To

Donald H. Schwartz

as a token of our good will and respect for receiving the highest score in the Army Achievement test in Geography, Term II, in the Basic Engineering Curriculum of the Army Specialized Training Program.

Verne H. Booth
Murray N. Friedman
Charles C. Mook
Anna M. Wellnitz

Brooklyn College
March 2, 1944

GOODE'S

SCHOOL ATLAS

PHYSICAL, POLITICAL, and ECONOMIC

FOR AMERICAN SCHOOLS AND COLLEGES

REVISED AND ENLARGED

BY

J. PAUL GOODE, Ph. D.

LATE PROFESSOR OF GEOGRAPHY
UNIVERSITY OF CHICAGO

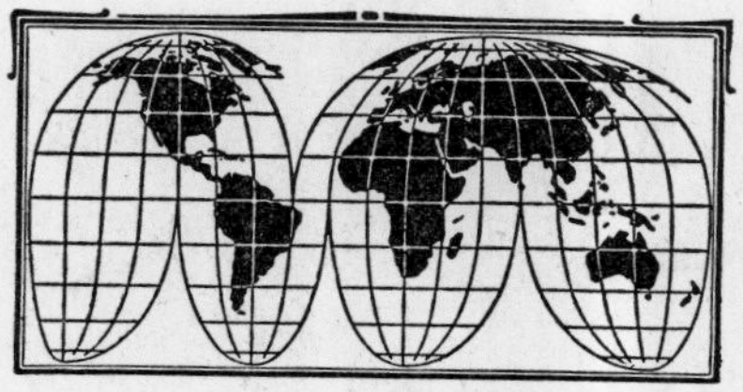

1943 EDITION

RAND McNALLY & COMPANY

NEW YORK CHICAGO SAN FRANCISCO

Printed in U. S. A.

THE RAND-McNALLY PRESS
R McN & Co
Made in U. S. A.

TO

LIVINGSTON C. LORD, LLD.

IN RECOGNITION OF MY DEBT TO HIM
FOR INTELLECTUAL INSPIRATION
FOR UNCOMPROMISING STANDARDS OF SCHOLARSHIP
AND FOR THE RARE GIFT OF HIS FRIENDSHIP
AND
TO THE SACRED MEMORY OF

KATHERINE

THE CONTENTS

	PAGE
To the Student and Teacher	xi
EARTH, SUN, AND MOON	1
LANDSCAPE WITH PHYSICAL FEATURES; PHYSICAL MAP	1
MAP PROJECTIONS	2
De Lisle's Conic; Polyconic; Central Cylindrical and Mercator's; Sinusoidal; Lambert's Azimuthal; Mollweide's Homolographic; Goode's Interruption of the Homolographic; Goode's Homolosine; Goode's Polar Adaptation of Werner's Equal Area	
A STUDY IN SCALES. Five maps	3
Central Part of Washington, D. C. Scale 1 inch to ¼ mile	
Part of Washington, D. C., 1 inch to 1 mile	
Washington and Vicinity, 1 inch to 4 miles	
Washington–Baltimore, 1 inch to 16 miles	
Washington–New York, 1 inch to 64 miles	
WORLD—PHYSICAL. Scale 1:100,000,000	4–5
Insets: Land Elevations in Profile; Ocean Depths in Profile	
WORLD—POLITICAL. Scale 1:100,000,000	6–7
Insets, Scale 1:4,000,000: Réunion; Mauritius; Guam; Yap; Part of Fiji Islands; Part of Samoa Islands; Martinique and St. Lucia; Trinidad; Ascension; Part of the Azores; St. Helena; Northwest group of Cape Verde Islands; Malta; Madeira Islands; Tenerife	
WORLD—DENSITY OF POPULATION. Scale 1:74,000,000	8–9
WORLD—THE OCEANS: COTIDAL LINES, RANGE OF TIDES; OCEAN DEPTHS. Scale 1:100,000,000	10–11
Twelve Insets: Estuaries with Exceptionally High Tides	
WORLD—CLIMATIC. EQUATORIAL ASPECT. Six maps	12–13
January Normal Surface Temperature	
January Isobars and Prevailing Winds	
July Normal Surface Temperature	
July Isobars and Prevailing Winds	
Rainfall, Nov. 1–Apr. 30	
Rainfall, May 1–Oct. 31	
WORLD IN HEMISPHERES—CLIMATIC. POLAR ASPECT. Four maps	14–15
January Normal Surface Temperature	
January Isobars and Prevailing Winds	
July Normal Surface Temperature	
July Isobars and Prevailing Winds	
Insets: Vertical sections showing Normal Surface Temperature and Atmospheric Pressure at Surface for the Northern and Southern Hemispheres in January and July	
WORLD—CLIMATIC: SURFACE TEMPERATURE REGIONS. Scale 1:74,000,000	16–17
WORLD—CLIMATIC: ANNUAL RAINFALL. Scale 1:74,000,000	18–19
WORLD—CLIMATIC: THE CLIMATIC REGIONS OF THE EARTH. Scale 1:100,000,000	20–21
WORLD—VEGETATION AND OCEAN CURRENTS. Scale 1:100,000,000	22–23
Insets: Distribution of Vegetation in Relation to Altitude	
WORLD—THE OCEANS: COMMUNICATIONS; VOLUME OF OCEAN COMMERCE. Scale 1:100,000,000	24–25
Insets: Races of Men; The Great Religions	
WORLD ECONOMIC MAPS. GOODE'S HOMOLOSINE EQUAL AREA PROJECTION, CONDENSED. Scale 1:140,000,000	26–45
WHEAT—COFFEE. Areas of Production, Output by Countries	26
RYE—TEA. Areas of Production, Output by Countries	26
OATS—CACAO. Areas of Production, Output by Countries	27
BARLEY—RICE. Areas of Production, Output by Countries	27
CORN (MAIZE)—TAPIOCA (CASSAVA, MANIOC) AND SAGO. Areas of Production, Output by Countries	28
GRAIN SORGHUMS AND MILLETS—FISHING PRODUCTS. Areas of Production, Output by Countries	28

PAGE

FORESTS AND WOOD PRODUCTS. Areas and Production by Countries 29

SUGAR—SPICES. Areas of Production, Output by Countries 29

GRAPES. Areas of Production, Output by Countries. 29

TEXTILE FIBERS: HEMP—ABACA (MANILA)—SISAL (HENEQUEN)—RAMIE—PHORMIUM. Areas of Production, Output by Countries . . . 30

RUBBER. Areas of Production, Output by Countries . 30

TEXTILE FIBERS (*cont.*): COTTON—FLAX—JUTE. Areas of Production, Output by Countries . . 30

TEXTILE FIBERS (*cont.*): SILK—RAYON. Areas of Production, Output by Countries 31

VEGETABLE OILS: SUNFLOWER—SESAME—PALM NUT—COPRA. Areas of Production, Output by Countries 31

VEGETABLE OILS (*cont.*): OLIVE—LINSEED—PEANUT —COTTONSEED—SOY BEAN—MAIZE—TUNG —RAPESEED. Areas of Production, Output by Countries 31

TOBACCO. Areas of Production, Output by Countries 32

FRUITS: CITROUS FRUITS—PINEAPPLES. Areas of Production, Output by Countries 32

FRUITS (*cont.*): APPLES—BANANAS—DATES—FIGS. Areas of Production, Output by Countries . 32

CATTLE—REINDEER—YAK. Areas of Distribution and Numbers by Countries 33

THE BEEF TRADE: EXPORT AND IMPORT OF BEEF AND BEEF PRODUCTS. Value by Countries . 33

SHEEP—ALPACA—LLAMA. Areas of Distribution and Numbers by Countries 34

THE WOOL TRADE: PRODUCTION, EXPORTS, AND IMPORTS. Value by Countries 34

SWINE—GOATS. Areas of Distribution and Numbers by Countries 35

HORSES—MULES—ASSES—CAMELS. Areas of Distribution and Numbers by Countries . . . 35

HIDES AND SKINS, FOR LEATHER. Value of Exports and Imports by Countries 36

FURS AND FUR SKINS. Value of Exports and Imports by Countries 36

THE PRECIOUS METALS: GOLD—SILVER—PLATINUM. Value of Production by Countries . . . 37

COPPER—TIN—LEAD—ZINC. Value of Output by Countries 37

PAGE

COAL. Production in Tons by Countries. . . . 38

DIAMONDS. Value of Output by Countries . . . 38

IRON ORE. Production in Tons of Iron Content by Countries 38

CHROMITE—MANGANESE—TUNGSTEN. Output by Countries 38

PETROLEUM. Output in Barrels by Countries. . . 39

MERCURY—BAUXITE (ALUMINUM ORE)—COBALT—VANADIUM. Output by Countries . . . 39

STEEL. Production in Tons by Countries. . . . 39

NICKEL—MOLYBDENUM—ANTIMONY. Output by Countries 39

WATER POWER. Total Resources and Power Developed by Countries 40

MINERAL FERTILIZERS: PHOSPHATE—FIXED NITROGEN—POTASH. Production by Countries . 40

AUTOMOTIVE VEHICLES. Number in Use by Countries 41

INTERNATIONAL TRADE. Value by Countries. . . 41

RAILWAY MILEAGE. By Countries 42

MERCHANT MARINE. Gross Tonnage by Countries . 42

POPULATION. Number in Millions by Countries . 43

WEALTH AND DEBT OF NATIONS. Amount in Billions of Dollars 43

WORLD—ECONOMIC: THE PRINCIPAL OCCUPATIONS OF MANKIND. Scale 1:74,000,000 . . . 44–45

NORTH AND SOUTH POLAR REGIONS 46

NORTH AMERICA—GLACIAL; LIFE ZONES . . . 47
Insets: Glacial Lake Agassiz; Ancient Lakes Lahontan and Bonneville; Glacial Laurentian Lakes, early stage; Glacial Laurentian Lakes, later stage

NORTH AMERICA. Scale 1:40,000,000 48–49
Insets, Scale 1:1,000,000: Puget Sound Region; Portland to the Sea; San Francisco and Vicinity

NORTH AMERICA. Eight maps 50–51
January Normal Surface Temperature
January Isobars, Prevailing Winds, and Rainfall (six months)
July Normal Surface Temperature
July Isobars, Prevailing Winds, and Rainfall (other six months)
Annual Rainfall
Vegetation
Land Relief
Density of Population

PAGE

ALASKA. Scale 1:12,000,000 52–53
Insets: The Valdez Region; Economic Map

CANADA AND NEWFOUNDLAND. Scale 1:12,000,000 . 54–55
Insets: Toronto; Ottawa; Halifax

CANADA AND NEWFOUNDLAND. Four maps . . 56–57
Vegetation
Minerals
Railways and Geology: Areas of Crystalline and Sedimentary Rocks
Density of Population
Insets, Scale 1:1,000,000: Prince Rupert; Winnipeg; Montreal; Quebec

UNITED STATES OF AMERICA. Scale 1:12,000,000 . . 58–59

U. S. A.—PHYSICAL AND ECONOMIC. Five maps . . 60
Pleistocene Glaciation
Gold, Silver, Copper: Production by States
Potential Water Power by States
Petroleum and Natural Gas: Output by States
Total Mineral Output by States

U. S. A.—PHYSICAL AND ECONOMIC. Five maps . . 61
Physiographic Divisions
Value of Forest Products by States
Value of All Farm Crops and Animal Products
Value Added by Manufacture by States
Production of Wealth by States

U. S. A.—ECONOMIC. Two maps 62
Coal Fields, Iron Deposits, Waterways.
Value Added by Manufacture in Leading Cities

U. S. A.—ECONOMIC. Two maps 63
Railways and Standard Time
Urban Population, 1930

U. S. A.—CLIMATIC. Five maps 64
Average Annual Precipitation
Early Frost
Late Frost
Average Frostless Season
Average Annual Sunshine

U. S. A.—ECONOMIC; CLIMATIC. Five maps . . . 65
Population Density by Counties, 1930
Paths of Lows
Paths of Highs
Seasons of Rain
Average Wind Velocity

UNITED STATES OF AMERICA—SOIL REGIONS. Scale 1:16,000,000 66–67

UNITED STATES OF AMERICA AND PART OF CANADA—NATIVE VEGETATION 68–69
Insets: Temperature Efficiency; Evaporation Provinces; Precipitation-Evaporation Ratio; Drouth

U. S. A.—NORTHWESTERN. Scale 1:4,000,000 . . 70–71

U. S. A. AND CANADA—CITIES AND ENVIRONS. Scale 1:1,000,000 72–73
Vancouver—Victoria; Pikes Peak; Colorado Piedmont; Los Angeles Piedmont; Wasatch Oasis; Birmingham; Atlanta

U. S. A.—SOUTHWESTERN. Scale 1:4,000,000 . . 74–75
Inset: San Diego and Vicinity. Scale 1:1,000,000

U. S. A.—NORTHERN INTERIOR. Scale 1:4,000,000 . 76–77

U. S. A.—CENTRAL. Scale 1:4,000,000 78–79

U. S. A.—WESTERN GULF REGION AND PART OF MEXICO. Scale 1:4,000,000 80–81
Inset: Houston—Galveston. Scale 1:1,000,000

U. S. A.—SOUTHEASTERN. Scale 1:4,000,000 . . . 82–83

U. S. A.—PART OF NORTHEASTERN U. S. A. Scale 1:4,000,000 84–85

U. S. A. AND CANADA—EASTERN GATEWAY OF CANADA, NORTHERN NEW ENGLAND, AND NEWFOUNDLAND. Scale 1:4,000,000 86–87
Inset: Boston and Vicinity. Scale 1:1,000,000

U. S. A.—CITIES AND THEIR ENVIRONS. Scale 1:500,000 88–89
Chicago; New York; Duluth; St. Mary's Falls (Scale 1 inch to 1 mi.); Buffalo; Niagara River; Niagara Falls (Scale 1 inch to 1 mi.); Baltimore; Philadelphia; Detroit; Cleveland; Norfolk-Portsmouth; St. Louis; Pittsburgh; Savannah; Minneapolis–St. Paul; Cincinnati; New Orleans to the Sea (Scale 1:1,000,000)

GULF AND CARIBBEAN LANDS. Scale 1:16,000,000 . 90–91
Insets: Panama Canal (Scale 1:1,000,000); Habana and Vicinity (Scale 1:500,000); Puerto Rico and Virgin Islands (Scale 1:4,000,000); St. Thomas Island (Scale 1:500,000)

MEXICO—CENTRAL. Scale 1:4,000,000 92–93
Inset: Mexico City and Environs. Scale 1:500,000

CENTRAL AMERICA. Scale 1:4,000,000 94–95
Insets: Yucatan Peninsula (Scale 1:4,000,000); Leeward and Windward Islands (Scale 1:4,000,000)

WEST INDIES—WESTERN. Scale 1:4,000,000 . . . 96–97
Cuba, Bahamas, Jamaica, Hispaniola

PAGE

Insets: Cuba, Density of Population; Sugar Production

SOUTH AMERICA. Scale 1:40,000,000 98–99
Insets, Scale 1:4,000,000: Rio de Janeiro; Buenos Aires-Montevideo; Valparaiso; Santiago; Magallanes and the Strait of Magellan

SOUTH AMERICA. Eight maps 100–101
January Normal Surface Temperature
January Isobars, Prevailing Winds, Rainfall (six months)
July Normal Surface Temperature
July Isobars, Prevailing Winds, Rainfall (other six months)
Annual Rainfall
Native Vegetation
Land Relief
Density of Population

SOUTH AMERICA—NORTHERN. Scale 1:16,000,000 102–103
Insets: Belém, Scale 1:4,000,000; São Salvador (Scale 1:4,000,000); Callao-Lima (Scale 1:500,000)

SOUTH AMERICA—SOUTHERN. Scale 1:16,000,000 . 104
Insets, Scale 1:500,000. Buenos Aires; Rio de Janeiro

ATLANTIC OCEAN. Scale 1:60,000,000 105
Ocean Depths, Prevailing Winds, Ocean Currents

EUROPE. Scale 1:16,000,000 106–107

EUROPE. Five maps 106A–107A
Languages
In the Great Ice Age
After the Great Baltic Glacier
Annual Storm Tracks
Sunshine in Hours per Year

EUROPE. Eight maps 108–109
January Normal Surface Temperature
January Isobars, Prevailing Winds, Rainfall (six months)
July Normal Surface Temperature
July Isobars, Prevailing Winds, Rainfall (other six months)
Annual Rainfall
Native Vegetation
Land Relief
Density of Population

EUROPE—WESTERN. Scale 1:10,000,000 . . . 110–111

EUROPE—EASTERN EUROPE AND ASIA MINOR. SOVIET UNION IN EUROPE. Scale 1:10,000,000 112–113

MEDITERRANEAN LANDS. Scale 1:10,000,000 . . 114–115

PAGE

EUROPE—BRITISH ISLES AND NORTH SEA LANDS. Scale 1:4,000,000 116–117

ENGLAND—CENTRAL MANUFACTURING REGION. Scale 1:1,000,000 118

EUROPE—CITIES AND THEIR ENVIRONS. Scale 1:500,000. LIVERPOOL—MANCHESTER; LONDON TO THE SEA; ANVERS (ANTWERP); HAMBURG; BERLIN; WIEN (VIENNA); NAPOLI (NAPLES) 119

EUROPE—SOUTHERN SCANDINAVIA AND THE EAST BALTIC STATES. Scale 1:4,000,000 . . 120–121

EUROPE—CENTRAL. Scale 1:4,000,000 122–123

EUROPE—FRANCE. Scale 1:4,000,000 124–125
Insets: Paris and Environs (Scale 1:500,000); Ancient Provinces; Ports, Canals, Navigable Rivers; Beverages: Producing Areas; Coal, Iron, and Railway Traffic

EUROPE—SPAIN AND PORTUGAL. Scale 1:4,000,000 126–127
Insets: Cities and Environs. Scale 1:1,000,000. Madrid; Barcelona; Lisboa (Lisbon); Cádiz

EUROPE—ITALY, YUGOSLAVIA, BULGARIA, AND GREECE. Scale 1:4,000,000 128–129

EUROPE—SOUTHWESTERN SOVIET UNION, MANUFACTURING REGION. Scale 1:4,000,000 . . 130–131

EUROPE—WEST CENTRAL—ECONOMIC. Two maps. Scale 1:14,000,000 132
Industrial Regions; Coal, Iron, Navigable Waters
Density of Population

EUROPE—ECONOMIC AND RELIGIOUS. Two maps. Scale 1:34,000,000 133
Railways
Religions

AFRICA. Scale 1:40,000,000 134–135
Insets: Gibraltar (Scale 1:1,000,000); Tunis (Scale 1:4,000,000); The Lower Congo (Scale 1:4,000,000); The Lower Nile Valley (Scale 1:4,000,000); The Suez Canal (Scale 1:1,000,000)

AFRICA. Eight maps 136–137
January Normal Surface Temperature
January Isobars, Prevailing Winds, and Rainfall (six months)
July Normal Surface Temperature
July Isobars, Prevailing Winds, and Rainfall (other six months)
Annual Rainfall
Native Vegetation
Land Relief
Density of Population

AFRICA—NORTHERN. Scale 1:16,000,000 . . . 138–139
Insets: Cape Verde Islands and the Azores. Same scale as the main map

PAGE

AFRICA—SOUTHERN. Scale 1:16,000,000 . . . 140–141
Insets: The Eastern Horn (Scale 1:16,000,000); The Zanzibar Region (Scale 1:4,000,000); Cairo and Environs (Scale 1:500,000); Cape Town and Environs (Scale 1:500,000)

SOUTH AFRICA. Scale 1:4,000,000 142–143

EURASIA. Scale 1:40,000,000 144–145
Insets, Scale 1:4,000,000: Palestine; The Region of Aden; The Region of Singapore

ASIA. Eight maps 146–147
January Normal Surface Temperature
January Isobars, Prevailing Winds, and Rainfall (six months)
July Normal Surface Temperature
July Isobars, Prevailing Winds, and Rainfall (other six months)
Annual Rainfall
Native Vegetation
Land Relief
Density of Population

SOVIET UNION IN ASIA; SIBERIA. Scale 1:16,000,000 148–149

ASIA—SOUTHWESTERN. Scale 1:16,000,000 . . 150–151
Insets: Ceylon (Scale 1:16,000,000); The Region of Khyber Pass (Scale 1:4,000,000); Bombay (Scale 1:1,000,000); India (Political)

CHINA AND JAPAN. Scale 1:16,000,000 . . . 152–153
Inset: Shanghai. Scale 1:250,000

PART OF SOUTHERN CHINA. Scale 1:4,000,000 . . 154–155
Lower Basins of Yangtze and Si (West) Rivers.

PART OF EASTERN CHINA AND CHOSEN (KOREA). Scale 1:4,000,000 156–157
Eastern part of the Hwang Ho Basin

JAPAN. Scale 1:10,000,000 158
Inset: Taiwan. Scale 1:10,000,000

PAGE

SOUTHERN JAPAN. Scale 1:4,000,000 159
Insets: Kobe; Osaka; Kyoto; Tokyo; Yokohama (Scale 1:1,000,000)

INDOCHINA AND EAST INDIES. Scale 1:16,000,000 160–161
Inset: Manila and Environs. Scale 1:1,000,000

PHILIPPINE ISLANDS. Scale 1:4,000,000 . . . 162–163
Inset: Batan Islands. Scale 1:4,000,000

AUSTRALIA. Scale 1:16,000,000 164–165

AUSTRALIA—SOUTHEASTERN. Scale 1:4,000,000 . 166–167

AUSTRALIA AND NEW ZEALAND. Eight maps . . 168
January Normal Surface Temperature
January Isobars, Prevailing Winds, and Rainfall (six months)
July Normal Surface Temperature
July Isobars, Prevailing Winds, and Rainfall (other six months)
Annual Rainfall
Vegetation
Land Relief
Density of Population

TASMANIA AND CITIES OF AUSTRALIA. Scale 1:4,000,000 169
Cities, Scale 1:500,000: Sydney; Melbourne; Perth; Adelaide
Part of Queensland and New South Wales. Scale 1:4,000,000

NEW ZEALAND. Scale 1:4,000,000 170–171
Insets, Scale 1:500,000: Auckland; Wellington; Dunedin; Christchurch

PACIFIC OCEAN. Scale 1:50,000,000 172–173
Ocean Depths; Prevailing Winds; Currents
Inset: Hawaiian Islands. Scale 1:4,000,000

WORLD COMPARISONS 174–175

PRONOUNCING INDEX 177

TO THE STUDENT AND TEACHER

Introductory. The first edition of *Goode's School Atlas* was issued June 23, 1923. The work was designed specifically for American schools and colleges. The choice of material and the order of presentation were made purposely to meet the needs of American students. The atlas met with a generous reception at the hands of the schools and students of America, and it is a matter of keen satisfaction to the author to add extensively in this edition to the cartographic material of large value in the teaching of modern geography. The first edition carried 96 pages of maps; this, the seventh edition, carries 173 pages.

This volume is an outgrowth of over forty years of experience in teaching geography in normal school, teachers college, and university. It represents the mature judgment of the author as to what charted material is of greatest teaching value in American schools, and as to best methods of cartographic presentation. The atlas is again offered to the teachers and students of America with the sincere hope that it will help toward the better teaching of geography, and toward a greater appreciation of fine maps and a keener pleasure in their use, both during and after school days.

The purpose of a school atlas. The goal of the modern study of geography is a thorough understanding of the relation between mankind and the physical forces of his environment. Geography is not merely a matter of space relation, neither is it a matter of description only. It is a science, and it may levy tribute for its facts on all the physical and biological sciences—astronomy, geology, meteorology, climatology, botany, zoölogy—as well as upon the social-science group—anthropology, ethnology, history, sociology, and economics. The areal distribution of the influences recorded in these far-flung fields of science calls for *maps*. And the complexity of physical influences at work upon a given human group calls for maps of land relief, presenting the highland areas, the lowlands, the mountain barriers; climatic maps, showing the distribution of sunshine, of temperature, of prevailing wind, of rainfall; vegetation maps, showing forest areas, grassland areas, desert areas; population maps, showing the distribution of mankind; economic maps, showing how men make their living—maps which present the producing areas of the chief commodities of commerce; transportation maps for land and sea; maps of important manufacturing regions; city maps; and, finally, political maps. And since human affairs naturally are of the most vital interest to all of us, mere place maps are of large importance, maps which show where people live.

Thus the point of view in geography and the scope of the interests studied determine the character and the variety of the maps to be entered in a school atlas. In this atlas space relations are presented first in a general way in maps showing world relations; then in a larger scale in continental unities; then in still larger-scale maps, presenting more and more detail, as the importance of the material and the limitations of space may determine.

The atlas habit. Every student of geography and every intelligent reader should acquire early the "atlas habit." One acquires the atlas habit by havng conveniently at hand on the study table an atlas which may be turned to instantly, when one is uncertain as to questions of location, relative size, direction or distance, or any one of the many geographic facts set down in the atlas. *An atlas and a dictionary should be the constant companions of every student.* Much of the map material here presented is of fundamental importance in a liberal education. No reasonable device should go unused that offers readily to fix these fundamental facts and relations in the mind of the student.

Because of a new point of view in geography and a new emphasis upon map study, a school atlas becomes a necessity in the equipment requisite for a wide range of school subjects.

The choice of map projections. It is quite impossible to transform the surface of a globe into a plane surface without sacrificing some elements of truth. It is not possible to have truth of scale, angle, shape, and area all in one flat map. In fact, it is not possible in flat maps to tell all the truth at any time. One must choose the element of truth it is desired to emphasize, and then sacrifice other elements of truth as the case may require. *For geographic use truth of area is of prime importance, and close to this is truth of form.* Most of the maps used in geography should be on an equal-area projection; that is, upon a projection in which any square inch in the map represents the

same number of square miles of the earth's surface as any other square inch in the map. Equal-area maps show continents, countries, states, in their true relative size. When countries or other areas are to be compared in size, such a comparison can be made *only* upon an equal-area projection.

In most geographic studies mere longitude is of little significance, but latitude is of very great importance. For studies of distribution in latitude it is desirable to have latitudes shown by parallel lines, as they are on the globe, either as arcs of circles or, better, as straight lines. All the world maps used in this atlas are on strictly equal-area projections, and all have latitudes shown by parallel lines.

Out of the scores of projections on record, five only have been chosen for use in this atlas (see p. 2 for projections): Lambert's azimuthal equal area, Goode's homolosine, the sinusoidal, De Lisle's conic, and the polyconic. The first three of these are equal-area projections. De Lisle's conic and the polyconic, as used in this atlas, depart but slightly from truth of area. They are used because they give excellent shapes in the areas covered, and because all the angles in the grill (or network of meridians and parallels) are right angles as on the globe.

It will be noticed that the Mercator projection is not used in this atlas. In all previous atlases for the past 362 years Mercator's projection has been used almost exclusively for world distributions, and this in spite of the facts that (1) it is impossible with this projection to show the earth's surface entire, the north and south poles being at infinity; and (2) distances and areas grow rapidly larger with increase of latitude, becoming enormous in higher latitudes. For example, on a Mercator map North America is much larger than Africa, although in fact North America is only seven-tenths the size of Africa. On a Mercator projection Greenland is much larger than South America, when in reality it is only one-ninth as large as South America. This distortion of area is so great that it becomes pedagogically unsound and very misleading to use Mercator's map to show areal distribution of any kind. Comparison in size of empires and states, annual rainfall, distribution of vegetation, and the like, all are untrue as shown upon a Mercator map. They are also untrue, but in lesser degree, when shown upon Gall's cylindrical or Van der Grinten's projections, which are used in some school texts. The best that can be said for these two projections is, that they are not quite so bad as the evil Mercator.

Although Mercator's projection is not adapted for general geographic use, it is one of the great contributions in cartography of all time. Mercator invented this projection avowedly for the use of mariners, and for this one use it has certain properties of outstanding value. On this projection the navigator can draw a straight line (called a rhumb line) between any two points, read the angle between the rhumb line and a meridian, set his compass to this angle, and go direct to his destination without change of compass. This advantage is so great that there is not at present any other projection that can take its place for purposes of navigation.

In this edition of the atlas Goode's homolosine equal-area projection is used for all world distributions, except where the earth's surface is shown in polar hemispheres. This projection has a number of significant advantages: (1) It presents the entire surface of the earth, which Mercator's projection cannot do. (2) It is strictly an equal-area projection. *There is no distortion of area.* (3) Parallels of latitude are represented by straight lines trending with the equator, a fine advantage in the study of comparative latitudes. (4) In this projection, as in the interrupted homolographic projection which was used in previous editions of this atlas, the grill is interrupted in the oceans, so as to give each continent in turn the advantage of being *in the center of the projection*, thus providing better shapes for the continents than any *uninterrupted* world map can give. In this projection the grill may also be interrupted through the continents, thus giving ocean unities, as on pp. 10–11, tidal phenomena; p. 105, the Atlantic Ocean, and pp. 172–73, the Pacific Ocean. The world ocean map throws the three great oceans into a plane, side by side, in the equatorial aspect, in better form for comparison than the globe itself can offer. No better projection has been devised for the display of all world phenomena which can best be studied in the equatorial aspect.

When the polar aspect of the earth is to be studied, the best presentation can be made on Lambert's azimuthal equal-area projection, as on pp. 14–15, where the great unities in world climate are shown.

For the series of continent maps Lambert's azimuthal equal-area projection is used, because this projection gives better shapes to the continental areas, as a whole, than is given by any other projection. For the United States of America and some other areas of similar position and size the polyconic projection is used. This projection was developed by the United States Coast and Geodetic Survey and has been much used in the official maps issued by the government. In this projection all meridians cross all parallels of latitude at right angles, as on the globe, while distances are true on the mid-meridian and on all parallels of latitude; therefore shapes are very good.

Though it is not an equal-area map, as used in this atlas the departure from truth of area is slight.

Where the area to be shown covers a wide range of longitude, De Lisle's conic projection is used, because the shapes are excellent, and the departure from the equal-area quality, as here used, is almost negligible. (See Canada, pp. 54–55, and Siberia, pp. 148–49.)

In all restricted areas of large scale, such as maps of cities and environs, the sinusoidal projection is used. In this projection the parallels of latitude are represented by straight parallel lines; distances are true on the mid-meridian and on all parallels of latitude. It is strictly equal area, and shapes are excellent. In low latitudes, areas of large extent can be shown well on this projection. (See South America, northern and southern sections, pp. 102–3 and 104, and the similar sections of Africa.)

The study of scale. Perhaps the most fundamental question in geography is, "Where in the world is it?"—a matter of latitude, and longitude, and direction. And almost as important is the question, "How big is it?" This is a matter of scale. As an introduction to the study of scale, on page 3 is given a series of maps which it is hoped may be found helpful, showing how the scale chosen for a map determines the scope of the map and fixes the amount of detail that may be entered on it profitably. Running across the page is a map of the central part of Washington, D. C., covering the area from the White House and the Monument to the Capitol and the Library of Congress. The scale is one inch to one-fourth mile. Then follow maps from the same center, but with decreasing scale—one inch to one mile, one inch to four miles, one inch to 16 miles, one inch to 64 miles. In the first map individual buildings are shown. In the final map the important area including Washington and New York City is shown, in which much detail and many cities of large size are omitted.

It is important that the student fix in mind the relative sizes of the continents, and of some countries and regions. No good purpose is served by fixing in his mind an erroneous impression that Greenland is larger than South America, or that North America is twice as large as Africa, or that New England is as large as the western half of the United States. To help the student acquire correct impressions of relative size, uniformity of scale for comparable areas is followed as far as possible. The two-page world maps are on a scale of approximately 1:100,000,000, and, since the homolosine is strictly an equal-area projection, the continents may be compared directly as to true relative size. North America, South America, Eurasia, and Africa are given as a series on a uniform scale of 1:40,000,000. This series is a striking feature of the atlas. It is based upon the largest map of Eurasia that can be put upon a two-page space in the book. With these continents on a uniform scale, the student, working over the various continents and comparing one with another, will fix them in his memory in their true relative sizes.

In similar fashion a series of regions comparable in area are presented in a uniform scale of 1:16,000,000, or one inch to 250 miles; a total of 23 pages of maps. In addition to this series are groups of maps on the still larger scale of 1:12,000,000, one inch to 190 miles, covering Alaska, Canada, the United States of America; and a still larger scale of 1:10,000,000, one inch to 160 miles, covering all Europe and northern Africa in six pages, and a one-page map carrying all of the Japanese Empire and Chosen. In these three scales are thirty-seven pages of maps. But far better than even these large-scale maps for place-name study are very detailed maps, on a scale of 1:4,000,000, or one inch to 64 miles. Sixteen two-page maps on this scale cover the entire United States and much of Canada; Latin America is given 6 pages, Europe 12, Asia 9, and the rest of the world 4; a total for the world of about 50 pages. These large-scale maps add greatly to the value of the work as a reader's reference atlas.

In addition to this list, 26 areas throughout the world, of large interest, such as Puget Sound and the Mississippi delta, have been shown on a scale of 1:1,000,000, or one inch to 16 miles. It is also of interest to see the areas occupied by the world's great cities brought to map on a uniform scale of 1:500,000, or one inch to 8 miles. This scale is so generous that the street pattern is shown, as well as parks, canals, docks, railway lines and terminals, and suburban cities and towns. There are 37 such maps, and all are contoured, showing elevation by tinting in color.

Accuracy and legibility. While accuracy is the highest virtue of any map, legibility is of almost equal importance; for, if the most accurate of maps cannot be read, its accuracy is of no avail. In so far as any data on a map cannot be grasped by the eye, and easily read, in just that measure is the map encumbered with useless material, and is a failure. Notice that these atlas maps are not burdened with detail. They are simple. The great facts presented for study stand out clearly. In many foreign maps hitherto so much information of varied kinds has been packed into a map, that to find a fact wanted one must bend laboriously over the page with a magnifier, and when the fact is so found it cannot be properly visualized because of the crowd of other material in the way. In this atlas, rather than have one map overloaded

with a great range of data, many maps are included, each map carrying one class of data, thus keeping the maps simple and readable. Aids to legibility have been studied carefully. Choice of color and color contrast, style and size of type, thickness of line, and the elimination of nonessentials have been studied at every stage and tested under actual use, to arrive at a norm of content and legibility.

The use of color. Color in map making is exceedingly important. Color is used primarily as an aid to legibility, distinguishing land from water, lowland from highland—in short, where for any reason one region must be distinguished from another. Where many regions are to be compared, contrasts are provided by difference in color, by tints and shades of color, and by pattern in color surface. So it has been possible, with printing ink in only five colors, to produce maps with luminous colors and adequate contrasts without obscuring the data entered, even in the most complicated map. (See the map of the United States of America, Soils, pp. 66–67, with 31 contrasting areas.)

In addition to its service in providing legibility, color has an esthetic value of large significance. We are all susceptible to the element of beauty. The colors chosen may be brilliant or dull, and color combinations may be harmonious or discordant. Color contrasts, particularly contrasts due to the light value of colors, may be physically measured. But color harmony is largely subjective, and may vary widely among different peoples and at different times. As Emerson has it, "Beauty is in the eye of the beholder." Pleasing colors contribute greatly to a favorable impression of a map or an atlas.

In this atlas the color scheme for the physical maps is essentially the same as the color scheme for the international one-to-one-million map of the world, but for good reasons color contrasts are stronger. The most fundamental distinction that a large-area map can carry, is the delimitation of land and water. This should be the strongest contrast in the map. In all the physical maps in this atlas this contrast is made positive by having the lowlands in a striking green, and the oceans in an equally positive blue, *but* omitting the blue over the continental shelves. So the lowland ends on the water side against the white paper—the strongest contrast in the maps. The next most fundamental fact in a physical map is the limitation of the lowland on the land side. In a human way the great lowlands are vastly more important than any other part of the earth's surface. About seven-eighths of all the inhabitants of the earth live on the lands less than a thousand feet above sea level. The highlands are of most significance to man as barriers to rain, transportation, and communication. So this exceedingly important 1,000-foot contour line, standing between the strong green and the bright yellow, is almost as prominent as the seashore itself.

Where possible, certain color conventions have been followed or created. Thus in all maps showing temperature of air or water, blue stands for cold and red for heat. By extension, red stands for hot deserts, yellow for grasslands, green for dense vegetation, and so on.

Comparison of units of measurement. A major fraction of the world is using the metric system of measures and the centigrade thermometer, and all forward-looking students are hoping for the time when these scientific systems of measurement will come into universal use. To help toward that great day, all measures in this atlas are given in the scientific system, as well as in the conventional but cumbersome and irrational English system. The scale for each map is given (1) as an arithmetical ratio, e.g., 1:1,000,000, or one inch to 16 miles; and (2) as a linear scale by which the actual distances in the map may be read directly. And in addition the linear scale of miles is placed very close alongside a linear scale of kilometers, with the *zero points together*. This makes it possible to take a given distance in miles and read it directly into kilometers, without computation, and vice versa. Also, areas given in square miles are given in square kilometers as well. Each physical map has a scale showing land relief. A height or depth given in feet may be read on the opposite scale in meters, without conversion.

In all temperature maps the same plan is carried out. At one side of the map isotherms are read in Fahrenheit degrees; at the other side in centigrade degrees. Likewise isobars are numbered at one side of the map in inches of mercury, at the other side in millimeters of mercury. Rainfall is given both in inches and in centimeters.

World relations. A strong feature of the atlas is the extended series of world maps carrying a mass of scientific information fundamental to the geographer's study of the relationship between man and his physical environment. Twenty double-page homolosine equal-area world maps carry a wealth of material of world-wide distribution. The two-page world maps present first, a physical world, pp. 4–5, with primary and secondary highland systems in each continent, and the great lowland plains between; the oceans, tinted for depth, bringing out clearly the continental shelves of shallow water where the world's food-fish supply is found; and at the other extreme the ocean

deeps in deepest blue. To contrast with this map a two-page political world map follows, pp. 6–7, with the areas of empires and countries and colonial possessions in vivid color. World climates, pp. 12–13, are shown in six world maps in the equatorial aspect presenting the great generalizations of distribution of temperature, pressure, and prevailing winds, and rainfall by seasons. Two pages more, pp. 14–15, carry four world maps presenting the same climatic information in polar hemispheres, the only way in which the hemispherical unities in climate can be shown at all. A temperature region map, pp. 16–17, and a world map of average annual rainfall, pp. 18–19, lead to a map of climatic regions, pp. 20–21. All these maps provide a sequence of causes, which find their effects in (1) the native vegetation regions of the world, pp. 22–23, and (2) the areal distribution of population density, pp. 8–9. In this latter case the continents are shown in an enlarged scale, by the omission of much open ocean. Pages 10–11 carry a very complete map of tidal phenomena, on the homolosine projection interrupted, to show ocean unities; and pp. 24–25 a similar ocean map with steamship routes and distances between ports.

For a wide variety of studies in cause and effect this series will be found invaluable. To cite but one: Eurasia, with a great central highland, provides deep reëntrant valley lowlands in its southeastern flank. This is a region of low latitude and constantly high temperatures. In the summer season the winds from the warm oceans at the southeast bring plentiful rain, while in the winter season the cool north winds bring little rain. Consequently this is a region of luxuriant vegetation ranging from tropical rain forests at the southeast to rich grasslands toward the interior. For all these reasons the region provides food for an exceedingly dense population, half of the people on earth being found in this area.

World economic maps. An important addition to the atlas is the inclusion of 37 world maps presenting an up-to-date study of the production and movement of the leading commodities of commerce. This series presents in graphic form the latest statistical information of 96 different commercial commodities or activities, the world total and the rank of the various countries readable at sight. The advantages of having all these data entered on an equal-area map will be obvious to every teacher, especially to those teachers who have tried to use economic maps in which no suggestion is made of the *rank* in production by countries or regions, or of the *date* of the information supplied. This economic series extends the very fertile opportunity for drill on cause and effect in the highest type of geographic study, which was begun in the first series of world maps. These economic studies can be prefaced in the case of every commodity by a study of the eight little maps provided for each continent—the significance of the latitude of the areas under discussion, of the distribution of highlands and lowlands, of the climatic conditions of temperature, wind, rain; the character of the native vegetation; and the position of the region with relation to the rest of the world. In short, all sorts of geographic relations can be read out of these eight little maps. Obviously these are valuable lessons in cause and effect, lessons fundamental in the study of geography.

Distribution of emphasis. Our own country is of largest significance to us. Next in importance are the countries of Europe, and next the Latin-American countries to the south of us. Other regions follow according to their importance to us. The distribution by number of maps and by pages is as follows: world relations in general, 59 maps using 42 pages, of which the series of economic relations runs to 34 maps, 18 pages; North America, 114 maps, 51 pages, of which the United States of America has 66 maps, 34 pages. South America has 21 maps, 8½ pages; Europe, 40 maps, 28 pages; Africa, 23 maps, 12 pages; Asia, 28 maps, 20 pages; Australia–New Zealand and the Atlantic and Pacific oceans, 24 maps, 11 pages.

As a reference atlas. Without doubt this atlas will be found of enduring value as a reader's reference atlas. Its page size permits it to go on the bookshelves along with other books, and to lie on the reader's table convenient at hand for immediate use by all those who have the atlas habit, or want to acquire it. The series of maps on the scale of 1:16,000,000, 1:12,000,000, and 1:10,000,000 cover the entire inhabited land surface of the earth, in 34 pages of maps; there is also a very significant series of 50 pages of maps on the 1:4,000,000 scale; also 28 maps of important regions on the 1:1,000,000 scale, and 37 maps of cities and environs on a scale of 1:500,000. All these maps together carry a total of over 30,000 place names, certainly a list large enough to satisfy the needs of most readers.

A pronouncing index. A new feature of great value has been introduced in the index, where an attempt is made to show the correct pronunciation of every one of the more than 30,000 geographic names. This is an invaluable advantage in a student's reference atlas.

Accuracy. Although a high level of achievement has been striven for at every turn, it is quite certain that it is humanly impossible to make an atlas without error. It will be a favor gratefully received if anyone will report any error found, or will offer constructive criticism.

Sources. Extreme care has been taken to have the latest, best, and most authentic sources for every entry in the atlas. All national and state official surveys have been called upon; charts by our Navy Department, the British Admiralty, the Institute Oceanographique de Monaco, and similar charts of other governments. For maps prepared especially for this atlas, some of which are published here for the first time, acknowledgments and thanks are extended: to Captain T. J. J. See, of the Hydrographic Office, U. S. N., for tidal data and their interpretation in the map of co-tidal lines, etc., pp. 10–11; to Professor Griffith Taylor, of the University of Chicago, for aid in the interpretation of the climatic data of Antarctica, pp. 14–15; to Professor Almon E. Parkins, of the George Peabody College, Nashville, Tenn., for his map of the Temperature Regions of the Earth, pp. 16–17; to Professor Preston E. James, of the University of Michigan, and to Professor Richard Joel Russell, of the Louisiana State University, for the revision of Koeppen's Climatic Regions of the Earth, pp. 20–21; to the Division of Statistical Research of the Department of Commerce, U. S. A., for generous aid in the accumulation of the data for the series of economic maps, pp. 26–43; to Dr. C. F. Marbut, Chief of the U. S. A. Bureau of Soils, for his soil map of U. S. A., pp. 66–67, reprinted from the previous edition of this atlas; to Dr. Burton E. Livingston, professor of plant physiology, Johns Hopkins University, and to Dr. Forrest Shreve, editor of *The Plant World*, for four climatic maps, on p. 69, reprinted from the previous edition; to Dr. H. M. Shantz, president of the University of Arizona, and to Professor Raphael Zon, director of the Lake States Forest Experiment Station, for the map of Native Vegetation of the U. S. A. and Part of Canada, pp. 68–69; and to the University of Chicago, owners of the copyright, for permission to use Goode's homolosine equal-area projection for the world maps in this edition.

The author's grateful thanks are due to the skilful draftsmen, engravers, and readers, whose careful work has made the production of this atlas a pleasure, and the final result possible.

J. Paul Goode

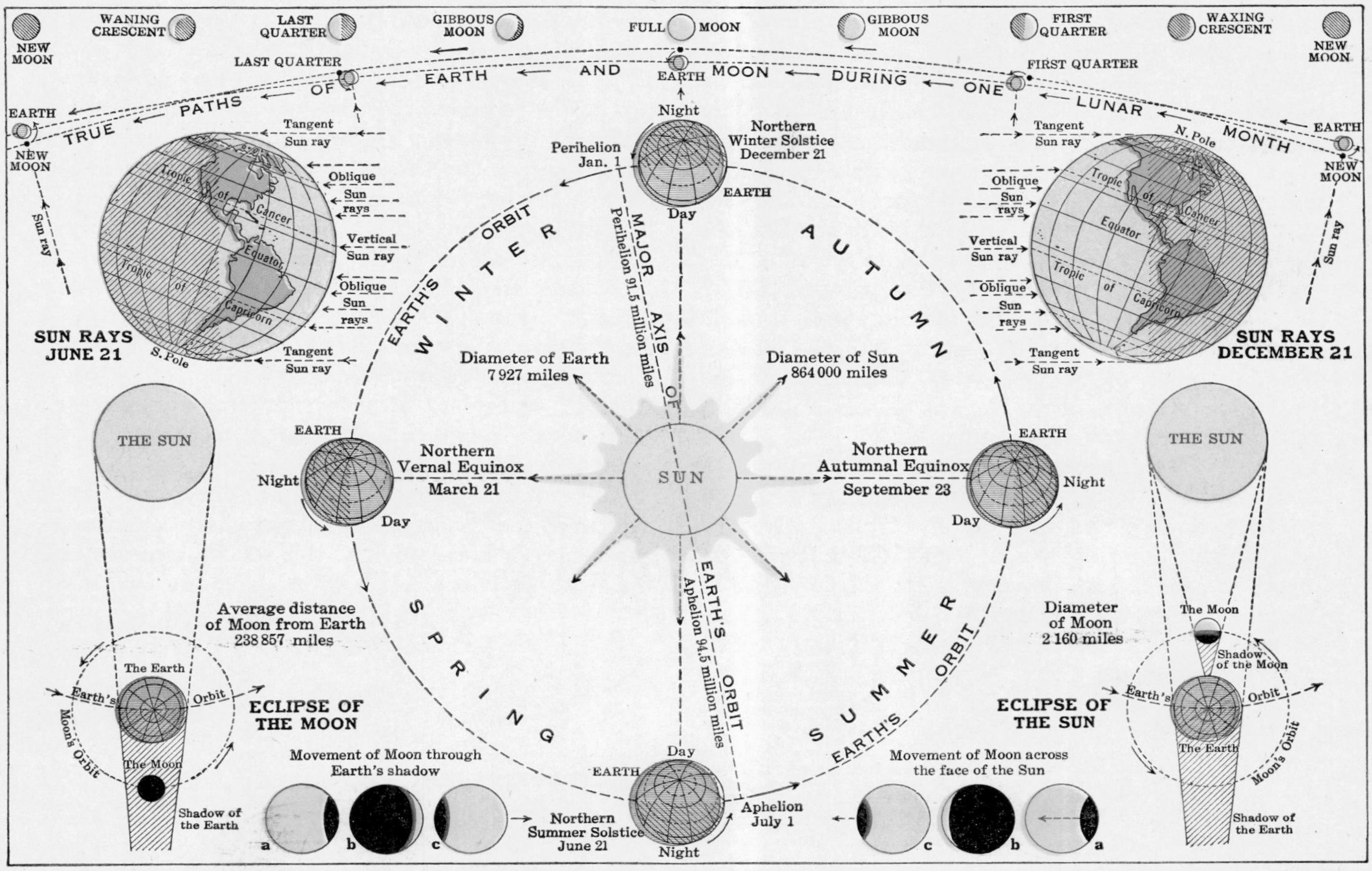

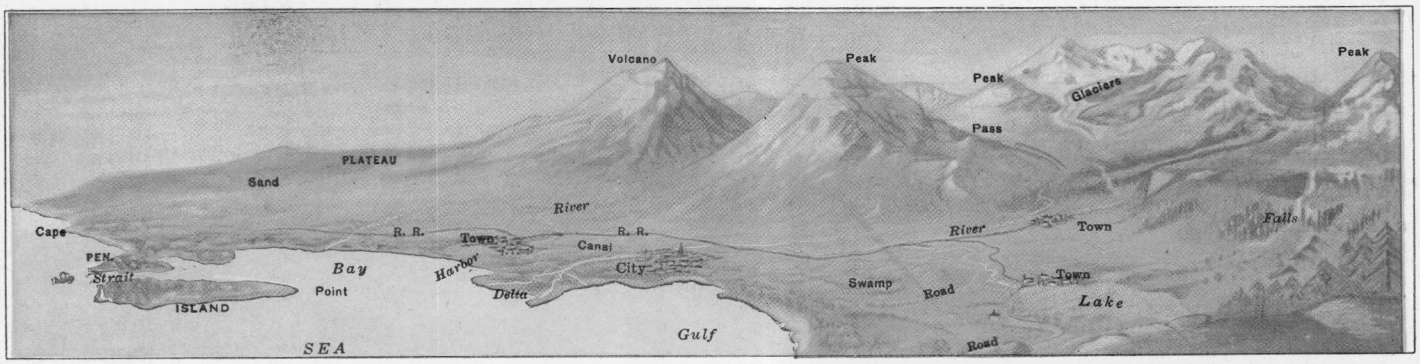

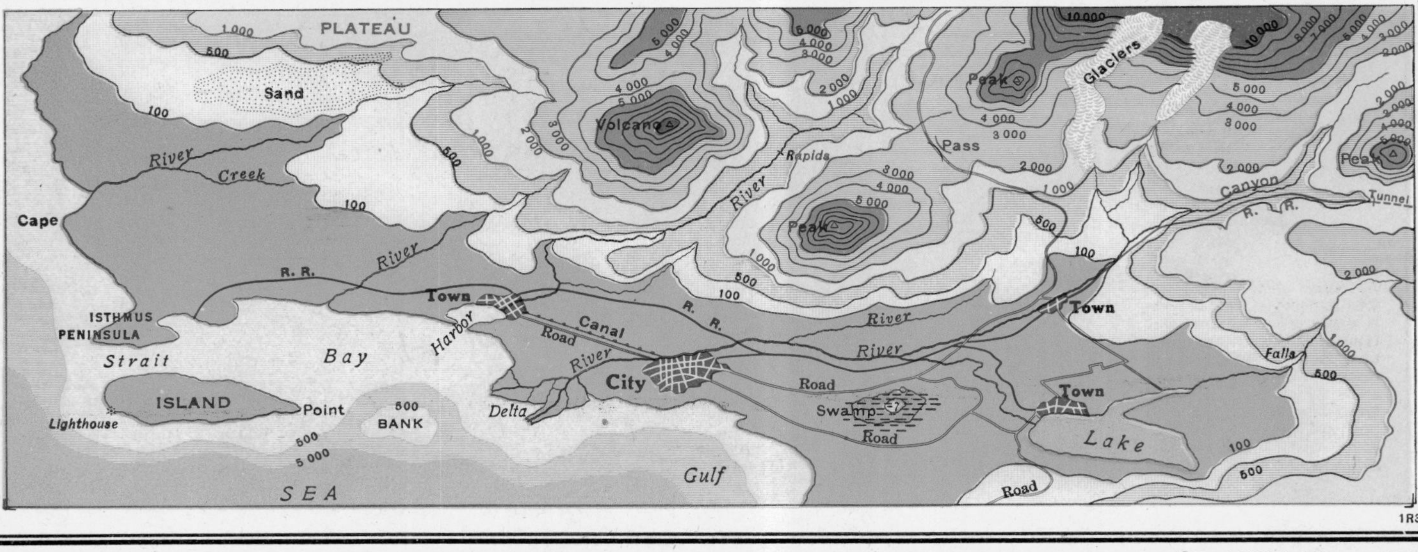

Elevations and depressions are given in feet

MAP PROJECTIONS

I. CONIC

In the simple conic projection, the eye or center of projection is at the center of the earth, *o*, and the surface of the earth is projected into the surface of a tangent cone, *a, d, e, f*. The surface of the cone unrolled becomes the plane of the map. The parallels of latitude become arcs of circles, struck with radii from the apex of the cone, as *ad, ae, af*. All meridians are straight lines crossing all parallels at right angles, as on the globe. At the parallel of tangency all elements of the map are true, angles, distances, shapes, areas. But departing from the tangent parallel, distances increase rapidly giving bad distortions of shapes and areas. For geographical purposes this simple projection is not used, but modifications, as at B, are of distinct value.

B. In this projection the cone intersects the sphere in two parallels, as at *f* and *g*, 60° and 35°. This is not an equal area projection, the space being reduced in size between the standard parallels or points of intersection, and progressively enlarged beyond the standard parallels. It gives very good shapes near the standard parallels and through the entire range of longitude and is much used for maps of Europe, Siberia, and Canada.

A. Simple Conic

Cone *a, b, c, d,* is tangent to the sphere at *t*. Latitudes are projected from the center as *os*. Half the unrolled cone is shown at *a, d, e, f*.

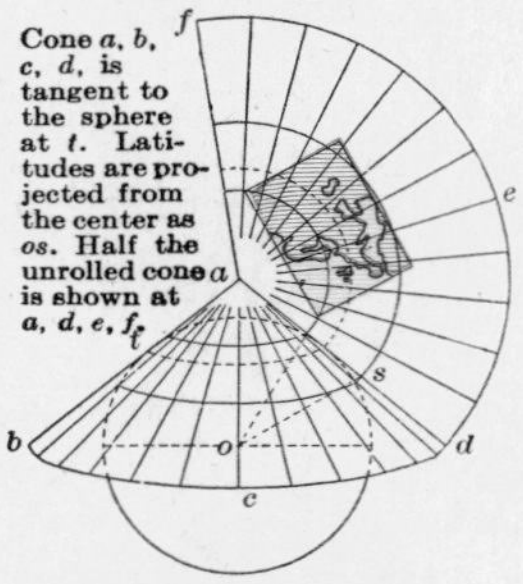

B. Modified Conic By Delisle 1745

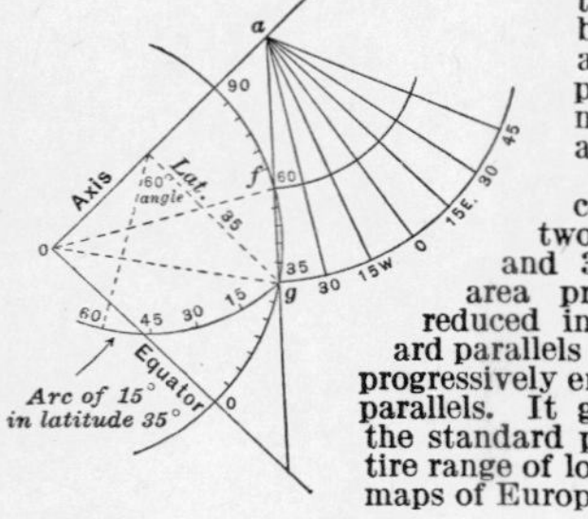

II. POLYCONIC

Not an equal area projection, since the arcs for the parallels are not concentric.

The mid-meridian is laid down as a straight line, *Tm*, and upon it latitude spaces are laid true to scale. Through each point is drawn the arc of a circle with a radius equal to the element of a cone tangent at that latitude, as *TP*. Meridian spaces are marked on each latitude arc at true distances from the mid-meridian. Through homologous points smooth curves are drawn for meridians.

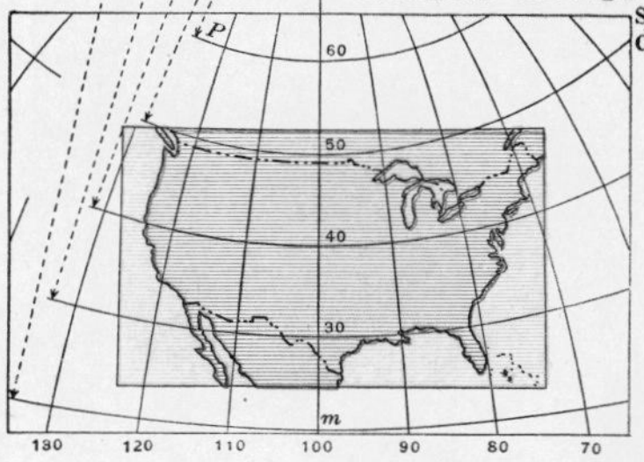

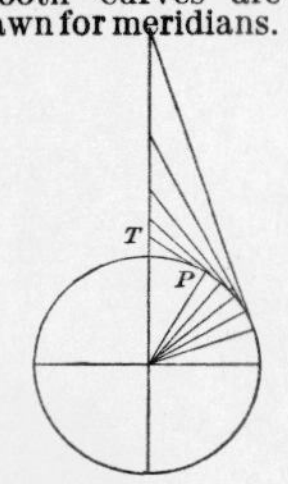

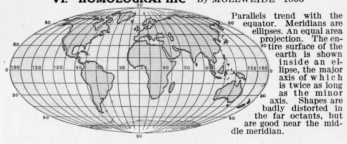

III. MERCATOR'S 1569

In the central cylindrical projection A, the eye at the center of the sphere projects the surface of the sphere into the surface of a cylinder tangent to the sphere at the equator. Meridians are straight lines normal to the equator and at true distances apart at the equator. But scale and area increase very rapidly with increase in latitude. This projection is not used for maps, but serves as starting point for Mercator's projection B. In Mercator's a constant relation is kept between latitude and longitude distances. It is useful for mariners, since a right line (loxodrome) can be drawn between two ports, the mariner setting his course to the angle between loxodrome and meridian and sailing straight to port without change of bearing. But distances, areas, and shapes are so badly distorted that for studies in comparative areas it is worse than useless.

A. Central Cylindrical

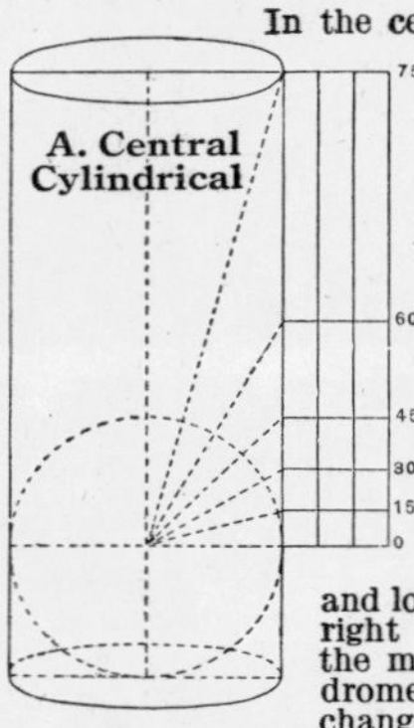

B. Mercator's

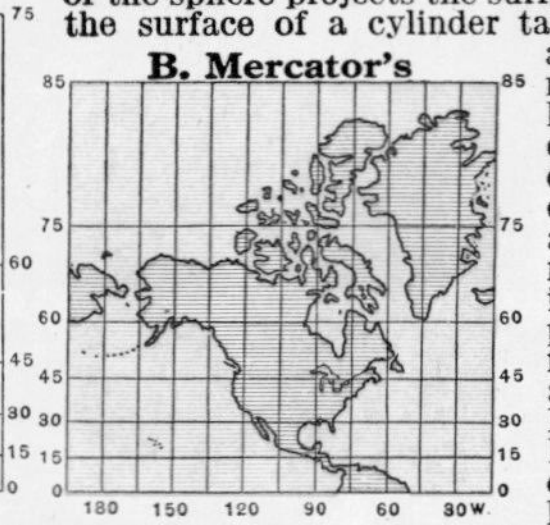

IV. SINUSOIDAL By SANSON 1650

An equal area projection. Parallels are straight lines trending with the equator, thus making studies in comparative latitudes easy. Meridians are sinusoids. Distances are true on the middle meridian and on all parallels. This projection is adapted to wide areas in low latitudes and small areas in all latitudes. The limiting sinusoid may be derived by construction as shown at the left. The sinusoidal projection is one of the best projections used by cartographers and the results are especially good in continent maps of South America and Africa.

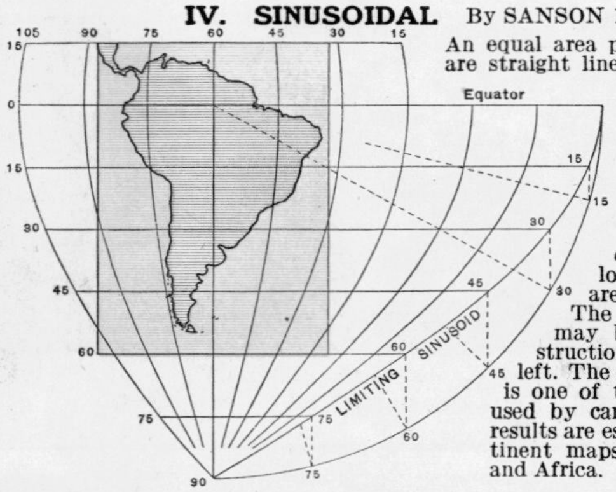

V. LAMBERT'S AZIMUTHAL 1772

A. Principle

The chords of latitudes are the radii for latitudes in the polar map.

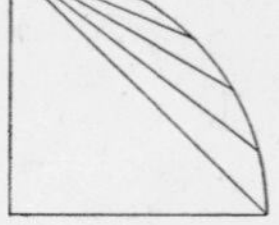

An equal-area projection. The surface to be mapped is deployed upon a plane tangent at the center of the area chosen. This projection gives the best shape to areas of continental size. Especially good for polar hemispheres. The principle of the polar projection is shown above at A.

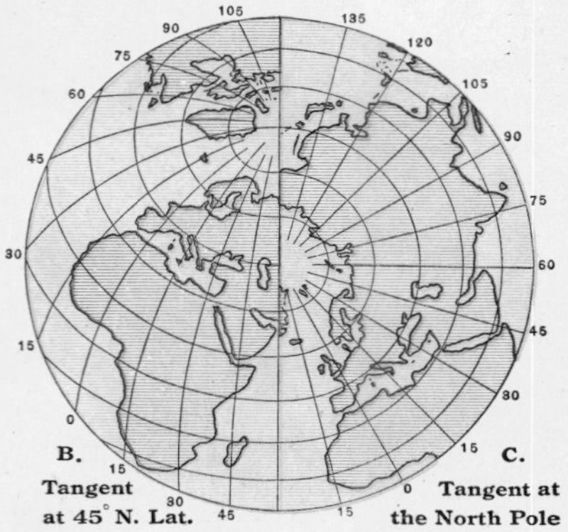

B. Tangent at 45° N. Lat.

C. Tangent at the North Pole

VI. HOMOLOGRAPHIC By MOLLWEIDE 1805

Parallels trend with the equator. Meridians are ellipses. An equal area projection. The entire surface of the earth is shown inside an ellipse, the major axis of which is twice as long as the minor axis. Shapes are badly distorted in the far octants, but are good near the middle meridian.

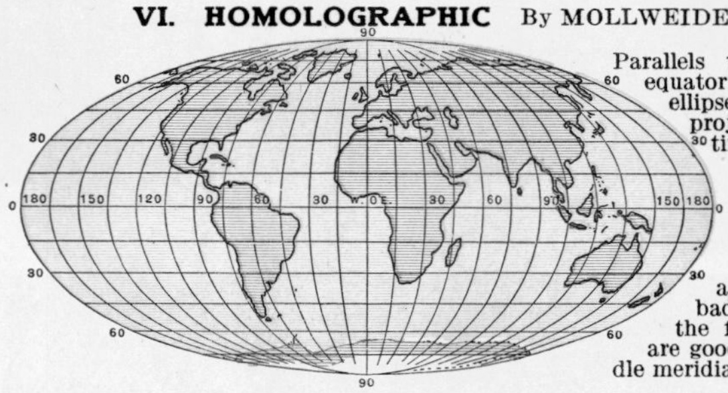

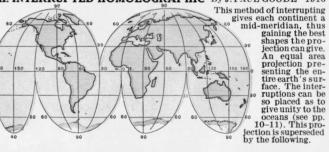

VII. INTERRUPTED HOMOLOGRAPHIC By J. PAUL GOODE 1916

This method of interrupting gives each continent a mid-meridian, thus gaining the best shapes the projection can give. An equal area projection presenting the entire earth's surface. The interruptions can be so placed as to give unity to the oceans (see pp. 10–11). This projection is superseded by the following.

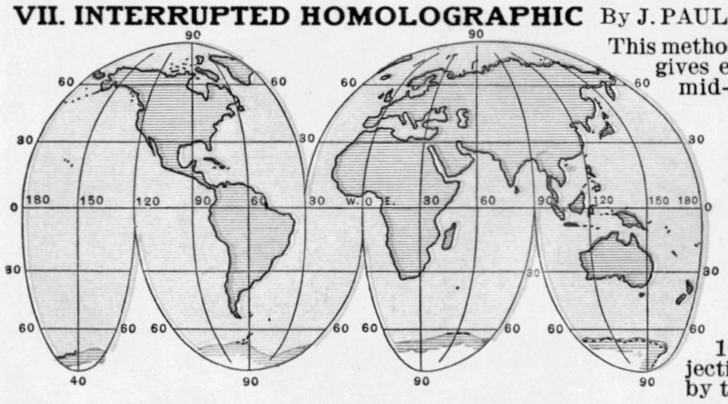

VIII. HOMOLOSINE By J. PAUL GOODE 1923

A combination using the sinusoidal projection from the equator to latitude 40° N. and S., and beyond these points the homolographic. An equal area projection. The straight parallels aid the comparison of similar latitudes. Good shapes in low latitudes.

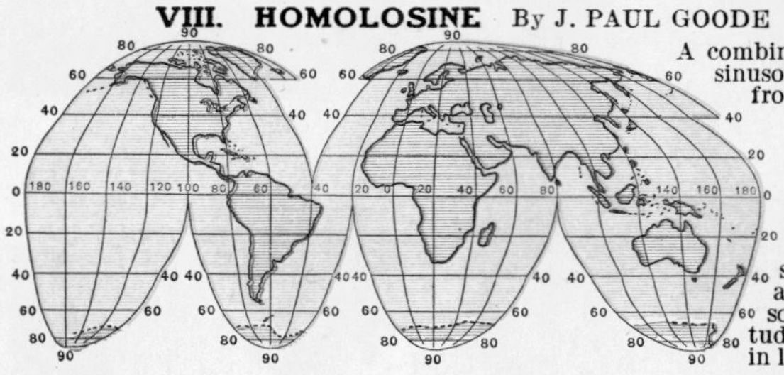

IX. POLAR EQUAL AREA By J. PAUL GOODE 1928

The continental land masses are deployed radially in a plane tangent at the North Pole. Each continent lobe is given a mid-meridian of its own, which is part of a radius from the pole. Parallels of latitudes are arcs of circles concentric from the pole. Distances are true on all the mid-meridians and on all the parallels of latitude. True space relations are shown across the North Pole and across the equator as well.

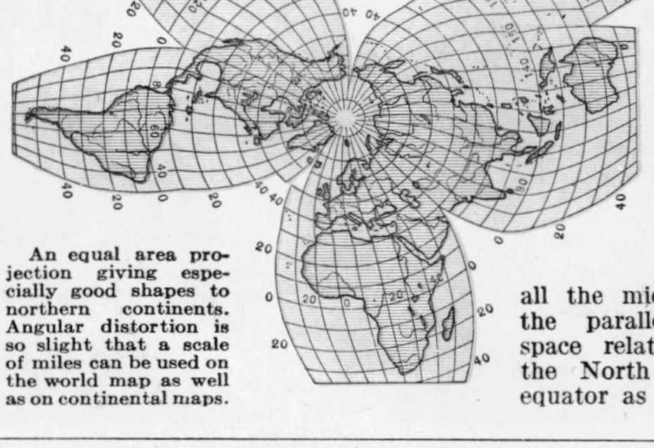

An equal area projection giving especially good shapes to northern continents. Angular distortion is so slight that a scale of miles can be used on the world map as well as on continental maps.

1N32

A STUDY IN SCALES

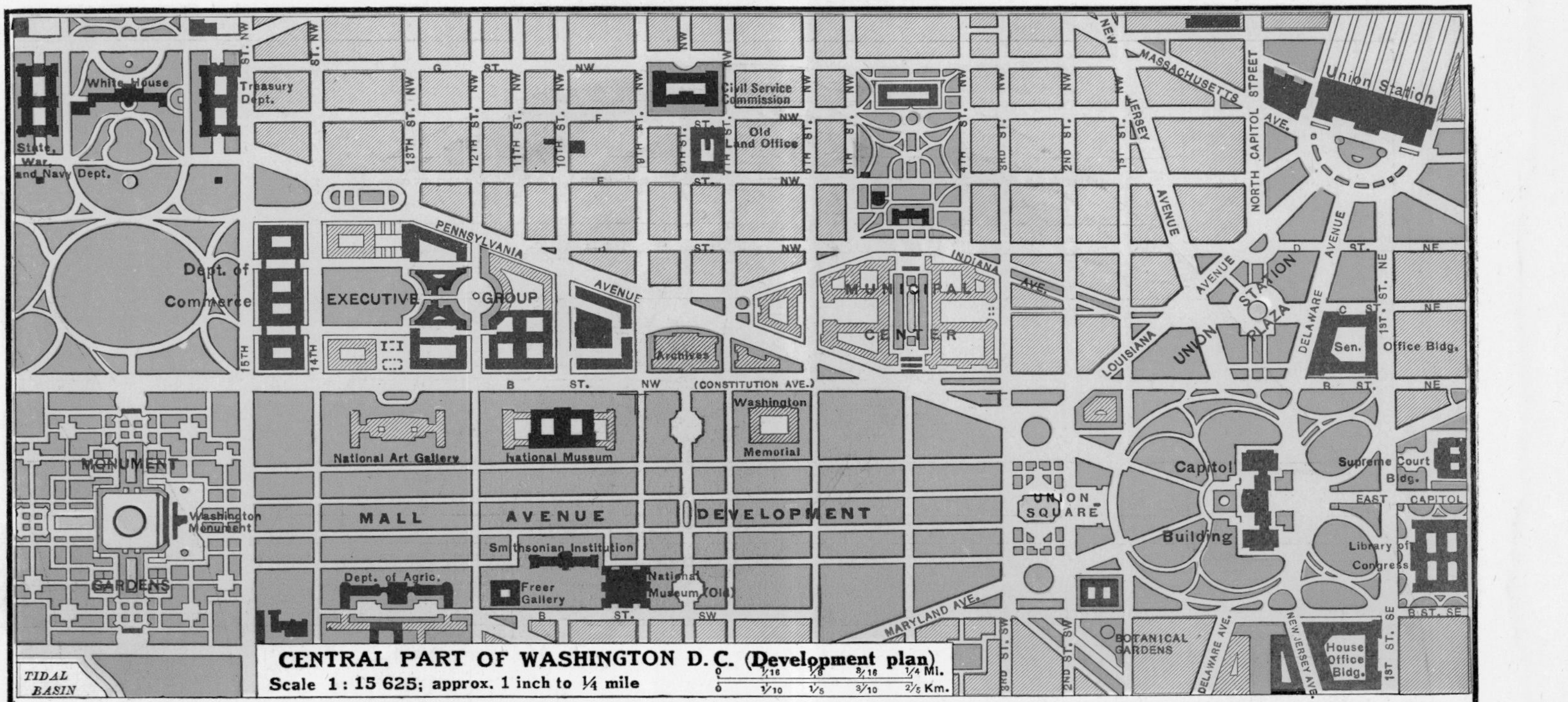

CENTRAL PART OF WASHINGTON D. C. (Development plan)
Scale 1 : 15 625; approx. 1 inch to ¼ mile

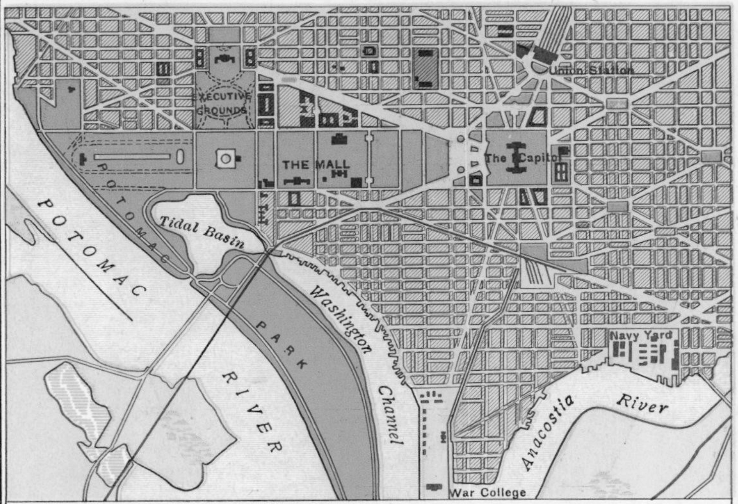

PART OF WASHINGTON, D. C.
Scale 1 : 62 500; approx. 1 inch to 1 mile

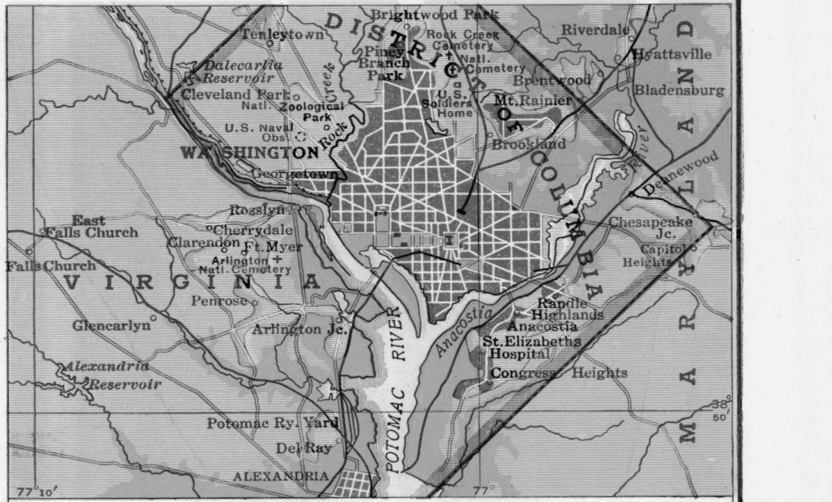

WASHINGTON AND VICINITY
Scale 1 : 250 000; approx. 1 inch to 4 miles

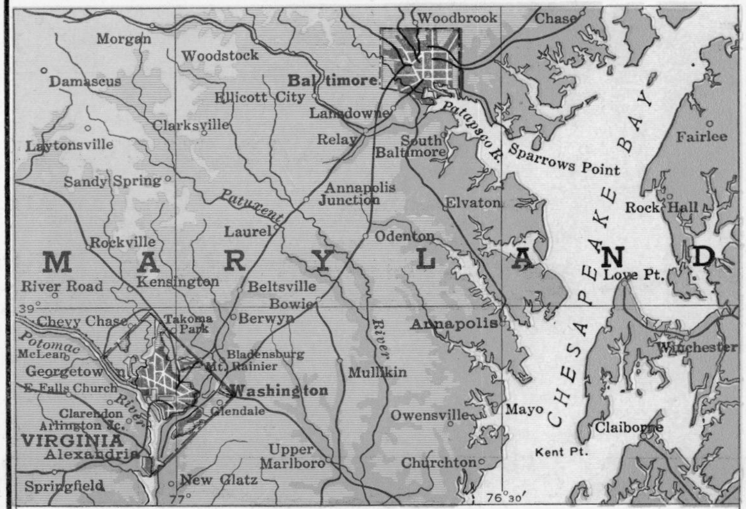

WASHINGTON TO BALTIMORE
Scale 1 : 1 000 000; approx. 1 inch to 16 miles

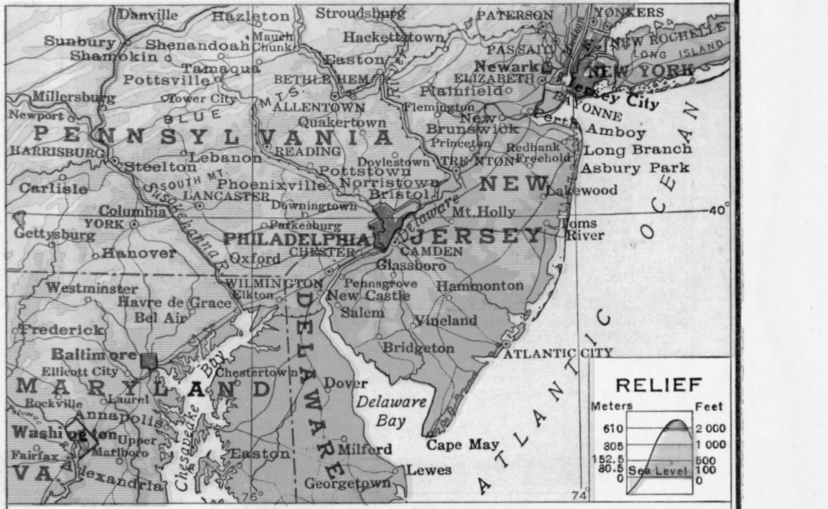

WASHINGTON TO NEW YORK
Scale 1 : 4 000 000; approx. 1 inch to 64 miles

Elevations and depressions are given in feet

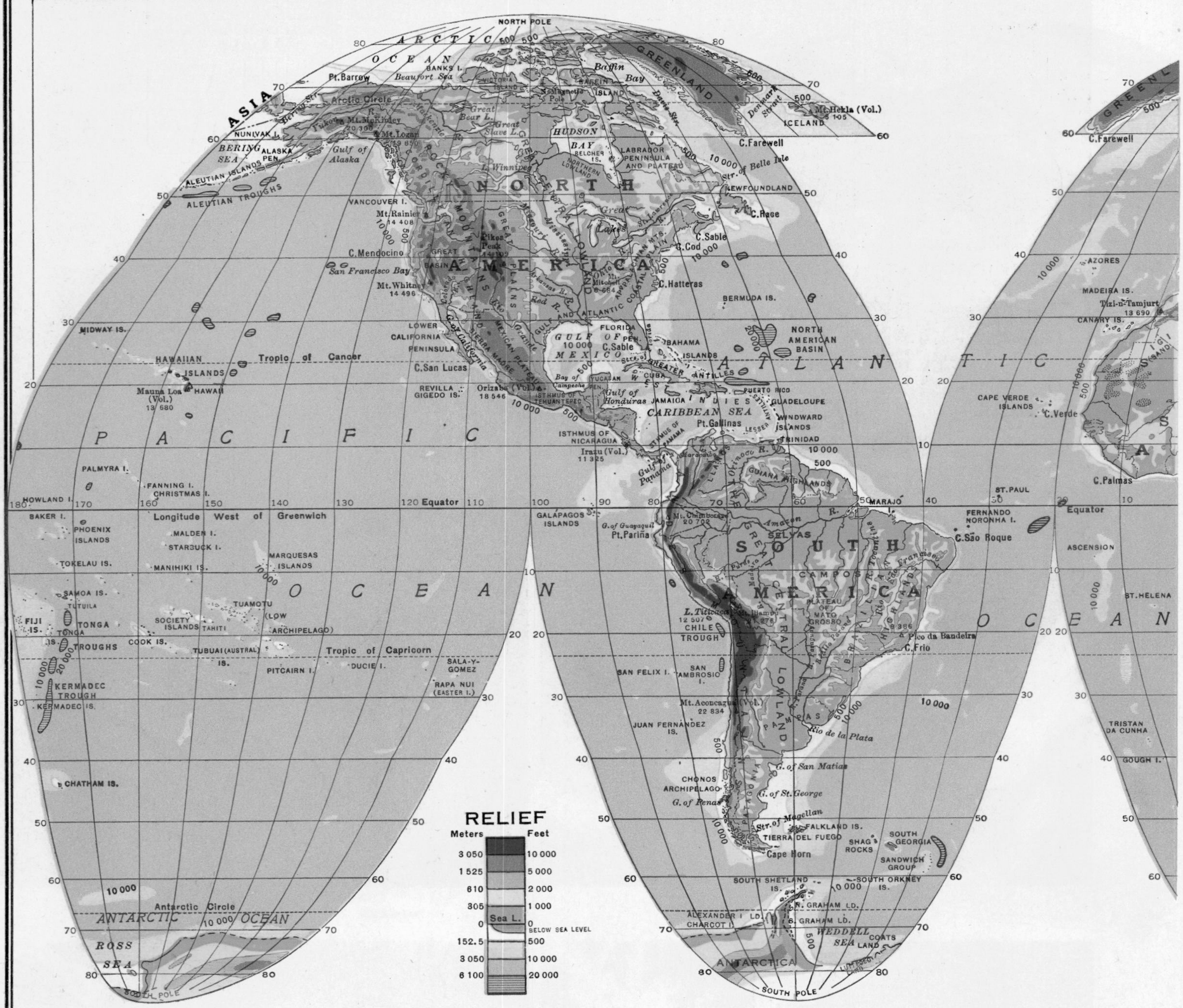

LAND ELEVATIONS

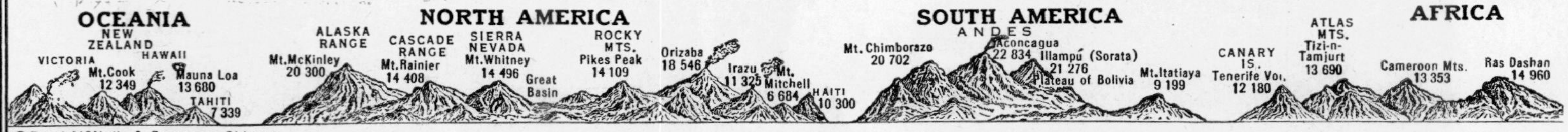

OCEAN DEPTHS

On the same vertical scale as

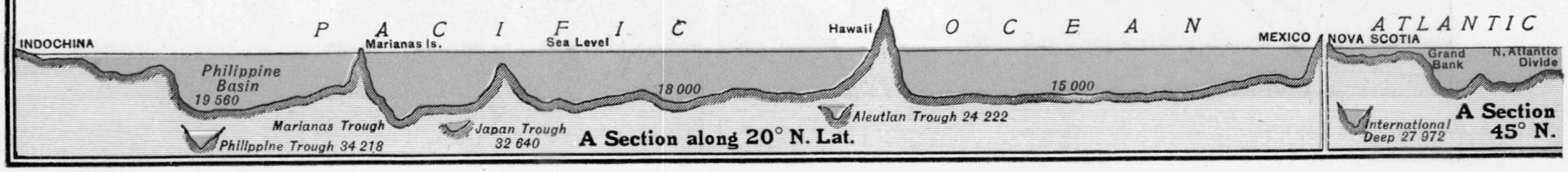

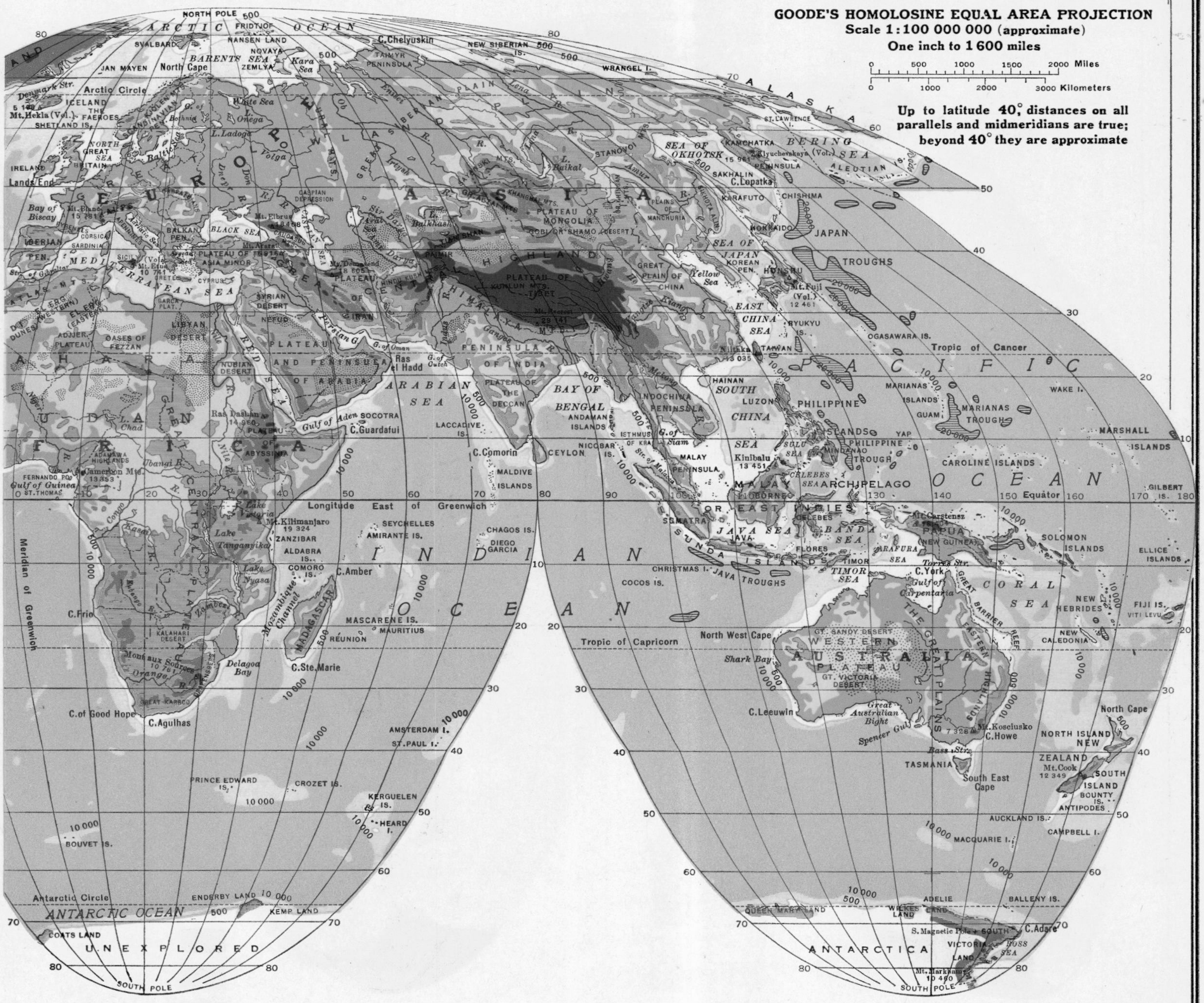

IN PROFILE

IN PROFILE

the land elevations

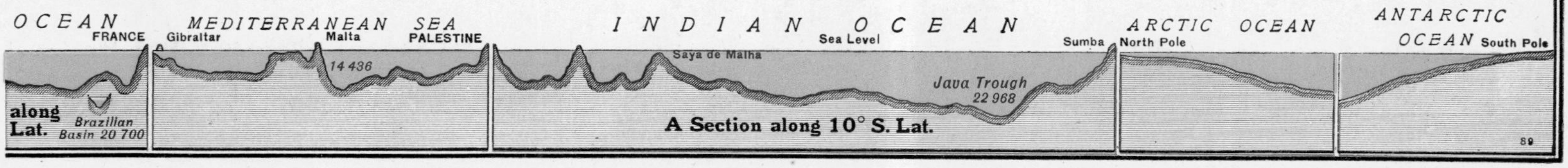

depressions are given in feet

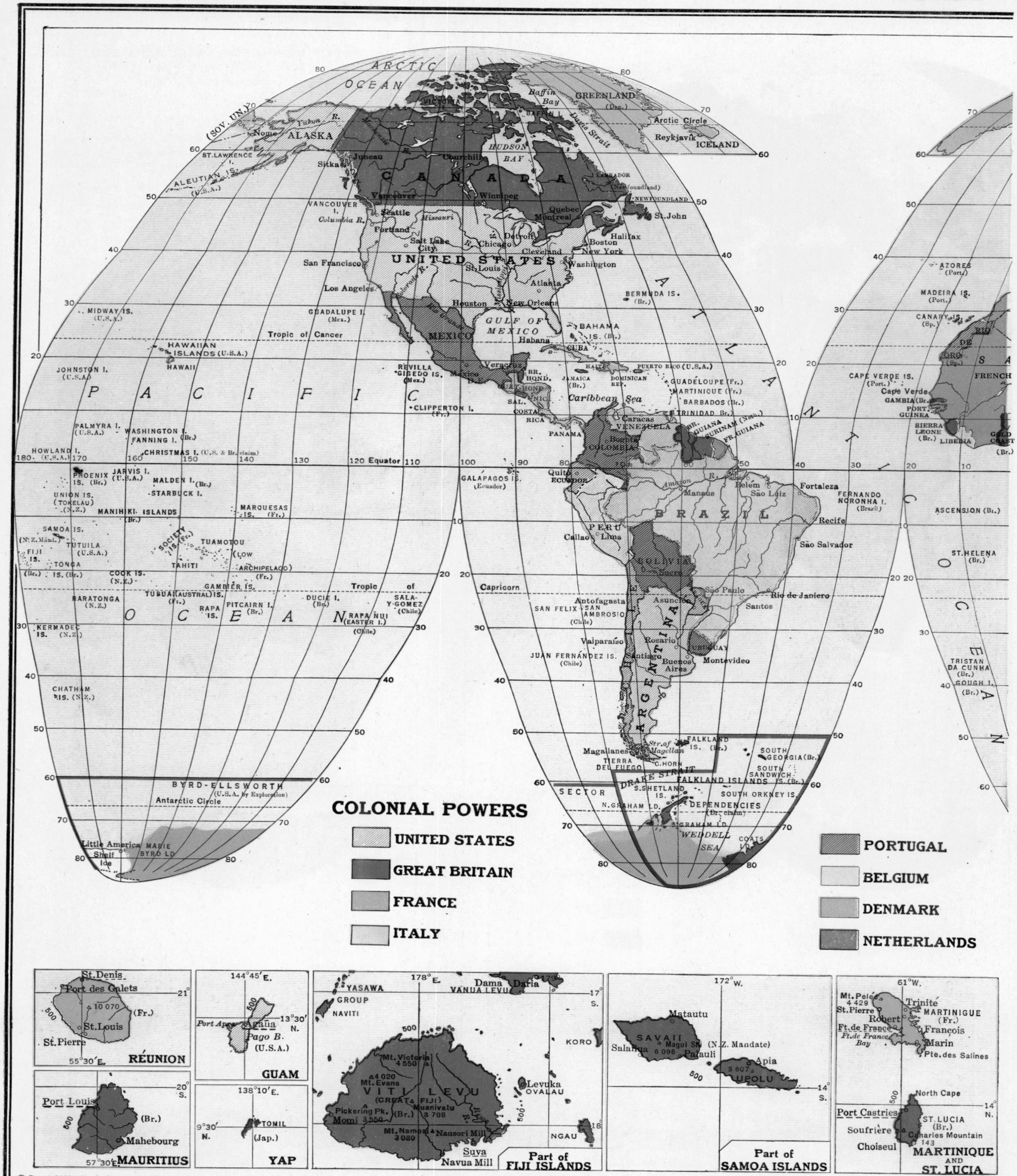
COLONIAL POWERS
UNITED STATES
GREAT BRITAIN
FRANCE
ITALY
PORTUGAL
BELGIUM
DENMARK
NETHERLANDS
ARCTIC OCEAN
ALASKA
CANADA
GREENLAND (Den.)
ICELAND
HUDSON BAY
NEWFOUNDLAND
UNITED STATES
GULF OF MEXICO
MEXICO
Caribbean Sea
PACIFIC OCEAN
ATLANTIC OCEAN
BRAZIL
PERU
BOLIVIA
ARGENTINA
COLOMBIA
VENEZUELA
URUGUAY
HAWAIIAN ISLANDS (U.S.A.)
BERMUDA IS. (Br.)
BAHAMA IS. (Br.)
PUERTO RICO (U.S.A.)
FALKLAND IS. (Br.)
SOUTH GEORGIA (Br.)
FALKLAND ISLANDS DEPENDENCIES (Br. claim)
BYRD-ELLSWORTH SECTOR (U.S.A. by Exploration)
WEDDELL SEA
DRAKE STRAIT
Tropic of Cancer
Equator
Tropic of Capricorn
Arctic Circle
Antarctic Circle
AZORES (Port.)
MADEIRA IS. (Port.)
CANARY IS. (Sp.)
CAPE VERDE IS. (Port.)
ASCENSION (Br.)
ST. HELENA (Br.)
TRISTAN DA CUNHA (Br.)
RÉUNION
MAURITIUS
GUAM
YAP
Part of FIJI ISLANDS
Part of SAMOA ISLANDS
MARTINIQUE AND ST. LUCIA

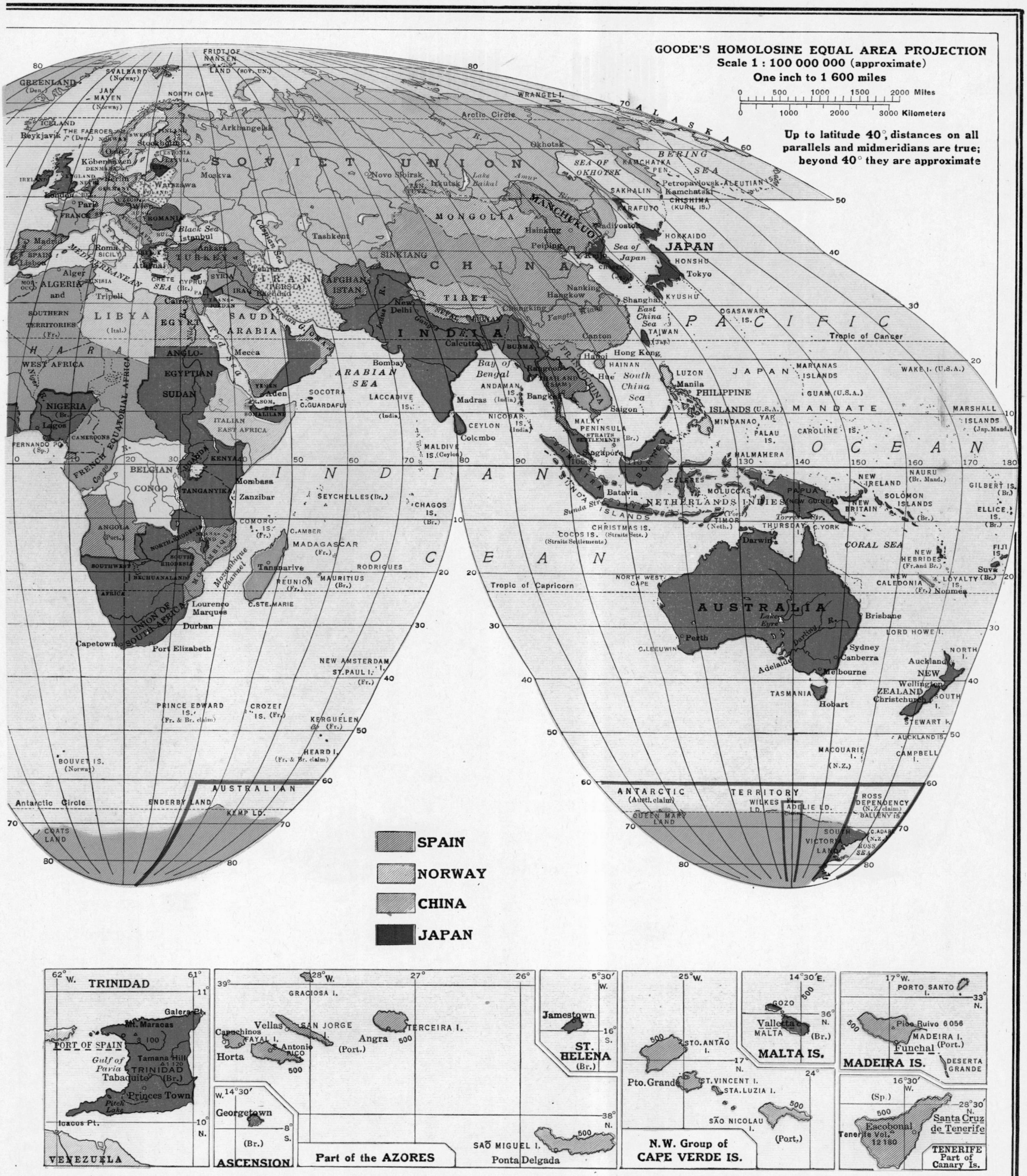

Scale for insets only 1 : 4 000 000; one inch to 64 miles

Elevations and depressions are given in feet

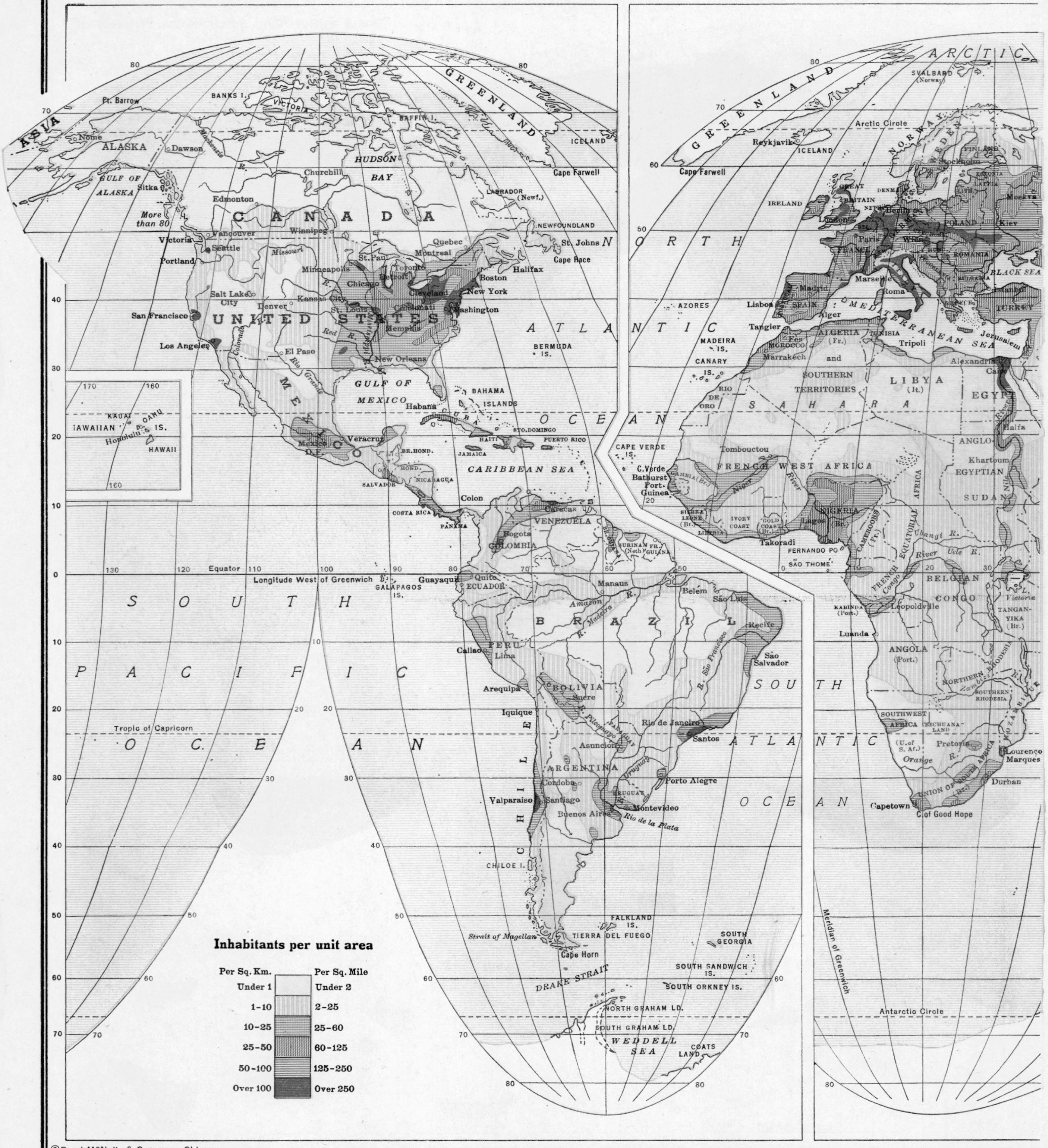
ARCTIC
GREENLAND
SVALBARD (Norway)
Pt. Barrow
BANKS I.
VICTORIA
BAFFIN I.
ASIA
Nome
ALASKA
Dawson
Mackenzie R.
ICELAND
Reykjavik
Arctic Circle
NORWAY
SWEDEN
FINLAND
HUDSON BAY
Churchill
GULF OF ALASKA
Sitka
Cape Farwell
LABRADOR (Newf.)
Edmonton
More than 80
CANADA
NEWFOUNDLAND
Winnipeg
Vancouver
Victoria
Seattle
Portland
Missouri
St. Paul
Minneapolis
Quebec
Montreal
Toronto
Detroit
Chicago
Boston
New York
Cleveland
Halifax
St. Johns
Cape Race
NORTH
GREAT BRITAIN
IRELAND
London
Berlin
Paris
Wien
POLAND
Kiev
FRANCE
ROMANIA
BLACK SEA
Salt Lake City
Denver
Kansas City
St. Louis
Cincinnati
Washington
San Francisco
UNITED STATES
Memphis
Red R.
Los Angeles
Colorado
El Paso
Rio Grande
New Orleans
Mississippi
AZORES
Madrid
SPAIN
Lisboa
Marseille
Roma
Istanbul
TURKEY
MEDITERRANEAN SEA
Alger
Tangier
ATLANTIC
BERMUDA IS.
MADEIRA IS.
CANARY IS.
MOROCCO
Fes
Marrakech
ALGERIA (Fr.)
and
SOUTHERN TERRITORIES
TUNISIA
Tripoli
Jerusalem
Alexandria
Cairo
LIBYA (It.)
EGYPT
SAHARA
RIO DE ORO
GULF OF MEXICO
MEXICO
Habana
BAHAMA ISLANDS
CUBA
OCEAN
HAWAIIAN IS.
KAUAI
OAHU
Honolulu
HAWAII
Veracruz
Mexico D.F.
BR. HOND.
HAITI
STO. DOMINGO
PUERTO RICO
JAMAICA
CARIBBEAN SEA
HOND.
SALVADOR
NICARAGUA
CAPE VERDE IS.
C. Verde
Bathurst
Port Guinea
Tombouctou
FRENCH WEST AFRICA
Niger
ANGLO-EGYPTIAN SUDAN
Khartoum
Nile
Colon
COSTA RICA
PANAMA
Caracas
VENEZUELA
Bogota
COLOMBIA
SURINAM (Neth.)
FR. GUIANA
SIERRA LEONE (Br.)
LIBERIA
IVORY COAST
GOLD COAST (Br.)
Lagos
NIGERIA (Br.)
CAMEROONS (Fr.)
FRENCH EQUATORIAL AFRICA
Ubangi R.
Uele R.
Takoradi
FERNANDO PO
SAO THOME
Equator
Longitude West of Greenwich
GALAPAGOS IS.
Guayaquil
Quito
ECUADOR
Manaus
Amazon R.
Belem
São Luis
Congo River
FRENCH Congo
BELGIAN CONGO
Leopoldville
L. Victoria
TANGANYIKA (Br.)
KABINDA (Port.)
SOUTH
PACIFIC
OCEAN
Madeira R.
BRAZIL
Recife
Luanda
ANGOLA (Port.)
PERU
Callao
Lima
São Francisco R.
São Salvador
NORTHERN RHODESIA
Zambezi R.
SOUTHERN RHODESIA
BOLIVIA
Sucre
Arequipa
Iquique
Pilcomayo R.
PARAGUAY
Rio de Janeiro
Santos
SOUTH ATLANTIC OCEAN
SOUTHWEST AFRICA
BECHUANALAND
(U. of S. Af.)
Pretoria
Orange R.
MOZAMBIQUE
Lourenço Marques
Tropic of Capricorn
Asuncion
ARGENTINA
Uruguay
Cordoba
URUGUAY
Porto Alegre
Valparaiso
Santiago
CHILE
Buenos Aires
Montevideo
Rio de la Plata
UNION OF SOUTH AFRICA
Durban
Capetown
C. of Good Hope
CHILOE I.
FALKLAND IS.
Strait of Magellan
TIERRA DEL FUEGO
Cape Horn
SOUTH GEORGIA
SOUTH SANDWICH IS.
SOUTH ORKNEY IS.
DRAKE STRAIT
NORTH GRAHAM LD.
SOUTH GRAHAM LD.
WEDDELL SEA
COATS LAND
Antarctic Circle
Meridian of Greenwich
Inhabitants per unit area
Per Sq. Km.
Per Sq. Mile
Under 1
Under 2
1-10
2-25
10-25
25-60
25-50
60-125
50-100
125-250
Over 100
Over 250

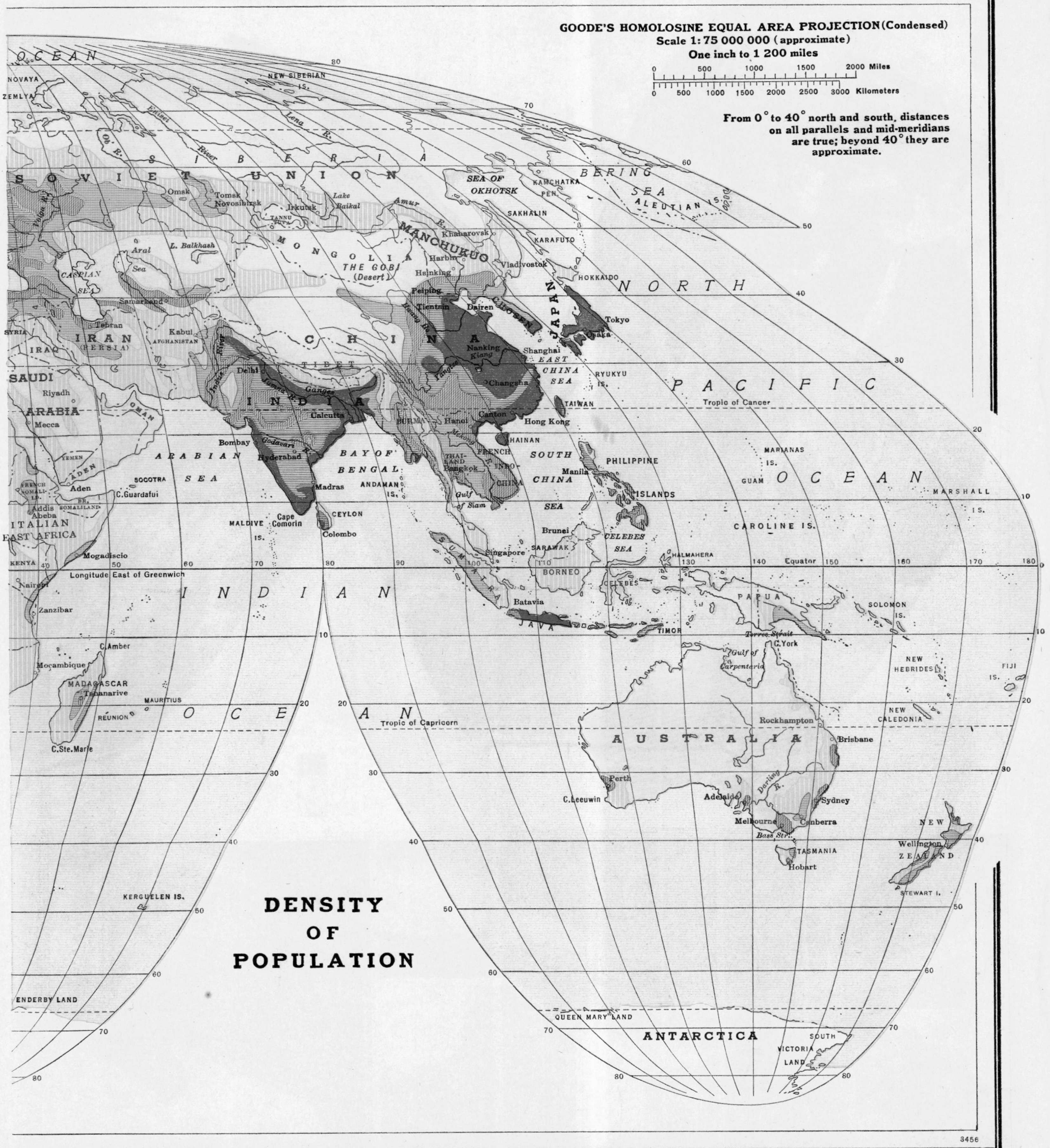
GOODE'S HOMOLOSINE EQUAL AREA PROJECTION (Condensed)
Scale 1: 75 000 000 (approximate)
One inch to 1 200 miles
0 500 1000 1500 2000 Miles
0 500 1000 1500 2000 2500 3000 Kilometers
From 0° to 40° north and south, distances on all parallels and mid-meridians are true; beyond 40° they are approximate.
DENSITY OF POPULATION
OCEAN
NOVAYA ZEMLYA
NEW SIBERIAN IS.
SIBERIA
SOVIET UNION
Omsk
Tomsk
Novosibirsk
Irkutsk
Lake Baikal
SEA OF OKHOTSK
KAMCHATKA PEN.
BERING SEA
ALEUTIAN IS.
SAKHALIN
KARAFUTO
MANCHUKUO
Khabarovsk
Harbin
Hsinking
Vladivostok
HOKKAIDO
MONGOLIA
THE GOBI (Desert)
Aral Sea
L. Balkhash
CASPIAN SEA
Samarkand
Tehran
Kabul
AFGHANISTAN
IRAN (PERSIA)
IRAQ
SYRIA
SAUDI ARABIA
Riyadh
Mecca
CHINA
TIBET
Peiping
Tientsin
Dairen
CHOSEN
JAPAN
Tokyo
Osaka
Nanking
Shanghai
Changsha
EAST CHINA SEA
RYUKYU IS.
TAIWAN
NORTH PACIFIC OCEAN
Tropic of Cancer
INDIA
Delhi
Ganges
Calcutta
Bombay
Hyderabad
Madras
Cape Comorin
CEYLON
Colombo
ARABIAN SEA
BAY OF BENGAL
ANDAMAN IS.
MALDIVE IS.
SOCOTRA
C. Guardafui
Aden
ADEN
YEMEN
OMAN
FRENCH SOMALILAND
BR. SOMALILAND
Addis Abeba
ITALIAN EAST AFRICA
KENYA
Mogadiscio
Nairobi
Zanzibar
BURMA
Hanoi
Canton
Hong Kong
HAINAN
THAILAND
Bangkok
FRENCH INDO-CHINA
Gulf of Siam
SOUTH CHINA SEA
Manila
PHILIPPINE ISLANDS
MARIANAS IS.
GUAM
MARSHALL IS.
CAROLINE IS.
Brunei
SARAWAK
CELEBES SEA
BORNEO
CELEBES
HALMAHERA
Singapore
SUMATRA
Batavia
JAVA
TIMOR
PAPUA
SOLOMON IS.
Torres Strait
C. York
Gulf of Carpentaria
NEW HEBRIDES
FIJI IS.
NEW CALEDONIA
Equator
Longitude East of Greenwich
INDIAN OCEAN
C. Amber
Mocambique
MADAGASCAR
Tananarive
MAURITIUS
REUNION
C. Ste. Marie
Tropic of Capricorn
AUSTRALIA
Rockhampton
Brisbane
Perth
C. Leeuwin
Adelaide
Darling R.
Sydney
Melbourne
Canberra
Bass Str.
TASMANIA
Hobart
NEW ZEALAND
Wellington
STEWART I.
KERGUELEN IS.
ENDERBY LAND
QUEEN MARY LAND
ANTARCTICA
SOUTH VICTORIA LAND
3456

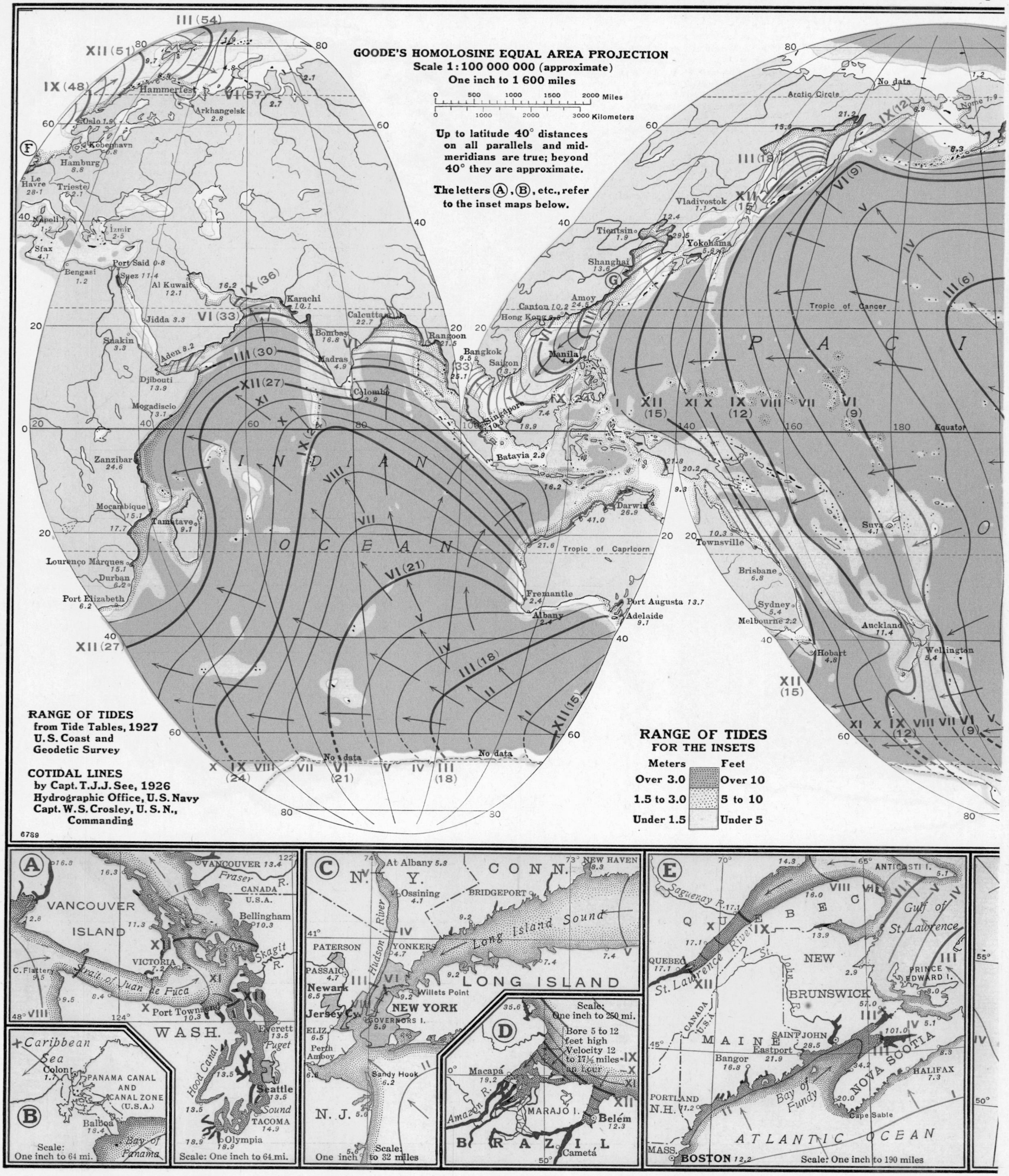
GOODE'S HOMOLOSINE EQUAL AREA PROJECTION
Scale 1:100 000 000 (approximate)
One inch to 1 600 miles
0 500 1000 1500 2000 Miles
0 1000 2000 3000 Kilometers
Up to latitude 40° distances on all parallels and mid-meridians are true; beyond 40° they are approximate.
The letters (A), (B), etc., refer to the inset maps below.
RANGE OF TIDES
from Tide Tables, 1927
U.S. Coast and Geodetic Survey
COTIDAL LINES
by Capt. T.J.J. See, 1926
Hydrographic Office, U.S. Navy
Capt. W.S. Crosley, U.S.N., Commanding
6789
RANGE OF TIDES FOR THE INSETS
Meters
Feet
Over 3.0
Over 10
1.5 to 3.0
5 to 10
Under 1.5
Under 5
INDIAN OCEAN
PACIFIC O
Tropic of Cancer
Tropic of Capricorn
Equator
Arctic Circle
No data
VANCOUVER ISLAND
WASH.
Scale: One inch to 64 mi.
PANAMA CANAL AND CANAL ZONE (U.S.A.)
Caribbean Sea
Bay of Panama
Scale: One inch to 64 mi.
CONN.
N. Y.
N. J.
Long Island Sound
LONG ISLAND
NEW YORK
One inch to 32 miles
Scale: One inch to 250 mi.
Bore 5 to 12 feet high Velocity 12 to 17½ miles an hour
BRAZIL
MARAJÓ I.
QUEBEC
NEW BRUNSWICK
MAINE
NOVA SCOTIA
Gulf of St. Lawrence
Bay of Fundy
ATLANTIC OCEAN
Scale: One inch to 190 miles

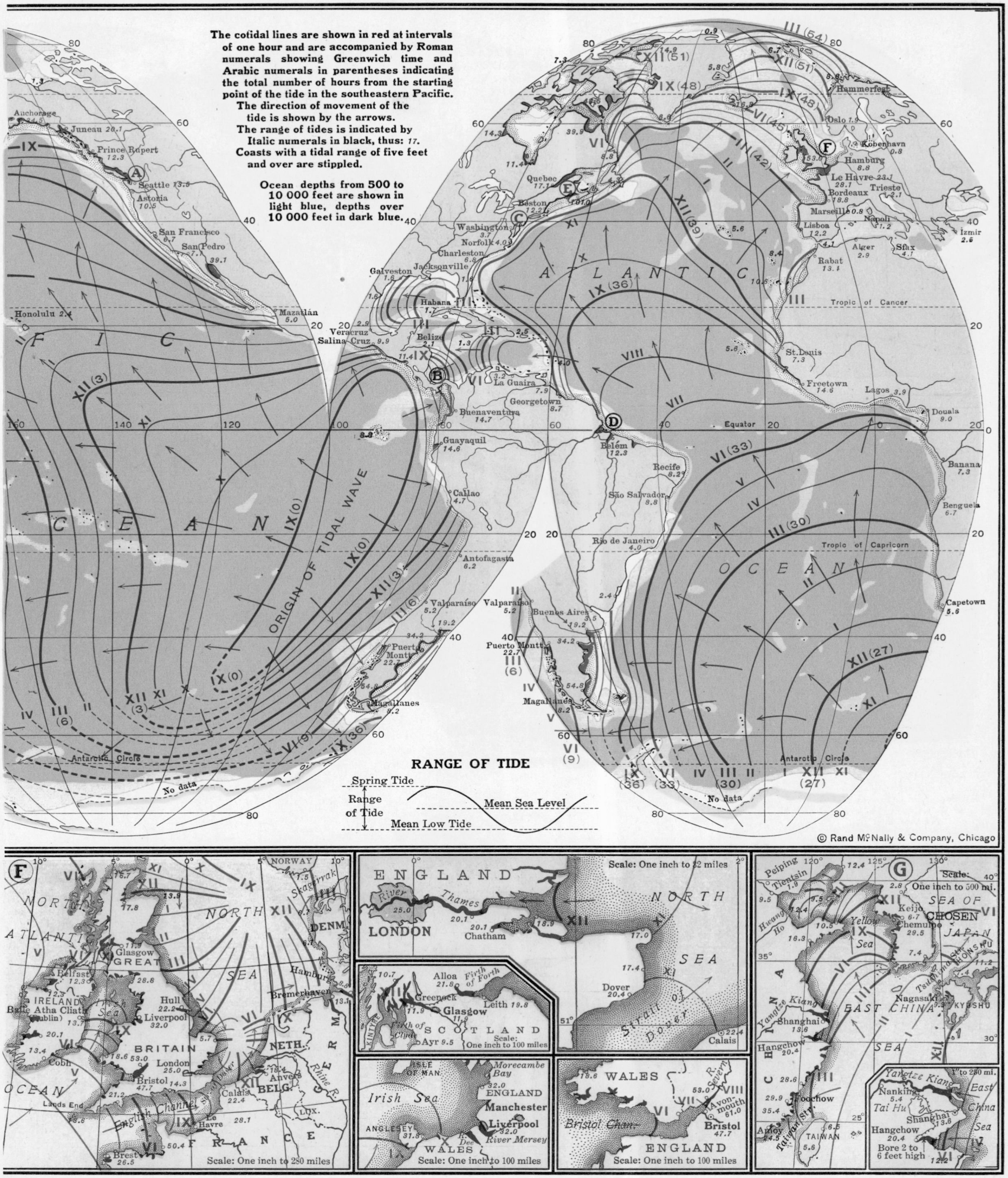
The cotidal lines are shown in red at intervals of one hour and are accompanied by Roman numerals showing Greenwich time and Arabic numerals in parentheses indicating the total number of hours from the starting point of the tide in the southeastern Pacific.
The direction of movement of the tide is shown by the arrows.
The range of tides is indicated by Italic numerals in black, thus: 17.
Coasts with a tidal range of five feet and over are stippled.
Ocean depths from 500 to 10 000 feet are shown in light blue, depths over 10 000 feet in dark blue.
ORIGIN OF TIDAL WAVE
ATLANTIC
OCEAN
RANGE OF TIDE
Spring Tide
Range of Tide
Mean Sea Level
Mean Low Tide
Equator
Tropic of Cancer
Tropic of Capricorn
Antarctic Circle
No data
Anchorage
Juneau 20.1
Prince Rupert 12.3
Seattle 13.5
Astoria 10.5
San Francisco 6.7
San Pedro 7.1
Honolulu 2.4
Mazatlán 5.0
Veracruz
Salina Cruz 9.9
Galveston 1.6
Jacksonville
Charleston 6.6
Norfolk 4.0
Washington 3.7
Boston 12.2
Quebec 17.1
Habana 1.7
Belize 2.1
La Guaira 3.2
Georgetown 8.7
Buenaventura 14.7
Guayaquil 14.6
Callao 4.7
Antofagasta 6.2
Valparaíso 5.2
Puerto Montt 22.7
Magallanes 8.2
Buenos Aires
Rio de Janeiro 4.0
São Salvador 8.8
Recife 8.2
Belém 12.3
Hammerfest
Oslo 1.9
København 0.8
Hamburg 8.8
Le Havre 23.1
Bordeaux 18.8
Marseille 0.8
Trieste 2.1
Napoli 1.2
Lisboa 12.2
Izmir 2.6
Alger 2.9
Sfax 4.1
Rabat 13.1
St. Louis 7.3
Freetown 14.6
Lagos 3.9
Douala 9.0
Banana 7.3
Benguela 6.7
Capetown 5.6
NORTH SEA
GREAT BRITAIN
IRELAND
Baile Atha Cliath (Dublin)
Glasgow
Belfast
Hull
Liverpool
London
Bristol
Cobh
Lands End
Brest 26.5
Le Havre
Calais
Anvers
BELG.
NETH.
Bremerhaven
Hamburg
DENM.
NORWAY
Skagerrak
English Channel
FRANCE
GERMANY
LUX.
Rhine R.
Scale: One inch to 280 miles
ENGLAND
River Thames
LONDON
Chatham
Dover
Strait of Dover
Calais
Scale: One inch to 32 miles
Alloa
Firth of Forth
Leith
Greenock
Glasgow
Firth of Clyde
Ayr
KINTYRE
SCOTLAND
Scale: One inch to 100 miles
ISLE OF MAN
Morecambe Bay
Irish Sea
ENGLAND
Manchester
Liverpool
River Mersey
Dee
ANGLESEY
WALES
Scale: One inch to 100 miles
WALES
R. Severn
Avonmouth
Bristol Chan.
Bristol
ENGLAND
Scale: One inch to 100 miles
Peiping
Tientsin
Hwang Ho
Yellow Sea
Keijo
Chemulpo
SEA OF CHOSEN
JAPAN
HONSHU
KYUSHU
Nagasaki
Tsushima Str.
EAST CHINA SEA
Yangtze Kiang
Shanghai
Hangchow
Foochow
Amoy
Taiwan Str.
TAIWAN
CHINA
Scale: One inch to 500 mi.
1" to 280 mi.
Nanking
Tai Hu
Bore 2 to 6 feet high

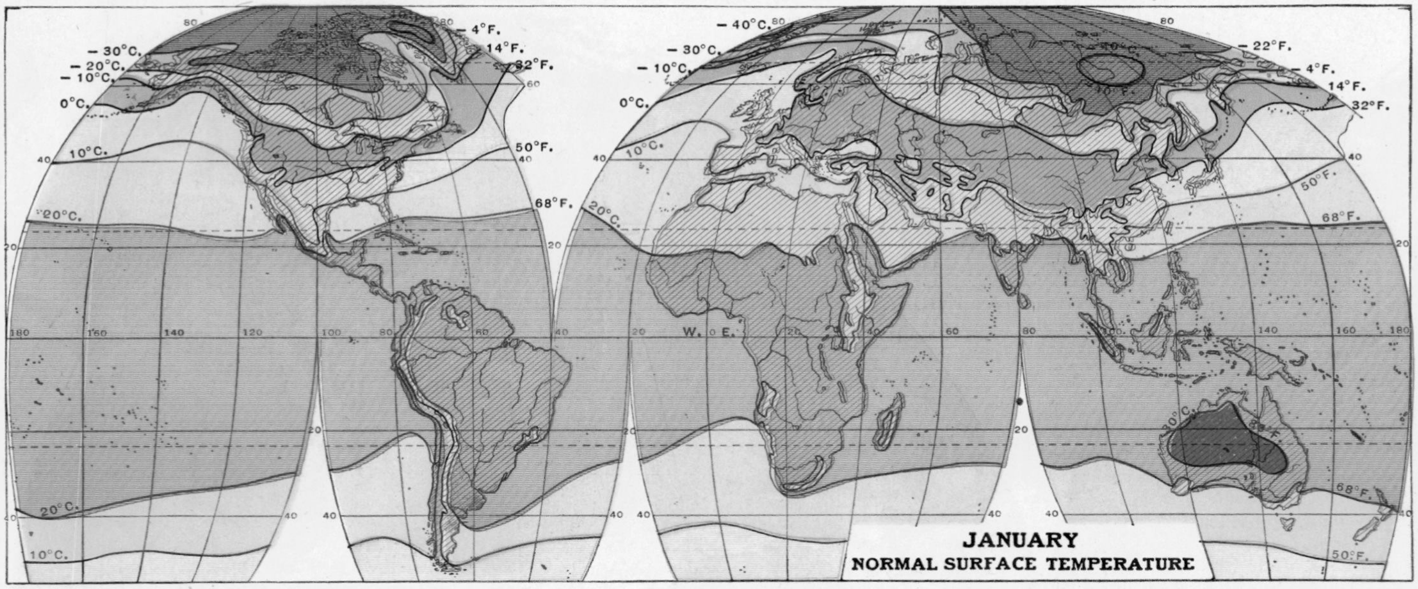
JANUARY
NORMAL SURFACE TEMPERATURE
−40°C.
−30°C.
−20°C.
−10°C.
0°C.
10°C.
20°C.
−22°F.
−4°F.
14°F.
32°F.
50°F.
68°F.
W.
E.

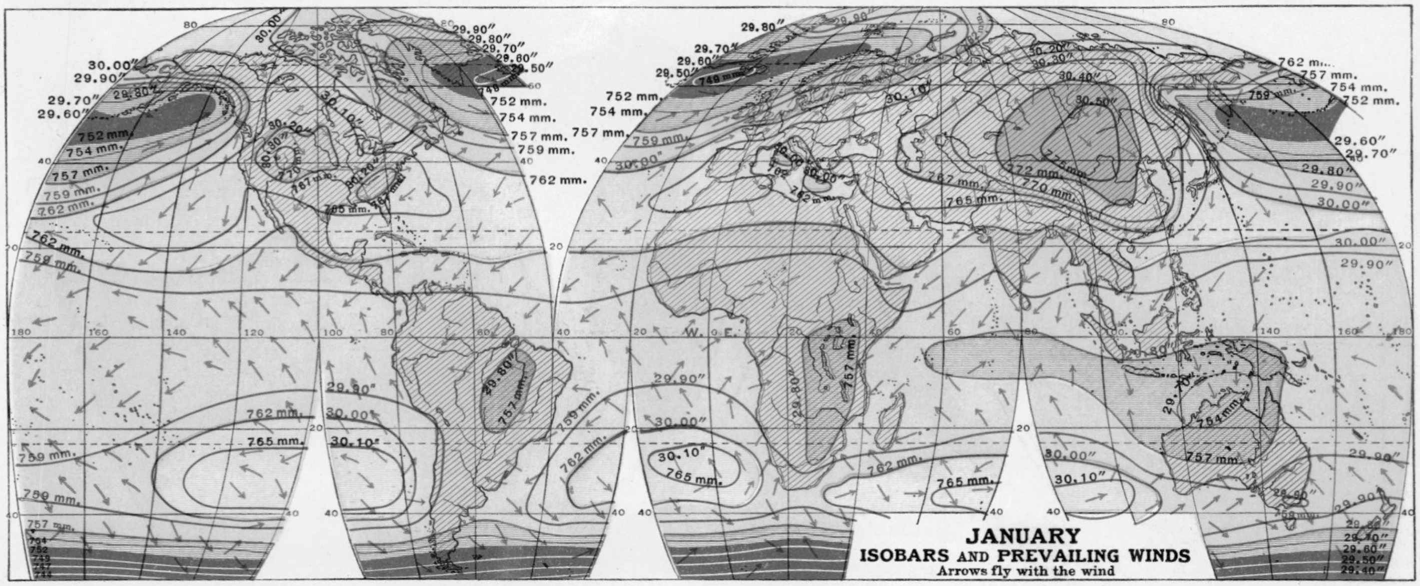
JANUARY
ISOBARS AND PREVAILING WINDS
Arrows fly with the wind
29.60″
29.70″
29.80″
29.90″
30.00″
30.10″
752 mm.
754 mm.
757 mm.
759 mm.
762 mm.
765 mm.
W.
E.

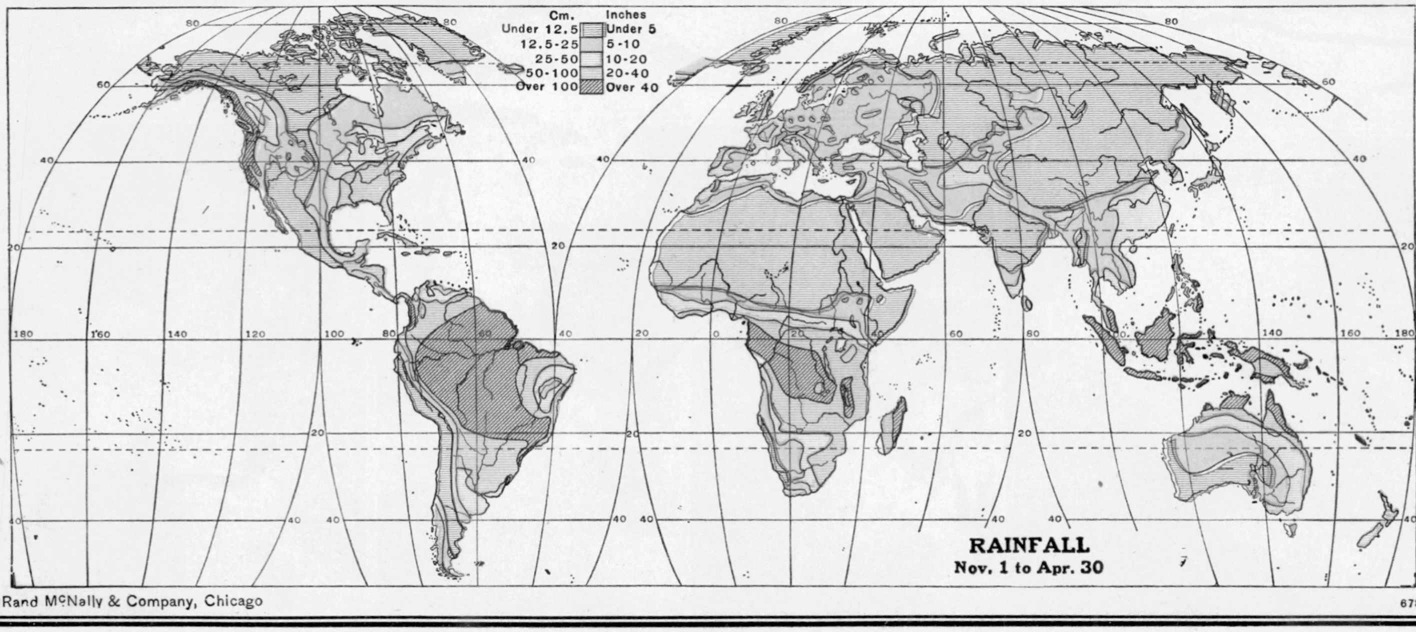
Cm. Inches
Under 12.5 Under 5
12.5-25 5-10
25-50 10-20
50-100 20-40
Over 100 Over 40
RAINFALL
Nov. 1 to Apr. 30

6789

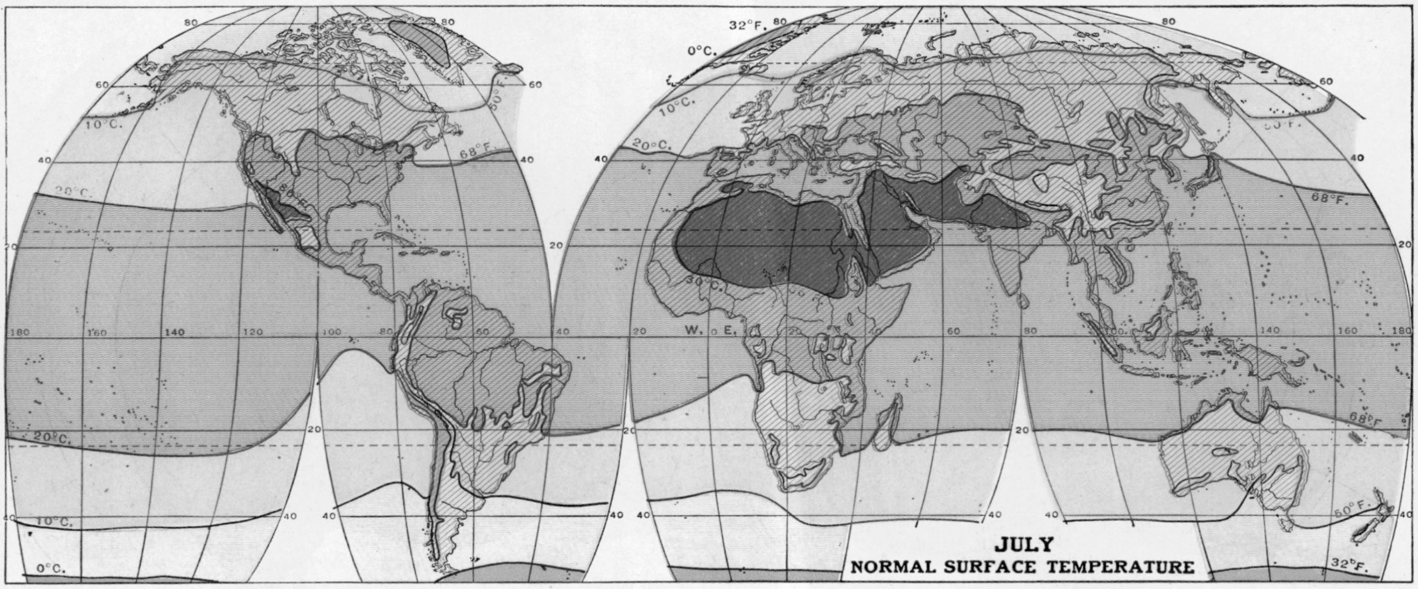

JULY
NORMAL SURFACE TEMPERATURE

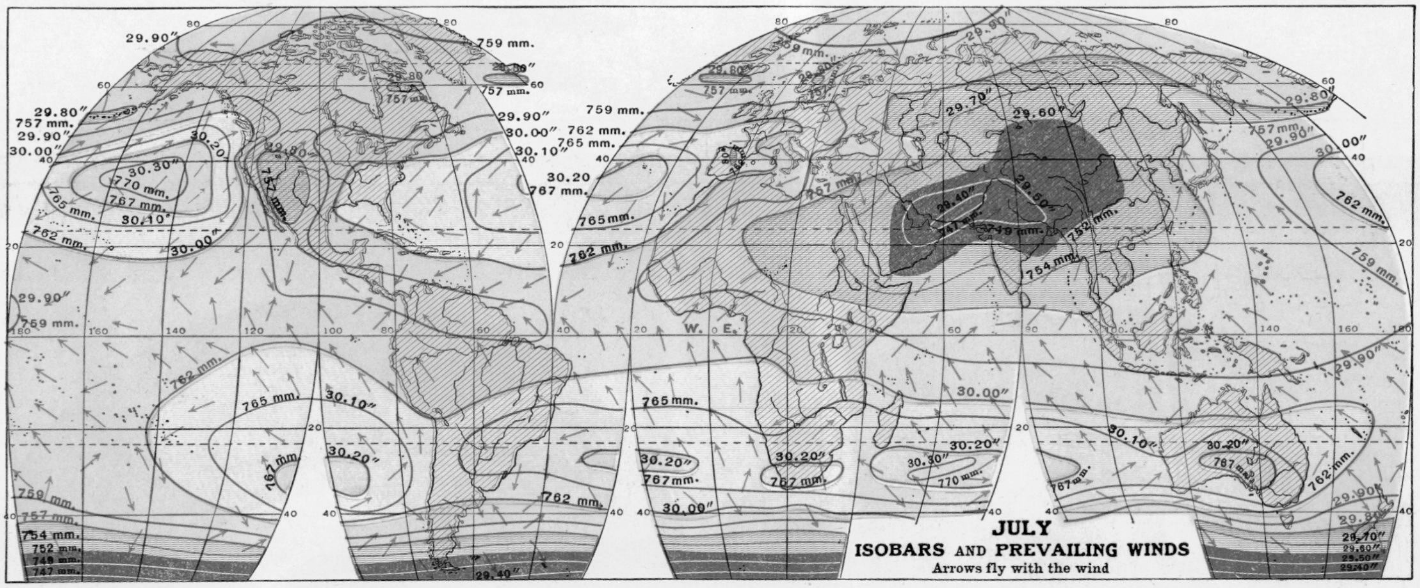

JULY
ISOBARS AND PREVAILING WINDS
Arrows fly with the wind

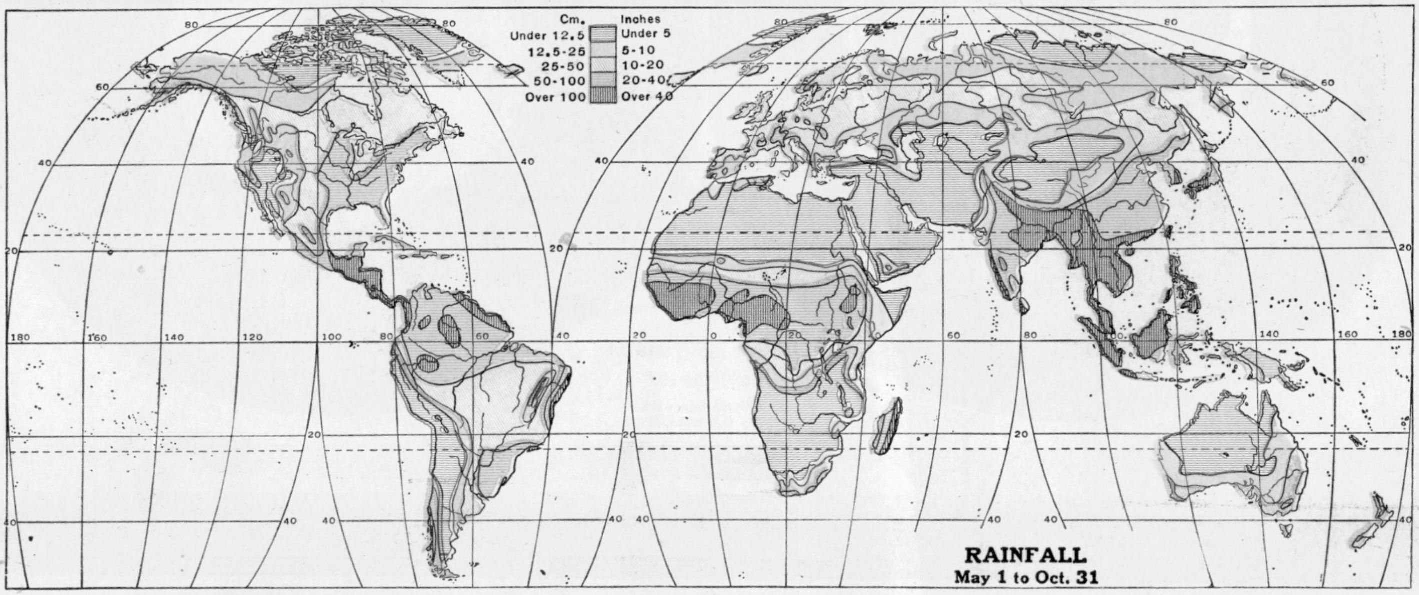

RAINFALL
May 1 to Oct. 31

1R32

Goode's Interrupted Homolographic Equal Area Projection

THE WORLD IN HEMISPHERES – Climatic

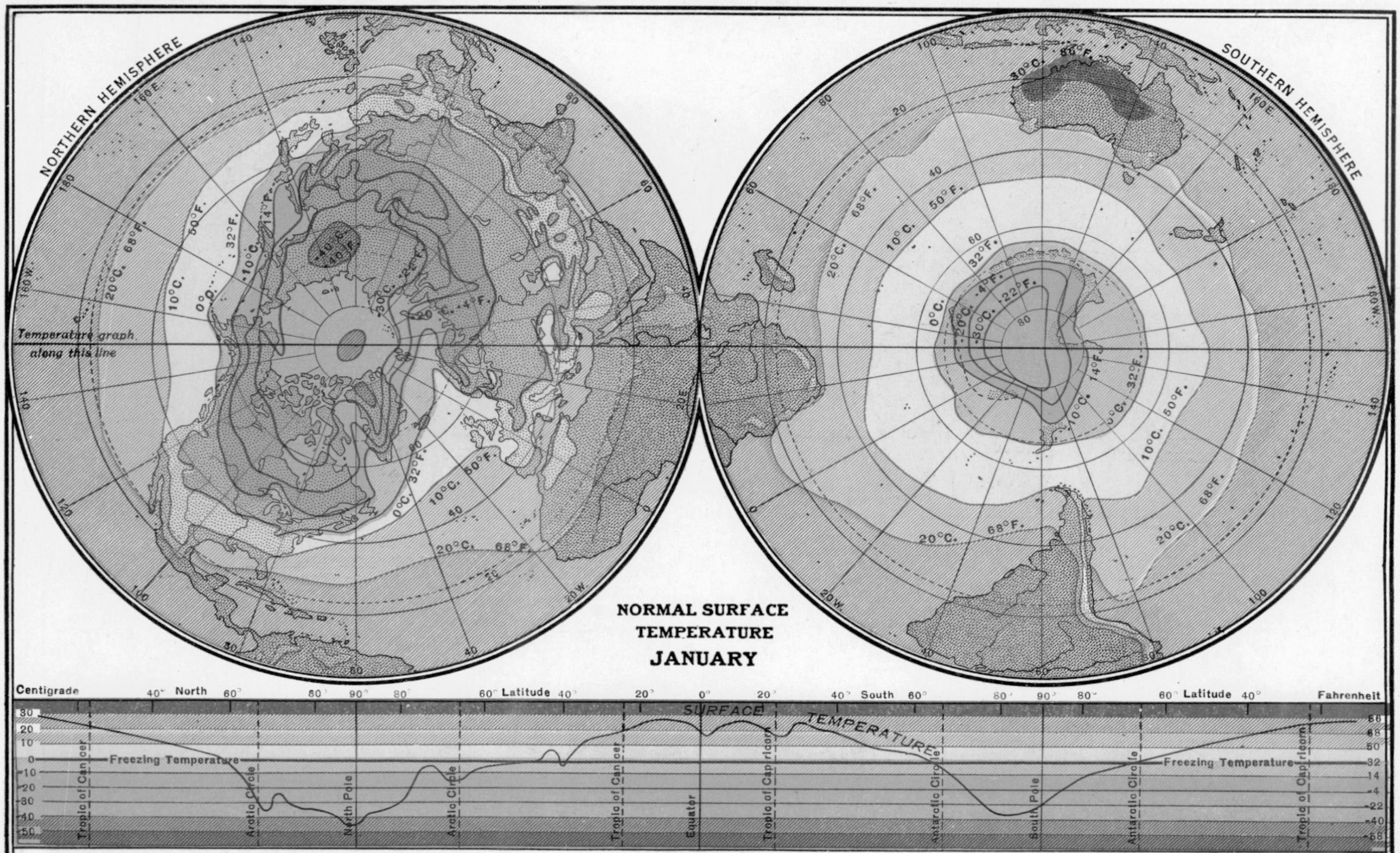

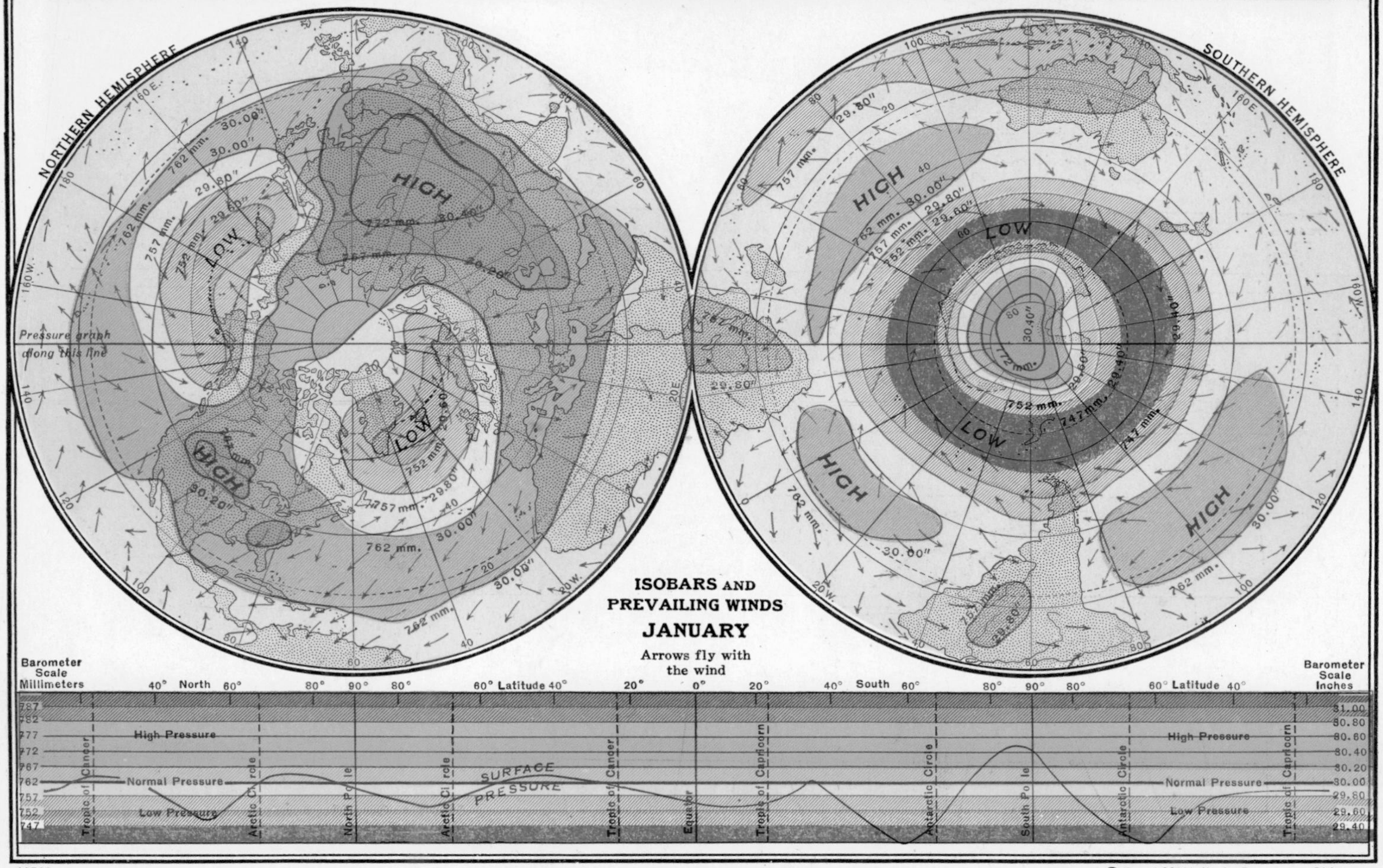

Lambert's Azimuthal Equal Area Projection

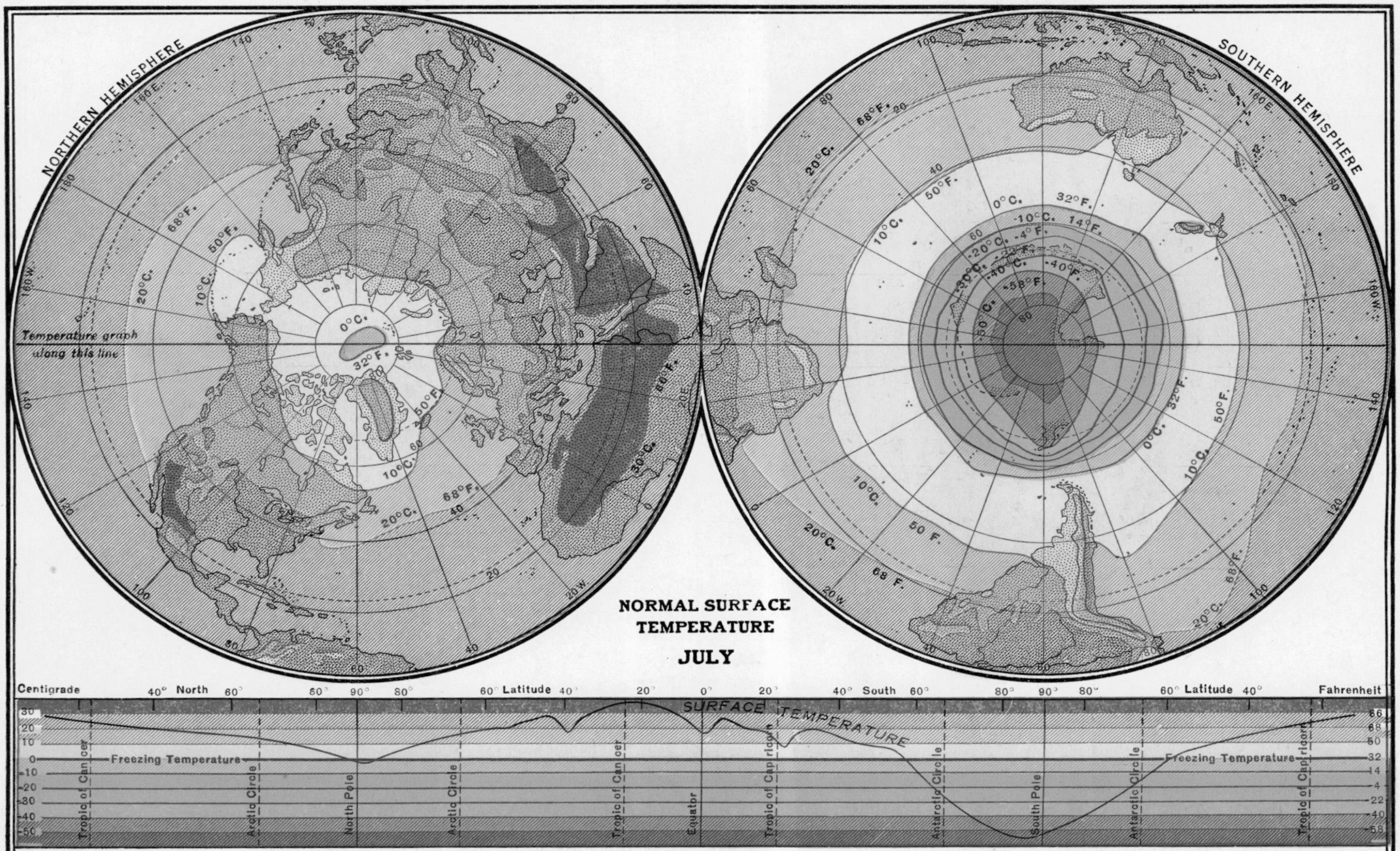

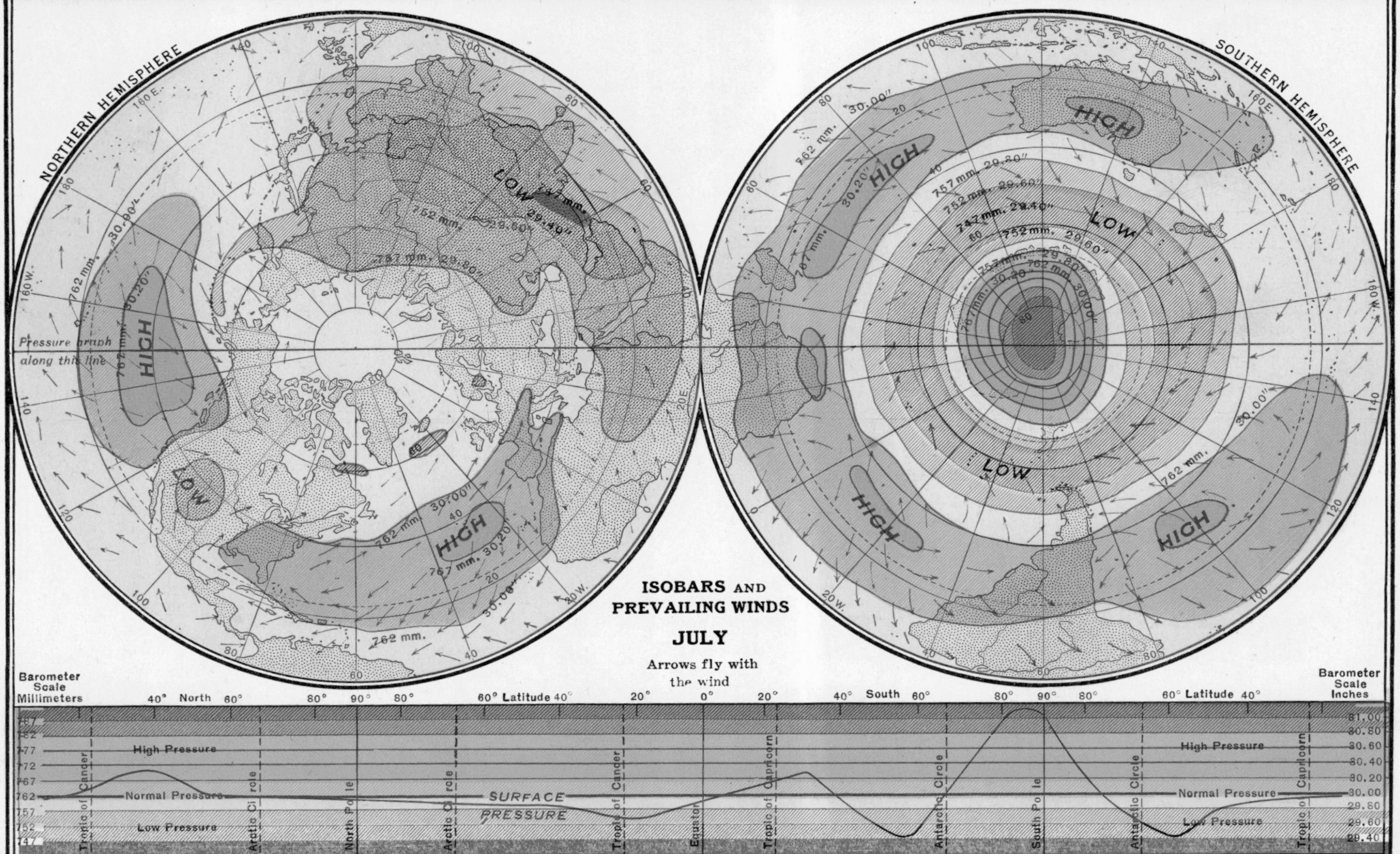

10R32

Lambert's Azimuthal Equal Area Projection

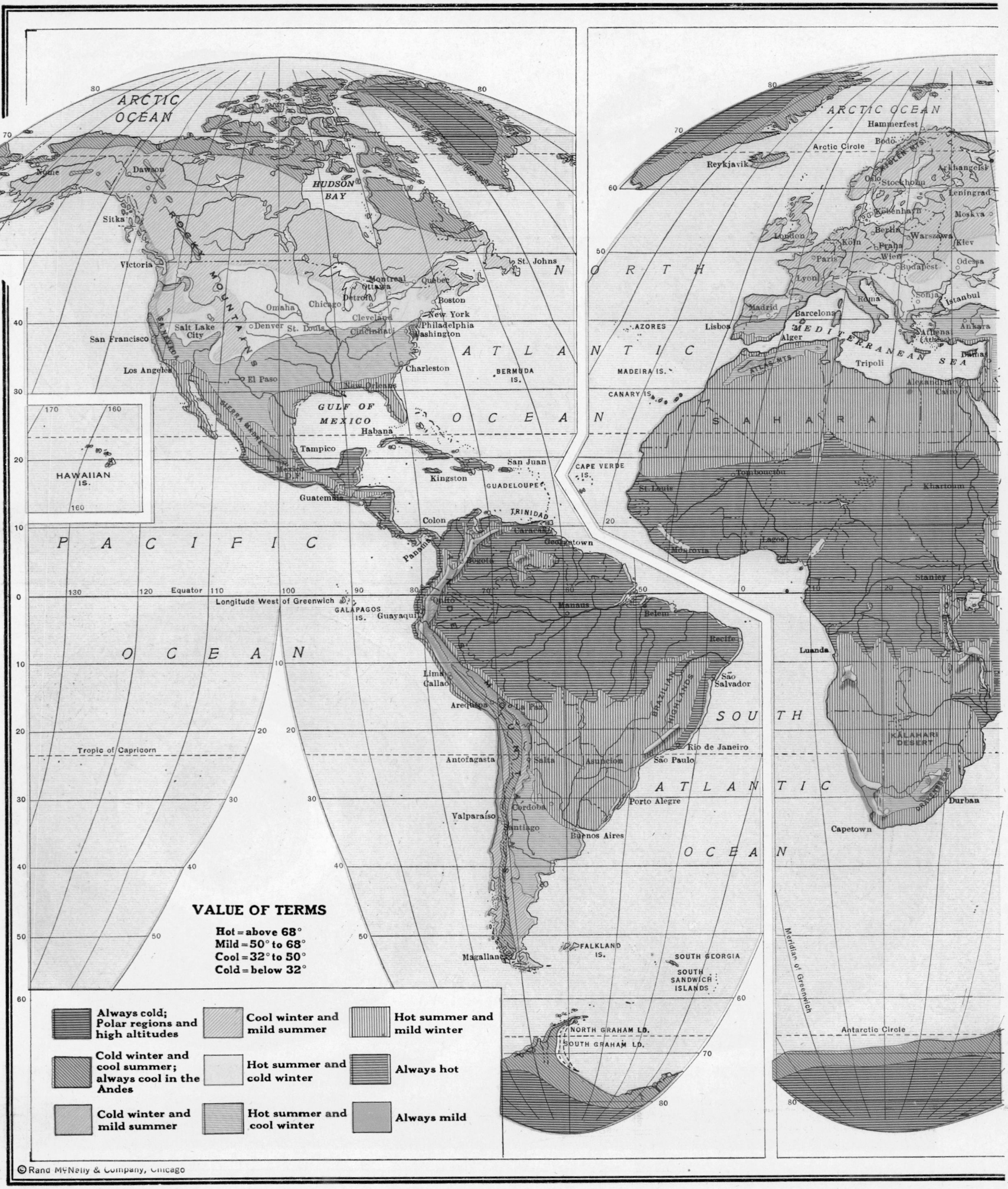
ARCTIC OCEAN
HUDSON BAY
ROCKY MOUNTAINS
SIERRA NEVADA
SIERRA MADRE
GULF OF MEXICO
HAWAIIAN IS.
PACIFIC OCEAN
Equator
Longitude West of Greenwich
GALAPAGOS IS.
Tropic of Capricorn
NORTH ATLANTIC OCEAN
AZORES
BERMUDA IS.
MADEIRA IS.
CANARY IS.
CAPE VERDE IS.
GUADELOUPE
TRINIDAD
BRAZILIAN HIGHLANDS
SOUTH ATLANTIC OCEAN
FALKLAND IS.
SOUTH GEORGIA
SOUTH SANDWICH ISLANDS
NORTH GRAHAM LD.
SOUTH GRAHAM LD.
Antarctic Circle
Arctic Circle
Meridian of Greenwich
ATLAS MTS.
SAHARA
MEDITERRANEAN SEA
KALAHARI DESERT
DRAKENSBERG
Nome
Dawson
Sitka
Victoria
San Francisco
Salt Lake City
Los Angeles
Denver
Omaha
Chicago
St. Louis
El Paso
Detroit
Cleveland
Cincinnati
Montreal
Ottawa
Quebec
Boston
New York
Philadelphia
Washington
Charleston
New Orleans
St. Johns
Tampico
Mexico D.F.
Guatemala
Habana
Kingston
San Juan
Colon
Panama
Caracas
Georgetown
Bogota
Quito
Guayaquil
Manaus
Belem
Recife
Lima
Callao
Arequipa
La Paz
São Salvador
Rio de Janeiro
São Paulo
Antofagasta
Salta
Asunción
Porto Alegre
Córdoba
Valparaíso
Santiago
Buenos Aires
Magallanes
Reykjavik
Hammerfest
Bodø
Oslo
Stockholm
Arkhangelsk
Leningrad
København
Moskva
London
Berlin
Warszawa
Köln
Praha
Kiev
Paris
Wien
Budapest
Odessa
Lyon
Roma
Sofija
Istanbul
Madrid
Barcelona
Lisboa
Alger
Athenai
Ankara
Tripoli
Alexandria
Cairo
Tombouctou
St. Louis
Khartoum
Monrovia
Lagos
Stanley
Luanda
Capetown
Durban
VALUE OF TERMS
Hot = above 68°
Mild = 50° to 68°
Cool = 32° to 50°
Cold = below 32°
Always cold; Polar regions and high altitudes
Cold winter and cool summer; always cool in the Andes
Cold winter and mild summer
Cool winter and mild summer
Hot summer and cold winter
Hot summer and cool winter
Hot summer and mild winter
Always hot
Always mild

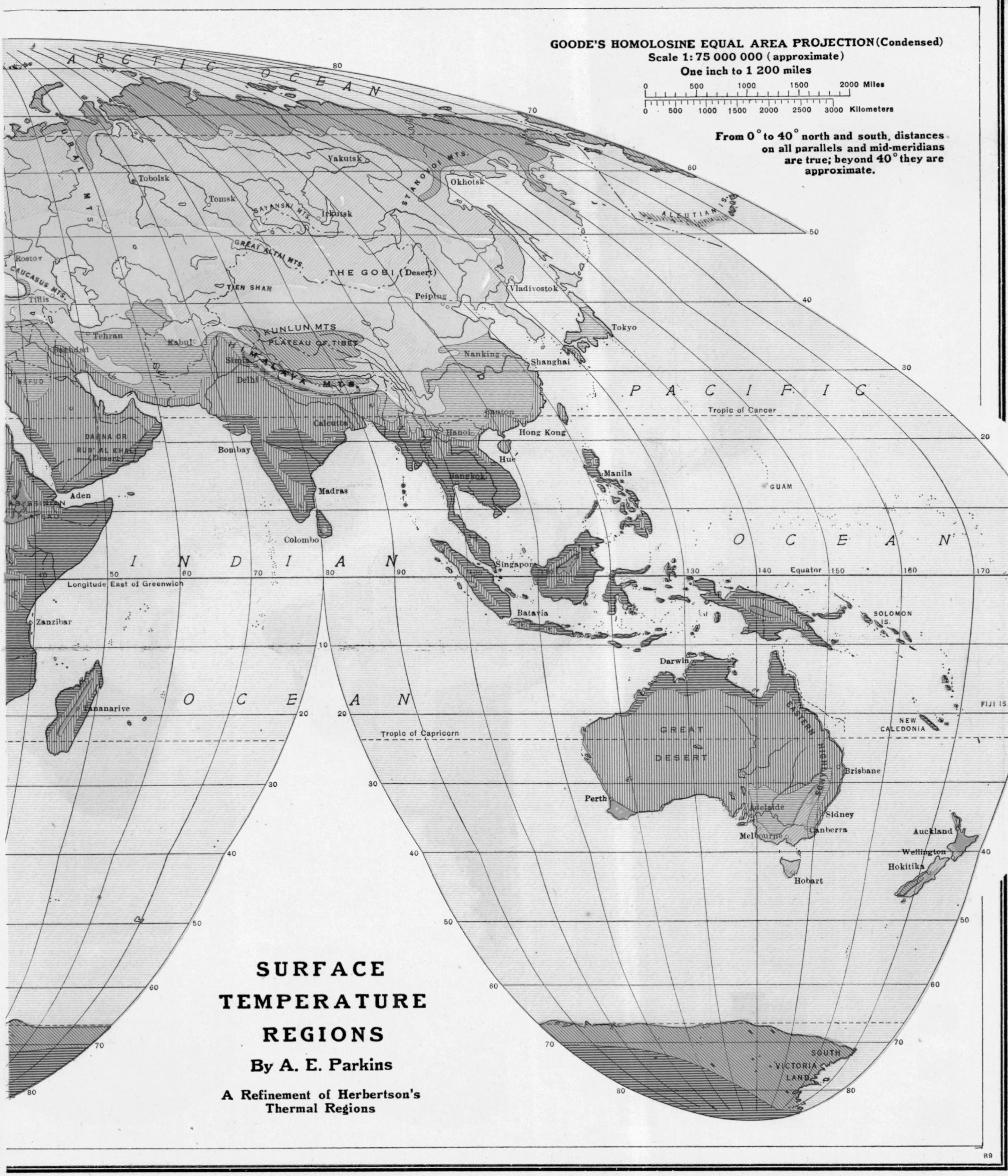

SURFACE TEMPERATURE REGIONS

By A. E. Parkins

A Refinement of Herbertson's Thermal Regions

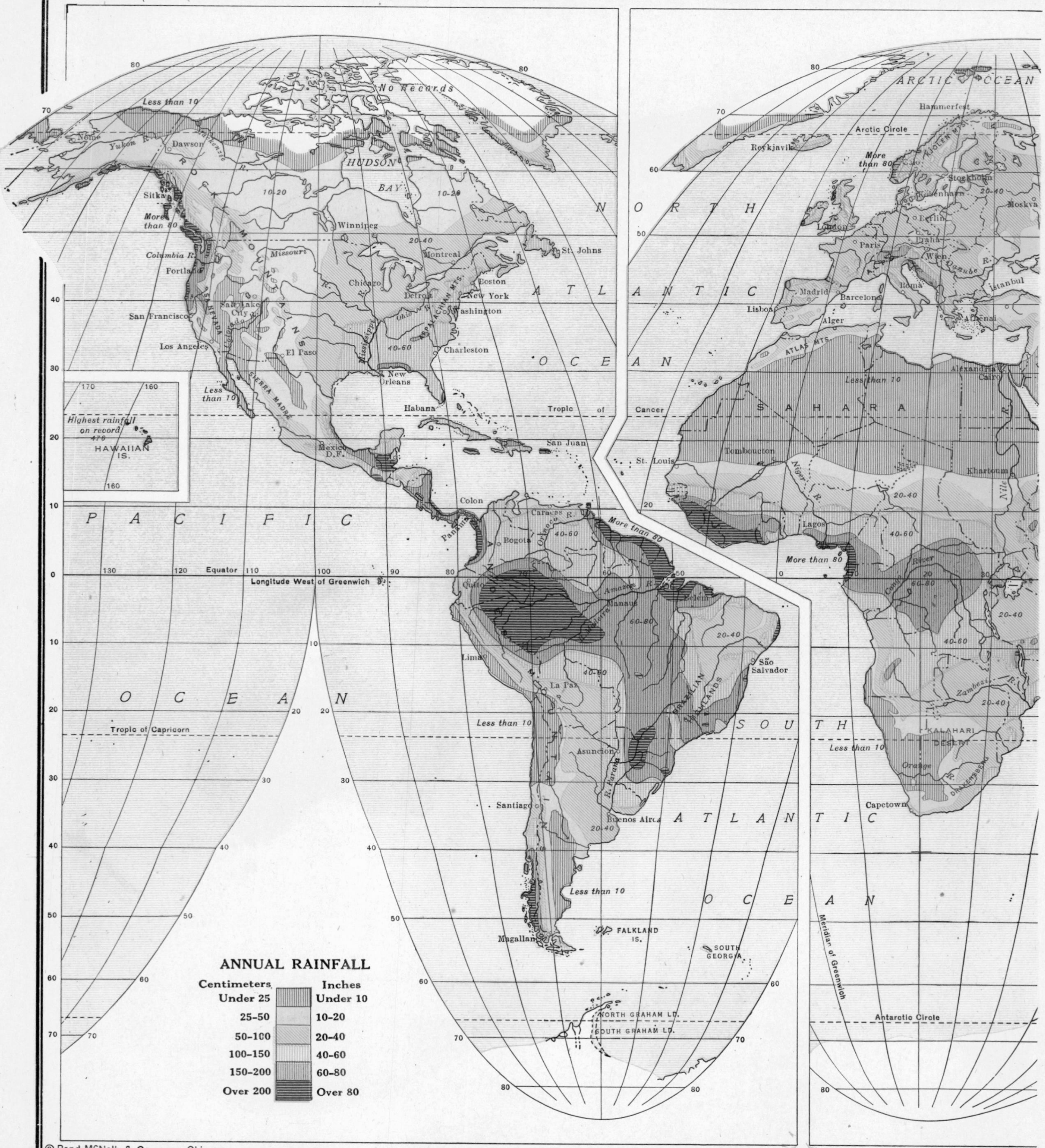
ANNUAL RAINFALL
Centimeters
Inches
Under 25
Under 10
25-50
10-20
50-100
20-40
100-150
40-60
150-200
60-80
Over 200
Over 80
HUDSON BAY
No Records
Less than 10
More than 80
Highest rainfall on record 476
HAWAIIAN IS.
P A C I F I C
O C E A N
N O R T H
A T L A N T I C
O C E A N
S O U T H
A T L A N T I C
O C E A N
ARCTIC OCEAN
S A H A R A
KALAHARI DESERT
Tropic of Cancer
Tropic of Capricorn
Equator
Longitude West of Greenwich
Meridian of Greenwich
Arctic Circle
Antarctic Circle
Dawson
Sitka
Winnipeg
Montreal
St. Johns
Boston
New York
Washington
Chicago
Detroit
Charleston
New Orleans
San Francisco
Salt Lake City
Portland
Los Angeles
El Paso
Habana
Mexico D.F.
San Juan
Colon
Caracas
Bogota
Quito
Lima
La Paz
Manaus
Belem
São Salvador
Asuncion
Santiago
Buenos Aires
Magallanes
FALKLAND IS.
SOUTH GEORGIA
NORTH GRAHAM LD.
SOUTH GRAHAM LD.
Reykjavik
Hammerfest
Stockholm
London
Paris
Berlin
Praha
Wien
Madrid
Lisbon
Barcelona
Roma
Alger
Athenai
Istanbul
Moskva
Alexandria
Cairo
Tombouctou
St. Louis
Lagos
Khartoum
Capetown
Nome
Yukon R.
Columbia R.
Missouri
Mississippi
Ohio
Amazon R.
Orinoco R.
Parana
Niger R.
Congo R.
Zambezi R.
Orange R.
Nile
Danube R.
ROCKY MOUNTAINS
SIERRA NEVADA
SIERRA MADRE
APPALACHIAN MTS.
ANDES
BRAZILIAN HIGHLANDS
ATLAS MTS.
KJOLEN MTS.
DRAKENSBERG

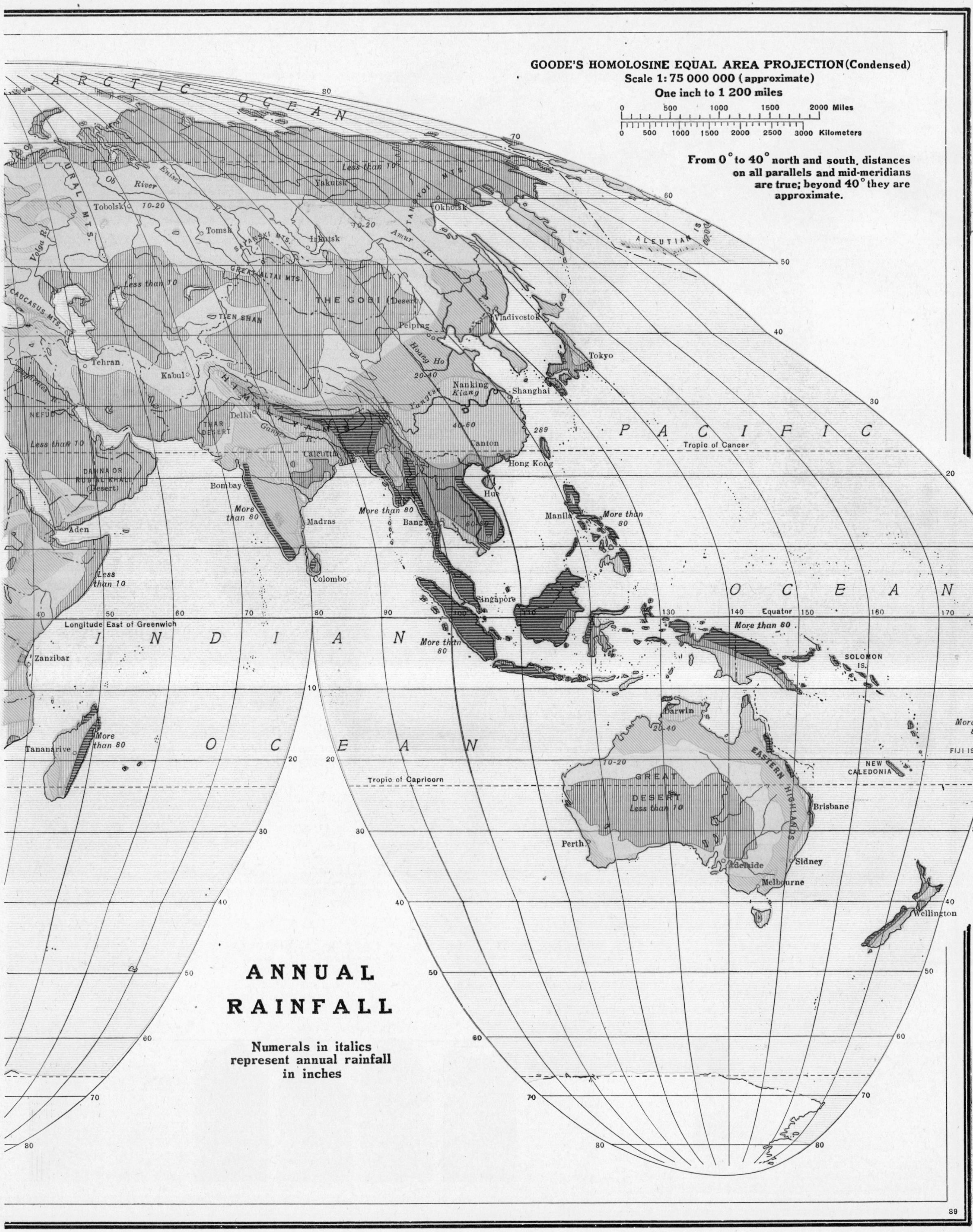
GOODE'S HOMOLOSINE EQUAL AREA PROJECTION (Condensed)
Scale 1: 75 000 000 (approximate)
One inch to 1 200 miles
0 500 1000 1500 2000 Miles
0 500 1000 1500 2000 2500 3000 Kilometers
From 0° to 40° north and south, distances on all parallels and mid-meridians are true; beyond 40° they are approximate.
ANNUAL RAINFALL
Numerals in italics represent annual rainfall in inches
ARCTIC OCEAN
PACIFIC OCEAN
INDIAN OCEAN
Tropic of Cancer
Tropic of Capricorn
Equator
Longitude East of Greenwich
URAL MTS.
Ob River
Enisei R.
Less than 10
10-20
20-40
40-60
More than 80
289
Volga R.
Tobolsk
Tomsk
Irkutsk
Yakutsk
Okhotsk
STANOVOI MTS.
SAYANSKI MTS.
Amur R.
GREAT ALTAI MTS.
THE GOBI (Desert)
TIEN SHAN
CAUCASUS MTS.
Vladivostok
Peiping
Hoang Ho
Tokyo
Nanking
Kiang
Yangtse
Shanghai
Tehran
Kabul
HIMALAYA
Delhi
THAR DESERT
Ganges R.
Calcutta
NEFUD
DAHNA OR RUB'AL KHALI (Desert)
Canton
Hong Kong
Hue
Bombay
Madras
Bangkok
Manila
Aden
Colombo
Singapore
ALEUTIAN IS.
Zanzibar
Tananarive
SOLOMON IS.
FIJI IS.
NEW CALEDONIA
Darwin
GREAT DESERT
EASTERN HIGHLANDS
Brisbane
Perth
Adelaide
Sidney
Melbourne
Wellington

THE CLIMATIC REGIONS of the EARTH

After W. Köppen and R. Geiger

With revision by Preston E. James, Richard Joel Russell, G. T. Renner

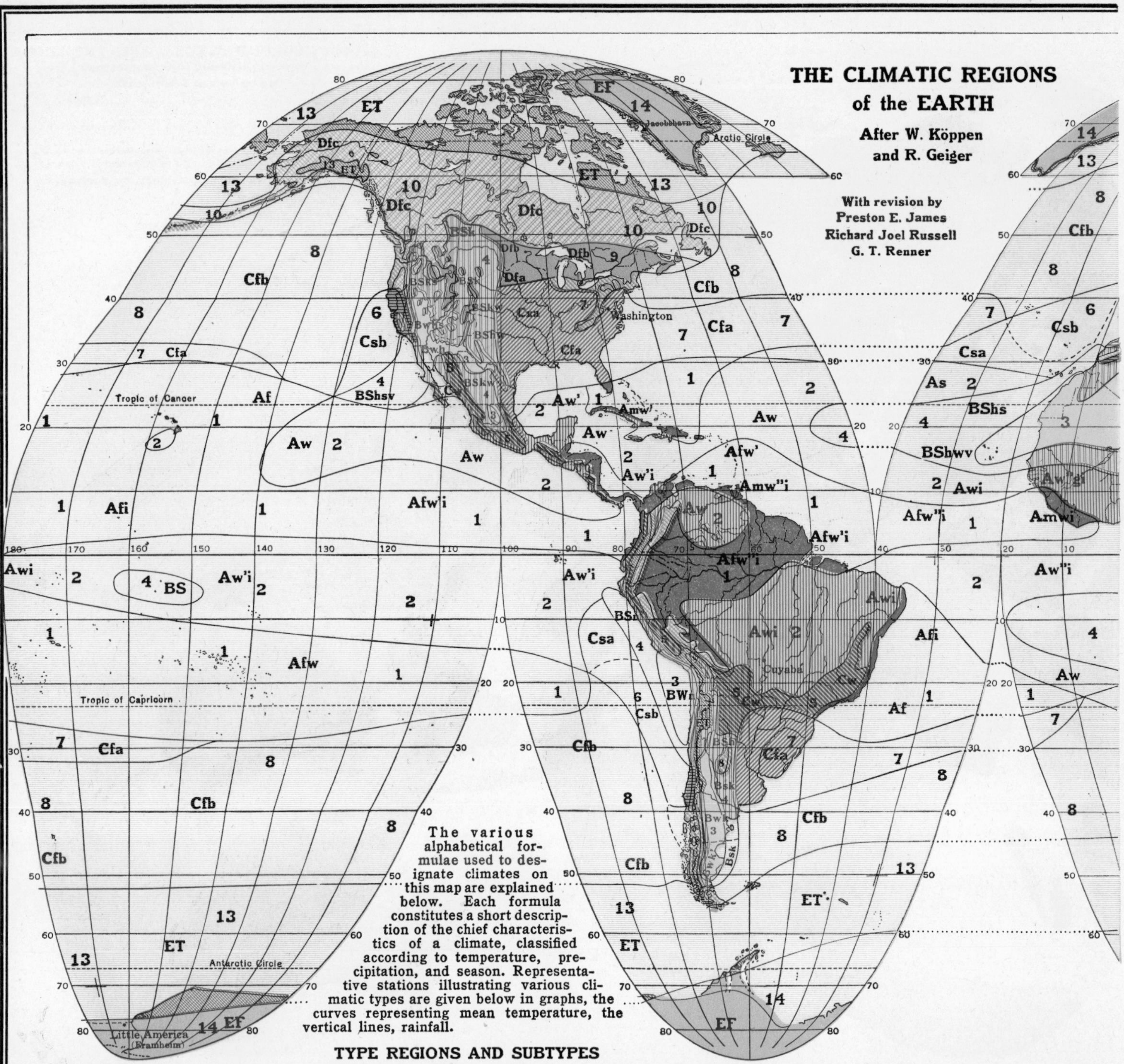

The various alphabetical formulae used to designate climates on this map are explained below. Each formula constitutes a short description of the chief characteristics of a climate, classified according to temperature, precipitation, and season. Representative stations illustrating various climatic types are given below in graphs, the curves representing mean temperature, the vertical lines, rainfall.

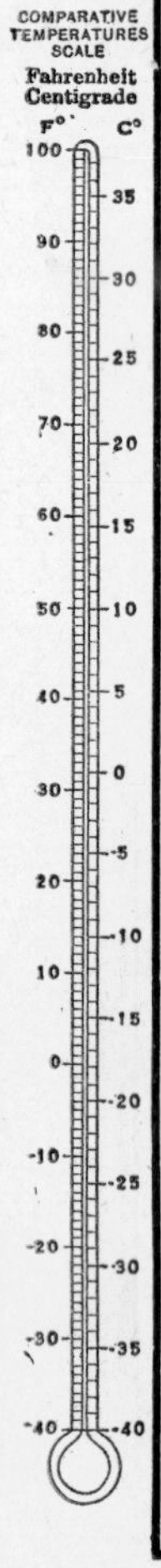

TYPE REGIONS AND SUBTYPES

A–Tropical climates: the average temperature of the coldest month over 18° C. (64.4° F.).

A, C, D–Tree climates: rainfall sufficient and warm season long enough for tall tree growth.

B–Arid climates (for limits see graph at right, p. 21).

C–Mesothermal climates: at least one month under 18° C. (64.4° F.); at least eight months over 1° C. (33.8° F.).

D–Microthermal, snow-forest climates: at least one month 10° C. to 18° C. (50° F. to 64.4° F.); at least four months under 1° C. (33.8° F.).

E–Ice climate: beyond the tree limits; warmest month under 10° C. (50° F.).

F–Perpetual frost; temperature all months under 0° C. (32° F.).

BS–Steppe climate (see graph at right, p. 21).

BW–Desert climate (see graph at right, p. 21).

ET–Tundra climate; warmest month between 0° and 10° C. (32° and 50° F.).

a–Temperature of warmest month over 22° C. (71.6° F.).

b–Warmest month under 22° C. (71.6° F.); at least four months over 10° C. (50° F.).

c–Less than four months over 10° C. (50° F.).

d–Same as **c**, with temperatures in the coldest month under –38° C. (–36.4° F.).

f–Constantly moist—rainfall all through the year.

g–Temperature maximum before the summer solstice and the rainy season. Ganges type of temperature curve.

g'–Coolest season after the summer solstice. Sudan type.

h–Hot and dry; annual average temperature over 18° C. (64.4° F.).

i–Isothermal climates; annual range less than 5° C. (9° F.).

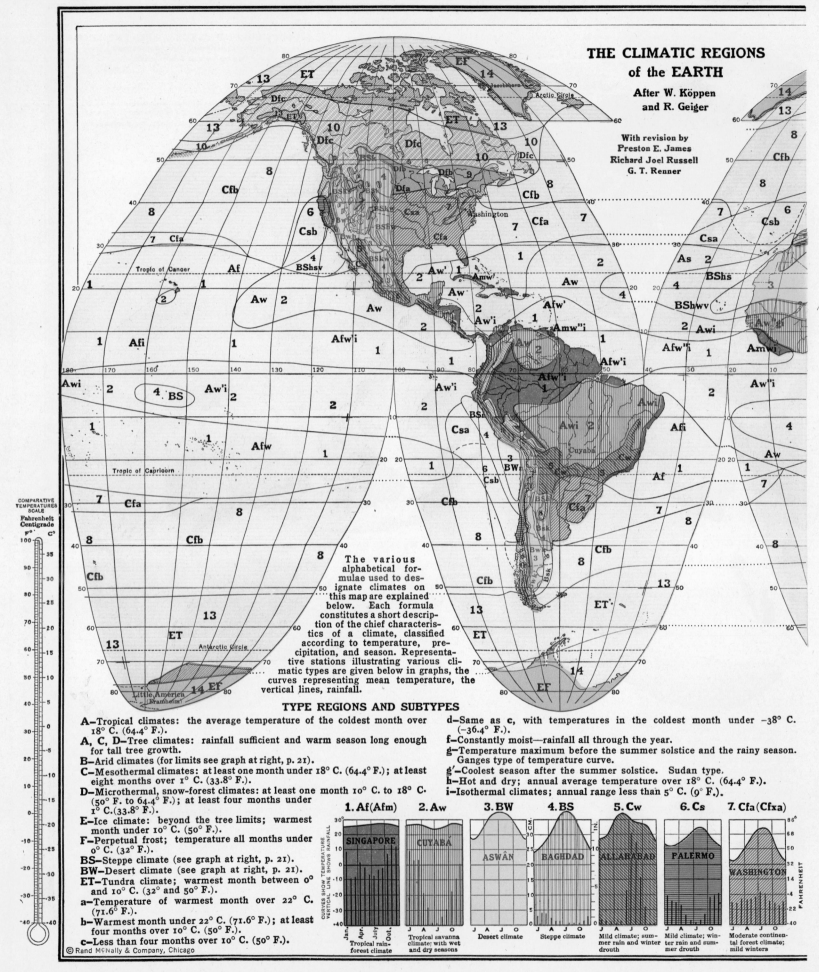

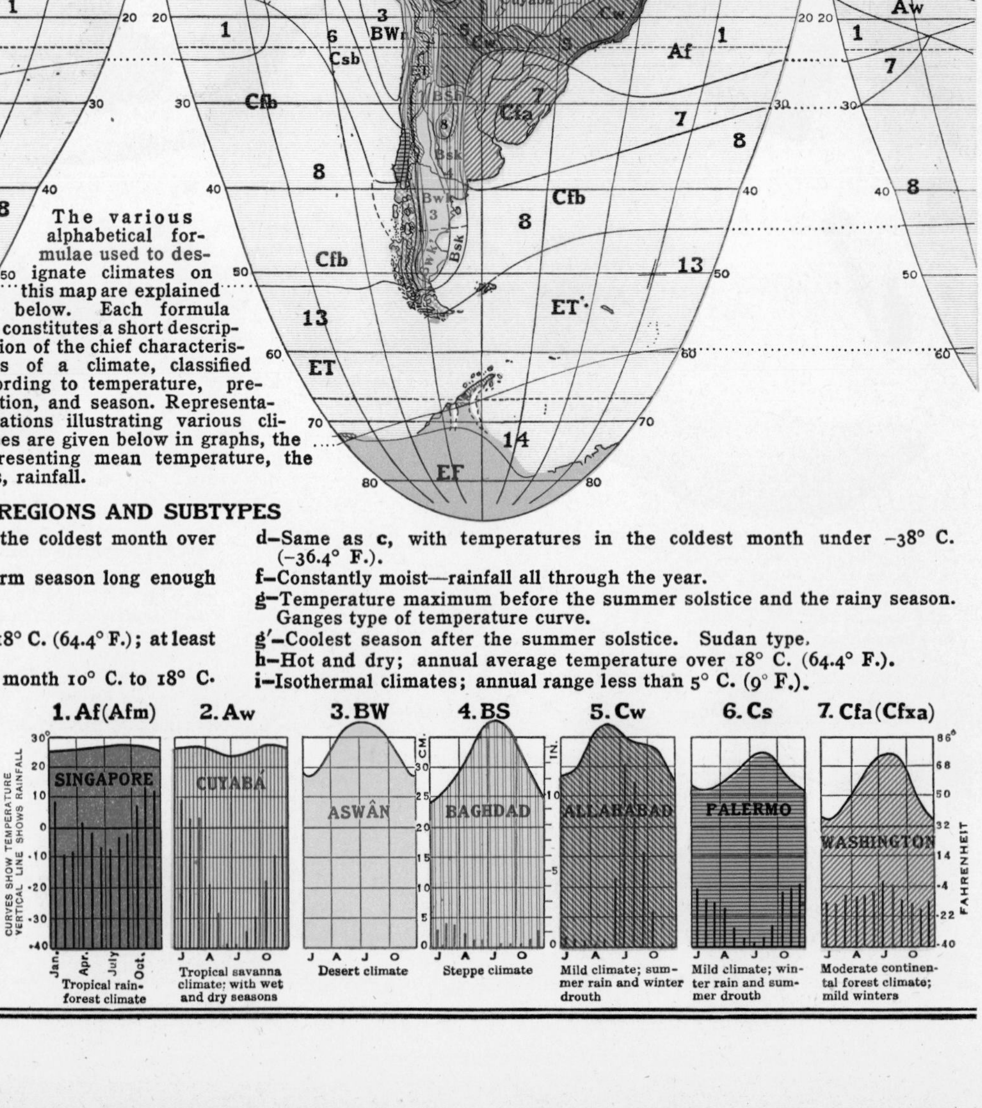

1. Tropical rain-forest climate
2. Tropical savanna climate; with wet and dry seasons
3. Desert climate
4. Steppe climate
5. Mild climate; summer rain and winter drouth
6. Mild climate; winter rain and summer drouth
7. Moderate continental forest climate; mild winters

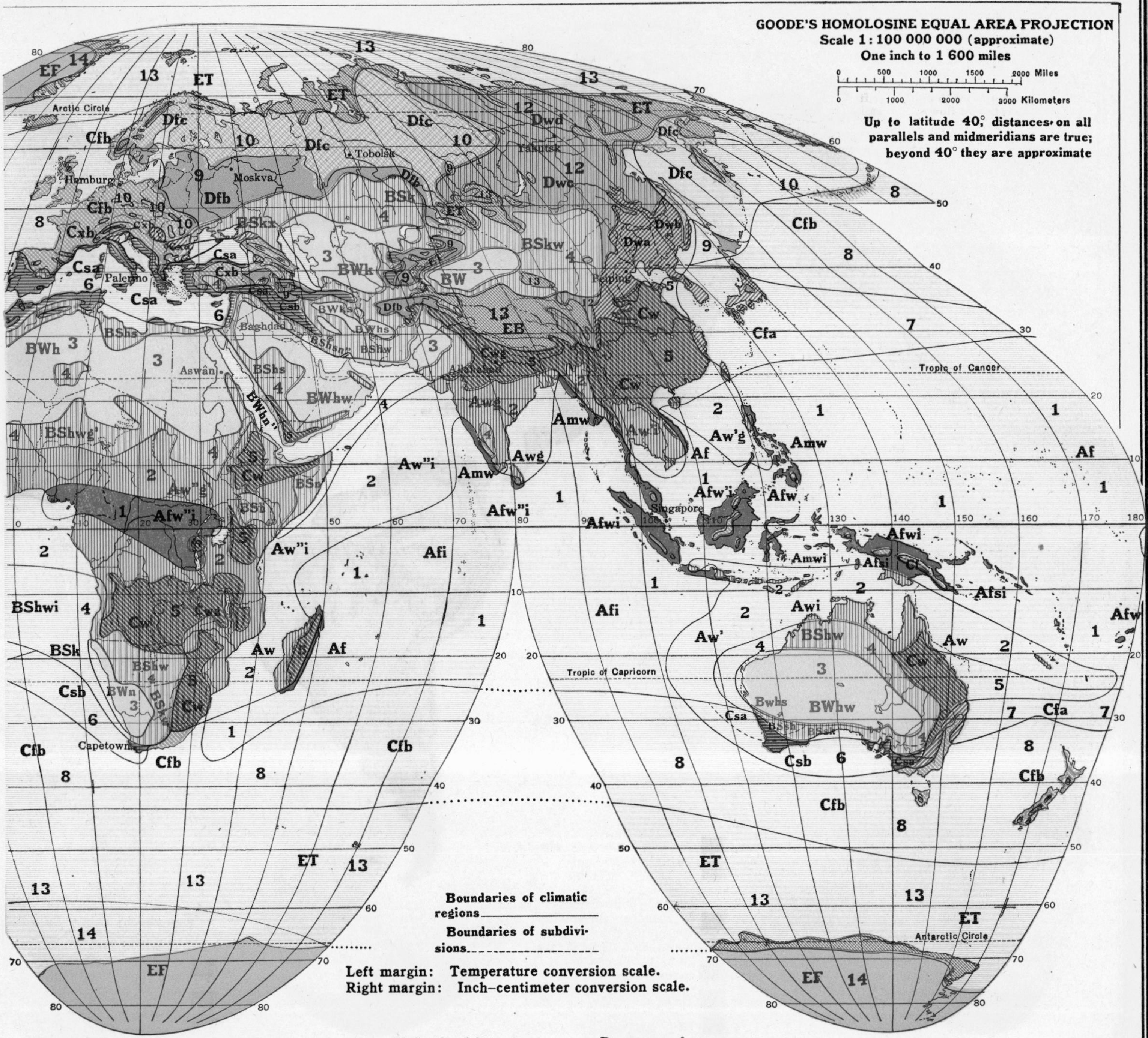

Left margin: Temperature conversion scale.
Right margin: Inch–centimeter conversion scale.

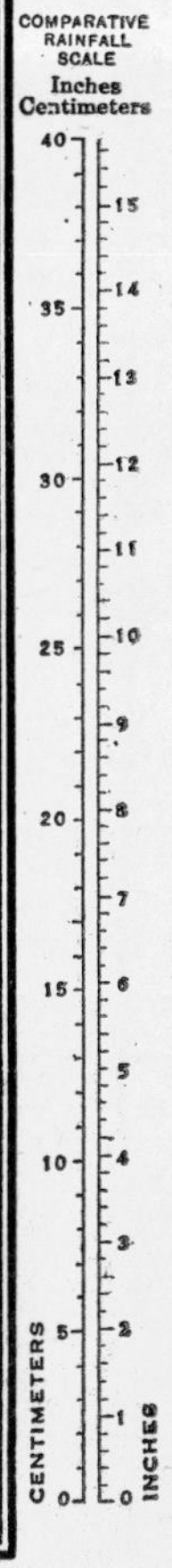

k–Cold and dry; annual average temperature under 18° C. (64.4° F.); warmest month over 18° C. (64.4° F.).
k′–Same as k, but the warmest month under 18° C. (64.4° F.).
m–Monsoon summer rain; forest climate in spite of dry season.
n–Frequent fog
n′–Infrequent fog, but high humidity and low rainfall with relative coolness; summer temperature under 24° C. (75.2° F.).
n″–Same as n′, but with summer temperature over 24° C. (75.2° F.).
s–Dry season in summer.
w–Dry season in winter.
s′w′–Rain in autumn.
w″–Two rainy seasons, longer dry season in winter.
v–Warmest season in autumn. Cape Verde type.
x–Rainiest month in early summer; clearer in late summer; driest in late winter.
x′–Infrequent but severe rain storms in all seasons.

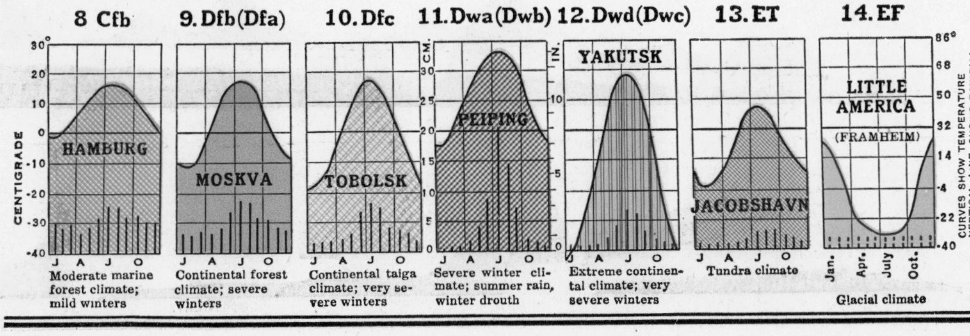

Moderate marine forest climate; mild winters
Continental forest climate; severe winters
Continental taiga climate; very severe winters
Severe winter climate; summer rain, winter drouth
Extreme continental climate; very severe winters
Tundra climate
Glacial climate

RELATION OF TEMPERATURE TO RAINFALL

Limits of the Regions of Dry Climate

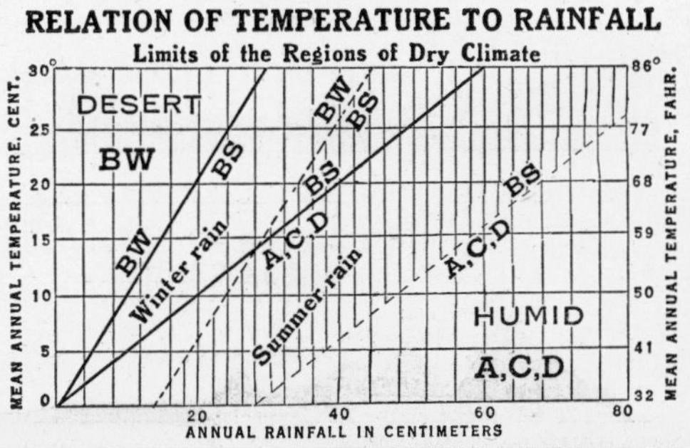

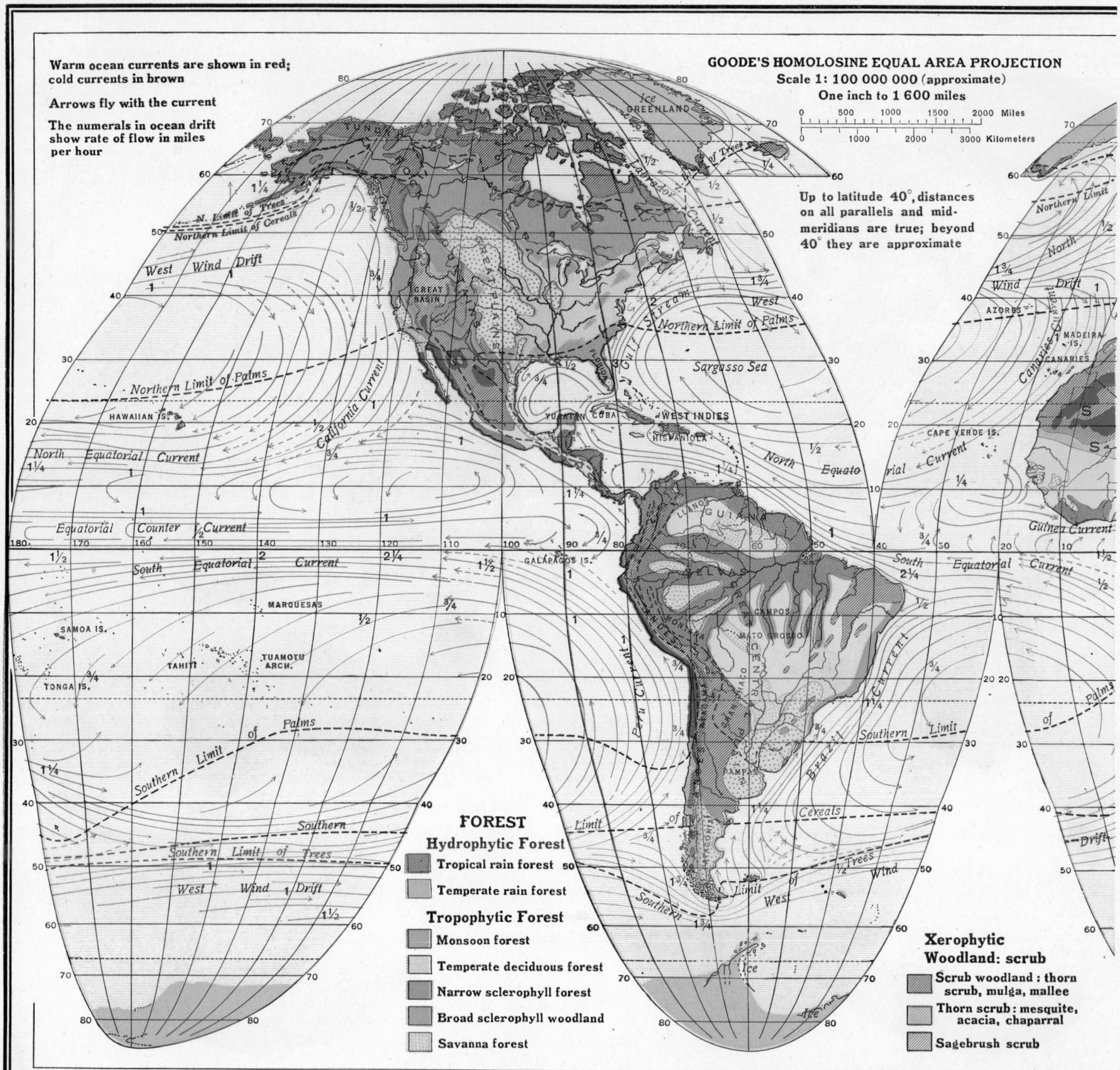

DISTRIBUTION OF VEGETATION

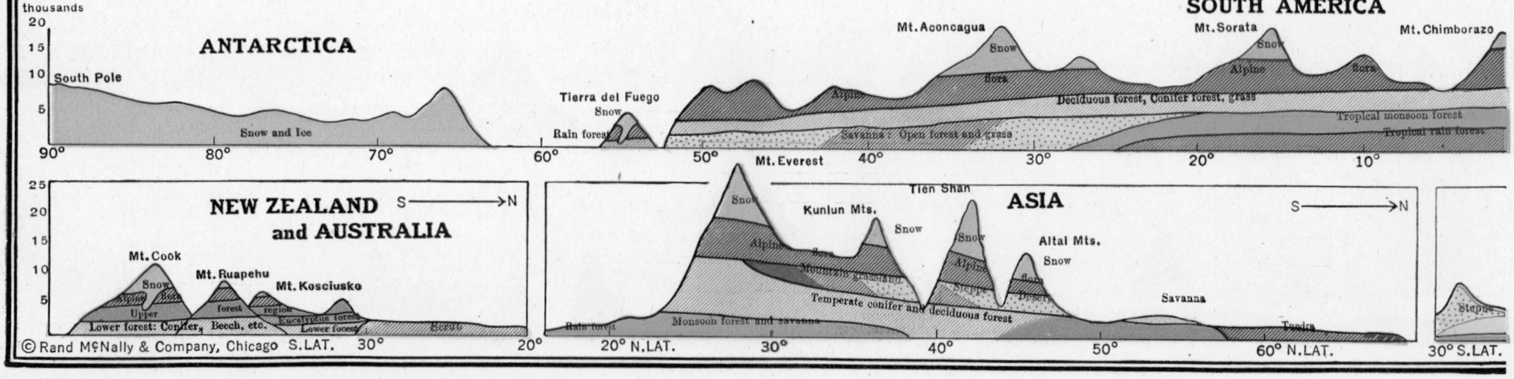

Vegetation areas after Schimper, Shreve, Harshberger, Shantz, Hauman, Griffith Taylor, and others

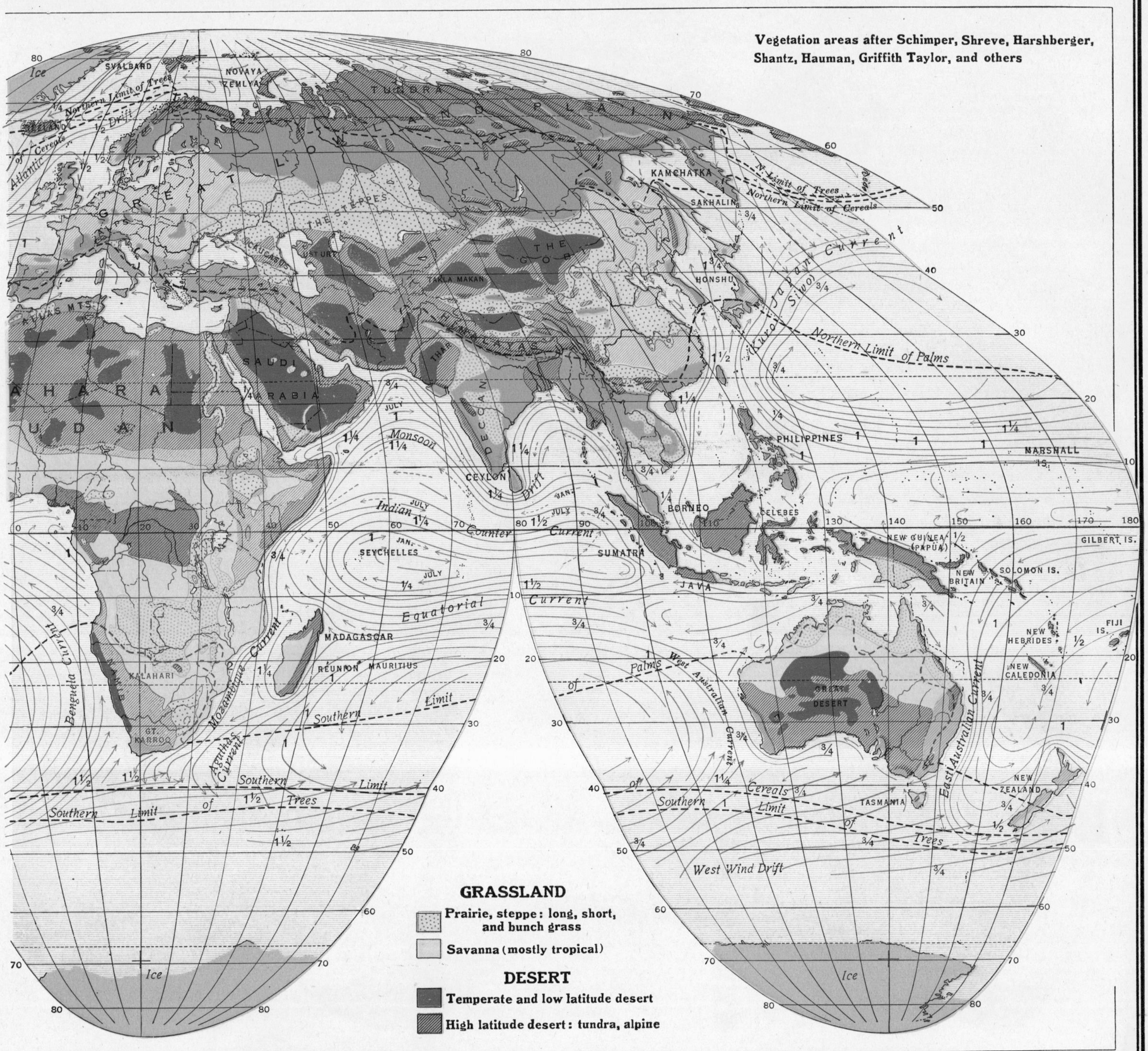

IN RELATION TO ALTITUDE

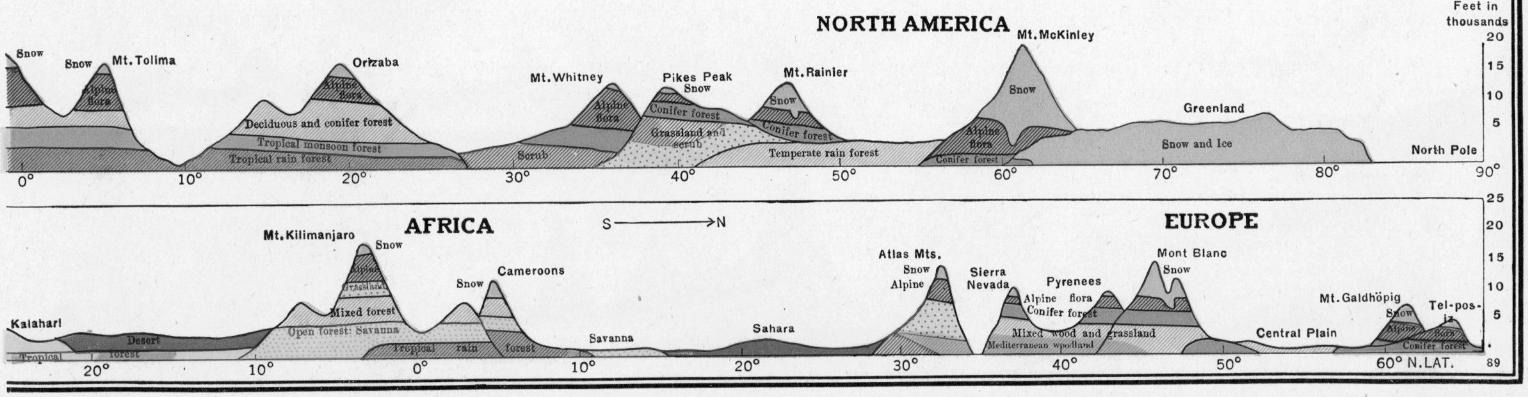

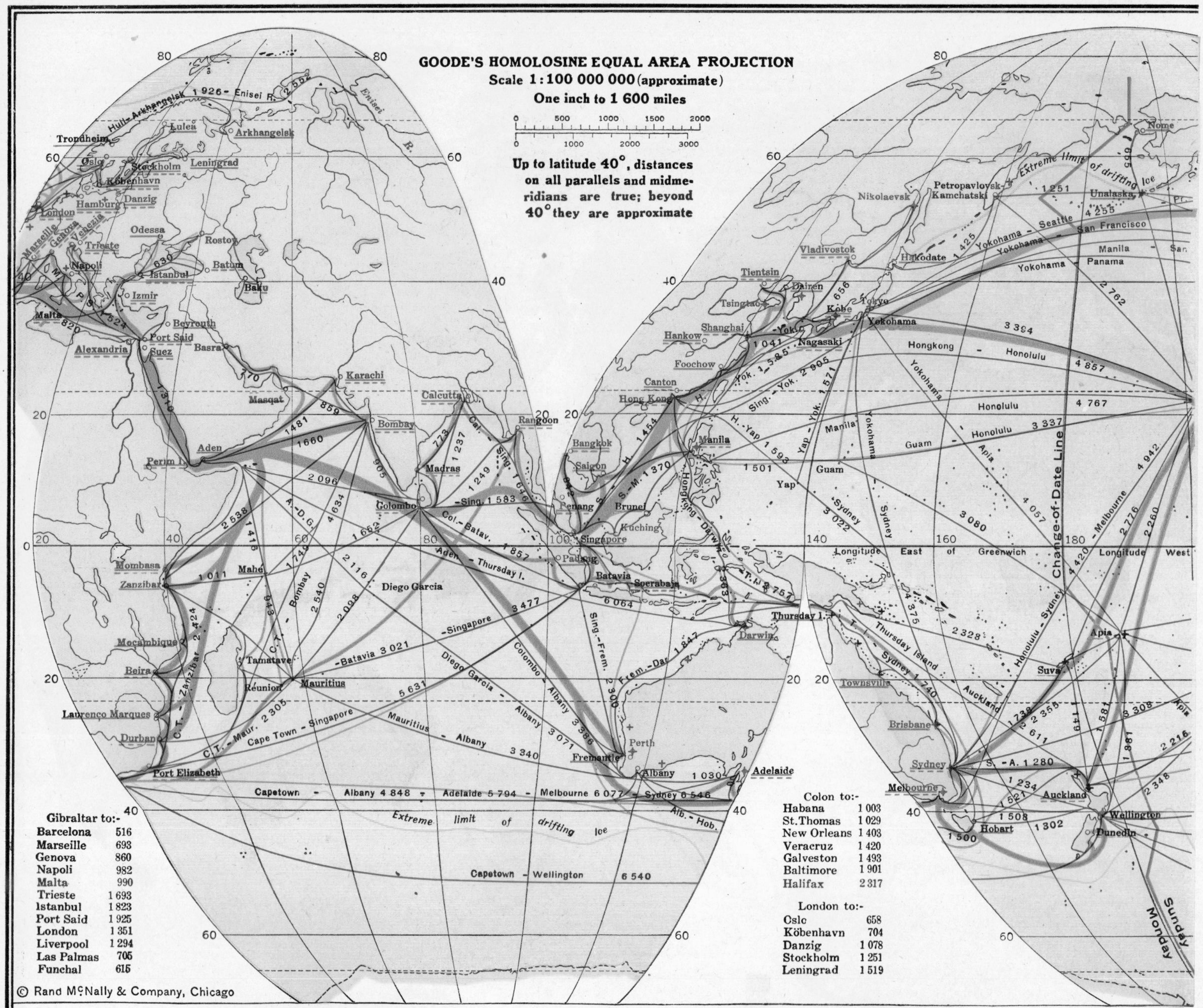
GOODE'S HOMOLOSINE EQUAL AREA PROJECTION
Scale 1:100 000 000 (approximate)
One inch to 1 600 miles
Up to latitude 40°, distances on all parallels and midmeridians are true; beyond 40° they are approximate
Gibraltar to:-
Barcelona 516
Marseille 693
Genova 860
Napoli 982
Malta 990
Trieste 1 693
Istanbul 1 823
Port Said 1 925
London 1 351
Liverpool 1 294
Las Palmas 705
Funchal 615
Colon to:-
Habana 1 003
St. Thomas 1 029
New Orleans 1 403
Veracruz 1 420
Galveston 1 493
Baltimore 1 901
Halifax 2 317
London to:-
Oslo 658
København 704
Danzig 1 078
Stockholm 1 251
Leningrad 1 519
Extreme limit of drifting ice
Change-of-Date Line
Sunday
Monday
Longitude East of Greenwich
Capetown - Albany 4 848 - Adelaide 5 794 - Melbourne 6 077 - Sydney 6 546
Capetown - Wellington 6 540

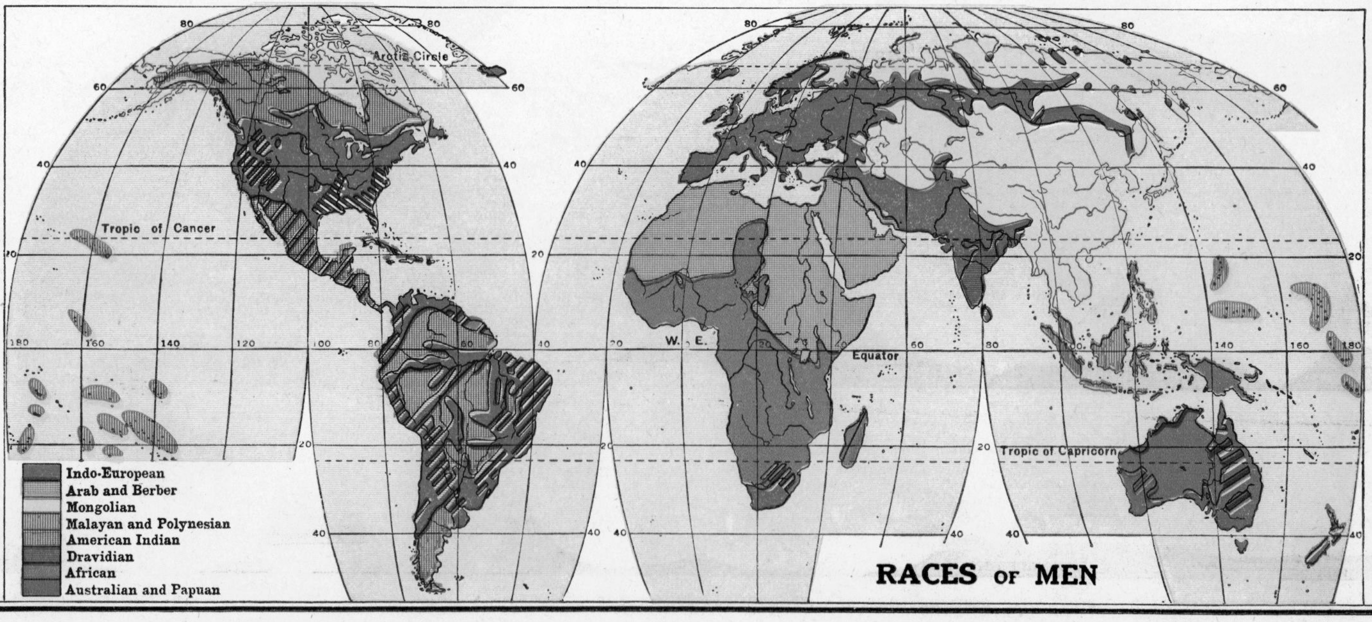
Indo-European
Arab and Berber
Mongolian
Malayan and Polynesian
American Indian
Dravidian
African
Australian and Papuan
Arctic Circle
Tropic of Cancer
Equator
Tropic of Capricorn

RACES OF MEN

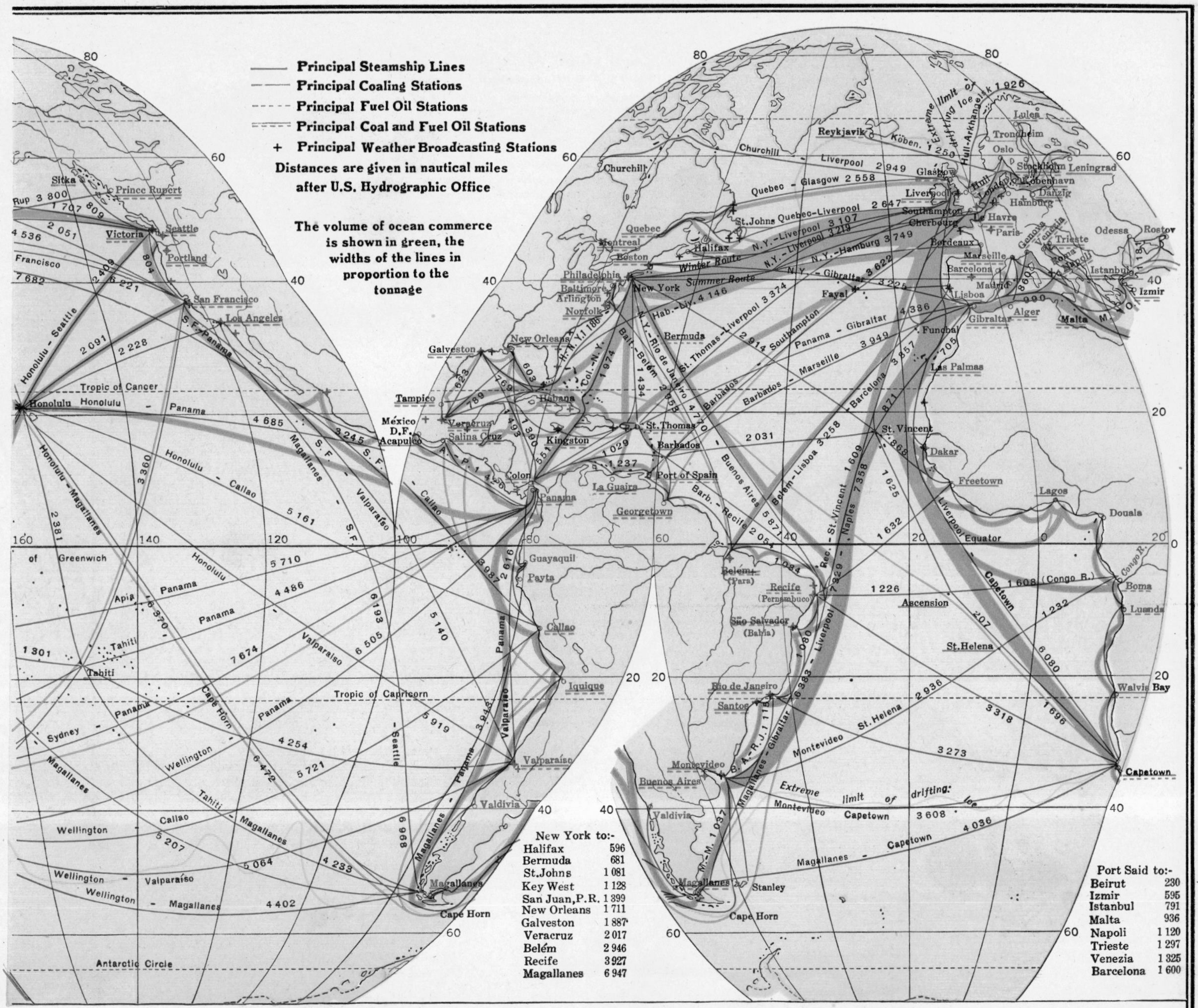

New York to:-	
Halifax	596
Bermuda	681
St.Johns	1 081
Key West	1 128
San Juan, P.R.	1 399
New Orleans	1 711
Galveston	1 887
Veracruz	2 017
Belém	2 946
Recife	3 927
Magallanes	6 947

Port Said to:-	
Beirut	230
Izmir	595
Istanbul	791
Malta	936
Napoli	1 120
Trieste	1 297
Venezia	1 325
Barcelona	1 600

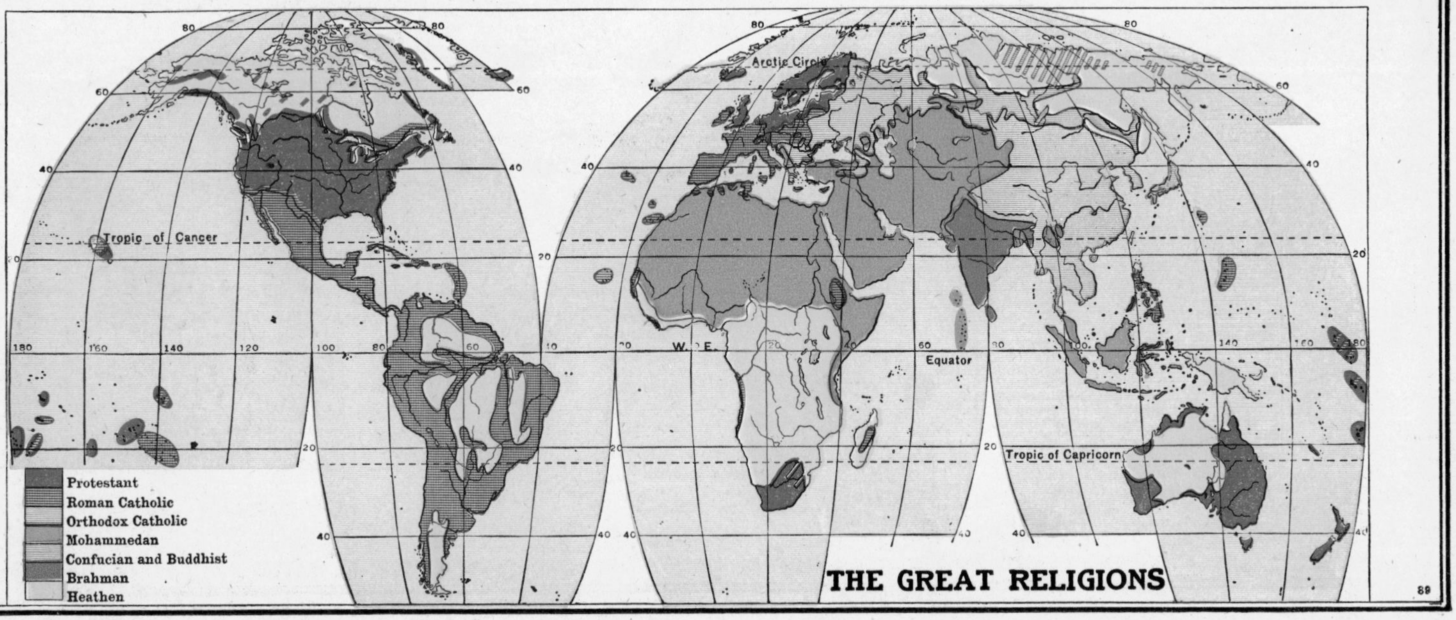

THE GREAT RELIGIONS

Equal Area Projection

WORLD—Economic

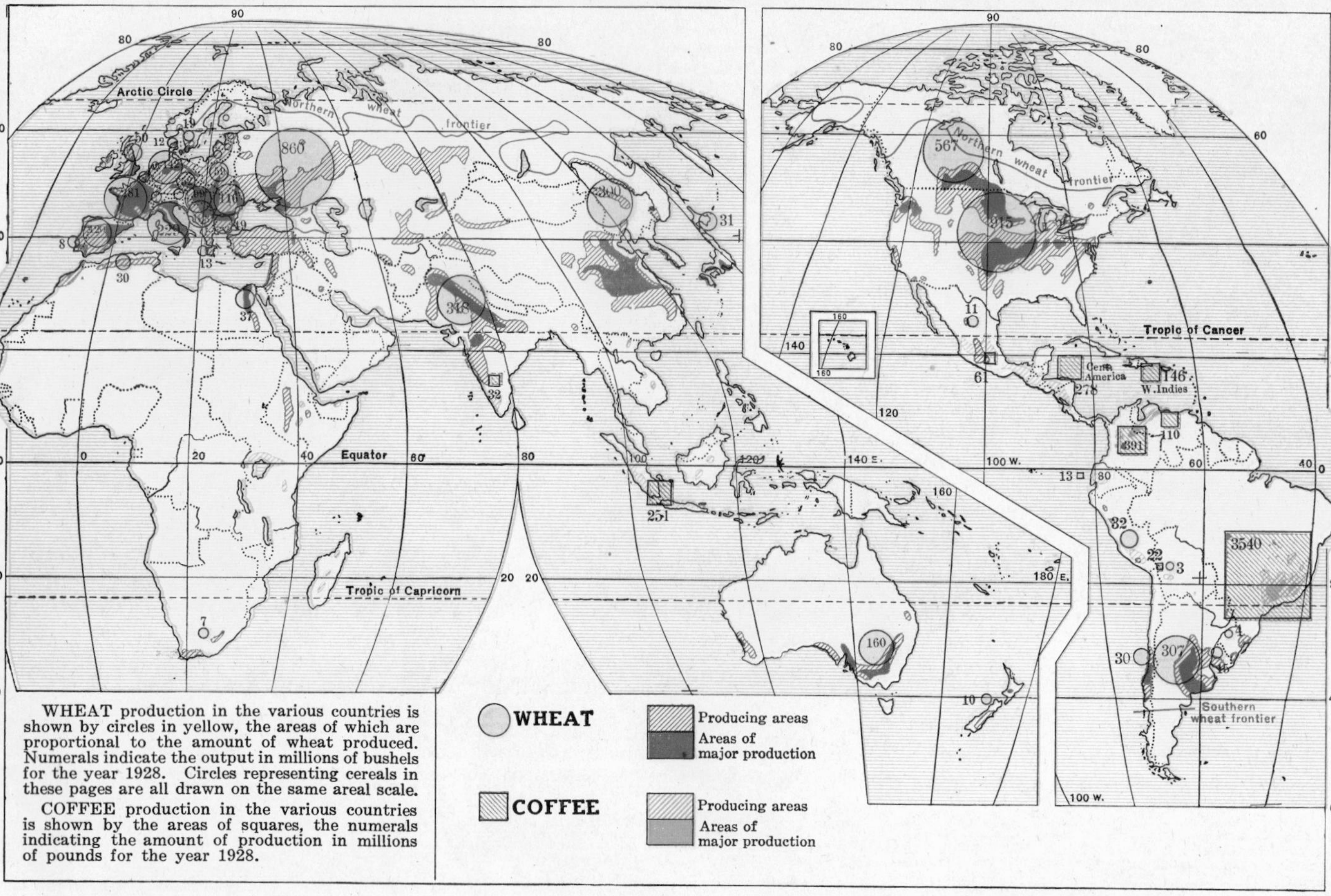

WHEAT production in the various countries is shown by circles in yellow, the areas of which are proportional to the amount of wheat produced. Numerals indicate the output in millions of bushels for the year 1928. Circles representing cereals in these pages are all drawn on the same areal scale.

COFFEE production in the various countries is shown by the areas of squares, the numerals indicating the amount of production in millions of pounds for the year 1928.

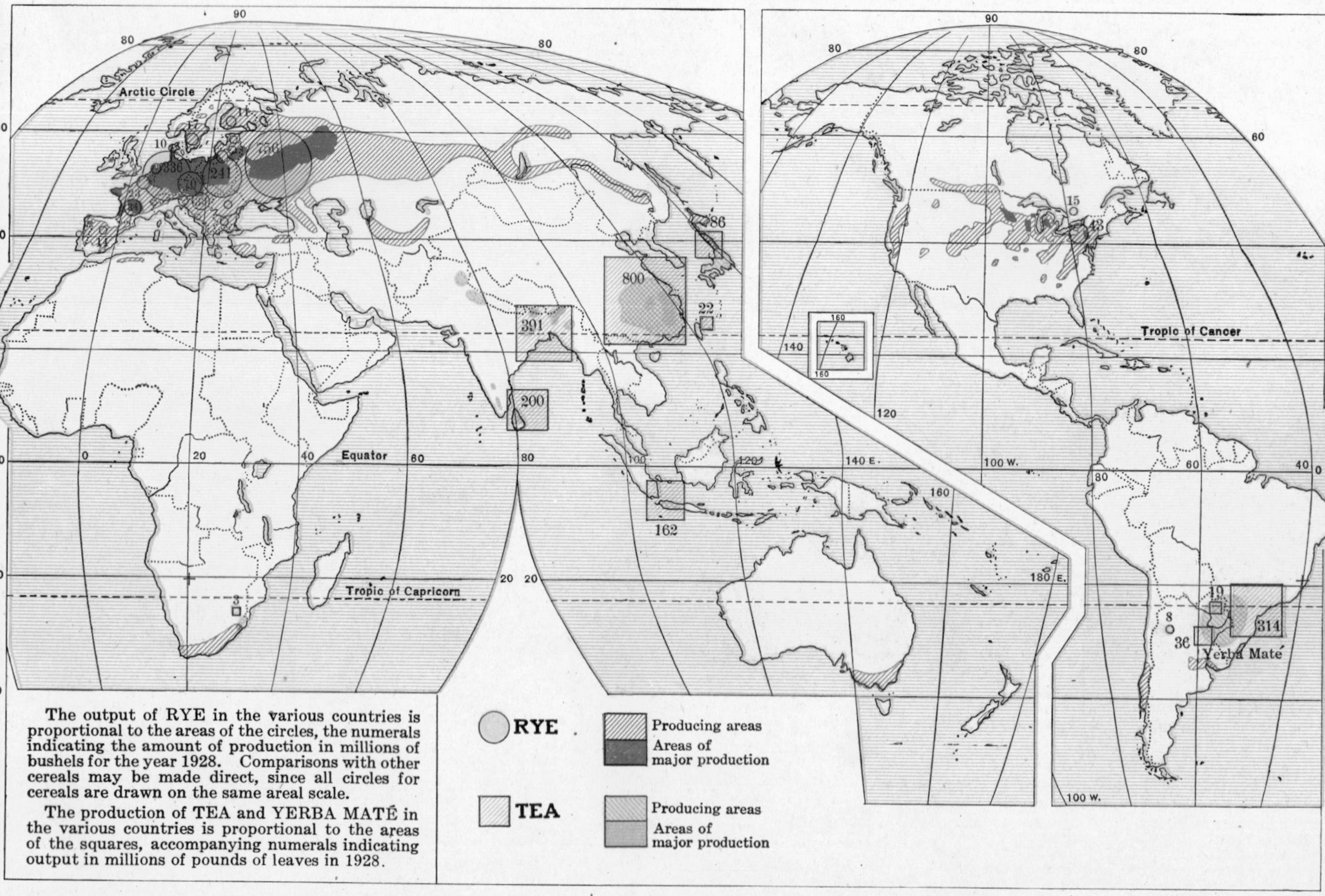

The output of RYE in the various countries is proportional to the areas of the circles, the numerals indicating the amount of production in millions of bushels for the year 1928. Comparisons with other cereals may be made direct, since all circles for cereals are drawn on the same areal scale.

The production of TEA and YERBA MATÉ in the various countries is proportional to the areas of the squares, accompanying numerals indicating output in millions of pounds of leaves in 1928.

6789

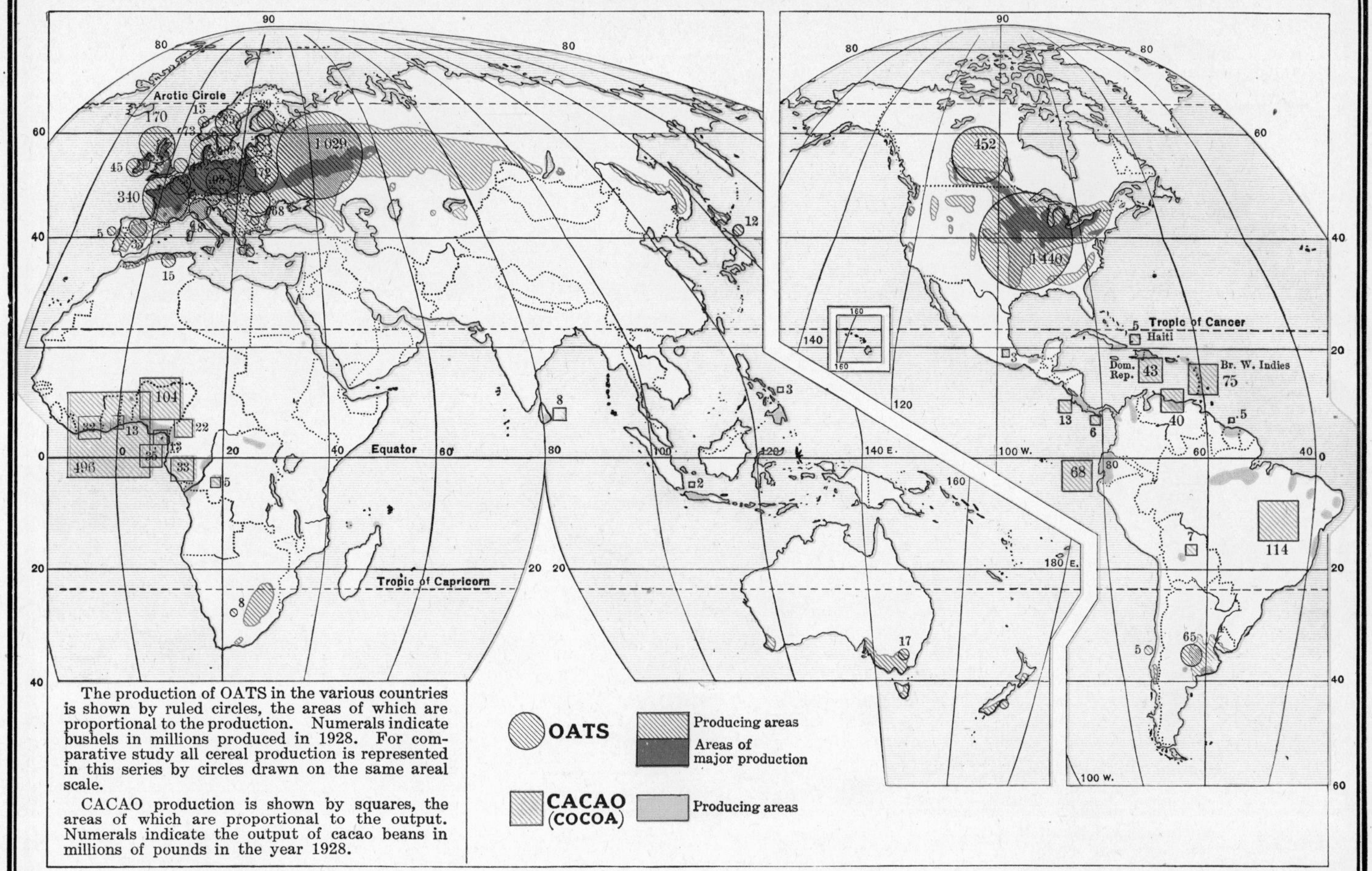

The production of OATS in the various countries is shown by ruled circles, the areas of which are proportional to the production. Numerals indicate bushels in millions produced in 1928. For comparative study all cereal production is represented in this series by circles drawn on the same areal scale.

CACAO production is shown by squares, the areas of which are proportional to the output. Numerals indicate the output of cacao beans in millions of pounds in the year 1928.

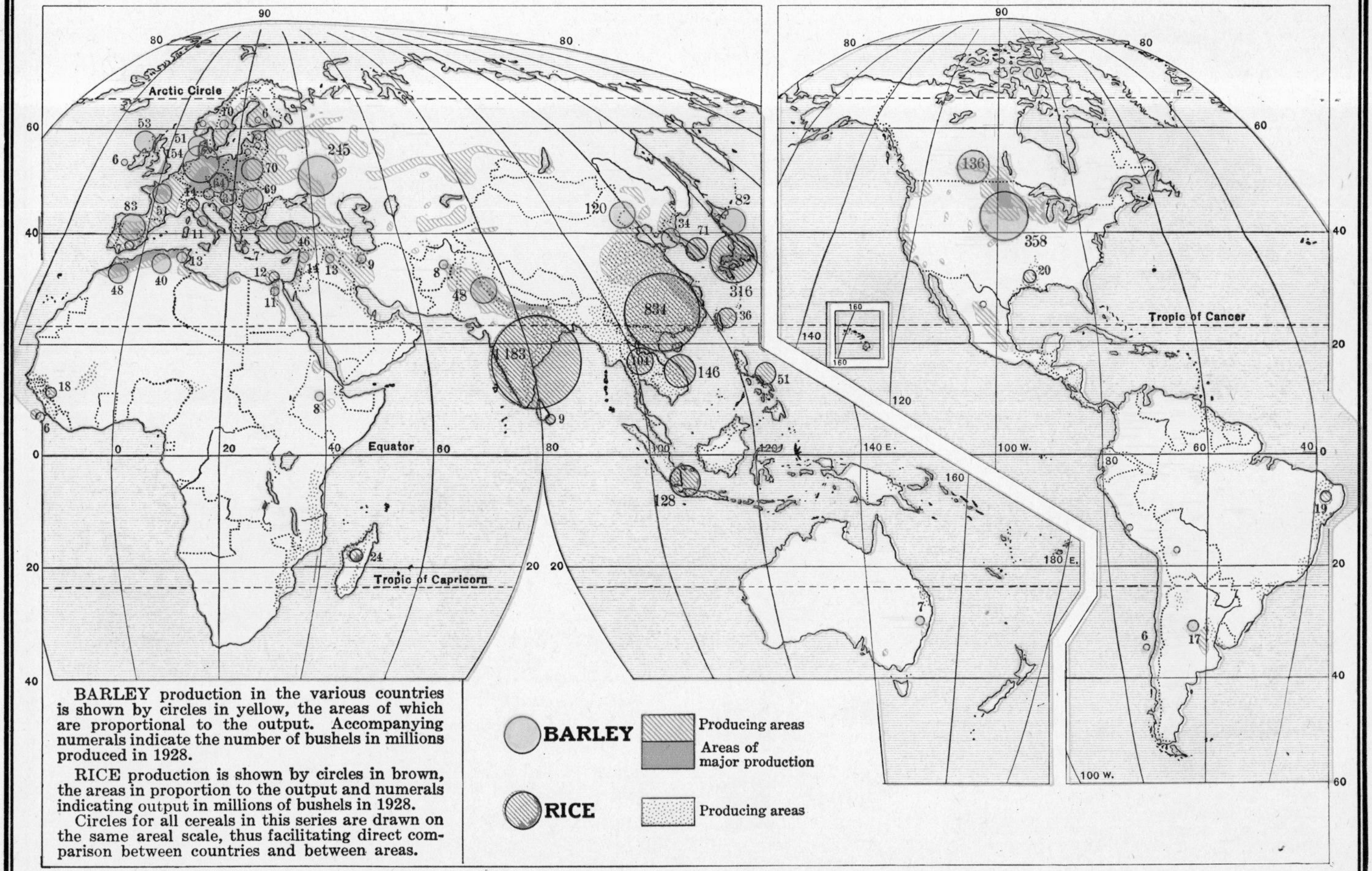

BARLEY production in the various countries is shown by circles in yellow, the areas of which are proportional to the output. Accompanying numerals indicate the number of bushels in millions produced in 1928.

RICE production is shown by circles in brown, the areas in proportion to the output and numerals indicating output in millions of bushels in 1928.

Circles for all cereals in this series are drawn on the same areal scale, thus facilitating direct comparison between countries and between areas.

6789

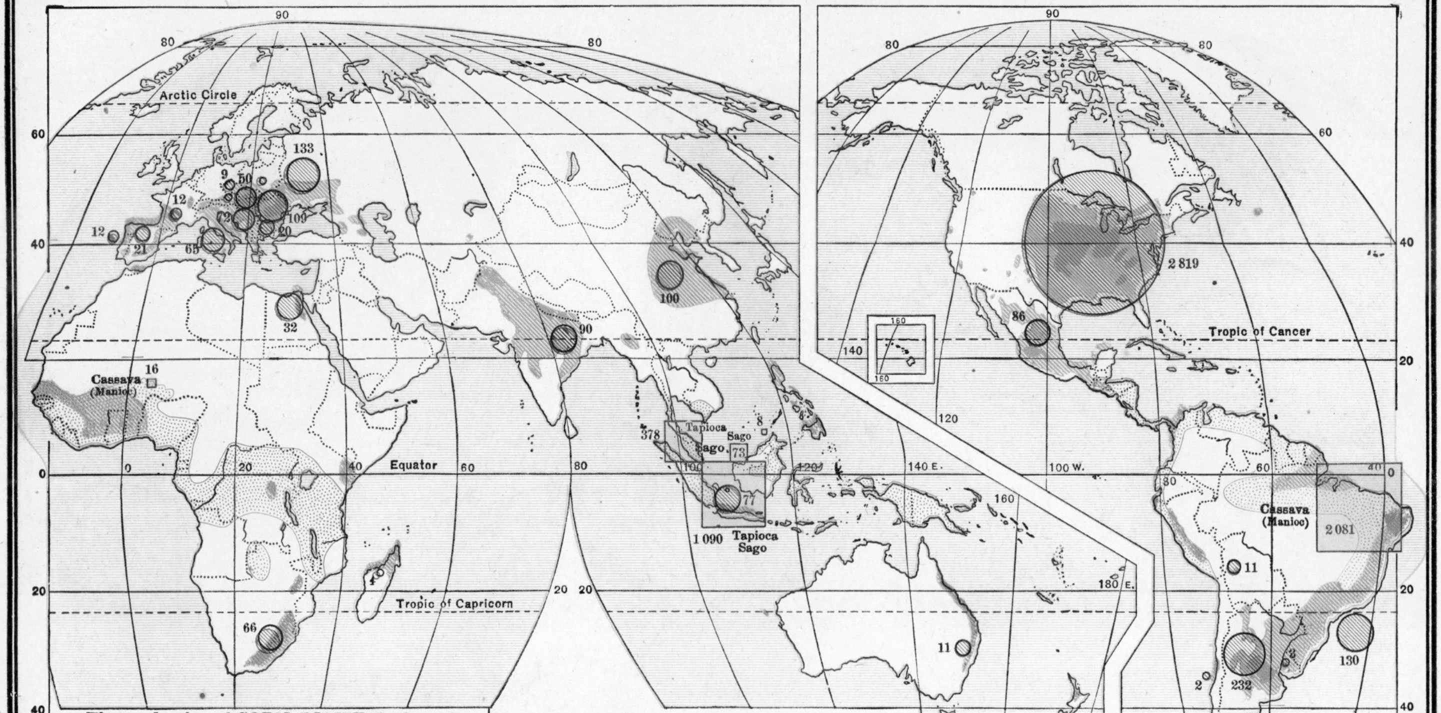

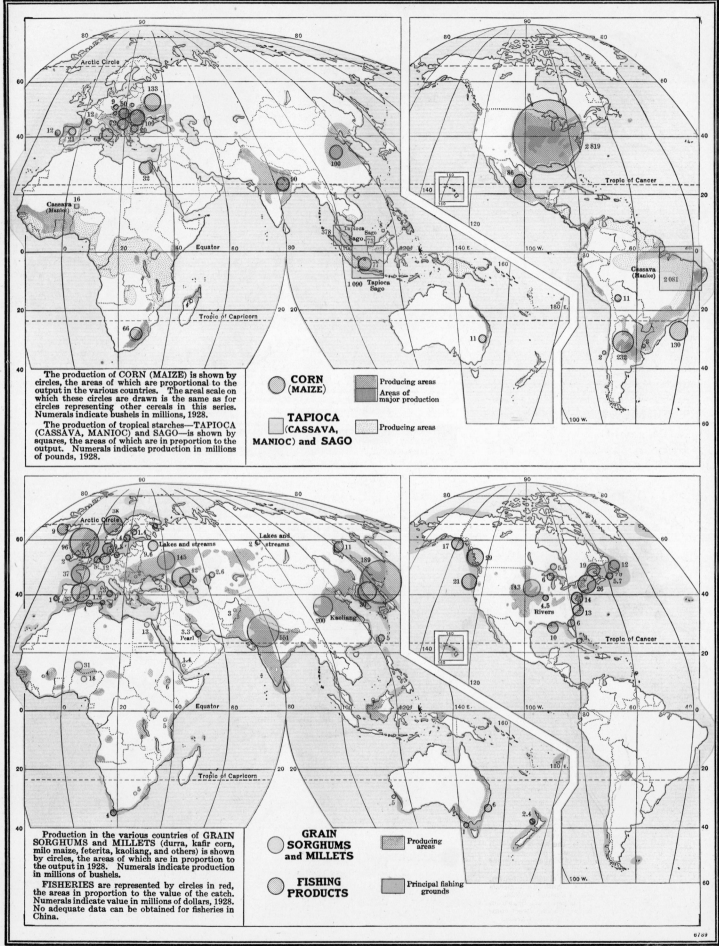

The production of CORN (MAIZE) is shown by circles, the areas of which are proportional to the output in the various countries. The areal scale on which these circles are drawn is the same as for circles representing other cereals in this series. Numerals indicate bushels in millions, 1928.

The production of tropical starches—TAPIOCA (CASSAVA, MANIOC) and SAGO—is shown by squares, the areas of which are in proportion to the output. Numerals indicate production in millions of pounds, 1928.

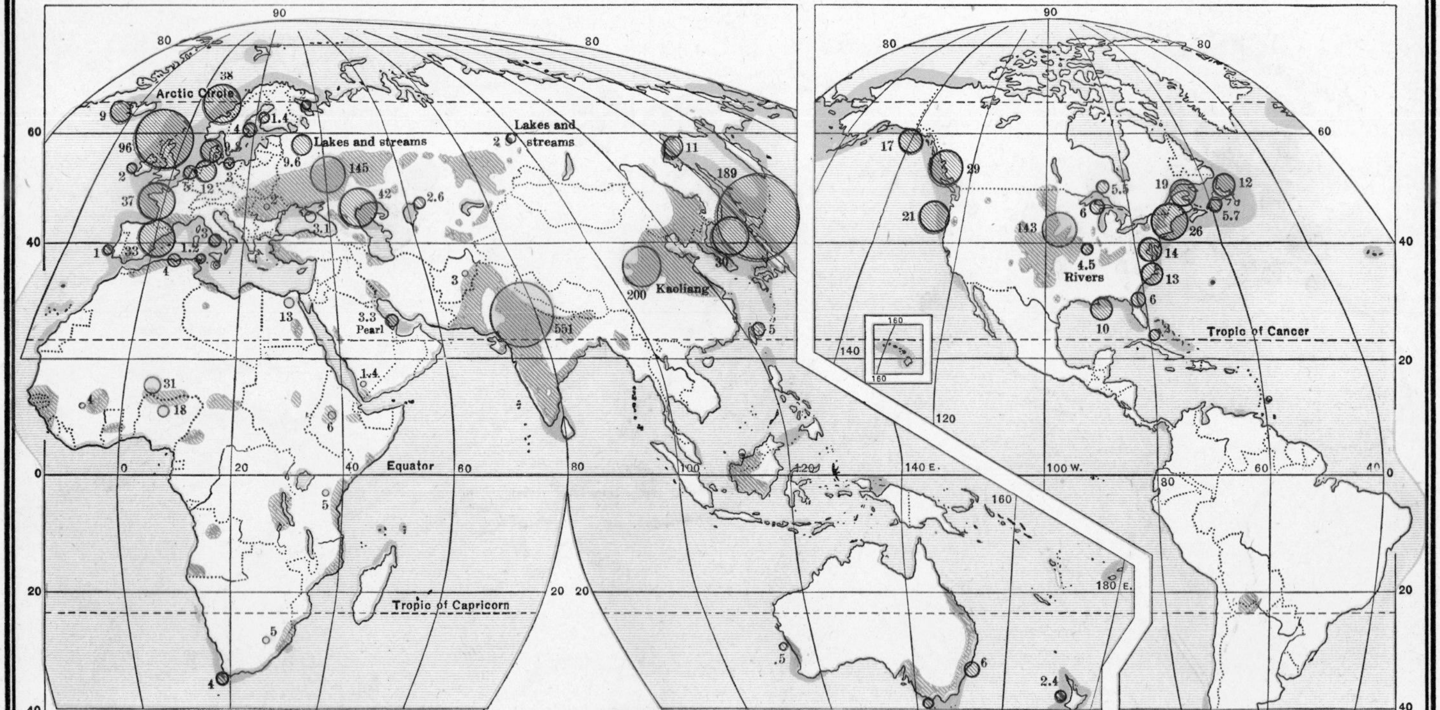

Production in the various countries of GRAIN SORGHUMS and MILLETS (durra, kafir corn, milo maize, feterita, kaoliang, and others) is shown by circles, the areas of which are in proportion to the output in 1928. Numerals indicate production in millions of bushels.

FISHERIES are represented by circles in red, the areas in proportion to the value of the catch. Numerals indicate value in millions of dollars, 1928. No adequate data can be obtained for fisheries in China.

6789

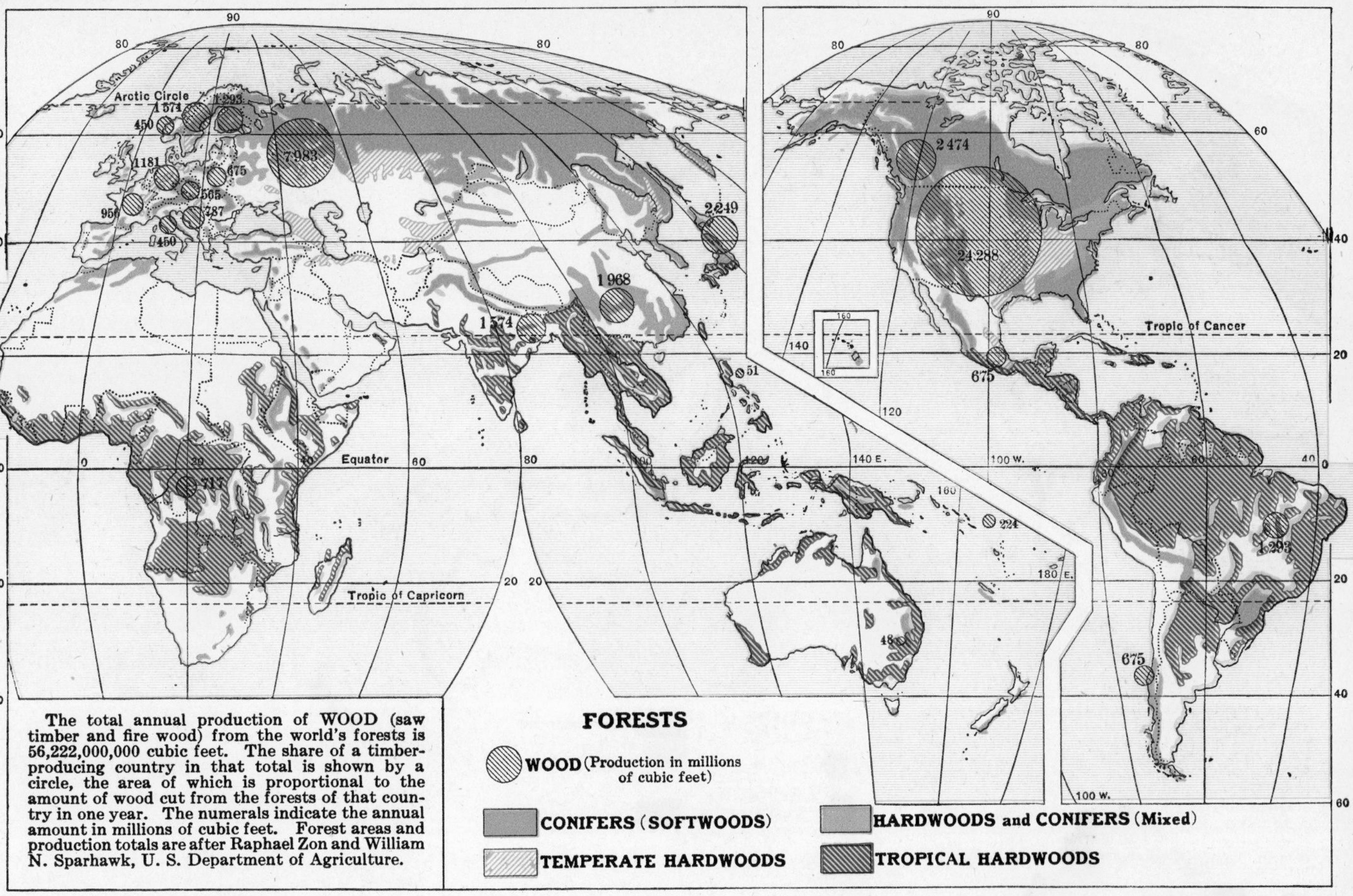

The total annual production of WOOD (saw timber and fire wood) from the world's forests is 56,222,000,000 cubic feet. The share of a timber-producing country in that total is shown by a circle, the area of which is proportional to the amount of wood cut from the forests of that country in one year. The numerals indicate the annual amount in millions of cubic feet. Forest areas and production totals are after Raphael Zon and William N. Sparhawk, U. S. Department of Agriculture.

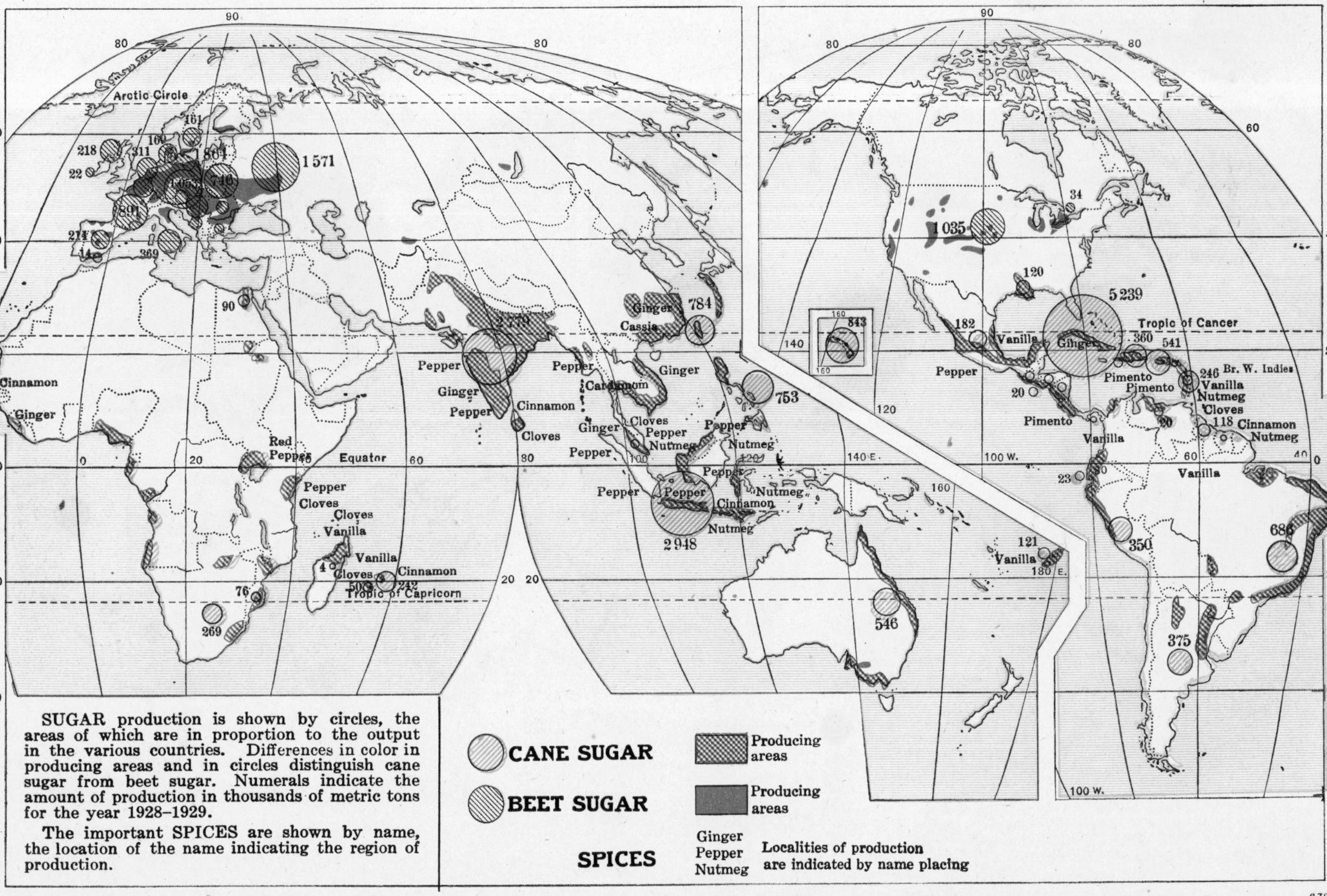

SUGAR production is shown by circles, the areas of which are in proportion to the output in the various countries. Differences in color in producing areas and in circles distinguish cane sugar from beet sugar. Numerals indicate the amount of production in thousands of metric tons for the year 1928–1929.

The important SPICES are shown by name, the location of the name indicating the region of production.

6789

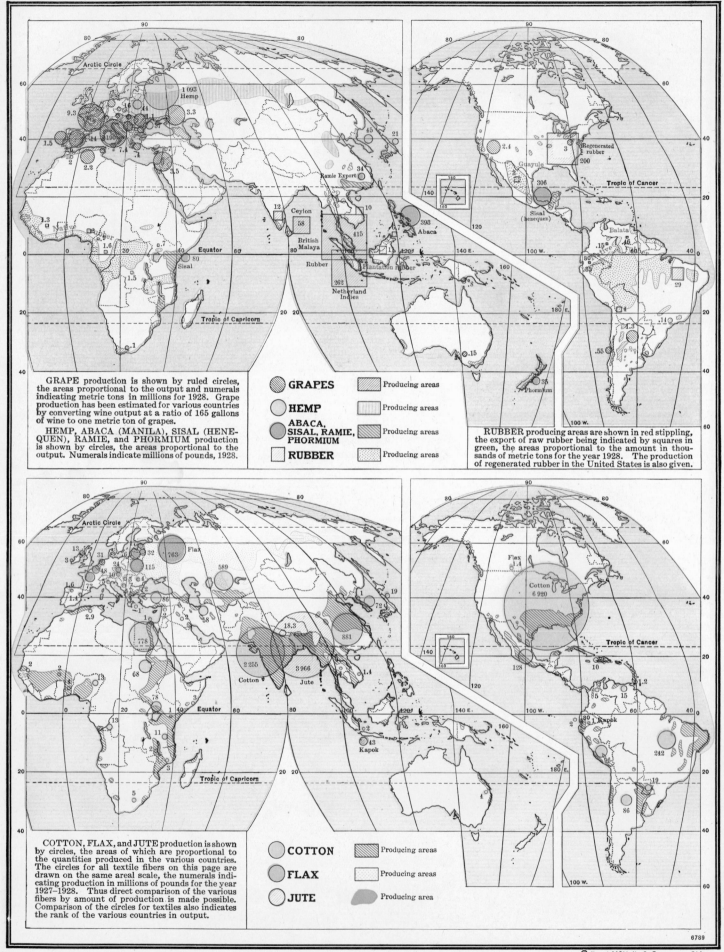

WORLD—Economic

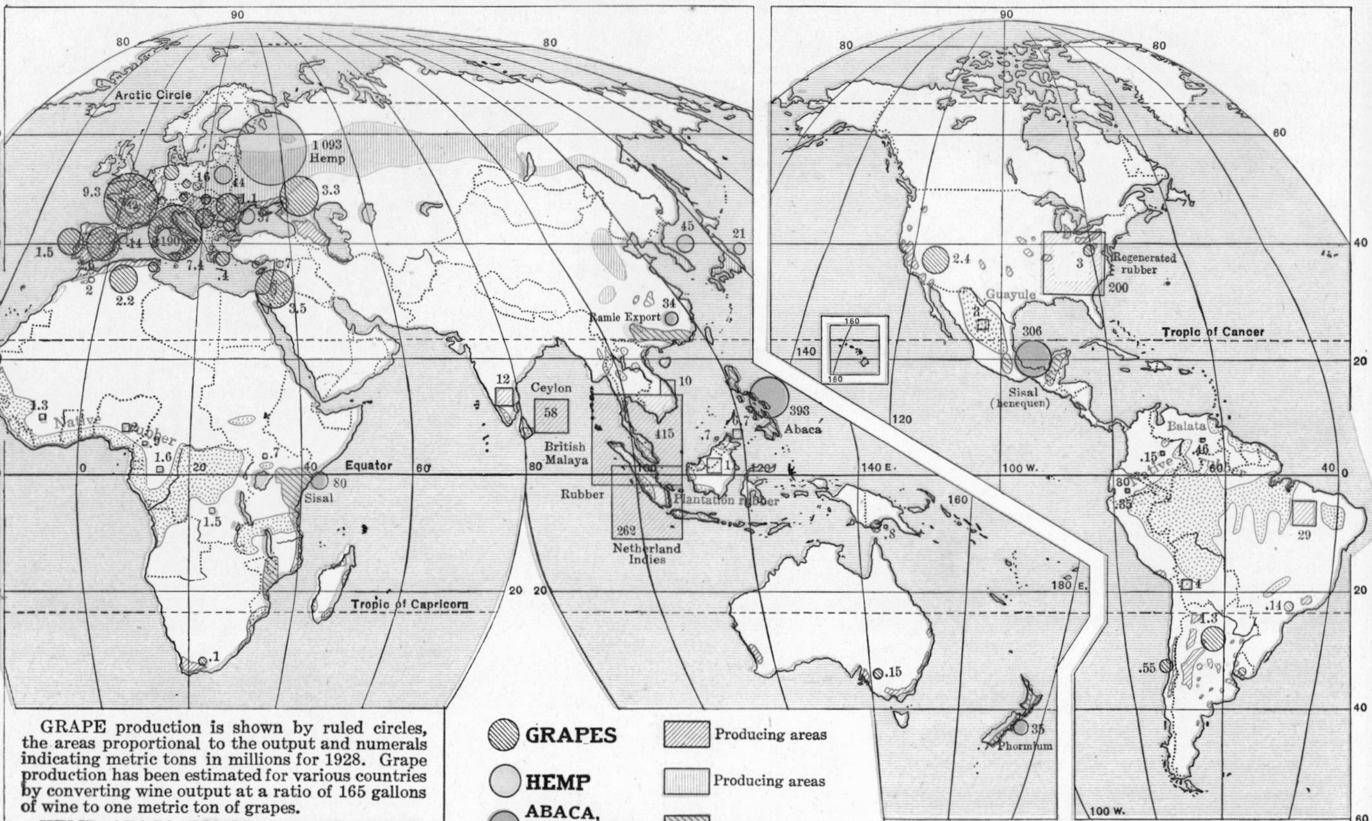

GRAPE production is shown by ruled circles, the areas proportional to the output and numerals indicating metric tons in millions for 1928. Grape production has been estimated for various countries by converting wine output at a ratio of 165 gallons of wine to one metric ton of grapes.

HEMP, ABACA (MANILA), SISAL (HENEQUEN), RAMIE, and PHORMIUM production is shown by circles, the areas proportional to the output. Numerals indicate millions of pounds, 1928.

GRAPES	Producing areas
HEMP	Producing areas
ABACA, SISAL, RAMIE, PHORMIUM	Producing areas
RUBBER	Producing areas

RUBBER producing areas are shown in red stippling, the export of raw rubber being indicated by squares in green, the areas proportional to the amount in thousands of metric tons for the year 1928. The production of regenerated rubber in the United States is also given.

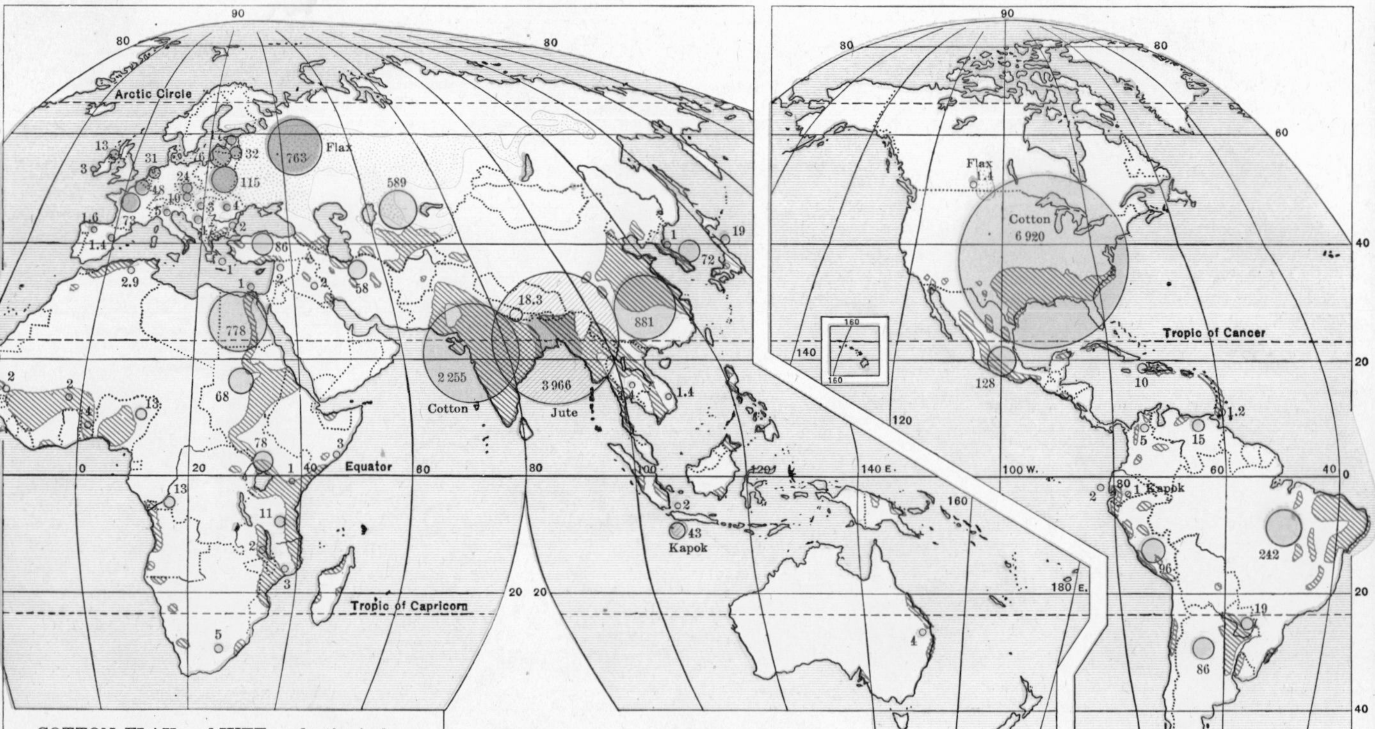

COTTON, FLAX, and JUTE production is shown by circles, the areas of which are proportional to the quantities produced in the various countries. The circles for all textile fibers on this page are drawn on the same areal scale, the numerals indicating production in millions of pounds for the year 1927–1928. Thus direct comparison of the various fibers by amount of production is made possible. Comparison of the circles for textiles also indicates the rank of the various countries in output.

COTTON	Producing areas
FLAX	Producing areas
JUTE	Producing area

6789

Goode's Homolosine Equal Area Projection, Condensed

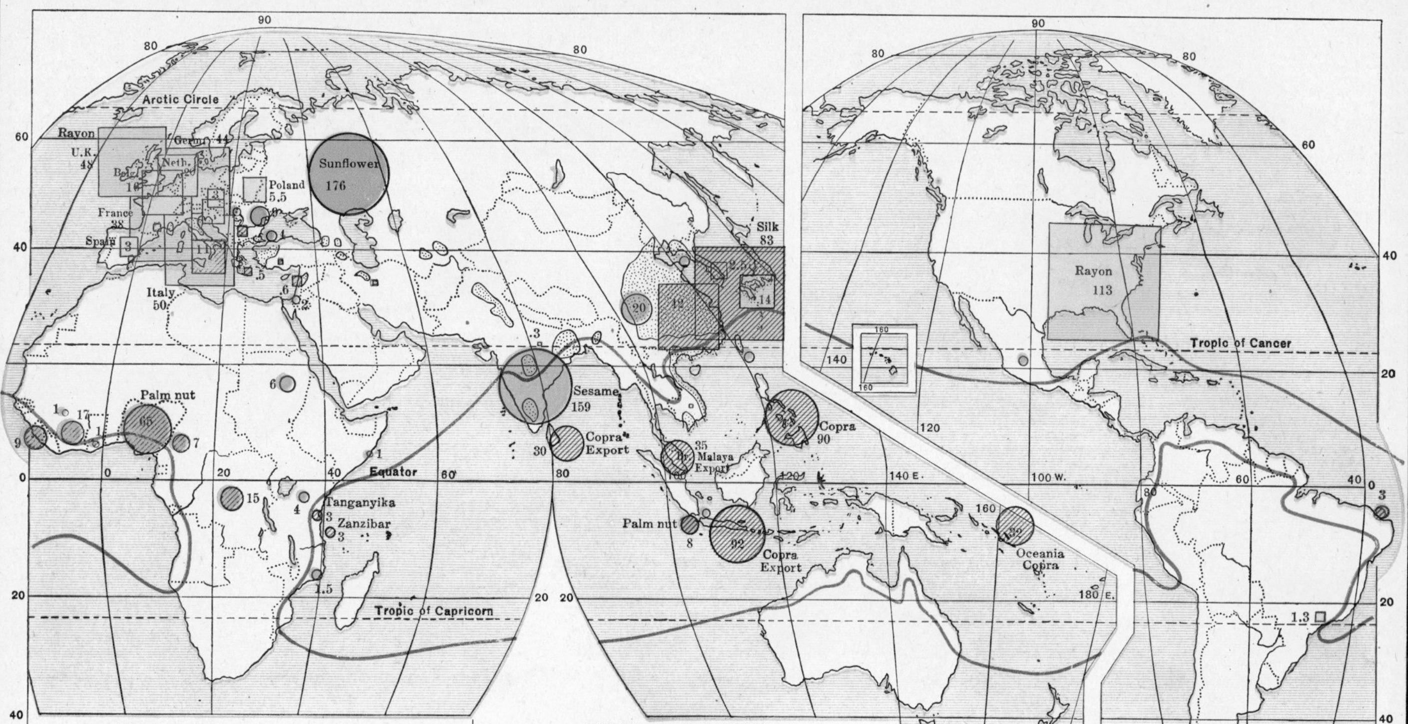

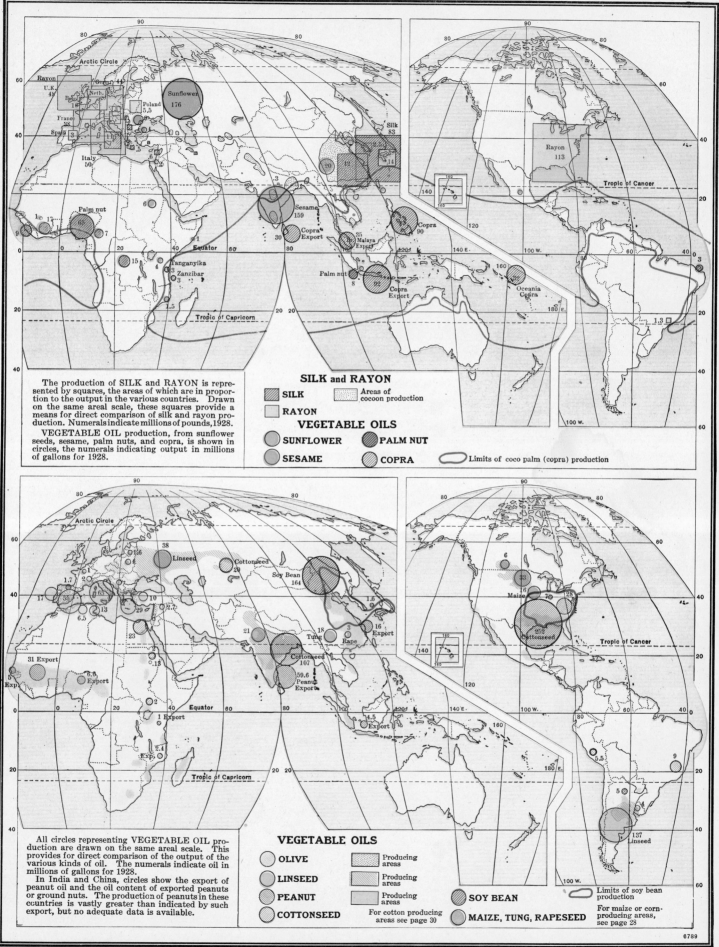

The production of SILK and RAYON is represented by squares, the areas of which are in proportion to the output in the various countries. Drawn on the same areal scale, these squares provide a means for direct comparison of silk and rayon production. Numerals indicate millions of pounds, 1928.

VEGETABLE OIL production, from sunflower seeds, sesame, palm nuts, and copra, is shown in circles, the numerals indicating output in millions of gallons for 1928.

SILK and RAYON

SILK — RAYON — Areas of cocoon production

VEGETABLE OILS

SUNFLOWER — SESAME — PALM NUT — COPRA — Limits of coco palm (copra) production

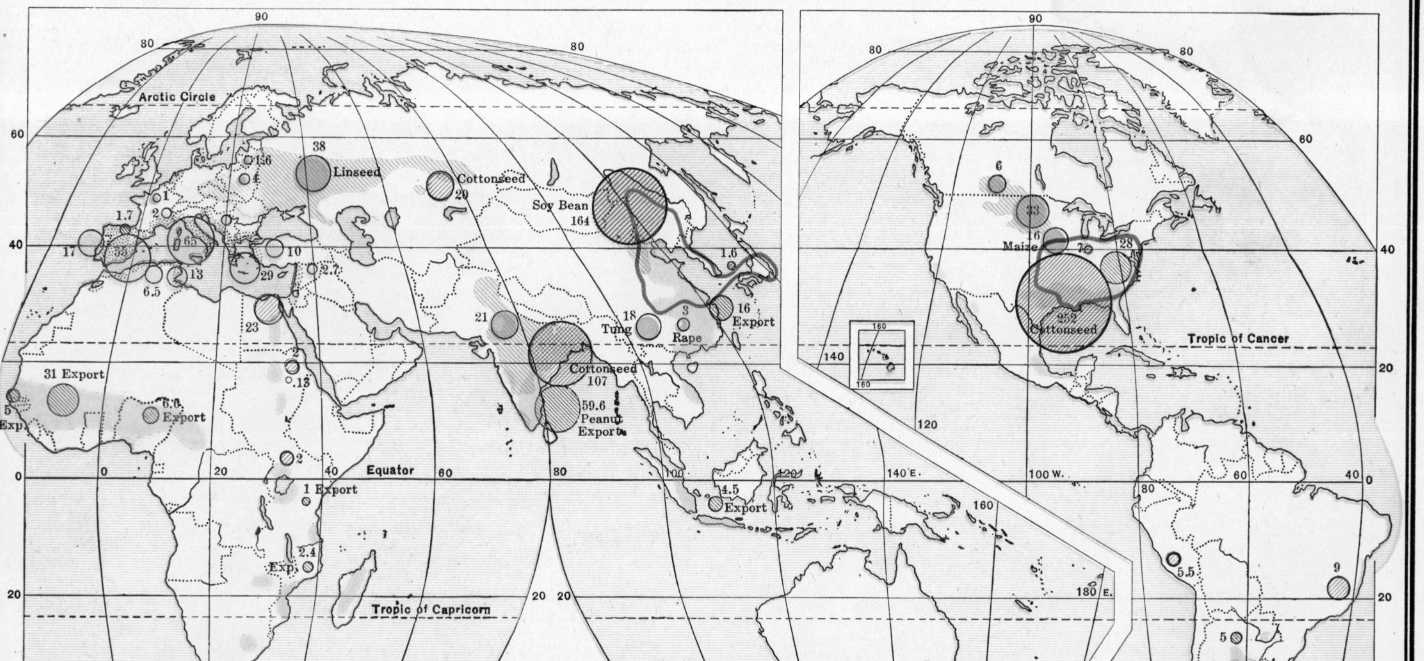

All circles representing VEGETABLE OIL production are drawn on the same areal scale. This provides for direct comparison of the output of the various kinds of oil. The numerals indicate oil in millions of gallons for 1928.

In India and China, circles show the export of peanut oil and the oil content of exported peanuts or ground nuts. The production of peanuts in these countries is vastly greater than indicated by such export, but no adequate data is available.

VEGETABLE OILS

OLIVE — Producing areas

LINSEED — Producing areas

PEANUT — Producing areas

COTTONSEED — For cotton producing areas see page 30

SOY BEAN — Limits of soy bean production

MAIZE, TUNG, RAPESEED — For maize or corn-producing areas, see page 28

6789

WORLD – Economic

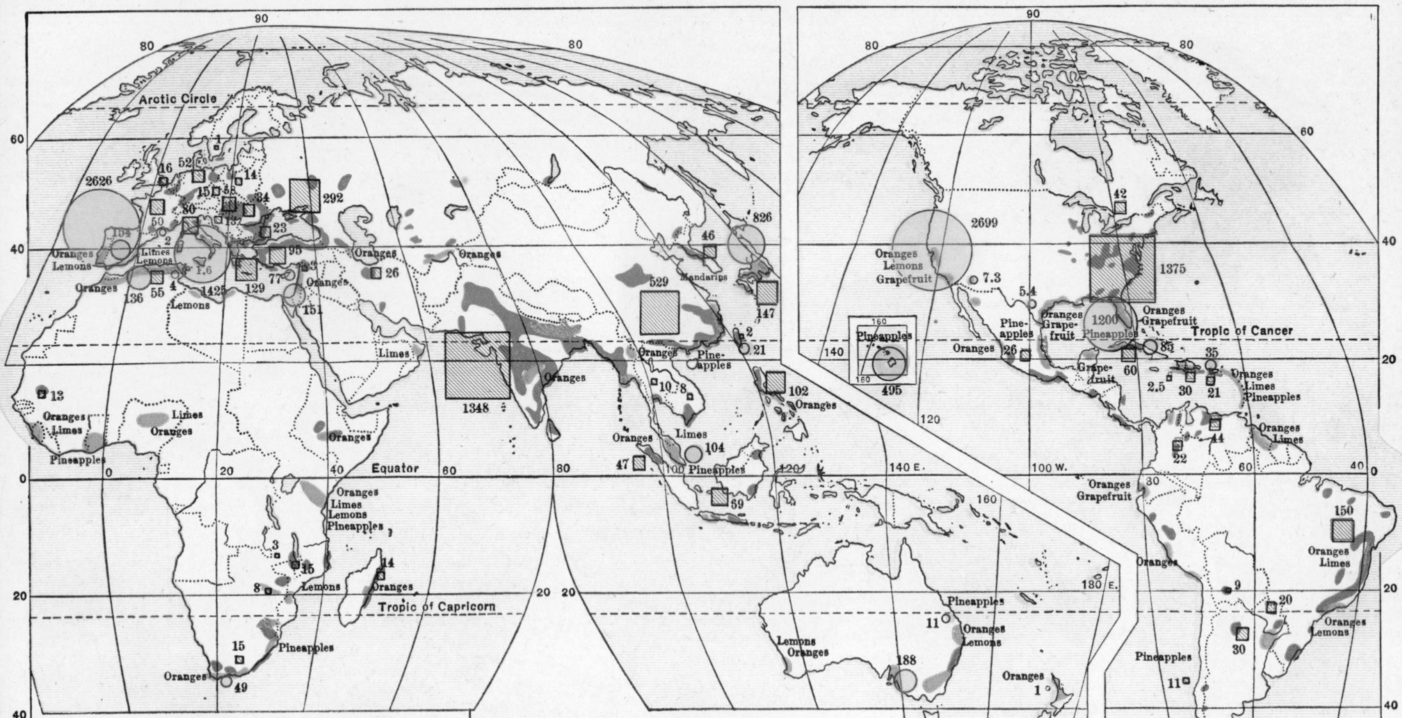

TOBACCO production is represented by squares, the areas of which are in proportion to the crop output. The numerals indicate millions of pounds of leaves produced in the various countries in 1928.

The areas of the circles for FRUITS are in proportion to the production. Numerals indicate millions of pounds in 1928. Circles for all fruits shown in this series are drawn on the same areal scale. Production of citrous fruits in Greece is large, but comparative statistics are not available.

TOBACCO — Producing areas

FRUITS

CITROUS FRUITS — Producing areas

PINEAPPLES

Localities of production are indicated by name placing

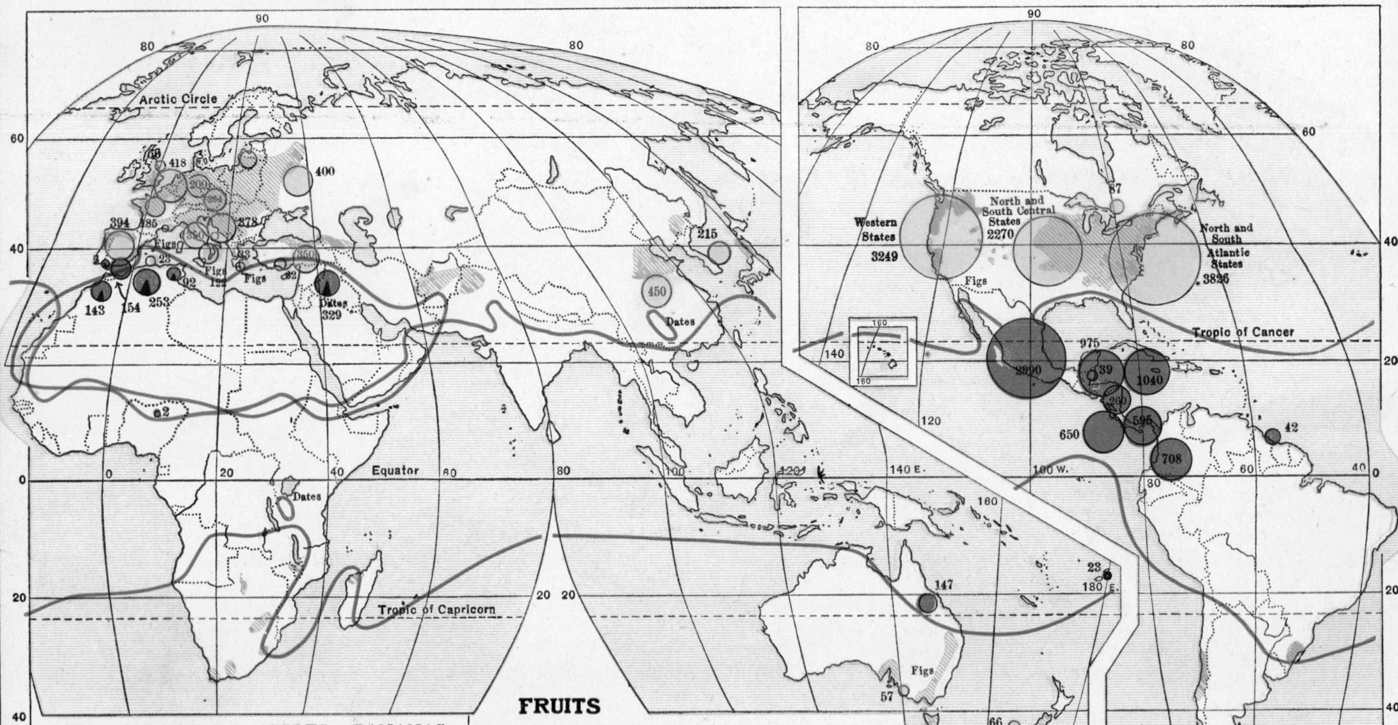

The production of APPLES, BANANAS, DATES, and FIGS is shown by circles, the areas proportional to the output. Numerals indicate production in millions of pounds of fruit for 1927–1928.

All the circles representing fruit production are drawn on the same areal scale. The comparison of the various fruits by quantity of production is thus made easy. Data available for apple production in countries other than the U. S. A. are largely incomplete and figures given are based on estimates.

FRUITS

APPLES

BANANAS

DATES

FIGS

Principal producing areas

Zone of production

Zone of production

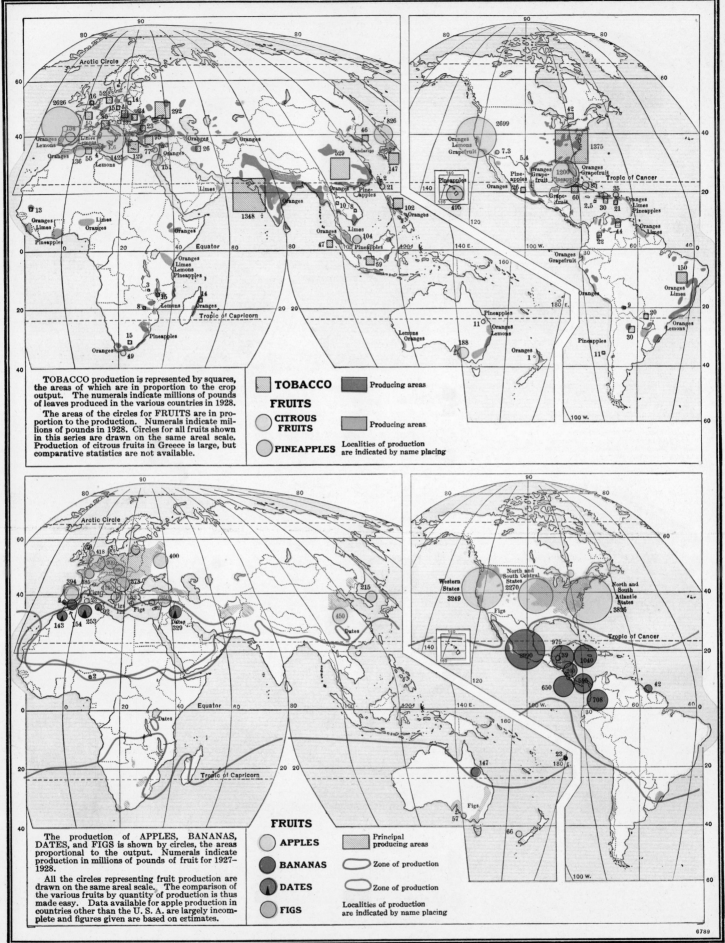

Localities of production are indicated by name placing

6789

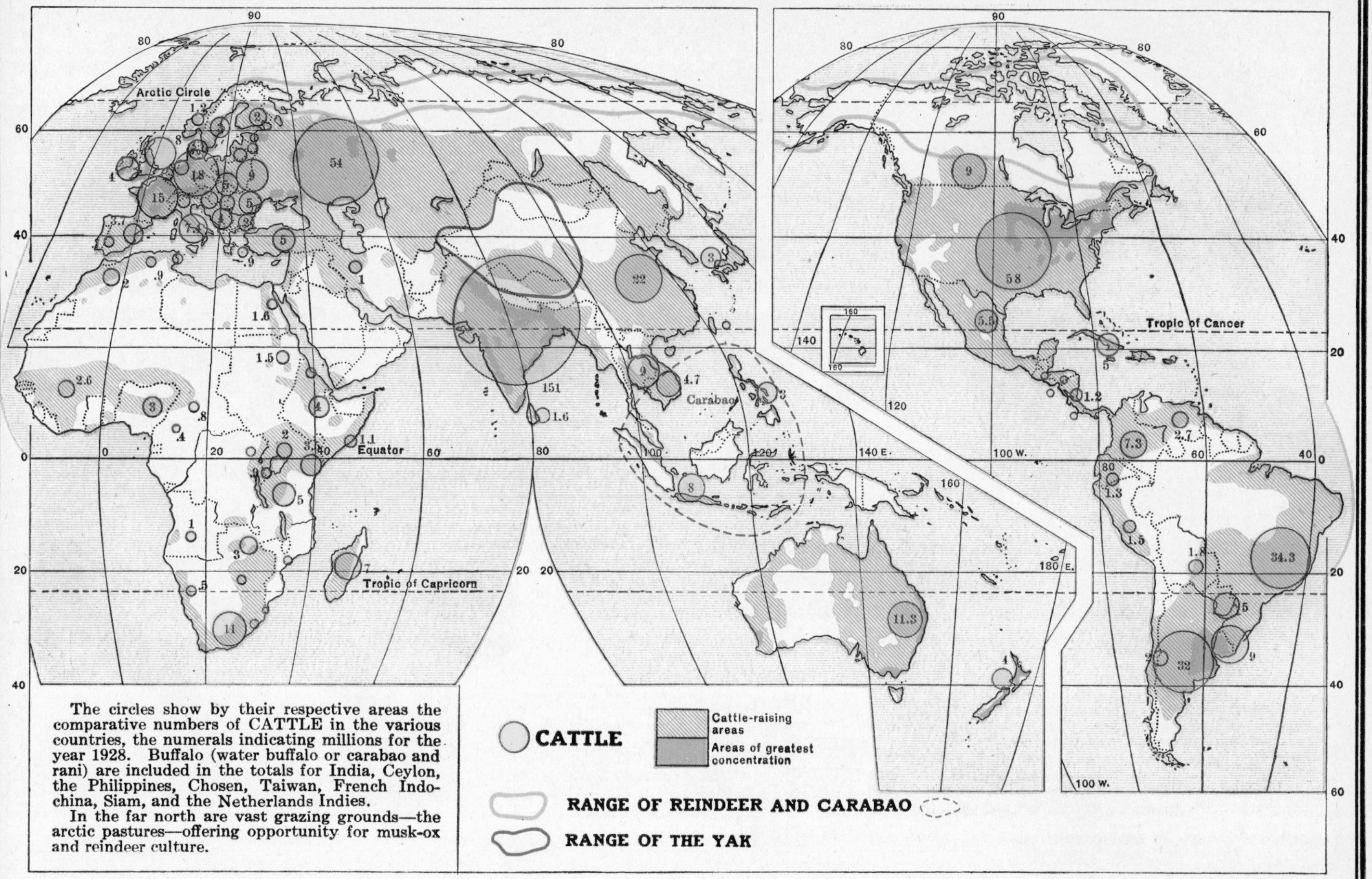

The circles show by their respective areas the comparative numbers of CATTLE in the various countries, the numerals indicating millions for the year 1928. Buffalo (water buffalo or carabao and rani) are included in the totals for India, Ceylon, the Philippines, Chosen, Taiwan, French Indo-china, Siam, and the Netherlands Indies.

In the far north are vast grazing grounds—the arctic pastures—offering opportunity for musk-ox and reindeer culture.

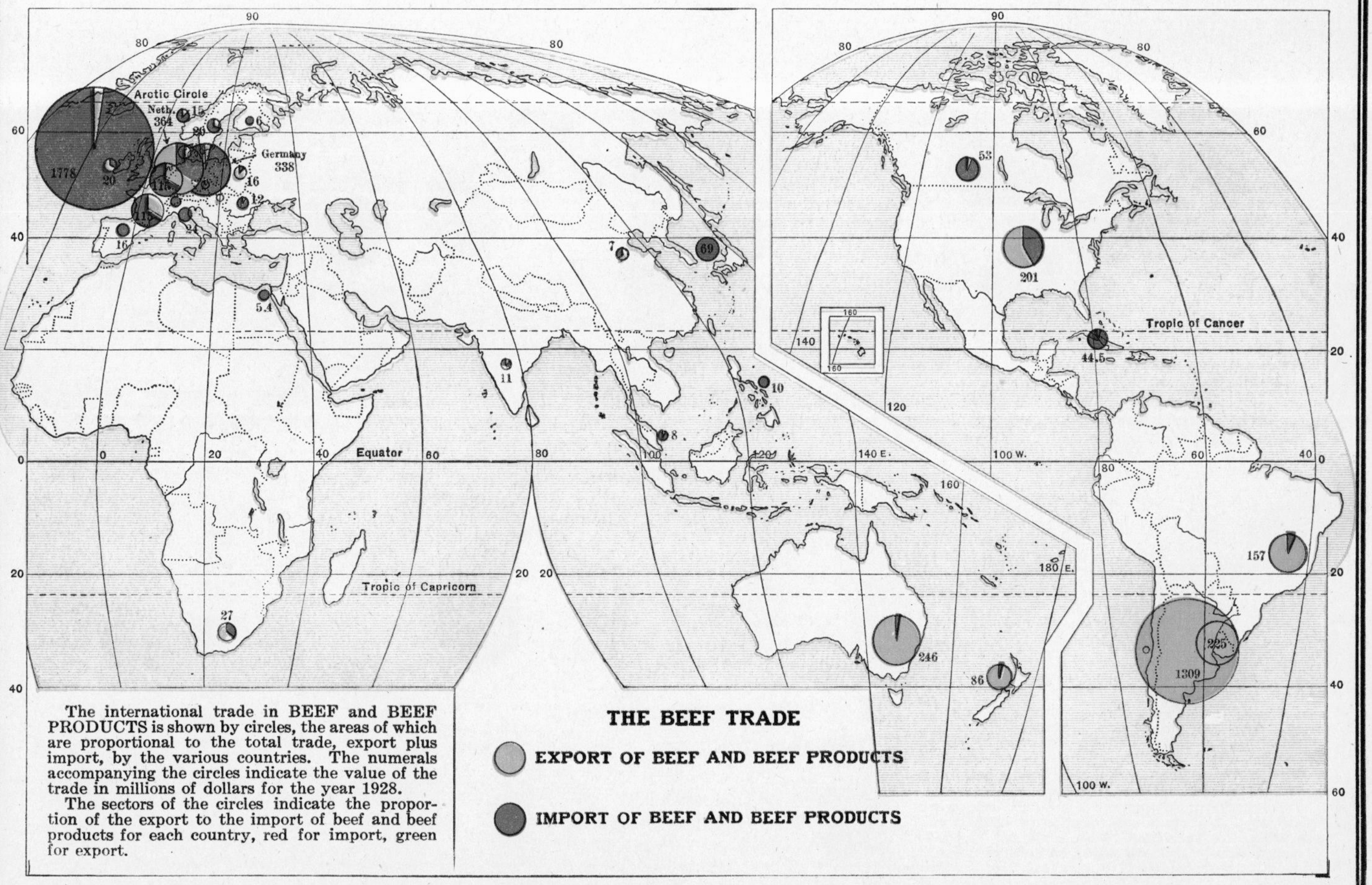

The international trade in BEEF and BEEF PRODUCTS is shown by circles, the areas of which are proportional to the total trade, export plus import, by the various countries. The numerals accompanying the circles indicate the value of the trade in millions of dollars for the year 1928.

The sectors of the circles indicate the proportion of the export to the import of beef and beef products for each country, red for import, green for export.

6789

WORLD – Economic

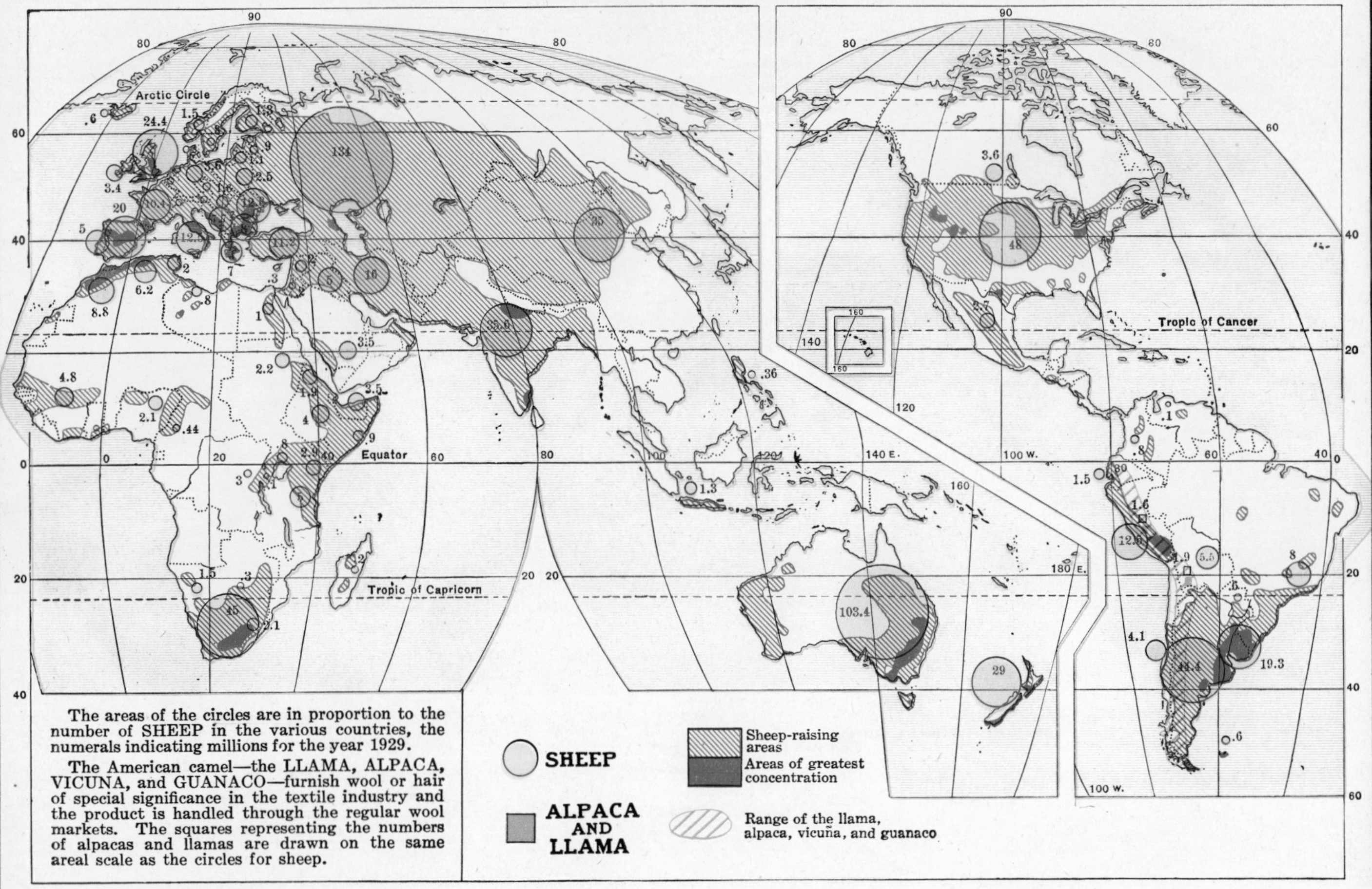

The areas of the circles are in proportion to the number of SHEEP in the various countries, the numerals indicating millions for the year 1929.

The American camel—the LLAMA, ALPACA, VICUNA, and GUANACO—furnish wool or hair of special significance in the textile industry and the product is handled through the regular wool markets. The squares representing the numbers of alpacas and llamas are drawn on the same areal scale as the circles for sheep.

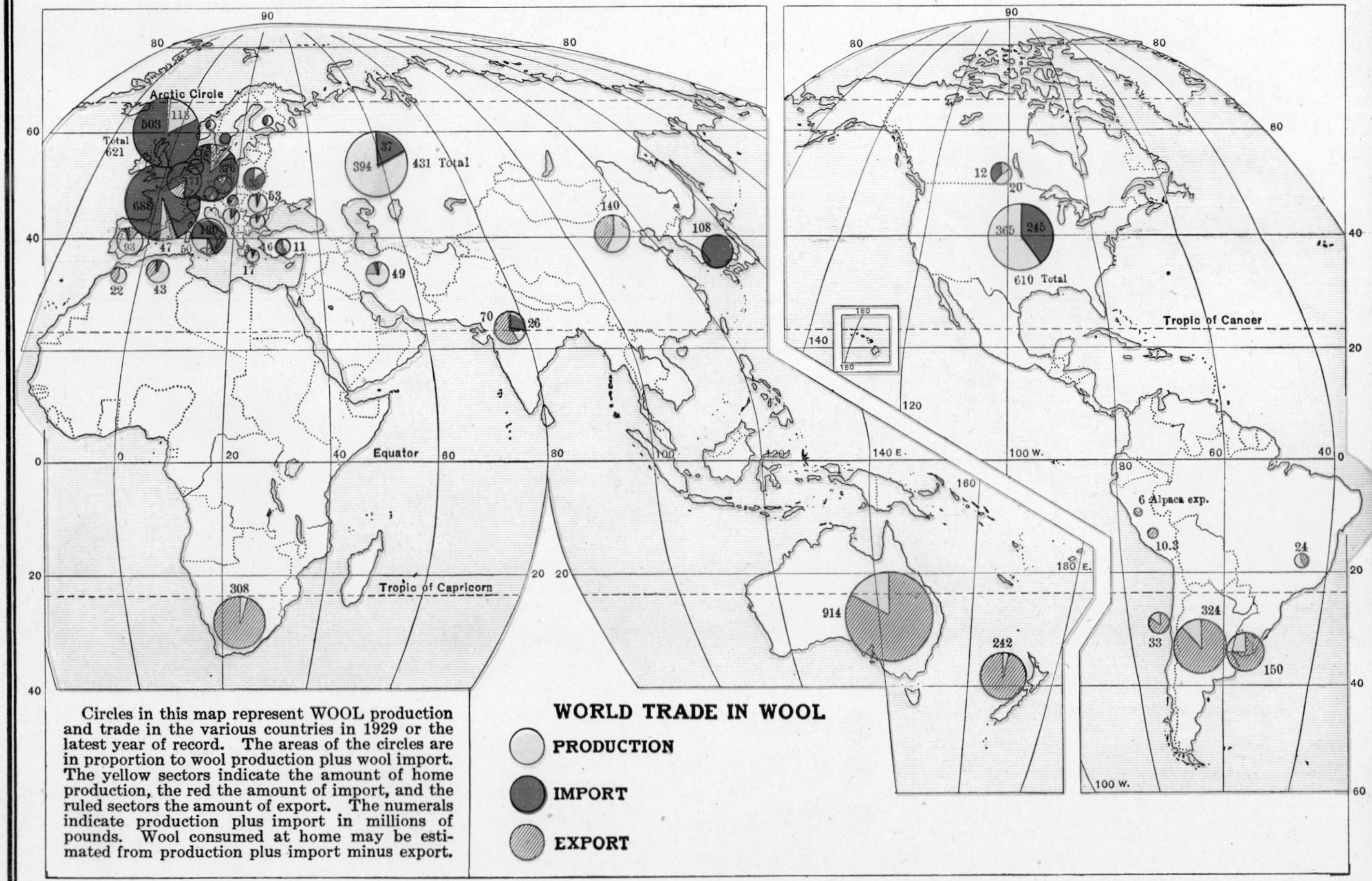

Circles in this map represent WOOL production and trade in the various countries in 1929 or the latest year of record. The areas of the circles are in proportion to wool production plus wool import. The yellow sectors indicate the amount of home production, the red the amount of import, and the ruled sectors the amount of export. The numerals indicate production plus import in millions of pounds. Wool consumed at home may be estimated from production plus import minus export.

6759

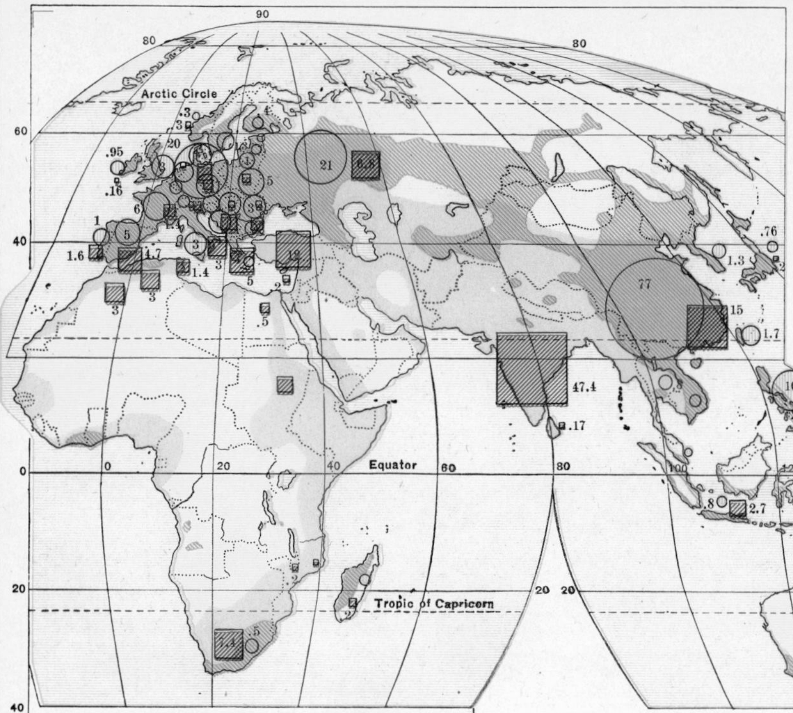

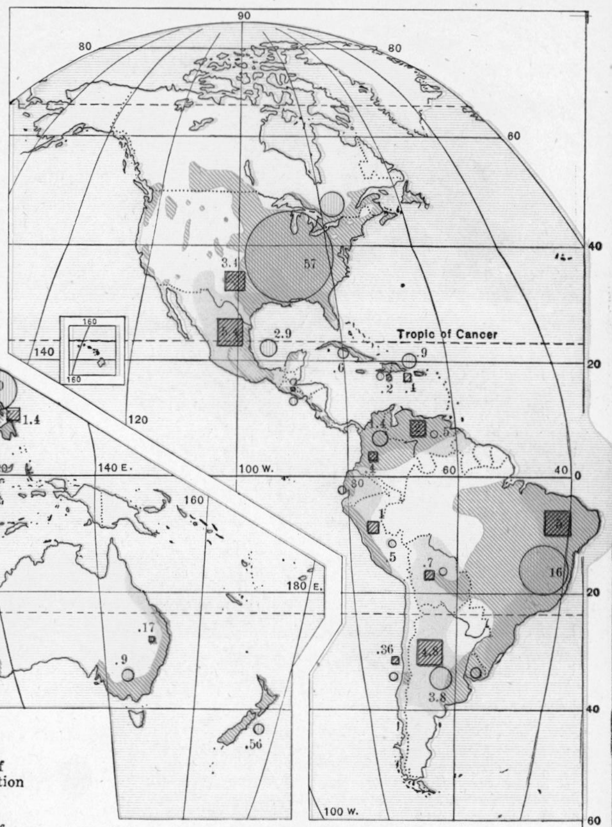

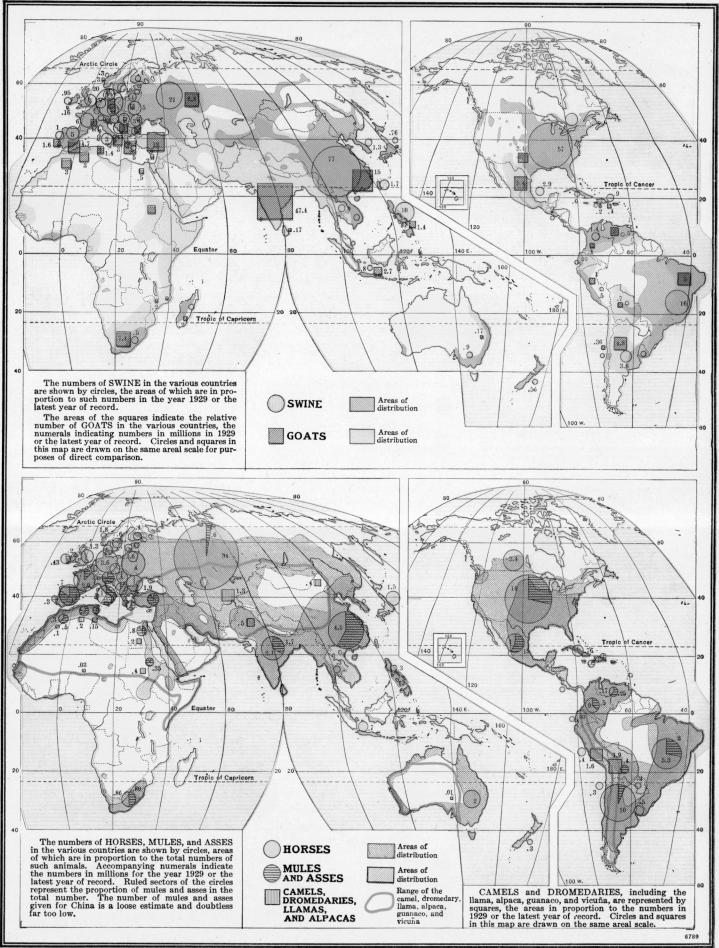

The numbers of SWINE in the various countries are shown by circles, the areas of which are in proportion to such numbers in the year 1929 or the latest year of record.

The areas of the squares indicate the relative number of GOATS in the various countries, the numerals indicating numbers in millions in 1929 or the latest year of record. Circles and squares in this map are drawn on the same areal scale for purposes of direct comparison.

SWINE — Areas of distribution

GOATS — Areas of distribution

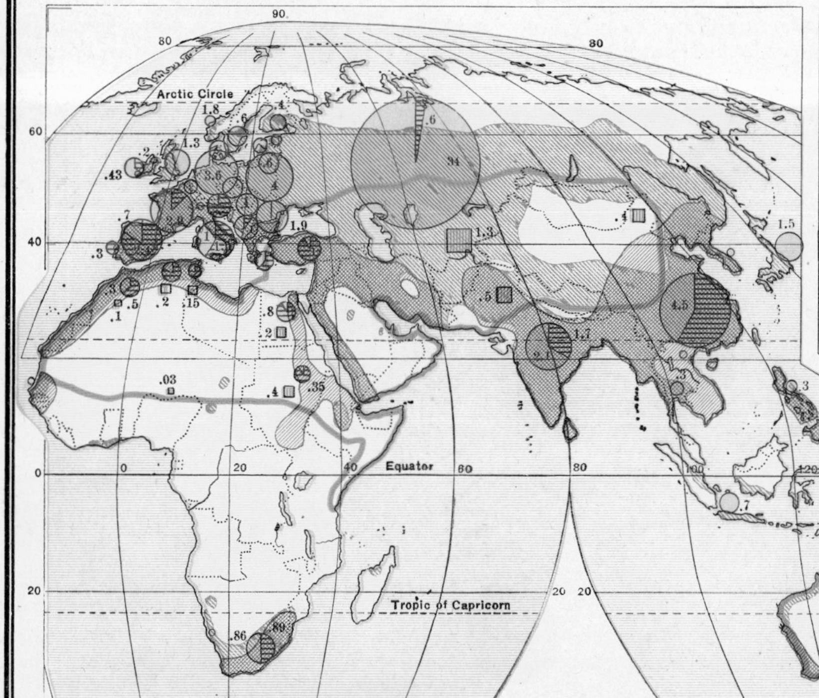

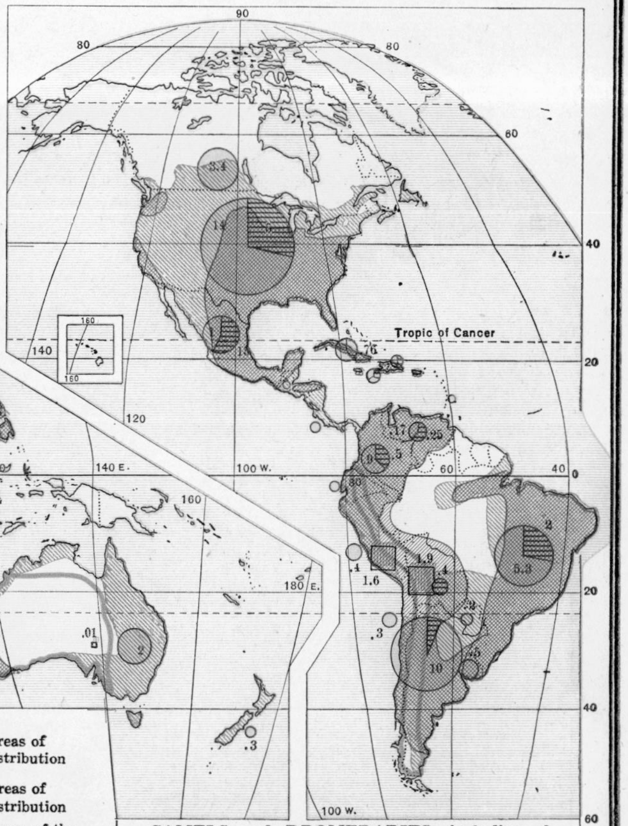

The numbers of HORSES, MULES, and ASSES in the various countries are shown by circles, areas of which are in proportion to the total numbers of such animals. Accompanying numerals indicate the numbers in millions for the year 1929 or the latest year of record. Ruled sectors of the circles represent the proportion of mules and asses in the total number. The number of mules and asses given for China is a loose estimate and doubtless far too low.

HORSES — Areas of distribution

MULES AND ASSES — Areas of distribution

CAMELS, DROMEDARIES, LLAMAS, AND ALPACAS — Range of the camel, dromedary, llama, alpaca, guanaco, and vicuña

CAMELS and DROMEDARIES, including the llama, alpaca, guanaco, and vicuña, are represented by squares, the areas in proportion to the numbers in 1929 or the latest year of record. Circles and squares in this map are drawn on the same areal scale.

6789

WORLD - Economic

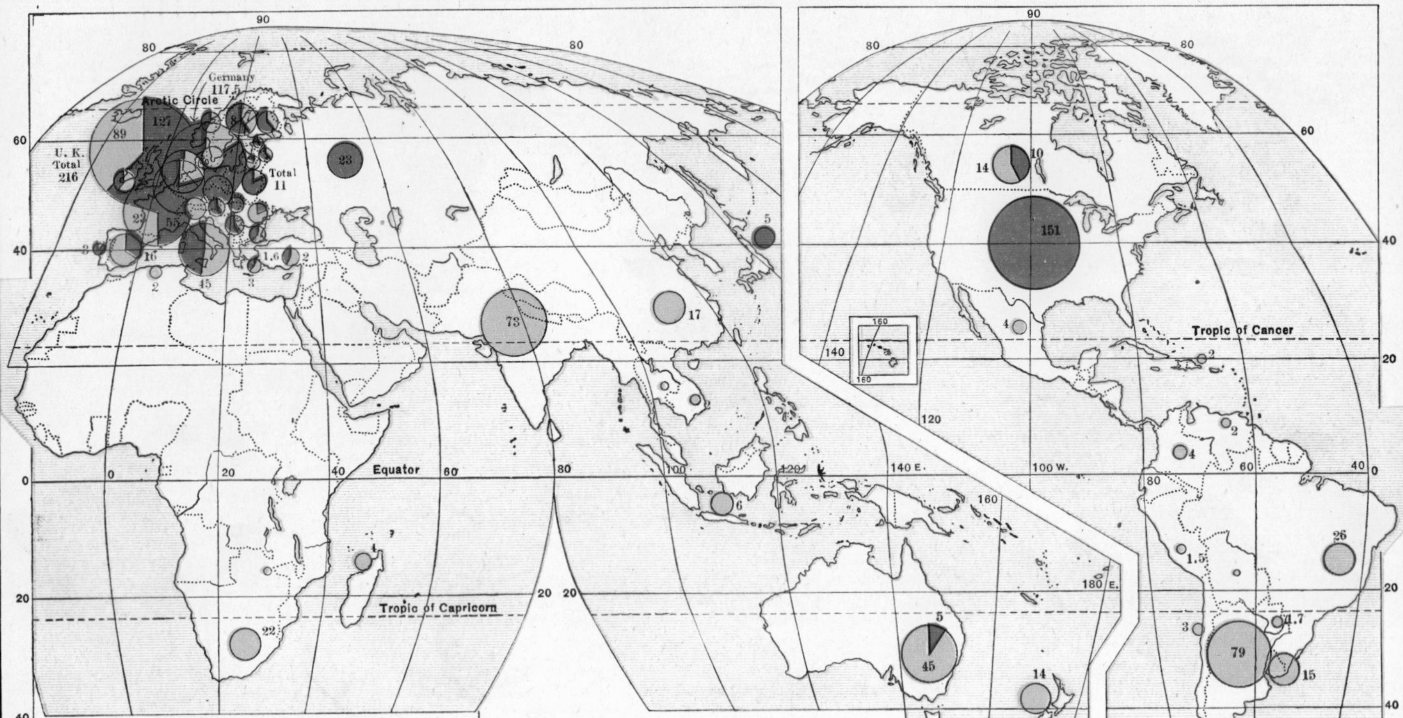

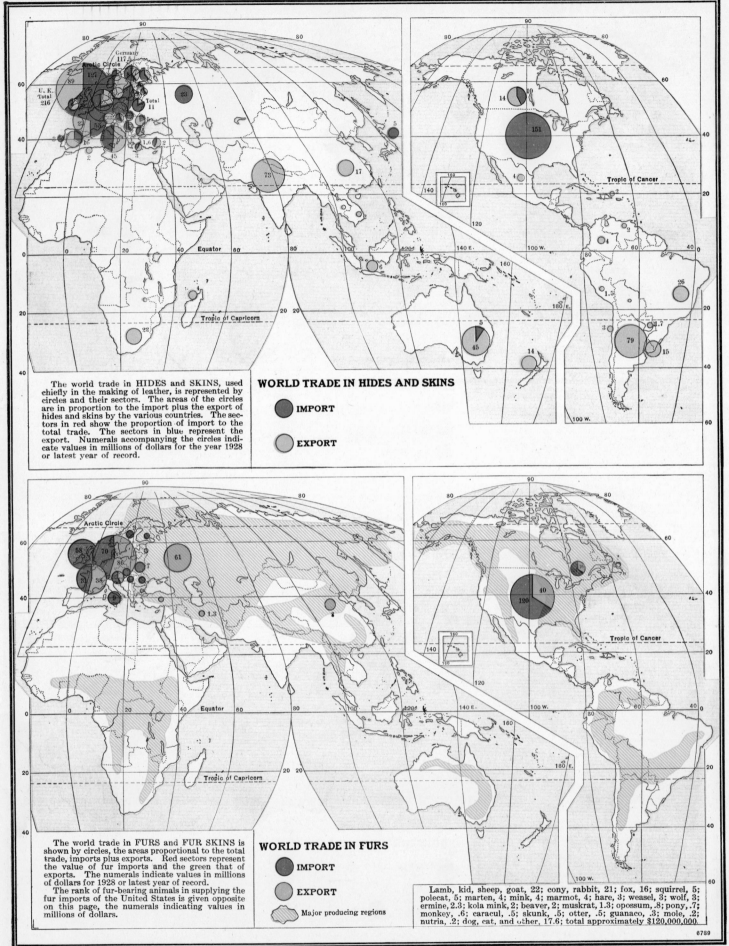

The world trade in HIDES and SKINS, used chiefly in the making of leather, is represented by circles and their sectors. The areas of the circles are in proportion to the import plus the export of hides and skins by the various countries. The sectors in red show the proportion of import to the total trade. The sectors in blue represent the export. Numerals accompanying the circles indicate values in millions of dollars for the year 1928 or latest year of record.

WORLD TRADE IN HIDES AND SKINS

IMPORT

EXPORT

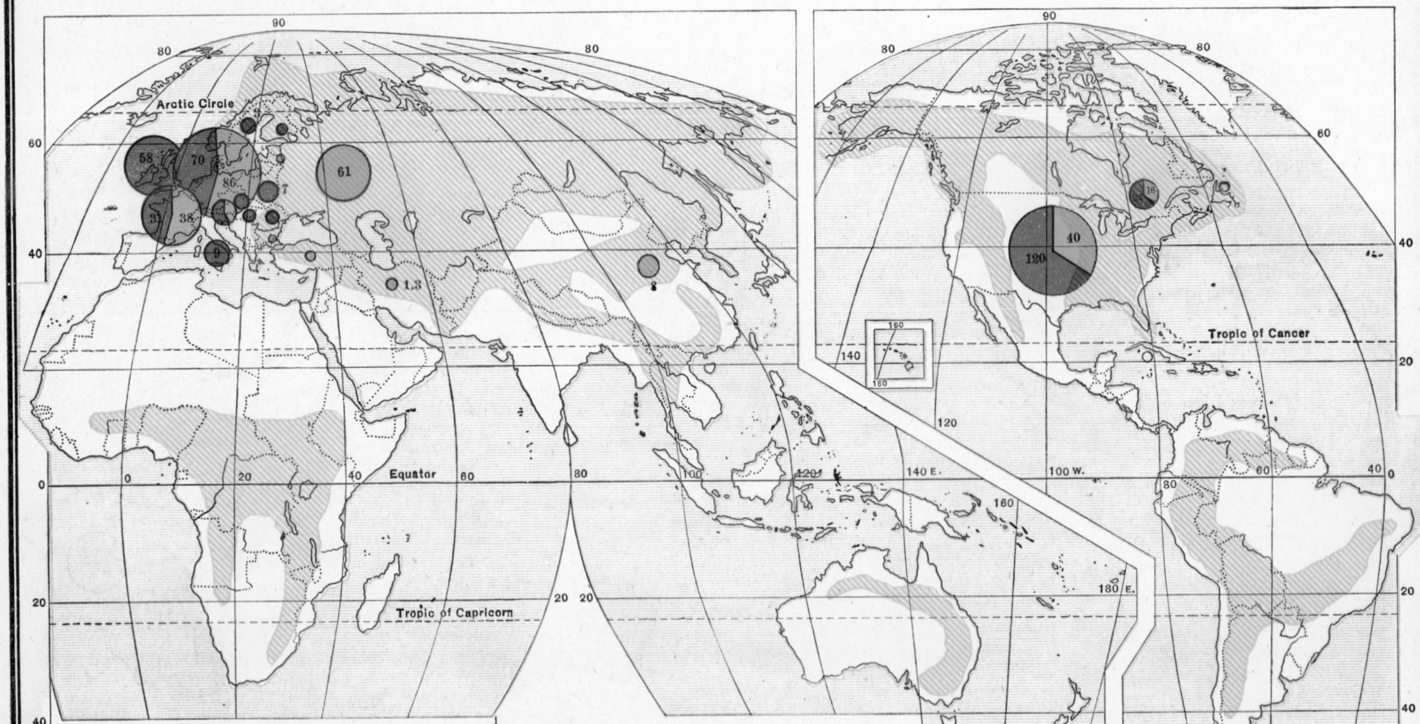

The world trade in FURS and FUR SKINS is shown by circles, the areas proportional to the total trade, imports plus exports. Red sectors represent the value of fur imports and the green that of exports. The numerals indicate values in millions of dollars for 1928 or latest year of record.
The rank of fur-bearing animals in supplying the fur imports of the United States is given opposite on this page, the numerals indicating values in millions of dollars.

WORLD TRADE IN FURS

IMPORT

EXPORT

Major producing regions

Lamb, kid, sheep, goat, 22; cony, rabbit, 21; fox, 16; squirrel, 5; polecat, 5; marten, 4; mink, 4; marmot, 4; hare, 3; weasel, 3; wolf, 3; ermine, 2.3; kola mink, 2; beaver, 2; muskrat, 1.3; opossum, .8; pony, .7; monkey, .6; caracul, .5; skunk, .5; otter, .5; guanaco, .3; mole, .2; nutria, .2; dog, cat, and other, 17.6; total approximately $120,000,000.

6789

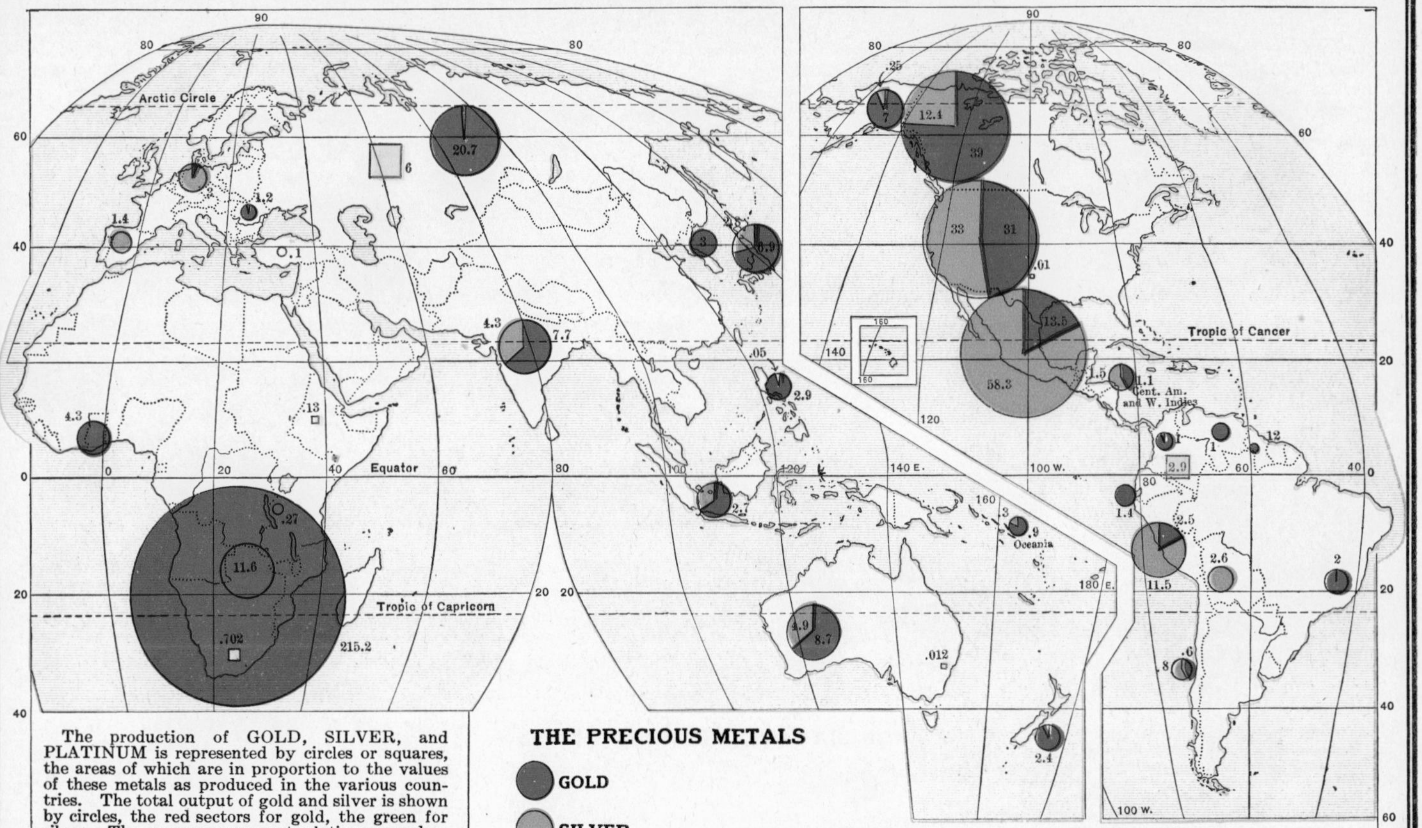

The production of GOLD, SILVER, and PLATINUM is represented by circles or squares, the areas of which are in proportion to the values of these metals as produced in the various countries. The total output of gold and silver is shown by circles, the red sectors for gold, the green for silver. The squares represent platinum production and are drawn on the same areal scale as the circles. Numerals indicate output value in millions of dollars, gold and silver in 1929, platinum in 1927.

THE PRECIOUS METALS

- GOLD
- SILVER
- PLATINUM

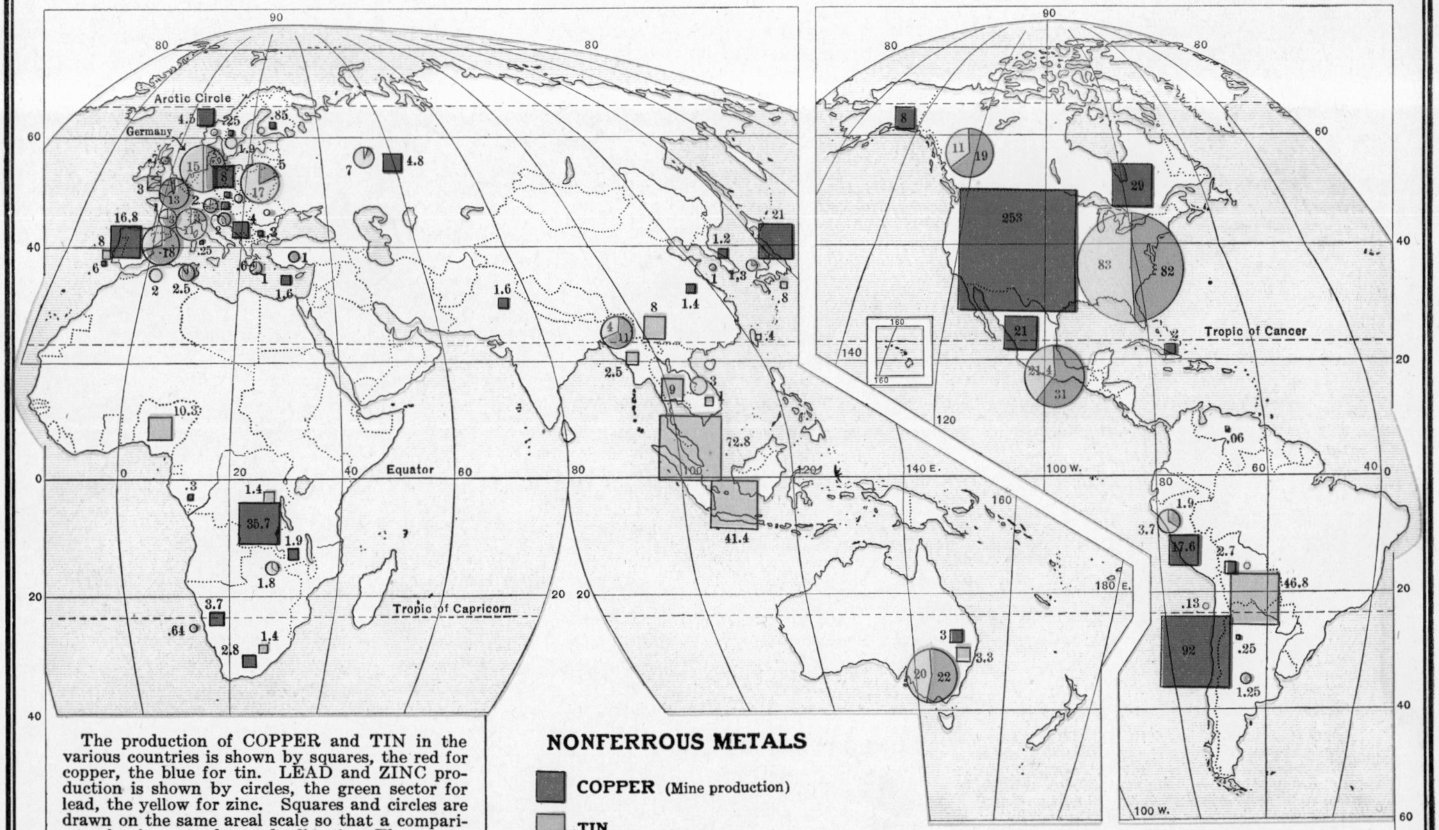

The production of COPPER and TIN in the various countries is shown by squares, the red for copper, the blue for tin. LEAD and ZINC production is shown by circles, the green sector for lead, the yellow for zinc. Squares and circles are drawn on the same areal scale so that a comparison of values can be made directly. The accompanying numerals indicate the value of the output of the various metals in millions of dollars for the year 1928.

NONFERROUS METALS

- COPPER (Mine production)
- TIN
- LEAD
- ZINC

6789

WORLD - Economic

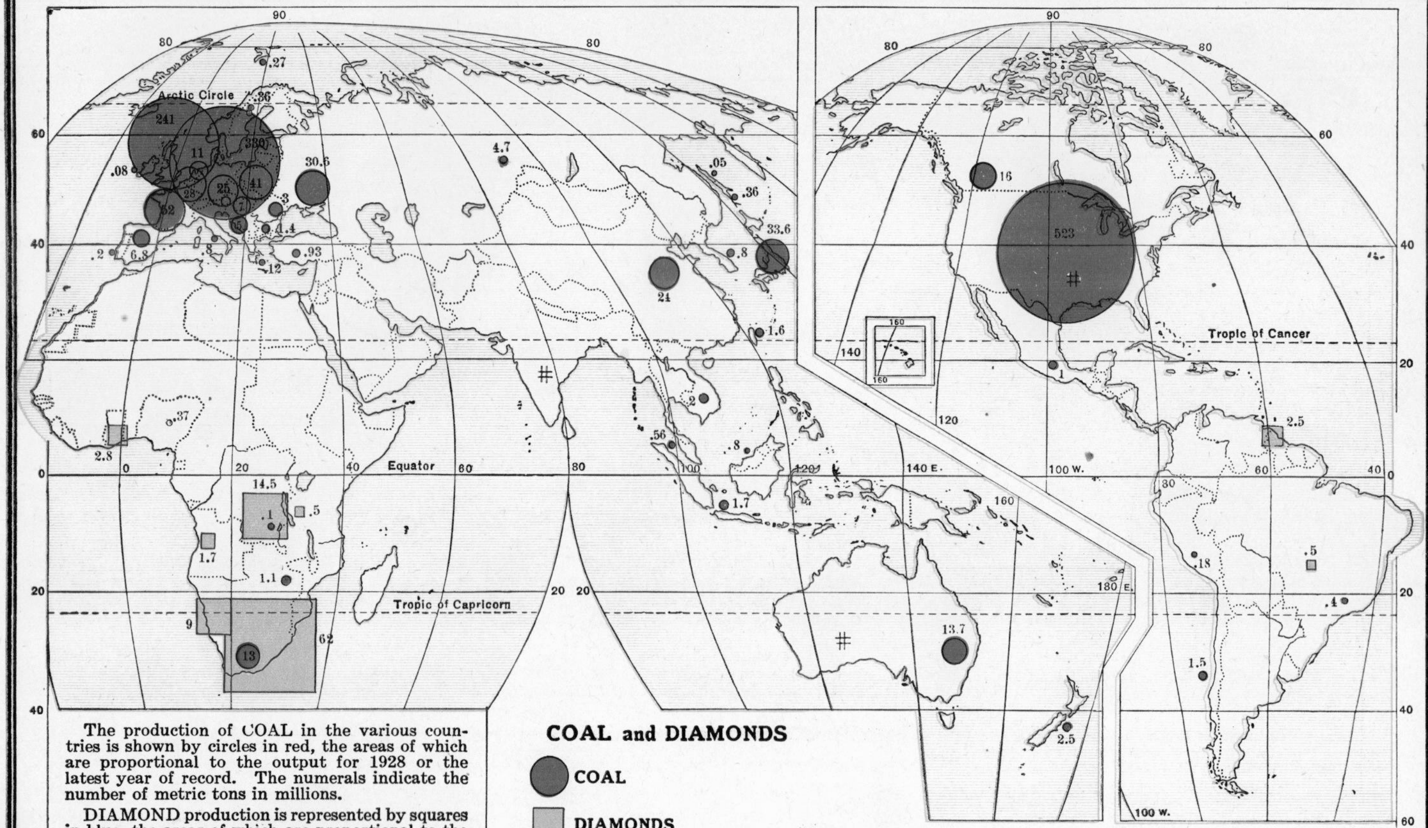

The production of COAL in the various countries is shown by circles in red, the areas of which are proportional to the output for 1928 or the latest year of record. The numerals indicate the number of metric tons in millions.

DIAMOND production is represented by squares in blue, the areas of which are proportional to the value of the output. The numerals indicate values in millions of dollars for the year 1928 or the latest year of record.

COAL and DIAMONDS

COAL

DIAMONDS

Occasional diamond finds

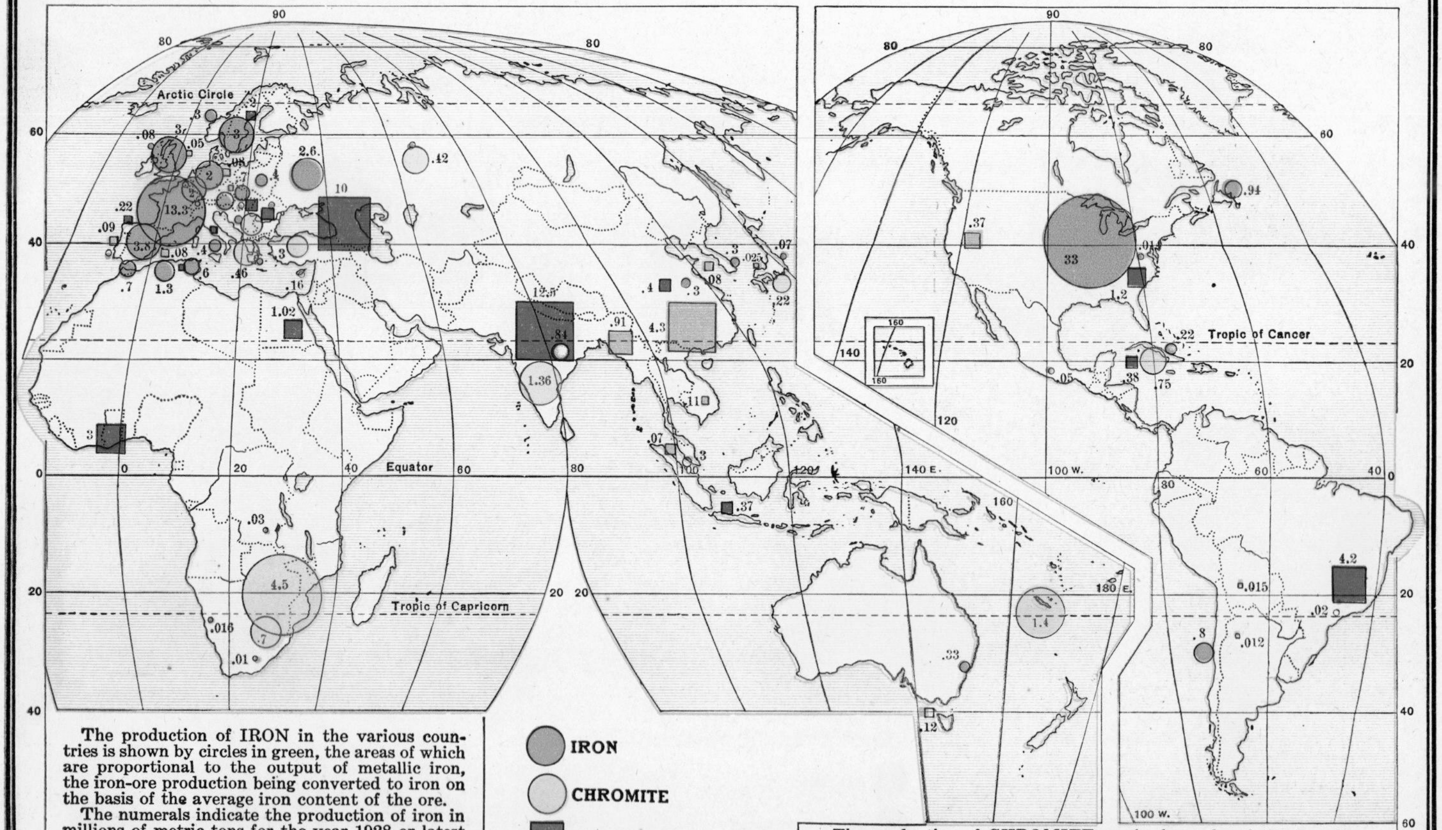

The production of IRON in the various countries is shown by circles in green, the areas of which are proportional to the output of metallic iron, the iron-ore production being converted to iron on the basis of the average iron content of the ore.

The numerals indicate the production of iron in millions of metric tons for the year 1928 or latest year of record. The areal scale of the circles is the same as for circles representing steel production on the following page.

IRON

CHROMITE

MANGANESE

TUNGSTEN

The production of CHROMITE ore is shown by circles in yellow, of MANGANESE ore by squares in red, and of TUNGSTEN ore by squares in blue, the areas in each case proportional to the output.

The numerals indicate the value of production in millions of dollars for the year 1928 or the latest year of record.

6789

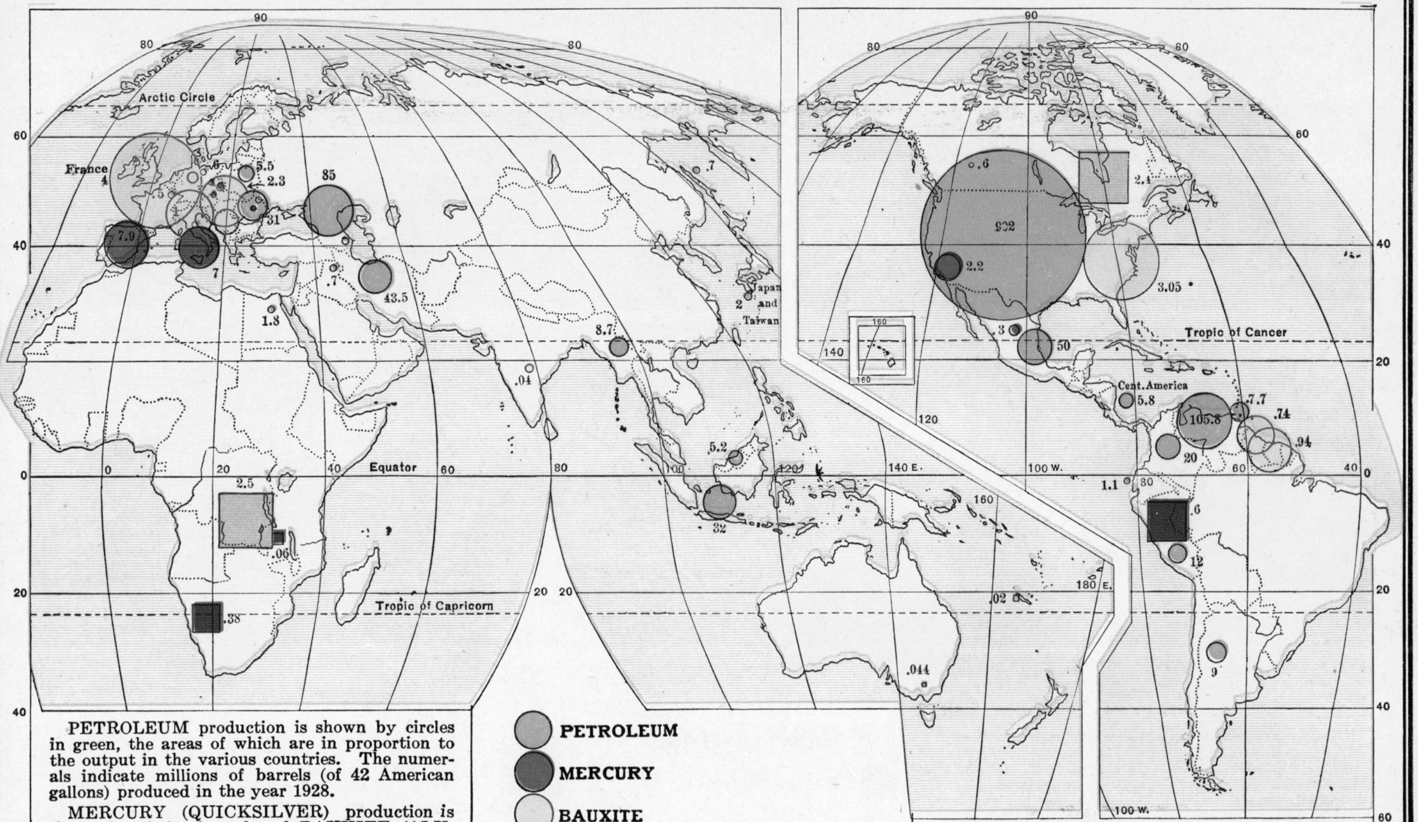

PETROLEUM production is shown by circles in green, the areas of which are in proportion to the output in the various countries. The numerals indicate millions of barrels (of 42 American gallons) produced in the year 1928.

MERCURY (QUICKSILVER) production is shown by circles in red and BAUXITE (ALUMINUM ORE) by circles in yellow, the areas in proportion to the output and numerals indicating value of output in millions of dollars for 1928.

COBALT production is shown by squares in blue and VANADIUM by squares in purple, the areas in proportion to the output. Numerals indicate value of output in millions of dollars for the year 1928.

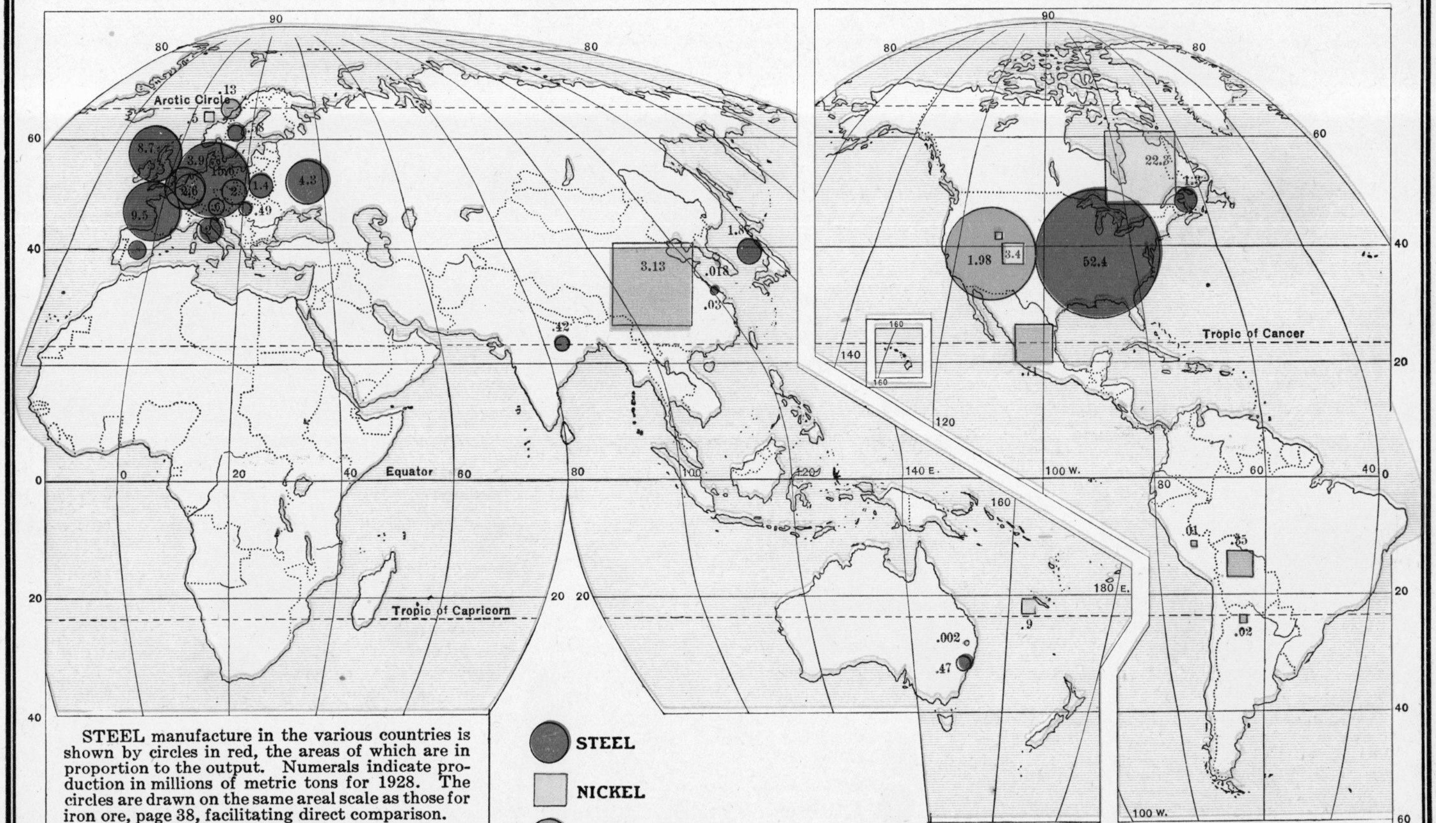

STEEL manufacture in the various countries is shown by circles in red, the areas of which are in proportion to the output. Numerals indicate production in millions of metric tons for 1928. The circles are drawn on the same areal scale as those for iron ore, page 38, facilitating direct comparison.

NICKEL production is shown by squares in yellow and ANTIMONY by squares in blue. Accompanying numerals indicate value of output in millions of dollars for the year 1928.

The production of MOLYBDENUM is represented by green circles, the areas of which are in proportion to the output. Numerals indicate the value of the output in millions of dollars.

6789

WORLD—Economic

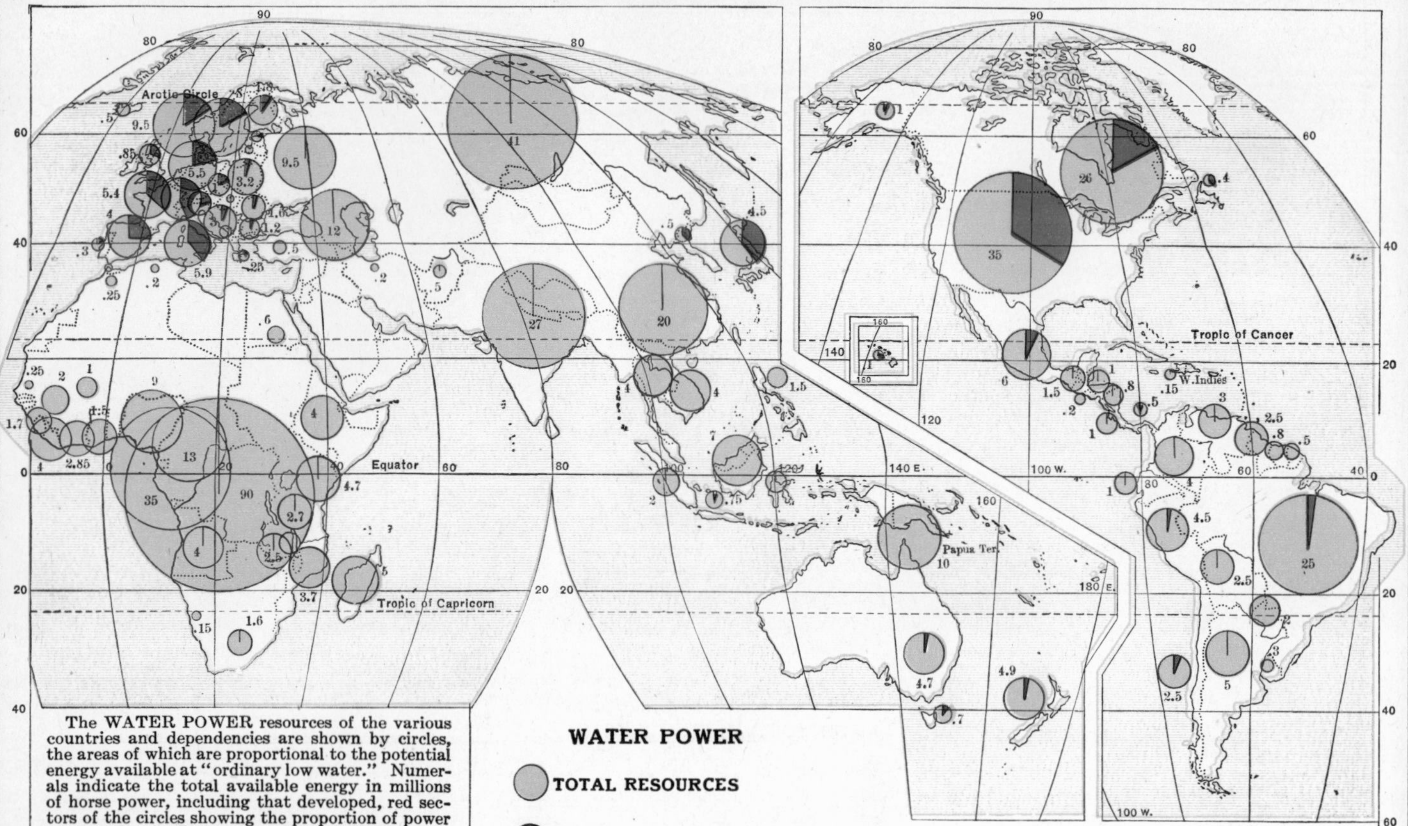

The WATER POWER resources of the various countries and dependencies are shown by circles, the areas of which are proportional to the potential energy available at "ordinary low water." Numerals indicate the total available energy in millions of horse power, including that developed, red sectors of the circles showing the proportion of power developed as at January 1, 1928. A single line in a circle represents very slight development. The available energy reported for India, China, and Brazil is tentative only and is doubtless far too low.

WATER POWER

TOTAL RESOURCES

POWER DEVELOPED, 1928

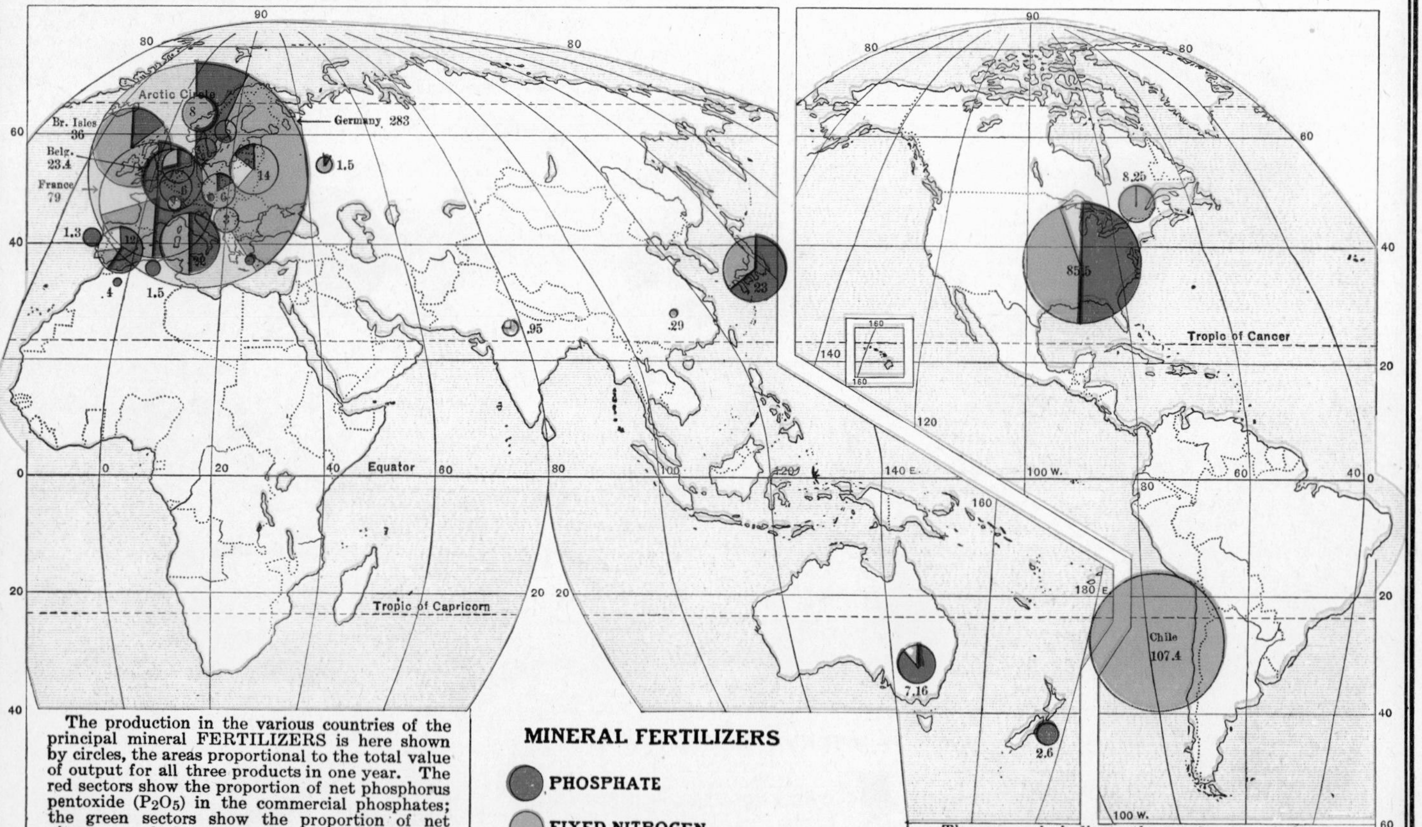

The production in the various countries of the principal mineral FERTILIZERS is here shown by circles, the areas proportional to the total value of output for all three products in one year. The red sectors show the proportion of net phosphorus pentoxide (P_2O_5) in the commercial phosphates; the green sectors show the proportion of net nitrogen, and the yellow that of the net potash (K_2O). Estimates are based on the average wholesale price of the commercial fertilizer, computed on the net chemical content.

MINERAL FERTILIZERS

PHOSPHATE

FIXED NITROGEN

POTASH

The numerals indicate the total value of the three forms of fertilizer in millions of dollars for the year 1928. The Chilean output is the natural mineral nitrate. In other lands the nitrates are largely synthetic, those from Norway being derived entirely from the air.

6789

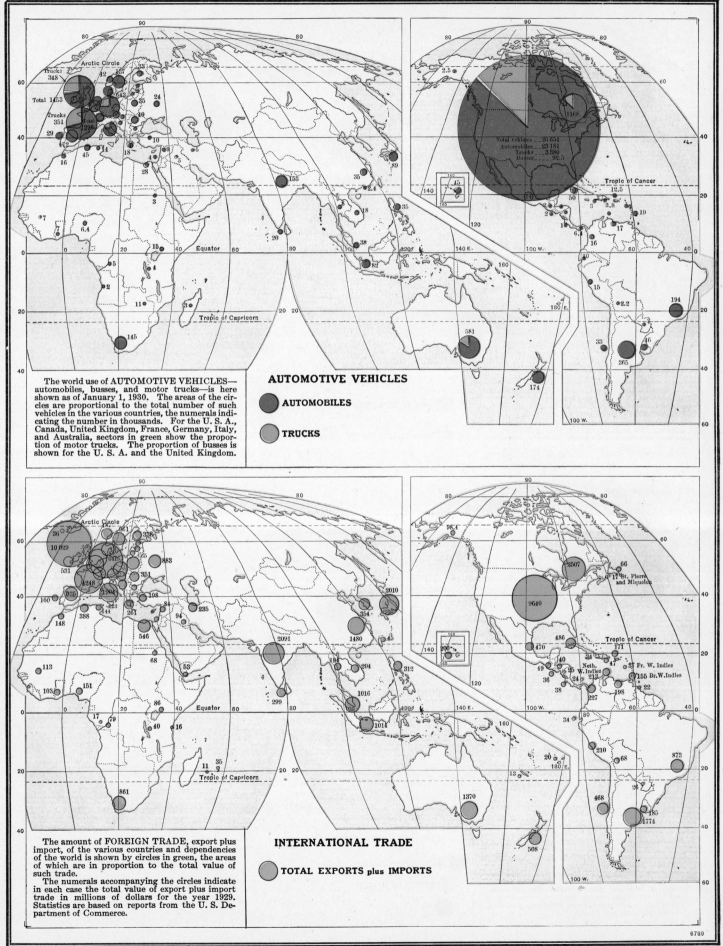

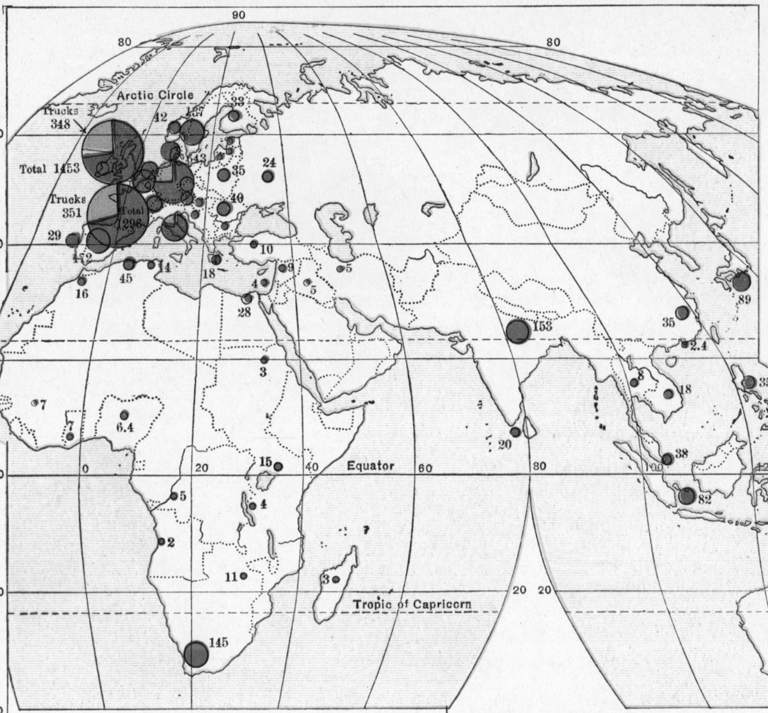

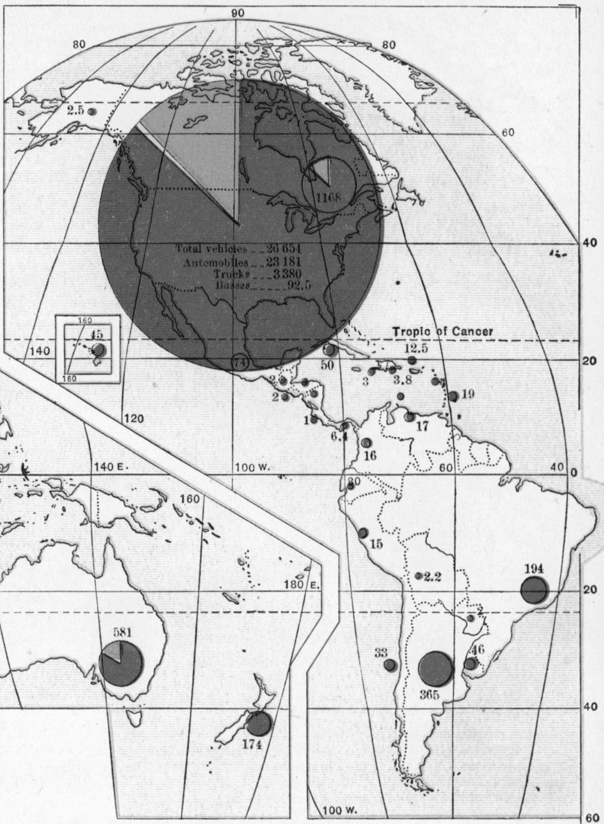

The world use of AUTOMOTIVE VEHICLES—automobiles, busses, and motor trucks—is here shown as of January 1, 1930. The areas of the circles are proportional to the total number of such vehicles in the various countries, the numerals indicating the number in thousands. For the U. S. A., Canada, United Kingdom, France, Germany, Italy, and Australia, sectors in green show the proportion of motor trucks. The proportion of busses is shown for the U. S. A. and the United Kingdom.

AUTOMOTIVE VEHICLES

AUTOMOBILES

TRUCKS

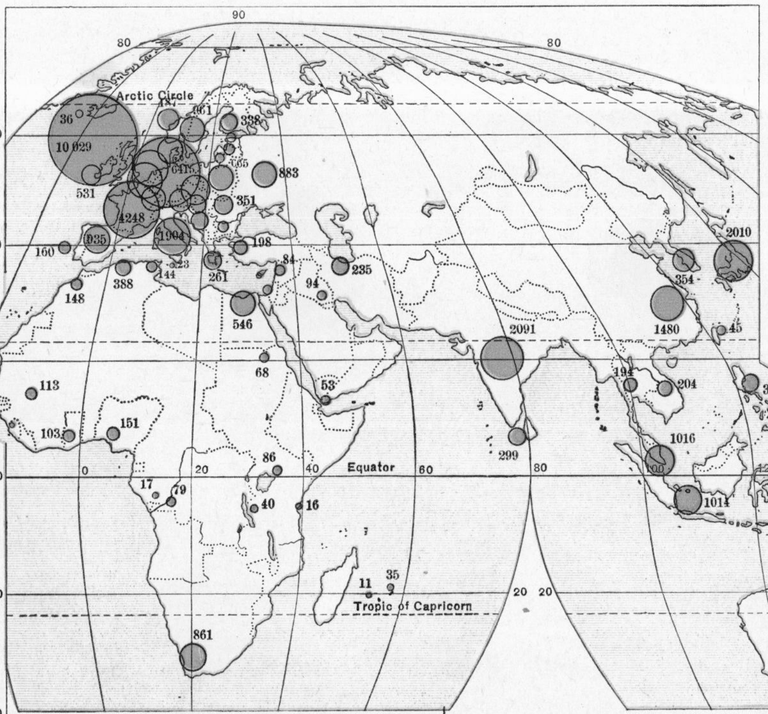

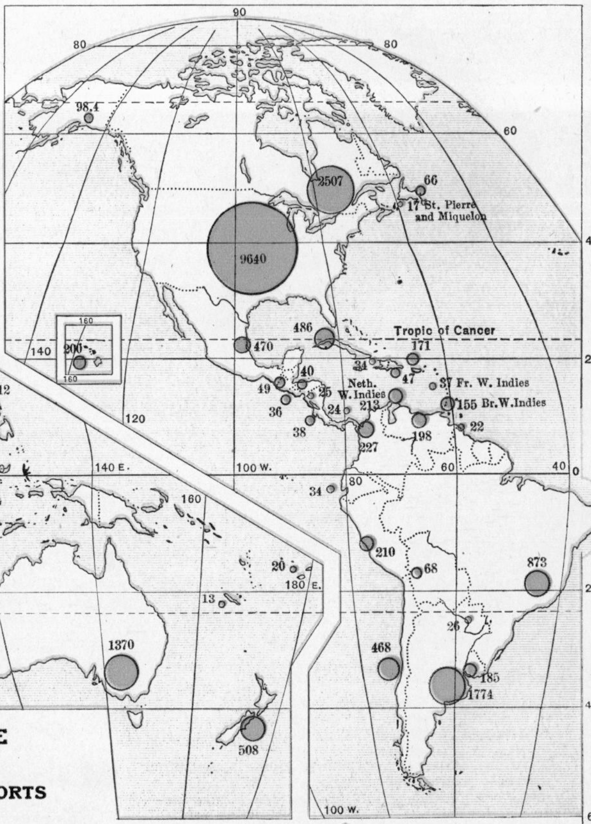

The amount of FOREIGN TRADE, export plus import, of the various countries and dependencies of the world is shown by circles in green, the areas of which are in proportion to the total value of such trade.

The numerals accompanying the circles indicate in each case the total value of export plus import trade in millions of dollars for the year 1929. Statistics are based on reports from the U. S. Department of Commerce.

INTERNATIONAL TRADE

TOTAL EXPORTS plus IMPORTS

6789

WORLD – Economic

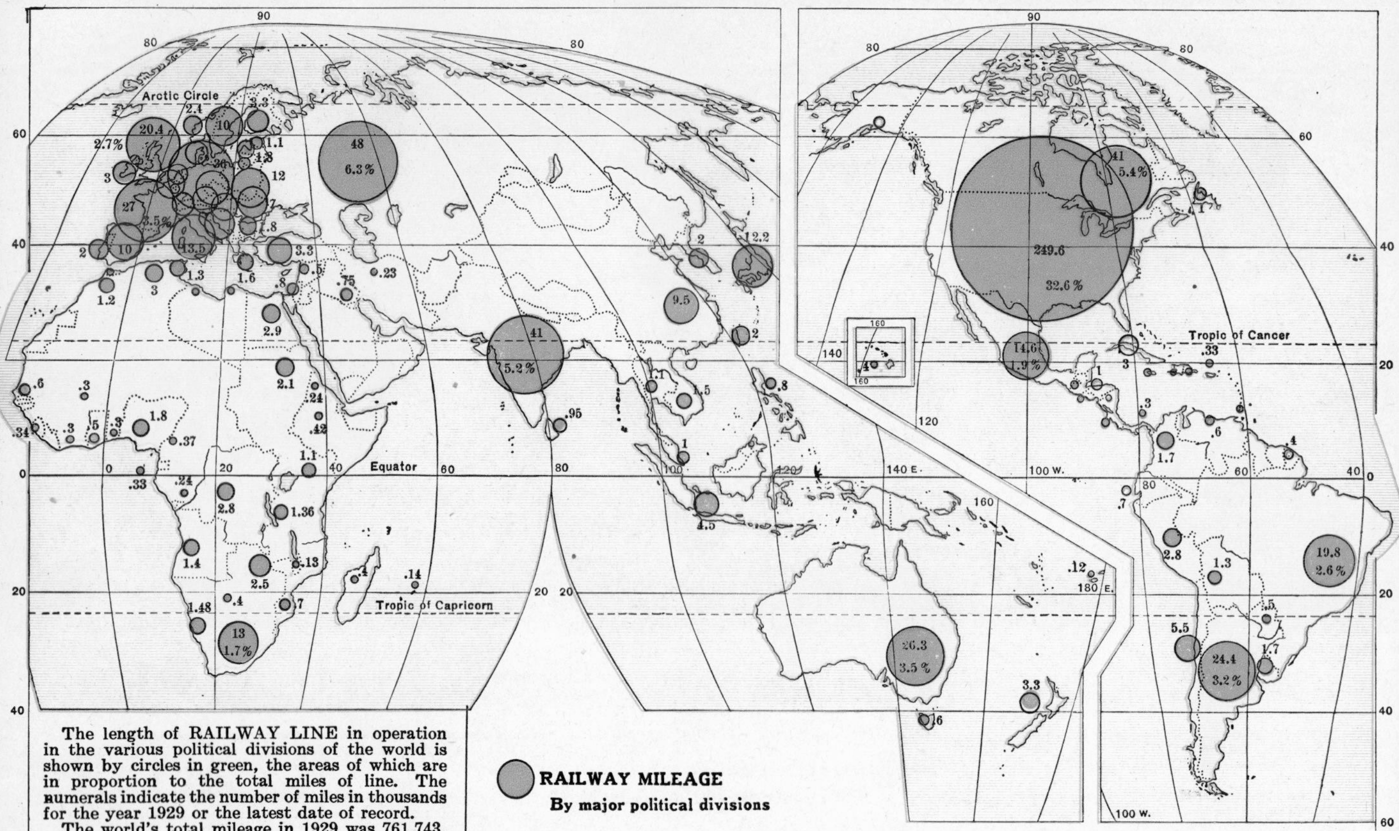

The length of RAILWAY LINE in operation in the various political divisions of the world is shown by circles in green, the areas of which are in proportion to the total miles of line. The numerals indicate the number of miles in thousands for the year 1929 or the latest date of record.

The world's total mileage in 1929 was 761,743, and the percentage of that world total is given in numerals accompanying the circles for countries of larger mileage.

RAILWAY MILEAGE
By major political divisions

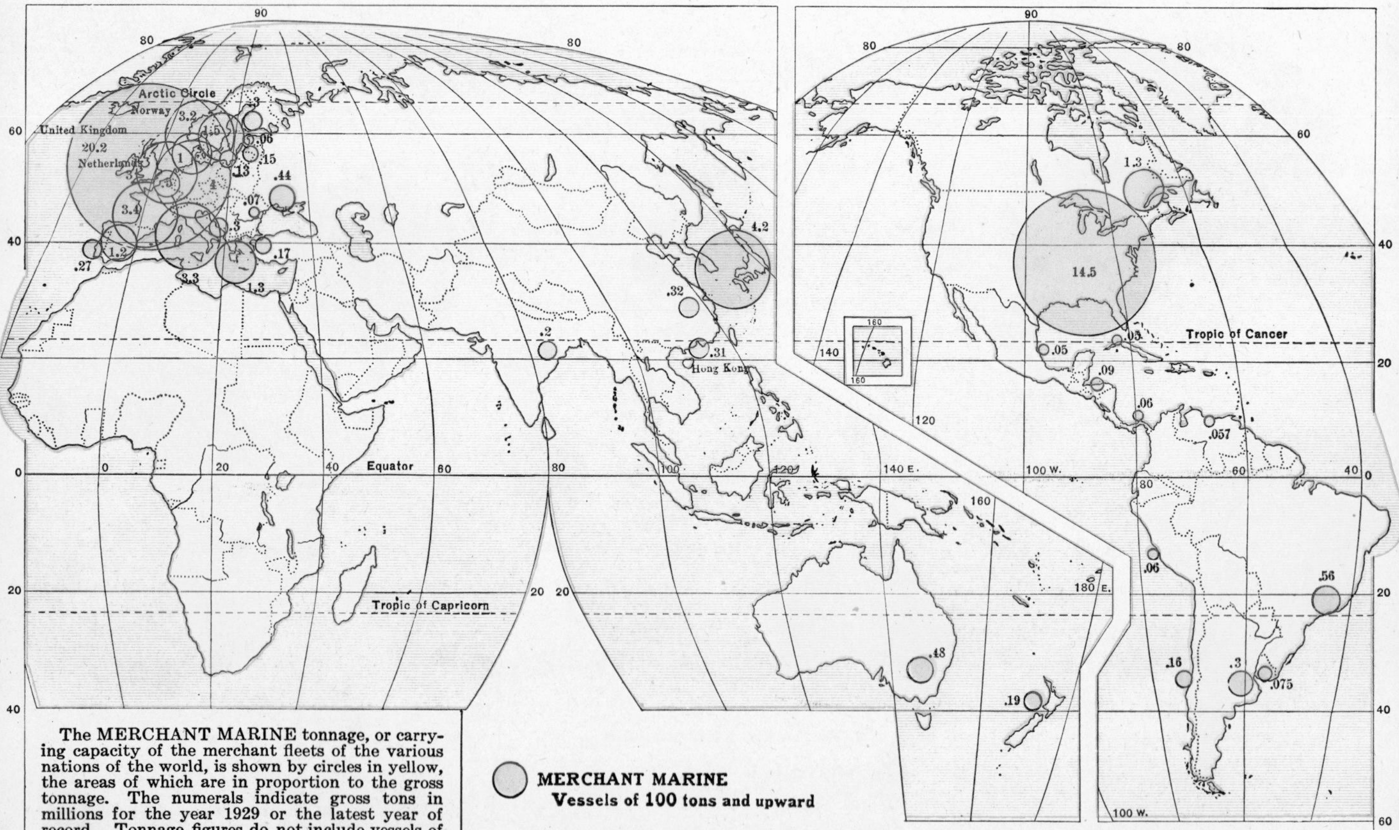

The MERCHANT MARINE tonnage, or carrying capacity of the merchant fleets of the various nations of the world, is shown by circles in yellow, the areas of which are in proportion to the gross tonnage. The numerals indicate gross tons in millions for the year 1929 or the latest year of record. Tonnage figures do not include vessels of less than 100 tons.

The tonnage of craft on lakes and rivers is not included in this record.

MERCHANT MARINE
Vessels of 100 tons and upward

6789

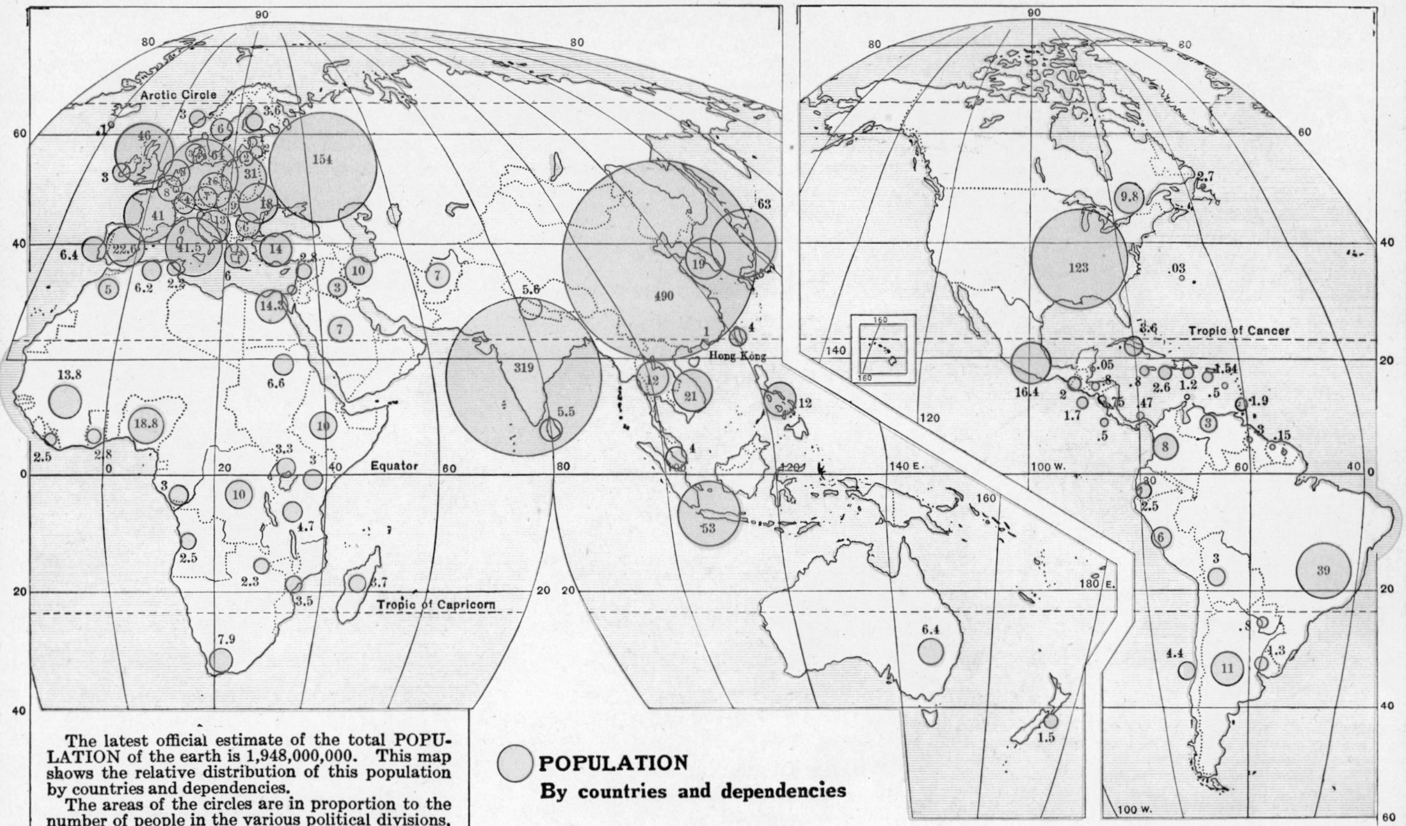

The latest official estimate of the total POPULATION of the earth is 1,948,000,000. This map shows the relative distribution of this population by countries and dependencies.

The areas of the circles are in proportion to the number of people in the various political divisions, the accompanying numerals indicating the number in millions as given by the latest census reports or by official estimate for the year 1930.

POPULATION
By countries and dependencies

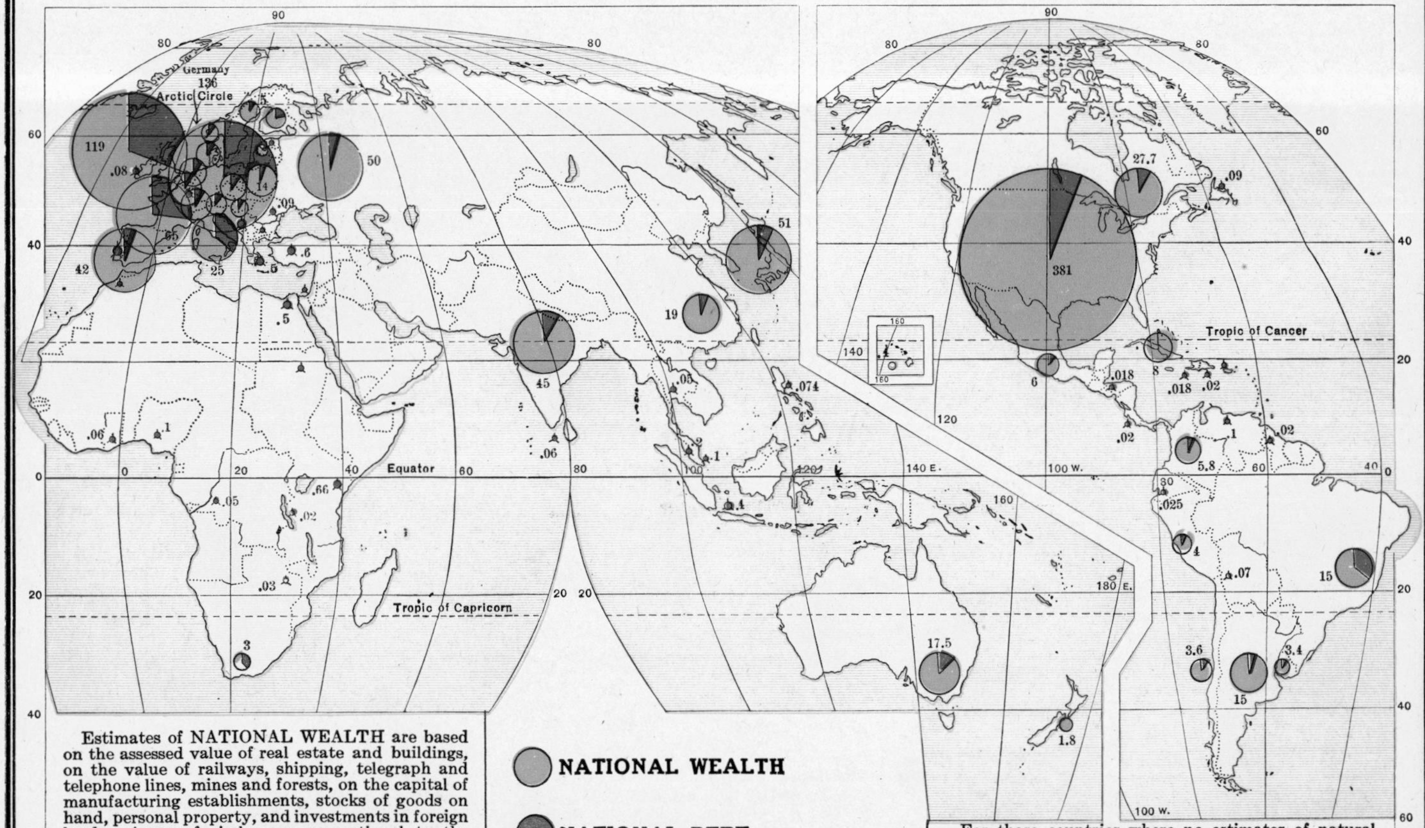

Estimates of NATIONAL WEALTH are based on the assessed value of real estate and buildings, on the value of railways, shipping, telegraph and telephone lines, mines and forests, on the capital of manufacturing establishments, stocks of goods on hand, personal property, and investments in foreign lands. Areas of circles are proportional to the total national wealth, numerals indicating billions of dollars for 1930 or the latest year of record.
Red sectors of the circles show national debt.

NATIONAL WEALTH

NATIONAL DEBT

For those countries where no estimates of natural wealth have been made, the national debt is indicated by circles in red on the same areal scale as those for national wealth. To aid in their identification these circles carry three spokes.

6789

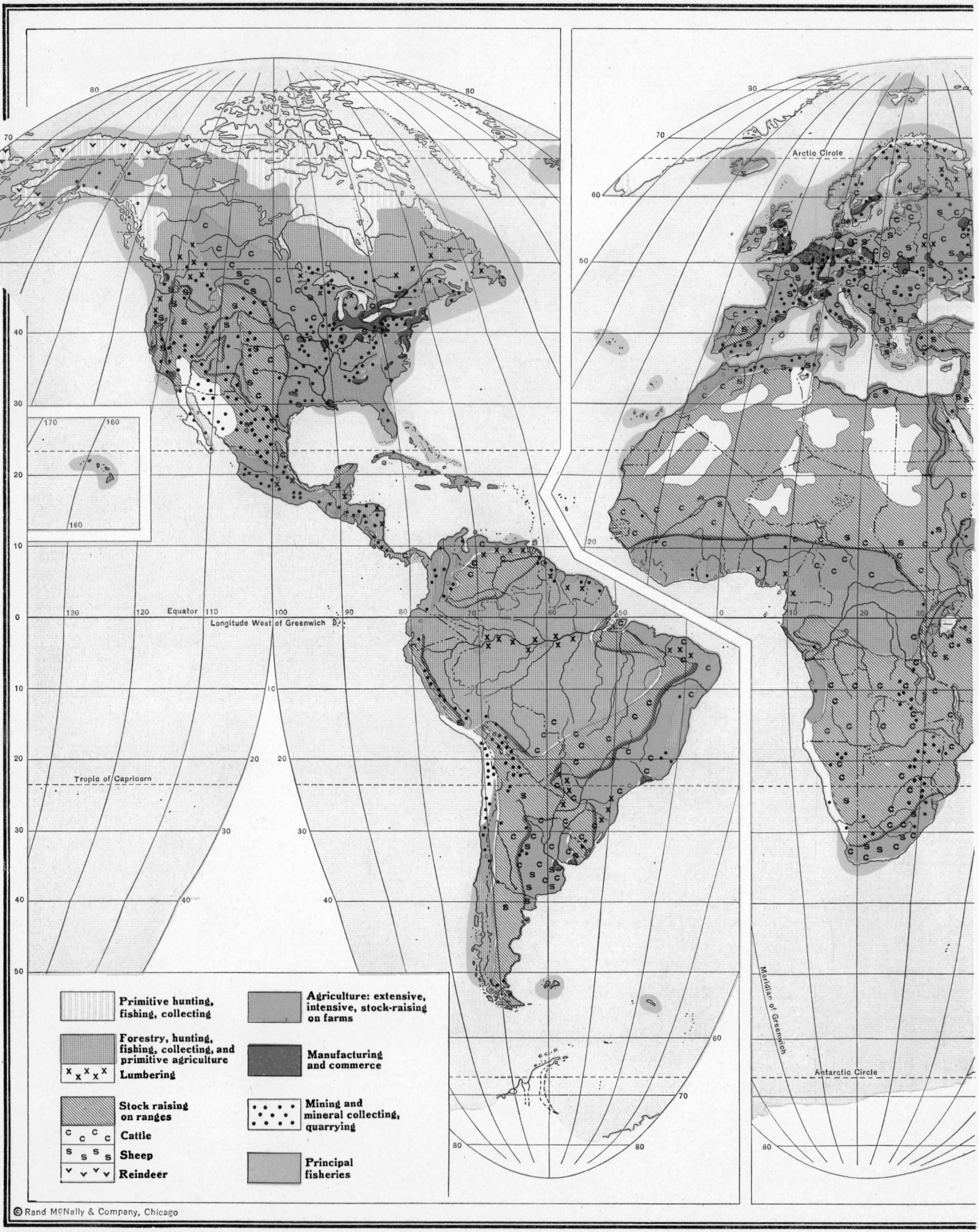
Arctic Circle
Equator
Longitude West of Greenwich
Tropic of Capricorn
Meridian of Greenwich
Antarctic Circle
Primitive hunting, fishing, collecting
Forestry, hunting, fishing, collecting, and primitive agriculture
Lumbering
Stock raising on ranges
Cattle
Sheep
Reindeer
Agriculture: extensive, intensive, stock-raising on farms
Manufacturing and commerce
Mining and mineral collecting, quarrying
Principal fisheries

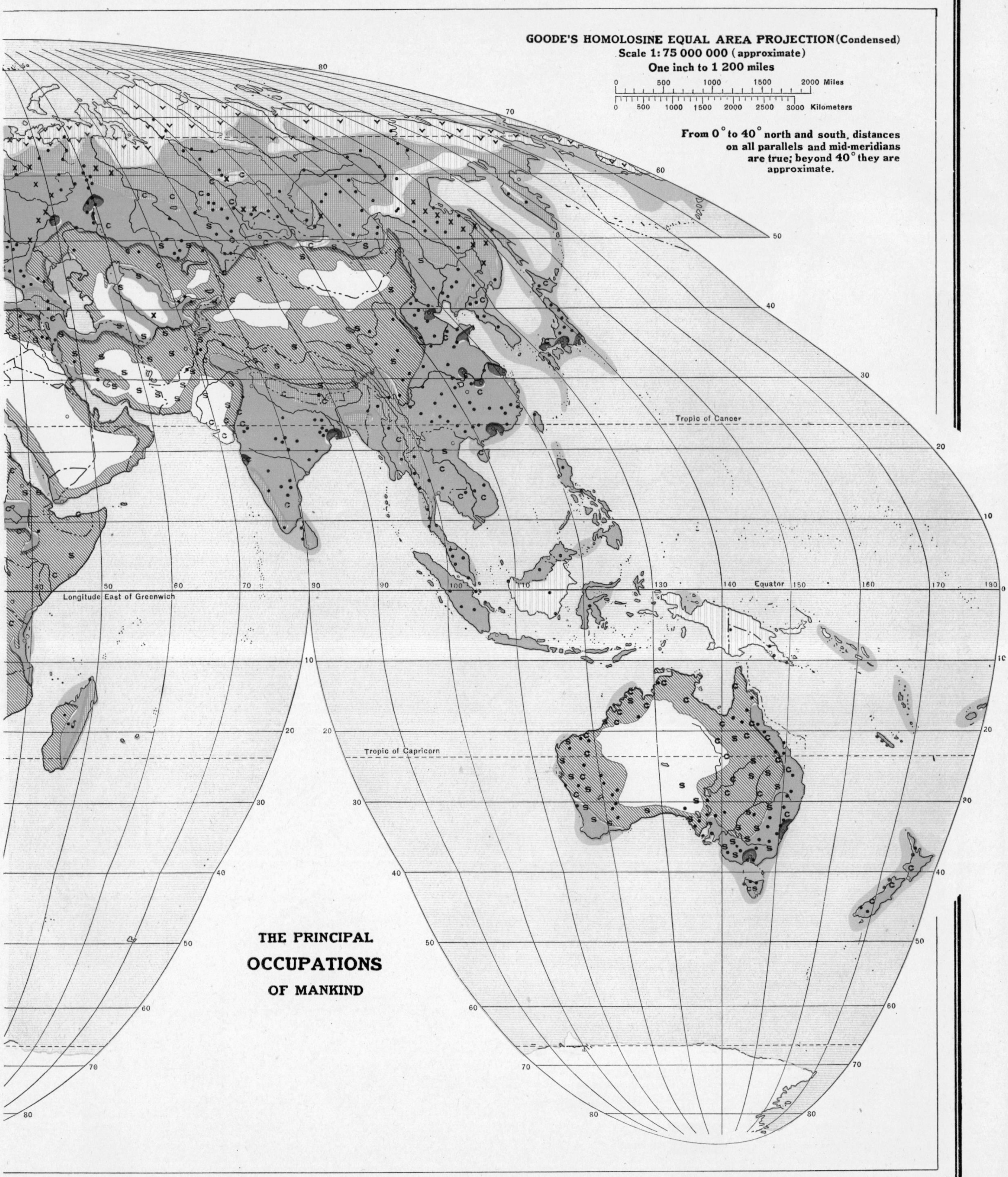
GOODE'S HOMOLOSINE EQUAL AREA PROJECTION (Condensed)
Scale 1: 75 000 000 (approximate)
One inch to 1 200 miles
0 500 1000 1500 2000 Miles
0 500 1000 1500 2000 2500 3000 Kilometers
From 0° to 40° north and south, distances on all parallels and mid-meridians are true; beyond 40° they are approximate.
Tropic of Cancer
Equator
Tropic of Capricorn
Longitude East of Greenwich
THE PRINCIPAL OCCUPATIONS OF MANKIND

NORTH AND SOUTH POLAR REGIONS

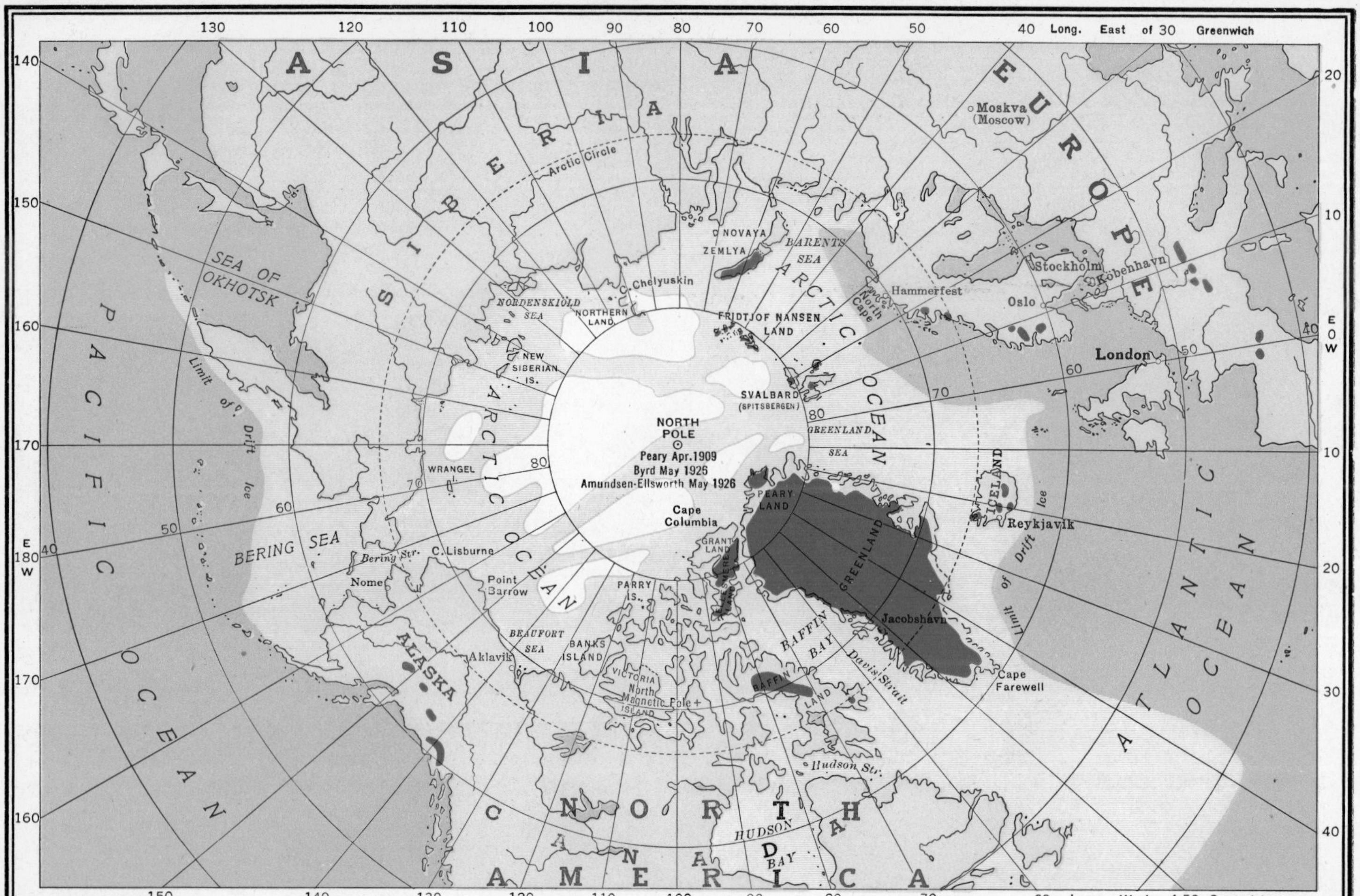

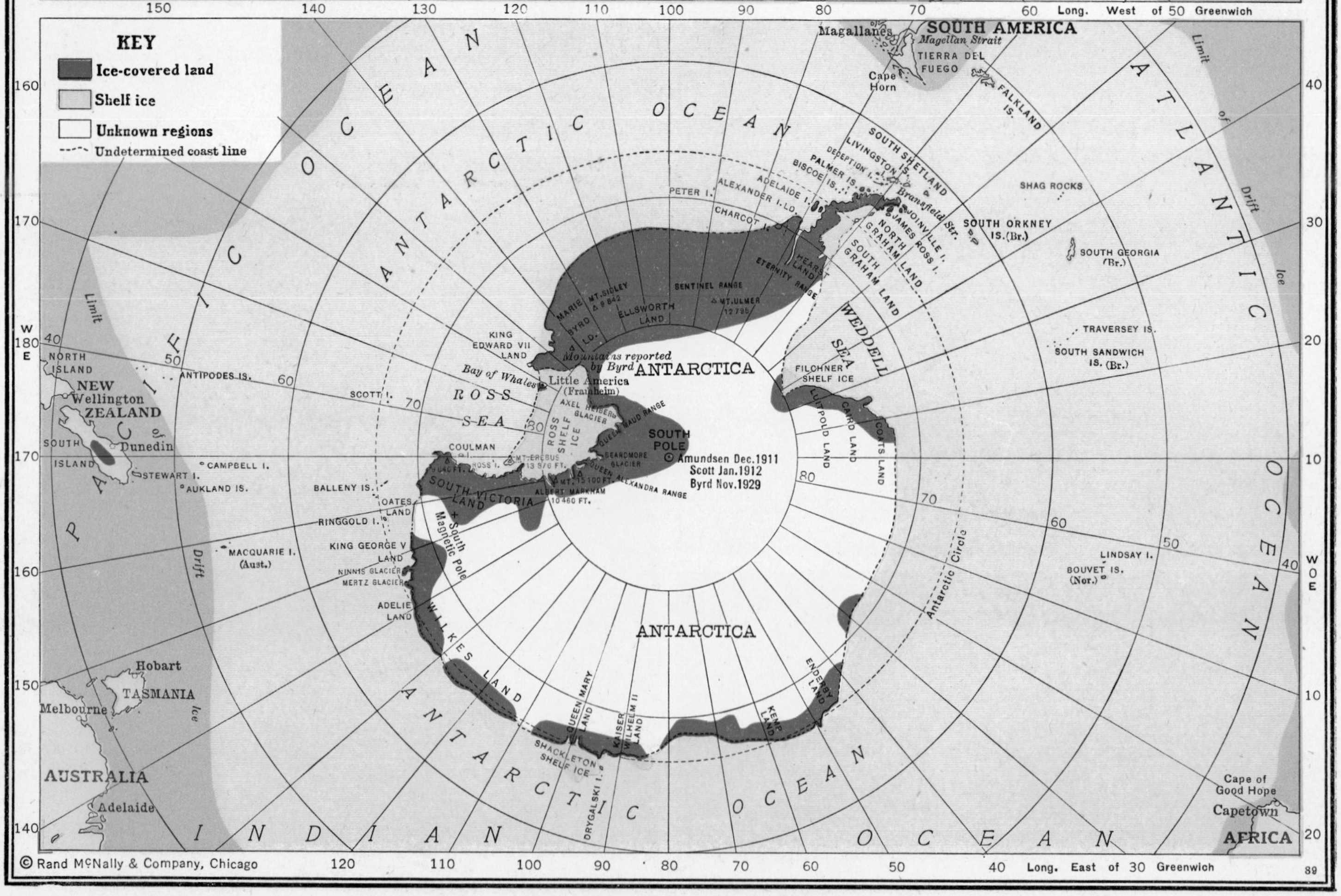

Lambert's Azimuthal Equal Area Projection

Scale 1 : 60 000 000; 15° latitude = 1 000 miles (approx.)

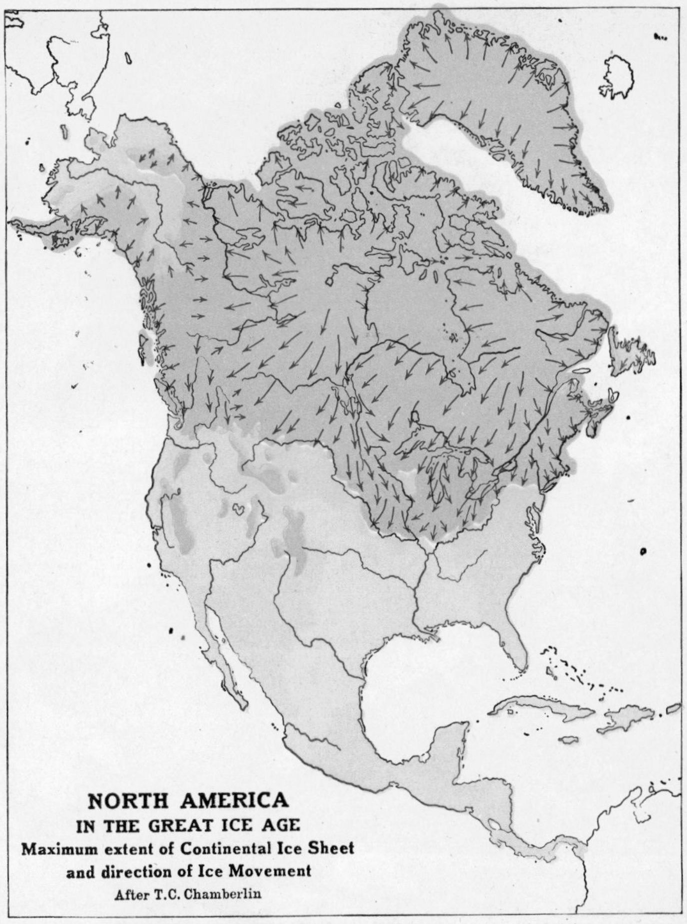
NORTH AMERICA
IN THE GREAT ICE AGE
Maximum extent of Continental Ice Sheet
and direction of Ice Movement
After T.C. Chamberlin

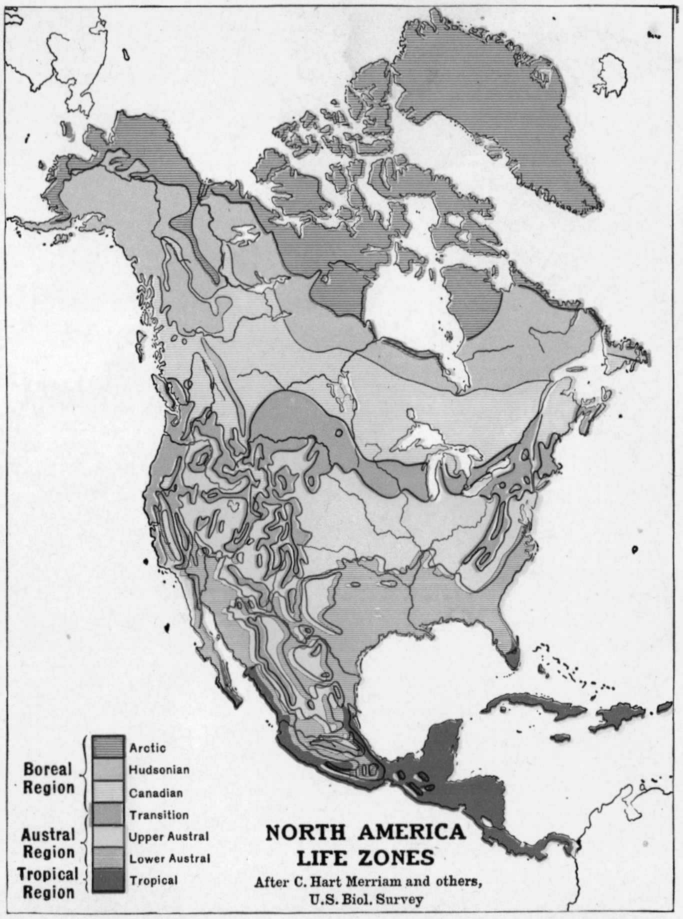

NORTH AMERICA
LIFE ZONES
After C. Hart Merriam and others,
U.S. Biol. Survey

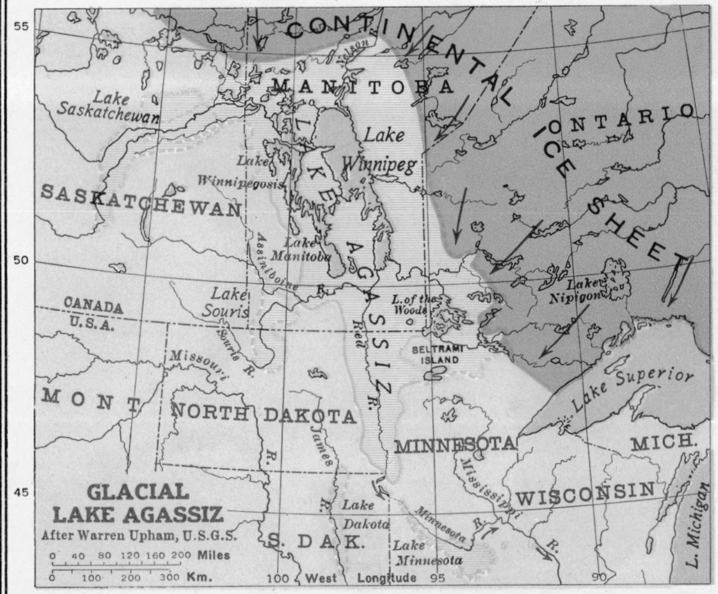

GLACIAL
LAKE AGASSIZ
After Warren Upham, U.S.G.S.

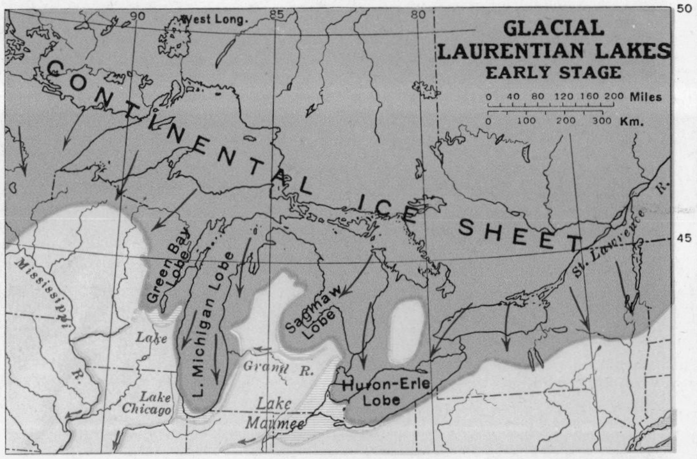

GLACIAL
LAUERENTIAN LAKES
EARLY STAGE

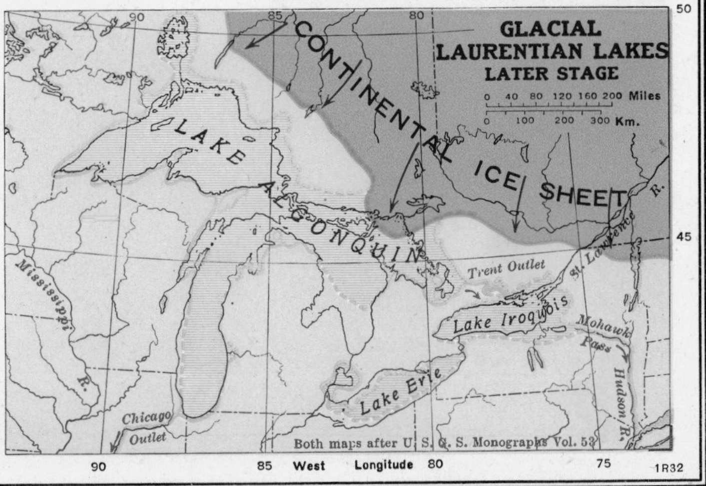

GLACIAL
LAURENTIAN LAKES
LATER STAGE

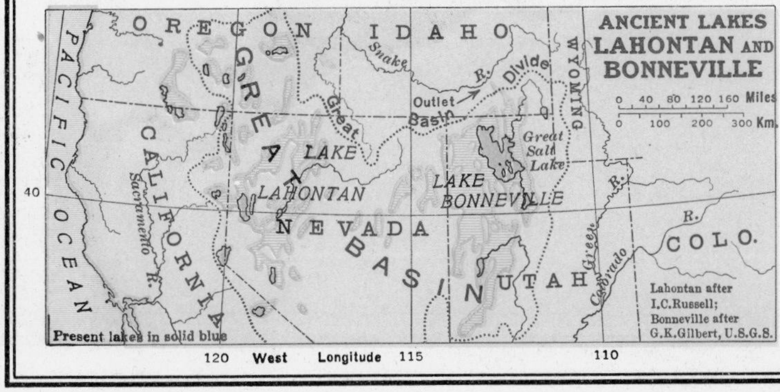

ANCIENT LAKES
LAHONTAN AND
BONNEVILLE

1R32

Red arrows in glacial maps show the direction of ice movement
Present lakes and rivers in black

NORTH AMERICA

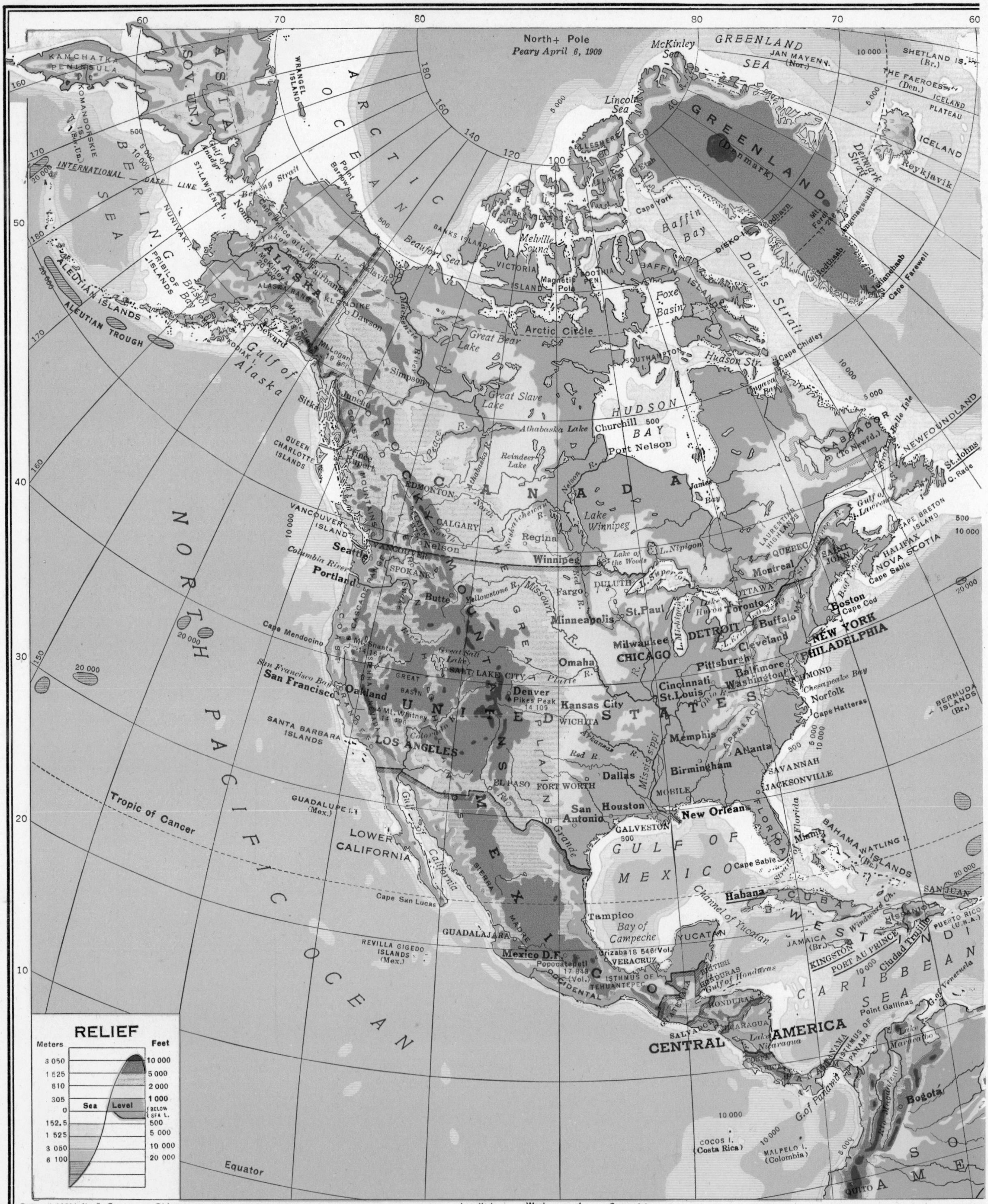

0 200 400 600 800 1000 Miles
0 400 800 1200 1600 Kilometers

Scale 1: 40 000 000; One inch to 630 miles. Lambert's Azimuthal Equal Area Projection

Elevations and depressions are given in feet

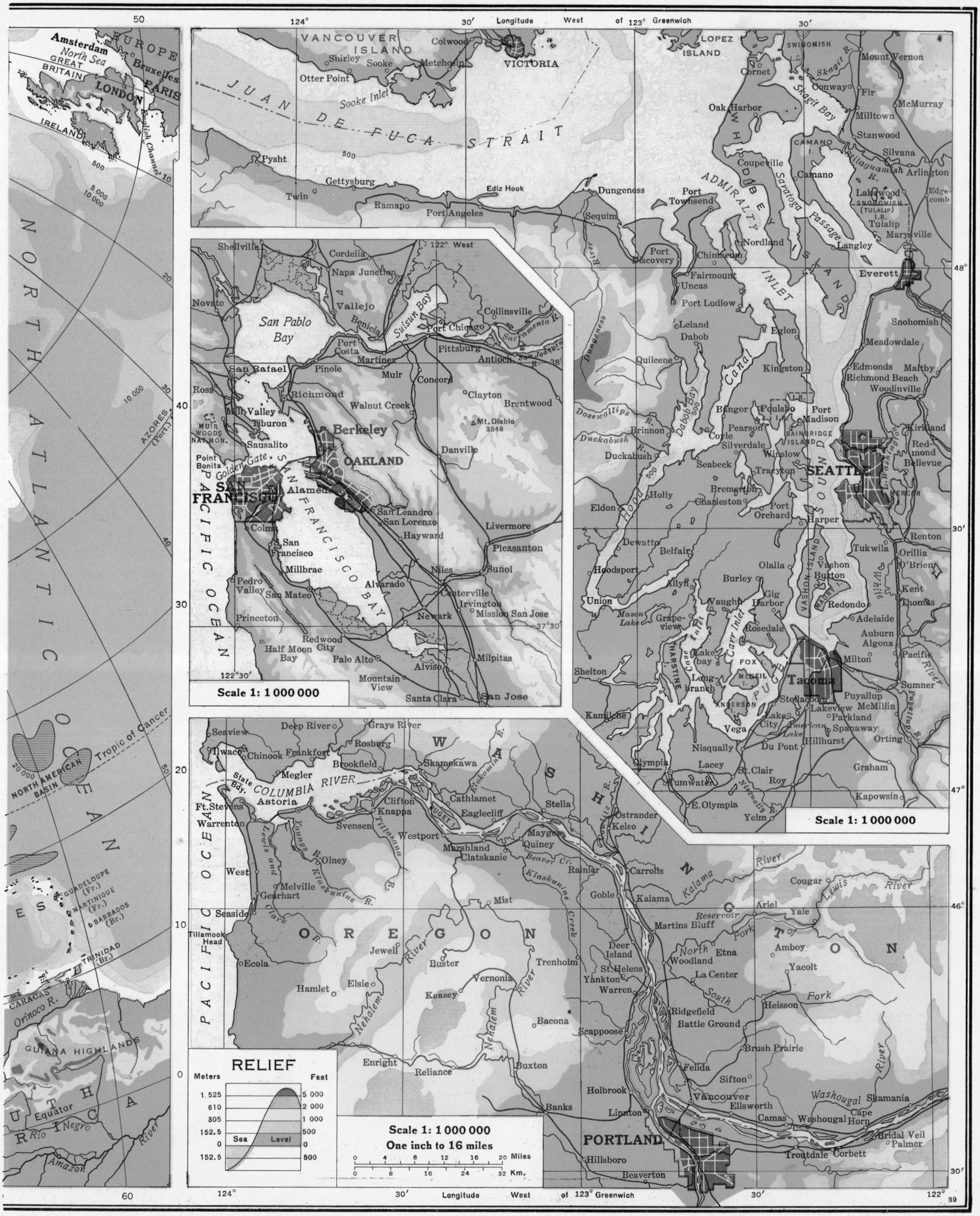
Longitude West of 123° Greenwich
VANCOUVER ISLAND
Colwood
VICTORIA
Shirley
Sooke
Metchosin
Otter Point
Sooke Inlet
JUAN DE FUCA STRAIT
Pysht
Twin
Gettysburg
Ramapo
Ediz Hook
Port Angeles
Dungeness
Sequim
LOPEZ ISLAND
SWINOMISH
Cornet
Skagit R.
Skagit Bay
Mount Vernon
Conway
Fir
McMurray
Milltown
Stanwood
Silvana
Arlington
Oak Harbor
WHIDBEY ISLAND
CAMANO I.
Camano
Coupeville
Saratoga Passage
Stillaguamish R.
Lakewood
SNOHOMISH (TULALIP) I.R.
Tulalip
Marysville
Edgecomb
ADMIRALTY INLET
Port Townsend
Nordland
Chimacum
Langley
Port Discovery
Fairmount
Uncas
Port Ludlow
Everett
Snohomish
Leland
Dabob
Eglon
Meadowdale
Quilcene
Dungeness R.
Canal
Kingston
Edmonds
Richmond Beach
Maltby
Woodinville
Dosewallips R.
Brinnon
Duckabush R.
Duckabush
Dabob Bay
Bangor
Poulsbo
Port Madison
BAINBRIDGE ISLAND
Pearson
Silverdale
Coyle
Winslow
Seabeck
Tracyton
Bremerton
Charleston
SEATTLE
Kirkland
Redmond
Bellevue
MERCER I.
Lake Washington
Port Orchard
Harper
Hood Canal
Holly
Eldon
Dewatto
Belfair
Renton
Tukwila
Orillia
O'Brien
Hoodsport
Olalla
Vashon
VASHON ISLAND
MAURY I.
Burton
Redondo
Kent
Thomas
White River
Union
Mason Lake
Allyn
Burley
Vaughn
Gig Harbor
Grapeview
Rosedale
Adelaide
Auburn
Algona
Case Inlet
Carr Inlet
HARSTINE I.
FOX I.
McNEIL I.
Lakebay
Longbranch
ANDERSON I.
PUGET SOUND
Tacoma
Milton
Pacific
Sumner
Shelton
Kamilche
Steilacoom
Puyallup
McMillin
Lakeview
Parkland
Puyallup R.
Vega
Lake City
American Lake
Spanaway
Hillhurst
Orting
Nisqually
Du Pont
Olympia
Lacey
St. Clair
Graham
Tumwater
Roy
Nisqually R.
E. Olympia
Yelm
Kapowsin
Scale 1: 1 000 000
Shellville
Cordelia
122° West
Napa Junction
Novato
Vallejo
Collinsville
San Pablo Bay
Benicia
Suisun Bay
Port Chicago
Sacramento R.
Port Costa
Pittsburg
Martinez
Antioch
San Joaquin R.
San Rafael
Pinole
Muir
Concord
Ross
Richmond
Clayton
Brentwood
Mill Valley
Tiburon
Walnut Creek
MUIR WOODS NAT. MON.
Berkeley
Mt. Diablo 3849
Sausalito
Point Bonita
Golden Gate
OAKLAND
Danville
SAN FRANCISCO
Alameda
San Leandro
San Lorenzo
Hayward
Livermore
Colma
South San Francisco
Pleasanton
Millbrae
SAN FRANCISCO BAY
Niles
Sunol
Pedro Valley
San Mateo
Alvarado
Centerville
Irvington
Mission San Jose
Princeton
Newark
Redwood City
Half Moon Bay
Palo Alto
Milpitas
Alviso
Mountain View
Santa Clara
San Jose
PACIFIC OCEAN
122°30′
Scale 1: 1 000 000
Seaview
Deep River
Grays River
Ilwaco
Chinook
Frankfort
Rosburg
Brookfield
Skamokawa
Elokomin R.
Megler
State Bdy.
COLUMBIA RIVER
Astoria
Cathlamet
Ft. Stevens
Warrenton
Clifton
Knappa
PUGET I.
Eaglecliff
Stella
Svensen
Westport
Ostrander
Kelso
Mayger
Quincy
Marshland
Clatskanie
Beaver Cr.
Rainier
Carrolls
West
Olney
Klaskanine R.
Lewis and Clark R.
Youngs R.
Tillamook R.
Nehalem R.
Klaskunine Creek
Goble
Kalama
Kalama River
Cougar
Lewis River
Gearhart
Melville
Mist
Yale
Ariel
Reservoir
Seaside
Martins Bluff
North Fork
Tillamook Head
OREGON
WASHINGTON
Amboy
Jewell
Deer Island
Woodland
Etna
Yacolt
Ecola
Buster
Trenholm
St. Helens
La Center
Vernonia
Elsie
Yankton
Warren
South Fork
Hamlet
Keasey
Heisson
Ridgefield
Bacona
Battle Ground
Scappoose
Brush Prairie
Enright
Reliance
Buxton
Felida
Sifton
Holbrook
Vancouver
Ellsworth
Washougal River
Skamania
Banks
Linnton
Camas
Washougal
Cape Horn
PORTLAND
Bridal Veil
Palmer
Troutdale
Corbett
Hillsboro
Beaverton
RELIEF
Meters
Feet
1 525
5 000
610
2 000
305
1 000
152.5
500
0
Sea Level
0
152.5
500
Scale 1: 1 000 000
One inch to 16 miles
Miles
0 4 8 12 16 20
Km.
0 8 16 24 32
124°
30′
Longitude West of 123° Greenwich
122°
48°
47°
46°
38°
37°30′
EUROPE
Amsterdam
North Sea
GREAT BRITAIN
LONDON
Bruxelles
PARIS
IRELAND
English Channel
NORTH ATLANTIC OCEAN
AZORES (Port.)
Tropic of Cancer
NORTH AMERICAN BASIN
GUADELOUPE (Fr.)
MARTINIQUE (Fr.)
BARBADOS (Br.)
TRINIDAD (Br.)
CARACAS
Orinoco R.
GUIANA HIGHLANDS
Equator
Rio Negro
Amazon River
SOUTH AMERICA
50
60
89

NORTH AMERICA

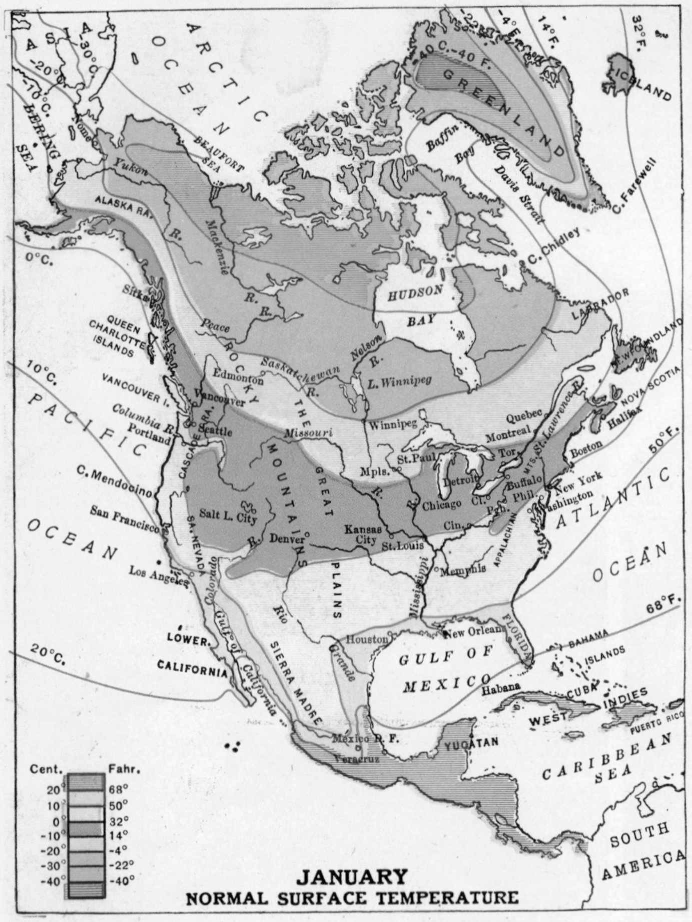

JANUARY
NORMAL SURFACE TEMPERATURE

JULY
NORMAL SURFACE TEMPERATURE

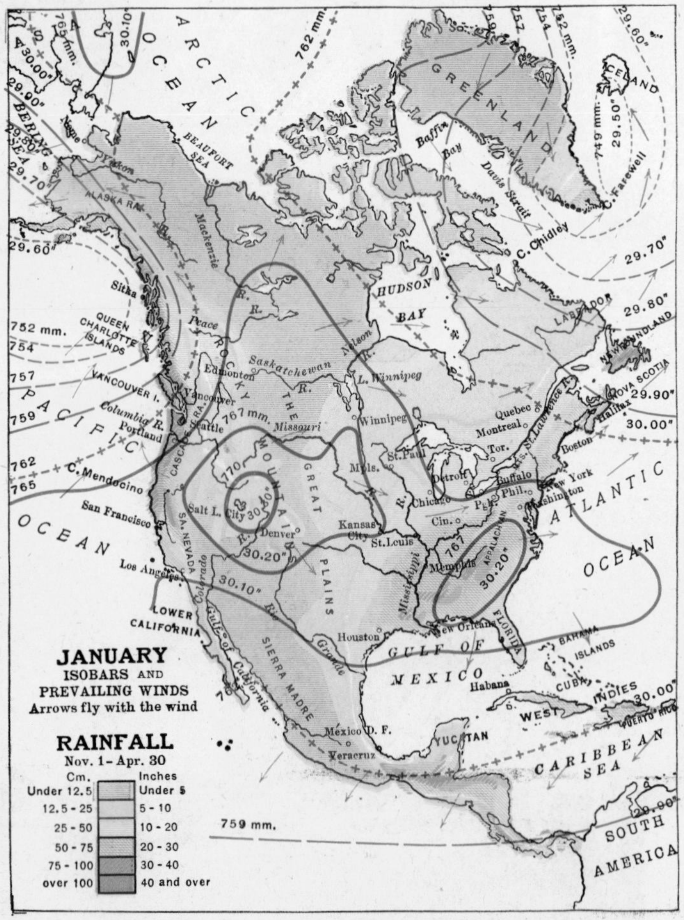

JANUARY
ISOBARS AND
PREVAILING WINDS
Arrows fly with the wind

RAINFALL
Nov. 1 - Apr. 30

JULY
ISOBARS AND
PREVAILING WINDS
Arrows fly with the wind

RAINFALL
May 1 - Oct. 31

ANNUAL RAINFALL
Cm. Inches
Under 25 Under 10
25 - 50 10 - 20
50 - 100 20 - 40
100 - 150 40 - 60
150 - 200 60 - 80
over 200 80 and over
ARCTIC OCEAN
PACIFIC OCEAN
ATLANTIC OCEAN
GULF OF MEXICO
CARIBBEAN SEA
HUDSON BAY
GREENLAND
SOUTH AMERICA

VEGETATION
Tropical rain forest
Temperate deciduous forest
Narrow sclerophyll forest
Scrub woodland: thorn scrub, mulga, mallee
Thorn scrub: mesquite, acacia, chaparrel
Sagebrush scrub
Prairie, steppe: long, short, and bunch grass
Savanna (mostly tropical)
Temperate and low latitude desert
High latitude desert: tundra, alpine
Snow and ice
ARCTIC OCEAN
PACIFIC OCEAN
ATLANTIC OCEAN
GULF OF MEXICO
CARIBBEAN SEA
HUDSON BAY
GREENLAND
SOUTH AMERICA

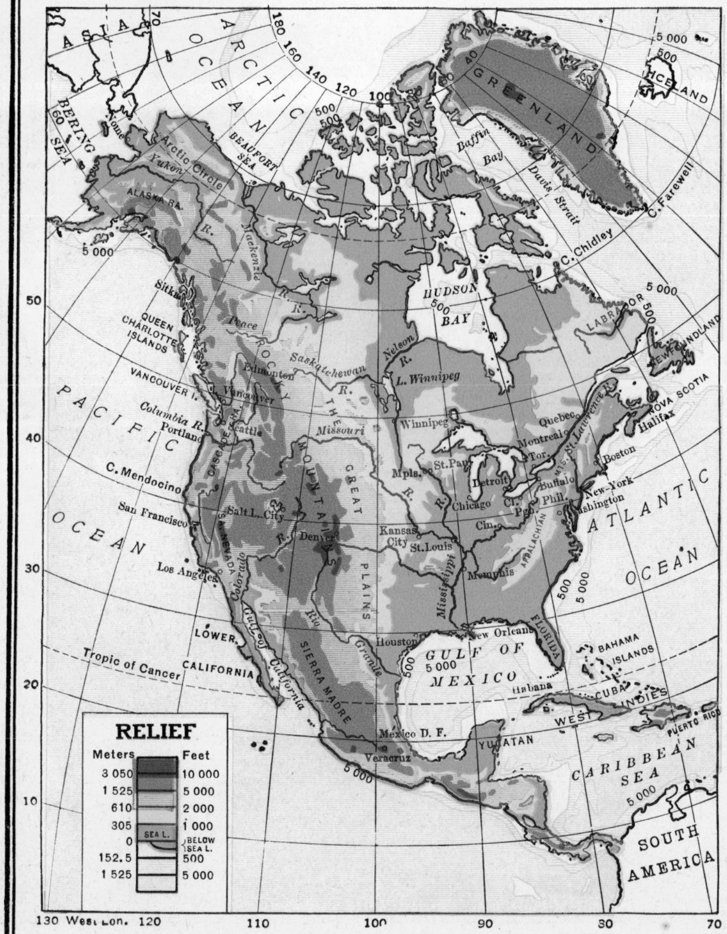
RELIEF
Meters Feet
3 050 10 000
1 525 5 000
610 2 000
305 1 000
0 SEA L. 0
BELOW SEA L.
152.5 500
1 525 5 000
130 West Lon. 120
110
100
90
80
70
Tropic of Cancer
ARCTIC OCEAN
PACIFIC OCEAN
ATLANTIC OCEAN
GULF OF MEXICO
CARIBBEAN SEA
HUDSON BAY
GREENLAND
SOUTH AMERICA

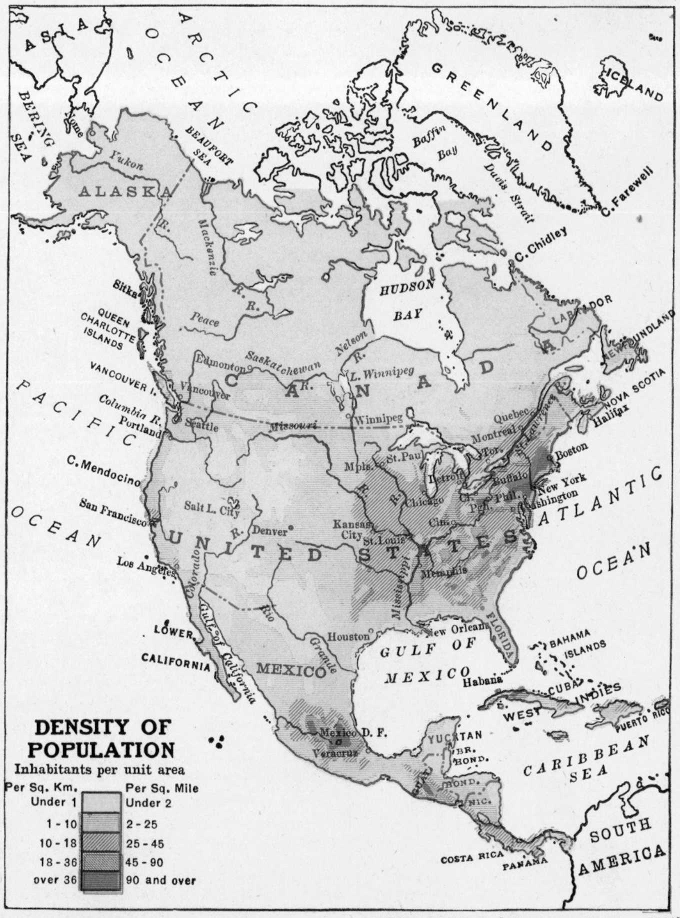
DENSITY OF POPULATION
Inhabitants per unit area
Per Sq. Km. Per Sq. Mile
Under 1 Under 2
1 - 10 2 - 25
10 - 18 25 - 45
18 - 36 45 - 90
over 36 90 and over
ALASKA
CANADA
UNITED STATES
MEXICO
ARCTIC OCEAN
PACIFIC OCEAN
ATLANTIC OCEAN
GULF OF MEXICO
CARIBBEAN SEA
HUDSON BAY
GREENLAND
SOUTH AMERICA

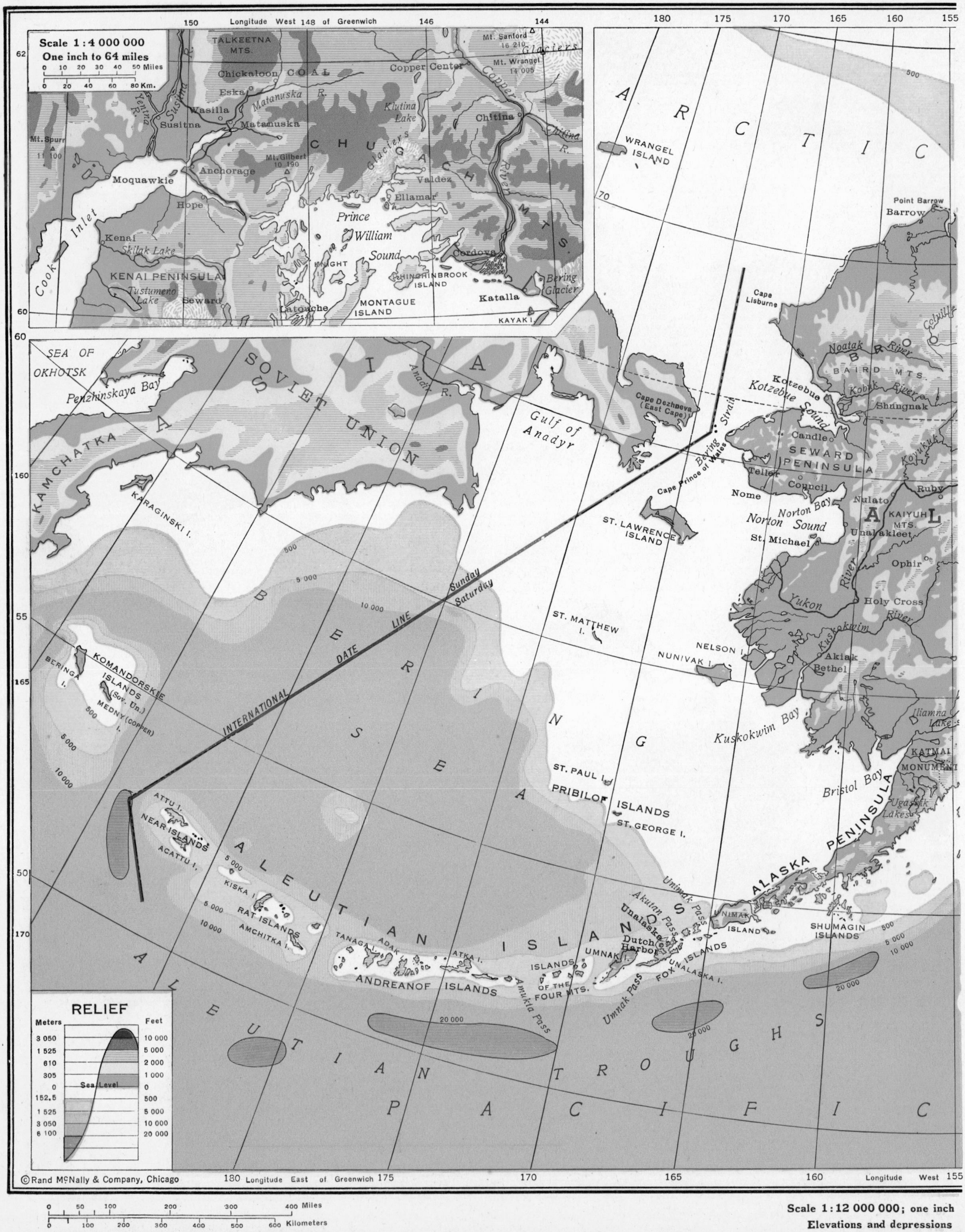

Scale 1:12 000 000; one inch
Elevations and depressions

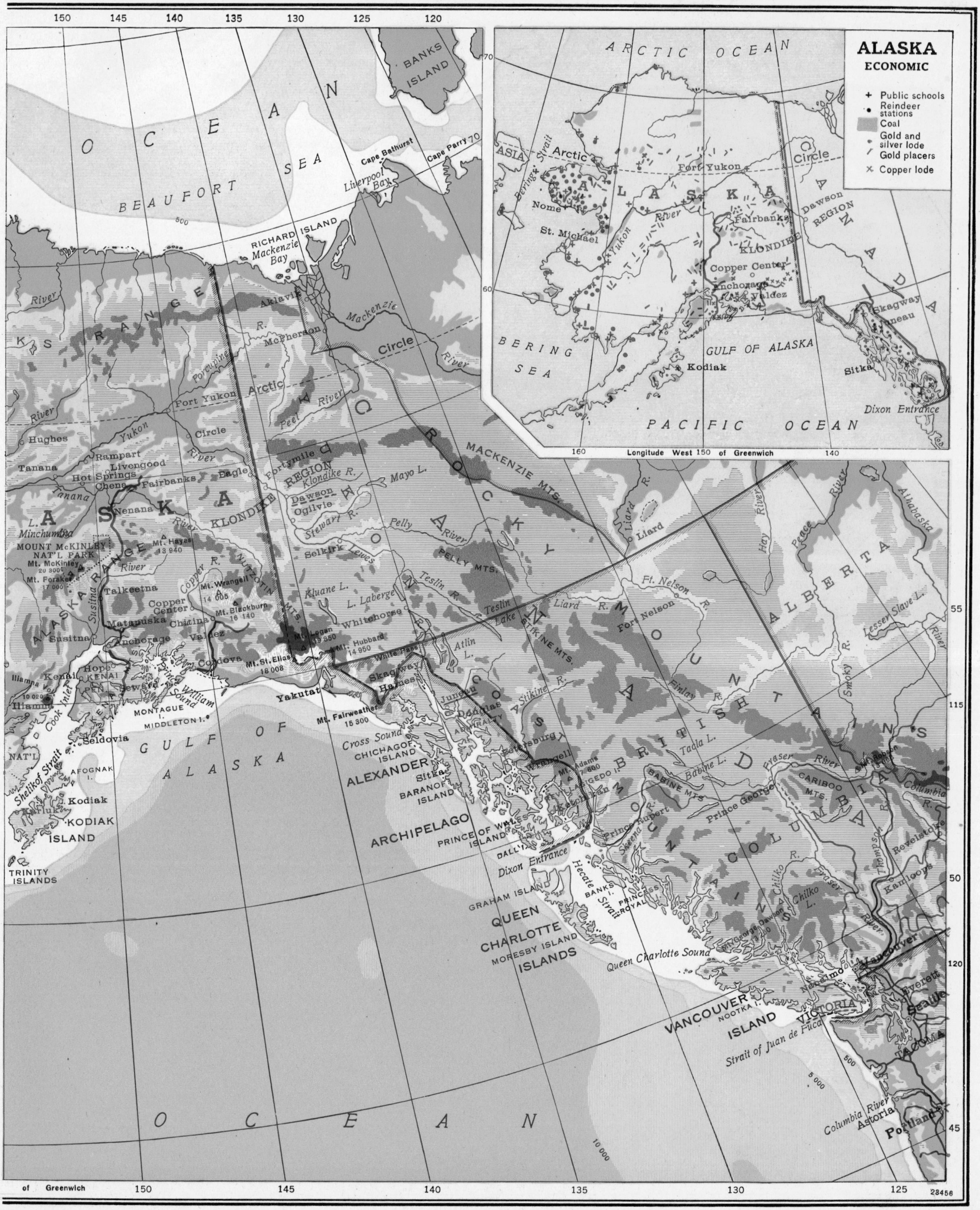

to 190 miles. Conic Projection
are given in feet

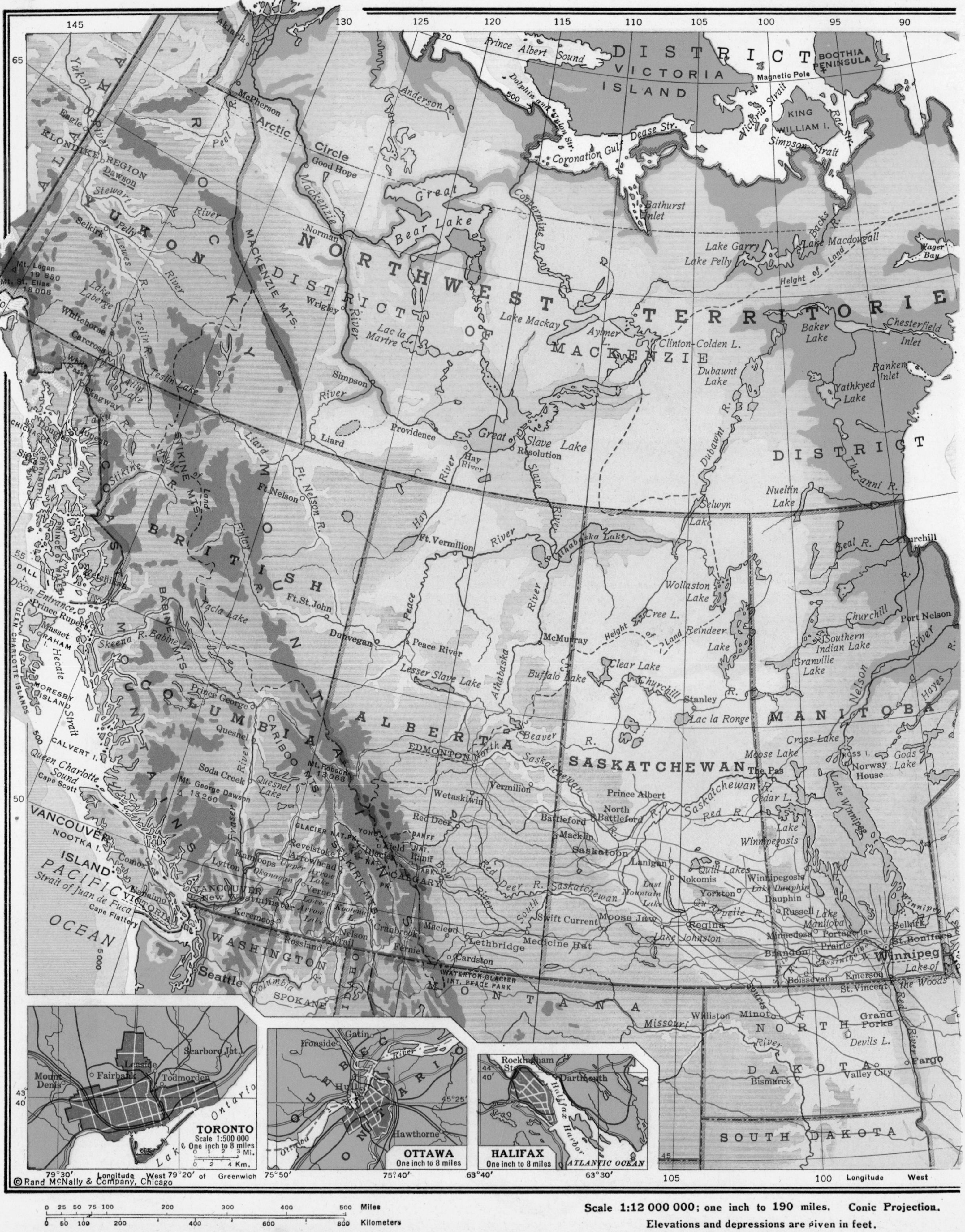

Scale 1:12 000 000; one inch to 190 miles. Conic Projection.

Elevations and depressions are given in feet.

RELIEF
Meters
Feet
3 050
1 525
610
305
152.5
0
152.5
1 525
3 050
10 000
5 000
2 000
1 000
500
0
500
5 000
10 000
Sea Level
West of Greenwich
QUEBEC
Gulf of St. Lawrence
Strait of Belle Isle
Cape Bauld
White Bay
C. St. John
Notre Dame Bay
Twillingate
Bonavista Bay
Bonavista
Trinity
Trinity Bay
Bay of Islands
Lake
C. St. George
St. George Bay
Robinson
NEWFOUNDLAND
Port aux Basques
Cape Ray
Cabot Strait
Cape North
CAPE BRETON ISLAND
MIQUELON I. (Fr.)
ST. PIERRE I. (Fr.)
Fortune B.
Placentia Bay
St. Johns
C. Race
ATLANTIC OCEAN
Same scale as map of Canada
BAFFIN ISLAND
FRANKLIN
Foxe Basin
Gulf of Boothia
MELVILLE PENINSULA
Arctic Circle
Foxe Channel
FOXE LAND
Netsalik Lake
Cumberland Sound
Amadjuak Lake
Frobisher Bay
RESOLUTION ISLAND
Cape Chidley
Hudson Strait
AKPATOK ISLAND
Roes Welcome
SOUTHAMPTON ISLAND
Fisher Strait
COATS I.
Lyon Strait
MANSEL ISLAND
MARBLE I.
KEEWATIN
HUDSON BAY
OTTAWA ISLANDS
BELCHER ISLANDS
UNGAVA PENINSULA
Payne Lake
Ungava Bay
Leaf River
Koksoak R.
Kaniapiskau
Hebron
Nain
Hopedale
Hamilton Inlet
Cartwright
Lake Melville
Naskaupi R.
Lake Michikamau
Hamilton River
LABRADOR
Strait of Belle Isle
NEWFOUNDLAND
Lake Minto
Apiskigamish Lake
Lake Kaniapiskau
Great Whale R.
Attikonak Lake
Height of Land
Natashkwan R.
Romaine R.
Ashuanipi Lake
Moisie R.
Nichikun Lake
Fort George R.
ANTICOSTI I.
Gulf of St. Lawrence
Robinson
Port aux Basques
CAPE BRETON ISLAND
Sydney
MAGDALEN ISLANDS
PRINCE EDWARD ISLAND
Charlottetown
Outarde R.
Manikuagan R.
Peribonka River
Mistassini R.
Bersimis
St. Lawrence River
Matane
Metis
Campbellton
Chaleur Bay
Bathurst
Newcastle
Chatham
NEW BRUNSWICK
Edmundston
Fraserville
Moncton
Truro
NOVA SCOTIA
HALIFAX
Windsor
Annapolis
Bay of Fundy
Yarmouth
Cape Sable
Fredericton
SAINT JOHN
Woodstock
York Factory
Port Severn
Winisk R.
Severn River
Trout Lake
Island Lake
Attawapiskat River
Albany
Martin Falls
Moosonee
Moose R.
James Bay
AKIMISKI ISLAND
Eastmain River
Opinaka R.
Rupert River
Rupert House
Lake Mistassini
Nottaway R.
Mattagami L.
Lake St. John
Roberval
Chicoutimi
Saguenay R.
LAURENTIDES PARK
Murray Bay
La Tuque
St. Maurice R.
QUEBEC
Levis
Montmagny
Megantic
Sherbrooke
MAINE
Shawinigan Falls
Trois Rivieres
Berthier
Sorel
Joliette
Montreal
St. Johns
Lachine
Valleyfield
ONTARIO
Trout Lake
Lake St. Joseph
Lac Seul
English R.
Lake Nipigon
Height of Land
Abitibi Lake
Abitibi R.
Missinaibi R.
Cochrane
Noranda
Rouyn
Matheson
Kirkland L.
L. Timiskaming
Cobalt
Ottawa R.
North Bay
Mattawa
ALGONQUIN PK.
OTTAWA
Cornwall
Kenora
Rainy Lake
Rainy R.
Red L.
Nipigon
Port Arthur
Fort William
Heron Bay
ISLE ROYALE NAT. PARK
MICHIPICOTEN I.
Lake Superior
+602
Sault Ste. Marie
Algoma
Sudbury
L. Nipissing
Pembroke
Renfrew
Bancroft
Parry Sound
Smiths Falls
Ogdensburg
Brockville
Kingston
MANITOULIN I.
Georgian Bay
Lake Huron
+581
Owen Sound
Collingwood
Lake Simcoe
Orillia
Lindsay
Peterborough
Trenton
Lake Ontario
+246
Rochester
Toronto
HAMILTON
Guelph
Niagara Falls
Buffalo
LONDON
Port Huron
Sarnia
L. St. Clair
DETROIT
Windsor
Lake Erie
+572
Toledo
Cleveland
MINNESOTA
DULUTH
Superior
Marquette
Escanaba
MICHIGAN
Lake Michigan
+581
WISCONSIN
St. Paul
Minneapolis
Mississippi R.
Green Bay
SAGINAW
Grand Haven
LANSING
NEW YORK
ALBANY
PENNSYLVANIA
Scranton
Jersey City
NEW YORK
LONG ISLAND
Hudson R.
VERMONT
NEW HAMPSHIRE
L. Champlain
MASSACHUSETTS
Boston
Cape Cod
Providence
CONN.
R.I.
PORTLAND
ATLANTIC OCEAN
Greenwich
6789

CANADA

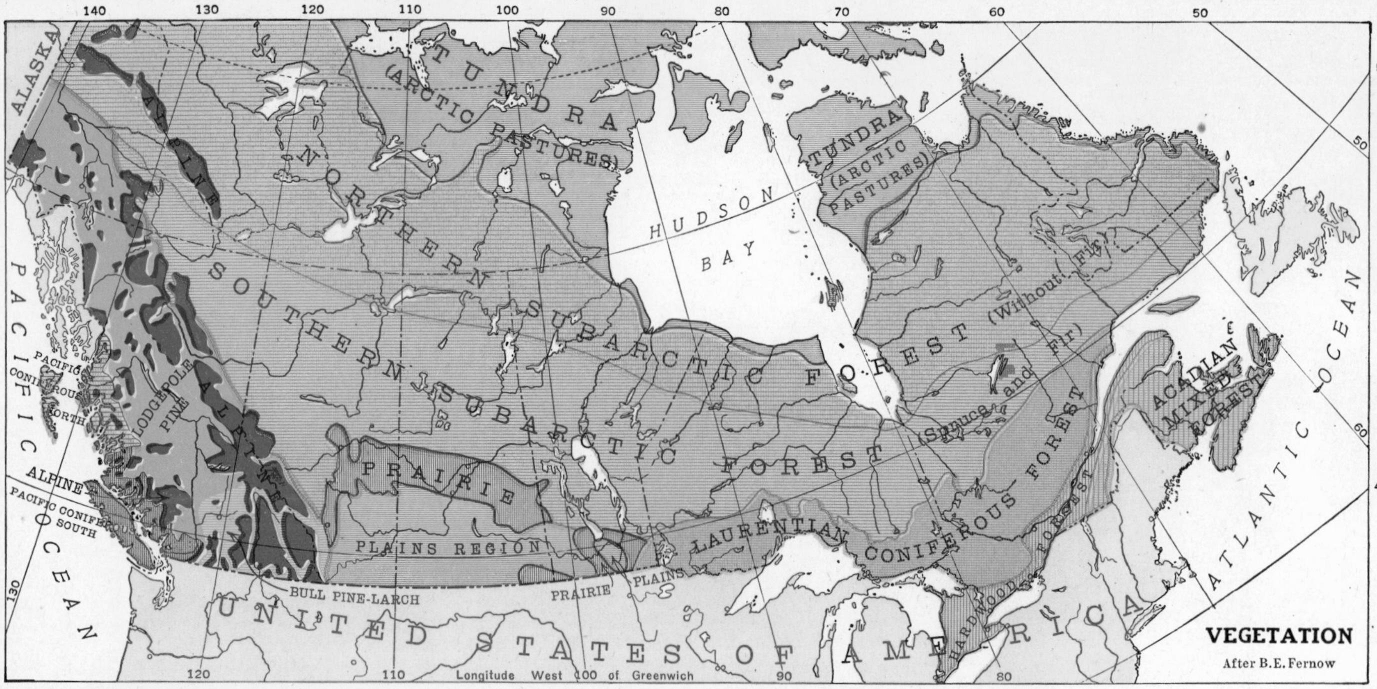

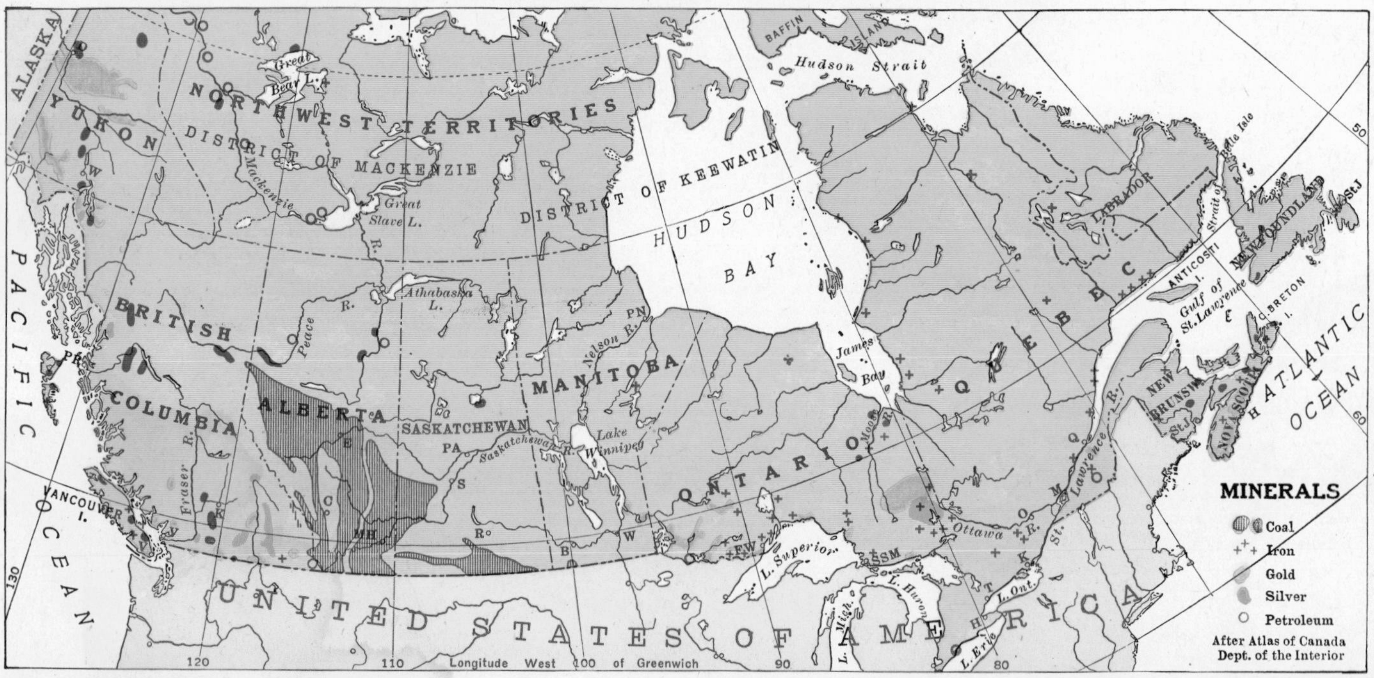

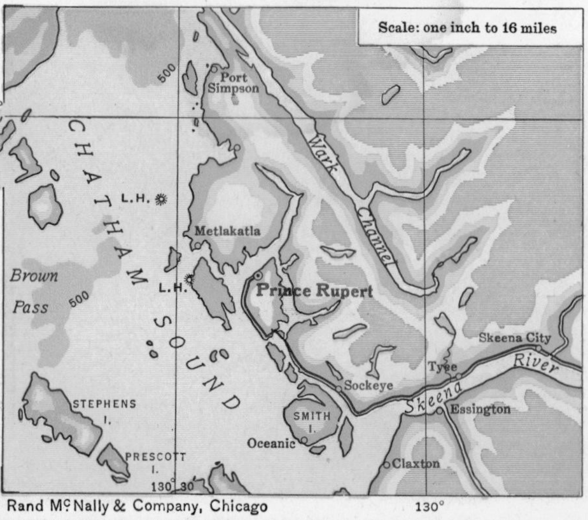

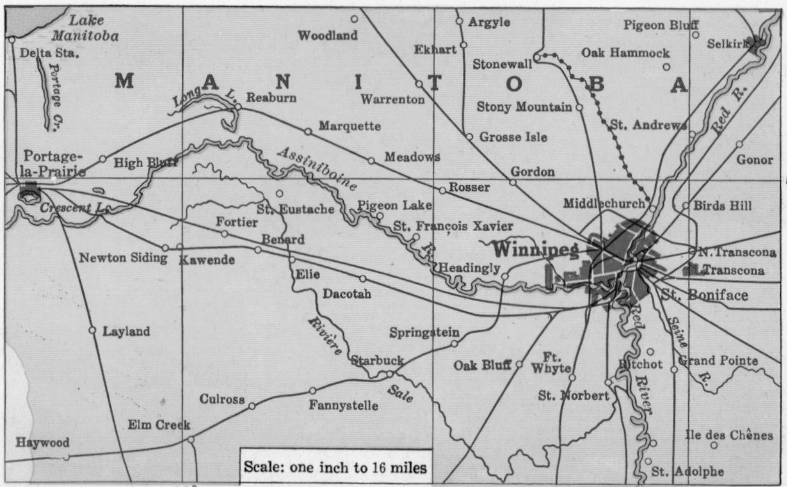

 130° 98° 97°30′ 97° 6789

For Canada: Conic Projection

Scale 1:30 000 000; one inch to 500 miles (approx.)

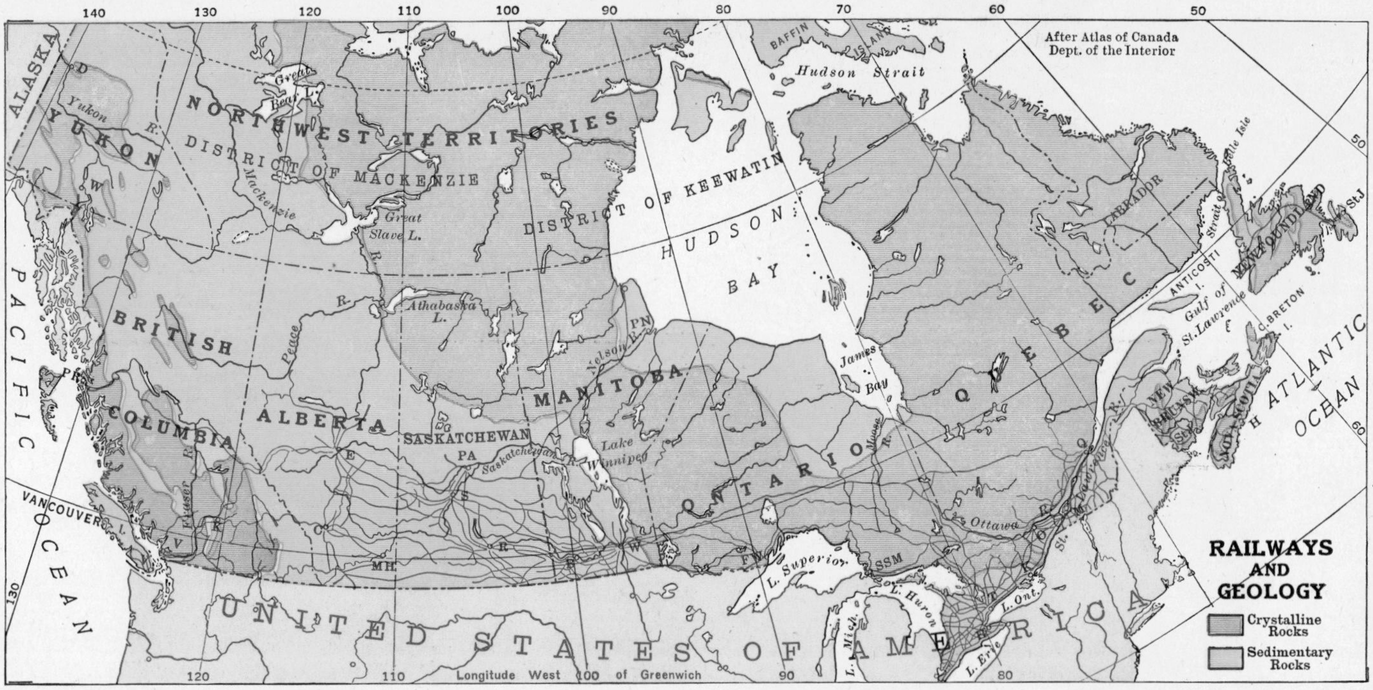

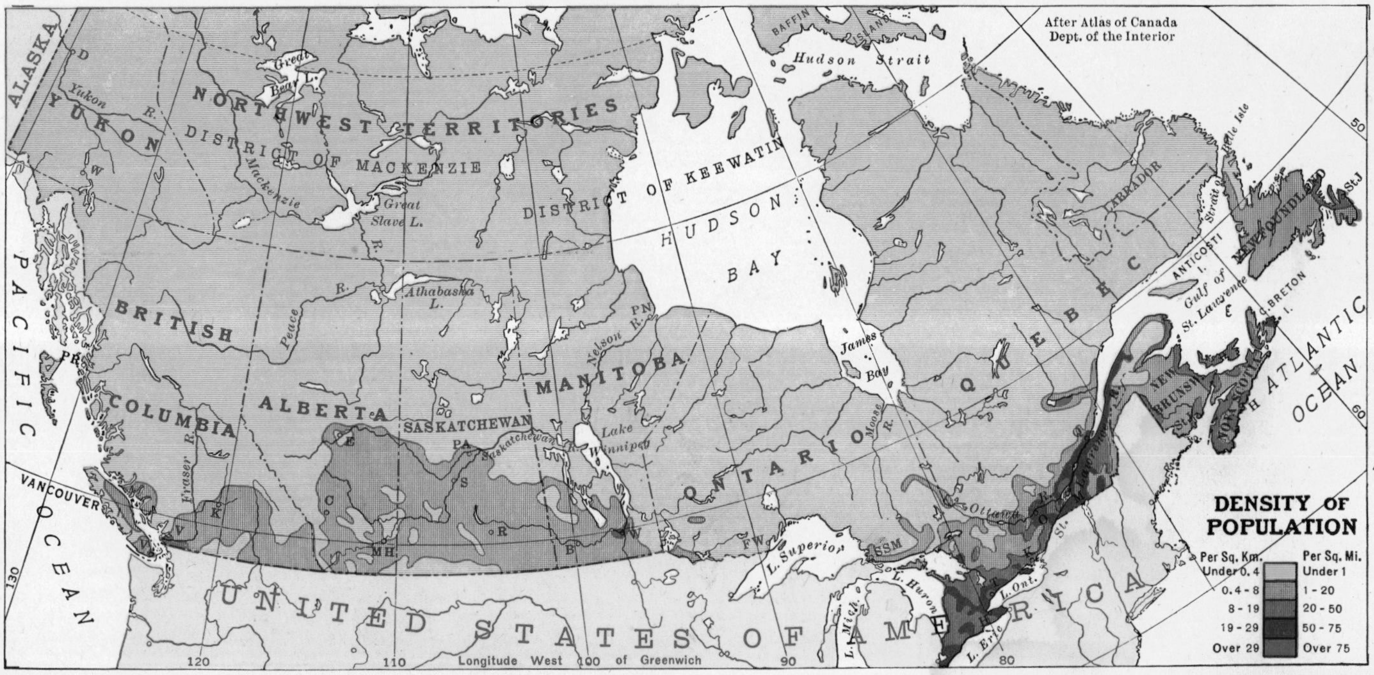

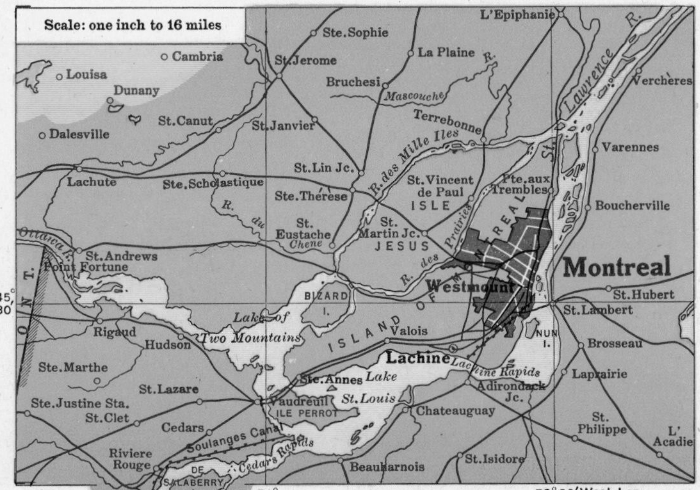

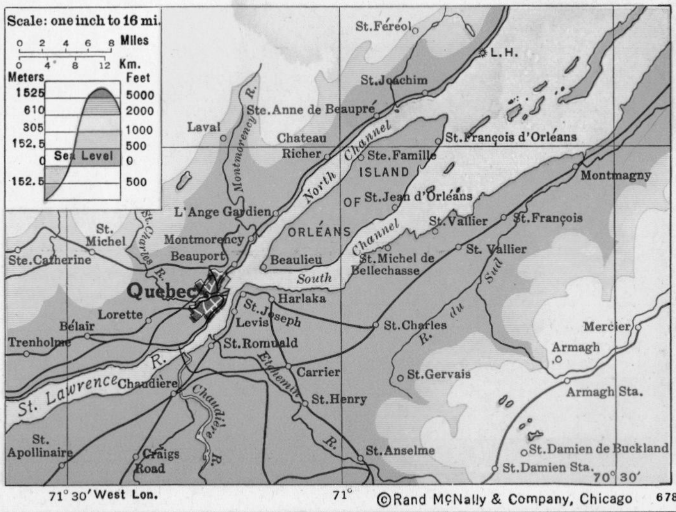

For Canada: Conic Projection

Scale 1 : 30 000 000; one inch to 500 miles (approx.)

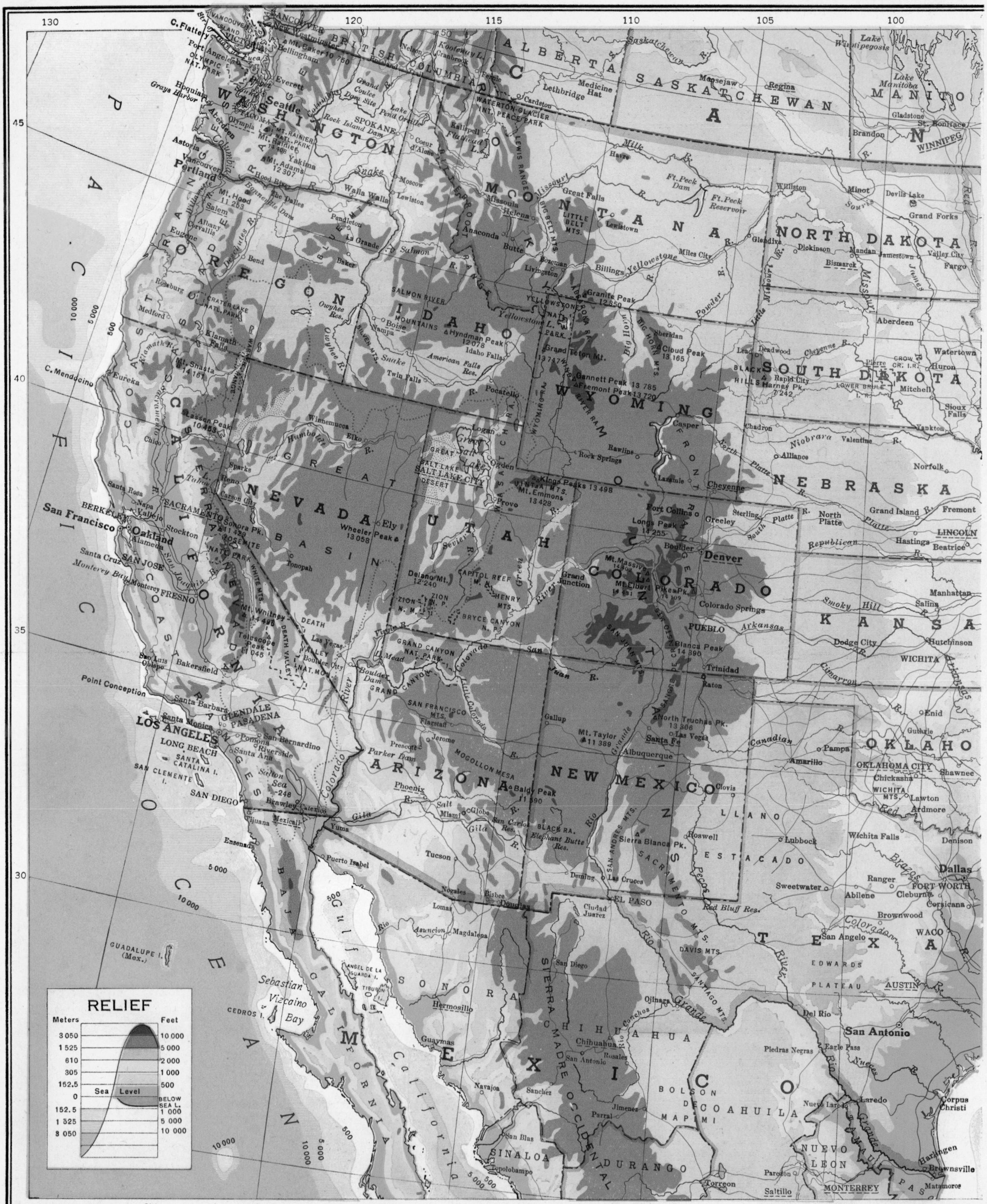

0 25 50 75 100 200 300 400 500 Miles

0 50 100 200 400 600 800 Kilometers

Scale 1:12 000 000; one inch to

Elevations and depressions

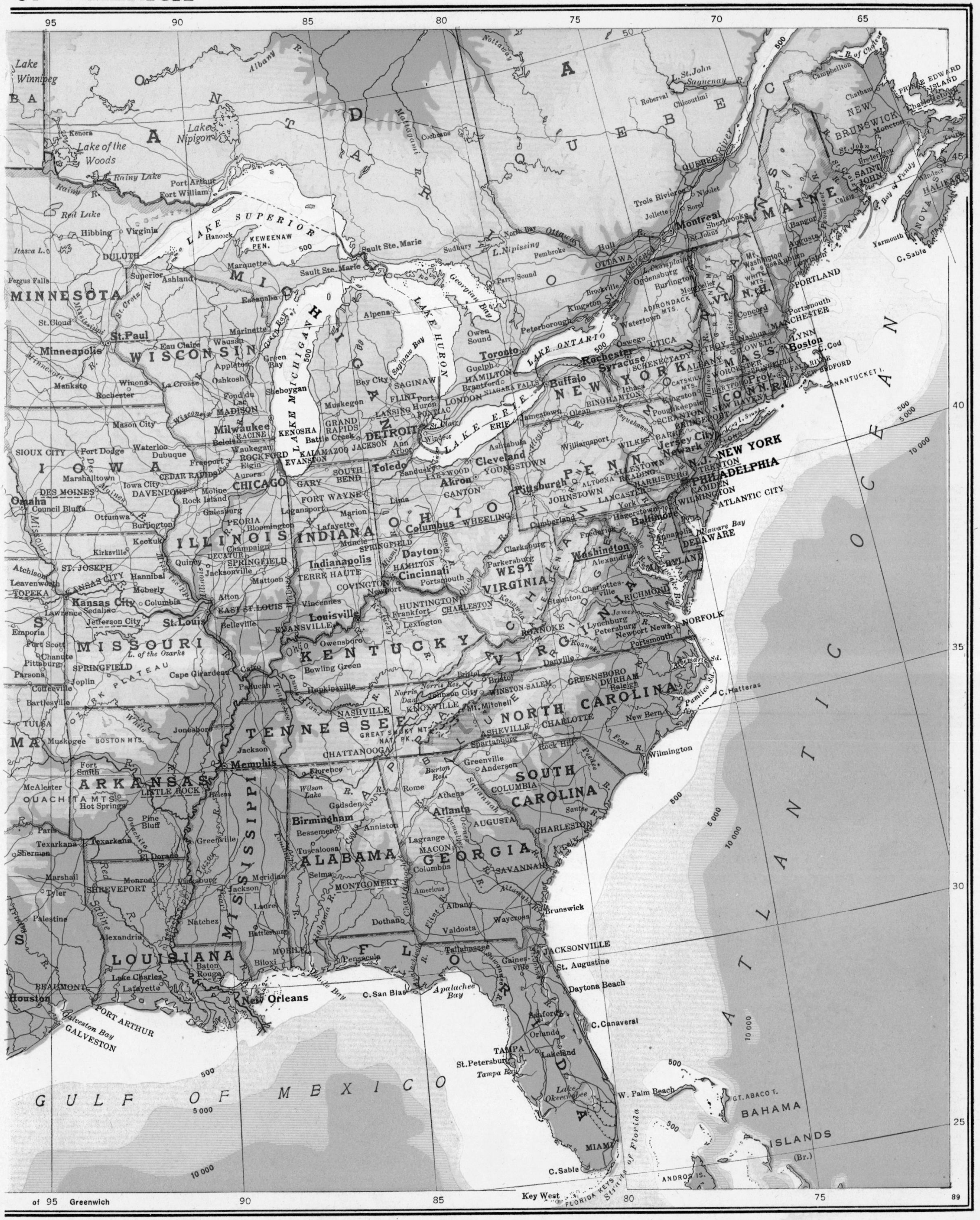

190 miles. **Polyconic Projection**

are given in feet

U. S. A.—Economic

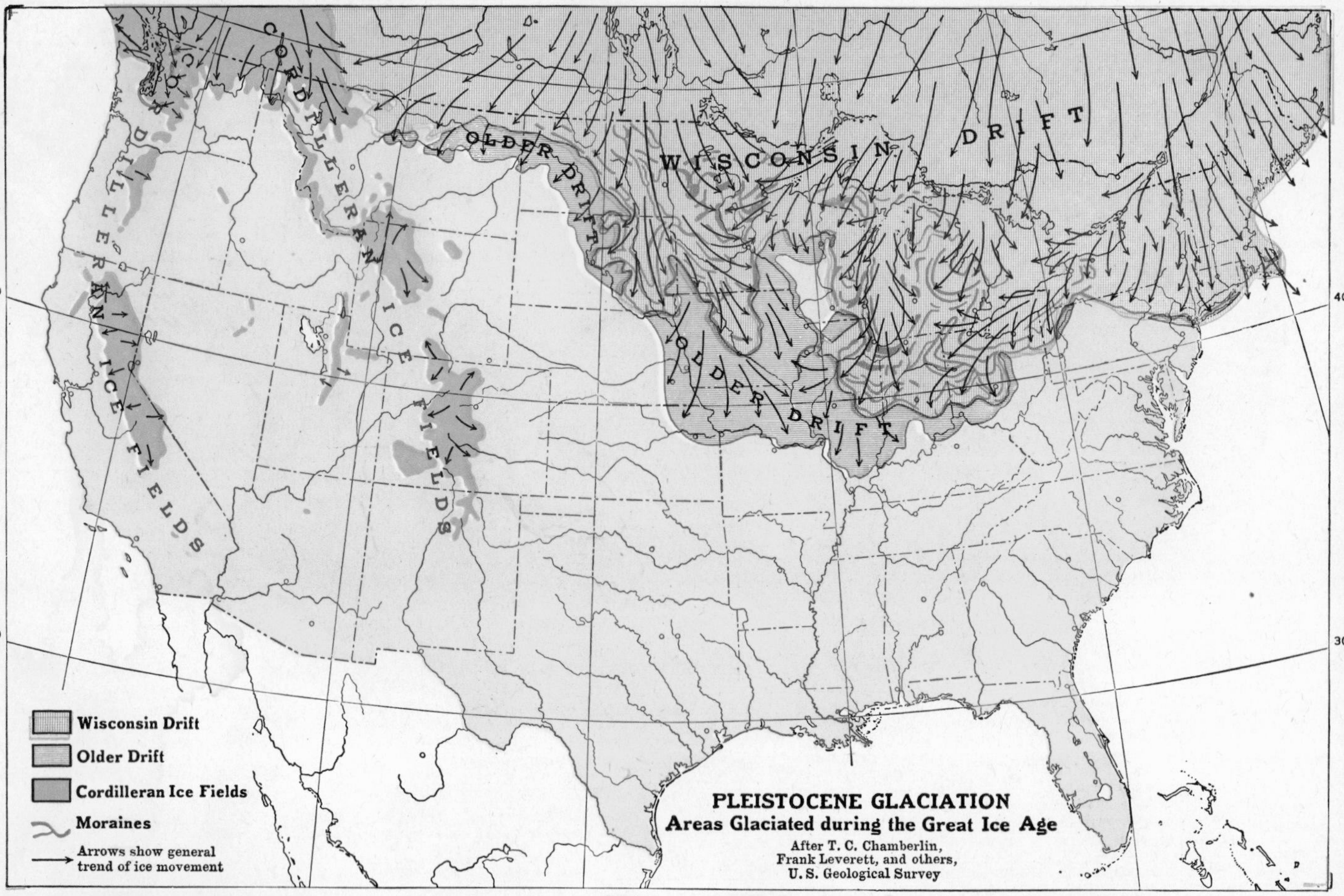
120
110 Longitude West 100 of Greenwich 90
80
70
40
30
CORDILLERAN ICE FIELDS
CORDILLERAN ICE FIELDS
OLDER DRIFT
WISCONSIN DRIFT
OLDER DRIFT
Wisconsin Drift
Older Drift
Cordilleran Ice Fields
Moraines
Arrows show general trend of ice movement
PLEISTOCENE GLACIATION
Areas Glaciated during the Great Ice Age
After T. C. Chamberlin, Frank Leverett, and others, U. S. Geological Survey

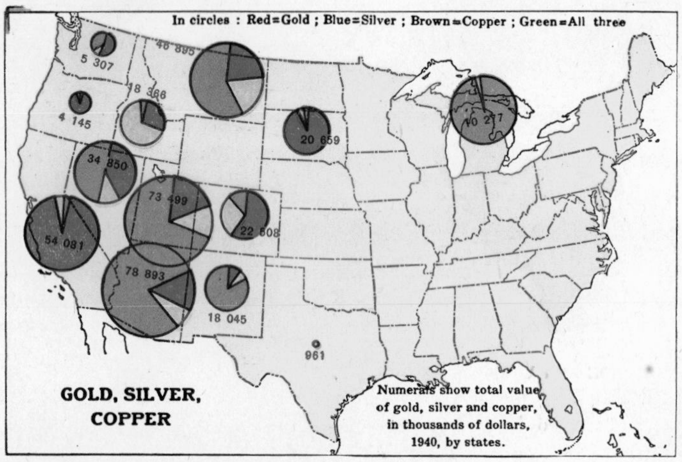
In circles : Red=Gold ; Blue=Silver ; Brown=Copper ; Green=All three
5 307
46 895
4 145
18 386
20 659
10 277
34 850
73 499
22 508
54 081
78 893
18 045
961
GOLD, SILVER, COPPER
Numerals show total value of gold, silver and copper, in thousands of dollars, 1940, by states.

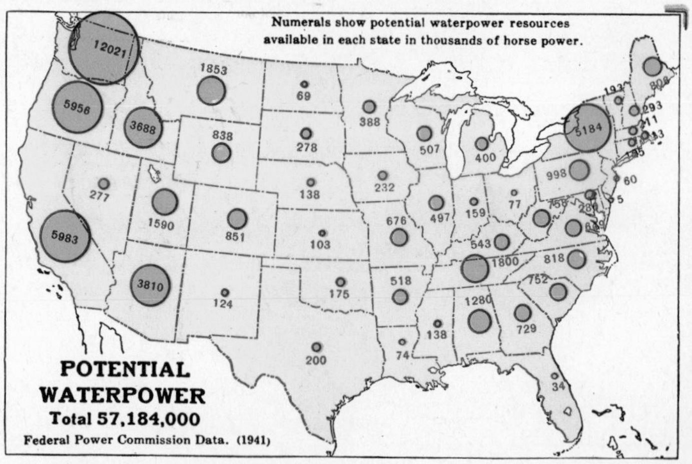
Numerals show potential waterpower resources available in each state in thousands of horse power.
12021
1853
5956
3688
838
69
278
388
507
400
5184
277
138
232
998
5983
1590
851
103
676
497
159
77
543
1800
818
3810
124
175
518
1280
752
729
138
200
74
34
POTENTIAL WATERPOWER
Total 57,184,000
Federal Power Commission Data. (1941)

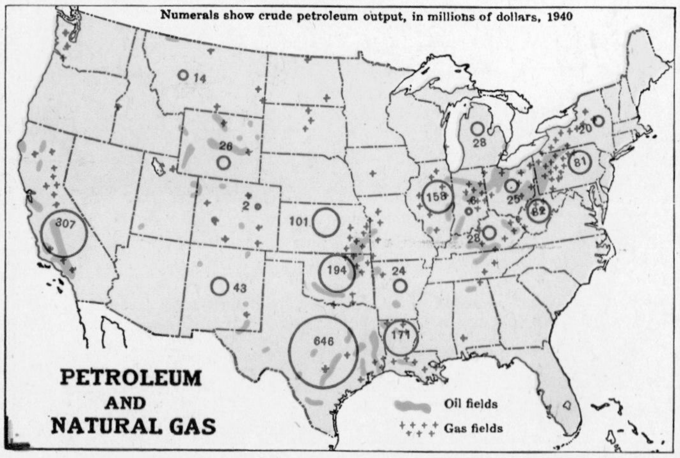
Numerals show crude petroleum output, in millions of dollars, 1940
14
26
28
81
2
158
25
307
101
62
28
194
24
43
171
646
PETROLEUM AND NATURAL GAS
Oil fields
Gas fields

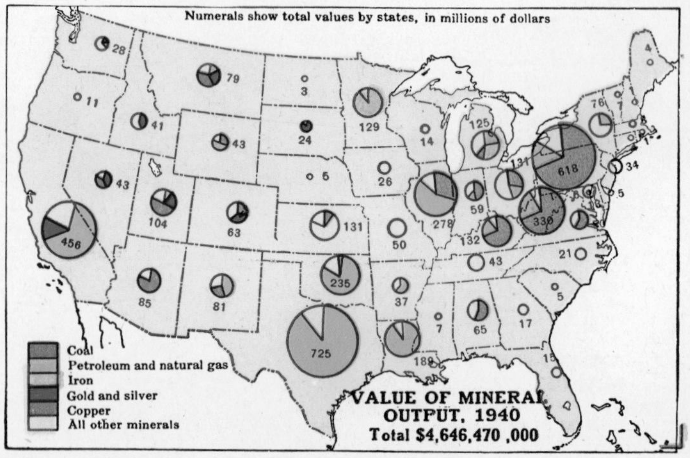
Numerals show total values by states, in millions of dollars
28
79
3
11
41
43
24
129
14
76
125
618
34
43
104
63
5
26
131
278
59
131
336
5
456
131
50
132
85
81
235
37
43
21
5
65
17
7
725
188
15
Coal
Petroleum and natural gas
Iron
Gold and silver
Copper
All other minerals
VALUE OF MINERAL OUTPUT, 1940
Total $4,646,470,000

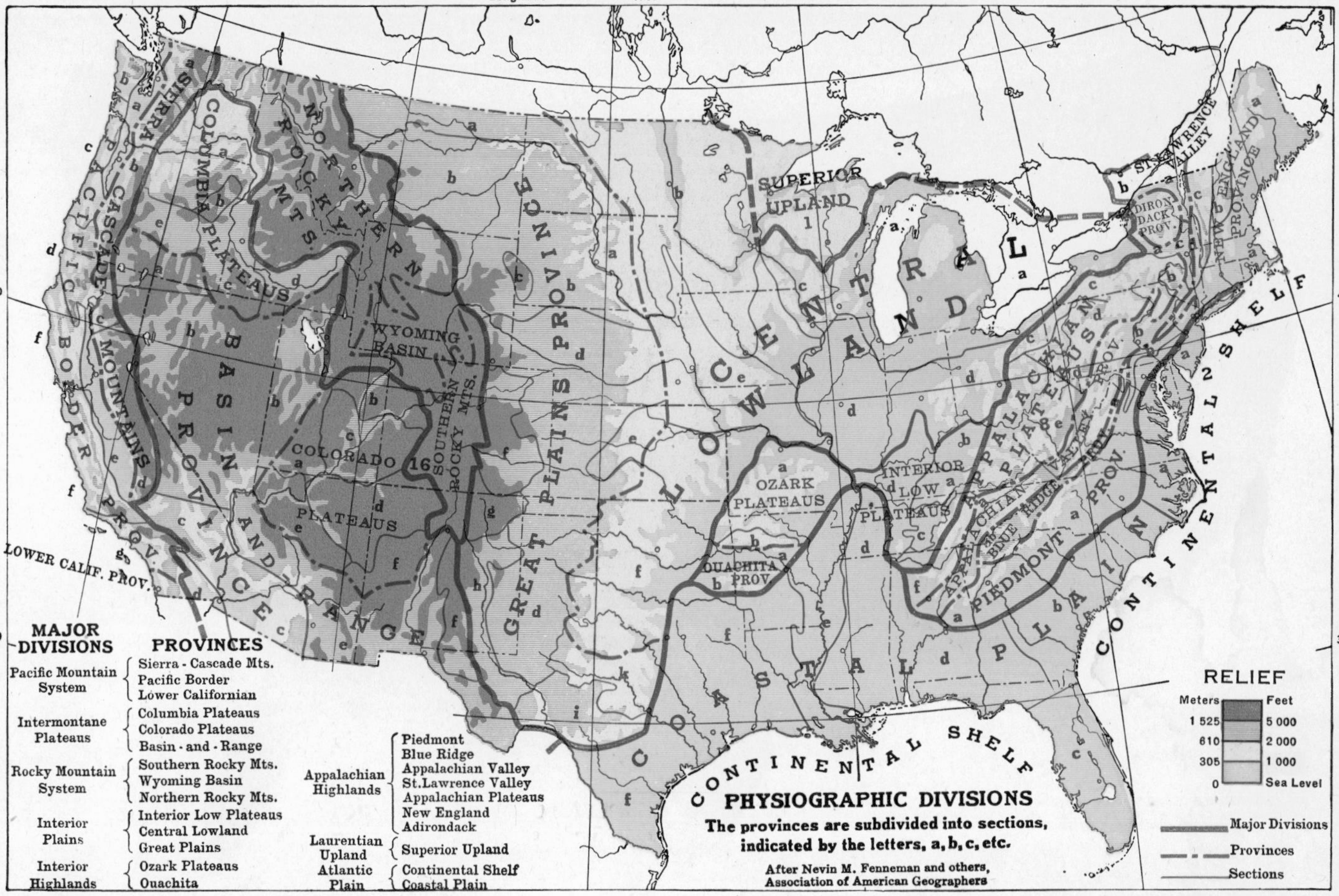
Longitude West of Greenwich
120
110
100
90
80
70
40
30
SIERRA CASCADE MTS.
PACIFIC BORDER PROV.
COLUMBIA PLATEAUS
NORTHERN ROCKY MTS.
WYOMING BASIN
SOUTHERN ROCKY MTS.
BASIN AND RANGE PROVINCE
COLORADO PLATEAUS
GREAT PLAINS PROVINCE
CENTRAL LOWLAND
SUPERIOR UPLAND
OZARK PLATEAUS
OUACHITA PROV.
INTERIOR LOW PLATEAUS
APPALACHIAN PLATEAUS
APPALACHIAN VALLEY
BLUE RIDGE PROV.
PIEDMONT PROV.
ST. LAWRENCE VALLEY
ADIRONDACK PROV.
NEW ENGLAND PROVINCE
COASTAL PLAIN
CONTINENTAL SHELF
LOWER CALIF. PROV.
MAJOR DIVISIONS
PROVINCES
Pacific Mountain System: Sierra - Cascade Mts., Pacific Border, Lower Californian
Intermontane Plateaus: Columbia Plateaus, Colorado Plateaus, Basin - and - Range
Rocky Mountain System: Southern Rocky Mts., Wyoming Basin, Northern Rocky Mts.
Interior Plains: Interior Low Plateaus, Central Lowland, Great Plains
Interior Highlands: Ozark Plateaus, Ouachita
Appalachian Highlands: Piedmont, Blue Ridge, Appalachian Valley, St.Lawrence Valley, Appalachian Plateaus, New England, Adirondack
Laurentian Upland: Superior Upland
Atlantic Plain: Continental Shelf, Coastal Plain
PHYSIOGRAPHIC DIVISIONS
The provinces are subdivided into sections, indicated by the letters, a, b, c, etc.
After Nevin M. Fenneman and others, Association of American Geographers
RELIEF
Meters / Feet
1 525 / 5 000
610 / 2 000
305 / 1 000
0 / Sea Level
Major Divisions
Provinces
Sections

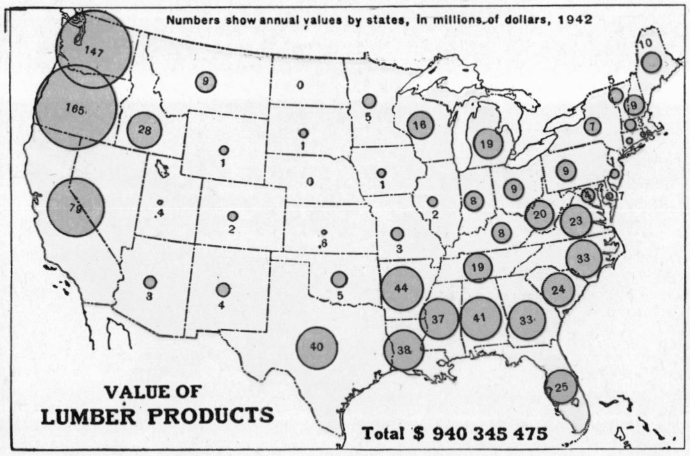
Numbers show annual values by states, in millions of dollars, 1942
VALUE OF LUMBER PRODUCTS
Total $ 940 345 475

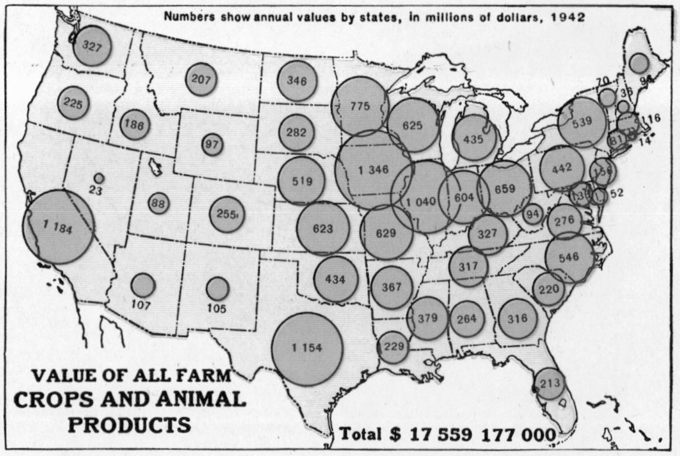
Numbers show annual values by states, in millions of dollars, 1942
VALUE OF ALL FARM CROPS AND ANIMAL PRODUCTS
Total $ 17 559 177 000

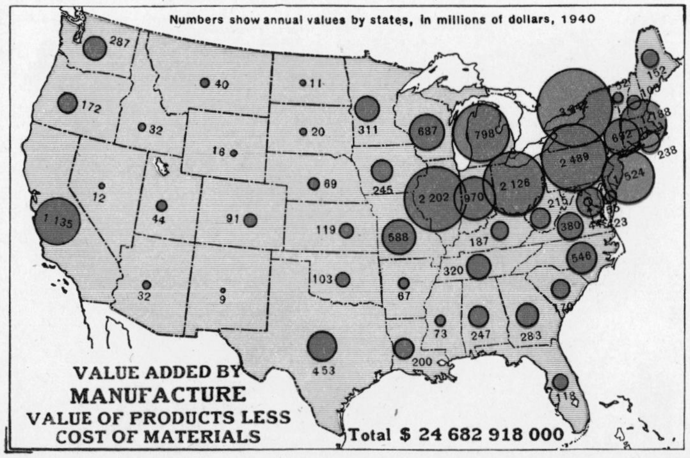
Numbers show annual values by states, in millions of dollars, 1940
VALUE ADDED BY MANUFACTURE
VALUE OF PRODUCTS LESS COST OF MATERIALS
Total $ 24 682 918 000

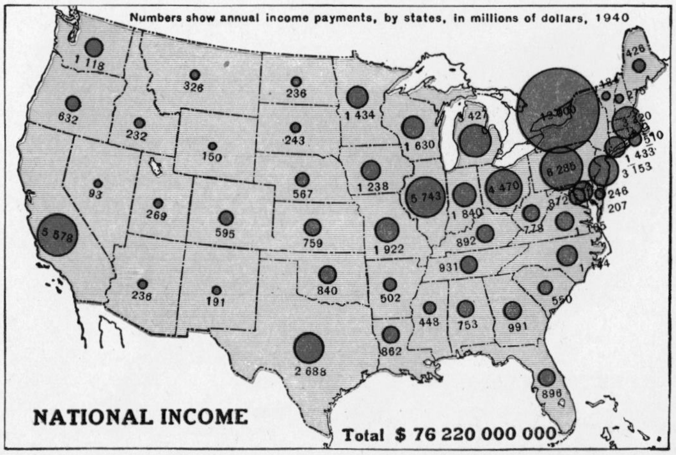
Numbers show annual income payments, by states, in millions of dollars, 1940
NATIONAL INCOME
Total $ 76 220 000 000

U. S. A.–Economic

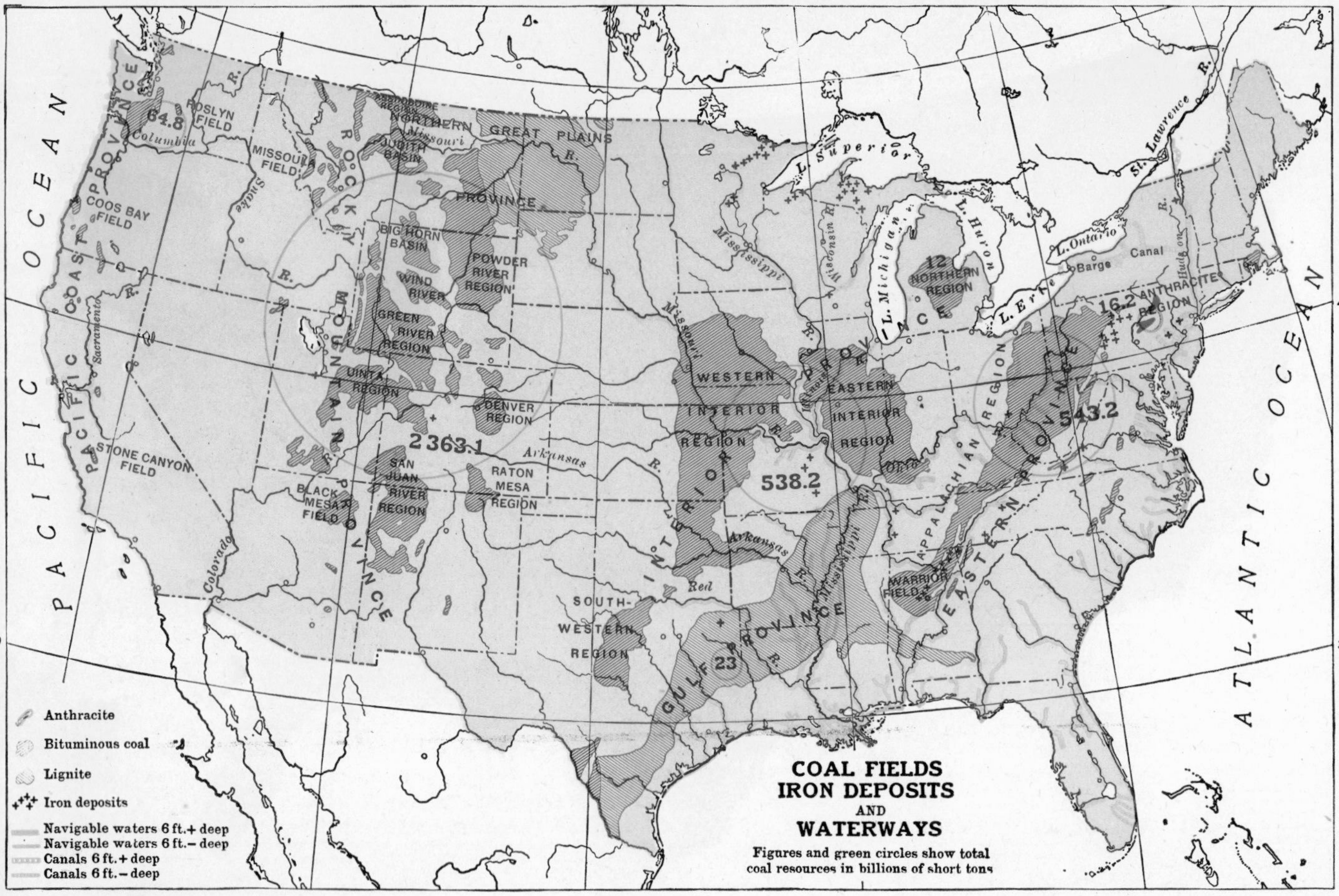

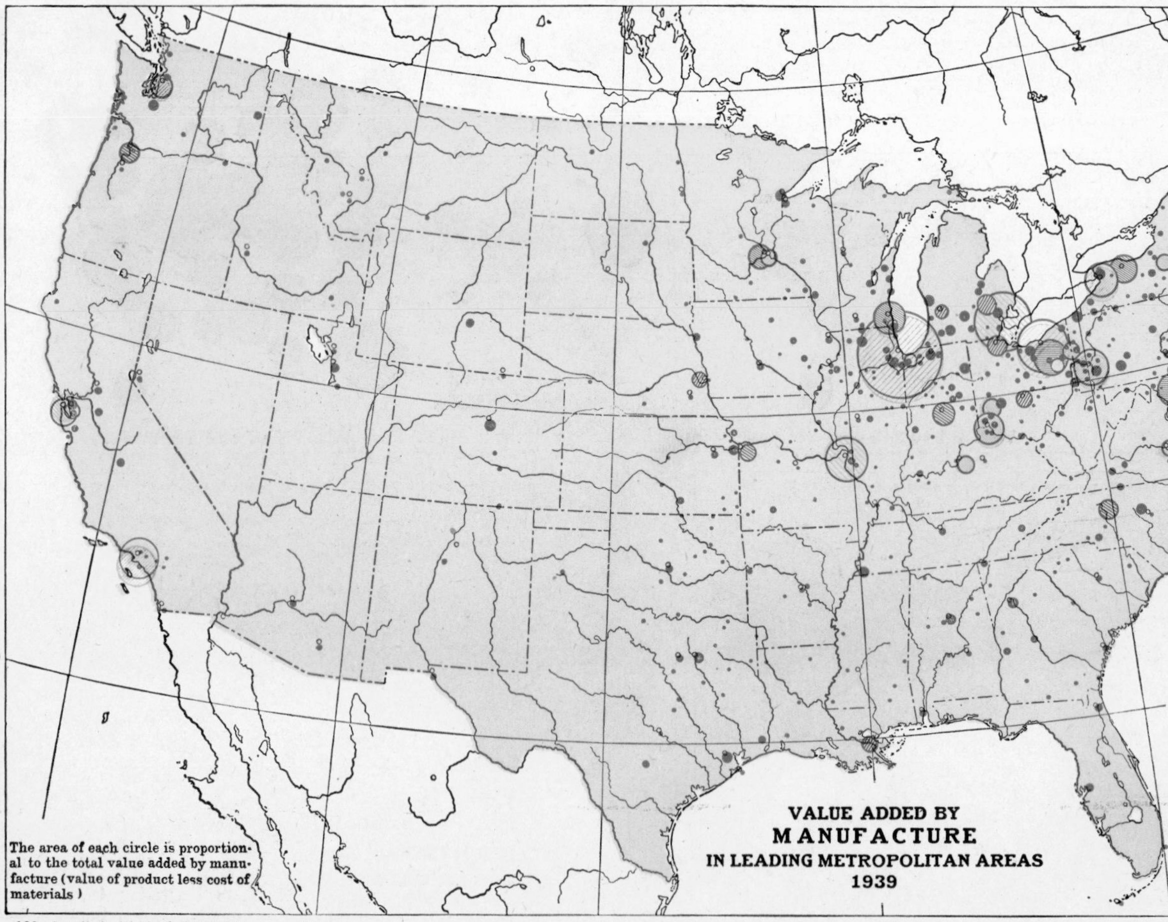

Rank of Metropolitan Areas in value added by Manufacture
In millions of dollars

1.	New York	3 061
2.	Chicago	1 910
3.	Detroit	1 069
4.	Philadelphia	1 041
5.	Boston	661
6.	Pittsburgh	643
7.	Cleveland	547
8.	Los Angeles	513
9.	St. Louis	464
10.	Buffalo	394
11.	Bridgeport	394
12.	Milwaukee	361
13.	San Francisco	360
14.	Baltimore	342
15.	Cincinnati	316
16.	Providence	315
17.	Youngstown	227

Scale for both maps; one inch to 400 miles

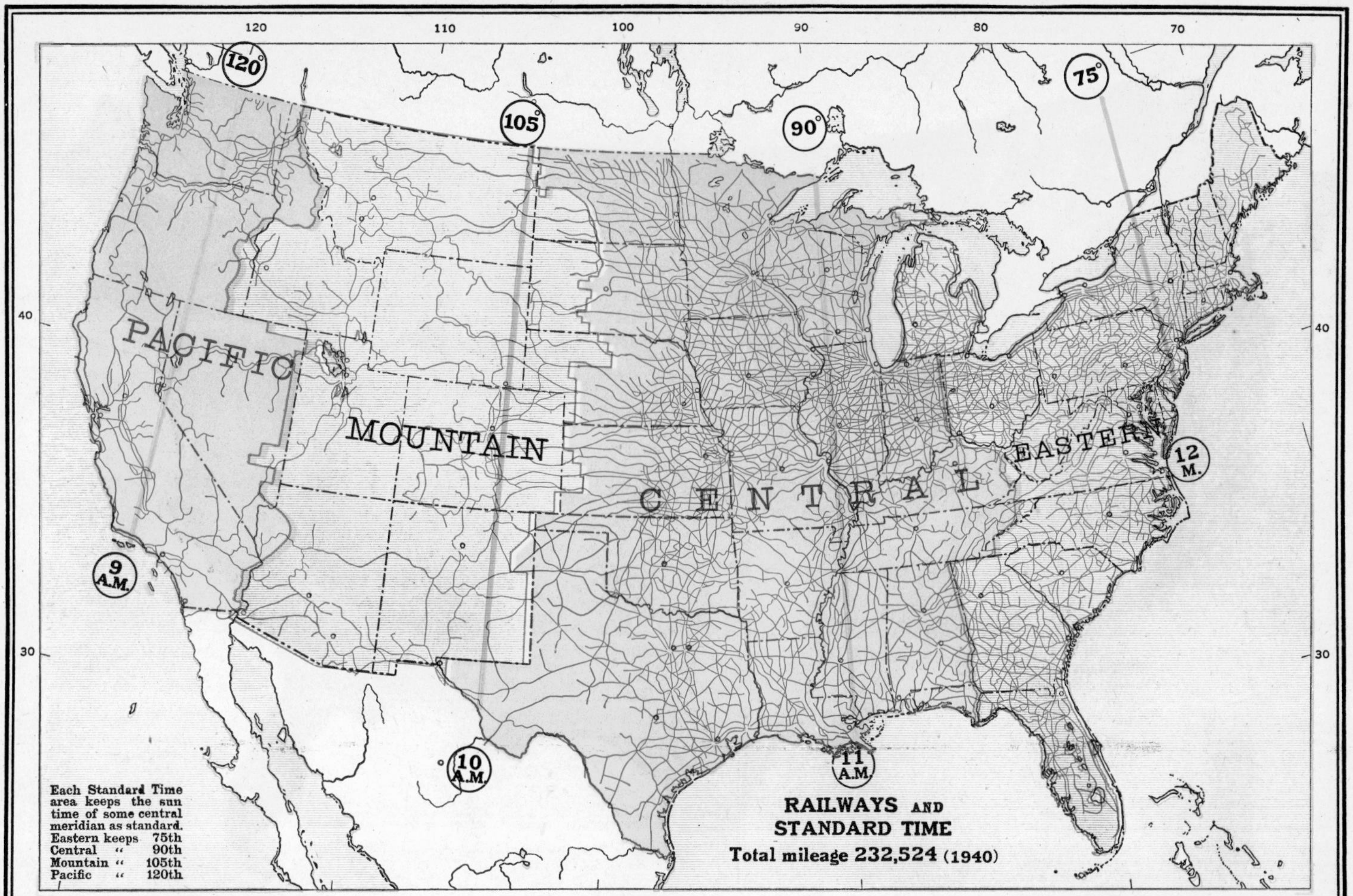
120
110
100
90
80
70
40
30
120°
105°
90°
75°
PACIFIC
MOUNTAIN
CENTRAL
EASTERN
9 A.M.
10 A.M.
11 A.M.
12 M.
Each Standard Time area keeps the sun time of some central meridian as standard.
Eastern keeps 75th
Central " 90th
Mountain " 105th
Pacific " 120th
RAILWAYS AND STANDARD TIME
Total mileage 232,524 (1940)

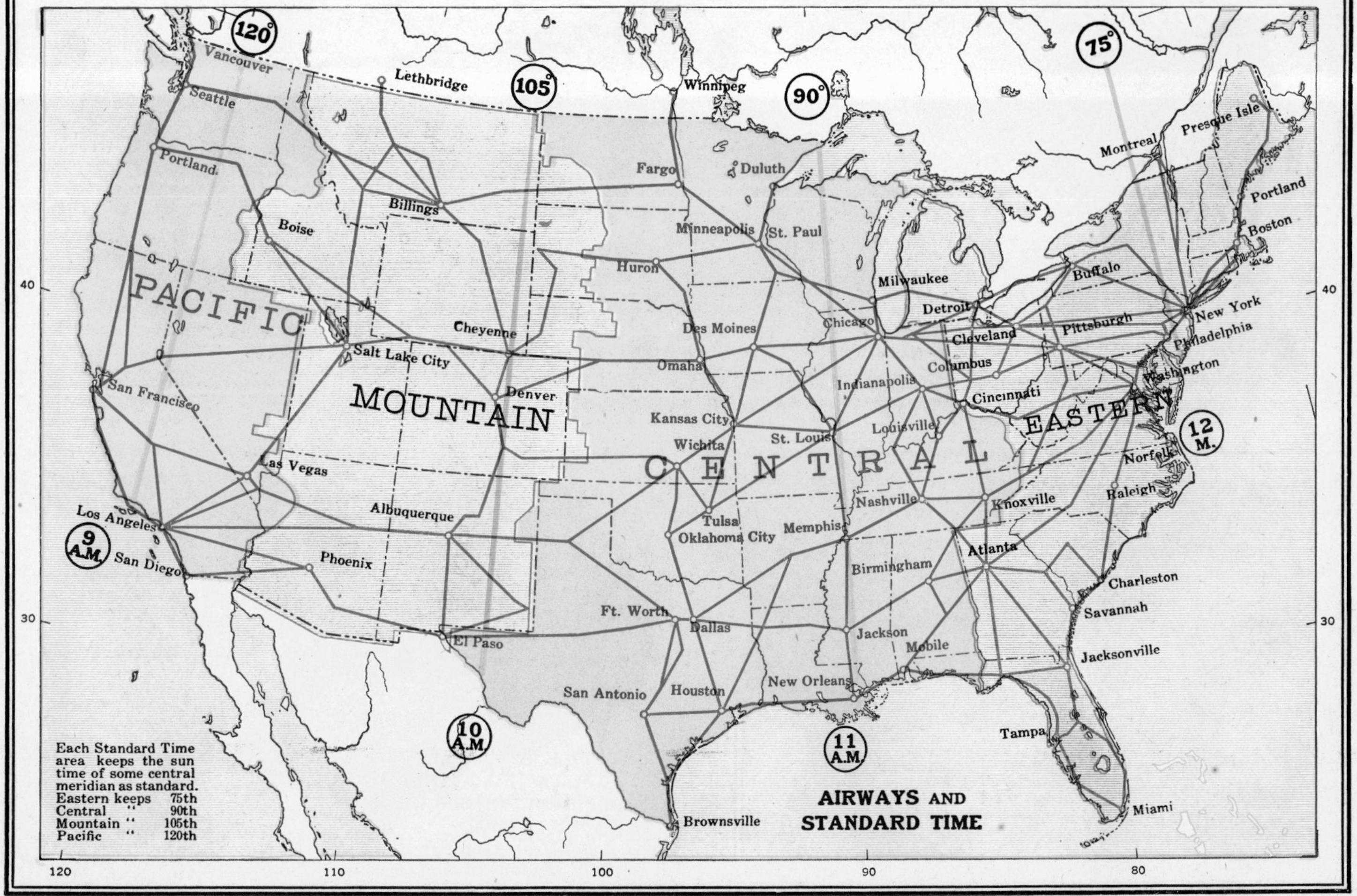
120°
105°
90°
75°
Vancouver
Seattle
Lethbridge
Winnipeg
Portland
Fargo
Duluth
Montreal
Presque Isle
Portland
Boston
Billings
Boise
Minneapolis
St. Paul
Huron
Milwaukee
Buffalo
Detroit
New York
Cheyenne
Des Moines
Chicago
Cleveland
Pittsburgh
Philadelphia
Salt Lake City
Omaha
Columbus
Washington
San Francisco
Denver
Indianapolis
Cincinnati
Kansas City
Louisville
St. Louis
Wichita
Norfolk
Las Vegas
Nashville
Knoxville
Raleigh
Los Angeles
Albuquerque
Tulsa
Oklahoma City
Memphis
Atlanta
San Diego
Phoenix
Birmingham
Charleston
Savannah
Ft. Worth
Dallas
Jackson
Mobile
Jacksonville
El Paso
San Antonio
Houston
New Orleans
Tampa
Miami
Brownsville
PACIFIC
MOUNTAIN
CENTRAL
EASTERN
9 A.M.
10 A.M.
11 A.M.
12 M.
40
30
120
110
100
90
80
Each Standard Time area keeps the sun time of some central meridian as standard.
Eastern keeps 75th
Central " 90th
Mountain " 105th
Pacific " 120th
AIRWAYS AND STANDARD TIME

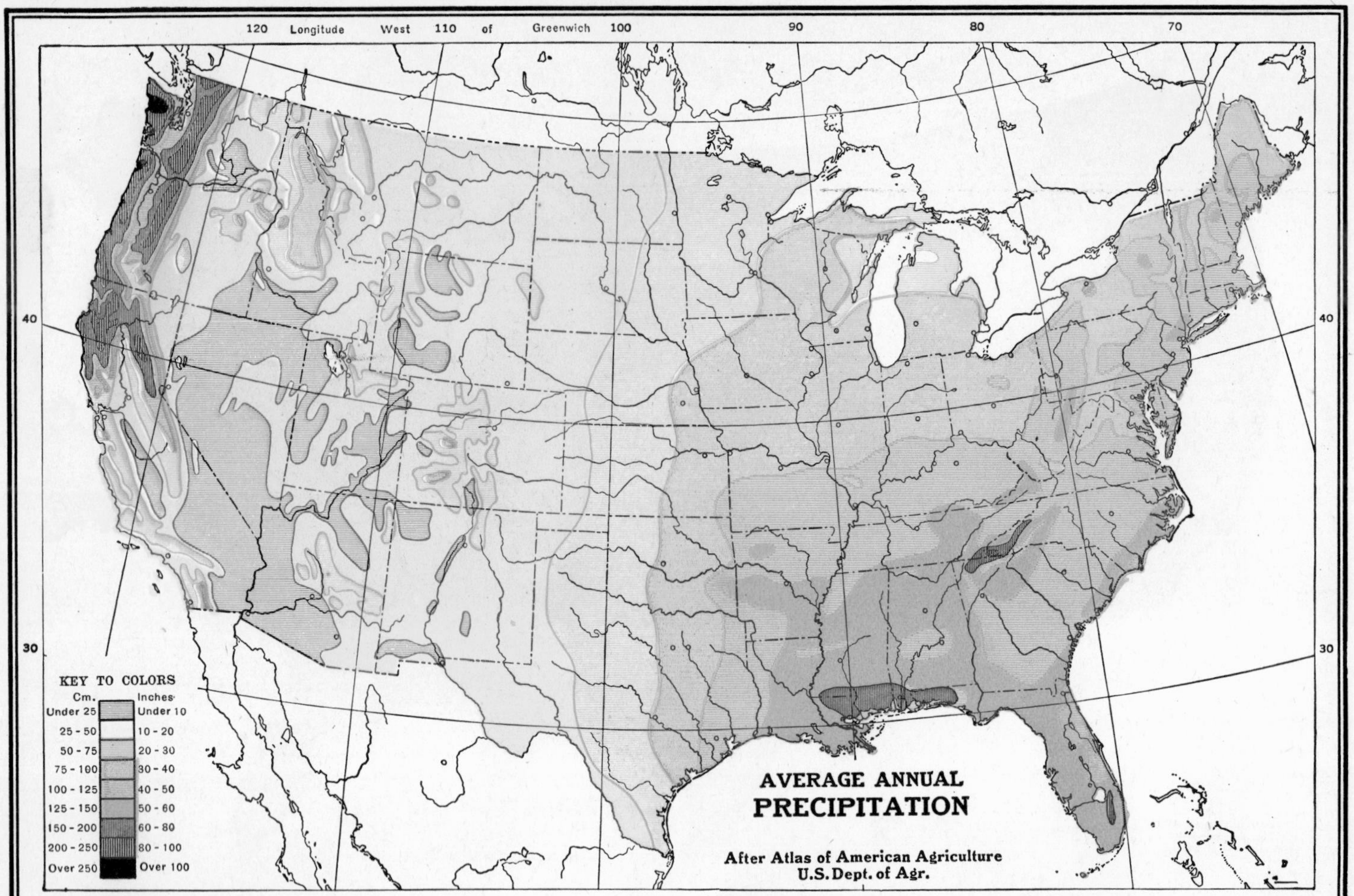
120 Longitude West 110 of Greenwich 100
90
80
70
40
30
KEY TO COLORS
Cm. Inches
Under 25 Under 10
25 - 50 10 - 20
50 - 75 20 - 30
75 - 100 30 - 40
100 - 125 40 - 50
125 - 150 50 - 60
150 - 200 60 - 80
200 - 250 80 - 100
Over 250 Over 100
AVERAGE ANNUAL
PRECIPITATION
After Atlas of American Agriculture
U.S. Dept. of Agr.

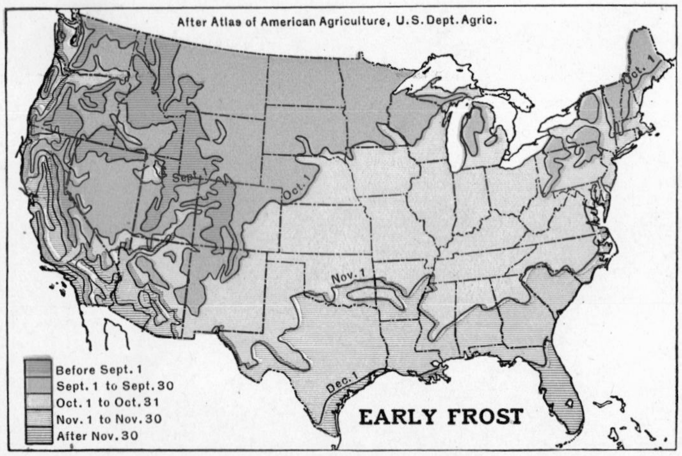
After Atlas of American Agriculture, U.S. Dept. Agric.
Sept. 1
Oct. 1
Nov. 1
Dec. 1
Before Sept. 1
Sept. 1 to Sept. 30
Oct. 1 to Oct. 31
Nov. 1 to Nov. 30
After Nov. 30
EARLY FROST

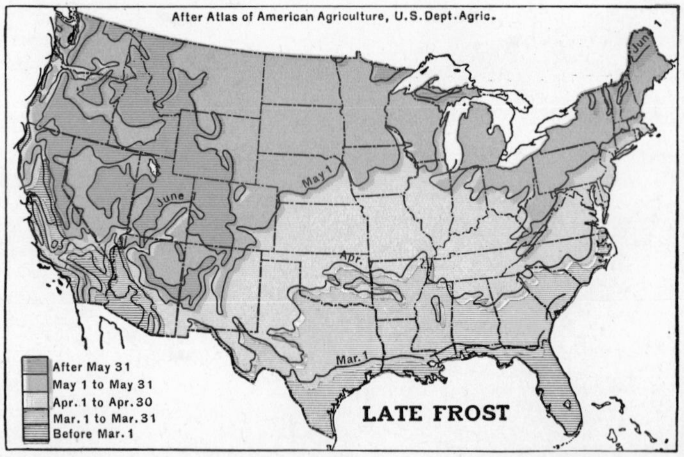
After Atlas of American Agriculture, U.S. Dept. Agric.
June
May 1
Apr.
Mar. 1
After May 31
May 1 to May 31
Apr. 1 to Apr. 30
Mar. 1 to Mar. 31
Before Mar. 1
LATE FROST

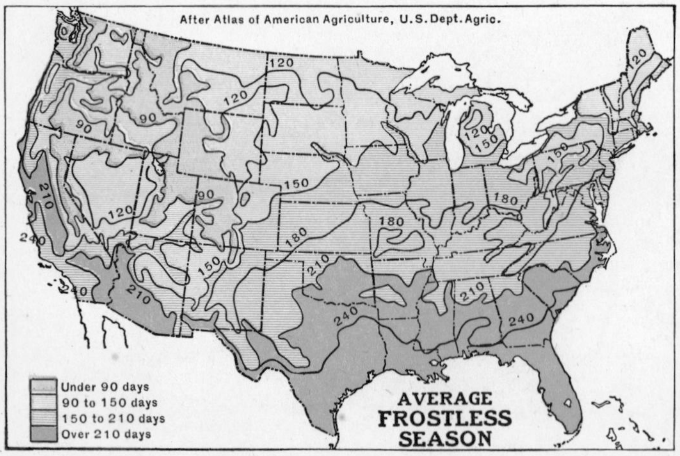
After Atlas of American Agriculture, U.S. Dept. Agric.
Under 90 days
90 to 150 days
150 to 210 days
Over 210 days
AVERAGE
FROSTLESS
SEASON

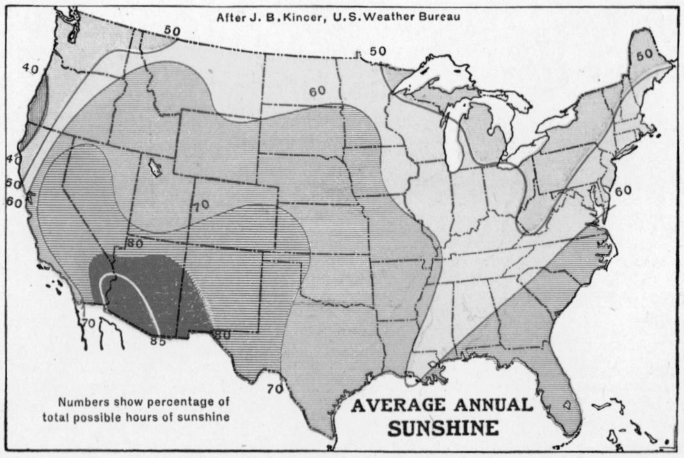
After J. B. Kincer, U.S. Weather Bureau
Numbers show percentage of
total possible hours of sunshine
AVERAGE ANNUAL
SUNSHINE

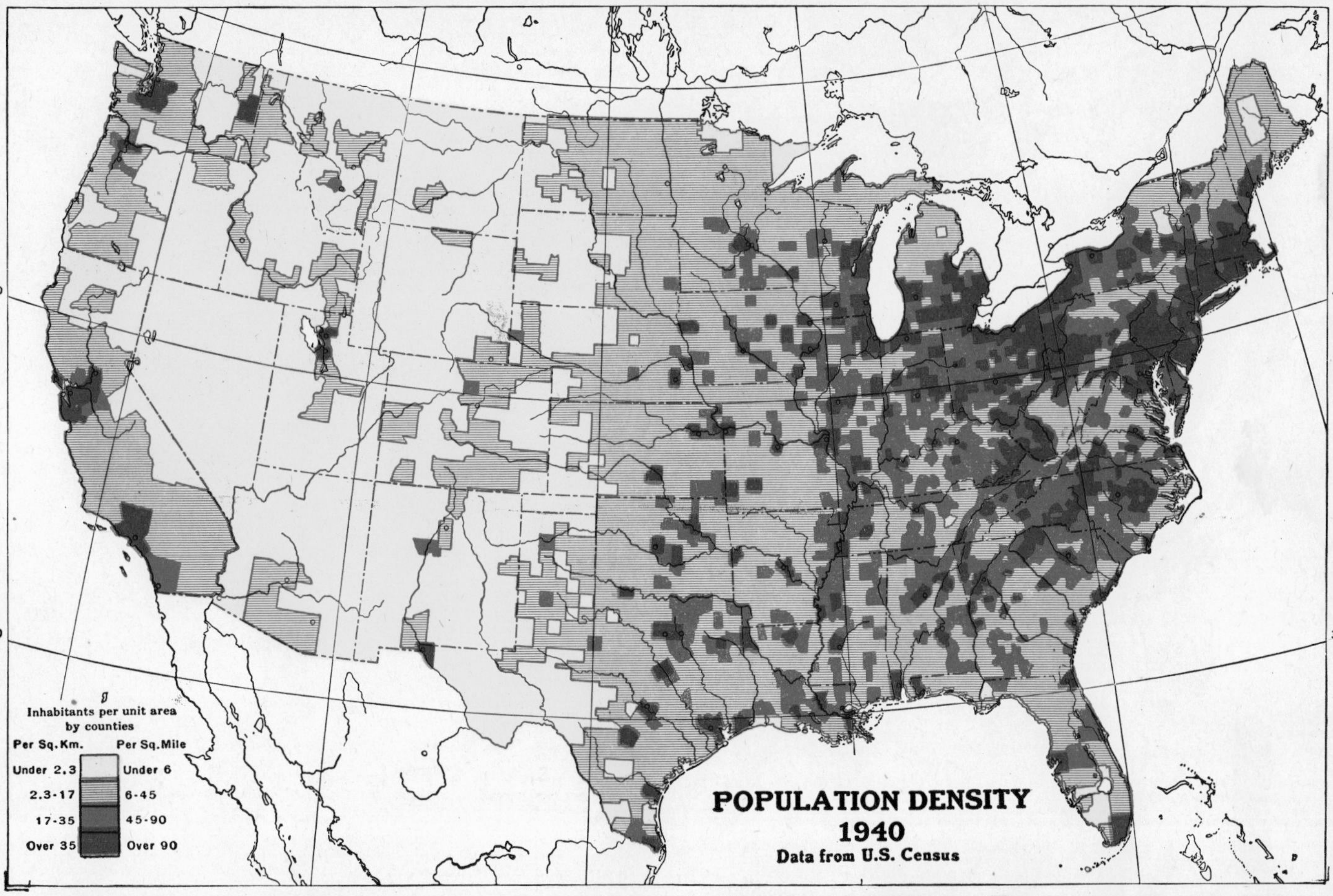

POPULATION DENSITY 1940
Data from U.S. Census

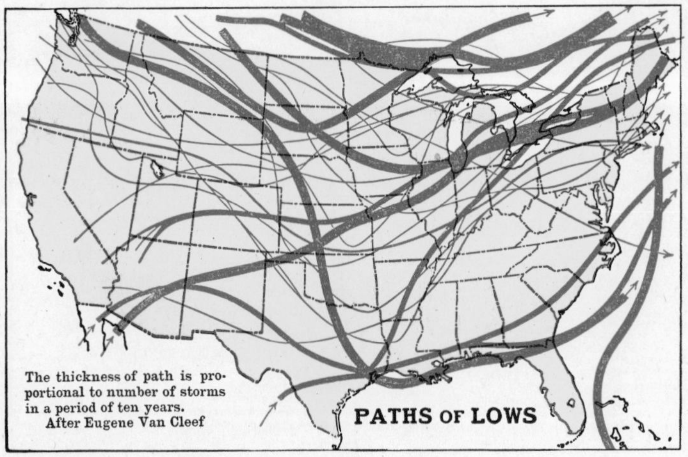
The thickness of path is proportional to number of storms in a period of ten years.
After Eugene Van Cleef
PATHS OF LOWS

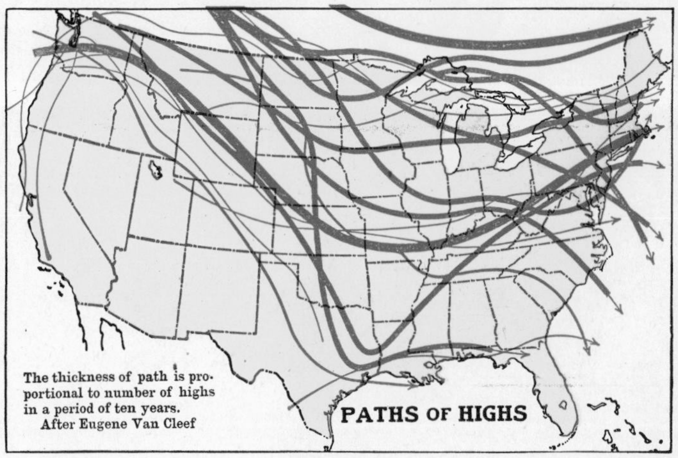
The thickness of path is proportional to number of highs in a period of ten years.
After Eugene Van Cleef
PATHS OF HIGHS

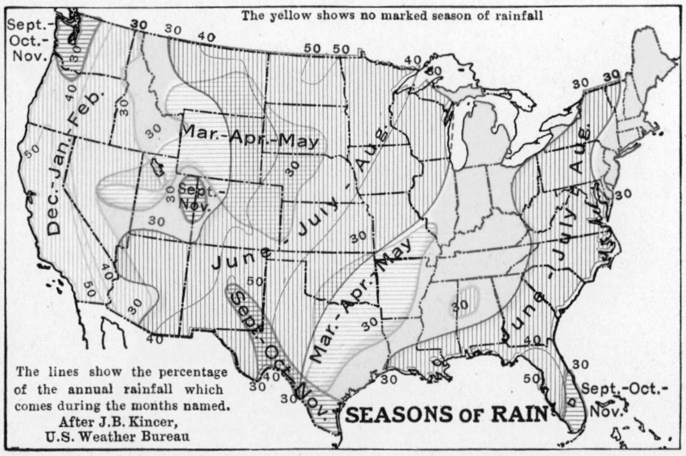

The lines show the percentage of the annual rainfall which comes during the months named.
After J.B. Kincer, U.S. Weather Bureau
SEASONS OF RAIN

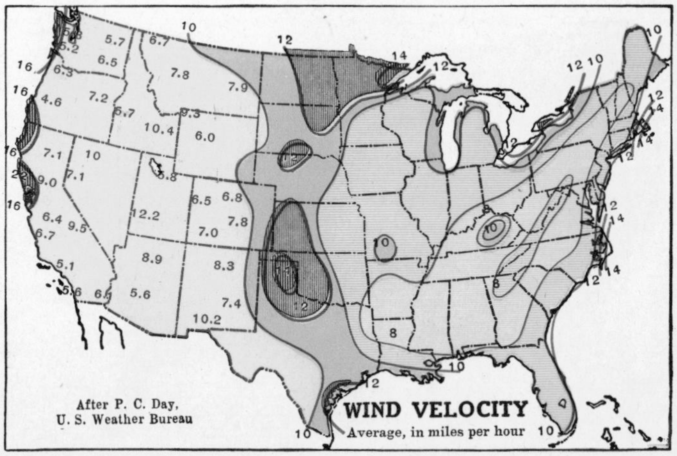
After P. C. Day, U. S. Weather Bureau
WIND VELOCITY
Average, in miles per hour

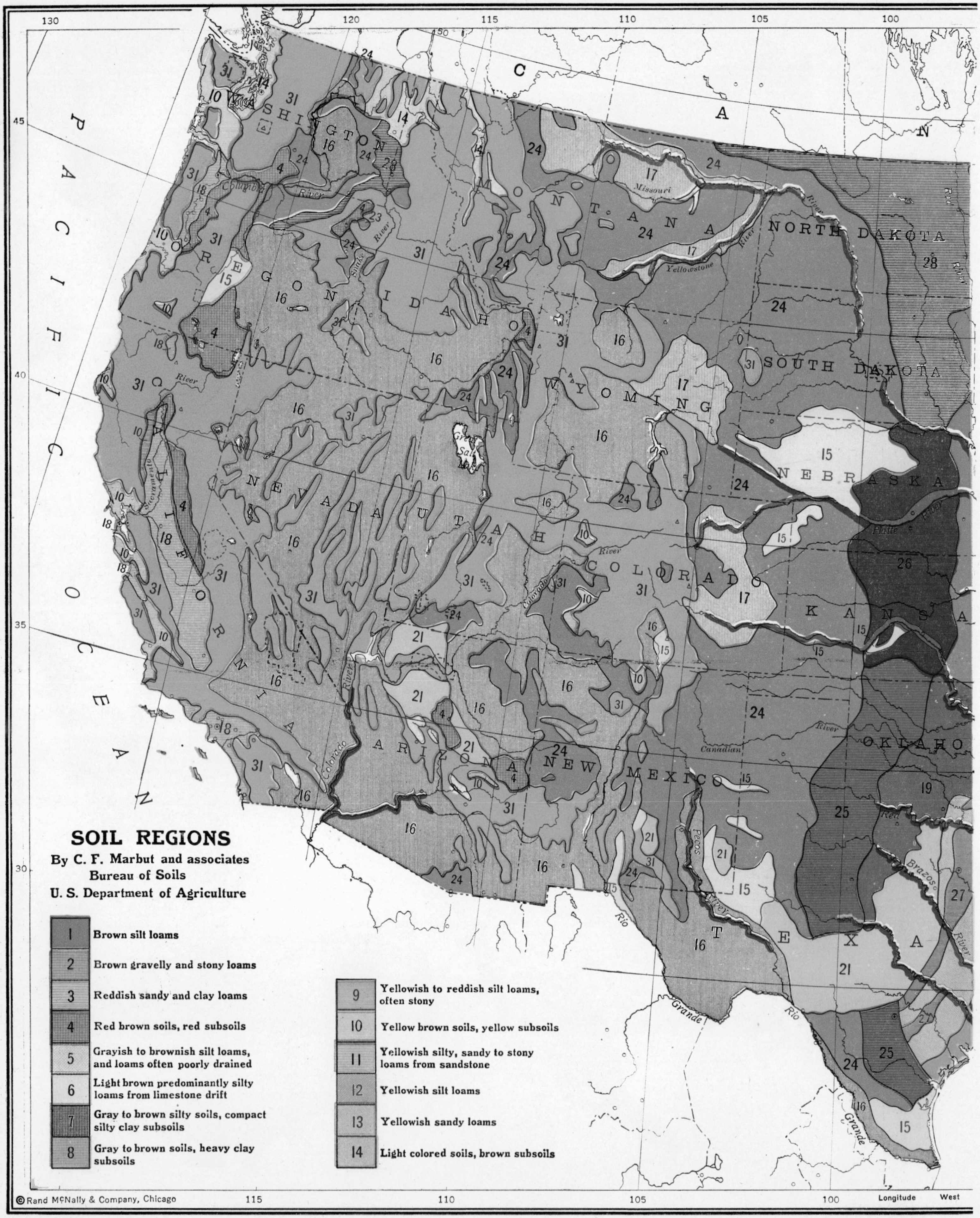
SOIL REGIONS
By C. F. Marbut and associates
Bureau of Soils
U. S. Department of Agriculture
1 Brown silt loams
2 Brown gravelly and stony loams
3 Reddish sandy and clay loams
4 Red brown soils, red subsoils
5 Grayish to brownish silt loams, and loams often poorly drained
6 Light brown predominantly silty loams from limestone drift
7 Gray to brown silty soils, compact silty clay subsoils
8 Gray to brown soils, heavy clay subsoils
9 Yellowish to reddish silt loams, often stony
10 Yellow brown soils, yellow subsoils
11 Yellowish silty, sandy to stony loams from sandstone
12 Yellowish silt loams
13 Yellowish sandy loams
14 Light colored soils, brown subsoils
PACIFIC OCEAN
WASHINGTON
OREGON
CALIFORNIA
NEVADA
IDAHO
MONTANA
WYOMING
UTAH
COLORADO
ARIZONA
NEW MEXICO
NORTH DAKOTA
SOUTH DAKOTA
NEBRASKA
KANSAS
OKLAHO
TEXAS
CANADA
Longitude West
Rand McNally & Company, Chicago

0 25 50 75 100 200 300 400 500 Miles
0 50 100 200 400 600 800 Kilometers

Scale 1:12 000 000; one inch

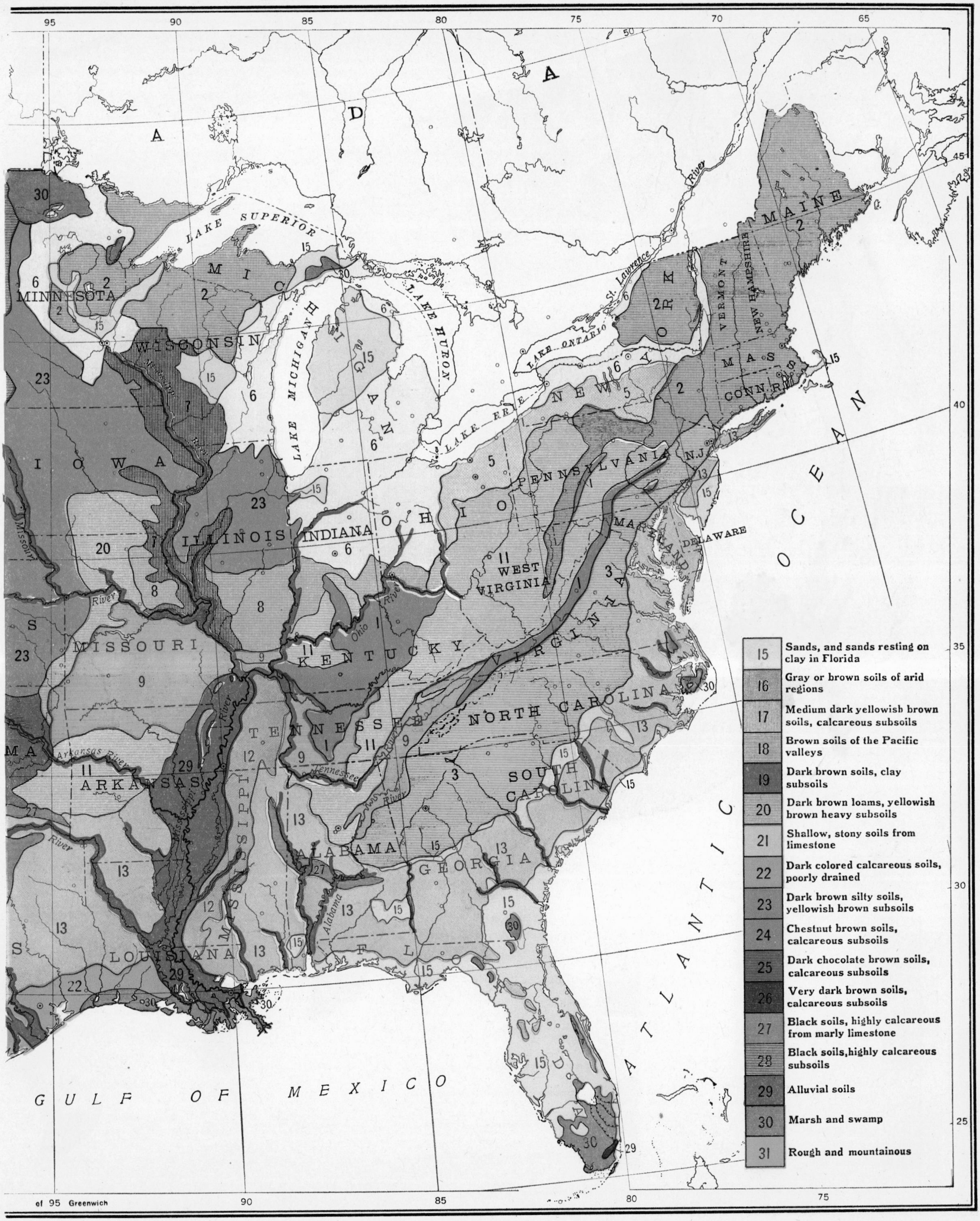

to 190 miles. Polyconic Projection

NATIVE VEGETATION

By Homer L. Shantz and Raphael Zon, U.S. Department of Agriculture, and B.E. Fernow for Canada

I. FOREST VEGETATION (WESTERN)

1. WOODLAND

- 1 Chaparral (Southwestern broad-leaved woodland)
- 2 Piñon-Juniper (Southwestern coniferous woodland)

2. TIMBERLAND

A. Western yellow pine-Douglas fir (Western pine forest)

- 3a Yellow pine-Sugar pine
- 3b Lodgepole pine
- 3c Yellow pine-Douglas fir

B. Cedar-Hemlock (Northwestern coniferous forest)

- 4a Western larch-Western white pine
- 4b Pacific Douglas fir
- 4c Redwood

- 5 **C. Spruce-Fir** (Northern coniferous forest)

II. FOREST VEGETATION (EASTERN)

- 5 **A. Spruce-Fir** (Northern coniferous forest)
- 7 **B. White, Norway, Jack pine** (Northeastern pine forest)
- 8 **C. Birch-Beech-Maple-Hemlock** (Northeastern hardwoods)

D. Oak (Southern hardwood forest)

- 9a Chestnut-Chestnut oak-Yellow poplar
- 9b Oak-Hickory
- 9c Oak-Pine

- 10 **E. Cypress-Tupelo-Red gum** (River bottom forest)
- 11 **F. Longleaf, Loblolly, Slash pine** (Southeastern pine forest)
- 12 **G. Mangrove** (Subtropical forest)

Miles: 0 50 100 200 300 400 500
Kilometers: 0 50 100 200 400 600 800

Scale 1:16 000 000; one inch to 250 miles. Polyconic Projection

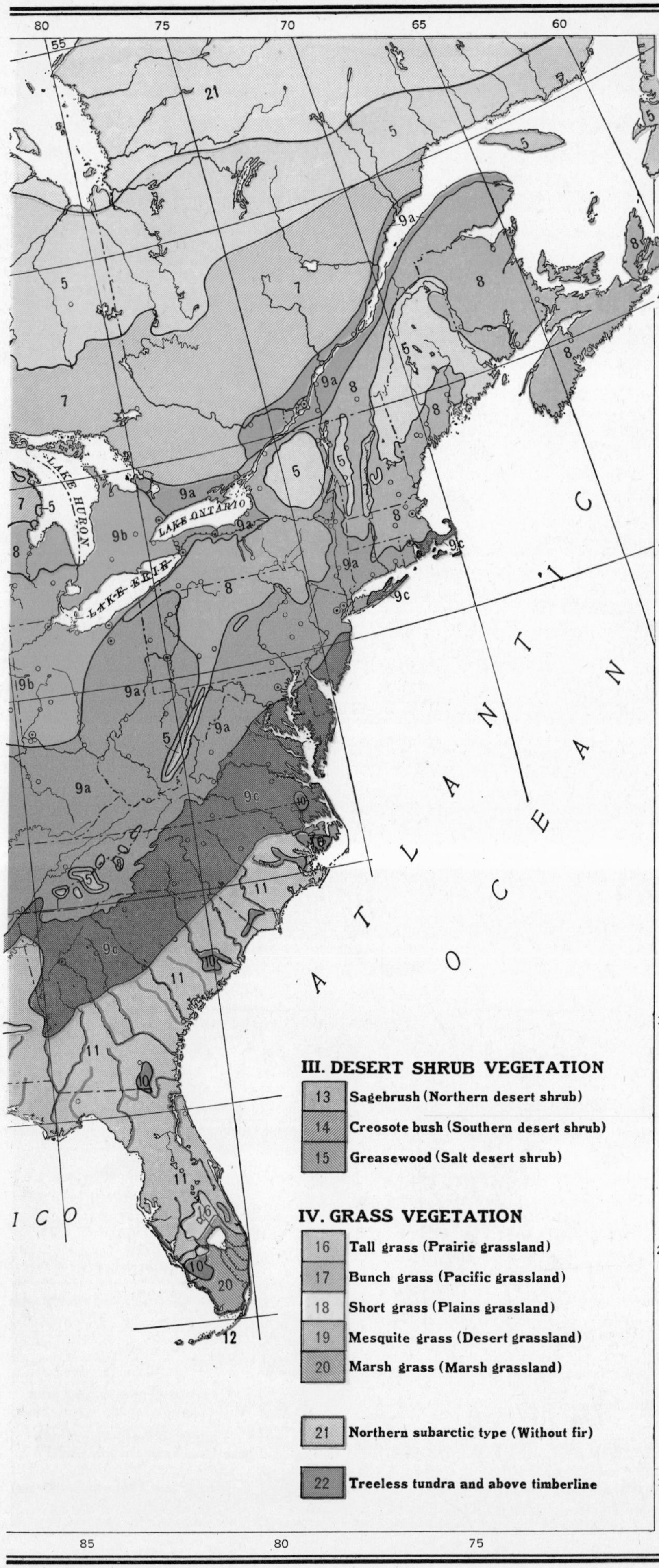
LAKE HURON
LAKE ONTARIO
LAKE ERIE
ATLANTIC OCEAN
III. DESERT SHRUB VEGETATION
13 Sagebrush (Northern desert shrub)
14 Creosote bush (Southern desert shrub)
15 Greasewood (Salt desert shrub)
IV. GRASS VEGETATION
16 Tall grass (Prairie grassland)
17 Bunch grass (Pacific grassland)
18 Short grass (Plains grassland)
19 Mesquite grass (Desert grassland)
20 Marsh grass (Marsh grassland)
21 Northern subarctic type (Without fir)
22 Treeless tundra and above timberline

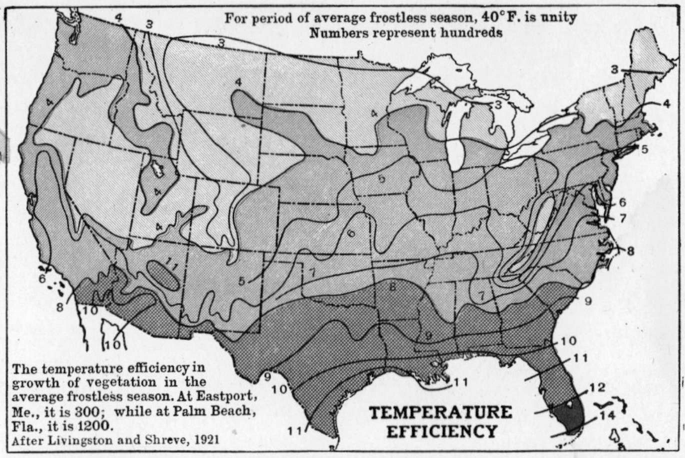
For period of average frostless season, 40°F. is unity
Numbers represent hundreds
The temperature efficiency in growth of vegetation in the average frostless season. At Eastport, Me., it is 300; while at Palm Beach, Fla., it is 1200.
After Livingston and Shreve, 1921
TEMPERATURE EFFICIENCY

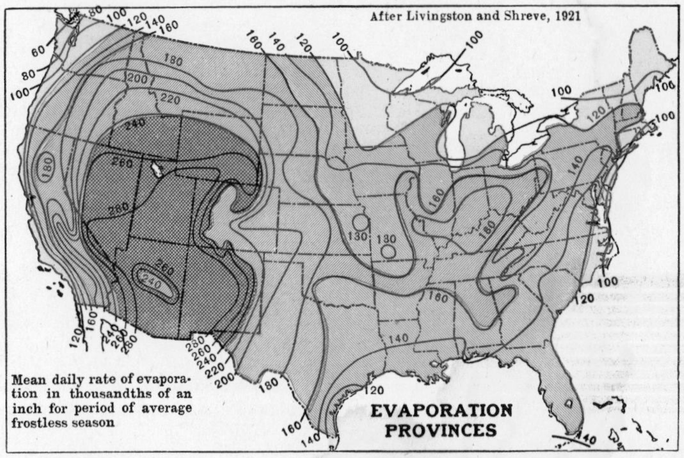
After Livingston and Shreve, 1921
Mean daily rate of evaporation in thousandths of an inch for period of average frostless season
EVAPORATION PROVINCES

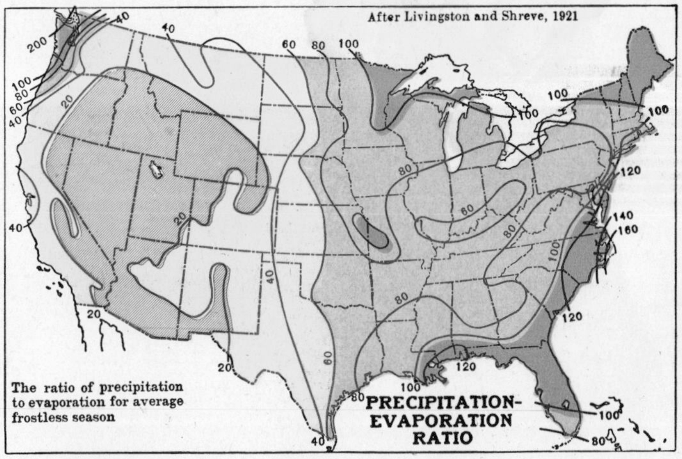
After Livingston and Shreve, 1921
The ratio of precipitation to evaporation for average frostless season
PRECIPITATION-EVAPORATION RATIO

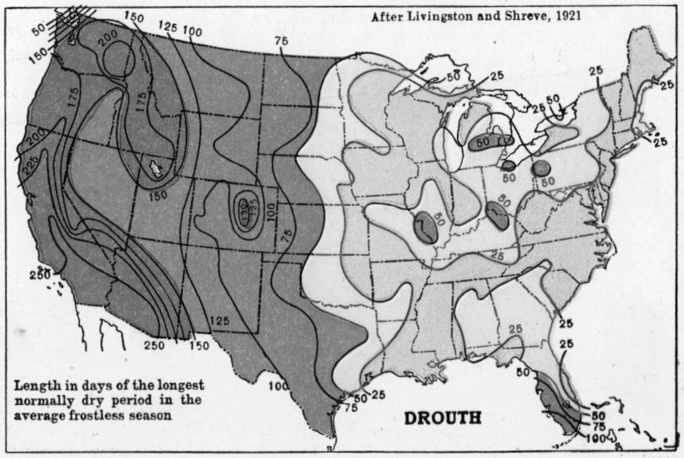
After Livingston and Shreve, 1921
Length in days of the longest normally dry period in the average frostless season
DROUTH

10R34

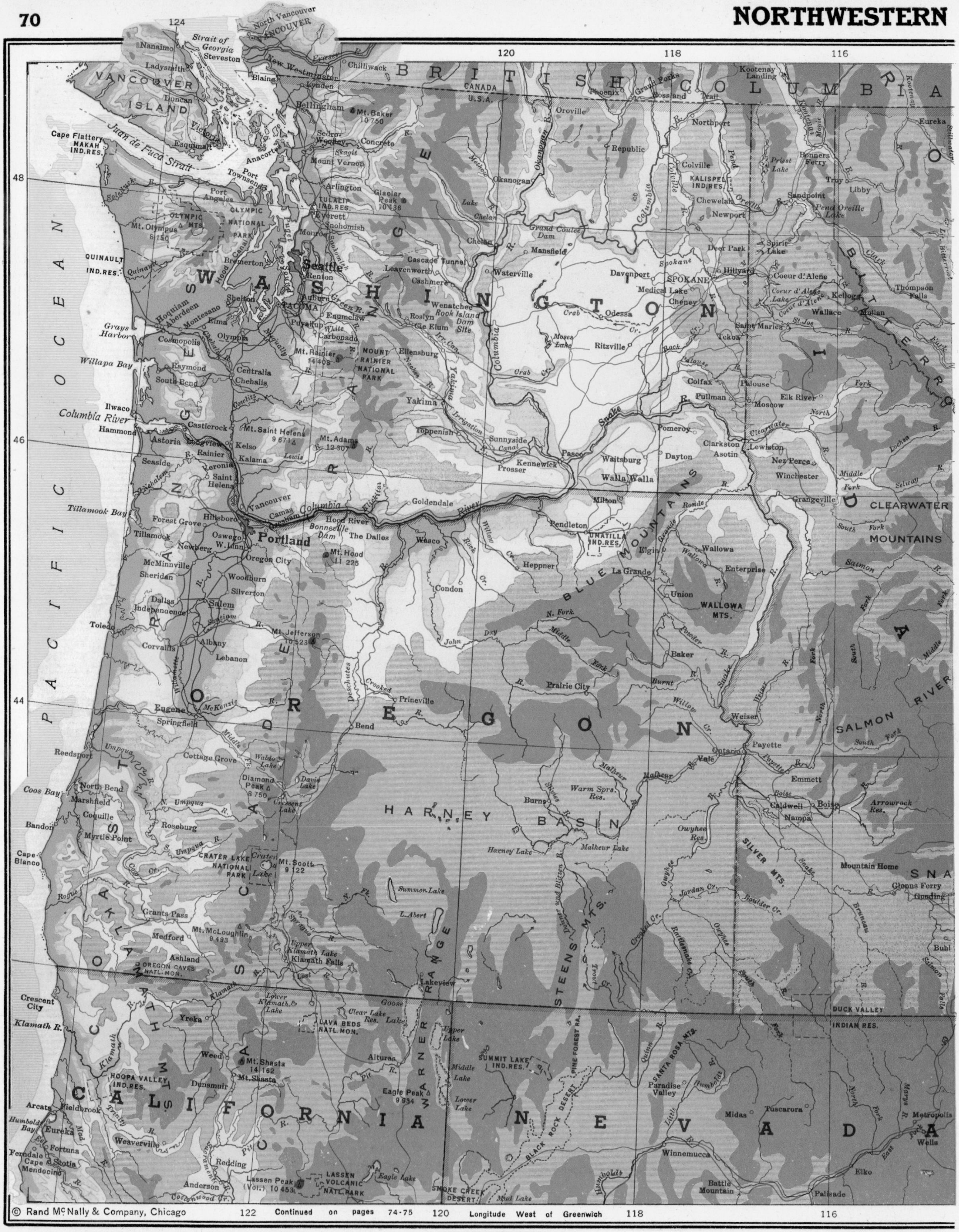

0 20 40 60 80 100 120 Miles

0 20 40 60 80 100 120 140 160 180 200 Kilometers

Scale 1:4 000 000; one inch to

Elevations and depressions

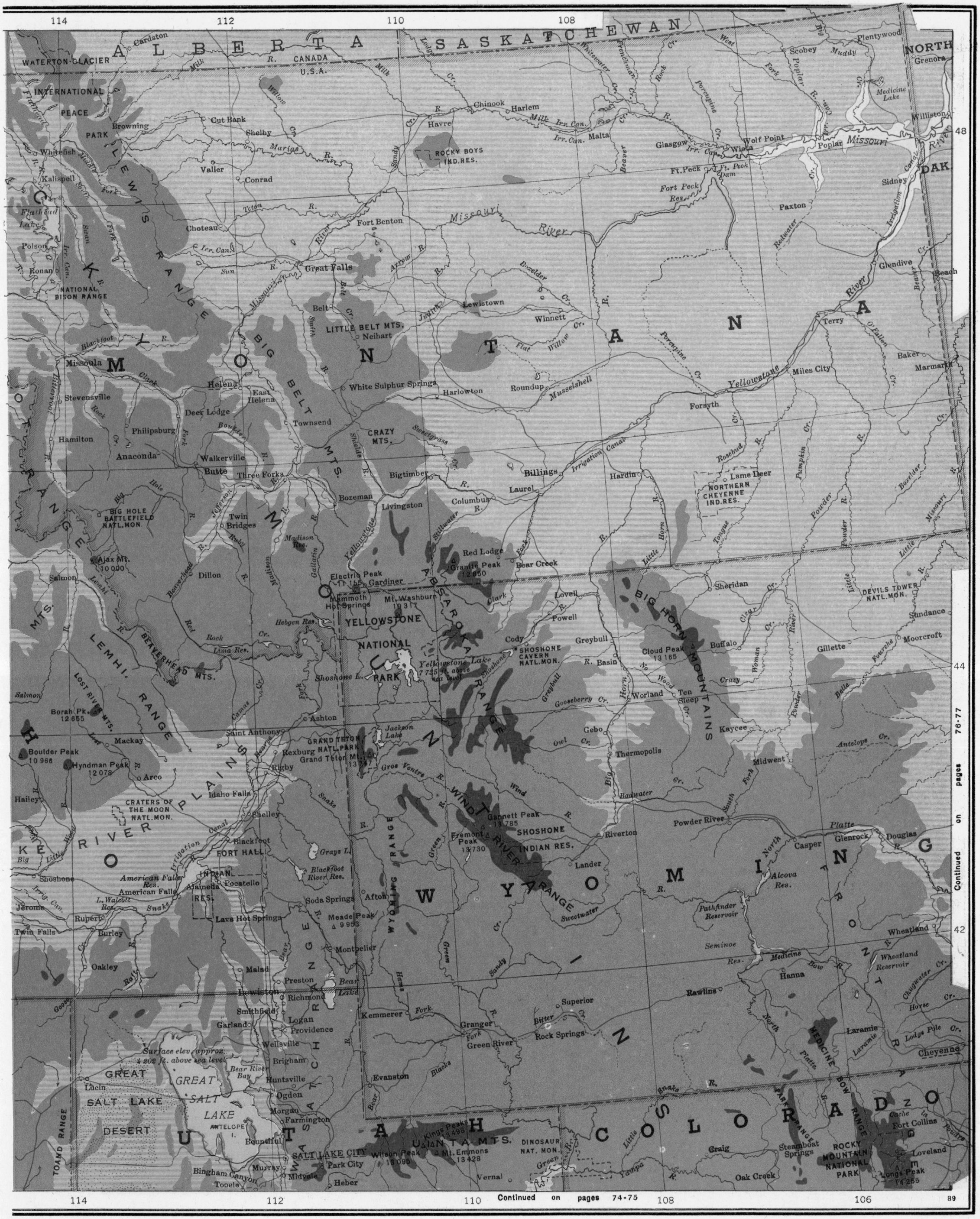

64 miles. Conic Projection

are given in feet

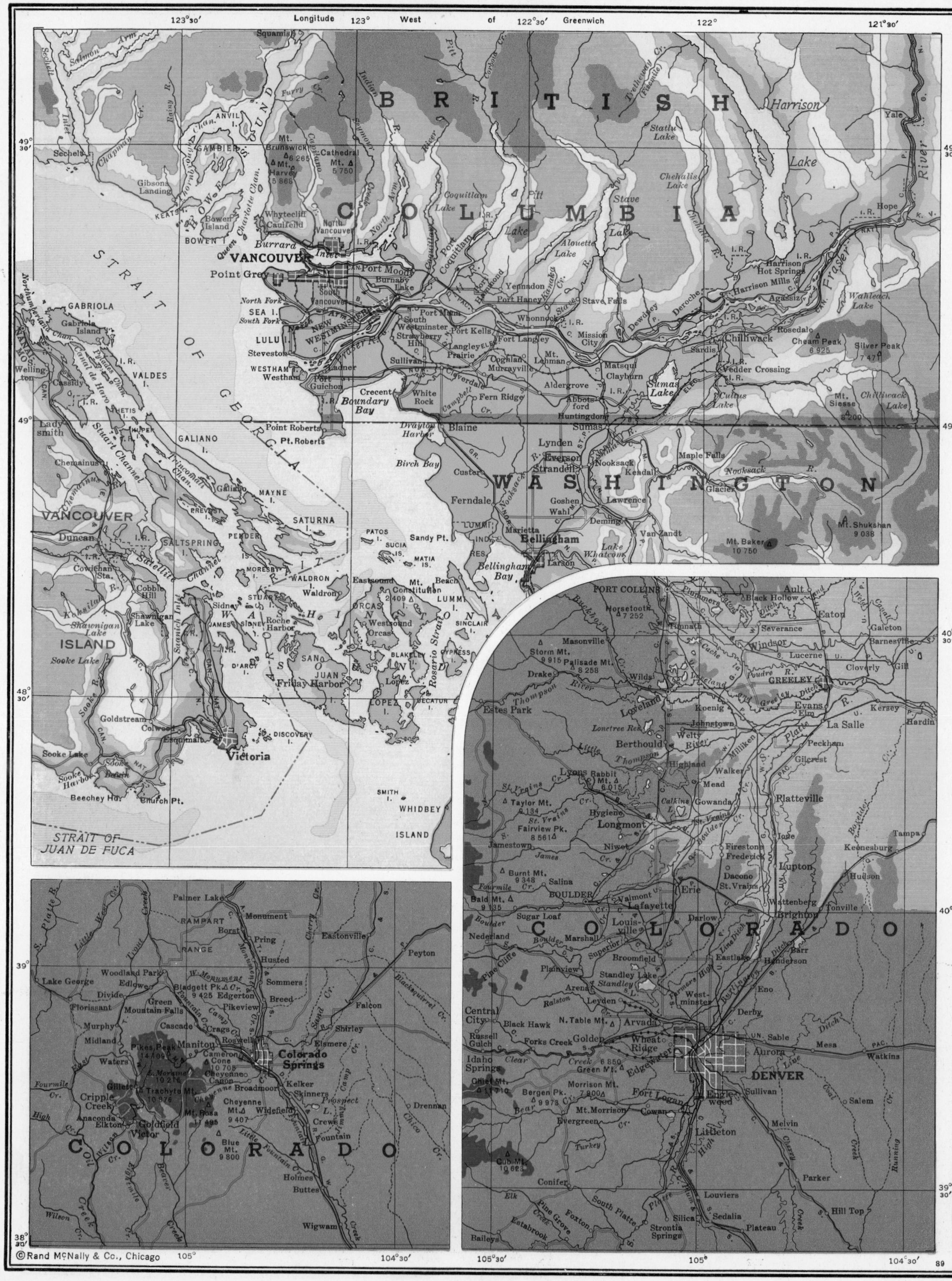

Scale 1:1 000 000; one inch to 16 miles

Elevations and depressions are given in feet

0 4 8 12 16 20 24 28 32 Miles

0 8 16 24 32 40 48 Kilometers

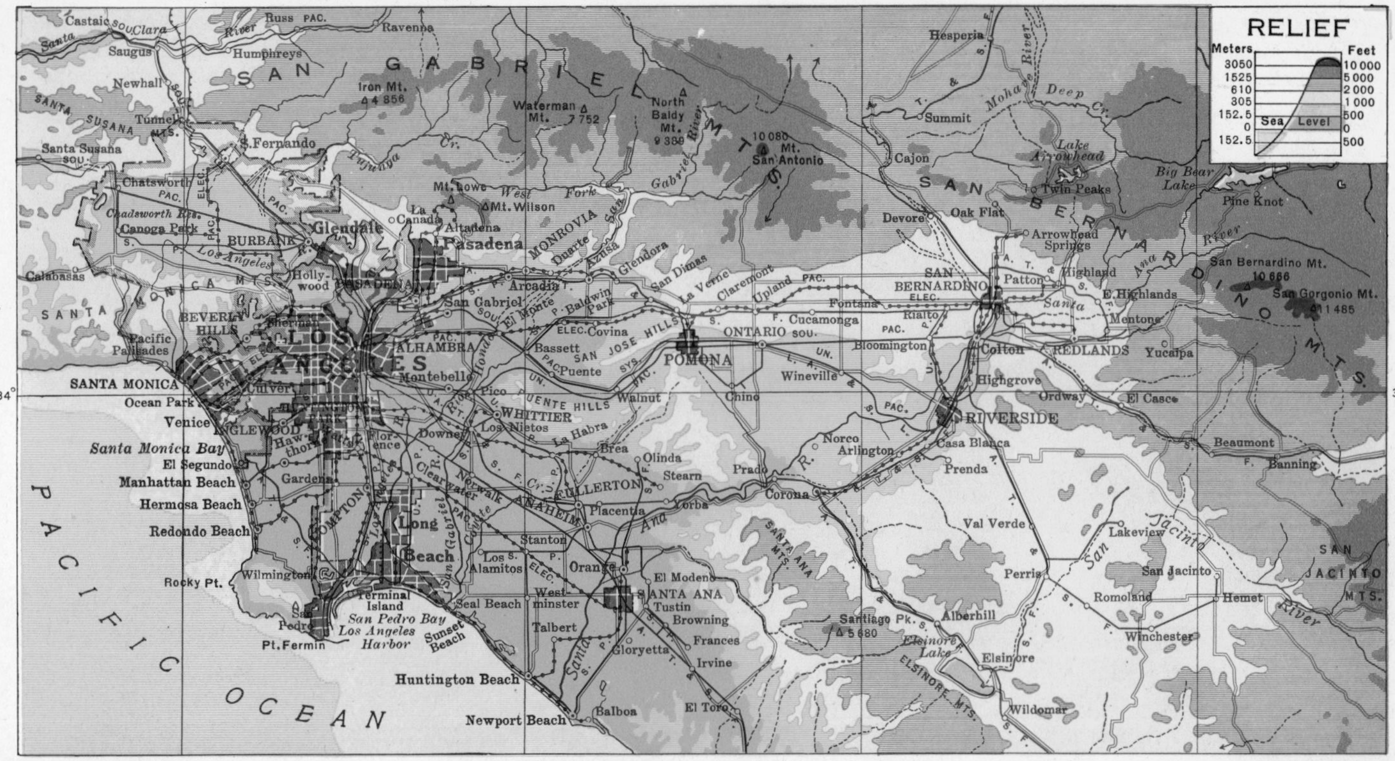

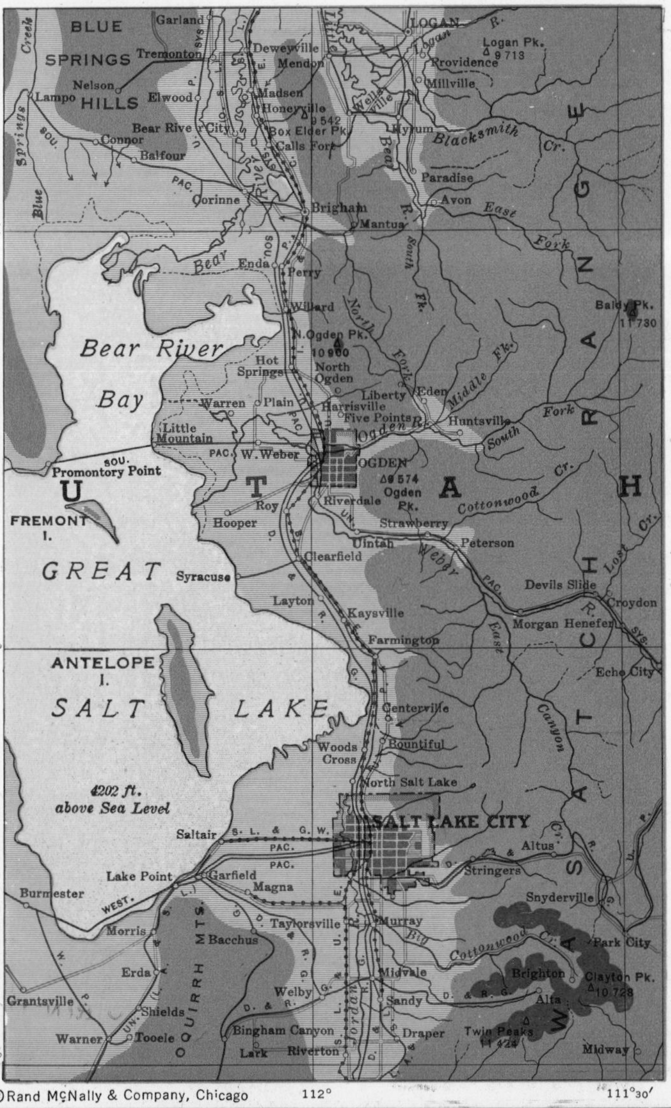

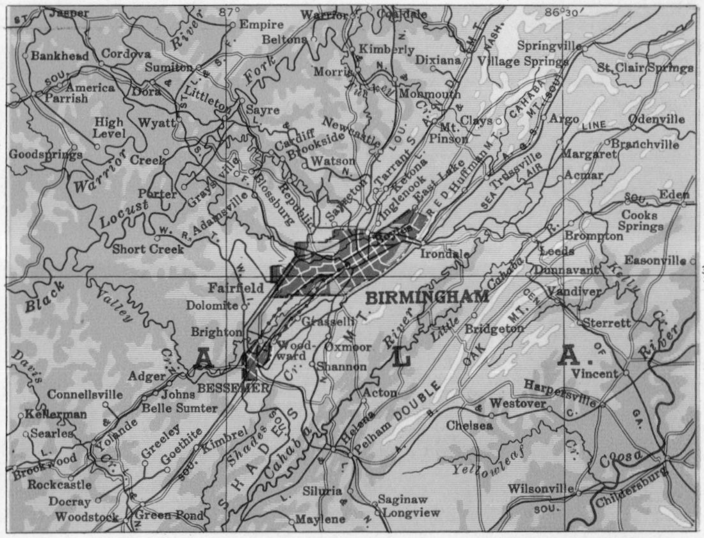

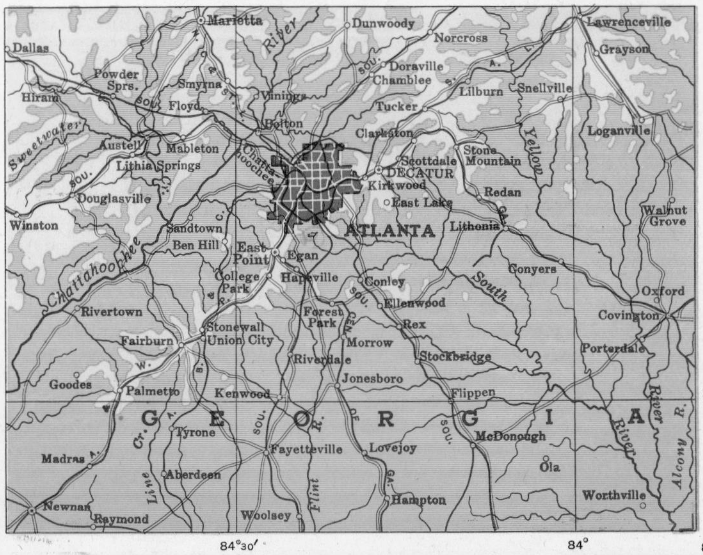

89

Scale 1 : 1 000 000; one inch to 16 miles

Miles 0 4 8 12 16 20 24 28 32

Kilometers 0 8 16 24 32 40 48

Elevations and depressions are given in feet

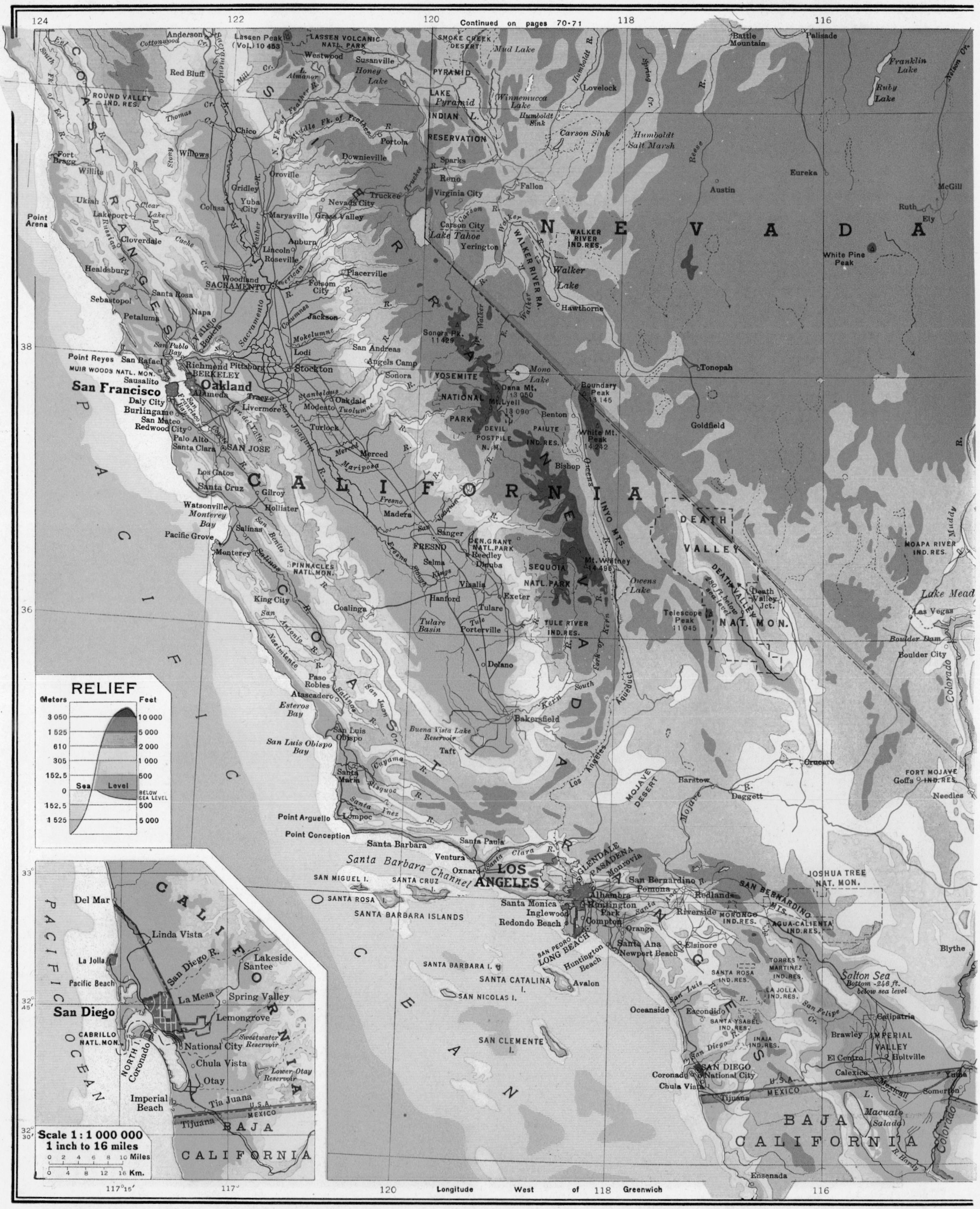

0 20 40 60 80 100 120 Miles

0 20 40 60 80 100 120 140 160 180 200 Kilometers

Scale 1 : 4 000 000; one inch to

Elevations and depressions

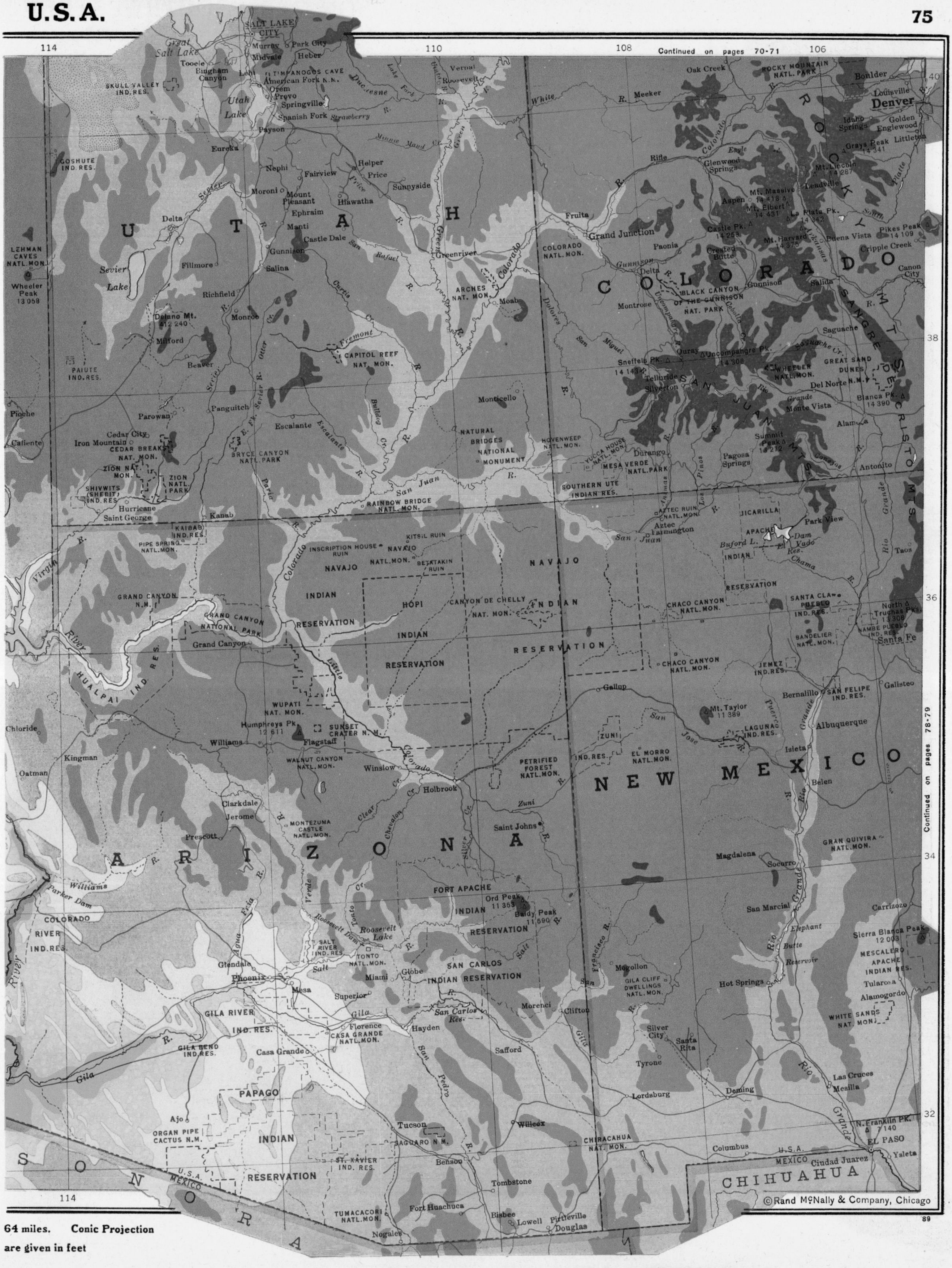

64 miles. Conic Projection

are given in feet

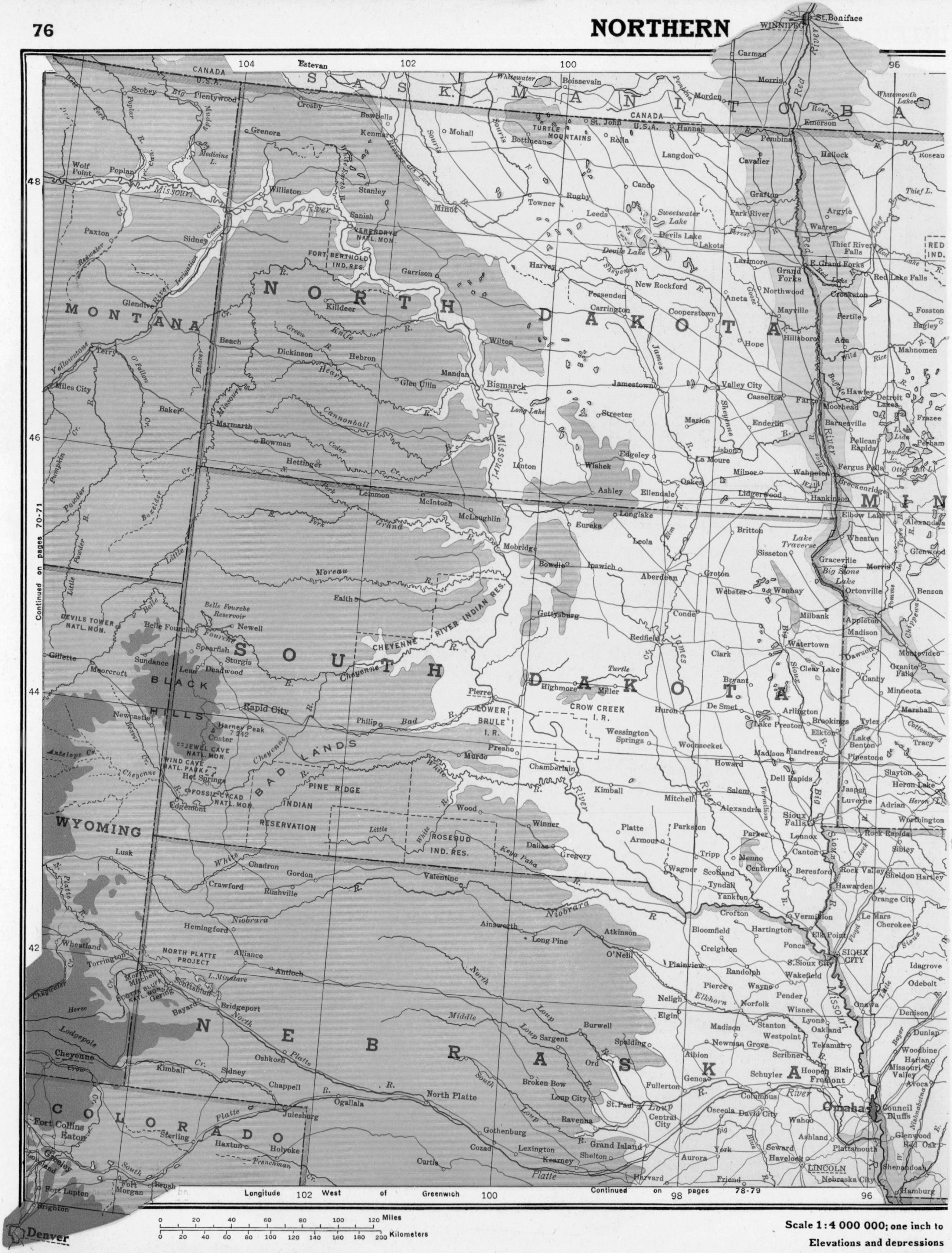

Scale 1:4 000 000; one inch to

Elevations and depressions

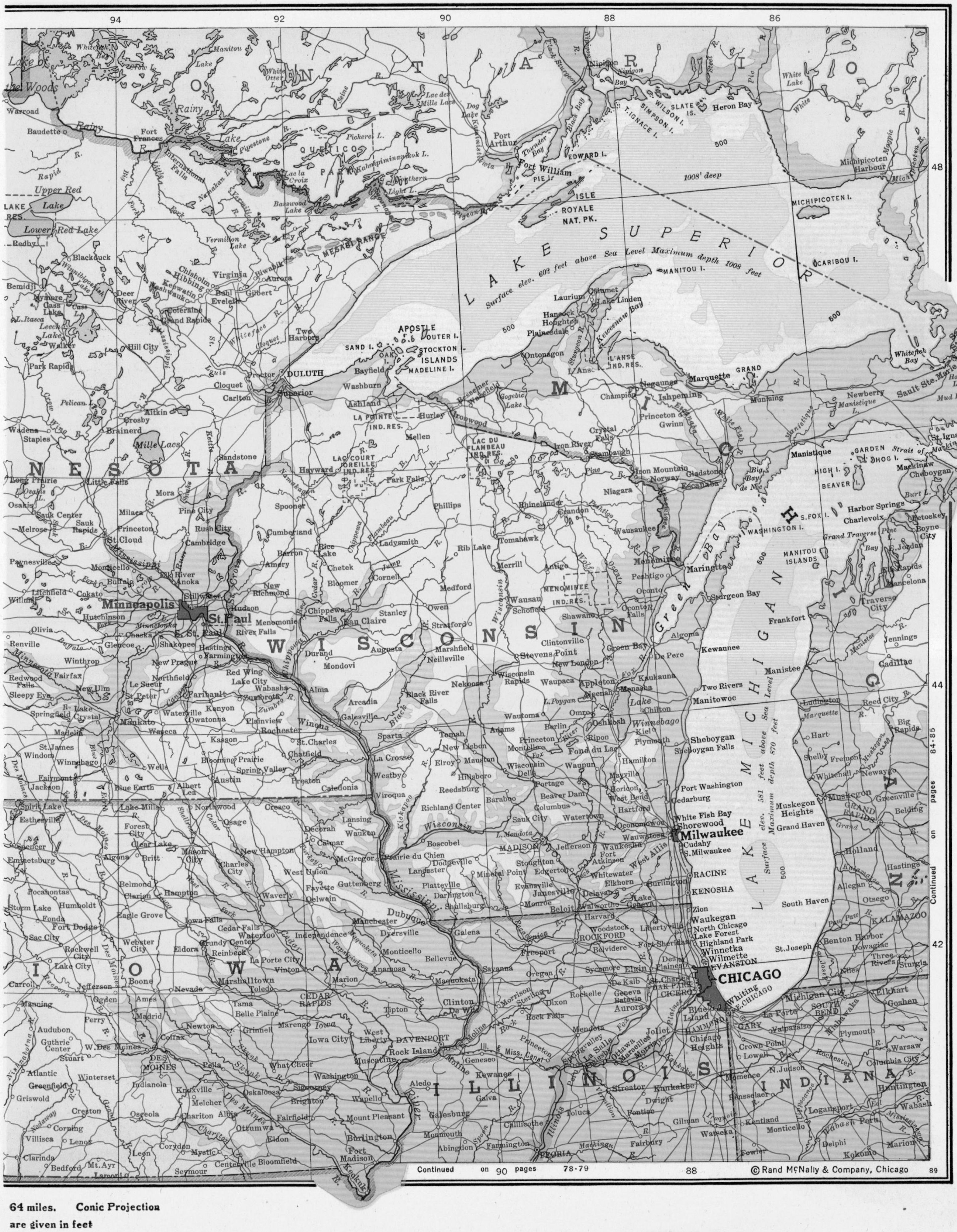

64 miles. Conic Projection

are given in feet

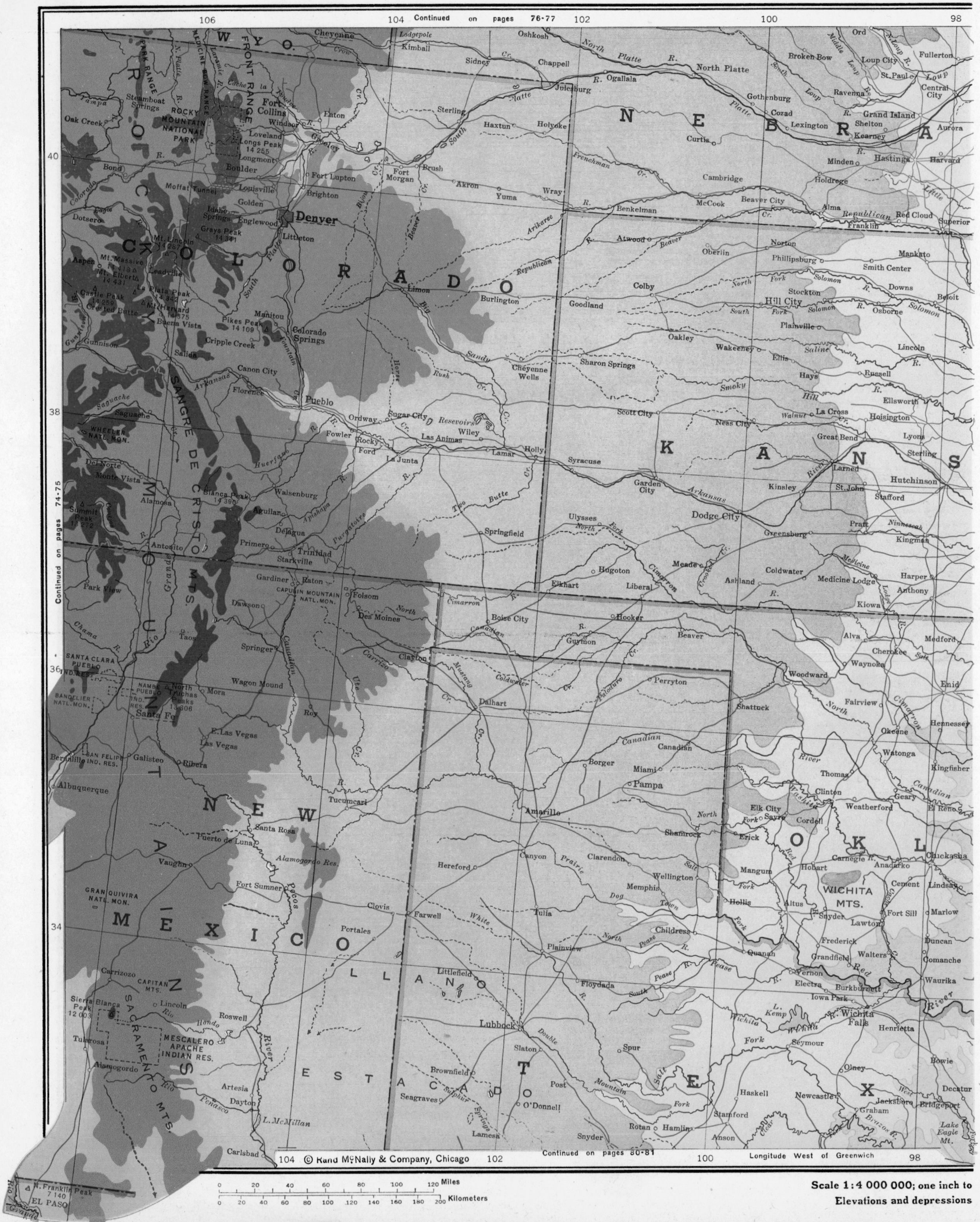

Scale 1 : 4 000 000; one inch to

Elevations and depressions

Continued on pages 76-77

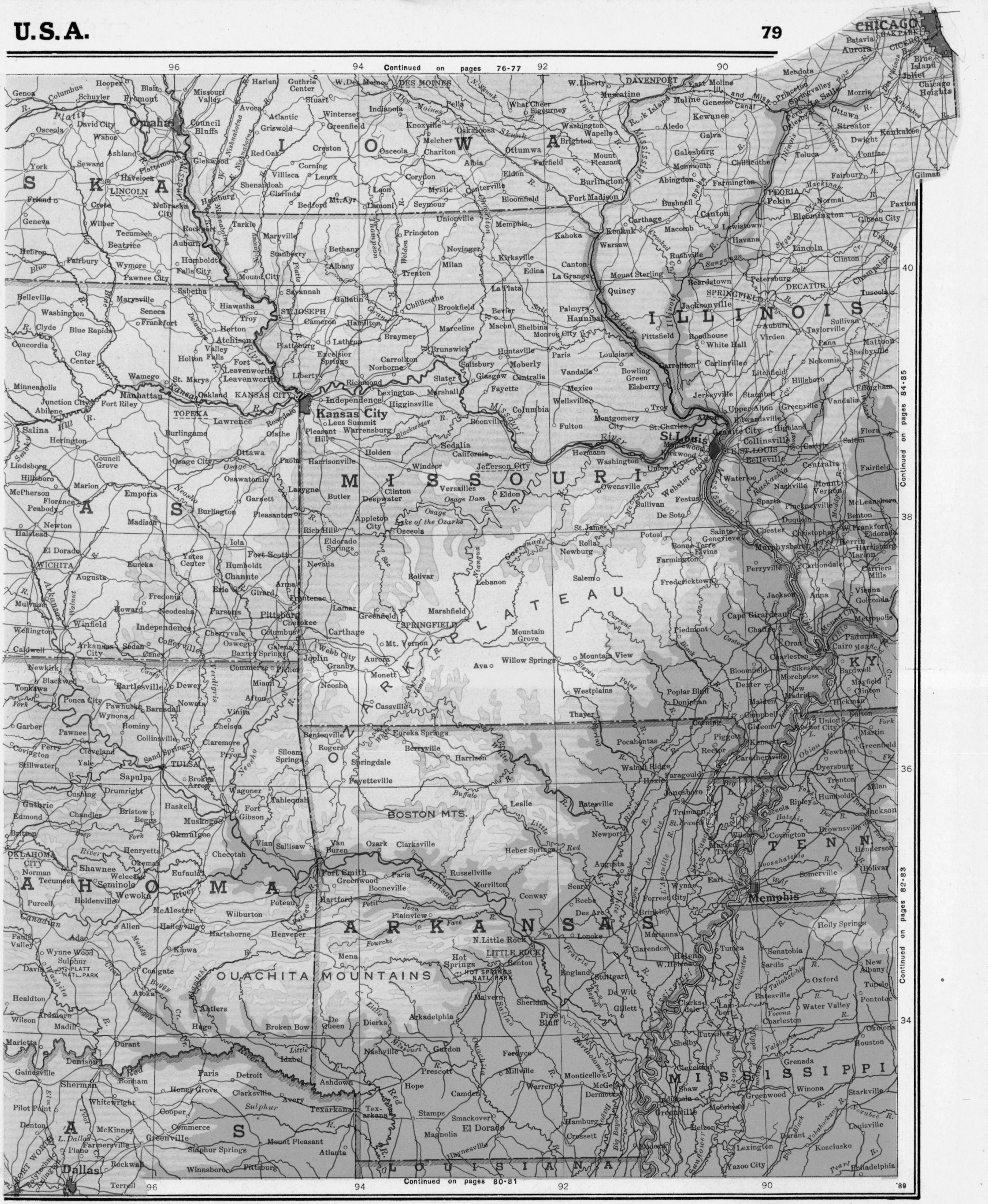

Continued on pages 84-85
Continued on pages 82-83
Continued on pages 80-81

64 miles. Conic Projection
are given in feet

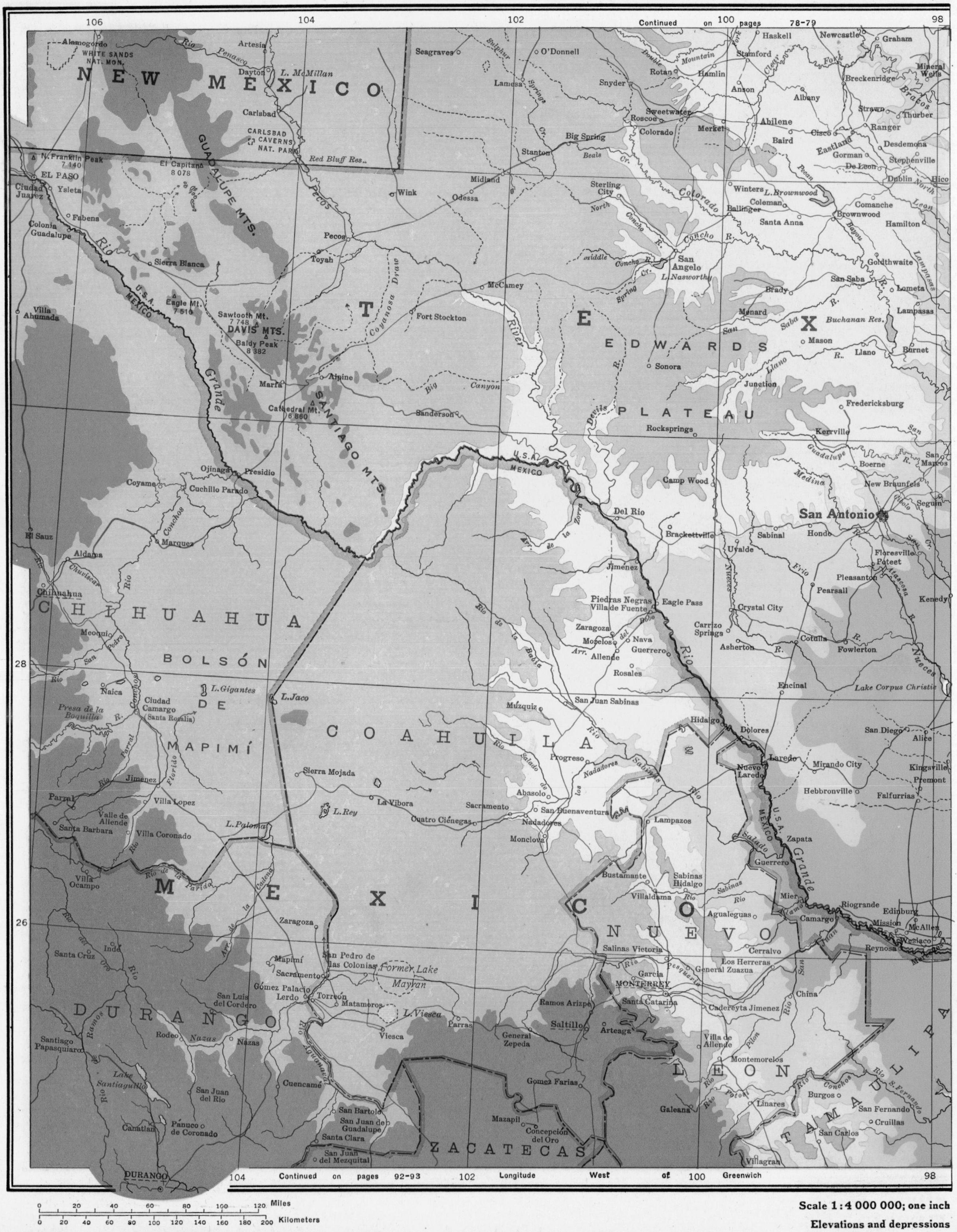

0 20 40 60 80 100 120 Miles

0 20 40 60 80 100 120 140 160 180 200 Kilometers

Scale 1:4 000 000; one inch

Elevations and depressions

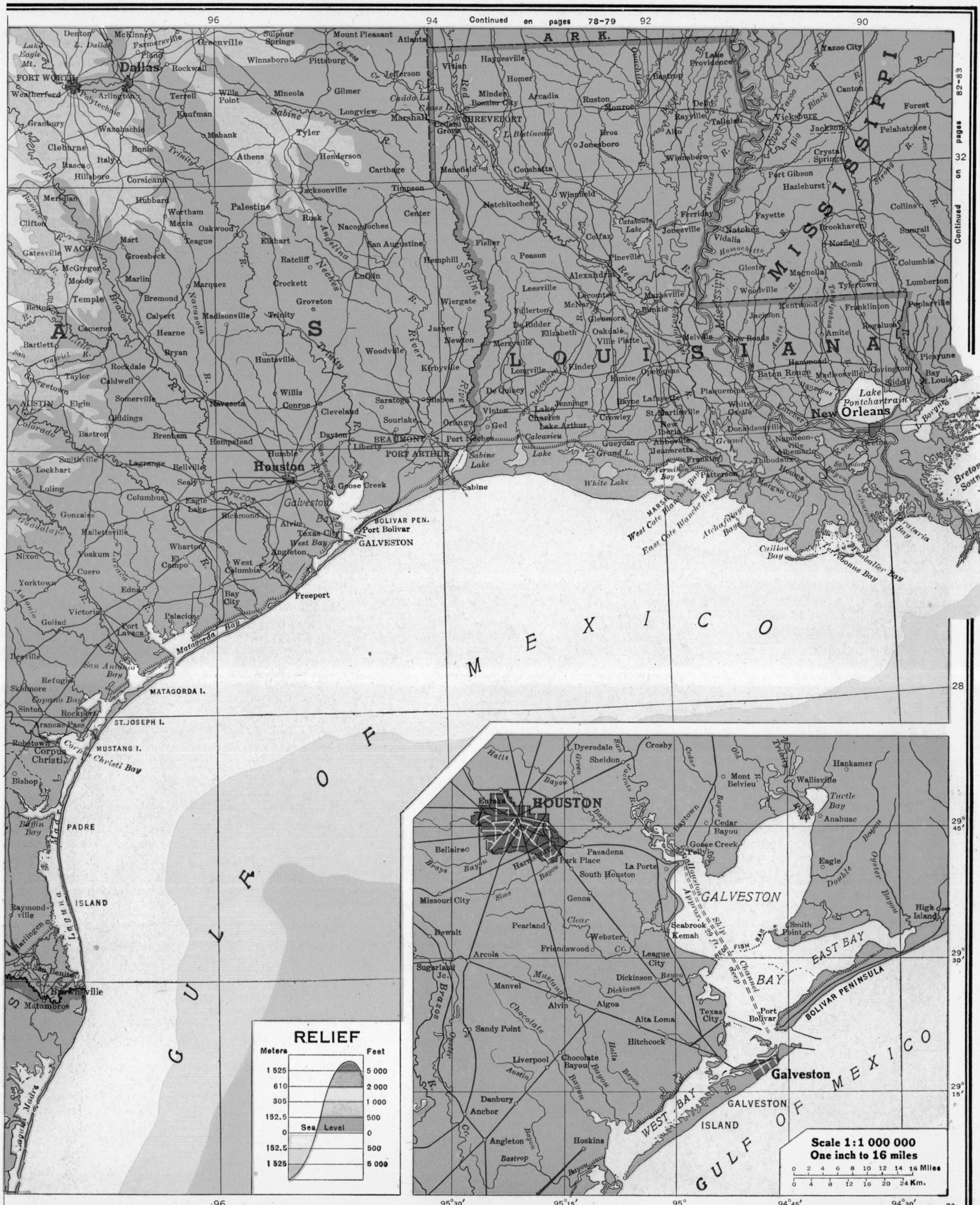

to 64 miles. Conic Projection

are given in feet

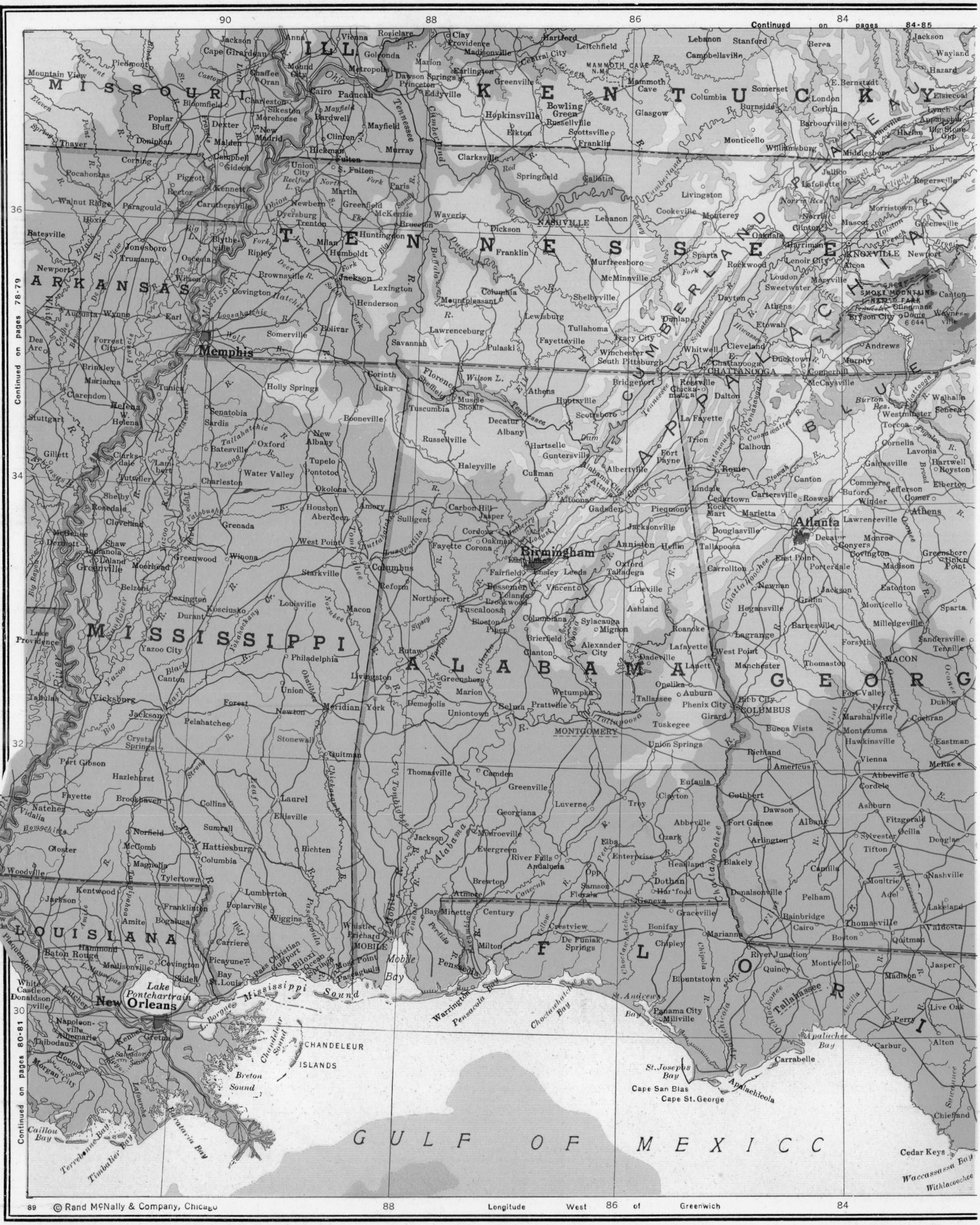

0 20 40 60 80 100 120 Miles
0 20 40 60 80 100 120 140 160 180 200 Kilometers

Scale 1:4 000 000; one inch to

Elevations and depressions

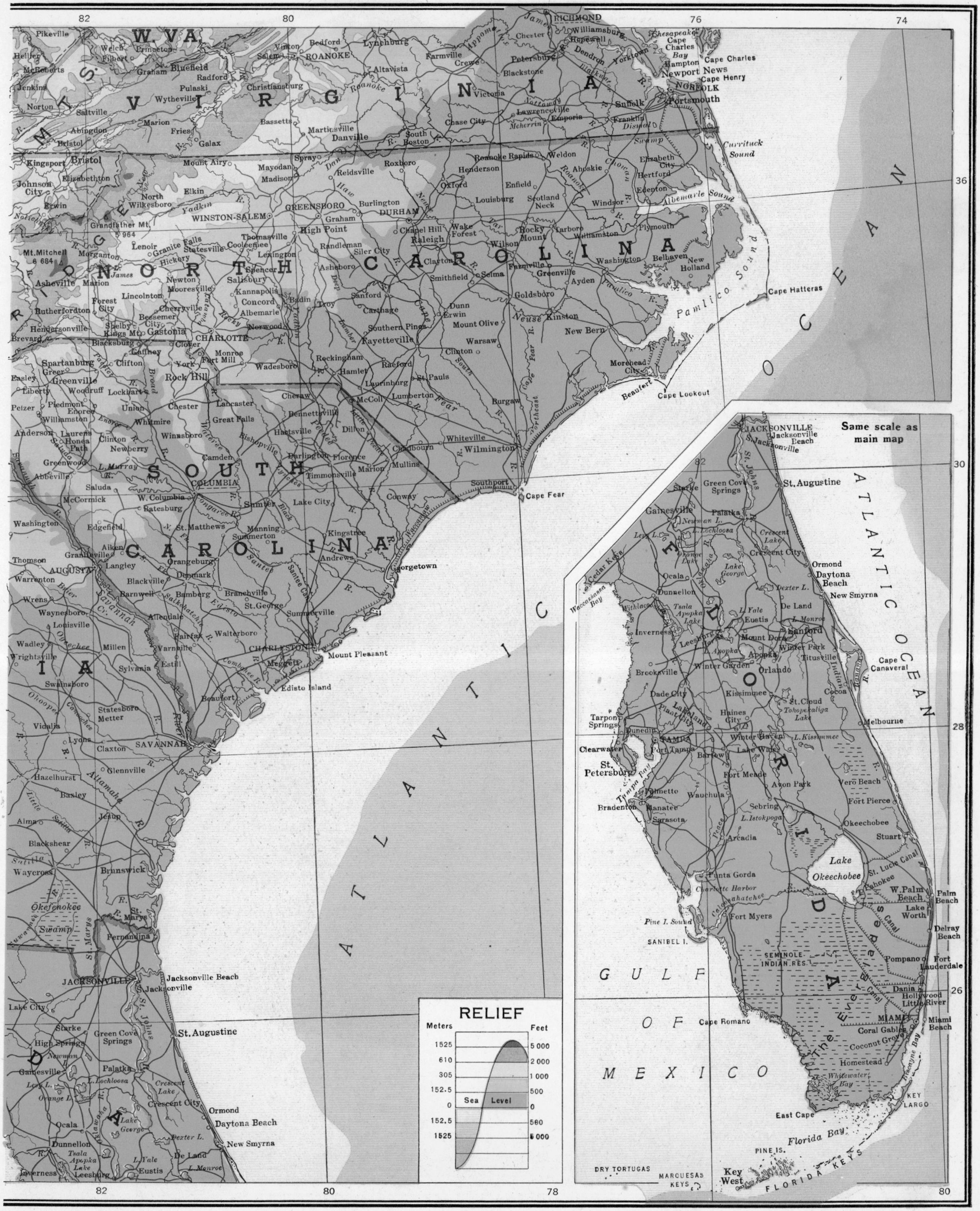
W. VA.
V I R G I N I A
N O R T H C A R O L I N A
S O U T H C A R O L I N A
F L O R I D A
A T L A N T I C
A T L A N T I C O C E A N
G U L F O F M E X I C O
RICHMOND
Petersburg
Williamsburg
Newport News
NORFOLK
Portsmouth
Cape Charles
Cape Henry
Lynchburg
ROANOKE
Danville
Bluefield
Bristol
Kingsport
Johnson City
Currituck Sound
Albemarle Sound
Pamlico Sound
Cape Hatteras
Cape Lookout
Cape Fear
WINSTON-SALEM
GREENSBORO
DURHAM
Raleigh
High Point
Asheville
Mt.Mitchell 6 684
Grandfather Mt. 5 964
CHARLOTTE
Gastonia
Fayetteville
Wilmington
New Bern
Morehead City
Beaufort
Spartanburg
Greenville
Rock Hill
COLUMBIA
Florence
Sumter
Georgetown
CHARLESTON
Mount Pleasant
Edisto Island
Beaufort
AUGUSTA
SAVANNAH
Brunswick
Waycross
Okefenokee Swamp
Fernandina
JACKSONVILLE
Jacksonville Beach
St. Augustine
Gainesville
Palatka
Ocala
Ormond
Daytona Beach
New Smyrna
De Land
Leesburg
Inverness
Same scale as main map
Orlando
Sanford
Cape Canaveral
Titusville
Cocoa
Melbourne
TAMPA
St. Petersburg
Clearwater
Tarpon Springs
Lakeland
Bradenton
Sarasota
Vero Beach
Fort Pierce
Stuart
Lake Okeechobee
St. Lucie Canal
W. Palm Beach
Palm Beach
Lake Worth
Delray Beach
Fort Lauderdale
Hollywood
MIAMI
Miami Beach
Coral Gables
Coconut Grove
Homestead
Fort Myers
Punta Gorda
Charlotte Harbor
SANIBEL I.
SEMINOLE INDIAN RES.
Cape Romano
East Cape
Florida Bay
KEY LARGO
FLORIDA KEYS
Key West
MARQUESAS KEYS
DRY TORTUGAS
PINE IS.
RELIEF
Meters
Feet
1525
610
305
152.5
0
152.5
1525
5 000
2 000
1 000
500
0
500
5 000
Sea Level
82
80
78
76
74
36
30
28
26

PART OF

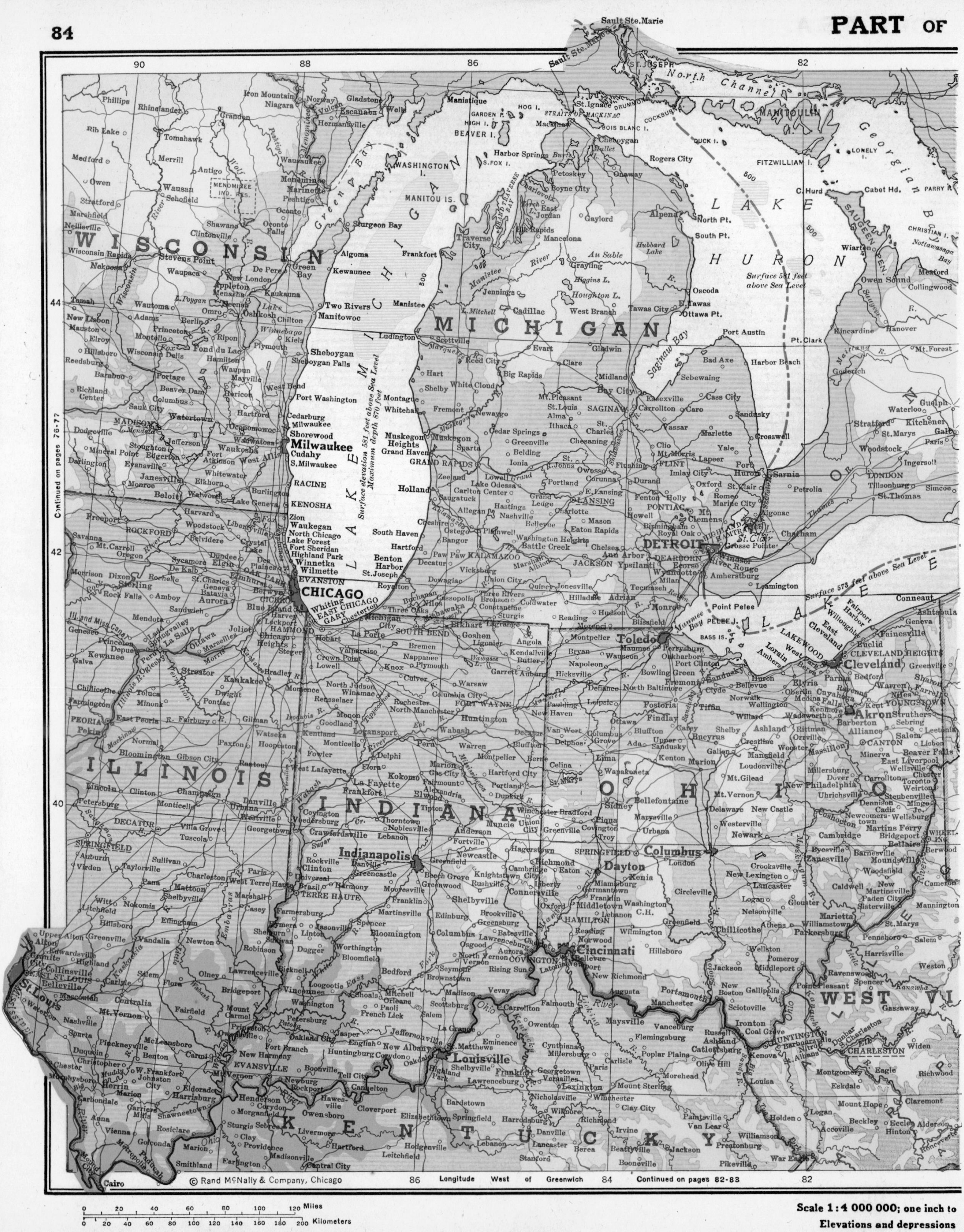

Scale 1 : 4 000 000; one inch to

Elevations and depressions

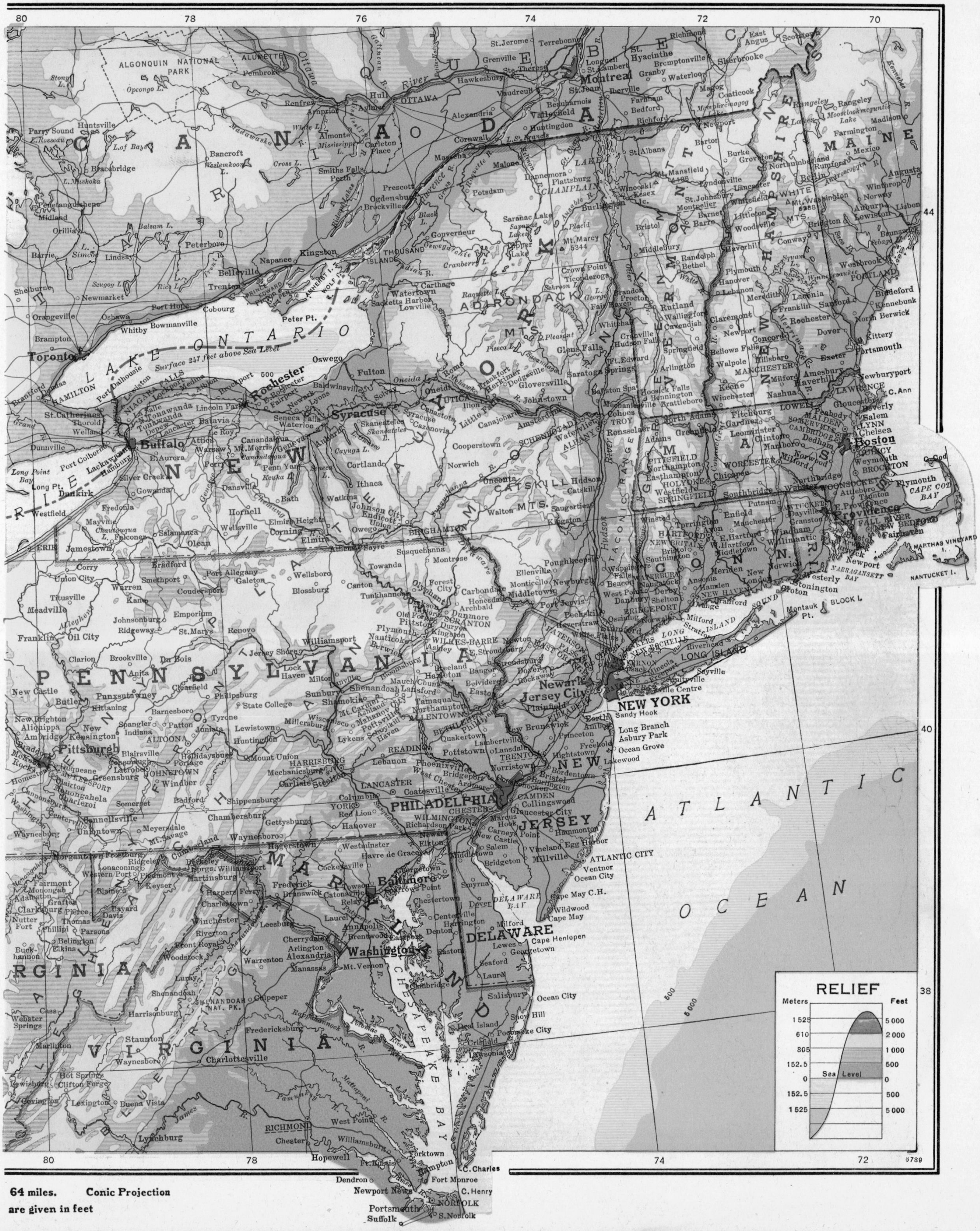

64 miles. Conic Projection

are given in feet

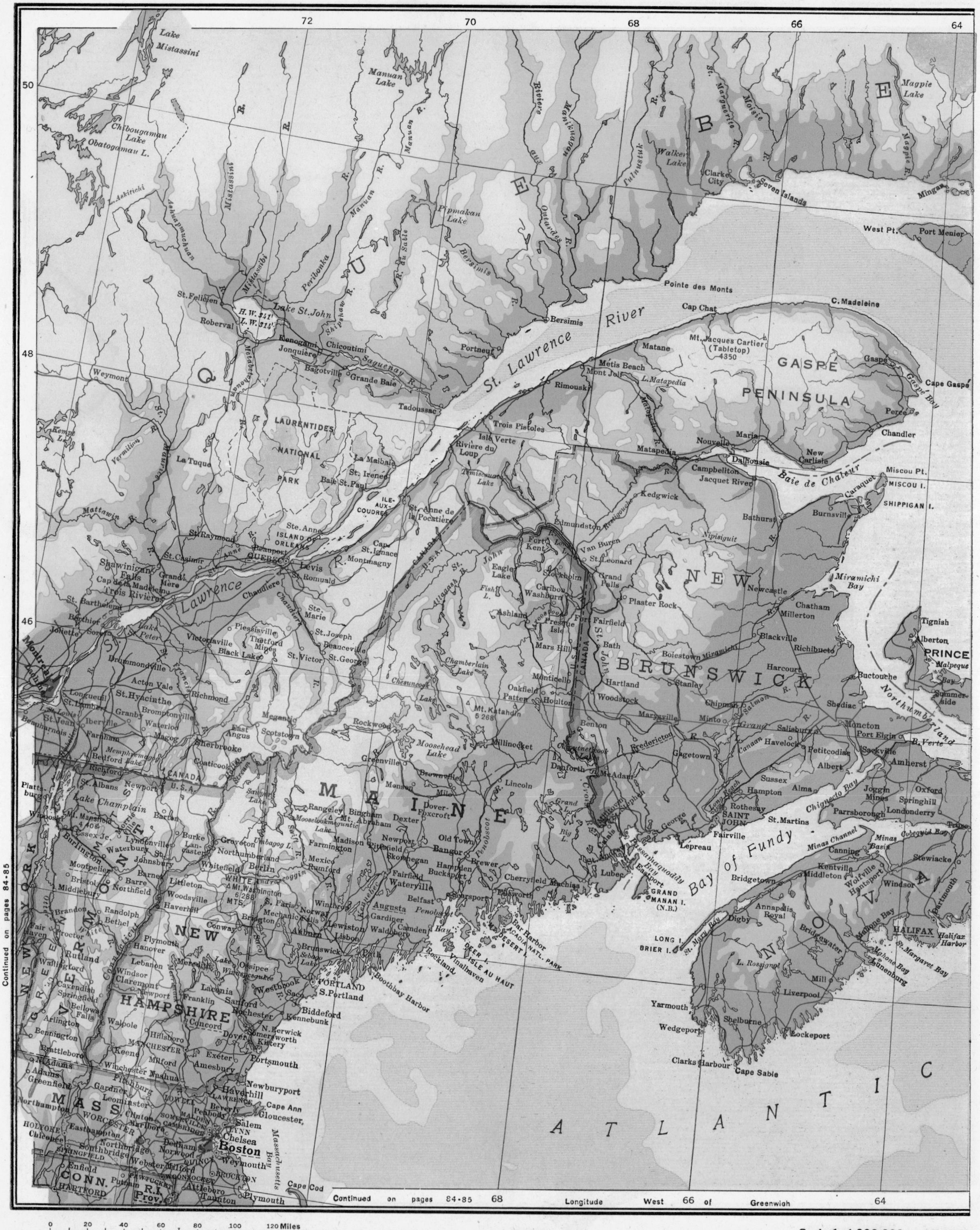

Continued on pages 84-85

Continued on pages 84-85

Scale 1:4 000 000; one inch to

Elevations and depressions

RELIEF

Meters	Feet
1 525	5 000
610	2 000
305	1 000
152.5	500
0 Sea Level	0
152.5	500
1 525	5 000

COAST OF LABRADOR (Newfoundland)
Strait of Belle Isle
C. Norman
Pistolet Bay
C. Bauld
GREENLY I.
SANDY I.
OUTER I.
Robertson L.
MECATINA I.
Mutton Bay
Pt. Ferolle
Hare Bay
GROAIS I.
BELL I.
Chimney Bay
Blue Mt. 2 085
L. Michel
LONG RANGE
2 075
ST. MARY IS.
Natashkwan
Romaine
Muskwaro Lake
ST. BARBE IS.
White Bay
Cape St. John
ANTICOSTI ISLAND (Quebec)
Jupiter R.
Heath Pt.
Notre Dame Bay
Twillingate
TWILLINGATE I.
FOGO
Fogo I.
C. Freels
Bonne Bay
Gros Morne 2 540
Mt. St. Gregory 2 240
Deer Lake
Deer L.
Sandy L.
Bay of Islands
Grand Lake
Hodges Hill 2 200
Lewisporte
Botwood Harbour
Grand Falls
Gander Lake
Glenwood
Rushy Pond
Millertown
Exploits R.
Gander R.
Humbermouth
Long Pt.
Port au Port Bay
SIR JOHN H. GLOVER I.
Red Indian Lake
Bonavista Bay
Bonavista
GULF OF ST. LAWRENCE
C. St. George
St. George Bay
St. Georges
Robinsons
NEWFOUNDLAND
Crooked Lake
Round Pond
Meelpaeg Lake
Trinity
Smith Sd.
RANDOM I.
Trinity Bay
Grates Pt.
Heart's Content
Carbonear
Harbor Grace
Conception Bay
Bay Roberts
Brigus
Torbay
St. Johns
C. Spear
C. Anguille
BRION I.
BIRD ROCK
C. Ray
Port au Basque
La Poile Bay
White Bear Bay
Hermitage Bay
Belle Bay
Harbour Breton
Fortune Bay
MERASHEEN I.
Placentia
Placentia Bay
Ferryland
Cabot Strait
MAGDALEN ISLANDS (Quebec)
ST. PAUL I.
BRUNETTE I.
GREAT MIQUELON (Fr.)
LITTLE MIQUELON (Fr.)
ST. PIERRE (Fr.)
Grand Bank
Burin
St. Marys Bay
Trepassey
C. Pine
C. Race
Cape North
Aspy Bay
EDWARD ISLAND
Souris
Charlottetown
Georgetown
Inverness
St. Ann Bay
Sydney Mines
New Waterford
Dominion
Glace Bay
N. Sydney
CAPE BRETON ISLAND
SCATARI I.
Louisburg
L. Ainslie
Port Hood
Strait
Strait of Canso
Bras d'Or Lake
St. Peters
Pictou
Trenton
Antigonish
George Bay
Port Hawkesbury
Westville
Stellarton
New Glasgow
Harbour au Bouche
Mulgrave
Arichat
MADAME I.
Chedabucto Bay
Canso
Cape Canso
Guysborough
Cole Harbour
SCOTIA
OCEAN
SABLE I. (N. S.)

Scale 1:1 000 000
One inch to 16 miles
0 4 8 12 16 Miles
0 4 8 12 16 20 24 Km.
Railways
Roads

Merrimac
Amesbury
Salisbury
Merrimack R.
Haverhill
Newburyport
W. Newbury
Newbury
Groveland
N.H. MASS.
Methuen
Georgetown
Rowley
Lawrence
Dracut
N. Andover
Ipswich
Rockport
Townsend
Pepperell
Tyngsboro
Lowell
Andover
Hamilton
Essex
FITCHBURG
Groton
Tewksbury
Middleton
Wenham
Gloucester
Lunenburg
Shirley
Ayer
Westford
Chelmsford
N. Reading
Beverly
Manchester
Billerica
Wilmington
Danvers
Reading
Leominster
Harvard
Littleton
Stoneham
Wakefield
SALEM
Peabody
Woburn
Winchester
Melrose
Saugus
Marblehead
Swampscott
Bedford
Acton
Lancaster
Maynard
Concord
Lexington
Medford
Malden
Lynn
Sterling
Clinton
Stow
Lincoln
Arlington
Somerville
Nahant
REVERE
Hudson
Sudbury
WALTHAM
Cambridge
Chelsea
Winthrop
W. Boylston
Wayland
Watertown
BOSTON
Marlboro
Weston
Newton
Holden
Northboro
Wellesley
Needham
BROOKLINE
Hull
Southboro
Worcester
Shrewsbury
Framingham
Natick
Quincy
Westboro
Ashland
Sherborn
Dedham
Milton
Cohasset
Millbury
Grafton
Hopkinton
Westwood
Braintree
Hingham
Weymouth
Upton
Holliston
Medfield
Norwood
Randolph
Scituate
Auburn
Sutton
Northbridge
Medway
Millis
Walpole
Canton
Holbrook
Norwell
Rockland
Oxford
Hopedale
Milford
Norfolk
Sharon
Stoughton
Avon
Hanover
Abington
Webster
Douglas
Uxbridge
Bellingham
Franklin
Wrentham
Foxboro
Brockton
Whitman
Hanson
Marshfield
Pembroke
MASSACHUSETTS BAY
42° 30′
71°
71° 30′
62
60
58
54
50
46

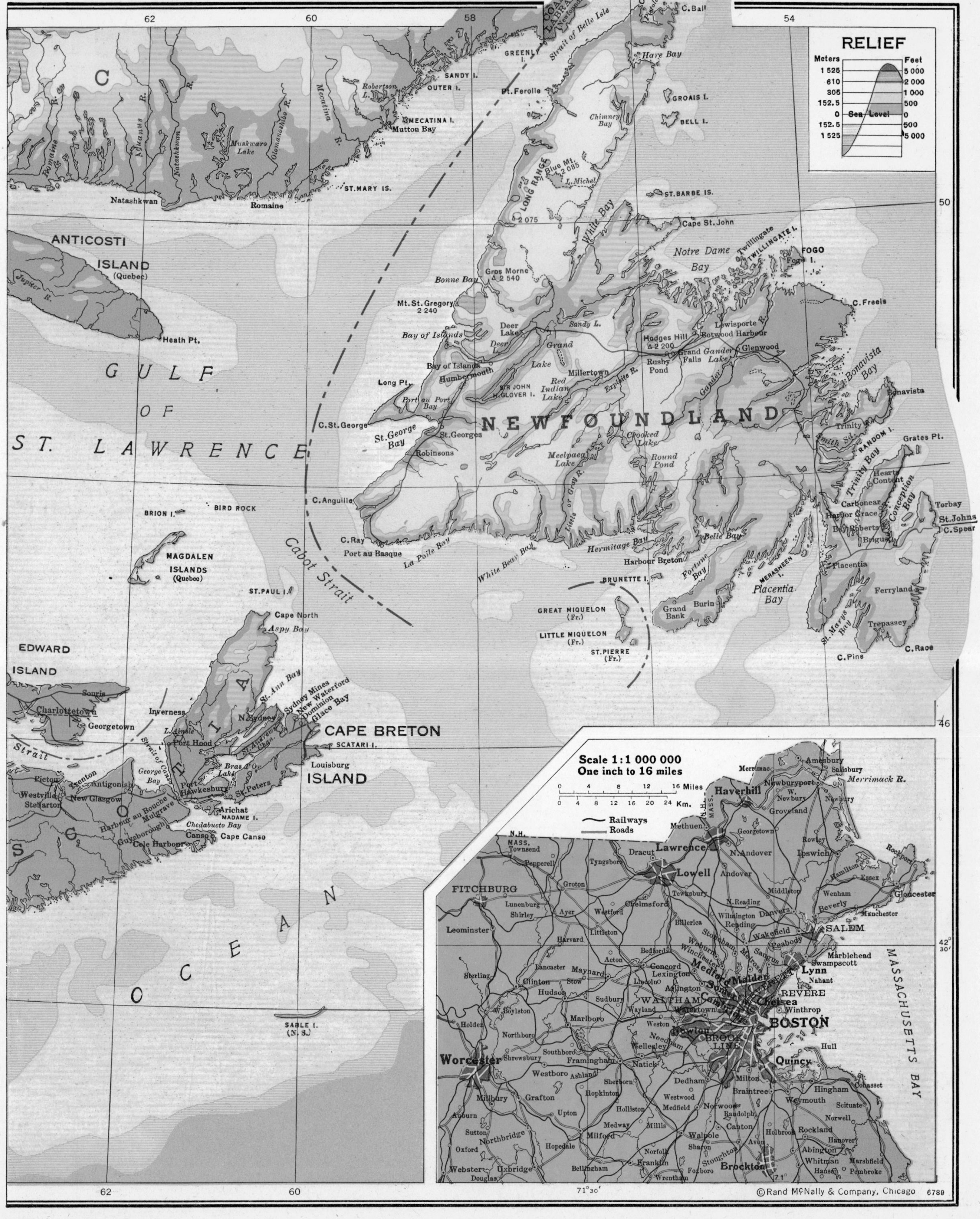

64 miles. Conic Projection

are given in feet

U. S. A.– Cities and their Environs

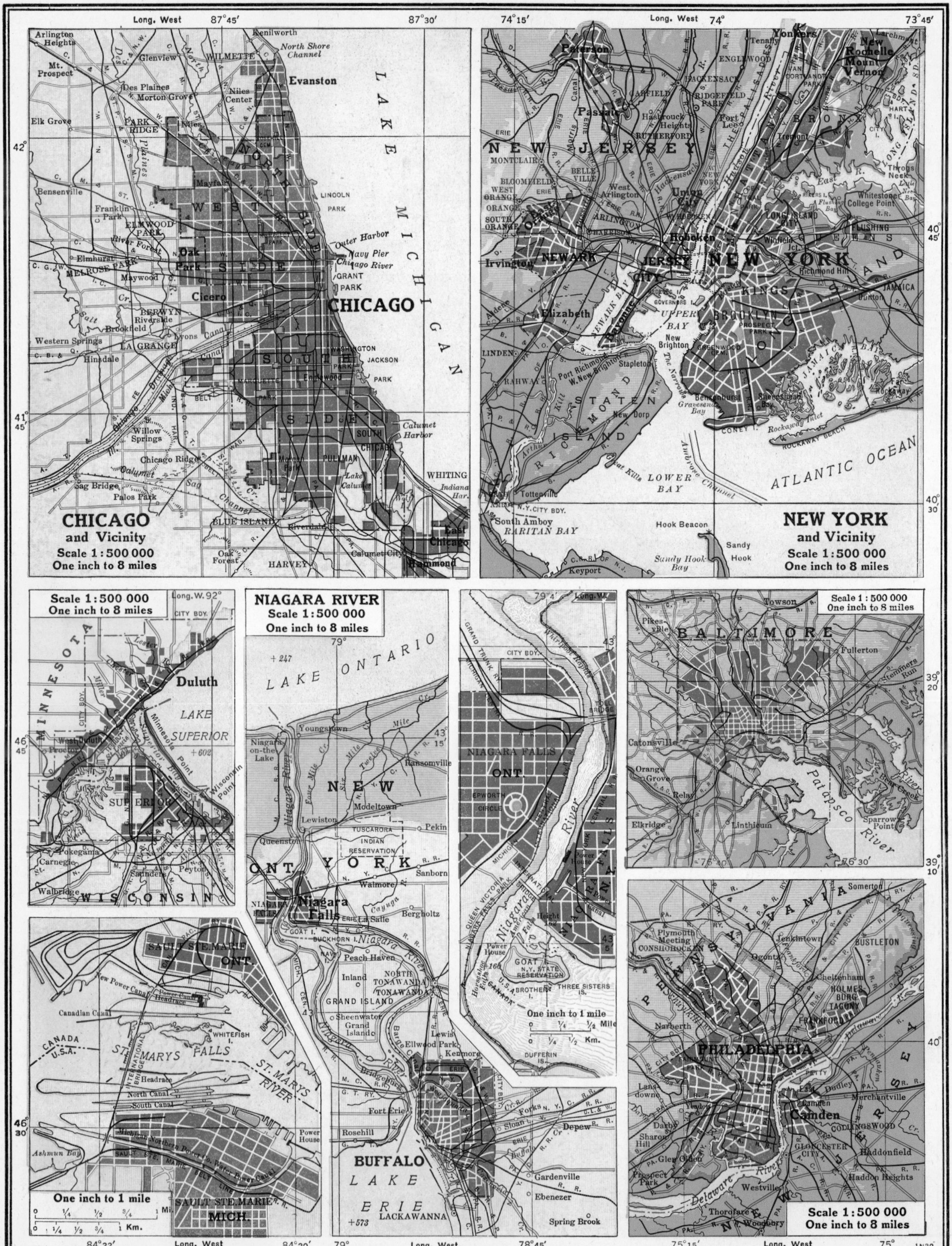

Scale 1:500 000; one inch to 8 miles
Elevations are given in feet

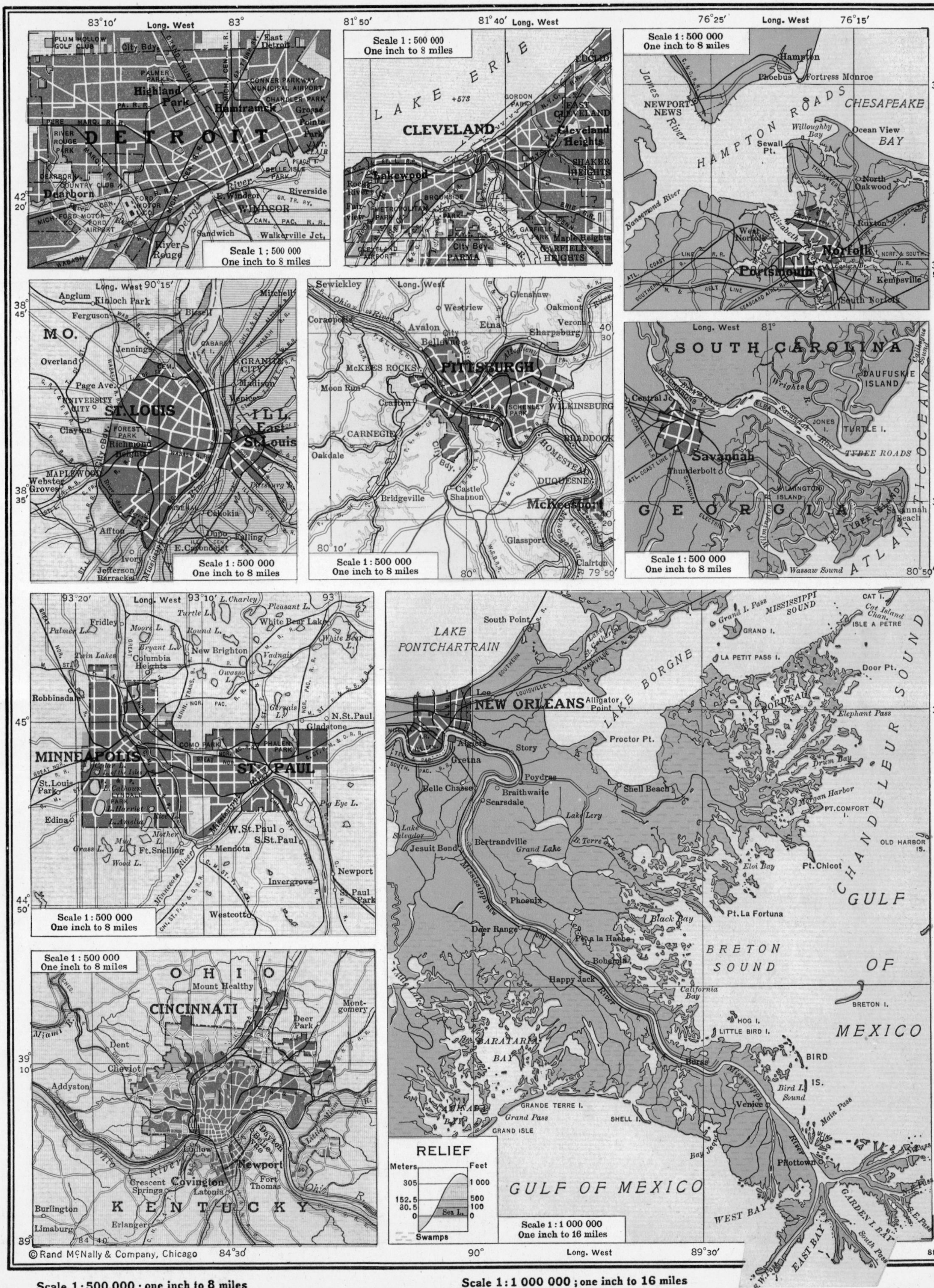

Scale 1 : 500 000 ; one inch to 8 miles

Scale 1 : 1 000 000 ; one inch to 16 miles

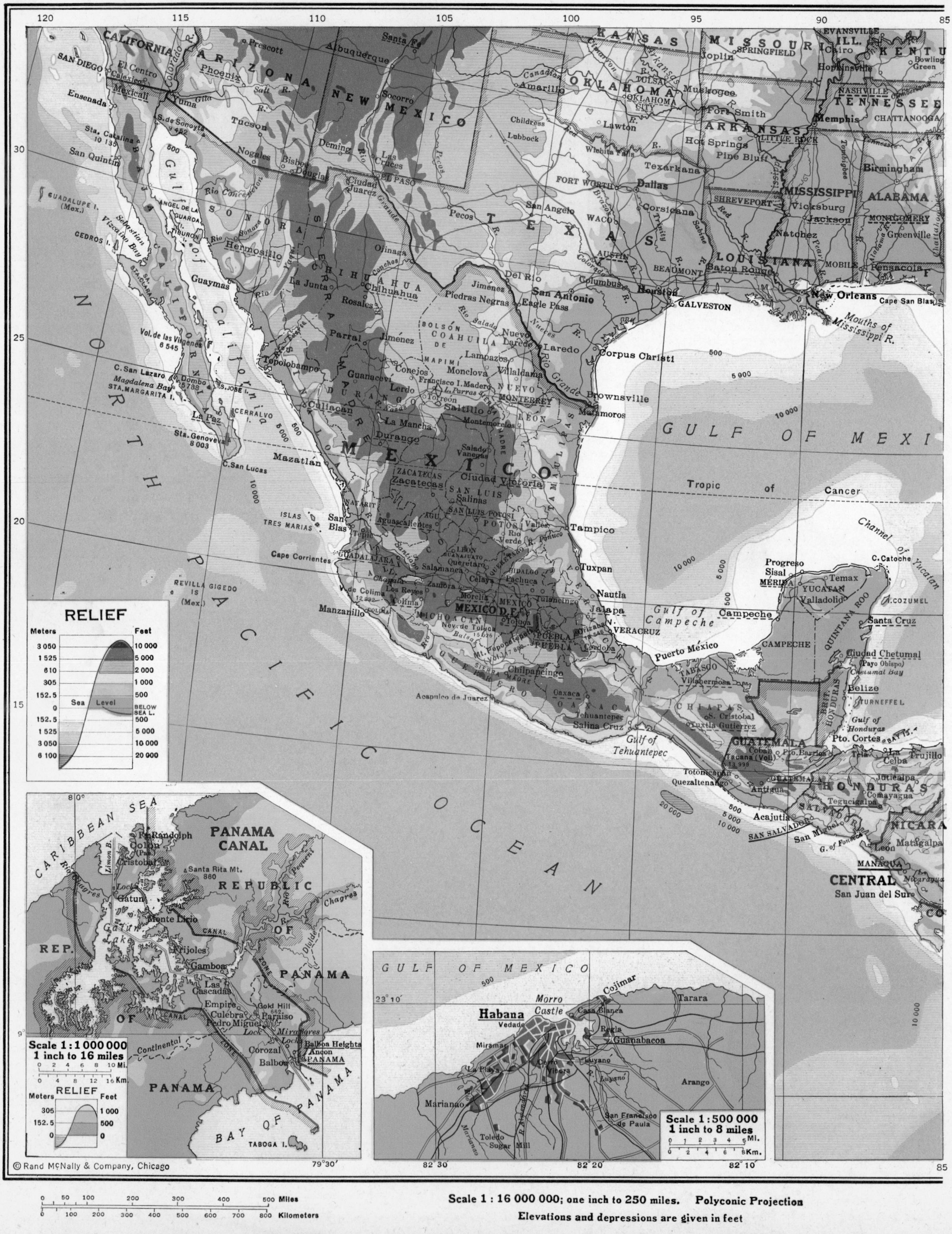

Scale 1 : 16 000 000; one inch to 250 miles. Polyconic Projection

Elevations and depressions are given in feet

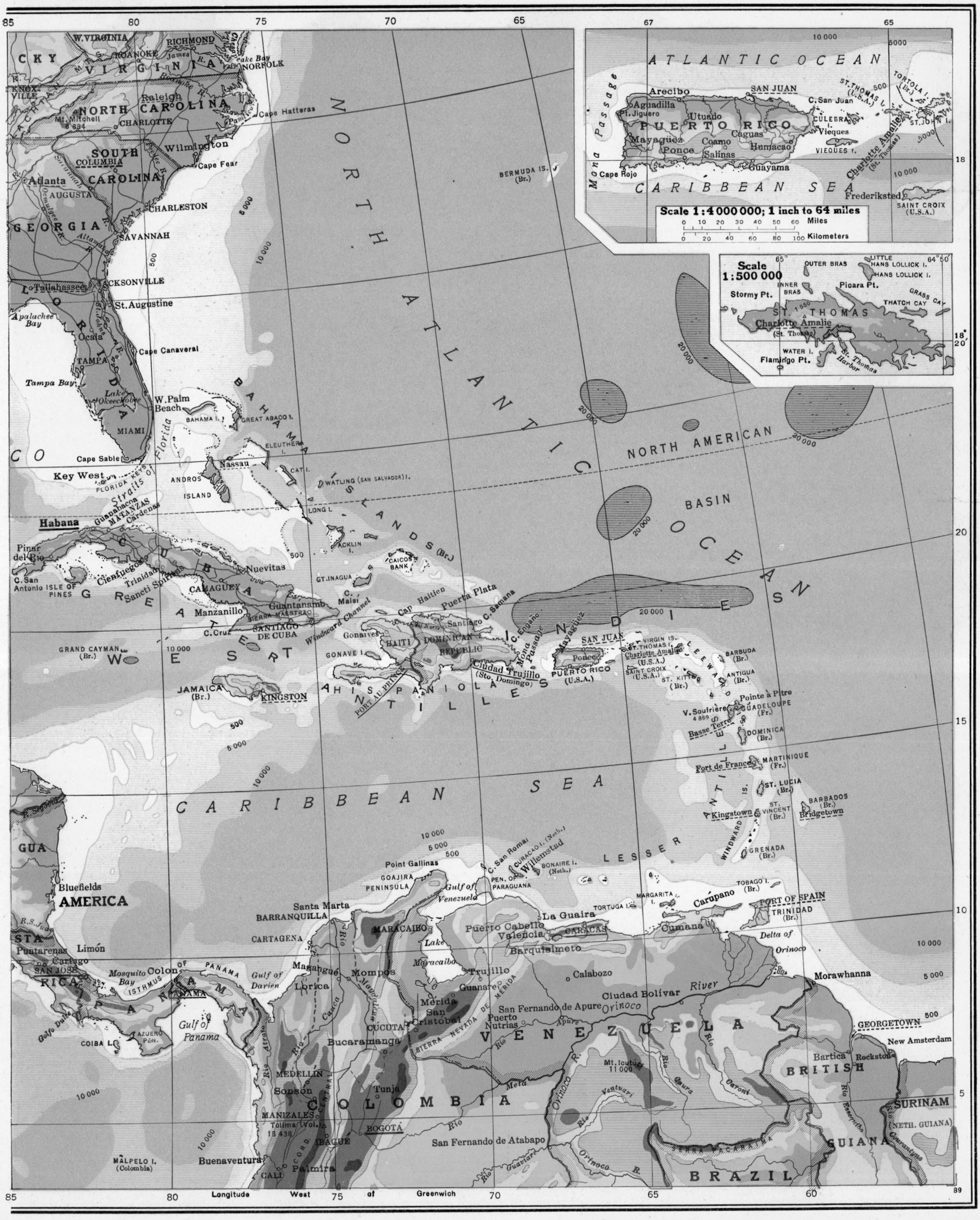
NORTH ATLANTIC OCEAN
NORTH AMERICAN BASIN
CARIBBEAN SEA
GREATER ANTILLES
LESSER ANTILLES
WEST INDIES
BAHAMA ISLANDS (Br.)
HISPANIOLA
CUBA
JAMAICA (Br.)
KINGSTON
HAITI
DOMINICAN REPUBLIC
PUERTO RICO (U.S.A.)
SAN JUAN
VIRGINIA
NORTH CAROLINA
SOUTH CAROLINA
GEORGIA
FLORIDA
COLOMBIA
VENEZUELA
BRITISH GUIANA
SURINAM (NETH. GUIANA)
BRAZIL
PANAMA
Habana
Ciudad Trujillo (Sto. Domingo)
PORT AU PRINCE
CARACAS
BOGOTÁ
GEORGETOWN
PORT OF SPAIN
TRINIDAD (Br.)
BERMUDA IS. (Br.)
Scale 1:4 000 000; 1 inch to 64 miles
ATLANTIC OCEAN
CARIBBEAN SEA
Mona Passage
Scale 1:500 000
ST. THOMAS
Charlotte Amalie (St. Thomas)
Longitude West of Greenwich

Continued on pages 80·81

0 20 40 60 80 100 120 Miles
0 20 40 60 80 100 120 140 160 180 200 Kilometers

Scale 1 : 4 000 000; one inch to
Elevations and depressions

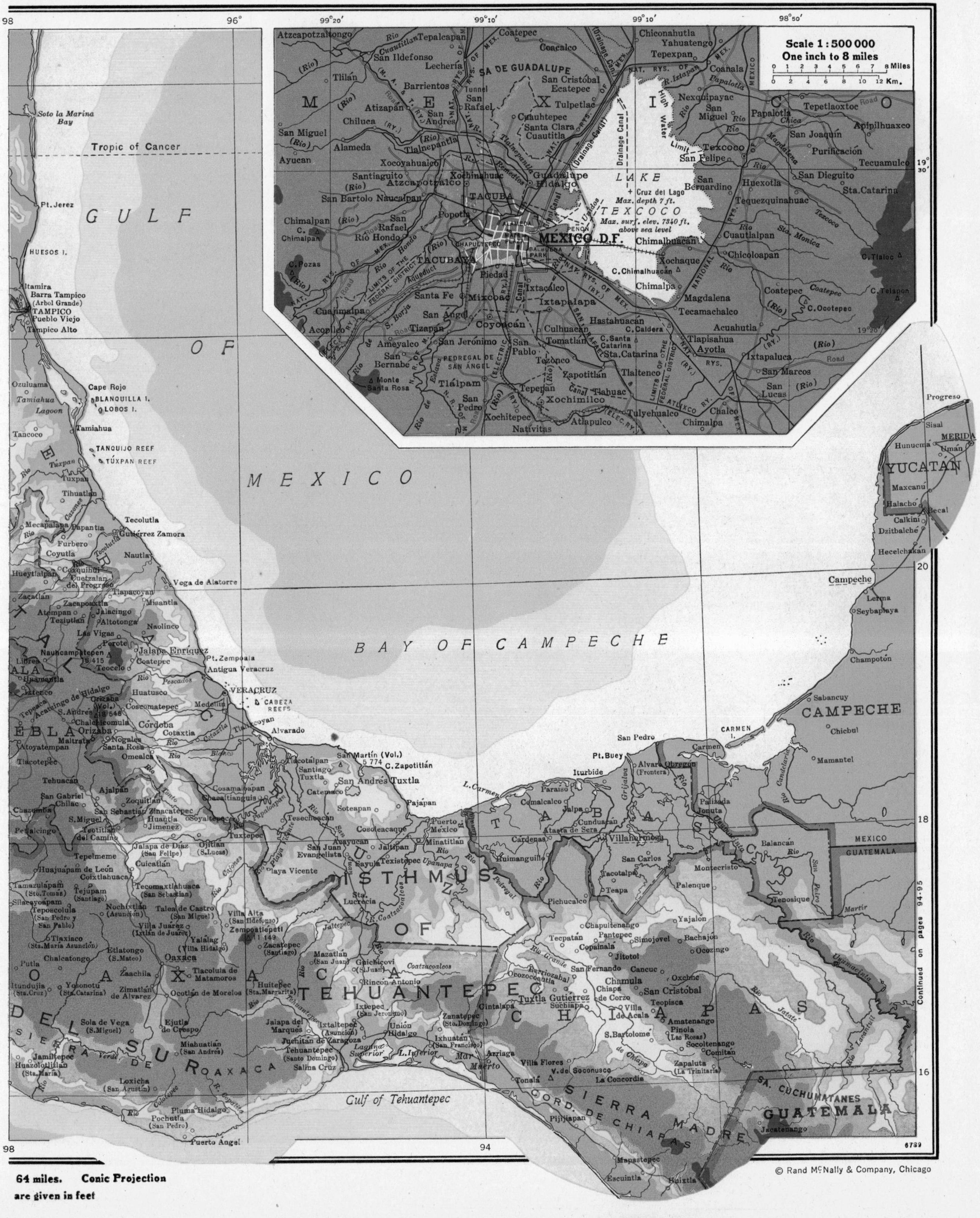

64 miles. Conic Projection
are given in feet

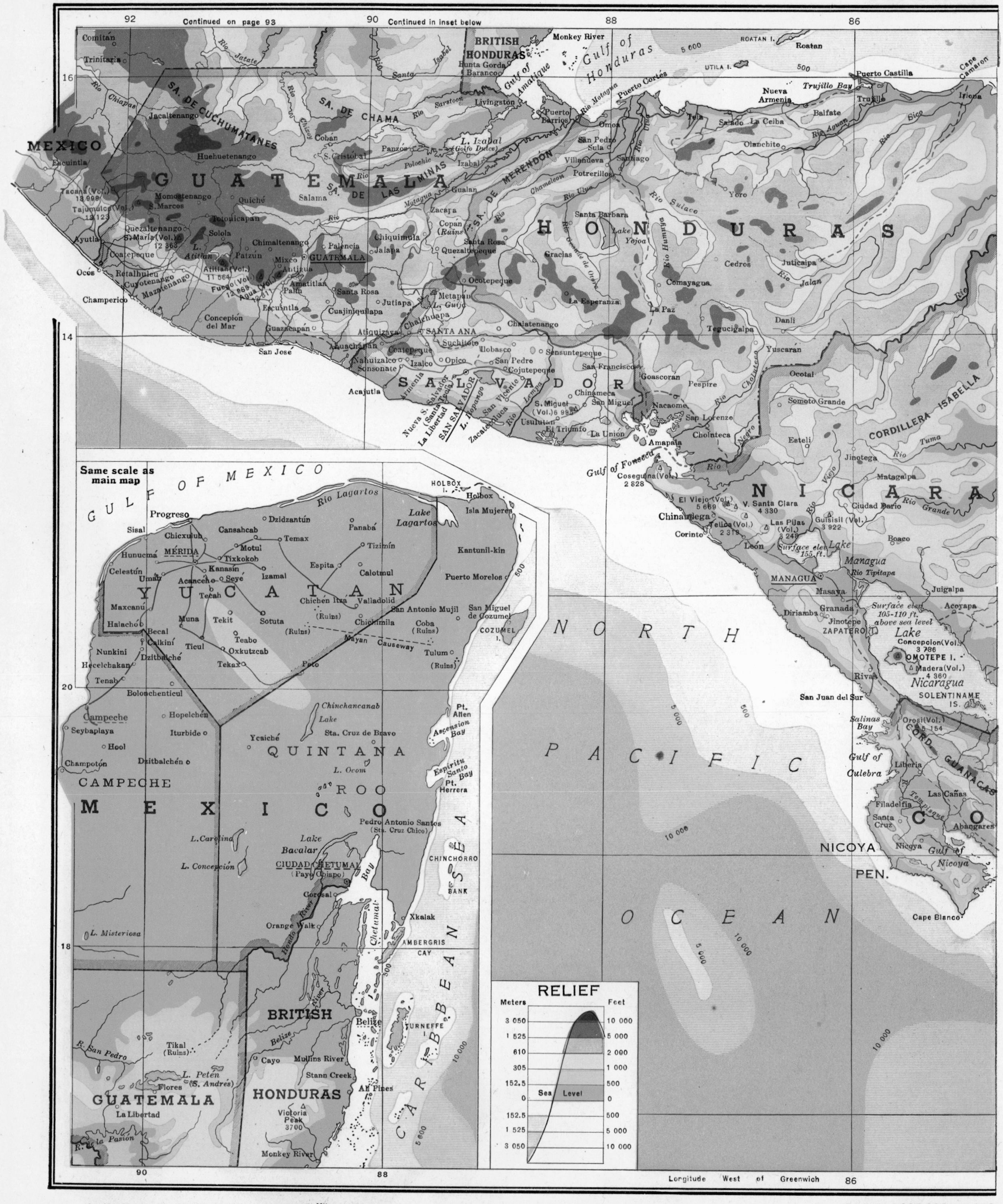

0 10 20 30 40 50 60 70 80 90 100 110 120 Miles

0 20 40 60 80 100 120 140 160 180 200 Kilometers

Scale 1:4 000 000; one inch

Elevations and depressions

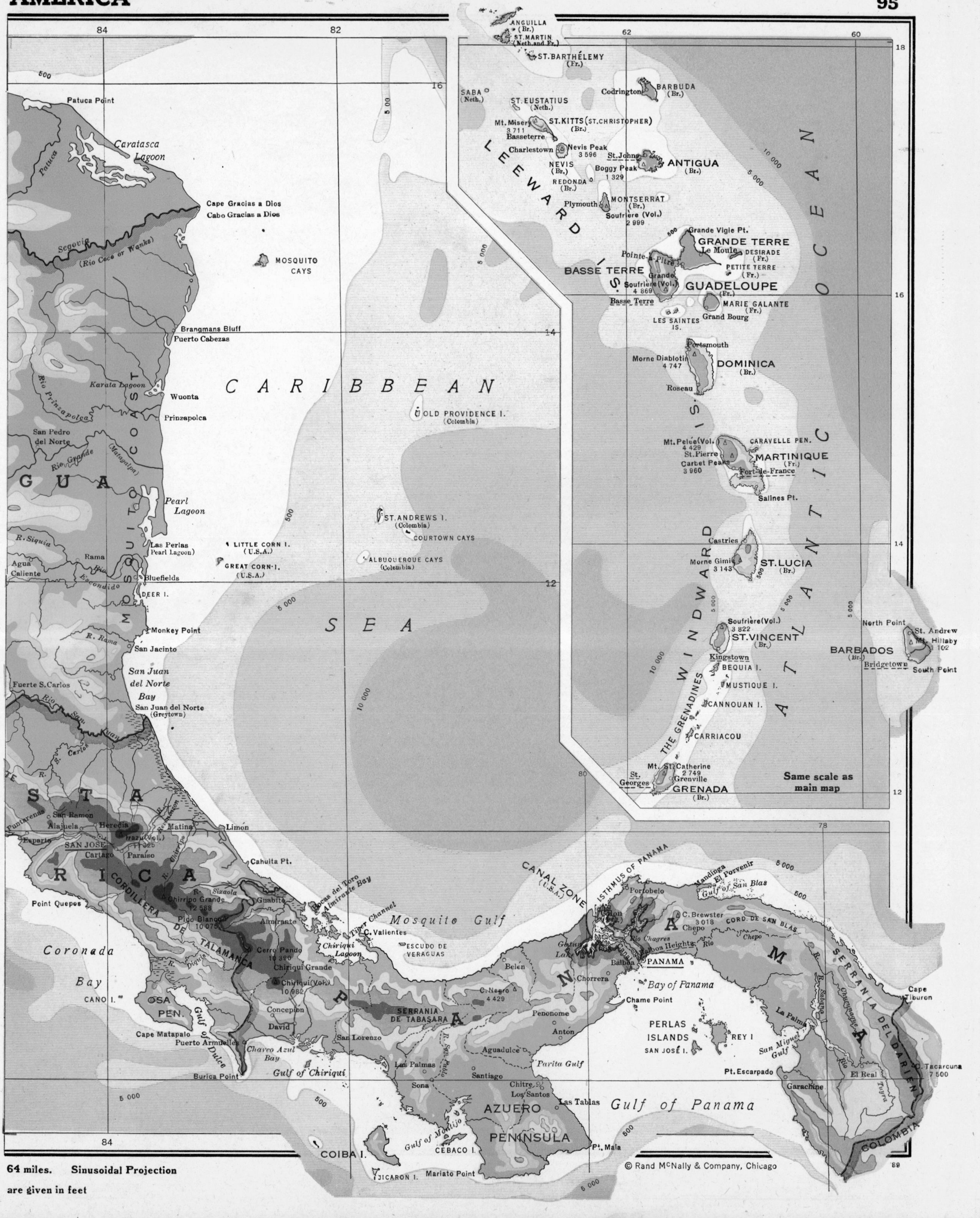

64 miles. Sinusoidal Projection

are given in feet

84 82 62 60 18 16 14 12 80 78 89
CARIBBEAN SEA
ATLANTIC OCEAN
LEEWARD IS.
WINDWARD IS.
ANGUILLA (Br.)
ST. MARTIN (Neth. and Fr.)
ST. BARTHÉLEMY (Fr.)
SABA (Neth.)
ST. EUSTATIUS (Neth.)
Codrington
BARBUDA (Br.)
Mt. Misery 3 711
ST. KITTS (ST. CHRISTOPHER) (Br.)
Basseterre
Charlestown
Nevis Peak 3 596
NEVIS (Br.)
St. Johns
ANTIGUA (Br.)
Boggy Peak 1 329
REDONDA (Br.)
Plymouth
MONTSERRAT (Br.)
Soufrière (Vol.) 2 999
Grande Vigie Pt.
GRANDE TERRE
Le Moule
DESIRADE (Fr.)
Pointe-à-Pitre
PETITE TERRE (Fr.)
BASSE TERRE
Grande
Soufrière (Vol.) 4 869
GUADELOUPE (Fr.)
Basse Terre
MARIE GALANTE (Fr.)
Grand Bourg
LES SAINTES IS.
Portsmouth
Morne Diablotin 4 747
DOMINICA (Br.)
Roseau
Mt. Pelée (Vol.) 4 429
CARAVELLE PEN.
St. Pierre
MARTINIQUE (Fr.)
Carbet Peaks 3 960
Fort-de-France
Salines Pt.
Castries
Morne Gimie 3 143
ST. LUCIA (Br.)
Soufrière (Vol.) 3 822
ST. VINCENT (Br.)
Kingstown
BEQUIA I.
MUSTIQUE I.
CANNOUAN I.
THE GRENADINES
CARRIACOU
Mt. St. Catherine 2 749
Grenville
St. Georges
GRENADA (Br.)
North Point
St. Andrew
Mt. Hillaby 1 102
BARBADOS (Br.)
Bridgetown
South Point
Same scale as main map
10 000 5 000 500
Patuca Point
Patuca
Caratasca Lagoon
Cape Gracias a Dios
Cabo Gracias a Dios
Segovia (Rio Coco or Wanks)
MOSQUITO CAYS
Brangmans Bluff
Puerto Cabezas
Karata Lagoon
Wuonta
Rio Prinzapolca
Prinzapolca
San Pedro del Norte
Rio Grande
Matagalpa
MOSQUITO COAST
GUA
Pearl Lagoon
R. Siquia
Las Perlas Pearl Lagoon
Rama
Agua Caliente
Escondido
Bluefields
LITTLE CORN I. (U.S.A.)
GREAT CORN I. (U.S.A.)
OLD PROVIDENCE I. (Colombia)
ST. ANDREWS I. (Colombia)
COURTOWN CAYS
ALBUQUERQUE CAYS (Colombia)
DEER I.
Monkey Point
R. Rama
San Jacinto
San Juan del Norte Bay
Fuerte S. Carlos
Rio San Juan
San Juan del Norte (Greytown)
S. Carlos
STA
RICA
Puntarenas
San Ramon
Alajuela
Heredia
Matina
Limon
Esparta
SAN JOSE
Irazu (Vol.) 11 325
Cartago
Paraiso
Reventazon
Cahuita Pt.
CORDILLERA DE TALAMANCA
Sixaola
Chirripo Grande 12 588
Point Quepos
Pico Blanco 10 075
Guabito
Bocas del Toro
Almirante Bay
Almirante
Tiger Channel
C. Valientes
Mosquito Gulf
Coronado Bay
Cerro Pando 10 390
Chiriqui Lagoon
ESCUDO DE VERAGUAS
Chiriqui Grande
Diquis
Chiriqui (Vol.) 10 982
CANO I.
OSA PEN.
Gulf of Dulce
Cape Matapalo
Puerto Armuelles
Burica Point
Concepcion
David
SERRANIA DE TABASARA
San Lorenzo
Charco Azul Bay
Gulf of Chiriqui
Las Palmas
Sona
COIBA I.
JICARON I.
Gulf of Montijo
CEBACO I.
Mariato Point
Santiago
AZUERO PENINSULA
Chitre
Los Santos
Las Tablas
Pt. Mala
Aguadulce
Parita Gulf
Anton
Penonome
C. Negro 4 429
Belen
PANAMA
CANAL ZONE (U.S.A.)
ISTHMUS OF PANAMA
Portobelo
Colon
Gatun Lake
Rio Chagres
Balboa Heights
Balboa
Chorrera
Chame Point
Bay of Panama
Mandinga
El Porvenir
Gulf of San Blas
C. Brewster 3 018
Chepo
CORD. DE SAN BLAS
PERLAS ISLANDS
REY I.
SAN JOSÉ I.
San Miguel Gulf
La Palma
Pt. Escarpado
Garachine
El Real
Tuyra
SERRANIA DEL DARIEN
Cape Tiburon
C. Tacarcuna 7 500
COLOMBIA
Gulf of Panama

WEST INDIES –

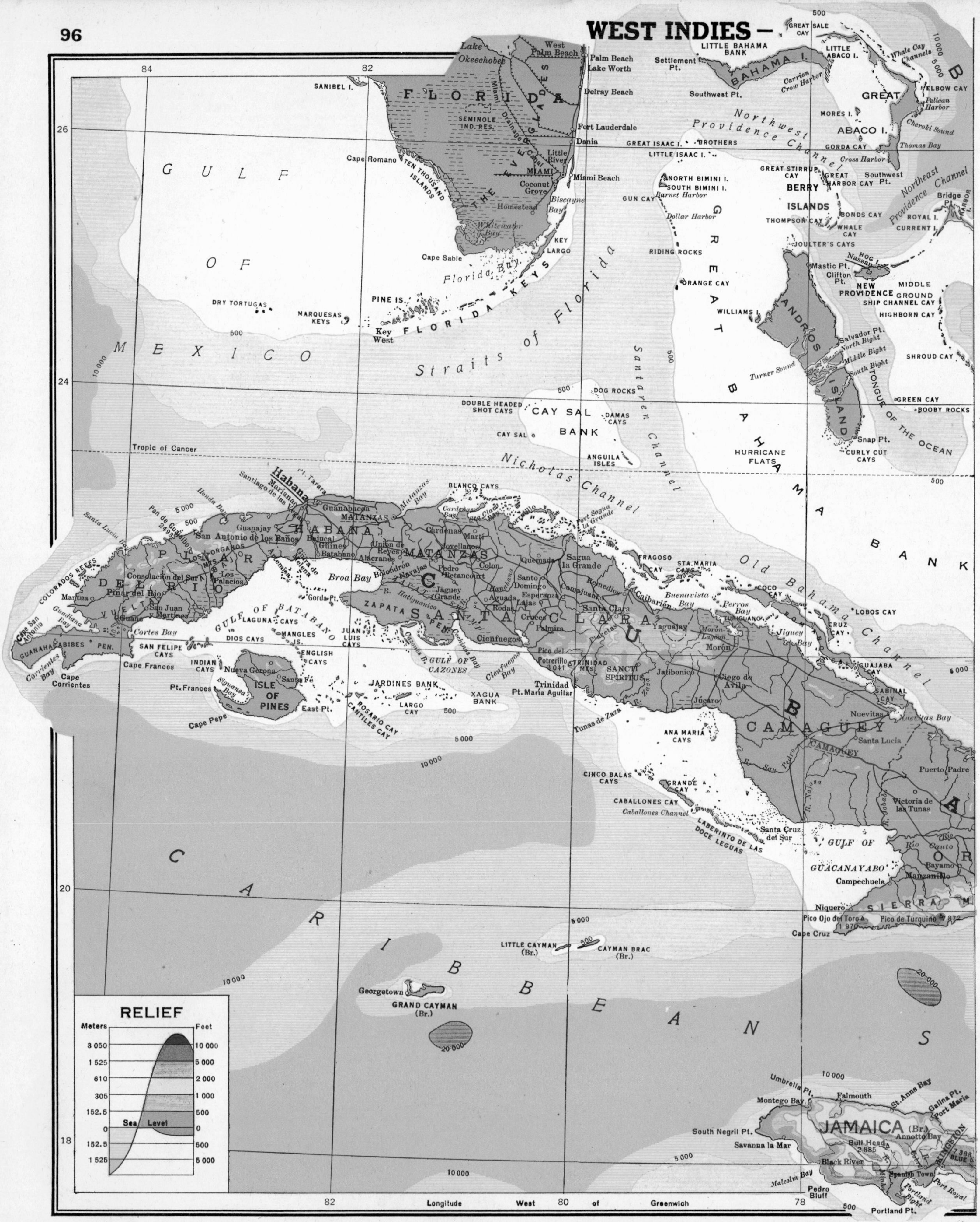

0 10 20 30 40 50 60 70 80 90 100 110 120 Miles
0 20 40 60 80 100 120 140 160 180 200 Kilometers

Scale 1 : 4 000 000; one inch

Elevations and depressions

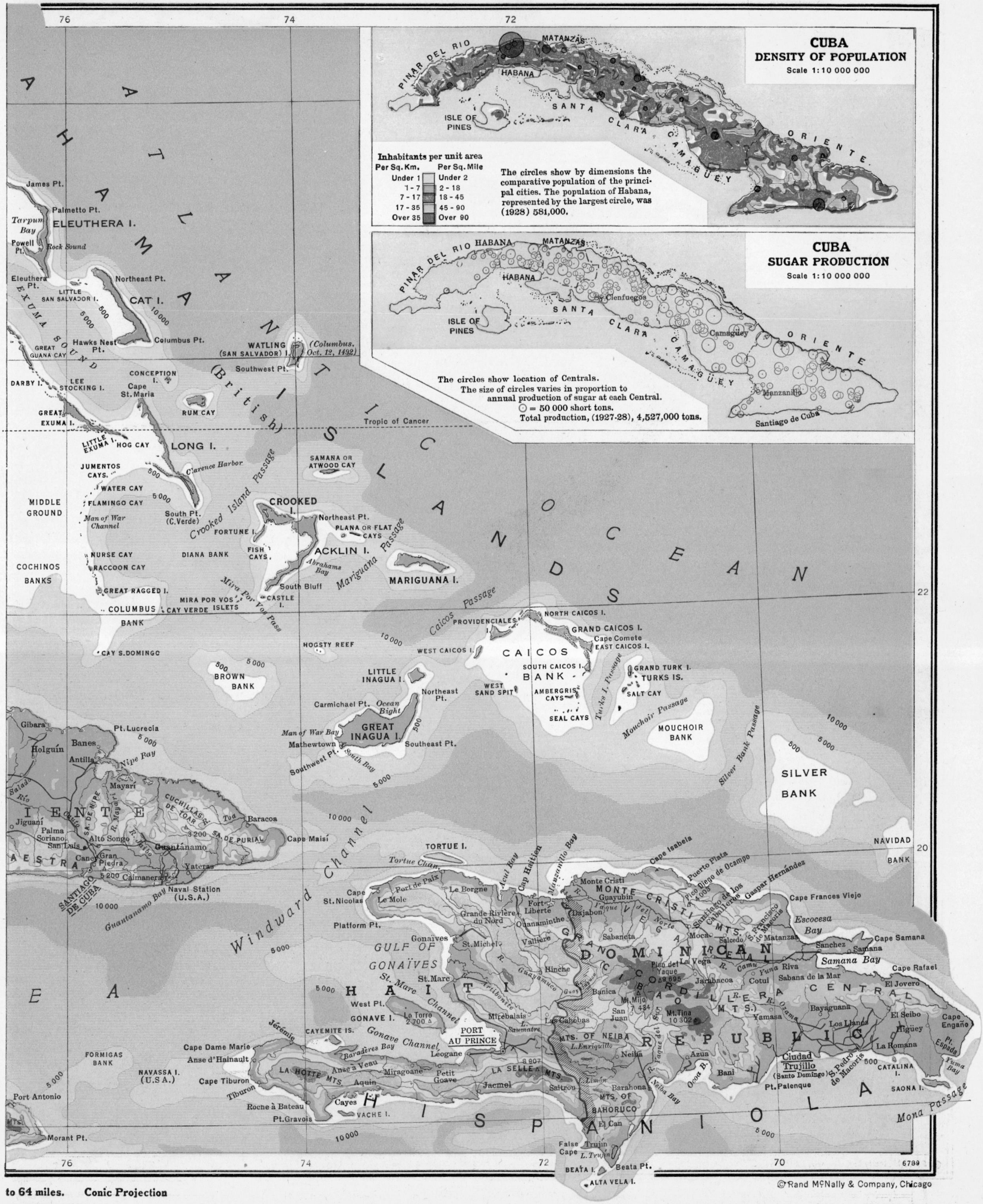
CUBA
DENSITY OF POPULATION
Scale 1:10 000 000
Inhabitants per unit area
Per Sq. Km. | Per Sq. Mile
Under 1 | Under 2
1 - 7 | 2 - 18
7 - 17 | 18 - 45
17 - 35 | 45 - 90
Over 35 | Over 90
The circles show by dimensions the comparative population of the principal cities. The population of Habana, represented by the largest circle, was (1928) 581,000.
PINAR DEL RIO
MATANZAS
HABANA
ISLE OF PINES
SANTA CLARA
CAMAGUEY
ORIENTE
CUBA
SUGAR PRODUCTION
Scale 1:10 000 000
The circles show location of Centrals.
The size of circles varies in proportion to annual production of sugar at each Central.
= 50 000 short tons.
Total production, (1927-28), 4,527,000 tons.
Cienfuegos
Camagüey
Manzanillo
Santiago de Cuba
BAHAMA ISLANDS (British)
ATLANTIC OCEAN
Tropic of Cancer
ELEUTHERA I.
CAT I.
WATLING (SAN SALVADOR) I.
(Columbus, Oct. 12, 1492)
EXUMA SOUND
LONG I.
RUM CAY
CONCEPTION I.
CROOKED I.
ACKLIN I.
MARIGUANA I.
SAMANA OR ATWOOD CAY
Crooked Island Passage
Mariguana Passage
Caicos Passage
Mira Por Vos Pass
CAICOS BANK
NORTH CAICOS I.
GRAND CAICOS I.
EAST CAICOS I.
SOUTH CAICOS I.
GRAND TURK I.
TURKS IS.
SALT CAY
Turks I. Passage
Mouchoir Passage
MOUCHOIR BANK
SILVER BANK
Silver Bank Passage
NAVIDAD BANK
HOGSTY REEF
LITTLE INAGUA I.
GREAT INAGUA I.
BROWN BANK
COLUMBUS BANK
CAY S.DOMINGO
MIDDLE GROUND
COCHINOS BANKS
DIANA BANK
Windward Channel
TORTUE I.
Tortue Chan.
GULF OF GONAÏVES
HAITI
GONAVE I.
Gonave Channel
St. Marc Channel
PORT AU PRINCE
LA HOTTE MTS.
LA SELLE MTS.
MTS. OF NEIBA
MTS. OF BAHORUCO
Cap Haitien
Jérémie
Jacmel
Léogane
Cayes
VACHE I.
FORMIGAS BANK
NAVASSA I. (U.S.A.)
DOMINICAN REPUBLIC
MONTE CRISTI MTS.
CORDILLERA CENTRAL
Pico del Yaque 9 695
Mt. Tina 10 302
Santiago de los Caballeros
Puerto Plata
Samana Bay
Ciudad Trujillo (Santo Domingo)
San Pedro de Macoris
La Romana
Cape Engaño
SAONA I.
CATALINA I.
BEATA I.
ALTA VELA I.
HISPANIOLA
Mona Passage
Guantanamo Bay
Naval Station (U.S.A.)
SANTIAGO DE CUBA
Baracoa
Cape Maisi
Holguín
Gibara
Banes
Nipe Bay
Mayari
ORIENTE
Port Antonio
Morant Pt.
76
74
72
70
22
20
6789

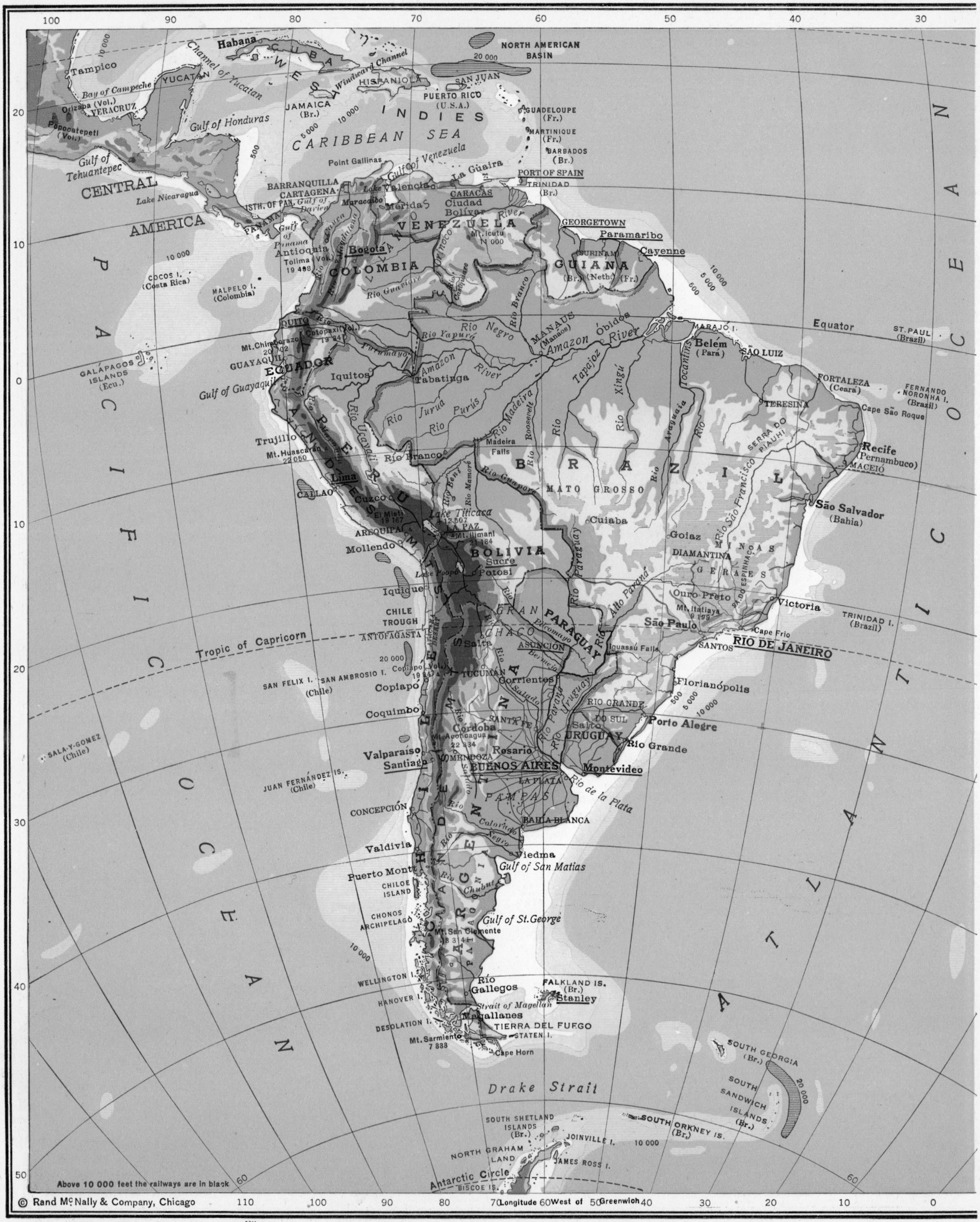

0 200 400 600 800 1000 Miles
0 400 800 1200 1600 Kilometers

Scale 1: 40 000 000; One inch to 630 miles. Lambert's Azimuthal, Equal Area Projection

Elevations and depressions are given in feet

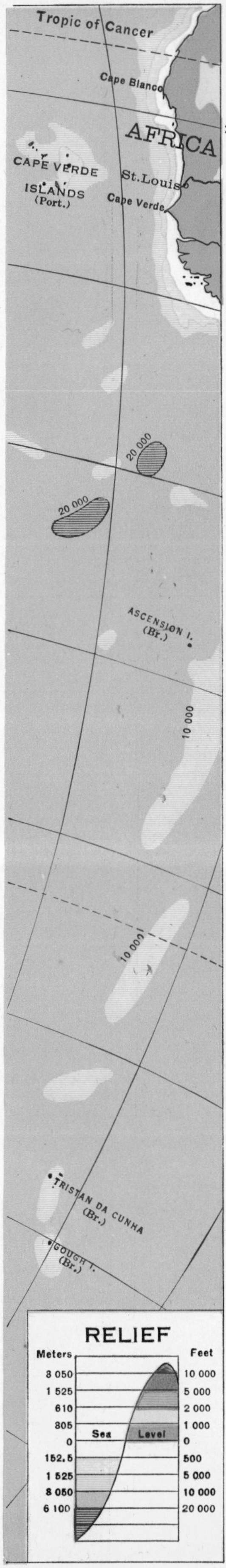
20
Tropic of Cancer
Cape Blanco
AFRICA
CAPE VERDE
ISLANDS
(Port.)
St.Louis
Cape Verde
20
10
0
20 000
20 000
ASCENSION I.
(Br.)
10 000
10
10 000
20
TRISTAN DA CUNHA
(Br.)
GOUGH I.
(Br.)
30
40
RELIEF
Meters
Feet
3 050
1 525
610
305
0
152.5
1 525
3 050
6 100
Sea
Level
10 000
5 000
2 000
1 000
0
500
5 000
10 000
20 000

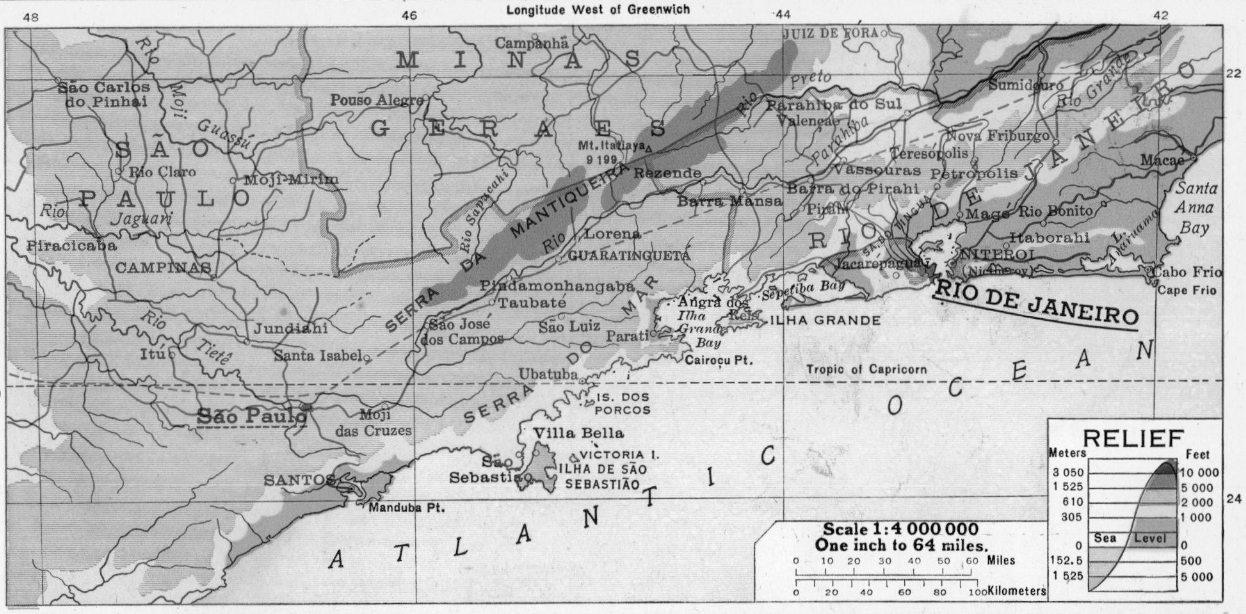
Longitude West of Greenwich
48
46
44
42
22
24
JUIZ DE FORA
Campanha
M I N A S
G E R A E S
São Carlos
do Pinhal
Pouso Alegre
Rio Moji Guassú
SÃO
PAULO
Rio Claro
Moji-Mirim
Rio Jaguari
Piracicaba
CAMPINAS
Mt. Itatiaya
9 199
SERRA DA MANTIQUEIRA
Rio Sapucahi
Rezende
Barra Mansa
Lorena
GUARATINGUETÁ
Pindamonhangaba
Taubaté
São José
dos Campos
São Luiz
Paratí
Ubatuba
SERRA DO MAR
Rio Tieté
Jundiahi
Itú
Santa Isabel
São Paulo
Moji
das Cruzes
SANTOS
Manduba Pt.
São
Sebastião
Villa Bella
IS. DOS
PORCOS
VICTORIA I.
ILHA DE SÃO
SEBASTIÃO
Angra dos
Reis
Ilha
Grande
Bay
Cairoçu Pt.
ILHA GRANDE
Sepetiba Bay
Rio Pyreto
Parahiba do Sul
Valença
Rio Parahiba
Vassouras
Barra do Pirahi
Pirahi
Teresopolis
Petropolis
Nova Friburgo
Sumidouro
Rio Grande
RIO DE JANEIRO
Jacarepaguá
NITEROI
(Nictheroy)
Magé
Rio Bonito
Itaborahi
Macaé
Santa
Anna
Bay
Cabo Frio
Cape Frio
RIO DE JANEIRO
Tropic of Capricorn
ATLANTIC OCEAN
Scale 1:4 000 000
One inch to 64 miles.
0 10 20 30 40 50 60 Miles
0 20 40 60 80 100 Kilometers
RELIEF
Meters
Feet
3 050
1 525
610
305
0
152.5
1 525
Sea
Level
10 000
5 000
2 000
1 000
0
500
5 000

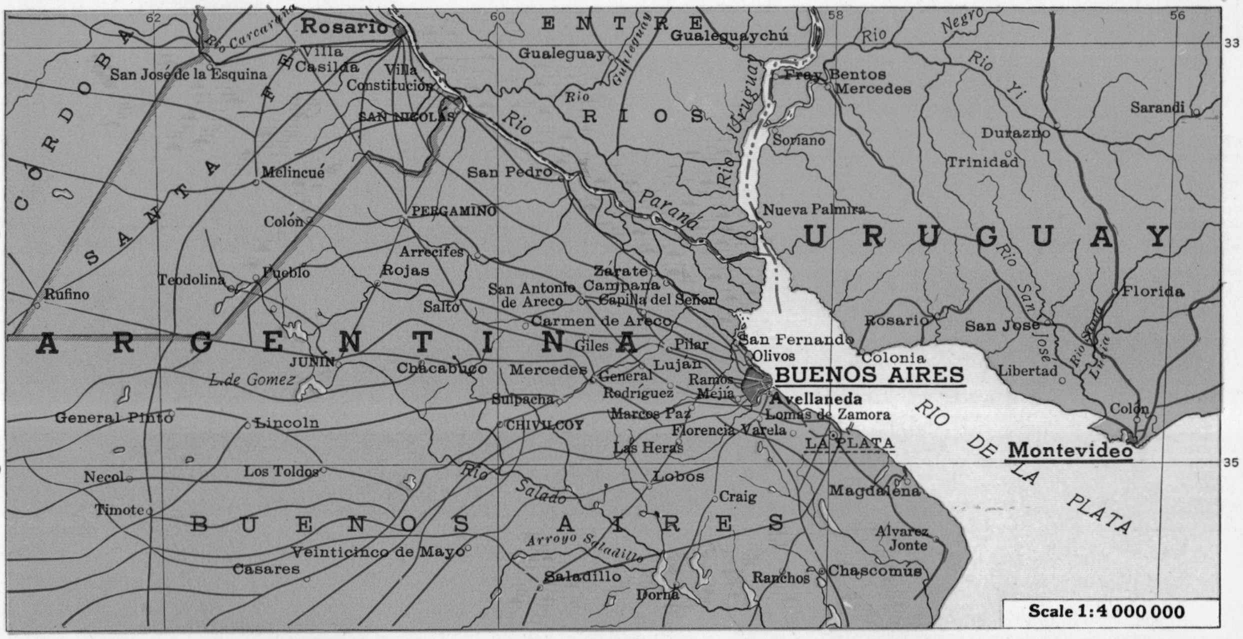
62
60
58
56
33
35
ENTRE RIOS
Rosario
Rio Carcarañá
Villa
Casilda
Villa
Constitución
SAN NICOLAS
San José de la Esquina
CORDOBA
SANTA FE
Melincué
Colón
PERGAMINO
Rufino
Teodolina
Pueblo
Arrecifes
Rojas
Salto
San Pedro
Rio Paraná
San Antonio
de Areco
Zarate
Campana
Capilla del Señor
Carmen de Areco
ARGENTINA
JUNIN
Chacabuco
Giles
Pilar
Lujan
Mercedes
General
Rodriguez
Ramos
Mejia
L.de Gomez
General Pinto
Lincoln
Suipacha
CHIVILCOY
Marcos Paz
Las Heras
Florencia Varela
Lobos
Necol
Timote
Los Toldos
Rio Salado
BUENOS AIRES
Arroyo Saladillo
Veinticinco de Mayo
Casares
Saladillo
Dorna
Craig
Ranchos
Chascomus
Magdalena
Alvarez
Jonte
LA PLATA
Lomas de Zamora
Avellaneda
BUENOS AIRES
Olivos
San Fernando
Gualeguay
Gualeguaychú
Rio Gualeguay
Rio Uruguay
Fray Bentos
Mercedes
Soriano
Nueva Palmira
URUGUAY
Rio Negro
Rio Yi
Sarandi
Durazno
Trinidad
Rio San José
Rio Santa Lucia
Florida
Rosario
Colonia
San José
Libertad
Colon
Montevideo
RIO DE LA PLATA
Scale 1:4 000 000

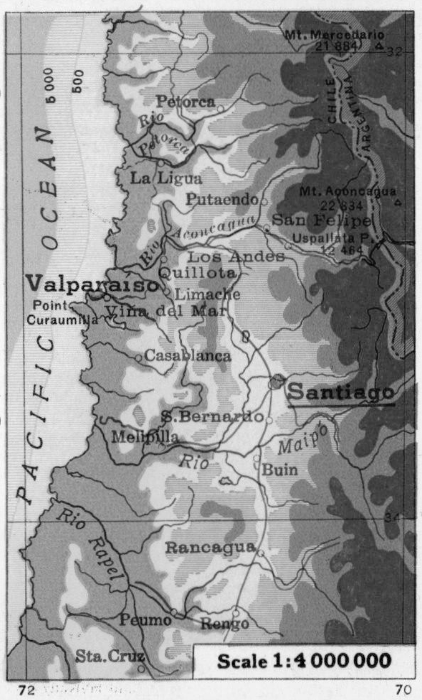
Mt. Mercedario
21 884
32
Petorca
Rio Petorca
La Ligua
Putaendo
Mt. Aconcagua
22 834
San Felipe
Uspallata P.
12 464
Rio Aconcagua
Los Andes
Quillota
Valparaiso
Point
Curaumilla
Limache
Viña del Mar
Casablanca
Santiago
S.Bernardo
Melipilla
Rio Maipo
Buin
Rio Rapel
Rancagua
Peumo
Rengo
Sta.Cruz
PACIFIC OCEAN
5 000
500
CHILE
ARGENTINA
34
Scale 1:4 000 000
72
70

Mt. Burnay
5 742
MUÑOZ
GAMERO
PEN.
Cape
Pilar
Strait of Magellan
DESOLATION
RIESCO ISLAND
Cord. Riesco
Skyring Water
Otway Water
L. Blanca
Pta. Dungeness
B. Lomas
Pta. Catalina
B. San
Felipe
Rio Side
Magallanes
PEN. BRUNSWICK
Cape
Froward
Strait of Magellan
Useless Bay
CORDOVA PEN.
Abra Canal
SANTA
INEZ
ISLAND
Barbara Chan.
PACIFIC
OCEAN
GRAFTON
ISLANDS
CLARENCE I.
DAWSON I.
Whiteside Canal
Admiralty Sound
Rio Grande
TIERRA DEL FUEGO
CHILE
ARGENTINA
ATLANTIC OCEAN
Cockburn Canal
BRECKNOCK PEN.
Mt. Sarmiento
7 333
CORD. DARWIN
Mt. Darwin
7 005
Beagle Channel
Ushuaia
CAMDEN
ISLANDS
STEWART I.
500
5 000
53
55
74
72
70
Scale 1:4 000 000

SOUTH AMERICA

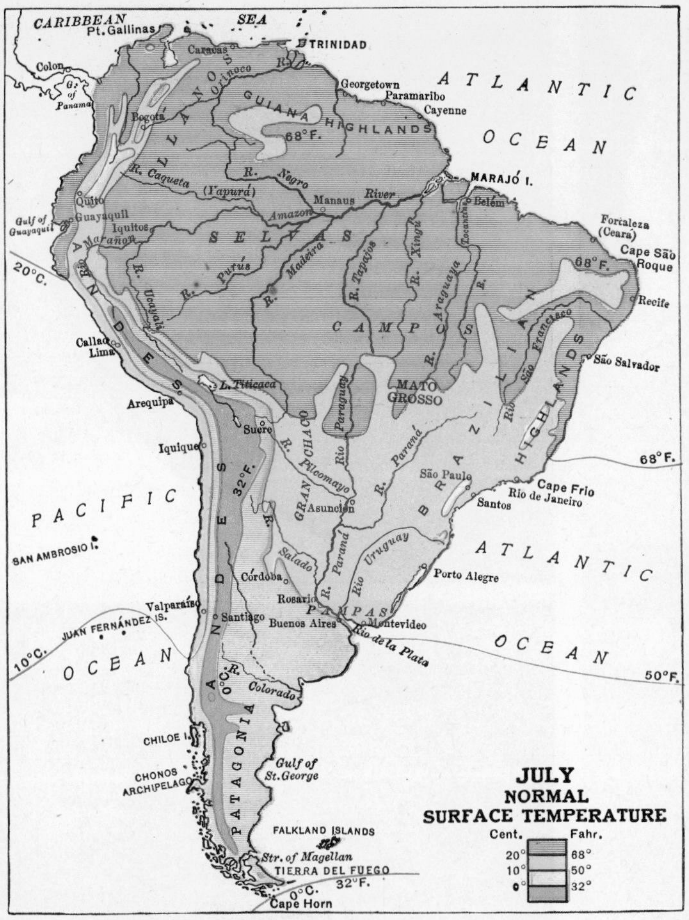

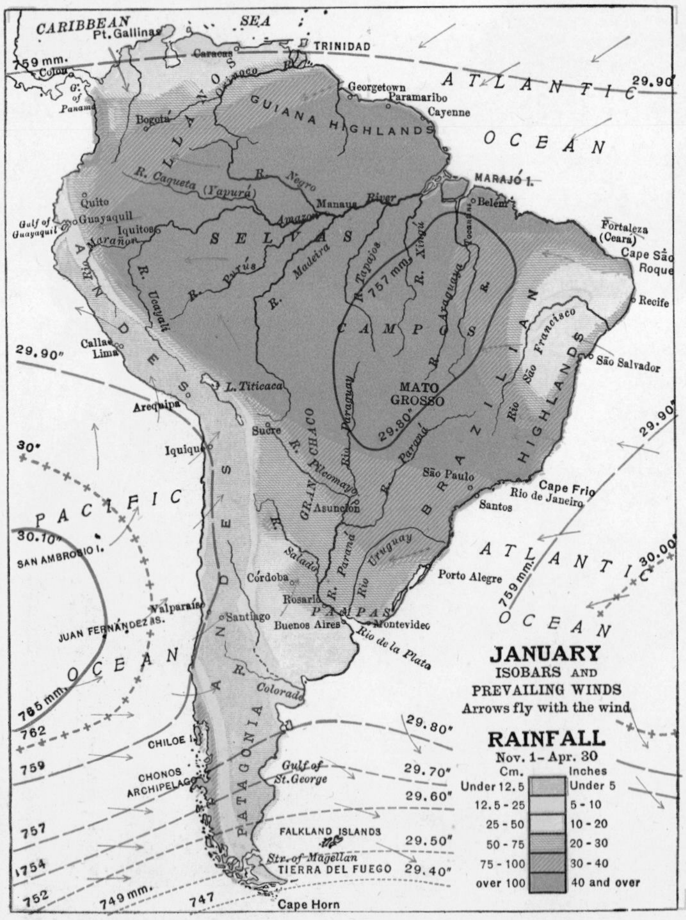

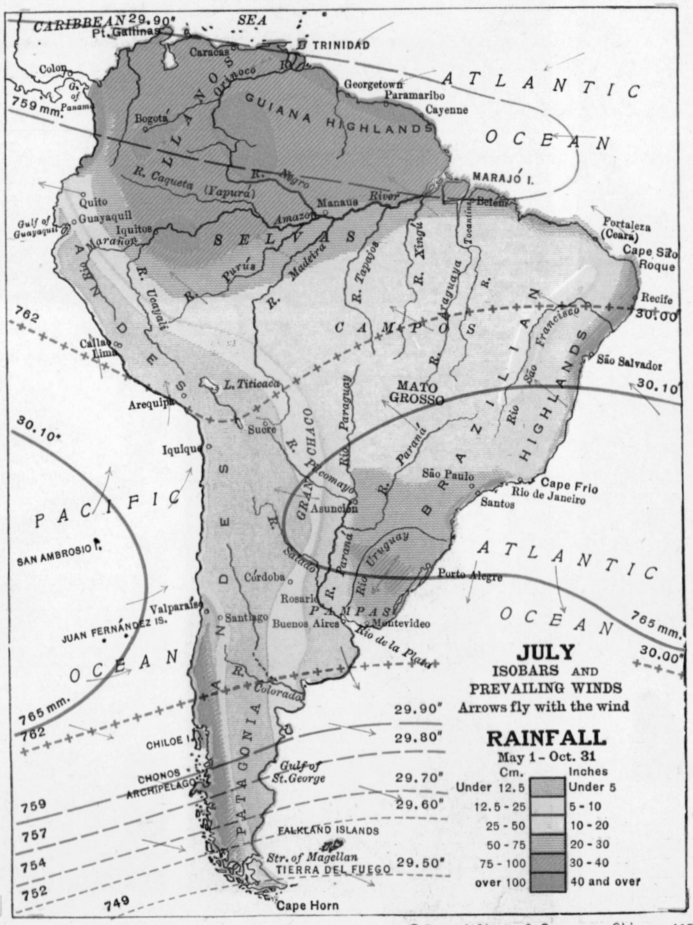

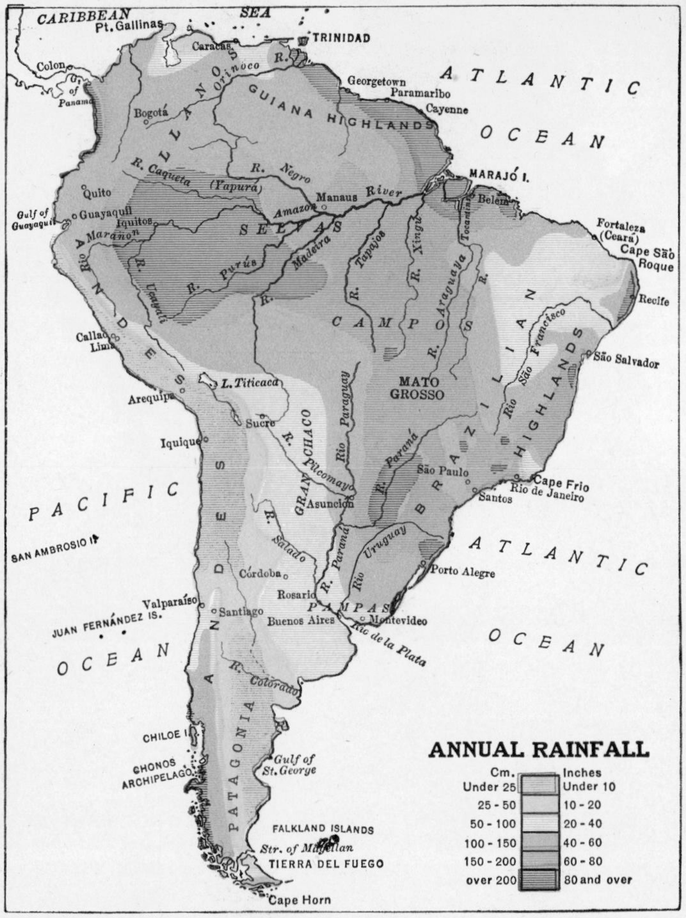
ANNUAL RAINFALL
Cm. | Inches
Under 25 | Under 10
25 - 50 | 10 - 20
50 - 100 | 20 - 40
100 - 150 | 40 - 60
150 - 200 | 60 - 80
over 200 | 80 and over
CARIBBEAN SEA
ATLANTIC OCEAN
PACIFIC OCEAN
GUIANA HIGHLANDS
LLANOS
SELVAS
CAMPOS
MATO GROSSO
BRAZILIAN HIGHLANDS
GRAN CHACO
PAMPAS
ANDES
PATAGONIA
FALKLAND ISLANDS
TIERRA DEL FUEGO
Cape Horn

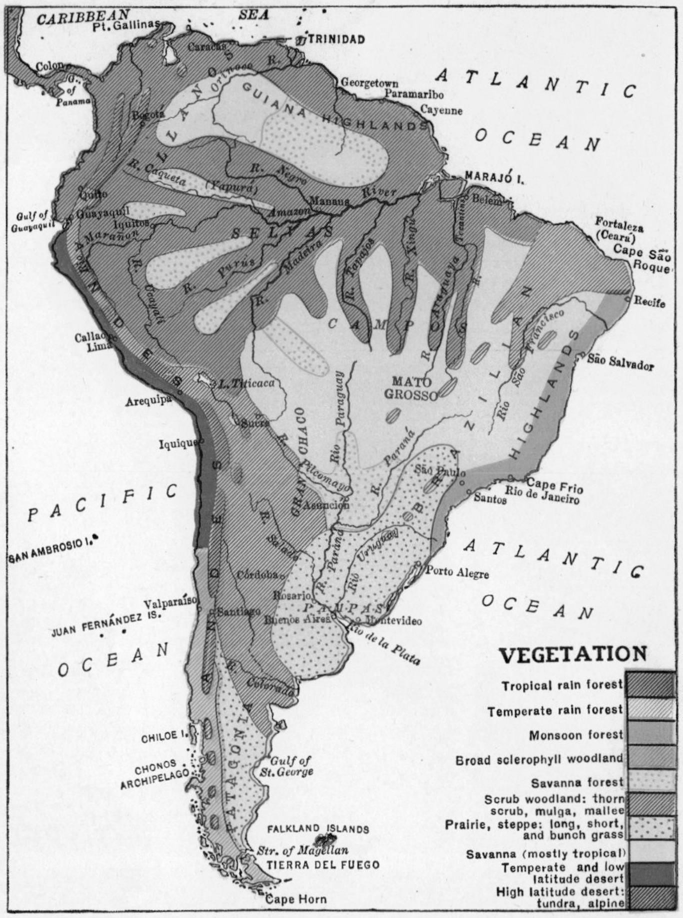
VEGETATION
Tropical rain forest
Temperate rain forest
Monsoon forest
Broad sclerophyll woodland
Savanna forest
Scrub woodland: thorn scrub, mulga, mallee
Prairie, steppe: long, short, and bunch grass
Savanna (mostly tropical)
Temperate and low latitude desert
High latitude desert: tundra, alpine
CARIBBEAN SEA
ATLANTIC OCEAN
PACIFIC OCEAN

RELIEF
Meters | Feet
3 050 | 10 000
1 525 | 5 000
610 | 2 000
305 | 1 000
0 | SEA L. | 0
152.5 | 500
1 525 | 5 000
Tropic of Capricorn
Equator
West Lon. 90 80 70 60 50 40 30 20
CARIBBEAN SEA
ATLANTIC OCEAN
PACIFIC OCEAN

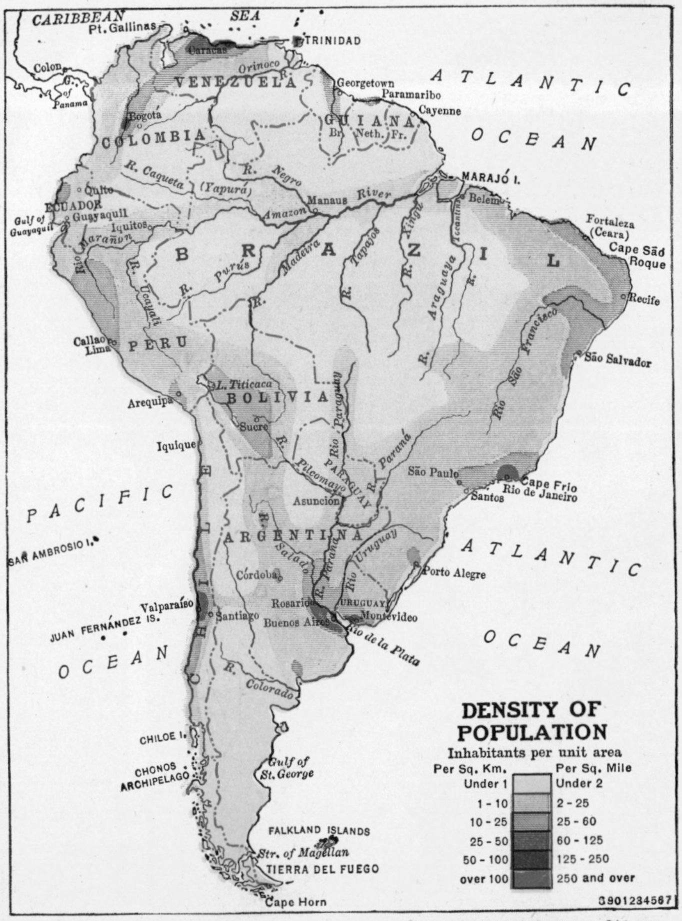
DENSITY OF POPULATION
Inhabitants per unit area
Per Sq. Km. | Per Sq. Mile
Under 1 | Under 2
1 - 10 | 2 - 25
10 - 25 | 25 - 60
25 - 50 | 60 - 125
50 - 100 | 125 - 250
over 100 | 250 and over
VENEZUELA
COLOMBIA
GUIANA
ECUADOR
PERU
BRAZIL
BOLIVIA
PARAGUAY
CHILE
ARGENTINA
URUGUAY
3901234567

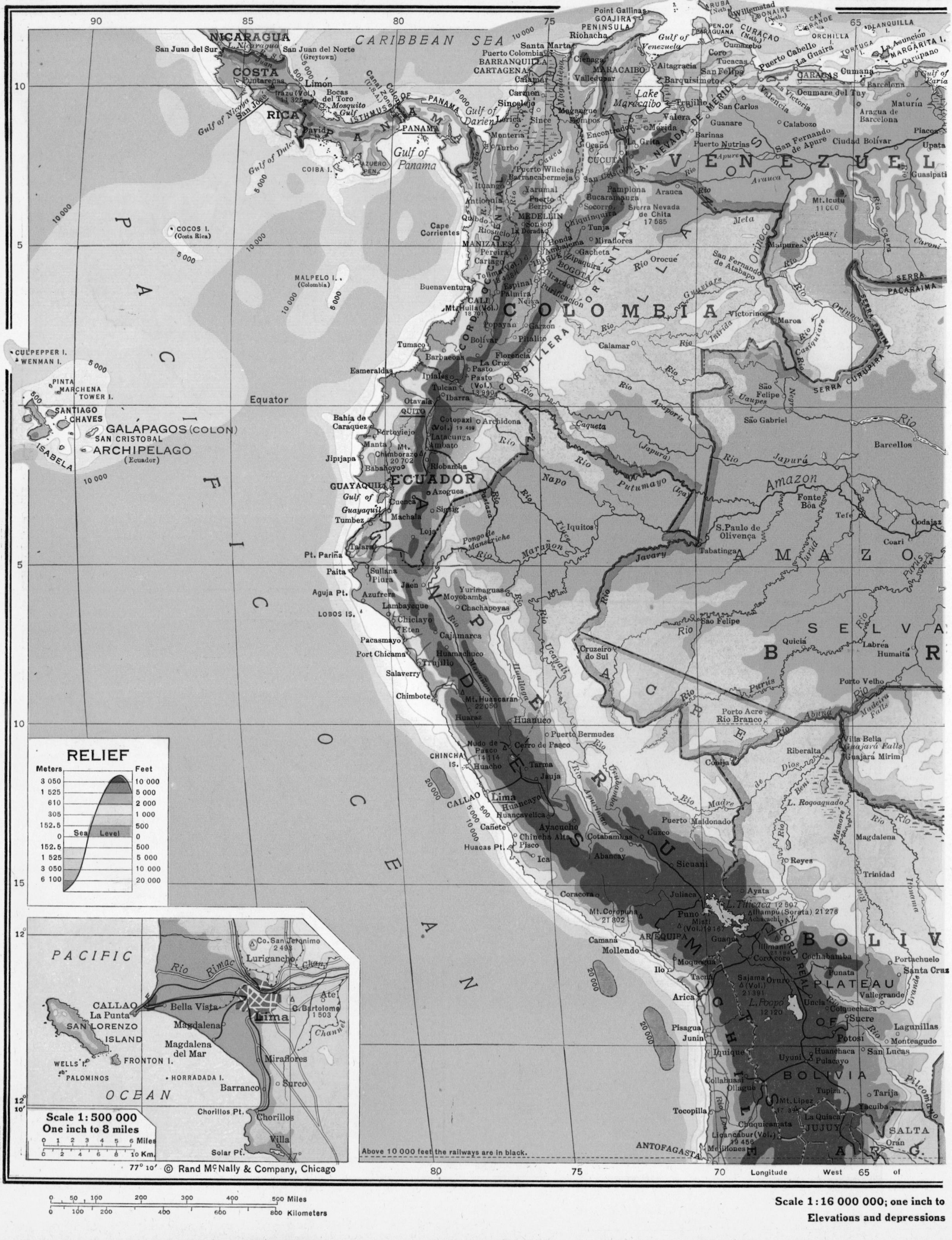

Scale 1:16 000 000; one inch to
Elevations and depressions

250 miles. Sinusoidal Projection

are given in feet

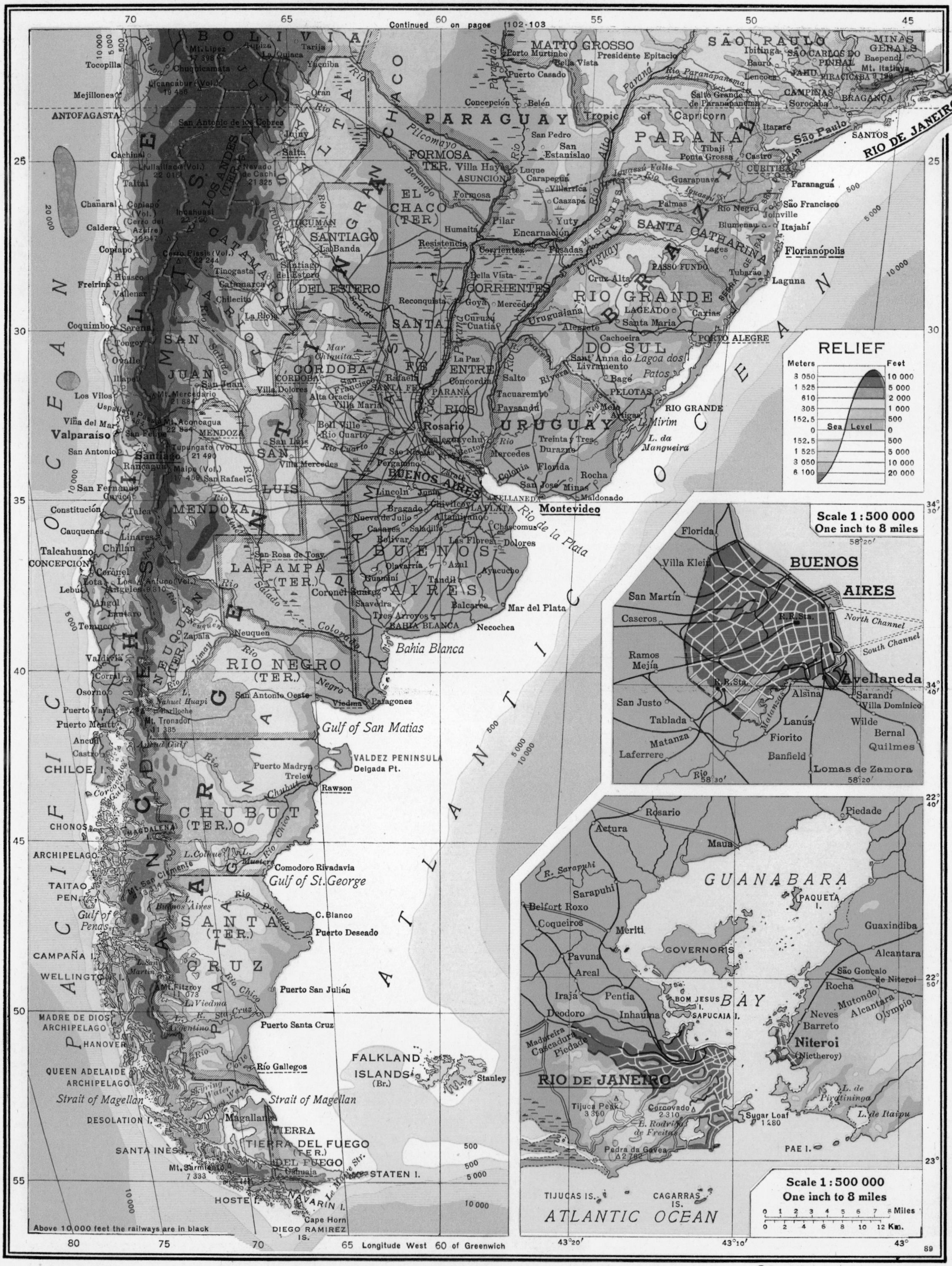

Scale 1:16 000 000; one inch to 250 miles. Sinusoidal Projection

Elevations and depressions are given in feet

ATLANTIC OCEAN

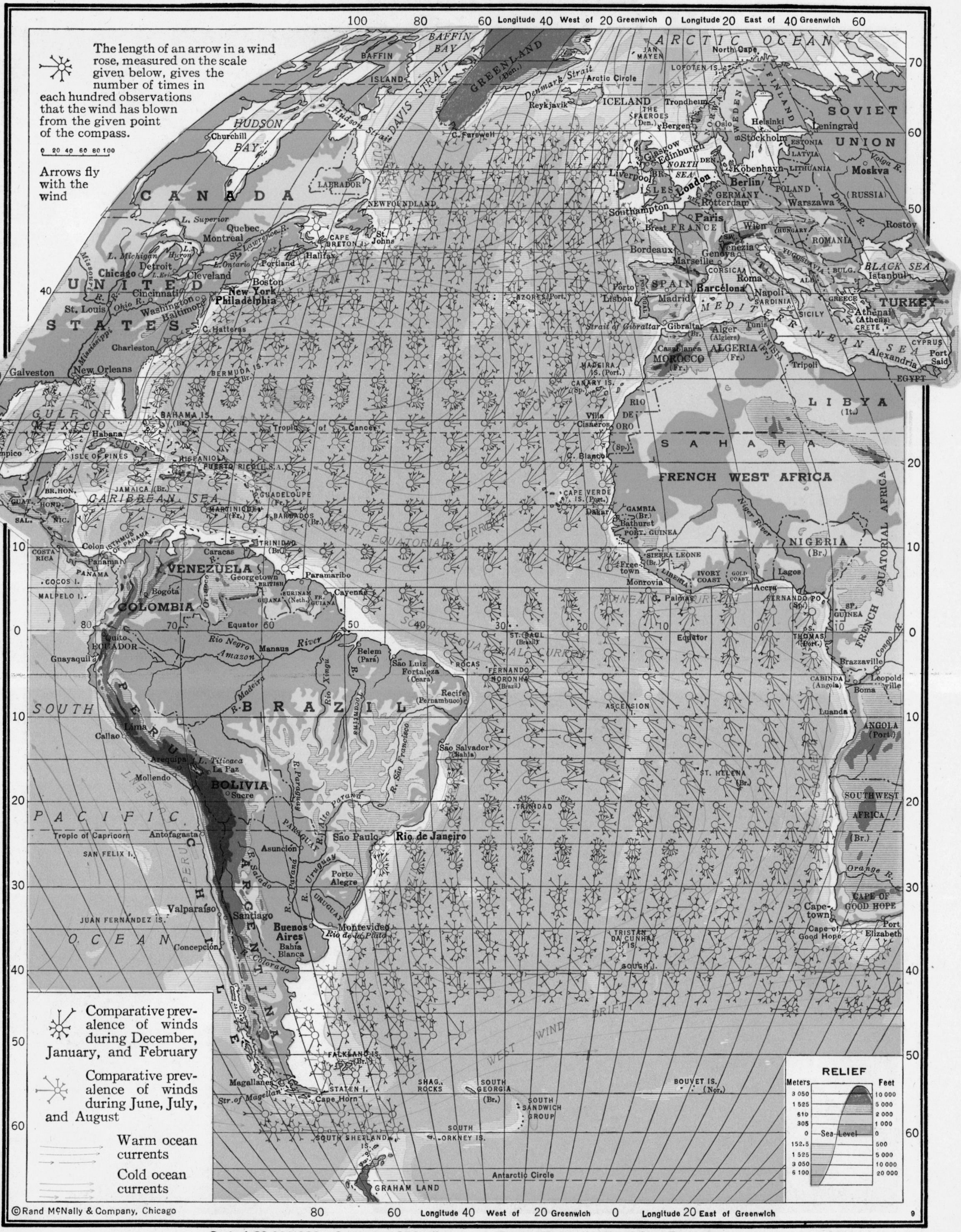

Scale 1:60 000 000; One inch to 950 miles. Goode's Homolosine Equal Area Projection.

0 50 100 200 300 400 500 Miles

0 100 200 400 600 800 Kilometers

Scale 1 : 16 000 000; one inch to 250 miles. **Conic Projection**

Elevations and depressions are given in feet

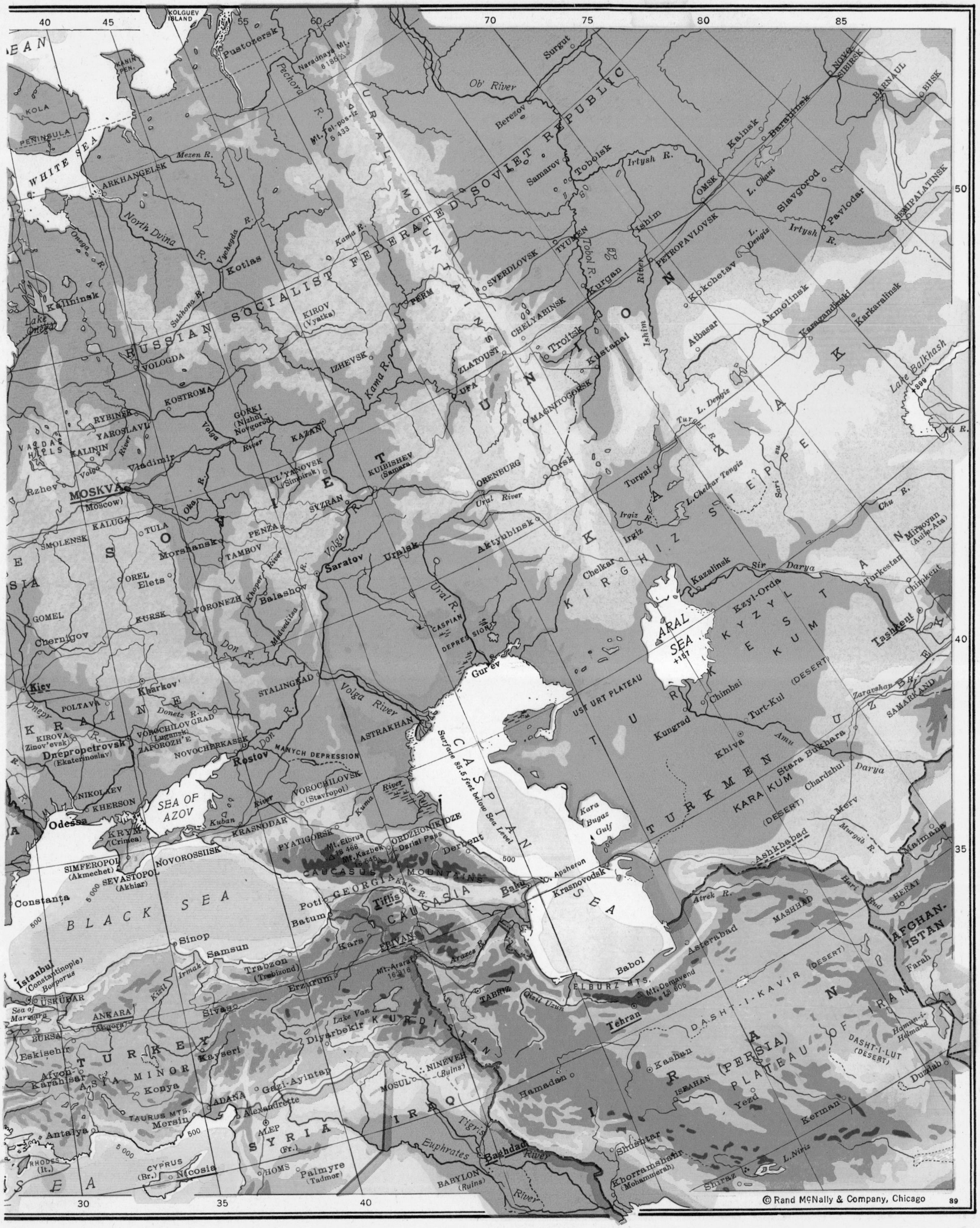
KOLGUEV ISLAND
Pustozersk
Naradnaya Mt. 6185
Pechora R.
KANIN PEN.
KOLA PENINSULA
WHITE SEA
Mt. Tel-pos-Iz 5 433
URAL MOUNTAINS
Ob' River
Surgut
NOVOSIBIRSK
BARNAUL
BIISK
Berezov
Mezen R.
ARKHANGELSK
RUSSIAN SOCIALIST FEDERATED SOVIET REPUBLIC
Samarov
Tobolsk
Irtysh R.
Kainsk
Barabinsk
OMSK
L. Chani
Slavgorod
SEMIPALATINSK
Pavlodar
North Dvina R.
Vychegda R.
Onega R.
Kama R.
SVERDLOVSK
TYUMEN
Tobol R.
Ishim
PETROPAVLOVSK
Dengiz
Irtysh R.
Kotlas
Kalininsk
Sukhona R.
Lake Onega
KIROV (Vyatka)
PERM
CHELYABINSK
Kurgan
Ishim River
Kokchetav
Akmolinsk
Karagandinski
Karkaralinsk
Atbasar
Troitsk
Kustanai
VOLOGDA
IZHEVSK
ZLATOUST
Lake Balkhash
RYBINSK
KOSTROMA
GORKI (Nizhni Novgorod)
Kama R.
UFA
MAGNITOGORSK
L. Dengiz
YAROSLAVL
VALDAI HILLS
KALININ
Volga River
KAZAN
Turgai R.
Vladimir
UL'YANOVSK (Simbirsk)
KUIBISHEV (Samara)
ORENBURG
Orsk
Turgai
L. Chelkar Tengiz
Sari su
Rzhev
MOSKVA (Moscow)
Oka R.
SYZRAN
Ural River
Irgiz R.
Chu R.
KALUGA
TULA
PENZA
Aktyubinsk
KIRGHIZ STEPPE
Mirsoyan (Aulie-Ata)
SMOLENSK
Morshansk
TAMBOV
Volga R.
Saratov
Uralsk
Chelkar
Irgiz
Kazalinsk
Sir Darya
Turkestan
Chimkent
OREL
Elets
Balashov
Khoper River
ARAL SEA +157
Kzyl-Orda
KYZYL KUM
GOMEL
KURSK
VORONEZH
Ural R.
CASPIAN DEPRESSION
Tashkent
Chernigov
Don R.
Medveditsa
Gur'ev
Kiev
Kharkov'
STALINGRAD
Volga River
UST URT PLATEAU
Chimbai
(DESERT)
Zaravshan R.
SAMARKAND
POLTAVA
Dnepr
Donetz R.
VOROSHILOVGRAD (Lugansk)
ZAPOROZH'E
ASTRAKHAN
Kungrad
Turt-Kul
Amu
UKRAINE
KIROVA Zinov'evsk
Dnepropetrovsk (Ekaterinoslav)
NOVOCHERKASSK
Rostov
Don R.
MANYCH DEPRESSION
Surface 85.5 feet below Sea Level
CASPIAN SEA
Khiva
Stara Bukhara
Chardzhui
Darya
TURKMEN
KARA KUM
(DESERT)
Merv
NIKOLAEV
KHERSON
SEA OF AZOV
VOROSHILOVSK (Stavropol)
Kuma R.
Kara Bugaz Gulf
Odessa
KRYM (Crimea)
Kuban
KRASNODAR
PYATIGORSK
ORDZHONIKIDZE
Mt. Elbrus 18 468
Mt. Kazbek 16 545
Darial Pass
Derbent
Ashkhabad
Murgab R.
Maimana
SIMFEROPOL (Akmechet)
SEVASTOPOL (Akbiar)
NOVOROSSIISK
CAUCASUS MOUNTAINS
GEORGIA
CAUCASIA
Baku
C. Apsheron
Krasnovodsk
Atrek R.
Hari Rud
HERAT
Constanța
BLACK SEA
Poti
Batum
Tiflis
Kura R.
MASHHAD
AFGHANISTAN
Sinop
Samsun
Kars
ERIVAN
Araxes R.
Asterabad
Farah
Istanbul (Constantinople)
Bosporus
Trabzon (Trebizond)
Erzurum
Mt. Ararat 16 916
Babol
ELBURZ MTS.
Mt. Demavend 18 606
DASHT-I-KAVIR (DESERT)
ÜSKÜDAR
Sea of Marmara
ANKARA (Angora)
Sivas
TABRIZ
Qizil Uzun
Tehran
BURSA
Eskisehir
TURKEY
Lake Van
KURDISTAN
Diyarbekir
Kayseri
DASHT-I-LUT (DESERT)
Hamun-i-Helmand
PLATEAU OF IRAN
Afyon Karahisar
ASIA MINOR
Konya
NINEVEH (Ruins)
MOSUL
Hamadan
Kashan
IRAN (PERSIA)
ISFAHAN
Yezd
Duzdab
ADANA
Gazi-Ayintap
Alexandretta
TAURUS MTS.
Mersin
ALEP
IRAQ
Tigris
Kerman
Antalya
SYRIA (Fr.)
Euphrates
Baghdad
Shushtar
L. Niriz
RHODES (It.)
CYPRUS (Br.)
Nicosia
HOMS
Palmyre (Tadmor)
BABYLON (Ruins)
Khorramshahr (Mohammerah)
Shiraz
SEA

89

Scale 1:16 000 000; one inch to 250 miles. Conic Projection.

After Language Map by Morris Jastrow

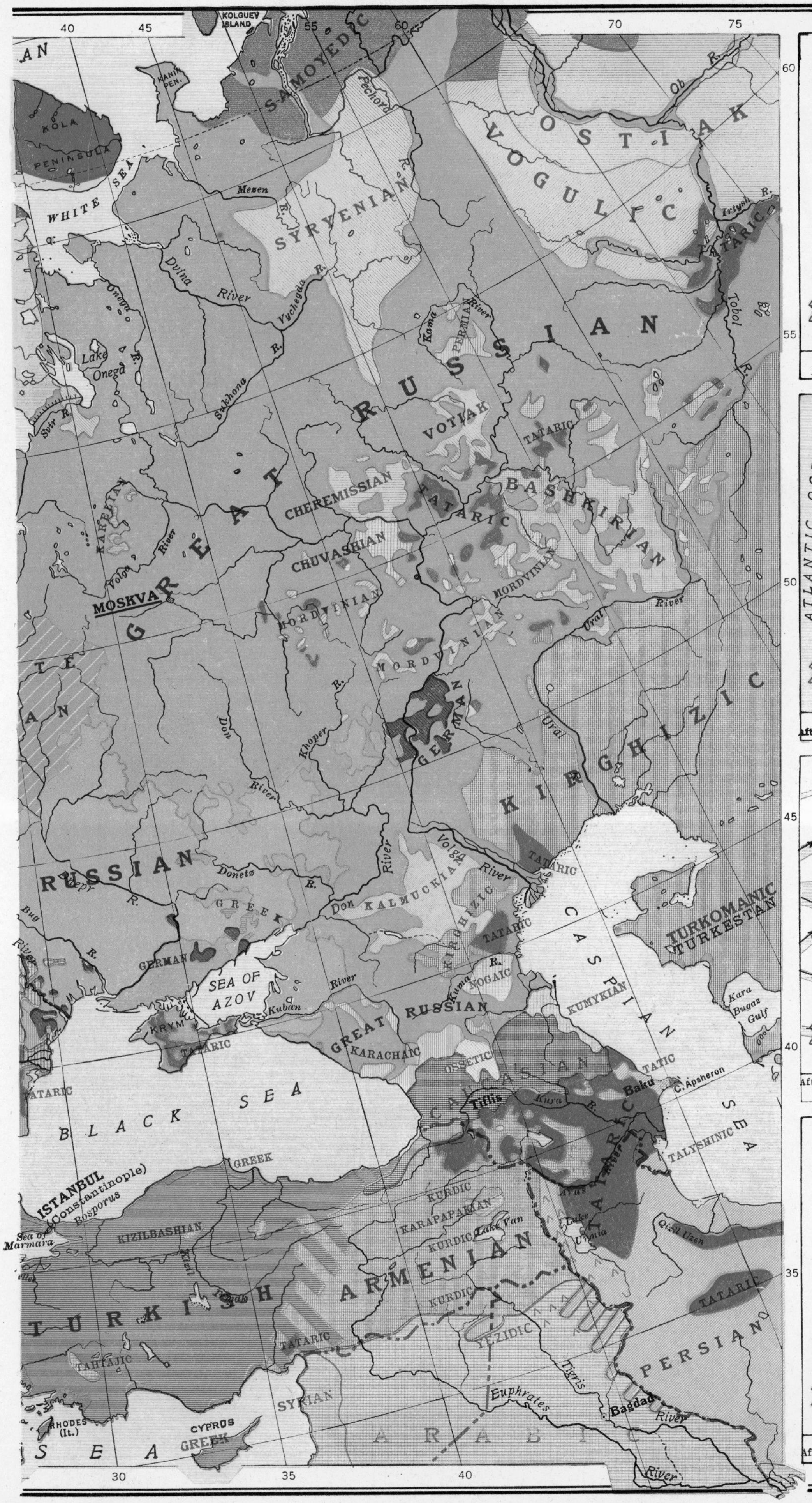

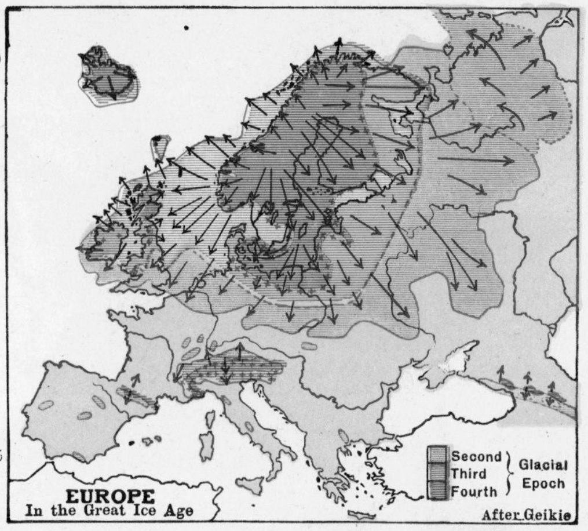

EUROPE
In the Great Ice Age
After Geikie

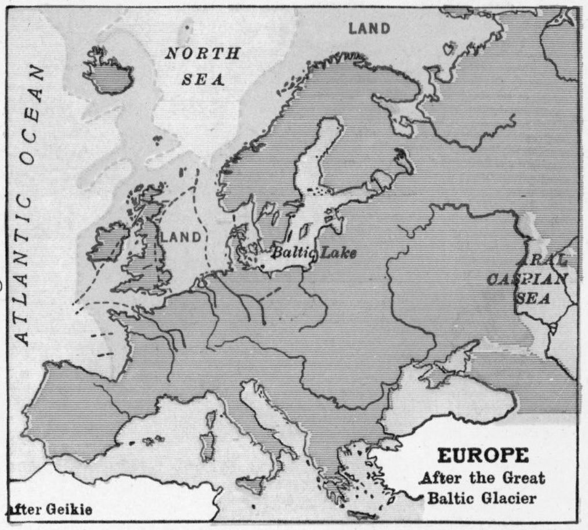

EUROPE
After the Great Baltic Glacier
After Geikie

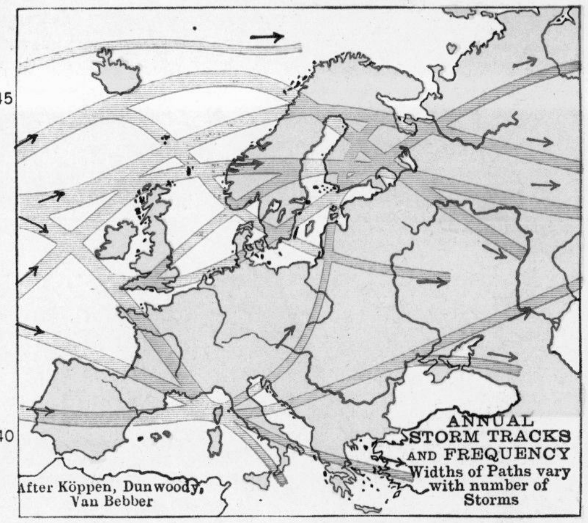

ANNUAL STORM TRACKS AND FREQUENCY
Widths of Paths vary with number of Storms
After Köppen, Dunwoody, Van Bebber

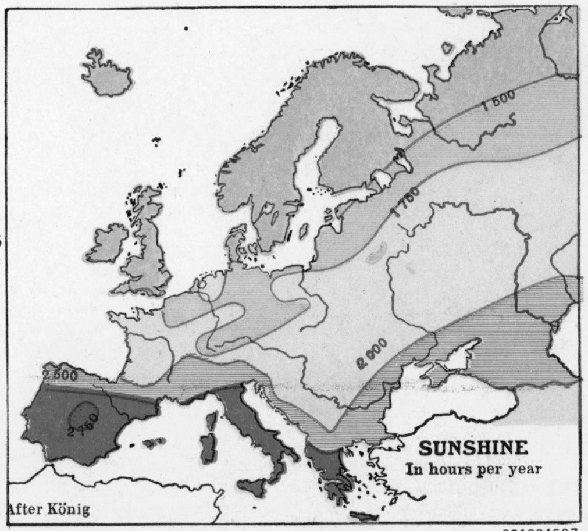

SUNSHINE
In hours per year
After König

901234567

EUROPE

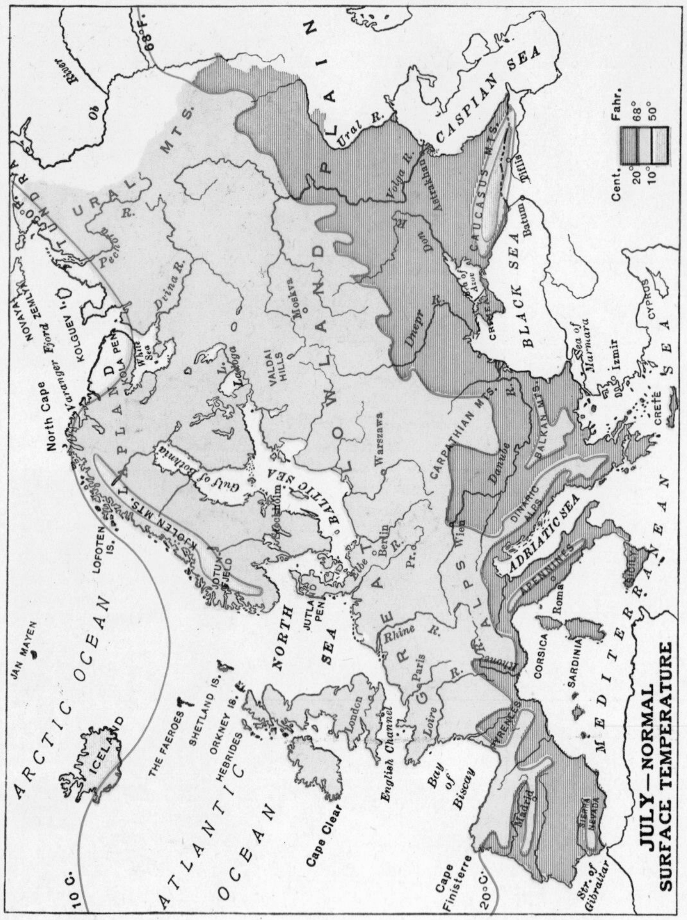
JULY—NORMAL
SURFACE TEMPERATURE
Cent. 20° 10°
Fahr. 68° 50°

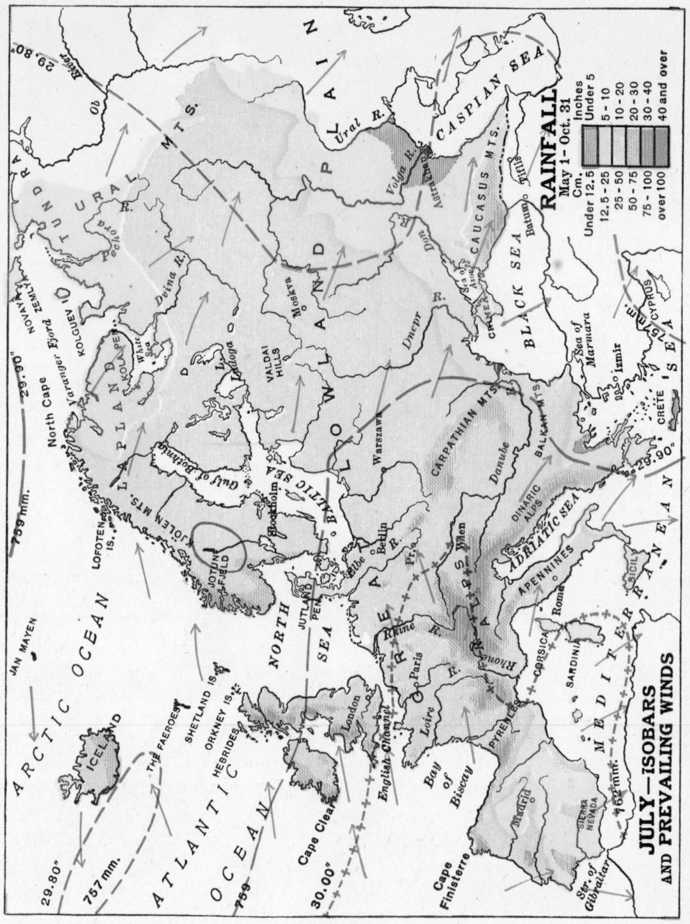
JULY—ISOBARS
AND PREVAILING WINDS
RAINFALL
May 1 - Oct. 31
Cm. Under 12.5, 12.5 - 25, 25 - 50, 50 - 75, 75 - 100, over 100
Inches Under 5, 5 - 10, 10 - 20, 20 - 30, 30 - 40, 40 and over

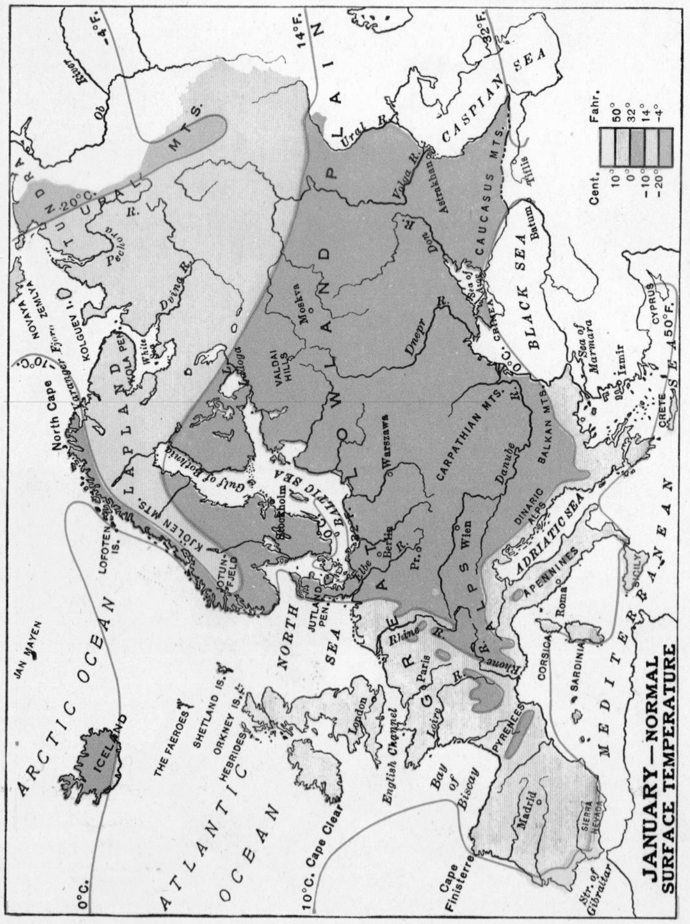
JANUARY—NORMAL
SURFACE TEMPERATURE
Cent. 10° 0° -10° -20°
Fahr. 50° 32° 14° -4°

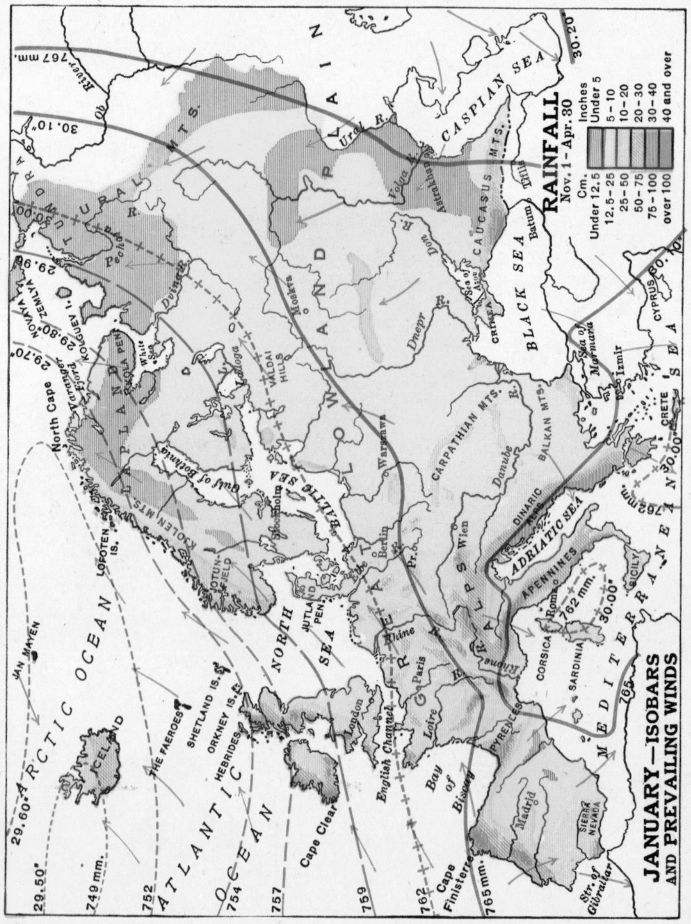
JANUARY—ISOBARS
AND PREVAILING WINDS
RAINFALL
Nov. 1 - Apr. 30
Cm. Under 12.5, 12.5 - 25, 25 - 50, 50 - 75, 75 - 100, over 100
Inches Under 5, 5 - 10, 10 - 20, 20 - 30, 30 - 40, 40 and over

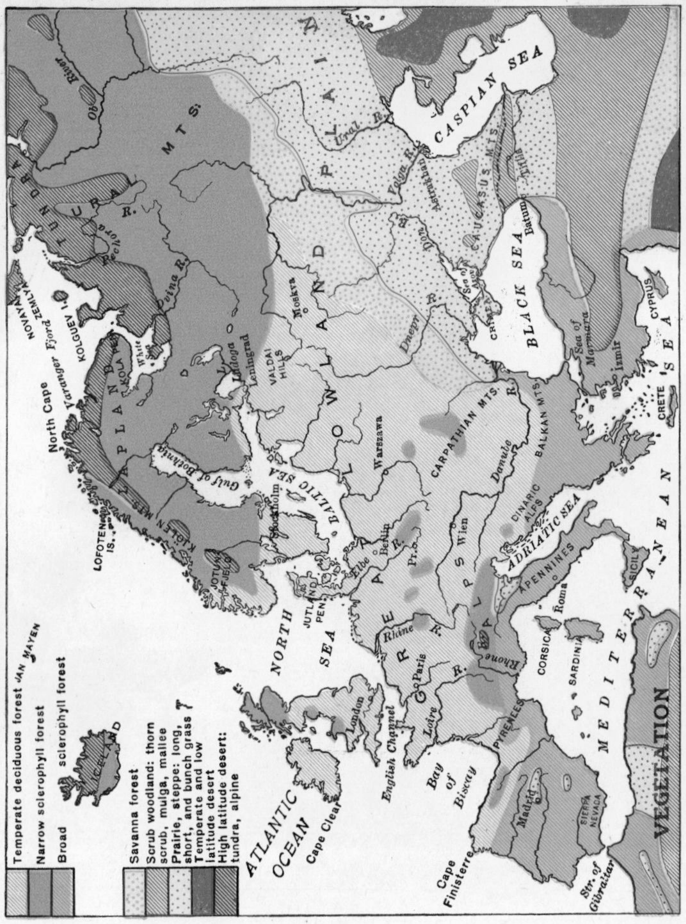

VEGETATION

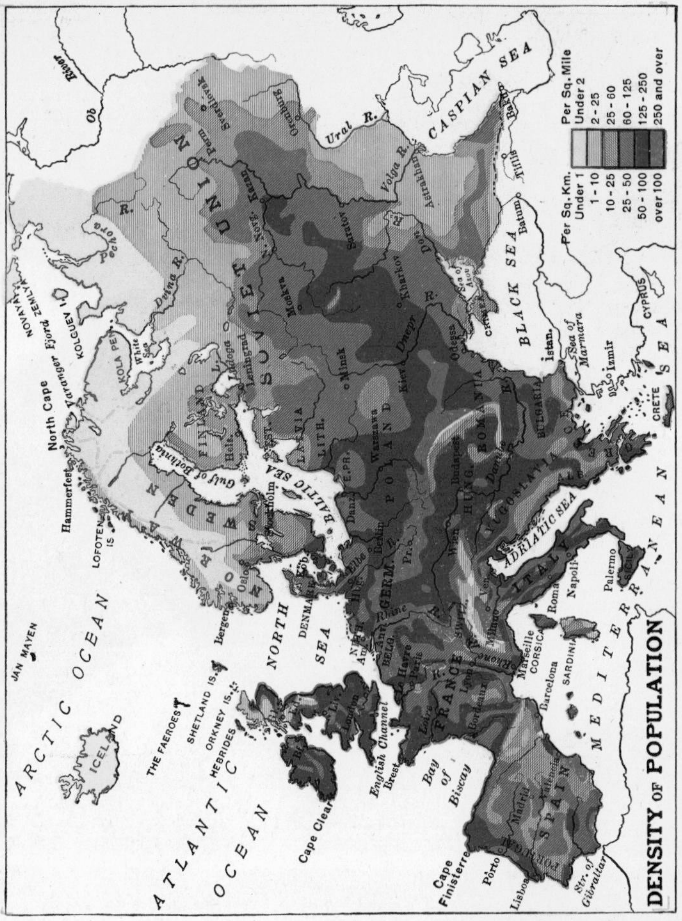

DENSITY OF POPULATION

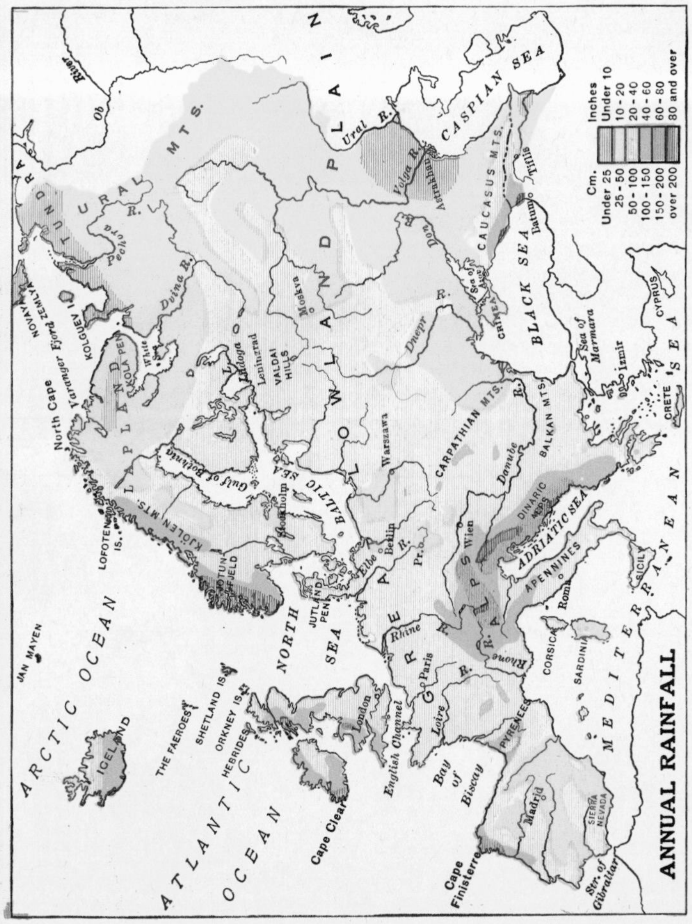

ANNUAL RAINFALL

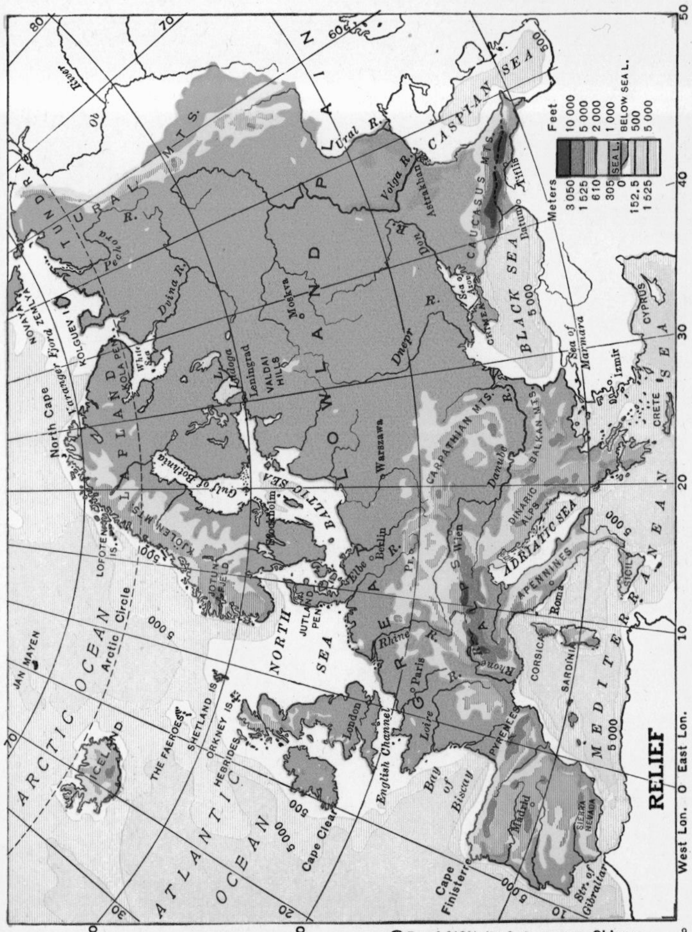

RELIEF

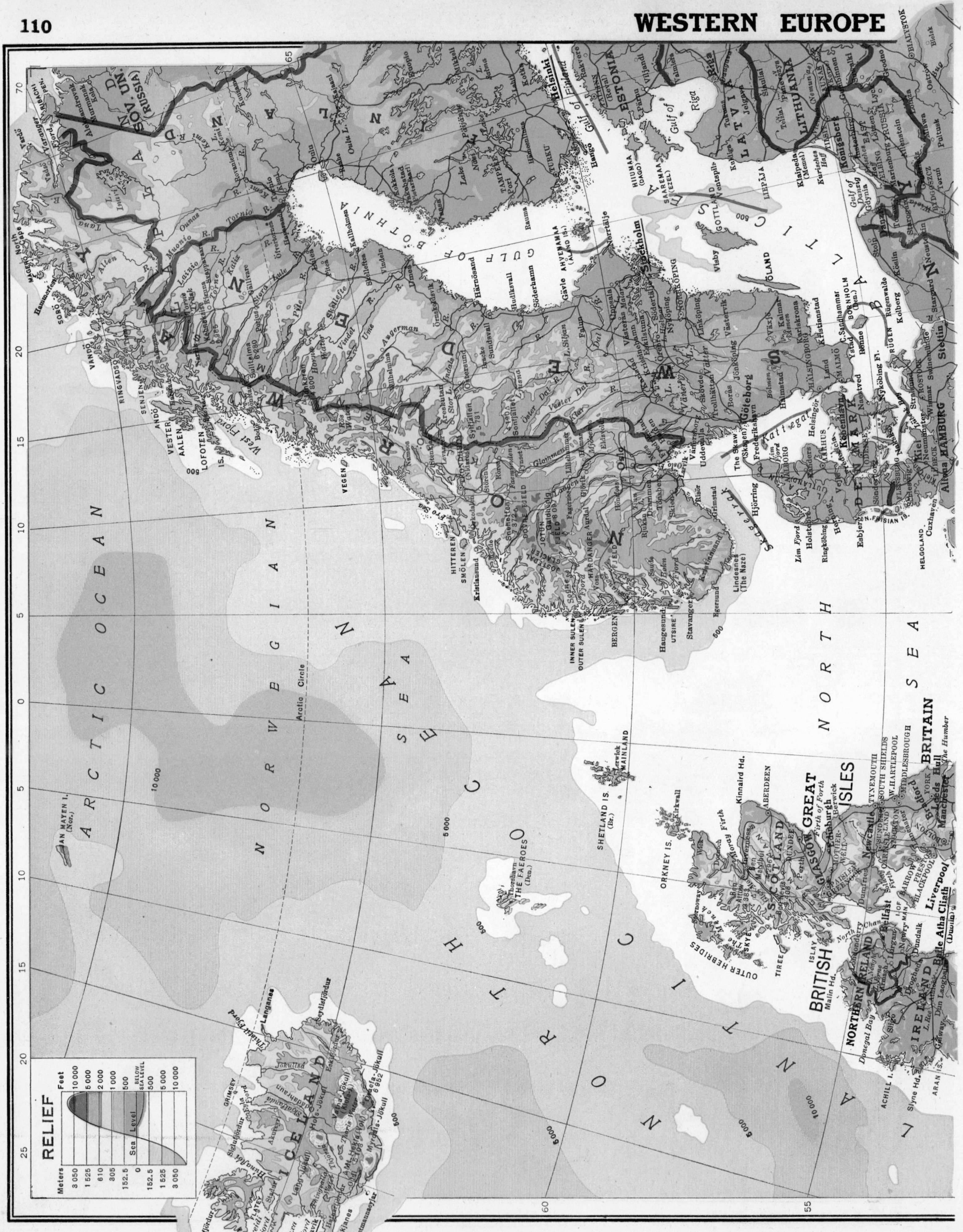
ARCTIC OCEAN
NORWEGIAN SEA
NORTH ATLANTIC OCEAN
NORTH SEA
GULF OF BOTHNIA
BALTIC SEA
ICELAND
THE FAEROES (Den.)
SHETLAND IS. (Br.)
ORKNEY IS.
BRITISH ISLES
GREAT BRITAIN
SCOTLAND
NORTHERN IRELAND
IRELAND
NORWAY
SWEDEN
FINLAND
DENMARK
ESTONIA
LATVIA
LITHUANIA
SOV. UN. (RUSSIA)
JAN MAYEN I. (Nor.)
Arctic Circle
Stockholm
Oslo
Helsinki
Riga
Reykjavik
RELIEF
Meters
Feet
Sea Level
BELOW SEA LEVEL
3 050
1 525
610
305
152.5
0
10 000
5 000
2 000
1 000
500

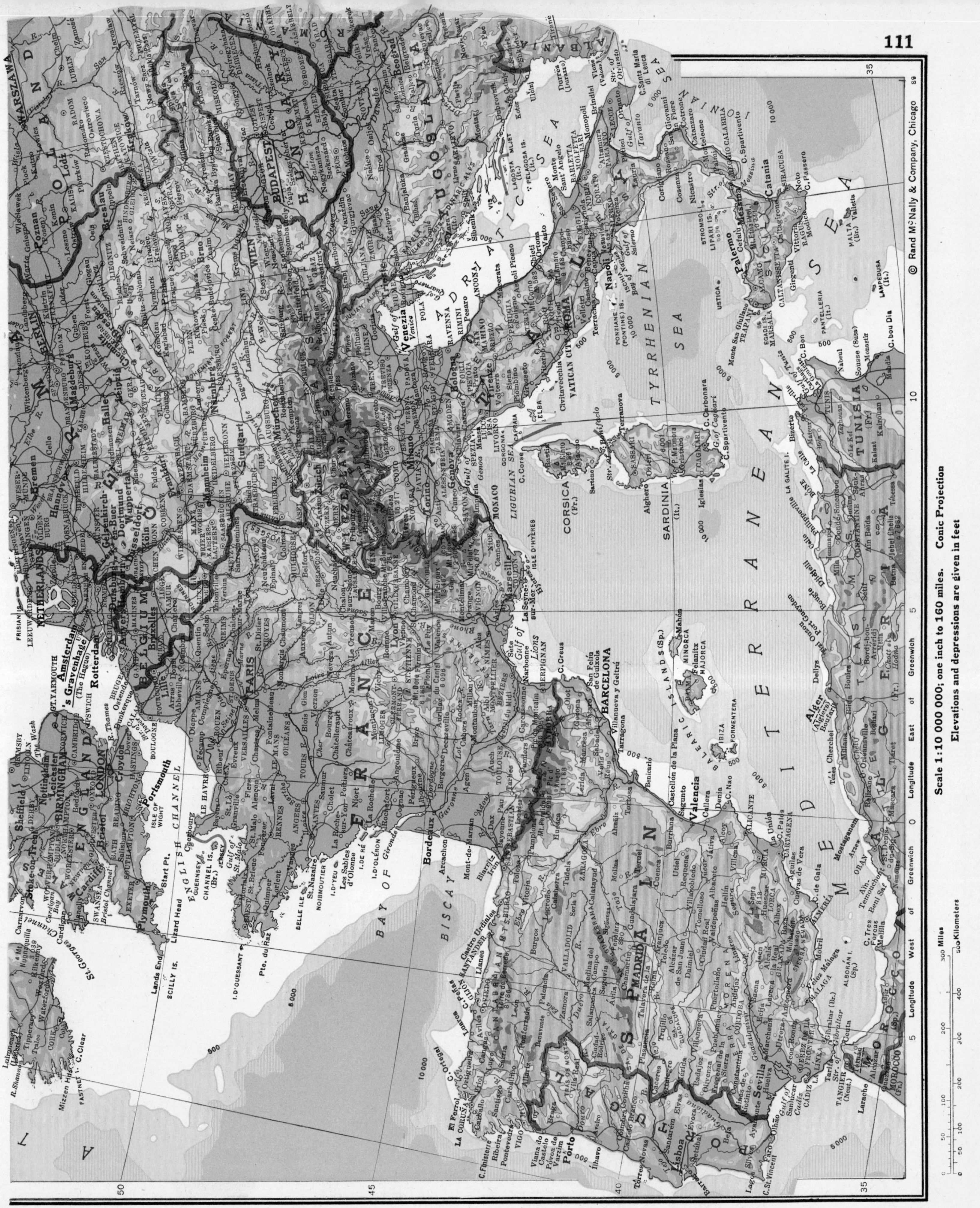

Scale 1:10 000 000; one inch to 160 miles. Conic Projection

Elevations and depressions are given in feet

SOVIET UNION IN EUROPE

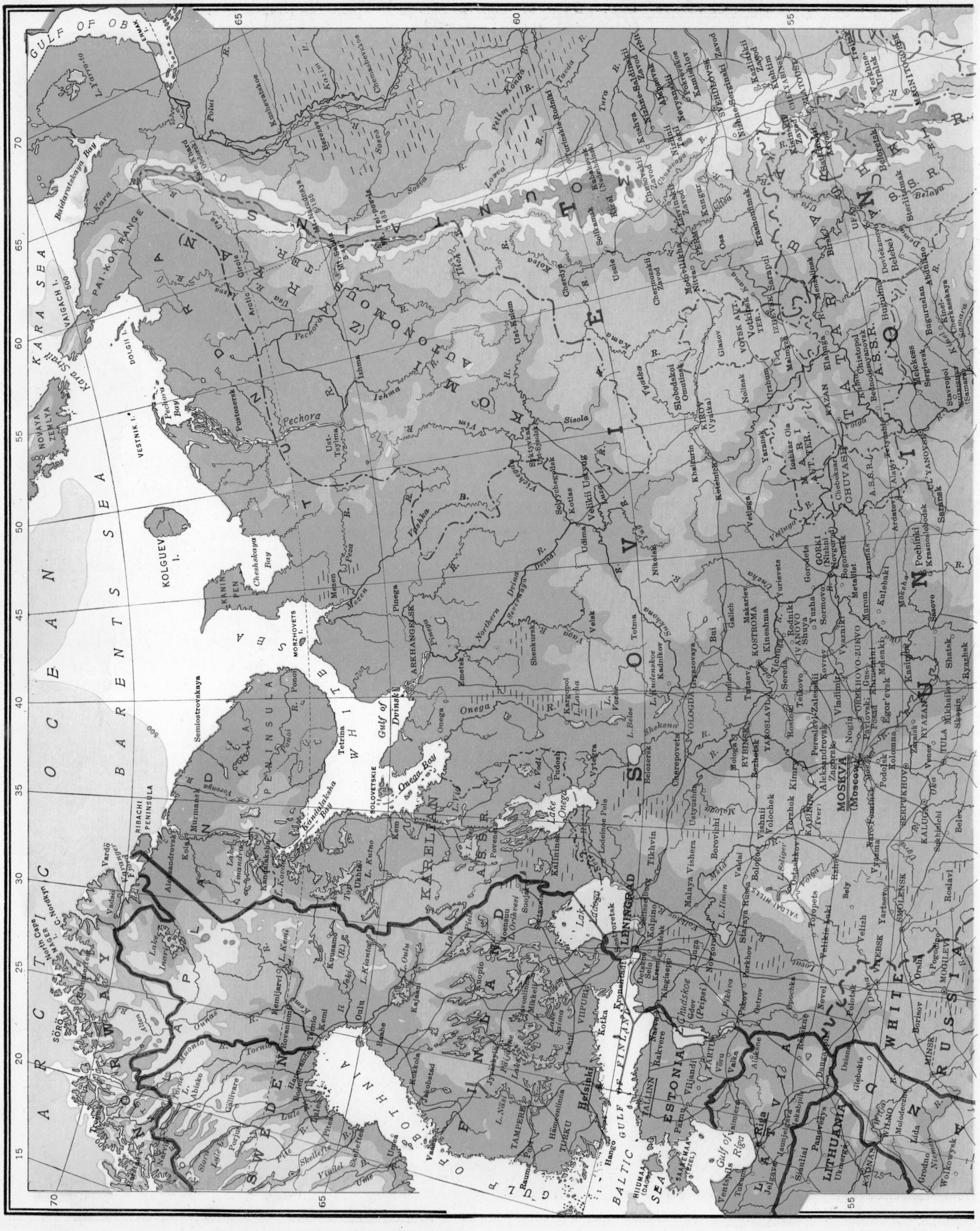

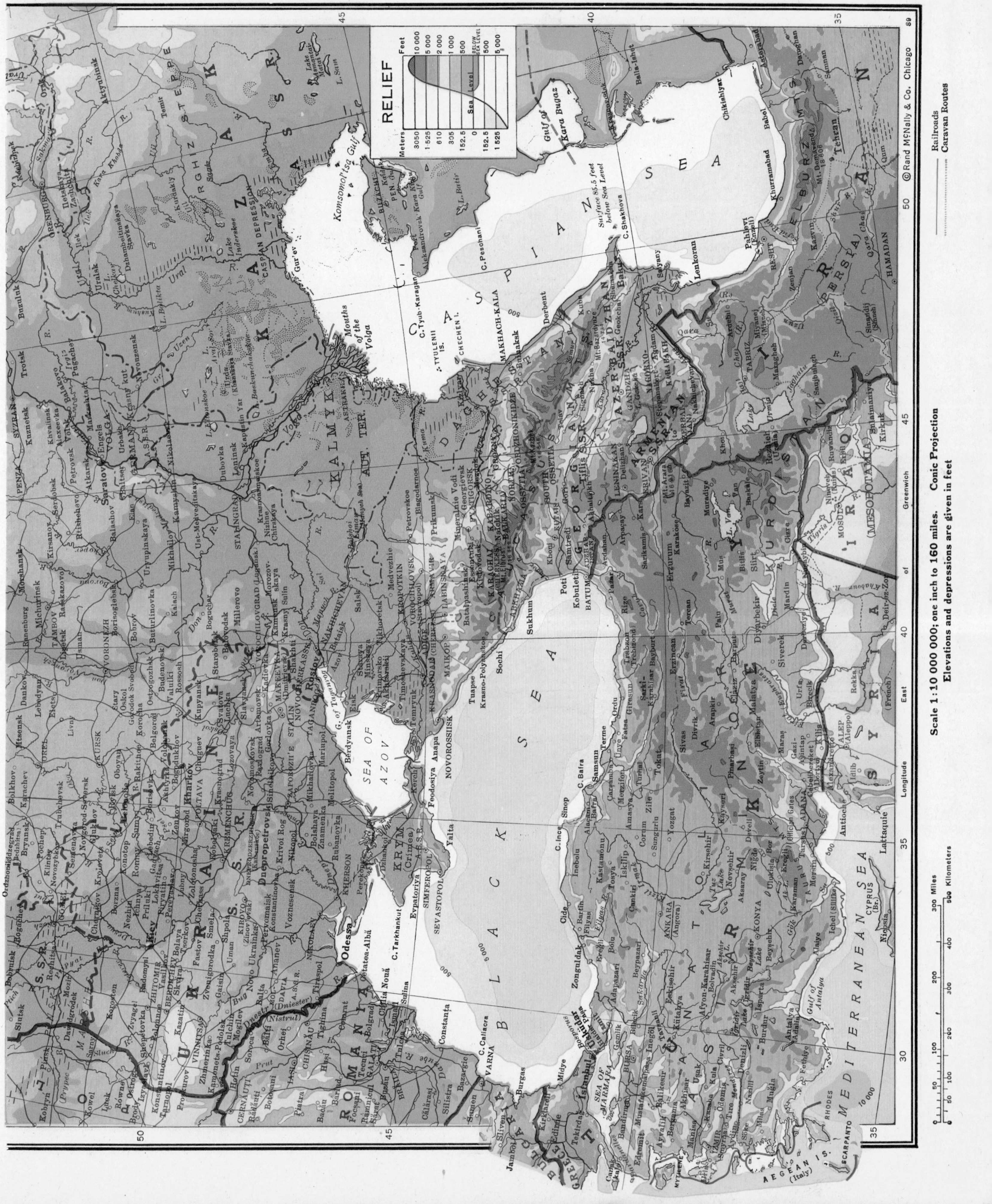
RELIEF
Meters
Feet
Sea Level
BELOW SEA LEVEL
BLACK SEA
CASPIAN SEA
SEA OF AZOV
MEDITERRANEAN SEA
TURKEY
PERSIA
IRAQ (MESOPOTAMIA)
SYRIA (French)
ROMANIA
KRYM (Crimea)
Scale 1:10 000 000; one inch to 160 miles. Conic Projection
Elevations and depressions are given in feet
© Rand McNally & Co. Chicago
Railroads
Caravan Routes
Miles
Kilometers

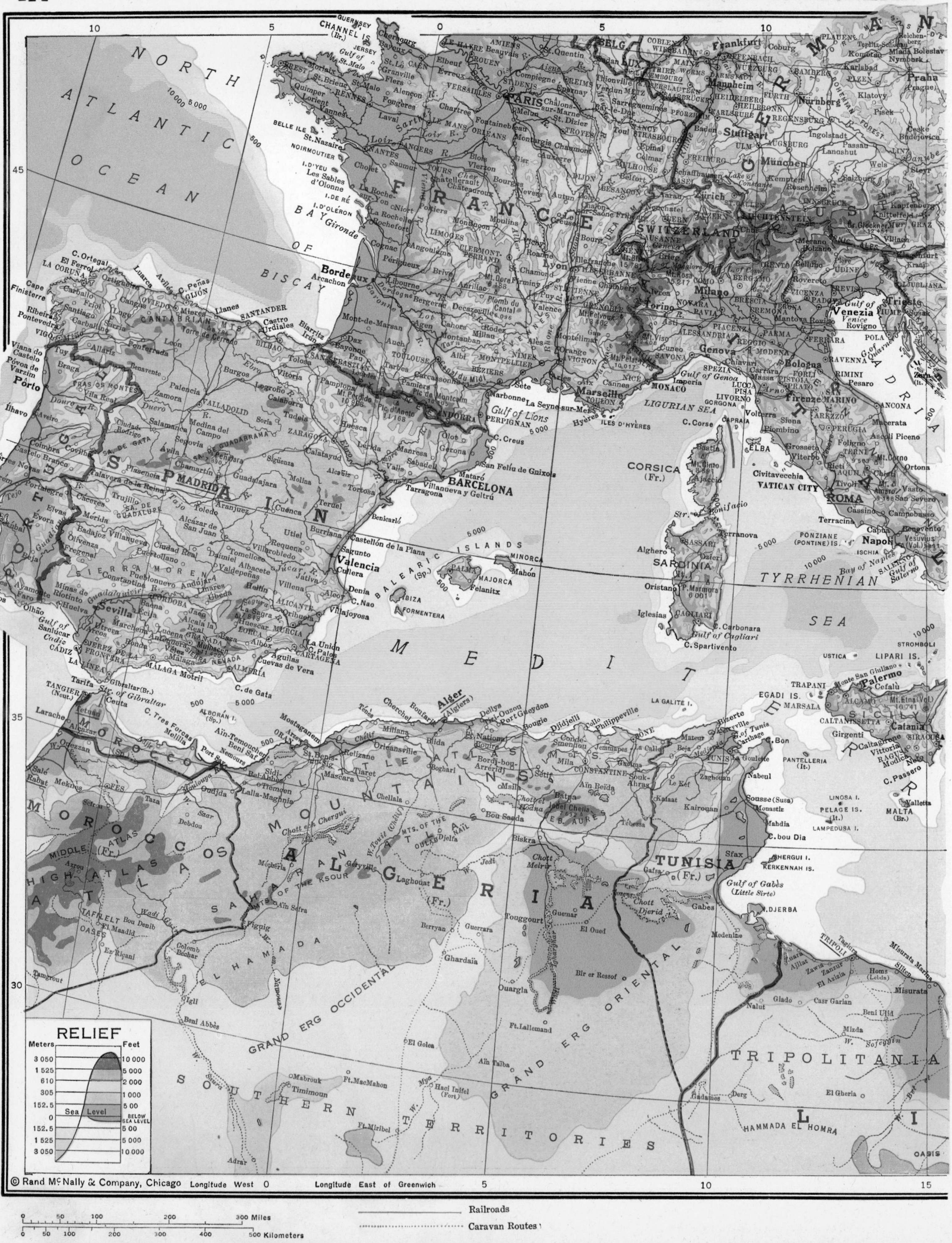
NORTH ATLANTIC OCEAN
BAY OF BISCAY
FRANCE
SPAIN
PORTUGAL
GERMANY
SWITZERLAND
ITALY
CORSICA (Fr.)
SARDINIA (It.)
BALEARIC ISLANDS
MAJORCA
MINORCA
IBIZA
FORMENTERA
Gulf of Lions
LIGURIAN SEA
TYRRHENIAN SEA
MEDITERRANEAN
ADRIATIC
VATICAN CITY
ANDORRA
MONACO
LIECHTENSTEIN
SICILY
MALTA (Br.)
MOROCCO
ALGERIA (Fr.)
TUNISIA (Fr.)
TRIPOLITANIA
LIBYA
SPANISH MOROCCO (Sp.)
TANGIER (Neut.)
Str. of Gibraltar
Gibraltar (Br.)
ATLAS MOUNTAINS
HIGH ATLAS
MIDDLE ATLAS
SAHARAN ATLAS
GRAND ERG OCCIDENTAL
GRAND ERG ORIENTAL
HAMMADA EL HOMRA
SOUTHERN TERRITORIES
PARIS
MADRID
Lisboa
BARCELONA
Valencia
Sevilla
Marseille
Lyon
Bordeaux
Milano
Torino
Genova
ROMA
Napoli
Palermo
Alger
Tunis
Tripoli
Frankfurt
Stuttgart
München
Praha
Venezia
Trieste
RELIEF
Meters
Feet
3 050
1 525
610
305
152.5
0
152.5
1 525
3 050
10 000
5 000
2 000
1 000
500
Sea Level
BELOW SEA LEVEL
© Rand McNally & Company, Chicago
Longitude West
Longitude East of Greenwich
Railroads
Caravan Routes
300 Miles
500 Kilometers

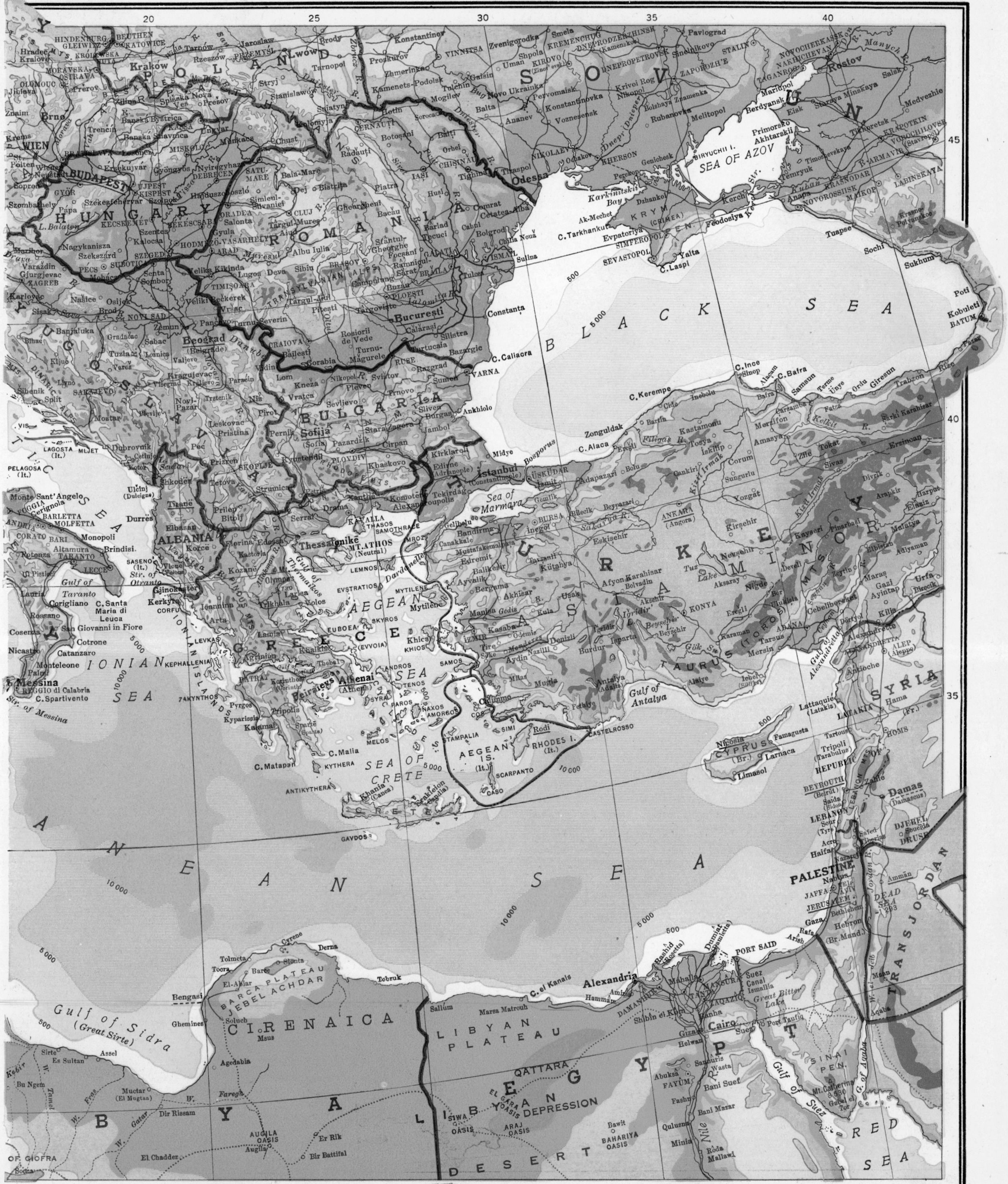

Scale 1:10 000 000; one inch to 160 miles. Bonne's Projection
Elevations and depressions are given in feet

0 10 20 40 60 80 100 120 Miles
0 20 40 80 120 160 200 Kilometers

Scale 1:4 000 000; one inch to 64 miles. Conic Projection

Elevations and depressions are given in feet

ENGLAND—Central Manufacturing Region

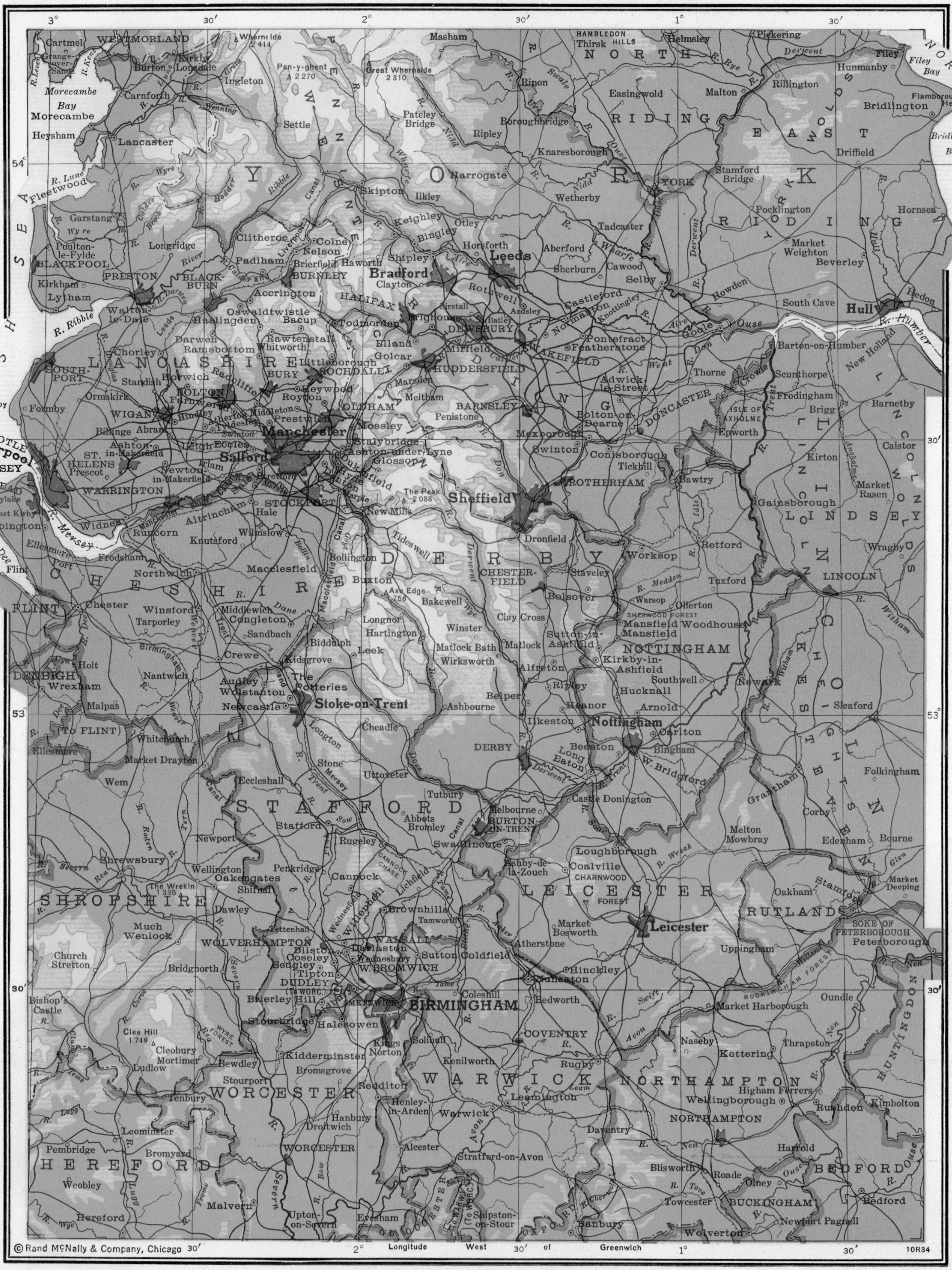

Scale 1:1 000 000; one inch to 16 miles. Sinusoidal Projection

Elevations and depressions are given in feet

Miles: 0 2 4 6 8 10 12 14 16 18 20

Kilometers: 0 4 8 12 16 20 24 28 32

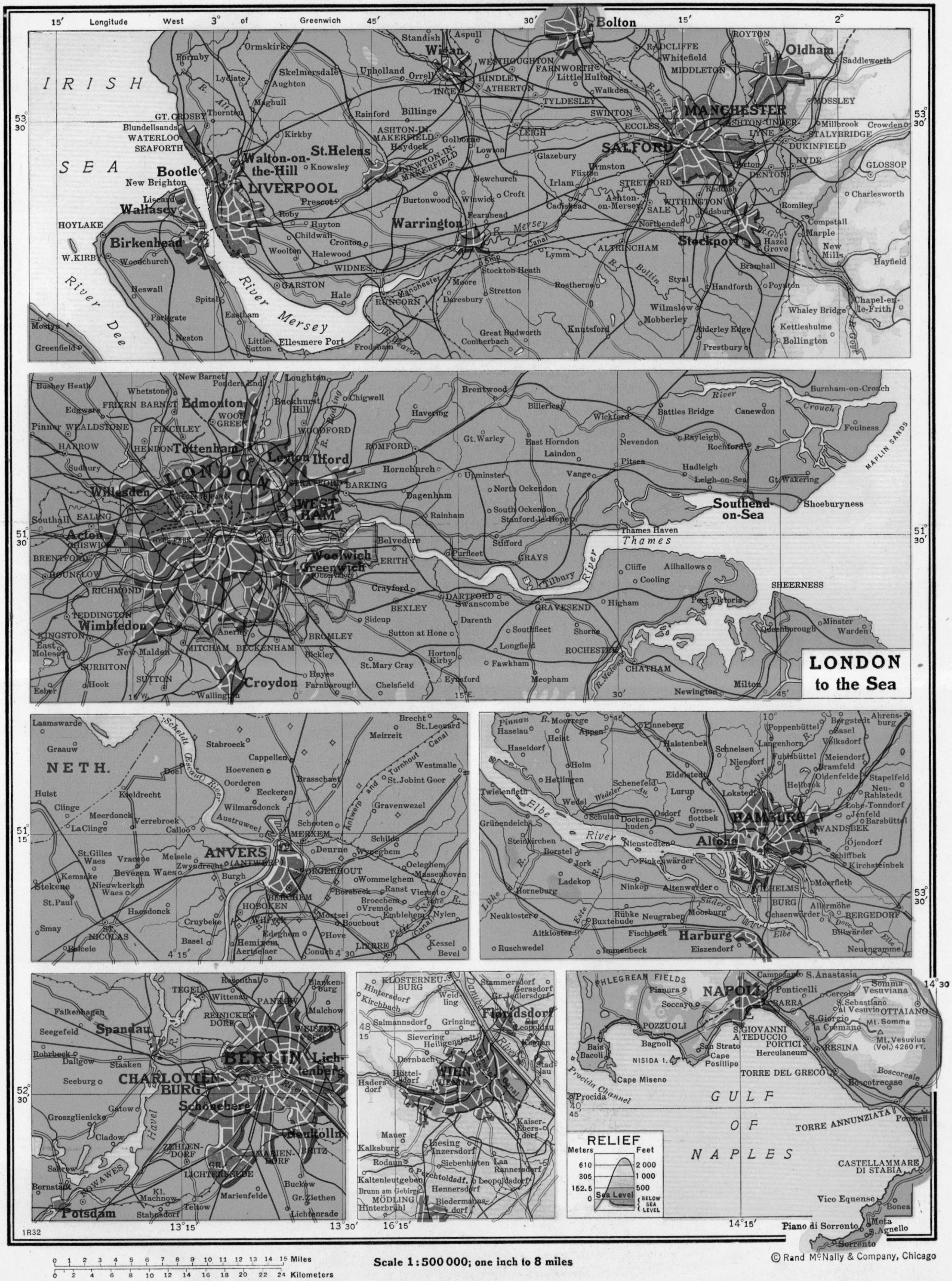

Scale 1:500 000; one inch to 8 miles

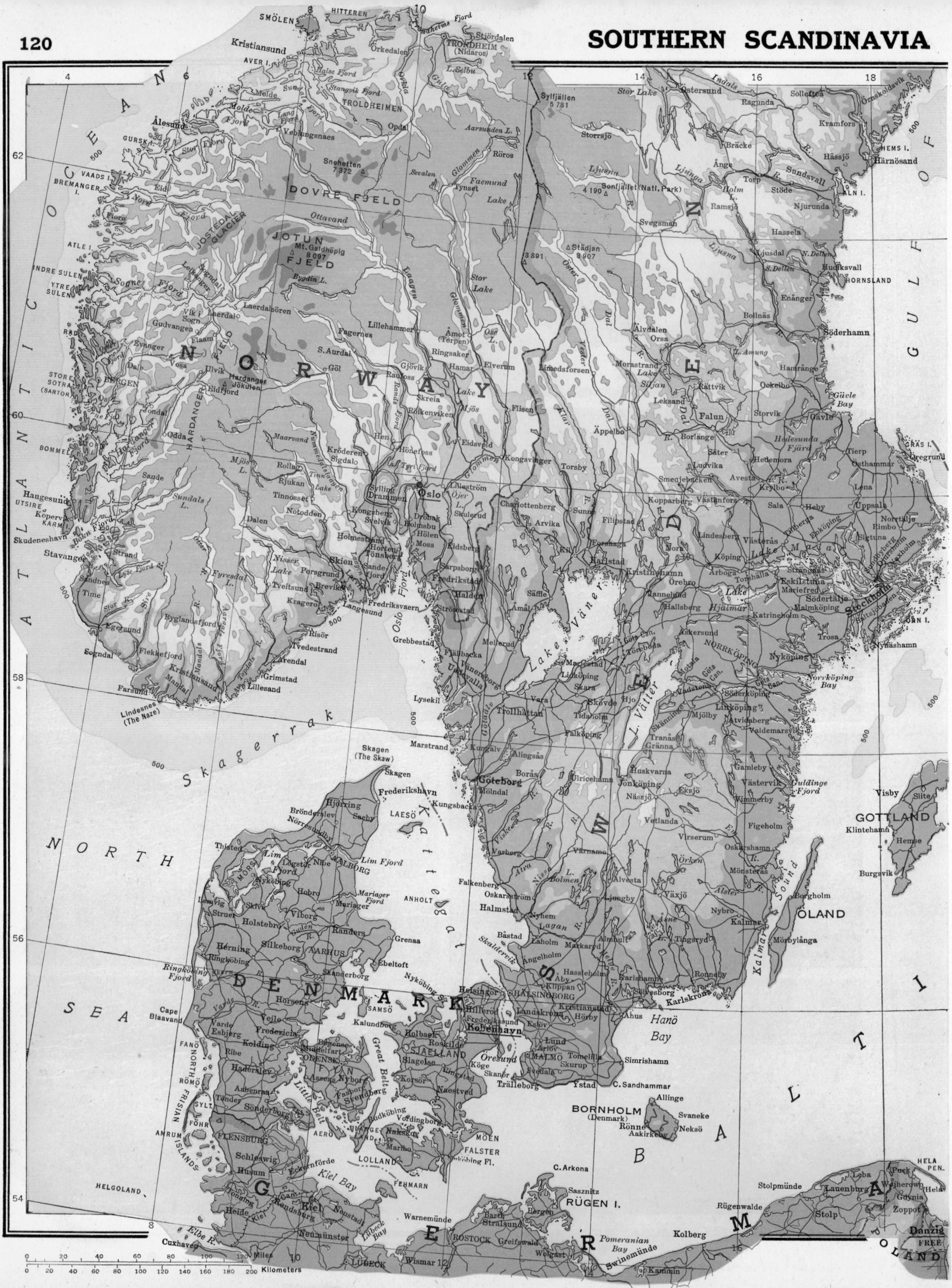
ATLANTIC OCEAN
NORWAY
SWEDEN
DENMARK
GERMANY
POLAND
NORTH SEA
BALTIC SEA
GULF OF BOTHNIA
Skagerrak
Kattegat
DOVRE FJELD
JOTUN FJELD
TROLDHEIMEN
JOSTEDAL GLACIER
HARDANGER JÖKULEN
Trondheim (Nidaros)
Kristiansund
Molde
Ålesund
Bergen
Stavanger
Haugesund
Egersund
Kristiansand
Mandal
Farsund
Lindesnes (The Naze)
Arendal
Grimstad
Lillesand
Risör
Kragerö
Skien
Larvik
Tönsberg
Horten
Drammen
Oslo
Moss
Sarpsborg
Fredrikstad
Halden
Lillehammer
Hamar
Gjövik
Kongsberg
Notodden
Rjukan
Elverum
Röros
Kongsvinger
Lake Väner
L. Vätter
Hjälmar Lake
Lake Mälar
Lake Siljan
Stockholm
Göteborg
Uppsala
Gävle
Falun
Karlstad
Örebro
Västerås
Norrköping
Nyköping
Linköping
Jönköping
Växjö
Kalmar
Karlskrona
Malmö
Lund
Hälsingborg
Halmstad
Trelleborg
Ystad
Simrishamn
Kalmar Sound
ÖLAND
GOTTLAND
Visby
BORNHOLM (Denmark)
Rönne
Hanö Bay
Östersund
Sundsvall
Härnösand
Söderhamn
Hudiksvall
København
Helsingör
Aalborg
Aarhus
Randers
Viborg
Esbjerg
Fredericia
Odense
Svendborg
Nyborg
Korsör
Slagelse
Kolding
Vejle
Horsens
Frederikshavn
Hjörring
Skagen (The Skaw)
Lim Fjord
SJAELLAND
FYN
LOLLAND
FALSTER
MÖEN
Great Belt
Little Belt
Öresund
Kiel Bay
Kiel
Flensburg
Schleswig
Husum
Rendsburg
Neumünster
Lübeck
Wismar
Rostock
Warnemünde
Stralsund
Greifswald
RÜGEN I.
Swinemünde
Kolberg
Rügenwalde
Stolp
Stolpmünde
Lauenburg
Danzig FREE
Gdynia
Zoppot
HELGOLAND
Cuxhaven
Elbe R.
NORTH FRISIAN ISLANDS
Pomeranian Bay
0 20 40 60 80 100 120 Miles
0 20 40 60 80 100 120 140 160 180 200 Kilometers

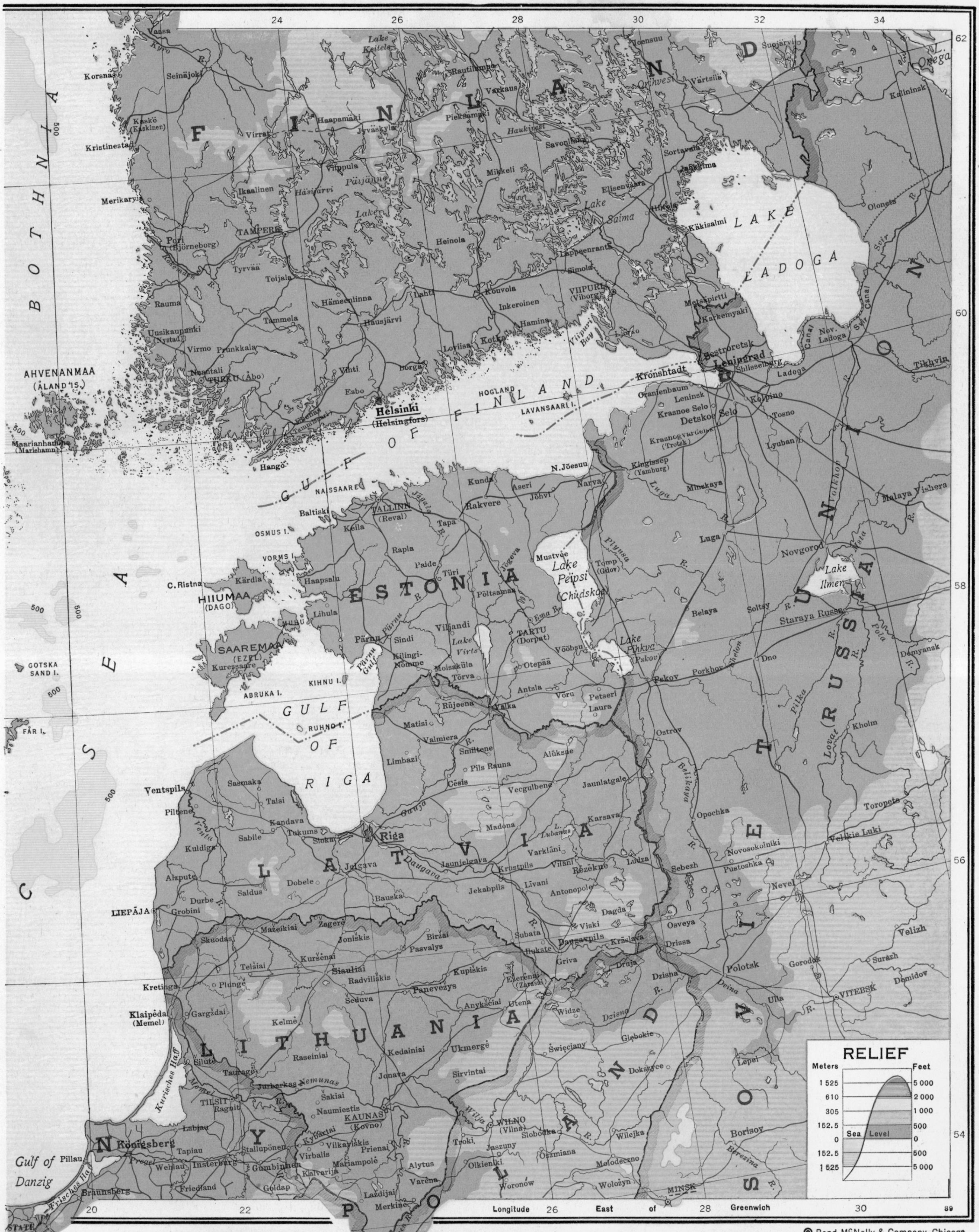

Scale 1 : 4 000 000; one inch to 64 miles.
Conic Projection
Elevations and depressions are given in feet

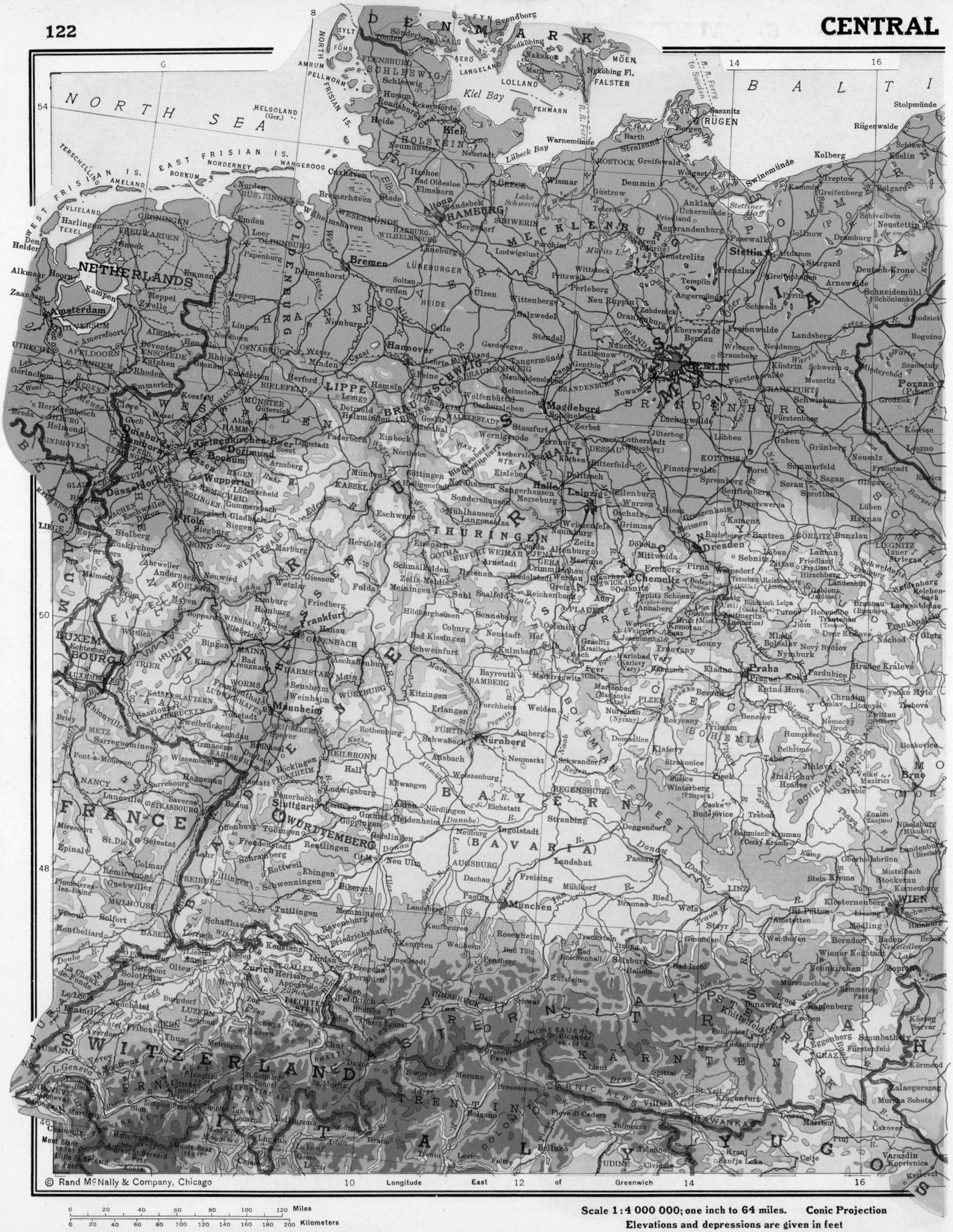

Scale 1 : 4 000 000; one inch to 64 miles. Conic Projection

Elevations and depressions are given in feet

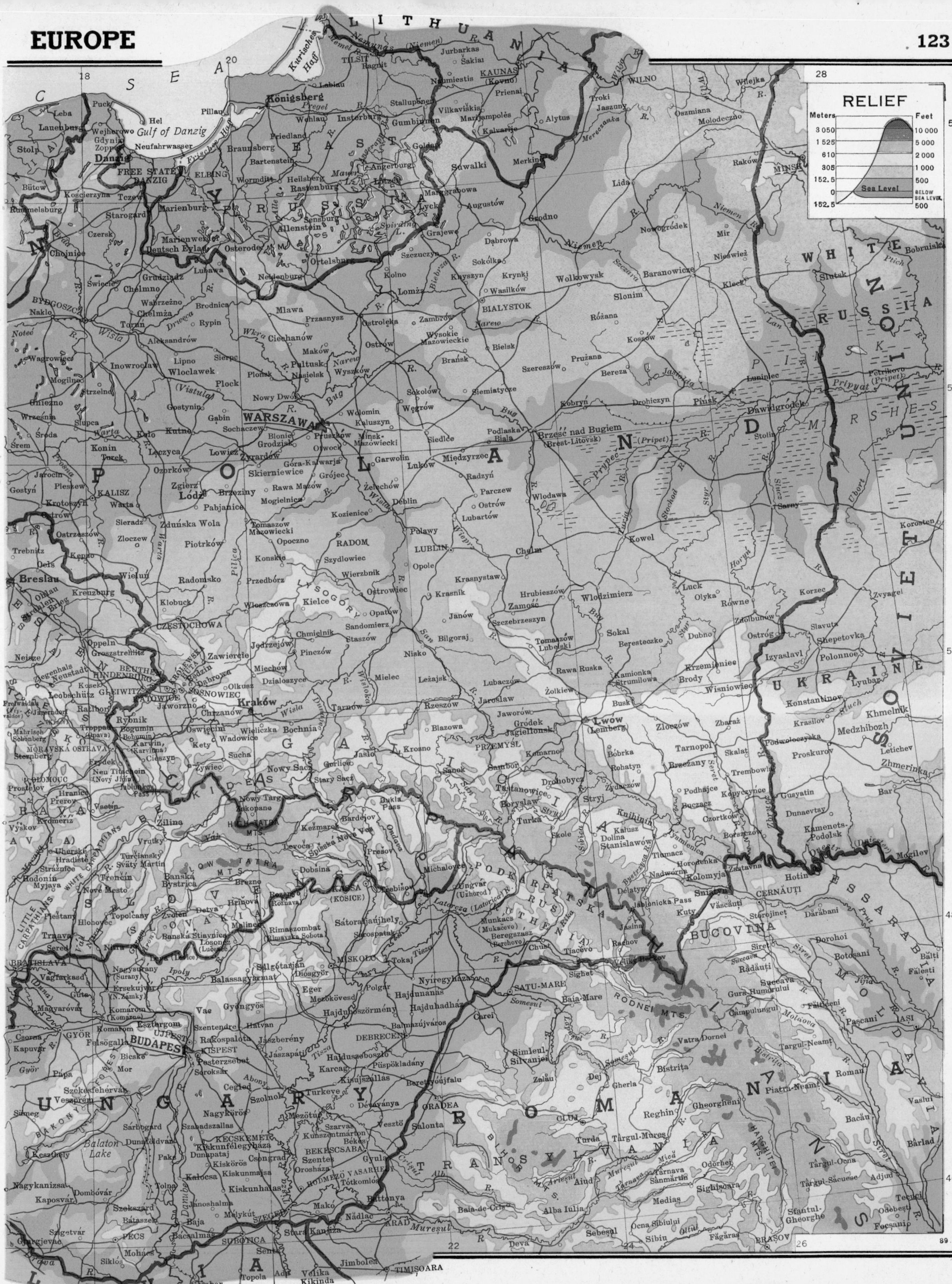
RELIEF
Meters
Feet
3 050
10 000
1 525
5 000
610
2 000
305
1 000
152.5
500
0
Sea Level
152.5
BELOW SEA LEVEL
500
LITHUANIA
EAST PRUSSIA
FREE STATE DANZIG
Gulf of Danzig
POLAND
WHITE RUSSIA
UKRAINE
SOVIET UNION
PRIPET MARSHES
GALICIA
CARPATHIANS
SLOVAKIA
PODKARPATSKA RUS (RUTHENIA)
HUNGARY
ROMANIA
TRANSYLVANIA
BUCOVINA
BESSARABIA
MOLDAVIA
HIGH TATRA MTS.
LOW TATRA MTS.
RODNEI MTS.
LYSOGÓRY
Balaton Lake
Königsberg
Danzig
Gdynia
WARSZAWA
Kraków
Lwow (Lemberg)
Łódź
KALISZ
BIAŁYSTOK
LUBLIN
RADOM
CZĘSTOCHOWA
KAUNAS (Kovno)
WILNO
MINSK
Breslau
BUDAPEST
DEBRECEN
KECSKEMÉT
SZEGED
CLUJ
CERNĂUŢI
SATU-MARE
ORADEA
ARAD
TIMIŞOARA
BRAŞOV
BRATISLAVA
KOŠICE
89

0 10 20 30 40 50 60 70 80 90 100 110 120 Miles
0 20 40 60 80 100 120 140 160 180 200 Kilometers

Scale 1 : 4 000 000; one inch to 64 miles. Conic Projection
Elevations and depressions are given in feet

SWITZERLAND
ITALY
LUXEMBOURG
Marseille
Genève (Geneva)
Torino
Strasbourg
RRANEAN SEA

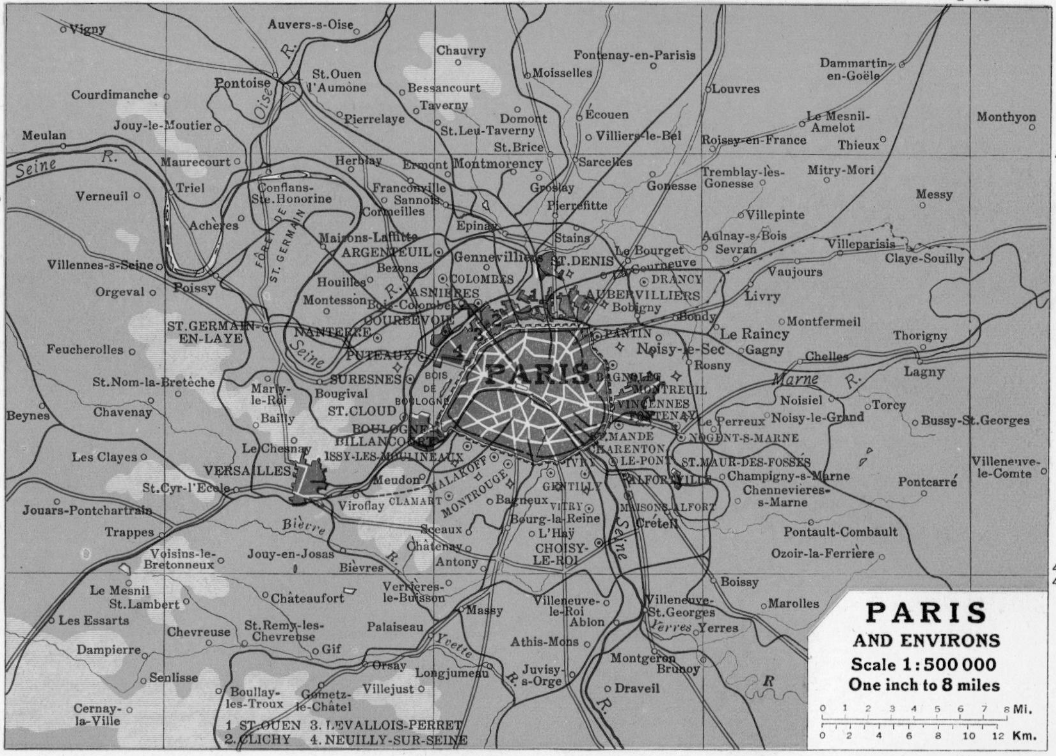
PARIS
AND ENVIRONS
Scale 1:500 000
One inch to 8 miles
Mi.
Km.
1 ST.OUEN 3. LEVALLOIS-PERRET
2. CLICHY 4. NEUILLY-SUR-SEINE
VERSAILLES
ST. DENIS
ARGENTEUIL
Seine R.
Marne R.

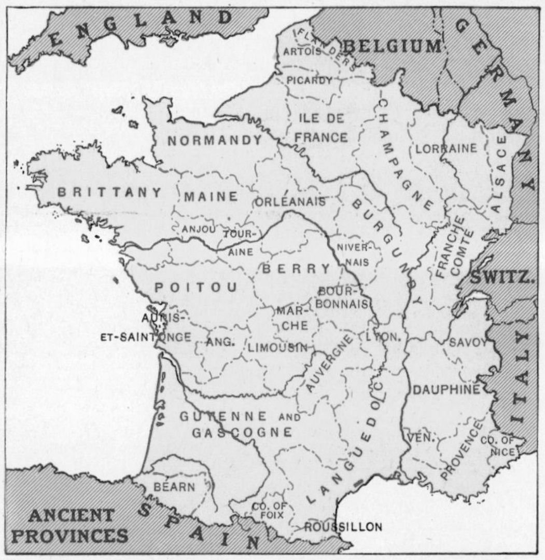
ANCIENT PROVINCES
ENGLAND
BELGIUM
GERMANY
SWITZ.
ITALY
SPAIN
NORMANDY
BRITTANY
MAINE
ORLEANAIS
ILE DE FRANCE
CHAMPAGNE
LORRAINE
ALSACE
BURGUNDY
FRANCHE COMTE
POITOU
BERRY
LIMOUSIN
AUVERGNE
GUIENNE AND GASCOGNE
LANGUEDOC
DAUPHINE
PROVENCE
BEARN
ROUSSILLON

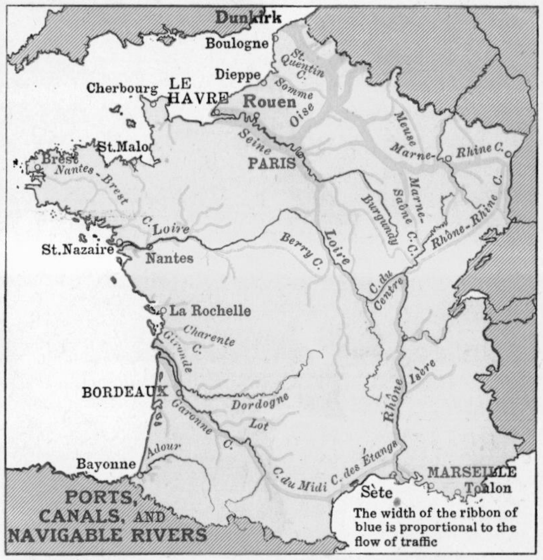
PORTS, CANALS, AND NAVIGABLE RIVERS
The width of the ribbon of blue is proportional to the flow of traffic
Dunkirk
Boulogne
Cherbourg
LE HAVRE
Rouen
PARIS
St.Malo
Brest
St.Nazaire
Nantes
La Rochelle
BORDEAUX
Bayonne
Sète
MARSEILLE
Toulon

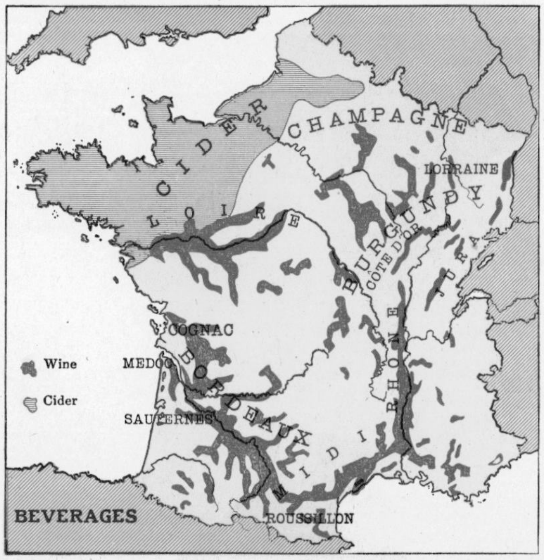
BEVERAGES
Wine
Cider
CIDER
CHAMPAGNE
LORRAINE
LOIRE
BURGUNDY
COTE D'OR
JURA
COGNAC
MEDOC
BORDEAUX
SAUTERNES
RHONE
MIDI
ROUSSILLON

COAL, IRON, AND RAILWAY TRAFFIC
Coal fields
Iron deposits
Railway traffic:
Width of brown ribbon is proportional to the flow of traffic
Calais
Lille
Paris
Strasbourg
Lyon
Marseille
Bordeaux
Toulouse

BAY OF BISCAY
ATLANTIC OCEAN
SPAIN
PORTUGAL
ASTURIAS
CANTABRIAN MTS.
GALICIA
VASCONGADAS
NAVARRA
CASTILLA LA VIEJA
CASTILLA LA NUEVA
EXTREMADURA
ANDALUCIA
MURCIA
LEON
MINHO
TRAS OS MONTES
BEIRA
ESTREMADURA
ALEMTEJO
ALGARVE
SIERRA DE GUADARRAMA
SIERRA DE GREDOS
SA. DE GATA
SA. DA ESTRELLA
SA. DE GUADALUPE
SIERRA MORENA
SIERRA NEVADA
MONTES UNIVERSALES
MADRID
Lisboa
Pôrto
Sevilla
Granada
Córdoba
Valladolid
Málaga
Cádiz
Gibraltar (Br.)
Tangier (Neutral)
Gulf of Cadiz
Strait of Gibraltar
Cape Finisterre
Cape Ortegal
Cape Roca
Cape St. Vincent
Cape Trafalgar
Cape de Gata
Cape Tres Forcas
JEBALA
MOROCCO (Spanish Prot.)
MELILLA
Ceuta
Tetuan
Larache
Arsila
ALBORAN I. (Sp.)
CHAFARINA IS.
ALHUCEMA IS.
MEDIT
Longitude West 8 of Greenwich
0 10 20 40 60 80 100 120 Miles
0 10 20 40 80 120 160 200 Kilometers

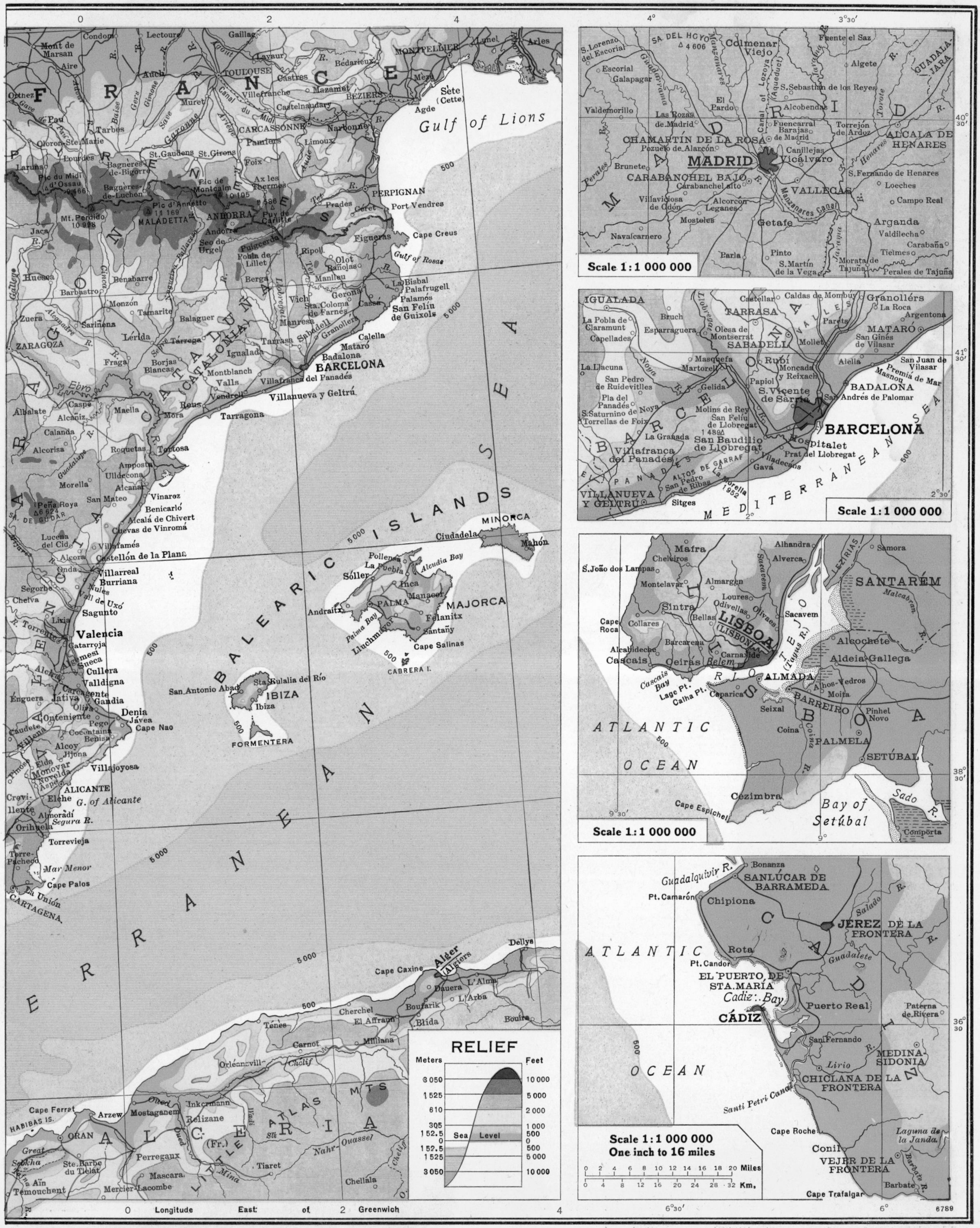

Scale 1:4 000 000; one inch to 64 miles. Conic Projection

Elevations and depressions are given in feet

Continued on pp. 122-123
Continued on pp. 124-125
SWITZERLAND
GERMANY
TRENTINO
SLOVENIA
CROATIA
SERBIA
YUGOSLAVIA
LOMBARDY
EMILIA
TUSCANY
UMBRIA
MARCHE
ABRUZZI
MOLISE
CAMPANIA
BASILICATA
CALABRIA
SICILY
CORSICA (Fr.)
SARDINIA
LIGURIAN SEA
ADRIATIC SEA
TYRRHENIAN SEA
Gulf of Genoa
Gulf of Venice
Gulf of Trieste
Gulf of Manfredonia
Gulf of Salerno
Gulf of Policastro
Gulf of Squillace
Gulf of Santa Eufemia
Gulf of Catania
Gulf of Cagliari
Gulf of Orosei
Gulf of Asinara
Strait of Bonifacio
Torino (Turin)
Milano (Milan)
Genova (Genoa)
Venezia (Venice)
Bologna
Firenze (Florence)
ROMA
VATICAN CITY
Napoli (Naples)
Palermo
Messina
Catania
Trieste
Bari
CRETE (Greece)
SEA OF CRETE
MEDITERRANEAN SEA
Same scale as main map
Miles
Kilometers

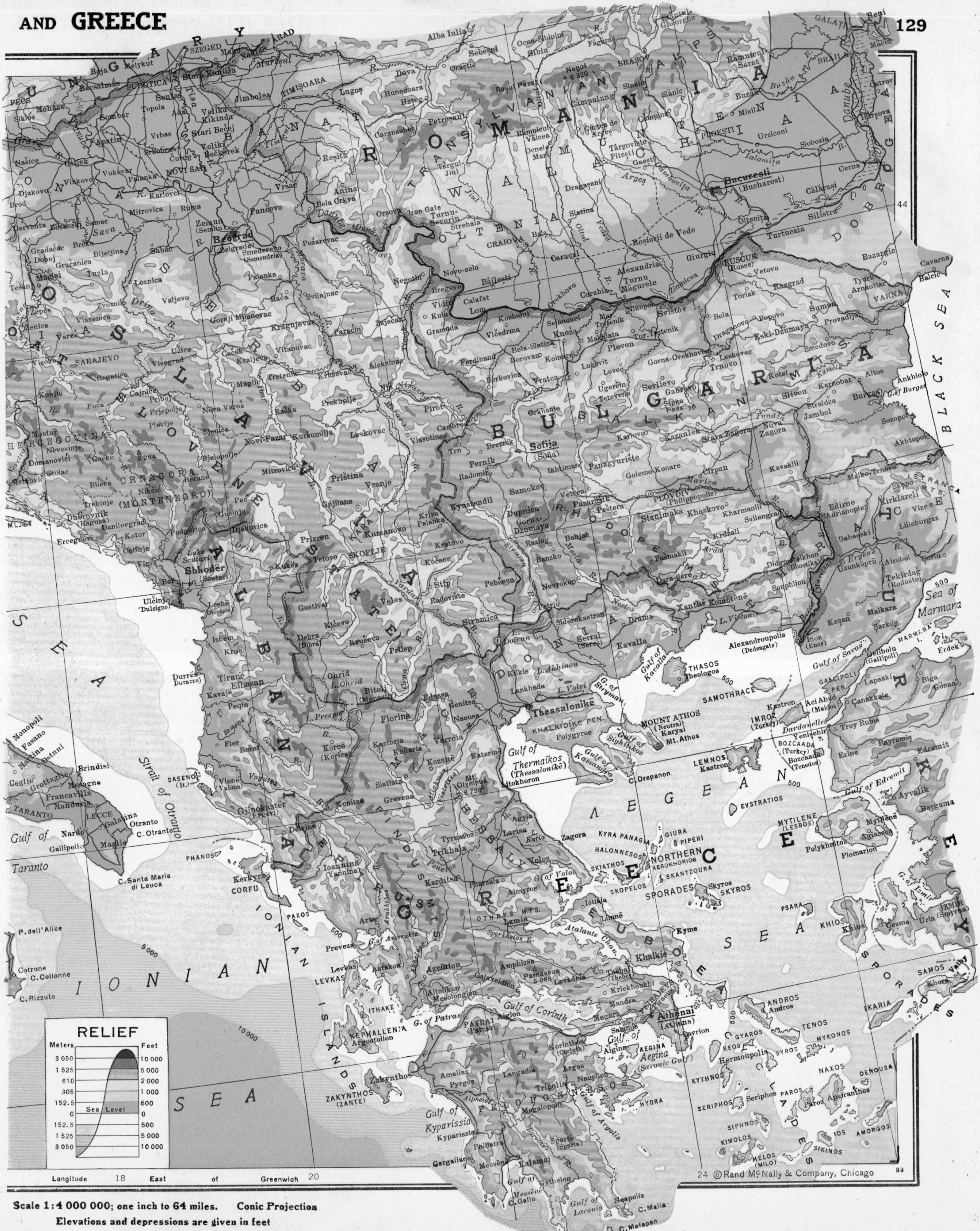

Scale 1:4 000 000; one inch to 64 miles. Conic Projection
Elevations and depressions are given in feet

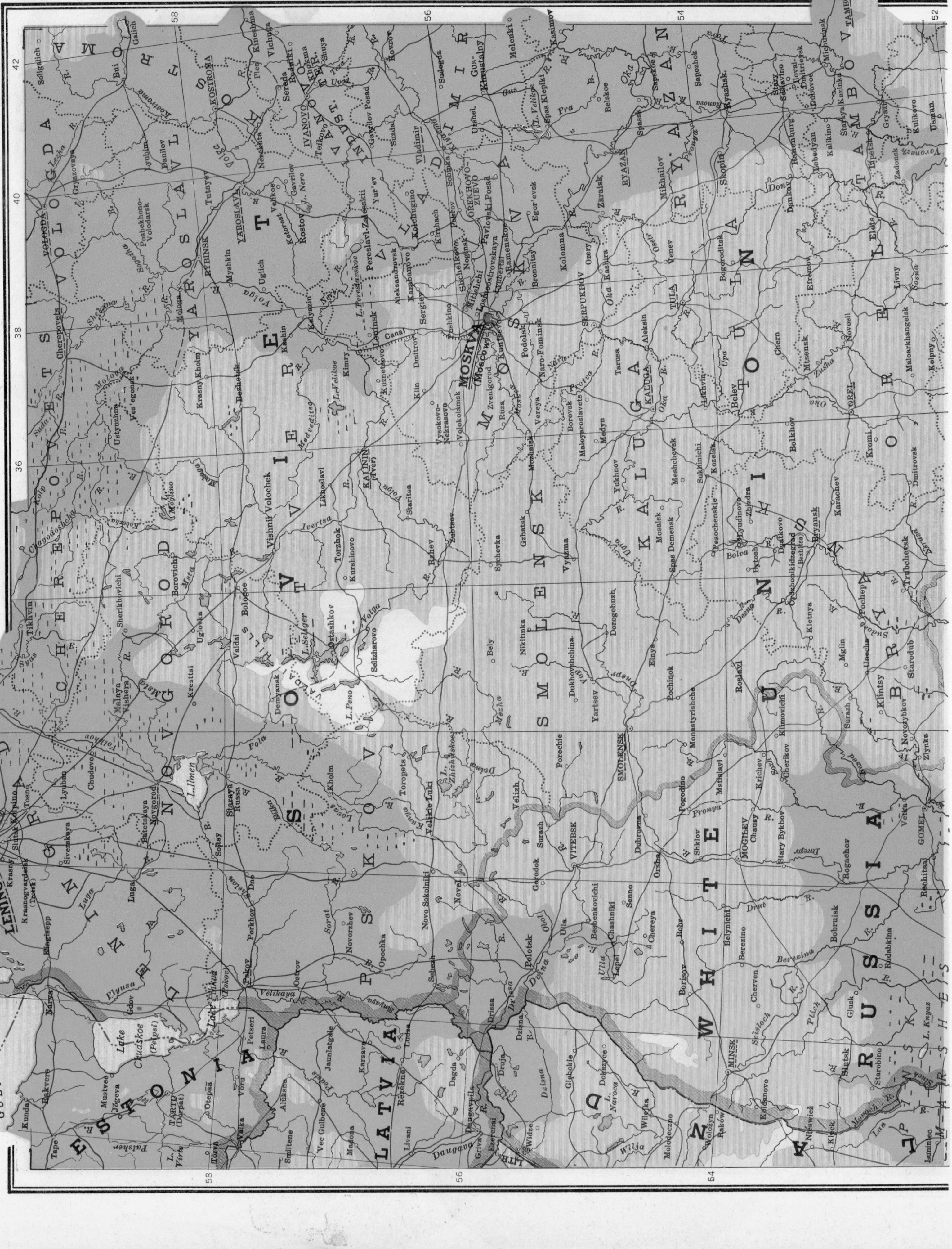
LENINGRAD
Kronshtadt
GULF OF FINLAND
ESTONIA
LATVIA
Lake Chudskoe (Peipsi)
L. Ilmen
Novgorod
NOVGOROD
PSKOV
Pskov
VOLOGDA
YAROSLAVL
Yaroslavl
KOSTROMA
IVANOVO
VLADIMIR
MOSKVA (Moscow)
SMOLENSK
Smolensk
KALUGA
Kaluga
TULA
Tula
RYAZAN
Ryazan
ORLOV
Orel
TAMBOV
Tambov
KALININ (Tver)
VITEBSK
MOGILEV
MINSK
GOMEL
WHITE RUSSIA
Volga
Dnepr

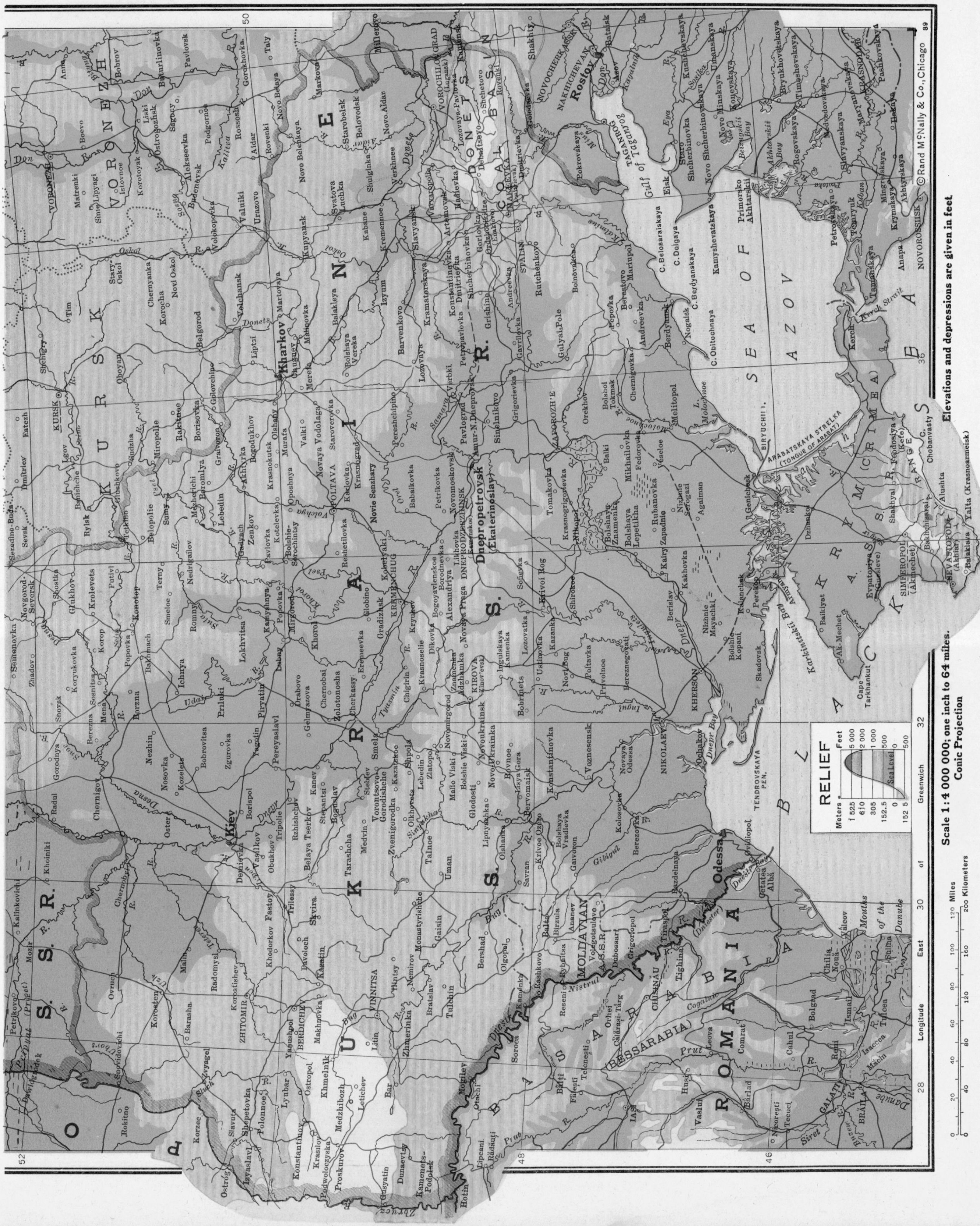
RELIEF
Elevations and depressions are given in feet.
Scale 1:4 000 000; one inch to 64 miles.
Conic Projection
Miles
Kilometers
©Rand McNally & Co., Chicago

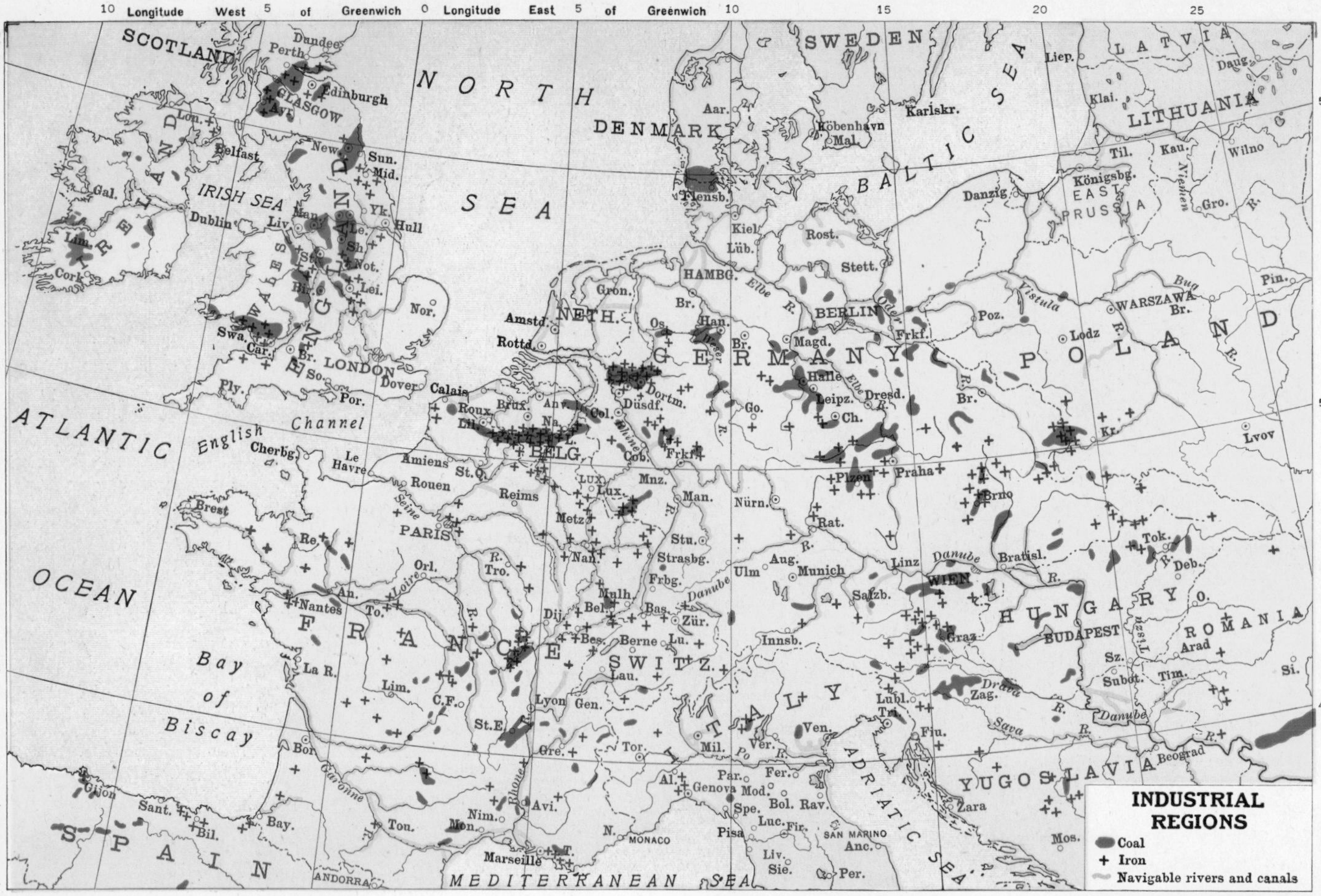

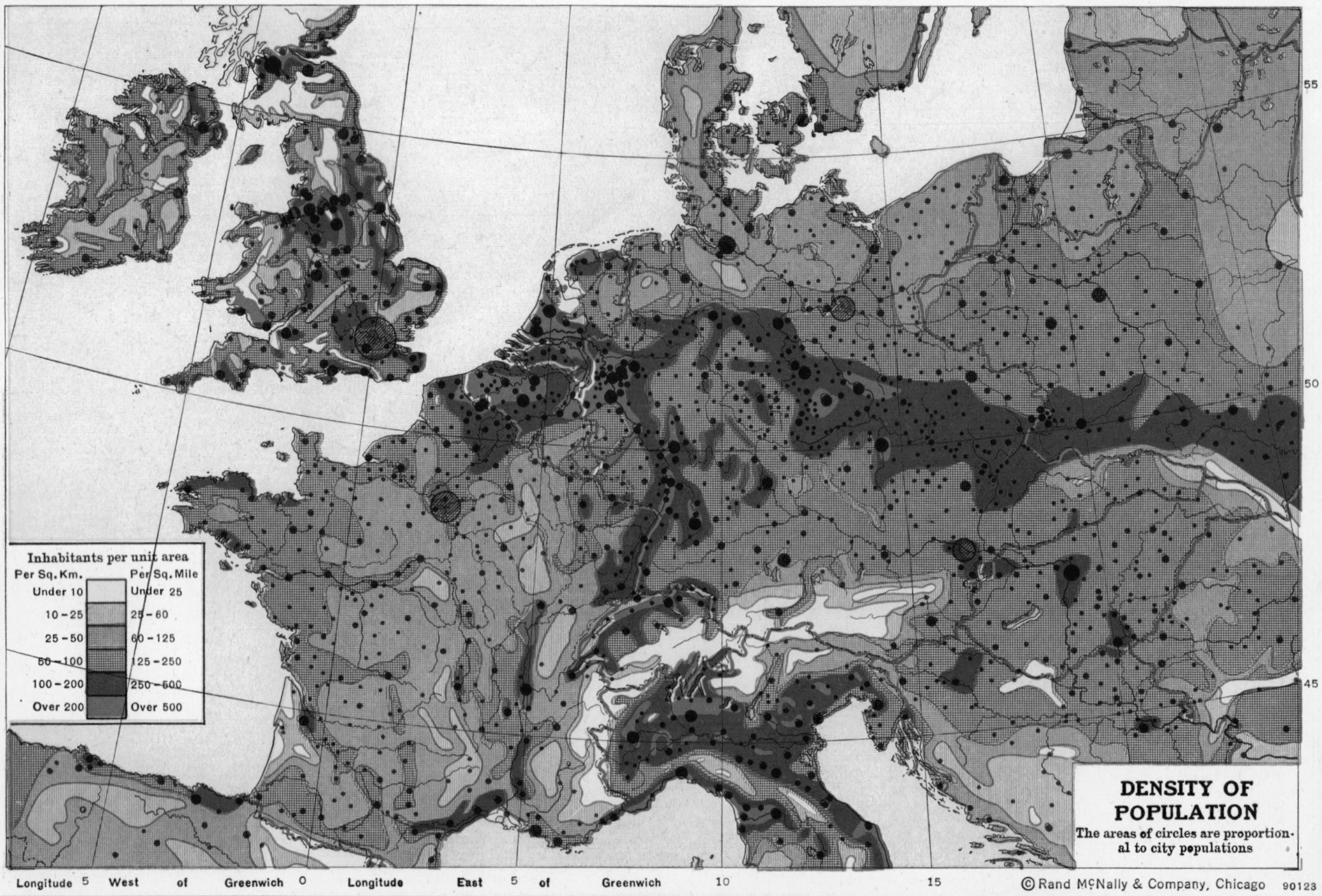

0 50 100 150 200 250 300 Miles
0 50 100 200 300 400 500 Km.

Scale for both maps: one inch to 216 miles

Conic Projection

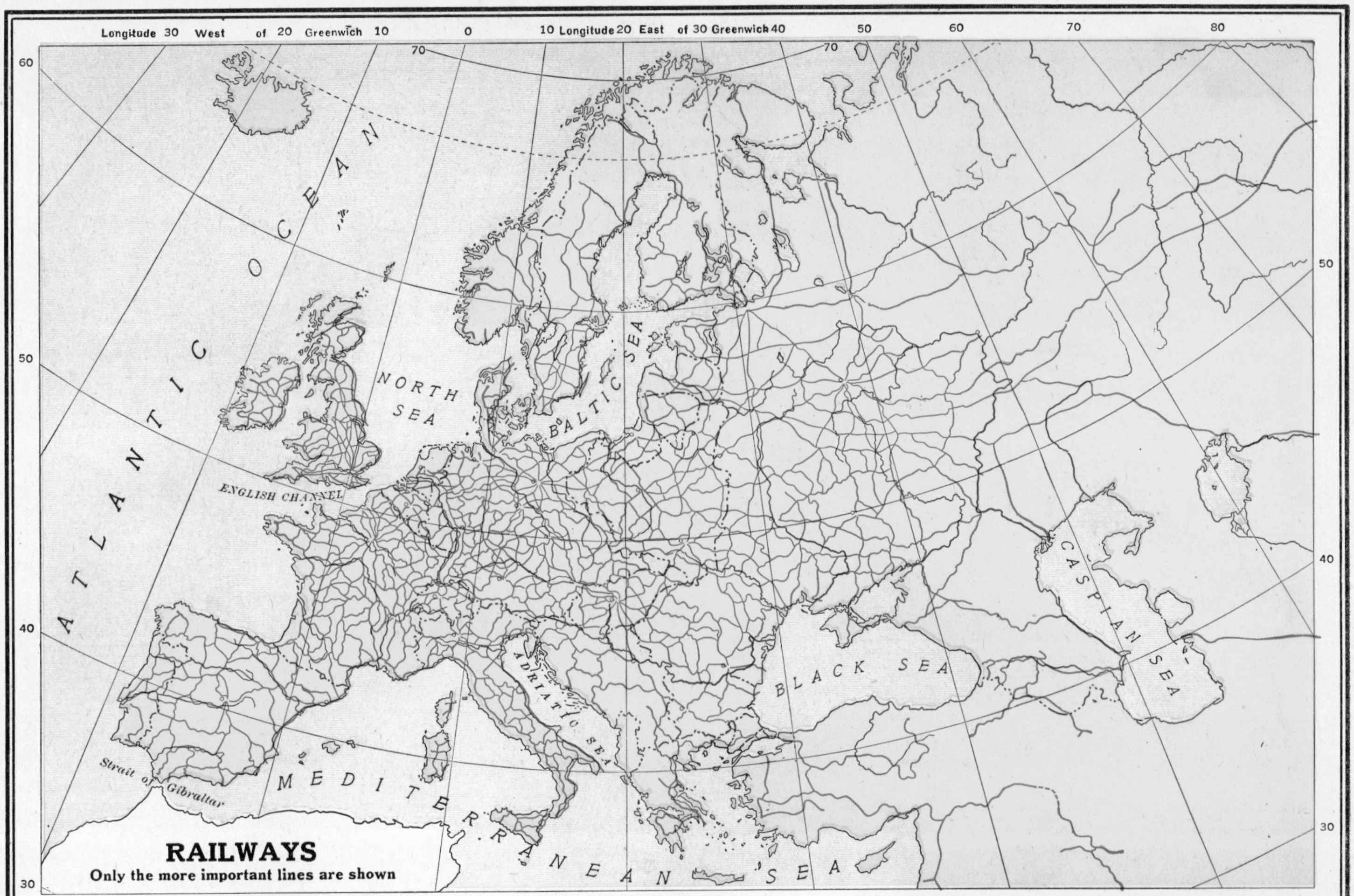

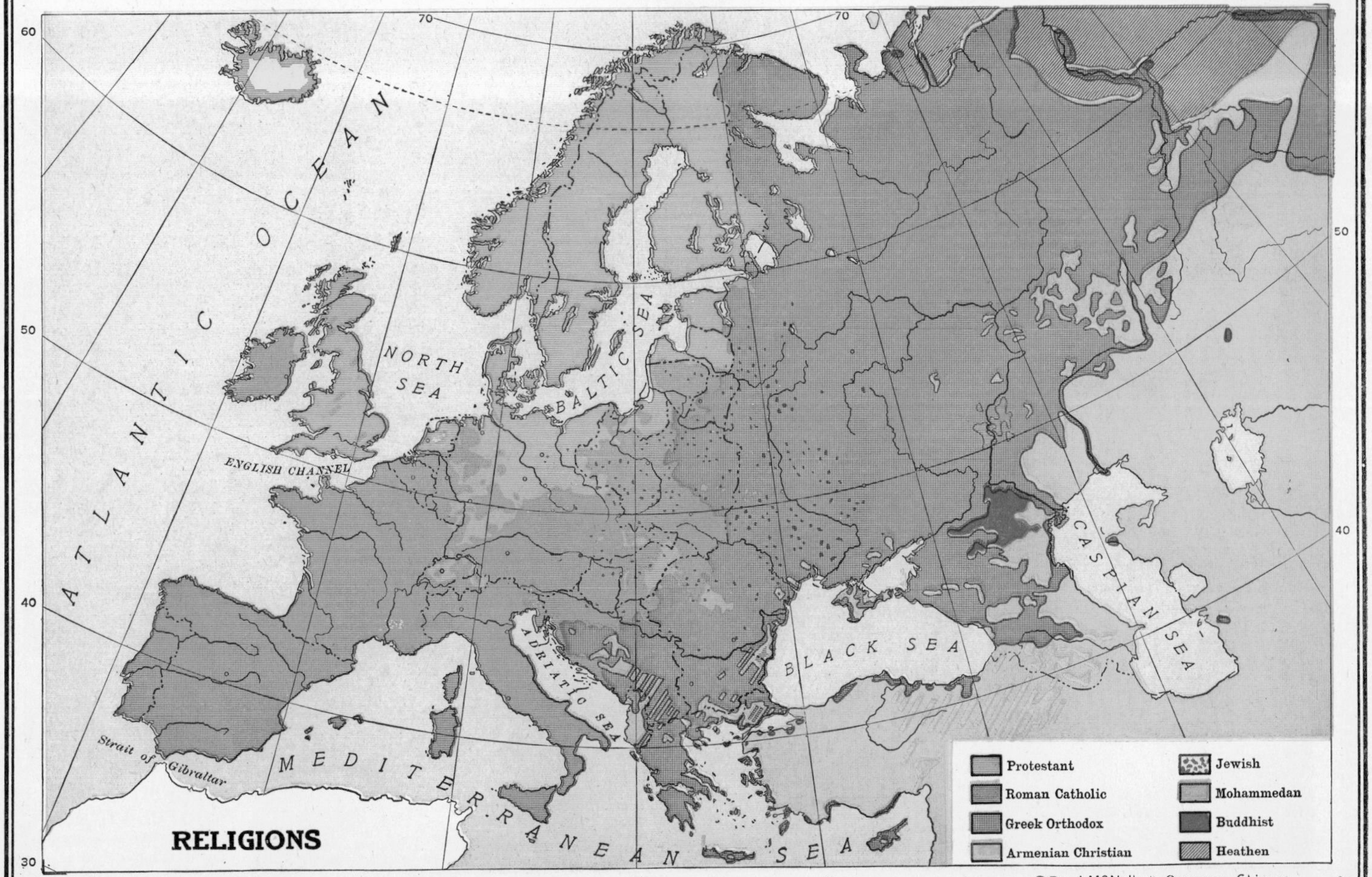

Scale for both maps: one inch to 530 miles

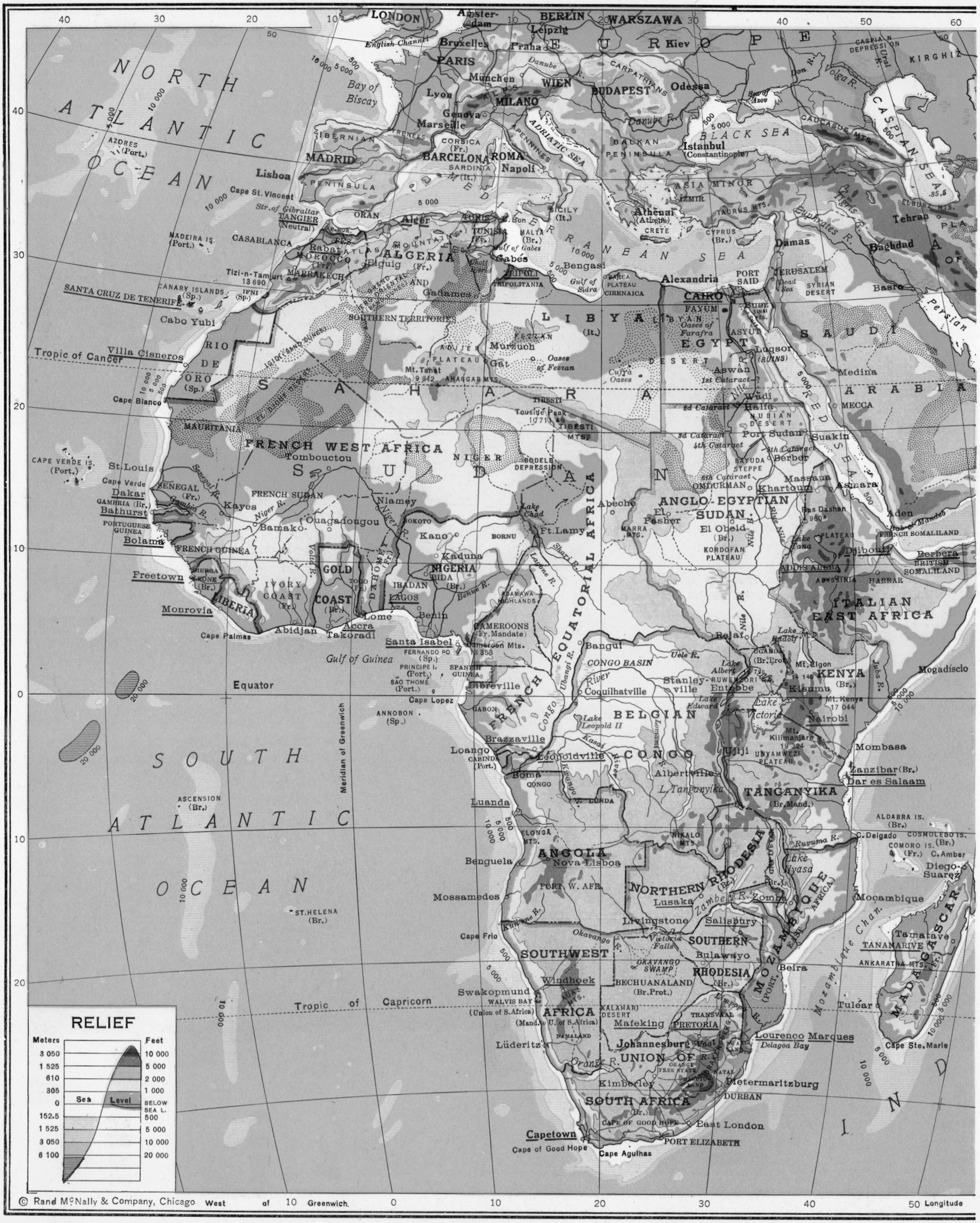

0 200 400 600 800 1000 Miles
0 400 800 1200 1600 Kilometers

Scale 1 : 40 000 000; one inch to 630 miles. Lambert's Azimuthal, Equal Area Projection

Elevations and depressions are given in feet

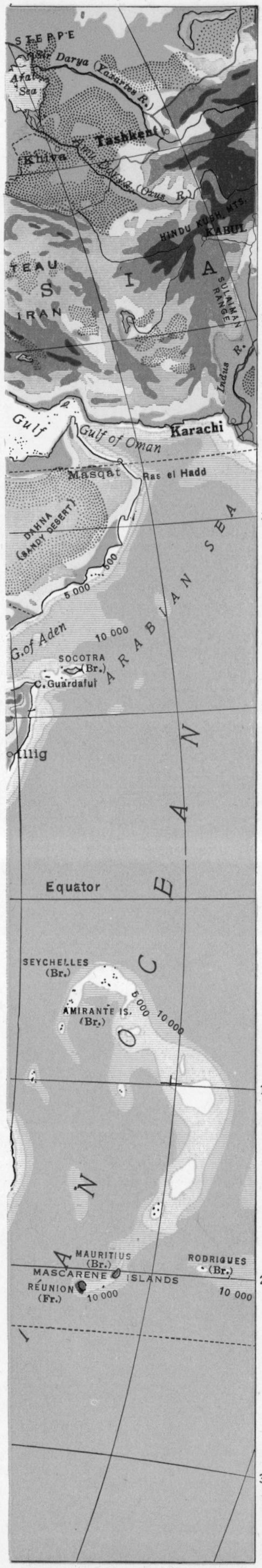
STEPPE
Syr Darya (Yaxartes R.)
Aral Sea
Tashkent
Khiva
Amu Darya (Oxus R.)
HINDU KUSH MTS.
KABUL
TEAU
IRAN
S I A
SULAIMAN RANGE
Indus R.
Karachi
Gulf of Oman
Masqat
Ras el Hadd
DAHNA (SANDY DESERT)
G. of Aden
SOCOTRA (Br.)
C. Guardafui
A R A B I A N S E A
Illig
Equator
SEYCHELLES (Br.)
AMIRANTE IS. (Br.)
MAURITIUS (Br.)
RODRIGUES (Br.)
MASCARENE ISLANDS
RÉUNION (Fr.)
I N D I A N O C E A N
East 60 of Greenwich 70

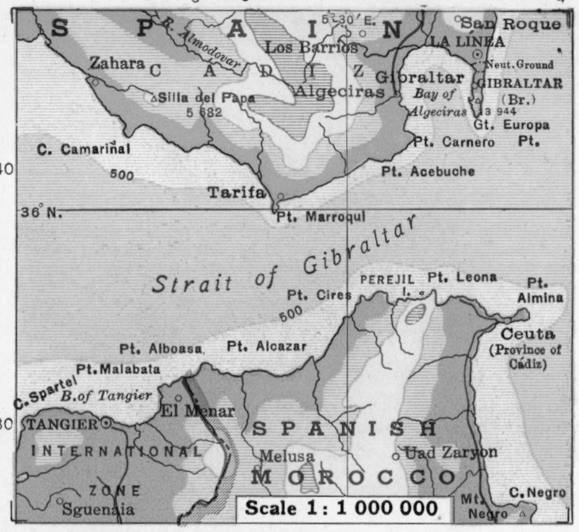
Longitude West of Greenwich
S P A I N
Los Barrios
Zahara
C A D I Z
Gibraltar
GIBRALTAR (Br.)
LA LINEA
San Roque
Algeciras
Bay of Algeciras
Silla del Papa 5 682
C. Camarinal
Pt. Carnero
Gt. Europa Pt.
Pt. Acebuche
Tarifa
Pt. Marroqui
36° N.
Strait of Gibraltar
PEREJIL
Pt. Leona
Pt. Almina
Pt. Cires
Ceuta (Province of Cadiz)
Pt. Alboasa
Pt. Alcazar
Pt. Malabata
C. Spartel
B. of Tangier
TANGIER
El Menar
INTERNATIONAL ZONE
Sguenzia
S P A N I S H M O R O C C O
Melusa
Uad Zaryon
C. Negro
Scale 1: 1 000 000

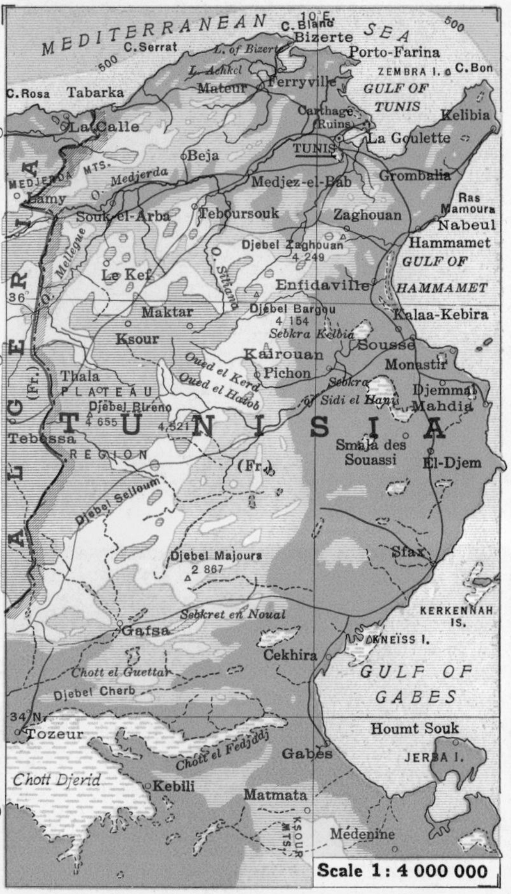
MEDITERRANEAN SEA
C. Blanc
Bizerte
C. Serrat
L. of Bizerte
L. Achkel
Porto-Farina
ZEMBRA I.
C. Bon
C. Rosa
Tabarka
Mateur
Ferryville
GULF OF TUNIS
Kelibia
La Calle
Carthage (Ruins)
TUNIS
La Goulette
MEDJERDA MTS.
Beja
Medjerda
Medjez-el-Bab
Grombalia
Souk-el-Arba
Teboursouk
Zaghouan
Ras Mamoura
Nabeul
Djebel Zaghouan 4 249
Hammamet
GULF OF HAMMAMET
Le Kef
Enfidaville
Maktar
Djebel Bargou 4 154
Sebkra Kelbia
Kalaa-Kebira
Ksour
Sousse
Kairouan
Monastir
Thala
Pichon
Oued el Hateb
Sebkra Sidi el Hani
Djemmal
Mahdia
PLATEAU
Djebel Bireno 4 655
T U N I S I A
Tebessa
REGION
A L G E R I A (Fr.)
Smaja des Souassi
El-Djem
Djebel Selloum
Djebel Majoura 2 867
Sfax
KERKENNAH IS.
Sebkret en Noual
Gafsa
CHERGUI I.
Cekhira
Chott el Guettar
Djebel Cherb
GULF OF GABES
Tozeur
Houmt Souk
JERBA I.
Chott el Fedjadj
Gabes
Chott Djerid
Kebili
Matmata
KSOUR MTS.
Medenine
Scale 1: 4 000 000

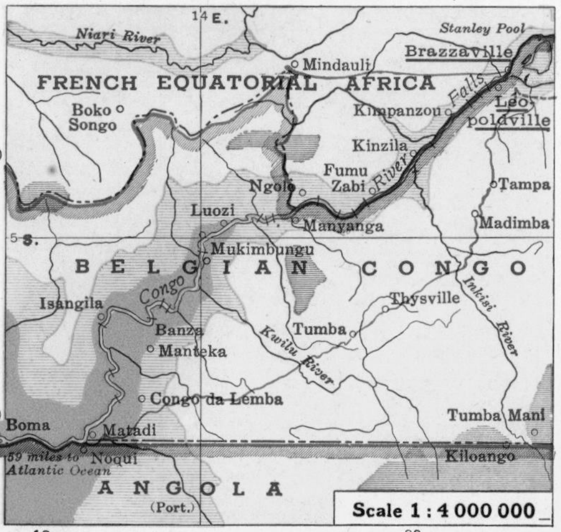
Niari River
Stanley Pool
Mindauli
Brazzaville
FRENCH EQUATORIAL AFRICA
Leopoldville
Boko Songo
Kimpanzou
Kinzila
Fumu Zabi
Ngolo
Tampa
Luozi
Manyanga
Madimba
Mukimbungu
B E L G I A N C O N G O
Isangila
Congo
Thysville
Inkisi River
Banza Manteka
Tumba
Kwilu River
Congo da Lemba
Boma
Matadi
Noqui
Tumba Mani
Kiloango
59 miles to Atlantic Ocean
A N G O L A (Port.)
Scale 1 : 4 000 000

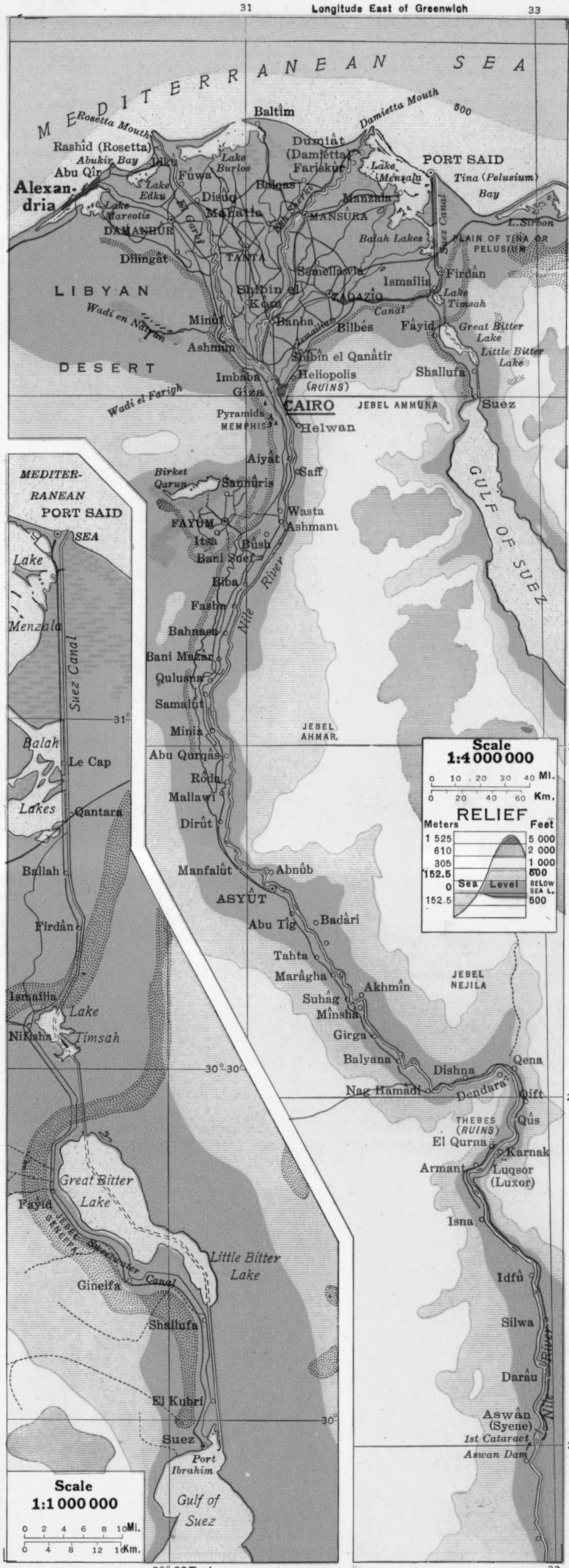
Longitude East of Greenwich
M E D I T E R R A N E A N S E A
Baltim
Rosetta Mouth
Damietta Mouth
Rashid (Rosetta)
Abukir Bay
Dumyat (Damietta)
Fariskur
PORT SAID
Tina (Pelusium) Bay
Abu Qir
Lake Burlos
Lake Menzala
Alexandria
Lake Edku
Fuwa
Disuq
Bilqas
Lake Mareotis
Mahalla
Manzala
DAMANHUR
MANSURA
L. Sirbon
Dilingat
TANTA
Balah Lakes
Suez Canal
PLAIN OF TINA OR PELUSIUM
L I B Y A N
Senellawein
Ismailia
Firdan
Shibin el Kom
ZAGAZIG
Lake Timsah
Wadi en Natrun
Minuf
Banha
Bilbes
Fayid
Great Bitter Lake
Little Bitter Lake
Ashmun
D E S E R T
Imbaba
Shibin el Qanatir
Shallufa
Giza
Heliopolis (RUINS)
Wadi el Farigh
Pyramids
MEMPHIS
CAIRO
JEBEL AMMUNA
Suez
Helwan
Birket Qarun
Sannuris
Aiyat
Saff
FAYUM
Itsa
Wasta
Ashmant
Bani Suef
Bush
Biba
Fashn
Bahnasa
Nile River
Bani Mazar
Qulusna
Samalut
G U L F O F S U E Z
Minia
JEBEL AHMAR
Abu Qurqas
Roda
Mallawi
Dirut
Manfalut
Abnub
ASYUT
Abu Tig
Badari
Tahta
Maragha
JEBEL NEJILA
Suhag
Akhmim
Minsha
Girga
Balyana
Dishna
Qena
Nag Hamadi
Dendara
Qift
THEBES (RUINS)
Qus
El Qurna
Karnak
Armant
Luqsor (Luxor)
Isna
Idfu
Silwa
Darau
Aswan (Syene)
1st Cataract
Aswan Dam
Scale 1:4 000 000
Mi.
Km.
RELIEF
Meters
Feet
1 525
610
305
152.5
0
152.5
5 000
2 000
1 000
500
Sea Level
BELOW SEA L.
500
MEDITERRANEAN
PORT SAID
SEA
Lake Menzala
Suez Canal
Balah Lakes
Le Cap
Qantara
Ballah
Firdan
Ismailia
Lake Timsah
Nifisha
Great Bitter Lake
Fayid
JEBEL GENEFFA
Sweetwater Canal
Little Bitter Lake
Geneifa
Shallufa
El Kubri
Suez
Port Ibrahim
Gulf of Suez
Scale 1:1 000 000
Mi.
Km.
32° 30' East

AFRICA

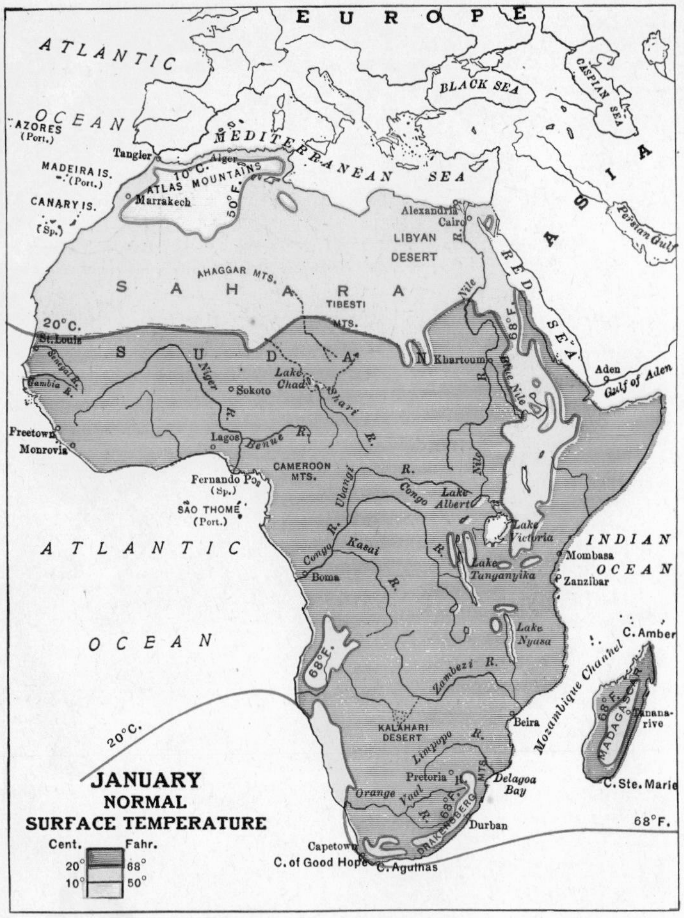

JANUARY
NORMAL
SURFACE TEMPERATURE
Cent. Fahr.
20° 68°
10° 50°
EUROPE
ATLANTIC OCEAN
MEDITERRANEAN SEA
BLACK SEA
CASPIAN SEA
ASIA
RED SEA
Persian Gulf
Gulf of Aden
INDIAN OCEAN
AZORES (Port.)
MADEIRA IS. (Port.)
CANARY IS. (Sp.)
Tangier
Alger
Marrakech
ATLAS MOUNTAINS
Alexandria
Cairo
LIBYAN DESERT
SAHARA
AHAGGAR MTS.
TIBESTI MTS.
SUDAN
St. Louis
Senegal R.
Gambia R.
Niger R.
Sokoto
Lake Chad
Shari R.
Khartoum
Blue Nile
Nile R.
Aden
Freetown
Monrovia
Lagos
Benue R.
CAMEROON MTS.
Fernando Po (Sp.)
SAO THOME (Port.)
Ubangi R.
Congo R.
Lake Albert
Lake Victoria
Mombasa
Zanzibar
Kasai R.
Boma
Lake Tanganyika
Lake Nyasa
Zambezi R.
C. Amber
Mozambique Channel
MADAGASCAR
Tananarive
KALAHARI DESERT
Limpopo R.
Beira
Pretoria
Delagoa Bay
Orange R.
Vaal R.
DRAKENSBERG MTS.
Durban
Capetown
C. of Good Hope
C. Agulhas
C. Ste. Marie
10° C.
50° F.
20° C.
68° F.

JULY
NORMAL
SURFACE TEMPERATURE
Cent. Fahr.
30° 86°
20° 68°
10° 50°
EUROPE
ATLANTIC OCEAN
MEDITERRANEAN SEA
BLACK SEA
CASPIAN SEA
ASIA
RED SEA
Persian Gulf
Gulf of Aden
INDIAN OCEAN
SAHARA
LIBYAN DESERT
SUDAN
KALAHARI DESERT
MADAGASCAR
30° C.
86° F.
20° C.
68° F.
10° C.
50° F.

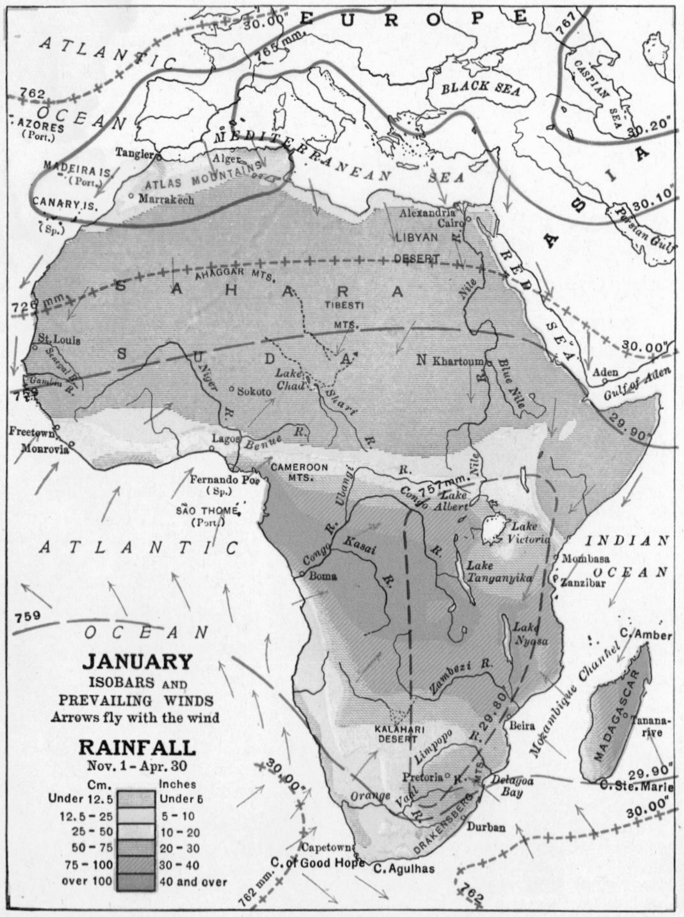

JANUARY
ISOBARS AND
PREVAILING WINDS
Arrows fly with the wind
RAINFALL
Nov. 1 - Apr. 30
Cm. Inches
Under 12.5 Under 5
12.5 - 25 5 - 10
25 - 50 10 - 20
50 - 75 20 - 30
75 - 100 30 - 40
over 100 40 and over
EUROPE
ATLANTIC OCEAN
MEDITERRANEAN SEA
BLACK SEA
CASPIAN SEA
ASIA
RED SEA
INDIAN OCEAN
SAHARA
SUDAN
MADAGASCAR
30.00"
30.10"
30.20"
29.90"
29.80"
765 mm.
762
759
757 mm.
726 mm.

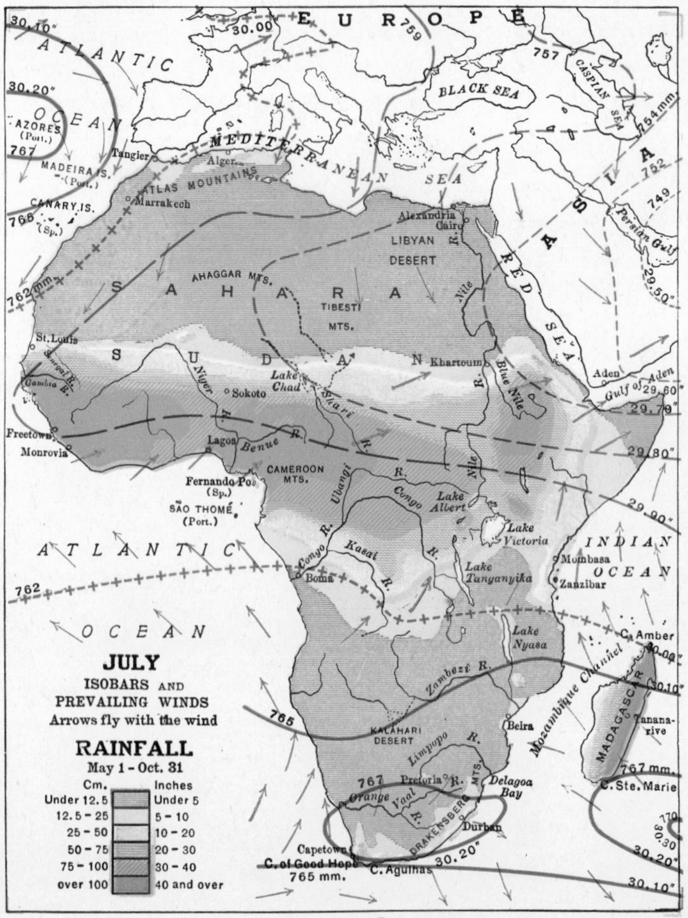

JULY
ISOBARS AND
PREVAILING WINDS
Arrows fly with the wind
RAINFALL
May 1 - Oct. 31
Cm. Inches
Under 12.5 Under 5
12.5 - 25 5 - 10
25 - 50 10 - 20
50 - 75 20 - 30
75 - 100 30 - 40
over 100 40 and over
EUROPE
ATLANTIC OCEAN
MEDITERRANEAN SEA
BLACK SEA
CASPIAN SEA
ASIA
RED SEA
INDIAN OCEAN
SAHARA
SUDAN
MADAGASCAR
30.10"
30.20"
30.00"
29.90"
29.80"
29.70"
29.50"
765 mm.
767 mm.
762 mm.
754 mm.

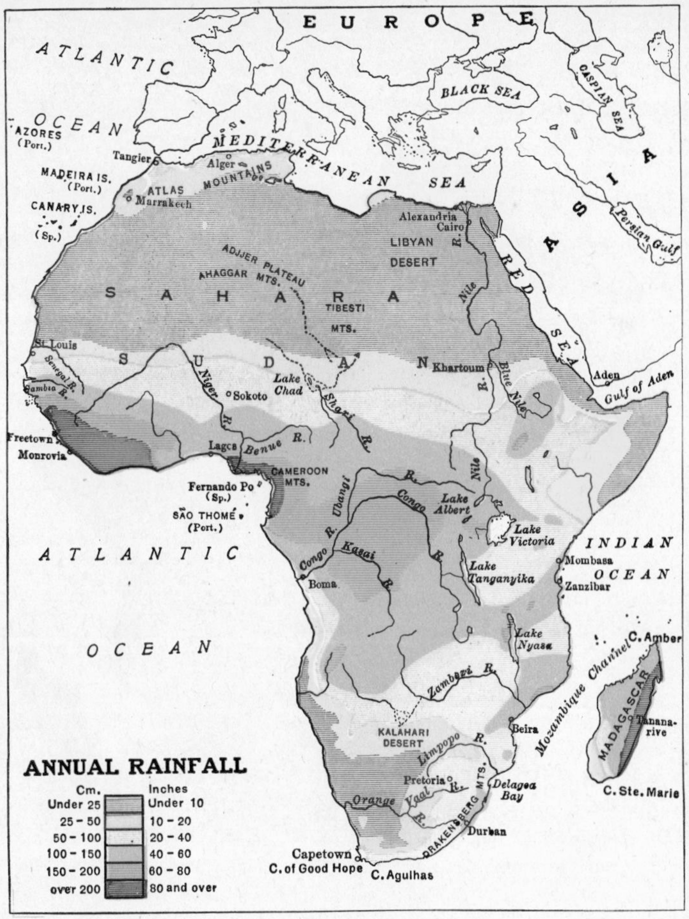
EUROPE
ATLANTIC OCEAN
AZORES (Port.)
MADEIRA IS. (Port.)
CANARY IS. (Sp.)
Tangier
Alger
MEDITERRANEAN SEA
ATLAS MOUNTAINS
Marrakech
BLACK SEA
CASPIAN SEA
ASIA
Persian Gulf
Alexandria
Cairo
LIBYAN DESERT
ADJER PLATEAU
AHAGGAR MTS.
SAHARA
TIBESTI MTS.
Nile R.
RED SEA
St. Louis
Senegal R.
Gambia R.
SUDAN
Khartoum
Blue Nile
Aden
Gulf of Aden
Lake Chad
Sokoto
Niger R.
Shari R.
Freetown
Monrovia
Lagos
Benue R.
CAMEROON MTS.
Fernando Po (Sp.)
SÃO THOMÉ (Port.)
Ubangi R.
Congo R.
Lake Albert
Lake Victoria
Kasai R.
Boma
Lake Tanganyika
Mombasa
Zanzibar
INDIAN OCEAN
ATLANTIC OCEAN
Lake Nyasa
Zambezi R.
C. Amber
Mozambique Channel
MADAGASCAR
Tananarive
Beira
KALAHARI DESERT
Limpopo R.
Pretoria
Orange
Vaal R.
DRAKENSBERG MTS.
Delagoa Bay
Durban
C. Ste. Marie
Capetown
C. of Good Hope
C. Agulhas
ANNUAL RAINFALL
Cm. Inches
Under 25 Under 10
25 - 50 10 - 20
50 - 100 20 - 40
100 - 150 40 - 60
150 - 200 60 - 80
over 200 80 and over

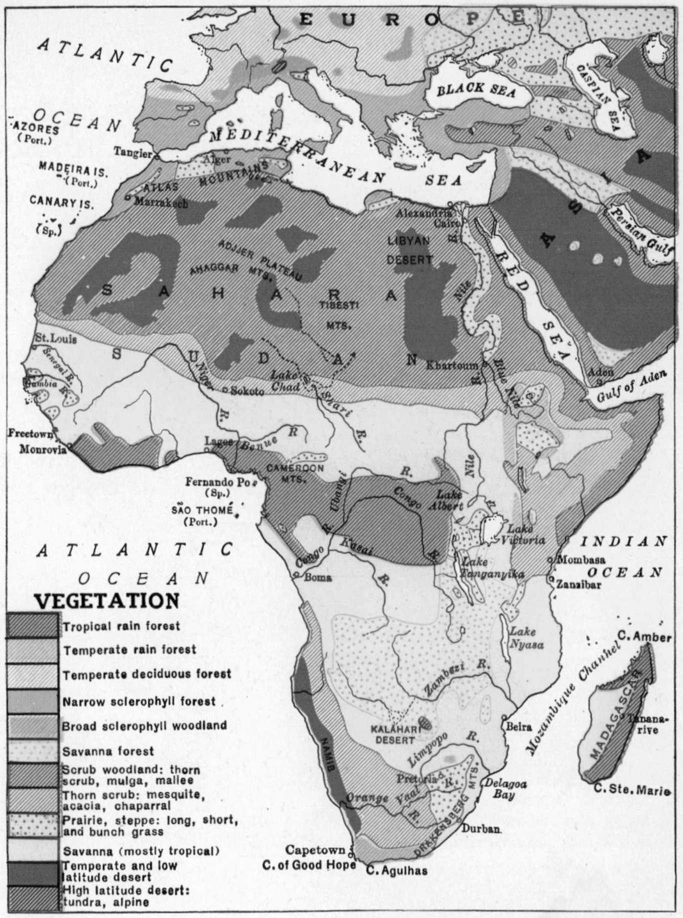
EUROPE
ATLANTIC OCEAN
AZORES (Port.)
MADEIRA IS. (Port.)
CANARY IS. (Sp.)
Tangier
MEDITERRANEAN SEA
ATLAS MOUNTAINS
Marrakech
BLACK SEA
CASPIAN SEA
ASIA
Persian Gulf
Alexandria
Cairo
LIBYAN DESERT
ADJER PLATEAU
AHAGGAR MTS.
SAHARA
TIBESTI MTS.
Nile R.
RED SEA
St. Louis
SUDAN
Khartoum
Aden
Gulf of Aden
Lake Chad
Sokoto
Freetown
Monrovia
Lagos
Benue R.
CAMEROON MTS.
Fernando Po (Sp.)
SÃO THOMÉ (Port.)
Ubangi
Congo R.
Lake Albert
Lake Victoria
Kasai
Boma
Lake Tanganyika
Mombasa
Zanzibar
INDIAN OCEAN
ATLANTIC OCEAN
Lake Nyasa
Zambezi R.
C. Amber
Mozambique Channel
MADAGASCAR
Tananarive
Beira
KALAHARI DESERT
NAMIB
Limpopo R.
Pretoria
Orange
Vaal R.
DRAKENSBERG MTS.
Delagoa Bay
Durban
C. Ste. Marie
Capetown
C. of Good Hope
C. Agulhas
VEGETATION
Tropical rain forest
Temperate rain forest
Temperate deciduous forest
Narrow sclerophyll forest
Broad sclerophyll woodland
Savanna forest
Scrub woodland: thorn scrub, mulga, mallee
Thorn scrub: mesquite, acacia, chaparral
Prairie, steppe: long, short, and bunch grass
Savanna (mostly tropical)
Temperate and low latitude desert
High latitude desert: tundra, alpine

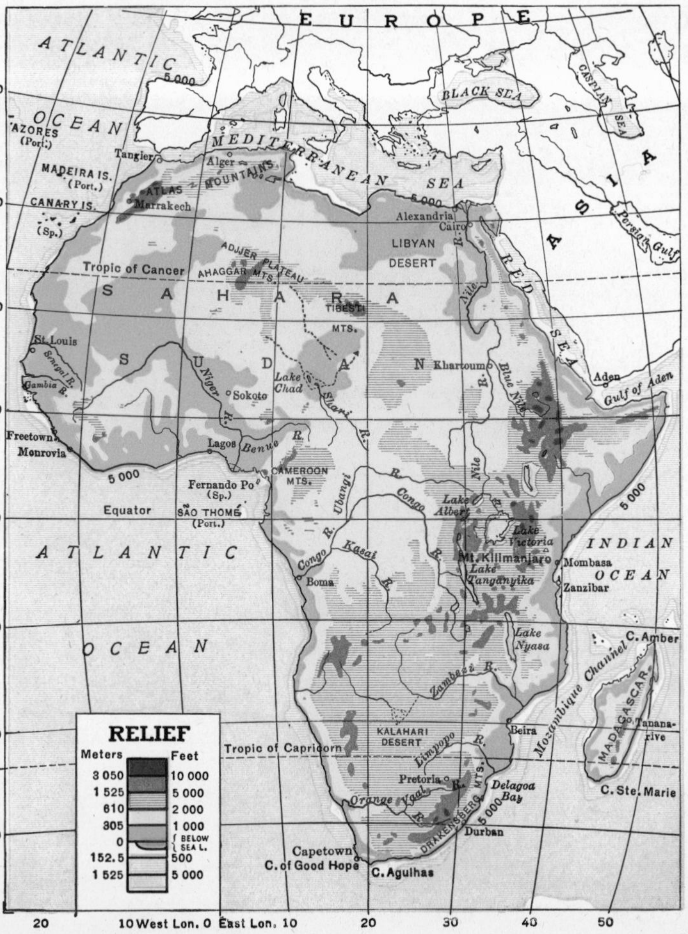
EUROPE
ATLANTIC OCEAN
5 000
AZORES (Port.)
MADEIRA IS. (Port.)
CANARY IS. (Sp.)
Tangier
Alger
MEDITERRANEAN SEA
ATLAS MOUNTAINS
Marrakech
BLACK SEA
CASPIAN SEA
ASIA
Persian Gulf
Alexandria
Cairo
LIBYAN DESERT
Tropic of Cancer
ADJER PLATEAU
AHAGGAR MTS.
SAHARA
TIBESTI MTS.
Nile R.
RED SEA
St. Louis
Senegal R.
Gambia R.
SUDAN
Khartoum
Blue Nile
Aden
Gulf of Aden
Lake Chad
Sokoto
Niger R.
Shari R.
Freetown
Monrovia
Lagos
Benue R.
CAMEROON MTS.
Fernando Po (Sp.)
Equator
SÃO THOMÉ (Port.)
Ubangi R.
Congo R.
Lake Albert
Lake Victoria
Mt. Kilimanjaro
Kasai R.
Boma
Lake Tanganyika
Mombasa
Zanzibar
INDIAN OCEAN
ATLANTIC OCEAN
Lake Nyasa
Zambezi R.
C. Amber
Mozambique Channel
MADAGASCAR
Tananarive
Beira
Tropic of Capricorn
KALAHARI DESERT
Limpopo R.
Pretoria
Orange
Vaal R.
DRAKENSBERG MTS.
Delagoa Bay
Durban
C. Ste. Marie
Capetown
C. of Good Hope
C. Agulhas
40
30
20
10
0
10
20
30
20
10 West Lon. 0 East Lon. 10
20
30
40
50
RELIEF
Meters Feet
3 050 10 000
1 525 5 000
610 2 000
305 1 000
0 BELOW SEA L.
152.5 500
1 525 5 000

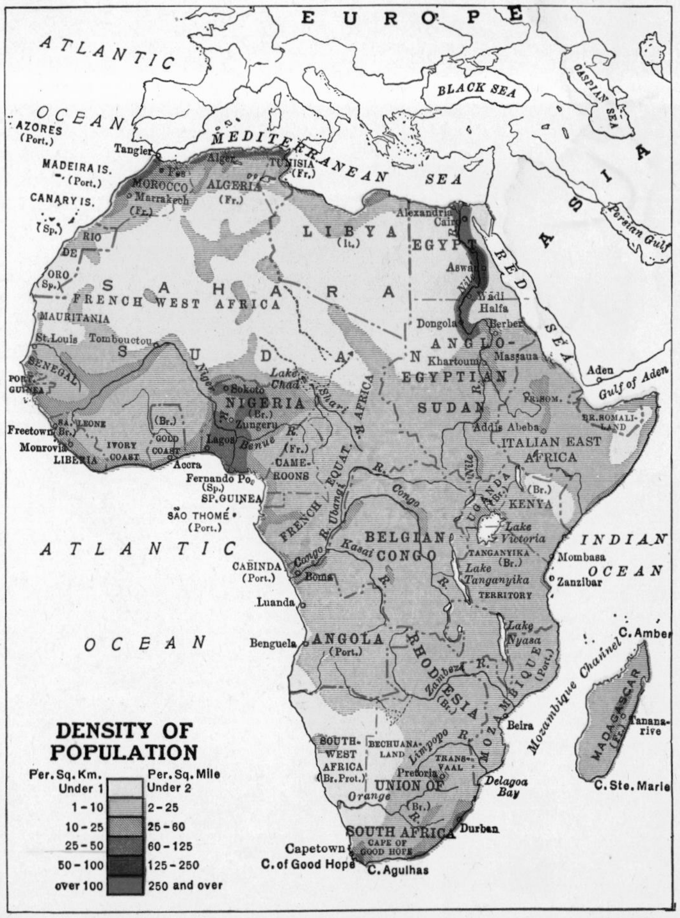
EUROPE
ATLANTIC OCEAN
AZORES (Port.)
MADEIRA IS. (Port.)
CANARY IS. (Sp.)
Tangier
MEDITERRANEAN SEA
MOROCCO (Fr.)
Marrakech
Alger
ALGERIA (Fr.)
TUNISIA (Fr.)
BLACK SEA
CASPIAN SEA
ASIA
Persian Gulf
RIO DE ORO (Sp.)
LIBYA (It.)
Alexandria
Cairo
EGYPT
Aswan
Wadi Halfa
SAHARA
FRENCH WEST AFRICA
MAURITANIA
RED SEA
St. Louis
Tombouctou
Dongola
Berber
ANGLO-EGYPTIAN SUDAN
Khartoum
Massaua
SENEGAL
Aden
Gulf of Aden
Lake Chad
Sokoto
NIGERIA (Br.)
Zungeru
FR. SOMALILAND
BR. SOMALILAND
Freetown
SIERRA LEONE (Br.)
Monrovia
LIBERIA
IVORY COAST
GOLD COAST (Br.)
Accra
Lagos
Benue R.
CAMEROONS (Fr.)
Addis Abeba
ITALIAN EAST AFRICA
Fernando Po (Sp.)
SP. GUINEA
SÃO THOMÉ (Port.)
FRENCH EQUAT. AFRICA
Congo
BELGIAN CONGO
UGANDA
KENYA (Br.)
Lake Victoria
INDIAN OCEAN
ATLANTIC OCEAN
CABINDA (Port.)
Boma
Kasai
TANGANYIKA (Br.)
Lake Tanganyika
TERRITORY
Mombasa
Zanzibar
Luanda
Benguela
ANGOLA (Port.)
RHODESIA (Br.)
Lake Nyasa
MOZAMBIQUE (Port.)
C. Amber
Mozambique Channel
MADAGASCAR (Fr.)
Tananarive
Zambezi R.
Beira
SOUTH-WEST AFRICA (Br. Prot.)
BECHUANALAND
Limpopo R.
TRANSVAAL
Pretoria
UNION OF SOUTH AFRICA
Orange
Delagoa Bay
Durban
C. Ste. Marie
CAPE OF GOOD HOPE
Capetown
C. of Good Hope
C. Agulhas
DENSITY OF POPULATION
Per. Sq. Km. Per. Sq. Mile
Under 1 Under 2
1-10 2-25
10-25 25-60
25-50 60-125
50-100 125-250
over 100 250 and over

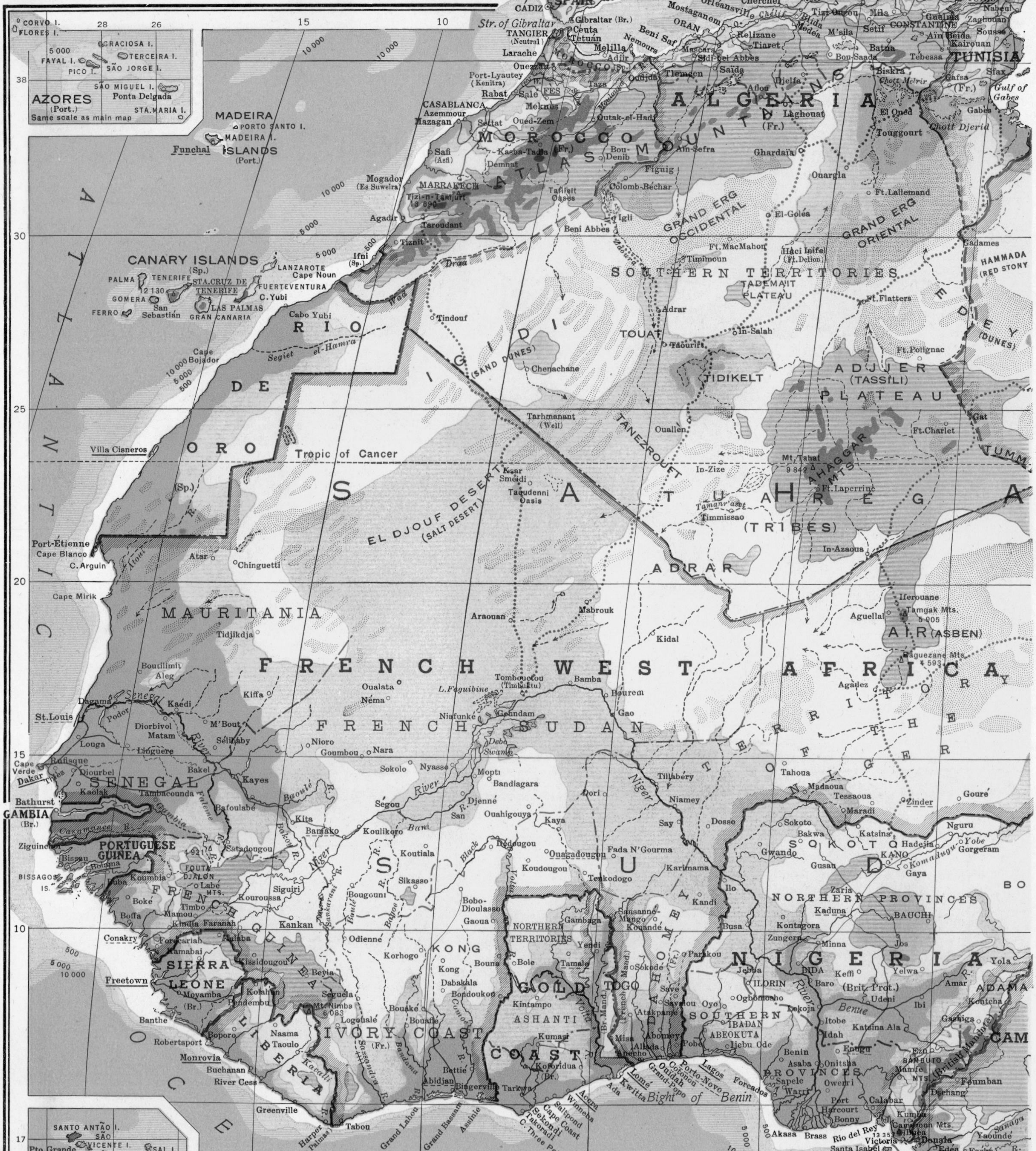

0 50 100 200 300 400 500 Miles
0 100 200 400 600 800 Kilometers

Scale 1:16 000 000; one inch to

Elevations and depressions

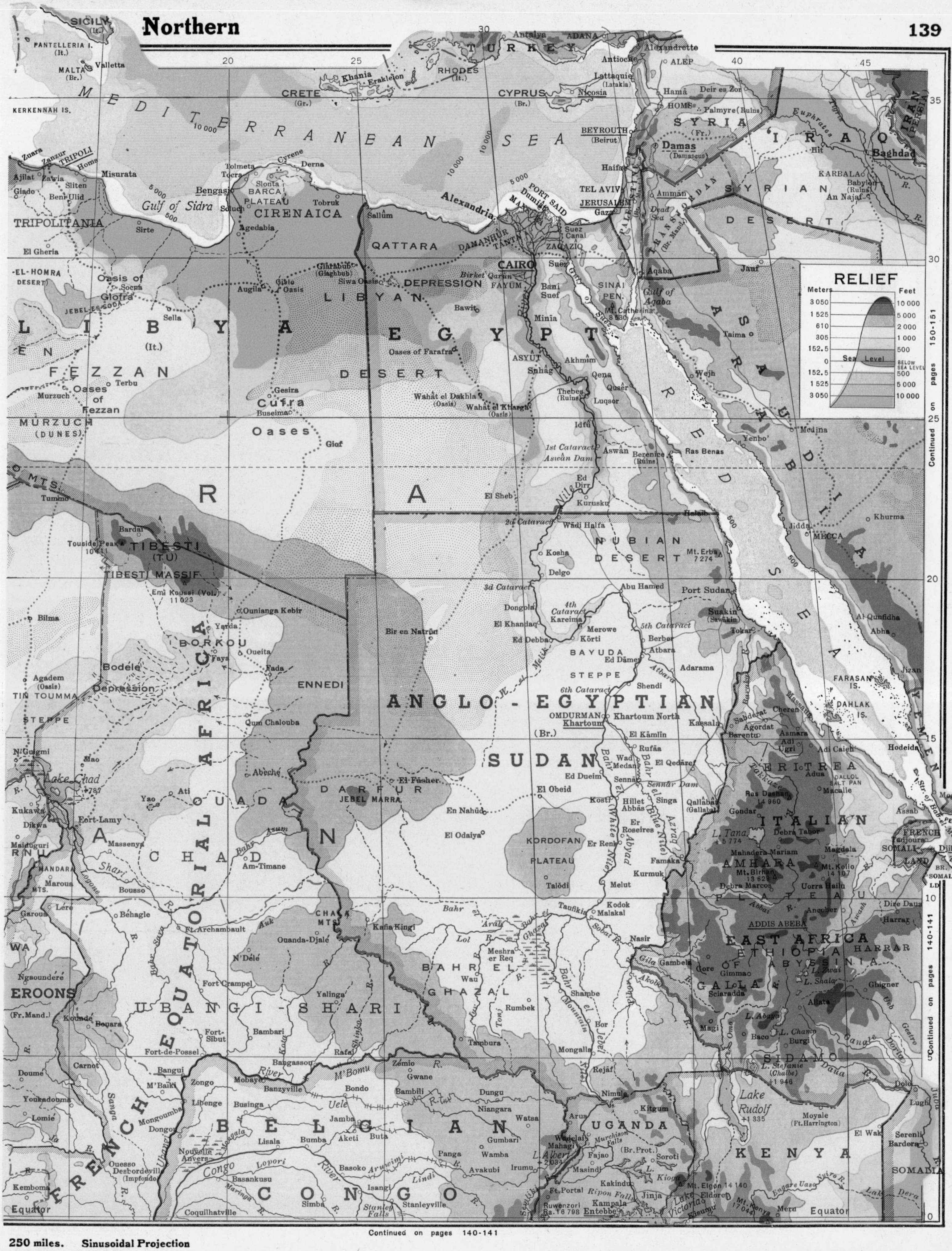

250 miles. Sinusoidal Projection

are given in feet

Continued on pages 140-141

Continued on pages 150-151

Continued on pages 140-141

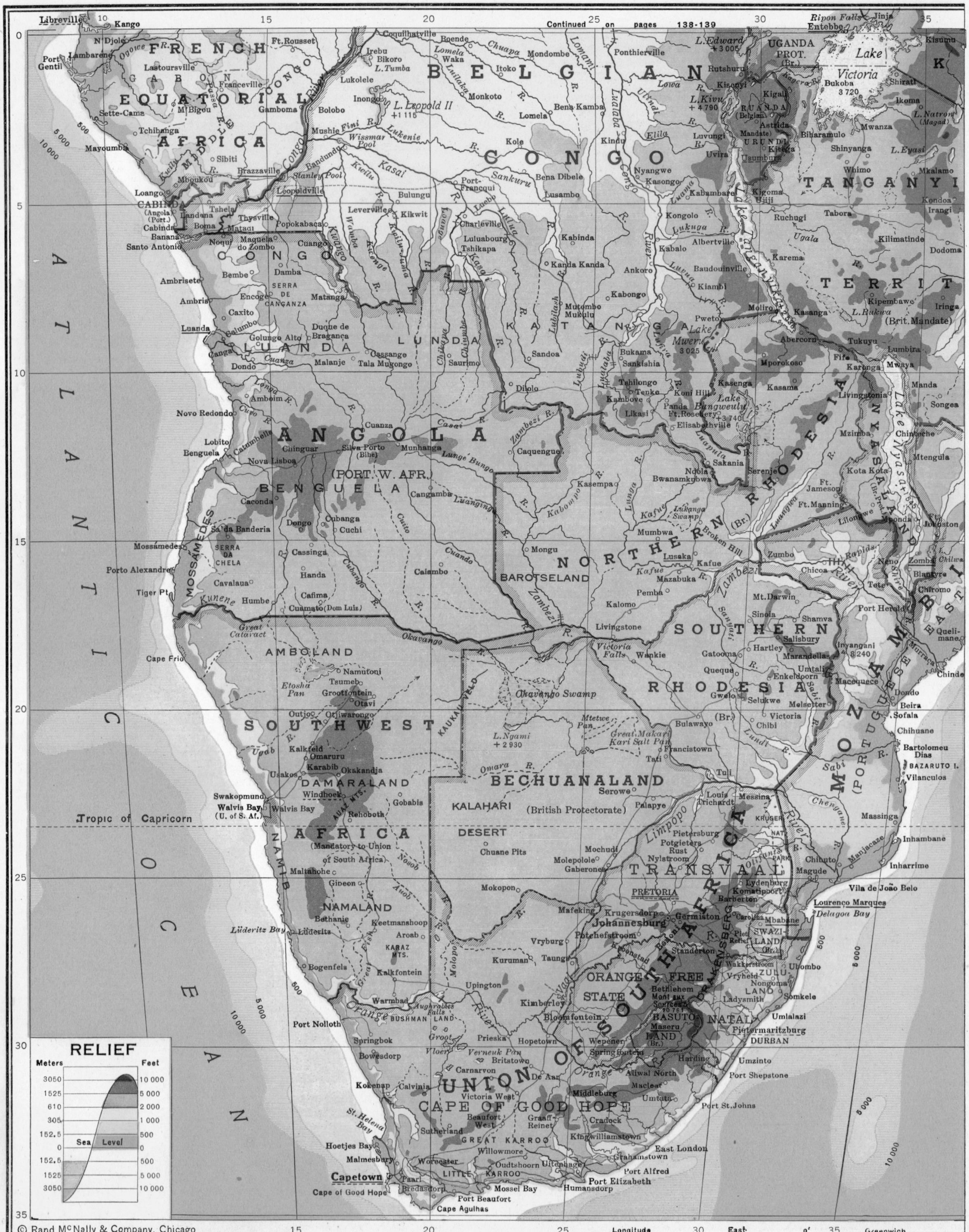

0 50 100 200 300 400 500 Miles
0 100 200 400 600 800 Kilometers

Scale 1:16 000 000; one inch to

Elevations and depressions

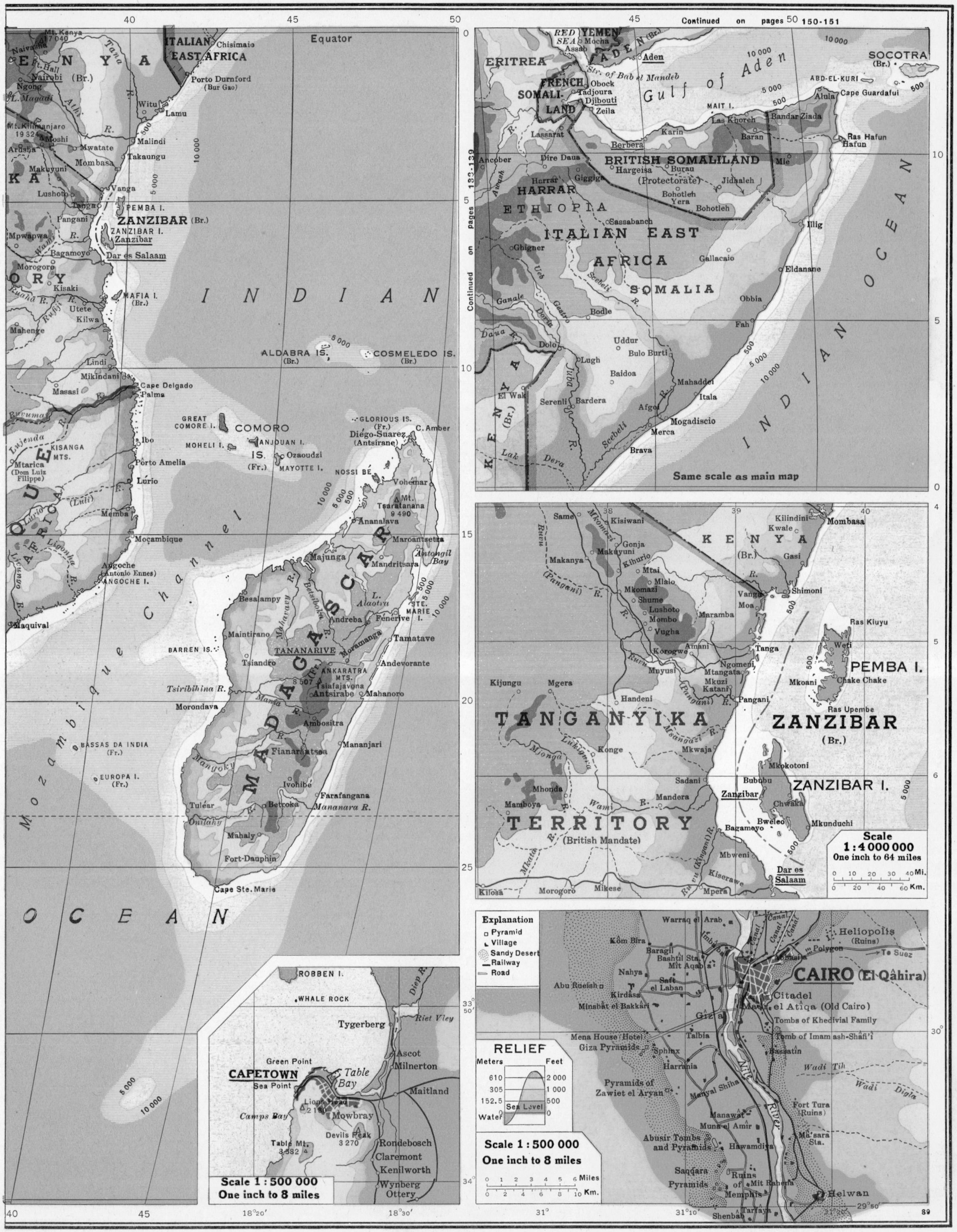

250 miles. Sinusoidal Projection

are given in feet

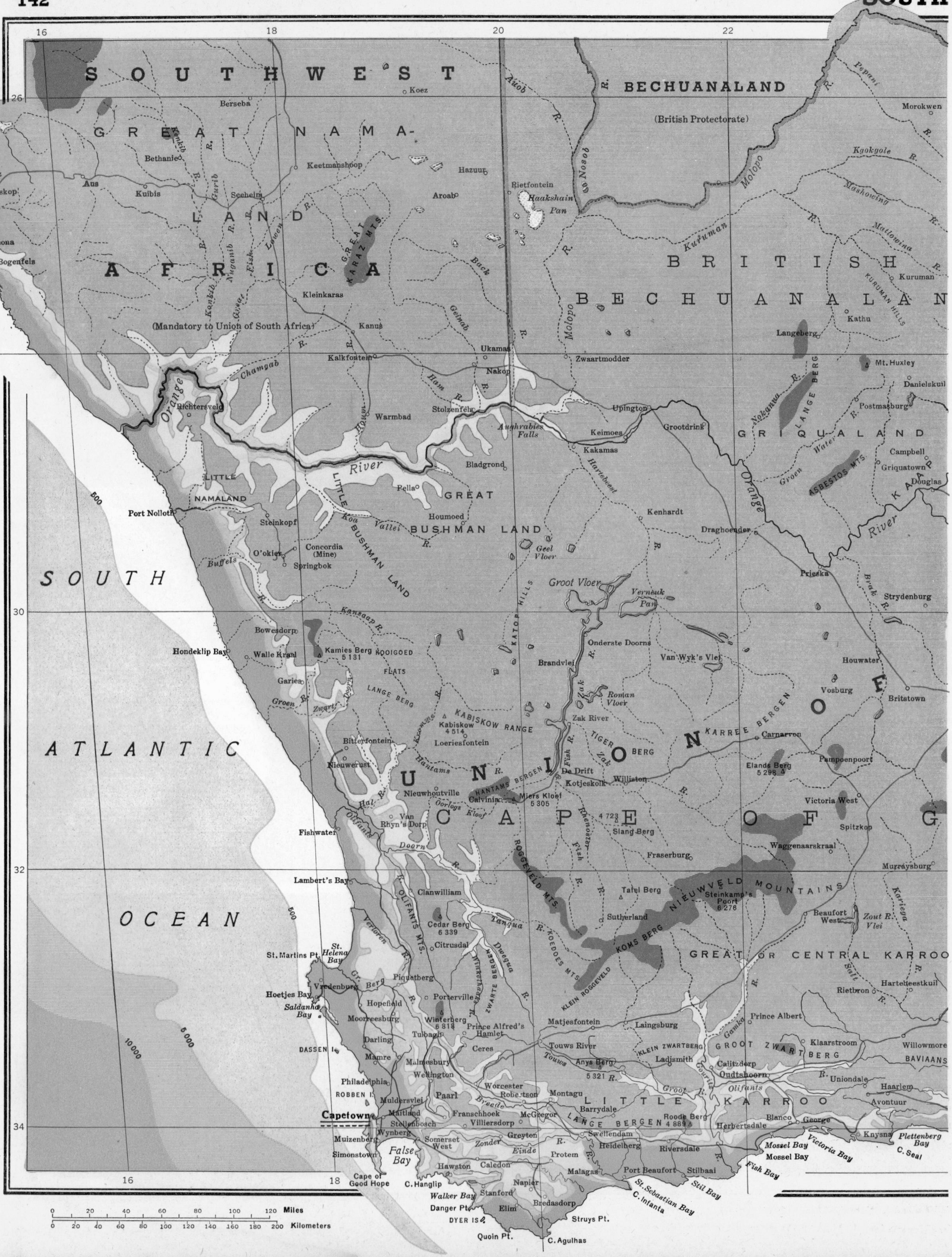
SOUTHWEST
GREAT NAMA-
LAND
AFRICA
(Mandatory to Union of South Africa)
BECHUANALAND
(British Protectorate)
BRITISH
BECHUANALAN
GRIQUALAND
UNION
OF
CAPE
OF G
SOUTH
ATLANTIC
OCEAN
LITTLE
NAMALAND
GREAT
BUSHMAN LAND
LITTLE BUSHMAN LAND
GREAT OR CENTRAL KARROO
LITTLE KARROO
Lüderitz
Kolmanskop
Pomona
Bogenfels
Aus
Kuibis
Bethanie
Berseba
Seeheim
Keetmanshoop
Koez
Hazuur
Aroab
Rietfontein
Haakshain Pan
Kleinkaras
Kanus
Kalkfontein
Ukamas
Nakop
Zwaartmodder
Warmbad
Stolzenfels
Richtersveld
Upington
Keimoes
Kakamas
Aughrabies Falls
Grootdrink
Bladgrond
Pella
Houmoed
Kenhardt
Draghoender
Port Nolloth
Steinkopf
O'okiep
Concordia (Mine)
Springbok
Geel Vloer
Groot Vloer
Verneuk Pan
Prieska
Strydenburg
Bowesdorp
Hondeklip Bay
Walle Kraal
Kamies Berg 5 131
KOIGOED FLATS
Garies
LANGE BERG
Onderste Doorns
Brandvlei
Van Wyk's Vlei
Roman Vloer
Houwater
Vosburg
Britstown
KABISKOW RANGE
Kabiskow 4 514
Loeriesfontein
Bitterfontein
Nieuwerust
Zak River
TIGER BERG
KARREE BERGEN
Carnarvon
Pampoenpoort
Elands Berg 5 298
De Drift
Williston
Kotjeskolk
HANTAMS BERGEN
Nieuwhoutville
Calvinia
Miers Kloof 5 305
Victoria West
Spitzkop
Van Rhyn's Dorp
Fishwater
4 723
Slang Berg
Waggenaarskraal
Fraserburg
Murraysburg
Lambert's Bay
Clanwilliam
ROGGEVELD MTS.
Tafel Berg
NIEUWVELD MOUNTAINS
Steinkamp's Poort 6 276
Sutherland
Beaufort West
Zout R. Vlei
Cedar Berg 6 339
Citrusdal
KOMS BERG
OLIFANTS MTS.
KOEDOES MTS.
KLEIN ROGGEVELD
ZWARTE BERGEN
St. Martins Pt.
St. Helena Bay
Vredenburg
Piquetberg
Hoetjes Bay
Saldanha Bay
Hopefield
Porterville
Moorreesburg
Winterberg 5 818
Prince Alfred's Hamlet
Matjesfontein
Laingsburg
Prince Albert
Rietbron
Harteheestkuil
Darling
Tulbagh
Ceres
Touws River
KLEIN ZWARTBERG
Ladismith
GROOT ZWARTBERG
Klaarstroom
Willowmore
BAVIAANS
DASSEN I.
Mamre
Malmesbury
Anys Berg 5 321
Calitzdorp
Oudtshoorn
Uniondale
Philadelphia
Wellington
Worcester
Robertson
Montagu
Haarlem
Avontuur
ROBBEN I.
Mulders Vlei
Paarl
Barrydale
Capetown
Maitland
Stellenbosch
Franschhoek
Villiersdorp
McGregor
LANGE BERGEN
Roode Berg 4 888
Blanco
George
Herbertsdale
Knysna
Plettenberg Bay
C. Seal
Wynberg
Muizenberg
Simonstown
False Bay
Somerset West
Greyton
Swellendam
Heidelberg
Riversdale
Mossel Bay
Victoria Bay
Hawston
Caledon
Protem
Malagas
Port Beaufort
Stilbaai
Fish Bay
Stil Bay
St. Sebastian Bay
C. Infanta
Cape of Good Hope
C. Hanglip
Walker Bay
Danger Pt.
Stanford
Napier
Elim
Bredasdorp
DYER IS.
Struys Pt.
Quoin Pt.
C. Agulhas
GREAT KARAS MTS.
KATOP HILLS
ASBESTOS MTS.
KURUMAN HILLS
LANGE BERG
Langeberg
Kathu
Kuruman
Mt. Huxley
Danielskuil
Postmasburg
Campbell
Griquatown
Douglas
Morokwen
Orange River
Molopo R.
Nosob R.
Auob R.
Kuruman R.
Fish R.
Olifants R.
Doorn R.
Groot R.
Gamka R.
Breede R.
Zonder Einde R.
Berg R.
Verloren
Buffels R.
Kansaap R.
Hartebeest R.
Brak R.
Zak R.
Groen R.
Hantams
16
18
20
22
26
28
30
32
34
500
5 000
10 000
0 20 40 60 80 100 120 Miles
0 20 40 60 80 100 120 140 160 180 200 Kilometers

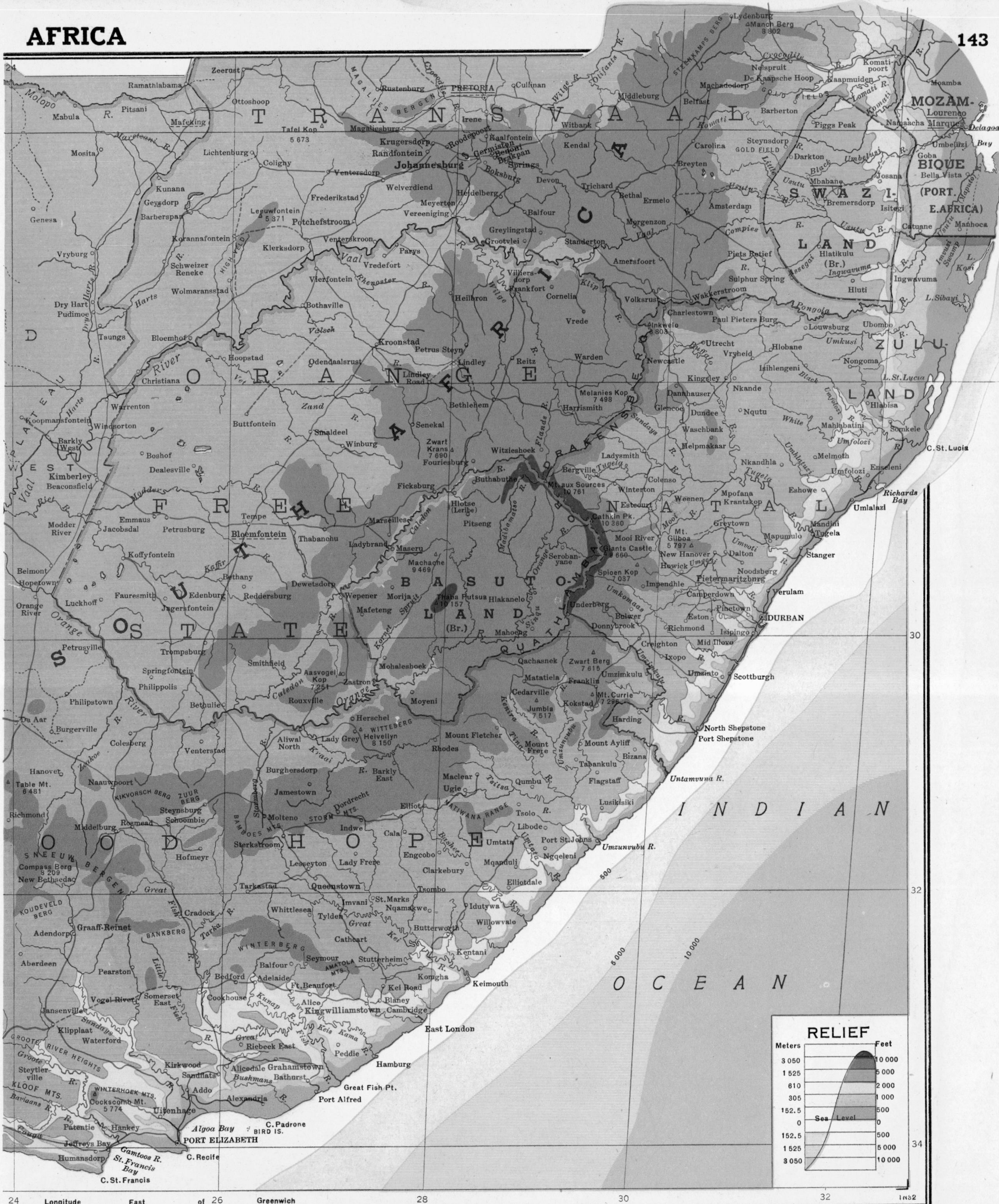

Scale 1:4 000 000; one inch to 64 miles. Sinusoidal Projection.

Elevations and depressions are given in feet

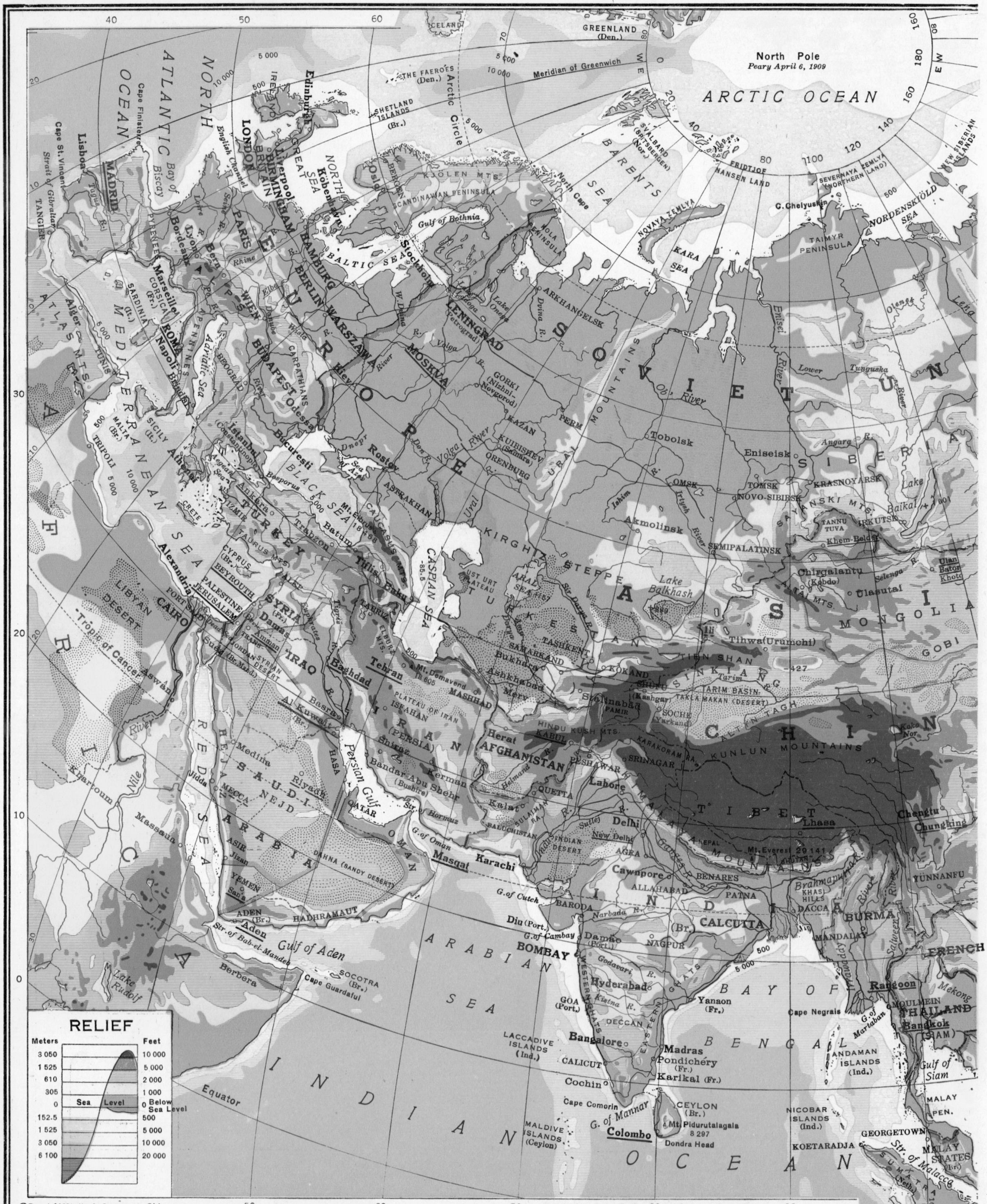

Scale 1 : 40 000 000; One inch to 630 miles. Lambert's Azimuthal, Equal Area Projection

Elevations and depressions are given in feet

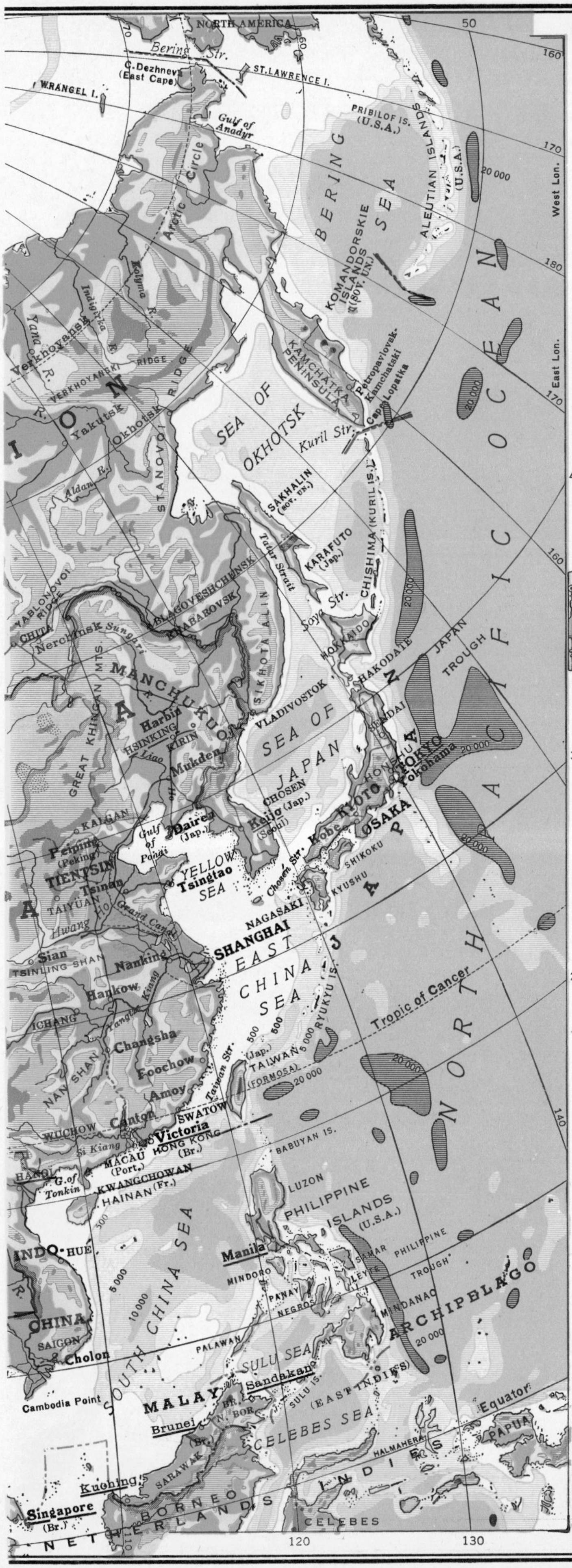
NORTH AMERICA
Bering Str.
C. Dezhnev (East Cape)
ST. LAWRENCE I.
WRANGEL I.
Gulf of Anadyr
Arctic Circle
PRIBILOF IS. (U.S.A.)
BERING SEA
ALEUTIAN ISLANDS (U.S.A.)
KOMANDORSKIE ISLANDS
KAMCHATKA PENINSULA
Petropavlovsk-Kamchatski
Cape Lopatka
Verkhoyansk
VERKHOYANSKI RIDGE
Yakutsk
Okhotsk
STANOVOI RIDGE
SEA OF OKHOTSK
Kuril Str.
SAKHALIN
Tatar Strait
KARAFUTO (Jap.)
CHISHIMA (KURIL IS.)
Soya Str.
BLAGOVESHCHENSK
KHABAROVSK
SIKHOTA ALIN
Nerchinsk
CHITA
MANCHUKUO
Harbin
HSINKING
KIRIN
Mukden
VLADIVOSTOK
SEA OF JAPAN
HOKKAIDO
HAKODATE
JAPAN TROUGH
SENDAI
HONSHU
TOKYO
Yokohama
KYOTO
OSAKA
Kobe
SHIKOKU
KYUSHU
NAGASAKI
CHOSEN
Keijo (Jap.) (Seoul)
Dairen (Jap.)
GREAT KHINGAN MTS.
KALGAN
Peiping (Peking)
TIENTSIN
Tsinan
Tsingtao
YELLOW SEA
TAIYUAN
Hwang
Grand Canal
Sian
TSINLING SHAN
Nanking
SHANGHAI
EAST CHINA SEA
Hankow
ICHANG
Changsha
NAN SHAN
Foochow
Amoy
Canton
SWATOW
Victoria
HONG KONG (Br.)
MACAU (Port.)
WUCHOW
Si Kiang
KWANGCHOWAN (Fr.)
HAINAN
G. of Tonkin
RYUKYU IS.
TAIWAN (FORMOSA)
Taiwan Str.
Tropic of Cancer
NORTH PACIFIC OCEAN
BABUYAN IS.
LUZON
PHILIPPINE ISLANDS (U.S.A.)
Manila
MINDORO
PANAY
NEGROS
SAMAR
LEYTE
MINDANAO
PHILIPPINE TROUGH
PALAWAN
SULU SEA
SOUTH CHINA SEA
Sandakan
SULU IS.
ARCHIPELAGO
MALAY
(EAST INDIES)
CELEBES SEA
Equator
PAPUA
HALMAHERA
Brunei
SARAWAK
BORNEO
Kuching
NETHERLANDS INDIES
CELEBES
Singapore (Br.)
INDO-CHINA
HUE
SAIGON
Cholon
Cambodia Point
West Lon.
East Lon.
50
160
170
180
40
30
20
10
0
120
130
140

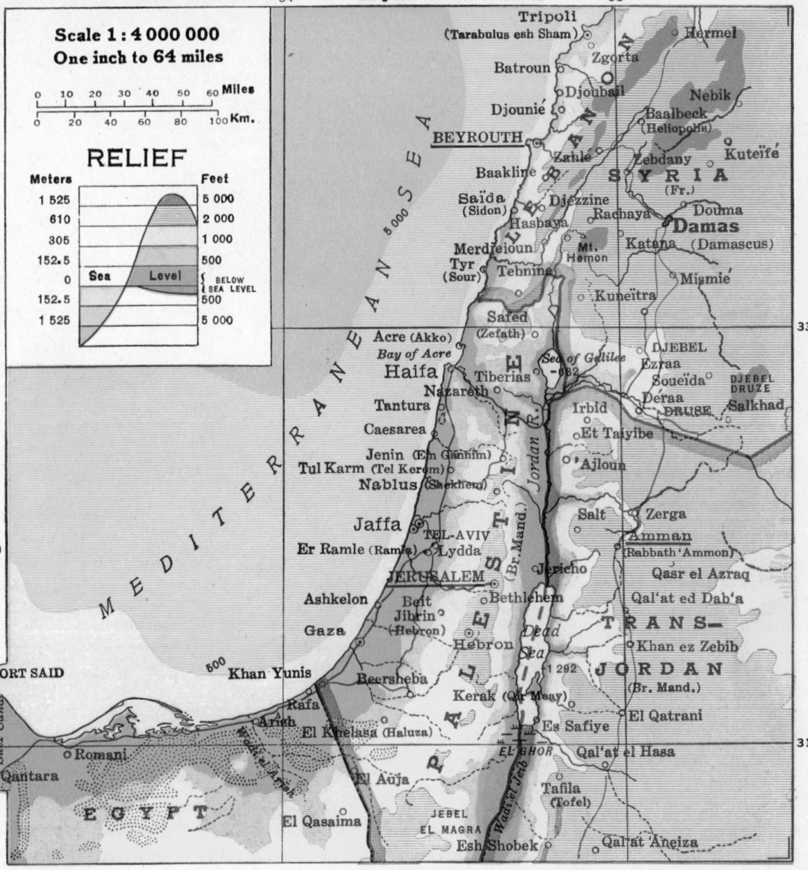
Scale 1 : 4 000 000
One inch to 64 miles
Miles
Km.
RELIEF
Meters
Feet
1 525
610
305
152.5
0
152.5
1 525
5 000
2 000
1 000
500
Sea Level
BELOW SEA LEVEL
500
5 000
Longitude East of Greenwich
34
36
Tripoli (Tarabulus esh Sham)
Hermel
Zgorta
Batroun
Djoubail
Nebik
Djounié
Baalbeck (Heliopolis)
BEYROUTH
Zahle
Zebdany
Kuteife
Baakline
SYRIA (Fr.)
Saïda (Sidon)
Djezzine
Douma
Hasbaya
Rachaya
Damas (Damascus)
Merdjeioun
Katana
Tyr (Sour)
Mt. Hermon
Tebnine
Mismie
Kuneitra
Safed (Zefath)
Acre (Akko)
Bay of Acre
Haifa
Sea of Galilee
Tiberias
Nazareth
DJEBEL
Ezraa
Soueida
DJEBEL DRUZE
Deraa
Salkhad
Tantura
Caesarea
Irbid
Et Taiyibe
Jenin (En Gannim)
Tul Karm (Tel Kerem)
Ajloun
Nablus (Shechem)
Jordan R.
MEDITERRANEAN SEA
Jaffa
TEL-AVIV
Salt
Zerga
Er Ramle (Ramla)
Lydda
Amman (Rabbath 'Ammon)
JERUSALEM
Jericho
Qasr el Azraq
Ashkelon
Beit Jibrin (Hebron)
Bethlehem
Qal'at ed Dab'a
Gaza
Hebron
Dead Sea
TRANS-JORDAN (Br. Mand.)
Khan ez Zebib
PALESTINE (Br. Mand.)
PORT SAID
Khan Yunis
Beersheba
Rafa
Arish
Kerak
Es Safiye
El Qatrani
El Khelasa (Haluza)
Romani
Suez Canal
Qantara
El Auja
EL GHOR
Qal'at el Hasa
EGYPT
Tafila (Tofel)
JEBEL EL MAGRA
El Qasaima
Esh Shobek
Qal'at Aneiza
Wadi el Arish
Wadi el Jeib
33
31

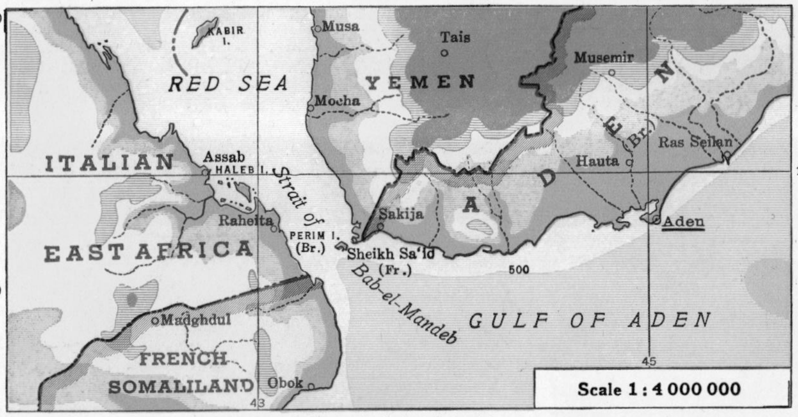
KABIR I.
Musa
Tais
RED SEA
YEMEN
Musemir
Mocha
ITALIAN EAST AFRICA
Assab
HALEB I.
Raheita
Strait of Bab-el-Mandeb
PERIM I. (Br.)
Sheikh Sa'id (Fr.)
Sakija
ADEN
Hauta
Ras Seilan
Aden
GULF OF ADEN
Madghdul
FRENCH SOMALILAND
Obok
500
43
45
13
Scale 1 : 4 000 000

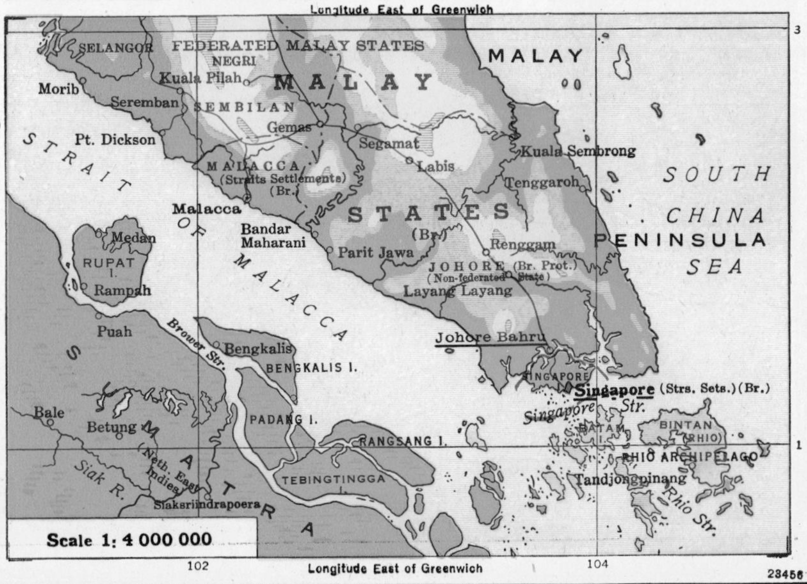
Longitude East of Greenwich
SELANGOR
FEDERATED MALAY STATES
NEGRI SEMBILAN
Kuala Pilah
MALAY
Morib
Seremban
Gemas
Pt. Dickson
Segamat
Kuala Sembrong
Labis
STRAIT OF MALACCA
MALACCA (Straits Settlements) (Br.)
Tenggaroh
SOUTH CHINA SEA
Malacca
Bandar Maharani
STATES (Br.)
PENINSULA
Medan
RUPAT I.
Parit Jawa
Renggam
Rampah
JOHORE (Non-federated State) (Br. Prot.)
Layang Layang
Puah
Brouwer Str.
Johore Bahru
Bengkalis
BENGKALIS I.
Singapore (Strs. Sets.) (Br.)
Singapore Str.
Bale
PADANG I.
BINTAN (RHIO)
Betung
SUMATRA (Neth. East Indies)
RANGSANG I.
RHIO ARCHIPELAGO
Siak R.
TEBINGTINGGA I.
Tandjongpinang
Rhio Str.
Siakrinndrapoera
102
104
3
1
Scale 1: 4 000 000
Longitude East of Greenwich

23456

JANUARY
NORMAL SURFACE TEMPERATURE

JULY
NORMAL SURFACE TEMPERATURE

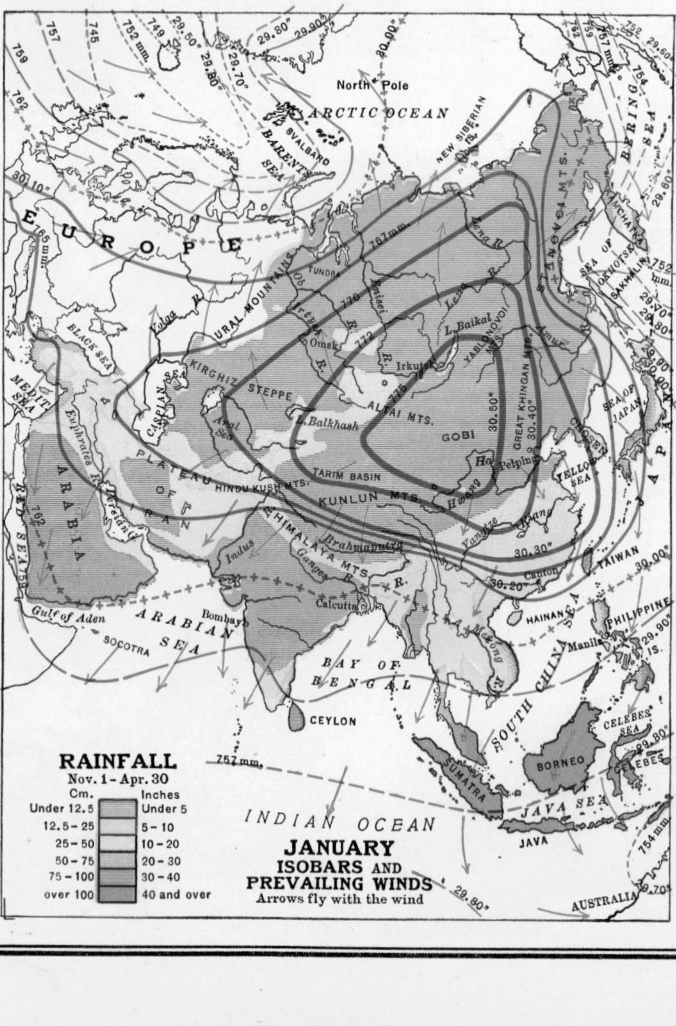

JANUARY
ISOBARS AND
PREVAILING WINDS
Arrows fly with the wind

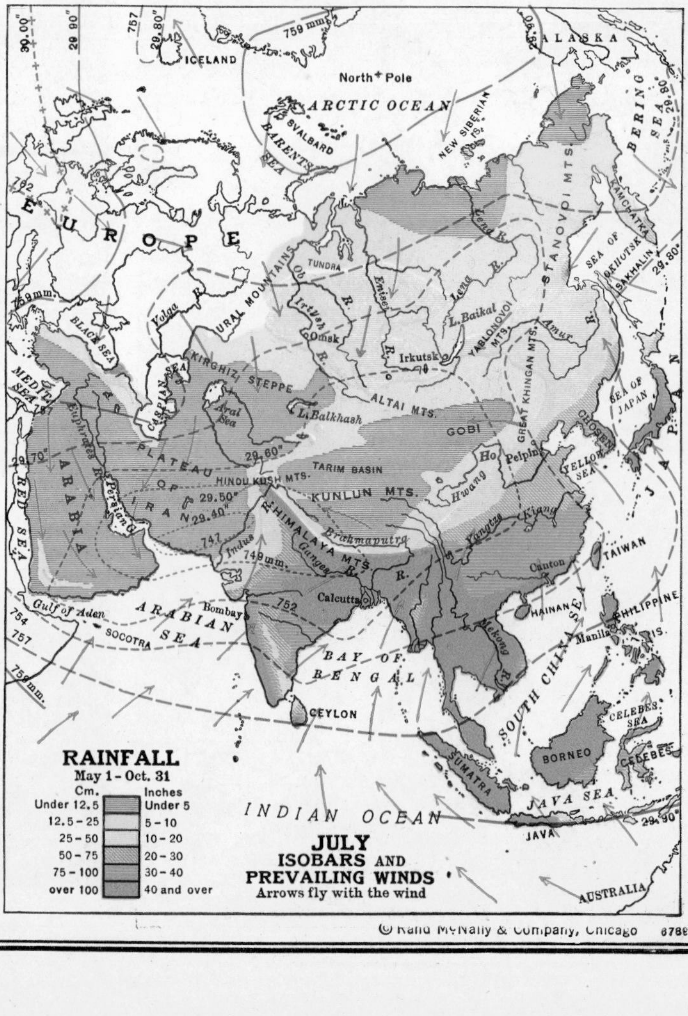

JULY
ISOBARS AND
PREVAILING WINDS
Arrows fly with the wind

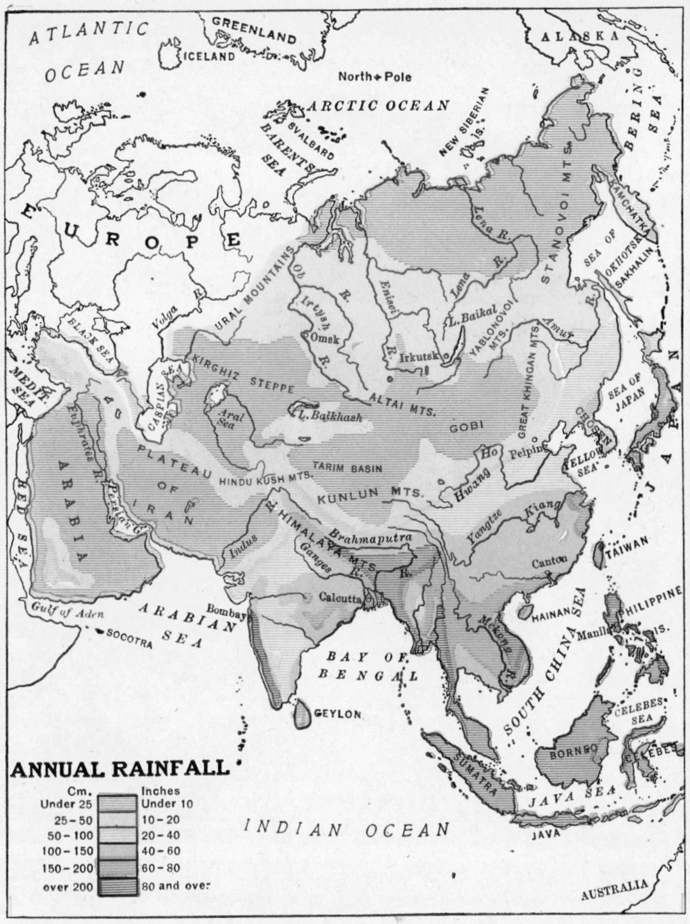
ANNUAL RAINFALL
Cm. Inches
Under 25 Under 10
25–50 10–20
50–100 20–40
100–150 40–60
150–200 60–80
over 200 80 and over
ATLANTIC OCEAN
ARCTIC OCEAN
EUROPE
ARABIA
PLATEAU OF IRAN
KIRGHIZ STEPPE
GOBI
TARIM BASIN
KUNLUN MTS.
HIMALAYA MTS.
ARABIAN SEA
BAY OF BENGAL
SOUTH CHINA SEA
INDIAN OCEAN
AUSTRALIA

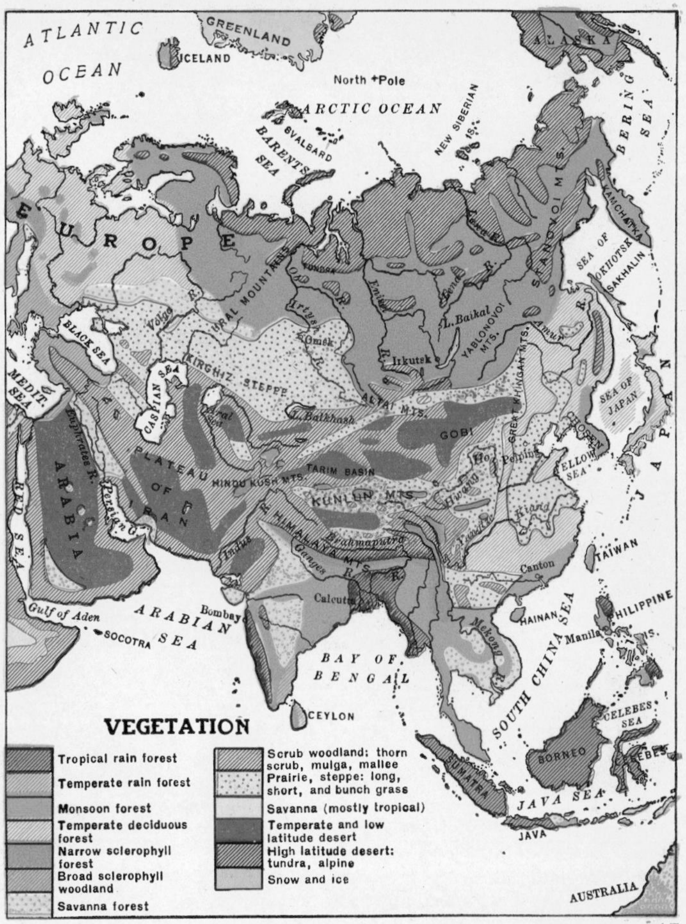
VEGETATION
Tropical rain forest
Temperate rain forest
Monsoon forest
Temperate deciduous forest
Narrow sclerophyll forest
Broad sclerophyll woodland
Savanna forest
Scrub woodland; thorn scrub, mulga, mallee
Prairie, steppe: long, short, and bunch grass
Savanna (mostly tropical)
Temperate and low latitude desert
High latitude desert: tundra, alpine
Snow and ice
ATLANTIC OCEAN
ARCTIC OCEAN
EUROPE
ARABIA
PLATEAU OF IRAN
GOBI
ARABIAN SEA
BAY OF BENGAL
SOUTH CHINA SEA
AUSTRALIA

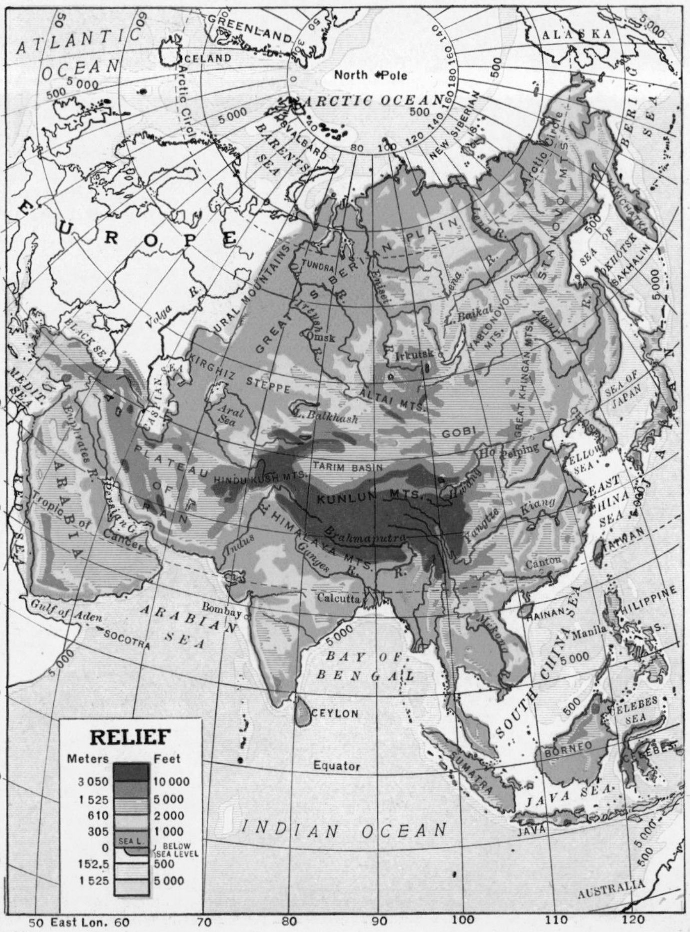
RELIEF
Meters Feet
3 050 10 000
1 525 5 000
610 2 000
305 1 000
0 SEA L. BELOW SEA LEVEL
152.5 500
1 525 5 000
ATLANTIC OCEAN
ARCTIC OCEAN
EUROPE
SIBERIAN PLAIN
ARABIA
PLATEAU OF IRAN
KUNLUN MTS.
HIMALAYA MTS.
ARABIAN SEA
BAY OF BENGAL
Equator
INDIAN OCEAN
AUSTRALIA
50 East Lon. 60 70 80 90 100 110 120

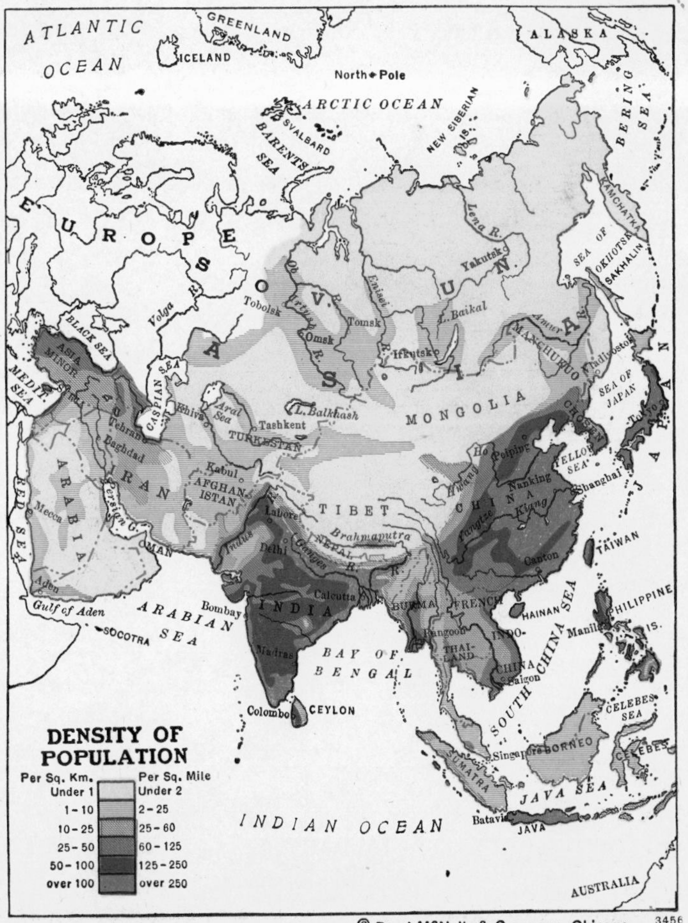
DENSITY OF POPULATION
Per Sq. Km. Per Sq. Mile
Under 1 Under 2
1–10 2–25
10–25 25–60
25–50 60–125
50–100 125–250
over 100 over 250
ATLANTIC OCEAN
ARCTIC OCEAN
EUROPE
SOVIET UNION
ASIA MINOR
ARABIA
IRAN
AFGHANISTAN
TURKESTAN
MONGOLIA
TIBET
CHINA
INDIA
BURMA
THAILAND
FRENCH INDO-CHINA
ARABIAN SEA
BAY OF BENGAL
INDIAN OCEAN
AUSTRALIA

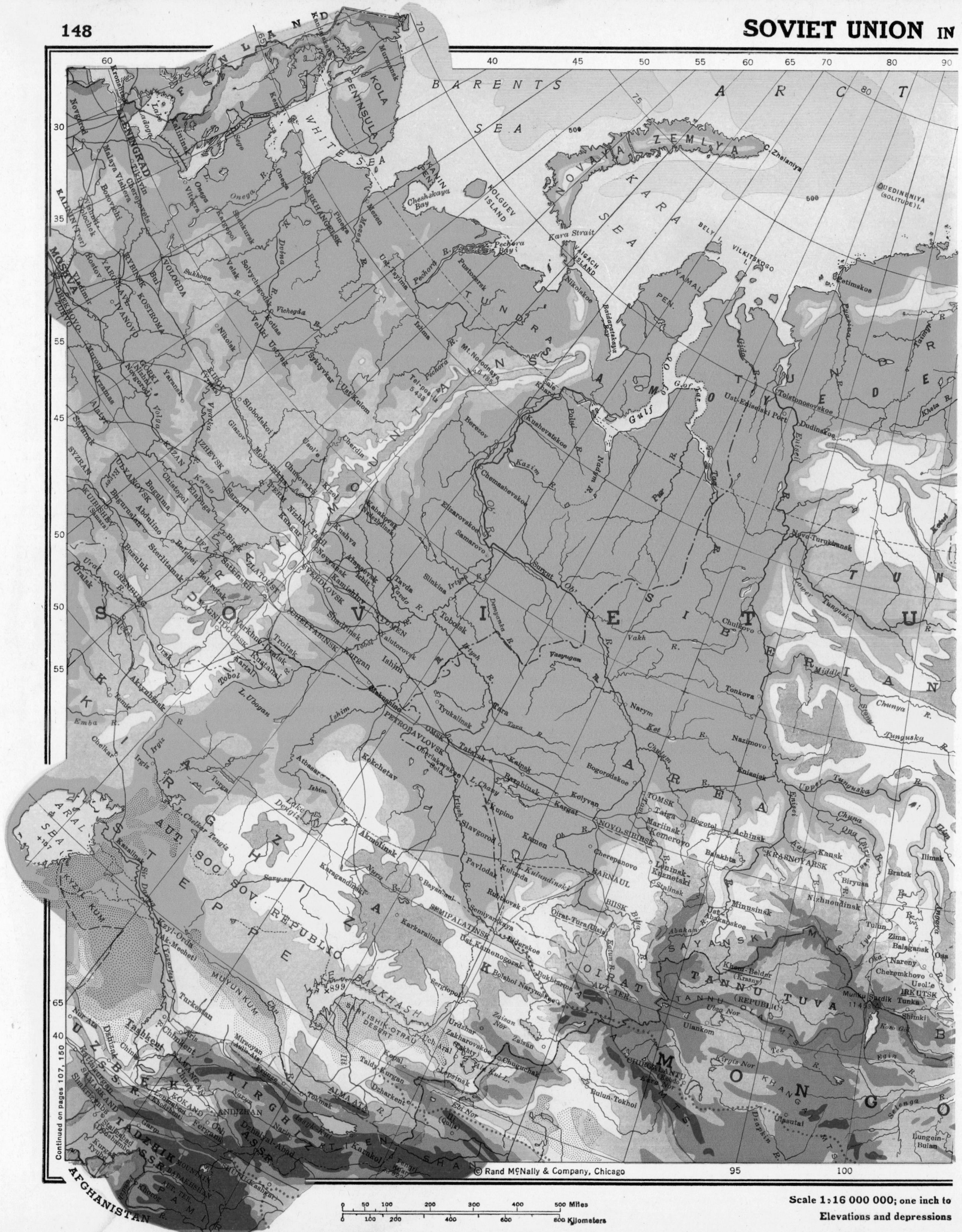

Continued on pages 107, 150

Scale 1:16 000 000; one inch to
Elevations and depressions

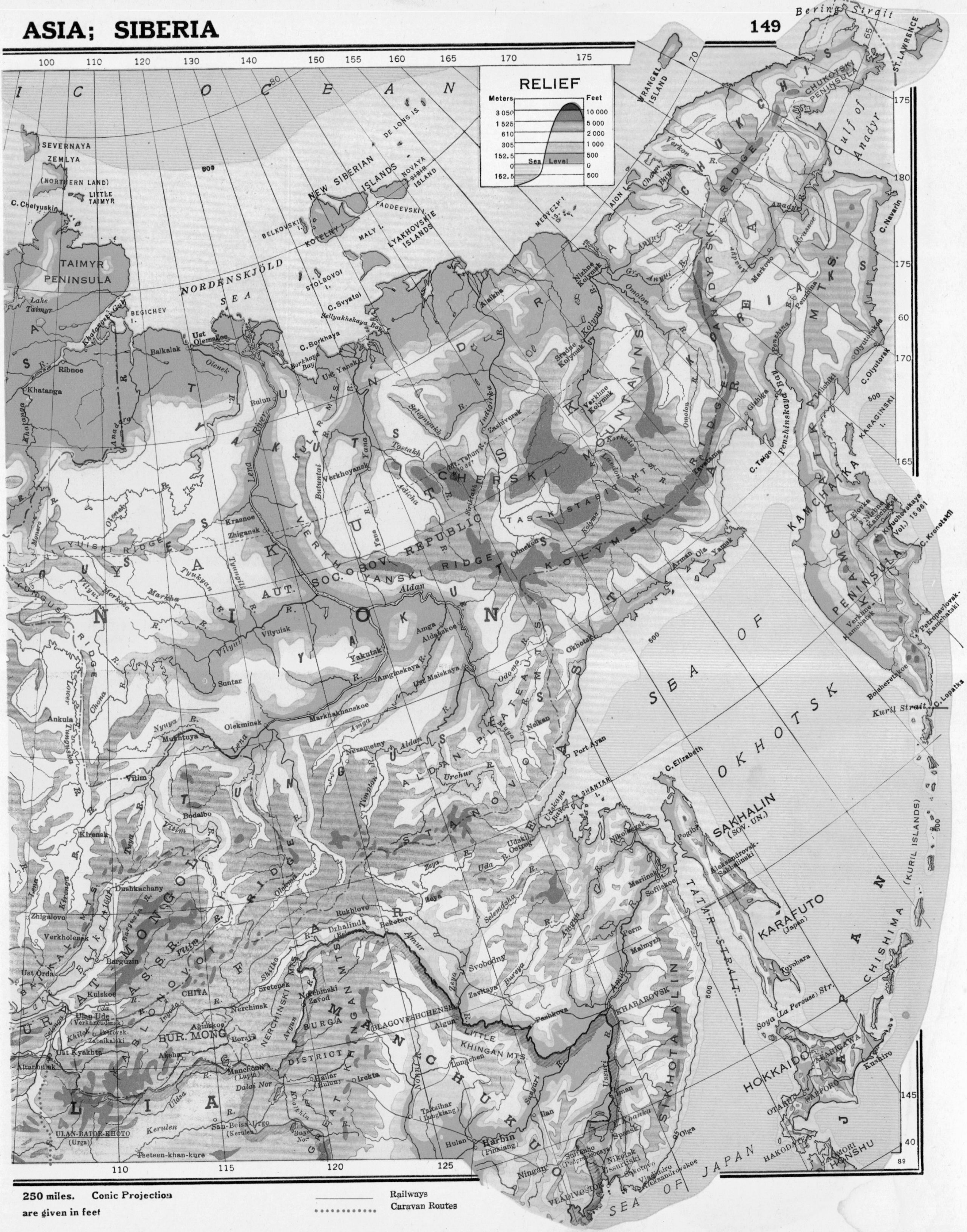

250 miles. Conic Projection

are given in feet

Railways

Caravan Routes

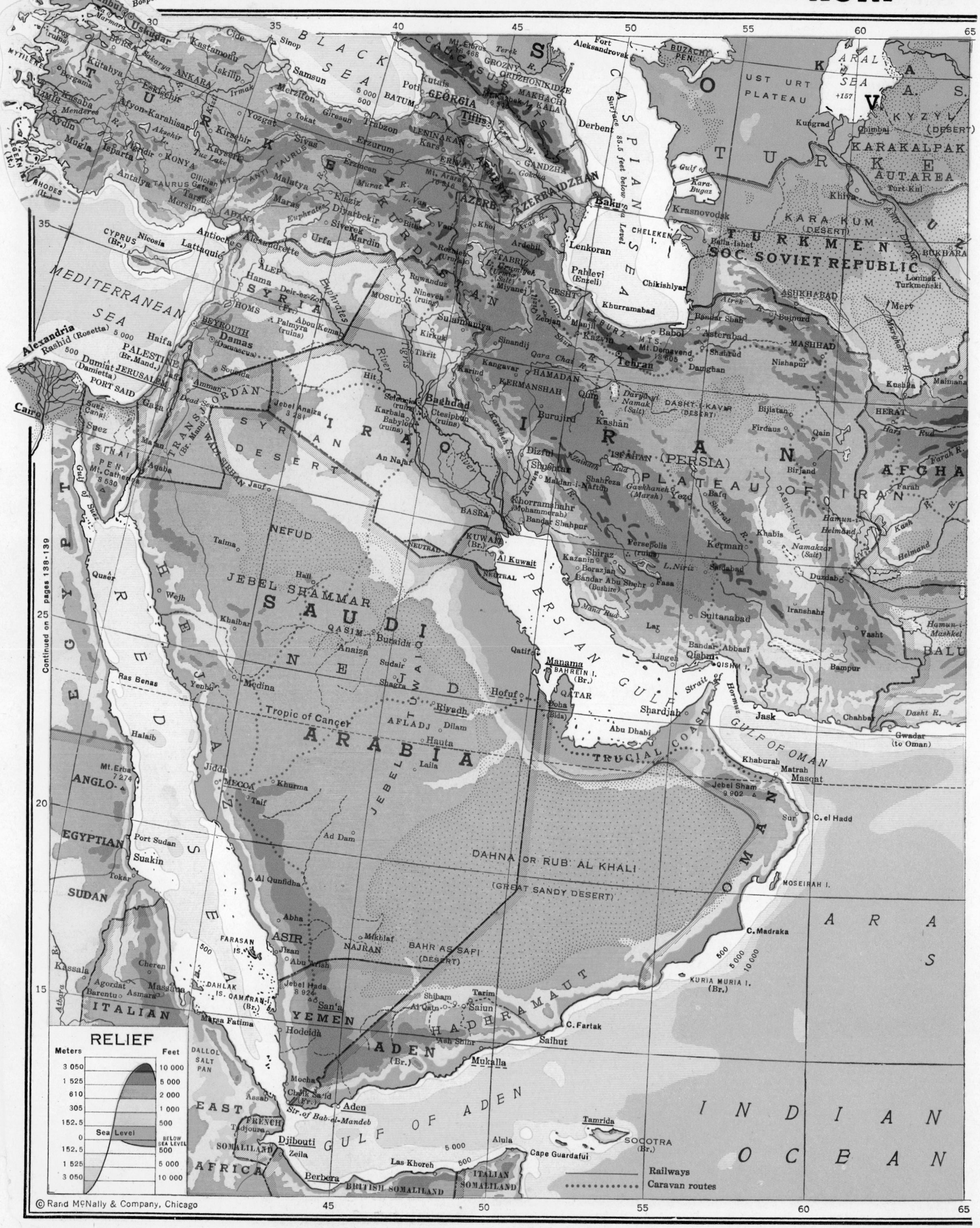

0 50 100 200 300 400 500 Miles
0 100 200 400 600 800 Kilometers

Scale 1 : 16 000 000; one inch to
Elevations and depressions

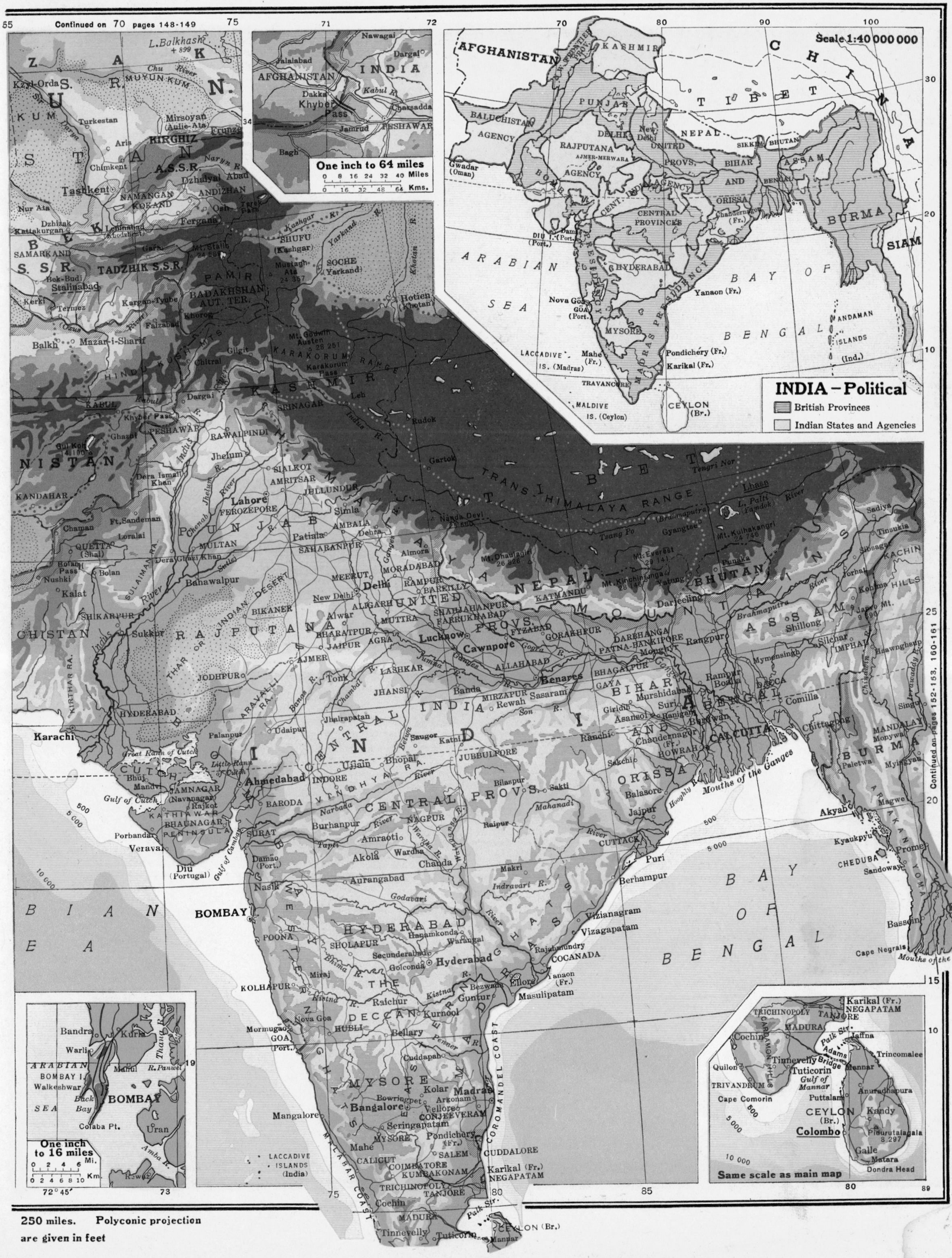

250 miles. Polyconic projection
are given in feet

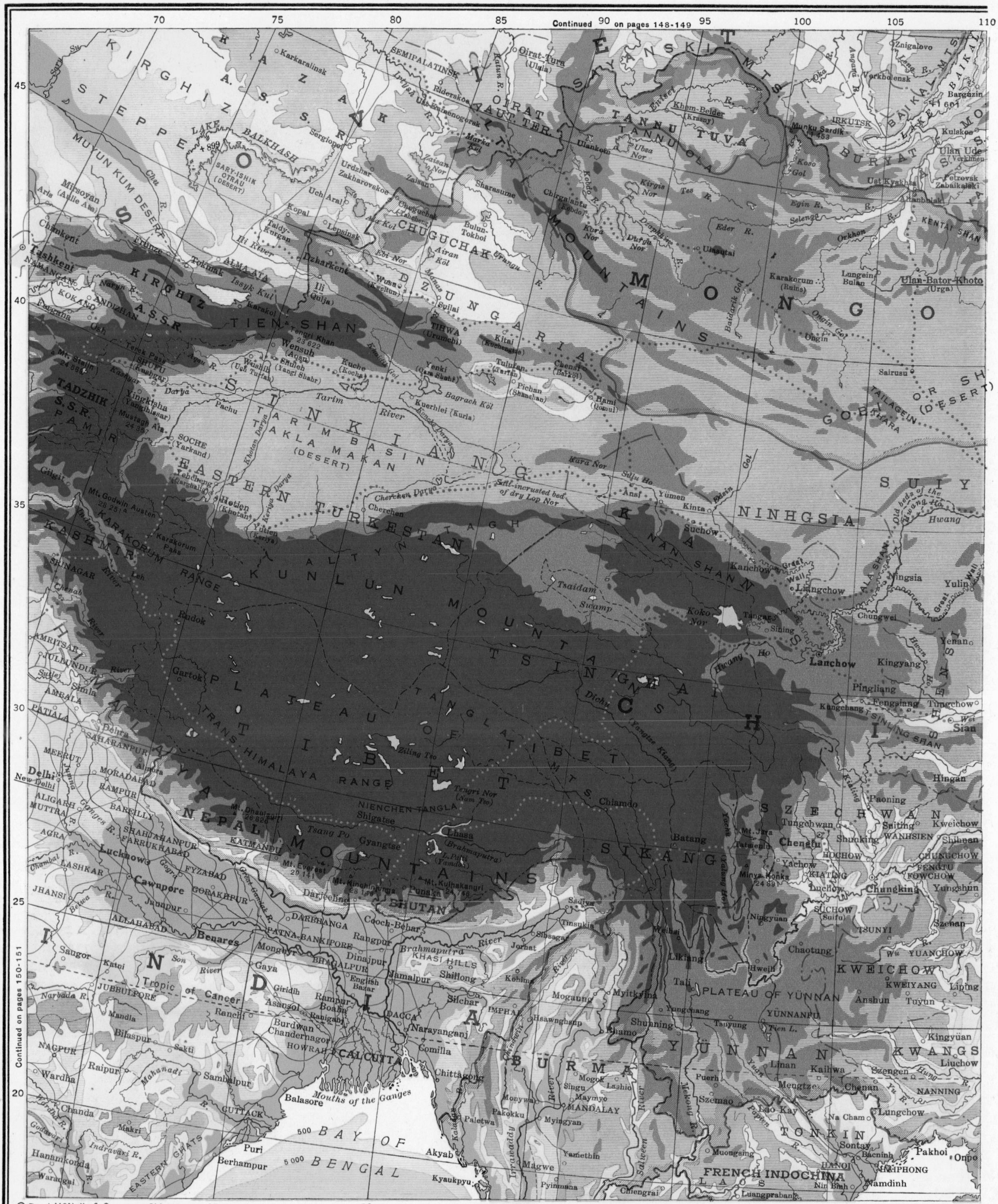

0 50 100 200 300 400 500 Miles
0 100 200 400 600 800 Kilometers

Railways
Caravan routes

Scale 1 : 16 000 000; one inch to
Elevations and depressions

250 miles. Polyconic Projection
are given in feet

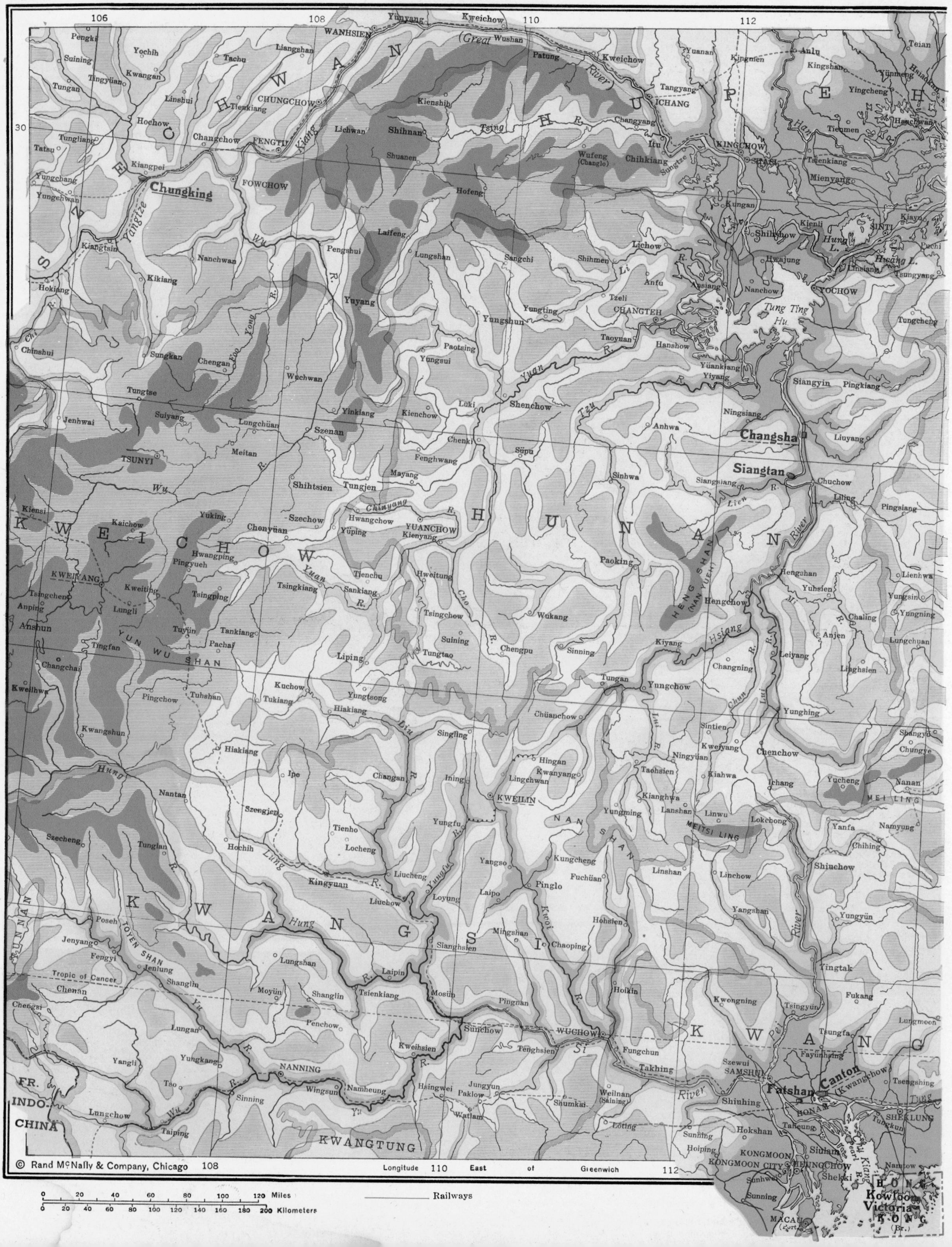

106
108
110
112
30
S Z E C H W A N
H U P E H
K W E I C H O W
H U N A N
K W A N G S I
K W A N G T U N G
YUNNAN
FR. INDO-CHINA
KWANGTUNG
Wanhsien
Yunyang
Kweichow
Wushan
(Great River) Yangtze
Patung
Ichang
Tangyang
Yuanan
Kingmen
Anlu
Teian
Kingshan
Yunmeng
Hsiaokan
Yingcheng
Hanchwan
Tienmen
Han
Pengki
Yochih
Suining
Tachu
Liangshan
Tingyüan
Kwangan
Tungan
Linshui
Chungchow
Tienkiang
Kienshih
Changyang
Hochow
Changchow
Fengtu
Lichwan
Shihnan
Tsing
Itu
Kingchow
Shasi
Tunglianp
Tatsu
Kiangpei
Chungking
Fowchow
Shuanen
Wufeng (Changlo)
Chihkiang
Tsienkiang
Mienyang
Yungchang
Yungchwan
Hofeng
Kungan
Kiangtsin
Nanchwan
Laifeng
Pengshui
Lungshan
Sangchi
Shihmen
Lichow
Shihshow
Kienli
Kiayu
Sinti
Hung L.
Hwang L.
Puchi
Linsiang
Tsungyang
Kikiang
Hokiang
Wu R.
Yuyang
Yungting
Anfu
Hwajung
Anhsiang
Tzeli
Nanchow
Yochow
Changteh
Tung Ting Hu
Yungshun
Tungcheng
Chinshui
Sungkan
Chengan
Paotsing
Yungsui
Taoyuan
Hanshow
Yüankiang
Yiyang
Wuchwan
Yuan R.
Siangyin
Pingkiang
Tungtse
Suiyang
Jenhwai
Lungchüan
Yinkiang
Kienchow
Luki
Shenchow
Tzu R.
Ningsiang
Anhwa
Changsha
Liuyang
Tsunyi
Meitan
Szenan
Chenki
Supu
Siangtan
Fenghwang
Mayang
Shihtsien
Tungjen
Sinhwa
Siangsiang
Chuchow
Liling
Pingsiang
Kiensi
Kaichow
Yuking
Szechow
Chenyüan
Chinyang R.
Hwangchow
Yüping
Yuanchow
Kienyang
Lien R.
Hsiang River
Paoking
Kweiyang
Tsingchen
Anping
Anshun
Pingyueh
Hwangping
Kweiting
Tsingping
Lungli
Tsingkiang
Tienchu
Sankiang
Hweitung
Heng Shan (Nan Yueh)
Hengshan
Yuhsien
Lienhwa
Yungsin
Yungning
Hengchow
Tsingchow
Wukang
Mi R.
Chaling
Anjen
Tuyün
Tankiang
Pachai
Tingfan
Yun Wu Shan
Changchai
Suining
Tungtao
Chengpu
Sinning
Kiyang
Leiyang
Lungchuan
Changning
Linghsien
Liping
Kweihwa
Kuchow
Tukiang
Yungtsung
Hiakiang
Tungan
Yungchow
Chun R.
Lui R.
Pingchow
Tuhshan
Chüanchow
Yunghing
Kwangshun
Singling
Sintien
Kweiyang
Chenchow
Shangyu
Chungyi
Hiakiang
Ipe
Changan
Ining
Hingan
Kwanyang
Lingchwan
Ningyüan
Taohsien
Kiahwa
Ichang
Yucheng
Nanan
Mei Ling
Nantan
Kweilin
Kianghwa
Lanshan
Linwu
Lokchong
Yanfa
Namyung
Szengjen
Yungfu
Yungming
Meitsi Ling
Chihing
Tienho
Nan Shan
Szecheng
Hochih
Locheng
Yangso
Kungcheng
Linshan
Linchow
Shiuchow
Tunglan
Lung R.
Liucheng
Pinglo
Fuchüan
Kingyuan
Liuchow
Loyung
Laipo
Yangshan
Yungyün
Poseh
Hung R.
Kwei R.
Hohsien
Jenyang
Toyen Shan
Mingshan
Chaoping
Fengyi
Lungshan
Sianghsien
Jenlung
Laipin
Tingtak
Tropic of Cancer
Shanglin
Hoikin
Chenan
Moyün
Shanglin
Tsienkiang
Mosün
Pingnan
Kwongning
Tsingyün
Fukang
Chengsi
Yu R.
Penchow
Sunchow
Lungmoon
Lungan
Kweihsien
Wuchow
Si R.
Tsungfa
Fayunhsing
Yangli
Yungkang
Tenghsien
Fungchun
Szewui
Samshui
Takhing
Nanning
Tso
Hsingwei
Jungyun
Paklow
Weilnan (Saining)
Canton
Fatshan
Kwangchow
Tsengshing
Tung
Honam
Wingsun
Namheung
Sinning
Shiuhing
Shumkai
Wu R.
Lungchow
Watlam
Hokshan
Tailuong
Sheklung
Loting
Taiping
Sunning
Hoiping
Kongmoon
Kongmoon City
Heungchow
Siulam
Chu Kiang
Pearl R.
Namtow
Sunwui
Shekki
Hong Kong
Kowloon
Victoria
Macau (Port.)
(Br.)
© Rand McNally & Company, Chicago
Longitude 110 East of Greenwich 112
0 20 40 60 80 100 120 Miles
0 20 40 60 80 100 120 140 160 180 200 Kilometers
Railways

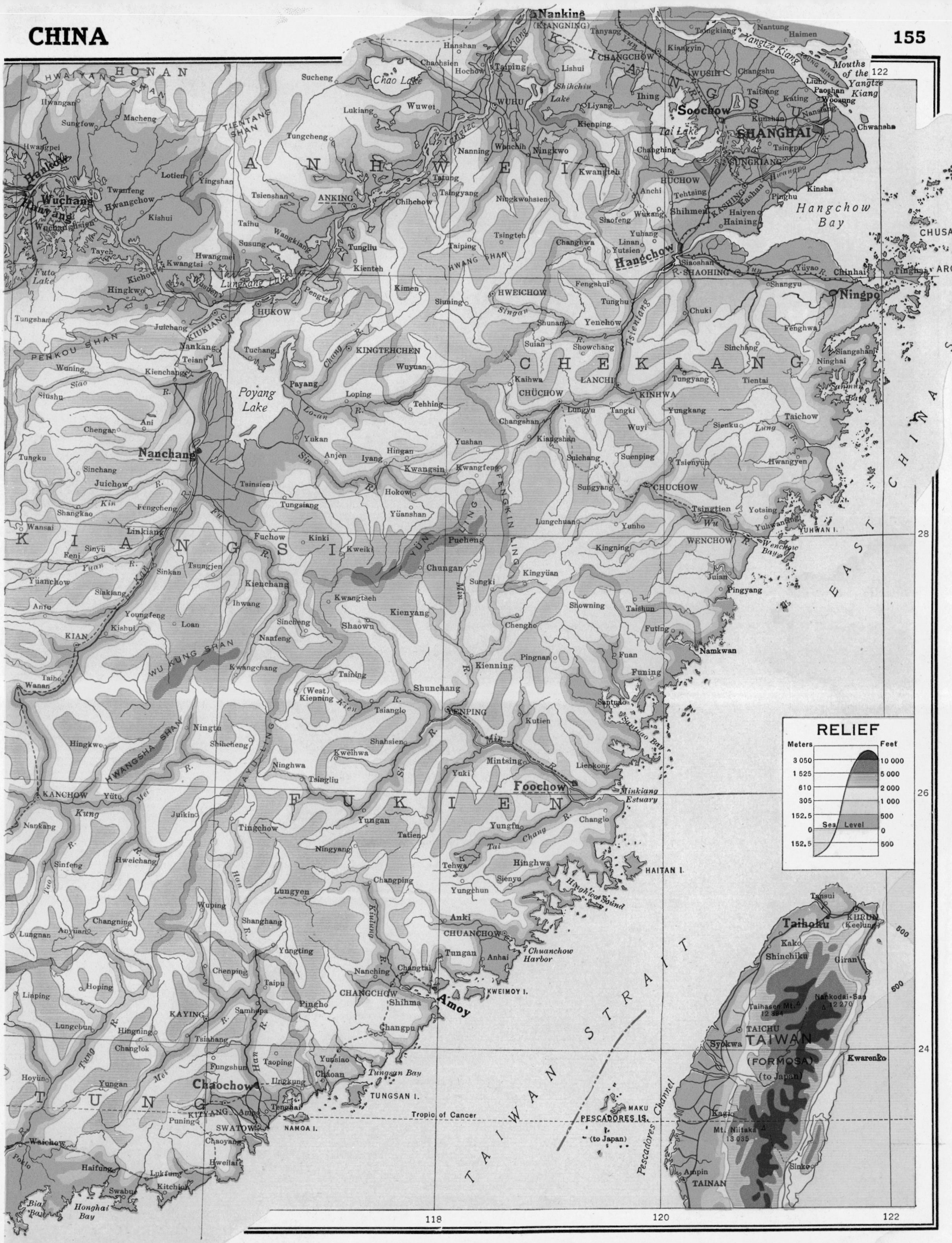

Scale 1:4 000 000; one inch to 64 miles. Conic Projection

Elevations and depressions are given in feet

PART OF EASTERN

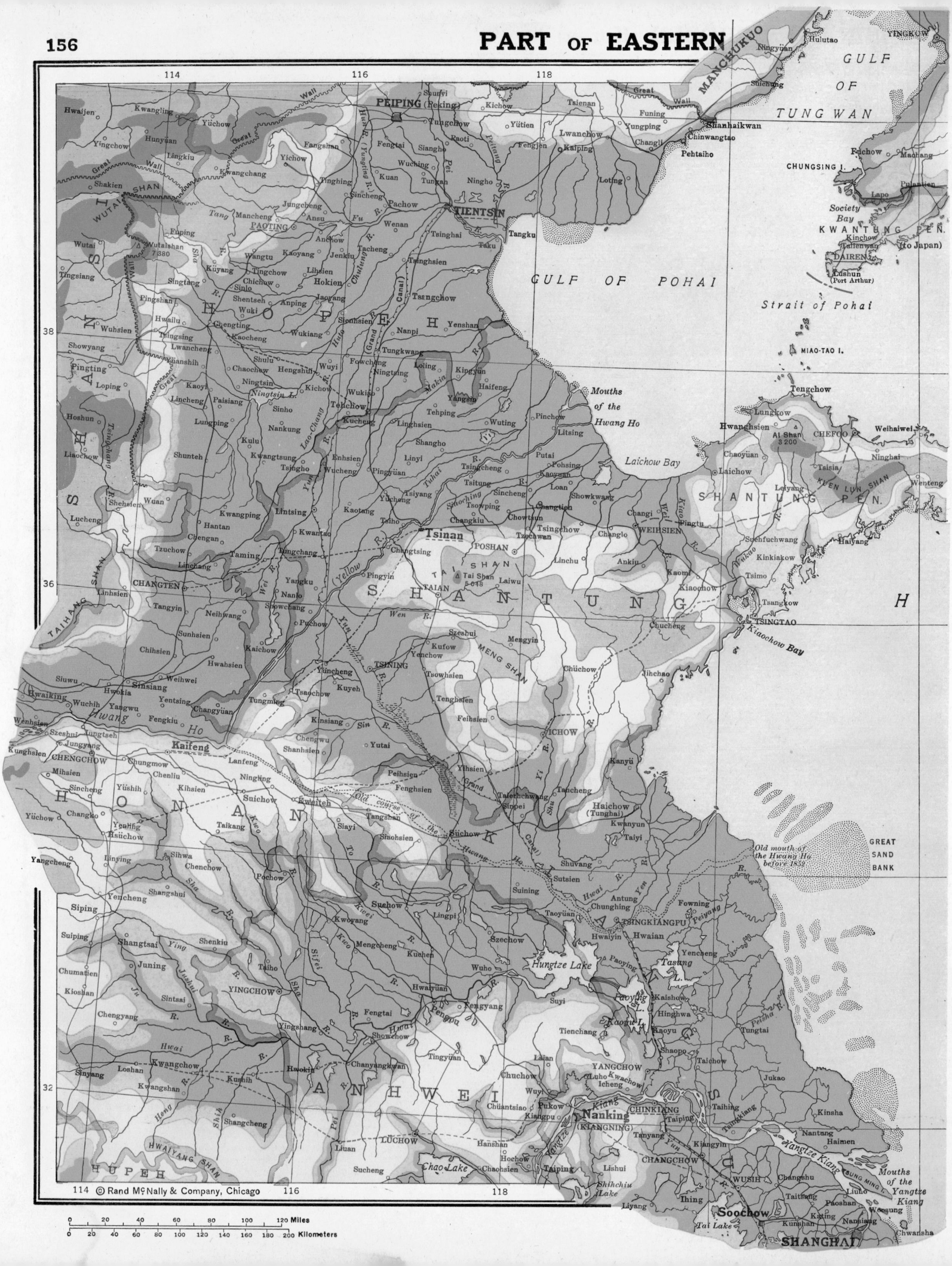

MANCHUKUO
GULF OF TUNG WAN
GULF OF POHAI
Strait of Pohai
KWANTUNG PEN.
DAIREN
Lushun (Port Arthur)
Society Bay
(to Japan)
CHUNGSING I.
MIAO-TAO I.
Laichow Bay
Mouths of the Hwang Ho
Kiaochow Bay
Old mouth of the Hwang Ho before 1852
GREAT SAND BANK
Mouths of the Yangtze Kiang
SUNG MING I.
Yangtze Kiang
HOPEH
SHANSI
SHANTUNG
SHANTUNG PEN.
HONAN
ANHWEI
KIANGSU
HUPEH
PEIPING (Peking)
TIENTSIN
Tangku
Taku
Shanhaikwan
Chinwangtao
Pehtaiho
Yingkow
Hulutao
Tsinan
TSINGTAO
CHEFOO
Weihaiwei
Tengchow
WEIHSIEN
Kaifeng
CHENGCHOW
Suchow
Nanking (KIANGNING)
CHINKIANG
YANGCHOW
Soochow
SHANGHAI
Hungtze Lake
Chao Lake
Tai Lake
Shihchiu Lake
TAI SHAN
Tai Shan 5 048
Ai Shan 3 200
Wutaishan 7 380
WUTAI SHAN
MENG SHAN
KUEN LUN SHAN
TAIHANG SHAN
HWAIYANG SHAN
Great Wall
Grand Canal
Hwang Ho
Old course of the Hwang Ho
Hwai R.
Yun R.
Wei R.
Sha R.
114
116
118
38
36
32
© Rand McNally & Company, Chicago
0 20 40 60 80 100 120 Miles
0 20 40 60 80 100 120 140 160 180 200 Kilometers

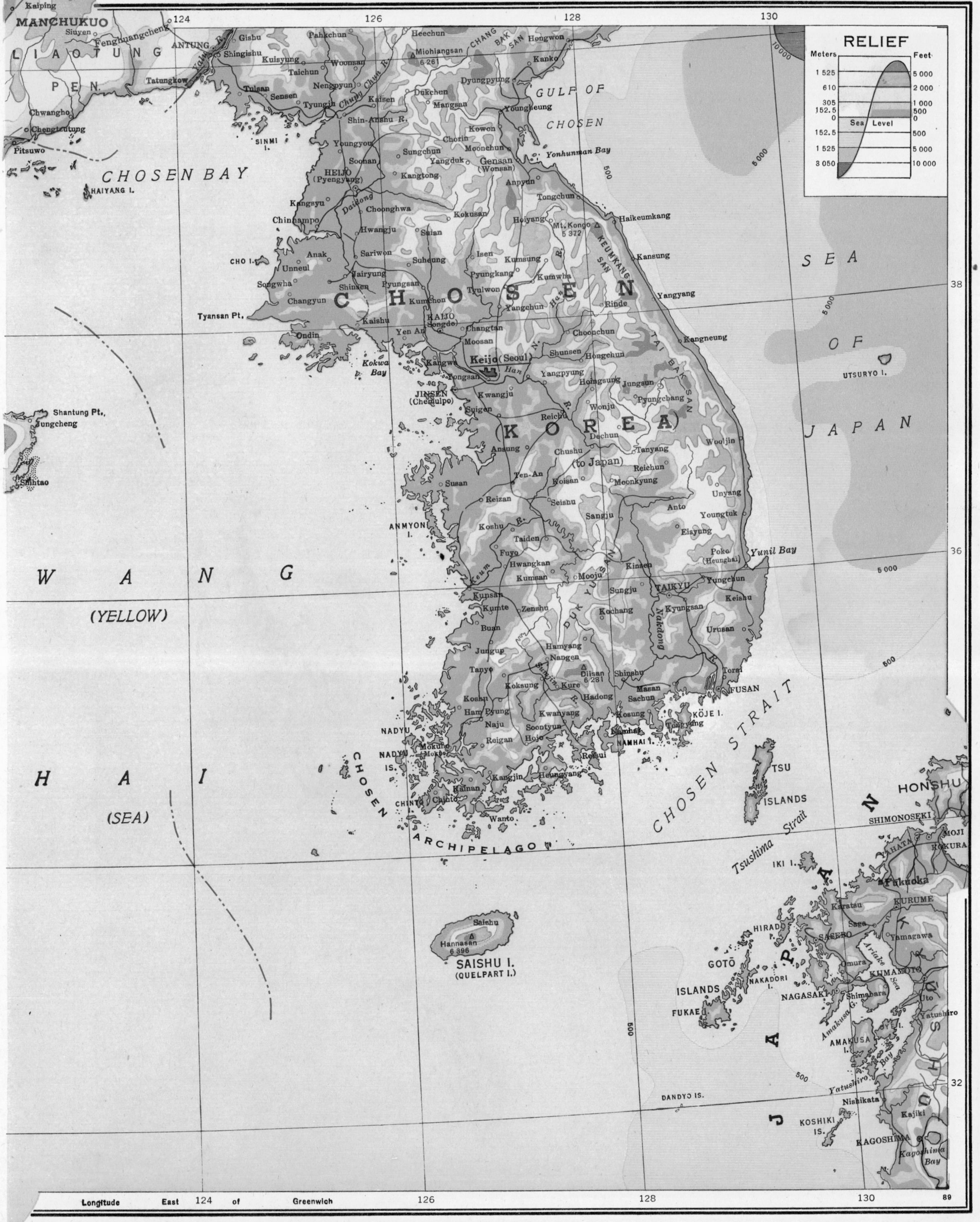

Scale 1:4 000 000; one inch to 64 miles. Conic Projection

Elevations and depressions are given in feet

JAPAN

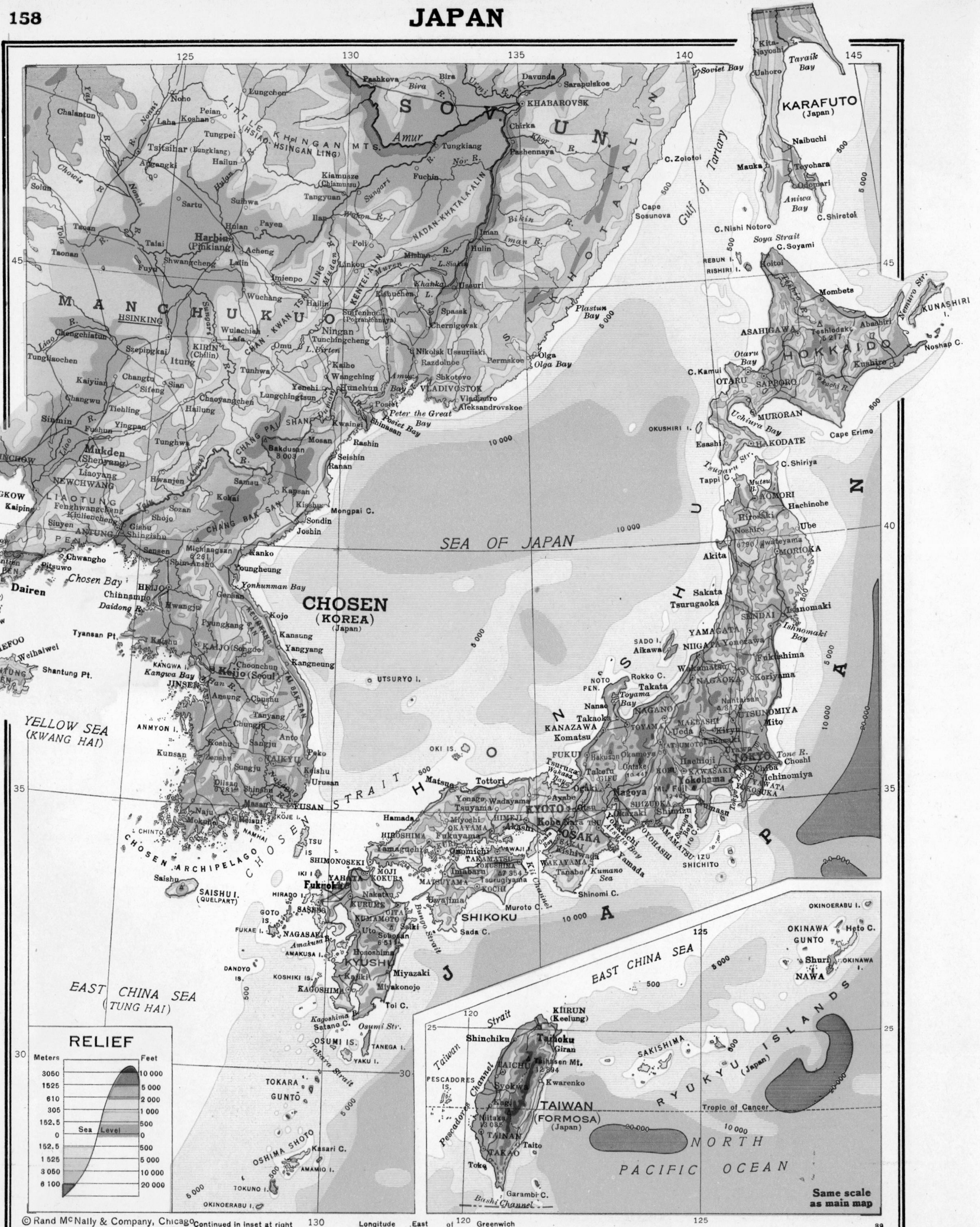

Scale 1:10 000 000; one inch to 160 miles. Bonne's Equal Area Projection

Elevations and depressions are given in feet

0 50 100 200 300 Miles

0 50 100 200 300 400 500 Kilometers

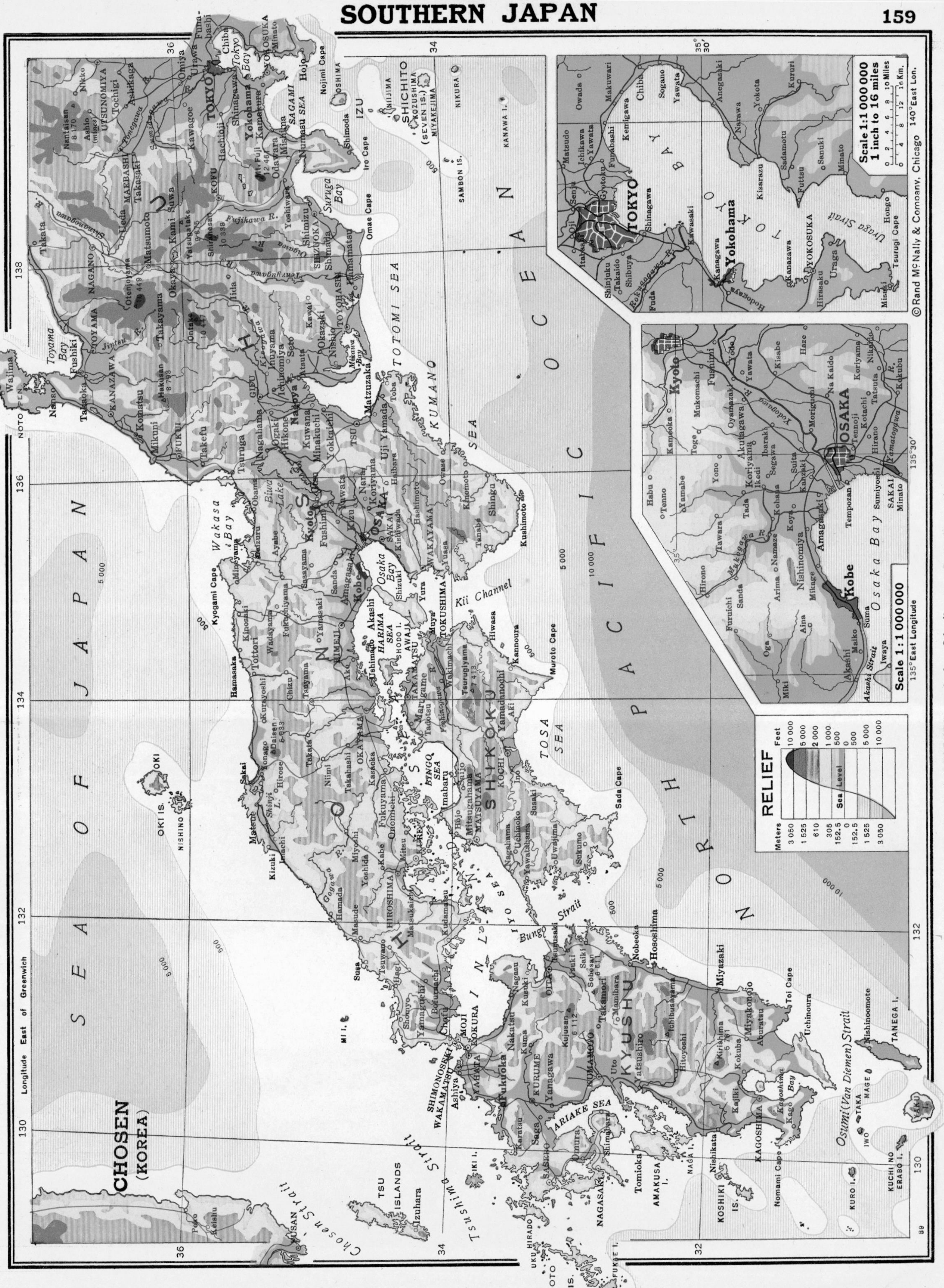

Scale 1:4 000 000; one inch to 64 miles. Conic Projection

Elevations and depressions are given in feet

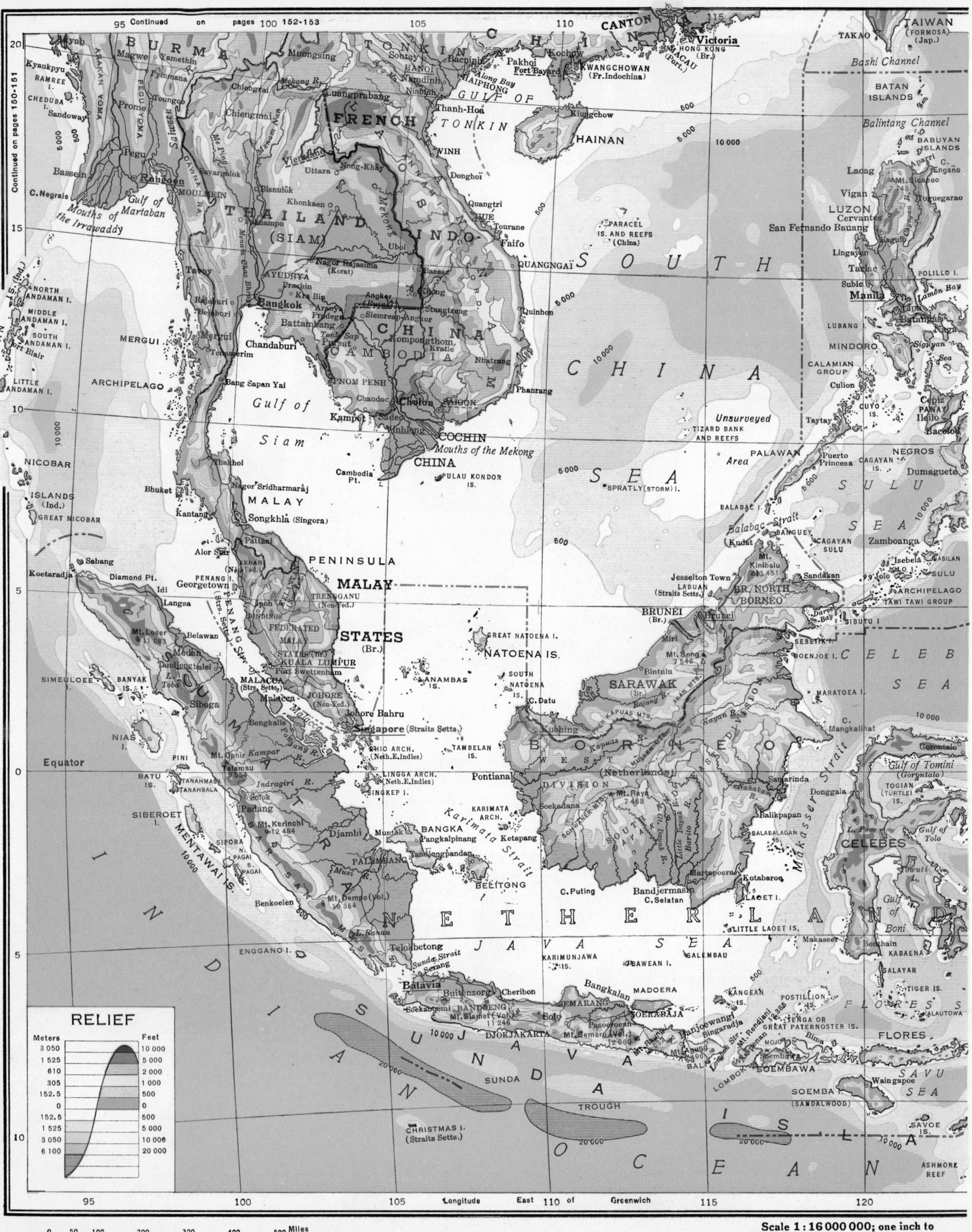

Miles 0 50 100 200 300 400 500
Kilometers 0 100 200 400 600 800

Scale 1 : 16 000 000; one inch to

Elevations and depressions

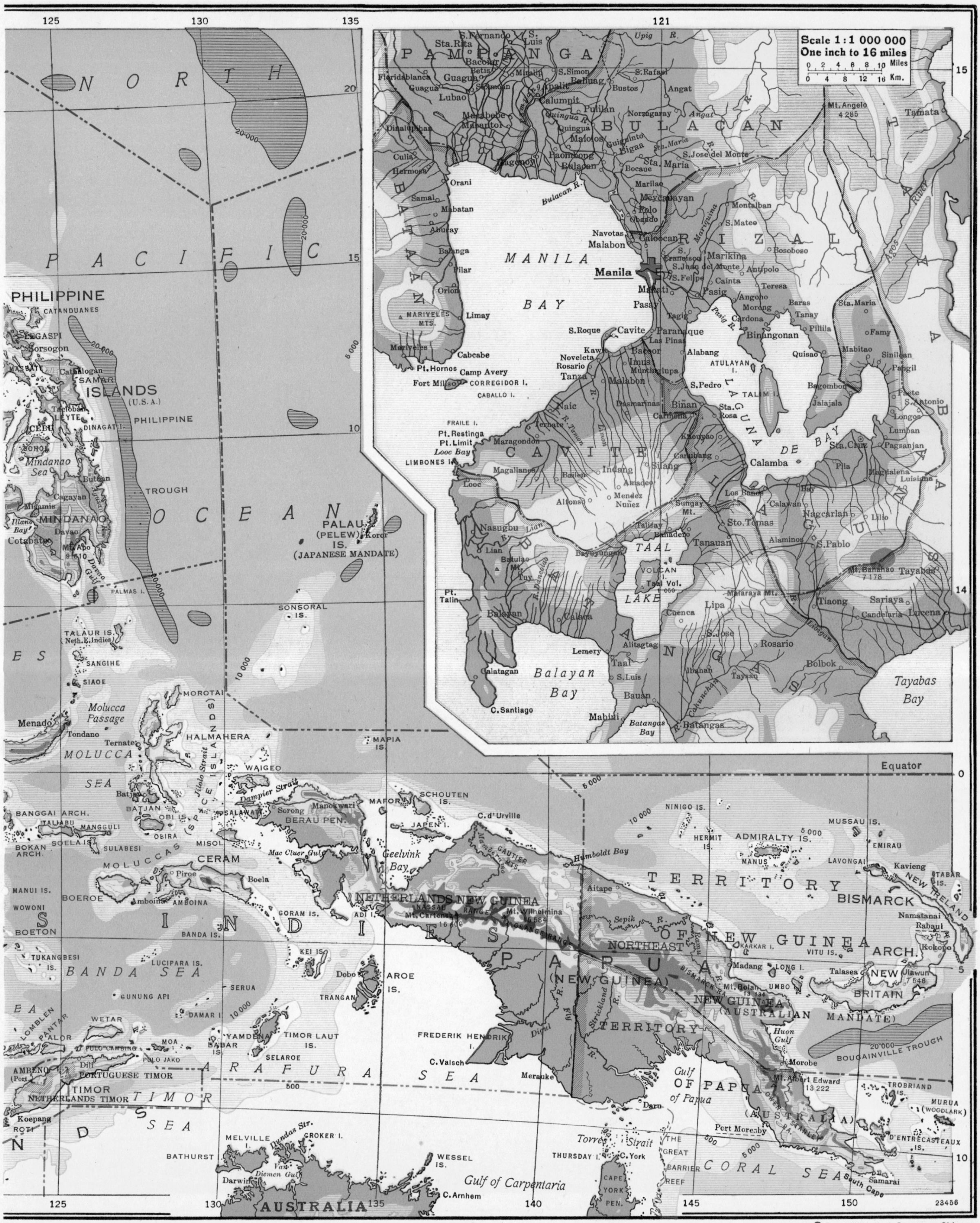

250 miles. Polyconic Projection

are given in feet

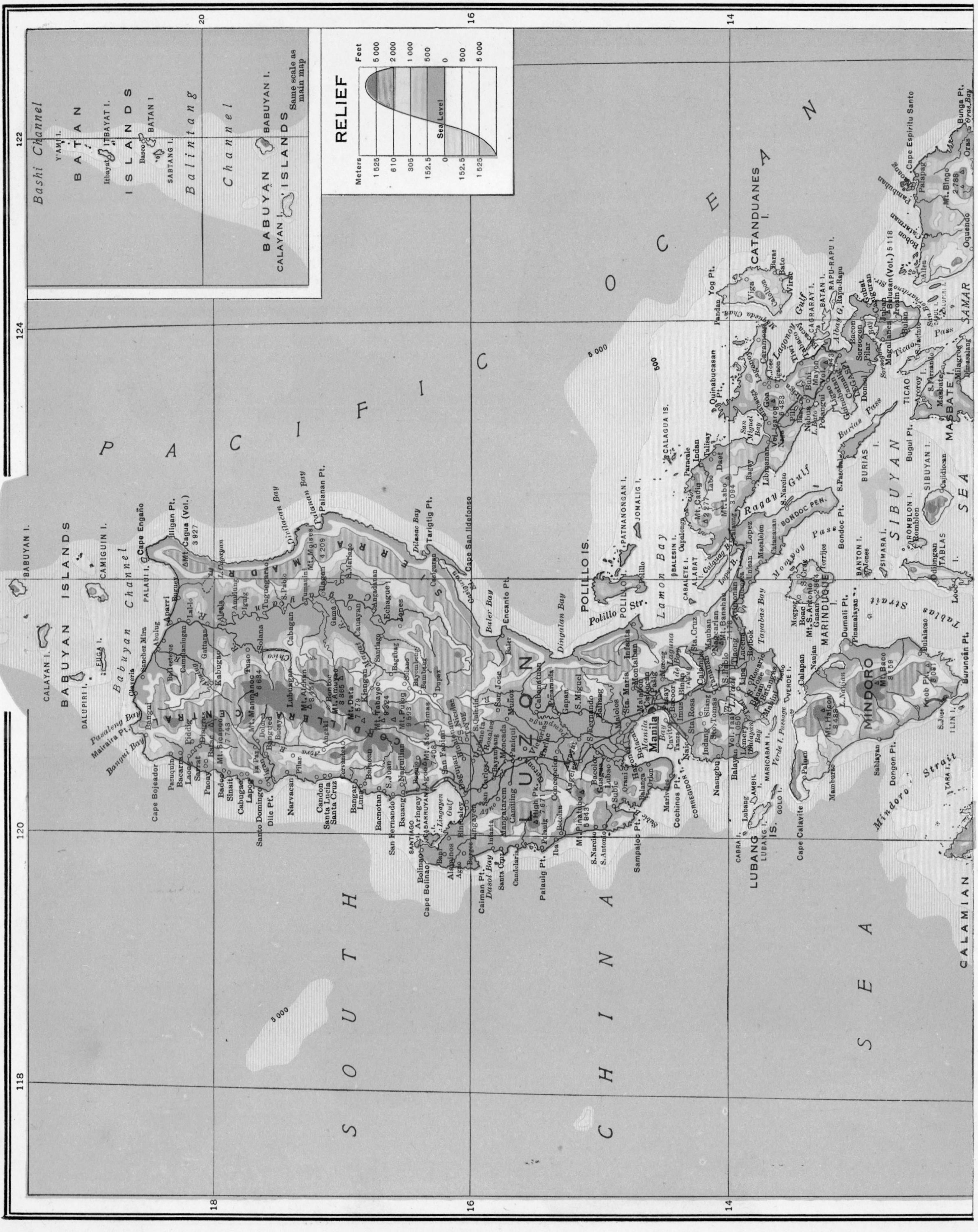
RELIEF
Feet
5 000
2 000
1 000
500
0
500
5 000
Meters
1 525
610
305
152.5
0
152.5
1 525
Sea Level
Bashi Channel
BATAN ISLANDS
Balintang Channel
BABUYAN ISLANDS
Same scale as main map
PACIFIC OCEAN
SOUTH CHINA SEA
SIBUYAN SEA
LUZON
MINDORO
MARINDUQUE
POLILLO IS.
CATANDUANES I.
MASBATE
SAMAR
TICAO
BURIAS
TABLAS
SIBUYAN I.
LUBANG IS.
CALAMIAN
Babuyan Channel
Lingayen Gulf
Manila
Manila Bay
Lamon Bay
Ragay Gulf
Lagonoy Gulf
Tayabas Bay
Mindoro Strait
Tablas Strait
Burias Pass
Sibuyan Sea
Cape Engaño
Cape Bojeador
Cape Bolinao
Cape San Ildefonso
Cape Calavite
Cape Espiritu Santo
Mt. Cagua (Vol.) 3 927
Mt. Halcon 8 488
Mt. Baco 8 159
Mt. Bulusan (Vol.) 5 118
Mt. Mayon (Vol.)
Mt. Pinatubo
Mt. Banahao
Aparri
Laoag
Vigan
San Fernando
Dagupan
Tarlac
Cavite
Batangas
Lucena
Naga
Legaspi
Sorsogon
Masbate
Calapan
5 000
500
118
120
122
124
14
16
18
20

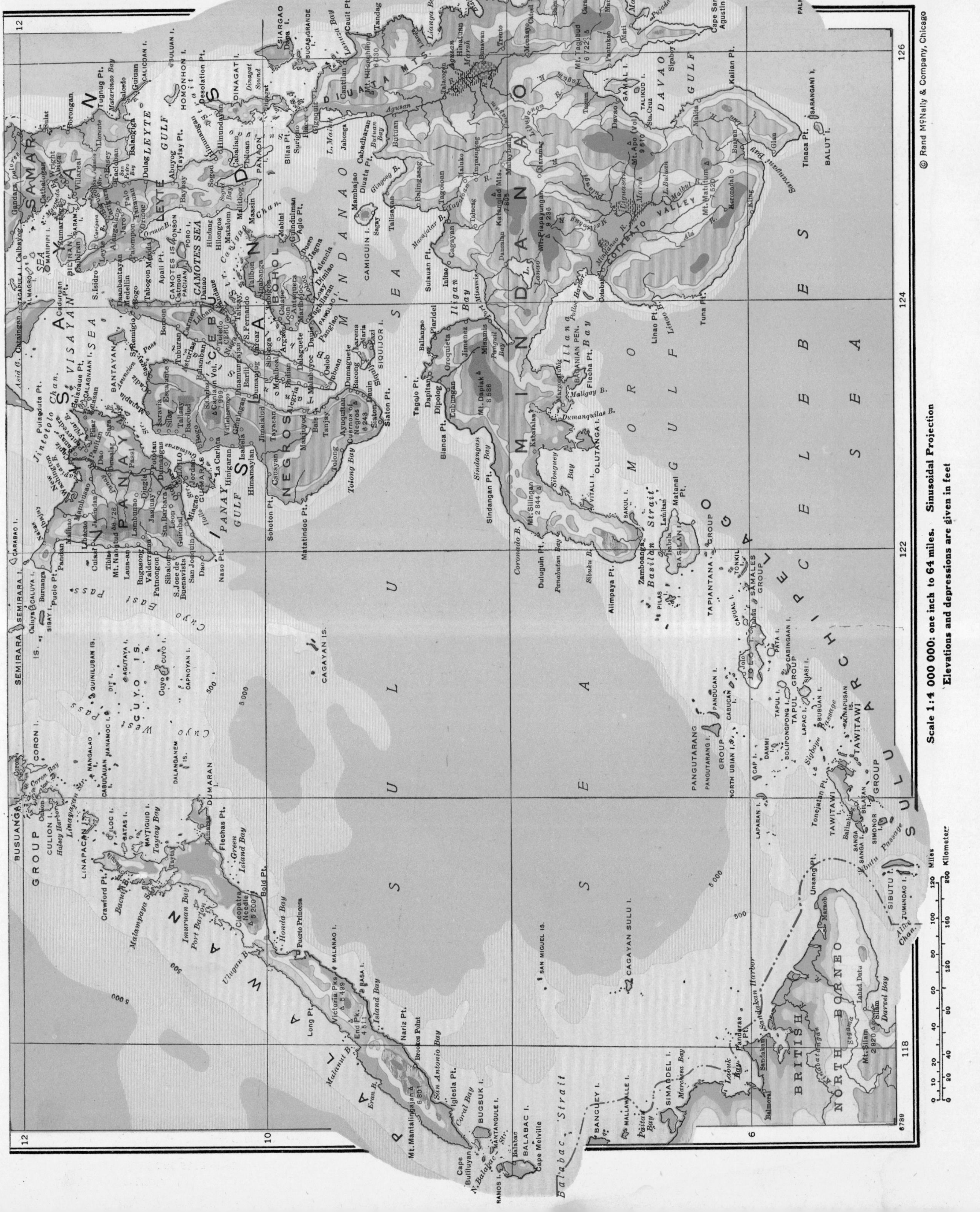
Scale 1:4 000 000: one inch to 64 miles. Sinusoidal Projection
Elevations and depressions are given in feet
© Rand McNally & Company, Chicago
SULU SEA
CELEBES SEA
MORO GULF
MINDANAO
MINDANAO SEA
VISAYAN SEA
CAMOTES SEA
SAMAR
LEYTE
PANAY
NEGROS
CEBU
BOHOL
PALAWAN
BRITISH NORTH BORNEO
SULU ARCHIPELAGO
DAVAO GULF
LEYTE GULF
PANAY GULF
Balabac Strait
Basilan Strait
Cuyo East Pass
Cuyo West Pass
Miles
Kilometers

0 50 100 200 300 400 500 600 Miles

0 100 200 400 600 800 1000 Kilometers

Scale 1:16 000 000; one inch to 250 miles.

Elevations and depressions

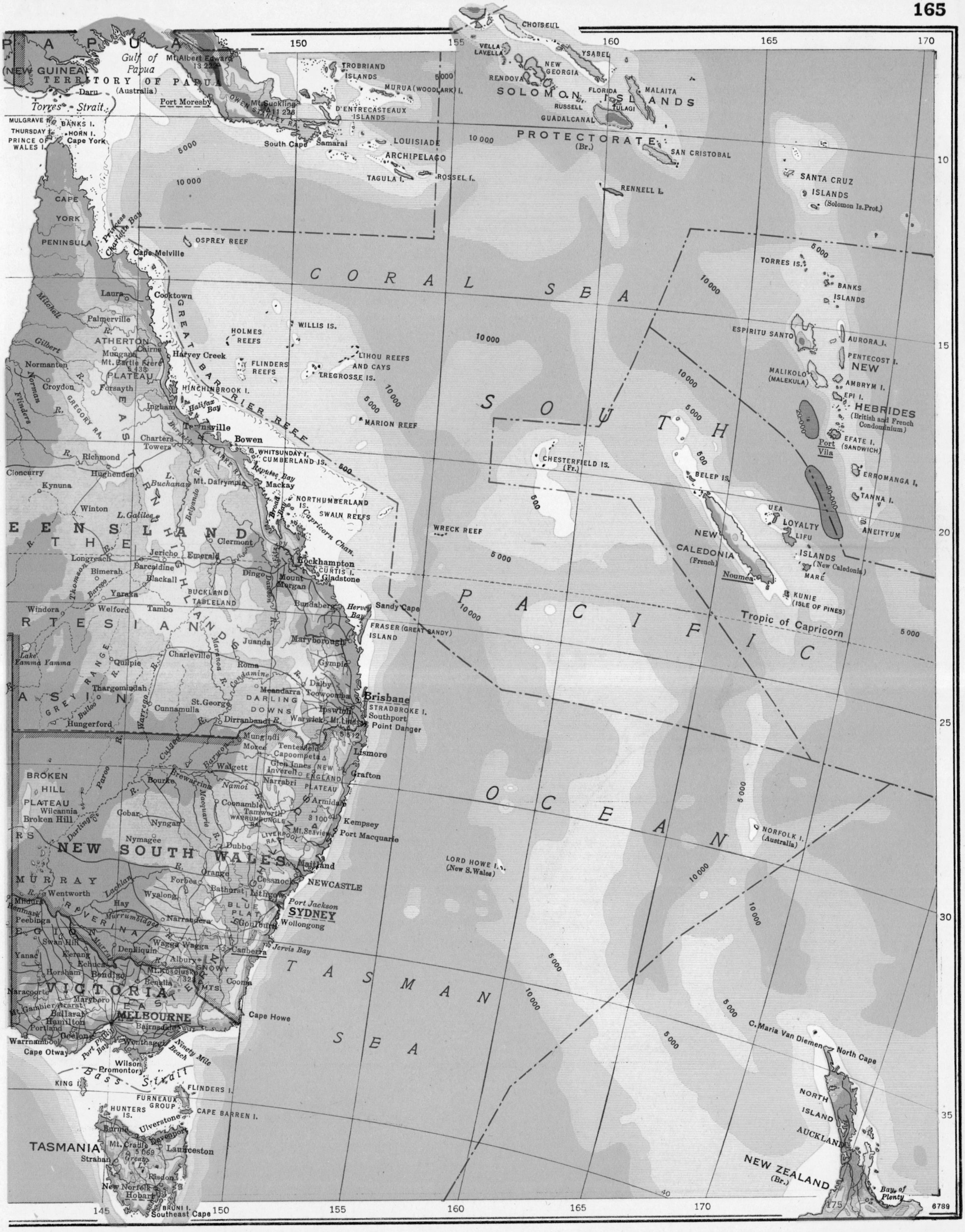

Lambert's Azimuthal, Equal Area Projection

are given in feet

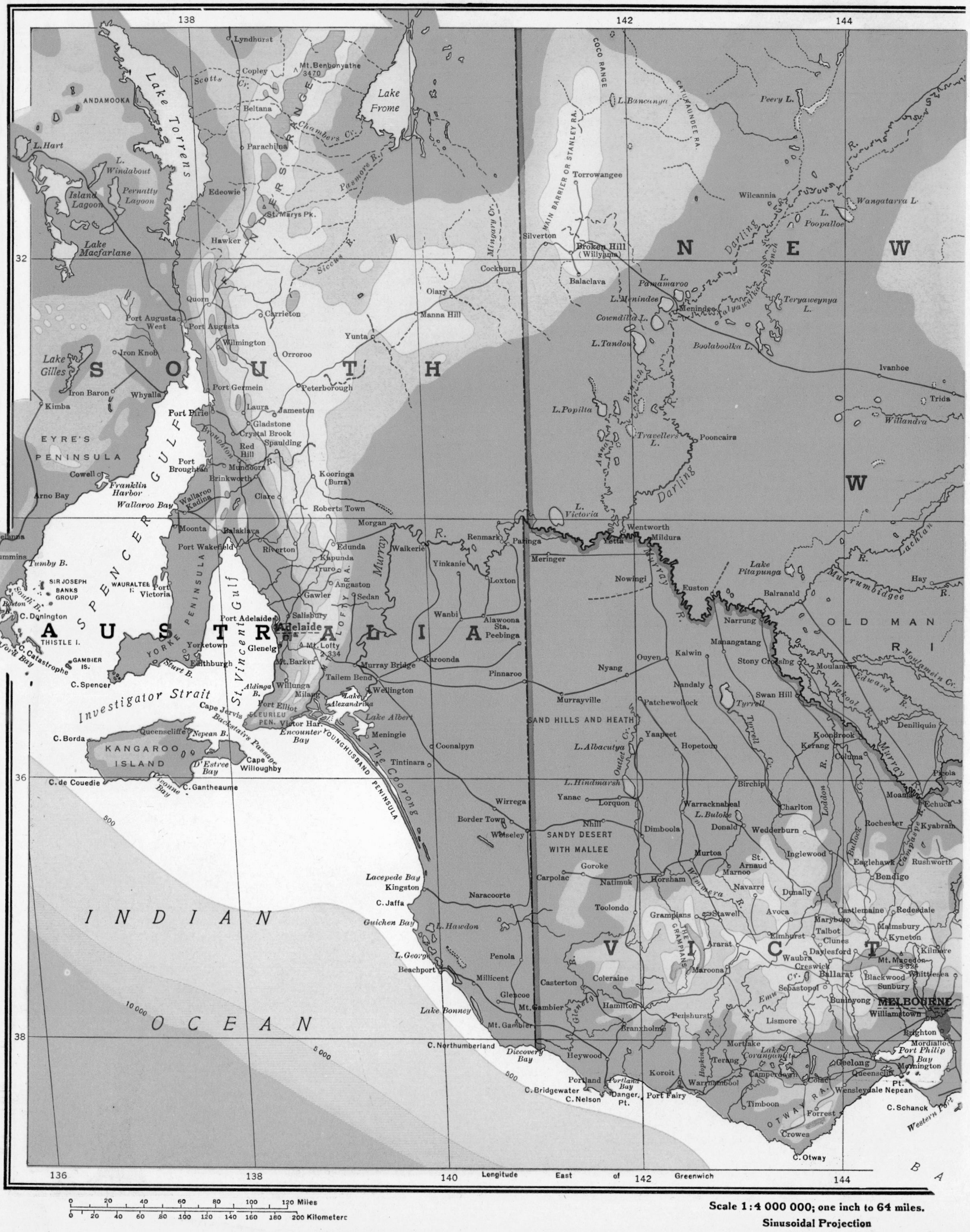

Scale 1 : 4 000 000; one inch to 64 miles.

Sinusoidal Projection

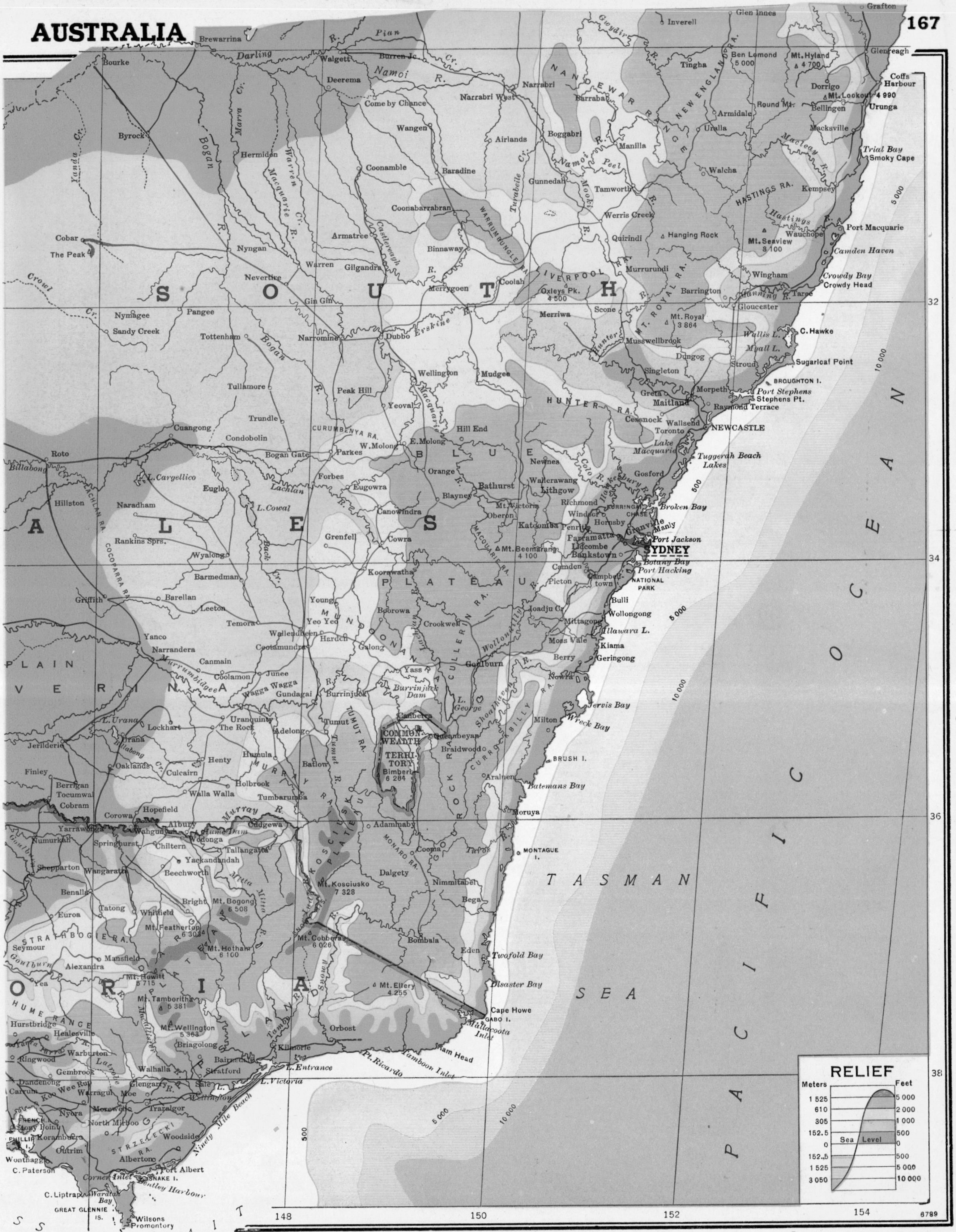

Elevations and depressions are given in feet

AUSTRALIA AND NEW ZEALAND

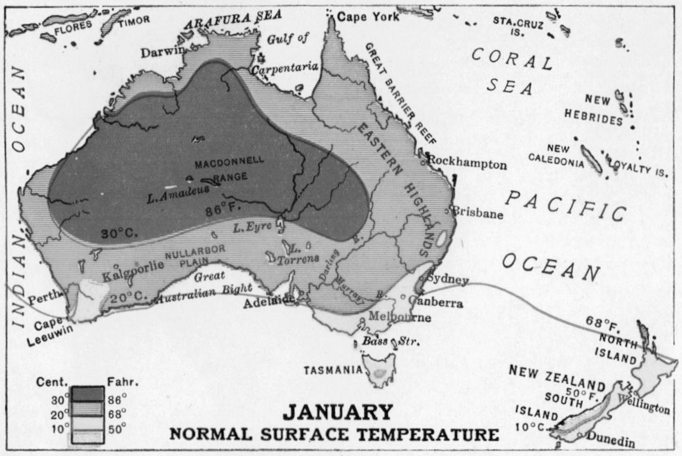

JANUARY
NORMAL SURFACE TEMPERATURE

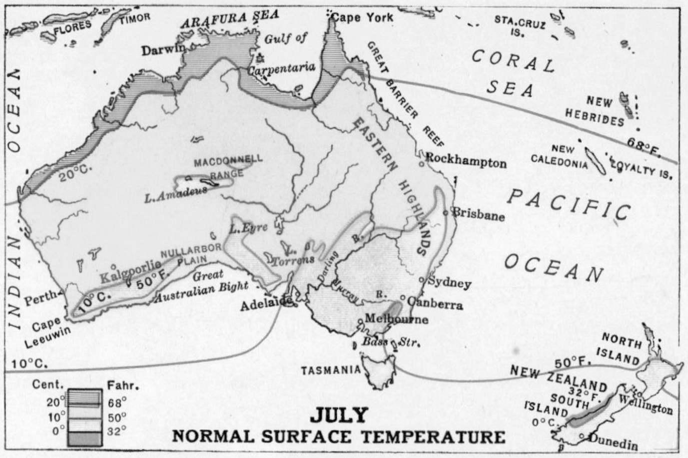

JULY
NORMAL SURFACE TEMPERATURE

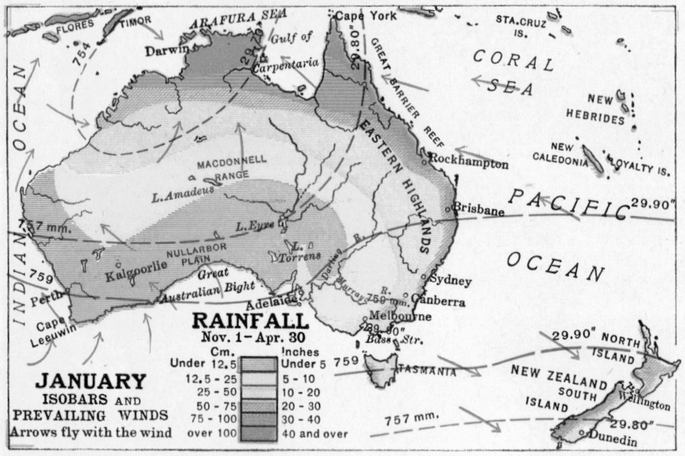

RAINFALL
Nov. 1 - Apr. 30
JANUARY
ISOBARS AND PREVAILING WINDS
Arrows fly with the wind

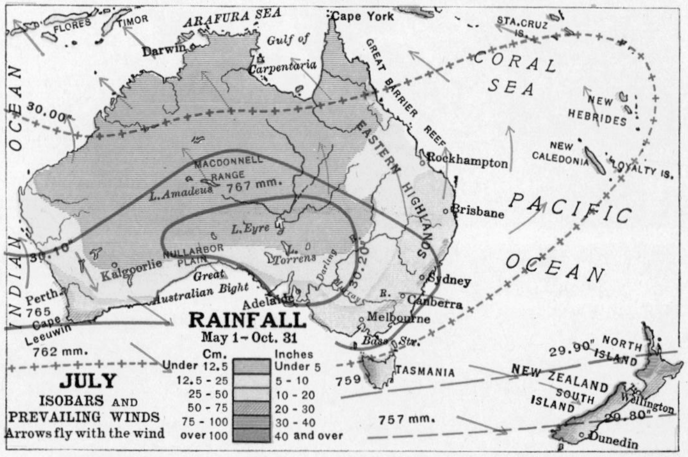

RAINFALL
May 1 - Oct. 31
JULY
ISOBARS AND PREVAILING WINDS
Arrows fly with the wind

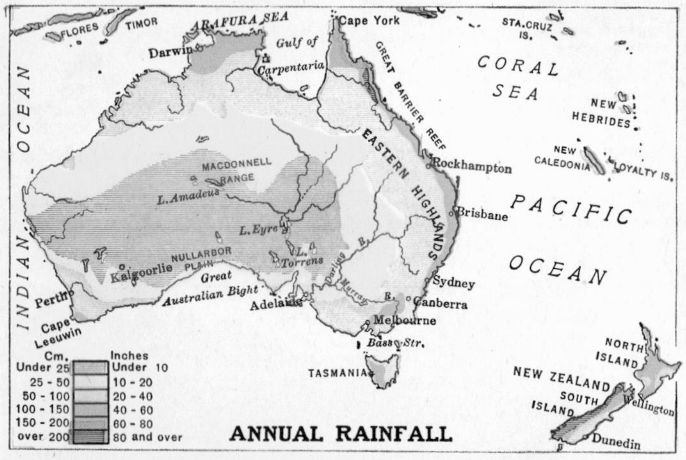

ANNUAL RAINFALL

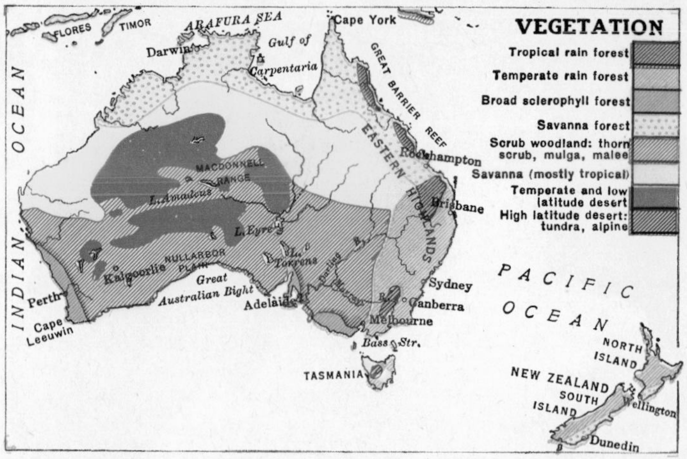

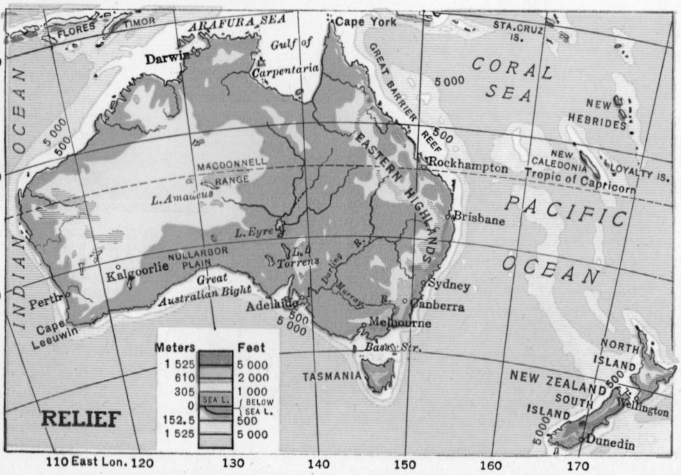

RELIEF

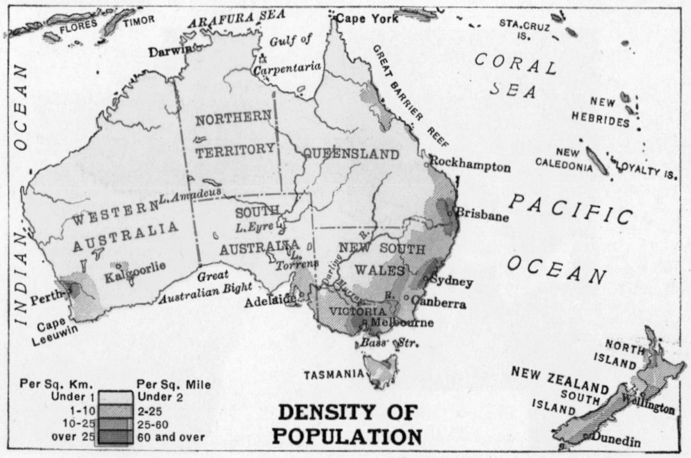

DENSITY OF POPULATION

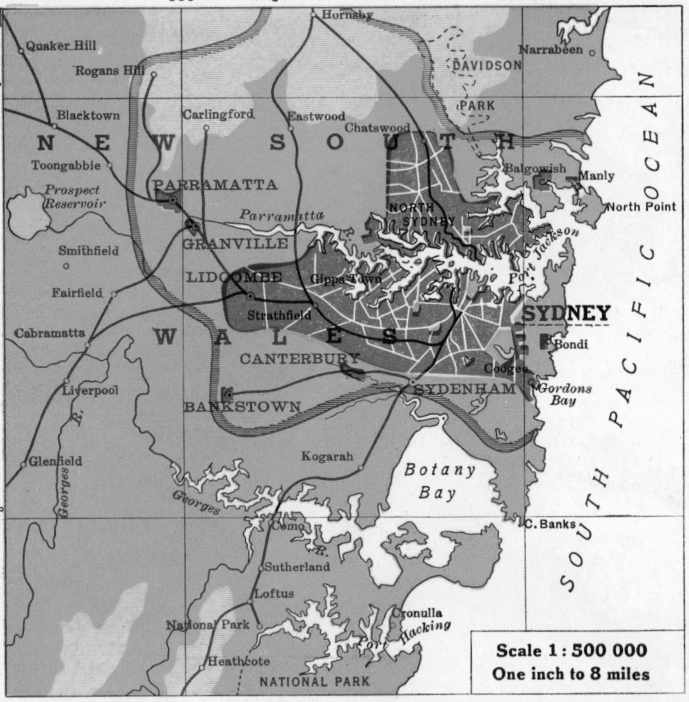

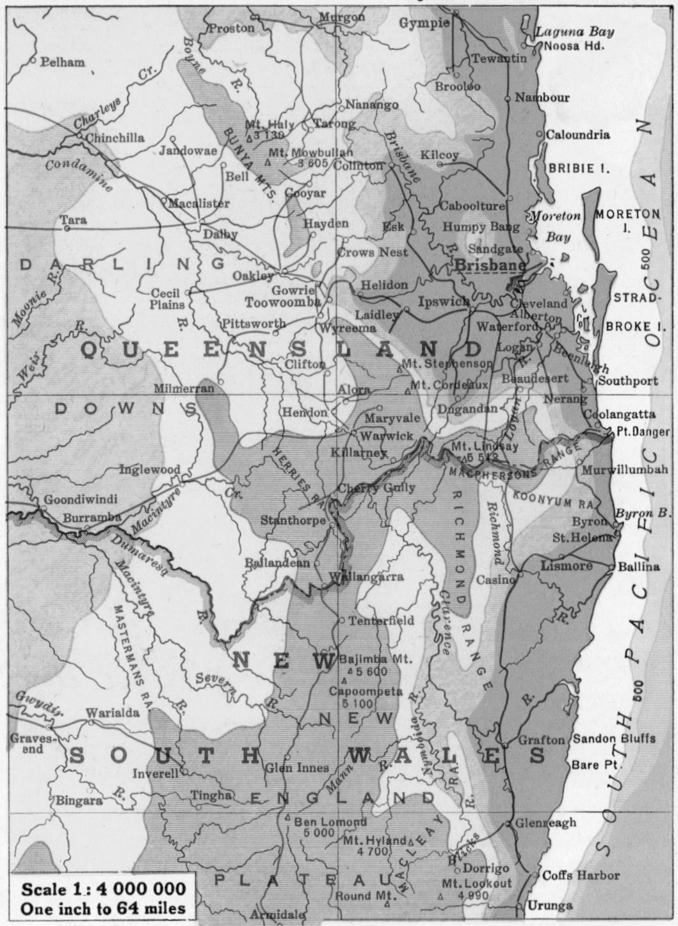

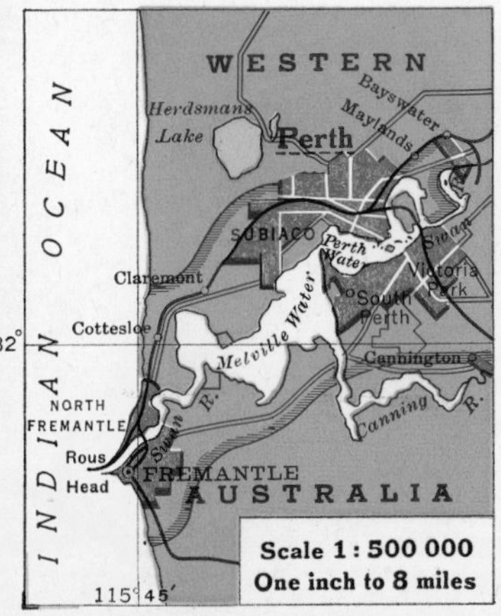

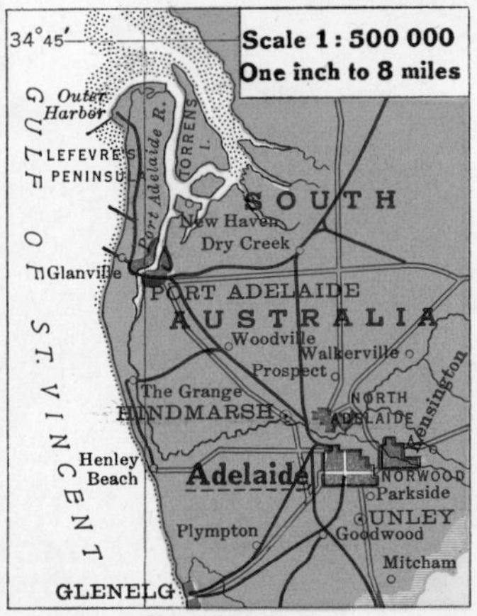

Scale 1 : 5 000 000

Miles 0 1 2 3 4 5 6 7 8 9 10

Kilometers 0 2 4 6 8 10 12 14 16

Elevations and depressions are given in feet

Scale 1 : 4 000 000

Miles 0 20 40 60

Kilometers 0 20 40 60 80 100

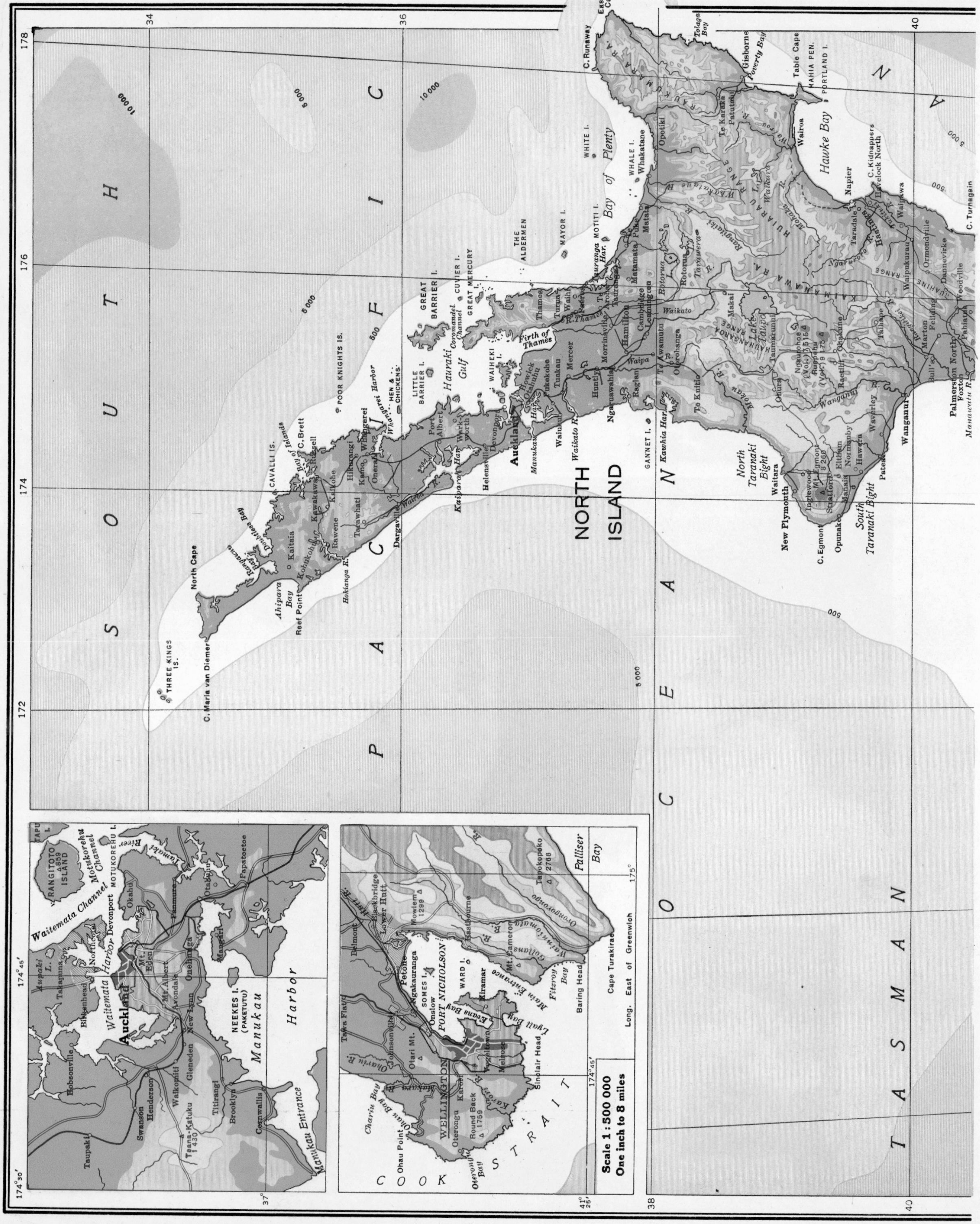
SOUTH PACIFIC OCEAN
TASMAN
NORTH ISLAND
THREE KINGS IS.
C. Maria van Diemen
North Cape
Reef Point
Ahipara Bay
CAVALLI IS.
POOR KNIGHTS IS.
HEN & CHICKENS
LITTLE BARRIER I.
GREAT BARRIER I.
CUVIER I.
GREAT MERCURY I.
Hauraki Gulf
Firth of Thames
Coromandel Channel
THE ALDERMEN
MAYOR I.
MOTITI I.
WHITE I.
WHALE I.
Bay of Plenty
C. Runaway
East Cape
Poverty Bay
Gisborne
Table Cape
MAHIA PEN.
PORTLAND I.
Hawke Bay
Wairoa
Napier
C. Kidnappers
Havelock North
C. Turnagain
Auckland
Hamilton
Rotorua
Lake Taupo
Whakatane
Opotiki
Thames
Dargaville
Kaitaia
Wanganui
Palmerston North
New Plymouth
C. Egmont
North Taranaki Bight
South Taranaki Bight
GANNET I.
Kawhia Har.
RANGITOTO ISLAND
Waitemata Channel
Motukorehu Channel
Waitemata Harbor
Devonport
Manukau Harbor
Manukau Entrance
NEEKES I. (PAKETUTU)
WELLINGTON
PORT NICHOLSON
Petone
Lower Hutt
Palliser Bay
Cape Turakirae
Baring Head
Fitzroy Bay
Main Entrance
Sinclair Head
Ohau Point
COOK STRAIT
Scale 1:500 000
One inch to 8 miles
Long. East of Greenwich

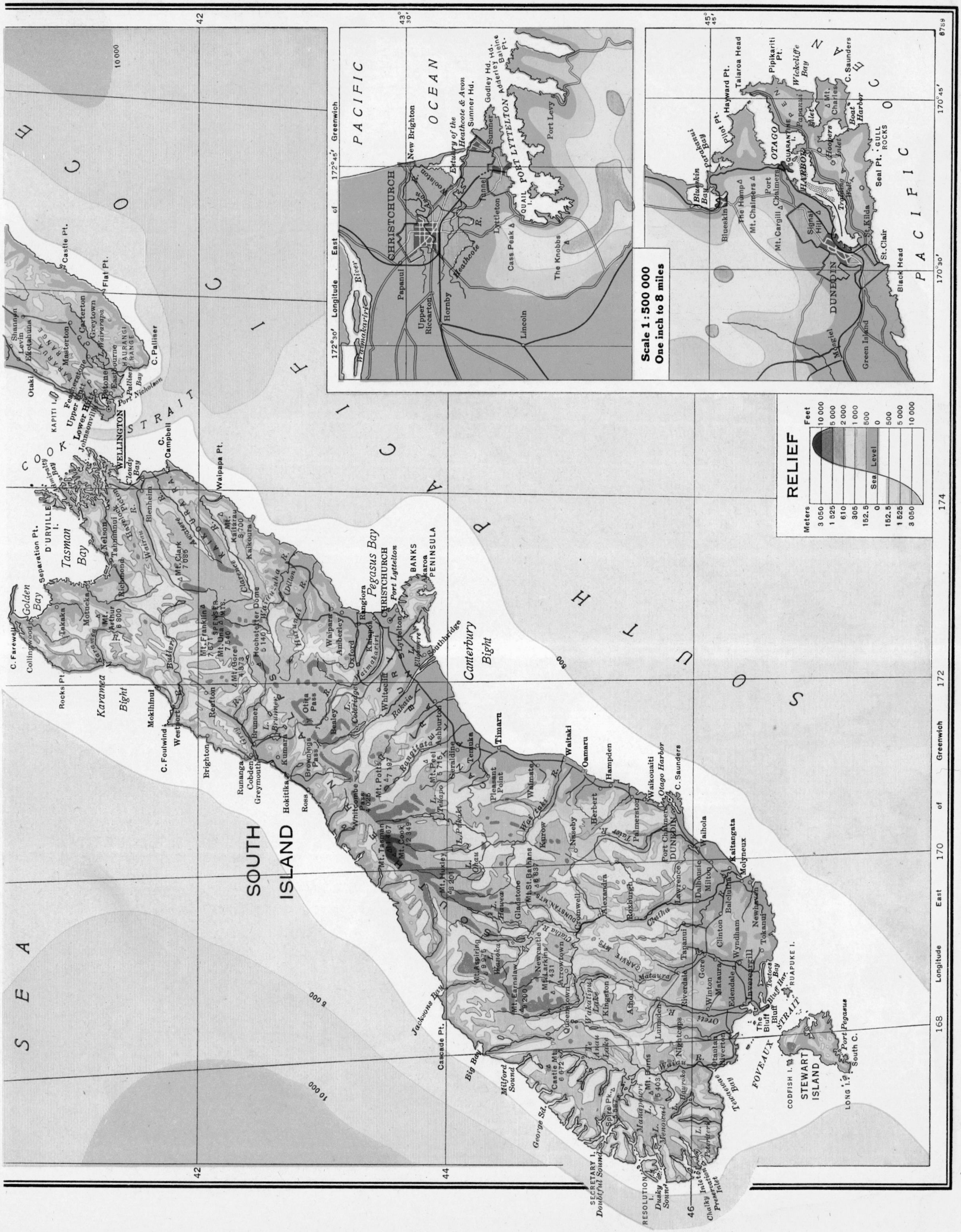

Scale 1:4 000 000; one inch to 64 miles. Conic Projection

Elevations and depressions are given in feet

PACIFIC

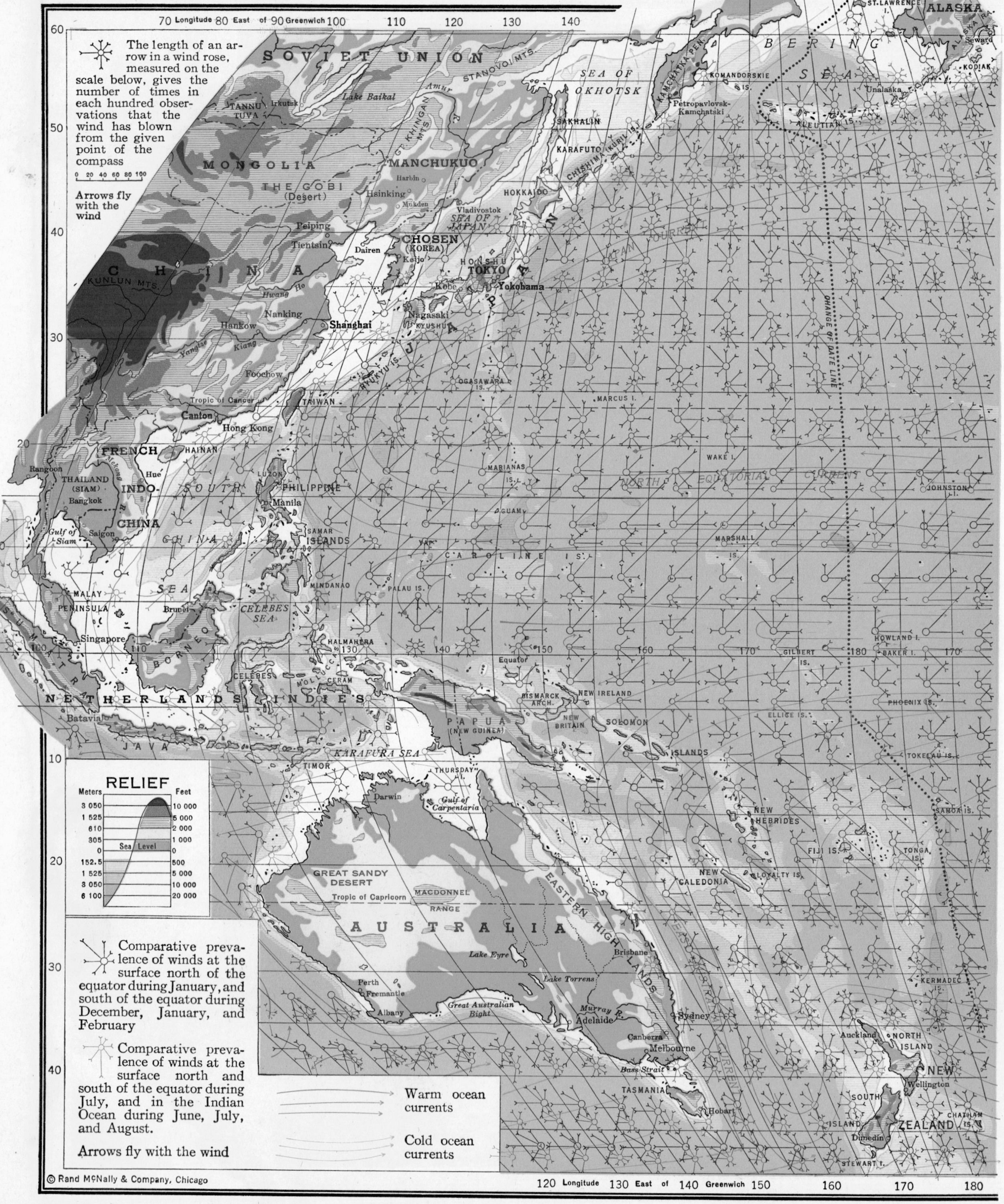
The length of an arrow in a wind rose, measured on the scale below, gives the number of times in each hundred observations that the wind has blown from the given point of the compass
0 20 40 60 80 100
Arrows fly with the wind
RELIEF
Meters Feet
3 050 10 000
1 525 5 000
610 2 000
305 1 000
0 Sea Level 0
152.5 500
1 525 5 000
3 050 10 000
6 100 20 000
Comparative prevalence of winds at the surface north of the equator during January, and south of the equator during December, January, and February
Comparative prevalence of winds at the surface north and south of the equator during July, and in the Indian Ocean during June, July, and August.
Arrows fly with the wind
Warm ocean currents
Cold ocean currents
Longitude East of Greenwich
SOVIET UNION
MONGOLIA
MANCHUKUO
CHINA
CHOSEN (KOREA)
JAPAN
FRENCH INDO-CHINA
THAILAND (SIAM)
PHILIPPINE ISLANDS
NETHERLANDS INDIES
PAPUA (NEW GUINEA)
AUSTRALIA
NEW ZEALAND
ALASKA
BERING SEA
SEA OF OKHOTSK
SEA OF JAPAN
SOUTH CHINA SEA
CELEBES SEA
KARAFURA SEA
CAROLINE IS.
MARSHALL IS.
NORTH EQUATORIAL CURRENT
CHANGE OF DATE LINE
Tropic of Cancer
Tropic of Capricorn
Equator
© Rand McNally & Company, Chicago

0 500 1000 1500 2000 Miles
0 1000 2000 3000 Kilometers

Goode's Homolosine Equal Area Projection.

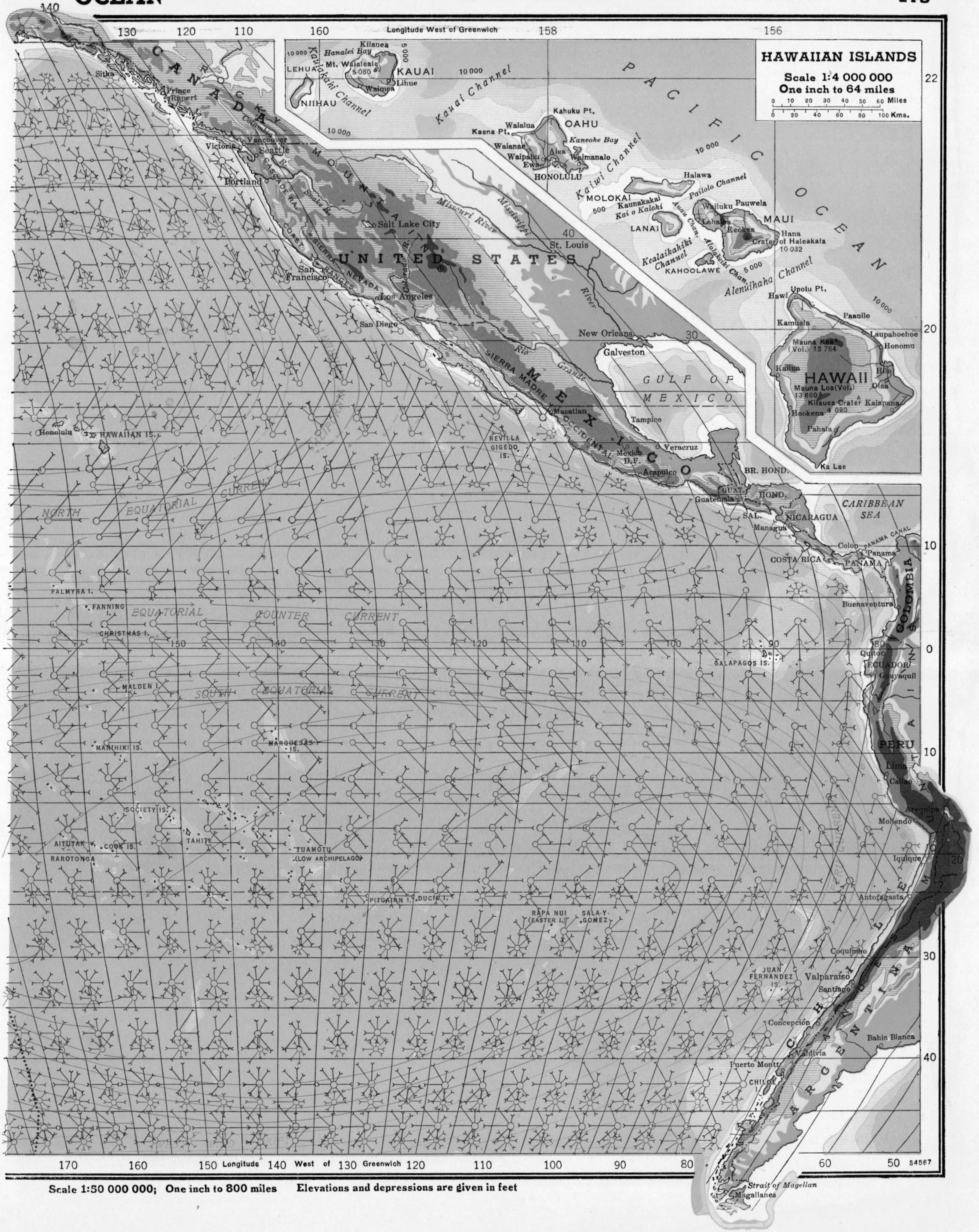

Scale 1:50 000 000; One inch to 800 miles   Elevations and depressions are given in feet

WORLD COMPARISONS

Miscellaneous Dimensions

Equatorial Diameter of the Earth (miles)	7,926.68
Polar Diameter of the Earth (miles)	7,899.99
Equatorial Circumference of the Earth (mi.)	24,902.37
Polar Circumference of the Earth (miles)	24,860.44
Area of the Earth (square miles)	196,940,400.00
Diameter of the Mean Sphere of the Earth (mi.)	7,917.57
Land Area of the Earth (sq. miles)	55,885,000.00
Water Area of the Earth (sq. miles)	141,055,400.00
Greatest Altitude of Land (feet), Mt. Everest, Asia	29,141.00
Lowest Altitude on Land (feet), Dead Sea, Palestine	—1,292.00
Greatest Depth of the Ocean (feet), off Phil. Is., Pacific O.	34,218.00
Population of the Earth (estimated number)	2,102,600,000
Distance from Earth to Sun (mean miles)	92,900,000.00
Distance from Earth to Moon (mean miles)	238,857.00
Africa Area (square miles)	11,529,480000
Antarctica Area (square miles)	5,362,626.00
Asia Area (square miles)	16,494,217.00
Australia Area (square miles)	2,974,581.00
Europe Area (square miles)	3,781,407.00
North America Area (square miles)	9,363,868.00
South America Area (square miles)	7,096,656.00

Principal Islands and Their Areas

Island	Area Sq. Miles
Baffin, Arctic Region	231,000
Banks, Arctic Region	25,000
Borneo, East Indies	282,416
Celebes, East Indies	72,679
Ceylon, Indian Ocean	25,332
Corsica, Mediterranean Sea	3,367
Crete, Mediterranean Sea	3,330
Cuba West Indies	44,164
Cyprus, Mediterranean Sea	3,584
Devon, Arctic Region	24,000
Ellesmere, Arctic Region	41,000
Great Britain, North Atlantic O.	88,745
Greenland, Arctic Region	837,620
Hainan, South China Sea	13,000
Hawaii, Pacific O.	4,015
Hispaniola, West Indies	29,536
Hokkaido, Japan	30,000
Honshu, Japan	87,500
Iceland, Arctic Region	39,709
Ireland, North Atlantic O.	31,829
Jamaica, West Indies	4,450
Java, East Indies	50,745
Luzon, Phil. Is.	40,814
Madagascar, Indian Ocean	228,707
Melville, Arctic Region	20,000
Mindanao, Phil. Is.	36,906
Mindoro, Phil. Is.	3,794
Negros, Phil. Is.	4,903
New Britain, East Indies	10,000
New Caledonia, South Pacific O.	8,458
Newfoundland, North Atlantic O.	42,734
New Ireland, East Indies	3,000
North Island (N. Zeal.), South Pacific O.	44,281
Novaya Zemlya, Arctic Region	35,150
Palawan, Phil. Is.	4,500
Panay, Phil. Is.	4,448
Papua (New Guinea), East Indies	342,232
Prince Edward, Arctic Region	2,184
Prince of Wales, Arctic Region	15,000
Puerto Rico, West Indies	3,534
Sakhalin, Japan	29,100
Samar, Phil. Is.	5,124
Sardinia, Mediterranean Sea	9,299
Sicily, Mediterranean Sea	9,935
Somerset, Arctic Region	12,000
South (N. Zeal.), South Pacific O.	58,092
Southampton, Hudson Bay	17,800
Sumatra, East Indies	163,138
Taiwan (Formosa), China Sea	13,836
Tasmania, Australia	26,215
Timor, East Indies	33,740
Vancouver, Canada	12,468
Victoria, Arctic Region	60,000
West Spitzbergen, Arctic Region	15,260
Wrangel, Arctic Region	1,806

Principal Lakes, Oceans, Seas, and Their Areas

Lake Country	Area Sq. Miles
Antarctic O.	5,731,400
Aral, L., Soviet Union	26,166
Arctic O.	5,541,000
Athabaska, L., Canada	2,842
Atlantic O.	31,529,000
Baikal, L., Soviet Union	13,197
Balkhash, L., Soviet Union	7,115
Baltic Sea, Europe	158,000
Bering Sea, N. Pacific	878,000
Black Sea	168,500
Caribbean Sea, W. Indies	750,000
Caspian Sea, Asia	169,383
Chad, L., Africa	10,400
East China Sea, Asia	480,000
Erie, L., U. S.–Canada	9,940
Eyre, L., Australia	3,700
Gairdner, L., Australia	3,000
Great Bear L., Canada	14,000
Great Salt L., United States	2,560
Great Slave L., Canada	7,100
Hudson Bay, N. America	472,000
Huron, L., U. S.–Canada	23,010
Indian O.	28,357,000
Japan Sea, Asia	405,000
Koko-Nor (L.), Tibet—China	2,300
Ladoga, L., Soviet Union	7,000
Leopold II, L., Belgian Congo	1,700
Manitoba, L., Canada	1,817
Mediterranean Sea, Eur.	1,145,000
Mexico, G. of, N. America	700,000
Michigan, L., United States	22,400
Nicaragua, L., Nicaragua	2,975
North Sea, Europe	221,000
Nyasa, L., Africa	10,231
Okhotsk Sea, Asia	582,000
Onega, L., Soviet Union	3,800
Ontario, L., U. S.–Canada	7,540
Pacific O.	63,985,000
Red Sea, Africa–Asia	178,000
Rudolf, L., Kenya	3,500
Superior, L., U. S.–Canada	31,810
Tanganyika, L., Africa	12,355
Titicaca, L., Peru-Bolivia	3,261
Torrens, L., Australia	2,400
Van, L., Turkey	2,500
Vänern (L.), Sweden	2,150
Victoria, L., Africa	26,828
Winnipeg, L., Canada	9,400
Winnipegosis, L., Canada	2,085
Yellow Sea, Asia	480,000

Principal Mountains and Their Heights

Mountain Country	Height in Feet
Aconcagua, Argentina	22,834
Albaron, France	12,014
Albert Edward, Papua	13,222
Albert Markham, Antarctica	10,459
Alestschhorn, Switzerland	13,803
Altar, Ecuador	17,730
Ampato, Peru	21,702
Ancohuma, Bolivia	21,490
Antisana, Ecuador	18,885
Apo, Philippine Islands	9,610
Ararat, Turkey	16,916
Arjias Dagh, Turkey	12,566
Aux Sources, Basutoland	22,834
Bear, Alaska	14,850
Blackburn, Alaska	16,140
Blanc, France-Italy	15,781
Blanca, Colorado, U. S.	14,390
Bona, Canada	16,422
Bonete, Argentina	21,031
Borah, Idaho, U. S.	12,655
Byelukha, Soviet Union	14,890
Caca Aca, Bolivia	20,329
Cachi, Argentina	21,326
Carstensz, Papua	16,404
Cayambe, Ecuador	19,023
Ceachuca, Bolivia	19,407
Charles Louis, Papua	18,000
Chimborazo, Ecuador	20,702
Cincel, Bolivia	20,102
Colima, Mexico	13,572
Colorados, Argentina-Chile	19,846
Condori, Peru	18,045
Condoriri, Bolivia	20,043
Cook, New Zealand	12,349
Copiapo, Chile	19,947
Coropuna, Peru	22,802
Cotopaxi, Ecuador	19,498
Cuzco (Ausangate), Peru	20,187
Del Acay, Argentina	20,801
Demavend, Iran	18,605
Dos Conos, Argentina	22,507
Dykh-tau, Soviet Union	17,054
Elbert, Colorado, U. S.	14,420
Elbrus, Soviet Union	18,468
Erebus, Antarctica	13,300
Etna, Sicily	10,755
Everest, Nepal	29,141
Fairweather, Alaska-Canada	15,399
Falso Azufre, Argentina–Chile	22,277
Foraker, Alaska	17,000
Forel, Greenland	11,286
Fremont, Wyoming, U. S.	13,730
Fujiyama, Japan	12,395
Godwin Austen, India	28,251
Grand Teton, Wyo. U. S.	13,747
Hekla, Iceland	5,105
Hood, Oregon, U. S.	11,253
Huanacuni, Bolivia	19,829
Huascaran, Peru	22,188
Hubbard, Canada	14,950
Huelacalloc, Bolivia	19,082
Huila, Colombia	18,701
Illampu, Bolivia	21,276
Illimani, Bolivia	21,282
Incahuasu, Argentina-Chile	21,720
Ixtaccihuatl, Mexico	17,338
Juncal, Argentina-Chile	19,965
Jungfrau, Switzerland	13,671
Kanchanganga, India	28,146
Kaufmann, Soviet Union	23,386
Kazbek, Soviet Union	16,546
Kenya, Africa	17,044
Kilimanjaro, Africa	19,324
Kinchinjunga, Nepal	28,146
King, Canada	16,971
Klyuchevskaya, Soviet Union	16,125
Koshtan-tau, Soviet Union	17,096
La Plata, Colorado, U. S.	14,342
Lassen, California, U. S.	10,453
Lincacabur, Chile-Bolivia	19,456
Llullaillaco, Argentina–Chile	22,015
Logan, Canada	19,850
Lucania, Canada	17,150
McKinley, Alaska	20,300
Maipo, Argentina-Chile	17,459
Matterhorn, Switz. Italy	14,780
Mauna Kea, Hawaii	13,784
Mauna Loa, Hawaii	13,680
Mercedario, Argentina–Chile	21,884
Misti, Peru	19,166
Mont Blanc, Italy	15,780
Monte Rosa, Italy-Switz.	15,217
Mustagh Ata, Turkestan	24,357
Nanga Parbat, India	26,629
Niitakayama, Taiwan	12,959
Ojos del Salado, Argentina–Chile	22,573
Ollague, Bolivia–Chile	19,259
Orizaba, Mexico	18,541
Payachata, Bolivia	20,768
Pelée, Martinique	5,200
Pichu Pichu, Peru	18,373
Pikes, Colorado, U. S.	14,109
Pili, Chile	19,850
Pissis, Argentina	22,245
Popocatepetl, Mexico	17,840
Porongos, Argentina-Chile	20,512
Pular, Chile	20,342
Quincy Adams, Alaska	15,560
Rainier, Washington, U. S.	14,408
Ras Dashan, Ethiopia	14,960
Ruwenzori, Belgian Congo	16,798
St. Elias, Alaska–Canada	18,008
Sajama, Bolivia	21,390
Sanford, Alaska	16,210
San Francisco, Arizona, U. S.	12,611
Sangay, Ecuador	17,465
San Jose, Argentina-Chile	20,067
Sarmiento, Chile	20,670
Semeru, Java	12,060
Shasta, California, U. S.	14,161
Socompa, Argentina-Chile	19,787
Steele, Canada	16,439
Taapaca, Bolivia	19,079
Tacora, Peru	19,521
Tengri Khan, Soviet Union	23,622
Tocorpuri Bolivia-Chile	22,163
Tolima, Colombia	19,482
Toluca, Mexico	15,448
Tortolas, de las, Chile	20,018
Tres Cruces, Chile	21,720
Turpungato, Chile	21,490
Ushba, Soviet Union	15,409
Vancouver, Canada	15,700
Veladero, Argentina	20,735
Vesuvius, Italy	4,012
Vilcanota, Peru	17,998
Weisshorn, Switzerland	14,804
Wheeler, Nevada, U. S.	13,058
White, Calif. U. S.	14,242
Whitney, California, U. S.	14,496
Wilhelmina, Papua	15,584
Wood, Canada	15,880
Wrangell, Alaska	14,005

Principal Rivers and Their Lengths

River Country	Length in Miles
Albany, North America	610
Amazon, South America	3,900
Amur, Asia	2,900
Araguaya, South America	1,550
Arkansas, North America	1,450
Athabaska, North America	750
Backs, North America	600
Brahmaputra, Asia	1,800
Branco, South America	580
Brazos, North America	950
Canadian, North America	760
Churchill, North America	1,000
Colorado, North America	1,650
Columbia, North America	1,270
Congo, Africa	2,900
Cumberland, North America	687
Danube, Europe	1,725
Dnieper, Europe	1,400
Dniester, Europe	800
Don, Europe	1,100
Donets, Europe	650
Dubawnt, North America	575
Dvina, Europe	1,100
Elbe, Europe	700
Euphrates, Asia	1,700
Fraser, North America	700
Ganges, Asia	1,455
Gila, North America	630
Green, North America	730
Hwang, Asia	2,700
Indus, Asia	2,000
Jurua, South America	1,200
Kama, Europe	1,115
Lena, Asia	2,860
Liard, North America	550
Loire, Europe	650
Mackenzie, North America	2,500
Madeira, South America	1,200
Magdalena, South America	950
Marañon, South America	1,000
Mekong, Asia	2,600
Meuse, Europe	575
Mississippi, North America	2,470
Mississippi-Missouri, N. A.	3,988
Missouri, North America	2,723
Nelson, North America	1,660
Niemen, Europe	550
Niger, Africa	2,600
Nile, Africa	4,000
Ob, Asia	3,200
Oder, Europe	550
Ohio, North America	1,306
Oka, Europe	914
Orinoco, South America	1,600
Ottawa, North America	690
Paraná, South America	2,450
Parnahyba, South America	850
Peace, North America	1,050
Pechora, Europe	1,000
Pilcomayo, South America	1,000
Plata-Paraguay, S. America	2,300
Platte, North America	1,030
Purus, South America	1,500
Putumayo, South America	900
Red, North America	1,018
Rhine, Europe	700
Rhone, Europe	500
Rio Grande, North America	1,800
Rio Negro, South America	1,400
Roosevelt, South America	950
St. Lawrence, North America	2,150
Salado, South America	1,000
São Francisco, South America	1,800
Saskatchewan, North America	1,205
Sava, Europe	550
Snake, North America	1,038
Tagus, Europe	550
Tapajos, South America	1,150
Tennessee, North America	862
Theiss, Europe	800
Tocantins, South America	1,000
Ucayali, South America	1,100
Ural, Europe	1,400
Uruguay, South America	1,100
Vistula, Europe	630
Volga, Europe	2,300
Vyatka, Europe	680
White, North America	690
Xingu, South America	1,300
Yangtze, Asia	3,100
Yapura, South America	1,200
Yellowstone, North America	671
Yenisei, Asia	2,800
Yukon, North America	2,100
Zambezi, Africa	1,600

PRINCIPAL COUNTRIES OF THE WORLD

Political Division	Area in sq. miles	Population	Pop. per sq. m.
Aden Protectorate . (Br.)	42,080	100,000	2.4
Aegean Is. . . . . (It.)	988	132,638	134.2
Afghanistan	245,000	12,000,000	48.9
Africa	11,529,480	155,475,000	13.5
Alabama . . . . (U. S.)	51,609	2,832,961	55.0
Alaska . . . . (U. S.)	586,400	72,524	0.1
Albania . . . . (It.)	10,629	1,135,000	107.0
Alberta . . . . (Can.)	255,285	788,393	3.5
Aldabra Is. . . . . (Br.)	60	127	2.1
Algeria . . . . (Fr.)	847,818	7,234,684	8.5
Andaman Is. . . . . . . (Br.)	2,508	19,223	7.6
Andorra	191	6,000	31.4
Anglo-Egyp. Sudan (Br.)	969,600	6,000,000	6.2
Angola . . . . (Port.)	484,729	3,225,015	6.2
Arabia	1,000,000	7,000,000	7.0
Argentina	1,079,965	13,000,000	12.0
Arizona . . . . (U. S.)	113,909	499,261	4.4
Arkansas . . . . (U. S.)	53,102	1,949,387	36.7
Ascension I. . . . . (Br.)	34	159	4.7
Asia	16,494,217	1,090,355,000	66.1
Australia . . . . (Br.)	2,974,581	6,959,913	2.4
Austria, see Germany	. . . .	. . . .	
Azores Is. . . . . (Port.)	990	253,935	256.5
Bahama Is. . . . . (Br.)	4,404	70,332	15.9
Bahrein Is. . . . . (Br.)	250	120,000	480.0
Basutoland . . . . (Br.)	11,716	562,311	47.9
Bechuanaland . . . . . (Br.)	275,000	265,756	0.9
Belgian Congo . . . . (Bel.)	941,809	13,829,293	14.6
Belgium	11,752	8,361,220	711.5
Belgium & Poss.	932,408	22,000,000	23.6
Bermuda Is. . . . . (Br.)	19	32,086	1688.7
Bhutan	18,000	300,000	16.7
Bolivia	514,468	3,282,736	6.4
Borneo, Netherlands	206,810	2,168,661	10.5
Brazil	3,285,319	44,116,000	13.4
British Columbia . (Can.)	366,255	809,203	2.2
British Honduras	8,598	59,965	7.0
British North Borneo	31,106	299,311	9.6
Brunei . . . . (Br.)	2,500	37,868	15.1
Bulgaria	42,814	6,734,232	157.3
California . . . . (U. S.)	158,693	6,907,387	43.7
Cameroons . . . . (Fr.)	166,489	2,609,508	15.6
Canada . . . . (Br.)	3,694,863	11,419,896	3.1
Canal Zone . . . . . . (U. S.)	554	51,830	93.6
Canary Is. . . . . (Sp.)	2,807	632,275	225.3
Cape Verde Is. . . . (Port.)	1,516	158,900	104.8
Celebes & Great East . . . . (Neth. Indies)	293,091	5,492,114	18.7
Ceylon . . . . (Br.)	25,332	5,712,000	225.5
Chile	286,322	5,044,446	17.6
China	3,756,102	422,527,000	112.5
Chosen . . . . (Jap.)	85,206	22,047,836	258.8
Colombia	441,651	8,702,000	19.7
Colorado . . . . (U. S.)	104,247	1,123,296	10.8
Connecticut . . . . . (U. S.)	5,009	1,709,242	341.2
Costa Rica	23,000	639,197	27.8
Cuba	44,164	4,252,959	96.3
Cyprus . . . . (Br.)	3,584	377,000	105.2
Czechoslovakia*	. . . .	. . . .	. . . . .
Danzig	754	407,517	540.5
Delaware . . . . (U. S.)	2,057	266,505	124.7
Denmark	16,571	3,776,328	227.8
Denmark & Poss.	854,731	3,820,000	4.5
Dist. of Columbia (U. S.)	69	663,091	9611.4
Dominican Republic	19,332	1,654,993	86.1
Ecuador	95,036	3,011,072	31.7
Egypt	383,000	15,951,800	41.6
England	50,874	38,173,950	750.4
Eritrea, see Italian East	Africa (It.)	. . . .	. . . . .
Estonia †	18,354	1,131,200	61.6
Ethiopia, see Italian East	Africa (It.)	. . . .	. . . . .
Europe	3,773,958	539,800,000	143.0
Faeroes, The . . . . . (Den.)	540	25,744	47.7
Falkland Is. . . . . (Br.)	4,618	2,440	0.5
Fed. Malay States . . (Br.)	27,506	2,125,000	77.2
Fiji Is. . . . . (Br.)	7,083	205,379	29.0
Finland	136,054	3,864,000	28.4
Florida . . . . (U. S.)	58,560	1,897,414	32.4
France	212,681	41,980,000	197.4
France & Poss.	4,805,646	108,000,000	22.4
French Equatorial Africa	912,049	3,422,815	3.8
French Indochina	259,522	23,250,000	89.2
French West Africa . (Fr.)	1,814,810	14,944,830	8.2
Gambia . . . . (Br.)	4,068	199,520	49.0
Georgia . . . . (U. S.)	58,876	3,123,723	53.1
Germany	246,342	84,022,066	341.1
Gibraltar . . . . (Br.)	2	21,372	10686.0
Gold Coast . . . . (Br.)	91,843	3,786,659	41.2
Great Britain & N. Ire.	94,278	46,688,814	495.2
Great Britain & Poss.	13,355,426	500,800,000	37.5
Greece	54,092	7,020,000	129.8

Political Division	Area in sq. miles	Population	Pop. per sq. m.
Greenland . . . . (Den.)	837,620	18,163	0.02
Guadeloupe & Dep. (Fr.)	688	308,000	447.7
Guam . . . . (U. S.)	206	22,077	107.2
Guatemala	42,353	3,284,269	77.5
Guiana, British	89,480	346,982	3.9
Guiana, Netherlands	54,291	182,396	3.3
Guiana, French & Inini	34,354	36,975	7.8
Guinea, Portuguese	13,944	390,400	28.0
Guinea, Spanish	10,860	140,000	12.8
Haiti	11,069	3,195,000	288.6
Hawaii . . . . (U. S.)	6,407	423,332	66.1
Honduras	44,275	962,700	21.7
Hong Kong . . . . (Br.)	391	1,007,000	2575.4
Hungary	61,723	13,412,667	217.3
Iceland	39,709	119,000	3.0
Idaho . . . . (U. S.)	83,557	524,873	6.3
Ifni . . . . (Sp.)	965	20,000	20.7
Illinois . . . . (U. S.)	56,400	7,897,241	140.0
India . . . . (Br.)	1,575,107	338,170,632	214.6
Indiana . . . . (U. S.)	36,291	3,427,796	94.4
Iowa . . . . (U. S.)	56,280	2,538,268	45.2
Iran (Persia)	628,000	15,055,115	23.9
Iraq	143,240	4,412,959	30.8
Ireland . . . . (Br.)	26,592	2,944,000	110.7
Italian E. Africa . . . . (It.)	585,783	12,100,000	20.6
Italy	119,703	44,530,000	372.0
Jamaica . . . . (Br.)	4,450	1,218,365	273.8
Japan (proper)	147,889	72,222,700	488.4
Japanese Empire	263,357	101,663,279	386.0
Java and Madoera . . . . (Neth. Indies)	51,029	41,718,364	817.5
Kansas . . . . (U. S.)	82,276	1,801,028	21.9
Kentucky . . . . (U. S.)	40,395	2,845,627	70.4
Kenya . . . . (Br.)	224,960	3,334,000	14.8
Kuwait . . . . (Br.)	1,930	80,000	41.5
Kwantung . . . . (Jap.)	1,435	1,657,000	1154.7
Labrador . . . . . . (Newfd.)	112,400	4,850	0.04
Latvia †	25,395	1,995,000	78.6
Leeward Is. . . . . (Br.)	410	96,994	236.5
Liberia	43,000	1,500,000	34.9
Libya . . . . (It.)	633,040	818,400	1.3
Liechtenstein	65	10,213	157.1
Lithuania †	20,584	2,879,000	139.8
Louisiana . . . . (U. S.)	48,523	2,363,880	48.7
Luxembourg	998	296,913	297.0
Mackenzie Dist. . . (Can.)	527,490	. . . .	. . . . .
Madagascar . . . . (Fr.)	228,707	3,797,936	16.5
Madeira Is. . . . . . . (Port.)	307	215,000	700.3
Maine . . . . (U. S.)	33,215	847,226	25.5
Manchukuo	503,013	36,933,000	73.4
Manitoba . . . . (Can.)	246,512	722,447	3.1
Maryland . . . . (U. S.)	10,577	1,821,244	172.2
Massachusetts . . . (U. S.)	8,257	4,316,721	524.3
Mauritius . . . . (Br.)	720	415,462	577.0
Mexico	760,290	19,470,094	25.6
Michigan . . . . (U. S.)	58,216	5,256,106	90.3
Minnesota . . . . (U. S.)	84,068	2,792,300	33.2
Mississippi . . . . . . (U. S.)	47,716	2,183,796	45.8
Missouri . . . . (U. S.)	69,674	3,784,664	54.3
Monaco	0.5	23,994	47988.0
Mongolia (Outer) . . . . (Sov. Rep.)	558,054	840,000	1.5
Montana . . . . (U. S.)	147,138	559,456	3.8
Morocco . . . . (Fr.)	200,000	6,245,222	31.2
Morocco . . . . (Sp.)	8,880	795,000	89.7
Mozambique . . . . . (Port.)	297,917	4,006,000	13.5
Nebraska . . . . (U. S.)	77,237	1,315,834	17.0
Nepal	54,000	5,600,000	107.0
Netherlands	13,202	8,728,569	661.1
Netherlands & Poss.	803,202	70,000,000	86.3
Netherlands Indies	733,790	60,727,233	82.8
Nevada . . . . (U. S.)	110,540	110,247	1.0
New Brunswick . . (Can.)	27,985	453,377	16.2
Newfoundland . . . . . (Br.)	42,734	292,000	6.8
New Guinea, Netherlands	incl. in Cel	ebes & Great	East
New Gui. Ter. . (Austl.)	91,000	755,882	8.3
New Hampshire . (U. S.)	9,304	491,524	52.8
New Hebrides Is. (Br. & Fr.)	5,700	43,000	7.5
New Jersey . . . . . . (U. S.)	7,836	4,160,165	530.8
New Mexico . . . . . (U. S.)	121,666	531,818	4.3
New York . . . . (U. S.)	49,576	13,479,142	271.9
New Zealand . . . . . . (Br.)	103,862	1,618,093	15.6
Nicaragua	51,660	1,380,287	26.7
Nigeria	372,674	20,190,771	54.2
Non-Fed. Mal. States (Br.)	23,486	1,817,283	77.4
North America	9,358,976	185,033,500	19.8
North Carolina . . . (U. S.)	52,712	3,571,623	69.6
North Dakota . . . (U. S.)	70,665	641,935	9.1
Northern Ireland . . (Br.)	5,237	1,279,753	244.4
Northwest Ter. . . . (Can.)	1,309,682	10,661	0.08
Norway	124,984	2,921,000	23.4

Political Division	Area in sq. miles	Population	Pop. per sq. m.
Norway & Poss.	148,926	2,923,000	19.7
Nova Scotia . . . . . (Can.)	21,068	573,190	27.2
Nyasaland . . . . (Br.)	37,596	1,639,329	43.6
Ohio . . . . (U. S.)	41,222	6,907,612	167.5
Oklahoma . . . . (U. S.)	69,919	2,336,434	33.4
Oman	82,000	500,000	6.1
Ontario . . . . (Can.)	412,582	3,756,632	9.1
Oregon . . . . (U. S.)	96,981	1,089,684	11.2
Palestine . . . . (Br.)	10,155	1,467,000	144.5
Panama	28,575	633,181	22.2
Papua Territory . (Austl.)	90,540	276,366	3.1
Paraguay	177,756	1,014,773	5.9
Pennsylvania . . . . (U. S.)	45,333	9,900,180	219.1
Peru	437,133	8,000,000	18.3
Philippine Is. . . . . (U. S.)	114,400	16,000,303	139.8
Poland	150,290	35,090,000	233.4
Portugal	34,904	6,991,260	200.3
Portugal & Poss.	847,196	15,825,705	18.7
Prince Edward I. (Can.)	2,184	93,919	43.0
Puerto Rico . . . . . (U. S.)	3,435	1,869,255	544.2
Quebec . . . . (Can.)	494,534	3,319,640	6.7
Rhode Island . . . . (U. S.)	1,214	713,346	587.6
Rhodesia, Northern (Br.)	290,320	1,380,754	4.7
Rhodesia, Southern (Br.)	150,354	1,383,540	9.2
Rio de Oro & Adrar (Sp.)	109,200	32,000	0.29
Romania	75,039	12,935,000	172.4
Salvador	13,176	1,787,930	135.7
San Marino	38	14,170	372.9
Sarawak . . . . (Br.)	42,000	442,900	10.5
Saskatchewan . . . . (Can.)	251,700	887,747	3.5
Saudi Arabia	413,792	5,500,000	13.3
Scotland . . . . (Br.)	30,405	4,916,000	161.7
Siam, see Thailand	. . . .	. . . .	. . . . .
Sierre Leone & Prot. (Br.)	31,000	1,672,057	53.9
Sinkiang . . . . (China)	550,050	2,552,000	4.6
Slovakia	14,668	2,410,000	164.3
Solomon Is. . . . . (Austl.)	3,400	44,113	12.9
Solomon Is. . . . . (Br.)	11,458	95,428	8.3
Somaliland, British	68,000	344,768	5.1
Somaliland, French	5,790	46,391	8.0
Somaliland, Italian	see Italian	East Africa (I	t.). . . .
South America	6,825,876	93,011,000	13.6
South Carolina . . (U. S.)	31,055	1,899,804	61.2
South Dakota . . . . (U. S.)	77,047	642,961	8.3
Southwest Africa . . (Br.)	322,393	288,000	0.9
Soviet Union	8,170,268	180,122,390	22.0
Soviet Union in Eur.	1,804,579	139,521,997	77.3
Spain	195,010	23,950,821	122.8
Spain & Poss.	323,706	25,517,782	78.8
Straits Settlements . (Br.)	1,600	1,357,854	848.7
Sumatra . . (Neth. Indies)	182,860	8,533,635	52.3
Svalbard . . . . (Nor.)	24,142	2,415	0.1
Swaziland . . . . (Br.)	6,705	156,715	23.4
Sweden	173,105	6,284,722	36.3
Switzerland	15,940	4,183,200	262.4
Syria . . . . (Fr.)	72,723	2,367,734	32.5
Taiwan . . . . (Jap.)	13,836	5,315,642	385.9
Tanganyika Ter. . . . (Br.)	363,548	5,258,000	14.4
Tangier Zone (Internat'l)	225	65,000	288.9
Tannu Tuva . (Sov. Rep.)	63,690	65,000	1.0
Tennessee . . . . (U. S.)	42,246	2,915,841	69.0
Texas . . . . (U. S.)	267,339	6,414,824	23.9
Thailand (Siam)	225,148	15,266,000	67.8
Tibet . . . . (China)	443,900	3,722,000	8.4
Timor, Netherlands	incl. in Cel	ebes & Great	East
Timor, Portuguese	7,330	460,655	63.1
Transjordan . . . . (Br.)	16,220	325,000	20.1
Trinidad & Tobago . (Br.)	1,976	484,900	245.4
Tunisia . . . . (Fr.)	48,300	2,608,300	49.9
Turkey	296,190	17,869,901	60.3
Uganda . . . . (Br.)	94,204	3,747,221	39.8
Union of S. Africa . . (Br.)	472,550	10,160,000	21.5
United States	3,022,387	131,669,275	43.6
United States & Poss.	3,734,010	150,147,000	40.2
Uruguay	72,153	2,093,331	29.0
Utah . . . . (U. S.)	84,916	550,310	6.5
Vatican City	0.5	1,025	2050.0
Venezuela	352,051	3,583,327	10.2
Vermont . . . . (U. S.)	9,609	359,231	37.3
Virgin Is. . . . . (U. S.)	133	24,889	187.1
Virginia . . . . (U. S.)	40,815	2,677,773	65.6
Wales . . . . (Br.)	7,466	2,176,050	291.5
Washington . . . . . . (U. S.)	68,192	1,736,191	25.4
West Virginia . . . . . (U. S.)	24,181	1,901,974	78.6
Windward Is. . . . . . . (Br.)	821	278,239	338.9
Wisconsin . . . . (U. S.)	56,154	3,137,587	55.9
Wyoming . . . . (U. S.)	97,914	250,742	2.5
Yemen	23,932	875,000	36.6
Yugoslavia	95,551	15,703,000	164.3
Yukon . . . . (Can.)	207,076	4,687	0.02
Zanzibar . . . . (Br.)	640	244,000	381.3

*Absorbed by Germany, Hungary and Poland. † Annexed to the Soviet Union.

ABBREVIATIONS OF GEOGRAPHICAL NAMES AND TERMS

A. E. Sud.	Anglo-Egyptian Sudan
Afg.	Afghanistan
Afr.	Africa
Agua	Aguascalientes
Ala.	Alabama
Alb.	Albania
Alg.	Algeria
Alsk.	Alaska
Alta.	Alberta
And.	Andorra
Ang.	Angola
Ant.	Antarctic, Antarctica
Arc.	Arctic
Arch.	Archipelago
Arg.	Argentina
Ariz.	Arizona
Ark.	Arkansas
A. S. S. R.	Autonomous Socialist Soviet Republic
Atl. O.	Atlantic Ocean
Austl.	Australia
Aut.	Autonomous
Az. Is.	Azores Is.
B.	Bay, Bahia
Ba. Is.	Bahama Is.
Baja Cal.	Baja California
Bal.	Baluchistan
Barb.	Barbados
Bas.	Basutoland
B. C.	British Columbia
Bdy.	Boundary
Bech.	Bechuanaland
Bel.	Belgium
Bel. Cong.	Belgian Congo
Ber. Is.	Bermuda Is.
Bg.	Berg
Bhu.	Bhutan
Bk.	Bank
Br.	British
Br. Gu.	British Guiana
Br. Hond.	British Honduras
B. N. B.	British North Borneo
Bol.	Bolivia
Braz.	Brazil
Brit. Prot.	British Protectorate
Br. Mal.	British Malaya
Br. Som.	British Somaliland
Bru.	Brunei
Bul.	Bulgaria
C.	Cape
Calif.	California
Cam.	Cameroons
Camp.	Campeche
Can.	Canal, Canada
Can. Is.	Canary Is.
Cel.	Celebes
Cen. Am.	Central America
Cey.	Ceylon
C. H.	Court House
Chan.	Channel
Chia.	Chiapas
Chih.	Chihuahua
Chl.	Chile
Chn.	China
Cho.	Chosen
Coa.	Coahuila
Co.	County
Col.	Colombia
Colim.	Colima
Colo.	Colorado
Conn.	Connecticut
Cor.	Corsica
C. R.	Costa Rica
Cr.	Creek
Cur.	Curaçao
C. V. Is.	Cape Verde Is.
Cyp.	Cyprus
C. Z.	Canal Zone
Czech.	Czechoslovakia
Dan.	Danzig
D. C.	District of Columbia
Del.	Delaware
Den.	Denmark
Dept.	Department
Des.	Desert
D. F.	Distrito Federal
Dist.	District
Dom.	Dominica
Dom. Rep.	Dominican Republic
Dur.	Durango
E.	East
Ec.	Ecuador
Eg.	Egypt
Elec.	Electric
Eng.	England
Est.	Estonia
Eur.	Europe
Faer.	The Faeroes
Falk. Is.	Falkland Is.
Fd.	Fjord
Fed.	Federated
Fed. Mal. States	Federated Malay States
Fin.	Finland
Fk.	Fork
Fla.	Florida
For.	Forest
Fr.	France
Fr. Eq. Afr.	French Equatorial Africa
Fr. Gu.	French Guiana
Fr. In. Chn.	French Indochina
Fr. Som.	French Somaliland
Fr. W. Afr.	French West Africa
Ft.	Fort
G.	Gulf
Ga.	Georgia
Gam.	Gambia
G. C.	Gold Coast
Ger.	Germany
Gib.	Gibraltar
Grc.	Greece
Gren.	Grenada
Grnld.	Greenland
Gt.	Great
Gt. Brit.	Great Britain
Guad.	Guadeloupe
Guan.	Guanajuato
Guat.	Guatemala
Guer.	Guerrero
Hai.	Haiti
Har., Hbr.	Harbor
Haw.	Hawaii
Hd.	Head
Hej.	Hejaz
Hid.	Hidalgo
Hond.	Honduras
Hong.	Hong Kong
Hts.	Heights
Hung.	Hungary
I.	Island
Ia.	Iowa
Ice.	Iceland
Ida.	Idaho
If.	Ifni
Ill.	Illinois
In.	Inset
Ind.	Indiana
Ind. O.	Indian Ocean
Ind. Res.	Indian Reservation
Iran	Iran
Ire.	Ireland
Is.	Islands
Isth.	Isthmus
It.	Italy
Ital.	Italian
It. E. Afr.	Italian East Africa
Jal.	Jalisco
Jam.	Jamaica
Jap.	Japan
Jc.	Junction
Kan.	Kansas
Kar.	Karafuto
Km.	Kilometer, Kilometers
Kuw.	Kuwait
Kwan.	Kwantung
Ky.	Kentucky
L.	Lake, Loch, Lough
La.	Louisiana
Lab.	Labrador
Lat.	Latitude, Latvia
Le. Is.	Leeward Is.
Lib.	Liberia
Liech.	Liechtenstein
Lith.	Lithuania
Long.	Longitude
Lux.	Luxembourg
M.	Mile, miles
Mack.	Mackenzie
Madag.	Madagascar
Mal.	Malta
Mal. St.	Malay States
Man.	Manitoba
Manch.	Manchukuo
Mand.	Mandate
Mar.	Maraski
Mart.	Martinique
Mass.	Massachusetts
Max.	Maximum
Max. surf. elev.	Maximum surface elevation
Md.	Maryland
Me.	Maine
Medit.	Mediterranean
Mex.	Mexico
Mich.	Michigan
Michoa.	Michoacan
Minn.	Minnesota
Miss.	Mississippi
Mo.	Missouri
Mong.	Mongolia
Mont.	Montana
Mor.	Morocco
Morel.	Morelos
Moz.	Mozambique
Mt.	Mount, mountain
Mts.	Mountains
N.	North
N. A.	North America
Nat.	National
Natl. Mon.	National monument
N. C.	North Carolina
Nay.	Nayarit
Neb.	Nebraska
N. D.	North Dakota
Neth.	Netherlands
Neth. Bor.	Netherlands Borneo
Neth. Ind.	Netherlands Indies
N. B.	New Brunswick
N. Cal.	New Caledonia
Nep.	Nepal
Nev.	Nevada
Newf.	Newfoundland
New Hebr.	New Hebrides
N. Gui. Ter.	New Guinea Ter.
N. H.	New Hampshire
Nic.	Nicaragua
Nig.	Nigeria
N. Ire.	Northern Ireland
N. J.	New Jersey
N. L.	Nuevo León
N. M.	New Mexico
Non-fed.	Non-federated
Nor.	Norway
N. Rh.	Northern Rhodesia
N. S.	Nova Scotia
N. Y.	New York
Nya.	Nyasaland
N. Z.	New Zealand
O.	Ocean
Oax.	Oaxaca
Okla.	Oklahoma
Ont.	Ontario
Ore.	Oregon
P.	Pass
Pa.	Pennsylvania
Pac. O.	Pacific Ocean
Pal.	Palestine
Pan.	Panama
Pap. Ter.	Papua Ter.
Par.	Paraguay
P. E. I.	Prince Edward I.
Pen.	Peninsula
P. I.	Philippine Islands
Pk.	Peak, park
Plat.	Plateau
P. O.	Post office
Pol.	Poland
Port.	Portugal
Port. Gui.	Portuguese Guinea
P. R.	Puerto Rico
Prot.	Protectorate
Prov.	Province
Pt.	Point
Pta.	Punta
Pte.	Pointe
Pueb.	Puebla
Que.	Quebec
Quer.	Querétaro
R.	River, Rio
R. de O.	Río de Oro
Ra.	Range
Reg.	Region
Rep.	Republic
Res.	Reservation
Rf.	Reef
R. I.	Rhode Island
Rom.	Romania
R. S. F. S. R.	Russian Socialist Federative Soviet Republic
Rus.	Russian
Ry.	Railway
Rys.	Railways
S.	San, Santo, South
Sa.	Serra, Sierra
S. A.	South America
Sal.	Salvador
Sam.	Samoa
Sar.	Sarawak
Sard.	Sardinia
Sask.	Saskatchewan
Sau. Ar.	Saudi Arabia
S. C.	South Carolina
Scot.	Scotland
S. D.	South Dakota
Sd.	Sound
S. F. S. R.	Socialist Federative Soviet Republic
Shet. Is.	Shetland Is.
Sin.	Sinaloa
Sink.	Sinkiang
S. L.	Sierra Leone
S. L. P.	San Luis Potosí
S. Mar.	San Marino
Soc.	Socialist
Son.	Sonora
Sov. Un.	Soviet Union
Sp.	Spain
Sp. Gui.	Spanish Guinea
Sp. Mor.	Spanish Morocco
S. Rh.	Southern Rhodesia
Spr., Sprs.	Spring, Springs
S. S. R.	Socialistic Soviet Republic
St.	Saint
Sta.	Santa
Sta. Luc.	Santa Lucia
St. Vin.	Saint Vincent
Ste.	Sainte
Str.	Strait
Strs. Sets.	Straits Settlements
Sum.	Sumatra
Sur.	Surinam
S.W.Afr.	Southwest Africa
Swaz.	Swaziland
Swe.	Sweden
Switz.	Switzerland
Syr.	Syria
Tab.	Tabasco
Tai.	Taiwan
Tam.	Tamaulipas
Tan.	Tanganyika
Tas.	Tasmania
Tenn.	Tennessee
Ter.	Territory
Tex.	Texas
Thai.	Thailand
Tib.	Tibet
Tim.	Timor
Tlax.	Tlaxcala
Transj.	Transjordan
Trin.	Trinidad
Tun.	Tunisia
Tur.	Turkey, Turski
Ug.	Uganda
Ur.	Uruguay
U. S., U. S. A.	United States of America
U. S. Afr.	Union of South Africa
Va.	Virginia
Ven.	Venezuela
Ver.	Veracruz
Vir. Is.	Virgin Is.
Vol.	Volcano
Vt.	Vermont
W.	West
W. I.	West Indies
Wind. Is.	Windward Islands
Wash.	Washington
West. Austl.	Western Australia
W. I.	West Indies
Wis.	Wisconsin
W. Va.	West Virginia
Wyo.	Wyoming
Yem.	Yemen
Yuc.	Yucatan
Yugo.	Yugoslavia
Yuk.	Yukon
Zac.	Zacatecas
Zan.	Zanzibar

PRONUNCIATION OF GEOGRAPHICAL NAMES

Key to the Sound Values of Letters and Symbols Used in the Index to Indicate Pronunciation

ă—ăt, căt, băttle
ă—*ă*ppeal, fin*ă*l
ā—rāte, elāte
ȧ—animȧte, senȧte
ä—cälm, ärm
à—àsk, bàth
a—m*a*rine, sof*a* (short neutral or indeterminate sound)
â—fâre, prepâre
ch—church, choose
dh—as th in other, either
ē—bē, ēve
ê—crêate, êvent
ĕ—bĕt, ĕnd
ĕ—rec*ĕ*nt (short neutral or indeterminate sound)
ẽ—cratẽr, cindẽr
g—gō, gāme
gh—gutteral g
ĭ—wĭll, bĭt
ĭ—short neutral or indeterminate sound
ī—rīde, bīte
ĸ—gutteral k as ch in German ich
ng—sing
ŋ—baŋk, liŋger
ɴ—indicates nasalized preceding vowel
ŏ—nŏd, ŏdd
ŏ—c*ŏ*mmit, c*ŏ*nnect
ō—ōld, bōld
ô—ôbey, hôtel
ô—ôrder, nôrth
o͞o—fo͞od, ro͞ot
o͝o—fo͝ot, wo͝od
ou—thou, out
s—as in soft, so, sane
sh—dish, finish
th—thin, thick
ū—pūre, cūre
û—ûnite, ûsurp
û—ûrn, fûr
ŭ—stŭd, ŭp
ü—as in French tu or as "y" in study
ŭ—circ*ŭ*s, s*ŭ*bmit
zh—as z in azure
'—indeterminate vowel sound

In many cases the spelling of foreign geographic names does not even remotely indicate the pronunciation to an American, i. e., Luck in Poland is pronounced wo͞otsk; Jujuy in Argentina is pronounced ho͞o-hwē'; Spezia in Italy is spät'sê-ä

This condition is hardly surprising, however, when we consider that in our own language Worcester, Massachusetts, is pronounced wo͝os'tẽr; Sioux City, Iowa, so͞o-sĭ'tĭ; Schuylkill Haven, Pennsylvania, sko͞ol'kĭl; Poughkeepsie, New York, pô-kĭp'sĭ.

The indication of pronunciation of geographic names presents several peculiar problems:

(1) Many foreign tongues use sounds that are not present in the English language and which an American cannot normally articulate. Thus, though the nearest English equivalent sound has been indicated, only approximate results are possible.

(2) There are several dialects in each foreign tongue which cause variation in the local pronunciation of names. This also occurs in identical names in the various divisions of a great language group, as the Slavic or the Latin.

(3) Within the United States there are marked differences in pronunciation, not only of local geographic names, but also of common words, indicating that the sound and tone values for letters as well as the placing of the emphasis vary considerably from one part of the country to another.

(4) A number of different letter and diacritical combinations could be used to indicate essentially the same or approximate pronunciations.

Some variation in pronunciation other than that indicated in this index may be encountered, but such a difference does not necessarily indicate that either is in error, and in many cases it is a matter of individual choice as to which is preferred. In fact, an exact indication of pronunciation of many foreign names using English letters and diacriticals is extremely difficult and sometimes impossible.

A PRONOUNCING INDEX

of over 30,000 Geographical Names

Page	Name Pronunciation Region	Lat. °′	Long. °′
120	Aabenraa (ô'bĕn-rô) Den.	55.2 N	9.22 E
122	Aachen (ä'kĕn) Ger.	50.47 N	6.6 E
120	Aakirkeby (ô-kĭr'kĕ-bü) Den.	55.3 N	14.56 E
120	Aalborg (ôl'bôr) Den.	57.0 N	9.55 E
122	Aalen (ä'lĕn) Ger.	48.50 N	10.6 E
120	Aaraals Fjord (ô'rôls fyōr') Nor.	58.40 N	7.55 E
122	Aarau (är'ou) Switz.	47.23 N	8.2 E
122	Aare R. (ä'rĕ) Switz.	47.14 N	7.43 E
120	Aarhus (ôr'hōōs) Den.	56.10 N	10.10 E
120	Aarsunden L. (ôr'sōōn-dĕn) Nor.	62.44 N	11.40 E
143	Aasvogel Kop (äs'fō-gĕl kŏp') (Mt.) U. S. Afr.	30.18 S	27.3 E
103	Abaeté (ä-bä-â-tā') Braz. (In.)	1.42 S	48.53 W
148	Abakan R. (ä-bä-kän') Sov. Un.	52.55 N	90.0 E
102	Abancay (ä-bän-kä'ê) Peru	13.52 S	72.45 W
94	Abangares (ä-bän-gä'räs) C. R.	10.10 N	85.2 W
127	Abanilla (ä-bä-nēl'yä) Sp.	38.14 N	1.5 W
158	Abashiri (ä-bä-shē'rê) Jap.	44.0 N	144.12 E
80	Abasolo (ä-bä-sō'lô) Mex.	27.11 N	101.25 W
92	Abasolo Mex.	24.4 N	98.23 W
139	Abaya, L. (ä-bä'yȧ) It. E. Afr.	6.15 N	37.55 E
139	Abbai R. (ä-bä'ê) It. E. Afr.	10.0 N	37.18 E
150	Abbasi (ä-bäs'ê) Iran	27.15 N	50.28 E
141	Abbasia (äb-bä'zē-ä) Eg.	30.4 N	31.16 E
82	Abbeville (ăb'ê-vĭl) Ala.	31.34 N	85.16 W
124	Abbeville (ȧb-vēl') Fr.	50.5 N	1.50 E
82	Abbeville (ăb'ê-vĭl) Ga.	31.59 N	83.22 W
81	Abbeville La.	29.59 N	92.7 W
83	Abbeville S. C.	34.11 N	82.23 W
12	Abbiategrasso (äb-byä'tä-gräs'sō) It.	45.23 N	8.54 E
118	Abbots Bromley (ăb'ŭts brŭm'lê) Gt. Brit.	52.49 N	1.52 W
72	Abbotsford (ăb'ŭts-fērd) Can. (Vancouver In.)	49.3 N	122.17 W
141	Abd-El-Kuri (I.) (ăbd-ĕl-kōō'rê) Ind. O.	12.13 N	52.10 E
112	Abdulino (äb-dōō-lē'nō) Sov. Un.	53.40 N	53.35 E
130	Abèché (ȧ-bĕ-shā') Fr. Eq. Afr.	13.56 N	20.34 E
138	Abeokuta (ä-bā-ô-kōō'tä) Nig.	7.12 N	3.21 E
116	Aberavon (ăb-ēr-ă'vŏn) Gt. Brit.	51.35 N	3.45 W
140	Abercorn (ăb'ēr-kôrn) N. Rh.	8.48 S	31.20 E
116	Aberdare (ăb-ēr-dâr') Gt. Brit.	51.43 N	3.29 W
73	Aberdeen (ăb-ēr-dēn') Ga. (Atlanta In.)	33.25 N	84.37 W
116	Aberdeen Gt. Brit.	57.9 N	2.9 W
82	Aberdeen Miss.	33.49 N	88.34 W
76	Aberdeen S. D.	45.28 N	98.29 W
143	Aberdeen U. S. Afr.	32.28 S	24.4 E
70	Aberdeen Wash.	46.57 N	123.48 W
118	Aberford (ăb'ēr-fērd) Gt. Brit.	53.51 N	1.21 W
116	Abergavenny (ăb-ēr-gȧ-vĕn'ĭ) Gt. Brit.	51.50 N	3.0 W
70	Abert, L. (ā'bērt) Ore.	42.38 N	120.15 W
116	Aberystwith (ăb-ēr-ĭst'wĭth) Gt. Brit.	52.25 N	4.5 W
150	Abha (äb-hä') Sau. Ar.	17.47 N	42.35 E
103	Abia, Serra do (sĕr'rȧ dōō ä-bē'ȧ) (Mts.) Braz. (In.)	13.25 S	39.35 W
115	Abiar, El (ĕl ä-bē-är') Libya	32.30 N	20.58 E
138	Abidjan (ä-bêd-zhäN') (ä-bê-jän') Fr. W. Afr.	5.17 N	4.3 W
79	Abilene (ăb'ĭ-lēn) Kan.	38.55 N	97.12 W
80	Abilene Tex.	32.26 N	99.45 W
79	Abingdon (ăb'ĭng-dŭn) Ill.	40.49 N	90.21 W
83	Abingdon Va.	36.43 N	81.59 W
87	Abington (ăb'ĭng-tŭn) Mass. (In.)	42.7 N	70.56 W
55	Abitibi L. (ăb-ĭ-tĭb'ĭ) Can.	48.48 N	79.45 W
55	Abitibi R. Can.	49.45 N	81.20 W
113	Abkhazia (Reg.) (ăb-кä'sê-ȧ) Sov. Un.	43.10 N	41.10 E
125	Ablon (ȧb-lôN') Fr. (In.)	48.43 N	2.25 E
135	Abnûb (ȧb-nōōb') Eg. (In.)	27.18 N	31.10 E
121	Åbo (Turku) (ô'bōō)(tōōr'kōō) Fin.	60.29 N	22.14 E
138	Abomey (äb-ô-mā') Fr. W. Afr.	7.12 N	2.1 E
123	Abony (ŏ'bô-ny') Hung.	47.11 N	20.0 E
150	Abou Kemal (ä'bōō kĕ'mȧl) Iraq	34.40 N	41.0 E
99	Abra Canal (ä'brä) Chl. (Magallanes In.)	53.25 S	73.30 W
162	Abra R. P. I.	17.15 N	120.40 E
86	Abraham, Mt. (ā'brȧ-hăm) Me.	44.56 N	70.19 W
97	Abrahams B. Ba. Is.	22.25 N	73.55 W
118	Abram (ā'brăm) Gt. Brit.	53.31 N	2.36 W
103	Abrantes (ä-brän'tĕs) (Braz. (In.)	12.51 S	38.19 W
126	Abrantes Port.	39.28 N	8.12 W
103	Abrolhos Is. (ä-brōl'yōs) Braz.	18.0 S	38.0 W
121	Abruka I. (ȧ-brōō'kȧ) Est.	58.8 N	22.32 E
141	Abruzzi (ä-brōōt'sē) It. E. Afr.	2.50 N	45.35 E
128	Abruzzi and Molise (provinces) (ä-brōōt'sē, mô'lē-zä) It.	42.0 N	14.0 E
71	Absaroka Range (ăb-sȧ-rō'kȧ) Wyo.	44.40 N	109.40 W
150	Abu Arish (ä'bōō ȧ-rēsh') Asir	16.50 N	43.0 E
161	Abucay (ä-bōō-kī') P. I. (Manila In.)	14.42 N	120.27 E
150	Abu Dhabi (ä'bōō dä'bê) Oman	24.30 N	54.28 E
139	Abu Hamed (ä'bōō hä'mĕd) A. E. Sud.	19.34 N	33.22 E
135	Abukir B. (ä-bōō-kēr') Eg. (In.)	31.15 N	30.10 E
162	Abulug (ä-bōō'lōōg) P. I.	18.26 N	121.27 E
162	Abulug R. P. I.	18.10 N	121.21 E
102	Abunã, R. (ä-bōō-nä') Bol.-Braz.	10.0 S	66.30 W
135	Abu Qîr (ä'bōō kēr') Eg. (In.)	31.18 N	30.5 E
135	Abu Qurqâs (ä'bōō kōōr-käs') Eg. (In.)	27.57 N	30.51 E
159	Aburatsu (ä'bōō-rät'sōō) Jap.	31.36 N	131.22 E
141	Abu Rueish (ä'bōō rōō'wāsh) Eg.	30.3 N	31.4 E
141	Abusir Tombs and Pyramids (ä-bōō-sēr') Eg.	29.54 N	31.12 E

Page	Name Pronunciation Region	Lat. °′	Long. °′
135	Abû Tîg ä'bōō tēg') Eg. (In.)	27.3 N	31.20 E
163	Abuyog (ä-bōō'yôg) P. I.	10.44 N	125.0 E
120	Åby Klippan (ô'bü klĭp'pän) Swe.	56.9 N	13.20 E
	Abyssinia (Ethiopia) (see Italian East Africa)		
139	Abyssinia, Plateau of	8.0 N	38.0 E
86	Acadia National Park (ȧ-kā'dĭ-ȧ) Me.	44.20 N	68.15 W
94	Acajutla (ä-kä-hōōt'lä) Sal.	13.37 N	89.50 W
92	Acámbaro (ä-käm'bä-rō) Mex.	20.2 N	100.42 W
92	Acapetlahuaya (ä-kä-pĕt'lä-hwä'-yä) Mex.	18.18 N	100.9 W
92	Acaponeta (ä-kä-pô-nā'tȧ) Mex.	22.30 N	105.23 W
92	Acaponeta, R. Mex.	22.40 N	105.21 W
92	Acapulco (ä-kä-pōōl'kō) Mex.	16.51 N	99.56 W
103	Acarahu (ä-kä-rä'ōō) Braz.	3.0 S	42.0 W
103	Acarahy Mts. (ä-kä-rä'ê) Br. Gu.-Braz.	1.30 N	58.0 W
92	Acatlán de Osorio (ä-kät-län'dä ô-sō'rē-ō) Mex.	18.12 N	98.3 W
52	Acattu I. (ä-kä'tū) Alsk.	52.30 N	173.30 E
92	Acatzingo de Hidalgo (ä-kät-zĭŋ'-gō dä ê-dhäl'gō) Mex.	18.59 N	97.48 W
93	Acayucan (ä-kä-yōō'kän) Mex.	17.56 N	94.55 W
84	Accoville (ăk'kô-vĭl) W. Va.	37.47 N	81.50 W
138	Accra (ă'krȧ) G. C.	5.37 N	0.10 W
118	Accrington (ăk'rĭng-tŭn) Gt. Brit.	53.45 N	2.21 W
135	Acebuche, Pt. (ä-thä-bōō'chä) Sp. (Gibraltar In.)	36.3 N	5.33 E
102	Achacachi (ä-chä-kä'chê) Bol.	17.0 S	68.44 W
115	Achdar, Jebel (Mt.) (jĕb'ĕl ăch-där') Libya	32.25 N	22.0 E
301	Acheng (ä'chĕng') Manch.	45.32 N	127.2 E
125	Achères (ä-shâr') Fr. (In.)	48.57 N	2.4 E
116	Achill (ă-chĭl') Ire.	53.55 N	9.55 W
116	Achill I. Ire.	54.0 N	10.0 W
148	Achinsk (ȧ-chênsk') Sov. Un.	56.10 N	90.25 E
135	Achkel, L. (äsh-kĕl') Tun. (In.)	37.8 N	9.43 E
129	Aci Abad (Maidos) (ăd'zhê ȧ'bad) (mȧ'dôs) Tur.	40.11 N	26.21 E
128	Acireale (ä-chê-rȧ-ä'lä) It.	37.36 N	15.9 E
97	Acklin I. (ăk'lĭn) Ba. Is.	22.29 N	73.55 W
73	Acmar (ăk'mȧr) Ala. (Birmingham In.)	33.37 N	86.30 W
104	Aconcagua, Mt. (ä-kôn-kä'gwä) Arg.	32.40 S	71.0 W
99	Aconcagua, R. Chl. (Valparaiso In.)	32.47 S	7.1 W
93	Acopilco (ä-kô-pēl'kō) Mex. (In.)	19.20 N	99.19 W
94	Acoyapa (ä-kô-yä'pä) Nic.	11.53 N	85.11 W
128	Acqui (äk'kwē) It.	44.40 N	8.30 E
102	Acre (State) (ä'krä) Braz.	9.0 S	70.30 W
145	Acre, B. of (ä'kēr (ä'kēr) Pal. (In.)	32.52 N	35.2 E
145	Acre (Akko) (ä'kēr) (äk'kô) Pal. (In.)	32.57 N	35.3 E
73	Acton (ăk'tŭn) Ala. (Birmingham In.)	33.21 N	86.48 W
116	Acton Gt. Brit.	51.30 N	0.15 W
87	Acton Mass. (In.)	42.29 N	71.26 W
86	Acton Vale Que.	45.38 N	72.34 W
92	Actopan (äk-tô-pän') Mex.	20.16 N	98.57 W
104	Actura (äk-tōō'rȧ) Braz. (In.)	22.42 S	43.18 W
93	Acuahutla (ä-kwä-ōōt'lȧ) Mex. (In.)	19.21 N	98.52 W
92	Acuitzio del Canje (ä-kwēt'zē-ō dĕl kän'hä) Mex.	19.30 N	101.12 W
97	Acul B. (ä-kōōl') Hai.	19.45 N	72.20 W
138	Ada (ä'dȧ) G. C.	5.52 N	0.32 E
76	Ada Minn.	47.18 N	96.30 W
84	Ada Ohio	40.47 N	83.43 W
79	Ada Okla.	34.45 N	96.43 W
129	Ada (ŏ'dŏ) Yugo.	45.48 N	20.8 E
52	Adak I. (ă-dăk') Alsk.	51.40 N	176.35 W
113	Adalia (Antalya) (ä-dä'lē-ä) (än-täl'yä) Tur.	36.55 N	30.50 E
138	Adamawa (Reg.) (ä-dȧ-mä'wä) Cam.	8.30 N	12.30 E
167	Adaminaby (ă-dȧ-mĭ'nȧ-bĭ) Austl.	36.3 S	148.41 E
80	Adamo, R. (ä-dä'mō) Mex.	26.30 N	99.30 W
86	Adams (ăd'ămz) Mass.	42.35 N	73.10 W
77	Adams Wis.	43.55 N	89.48 W
151	Adams Bridge India-Cey. (Cey. In.)	9.10 N	79.30 E
53	Adams, Mt. Alsk.	55.55 N	130.30 W
70	Adams, Mt. Wash.	46.12 N	121.30 W
169	Adamson Peak (ăd'ăm-sŭn) Austl. (Tas. In.)	43.21 S	146.50 E
85	Adamstown W. Va.	39.18 N	80.2 W
73	Adamsville Ala. (Birmingham In.)	33.36 N	86.57 W
113	Adana (ä'dä-nä) Tur.	37.0 N	35.20 E
113	Adapazari (ä'dä-pä-zä'rê) Tur.	40.45 N	30.15 E
139	Adarama (ä-dä-rä'mä) A. E. Sud.	17.10 N	34.58 E
128	Adda R. (äd'dä) It.	45.36 N	9.30 E
150	Ad Dam (äd däm') Sau. Ar.	20.35 N	44.38 E
171	Adderley Head (ăd-ēr-lĭ hĕd') N. Z. (In.)	43.36 S	172.51 E
139	Addis Abeba (äd'dĭs ä'bĕ-bä) It. E. Afr.	9.2 N	38.49 E
143	Addo (ăd'dô) U. S. Afr.	33.32 S	25.41 E
89	Addyston (ăd'ê-stŭn) Ohio (Cincinnati In.)	39.9 N	84.43 W
82	Adel (ā-dĕl') Ga.	31.7 N	83.27 W
166	Adelaide (ăd'ê-lăd) Austl.	34.55 S	138.36 E
166	Adelaide Austl. (In.)		
143	Adelaide U. S. Afr.	32.42 S	26.19 E
49	Adelaide Wash. (In.)	47.19 N	122.22 W
46	Adelaide I. Ant. O.	67.0 S	69.0 W
46	Adélie Land (Reg.) (ȧ-dȧ-lē') Ant.	66.0 S	140.0 E
167	Adelong (ăd-ê-lông') Austl.	35.19 S	148.5 E
150	Aden (ä'dĕn) Aden	12.45 N	45.5 E
150	Aden Asia	14.30 N	47.0 E
150	Aden, G. of Asia	12.0 N	47.0 E

Page	Name Pronunciation Region	Lat. °′	Long. °′
143	Adendorp (ä'dĕn-dôrp) U. S. Afr.	32.19 S	24.32 E
128	Aderno (ä-dĕr-nô') It.	37.40 N	14.50 E
73	Adger (ăj'ēr) Ala. (Birmingham In.)	33.23 N	87.5 W
161	Adi I. (ä'dē) Neth. Ind.	4.15 S	133.30 E
139	Adi Caieh (ä'dê kī'ä) It. E. Afr.	14.50 N	39.20 E
149	Adicha R. (ä'dĭ-chȧ) Sov. Un.	66.0 N	136.30 E
128	Adige R. (ä'dê-jä) It.	45.40 N	10.54 E
113	Adige (Cherkess) (Reg.) (ä'dĭ-gä) Sov. Un.	45.0 N	40.5 E
57	Adirondack Junction Can. (Montreal In.)	45.24 N	73.39 W
85	Adirondack Mts. (ăd-ĭ-rŏn'dăk) N. Y.	43.40 N	74.30 W
112	Adisko (ä-dēs'kō) Swe.	68.30 N	18.55 E
139	Adi Ugri (ä-dē ōō'grē) It. E. Afr.	14.50 N	38.58 E
138	Adjjer (Tassili) Plat. (ä'jĕr tȧs'ê-lê) Alg.	26.0 N	7.0 E
138	Adjir (ăd-jēr') Sp. Mor.	35.10 N	3.55 W
123	Adjud (äd'zhōōd) Rom.	46.5 N	27.8 E
171	Admiralty B. (ăd'mĭ rȧl-tê) N. Z.	40.50 S	174.0 E
49	Admiralty Inlet Wash. (In.)	48.5 N	122.40 W
53	Admiralty I. Alsk.	57.40 N	135.30 W
161	Admiralty Is. N. Gui. Ter.	2.0 S	147.0 E
99	Admiralty Sd. Chl. (Magallanes In.)	54.20 S	69.30 W
124	Adour R. (ȧ-dōōr') Fr.	43.45 N	1.15 W
126	Adouz (ȧ-dōōz') Mor.	35.11 N	4.9 W
126	Adra (ä'drä) Sp.	36.46 N	3.1 W
138	Adrar (ä-drär') Alg.	27.55 N	0.19 W
138	Adrar (Reg.) Fr. W. Afr.-Alg.	20.30 N	2.0 E
128	Adria (ä'drê-ä) It.	45.4 N	12.8 E
84	Adrian (ā'drĭ-ăn) Mich.	41.55 N	84.3 W
76	Adrian Minn.	43.38 N	95.55 W
113	Adrianople (Edirne) (ā-drĭ-ăn-ō'pl) (ĕ-dĭr'nĕ)) Tur.	41.40 N	26.35 E
128	Adriatic Sea (ā-drĭ-ăt'ĭk) It.-Yugo.	42.50 N	15.40 E
139	Adua (ä'dōō-ä) It. E. Afr.	14.6 N	39.0 E
169	Adventure B. Austl. (Tas. In.)	43.18 S	147.35 E
118	Adwick-le-Street (ăd'wĭk-lê-strēt') Gt. Brit.	53.34 N	1.11 W
131	Adzhamka (äd-zhäm'kȧ) Sov. Un.	48.33 N	32.26 E
113	Adzharistan (Reg.) (äd-zhär'ĭ-stän) Sov. Un.	41.45 N	42.15 E
112	Adzva R. (ädz'vä) Sov. Un	67.0 N	59.45 E
128	Aegadian (Egadi) Is. (ê-gā'dĭ-ăn) (ä'gä-dē) It.	38.55 N	12.20 E
113	Aegean Is. Medit. Sea	36.30 N	27.0 E
129	Aegean Sea (ê-jē'ăn) Gr.-Tur.	39.0 N	24.50 E
129	Aegina, G. of (Saronic G.) (ê-jī'nȧ) Gr.	37.35 N	23.40 E
129	Aegina (I.) Gr.	37.45 N	23.30 E
120	Aerö (I.) (âr'ö) Den.	54.48 N	10.25 E
119	Aertselaer (ärt'sĕ-lär) Bel. (Anvers In.)	51.8 N	4.23 E
103	Affonso Penna (ä-fōn'sōō pĕn'nȧ) Braz. (In.)	12.50 S	39.15 W
89	Affton (ăf'tŭn) Mo. (St. Louis In.)	38.33 N	90.20 W
150	Afghanistan (ăf-găn-ĭ-stăn') Asia	33.0 N	65.0 E
141	Afgoi (äf-gô'ĭ) It. E. Afr.	2.5 N	45.5 E
150	Afladj (Reg.) (ä-flädj') Nejd	24.0 N	46.0 E
138	Aflou (ä flōō') Alg.	34.2 N	2.2 E
53	Afognak I. (ä-fŏg-năk') Alsk.	58.15 N	152.30 W
134	Africa (ăf'rĭ-kȧ)		
79	Afton (ăf'tŭn) Okla.	36.41 N	94.56 W
113	Afyon-Karahisar (ä-fê-ōn-kä-rȧ-hê-sär') Tur.	38.45 N	30.20 E
139	Agedabia (ä-gä-dä'bê-ä) Libya	30.45 N	20.15 E
139	Agadem (Oasis) (ä'gȧ-dĕm) Fr. W. Afr.	16.52 N	13.15 E
138	Agadez (ä'gȧ-dĕz) Fr. W. Afr.	17.0 N	7.58 E
138	Agadir (ä-gȧ-dēr') Mor.	30.30 N	9.33 W
131	Agaiman (ä-gä-ê-män') Sov. Un.	46.40 N	34.16 E
6	Agaña (ä-gän'yȧ) Guam. (In.)	13.23 N	144.45 E
72	Agassiz (ăg'ȧ-sê) Can. (Vancouver In.)	49.14 N	121.46 W
113	Agdam (ăg'dăm) Sov. Un.	39.59 N	46.58 E
124	Agde (ägd) Fr.	43.20 N	3.30 E
124	Agen (ȧ-zhäN') Fr.	44.12 N	0.35 E
129	Agiassos (ĭ'yä-sŏs) Grc.	39.5 N	26.22 E
149	Aginskoe (ä-hĭn'skô-yĕ) Sov. Un.	51.15 N	114.59 E
163	Agio Pt. (ä-jē'ō) P. I.	9.43 N	124.32 E
149	Aion I. (ä'yŏn) Sov. Un.	69.50 N	168.50 E
128	Agira (ä-jē'rä) It.	37.39 N	14.31 E
162	Agno (äg'nō) P. I.	16.8 N	119.48 E
162	Agno R. P. I.	15.47 N	120.20 E
128	Agnone (än-yō'nä) It.	41.48 N	14.22 E
162	Agoo (ä'gōō) P. I.	16.19 N	120.22 E
139	Agordat (ä-gōr'dät) It. E. Afr.	15.33 N	37.58 E
161	Agos R. (ä'gōs) P. I. (Manila In.)	14.47 N	121.37 E
124	Agout (ȧ-gōō') Fr.	43.40 N	2.0 E
151	Agra (ä'grä) Ind.	27.10 N	78.8 E
	Agram, see Zagreb, Yugo.		
128	Agri R. (ä'grē) It.	40.16 N	16.10 E
129	Agrinion (ä-grē'nyôn) Grc.	38.37 N	21.26 E
94	Agua (Vol.) (ä'gwä) Guat.	14.28 N	90.44 W
74	Agua Calienta Ind. Res. (ä'gwä käl yĕn'tä) Calif.	33.50 N	116.32 W
95	Agua Caliente (ä'gwä kä-lyĕn'tä) Nic.	12.10 N	84.37 W
96	Aguada (ä-gwä'dä) Cuba	22.25 N	80.48 W
91	Aguadilla (ä-gwä-dēl'yä) P. R. (In.)	18.25 N	67.15 W
95	Aguadulce (ä-gwä-dōōl'sä) Pan.	8.15 N	80.32 W
75	Agua Fria R. (ä'gwä frē'ȧ) Ariz.	33.45 N	112.18 W
80	Agualegnas (ä-gwä lān'yäs) Mex.	26.18 N	99.33 W
94	Aguan, R. (ä-gwän') Hond.	15.34 N	86.10 W
80	Aguanaval, R. (ä-guä-nä-väl') Mex.	25.0 N	103.15 W
87	Aguanus R. (ä'gwȧ-nŭs) Que.	50.50 N	62.5 W
92	Aguascalientes (ä'gwäs-käl-yĕn'täs) Mex.	21.52 N	102.17 W

Page	Name Pronunciation Region	Lat. °′	Long. °′
92	Aguascalientes (State) Mex.	22.0 N	102.30 W
126	Agueda (ä-gwā'dȧ) Port.	40.35 N	8.25 W
126	Agueda R. Sp.-Port.	40.40 N	6.40 W
138	Aguellal (ä-gĕl-yäl') Fr. W. Afr.	19.12 N	8.15 E
78	Aguilar (ä-gê-lär') Colo.	37.24 N	104.39 W
126	Aguilar Sp.	37.31 N	4.39 W
126	Aguilas (ä'gê-läs) Sp.	37.25 N	1.35 W
102	Aguja Pt. (ä-gōō'hä) Peru	5.58 S	81.10 W
142	Agulhas, C. (ä-gōōl'yȧs) U. S. Afr.	34.50 S	20.0 E
160	Agung, Mt. (ä-gōōng') Neth. Ind.	8.28 S	115.22 E
163	Agusan Marsh (ä-gōō'sän) P. I.	8.15 N	125.50 E
163	Agusan R. P. I.	8.40 N	125.37 E
163	Agutaya I. (ä-gōō-tä'yä) P. I.	11.9 N	120.58 E
129	Agyia (äī-yä') Grc.	39.41 N	22.45 E
138	Ahaggar Mts. (ȧ-hä-gär') Alg.	23.30 N	6.30 E
170	Ahipara B. (ä-hī-pä'rȧ) N. Z.	35.5 S	173.5 E
122	Ahlen (ä'lĕn) Ger.	51.46 N	7.53 E
135	Ahmar, Jebel (Mts.) (jĕb'ĕl ä'-mär) Eg. (In.)	28.5 N	31.30 E
151	Ahmedabad (ŭ-mĕd-ä-bäd') Ind.	23.0 N	72.44 E
83	Ahoskie (ā-hŏs'kē) N. C.	36.17 N	76.59 W
119	Ahrensburg (ä'rĕns-bōōrg) Ger. (Hamburg In.)	53.40 N	10.13 E
122	Ahrweiler (är'vī-lĕr) Ger.	50.34 N	7.3 E
92	Ahuacatlan (ä-wä-kät-län') Mex.	21.5 N	104.27 W
94	Ahuachapan (ä-wä-chä-pän') Sal.	13.57 N	89.52 W
92	Ahualulco (ä-wä-lōōl'kō) Mex.	20.43 N	103.58 W
120	Åhus (ô'hōōs) Swe.	55.56 N	14.19 E
121	Ahvenanmaa (Åland Is.) (ä'vĕ-nän-mô) (ô'lănd) Fin.	60.20 N	20.0 E
131	Aidar (ä'ī-där) Sov. Un.	50.2 N	38.52 E
131	Aidar R. Sov. Un.	49.8 N	38.56 E
173	Aiea (äē'ä) Haw.	21.20 N	157.55 W
129	Aigina (ä-yē'nä) Grc.	37.45 N	23.26 E
129	Aigion (ä'yôn) Grc.	38.14 N	22.5 E
124	Aiguesmortes (ĕg'-môrt) Fr.	43.35 N	4.10 E
153	Aigun (ī-gōōn') Manch.	49.50 N	127.28 E
158	Aikawa (ī-kä'wä) Jap.	38.0 N	138.25 E
83	Aiken (ā'kĕn) S. C.	33.34 N	81.44 W
159	Aina (ī'nä) Jap. (Osaka In.)	34.45 N	135.6 E
138	Aïn Beida (ä'ēn bā'ē-dä) Alg.	35.51 N	7.27 E
138	Aïn Sefra (ä'ēn sĕf'rä) Alg.	32.50 N	0.40 W
87	Ainsle, L. (ăn'slē) Can.	46.10 N	61.10 W
76	Ainsworth (ānz'wûrth) Neb.	42.33 N	99.51 W
114	Aïn Taïba (ä'ēn tä'ē-bä) Alg.	30.21 N	5.28 E
114	Aïn Temouchent (ä'ēn tĕ-mōō-shäN') Alg.	35.18 N	1.8 W
138	Aïr (Asben) (Reg.) (ä'ēr) (äs'bĕn) Fr. W. Afr.	18.35 N	9.0 E
152	Airan Köl (L.) (ä'ē-rän kûl') Chn.	45.35 N	85.20 E
129	Airbol (ä-ēr-bôl') Tur.	41.12 N	27.6 E
124	Aire (âr) Fr.	43.41 N	0.18 W
124	Aire Fr.	50.41 N	2.22 E
118	Aire R. Gt. Brit.	53.50 N	1.42 W
167	Airlands (âr'lănds) Austl.	30.43 S	149.35 E
156	Ai Shan (Mt.) (ī'shän') Chn.	37.31 N	120.40 E
124	Aisne R. (ăn) Fr.	49.25 N	3.20 E
161	Aitape (ä-ē-tä'pā) N. Gui. Ter.	3.12 S	142.10 E
77	Aitkin (āt'kĭn) Minn.	46.32 N	93.42 W
129	Aitolikon (ā-tō'lĭ-kŏn) Grc.	38.27 N	21.22 E
129	Aitos (ä-ē'tōs) Bul.	42.41 N	27.18 E
129	Aiud (ä'ē-ŏŏd) Rom.	46.20 N	23.42 E
125	Aix (ĕks) Fr.	43.32 N	5.28 E
	Aix-la-Chapelle, see Aachen, Ger.		
125	Aix-les-Bains (ĕks'-lā-băN') Fr.	45.41 N	5.59 E
135	Aiyât (ä-ē-yät') Eg. (In.)	29.38 N	31.18 E
121	Aizpute (ä'ēz-pōō-tĕ) Lat.	56.44 N	21.40 E
124	Ajaccio (ä-yät'chō) Cor. (In.)	41.55 N	8.42 E
124	Ajaccio, G. of Cor. (In.)	41.55 N	8.40 E
93	Ajalpan (ä-häl'pän) Mex.	18.21 N	97.15 W
71	Ajax Mt. (ā'jăks) Mont.-Ida.	45.18 N	113.43 W
139	Ajilat (ä'jē-lät) Libya	32.41 N	12.28 E
145	Ajloun (äj-lōōn') Transj. (In.)	32.21 N	35.41 E
151	Ajmer (ŭj-mēr') India.	26.31 N	74.32 E
75	Ajo (ä'hō) Ariz.	32.22 N	112.53 W
92	Ajuchitlán del Progreso (ä-hōō-chet-län') Mex.	18.2 N	100.20 W
163	Ajuy (äj-wē') P. I.	11.9 N	123.2 E
113	Ak L. (äk) Tur.	37.30 N	33.45 E
171	Akaroa (ä-kä-rō'ä) N. Z.	43.57 S	172.58 E
171	Akaroa Har. N. Z.	43.50 S	172.57 E
138	Akasa (ä-käs'ä) Nig.	4.27 N	6.2 E
159	Akashi (ä'kä-shē) Jap.	34.40 N	135.2 E
159	Akashi Str. (ä'kä-shē) Jap. (Osaka In.)	34.38 N	135.0 E
139	Aketi (ä-kä-tē') Bel. Cong.	2.46 N	24.0 E
113	Akhaltsikh (ä-käl-tsēk') Sov. Un.	41.38 N	42.58 E
129	Akheloos R. (ä-hĕ'lō-ōs) Grc.	39.0 N	21.25 E
131	Akhiar (Sevastopol) (äk'yär) (syĕ-väs'tō-pôl') Sov. Un.	44.35 N	33.32 E
129	Akhinou L. (ä-kē'-nōō) Grc.	40.55 N	23.40 E
113	Akhisar (äk-hĭs-sär') Tur.	38.58 N	27.57 E
139	Akhmîm (äk-mēm') Eg.	26.40 N	31.48 E
131	Akhtarskii B. (äk-tär'skĭ-ĕ) Sov. Un.	45.53 N	38.16 E
129	Akhtopol (äk'tō-pōl) Bul.	42.6 N	27.53 E
131	Akhtyrka (äk-tür'kä) Sov. Un.	50.18 N	34.52 E
131	Akhtyrskaya (äk-tür' skä-yȧ) Sov. Un.	44.52 N	38.11 E
159	Aki (ä'kē) Jap.	33.30 N	133.50 E
52	Akiak (äk'yäk) Alsk.	61.0 N	161.30 W
55	Akimiski I. (ä-kĭ-mĭ'skĭ) Can.	53.0 N	81.30 W
158	Akita (ä'kē-tä) Jap.	39.45 N	140.10 E
	Akkerman, see Cetatea Alba, Rom.		
145	Akko (Acre) (äk'kō) (ä'kĕr) Pal. (In.)	32.57 N	35.3 E
53	Aklavik (äk'lä-vĭk) Can.	68.20 N	135.30 W
131	Ak-Mechet (äk-mĕ'ch-ĕt) Sov. Un.	45.30 N	32.39 E
148	Ak-Mechet (Kzyl-Orda) (kzêl'-ôr'-dä) Sov. Un.	44.50 N	65.30 E
131	Akmechet (Simferopol) (sêm-fĕ-rô'-pôl') Sov. Un.	44.57 N	34.4 E
148	Akmolinsk (äk'mô-lênsk) Sov. Un.	51.15 N	71.25 E
159	Ako (ä'kô) Jap.	34.45 N	134.21 E
139	Akobo R. (ä-kô'bô) A. E. Sud.	7.0 N	34.30 E
151	Akola (ȧ-kō'lä) India	20.40 N	77.0 E
55	Akpatok I. (äk'pȧ-tŏk) Can.	60.30 N	68.0 W
78	Akron (ăk'rŭn) Colo.	40.8 N	103.13 W
84	Akron Ohio	41.5 N	81.30 W
113	Aksaray (äk-sȧ-rī') Tur.	38.25 N	34.5 E
113	Akşehir (äk'shȧ-hēr) Tur.	38.28 N	31.20 E
113	Akşehir L. Tur.	38.33 N	31.30 E
149	Aksha (äk'shȧ) Sov. Un.	50.20 N	113.25 E
148	Aktyubinsk (äk'tyōō-bĕnsk) Sov. Un.	50.15 N	57.20 E
110	Akureyri (ä-kōō-rä'rē) Ice.	65.40 N	18.14 W
159	Akutagawa (ä-kōō'tȧ-gä'wä) Jap. (Osaka In.)	34.53 N	135.37 E
52	Akutan Pass (ä-kōō-tän') Alsk.	54.0 N	166.0 W
151	Akyab (äk-yŭb') India	20.15 N	92.55 E
163	Ala R. (ä'lä) P. I.	6.30 N	124.33 E
82	Alabama (State) (ăl-ȧ-băm'ȧ) U. S.	32.45 N	86.45 W
82	Alabama R. Ala.	32.5 N	87.20 W
82	Alabama City Ala.	34.1 N	86.3 W
161	Alabang (ä-lä-băng') P. I. (Manila In.)	14.27 N	121.3 E
162	Alabat I. (ä-lä-bät') P. I.	14.7 N	122.4 E
113	Alaçam (ä-lä-chäm') Tur.	41.35 N	35.40 E
96	Alacranes (ä-lä-krä'nås) Cuba	22.42 N	81.35 W
103	Alagôas (State) (ä-lä-gō'äzh) Braz.	9.30 S	37.0 W
103	Alagoinhas (ä-lä-gō-ēn'yäzh) Braz. (In.)	12.7 S	38.18 W
126	Alagón (ä-lä-gōn') Sp.	41.47 N	1.8 W
126	Alagón R. Sp.	40.0 N	6.17 W
113	Alaiye (ä-lī'yä) Tur.	36.35 N	32.5 E
148	Ala Kul (L.) (ä'lä-kûl') Sov. Un.	46.20 N	82.0 E
149	Alaikha (ä-lī'kȧ) Sov. Un.	70.30 N	148.59 E
95	Alajuela (ä-lä-hwā'lä) C. R.	10.1 N	84.13 W
173	Alalakeiki Chan. (ä-lä-lä-kā'kē) Haw.	20.35 N	156.30 W
74	Alameda (ăl-ȧ-mā'dȧ) Calif.	37.46 N	122.15 W
71	Alameda Ida.	42.51 N	112.37 W
93	Alameda Mex. (In.)	19.32 N	99.19 W
162	Alaminos (ä-lä-mē'nōs) P. I.	16.10 N	119.58 E
161	Alaminos P. I. (Manila In.)	14.5 N	121.15 E
75	Alamogordo (ăl-ȧ-mō-gôr'dō) N. M.	32.54 N	105.58 W
78	Alamogordo Reservoir N. M.	34.35 N	104.20 W
78	Alamosa (ăl-ȧ-mō'sȧ) Colo.	37.27 N	105.51 W
121	Aland (Ahvenanmaa) Is. (ô'lănd) (ä'vĕ-nän-mô) Fin.	60.38 N	20.0 E
163	Alangalang (ä-läŋ-gä-läng') P. I.	11.12 N	124.50 E
171	Alaotra, L. (ä-lä-ō'trȧ) Madag.	16.25 S	48.35 E
148	Alapaevsk (ä'lä-pȧ-yĕfsk') Sov. Un.	57.57 N	61.57 E
92	Alaquines (ȧ-lȧ-kē'nås) Mex.	22.8 N	99.35 W
152	Ala Shan (Mts.) (ä'lä-shän') Chn.	39.0 N	105.45 E
53	Alaska (Ter.) (ȧ-lăs'kȧ) N. A.	65.0 N	150.0 W
53	Alaska, G. of Alsk.	58.30 N	145.0 W
53	Alaska Pen. Alsk.	57.0 N	158.0 W
53	Alaska Ra. (Mts.) Alsk.	62.40 N	150.30 W
112	Alatyr (ä'lä-tür) Sov. Un.	54.48 N	46.35 E
166	Alawoona Station (ȧ-lȧ-wōō'nȧ) Austl.	34.45 S	140.32 E
128	Alba (äl'bä) It.	44.40 N	8.2 E
126	Albacete (äl-bä-thā'tā) Sp.	39.0 N	1.50 W
166	Albacutya, L. (äl-bȧ-kŭt'yȧ) Austl.	35.45 S	141.57 E
126	Alba de Tormes (äl'bä dä tôr'mås) Sp.	40.49 N	5.29 W
123	Alba Iulia (äl'bä yōō'lyä) Rom.	46.6 N	23.34 E
127	Albalate (äl-bä-lä'tā) Sp.	41.7 N	0.31 W
129	Albania (ăl-bā'nĭ-ȧ) Eur.	41.0 N	20.0 E
128	Albano Laziale (äl-bä'nō lät-zē-ä'lä) It.	41.43 N	12.38 E
82	Albany (ôl'bȧ-nĭ) Ala.	34.34 N	86.59 W
164	Albany Austl.	34.57 S	117.58 E
82	Albany Ga.	31.35 N	84.11 W
79	Albany Mo.	40.15 N	94.20 W
85	Albany N. Y.	42.42 N	73.46 W
70	Albany Ore.	44.38 N	123.6 W
80	Albany Tex.	32.43 N	99.18 W
55	Albany R. Can.	51.28 N	86.30 W
162	Albay G. (äl-bä'ē) P. I.	13.10 N	124.0 E
81	Albemarle (ăl'bē-märl) La.	29.53 N	91.2 W
83	Albemarle N. C.	35.23 N	80.11 W
83	Albemarle Sd. N. C.	36.0 N	76.0 W
128	Albenga (äl-bĕŋ'gä) It.	44.3 N	8.12 E
126	Alberche R. (äl-bĕr'chā) Sp.	40.20 N	4.15 W
164	Alberga (R.) (ăl-bûr'gȧ) Austl.	27.0 S	135.0 E
126	Albergaria-a-Velha (äl-bĕr-gä-rē'ȧ-ȧ-väl'yȧ) Port.	40.41 N	8.29 W
73	Alberhill (ăl'bĕr-hĭl) Calif. (Los Angeles In.)	33.44 N	117.23 W
124	Albert (äl-bâr') Fr.	50.0 N	2.40 E
86	Albert (ăl'bērt) N. B.	45.45 N	64.44 W
166	Albert, L. Austl.	35.35 S	139.18 E
139	Albert, L. (ăl'bērt) (äl-bâr')) Bel. Cong.-Ug.	1.45 N	30.50 E
170	Albert, Mt. N. Z. (In.)	36.54 S	174.43 E
54	Alberta (Prov.) (ăl-bûr'tȧ) Can.	54.15 N	115.0 W
161	Albert Edward, Mt. (ăl'bērt ĕd'wērd) Pap. Ter.	8.25 S	147.15 E
77	Albert Lea (ăl'bērt lē') Minn.	43.39 N	93.21 W
46	Albert Markham, Mt. (märk'ăm) Ant.	81.0 S	160.0 E
167	Alberton (ăl'bēr-tŭn) Austl.	38.37 S	146.39 E
169	Alberton Austl. (In.)	27.41 S	153.15 E
86	Alberton P. E. I.	46.50 N	64.4 W
82	Albertville (ăl'bērt-vĭl) Ala.	34.17 N	86.12 W
140	Albertville (äl-bêr-vēl') Bel. Cong.	5.55 S	29.12 E
125	Albertville Fr.	45.40 N	6.28 E
124	Albi (äl-bē') Fr.	43.55 N	2.10 E
77	Albia (ăl'bĭ-ȧ) Ia.	41.1 N	92.48 W
79	Albia Ia.	41.1 N	92.49 W
103	Albina (äl-bē'nä) Sur.	5.29 N	54.2 W
84	Albion (ăl'bĭ-ŭn) Mich.	42.16 N	84.50 W
76	Albion Neb.	41.42 N	98.0 W
85	Albion N. Y.	43.15 N	78.12 W
135	Alboasa, Pt. (äl-bō-ä'sä) Sp. Mor. (Gibraltar In.)	35.50 N	5.19 E
126	Alborán I. (äl-bō-rän') Sp.	35.58 N	3.0 W
126	Albox (äl-bōk') Sp.	37.23 N	2.8 W
126	Albufeira (äl-bōō-fā'ē-rȧ) Port.	37.6 N	8.15 W
126	Albuñol (äl-bōōn-yōl') Sp.	36.48 N	3.12 W
78	Albuquerque (ăl-bû-kûr'kē) N. M.	35.5 N	106.39 W
126	Albuquerque (äl-boo-kĕr'kä) Sp.	39.14 N	7.0 W
95	Albuquerque Cays (Is.) (ăl-bû-kûr'kē kāz') W. I.	12.12 N	81.50 W
165	Albury (ôl'bēr-ē) Austl.	35.59 S	146.59 E
167	Albury Austl.	36.5 S	146.55 E
127	Alcabideche (äl-kȧ-bē-dā'chȧ) Port. (In.)	38.43 N	9.24 W
126	Alcácer do Sal (äl-kä'sĕr dōō säl') Port.	38.22 N	8.31 W
162	Alcala (äl-kä-lä') P. I.	17.56 N	121.39 E
126	Alcalá Sp.	37.21 N	5.50 W
127	Alcalá de Chivert (äl-kä-lä' dä chē-vĕrt') Sp.	40.18 N	0.12 E
127	Alcalá de Henares (äl-kä-lä'dä ā nä'räs) Sp. (In.)	40.29 N	3.22 W
126	Alcalá de los Gazules (äl-kä-lä'dä lōs gä thōō'läs) Sp.	36.29 N	5.43 W
126	Alcalá la Real (äl-kä-lä'lä rā-äl') Sp.	37.27 N	3.55 W
128	Alcamo (äl'kä-mō) It.	37.57 N	12.58 E
127	Alcanadre R. (äl-kä-nä'drā) Sp.	41.45 N	0.10 W
127	Alcanar (äl-kä-när') Sp.	40.34 N	0.29 E
127	Alcañiz (äl-kän-yēth') Sp.	41.4 N	0.8 W
103	Alcantara (äl-kän'tȧ-rȧ) Braz.	2.27 S	44.28 W
104	Alcantara Braz. (In.)	22.48 S	43.2 W
126	Alcaraz (äl-kä-räth') Sp.	38.39 N	2.29 W
126	Alcaudete (äl-kou-dhā'tā) Sp.	37.35 N	4.5 W
114	Alcázar (äl-kä'thär) Mor.	35.0 N	5.47 W
135	Alcázar, Pt. Sp. Mor. (Gibraltar In.)	35.50 N	5.27 E
126	Alcázar de San Juan (äl-kä'thär dä sän hwän') Sp.	39.23 N	3.12 W
118	Alcester (ôl'stēr) Gt. Brit.	52.13 N	1.52 W
162	Alchan, Mt. (äl-chän') P. I.	17.15 N	121.0 E
127	Alcira (äl-thē'rä) Sp.	39.9 N	0.26 W
82	Alcoa (ăl-kō'ȧ) Tenn.	35.46 N	84.0 W
103	Alcobaça (äl-kō-bä'sä) Braz.	3.33 S	49.34 W
127	Alcobendas (äl-kō-bĕn'däs) Sp. (In.)	40.31 N	3.39 W
127	Alcochete (äl-kō-chä'tä) Port. (In.)	38.45 N	8.58 W
73	Alcony R. (ăl-kō'nē) Ga. (Atlanta In.)	33.25 N	83.50 W
127	Alcora (äl-kō'rä) Sp.	40.6 N	0.13 W
127	Alcorcón (äl-kôr-kōn') Sp. (In.)	40.21 N	3.50 W
127	Alcorisa (äl-kō-rē'sä) Sp.	40.55 N	0.19 W
71	Alcova Reservoir (ăl-kō'vȧ) Wyo.	42.35 N	106.45 W
127	Alcoy (äl-koi') Sp.	38.42 N	0.27 W
127	Alcudia B. (äl-kōō-dhē'ä) Sp.	39.45 N	3.15 E
141	Aldabra Is. (äl-dä'brä) Ind. O.	9.20 S	46.20 E
92	Aldama (äl-dä'mä) Mex.	22.56 N	98.3 W
80	Aldama Mex.	28.50 N	105.53 W
149	Aldan Plat. (äl-dän') Sov. Un.	58.0 N	134.0 E
149	Aldan R. Sov. Un.	61.50 N	135.20 E
149	Aldanskoe (äl-dän'skô-yĕ) Sov. Un.	61.45 N	135.20 E
126	Aldeia Gallega do Ribatejo (äl-dā'-yȧ gä-lä'gȧ dōō rē-bä-tā'hōō) Port.	38.42 N	8.58 W
88	Aldene (ôl'dēn) N. J. (N. Y. In.)	40.40 N	74.16 W
72	Aldergrove (ôl'dĕr-grōv) Can. (Vancouver In.)	49.3 N	122.28 W
119	Alderley Edge (ôl'dēr-lē ĕj') Gt. Brit. (Liverpool In.)	53.18 N	2.14 W
170	Aldermen, The (Is.) (ôl'dēr-mĕn) N. Z.	36.57 S	176.7 E
124	Alderney (I.) (ôl'dēr-nĭ) Gt. Brit.	49.41 N	2.11 W
116	Aldershot (ôl'dēr-shŏt) Gt. Brit.	51.15 N	0.50 W
85	Alderson (ôl-dēr-sŭn) W. Va.	37.43 N	80.39 W
166	Aldinga B. (ôl-dĭŋ'gȧ) Austl.	35.20 S	138.22 E
79	Aledo (ȧ-lē'dō) Ill.	41.12 N	90.44 W
138	Aleg (ä-lĕg') Fr. W. Afr.	17.10 N	14.0 W
104	Alegrete (ä-lä-grä'tā) Braz.	29.45 S	55.51 W
163	Alegria (ä-lä-grē'ä) P. I.	9.43 N	123.22 E
130	Aleksandrovsk (ȧ-lyĕk-sän'drôfsk) Sov. Un.	56.25 N	38.41 E
149	Aleksandrovsk-Sakhalinski Sov. Un.	50.55 N	142.10 E
123	Aleksandrów (ä-lĕk-sän'drōōf) Pol.	52.44 N	18.45 E
131	Alekseevka (ä-lyĕk-sä-yĕf'kȧ) Sov. Un.	50.38 N	38.40 E
130	Aleksin (ä-lyĕk-sēn) Sov. Un.	54.31 N	37.5 E
129	Aleksinac (ä-lyĕk-sē-näk') Yugo.	43.32 N	21.43 E
127	Alella (ä-läl'yä) Sp. (In.)	41.29 N	2.17 E
124	Alençon (ä-läN-sôN') Fr.	48.25 N	0.5 E
103	Alenquer (ä-lĕŋ-kĕr') Braz.	2.3 S	54.48 W
126	Alenquer Port.	39.3 N	9.1 W
126	Alentejo (Prov.) (ä-lĕŋ-tā'zhōō) Port.	38.20 N	7.35 W
173	Alenuihaha Chan. (ä'lä-nōō-ē-hä'hä) Haw.	20.25 N	156.0 W
150	Alep (Aleppo) (ä-lĕp') (ȧ-lĕp'ō) Syr.	36.0 N	37.20 E
124	Aleria (ä-lā'rĭ-ȧ) Cor. (In.)	42.5 N	9.30 E
124	Alès (ä-lĕs') Fr.	44.8 N	4.5 E
128	Alessandria (ä-lĕs-sän'drē-ä) It.	44.52 N	8.37 E
129	Alessio (Leshë) (ä-lĕs'syō) (lyĕsh) Alb.	41.47 N	19.40 E
120	Alesund (ô'lĕ-sōōn') Nor.	62.28 N	6.12 E
52	Aleutian Is. (ȧ-lū'shăn) Alsk.	52.40 N	175.0 W
52	Aleutian Troughs Pac. O.	52.0 N	170.0 W
53	Alexander Archipelago (ăl-ĕg-zăn'dēr) Alsk.	57.0 N	135.0 W
46	Alexander I. Ant. O.	69.0 S	70.0 W

ăt; finȧl; rāte; senȧte; ärm; ȧsk; sofȧ; fâre; ch-choose; dh-as th in other; bē; ēvent; bĕt; recĕnt; cratēr; g-go; gh-gutteral g; bĭt; ĭ-short neutral; rīde; K-gutteral k as ch in German ich;

Page	Name Pronunciation Region	Lat. °′	Long. °′
82	Alexander City ... Ala.	32.56 N	85.57 W
167	Alexandra (ăl-ĕg-zăn'drȧ) ... Austl.	37.11 S	145.41 E
171	Alexandra ... N. Z.	45.13 S	169.25 E
46	Alexandra Mts. ... Ant.	76.0 S	148.0 W
150	Alexandrette (ȧ-lĕg-zäN-drĕt'). Syr.	36.35 N	36.15 E
85	Alexandria (ăl-ĕg-zăn'drĭ-ȧ) .. Can.	45.17 N	74.35 W
139	Alexandria ... Eg.	31.12 N	29.52 E
84	Alexandria ... Ind.	40.17 N	85.41 W
81	Alexandria ... La.	31.18 N	92.26 W
76	Alexandria ... Minn.	45.53 N	95.21 W
129	Alexandria ... Rom.	43.57 N	25.19 E
76	Alexandria ... S. D.	43.39 N	97.44 W
143	Alexandria ... U. S. Afr.	33.40 S	26.24 E
85	Alexandria ... Va.	38.49 N	77.4 W
166	Alexandrina, L. (ăl-ĕg-zăn-drē'nȧ) Austl.	35.25 S	139.10 E
131	Alexandriya (ȧ'lyĕk-sän'drē-yȧ) Sov. Un.	48.41 N	33.9 E
129	Alexandroupolis (Dedeagats) (ȧ-lĕk-sän-drōō'pō-lĭs) (dĕ'dĕ-ȧ-gäts). Grc.	40.51 N	25.51 E
	Alexandrovka (see Vladimiro Aleksandrovskoe.)		
112	Alexandrovsk (ȧ-lyĕk-sän'drôfsk) Sov. Un.	69.4 N	33.20 E
113	Alexeevka (ȧ-lyĕk-sā-yĕf'kȧ) Sov. Un.	52.15 N	48.0 E
126	Alfaro (äl-fä'rō) ... Sp.	42.10 N	1.45 W
161	Alfonso (äl-fōn'sō) P. I. (Manila In.)	14.10 N	120.50 E
118	Alfreton (ôl'fēr-tŭn) ... Gt. Brit.	53.6 N	1.24 W
126	Algarve (Prov.) (äl-gär'vĕ) .. Port.	37.15 N	8.5 W
126	Algeciras (äl-hā-thē'räs) ... Sp.	36.7 N	5.28 W
126	Algeciras, B. of ... Sp.	36.8 N	5.25 W
127	Algemesi (äl-hā-mā-sē') ... Sp.	39.12 N	0.27 W
138	Alger (Algiers) (àl-zhā') (ăl-jērz') Alg.	36.50 N	3.0 E
138	Algeria (ăl-gē'rĭ-ȧ) ... Afr.	30.0 N	4.0 E
127	Algete (äl-hā'tā) ... Sp. (In.)	40.36 N	3.30 W
128	Alghero (Sard.) (äl-gâ'rō) ... It.	40.34 N	8.22 E
89	Algiers (ăl-jērz') La. (New Orleans In.)	29.57 N	90.3 W
138	Algiers (Alger) (ăl-jērz') (àl-zhā') Alg.	36.50 N	3.0 E
81	Algoa (ăl-gō'ȧ) ... Tex. (In.)	29.24 N	95.10 W
143	Algoa B. ... U. S. Afr.	33.50 S	25.50 E
55	Algoma (ăl-gō'mȧ) ... Can.	46.15 N	82.50 W
77	Algoma ... Wis.	44.37 N	87.28 W
77	Algona (ăl-gō'nȧ) ... Ia.	43.5 N	94.11 W
49	Algona ... Wash. (In.)	47.16 N	122.15 W
84	Algonac (ăl'gō-năk) ... Mich.	42.38 N	82.33 W
85	Algonquin Pk. (ăl-gŏn'kwĭn) .. Can.	45.50 N	78.20 W
126	Alhama (äl-hä'mä) ... Sp.	37.1 N	3.59 W
126	Alhama ... Sp.	37.54 N	1.24 W
74	Alhambra (ăl-hăm'brȧ) ... Calif.	34.5 N	118.9 W
127	Alhandra (äl-yän'drȧ) .. Port. (In.)	38.55 N	9.2 W
126	Alhaurín (ä-lou-rēn') ... Sp.	36.39 N	4.41 W
127	Alhos-Vedros (äl'yōs-vä'drōs) Port. (In.)	38.39 N	9.2 W
114	Alhucema Is. (äl-ōō-thā'mä) .. Mor.	35.15 N	4.0 W
129	Aliakmon (Vistritsa) R. (äl-ē-äk'-mōn) (vē-strĕt'sä). Grc.	40.20 N	22.10 E
127	Alicante (ä-lē-kän'tā) ... Sp.	38.21 N	0.29 W
127	Alicante, G. of ... Sp.	38.15 N	0.23 W
80	Alice (ăl'ĭs) ... Tex.	27.45 N	98.4 W
143	Alice ... U. S. Afr.	32.48 S	26.50 E
143	Alicedale (ăl'ĭs-dāl) ... U. S. Afr.	33.19 S	26.8 E
129	Alice, Point dell' (dĕl ä-lē'chä) .. It.	39.24 N	17.8 E
164	Alice Sprs. (Stuart) (ăl'ĭs) (stū'ērt) Austl.	23.38 S	133.50 E
128	Alicudi (I.) (ä-lē-kōō'dē) ... It.	38.31 N	14.22 E
151	Aligarh (ä-lē-gŭr') ... India	27.45 N	78.15 E
163	Alimpaya Pt. (ä-lēm-pä'yä) .. P. I.	7.8 N	121.54 E
120	Alingsås (ä'lĭŋ-sōs) ... Swe.	57.57 N	12.32 E
85	Aliquippa (ăl-ĭ-kwĭp'ȧ) ... Pa.	40.38 N	80.15 W
161	Alitagtag (ä-lē-täg'täg) P. I. (Manila In.)	13.53 N	120.55 E
143	Aliwal North (ä-lē-wäl') U. S. Afr.	30.42 S	26.41 E
126	Aljezur (äl-zhā-zōōr') ... Port.	37.19 N	8.49 W
126	Aljustrel (äl-zhōō-strĕl') ... Port.	37.52 N	8.11 W
122	Alkmaar (älk-mär') ... Neth.	52.36 N	4.45 E
150	Al Kuwait (äl-kōō-wīt') ... Kuw.	29.17 N	48.2 E
138	Allada (äl-lä'dä) ... Fr. W. Afr.	6.40 N	2.10 E
86	Allagash R. (ăl'ȧ-găsh) ... Me.	46.45 N	69.25 W
151	Allahabad (ŭl-ŭ-hä-bäd') ... India	25.30 N	81.58 E
126	Allande (äl-yän'dä) ... Sp.	43.17 N	6.37 W
126	Allariz (äl-yä-rēth') ... Sp.	42.11 N	7.48 W
139	Allata (ä-lä'tä) ... It. E. Afr.	6.32 N	38.30 E
123	Alle, R. (äl'ĕ) ... Ger.	54.20 N	20.40 E
84	Allegan (ăl'ē-găn) ... Mich.	42.34 N	85.52 W
85	Allegheny Front (Mts.) (ăl-ē-gā'-nĭ) .. U. S. A.	40.0 N	79.0 W
84	Allegheny Plat. ... U. S. A.	40.50 N	79.0 W
85	Allegheny R. ... Pa.	41.40 N	79.25 W
79	Allen (ăl'ĕn) ... Okla.	34.52 N	96.25 W
162	Allen ... P. I.	12.30 N	124.19 E
116	Allen, Lough (lŏk ăl'ĕn) ... Ire.	54.5 N	8.5 W
83	Allendale (ăl'ĕn-dāl) ... S. C.	33.0 N	81.18 W
80	Allende (äl-yĕn'dā) ... Mex.	28.20 N	100.51 W
123	Allenstein (äl'ĕn-stīn) ... Ger.	53.46 N	20.27 E
85	Allentown (ăl'ĕn-toun) ... Pa.	40.36 N	75.30 W
126	Aller (äl-yär') ... Sp.	43.11 N	5.36 W
122	Aller R. (äl'ēr) ... Ger.	52.35 N	10.10 E
119	Allermöhe (äl'ēr-mû'ĕ) Ger. (Hamburg In.)	53.29 N	10.7 E
119	Allhallows (ôl-hăl'ōs) Gt. Brit. (London In.)	51.28 N	0.38 E
76	Alliance (ȧ-lī'ăns) ... Neb.	42.5 N	102.51 W
84	Alliance ... Ohio	40.56 N	81.7 W
125	Allier R. (ȧ-lyā') ... Fr.	46.40 N	3.15 E
89	Alligator Pt. (ăl'ĭ-gā-tēr) La. (New Orleans In.)	30.1 N	89.43 W
120	Allinge (äl'ĭŋ-ĕ) ... Den.	55.14 N	14.50 E

Page	Name Pronunciation Region	Lat. °′	Long. °′
116	Alloa (ăl'ō-ȧ) ... Gt. Brit.	56.5 N	3.45 W
88	Allouez R. (ăl-ōō-ā') Wis. (Duluth In.)	46.40 N	92.2 W
49	Allyn (ăl'ĭn) ... Wash. (Seattle In.)	47.23 N	122.51 W
83	Alma (ăl'mȧ) ... Ga.	31.31 N	82.30 W
84	Alma ... Mich.	43.24 N	84.38 W
78	Alma ... Neb.	40.8 N	99.21 W
86	Alma ... Can.	45.35 N	65.0 W
77	Alma ... Wis.	44.21 N	91.56 W
148	Alma Ata (Verny) (äl'mȧ ȧ'tȧ) (vyĕr'nĕ) ... Sov. Un.	43.30 N	77.0 E
127	Almada (äl-mä'dä) ... Port. (In.)	38.40 N	9.9 W
126	Almadén (äl-mȧ-dhān') ... Sp.	38.47 N	4.49 W
126	Almagro (äl-mä'grō) ... Sp.	38.53 N	3.42 W
163	Almagro I. ... P. I.	11.56 N	124.18 E
74	Almanor, L. (ăl-măn'ôr) ... Calif.	40.15 N	121.10 W
126	Almansa (äl-män'sä) ... Sp.	38.53 N	1.8 W
126	Almanzora R. (äl-män-thō'rä). Sp.	37.21 N	2.10 W
127	Almargen (äl-mär-zhān') Port. (In.)	38.51 N	9.16 W
126	Almazán (äl-mȧ-thän') ... Sp.	41.30 N	2.31 W
126	Almeirim (äl-māī-rēN') ... Port.	39.12 N	8.39 W
122	Almelo (äl'mē-lō) ... Neth.	52.21 N	6.43 E
90	Almendares, R. (äl-män-dä'räs) Cuba (Habana In.)	23.4 N	82.25 W
126	Almendralejo (äl-män-drä-lā'hō) Sp.	38.41 N	6.22 W
126	Almería (äl-mā-rē'ä) ... Sp.	36.51 N	2.28 W
126	Almería, G. of ... Sp.	36.45 N	2.25 W
126	Almería R. ... Sp.	37.5 N	2.40 W
120	Almhult (älm'hōōlt) ... Swe.	56.34 N	14.8 E
135	Almina, Pt. (äl-mē'nä) Sp. Mor. (Gibraltar In.)	35.52 N	5.43 E
95	Almirante (äl-mē-rän'tā) ... Pan.	9.17 N	82.23 W
95	Almirante B. ... Pan.	9.30 N	82.0 W
126	Almodóvar (äl-mō-dō'vär) ... Port.	37.33 N	8.3 W
126	Almodóvar (äl-mô-dhō'vär) ... Sp.	38.44 N	4.11 W
135	Almodóvar R. Sp. (Gibraltar In.)	36.10 N	5.21 E
126	Almogía (äl-mō-hē'ä) ... Sp.	37.0 N	5.0 W
92	Almoloya (äl-mō-lō'yä) ... Mex.	19.23 N	99.45 W
126	Almonaster (äl-mō-näs-tĕr') ... Sp.	37.53 N	6.47 W
85	Almonte (ăl-mŏn'tē) ... Can.	45.15 N	76.15 W
126	Almonte (äl-mōn'tā) ... Sp.	37.16 N	6.30 W
126	Almonte R. ... Sp.	39.25 N	5.28 W
151	Almora (ŭl-mō'rä) ... India	29.31 N	79.45 E
127	Almoradí (äl-mō-rä-dhē') ... Sp.	38.9 N	0.48 W
126	Almuñécar (äl-mōōn-yä'kär) ... Sp.	36.45 N	3.41 W
129	Almyros (äl'mē-rōs) ... Grc.	39.10 N	22.47 E
120	Aln I. (äln) ... Swe.	62.27 N	17.25 E
160	Along B. (ä-lông') ... Fr. In. Chn.	20.50 N	107.15 E
161	Alor (I.) (ä'lôr) ... Neth. Ind.	8.20 S	124.45 E
169	Alora (ăl'ō-rä) ... Austl. (In.)	28.2 S	152.3 E
126	Alora (ä'lô-rä) ... Sp.	36.49 N	4.42 E
160	Alor Star (ä'lôr stär) ... Siam	6.30 N	100.10 E
126	Alosno (ä-lôs'nō) ... Sp.	37.33 N	7.8 W
117	Alost (ä'lôst) ... Bel.	51.0 N	4.5 E
72	Alouette L. (ä-lōō-ĕt') Can. (Vancouver In.)	49.19 N	122.25 W
84	Alpena (ăl-pē'nȧ) ... Mich.	45.4 N	83.26 W
129	Alpheios R. (ăl'fā-ōs) ... Grc.	37.30 N	22.0 E
126	Alpiarça (äl-pyär'sä) ... Port.	39.17 N	8.35 W
80	Alpine (ăl'pīn) ... Tex.	30.21 N	103.40 W
128	Alps, The (Mts.) (ălps) ... Eur.	46.5 N	10.45 E
128	Alps, Bergamo (Mts.) (bĕr'gä-mō) It.	46.5 N	9.50 E
122	Alps, Bernese (bûr'nēz) ... Switz.	46.33 N	7.42 E
122	Alps, Carnic (Mts.) (kär'nĭk) Ger.-It.	46.43 N	12.50 E
128	Alps, Cottian (Mts.) (kŏt'ĭ-ăn) Fr.-It.	44.45 N	7.0 E
128	Alps, Dinaric (Mts.) (dĭ-năr'ĭk) Yugo	43.40 N	16.30 E
122	Alps, Eastern (Mts.) ... Ger.	47.17 N	12.10 E
128	Alps, Graian (Mts.) (grā'yăn) It.-Fr.	45.28 N	7.15 E
128	Alps, Julian (Mts.) (jōō'lyăn) Yugo.	46.0 N	14.0 E
128	Alps, Maritime (Mts.) (măr'ĭ-têm) It.-Fr.	44.10 N	7.5 E
128	Alps, Pennine (Mts.) (pĕn'īn) ... It.	46.5 N	9.50 E
122	Alps, Pennine (Mts.) (pĕn'īn) Switz.-Fr.	46.5 N	7.20 E
128	Alps, Rhaetian (Mts.) (rē'shăn). It.	46.30 N	11.0 E
129	Alps, Transylvanian (Mts.) (trăn-sĭl-vā'nĭ-ăn). Rom.	45.20 N	24.0 E
128	Alps, Venetian (Mts.) (vē-nē'shĭ-ăn) It.	46.5 N	12.30 E
122	Alps, Western (Mts.) ... Switz.-Fr.	46.25 N	7.45 E
126	Alpujarras (Mts.) (äl-pōō-här'räs) Sp.	36.56 N	3.15 W
150	Al Qatn (äl kät) ... Aden	16.00 N	43.30 E
150	Al Qunfidha (Qunfidha) (äl kŭn'fēd'hä) .. Sau. Ar.	18.59 N	41.29 E
120	Als (I.) (äls) ... Den.	54.57 N	9.54 E
104	Alsina (äl-sē'nä) ... Arg. (In.)	34.40 S	58.25 W
119	Alster R. (äl'stēr) Ger. (Hamburg In.)	53.37 N	10.0 E
120	Alster R. ... Swe.	57.0 N	16.0 E
119	Alt, R. (ălt) Gt. Brit. (Liverpool In.)	53.31 N	2.58 W
73	Alta (ăl'tȧ) Utah (Salt Lake City In.)	40.36 N	111.38 W
73	Altadena (ăl-tȧ-dē'nȧ) Calif. (Los Angeles In.)	34.12 N	118.8 W
104	Alta Gracia (äl'tä grä'thē-ä) .. Arg.	31.45 S	64.15 W
102	Altagracia ... Ven.	10.32 N	71.30 W
152	Altai Mts. (äl'tī') ... Chn.-Sov. Un.	47.0 N	92.0 E
81	Alta Loma (ăl'tȧ lō'mȧ) Tex. (In.)	29.22 N	95.5 W
83	Altamaha R. (ôl-tȧ-mȧ-hô') ... Ga.	31.30 N	81.40 W
103	Altamira (äl-tä-mē'rä) ... Braz.	3.2 S	52.46 W
93	Altamira ... Mex.	22.24 N	97.56 W
104	Altamirano (äl-tä-mē-rä'nō) .. Arg.	35.31 S	58.15 W

Page	Name Pronunciation Region	Lat. °′	Long. °′
128	Altamura (äl-tä-mōō'rä) ... It.	40.49 N	16.33 E
152	Altanbulak (äl'tän-bōō-läk'). Chn.	50.12 N	106.31 E
97	Alta Vela I. (äl'tä vā'lä) ... Hai.	17.28 N	71.40 W
83	Altavista (ăl-tȧ-vĭs'tȧ) ... Va.	37.7 N	79.17 W
122	Altdamm (ält'dăm) ... Ger.	53.24 N	14.41 E
110	Alten R. (äl'tĕn) ... Nor.	69.20 N	24.8 E
122	Altenburg (äl'tĕn-bōōrgh) ... Ger.	50.58 N	12.26 E
119	Altenwerder (äl-tĕn-vĕr'dēr) Ger. (Hamburg In.)	53.31 N	9.55 E
126	Alter do Chão (äl-tĕr'dōō chä'ōō) Port.	39.14 N	7.39 W
119	Altkloster (ält-klō'stēr) Ger. (Hamburg In.)	53.28 N	9.41 E
122	Altmühl R. (ält'mül) ... Ger.	48.54 N	11.0 E
81	Alto (ăl'tō) ... La.	32.20 N	91.50 W
82	Alton (ôl'tŭn) ... Fla.	30.3 N	83.9 W
79	Alton ... Ill.	38.54 N	90.9 W
122	Altona (äl'tō-nä) ... Ger.	53.33 N	9.55 E
82	Altoona (ăl-tōō'nȧ) ... Ala.	34.2 N	86.19 W
85	Altoona ... Pa.	40.32 N	78.26 W
103	Alto Paraná, R. (äl'tō pä-rä-nä') Braz.	22.0 S	52.30 W
127	Altos de Garraf (Mts.) (äl'tōs dā gär-äf'). Sp. (In.)	41.18 N	1.54 E
97	Alto Songo (äl'tō sŏŋ'gō) ... Cuba	20.11 N	75.44 W
93	Altotonga (äl-tō-tŏŋ'gä) ... Mex.	19.45 N	97.14 W
118	Altrincham (ôl'trĭng-ăm). Gt. Brit.	53.23 N	2.21 W
70	Alturas (ăl-tōō'rȧs) ... Calif.	41.29 N	120.32 W
78	Altus (ăl'tŭs) ... Okla.	34.37 N	99.21 W
73	Altus ... Utah (Salt Lake City In.)	40.45 N	111.37 W
152	Altyn Tagh (Mts.) (äl-tēn'täg') Chn.	37.30 N	88.0 E
121	Aluksne (ä'lōōks-nĕ) ... Lat.	57.24 N	27.4 E
141	Alula (ä-lōō'lä) ... It. E. Afr.	11.52 N	50.42 E
85	Alumette I. (ȧ-lü-mĕt') ... Can.	45.50 N	77.0 W
131	Alushta (ä'lōōsh-tȧ) ... Sov. Un.	44.39 N	34.21 E
78	Alva (ăl'vȧ) ... Okla.	36.47 N	98.40 W
49	Alvarado (ăl-vȧ-rä'dō) Calif. (San Francisco In.)	37.35 N	122.4 W
93	Alvarado (äl-vä-rä'dhō) ... Mex.	18.48 N	95.46 W
99	Alvarez Jonte (äl-vä'räth hōn'tä) Arg. (Buenos Aires In.)	35.21 S	57.21 W
93	Alvaro Obregon (Frontera) (äl-vä'-rō ô-brä-gōn') (frōn-tä'rä). Mex.	18.32 N	92.38 W
120	Alvdalen (ĕlv'dä-lĕn) ... Swe.	61.13 N	14.2 E
127	Alverca (äl-vĕr'kȧ) ... Port. (In.)	38.54 N	9.3 W
120	Alvesta (äl-vĕs'tä) ... Swe.	56.57 N	14.31 E
81	Alvin (ăl'vĭn) ... Tex. (In.)	29.26 N	95.15 W
49	Alviso (ăl-vī'sō) Calif. (San Francisco In.)	37.25 N	121.58 W
151	Alwar (ŭl'wŭr) ... India	27.32 N	76.40 E
118	Alyn, R. (ăl'ĭn) ... Gt. Brit.	53.6 N	2.57 W
121	Alytus (ä'lē-tōōs) ... Lith.	54.24 N	24.4 E
92	Ama, R. (ä'mä) ... Mex.	21.0 N	99.0 W
161	Amadeo (ä-mä-dā'ō) P. I. (Manila In.)	14.12 N	120.54 E
164	Amadeus, L. (ăm-ȧ-dē'ŭs) .. Austl.	24.45 S	130.50 E
55	Amadjuak L. (ä-mädj'wäk) .. Can.	64.40 N	71.28 W
159	Amagasaki (ä'mä-gä-sä'kē) ... Jap.	34.44 N	135.23 E
158	Amakusa B. (ä-mä-kōō'sä) ... Jap.	32.32 N	130.0 E
159	Amakusa I. ... Jap.	32.28 N	130.8 E
120	Amål (ô'môl) ... Swe.	59.3 N	12.42 E
129	Amalias (ä-mäl'yäs) ... Grc.	37.48 N	21.21 E
141	Amani (ä-mä'nē) ... Tan.	5.5 S	38.39 E
94	Amapala (ä-mä-pä'lä) ... Hond.	13.16 N	87.38 W
138	Amar (ä-mär') ... Nig.	8.45 N	10.20 E
103	Amarante (ä-mä-rän'tä) ... Braz.	1.16 S	42.45 W
103	Amargosa (ä-mär-gō'sȧ) Braz. (In.)	13.2 S	39.41 W
78	Amarillo (ăm-ȧ-rĭl'ō) ... Tex.	35.13 N	101.49 W
128	Amaro, Mt. (ä-mä'rō) ... It.	42.5 N	14.4 E
113	Amasya (ä-mä'sē-ä) ... Tur.	40.40 N	35.55 E
93	Amatenango (ä-mä-tä-näŋ'gō) Mex.	16.31 N	92.27 W
94	Amatique, G. of (ä-mä-tē'kä) Br. Hond.-Guat.	16.0 N	88.45 W
94	Amatitlán (ä-mä-tē-tlän') ... Guat.	14.27 N	90.38 W
92	Amatlán de Cañas (ä-mät-län' dä kän-yäs) Mex.	20.50 N	104.28 W
143	Amatola Mts. (ä'mä-tō'lä) U. S. Afr.	32.35 S	27.5 E
103	Amazon R. (ăm'ȧ-zŏn) ... Braz.	3.1 S	60.0 W
102	Amazonas (State) (ä-mä-thō'-näs) Braz.	7.0 S	64.0 W
151	Amba R. (ŭm'bä) India (Bombay In.)	18.49 N	72.58 E
151	Ambala (ŭm-bä'lŭ) ... India	30.15 N	76.55 E
102	Ambalema (äm-bä-lā'mä) ... Col.	4.45 N	76.0 W
102	Ambato (äm-bä'tō) ... Ec.	1.29 S	78.33 W
161	Ambeno (Ter.) (äm-bā'nō) ... Tim.	9.20 S	124.20 E
141	Amber, Cape (ăm'bēr) ... Madag.	11.54 S	49.15 E
122	Amberg (äm'bĕrgh) ... Ger.	49.26 N	11.50 E
94	Ambergris Cay (I.) (ăm'bēr-grēs kā) Br. Hond. (In.)	18.0 N	87.56 W
97	Ambergris Cays (Is.) (ăm'bēr-grēs kāz). Ba. Is.	21.18 N	71.38 W
125	Ambérieu (äN-bā-rē-û') ... Fr.	45.58 N	5.20 E
171	Amberley (ăm'bēr-lē) ... N. Z.	43.8 S	172.43 E
124	Ambert (äN-bĕr') ... Fr.	45.31 N	3.45 E
162	Ambil I. (äm'bēl) ... P. I.	13.48 N	120.18 E
140	Amboim (äm-bô-ēn') ... Ang.	10.45 S	14.13 E
161	Amboina (ăm-boi'nȧ) ... Neth. Ind.	3.47 S	128.16 E
161	Amboina (I.) ... Neth. Ind.	3.45 S	128.15 E
124	Amboise (äN-bwäz') ... Fr.	47.25 N	1.0 E
140	Amboland (Dist.) (äm'bō-länd) S. W. Afr.	18.15 S	16.15 E
141	Ambositra (äN-bô-sē'trä) .. Madag.	20.30 S	47.20 E
49	Amboy (ăm'boi) Wash. (Portland In.)	45.54 N	122.26 W
85	Ambridge (ăm'brĭdj) ... Pa.	40.37 N	80.14 W
140	Ambris (äm-brēzh') ... Ang.	7.47 S	13.13 E
140	Ambrisete (äm-brē-zā'tä) ... Ang.	7.13 S	12.58 E
88	Ambrose Chan. (ăm'brōz) N. Y. (N. Y. In.)	40.33 N	74.0 W

ng-sing; ŋ-baŋk; N-nasalized n; nŏd; cŏmmit; ōld; ôbey; ôrder; fōōd; fŏŏt; ou-out; s-soft; sh-dish; th-thin; pūre; ûnite: ûrn; stŭd; circŭs; ü-as "y" in study; '-indeterminate vowel.

Page	Name Pronunciation Region	Lat. °'	Long. °'
165	Ambrym I. (ăm-brēm') New Hebr.	16.20 S	168.10 E
52	Amchitka I. (ăm-chĭt'kȧ) .... Alsk.	51.20 N	179.0 E
92	Amealco (ä-mä-äl'kō) .... Mex.	20.13 N	100.9 W
92	Ameca (ä-mā'kä) .... Mex.	20.32 N	104.2 W
92	Ameca, R. .... Mex.	20.40 N	104.30 W
92	Amecameca (ä'mȧ-kä-mä'kä) Mex.	19.7 N	98.45 W
122	Ameland (I.) (ä'mĕ-länd) ... Neth.	53.27 N	5.45 E
89	Amelia, L. (ȧ-mē'lyȧ) Minn. (Minneapolis In.)	44.54 N	93.15 W
122	Amerfoort (ä'mĕr-fōort) .... Neth.	52.10 N	5.24 E
73	America (ȧ-mĕr'ĭ-kȧ) Ala. (Birmingham In.)	33.44 N	87.15 W
48	America, North (ȧ-mĕr'ĭ-kȧ)		
98	America, South		
71	American Falls (ȧ-mĕr'ĭ-kăn) . Ida.	42.46 N	112.52 W
71	American Falls Reservoir ..... Ida.	42.56 N	112.43 W
75	American Fork .... Utah	40.22 N	111.50 W
49	American L.... Wash. (Seattle In.)	47.7 N	122.34 W
74	American R. .... Calif.	38.37 N	121.15 W
82	Americus (ȧ-mĕr'ĭ-kŭs) .... Ga.	32.4 N	84.14 W
143	Amersfoort (ä'mĕrs-fōrt). U. S. Afr.	27.2 S	29.52 E
77	Amery (ā'mēr-ē) .... Wis.	45.19 N	92.21 W
77	Ames (āmz) .... Ia.	42.1 N	93.35 W
86	Amesbury (āmz'bĕr-ē) ...... Mass.	42.50 N	70.57 W
93	Ameyalco (ä-mā-yäl'kō) Mex. (In.)	19.20 N	99.16 W
149	Amga (äm-gä') .... Sov. Un.	62.0 N	134.10 E
149	Amga R. .... Sov. Un.	60.0 N	129.0 E
149	Amginskaya (äm-gēn'skȧ-yȧ) Sov. Un.	60.5 N	132.0 E
149	Amgun R. (äm-gōōn') .... Sov. Un.	52.0 N	136.0 E
139	Amhara (äm-hä'rä) (Division) It. E. Afr.	12.30 N	37.30 E
86	Amherst (ăm'hērst) .... N. S.	45.49 N	64.12 W
84	Amherst .... Ohio	41.22 N	82.14 W
85	Amherst I. .... Can.	44.10 N	76.40 W
84	Amherstburg (ăm'hērst-bûrg) Can.	42.8 N	83.7 W
124	Amiens (ä-myăN') .... Fr.	49.55 N	2.20 E
81	Amite (ă-mēt') .... La.	30.43 N	90.31 W
85	Amityville (ăm'ĭ-tĭ-vĭl) ..... N. Y.	40.42 N	73.25 W
150	Amman (Rabbath Ammon) (äm'-män) (rä'bät äm'mōn). Transj.	32.0 N	36.0 E
135	Ammuna, Jebel (Mts.) (jĕb'ĕl ä-mōō'nä) Eg. (In.)	29.57 N	32.0 E
129	Amorgos (I.) (ä-môr'gōs) ..... Grc.	36.50 N	25.55 E
82	Amory (ā'mō-rē) .... Miss.	33.58 N	88.28 W
120	Åmot (Torpen) (ô'mōt) (tôr'pĕn) Nor.	61.7 N	11.18 E
155	Amoy (ä-moi') .... Chn.	24.28 N	117.58 E
160	Ampenan (äm'pē-nän) . Neth. Ind.	8.45 S	116.7 E
129	Amphissa (äm-fĭs'-ȧ) .... Grc.	38.31 N	22.22 E
155	Ampo (äm'pō') .... Chn.	23.27 N	116.25 E
127	Amposta (äm-pōs'tä) .... Sp.	40.42 N	0.34 E
151	Amraoti (ŭm-rŭ-ô'tē) .... India	20.59 N	77.50 E
151	Amritsar (ŭm-rĭt'sŭr) .... India	31.45 N	74.58 E
122	Amrum (I.) (äm'rōōm) .... Ger.	54.38 N	8.20 E
122	Amsterdam (äm-stēr-däm') .. Neth.	52.22 N	4.56 E
85	Amsterdam (ăm'stēr-dăm) .. N. Y.	42.56 N	74.10 W
143	Amsterdam (äm-stēr-däm') (ăm'stēr-dăm). U. S. Afr.	26.39 S	30.39 E
122	Amstetten (äm'stĕt-ĕn) .... Ger.	48.9 N	14.53 E
139	Am-Timane (äm'-tē-män') Fr. Eq. Afr.	11.15 N	20.30 E
150	Amu Darya (Oxus) R. (ä-mōō dä'rēä) .. Asia	40.15 N	62.30 E
52	Amukta Pass (ä-mōōk'tȧ) ... Alsk.	52.0 N	172.0 W
162	Amulung (ä'mōō'-lōōng) ..... P. I.	17.50 N	121.43 E
120	Amung, L. (ä'mōōng) .... Swe.	61.6 N	15.40 E
301	Amur B. (ä-mōōr') ...... Sov. Un.	43.15 N	131.56 E
149	Amur R. (ä-mōōr') Sov. Un.-Chn.	49.0 N	130.0 E
131	Amur-Novo Dneprovsk (ä-mōōr' nô'vô dnyĕ'-prôfsk) .. Sov. Un.	48.29 N	35.5 E
162	Amuyao, Mt. (ä-mōō-yä'ō) ... P. I.	16.17 N	121.3 E
92	Amuzgos (San Pedro) (ä-mōōz'gōz) Mex.	16.38 N	98.6 W
129	Amvrakia, G. of (äm-vrä'kē-ȧ) Grc.	38.58 N	21.0 E
72	Anaconda (ăn-ȧ-kŏn'dȧ) Colo. (Colo. Sprs. In.)	38.44 N	105.10 W
71	Anaconda .... Mont.	46.7 N	112.58 W
70	Anacortes (ăn-ȧ-kôr'tĕz) .... Wash.	48.29 N	122.38 W
149	Anadara R. (ăn-ȧ-där'ȧ) . Sov. Un.	71.0 N	113.0 E
78	Anadarko (ăn-ȧ-där'kō) ..... Okla.	35.4 N	98.15 W
149	Anadyr, G. of .... Sov. Un.	64.35 N	178.0 E
149	Anadyr Ridge (Mts.) .... Sov. Un.	67.0 N	170.0 E
149	Anadyr R. .... Sov. Un.	65.0 N	172.0 E
73	Anaheim (ăn'ȧ-hīm) Calif. (Los Angeles In.)	33.50 N	117.55 W
81	Anahuac (ä-nä'wäk) .... Tex. (In.)	29.41 N	94.40 W
150	Anaiza (ȧ-nī'zȧ) .... Sau. Ar.	26.5 N	44.15 E
157	Anak (ăn'äk') .... Cho.	38.32 N	125.27 E
96	Ana Maria Cays (Is.) (ä'nȧ mȧ rē'ȧ kāz'). Cuba	21.25 N	78.45 W
103	Anambari, Serra de (Mts.) (sĕr'rȧ dā ä-mȧn-bä'rē). Braz.	21.30 S	56.0 W
160	Anambas Is. (ä-näm'bäs) Neth. Ind.	3.0 N	106.0 E
158	Anamio I. (ä-nä'myō) .... Jap.	28.20 N	129.30 E
77	Anamosa (ăn-ȧ-mō'sȧ) .... Ia.	42.8 N	91.17 W
141	Ananalava (ä-nä-nä-lä'vä). Madag.	14.35 S	47.43 E
131	Ananev (ȧ-nä'nyĕf) ...... Sov. Un.	47.42 N	29.59 E
131	Anapa (ȧ-nä'pä) .... Sov. Un.	44.54 N	37.21 E
113	Anatolia (Reg.) (ăn-ȧ-tō'lĭ-ȧ). Tur.	39.15 N	33.45 E
124	Ancenis (äN-sē-nē') .... Fr.	47.25 N	1.10 W
155	Anchi (än'chē') .... Chn.	30.39 N	119.43 E
118	Ancholme, R. (ăn'chŭm) .. Gt. Brit.	53.30 N	0.29 W
81	Anchor (ăŋ'kēr) .... Tex. (In.)	29.12 N	95.28 W
53	Anchorage (ăŋ'kēr-āj) .... Alsk.	61.10 N	149.45 W
156	Anchow (än'chō') .... Chn.	38.58 N	115.41 E
90	Ancon (äŋ-kōn') .... C. Z. (In.)	8.58 N	79.33 W
128	Ancona (än-kō'nä) .... It.	43.36 N	13.31 E
104	Ancud (äŋ-kōōdh') .... Chl.	41.58 S	73.45 W
104	Ancud G. .... Chl.	42.10 S	72.32 W
126	Andalucía (Reg.) (än-dä-lōō-thē'ä) Sp.	37.30 N	5.0 W
82	Andalusia (ăn-dȧ-lōō'zhĭ-ȧ) ... Ala.	31.18 N	86.28 W
160	Andaman Is. (ăn-dȧ-măn') ... India	12.0 N	92.45 E
160	Andaman I., Little .... India	10.40 N	92.40 E
160	Andaman I., Middle .... India	12.30 N	92.45 E
160	Andaman I., North .... India	13.15 N	92.50 E
160	Andaman I., South .... India	12.0 N	92.45 E
166	Andamooka I. (ăn-dȧ-mōō'kȧ) Austl.	30.49 S	137.35 E
117	Anderlecht (än'dĕr-lĕkt) ..... Bel.	50.49 N	4.15 E
122	Andernach (än'dĕr-näĸ) ..... Ger.	50.25 N	7.23 E
74	Anderson (ăn'dĕr-sŭn) ...... Calif.	40.27 N	122.19 W
84	Anderson .... Ind.	40.5 N	85.31 W
83	Anderson .... S. C.	34.30 N	82.39 W
49	Anderson I.... Wash. (Seattle In.)	47.10 N	122.42 W
54	Anderson R. .... Can.	68.30 N	123.30 W
98	Andes Mts. (ăn'dēz) (än-dās') S. A.		
141	Andevorante (än-dā-vō-rän'tā) Madag.	18.52 S	49.8 E
148	Andizhan (än-dē-zhän') .. Sov. Un.	40.45 N	72.25 E
110	Andö (I.) (änd'û) .... Nor.	69.5 N	15.45 E
127	Andorra (än-dôr'rä) .... And.	42.29 N	1.29 E
127	Andorra .... Eur.	42.32 N	1.30 E
87	Andover (ăn'dō-vēr) .. Mass. (In.)	42.39 N	71.8 W
127	Andraitx (än-drä-ītsh') ...... Sp.	39.34 N	2.25 E
52	Andreanof Is. (än-drā-ä'nôf). Alsk.	52.0 N	176.0 W
141	Andreba (än-drā'bä) ...... Madag.	17.35 S	48.39 E
131	Andreevka (än-drā-yĕf'kȧ) Sov. Un.	47.4 N	36.34 E
131	Andreevka .... Sov. Un.	48.2 N	37.0 E
82	Andrews (ăn'drōōz) .... N. C.	35.12 N	83.49 W
83	Andrews .... S. C.	33.26 N	79.33 W
128	Andria (än'drē-ä) .... It.	41.13 N	16.18 E
129	Andros (än'dhrōs) .... Grc.	37.50 N	24.55 E
96	Andros I. (ăn'drŏs) .... Ba. Is.	24.21 N	77.55 W
129	Andros (I.) (än'dhrōs) ...... Grc.	37.50 N	24.52 E
86	Androscoggin R. (ăn-drŭs-kŏg'ĭn) Me.	44.25 N	70.35 W
126	Andújar (än-dōō'här) .... Sp.	38.3 N	4.3 W
138	Anécho (ä-nā'chō) .... Fr. W. Afr.	6.27 N	1.32 E
159	Anegasaki (ä'nā-gä-sä'kē) Jap. (Tokyo In.)	35.28 N	140.3 E
119	Anerley (ăn'ēr-lē) Gt. Brit. (London In.)	51.25 N	0.4 W
76	Aneta (ă-nē'tȧ) .... N. D.	47.41 N	97.58 W
165	Aneityum (I.) (ä-nā-ē'tē-ŭm) New Hebr.	20.8 S	169.45 E
154	Anfu (än'fōō') .... Chn.	29.22 N	111.15 E
155	Anfu .... Chn.	27.17 N	114.25 E
162	Angadanan (äŋ-gȧ-dä'nȧn) ... P. I.	16.45 N	121.45 E
162	Angaki (äŋ-gä'kē) .... P. I.	17.8 N	120.39 E
92	Angamacutiro (än'gȧ-mä-kōō-tē'rō) Mex.	20.7 N	101.44 W
152	Angangchi (äng'gäng'kē') .. Manch.	47.8 N	123.54 E
92	Angangueo (än-gäŋ'gwä-ō) ... Mex.	19.37 N	100.17 W
166	Angaston (äŋ-gäs'tŭn) .... Austl.	34.29 S	139.3 E
161	Angat (än-gät'). P. I. (Manila In.)	14.57 N	121.1 E
161	Angat R. .... P. I. (Manila In.)	14.55 N	121.5 E
120	Ånge (ông'ĕ) .... Swe.	62.33 N	15.40 E
120	Angeland (I.) (äng'ĕ-länd) ... Den.	54.54 N	10.45 E
162	Angeles (än'hä-lās) .... P. I.	15.8 N	120.35 E
120	Angelholm (ĕng'ĕl-hōlm) ...... Swe.	56.14 N	12.51 E
81	Angelina R. (ăn-jē-lē'nȧ) ..... Tex.	31.30 N	94.50 W
161	Angelo, Mt. (än'jĕ-lō) (än'hä-lō) P. I. (Manila In.)	14.56 N	121.23 E
74	Angels Camp (ăn'jĕls kămp') Calif.	38.3 N	120.33 W
123	Angerapp R. (äng'ĕr-äp) ..... Ger.	54.25 N	22.3 E
123	Angerburg (äng'ĕr-bōōrgh) ... Ger.	54.14 N	21.46 E
110	Angerman R. (ông'ĕr-män) ... Swe.	64.10 N	17.20 E
122	Angermünde (äng'ĕr-mûn-dĕ). Ger.	53.2 N	14.0 E
124	Angers (äN-zhā') .... Fr.	47.30 N	0.30 W
160	Angkor (Ruins) (äng-kōr') Fr. In. Chn.	13.40 N	103.55 E
116	Anglesey (ăŋ'g'l-sē) ..... Gt. Brit.	53.20 N	4.20 W
81	Angleton (ăŋ-g'l-tŭn) .... Tex.	29.10 N	95.26 W
81	Angleton .... Tex. (In.)	29.10 N	95.26 W
139	Anglo Egyptian Sudan (ăŋ'glō ē-jĭp'shăn sōō-dän'). Afr.	15.0 N	30.0 E
89	Anglum (ăŋ'glŭm) Mo. (St. Louis In.)	38.45 N	90.22 W
48	Angmagssalik (äŋ-mä'sȧ-lĭk) Grnld.	65.40 N	37.40 W
141	Angoche (Antonio Enes) (äŋ-gō' chä) (än-tō'nē-ōō ĕn-nezh') Moz.	16.10 S	39.55 E
141	Angoche I. .... Moz.	16.15 S	39.50 E
104	Angol (äŋ-gōl') .... Chl.	37.46 S	72.42 W
140	Angola (ăŋ-gō'lȧ) .... Afr.	12.30 S	18.30 E
84	Angola .... Ind.	41.38 N	85.2 W
161	Angono (äŋ-gō'nō) P. I. (Manila In.)	14.33 N	121.10 E
113	Angora (Ankara) (äŋ-gō'rȧ) (äŋ'-kä-ra). Tur.	39.55 N	32.55 E
124	Angoulême (äŋ-gōō-lām') ...... Fr.	45.40 N	0.15 E
7	Angra (äŋ'grä) .... Az. Is. (In.)	38.40 N	27.16 W
99	Angra dos Reis (äŋ'grȧ dōs rā'ēs) Braz. (Rio de Janeiro In.)	23.3 S	44.17 W
96	Anguilla Isles (äŋ-gwĭl'ȧ) ..... W. I.	23.30 N	79.35 W
95	Anguilla (I.) (äŋ-gwĭl'ȧ) W. I. (In.)	18.13 N	63.0 W
87	Anguille, C. (äŋ-gē'yē) ...... Newf.	47.55 N	59.25 W
155	Anhai (än'hī') .... Chn.	24.43 N	118.23 E
122	Anhalt (State) (än'hält) ...... Ger.	51.45 N	11.45 E
120	Anholt (I.) (än'hōlt) .... Den.	56.42 N	11.35 E
154	Anhwa (än'hwä') .... Chn.	28.11 N	111.21 E
155	Anhwei (Prov.) (än'hwā') .... Chn.	30.50 N	117.20 E
155	Ani (ä'nē') .... Chn.	28.46 N	115.16 E
75	Animas R. (ä'nē-mäs). Colo.-N. M.	37.0 N	107.52 W
129	Anina (ä-nē'nä) .... Rom.	45.2 N	21.49 E
85	Anita (ȧ-nē'tȧ) .... Pa.	41.3 N	79.0 W
158	Aniwa B. (ä'nē-wä') .... Kar.	46.28 N	142.45 E
154	Anjen (än'jĕn') .... Chn.	26.40 N	113.0 E
155	Anjen .... Chn.	28.33 N	116.55 E
141	Anjouan I. (än-jōō-än') .... Ind. O.	12.10 S	44.18 E
113	Ankara (Angora) (äŋ'kȧ-rä) (äŋ-gō'rȧ). Tur.	39.55 N	32.55 E
141	Ankaratra Mts. (äŋ-kȧ-rä'trä) Madag.	19.15 S	48.0 E
118	Anker R. (ăŋ'kēr) .... Gt. Brit.	52.36 N	1.34 W
129	Ankhiolo (äŋ-kē-ō'lō) .... Bul.	42.33 N	27.41 E
155	Anki (än'kē') .... Chn.	25.0 N	118.3 E
155	Anking (än'kĭng') .... Chn.	30.32 N	117.8 E
156	Ankiu (än'kē-ōō') .... Chn.	36.27 N	119.13 E
122	Anklam (än'kläm) .... Ger.	53.52 N	13.42 E
139	Ankober (äŋ-kō'bĕr) .... It. E. Afr.	9.41 N	39.52 E
140	Ankoro (äŋ-kō'rō) ..... Bel. Cong.	6.46 S	26.45 E
149	Ankula (än'kōō-lä) ...... Sov. Un.	61.10 N	107.59 E
154	Anlu (än'lōō') .... Chn.	31.10 N	112.28 E
157	Anmyon I. (än'myŏn') ...... Cho.	36.30 N	126.18 E
86	Ann, C. (ăn) .... Mass.	42.49 N	70.35 W
79	Anna (ăn'ȧ) .... Ill.	37.28 N	89.14 W
131	Anna (än'ä) .... Sov. Un.	51.28 N	40.21 E
122	Annaberg (än'ä-bĕrgh) ...... Ger.	50.35 N	13.1 E
166	Anna Branch (R.) (ăn'ȧ-brănch) Austl.	33.13 S	142.0 E
150	An Najaf (än nȧ-zhăf') ...... Iraq	31.40 N	44.38 E
160	Annam (State) (ăn-năm') Fr. In. Chn.	15.0 N	108.0 E
160	Annamitic Cord. (Mts.) (ă-nȧ-mĭt'-ĭk kôr-dĭl-yä'rȧ ..... Fr. In. Chn.	16.0 N	107.0 E
55	Annapolis (ă-năp'ō-lĭs) ...... Can.	44.45 N	65.35 W
85	Annapolis .... Md.	38.58 N	76.30 W
84	Ann Arbor (ăn är'bēr) ..... Mich.	42.17 N	83.44 W
125	Annecy (ăn'sē') .... Fr.	45.55 N	6.5 E
125	Annemasse (ăn'măs') .... Fr.	46.10 N	6.12 E
82	Anniston (ăn'ĭs-tŭn) .... Ala.	33.38 N	85.50 W
127	Anneto, Pic d' (Mt.) (pēk'dä-nā'tō) Sp.	42.38 N	0.38 W
124	Annonay (ȧ-nō-nĕ') .... Fr.	45.15 N	4.41 E
96	Annotto B. (ăn-nō'tō) .... Jam.	18.16 N	76.47 W
77	Anoka (ȧ-nō'kȧ) .... Minn.	45.11 N	93.23 W
154	Anping (än'pĭng') .... Chn.	26.21 N	106.2 E
156	Anping .... Chn.	38.20 N	115.31 E
157	Anpyun (än'pyōōn') .... Cho.	39.04 N	127.33 E
122	Ansbach (äns'bäĸ) .... Ger.	49.18 N	10.34 E
97	Anse à Veau (äNs'ȧ-vō') ...... Hai.	18.30 N	73.22 W
97	Anse d' Hainault (äNs' dĕ nō'). Hai.	18.30 N	74.27 W
154	Anshun (än-shōōn') .... Chn.	26.10 N	105.47 E
152	Ansi (än'sē') .... Chn.	40.30 N	95.48 E
154	Ansiang (än'sē-äng') .... Chn.	29.20 N	111.58 E
80	Anson (ăn'sŭn) .... Tex.	32.45 N	99.54 W
164	Anson B. (ăn'sŭn) .... Austl.	13.25 S	130.15 E
85	Ansonia (ăn-sō'nĭ-ȧ) .... Conn.	41.23 N	73.5 W
156	Ansu (än'sōō') .... Chn.	39.6 N	115.30 E
157	Ansung (än'sōōng') .... Cho.	37.2 N	127.14 E
113	Antalya (Adalia) (än-tä'lē-ä) (ä-dä'-lē-ä). Tur.	36.55 N	30.50 E
113	Antalya, G. of .... Tur.	36.35 N	31.20 E
	Antananarivo, see Tananarive, Madag.		
46	Antarctica		
46	Antarctic Ocean (ănt-ärk'tĭk) Ant.	63.0 S	
71	Antelope Cr. (ăn'tē-lōp) .... Wyo.	43.30 N	105.30 W
71	Antelope I. .... Utah	40.58 N	112.13 W
163	Antequera (än-tä-kä'rä) .... P. I.	9.47 N	123.54 E
126	Antequera .... Sp.	37.1 N	4.32 W
78	Anthony (ăn'thō-nē) .... Kan.	37.8 N	98.3 W
125	Antibes (äN-tēb') .... Fr.	43.35 N	7.10 E
87	Anticosti I. (ăn-tĭ-kŏs'tē) .... Can.	49.50 N	6.30 W
77	Antigo (ăn'tĭ-gō) .... Wis.	45.9 N	89.9 W
87	Antigonish (ăn-tĭ-gō-nēsh') .. Can.	45.39 N	61.59 W
94	Antigua (än-tē'gwä) .... Guat.	14.33 N	90.43 W
91	Antigua (I.) .... W. I.	17.5 N	61.37 W
93	Antigua Veracruz (än-tē'gwä vā-rä-krōōz'). Mex.	19.19 N	96.20 W
97	Antilla (än-tē'lyä) .... Cuba	20.50 N	75.44 W
49	Antioch (ăn'tĭ-ŏk) Calif. (San Francisco In.)	38.1 N	121.48 W
76	Antioch .... Neb.	42.3 N	102.34 W
150	Antioche (äN-tē-ôsh') .... Syr.	36.5 N	36.15 E
102	Antioquia (än-tē-ō'kēä) ...... Col.	6.20 N	76.3 W
46	Antipodes Is. (ăn-tĭp'ō-dēz) Ant. O.	49.0 S	180.0 E
161	Antipolo (än-tē'pō-lō) P. I. (Manila In.)	14.37 N	121.12 E
79	Antlers (ănt'-lērz) .... Okla.	34.13 N	95.38 W
157	Anto (än'tō) .... Cho.	36.38 N	128.38 E
104	Antofagasta (än-tō-fä-gäs'tä) Chl.	23.31 S	70.20 W
95	Antón (än-tōn') .... Pan.	8.21 N	80.14 W
141	Antongil B. (äN-tôN-zhēl') Madag.	15.30 S	49.50 E
141	Antonio Enes (Angoche) (än-tō'-nē-ōō ĕn-nĕzh') (äŋ-gō'chä). Moz.	16.10 S	39.55 E
78	Antonito (ăn-tō-nē'tō) .... Colo.	37.4 N	106.1 W
121	Antonopole (än'tō-nō-pō'lyĕ) . Lat.	56.21 N	27.10 E
125	Antony (äN-tō-nē') .... Fr. (In.)	48.45 N	2.17 E
116	Antrim, Mts. of (ăn'trĭm) .. N. Ire.	55.0 N	6.10 W
141	Antsirabe (änt-sē-rä'bā) ... Madag.	19.50 S	47.10 E
141	Antsirane (Diégo-Suarez) (änt-sē-rä'nā) (dē-ā'gō-sōō-ä'räs). Madag.	12.10 S	49.13 E
121	Antsla (änt'slä) .... Est.	57.50 N	26.35 E
104	Antuco (Vol.) (än-tōō'kō) ..... Chl.	37.25 S	71.30 W
156	Antung (än'tōōng') .... Chn.	33.44 N	119.17 E
157	Antung .... Manch.	40.9 N	124.22 E
117	Antwerp (Anvers) (ănt'wērp) (äN-vär'). Bel.	51.15 N	4.25 E
119	Antwerp and Turnhout Canal (ănt'wērp tŭrn'hout) Bel. (Anvers In.)	51.18 N	4.33 E
151	Anuradhapura (ŭ-nōō'rä-dŭ-pōō'rŭ) Cey.	8.25 N	80.25 E
117	Anvers (Antwerp) (äN-vär') (ănt'wērp). Bel.	51.15 N	4.25 E
119	Anvers (Antwerp) ...... Bel. (In.)		
72	Anvil I. (ăn'vĭl) Can. (Vancouver In.)	49.32 N	123.19 W
121	Anykščiai (ä-nīksh'chē-ī) .... Lith.	55.32 N	25.4 E
142	Anys Berg (Mt.) (ăn'ĭs bĕrg) U. S. Afr.	33.31 S	20.35 E

ăt; finăl; rāte; senāte; ärm; åsk; sofȧ; fâre; ch-choose; dh-as th in other; bē; ēvent; bĕt; recĕnt; cratēr; g-go; gh-gutteral g; bĭt; ĭ-short neutral; rīde; ĸ-gutteral k as ch in German ich;

Page	Name Pronunciation	Region	Lat. °′	Long. °′
155	Anyüan (än'yü-än')	Chn.	24.50 N	114.56 E
149	Anyui R. (än'yōō-ē')	Sov. Un.	68.0 N	165.0 E
124	Anzin (äN-zăN')	Fr.	50.24 N	3.30 E
128	Anzio (änt'zê-ō)	It.	41.27 N	12.38 E
158	Aomori (ä-ô-mō'rê)	Jap.	40.45 N	140.45 E
128	Aosta (ä-ôs'tä)	It.	45.44 N	7.19 E
82	Apalachee B. (ăp-ȧ-lăch'ē)	Fla.	30.0 N	84.10 W
82	Apalachicola (ăp-ȧ-lăch-ĭ-kō'lȧ)	Fla.	29.44 N	85.0 W
82	Apalachicola R.	Fla.	30.10 N	85.2 W
163	Apali Pt. (ä-pä'lê)	P. I.	10.50 N	124.30 E
161	Apalit (ä-pä'lêt)	P. I. (Manila In.)	14.48 N	120.44 E
92	Apam (ä-päm')	Mex.	19.41 N	98.28 W
92	Apango (ä-päŋ'gō)	Mex.	17.39 N	99.24 W
102	Apaporis, R. (ä-pä-pô'rĭs)	Col.	0.0	70.30 W
162	Aparri (ä-pär'rē)	P. I.	18.20 N	121.39 E
92	Apaseo (ä-pä'sâ-ō)	Mex.	20.34 N	100.40 W
129	Apatin (ŏ'pŏ-tĭn)	Yugo.	45.41 N	19.0 E
92	Apatzingán de la Constitución (ä-pät-zĭŋ-gän' dā lä cōn-stĭ-tōō-sê-ōn')	Mex.	19.5 N	102.15 W
129	Apeiranthos (ä-pĭr'än-thôs)	Grc.	37.4 N	25.32 E
122	Apeldoorn (ä'pĕl-dōōrn)	Neth.	52.12 N	5.56 E
128	Apennines (Mts.) (ăp'ĕ-nīnz)	It.	42.0 N	14.0 E
6	Apia (ä'pê-ä)	Sam. (In.)	13.49 S	171.48 W
93	Apipilhuaxco (ä-pĭ-pĭl-hwȧz'kō)	Mex. (In.)	19.32 N	98.45 W
92	Äpipilulco (ä-pĭ-pĭ-lōōl'kō)	Mex.	18.9 N	99.39 W
78	Apishapa R. (ăp-ĭ-shä'pȧ)	Colo.	37.35 N	104.15 W
55	Apiskigamish L. (ȧ-pĭs-kĭ-gȧ-mēsh')	Can.	55.15 N	73.30 W
92	Apizaco (ä-pê-zä'kō)	Mex.	19.25 N	98.7 W
163	Apo, Mt. (Vol.) (ä'-pō)	P. I.	6.59 N	125.17 E
122	Apolda (ä-pôl'dä)	Ger.	51.2 N	11.31 E
83	Apopka (ă-pŏp'kȧ)	Fla. (In.)	28.38 N	81.30 W
83	Apopka, L.	Fla. (In.)	28.38 N	81.35 W
92	Aporo (ä-pô'rō)	Mex.	19.43 N	100.25 W
77	Apostle Is. (ă-pŏs'l)	Wis.	46.55 N	90.35 W
82	Appalachia (ăpȧ-lăch'ĭ-ȧ)	Va.	36.56 N	82.48 W
59	Appalachian Mts. (ăp-ȧ-lăch'ĭ-ăn)	U. S.	38.0 N	80.30 W
120	Äppelbo (ĕp'ĕl-bŏŏ)	Swe.	60.30 N	14.0 E
119	Appen (äp'ĕn)	Ger. (Hamburg In.)	53.40 N	9.44 E
122	Appenzell (äp'ĕn-tsĕl)	Switz.	47.19 N	9.24 E
76	Appleton (ăp''l-tŭn)	Minn.	45.11 N	96.1 W
77	Appleton	Wis.	44.15 N	88.25 W
79	Appleton City	Mo.	38.12 N	94.3 W
83	Appomattox R. (ăp-ô-măt'ŭks)	Va.	37.30 N	78.0 W
128	Aprilia (ȧ-prē'lĭȧ)	It.	41.35 N	12.40 E
169	Apsley (ăps'lê)	Austl. (Tas. In.)	42.26 S	147.9 E
125	Apt (äpt)	Fr.	43.55 N	5.20 E
128	Apulia (Prov.) (ȧ-pū'lĭ-ȧ)	It.	41.15 N	16.10 E
102	Apure, R. (ä-pōō'rā)	Ven.	8.0 N	69.30 W
102	Apurimac, R. (ä-pōō-rê-mäk')	Peru	12.0 S	74.0 W
150	Aqaba (ä'kȧ-bȧ)	Transj.	29.30 N	35.5 E
152	Aqsu (Wensuh) (äk-sōō') (wĕn'sōō')	Chn.	41.40 N	80.5 E
152	Aqsu R.	Chn.	40.45 N	78.0 E
128	Aquila (ä'kwê-lä)	It.	42.22 N	13.24 E
92	Aquililla de Iturbide (ä-kwê-lē'yȧ dā ê-tōōr-bē'dhā)	Mex.	18.44 N	102.43 W
97	Aquin (ä-kăN')	Hai.	18.15 N	73.24 W
131	Arabatskaya Strelka (Tongue of Arabat) (Pen.) (ä-rä-bät'-skȧ-yȧ strĕl'kȧ) (ă-rȧ-băt')	Sov. Un.	45.50 N	35.0 E
150	Arabian Peninsula (ȧ-rā'bĭ-ăn)	Asia	24.0 N	45.0 E
150	Arabian Sea	Asia	19.0 N	65.0 E
103	Aracajú (ä-rä'kȧ-zhōō')	Braz.	10.59 S	37.1 W
103	Aracati (ä-rä'kȧ-tē')	Braz.	4.30 S	37.45 W
126	Aracena (ä-rä-thā'nä)	Sp.	37.54 N	6.35 W
124	Arachon (ä-rä-shôN')	Fr.	44.40 N	1.10 W
123	Arad (ŏ'rŏd)	Rom.	46.11 N	21.19 E
126	Araduey R. (ä-rä-dōō-ā'ĭ)	Sp.	42.0 N	5.18 W
161	Arafura Sea (ä-rä-fōō'rä)	Neth. Ind.	9.0 S	134.0 E
127	Aragón (Reg.) (ä-rȧ-gōn')	Sp.	41.30 N	0.30 W
126	Aragón R.	Sp.	42.32 N	1.20 W
102	Aragua de Barcelona (ä-rä'gwä dā bär-thȧ-lō'nä)	Ven.	9.29 N	64.58 W
103	Araguaia, R. (ä-rä-gwä'yä)	Braz.	9.0 S	50.0 W
103	Araguari (ä-rä-gwä'rê)	Braz.	18.45 S	48.2 W
151	Arakan Yoma (Mts.) (ŭ-rŭ-kŭn' yō'mȧ)	India	19.0 N	94.40 E
129	Arakhthos R. (är'äK-thôs)	Grc.	39.20 N	21.4 E
148	Aral Sea (ȧ-räl')	Sov. Un.	45.0 N	60.0 E
167	Aralnen (ȧ-räl'nĕn)	Austl.	35.39 S	149.48 E
113	Aral-Sor, L. (ȧ-räl'sôr')	Sov. Un.	49.10 N	48.15 E
92	Aramberri (ä-räm-bĕr-rē')	Mex.	24.6 N	99.48 W
126	Aranda de Duero (ä-rän'dä dā dwā'rō)	Sp.	41.41 N	3.41 W
92	Arandas (ä-rän'däs)	Mex.	20.44 N	102.17 W
90	Arango (ä-raŋ'gō)	Cuba (Habana In.)	23.5 N	82.12 W
116	Aran I. (ăr'ăn)	N. Ire.	55.0 N	8.25 W
116	Aran Is.	Ire.	53.5 N	9.45 W
126	Aranjuez (ä-rän-hwāth')	Sp.	40.2 N	3.36 W
81	Aransas Pass (ȧ-răn'sȧs)	Tex.	27.55 N	97.8 W
160	Aranya Pradega (ȧ-rän'yä prȧ-dā'gä)	Thai.	13.35 N	102.15 E
138	Araouan (ȧ-rou-äN')	Fr. W. Afr.	19.0 N	3.35 W
113	Arapkir (ä-räp-kēr')	Tur.	38.55 N	38.15 E
166	Ararat (ăr'ȧ-răt)	Austl.	37.16 S	142.58 E
113	Ararat, Mt.	Tur.	39.45 N	44.18 E
99	Araruama, L. (ä-rä-rōō-ä'mä)	Braz. (Rio De Janeiro In.)	22.54 S	42.15 W
113	Aras R. (ȧ-räs)	Sov. Un.-Iran	39.25 N	47.15 E
103	Aratuhipe (ä-rä-tōō-ē'pȧ)	Braz. (In.)	13.5 S	39.5 W
102	Arauca (ä-rou'kä)	Col.	7.0 N	70.30 W
102	Arauca, R.	Ven.	7.15 N	67.30 W
151	Aravalli Range (Mts.) (ä-rä'vŭ-lê)	India	23.30 N	73.30 E
162	Arayat (ä rä'yät)	P. I.	15.9 N	120.45 E
120	Arboga (är-bō'gä)	Swe.	59.24 N	15.41 E
125	Arbois (ȧr-bwä')	Fr.	46.54 N	6.45 E
116	Arbroath (är-brōth')	Gt. Brit.	56.35 N	2.35 W
73	Arcadia (är-kā'dĭ-ȧ)	Calif. (Los Angeles In.)	34.9 N	118.1 W
83	Arcadia	Fla. (In.)	27.12 N	81.51 W
81	Arcadia	La.	32.32 N	92.57 W
77	Arcadia	Wis.	44.15 N	91.29 W
70	Arcata (är-kȧ'tȧ)	Calif.	40.53 N	124.6 W
92	Arcelia (är-sā'lê-ä)	Mex.	18.17 N	100.22 W
112	Archangel (Arkhangelsk) (ärk'-ān-jĕl) (ȧr-Käŋ'gĕlsk)	Sov. Un.	64.30 N	40.40 E
85	Archbald (ärch'bôld)	Pa.	41.37 N	75.32 W
	Arches Natl. Monument	Utah	38.42 N	109.35 W
102	Archidona (är-chê-do'nä)	Ec.	0.31 S	76.59 W
126	Archidona	Sp.	37.7 N	4.22 W
124	Arcis-sur-Aube (är-sēs'sûr-ōb')	Fr.	48.31 N	4.9 E
71	Arco (är'kô)	Ida.	43.39 N	113.18 W
81	Arcola (är-kō'lȧ)	Tex. (In.)	29.30 N	95.27 W
126	Arcos (är'kōs)	Sp.	36.45 N	5.49 W
46	Arctic Ocean (ärk'tĭk)	Arc.	74.0 N	
46	Arctic Regions			
129	Arda R. (är'dä)	Bul.	41.37 N	25.30 E
113	Ardahan (är-dȧ-hän')	Tur.	41.10 N	42.40 E
112	Ardatov (är-dȧ-tôf')	Sov. Un.	54.55 N	46.15 E
150	Ardebil (är-dē-bēl')	Iran	38.20 N	48.2 E
117	Ardennes (ȧr-dĕn')	Bel.	50.20 N	5.30 E
126	Ardila R. (är-dē'lȧ)	Port.	38.12 N	7.0 W
79	Ardmore (ärd'mōr)	Okla.	34.11 N	97.8 W
85	Ardmore	Pa.	40.1 N	75.20 W
118	Ardsley (ärdz'lê)	Gt. Brit.	53.42 N	1.26 W
104	Areal (ä-râ-äl')	Braz. (In.)	22.50 S	43.20 W
91	Arecibo (ä-râ-sē'bō)	P. R. (In.)	18.27 N	66.43 W
103	Areia (ä-rā'yȧ)	Braz. (In.)	13.16 S	39.41 W
103	Areia Branca (bräŋ'kȧ)	Braz.	5.0 S	37.2 W
72	Arena (ȧ-rē'nȧ)	Colo. (Denver In.)	39.52 N	105.15 W
74	Arena, Pt. (ä-rā'nȧ)	Calif.	38.57 N	123.44 W
126	Arenas de San Pedro (ä-rā'nȧs dā sän pā'drō)	Sp.	40.13 N	5.4 W
120	Arendal (ä'rĕn-däl)	Nor.	58.29 N	8.43 E
102	Arequipa (ä-râ-kē'pä)	Peru	16.28 S	71.30 W
110	Areskutan (ä-rês'kōō-tă)	Swe.	63.28 N	13.5 E
124	Areyron R. (ä-râ-rôN')	Fr.	44.5 N	1.40 E
128	Arezzo (ä-rĕt'sō)	It.	43.29 N	11.53 E
126	Arga R. (är'gä)	Sp.	42.30 N	1.50 W
127	Arganda (är-gän'dä)	Sp. (In.)	40.18 N	3.27 W
163	Argao (är-gä'ō)	P. I.	9.52 N	123.36 E
148	Argara R. (är-gä'rä)	Sov. Un.	54.0 N	103.10 E
124	Argelès-Gazost (är-zhē-lâs'-gä-zō')	Fr.	43.0 N	0.6 W
124	Argentan (ȧr-zhäN-täN')	Fr.	48.45 N	0.1 E
124	Argentat (ȧr-zhäN-tä')	Fr.	45.5 N	1.55 E
124	Argenteuil (är-zhäN-tû'y')	Fr.	48.56 N	2.15 E
104	Argentina (är-jĕn-tē'nȧ)	S. A.	35.30 S	67.0 W
104	Argentina, I.	Arg.	50.15 S	72.30 W
124	Argenton (är-zhäN'tôN')	Fr.	46.35 N	1.30 E
127	Argentona (är-Kĕn-tō'nä)	Sp. (In.)	41.34 N	2.24 E
129	Argeș R. (ȧr'zhĕsh)	Rom.	44.34 N	25.30 E
73	Argo (är'gô)	Ala. (Birmingham In.)	33.42 N	86.32 W
129	Argolis, G. of (är'gô-lĭs)	Grc.	37.25 N	22.55 E
129	Argos (är'gŏs)	Grc.	37.37 N	22.44 E
129	Argostolion (är-gŏs-tô'lê-ōn)	Grc.	38.11 N	20.30 E
74	Arguello, Pt. (är-gwāl'yō)	Calif.	34.33 N	120.39 W
138	Arguin, C. (är-gōō-ēn') (ȧr-găN')	Fr. W. Afr.	20.32 N	16.30 W
149	Argun R. (ȧr-gōōn')	Chn.-Sov. Un.	51.45 N	120.0 E
56	Argyle (är'gīl)	Can. (Winnipeg In.)	50.12 N	97.27 W
76	Argyle	Minn.	48.19 N	96.48 W
164	Argyle Downs	Austl.	16.20 S	128.58 E
159	Ariake Sea (ä'rê-ä'kȧ)	Jap.	32.57 N	130.23 E
128	Ariano (ä-rê-ä'nō)	It.	41.8 N	15.6 E
102	Arica (ä-rē'kä)	Chl.	18.30 S	70.20 W
87	Arichat (ä-rĭ-shät')	Can.	45.31 N	61.0 W
124	Ariège R. (ȧ-rê-ĕzh')	Fr.	43.15 N	1.25 E
49	Ariel (ā'rĭ-ĕl)	Wash. (Portland In.)	45.59 N	122.30 W
123	Arieșul R. (ä-rê-ā'shŏŏl)	Rom.	46.25 N	23.25 E
78	Arikaree R. (ă-rĭ-kȧ-rē')	Colo.-Neb.	40.0 N	102.0 W
159	Arima (ä'rê-mä')	Jap. (Osaka In.)	34.48 N	135.15 E
162	Aringay (ä-rĭŋ-gä'ê)	P. I.	16.24 N	120.21 E
103	Arinos, R. (ä-rē'nôzh)	Braz.	12.30 S	56.30 W
92	Ario de Rosales (ä'rê-ô dā rō-sä'lâs)	Mex.	19.12 N	101.44 W
103	Aripuaña, R. (ä-rê-pwän'yȧ)	Braz.	8.0 S	60.0 W
148	Ariz (ȧ-rēs')	Sov. Un.	42.35 N	69.20 E
145	Arîsh (ȧ-rēsh')	Eg. (In.)	31.7 N	33.51 E
145	Arîsh, Wadi el (R.) (wä'dê ĕl ȧ-rēsh')	Eg. (In.)	31.0 N	33.53 E
75	Arizona (State) (ăr-ĭ-zō'nȧ)	U. S.	34.25 N	111.40 W
126	Arjona (är-hō'nä)	Sp.	37.56 N	4.4 W
79	Arkadelphia (är-kȧ-dĕl'fĭ-ȧ)	Ark.	34.7 N	93.3 W
79	Arkansas (State) (är'kăn-sô) (är-kăn'sȧs)	U. S.	34.50 N	93.0 W
79	Arkansas City	Kan.	37.3 N	97.2 W
79	Arkansas R.	U. S.	37.30 N	97.15 W
79	Arkansas R., Salt Fk. of	Okla.	36.40 N	97.40 W
112	Arkhangelsk (Archangel) (ȧr-Kän'-gĕlsk) (ärk'ān-jĕl)	Sov. Un.	64.30 N	40.40 E
116	Arklow (ärk'lō)	Ire.	52.45 N	6.10 W
151	Arkonam (är-kō-näm')	India	13.5 N	79.38 E
126	Arlanzá R. (är-län-thä')	Sp.	42.4 N	3.30 W
126	Arlanzón (är-län-thōn')	Sp.	42.20 N	4.10 W
122	Arlberg Tunnel (ärl'bĕrgh)	Ger.	47.8 N	10.12 E
124	Arles (ärl)	Fr.	43.39 N	4.41 E
73	Arlington (är'lĭng-tŭn)	Calif. (Los Angeles In.)	33.55 N	117.26 W
82	Arlington	Ga.	31.26 N	84.43 W
87	Arlington	Mass. (In.)	42.25 N	71.11 W
88	Arlington	N. J. (N. Y. In.)	40.46 N	74.9 W
76	Arlington	S. D.	44.22 N	97.8 W
81	Arlington	Tex.	32.44 N	97.6 W
86	Arlington	Vt.	43.5 N	73.5 W
85	Arlington	Va.	38.53 N	77.17 W
70	Arlington	Wash.	48.11 N	122.8 W
88	Arlington Heights	Ill. (Chicago In.)	42.5 N	87.59 W
120	Arlöv (är'lûf)	Swe.	55.37 N	13.5 E
164	Arltunga (ärl-tōōŋ'gȧ)	Austl.	23.20 S	134.45 E
79	Arma (är'mȧ)	Kan.	37.34 N	94.43 W
92	Armadillo (är-mä-dēl'yō)	Mex.	22.15 N	100.39 W
57	Armagh (är-mä') (är-mäK')	Can. (Que. In.)	46.45 N	70.36 W
116	Armagh	Gt. Brit.	54.21 N	6.42 W
57	Armagh Station	Can. (Que. In.)	46.44 N	70.36 W
149	Arman (är-män')	Sov. Un.	59.45 N	149.50 E
135	Armant (är-mänt')	Eg. (In.)	25.37 N	32.30 E
167	Armatree (är'mȧ-trē)	Austl.	31.28 S	148.31 E
113	Armavir (ȧr-mȧ-vĭr')	Sov. Un.	44.58 N	41.5 E
94	Armenia (är-mā'nê-ä)	Sal.	13.31 N	89.40 W
113	Armenia (Soviet Rep.) (är-mē'nĭ-ȧ)	Sov. Un.	40.0 N	45.15 E
124	Armentières (ȧr-mäN-tyâr')	Fr.	50.45 N	2.50 E
92	Armería, R. (är-mâ-rē'ä)	Mex.	19.40 N	104.8 W
165	Armidale (är'mĭ-dāl)	Austl.	30.30 S	151.46 E
167	Armidale	Austl.	30.31 S	151.40 E
76	Armour (är'mēr)	S. D.	43.19 N	98.20 W
131	Armyansk (ärm'yȧnsk)	Sov. Un.	46.5 N	33.43 E
126	Arnedo (är-nā'dō)	Sp.	42.12 N	2.3 W
122	Arnhem (ärn'hĕm)	Neth.	51.59 N	5.56 E
164	Arnhem, C.	Austl.	12.15 S	136.58 E
164	Arnhemland (ärn'hĕm-lănd)	Austl.	13.15 S	134.0 E
166	Arno B. (är'nō)	Austl.	33.53 S	136.35 E
118	Arnold (är'nŭld)	Gt. Brit.	53.0 N	1.8 W
128	Arno R.	It.	43.46 N	11.20 E
85	Arnprior (ärn-prī'ēr)	Can.	45.27 N	76.21 W
122	Arnsberg (ärns'bĕrgh)	Ger.	51.24 N	8.2 E
122	Arnstadt (ärn'shtät)	Ger.	50.51 N	10.56 E
122	Arnswalde (ärns'väl-dĕ)	Ger.	53.10 N	15.26 E
140	Aroab (är'ō-ȧb)	S. W. Afr.	26.47 S	19.43 E
161	Aroe Is. (ä-rō'ē)	Neth. Ind.	6.15 S	134.30 E
86	Aroostook R. (ȧ-rōōs'tŏŏk)	Me.-N. B.	46.40 N	68.18 W
162	Aroroy (ä-rô-rō'ê)	P. I.	12.30 N	123.24 E
113	Arpaçay (är-pȧ-chä'ê)	Tur.	40.50 N	43.15 E
126	Arraiolos (är-rī-ō'lōzh)	Port.	38.45 N	7.59 W
116	Arran (I.) (ă'răn)	Gt. Brit.	55.35 N	5.15 W
124	Arras (ȧ-räs')	Fr.	50.20 N	2.45 E
103	Arrasuahi (är-rȧ-swä'ê)	Braz.	17.0 S	42.0 W
99	Arrecifes (är-râ-sē'fās)	Arg. (Buenos Aires In.)	34.0 S	60.8 W
124	Arrée Mts. (är-rā')	Fr.	48.30 N	3.45 W
93	Arriaga (är-rê-ä'gä)	Mex.	16.14 N	93.56 W
54	Arrowhead (ăr'ō-hĕd)	Can.	50.47 N	117.57 W
73	Arrowhead, L.	Calif. (Los Angeles In.)	34.16 N	117.12 W
73	Arrowhead Springs	Calif. (Los Angeles In.)	34.12 N	117.15 W
71	Arrow R. (ăr'ō)	Mont.	47.29 N	110.0 W
70	Arrowrock Reservoir	Ida.	43.36 N	115.50 W
171	Arrowtown	N. Z.	44.58 S	168.50 E
80	Arroyo de la Cadena (är-rō'yō dā lä kä-dā'nä)	Mex.	26.15 N	104.0 W
80	Arroyo de la Zorro (är-rō'yō dā lä zôr'rō)	Mex.	29.10 N	101.30 W
80	Arroyo del Bobo (är-rō'yō dĕl bō'bō)	Mex.	28.25 N	101.0 W
126	Arroyo del Puerco (är-rō'yō dĕl pwĕr'kō)	Sp.	39.27 N	6.32 W
92	Arroyo Seco (är-rō'yō sä'kō)	Mex.	21.32 N	99.42 W
89	Arsenal I. (är'sê-năl)	Ill. (St. Louis In.)	38.34 N	90.14 W
126	Arsila (är-sē'lä)	Mor.	35.29 N	6.2 W
129	Arta (är'tä)	Grc.	39.7 N	21.0 E
80	Arteaga (är-tā-ä'gä)	Mex.	25.28 N	100.50 W
126	Arteijo (är-tā'hō)	Sp.	43.18 N	8.29 W
96	Artemisa (är-tâ-mē'sä)	Cuba	22.48 N	82.46 W
131	Artemovsk (är'tĕ-môfsk)	Sov. Un.	48.36 N	38.0 E
78	Artesia (är-tē'sĭ-ȧ)	N. M.	32.52 N	104.23 W
165	Artesian Basin, The (är-tē'zhăn)	Austl.	27.0 S	143.0 E
88	Arthur Kill (Inlet)	N. J.-N. Y. (N. Y. In.)	40.36 N	74.12 W
171	Arthur Mt. (är'thŭr)	N. Z.	41.12 S	172.42 E
169	Arthur R.	Austl. (Tas. In.)	41.5 S	145.10 E
169	Arthurs Cr.	Austl. (Melbourne In.)	37.42 S	145.9 E
97	Artibonite R. (är-tê-bô-nē'tā)	Hai.	19.2 N	72.21 W
104	Artigas (är-tē'gäs)	Ur.	32.40 S	53.24 W
139	Arua (ä'rōō-ä)	Ug.	3.2 N	30.57 E
102	Aruba (I.) (ä-rōō'bȧ)	W. I.	12.30 N	70.0 W
164	Arunta Desert (ȧ-rōōn'tȧ)	Austl.	22.30 S	137.15 E
141	Arusha (ȧ-rōō'shä)	Tan.	3.18 S	36.40 E
139	Aruwimi R. (ä-rŏŏ-wē'mê)	Bel. Cong.	1.30 N	27.15 E
72	Arvada (är-vă'dȧ)	Colo. (Denver In.)	39.48 N	105.5 W
120	Arvika (är-vē'kȧ)	Swe.	59.39 N	12.36 E
112	Arzamas (är-zä-mäs')	Sov. Un.	55.20 N	43.45 E
114	Arzew (är-zâ-ōō')	Alg.	35.52 N	0.19 W
126	Arzua (är-thōō'ä)	Sp.	42.55 N	8.10 W
	Aš (Czech.), see Asch, Ger.			
138	Asaba (ä-sä'bä)	Nig.	6.18 N	6.38 E
158	Asahigawa (ȧ-sä'hê-gä'wä)	Jap.	43.50 N	142.16 E
151	Asansol (ä-sȧn-sôl')	India	23.40 N	86.45 E
138	Asben (Air) (Reg.) (äs'bĕn) (ä'êr)	Fr. W. Afr.	18.35 N	9.0 E
142	Asbestos Mts. (ăs-bĕs'tŭs)	Bech.	29.0 S	22.50 E
85	Asbury Park (ăz'bĕr-ĭ)	N. J.	40.15 N	74.0 W
7	Ascension (I.) (ȧ-sĕn'shŭn)	Atl. O. (In.)	7.57 S	14.22 W
92	Ascensión (äs-sĕn-sê-ōn')	Mex.	24.21 N	99.55 W
122	Asch (Aš), (äsh)	Ger.	50.12 N	12.12 E
122	Aschaffenburg (ä-shäf'ĕn-bŏŏrgh)	Ger.	49.59 N	9.10 E
122	Aschersleben (äsh'ērs-lā-bĕn)	Ger.	51.45 N	11.27 E
128	Ascoli Piceno (äs'kô-lēpê-chā'nō)	It.	42.49 N	13.33 E
141	Ascot (ăs'kŏt)	U. S. Afr.	33.52 S	18.29 E
121	Aseri (ȧ'sĕ-rĭ)	Est.	59.26 N	26.50 E
138	Asfi (Safi) (äs'fê) (sä'fê)	Mor.	32.24 N	9.12 W

ng-sing; ŋ-baŋk; N-nasalized n; nŏd; cŏmmit; ōld; ôbey; ôrder; fōōd; fŏŏt; ou-out; s-soft; sh-dish; th-thin; pūre; ûnite ûrn; stŭd; circŭs; ü-as "y" in study; '-indeterminate vowel.

Page	Name Pronunciation Region	Lat. °′	Long. °′
138	Ashanti (Ter.) (ȧ-shăn′tē)...G. C.	7.30 N	1.30 W
118	Ashbourne (ăsh′bŭrn)....Gt. Brit.	53.1 N	1.44 W
82	Ashburn (ăsh′bŭrn)..........Ga.	31.42 N	83.41 W
171	Ashburton (ăsh′bûr-tŭn)....N. Z.	43.53 S	171.48 E
164	Ashburton R..............Austl.	23.15 S	116.30 E
118	Ashby-de-la-Zouch (ăsh′bĭ-dē-lȧ-zōōsh′). Gt. Brit.	52.45 N	1.28 W
79	Ashdown (ăsh′doun).........Ark.	33.41 N	94.7 W
83	Asheboro (ăsh′bŭr-ō).......N. C.	35.42 N	79.49 W
80	Asherton (ăsh′ēr-tŭn)........Tex.	28.26 N	99.46 W
83	Asheville (ăsh′vĭl)..........N. C.	35.35 N	82.34 W
159	Ashikaga (ä′shē-kä′gȧ).......Jap.	36.21 N	139.28 E
159	Ashio (Mines) (ä′shē-ō′)......Jap.	36.48 N	139.28 E
159	Ashiya (ä′shē-yä′)...........Jap.	33.55 N	130.40 E
145	Ashkelon (äsh′kĕ-lōn)...Pal. (In.)	31.40 N	34.33 E
150	Ashkhabad (ŭsh-кä-bät′) Sov. Un.	37.50 N	58.15 E
82	Ashland (ăsh′lănd)..........Ala.	33.16 N	85.50 W
78	Ashland....................Kan.	37.11 N	99.47 W
84	Ashland....................Ky.	38.28 N	82.40 W
86	Ashland....................Me.	46.37 N	68.25 W
87	Ashland.............Mass. (In.)	42.15 N	71.28 W
76	Ashland....................Neb.	41.2 N	96.22 W
84	Ashland....................Ohio	40.53 N	82.17 W
70	Ashland....................Ore.	42.11 N	122.42 W
85	Ashland....................Pa.	40.46 N	76.22 W
77	Ashland....................Wis.	46.35 N	90.54 W
76	Ashley (ăsh′lē).............N. D.	46.2 N	99.22 W
85	Ashley.....................Pa.	41.12 N	75.54 W
135	Ashmant (ȧsh-mänt′)....Eg. (In.)	29.17 N	31.15 E
160	Ashmore Reef (ăsh′mōr) Neth. Ind.	12.15 S	122.30 E
135	Ashmûn (ȧsh-mōōn′). (In.)...Eg.	30.19 N	30.59 E
88	Ashmun B. (ăsh′mŭn) Mich. (Sault Ste. Marie In.)	46.30 N	84.22 W
150	Ash Shihr (shēr)............Aden	14.50 N	44.50 E
84	Ashtabula (ăsh-tȧ-bū′lȧ).....Ohio	41.54 N	80.47 W
71	Ashton (ăsh′tŭn)............Ida.	44.4 N	111.29 W
118	Ashton-in-Makerfield (ăsh′tŭn-ĭn-māk′ēr-fēld). Gt. Brit.	53.29 N	2.39 W
119	Ashton-on-Mersey (ăsh′tŭn-ŏn-mûr′-zĭ). Gt. Brit. (Liverpool In.)	53.25 N	2.18 W
118	Ashton-under-Lyne (ăsh′tŭn-ŭn-dēr-līn′) Gt. Brit.	53.29 N	2.4 W
55	Ashuanipi L. (ăsh-wȧ-nĭp′ĭ)..Lab.	52.15 N	66.15 W
86	Ashuapmuchuan R. (ăsh-wăp-mōō-chwăn′). Que.	49.8 N	73.6 W
144	Asia (ā′shȧ)		
113	Asia Minor (Reg.)...........Asia	38.45 N	34.30 E
163	Asid G. (ä-sĭd′).............P. I.	12.5 N	123.30 E
92	Asientos (ä-sē-ĕn′tōs).......Mex.	22.14 N	102.7 W
128	Asinara, G. of (ä-sē-nä′rä)...Sard.	40.55 N	8.35 E
128	Asinara I...................Sard.	41.5 N	8.20 E
150	Asir (ä-sēr′)................Asia	17.30 N	43.0 E
120	Askersund (äs′kĕr-sŏŏnd)....Swe.	58.53 N	14.54 E
86	Askitichi, L. (ăs-kĭ-tĭ′chĭ)....Can.	49.12 N	74.8 W
113	Asmantai-Matai, L. (ăs-măn-tä′ĭ-mä-tä′ĭ). Sov. Un.	45.45 N	57.15 E
139	Asmara (äs-mä′rä).....It. E. Afr.	15.20 N	39.0 E
120	Asne L. (ôs′nĕ)..............Swe.	56.35 N	14.45 E
125	Asnières (ä-nyâr′).......Fr. (In.)	48.54 N	2.17 E
70	Asotin (ȧ-sō′tĭn)...........Wash.	46.19 N	117.3 W
127	Aspe (äs′pä).................Sp.	38.21 N	0.45 W
78	Aspen (ăs′pĕn)..............Colo.	39.11 N	106.50 W
169	Aspendale (ăs′pĕn-dāl) Austl. (Melbourne In.)	38.2 S	145.6 E
171	Aspiring Mt. (ăs-pīr′ĭng)....N. Z.	44.18 S	168.50 E
119	Aspull (ăs′pōōl) Gt. Brit. (Liverpool In.)	53.35 N	2.35 W
87	Aspy B. (ăs′pē).............Can.	46.55 N	60.28 W
139	Assab (ȧs-säb′).........It. E. Afr.	13.0 N	42.35 E
151	Assam (Prov.) (ăs-săm′).....India	25.30 N	92.0 E
143	Assegai R. (ăs′ē-gī).........Swaz.	27.5 S	31.5 E
115	Assel (äs-sĕl′)..............Libya	30.58 N	17.32 E
120	Assens (äs′sĕns)............Den.	55.15 N	9.53 E
54	Assiniboine R. (ă-sĭn′ĭ-boin)..Can.	49.35 N	98.45 W
138	Assinie (ȧ-sē-nē′).....Fr. W. Afr.	5.7 N	3.11 W
129	Astakos (äs′tä-kōs)..........Grc.	38.41 N	20.58 E
150	Asterabad (äs′tĕ-rä-bäd′).....Iran	36.47 N	54.32 E
128	Asti (äs′tē)...................It.	44.54 N	8.12 E
126	Astorga (äs-tôr′gä)...........Sp.	42.27 N	6.5 W
70	Astoria (ăs-tō′rĭ-ȧ)..........Ore.	46.10 N	123.49 W
113	Astrakhan (äs-trȧ-кän′)..Sov. Un.	46.20 N	48.0 E
140	Astrida (äs-trē′dȧ).....Bel. Cong.	2.38 S	29.48 E
163	Asturias (äs-tōō′rē-äs).......P. I.	10.34 N	123.43 E
126	Asturias (Reg.)...............Sp.	43.20 N	6.0 W
104	Asunción (ä-sōōn-syōn′)......Par.	25.15 S	57.40 W
93	Asunción (Ixtaltepec).......Mex.	16.30 N	95.1 W
93	Asunción (Nochixtlan)......Mex.	17.27 N	97.13 W
163	Asuncion Pass...............P. I.	11.5 N	123.30 E
139	Aswân Dam (ä-swän′)........Eg.	23.45 N	32.50 E
139	Aswân (Syene) (ä-swän′) (sē-ā′nĕ) Eg.	24.7 N	32.58 E
139	Asyût (ä-syōōt′).............Eg.	27.10 N	31.10 E
138	Atakpamé (ä′tȧk-pȧ-mā′) Fr. W. Afr.	7.36 N	1.05 E
129	Atalante Chan. (ä-tȧ-län′tē)..Grc.	38.40 N	23.20 E
82	Atalla (ă-tăl′ȧ)...............Ala.	34.2 N	86.5 W
138	Atar (ä-tär′)..........Fr. W. Afr.	20.37 N	13.8 W
74	Atascadero (ăt-ăs-kȧ-dâ′rō) .Calif.	35.27 N	120.41 W
80	Atascosa R. (ăt-ăs-kō′sȧ).....Tex.	29.0 N	98.30 W
93	Atasta de Sera (ä-täs′tä-dā-sā′rä) Mex.	17.58 N	92.57 W
139	Atbara (ät′bȧ-rä)......A. E. Sud.	17.45 N	34.0 E
139	Atbara R..............A. E. Sud.	16.0 N	35.33 E
148	Atbasar (ät′bä-sär′)......Sov. Un.	51.50 N	68.25 E
81	Atchafalaya B. (ăch-ȧ-fȧ-lī′ȧ)..La.	29.25 N	91.15 W
81	Atchafalaya R.................La.	30.40 N	91.45 W
79	Atchison (ăch′ĭ-sŭn) ....Kan.	39.33 N	95.8 W
102	Ate (ä′tā)............Peru (In.)	12.4 S	76.58 W
93	Atempan (ä-tĕm-pän′)......Mex.	19.50 N	97.26 W
92	Atenco, R. de (ä-tĕŋ′kō).....Mex.	22.30 N	104.6 W
54	Athabaska L. (ăth-ȧ-băs′kȧ) .Can.	59.15 N	110.0 W
54	Athabaska R.................Can.	55.45 N	112.45 W
129	Athēnai (Athens) (ȧ-thē′nā) ..Grc.	37.54 N	23.52 E

Page	Name Pronunciation Region	Lat. °′	Long. °′
82	Athens (ăth′ĕnz)............Ala.	34.48 N	86.59 W
82	Athens......................Ga.	33.57 N	83.25 W
129	Athens (Athēnai) ....Grc.	37.54 N	23.52 E
84	Athens.....................Ohio	39.23 N	82.9 W
85	Athens......................Pa.	41.59 N	76.30 W
82	Athens.....................Tenn.	35.36 N	84.37 W
81	Athens.....................Tex.	32.13 N	95.51 W
118	Atherstone (ăth′ēr-stŭn) .Gt. Brit.	52.34 N	1.32 W
119	Atherton (ăth′ēr-tŭn) Gt. Brit. (Liverpool In.)	53.31 N	2.29 W
118	Atherton..............Gt. Brit.	53.32 N	2.30 W
165	Atherton Plat.............Austl.	17.50 S	144.30 E
141	Athi R. (ä′tē)..............Kenya	3.0 S	38.40 E
125	Athis-Mons (ȧ-tēs′môɴ′). Fr. (In.)	48.42 N	2.23 E
116	Athlone (ăth-lōn′)...........Ire.	53.25 N	7.55 W
171	Athol (ăth′ŏl)..............N. Z.	45.30 S	108.38 E
129	Athos, Mt. (ăth′ŏs) ....Grc.	40.7 N	24.19 E
116	Athy (ȧ-thī)..................Ire.	52.55 N	6.55 W
139	Ati (ȧ-tē′)...........Fr. Eq. Afr.	13.16 N	18.6 E
162	Atimonan (ä-tē-mō′nän).....P. I.	14.0 N	121.55 E
94	Atiquizaya (ä′tē-kē-zä′yä) ...Sal.	14.0 N	89.41 W
94	Atitlan, L. (ä-tē-tlän′)......Guat.	14.40 N	91.10 W
94	Atitlan (Vol.).............Guat.	14.30 N	91.12 W
93	Atizapán (ä′tē-zȧ-pän′). Mex. (In.)	19.34 N	99.15 W
52	Atka I. (ăt′kȧ).............Alsk.	52.10 N	174.30 W
113	Atkarsk (ät′kȧrsk) ......Sov. Un.	51.48 N	45.0 E
76	Atkinson (ăt′kĭn-sŭn) ....Neb.	42.33 N	98.58 W
82	Atlanta (ăt-lăn′tȧ)...........Ga.	33.45 N	84.25 W
73	Atlanta, Ga. (In.)		
79	Atlanta.....................Tex.	33.08 N	94.10 W
77	Atlantic (ăt-lăn′tĭk)..........Ia.	41.24 N	95.0 W
85	Atlantic City..............N. J.	39.21 N	74.27 W
105	Atlantic Ocean		
93	Atlapulco (ät-lä-pōōl′kō) Mex. (In.)	19.15 N	99.3 W
114	Atlas, High (Mts.) (ăt′lăs)...Mor.	32.30 N	4.35 W
114	Atlas, Little (Mts.)..........Alg.	35.25 N	2.10 E
114	Atlas, Middle (Mts.)........Mor.	33.0 N	5.0 W
138	Atlas Mts.............Mor.-Alg.	32.30 N	2.0 W
114	Atlas, Saharan (Mts.).......Mor.	34.0 N	1.0 E
120	Atle I. (ät′lĕ)...............Nor.	61.22 N	5.0 E
92	Atliaca (ät-lē-ä′kä) ....Mex.	17.42 N	99.23 W
54	Atlin L. (ăt′lĭn).............Can.	59.45 N	133.40 W
92	Atlixco (ät-lēz′kō)..........Mex.	18.54 N	98.27 W
82	Atmore (ăt′mōr).............Ala.	31.1 N	87.32 W
79	Atoka (ȧ-tō′kȧ).............Okla.	34.23 N	96.8 W
92	Atotonilco el Alto (ä′tō-tō-nēl′kō ĕl äl′tō). Mex.	20.37 N	102.27 W
92	Atotonilco el Grande (ä′tō-tō-nēl′-kō ĕl grän′dā). Mex.	20.17 N	98.40 W
138	Atoui R. (ȧ-tōō-ē′)....Fr. W. Afr.	21.0 N	15.40 W
92	Atoyac (ä-tō-yäk′)..........Mex.	20.0 N	103.29 W
92	Atoyac de Álvarez (ä-tō-yäk′dā äl′-vä-rāz). Mex.	17.12 N	100.26 W
92	Atoyac, R...................Mex.	18.40 N	98.0 W
93	Atoyatempan (ä-tō′yȧ-tĕm-pän′) Mex.	18.48 N	97.55 W
120	Ätra R. (ĕt′rä) ....Swe.	57.6 N	12.50 E
102	Atrato, R. (ä-trä′tō)........Colo.	7.30 N	77.0 W
150	Atrek R. (ä′trĕk)............Iran	37.45 N	56.30 E
159	Atsuta (ät′sōō-tä)...........Jap.	35.7 N	136.54 E
158	Atsuta B....................Jap.	34.45 N	136.45 E
55	Attawapiskat R. (ăt′ȧ-wȧ-pĭs′kăt) Can.	52.45 N	86.30 W
85	Attica (ăt′ĭ-kȧ).............N. Y.	42.55 N	78.17 W
55	Attikonak L. (ăt′ĭ-kō-năk′)...Lab.	52.45 N	64.32 W
86	Attleboro (ăt′′l-bŭr-ō)......Mass.	41.55 N	71.15 W
52	Attu Is. (ăt-tōō′)...........Alsk.	52.50 N	173.0 E
104	Atuel, R. (ä-tōō-ĕl′).........Arg.	35.40 S	67.30 W
161	Atulayan I. (ä-tōō-lä-yän′) P. I. (Manila In.)	14.25 N	121.13 E
120	Åtvidaberg (ôt-vē′dȧ-bĕrgh) .Swe.	58.11 N	15.57 E
78	Atwood (ăt′wŏŏd)...........Kan.	39.49 N	101.6 W
93	Atzcapotzalco (ät′zkä-pō-tzäl′kō) Mex. (In.)	19.29 N	99.11 W
93	Atzcapotzaltongo (ät′zkä-pō-tzäl-tōŋ′gō). Mex. (In.)	19.38 N	99.19 W
173	Auau Chan .(ä′ŏŏ-ä′ŏŏ).....Haw.	20.55 N	156.45 W
140	Auaz Mts. (ä′wäs).....S. W. Afr.	22.45 S	17.15 E
125	Aubagne (ō-bän′y′)...........Fr.	43.18 N	5.35 E
125	Aube R. (ōb).................Fr.	48.35 N	4.0 E
124	Aubenas (ōb′-näs′)...........Fr.	44.38 N	4.22 E
125	Aubervilliers (ō-bĕr-vē-yā′) Fr. (In.)	48.54 N	2.24 E
124	Aubière (ō-byâr′)............Fr.	45.44 N	3.5 E
124	Aubigny-sur-Nère (ō-bēn-yē′sür-nâr′). Fr.	47.30 N	2.28 E
124	Aubin (ō-băɴ′)...............Fr.	44.30 N	2.15 E
82	Auburn (ô′bŭrn).............Ala.	32.35 N	85.30 W
74	Auburn....................Calif.	38.54 N	121.5 W
79	Auburn......................Ill.	39.35 N	89.45 W
84	Auburn.....................Ind.	41.22 N	85.2 W
86	Auburn.....................Me.	44.12 N	70.15 W
87	Auburn.............Mass. (In.)	42.11 N	71.50 W
79	Auburn.....................Neb.	40.24 N	95.51 W
85	Auburn....................N. Y.	42.55 N	76.36 W
70	Auburn....................Wash.	47.16 N	122.15 W
124	Aubusson (ō-bü-sôɴ′) ....Fr.	45.58 N	2.10 E
124	Auch (ōsh)...................Fr.	43.39 N	0.35 E
82	Aucilla, R. (ô-sĭl′ȧ)..........Fla.	30.25 N	83.45 W
170	Auckland (ôk′lănd)....N. Z. (In.)	36.52 S	174.45 E
46	Auckland Is..............Ant. O.	50.30 S	166.30 E
124	Aude R. (ōd).................Fr.	43.5 N	2.15 E
124	Audierne (ō-dyĕrn′)..........Fr.	48.0 N	4.30 W
125	Audincourt (ō-dăɴ-kōōr′).....Fr.	47.30 N	6.50 E
118	Audley (ôd′lĭ) ....Gt. Brit.	53.3 N	2.18 W
77	Audubon (ô′dŏŏ-bŏn)..........Ia.	41.44 N	94.55 W
122	Aue (ou′ē)..................Ger.	50.36 N	12.44 E
142	Aughrabies Falls (ô-grä′bēs) U. S. Afr.	28.30 S	20.15 E
119	Aughton (ô′tŭn) Gt. Brit. (Liverpool In.)	53.32 N	2.55 W
139	Augila (ou-jē′lȧ)...........Libya	29.6 N	21.11 E
115	Augila Oasis...............Libya	29.15 N	21.15 E

Page	Name Pronunciation Region	Lat. °′	Long.
122	Augsburg (ouks′bŏŏrgh) .....Ger.	48.23 N	10.53 E
79	Augusta (ô-gŭs′tȧ)..........Ark.	35.17 N	91.21 W
83	Augusta.....................Ga.	33.28 N	81.59 W
79	Augusta....................Kan.	37.40 N	96.59 W
84	Augusta....................Ky.	38.45 N	84.0 W
86	Augusta....................Me.	44.19 N	69.50 W
77	Augusta....................Wis.	44.41 N	91.8 W
123	Augustów (ou-gŏŏs′tŏŏf) .....Pol.	53.50 N	22.59 E
139	Auk, R. (ouk)........Fr. Eq. Afr.	9.38 N	20.0 E
125	Aulnay-s-Bois (ō-nĕ′sōō-bwä′) Fr. (In.)	48.56 N	2.30 E
72	Ault (ôlt).....Colo. (Denver In.)	40.35 N	104.44 W
124	Aune R. (ōn)................Fr.	48.15 N	4.0 W
140	Auob R. (ä′wŏb) S.W.Afr.-U.S. Afr.	25.45 S	19.43 E
170	Aupaki L. (ô-pä′kĭ)....N. Z. (In.)	36.47 S	174.46 E
151	Aurangabad (ou-rŭŋ-gä-bäd′) India	19.55 N	75.55 E
124	Auray (ō-rĕ′).................Fr.	47.41 N	31.0 W
120	Aurdal, S. (our′dāl).........Nor.	60.55 N	9.28 E
114	Aurès, Jebel (Mts.) (jĕb′ĕl ō-rĕs′) Alg.	35.25 N	6.30 E
124	Aurillac (ō-rē-yȧk′)...........Fr.	44.55 N	2.29 E
72	Aurora (ô-rō′rȧ) Colo. (Denver In.)	39.45 N	104.53 W
79	Aurora.......................Ill.	41.45 N	88.19 W
84	Aurora......................Ind.	39.5 N	84.56 W
77	Aurora.....................Minn.	47.31 N	92.16 W
79	Aurora......................Mo.	36.58 N	93.42 W
76	Aurora......................Neb.	40.52 N	98.1 W
85	Aurora, E..................N. Y.	42.49 N	78.39 W
165	Aurora I. ....New Hebr.	15.0 S	168.8 E
142	Aus (ous)............S. W. Afr.	26.37 S	16.16 E
84	Au Sable R. (ô-sā′b′l).......Mich.	44.37 N	83.50 W
85	Ausable R..................N. Y.	44.25 N	73.46 W
122	Aussig (Ustí) (ous′ĭk (ōōs′tē). Ger.	50.40 N	14.1 E
73	Austell (ôs-tĕl′)..Ga. (Atlanta In.)	33.48 N	84.38 W
77	Austin (ôs′tĭn).............Minn.	43.40 N	92.58 W
74	Austin......................Nev.	38.29 N	117.5 W
81	Austin......................Tex.	30.16 N	97.43 W
81	Austin Bayou (ôs′tĭn bī-ōō′) Tex. (In.)	29.15 N	95.20 W
164	Austin, L..................Austl.	27.40 S	118.10 E
6	Austral (Tubuai) Is. (ôs′trȧl) (tōō-bŏŏ-ä′ē). Pac. O.	23.0 N	150.0 W
164	Australia (ôs-trā′lĭ-ȧ)		
164	Australia, Western (State) ..Austl.	25.0 S	120.0 E
122	Austria (ôs′trĭ-ȧ)............Eur.	47.20 N	13.20 E
119	Austruweel (ous-trû-vāl′) Bel. (Anvers In.)	51.15 N	4.23 E
92	Autlán (ä-ōōt-län′)..........Mex.	19.47 N	104.21 W
124	Autun (ō-tŭɴ′) ....Fr.	46.59 N	4.19 E
124	Auvergne Mts. (ō-vĕrn′y′).....Fr.	45.20 N	2.40 E
125	Auvers-s-Oise (ō-vâr′sür-wäz′) Fr. (In.)	49.4 N	2.11 E
124	Auxerre (ō-sâr′)..............Fr.	47.49 N	3.35 E
125	Auxonne (ō-sôn′).............Fr.	47.15 N	5.25 E
79	Ava (ā′vȧ)...................Mo.	36.57 N	92.39 W
139	Avakubi (ä-vȧ-kōō′bē) .Bel. Cong.	1.21 N	27.32 E
170	Avalli I. (ȧ-văl′lē)..........N. Z.	35.0 S	174.0 E
124	Avallon (ȧ-vȧ-lôɴ′)...........Fr.	47.29 N	3.53 E
74	Avalon (ăv′ȧ-lŏn) ....Calif.	33.20 N	118.21 W
89	Avalon.......Pa. (Pittsburgh In.)	40.30 N	80.4 W
103	Avari, L. (ȧ-vä′rē).....Braz. (In.)	0.40 S	49.20 W
126	Aveiro (ä-vā′rŏŏ)...........Port.	40.39 N	8.39 W
104	Avellaneda (ä-vĕl-yä-nā′dhä) Arg. (In.)	34.40 S	58.21 W
128	Avellino (ä-vĕl-lē′nō).........It.	40.55 N	14.50 E
120	Aver I. (ä′vĕr)..............Nor.	63.0 N	7.35 E
128	Aversa (ä-vĕr′sä)..............It.	40.58 N	14.12 E
79	Avery (ā′vēr-ĭ)...............Tex.	33.33 N	94.46 W
120	Avesta (ä-vĕs′tä)............Swe.	60.8 N	16.10 E
128	Avezzano (ä-vȧt-sä′nō)........It.	42.3 N	13.24 E
128	Avigliano (ä-vēl-yä′nō).......It.	40.44 N	15.43 E
124	Avignon (ȧ-vē-nyôɴ′).........Fr.	43.55 N	4.50 E
126	Ávila (ä′vē-lä)...............Sp.	40.38 N	4.42 W
126	Avilés (ä-vē-lās′).............Sp.	43.34 N	5.57 W
166	Avoca (ȧ-vō′kȧ)...........Austl.	37.4 S	143.29 E
76	Avoca........................Ia.	41.30 N	95.20 W
85	Avon (ā′vŏn)...............Conn.	41.49 N	72.51 W
87	Avon.................Mass. (In.)	41.8 N	71.2 W
73	Avon...Utah (Salt Lake City In.)	41.32 N	111.48 W
170	Avondale (ăv′ŏn-dāl) ..N. Z. (In.)	36.54 S	174.42 E
83	Avon Park (ā′vŏn-pärk′) Fla. (In.)	27.35 N	81.28 W
116	Avon, R................Gt. Brit.	51.0 N	1.50 W
171	Avon R...............N. Z. (In.)	43.31 S	172.41 E
142	Avontuur (ăv-ŏn-tür′) ..U. S. Afr.	33.44 S	23.20 E
124	Avranches (ȧ-vränsh′).........Fr.	48.40 N	1.20 W
159	Awaji I. (ä′wä-jē)...........Jap.	34.20 N	134.52 E
139	Awash R. (ȧ-wäsh′)....It. E. Afr.	10.0 N	40.22 E
171	Awatere R. (ä-wä-tā′rȧ).....N. Z.	41.53 S	173.40 E
118	Axe Edge (Mt.) (ăks′ĕj) .Gt. Brit.	53.13 N	1.55 W
46	Axel Heiberg Glacier (äk′sĕl hī′-bĕrgh). Ant.	82.0 S	164.0 W
118	Axholme, Isle of (ăks′hōm) Gt. Brit.	53.33 N	0.48 W
124	Ax-les Thermes (äks′lā-tĕrm′)..Fr.	42.45 N	1.50 E
92	Axochiapan (äks-ō-chyä′pän) Mex.	18.30 N	98.45 W
124	Ay (ȧ′ē)......................Fr.	49.5 N	4.0 E
159	Ayabe (ä′yä-bĕ)..............Jap.	35.15 N	135.16 E
104	Ayacucho (ä-yä-kōō′chō).....Arg.	37.10 S	58.30 W
102	Ayacucho...................Peru	13.0 S	74.16 W
126	Ayamonte (ä-yä-mōn′tā)......Sp.	37.14 N	7.25 W
102	Ayata (ä-yä′tä)..............Bol.	15.5 S	68.45 W
83	Ayden (ā′dĕn)..............N. C.	35.28 N	77.26 W
113	Aydin (ȧ′ĭ-dĭn)..............Tur.	37.55 N	27.55 E
87	Ayer (âr)............Mass. (In.)	42.33 N	71.36 W
116	Aylesbury (ālz′bēr-ĭ) ....Gt. Brit.	51.50 N	0.45 W
85	Aylmer (āl′mēr)............Can.	45.26 N	75.56 W
54	Aylmer L...................Can.	64.15 N	108.30 W
92	Ayo el Chico (ä′yō-ĕl-chē′kō). Mex.	20.33 N	102.20 W
127	Ayora (ä-yō′rä)...............Sp.	39.5 N	1.4 W
93	Ayotla (ä-yōt′lä) ......Mex. (In.)	19.19 N	98.56 W
116	Ayr (âr) ....Gt. Brit.	55.25 N	4.37 W
116	Ayr, R.................Gt. Brit.	55.30 N	4.25 W
93	Ayucan (ä-yōō′kän)....Mex. (In.)	19.31 N	99.22 W
160	Ayudhyâ (ȧ-yōōt′hē′ä)......Thai.	14.17 N	100.33 E
163	Ayuquitan (ä-yōō-kē′tän)....P. I.	9.24 N	123.14 E

ăt; finăl; rāte; senâte; ärm; ȧsk; sofȧ; fâre ch-choose; dh-as th in other; bē; ēvent; bĕt; recĕnt; cratēr; g-go; gh-gutteral g; bĭt; ĭ-short neutral; rīde; к-gutteral k as ch in German ich;

Page	Name Pronunciation Region	Lat. °′	Long. °′
94	Ayutla (ä-yōōt'lä) ....Guat.	14.44 N	92.11 W
92	Ayutla....................Mex.	16.51 N	99.15 W
92	Ayutla....................Mex.	20.10 N	104.19 W
113	Ayvalik (aï-vä'lěk)..........Tur.	39.18 N	26.50 E
138	Azemmour (ȧ-zẽ-mōōr') .....Mor.	33.20 N	8.15 W
113	Azerbaidzhan (Soviet Rep.) (ä'zẽr-bä-ē-jän')...Sov. Un.	40.50 N	47.0 E
102	Azogues (ä-sō'gās)............Ec.	2.45 S	78.32 W
138	Azores (Is.) (ȧ-zōrz')..Atl. O. (In.)	38.30 N	28.0 W
131	Azov (ȧ-zôf') (ä'zôf).....Sov. Un.	47.6 N	39.22 E
131	Azov, Sea of...........Sov. Un.	45.50 N	36.22 E
92	Azoyú (ä-zô-yōō')...........Mex.	16.37 N	98.39 W
114	Azrou (äz-rōō')..............Mor.	32.28 N	5.12 W
75	Aztec (ăz'tĕk)..............N. M.	36.48 N	108.1 W
75	Aztec Ruin Natl. Mon. .....N. M.	36.51 N	108.5 W
97	Azua (ä'swä).........Dom. Rep.	18.27 N	70.46 W
126	Azuaga (ä-thwä'gä)..........Sp.	38.15 N	5.41 W
95	Azuero Pen. (ä-swā'rō).......Pan.	7.40 N	80.35 W
104	Azufre, Cerro del (Copiapó) (Vol.) (sĕr'rō dĕl ä-sōō'frā)(kō-pē-äpō') Chl.	27.15 S	69.10 W
102	Azufrera (ä-sōō-frā'rä).......Peru	6.6 S	80.53 W
104	Azul (ä-sōōl')..............Arg.	36.48 S	59.50 W
73	Azusa (ȧ-zōō'sȧ) Calif. (Los Angeles In.)	34.8 N	117.54 W
145	Baakline (bäk-lēn').....Syr. (In.)	33.43 N	34.34 E
145	Baalbeck (Heliopolis) (bäl'-bĕk) (hē-lĭ-ŏp'ō-lĭs).Syr. (In.).	33.59 N	36.9 E
162	Baao (bä'ō)..................P. I.	13.27 N	123.22 E
129	Babaeski (bä'bä ĕs'kĭ).......Tur.	41.24 N	27.5 E
102	Babahoyo (bä-bä-ō'yō).......Ec.	2.0 S	79.30 W
161	Babar Is. (bä'bär)......Neth. Ind.	8.0 S	129.45 E
150	Bab-el-Mandeb (Str.) (bäb' ĕl män'dĕb).Asia	12.30 N	44.0 E
80	Babia, R. de la (rē'ō-dā-lä-bä'-bē-ä).Mex.	28.36 N	102.0 W
131	Babaikovka (bä'bȧ-ĭ-kôf'kȧ) Sov. Un.	49.0 N	34.30 E
54	Babine L. (băb'ēn)..........Can.	55.0 N	126.30 W
54	Babine Mts..................Can.	55.0 N	127.30 W
150	Babol (bä-bôl')..............Iran	36.30 N	52.50 E
162	Babuyan Chan. (bä-bōō-yän')P. I.	18.40 N	121.40 E
162	Babuyan I...................P. I.	19.30 N	121.55 E
162	Babuyan Is..................P. I.	19.10 N	121.30 E
129	Babjak (bäb'zhȧk)............Bul.	41.58 N	23.41 E
150	Babylon (Ruins) (băb'ĭ-lŏn)..Iraq	32.45 N	44.30 E
103	Bacabal (bä-kȧ-bäl')........Braz.	5.20 S	56.14 W
162	Bacacay (bä-kä-kī').........P. I.	13.17 N	123.47 E
94	Bacalar, L. (bä-kä-lär') Br. Hond.-Mex. (In.)	18.45 N	88.30 W
162	Bacarra (bä-kär'rä)..........P. I.	18.16 N	120.37 E
129	Bacău (bȧ'kŭ-ōō)............Rom.	46.33 N	26.57 E
125	Baccarat (bȧ-kȧ-rä')..........Fr.	48.30 N	6.45 E
73	Bacchus (băk'ŭs) Utah (Salt Lake City In.)	40.40 N	112.6 W
93	Bachajón (bä-chä-hōn').....Mex.	17.8 N	92.17 W
151	Back B.(băk)..India (Bombay In.)	18.55 N	72.48 E
167	Back Cr.....................Austl.	34.4 S	147.38 E
88	Back R......Md. (Baltimore In.)	39.16 N	76.26 W
89	Back R......S. C. (Savannah In.)	32.6 N	81.5 W
142	Back R..............S. W. Afr.	27.35 S	19.50 E
54	Backs R. (băks)............Can.	66.30 N	97.0 W
166	Backstairs Passage (băk-stârs'-päs sĕj).Austl.	35.40 S	138.10 E
160	Bacninh (bäk'nĕn'')..Fr. In. Chn.	21.7 N	106.8 E
162	Bacnotan (bäk-nō-tän').......P. I.	16.42 N	120.22 E
162	Baco, Mt. (bä'kō)............P. I.	12.51 N	121.12 E
119	Bacoli (bä-kō-lē')..It. (Napoli In.)	40.48 N	14.5 E
163	Bacolod (bä-kō'lōd)..........P. I.	10.39 N	122.57 E
162	Bacolor (bä-kō-lōr')..........P. I.	15.1 N	120.39 E
162	Bacon (bä-kōn')..............P. I.	13.2 N	124.2 E
49	Bacona (bā-kō'nȧ) Ore. (Portland In.)	45.46 N	123.8 W
163	Bacong (bä-kông')...........P. I.	9.14 N	123.17 E
162	Bacoor (bä-kō-ōr')...........P. I.	14.27 N	120.57 E
161	Bacoor..........P. I. (Manila In.)	14.28 N	120.55 E
123	Bácsalmás (bäch'ôl-mäs)...Hung.	46.7 N	19.19 E
163	Bacuit (bä-kōō-ēt')...........P. I.	11.11 N	119.24 E
163	Bacuit B.....................P. I.	11.7 N	119.22 E
118	Bacup (băk'ŭp)..........Gt. Brit.	53.42 N	2.12 W
76	Bad R. (băd).................S. D.	44.5 N	101.0 W
127	Badalona (bä-dhä-lō'nä)..Sp. (In.)	41.27 N	2.15 E
126	Badajoz (bä-dhä-hōth').......Sp.	38.52 N	6.58 W
151	Badakhshan (Aut. Area) (bŭd-ŭk-shän').Sov. Un.	37.30 N	73.15 E
135	Badâri (bȧ-dä'rē).......Eg. (In.)	27.0 N	31.29 E
84	Bad Axe (băd' ăks)..........Mich.	43.48 N	82.56 W
122	Baden (bä'dĕn)...............Ger.	48.1 N	16.13 E
122	Baden (State)................Ger.	48.48 N	8.18 E
122	Baden.......................Switz.	47.27 N	8.17 E
163	Badian (bä-dē-än')...........P. I.	9.51 N	123.24 E
83	Badin (bă'dĭn)...............N. C.	35.24 N	80.6 W
122	Bad Ischl (bät ĭsh''l).........Ger.	47.44 N	13.35 E
122	Bad Kissingen(bät kĭs'ĭng-ĕn).Ger.	50.12 N	10.4 E
122	Bad Kreuznach (bät kroits'näĸ) Ger.	49.51 N	7.51 E
76	Bad Lands (băd' lănds).....S. D.	43.43 N	102.30 W
162	Badoc (bä-dōk')..............P. I.	17.56 N	120.30 E
122	Bad Oldesloe (bät ôl'dĕs-lōē..Ger.	53.48 N	10.21 E
71	Badwater Cr. (băd'wô-tẽr)..Wyo.	43.16 N	107.50 W
126	Baena (bä-ā'nä)...............Sp.	37.37 N	4.19 W
103	Baependi (bä-ȧ-pĕn'dĭ).......Braz.	21.59 S	44.59 W
48	Baffin B. (băf'ĭn)...........Can.	72.0 N	65.0 W
81	Baffin Bay...................Tex.	27.15 N	97.35 W
55	Baffin I.....................Can.	67.20 N	71.0 W
138	Bafoulabé (bä-fōō-lä-bā') Fr. W. Afr.	13.56 N	10.48 W
150	Bafq (bäfk) ....Iran	31.50 N	55.29 E
113	Bafra (bäf'rä).................Tur.	41.31 N	35.58 E
113	Bafra, C.....................Tur.	41.40 N	35.59 E
162	Bagabag (bä-gä-bäg')........P. I.	16.37 N	121.15 E
141	Bagamoyo (bä-gä-mō'yō)....Tan.	6.20 S	38.50 E
163	Baganga (bä-gäŋ'gä).........P. I.	7.33 N	126.34 E

Page	Name Pronunciation Region	Lat. °′	Long. °′
163	Baganian Pen. (bȧ-gä'nĭ-ȧn)..P. I.	7.25 N	123.25 E
104	Bagé (bä-gā')..............Braz.	31.28 S	54.10 W
151	Bagh (bäĸ).................Afg.	33.48 N	70.45 E
150	Baghdad (bȧgh-dȧd') (băg'dăd) Iraq	33.15 N	44.30 E
128	Bagheria (bä-gȧ-rē'ä).........It.	38.4 N	13.31 E
76	Bagley (băg'lē).............Minn.	47.31 N	95.21 W
128	Bagnara (bän-yä'rä)..........It.	38.17 N	15.49 E
124	Bagnères-de-Biggorre (bän-yâr' dē bē-gôr').Fr.	43.5 N	0.10 E
124	Bagnères-de-Luchon (bän-yâr' dē lü-chôɴ').Fr.	42.45 N	0.35 E
124	Bagneux (bän-yû')........Fr. (In.)	48.47 N	2.18 E
119	Bagnoli (bän'yō-lē)It. (Napoli In.)	40.49 N	14.10 E
124	Bagnols (bä-nyôl')............Fr.	44.10 N	4.40 E
163	Bago (bä'gō)..................P. I.	10.31 N	122.51 E
138	Bagoe, R. (bȧ-gō'ȧ)...Fr. W. Afr.	11.30 N	6.30 W
161	Bagombon (bä-gōm'bōn) P. I. (Manila In.)	14.23 N	121.27 E
86	Bagotville (bȧ-gō-vēl').......Can.	48.19 N	70.54 W
152	Bagrach Kol (L.) (bä'grȧch kûl') Chn.	42.0 N	87.0 E
138	Baguezane Mts. (bȧ-gē-zän') Fr. W. Afr.	17.50 N	8.40 E
162	Baguio (bä-gē-ō')............P. I.	16.25 N	120.36 E
96	Bahama I. (bȧ-hä'mȧ).....Ba. Is.	26.40 N	78.20 W
96	Bahama Is................Atl. O.	23.30 N	75.0 W
115	Bahariya Oasis (bȧ-hä-rē'yȧ)..Eg.	28.0 N	29.0 E
151	Bahawalpur (bŭ-hä'wŭl-pōōr) India	29.15 N	71.33 E
103	Bahia (State) (bä-ē'ȧ)......Braz.	12.30 S	42.0 W
104	Bahia Blanca (bä-ē'-ä bläŋ'kä) Arg.	38.45 S	62.1 W
104	Bahia Blanca (B.)...........Arg.	39.28 S	61.45 W
102	Bahia de Caráquez (bä-ē'ä dä kä-rä'kĕz).Ec.	0.45 S	80.29 W
103	Bahia Negra (bä-ē'ä nā'grä)..Par.	20.1 S	58.15 W
103	Bahia (São Salvador) (bä-ē'ä) (souɴ'säl-vȧ-dōr').Braz.	13.0 S	38.30 W
135	Bahnasa (bä'nȧ-sȧ).......Eg. (In.)	28.40 N	30.51 E
97	Bahoruco, Mts. of (bä-ō-rōō'kō) Hai.	18.5 N	71.25 W
150	Bahr As Safi (Des.) (bär' äs sä'-fē).Arabia	17.30 N	48.0 E
150	Bahrein I. (bä-rān')..........Asia	26.10 N	50.40 E
139	Bahr el Abyad (White Nile) (R.) (bär ĕl äb'yȧd).A. E. Sud.	13.0 N	32.45 E
139	Bahr el Arab (R.) (bär ĕl ä'räb) A. E. Sud.	9.45 N	27.30 E
139	Bahr el Azraq (Blue Nile) (R.) (äz-räk').A. E. Sud.-Eth.	13.0 N	34.0 E
139	Bahr Azum (R.) (ä-zōōm') Fr. Eq. Afr.	11.20 N	20.30 E
139	Bahr el Ghazal (Reg.) (gȧ-zäl') A. E. Sud.	7.30 N	27.30 E
139	Bahr el Ghazal (R.)....A. E. Sud.	9.25 N	30.0 E
139	Bahr el Jebel (Mountain Nile) (R.) (jĕb'ĕl).Afr.	7.0 N	31.0 E
139	Bahr Sara (R.) (sȧ-rä') Fr. Eq. Afr.	8.0 N	17.36 E
119	Baia (bä'yä).......It. (Napoli In.)	40.49 N	14.5 E
123	Baia-de-Cris (bä'yȧ dā krēs').Rom.	46.10 N	22.40 E
123	Baia-Mare (bä'yä-mä'rä)....Rom.	47.40 N	23.36 E
148	Baidaratskaya B. (bī'dä-rät-skä'yä).Sov. Un.	69.15 N	67.30 E
152	Baidarik Gol (R.) (bī'dä-rĭk gōl').Chn.	46.0 N	99.10 E
141	Baidoa (bä-ĭ-dō'ä)......It. E. Afr.	3.7 N	43.38 E
86	Baie St. Paul (bā'sănt-pôl')..Can.	47.27 N	70.31 W
149	Baikal, L. (bī'käl') (bī'kôl) Sov. Un.	54.0 N	108.40 E
149	Baikal Mts...........Sov. Un.	54.0 N	108.0 E
131	Baikiyat (bī-kē'ät).......Sov. Un.	45.40 N	33.0 E
116	Baile Atha Cliath (Dublin) (bŏ'lĕ ô'hō clē'ŏh) (dŭb'lĭn)...Ire.	53.20 N	6.15 W
161	Bailen (bä-ē-län') P. I. (Manila In.)	14.13 N	120.45 E
126	Bailén (bä-ē-lān')............Sp.	38.7 N	3.38 W
129	Băileşti (bȧ-ĭ-lĕsh'tĭ).......Rom.	44.1 N	23.21 E
72	Baileys (bā'lĭz)..Colo.(Denver In.)	39.25 N	105.29 W
125	Bailly (bȧ-yē')........Fr. (In.)	48.50 N	2.5 E
124	Bain (băɴ)....................Fr.	47.51 N	1.39 W
82	Bainbridge (bān'brĭj)..........Ga.	30.53 N	84.34 W
49	Bainbridge I...Wash. (Seattle In.)	47.40 N	122.30 W
129	Bairamiş (bä-ē-rä'mĭsh)......Tur.	39.47 N	26.38 E
80	Baird (bârd)..................Tex.	32.22 N	99.23 W
52	Baird Mts....................Alsk.	67.40 N	160.0 W
167	Bairnsdale (bârnz'dāl)......Austl.	37.47 S	147.35 E
163	Bais (bä-ēs')..................P. I.	9.35 N	123.8 E
124	Baïse R. (bȧ-ēz')..............Fr.	43.50 N	0.20 E
123	Baja (bŏ'yŏ)..................Hung.	46.11 N	18.58 E
74	Baja California (bä-hä)......Mex.	32.20 N	116.0 W
169	Bajemba Mt. (bȧ-jĕm'bȧ) Austl. (In.)	29.20 S	152.4 E
158	Bakdusan (Mt.) (bäk-dōō-sän') Cho.	42.0 N	128.0 E
138	Bakel (bȧ-kĕl')......Fr. W. Afr.	14.52 N	12.30 W
71	Baker (bā'kẽr)..............Mont.	46.23 N	104.17 W
70	Baker..........................Ore.	44.47 N	117.50 W
54	Baker L.......................Can.	64.15 N	96.25 W
70	Baker, Mt....................Wash.	48.47 N	121.49 W
74	Bakersfield (bā'kẽrz-fēld)....Calif.	35.23 N	119.1 W
118	Bakewell (băk'wĕl).......Gt. Brit.	53.12 N	1.40 W
131	Bakhchisarai (bäĸ'chē-sȧ-rī') Sov. Un.	44.44 N	33.54 E
131	Bakhmach (bȧĸ-mȧch')..Sov. Un.	51.9 N	32.48 E
148	Bakhti (Zakarovskoe) (bäĸ-tē') (zä'kȧ-rôf-skō'yĕ)...Sov. Un.	46.58 N	82.50 E
139	Bako (bä'kō)............It. E. Afr.	5.46 N	36.37 E
123	Bakony Forest (Mts.) (bȧ-kōn'y') Hung.	47.10 N	17.55 E
138	Bakoy, R. (bȧ-kô'ē)...Fr. W. Afr.	12.45 N	9.30 W

Page	Name Pronunciation Region	Lat. °′	Long. °′
113	Baku (bȧ-kōō')..........Sov. Un.	40.28 N	49.45 E
138	Bakwa (bäk'wä)...............Nig.	12.42 N	5.58 E
163	Balabac (bä-lä'bäk)..........P. I.	7.59 N	117.3 E
163	Balabac I.....................P. I.	7.57 N	117.0 E
160	Balabac Str.............B. N. B.	7.30 N	117.0 E
163	Balabac Str., N..............P. I.	7.35 N	117.0 E
160	Balabalagan (I.) (bä-lä-bä'lä-gän).Neth. Ind.	2.30 S	117.30 E
148	Balagansk (bä-lä-gänsk').Sov. Un.	53.59 N	103.10 E
127	Balaguer (bä-lä-gĕr')..........Sp.	41.48 N	0.49 E
135	Balah Lakes (bä'lȧ) Eg. (Suez Can. In.)	30.54 N	32.18 E
148	Balakhta (bä'läĸ-tä')....Sov. Un.	55.25 N	91.35 E
166	Balaklava (bȧ-lȧ-klä'vȧ)....Austl.	34.9 S	138.25 E
131	Balaklava...............Sov. Un.	44.29 N	33.40 E
131	Balakleya (bä'lä-klā'yä) .Sov. Un.	49.28 N	36.51 E
113	Balakovo (bä'lȧ-kō'vō)..Sov. Un.	52.0 N	47.48 E
163	Balamban (bä-läm-bän')......P. I.	10.29 N	123.44 E
93	Balancán (bä-läŋ-kän')......Mex.	17.47 N	91.32 W
162	Balanga (bä-läŋ'gä)...........P. I.	14.40 N	120.32 E
163	Balangiga (bä-läŋ-hē'gä).....P. I.	11.7 N	125.23 E
162	Balaoan (bä-lou'än)..........P. I.	16.49 N	120.24 E
163	Balasan (bä-lä'sän) ....P. I.	11.28 N	123.7 E
113	Balashov (bä-lä-shôf)....Sov. Un.	51.28 N	43.15 E
151	Balasore (bä-lȧ-sōr')........India	21.28 N	86.59 E
123	Balassagyarmat (bô'lôsh-shô-dyôr'môt).Hung.	48.4 N	19.19 E
123	Balaton L. (bô'lō-tôn)......Hung.	46.50 N	17.45 E
162	Balayan (bä-lä-yän')..........P. I.	13.57 N	120.43 E
162	Balayan B....................P. I.	13.50 N	120.48 E
73	Balboa (băl-bō'ȧ) Calif. (Los Angels In.)	33.36 N	117.55 W
90	Balboa........................C. Z.	8.58 N	79.32 W
90	Balboa Heights...............C. Z.	8.58 N	79.33 W
93	Balbuena Park (bäl-bwā'nä) Mex. (In.)	19.25 N	99.7 W
104	Balcarce (bäl-kär'sä).........Arg.	37.50 S	58.20 W
129	Balcic (bäl-chēk')............Rom.	43.25 N	28.11 E
171	Balclutha (băl-clōō'thȧ).....N. Z.	46.15 S	169.48 E
72	Bald, Mt. (bôld) Colo. (Denver In.)	40.2 N	105.28 W
73	Baldwin Park (bôld'wĭn) Calif. (Los Angeles In.)	34.5 N	117.56 W
85	Baldwinsville (bôld'wĭns-vĭl) N. Y.	43.9 N	76.20 W
75	Baldy Peak (bôl'dē)..........Ariz.	33.53 N	109.35 W
80	Baldy Peak....................Tex.	30.39 N	104.12 W
73	Baldy Peak Utah (Salt Lake City In.)	41.24 N	111.29 W
145	Bale (bä'lä)......Neth. Ind. (In.)	1.8 N	101.16 E
122	Bâle (Basel) (bäl) (bä'zĕl)...Switz.	47.33 N	7.35 E
127	Balearic Is. (băl-ē-ăr'ĭk) ....Sp.	39.40 N	2.30 E
171	Baleine Point (bȧ-lăn').N. Z. (In.)	43.36 S	172.53 E
162	Baler (bä-lär')................P. I.	15.45 N	121.33 E
162	Baler B.......................P. I.	15.50 N	121.36 E
162	Balesin I. (bä-lē-sēn')........P. I.	14.25 N	122.2 E
94	Balfate (bĕl'fät)..............Hond.	15.50 N	86.17 W
143	Balfour (băl'fōōr)......U. S. Afr.	26.39 S	28.38 E
143	Balfour...................U. S. Afr.	32.32 S	26.38 E
73	Balfour. Utah (Salt Lake City In.)	41.35 N	112.17 W
169	Balfour Mt. (băl'fōōr) Austl. (Tas. In.)	41.22 S	144.57 E
169	Balgowish (băl'gō-wĭsh) Austl. (Sydney In.)	33.48 S	151.16 E
160	Bali (I.) (bä'lē)........Neth. Ind.	8.30 S	115.0 E
163	Baliangao (bä'lē-äŋ-gä'ō)....P. I.	8.38 N	123.38 E
113	Balikesir (bä-lĭ-kē-sēr')......Tur.	39.42 N	28.0 E
160	Balikpapan (bä'lĕk-pä'pän) Neth. Ind.	108.0 S	116.50 E
113	Balikta, L. (bä-lĕk'tä) ...Sov. Un.	50.0 N	50.45 E
163	Balimbing (bä-lĭm-bĕng') ....P. I.	5.6 N	119.57 E
162	Balingasag (bä-lĭŋ'gä-säg')...P. I.	8.43 N	124.47 E
160	Balintang Chan. (bä-lĭn-täng)P. I.	19.45 N	121.30 E
162	Baliuag (bä-lē'-wäg)..........P. I.	14.58 N	120.54 E
149	Balkalakh (bäl-kä-läĸ')..Sov. Un.	72.50 N	119.40 E
129	Balkan Mts. (bô'kȧn)..........Bul.	42.40 N	25.25 E
151	Balkh (bälk)....................Afg.	36.44 N	66.58 E
148	Balkhash, L.(bäl-käsh')..Sov. Un.	46.35 N	76.0 E
131	Balki (bäl'kĭ).............Sov. Un.	47.23 N	34.53 E
87	Ball, C. (bäl)...............Newf.	51.35 N	55.25 W
135	Ballah (bä'lä).Eg. (Suez Can. In.)	30.47 N	32.21 E
113	Balla-Ishet (bä'lȧ-ĭsh-ĕt') Sov. Un.	39.28 N	54.30 E
169	Ballandean (băl'ăn-dēn) Austl. (In.)	28.48 S	151.53 E
166	Ballarat (băl'ȧ-răt).........Austl.	37.33 S	143.51 E
164	Ballard, L. (băl'ȧrd).......Austl.	29.30 S	120.47 E
116	Ballater (băl'ȧ-tẽr)......Gt. Brit.	57.5 N	3.0 W
46	Balleny Is. (băl'ĕ-nĕ)......Ant. O.	67.0 S	164.0 E
162	Ballesteros (bäl-yĕs-tā'rōs)...P. I.	18.23 N	121.31 E
169	Ballina (băl-ĭ-nȧ')......Austl. (In.)	28.49 S	153.32 E
116	Ballina........................Ire.	54.8 N	9.10 W
116	Ballinasloe (băl'ĭ-nȧ-slō')......Ire.	53.20 N	8.0 W
80	Ballinger (băl'ĭn-jẽr)..........Tex.	31.45 N	99.57 W
85	Ballston Spa (bôls'tŭn spä').N. Y.	43.0 N	73.52 W
116	Ballycastle (băl-ĭ-căs''l)....N. Ire.	55.10 N	6.15 W
123	Balmazújváros (bŏl'mŏz-ōō'y'vä'-rōsh).Hung.	47.37 N	21.22 E
163	Balmoral (băl'mō-răl)....B. N. B.	5.53 N	117.39 E
116	Balmoral..................Gt. Brit.	57.0 N	3.10 W
135	Balqas (bäl-käs).........Eg. (In.)	31.13 N	31.23 E
166	Balronald (băl-rŏ'nȧld).......Austl.	34.38 S	143.35 E
129	Bălş (bălsh)..................Rom.	44.20 N	24.6 E
85	Balsam L. (bôl'sȧm).........Can.	44.30 N	78.30 W
92	Balsas R. (bäl'säs)............Mex.	18.30 N	101.0 W
131	Balta (bäl'tä)..............Sov. Un.	47.57 N	29.39 E
123	Bălti (bĕl'tsē)................Rom.	47.45 N	27.57 E
	Baltic Port, see Baltiski, Est.		
120	Baltic Sea (bôl'tĭk)............Eur.	55.20 N	16.45 E
135	Baltîm (bäl-tēm')........Eg. (In.)	31.31 N	31.5 E
85	Baltimore (bôl'tĭ-mōr).........Md.	39.18 N	76.38 W
88	Baltimore, Md. (In.)		
121	Baltiski (bäl'tĭ-skē)...........Est.	59.20 N	24.4 E

-sing; ŋ-baŋk; ɴ-nasalized n; nŏd; cŏmmit; ōld; ōbey; ôrder; fōōd; fŏŏt; ou-out; s-soft; sh-dish; th-thin; pūre; ůnite; ûrn; stŭd; circŭs; ü-as "y" in study; '-indeterminate vowel

Page	Name Pronunciation Region	Lat. °'	Long. °'
113	Baltser (bält-sĕr') Sov. Un.	51.0 N	45.40 E
150	Baluchistan (Dist.) (bȧ-lōō-chi-stän'). India	27.30 N	65.30 E
163	Balut I. (bȧ-lōōt') P. I.	5.24 N	125.23 E
135	Balyana (bäl'yȧ-nȧ) Eg. (In.)	6.12 N	32.2 E
138	Bamako (bä-mȧ-kō') Fr. W. Afr.	12.42 N	7.58 W
138	Bamba (bȧm-bä') Fr. W. Afr.	17.9 N	1.28 W
162	Bambang (bäm-bäng') P. I.	16.23 N	121.7 E
139	Bambari (bäm-bȧ-rē'). Fr. Eq. Afr.	5.37 N	20.36 E
122	Bamberg (bäm'bĕrgh) Ger.	49.55 N	10.52 E
83	Bamberg (băm'bûrg) S. C.	33.17 N	81.3 W
139	Bambili (bäm-bē-lē') Bel. Cong.	3.47 N	26.4 E
143	Bamboes Mts. (bäm'bōōz) U. S. Afr.	31.30 S	26.20 E
138	Bambuto Mts. (bäm-bōō'tō). Nig.	6.0 N	9.45 E
150	Bampur (bŭm-pōōr') Iran	27.27 N	60.28 E
161	Banadero (bä-nä-dā'rō) P. I. (Manila In.)	14.7 N	121.4 E
162	Banahao, Mt. (bä-nä-hä'ō) P. I.	14.4 N	121.30 E
140	Banana (bȧ-nä'nȧ) Bel. Cong.	5.55 S	12.23 E
83	Banana R. (bȧ-nȧ'nȧ) Fla. (In.)	28.30 N	80.35 W
103	Bananal I. (bä-nä-näl') Braz.	11.30 S	50.15 W
151	Banas R. (bän-äs') India	25.30 N	75.0 E
129	Banat (Prov.) (bä'nät) Rom.-Yugo.	45.25 N	22.0 E
95	Banbana, R. (bän-bän'ä) Nic.	13.35 N	84.0 W
118	Banbury (băn'bĕr-ĭ) Gt. Brit.	52.44 N	1.20 W
166	Bancanya, L. (băn-căn'yȧ) Austl.	30.48 S	141.52 E
55	Bancroft (băn'krôft) Can.	45.5 N	77.50 W
151	Banda (bän'dä) India	25.27 N	80.25 E
161	Banda Is. Neth. Ind.	4.38 S	129.55 E
161	Banda Sea Neth. Ind.	6.0 S	127.30 E
138	Bandama R. (bän-dä'mä) Fr. W. Afr.	6.30 N	5.30 W
150	Bandar 'Abbasi (bŭn'dȧr ȧb-bäs'ē). Iran	27.30 N	56.29 E
150	Bandar Abu Shehr (Bushire) (bŭn'dȧr ä'bōō shär'). Iran	28.47 N	50.47 E
145	Bandar Maharani (bŭn'dȧr mä-hä-rä'nē). Non-fed. Mal. St. (In.)	22.0 N	102.35 E
150	Bandar Shab (bŭn'dȧr shäb) Iran	37.0 N	54.25 E
150	Bandar Shapur (bŭn'dȧr shä-pōōr'). Iran	30.29 N	48.59 E
141	Bandar Ziada (bŭn-dȧr' zē-ä'dä) Br. Som.	11.8 N	48.52 E
126	Bande (bän'dhä) Sp.	42.2 N	7.58 W
103	Bandeira, Pico de (Mt.) (pē'kōō dä bän-dā'rȧ). Braz.	20.29 S	41.58 W
75	Bandelier Natl. Mon. (băn-dĕ-lēr') N. M.	35.45 N	106.18 W
92	Banderas B. (bän-dā'räs) Mex.	20.35 N	105.30 W
138	Bandiagara (bän-dē-ȧ-gä'rȧ) Fr. W. Afr.	14.26 N	3.40 W
113	Bandirma (bän-dĭr'mȧ) Tur.	40.20 N	28.0 E
160	Bandjermasin (bän-jĕr-mä'sĕn) Neth. Ind.	3.21 S	114.34 E
160	Bandoeng (bän'dōōng). Neth. Ind.	6.59 S	107.38 E
70	Bandon (băn'dŭn) Ore.	43.5 N	124.25 W
140	Bandundu (bän-dōōn'dōō) Bel. Cong.	3.20 S	17.20 E
97	Banes (bä'näs) Cuba	20.58 N	75.45 W
54	Banff (bănf) Can.	51.15 N	115.29 W
116	Banff Gt. Brit.	57.40 N	2.32 W
54	Banff National Park Can.	51.0 N	116.0 W
104	Banfield (băn'fēld) Arg. (In.)	34.44 S	58.23 W
163	Bangai Pt. (bäŋ-gī') P. I.	7.42 N	126.35 E
151	Bangalore (băŋ-gȧ-lōr') India	12.59 N	77.28 E
162	Bangar (bäŋ-gär') P. I.	16.54 N	120.25 E
139	Bangassou (bäN-gȧ-sōō') Fr. Eq. Afr.	4.46 N	22.48 E
152	Bangfu (bäng'fōō') Chn. (Shanghai In.)	31.13 N	121.24 E
161	Banggai Arch. (bäng-gī') Neth. Ind.	1.15 S	123.15 E
160	Bangka (I.) (bäŋ'kȧ) Neth. Ind.	2.30 S	106.0 E
160	Bangkalan (bäng-kȧ-län') Neth. Ind.	7.8 S	112.50 E
160	Bangkok (băng-kŏk') Thai.	13.45 N	100.30 E
116	Bangor (băŋ'gŏr) (băŋ'gĕr) Gt. Brit.	53.12 N	4.5 W
86	Bangor (băn'gôr) Me.	44.47 N	68.47 W
84	Bangor Mich.	42.22 N	86.7 W
85	Bangor (băŋ'gĕr) Pa.	40.54 N	75.12 W
49	Bangor Wash. (Seattle In.)	47.43 N	122.45 W
160	Bang Sapan Yai (bäng'sä'pän-yī') Thai.	11.15 N	99.32 E
162	Bangued (bän-gād') P. I.	17.36 N	120.37 E
160	Banguey I. (bän-gā') B. N. B.	7.15 N	117.10 E
139	Bangui (bäŋ gē') Fr. Eq. Afr.	4.28 N	18.33 E
162	Bangui (bän'gē) P. I.	18.31 N	120.46 E
162	Bangui B. P. I.	18.35 N	120.35 E
140	Bangweulu, L. (băng-wē-ōō'lōō) N. Rh.	11.0 S	29.50 E
135	Banha (bän'hȧ) Eg. (In.)	30.26 N	31.11 E
97	Bani (bä'nē) Hai.	18.16 N	70.24 W
162	Bani P. I.	16.12 N	119.51 E
97	Banica (bä'nē-kȧ) Hai.	18.59 N	71.37 W
135	Bani Mazâr (bä'nē-mȧ-zär') Eg. (In.)	28.30 N	30.49 E
138	Bani R. (bä'nē) Fr. W. Afr.	13.30 N	5.0 W
131	Banishche (bä'nĭsh-chĕ) Sov. Un.	51.42 N	35.2 E
139	Bani Suef (bä'nē sōō-ĕf') Eg.	29.12 N	31.2 E
128	Banjaluka (bän-yä-lōō'kȧ) Yugo.	44.47 N	17.12 E
160	Banjoewangi (bän-jōō-wäŋ'gē) Neth. Ind.	8.15 S	114.18 E
143	Bankberg (bănk'bûrg) U. S. Afr.	32.17 S	25.25 E
73	Bankhead (bănk'hĕd) Ala. (Birmingham In.)	33.46 N	87.18 W
49	Banks (bănks) Ore. (Portland In.)	45.36 N	123.6 W
169	Banks, C. Austl. (Sydney In.)	34.0 S	151.15 E
53	Banks I. Can.	53.20 N	130.0 W
48	Banks I. Can.	73.0 N	123.0 W
165	Banks I. Pap. Ter.	10.10 S	142.10 E
165	Banks Is. Austl.	13.40 S	167.30 E
171	Banks Pen. N. Z.	43.45 S	173.0 E
169	Banks Str. Austl. (Tas. In.)	40.38 S	148.5 E
167	Bankstown Austl.	33.57 S	151.1 E
116	Bann, R. (băn) N. Ire.	55.0 N	6.35 W
73	Banning (băn'ĭng) Calif. (Los Angeles In.)	33.55 N	116.53 W
127	Bañolas (bän-yō'läs) Sp.	42.6 N	2.46 E
123	Banská Bystrica (bän'skä bē'strē-tzȧ). Czech.	48.45 N	19.9 E
123	Banská Stiavinica (bän'skä shtē'-äv-nyē'tsä). Czech.	48.27 N	18.52 E
129	Bansko (bän'skō) Bul.	41.51 N	23.32 E
163	Bantayan I. (bän-tä-yän') P. I.	11.14 N	123.44 E
138	Banthe (bän'thē) S. L.	7.32 N	12.36 W
162	Banton I. (bän-tōn') P. I.	12.56 N	122.3 E
116	Bantry (băn'trĭ) Ire.	51.37 N	9.28 W
116	Bantry B. Ire.	51.35 N	9.50 W
160	Banyak Is. (bän'yăk) Neth. Ind.	2.10 N	97.15 E
135	Banza Manteka (bän'zȧ män-tā'kȧ) Bel. Cong. (Brazzaville In.)	5.31 S	13.46 E
139	Banzyville (bäN-zē-vēl') Bel. Cong.	4.15 N	21.8 E
138	Baoulé R. (bȧ-ōō-lā') Fr. W. Afr.	14.0 N	9.0 W
131	Bar (bär) Sov. Un.	49.3 N	27.41 E
129	Bar Yugo.	42.4 N	19.8 E
148	Barabinsk (bȧ'rȧ-bĭnsk) Sov. Un.	55.40 N	79.59 E
77	Baraboo (bär'ȧ-bōō) Wis.	43.30 N	89.44 W
97	Baracoa (bä-rä-kō'ȧ) Cuba	20.20 N	74.28 W
97	Baradères B. (bȧ-rä-dâr') Hai.	18.35 N	73.37 W
167	Baradine (bă'rȧ-dĭn) Austl.	30.58 S	149.6 E
141	Baragil (bȧ-rä-gēl') Eg.	30.5 N	31.9 E
97	Barahona (bä-rä-hō'nä) Hai.	18.12 N	71.5 W
127	Barajas de Madrid (bä-rä'häs dä mä-drēdh'). Sp. (In.)	40.28 N	3.36 W
139	Baraka R. (bȧ-rä'kä) It. E. Afr.-A. E. Sud.	17.0 N	37.30 E
141	Baran (bȧ-rän') Br. Som.	10.40 N	48.30 E
94	Baranco (bä-räŋ'kō) Br. Hond.	16.1 N	88.56 W
53	Baranof I. (bä-rä'nôf) Alsk.	57.0 N	135.0 W
123	Baranowicze (bä'rä-nō-vē'chä) Pol.	53.7 N	25.59 E
162	Baras (bä-räs') P. I.	13.39 N	124.22 E
161	Baras P. I. (Manila In.)	14.33 N	121.18 E
131	Barasha (bä'rȧ-shȧ) Sov. Un.	50.45 N	28.2 E
81	Barataria B. (bär-ȧ-tä'rē-ȧ) La.	29.20 N	89.55 W
103	Barbacena (bär-bä-sā'nȧ) Braz.	21.15 S	43.50 W
102	Barbacoas (bär-bä-kō'äs) Col.	1.40 N	78.1 W
91	Barbados (I.) (bär-bä'dōz) W. I.	13.15 N	59.30 W
99	Barbara Chan. (bär'bä-rä) Chl. (Magallanes In.)	54.0 S	72.25 W
127	Barbastro (bär-bäs'trō) Sp.	42.2 N	0.6 E
127	Barbate (bär-bä'tä) Sp. (In.)	36.12 N	5.55 W
127	Barbate R. Sp. (In.)	36.15 N	5.55 W
143	Barberspan (bär'bĕrs-păn) U. S. Afr.	25.37 S	25.36 E
84	Barberton (bär'bĕr-tŭn) Ohio	41.3 N	81.37 W
143	Barberton U. S. Afr.	25.47 S	31.2 E
124	Barbezieux (bärb'zyû') Fr.	45.29 N	0.10 W
84	Barboursville W. Va.	38.24 N	82.17 W
82	Barbourville (bär'bĕr-vĭl) Ky.	36.53 N	83.53 W
91	Barbuda (I.) (bär-bōō'dȧ) W. I.	17.35 N	61.35 W
126	Barca d'Alva (bär'kȧ däl'vä). Port.	41.1 N	6.58 W
165	Barcaldine (bär'kôl-dīn) Austl.	23.40 S	145.20 E
139	Barca Plat. (bär'kä) Libya	32.0 N	21.30 E
103	Barcarena (bär-kä-rā' nä) Braz. (In.)	1.31 S	48.41 W
127	Barcarena Port. (In.)	38.44 N	9.18 W
126	Barcarrota (bär-kär-rō'tä) Sp.	38.31 N	6.51 W
115	Barce (bär'chä) Libya	32.45 N	21.2 E
128	Barcellona (bär-chĕl-lō'nä) It.	38.7 N	15.12 E
126	Barcellonnette (bär-sĕ-lō-nĕt') Fr.	44.25 N	6.41 E
102	Barcellos (bär-säl'yōs) Braz.	1.1 S	63.1 W
127	Barcelona (bär-thä-lō'nä) Sp. (In.)	41.23 N	2.11 E
127	Barcelona (Prov.) Sp. (In.)	41.27 N	1.57 E
102	Barcelona (bär-sä-lō'nä) Ven.	10.10 N	64.45 W
126	Barcelos (bär-thä'lōs) Port.	41.33 N	8.38 W
165	Barcoo (R.) (bär'kōō) Austl.	28.0 S	139.15 E
139	Bardaï (bär-dä'ē) Fr. W. Afr.	21.22 N	16.56 E
123	Bardějov (bär'dyĕ-yôf) Czech.	49.17 N	21.17 E
139	Bardera (bär-dā'rä) It. E. Afr.	2.22 N	42.22 E
116	Bardsey I. (bärd'sē) Gt. Brit.	52.45 N	4.45 W
84	Bardstown (bärds'town) Ky.	37.48 N	85.29 W
82	Bardwell (bärd'wĕl) Ky.	36.54 N	89.2 W
151	Bareilly (bŭ-rä'lē) India	28.15 N	79.25 E
167	Barellan (băr'ĕl-ăn) Austl.	34.15 S	146.36 E
124	Barentin (bȧ-räN-tăN') Fr.	49.35 N	0.59 E
112	Barents Sea (bä'rĕnts) Asia	70.15 N	41.0 E
139	Barentu (bä-rĕn'tōō) It. E. Afr.	15.6 N	37.35 E
169	Bare Point (bâr) Austl. (In.)	29.45 S	153.18 E
124	Barfleur, Pt. de (bär-flûr') Fr.	49.45 N	1.15 W
	Barfrush, see Babol, Persia		
135	Bargou, Djebel (Mt.) (jĕb'ĕl bär-gōō'). Tun. (In.)	36.3 N	9.40 E
149	Barguzin (bär'gōō-zĭn) Sov. Un.	53.40 N	109.30 E
149	Barguzin R. Sov. Un.	54.35 N	110.20 E
86	Bar Harbor (bär här'bĕr) Me.	44.23 N	68.14 W
128	Bari (bä'rē) It.	41.6 N	16.52 E
163	Barili (bä-rē'lē) P. I.	10.16 N	123.31 E
104	Bariloche (bä-rē-lō'chä) Arg.	41.15 S	71.29 W
103	Barima (bä-rē'mä) Br. Gu.	7.58 N	60.2 W
102	Barinas (bä-rē'näs) Ven.	8.31 N	70.13 W
170	Baring Head (C.) (bâr'ĭng hĕd) N. Z. (In.)	41.24 S	174.53 E
160	Barisan Mts. (bä-rē-sän') Neth. Ind.	4.0 S	103.0 E
160	Barito R. (bä-rē'tō) Neth. Ind.	1.0 S	114.50 E
166	Barker, Mt. (bär'kĕr) Austl.	35.5 S	138.52 E
119	Barking (bär'kĭng) Gt. Brit. (London In.)	51.32 N	0.5 E
143	Barkly East (bär'klē ēst) U. S. Afr.	30.59 S	27.35 E
164	Barkly Tableland Austl.	19.0 S	137.30 E
143	Barkly West Bech.	28.31 S	24.32 E
152	Barköl (Chensi) (bär'kûl') (chĕn'sē'). Chn.	43.32 N	93.0 E
123	Bârlad (bûr'lät) Rom.	46.16 N	27.39 E
124	Bar-le-Duc (bär-lē-dük') Fr.	48.48 N	5.5 E
164	Barlee, L. (bär-lē') Austl.	29.15 S	119.30 E
128	Barletta (bär-lĕt'tä) It.	41.18 N	16.28 E
167	Barmedman (bär-mĕd'mȧn) Austl.	34.7 S	147.23 E
148	Barnaul (bär-nä-ōōl') Sov. Un.	53.58 N	83.50 E
85	Barnesboro (bärnz'bĕr-ô) Pa.	40.44 N	78.50 W
72	Barnesville (bärnz'vĭl) Colo. (Denver In.)	40.29 N	104.28 W
82	Barnesville Ga.	33.3 N	84.10 W
76	Barnesville Minn.	46.39 N	96.25 W
84	Barnesville Ohio	38.58 N	81.10 W
86	Barnet (bär'nĕt) Vt.	44.15 N	72.5 W
118	Barnetby (bär'nĕt-bĭ) Gt. Brit.	53.34 N	0.25 W
96	Barnet Har. Ba. Is.	25.38 N	79.11 W
79	Barnsdall (bärnz'dôl) Okla.	36.36 N	96.13 W
116	Barnsley (bärnz'lĭ) Gt. Brit.	53.32 N	1.30 W
116	Barnstaple (bärn'stȧ-p'l). Gt. Brit.	51.5 N	4.5 W
83	Barnwell (bärn'wĕl) S. C.	33.14 N	81.22 W
138	Baro (bä'rō) Nig.	8.37 N	6.28 E
151	Baroda (bȧ-rō'dä) India	22.20 N	73.20 E
140	Barotseland (Dist.) (bȧ-rŏt'sĕ-lănd) N. Rh.	16.15 S	23.30 E
102	Barquisimeto (bär-kē-sē-mā'tō) Ven.	10.2 N	69.18 W
125	Barr (bär) Fr.	48.25 N	7.28 E
119	Barra (bär'rä) It. (Napoli In.)	40.50 N	14.19 E
167	Barraba (bă'rȧ-ba) Austl.	30.23 S	150.39 E
103	Barra do Corda (bär'rä dōō cōr'dä) Braz.	5.30 S	45.15 W
99	Barra do Pirahi (bär'rä dōō pē-rȧ'ē) Braz. (Rio de Janeiro In.)	22.30 S	43.52 W
103	Barra do Rio Grande (bär'rä dōō rē'ōō grän'dē). Braz.	11.2 S	43.2 W
116	Barra Head (C.) (băr'ȧ). Gt. Brit.	56.45 N	7.45 W
116	Barra Isles Gt. Brit.	56.55 N	7.30 W
99	Barra Mansa (bär'rä-män'sä) Braz. (Rio de Janeiro In.)	22.32 S	44.14 W
102	Barrancabermeja (bär-räŋ'kä-bĕr-mä'hä). Col.	7.2 N	73.58 W
102	Barranco (bär-räŋ'kō) Peru (In.)	12.9 S	77.2 W
102	Barranquilla (bär-rän-kēl'yä). Col.	10.59 N	74.58 W
93	Barra Tampico (Arbol Grande) (bär'rä täm-pē'kō) (är-bōl'grän'dä). Mex.	22.18 N	97.53 W
86	Barre (băr'ē) Vt.	44.11 N	72.31 W
127	Barreiro (bär-rĕ'ē-rōō). Port. (In.)	38.39 N	9.4 W
141	Barren Is. (băr'ĕn) Madag.	18.20 S	43.45 E
82	Barren R. Ky.	37.0 N	86.22 W
97	Barreto (bär-rā'tōō) Braz. (In.)	22.52 S	43.6 W
103	Barretos (bär-rā'tōs) Braz.	20.32 S	48.32 W
85	Barrie (băr'ĭ) Can.	44.22 N	79.40 W
93	Barrientos (bär-rē-ĕn'tōs) Mex. (In.)	19.35 N	99.12 W
169	Barring, Pt. (băr'ĭng) Austl. (Melbourne In.)	38.0 S	145.2 E
167	Barrington (băr'ĭng-tŭn) Austl.	31.58 S	151.52 E
72	Barr (bär) Colo. (Denver In.)	39.57 N	104.46 W
97	Barron (băr'ŭn) Wis.	45.25 N	91.51 W
52	Barrow (băr'ō) Alsk.	71.15 N	156.12 W
116	Barrow Gt. Brit.	54.10 N	3.10 W
164	Barrow I. Austl.	20.40 S	115.28 E
169	Barrow Mt. Austl. (Tas. In.)	41.23 S	147.25 E
52	Barrow, Pt. Alsk.	71.20 N	156.0 W
116	Barrow, R. Ire.	52.45 N	7.0 W
164	Barrows Creek (băr'ōz) Austl.	21.20 S	133.50 E
126	Barruelo de Santullan (bär-rōō-ā-lō dä sän-tōō-lyän'). Sp.	42.55 N	4.17 W
142	Barrydale (băr'ĭ-dāl) U. S. Afr.	33.54 S	20.41 E
119	Barsbüttel (bärs-büt''l) Ger. (Hamburg In.)	53.34 N	10.9 E
74	Barstow (bär'stō) Calif.	34.52 N	117.2 W
124	Bar-sur-Aube (bär'sür-ōb) Fr.	48.15 N	4.40 E
123	Bartenstein (bär'tĕn-stīn) Ger.	54.15 N	20.50 E
122	Barth (bärt) Ger.	54.21 N	12.43 E
79	Bartholomew Bayou (bär-thŏl'ō-mū). Ark.	33.45 N	91.34 W
103	Bartica (bär'tĭ-kȧ) Br. Gu.	6.18 N	57.33 W
113	Bartin (bär'tĭn) Tur.	41.42 N	32.18 E
165	Bartle Frere, Mt. (bärt''l frēr') Austl.	17.29 S	145.52 E
79	Bartlesville (bär'tlz-vĭl) Okla.	36.46 N	95.58 W
81	Bartlett (bärt'lĕt) Tex.	30.48 N	97.26 W
102	Bartolomé, Cerro (Mt.) (bär-tō-lō-mā'). Peru (In.)	12.4 S	77.0 W
140	Bartolomeu Dias (bär-tō-lō-mā'ōō dē'äzh). Moz.	21.12 S	35.10 E
86	Barton (bär'tŭn) Vt.	44.45 N	72.10 W
118	Barton-on-Humber (bär'tŭn-ŏn-hŭm'bĕr). Gt. Brit.	53.41 N	0.26 W
83	Bartow (bär'tō) Fla. (In.)	27.53 N	81.50 W
122	Bartsch R. (bärch) Ger.	51.28 N	17.5 E
163	Barugo (bä-rōō'gō) P. I.	11.18 N	124.44 E
131	Barvenkovo (bär-vĕn-kô'vô) Sov. Un.	48.57 N	36.59 E
165	Barwon R. (bär'wŭn) Austl.	29.0 S	148.45 E
139	Basankusu (bä-sän-kōō'sōō) Bel. Cong.	1.10 N	19.40 E
123	Basarabia (Bessarabia) (Prov.) (bäz-ȧ-rä'bē-ȧ) (bĕs-ȧ-rä'bĭ-ȧ) Rom.	47.10 N	28.40 E
162	Basco (bäs'kō) P. I. (In.)	20.28 N	121.59 E
119	Basel (bä-sĕl') Bel. (Anvers In.)	51.9 N	4.18 E
122	Basel (Bâle) (bä'zĕl) (bäl) Switz.	47.33 N	7.35 E
163	Basey (bä'sä) P. I.	11.17 N	125.4 E
143	Bashee R. (băsh'ē) U. S. Afr.	1.55 S	28.25 E
160	Bashi Chan. (bä'shē) Jap.	21.30 N	121.0 E
162	Bashi Chan. (băsh'ē) P. I. (In.)	21.15 N	121.50 E
112	Bashkir (Soviet Rep.) (băsh-kēr') Sov. Un.	54.12 N	57.15 E

Page	Name Pronunciation Region	Lat. °'	Long. °'
141	Bashtil Station (bäsh'tĭl) Eg. (Cairo In.)	30.4 N	31.11 E
163	Basilan I. (bä-sē'län) P. I.	6.35 N	122.0 E
163	Basilan Str. P. I.	6.48 N	122.5 E
128	Basilicata (Prov.) (bä-zē-lē-kä'tä) It.	40.30 N	16.10 E
71	Basin (bā'sĭn) Wyo.	44.23 N	108.4 W
116	Basingstoke (bā'zĭng-stōk) Gt. Brit.	51.15 N	1.5 W
128	Bâska (bäsh'ka) Yugo.	44.58 N	14.43 E
113	Başkale (bäsh-kä'lĕ) Tur.	38.10 N	44.5 E
113	Baskunchakskoe, L. (bäs'kōōn-chäk-skō'yē) Sov. Un.	48.10 N	46.55 E
139	Basoko (bȧ-sō'kō) Bel. Cong.	1.21 N	23.40 E
81	Basque R. (bȧsk) Tex.	31.40 N	97.30 W
150	Basra (bŭs'rȧ') Iraq	30.30 N	47.58 E
160	Bassac (bä-säk') Fr. Ind. Chn.	14.55 N	105.38 E
128	Bassano (bäs-sän'ō) It.	45.47 N	11.43 E
141	Bassas da India (I.) (bäs'säs dä ēn'dē-ȧ). Ind. O.	21.20 S	39.40 E
141	Bassatîn (bäs-sȧ-tēn') Eg.	29.59 N	31.16 E
151	Bassein (bŭ-sēn') India	16.45 N	94.45 E
95	Basse Terre (bäs'târ'). Guad. (In.)	17.19 N	62.43 W
95	Basse Terre (I.) Guad. (In.)	16.10 N	26.10 W
73	Bassett (băs'sĕt) Calif. (Los Angeles In.)	34.3 N	118.0 W
83	Bassetts (băs'sĕts) Va.	36.46 N	79.58 W
124	Bassin d' Arcachon (L.) (bȧ-săN' dȧr-kȧ-shôN'). Fr.	44.45 N	1.20 W
84	Bass Is. (băs) Mich.	41.40 N	82.48 W
167	Bass Str. Austl.	39.15 S	146.0 E
77	Basswood L. (băs'wŏŏd). Can.-U. S. A.	48.5 N	91.35 W
120	Båstad (bô'städ) Swe.	56.26 N	12.48 E
124	Bastelica (bä-stä'lē-kä). Cor. (In.)	42.0 N	9.0 E
124	Bastia (bäs'tē-ä) Cor. (In.)	42.40 N	9.28 E
117	Bastogne (bȧs-tôn'y') Bel.	50.0 N	5.45 E
81	Bastrop (băs'trŭp) La.	32.45 N	91.54 W
81	Bastrop Tex.	30.8 N	97.18 W
81	Bastrop Bayou Tex. (In.)	29.6 N	95.20 W
143	Basutoland (bȧ-sōō'tō-lănd). Afr.	29.32 S	28.20 E
138	Bata (bä'tä) Sp. Gui.	1.57 N	9.50 E
161	Bataan (Prov.) (bä-tä-än') P. I. (Manila In.)	14.40 N	120.25 E
96	Batabanó (bä-tä-bä-nō') Cuba	22.42 N	82.19 W
96	Batabanó, G. of Cuba	22.20 N	82.40 W
162	Batac (bä'täk) P. I.	18.4 N	120.34 E
131	Bataisk (bä-tīsk') Sov. Un.	47.8 N	39.46 E
113	Batalpashinsk (bȧ'tâl-pȧ-shēnsk') Sov. Un.	44.15 N	42.2 E
145	Batam I. (bä-täm') Neth. Ind. (In.)	15.0 N	104.2 E
162	Batan I. (bä-tän') P. I.	13.15 N	124.0 E
162	Batan I. P. I. (In.)	20.25 N	122.0 E
160	Batan Is. P. I.	20.45 N	122.0 E
152	Batang (bä'täng') Chn.	30.4 N	99.4 E
162	Batangas (bä-tän'gäs) P. I.	13.45 N	121.3 E
161	Batangas (Prov.) P. I. (Manila In.)	13.53 N	121.0 E
161	Batangas B. P. I. (Manila In.)	13.45 N	120.57 E
163	Batas I. (bä-täs') P. I.	11.10 N	119.35 E
123	Bátaszek (bä'tȧ-sĕk) Hung.	46.11 N	18.43 E
79	Batavia (bȧ-tā'vĭ-ȧ) Ill.	41.51 N	88.18 W
160	Batavia (bȧ-tä'vĭ-ä) Neth. Ind.	6.16 S	106.48 E
85	Batavia (bȧ-tā'vĭ-ȧ) N. Y.	43.0 N	78.12 W
167	Batemans B. (bāt'mȧnz) Austl.	35.45 S	150.15 E
83	Batesburg (bāts'bûrg) S. C.	33.54 N	81.32 W
79	Batesville (bāts'vĭl) Ark.	35.46 N	91.38 W
84	Batesville Ind.	39.15 N	85.17 W
82	Batesville Miss.	34.17 N	89.58 W
130	Batetskaya (bȧ'tĕt-skȧ'yȧ) Sov. Un.	58.35 N	30.20 E
116	Bath (bȧth) Gt. Brit.	51.25 N	2.25 W
86	Bath Me.	43.55 N	69.50 W
86	Bath Can.	46.31 N	67.35 W
85	Bath N. Y.	42.23 N	77.21 W
167	Bathurst (băth'ŭrst) Austl.	33.25 S	149.30 E
55	Bathurst Can.	47.33 N	65.33 W
138	Bathurst Gam.	13.28 N	16.42 W
143	Bathurst U. S. Afr.	33.28 S	26.50 E
53	Bathurst, C. Can.	70.40 N	127.30 W
169	Bathurst Har. Austl. (Tas. In.)	43.19 S	146.1 E
54	Bathurst Inlet Can.	67.5 N	108.30 W
164	Bathurst I. Austl.	11.40 S	130.15 E
113	Batir, L. (bä-têr') Sov. Un.	43.28 N	51.50 E
161	Batjan (bät-jän') Neth. Ind.	0.41 S	127.32 E
161	Batjan (I.) Neth. Ind.	0.30 S	127.30 E
116	Batley (băt'lĭ) Gt. Brit.	53.45 N	1.40 W
167	Batlow (băt'lō) Austl.	35.32 S	148.9 E
138	Batna (bät'nä) Alg.	35.37 N	6.15 E
162	Bato (bä'tō) P. I.	13.36 N	124.20 E
162	Bato, L. P. I.	13.20 N	123.22 E
81	Baton Rouge (băt'ŭn rōōzh') La.	30.28 N	91.10 W
145	Batroun (bȧ-trō-ūN') Syr. (In.)	34.15 N	35.40 E
160	Battambang (bät-tȧm-bäng') Fr. Ind. Chn.	13.5 N	103.15 E
74	Battle Mountain (băt''l) Nev.	40.38 N	116.58 W
85	Battle Creek (băt''l krēk') Mich.	42.19 N	85.11 W
54	Battleford (băt''l-fērd) Can.	52.47 N	108.30 W
49	Battle Ground (băt''l ground) Wash. (Portland In.)	45.46 N	122.31 W
119	Battles Bridge (băt''lz brĭj') Gt. Brit. (London In.)	51.37 N	0.34 E
123	Battonya (bät-tô'nyä) Hung.	46.16 N	21.1 E
160	Batu Is. (bä'tōō) Neth. Ind.	0.15 S	98.30 E
161	Batulao Mt. (bä-tōō-lä'ō) P. I. (Manila In.)	14.2 N	120.37 E
113	Batum (bȧ-tōōm') Sov. Un.	41.40 N	41.35 E
103	Baturité (bä-tōō-rē-tā') Braz.	4.20 S	38.55 E
162	Bauan (bä'wän) P. I.	13.47 N	121.0 E
162	Bauang (bä'wäng) P. I.	16.31 N	120.20 E
138	Bauchi (bä-ōō'chē) Nig.	10.25 N	9.50 E
77	Baudette (bô-dĕt') Minn.	48.41 N	94.35 W
140	Baudouinville (bō-dwăN-vēl') Bel. Cong.	7.12 S	29.40 E
103	Baurú (bou-rōō') Braz.	22.28 S	49.1 W
121	Bauska (bou'skȧ) Lat.	56.25 N	24.11 E
122	Bautzen (bout'sĕn) Ger.	51.10 N	14.26 E
122	Bavaria (Bayern) (State) (bȧ-vā'rĭ-ȧ) (bī'ĕrn). Ger.	48.47 N	11.55 E
143	Baviaans R. (bä'vē-äns) U. S. Afr.	33.37 S	24.15 E
142	Baviaans Kloof Mts. (bä'vē-äns klōōf). U. S. Afr.	33.28 S	24.0 E
160	Bawean I. (bȧ've-än) Neth. Ind.	5.52 S	112.37 E
139	Bawit (bȧ-wēt') Eg.	28.26 N	28.58 E
118	Bawtry (bô'trĭ) Gt. Brit.	53.26 N	1.1 W
83	Baxley (băks'lĭ) Ga.	31.46 N	82.22 W
79	Baxter Springs (băks'tēr springs') Kan.	37.2 N	94.45 W
161	Bay (bä'ē) P. I. (Manila In.)	14.12 N	121.20 E
97	Bayaguana (bä-yä-gwä'nä) Hai.	18.44 N	69.37 W
162	Bayambang (bä-yäm-bäng') P. I.	15.49 N	120.27 E
96	Bayamo (bä-yä'mō) Cuba	20.22 N	76.39 W
148	Bayan-aul (bä'yän-oul') Sov. Un.	50.50 N	75.40 E
76	Bayard (bā'ērd) Neb.	41.45 N	103.20 W
85	Bayard W. Va.	39.17 N	79.23 W
113	Bayazit (bä'yȧ-zĭt') Turk.	39.35 N	44.2 E
163	Baybay (bī'bī) P. I.	10.40 N	124.48 E
113	Bayburt (bä'ĭ-bŏŏrt) Tur.	40.20 N	40.8 E
84	Bay City Mich.	43.37 N	83.53 W
81	Bay City Tex.	28.59 N	95.58 W
122	Bayern (Bavaria) (State) (bī'ērn) (bȧ-vä'rĭ-ȧ). Ger.	48.47 N	11.55 E
124	Bayeux (bȧ-yû') Fr.	49.19 N	0.40 W
77	Bayfield (bā'fēld) Wis.	46.48 N	90.50 W
82	Bay Minette (bā'mĭn-ĕt') Ala.	30.52 N	87.47 W
162	Bayombong (bä-yôm-bông') P. I.	16.38 N	121.9 E
124	Bayonne (bȧ-yôn') Fr.	43.30 N	1.28 W
85	Bayonne (bā-yōn') N. J.	40.40 N	74.7 W
122	Bayreuth (bī-roit') Ger.	49.57 N	11.35 E
87	Bay Roberts (bā rŏb'ērts) Newf.	47.35 N	53.15 W
85	Bays, L. of (bās) Can.	45.12 N	79.12 W
82	Bay St. Louis (bā'sânt lōō'ĭs) Miss.	30.19 N	89.21 W
169	Bayswater (bāz'wô-tēr) Austl. (Perth In.)	31.55 S	115.55 E
81	Baytown (bā'toun) Tex. (In.)	29.44 N	95.0 W
139	Bayuda Steppe (bä-yōō'dȧ) A. E. Sud.	17.30 N	32.30 E
161	Bayuyungan (bä-yōō-yōōŋ'gän) P. I. (Manila In.)	14.5 N	120.55 E
126	Baza (bä'thȧ) Sp.	37.29 N	2.47 W
113	Bazardyuze, Mt. (bȧ'zär-dyōōz'ĕ) Sov. Un.	41.15 N	47.45 E
129	Bazargic (bȧ-zär'jĭk) Rom.	43.34 N	27.51 E
140	Bazaruto I. (bä-zä-rōō'tō) Afr.	21.40 S	35.25 E
126	Baztán (Elizonda) (bȧth-tän') (ä-lē-thôn'dä). Sp.	43.11 N	1.32 W
76	Beach (bēch) N. D.	46.55 N	104.0 W
72	Beach Wash. (Vancouver In.)	48.43 N	122.41 W
166	Beachport (bēch'pōrt) Austl.	37.28 S	139.59 E
85	Beacon (bē'kŭn) N. J.	41.29 N	73.58 W
169	Beaconsfield (bē'kŭnz-fēld) Austl. (Tas. In.)	41.12 S	146.50 E
143	Beaconsfield Bech.	28.45 S	24.48 E
99	Beagle Canal (bē'g'l) Chl.	54.50 S	71.0 W
169	Beagle Reef Austl. (Tas. In.)	39.40 S	147.40 E
171	Bealey (bē'lĭ) N. Z.	43.2 S	171.38 E
80	Beals Cr. (bēls) Tex.	32.13 N	101.15 W
72	Bear Cr. Colo (Denver In.)	39.38 N	105.25 W
88	Bear Creek Md. (Baltimore In.)	39.15 N	76.29 W
71	Bear Creek Mont.	45.9 N	109.8 W
46	Beardmore Glacier (bērd'môr) Ant.	86.0 S	170.0 E
79	Beardstown (bērds'toun) Ill.	40.1 N	90.26 W
71	Bear L. Ida.-Utah	42.0 N	111.20 W
71	Bear R. U. S.	42.20 N	111.44 W
71	Rear River Bay Utah	41.25 N	112.17 W
73	Bear River City Utah (Salt Lake City In.)	41.37 N	112.8 W
126	Beas de Segura (bā'äs dā sä-gōō'rä). Sp.	38.16 N	2.52 W
97	Beata I. (bā-ä'tä) Hai.	17.35 N	71.32 W
97	Beata Pt. Hai.	17.36 N	71.26 W
79	Beatrice (bē'ȧ-trĭs) Neb.	40.15 N	96.45 W
84	Beattyville (bēt'ē-vĭl) Ky.	37.35 N	83.42 W
124	Beaucaire (bō-kâr') Fr.	43.50 N	4.40 E
86	Beauceville (bōs'vēl) Can.	46.13 N	70.45 W
125	Beaucourt (bō-kōōr') Fr.	47.30 N	6.55 E
169	Beaudesert (bō-dĕ-zērt') Austl. (In.)	27.58 S	153.1 E
83	Beaufort (bō'fērt) (bū'fērt) N. C.	34.43 N	76.40 W
83	Beaufort S. C.	32.26 N	80.40 W
53	Beaufort Sea Arc. O.	71.0 N	140.0 W
142	Beaufort West U. S. Afr.	32.20 S	22.32 E
124	Beaugency (bō-zhäN-sē') Fr.	47.50 N	1.45 E
86	Beauharnois (bō-ăr-nwä') Can.	45.18 N	73.51 W
86	Beaulieu (bō-lyû'). Can. (Que. In.)	46.52 N	71.8 W
73	Beaumont (bō'mŏnt) Calif. (Los Angeles In.)	33.55 N	116.59 W
81	Beaumont Tex.	30.5 N	94.7 W
124	Beaune (bōn) Fr.	47.0 N	4.50 E
86	Beauport (bō-pōr') Can.	46.50 N	71.15 W
124	Beauvais (bō-vĕ') Fr.	49.25 N	2.5 E
79	Beaver (bē'vēr) Okla.	36.47 N	100.31 W
75	Beaver Utah	38.17 N	112.40 W
78	Beaver City Neb.	40.9 N	99.51 W
78	Beaver Cr. Colo.	39.50 N	103.35 W
78	Beaver Cr. Kan.-Neb.	39.55 N	100.40 W
71	Beaver Cr. Mont.	48.10 N	107.31 W
71	Beaver Cr. Mont.-N. D.	47.0 N	104.11 W
49	Beaver Cr. Ore. (Portland In.)	46.6 N	123.7 W
76	Beaver Cr. Wyo.	43.45 N	104.20 W
77	Beaver Dam Wis.	43.30 N	88.49 W
85	Beaver Falls Pa.	40.47 N	80.22 W
71	Beaverhead Mts. Ida.-Mont.	44.34 N	113.0 W
71	Beaverhead R. Mont.	45.10 N	112.42 W
84	Beaver I. Mich.	45.40 N	85.35 W
54	Beaver R. Can.	54.30 N	111.0 W
49	Beaverton (bē'vēr-tŭn) Ore. (Portland In.)	45.29 N	122.49 W
118	Bebington (bē'bĭng-tŭn) Gt. Brit.	53.20 N	3.0 W
93	Becal (bā-käl') Mex.	20.26 N	90.3 W
126	Becerrea (bā-thä'rē-ä) Sp.	42.51 N	7.10 W
140	Bechuanaland (bĕch-ōō-ä'nȧ-lănd) Afr.	21.30 S	24.0 E
119	Beckenham (bĕk'ĕn-ȧm) Gt. Brit. (London In.)	51.24 N	0.2 W
84	Beckley (bĕk'lĭ) W. Va.	37.44 N	81.17 W
124	Bédarieux (bā-dȧ-ryû') Fr.	43.35 N	3.10 E
86	Bedford (bĕd'fērd) Can.	45.5 N	73.0 W
116	Bedford Gt. Brit.	52.12 N	0.28 W
84	Bedford Ind.	38.50 N	86.28 W
77	Bedford Ia.	40.40 N	94.44 W
87	Bedford Mass. (In.)	42.29 N	71.16 W
84	Bedford Ohio	41.22 N	81.30 W
85	Bedford Pa.	40.3 N	78.28 W
143	Bedford U. S. Afr.	32.41 S	26.8 E
83	Bedford Va.	37.20 N	79.32 W
118	Bedford Co. Gt. Brit.	52.12 N	0.30 W
116	Bedlington (bĕd'lĭng-tŭn) Gt. Brit.	55.5 N	1.39 W
112	Bednodemyanovsk (byĕd'nō-dĕm-yä'nôfsk). Sov. Un.	55.2 N	49.28 E
118	Bedworth (bĕd'wērth) Gt. Brit.	52.29 N	1.28 W
123	Bedzin (băsc'jēn) Pol.	50.18 N	19.11 E
79	Beebe (bē'bē) Ark.	35.2 N	91.52 W
72	Beechey Hd. (bē'chĭ hĕd) Can. (Vancouver In.)	48.19 N	123.39 W
84	Beech Grove (bēch grōv) Ind.	39.42 N	86.6 W
167	Beechworth (bēch'wērth) Austl.	36.22 S	146.41 E
167	Beemarang, Mt. (bē-mȧ-răng') Austl.	33.55 S	149.50 E
169	Beenleigh (bĭn'lā) Austl. (In.)	27.42 S	153.12 E
145	Beersheba (bēr-shē'bȧ) Pal. (In.)	31.15 N	34.45 E
118	Beeston (bēs't'n) Gt. Brit.	52.56 N	1.11 W
81	Beeville (bē'vĭl) Tex.	28.25 N	97.43 W
167	Bega (bē'gȧ) Austl.	36.42 S	149.51 E
79	Beggs (bĕgz) Okla.	35.46 N	96.6 W
149	Begichev I. (bĕg-ĭ-chĕf') Sov. Un.	74.25 N	112.50 E
124	Bègles (bĕ'gl') Fr.	44.48 N	0.30 W
139	Béhagle (bā-ä'gl') Fr. Eq. Afr.	9.28 N	16.21 E
140	Beira (bā'ērȧ) Moz.	19.50 S	34.52 E
126	Beira (Prov.) Port.	40.30 N	8.0 W
	Beirut, see Beyrouth, Syria.		
145	Beit Jibrin (Hebron) (bāt jē'brēn) Pal. (In.)	31.37 N	34.57 E
131	Beizugskii B. (bĕ-ĭ-zōōg'skĭ-yē) Sov. Un.	46.8 N	38.35 E
126	Beja (bā'zhȧ) Port.	38.2 N	7.52 W
135	Beja (bā-zhä') Tun. (In.)	36.42 N	9.18 E
160	Bejaburi (bā-jȧ-bōō'rē) Thai.	13.8 N	99.58 E
126	Béjar (bā'här) Sp.	40.24 N	5.45 W
96	Bejucal (bā-hōō-käl') Cuba	22.55 N	82.23 W
123	Békés (bā'kāsh) Hung.	46.45 N	21.7 E
123	Bekescsaba (bā'kāsh-chô'bô) Hung.	46.40 N	21.5 E
149	Beketovo (bĕk'ĕ-tō'vō) Sov. Un.	53.15 N	125.10 E
129	Bela (bĕ'lȧ) Bul.	43.26 N	25.43 E
129	Bela Crkva (bā'lȧ tsĕrk'vȧ). Yugo.	44.53 N	21.24 E
57	Belair (bĕ-lâr') Can. (Que. In.)	46.47 N	71.28 W
126	Belalcázar (bāl-äl-kä'thär) Sp.	38.34 N	5.10 W
129	Bela-Slatina (bĕl'ȧ-slä-tē'nä) Bul.	43.27 N	23.57 E
160	Belawan (bā-lä'wän) Neth. Ind.	3.45 N	98.44 E
112	Belaya R. (byĕ'lĭ yȧ) Sov. Un.	53.15 N	55.50 E
131	Belaya Tserkov (byĕ'lĭ-yȧ tsĕr'-kôf). Sov. Un.	49.48 N	30.9 E
119	Belcele (bĕl'sĕ-lĕ) Bel. (Anvers In.)	51.9 N	4.5 E
55	Belcher Is. (bĕl'chēr) Can.	56.25 N	80.30 W
84	Belding (bĕl'dĭng) Mich.	43.5 N	85.21 W
112	Belebei (byĕ'lĕ-bā'ĭ) Sov. Un.	54.2 N	54.2 E
114	Bel el Kebir, Wadi (R.) wä'dē bĕl'ĕl kĕ-bēr') Libya	30.30 N	14.45 E
127	Belem (bȧ-lĕN') Port. (In.)	38.42 N	9.12 W
103	Belém (Pará) (bā-lĕN') (pä-rä') Braz. (In.)	1.28 S	48.29 W
75	Belen (bĕ-län') N. M.	34.38 N	106.47 W
95	Belén (bā-län') Pan.	8.58 N	80.42 W
104	Belén Par.	23.27 S	57.15 W
165	Belep Is. (bĕl'ĕp) N. Cal.	19.40 S	163.40 E
130	Belev (byĕl'yĕf) Sov. Un.	53.49 N	36.8 E
49	Belfair (bĕl'fâr) Ore. (Portland In.)	46.12 N	123.28 W
86	Belfast (bĕl'fȧst) Me.	44.26 N	69.1 W
116	Belfast N. Ire.	54.42 N	6.15 W
143	Belfast U. S. Afr.	25.42 S	30.2 E
116	Belfast Lough (L.) N. Ire.	54.45 N	5.32 W
125	Belfort (bĕl-fôr') Fr.	47.40 N	6.51 E
104	Belfort Roxo (bĕl'fôrt rō'shō) Braz. (In.)	22.46 S	43.23 W
122	Belgard (bĕl'gärt) Ger.	54.0 N	16.1 E
139	Belgian Congo (bĕl'jĭ-ăn kŏŋ'gō) Afr.	2.0 N	25.0 E
117	Belgium (bĕl'jĭ-ŭm) Eur.	35.0 N	4.40 E
131	Belgorod (byĕl'gō-rŭd) Sov. Un.	50.36 N	36.35 E
129	Belgrade (Beograd) (bĕl-grād') (bĕ-ō'grȧd). Yugo	44.52 N	20.32 E
83	Belhaven (bĕl'hā-vĕn) N. C.	35.33 N	76.36 W
85	Belington (bĕl'ĭng-tŭn) W. Va.	39.0 N	79.56 W
160	Belitong (bȧ-lē'tông) Neth. Ind.	2.45 S	108.0 E
94	Belize (bĕ-lēz') Br. Hond.	17.30 N	88.12 W
94	Belize R. Br. Hond.-Guat. (In.)	17.20 N	88.45 W
149	Belkovski I. (byĕl-kôf'skĭ) Sov. Un.	75.30 N	137.0 E
169	Bell (bĕl) Austl. (In.)	26.54 S	151.22 E
85	Bellaire (bĕl-âr') Ohio	40.2 N	80.46 W
81	Bellaire Tex. (In.)	29.42 N	95.27 W
151	Bellary (bĕl-lä'rē) India	15.10 N	77.0 E

Page	Name Pronunciation	Region	Lat. °′	Long. °′
127	Bellas (bĕl′äs)	Port. (In.)	38.47 N	9.16 W
104	Bella Vista (bä′lyȧ vēs′tȧ)	Arg.	28.30 S	59.0 W
103	Bella Vista (bĕl′ȧ vēs′tȧ)	Braz.	17.0 S	49.0 W
143	Bella Vista	Moz.	26.22 S	32.38 E
104	Bella Vista (bä′lyȧ vēs′tȧ)	Par.	22.1 S	56.28 W
102	Bella Vista	Peru (In.)	12.4 S	77.8 W
87	Belle B. (bĕl)	Newf.	47.35 N	55.18 W
89	Belle Chasse (bĕl shäs′)	La. (New Orleans In.)	29.52 N	90.0 W
84	Bellefontaine (bĕl-fŏn′tân)	Ohio	40.25 N	83.48 W
76	Belle Fourche (bĕl′fōōrsh′)	S. D.	44.39 N	103.40 W
76	Belle Fourche Reservoir	S. D.	44.45 N	103.43 W
76	Belle Fourche R.	S. D.-Wyo.	44.40 N	103.30 W
125	Bellegarde (bĕl-gärd′)	Fr.	46.4 N	5.50 E
124	Belle Ile (bĕl-el′)	Fr.	47.20 N	3.10 W
87	Belle Isle, Str. of	Newf.-Can.	51.40 N	56.30 W
77	Belle Plaine (bĕl plān′)	Ia.	41.54 N	92.18 W
169	Bellerive (bĕl′ĕ-rīv) (bĕl-rēv′)	Austl. (Tas. In.)	42.51 S	147.24 E
73	Belle Sumter (bĕl sŭm′tẽr)	Ala. (Birmingham In.)	33.22 N	87.8 W
85	Belleville (bĕl′vĭl)	Can.	44.10 N	77.21 W
124	Belleville (bĕl-vēl′)	Fr.	46.10 N	4.45 E
79	Belleville (bĕl′vĭl)	Ill.	38.31 N	89.58 W
79	Belleville	Kan.	39.49 N	97.37 W
88	Belleville	N. J. (N. Y. In.)	40.48 N	74.10 W
77	Bellevue (bĕl′vū)	Ia.	42.16 N	90.28 W
84	Bellevue	Ky.	39.7 N	84.28 W
84	Bellevue	Mich.	42.29 N	85.0 W
84	Bellevue	Ohio	41.17 N	82.48 W
89	Bellevue	Pa. (Pittsburgh In.)	40.29 N	80.3 W
49	Bellevue	Wash. (Seattle In.)	47.36 N	122.12 W
125	Belley (bĕ-lĕ′)	Fr.	45.45 N	5.41 E
87	Bell I. (bĕl)	Newf.	50.45 N	55.33 W
167	Bellingen (bĕl′ĭng-ĕn)	Austl.	30.27 S	152.51 E
87	Bellingham (bĕl′ĭng-hăm)	Mass. (In.)	42.5 N	71.27 W
70	Bellingham	Wash.	48.45 N	122.29 W
72	Bellingham B.	Wash. (Vancouver In.)	48.44 N	122.35 W
122	Bellinzona (bĕl-ĭn-tsō′nä)	Switz.	46.12 N	9.3 E
103	Bello Horizonte (bĕl′ŏŏ ō-rē-zôn′tā)	Braz.	19.59 S	43.59 W
86	Bellows Falls (bĕl′ōz fôls)	Vt.	43.10 N	72.30 W
128	Belluno (bĕl-lōō′nō)	It.	46.9 N	12.13 E
104	Bell Ville (bĕl vēl′)	Arg.	32.45 S	62.45 W
81	Bellville (bĕl′vĭl)	Tex.	29.57 N	96.17 W
126	Bélmez (bĕl′māth)	Sp.	38.17 N	5.13 W
77	Belmond (bĕl′mŏnd)	Ia.	42.53 N	93.35 W
143	Belmont (bĕl′mŏnt)	Bech.	29.25 S	24.21 E
170	Belmont	N. Z. (In.)	41.12 S	174.56 E
103	Belmonte (bĕl-mōn′tȧ)	Braz.	15.45 S	38.59 W
126	Belmonte	Sp.	43.17 N	6.11 W
112	Beloe, L. (byĕ′lō-yĕ)	Sov. Un.	60.15 N	37.45 E
78	Beloit (bē-loit′)	Kan.	39.27 N	98.7 W
77	Beloit	Wis.	42.31 N	89.1 W
131	Belopolie (byĕ′lô-pôl′yĕ)	Sov. Un.	51.7 N	34.19 E
112	Beloretsk (bye′lō-rĕtsk)	Sov. Un.	53.58 N	58.28 E
131	Belosaraiskaya, C. (byĕ′lô-sä-rä′ĭ-skä′yä)	Sov. Un.	46.52 N	37.20 E
131	Belovodsk (byĕ′lô-vôdsk)	Sov. Un.	49.11 N	39.32 E
112	Belozersk (byĕ′lô-zyĕrsk)	Sov. Un.	60.0 N	37.45 E
118	Belper (bĕl′pẽr)	Gt. Brit.	53.1 N	1.28 W
130	Belskoe (byĕl′skō-yĕ)	Sov. Un.	54.41 N	40.21 E
71	Belt (bĕlt)	Mont.	47.10 N	110.57 W
166	Beltana (bĕl-tȧ′nȧ)	Austl.	30.51 S	138.25 E
71	Belt Cr.	Mont.	47.10 N	110.56 W
81	Belton (bĕl′tŭn)	Tex.	31.3 N	97.29 W
73	Beltona (bĕl-tō′nȧ)	Ala. (Birmingham In.)	33.47 N	86.52 W
119	Belvedere (bĕl-vĕ-dēr′)	Gt. Brit. (London In.)	51.29 N	0.9 E
77	Belvidere (bĕl-vĭ-dēr′)	Ill.	42.15 N	88.50 W
85	Belvidere	N. J.	40.49 N	75.6 W
130	Bely (byĕ′lĭ)	Sov. Un.	55.51 N	32.59 E
165	Belyando R. (bĕl-yăn′dō)	Austl.	21.30 S	146.45 E
148	Belyi (White) I. (bĕl′yē)	Sov. Un.	73.20 N	71.0 E
130	Belynichi (byĕl-ĭ-nĭ′chĭ)	Sov. Un.	54.0 N	29.42 E
82	Belzoni (bĕl-zō′nē)	Miss.	33.11 N	90.30 W
140	Bembe (bĕɴ′bĕ)	Ang.	7.2 S	14.29 E
126	Bembezar R. (bĕm-bā-thär′)	Sp.	38.0 N	5.20 W
103	Bemfica (bĕɴ-fē′kȧ)	Braz. (In.)	1.13 S	48.18 W
77	Bemidji (bē-mĭj′ĭ)	Minn.	47.28 N	94 51 W
127	Benabarre (bā-nȧ-bär′rȧ)	Sp.	42.5 N	0.29 E
140	Bena Dibele (bĕn′ȧ dē-bĕ′lĕ)	Bel. Cong.	4.2 S	22.50 E
140	Bena Kamba (bĕn′ȧ käm′bȧ)	Bel. Cong.	2.22 S	25.12 E
167	Benalla (bĕn-ăl′ȧ)	Austl.	36.32 S	145.59 E
56	Benard (bĕ-närd′)	Can. (Winnipeg In.)	49.55 N	97.51 W
151	Benares (bĕ-nä′rēz)	India	25.17 N	83.8 E
139	Benas, Ras (C.) (räs bȧ-näs′)	Eg.	23.56 N	35.52 E
116	Ben Attow (Mt.) (bĕn ăt′tō)	Gt. Brit.	57.15 N	5.15 W
126	Benavente (bā-nä-vĕn′tā)	Sp.	42.1 N	5.41 W
166	Benbonyathe, Mt. (bĕn-bō-nyăth′)	Austl.	30.33 S	138.58 E
70	Bend (bĕnd)	Ore.	44.3 N	121.18 W
116	Ben Dearg (Mt.) (bĕn dĕrk)	Gt. Brit.	57.48 N	4.55 W
166	Bendigo (bĕn′dĭ-gō)	Austl.	36.45 S	144.17 E
122	Benešov (bĕn′ĕ-shôf)	Czech.	49.47 N	14.42 E
128	Benevento (bā-nā-vĕn′tō)	It.	41.7 N	14.45 E
103	Benevides (bā-nȧ-vē′dĕzh)	Braz. (In.)	1.21 S	48.15 W
151	Bengal (Presidency) (bĕn-gôl′)	India	23.30 N	89.45 E
151	Bengal, B. of	India	18.0 N	90.0 E
139	Bengasi (bĕn-gä′sē)	Libya	32.6 N	20.4 E
160	Bengkalis (bĕng-kä′lĭs)	Neth. Ind.	1.35 N	102.7 E
145	Bengkalis I.	Neth. Ind. (In.)	1.25 N	102.20 E
140	Benguela (bĕn-gĕl′ȧ)	Ang.	12.32 S	13.28 E
140	Benguela (Dist.)	Ang.	13.30 S	17.0 E
73	Ben Hill (bĕn hĭl)	Ga. (Atlanta In.)	33.41 N	84.31 W
116	Ben Hope (Mt.) (bĕn hōp)	Gt. Brit.	58.25 N	4.35 W
138	Beni Abbès (bā′nē ȧ-bĕs′)	Alg.	30.6 N	2.12 W
127	Benicarló (bā-nē-kär-lō′)	Sp.	40.26 N	0.25 E
74	Benicia (bē-nĭsh′ĭ-ȧ)	Calif.	38.4 N	122.11 W
138	Benin (bĕn-ēn′)	Nig.	6.27 N	5.34 E
138	Benin, Bight of	Fr. W. Afr.	5.0 N	3.0 E
102	Beni, R. (bā′nē)	Bol.	12.30 S	67.18 W
127	Benisa (bā-nē′sä)	Sp.	38.42 N	0.1 E
138	Beni Saf (bā′nē säf′)	Alg.	35.22 N	1.23 W
139	Beni Ulid (bā′nē ōō-lēd′)	Libya	31.45 N	14.0 E
78	Benkelman (bĕn-kĕl-mȧn)	Neb.	40.4 N	101.33 W
160	Benkoelen (bĕn-kōō′lĕn)	Neth. Ind.	3.45 S	102.15 E
128	Benkovac (bĕn′kō-vȧts)	Yugo.	44.2 N	15.38 E
169	Ben Lomond (Mt.) (bĕn lō′mŭnd)	Austl. (Tas. In.)	41.36 S	147.44 E
116	Ben Macdhui (Mt.) (bĕn măk-dōō′ē)	Gt. Brit.	57.5 N	3.35 W
116	Ben More (Mt.) (bĕn mōr)	Gt. Brit.	58.5 N	5.0 W
83	Bennettsville (bĕn′ĕts-vĭl)	S. C.	34.36 N	79.40 W
116	Ben Nevis (Mt.) (bĕn nĕ′vĭs)	Gt. Brit.	56.55 N	4.55 W
86	Bennington (bĕn′ĭng-tŭn)	Vt.	42.52 N	73.10 W
143	Benoni (bĕ-nō′nī)	U. S. Afr.	26.11 S	28.19 E
88	Bensenville (bĕn′sĕn-vĭl)	Ill. (Chicago In.)	41.57 N	87.56 W
122	Bensheim (bĕns′hīm)	Ger.	49.42 N	8.38 E
75	Benson (bĕn-sŭn)	Ariz.	31.58 N	110.18 W
76	Benson	Minn.	45.19 N	95.35 W
88	Bensonhurst (bĕn′sŭn-hûrst)	N. Y.	40.36 N	74.0 W
167	Bentley Har. (bĕnt′lĭ här′bẽr)	Austl.	38.48 S	146.30 E
79	Benton (bĕn′tŭn)	Ark.	34.35 N	92.35 W
74	Benton	Calif.	37.45 N	118.25 W
79	Benton	Ill.	38.0 N	88.55 W
86	Benton	N. B.	45.58 N	67.37 W
85	Benton Harbor	Mich.	42.5 N	86.28 W
79	Bentonville (bĕn′tŭn-vĭl)	Ark.	36.22 N	94.12 W
138	Benue R. (bā′nōō-ȧ)	Nig.-Cam.	8.30 N	10.0 E
129	Beograd (Belgrade) (bĕ-ō′grad) (bĕl-grād′)	Yugo.	44.52 N	20.32 E
159	Beppo (bĕ′pō)	Jap.	33.18 N	131.25 E
95	Bequia I. (bĕk-ē′ä)	Wind. Is.	13.0 N	61.15 W
129	Berane (bȧ-rä′nȧ)	Yugo.	42.47 N	19.51 E
129	Berat (bā-rät′)	Alb.	40.43 N	19.59 E
161	Berau Pen. (bȧ-rou′)	Neth. Ind.	1.30 S	133.0 E
139	Berber (bûr′bĕr)	A. E. Sud.	18.5 N	34.0 E
141	Berbera (bûr′bẽr-ȧ)	Br. Som.	10.25 N	45.3 E
124	Berck (bĕrk)	Fr.	50.25 N	1.39 E
131	Berdichev (bĕr-dē′chĕf)	Sov. Un.	49.53 N	28.32 E
131	Berdyansk (bĕr-dyänsk′)	Sov. Un.	46.46 N	36.49 E
131	Berdyanskaya, C. (bĕr-dyän′skä-yä)	Sov. Un.	46.37 N	36.48 E
84	Berea (bē-rē′ȧ)	Ky.	37.35 N	84.21 W
84	Berea	Ohio	41.24 N	81.49 W
123	Beregszász (Berehovo) (bĕ′rĕg-säs) (bĕ′rĕ-hô-vô)	Hung.	48.13 N	22.40 E
	Berehovo see Beregszász, Hung.			
	Berenice, see Bengasi, Libya.			
139	Berenice (Ruins) (bĕr-ē-nī′sē)	Eg.	23.58 N	35.27 E
76	Beresford (bĕr′ĕs-fẽrd)	S. D.	43.6 N	96.46 W
123	Beresteczko (bĕr-ĕs-tĕch′kô)	Pol.	50.20 N	25.7 E
131	Berestovo (bĕr′yĕs-tô′vô)	Sov. Un.	47.7 N	36.44 E
123	Berettyóújfalu (bĕ′rĕt-tyō-ōō′y′fô-lōō)	Hung.	47.13 N	21.33 E
123	Bereza (bĕ-rā′zȧ)	Pol.	52.30 N	24.59 E
130	Berezina R. (byĕr-yä′zē-nȧ)	Sov. Un.	53.25 N	29.2 E
130	Berezino (byĕr-yä′zē-nô)	Sov. Un.	53.50 N	28.58 E
131	Berezna (bĕr-yôz′nȧ)	Sov. Un.	51.32 N	31.46 E
131	Bereznegovati (bĕr-yôz′nyĕ-gô′vä-tē)	Sov. Un.	47.18 N	32.55 E
148	Berezov (bĕr-yôz′ôf)	Sov. Un.	63.58 N	64.59 E
131	Berezovka (bĕr-yôz′ôf-kȧ)	Sov. Un.	47.12 N	30.56 E
127	Berga (bĕr′gä)	Sp.	42.7 N	1.50 E
113	Bergama (bĕr′gä-mä)	Tur.	39.10 N	27.15 E
128	Bergamo (bĕr′gä-mō)	It.	45.42 N	9.40 E
122	Bergedorf (bĕr′gē-dôrf)	Ger.	53.30 N	10.14 E
122	Bergen (bĕr′gĕn)	Ger.	54.26 N	13.25 E
117	Bergen	Neth.	51.30 N	4.19 E
120	Bergen	Nor.	60.24 N	5.22 E
72	Bergen Pk. (bûr′gĕn)	Colo. (Denver In.)	39.39 N	105.24 W
124	Bergerac (bĕr-zhē-rȧk′)	Fr.	44.50 N	0.30 E
88	Bergholz (bûrg′hŭls)	N. Y. (Niagara Falls In.)	43.6 N	78.54 W
122	Bergisch-Gladbach (bĕrg′ĭsh-glät′bäᴋ)	Ger.	51.0 N	7.8 E
119	Bergstedt (bĕrg′shtĕt)	Ger. (Hamburg In.)	53.40 N	10.7 E
143	Bergville (bûrg′vĭl)	U. S. Afr.	28.43 S	29.22 E
151	Berhampur (bûr′ŭm-pōōr)	India	19.15 N	84.45 E
52	Bering Glacier (bē′rĭng)	Alsk. (In.)	60.15 N	144.20 W
52	Bering Sea	Pac. O.	58.0 N	175.0 W
52	Bering Str.	Alsk.	65.40 N	169.0 W
131	Berislav (byĕr′ĭ-släf)	Sov. Un.	46.50 N	33.24 E
126	Berja (bĕr′hä)	Sp.	36.51 N	2.57 W
74	Berkeley (bûrk′lĭ)	Calif.	37.52 N	122.18 W
85	Berkeley Springs	W. Va.	39.38 N	78.26 W
129	Berkovica (bĕr-kō′vē-tsȧ)	Bul.	43.14 N	23.7 E
126	Berlengas Is. (bĕr-lĕɴ′gäzh)	Port.	39.25 N	9.32 W
122	Berlin (bĕr-lēn′)	Ger.	52.30 N	13.25 E
119	Berlin	Ger. (In.)		
86	Berlin (bûr′lĭn)	N. H.	44.29 N	71.12 W
77	Berlin	Wis.	43.58 N	88.56 W
104	Bermejo, R. (bĕr-mā′hō)	Arg.	24.30 S	61.30 W
126	Bermeo (bĕr-mā′yō)	Sp.	43.24 N	2.45 W
91	Bermuda Is. (bẽr-mū′dȧ)	Atl. O.	32.20 N	64.55 W
122	Bern (bĕrn)	Switz.	46.56 N	7.23 E
104	Bernal (bĕr-näl′)	Arg. (In.)	34.42 S	57.17 W
78	Bernalillo (bĕr-nä-lē′yō)	N. M.	35.21 N	106.29 W
122	Bernau (bĕr′nou)	Ger.	52.41 N	13.36 E
124	Bernay (bĕr-nĕ′)	Fr.	49.5 N	0.35 E
122	Bernburg (bĕrn′bŏŏrgh)	Ger.	51.47 N	11.43 E
122	Berndorf (bĕrn′dôrf)	Ger.	47.57 N	16.6 E
84	Berne (bûrn)	Ind.	40.42 N	84.57 W
164	Bernier I. (bẽr-nēr′)	Austl.	24.47 S	113.5 E
117	Berohem (bĕ′rô-hĕm)	Bel.	51.9 N	4.10 E
122	Beroun (bā′rōn)	Czech.	49.58 N	14.3 E
122	Berounka R. (bĕ-rōn′kȧ)	Czech.	50.1 N	13.50 E
167	Berrigan (bĕr′ĭ-gȧn)	Austl.	35.41 S	145.50 E
93	Berriozabal (bā′rēō-zä-bäl′)	Mex.	16.47 N	93.15 W
167	Berry (bĕr′ē)	Austl.	34.47 S	150.41 E
114	Berryan (bĕr-ē-äɴ′)	Alg.	32.48 N	3.44 E
96	Berry Is.	Ba. Is.	25.35 N	77.45 W
79	Berryville (bĕr′ē-vĭl)	Ark.	36.21 N	93.34 W
142	Berseba (bĕr′sē-bȧ)	S. W. Afr.	26.2 S	17.47 E
131	Bershad (byĕr′shät)	Sov. Un.	48.21 N	29.32 E
55	Bersimis (bĕr-sē-mē′)	Can.	49.8 N	68.48 W
86	Bersimis R.	Can.	49.14 N	69.35 W
55	Berthier (bĕr-tyā′)	Can.	46.12 N	73.0 W
72	Berthould (bûr′thōld)	Colo. (Denver In.)	40.18 N	105.5 W
89	Bertrandville (bûr′trȧnd-vĭl)	La. (New Orleans In.)	29.45 N	90.0 W
116	Berwick (bûr′ĭk)	Gt. Brit.	55.45 N	2.0 W
85	Berwick	Pa.	41.5 N	76.13 W
84	Berwood (bûr′wŏŏd)	W. Va.	40.0 N	80.44 W
116	Berwyn Range Mts.)((bûr′wĭn)	Gt. Brit.	52.50 N	3.25 W
141	Besalampy (bĕz-ȧ-läm-pē′)	Madag.	16.40 S	44.30 E
125	Besançon (bē-säɴ-sôɴ)	Fr.	47.15 N	6.1 E
130	Besed R. (byĕ′syĕt)	Sov. Un.	52.55 N	31.22 E
130	Beshenkovichi (byĕ′shĕn-kō-vē′-chĭ)	Sov. Un.	55.4 N	29.26 E
123	Beskides (Mts.) (bĕs′kēdz′)	Czech.-Pol.	49.30 N	19.20 E
125	Bessancourt (bĕs-säɴ-kōōr′)	Fr. (In.)	49.2 N	2.13 E
123	Bessarabia (Basarabia) (Prov.) (bĕs-ȧ-rā′bĭ-ȧ) (bäz-ȧ-rä′bē-ä)	Rom.	47.10 N	28.40 E
124	Besseges (bĕ-sĕzh′)	Fr.	44.19 N	4.9 E
82	Bessemer (bĕs′ē-mẽr)	Ala.	33.24 N	86.58 W
77	Bessemer	Mich.	46.29 N	90.2 W
83	Bessemer City	N. C.	35.17 N	81.17 W
126	Betánzos (bĕ-tän′thōs)	Sp.	43.17 N	8.14 W
75	Betatakin Ruin (bĕt-ȧ-täk′ĭn)	Ariz.	36.38 N	110.29 W
143	Bethal (bĕth′ȧl)	U. S. Afr.	26.29 S	29.28 E
142	Bethanie (bĕth′ȧ-nĭ)	S. W. Afr.	26.29 S	17.7 E
79	Bethany (bĕth′ȧ-nĭ)	Mo.	40.15 N	94.2 W
143	Bethany	U. S. Afr.	29.32 S	25.56 E
52	Bethel (bĕth′ĕl)	Alsk.	60.35 N	162.5 W
86	Bethel	Vt.	43.50 N	72.39 W
145	Bethlehem (bĕth′lē-hĕm)	Pal. (In.)	31.41 N	35.11 E
85	Bethlehem	Pa.	40.39 N	75.23 W
143	Bethlehem	U. S. Afr.	28.8 S	28.23 E
143	Bethulie (bē-tōō′lē)	U. S. Afr.	30.31 S	25.59 E
124	Bethune (bā-tün′)	Fr.	50.32 N	2.38 E
161	Betis (bā′tēs)	P. I. (Manila In.)	15.0 N	120.36 E
126	Betoya B. (bĕ-tō′yȧ)	Mor.	35.15 N	3.25 W
141	Betroka (bĕ-trōk′ȧ)	Madag.	23.5 S	46.10 E
141	Betsiboka R. (bĕt-sĭ-bō′kȧ)	Madag.	17.15 S	47.15 E
138	Bettié (bĕt-tyā′)	Fr. W. Afr.	6.1 N	3.31 W
145	Betung (bȧ-tŏŏng′)	Neth. Ind. (In.)	1.4 N	101.37 E
151	Betwa R. (bĕt′wȧ)	India	25.0 N	78.30 E
123	Beuthen (boi′tĕn)	Ger.	50.21 N	18.55 E
119	Bevel (bā′vĕl)	Bel. (Anvers In.)	51.8 N	4.40 E
119	Beveren Waes (bā′vĕ-rĕn väs)	Bel. (Anvers In.)	51.13 N	4.15 E
116	Beverley (bĕv′ẽr-lĭ)	Gt. Brit.	53.48 N	0.25 W
86	Beverly	Mass.	42.35 N	70.55 W
73	Beverly Hills	Calif. (Los Angeles In.)	34.4 N	118.25 W
79	Bevier (bē-vēr′)	Mo.	39.44 N	92.35 W
118	Bewdley (būd′lĭ)	Gt. Brit.	52.22 N	2.19 W
117	Bexhill (bĕks′hĭl)	Gt. Brit.	50.50 N	0.30 E
119	Bexley (bĕks′lĭ)	Gt. Brit. (London In.)	51.26 N	0.9 E
138	Beyla (bā′lȧ)	Fr. W. Afr.	8.44 N	8.32 W
125	Beynes (bān)	Fr.	48.51 N	1.53 E
113	Beypazari (bā-pȧ-zä′rĭ)	Tur.	40.12 N	31.45 E
150	Beyrouth (Beirut) (bā-rōōt′) (bā′rōōt)	Syr.	33.55 N	35.30 E
113	Beyşehir (bā-shĕ′h′r)	Tur.	37.40 N	31.45 E
113	Beyşehir L.	Tur.	37.45 N	31.30 E
130	Bezhetsk (byĕ-zhĕtsk′)	Sov. Un.	57.47 N	36.41 E
	Bezhitsa (see Ordzhonikidzegrad),	Sov. Un.		
124	Béziers (bā-zyā′)	Fr.	43.21 N	3.15 E
125	Bezons (bē-zôɴ′)	Fr. (In.)	48.55 N	2.13 E
151	Bezwada (bĕz-wä′dȧ)	India	16.38 N	80.38 E
151	Bhagalpur (bä′gŭl-pōōr)	India	25.20 N	86.30 E
152	Bhamo (bŭ-mō′)	India	24.16 N	97.11 E
151	Bharatpur (bŭrt′pōr)	India	27.8 N	77.32 E
151	Bhaunagar (bäv-nŭg′ŭr)	India	21.45 N	72.8 E
151	Bhima R. (bē′mȧ)	India	17.15 N	76.0 E
151	Bhopal (bō-päl′)	India	23.15 N	77.30 E
151	Bhuj (bōōj)	India	23.15 N	69.32 E
160	Bhuket (bōō-kĕt′)	Thai.	7.59 N	98.26 E

ăt; finăl; rāte; senȧte; ärm; ȧsk; sofȧ; fâre; ch-choose; dh-as th in other; bē; ēvent; bĕt; recĕnt; cratẽr; g-go; gh-gutteral g; bĭt; ĭ-short neutral; rīde; ᴋ-gutteral k as ch in German ich;

Page	Name Pronunciation Region	Lat. °′	Long. °′
151	Bhutan (bōō-tän′)..........Asia	27.15 N	90.0 E
138	Biafra, Bight of (bē-ä′frä).Sp. Gu.	2.0 N	9.0 E
123	Biala Podlaska (byä′wä pōd′läs-kä)..Pol.	52.2 N	23.7 E
123	Bialystok (byä-wis′tōk)......Pol.	53.7 N	23.11 E
124	Biarritz (byä-rēts′)..........Fr.	43.25 N	1.35 W
155	Bias B. (byäs)..............Chn.	22.44 N	114.33 E
135	Biba (bē′bä)...........Eg. (In.)	28.55 N	31.0 E
82	Bibb City (bĭb′sĭ′tē)...........Ga.	32.31 N	84.59 W
122	Biberach (bē′bēr-äk)........Ger.	48.7 N	9.48 E
119	Bickley (bĭk′lĭ) Gt. Brit. (London In.)	51.24 N	0.2 E
84	Bicknell (bĭk′nĕl)...........Ind.	38.47 N	87.18 W
123	Bicske (bĭsh′kĕ)..........Hung.	47.29 N	18.38 E
138	Bida (bē′dä)................Nig.	9.5 N	6.0 E
150	Bida (Doha) (bē′dä) (dō′hä) Sau. Ar.	25.15 N	51.45 E
86	Biddeford (bĭd′ē-fērd)........Me.	43.30 N	70.30 W
118	Biddulph (bĭd′ŭlf).......Gt. Brit.	53.7 N	2.10 W
122	Biebrich (bē′brĭk)..........Ger.	50.3 N	8.16 E
123	Biebrza R. (byĕb′zhä)........Pol.	53.26 N	22.35 E
119	Biedermannsdorf (bē′dēr-mäns-dôrf). Aus. (Wien In.)	48.4 N	16.21 E
122	Biel (bēl)..................Switz.	47.8 N	7.14 E
122	Bielefeld (bē′lē-fēlt)........Ger.	52.2 N	8.32 E
128	Biella (byĕl′lä)...............It.	45.34 N	8.4 E
123	Bielsk (byĕlsk)..............Pol.	52.45 N	23.12 E
125	Bièvre R. (byĕv′r′)......Fr. (In.)	48.46 N	2.7 E
125	Bièvres.................Fr. (In.)	48.46 N	2.12 E
128	Biferno R. (bē-fĕr′nō)..........It.	41.43 N	14.40 E
129	Biğa (bē′ghä)................Tur.	40.13 N	27.13 E
161	Bigaa (bē-gä-ä′).P. I. (Manila In.)	14.50 N	120.53 E
171	Big B.......................N. Z.	44.15 S	168.0 E
77	Big Bay de Noc (bĭg bā dē nŏk′) Mich.	45.45 N	86.45 W
79	Big Bayou (bĭg′ bī′yōō)......Ark.	33.15 N	91.25 W
73	Big Bear L. (bĭg bâr lāk) Calif. (Los Angeles In.)	34.15 N	116.55 W
71	Big Belt Mts...............Mont.	46.30 N	111.25 W
82	Big Black R................Miss.	32.20 N	90.40 W
79	Big Blue R...........Neb.-Kan.	39.50 N	96.38 W
80	Big Canyon..................Tex.	30.28 N	102.30 W
73	Big Cottonwood Cr. Utah (Salt Lake City In.)	40.38 N	111.45 W
89	Big Cr.......Ohio (Cleveland In.)	41.27 N	81.47 W
77	Big Fork R..................Minn.	48.20 N	93.50 W
71	Big Hole Battlefield Natl. Mon. Mont.	45.40 N	113.39 W
71	Big Hole R.................Mont.	45.40 N	113.2 W
71	Big Horn Mts...............Wyo.	44.30 N	107.20 W
71	Big Horn R.........Wyo.-Mont.	44.0 N	157.58 W
79	Big L........................Ark.	35.55 N	90.5 W
86	Big L........................Me.	45.10 N	67.42 W
71	Big Muddy Cr..............Mont.	48.52 N	105.0 W
79	Big Muddy R...................Ill.	38.0 N	88.58 W
84	Big Rapids..................Mich.	43.43 N	85.30 W
78	Big Sandy Cr.................Colo.	38.47 N	103.0 W
84	Big Sandy R.........Ky.-W. Va.	38.15 N	82.37 W
82	Big Sandy R.................Tenn.	36.10 N	88.10 W
76	Big Sioux R. (bĭg sōō)...S. D.-Ia.	44.0 N	96.36 W
80	Big Spring...................Tex.	32.15 N	101.28 W
82	Big Stone Gap.................Va.	36.53 N	82.50 W
76	Big Stone L...........Minn.-S. D.	45.25 N	96.40 W
71	Bigtimber (bĭg′tĭm-bēr)....Mont.	45.50 N	109.57 W
84	Big Vermilion R. (bĭg′ vēr-mĭl′yŭn).Ill.-Ind.	40.10 N	87.38 W
71	Big Wood R...................Ida.	43.10 N	114.20 W
128	Bihać (bē′häch)............Yugo.	44.48 N	15.51 E
140	Biharamulo (bē-hä-rä-mōō′lō) Tan.	2.38 S	31.20 E
151	Bihar and Orissa (Prov.) (bē-här′; ô-rĭs′ȧ).India	23.30 N	86.45 E
140	Bihe (Silva Porto) (bē′ĕ) (sēl′vä pôr′tōō).Ang.	12.22 S	17.5 E
123	Bihor Mts. (bē′hōr)..........Rom.	46.47 N	22.50 E
148	Biisk (bēsk).............Sov. Un.	52.40 N	85.15 E
129	Bijeljina (bē-yĕl′yē-nä)......Yugo.	44.45 N	19.13 E
150	Bijistan (bē-jĭ-stän′)........Iran	34.29 N	58.28 E
78	Bijou Cr. (bē′zhōō)..........Colo.	40.0 N	104.5 W
151	Bikaner (bē-kä-nēr′)........India	28.0 N	73.14 E
158	Bikin R. (bē-kēn′)........Sov. Un.	46.30 N	135.0 E
140	Bikoro (bē-kō′rō)......Bel. Cong.	0.42 S	18.12 E
163	Bilaa Pt. (bē-lä-ä′)..........P. I.	9.48 N	125.28 E
151	Bilaspur (bē-läs′pōōr)........India	22.10 N	82.10 E
163	Bilatan I. (bē-lä′tän) ....P. I.	5.0 N	120.0 E
126	Bilbao (bĭl-bä′ō)...............Sp.	43.16 N	2.55 W
135	Bilbês (bĭl-bās′)..........Eg. (In.)	30.26 N	31.37 E
129	Bileća (bē-lăt′yä)..........Yugo.	42.52 N	18.26 E
113	Bilecik (bē-lĕd-zhĕk′)..........Tur.	40.10 N	29.59 E
123	Bilgoraj (bĭl-gō′rĭ)...........Pol.	50.31 N	22.43 E
163	Biliran I. (bē-lē′rän)........P. I.	11.35 N	124.30 E
167	Billabong Cr. (bĭl′ȧ-bŏng)...Austl.	35.40 S	146.40 E
87	Billerica (bĭl′rĭk-ȧ)....Mass. (In.)	42.33 N	71.16 W
119	Billericay (bĭl′rĭk-ȧ) Gt. Brit. (London In.)	51.37 N	0.25 E
118	Billinge (bĭl′ĭng).........Gt. Brit.	53.30 N	2.41 W
71	Billings (bĭl′ĭngz)...........Mont.	45.47 N	108.30 W
119	Billwärder (bĭl′vĕr-dĕr) Ger. (Hamburg In.)	53.28 N	10.10 E
139	Bilma (bēl′mä).......Fr. W. Afr.	18.42 N	13.25 E
82	Biloxi (bĭ-lŏk′sĭ).............Miss.	30.24 N	88.53 W
118	Bilston (bĭl′stŭn)........Gt. Brit.	52.34 N	2.4 W
160	Bima (bē′mä)..........Neth. Ind.	8.30 S	118.50 E
167	Bimberi (Mt.) (bĭm′bēr-ĭ)...Austl.	35.39 S	148.46 E
165	Bimerah (bĭm′ēr-ȧ)..........Austl.	24.15 S	143.45 E
163	Binalonan (bē-nä-lō′nän)....P. I.	16.3 N	120.36 E
162	Binan (bē′nän) ....P. I.	14.20 N	121.5 E
161	Binangonan (bē-näng-ō′nän) P. I. (Manila In.)	14.30 N	121.12 E
169	Bingara (bĭŋ-gä′rä)....Austl. (In.)	29.53 S	150.36 E
122	Bingen (bĭng′ĕn)..............Ger.	49.57 N	7.54 E
138	Bingerville (băn-zhä-vēl′) Fr. W. Afr.	5.25 N	3.58 W
118	Bingham (bĭng′ȧm)......Gt. Brit.	52.57 N	0.57 W
86	Bingham.......................Me.	45.3 N	69.51 W
75	Bingham Canyon..............Utah	40.32 N	112.9 W
85	Binghamton (bĭng′ȧm-tŭn)..N. Y.	42.7 N	75.55 W
118	Bingley (bĭng′lĭ).........Gt. Brit.	53.51 N	1.51 W
162	Bingo, Mt. (bĭn-gō′) ....P. I.	12.12 N	125.8 E
159	Bingo, Sea (bĭn′gō)............Jap.	34.10 N	133.25 E
162	Binmaley (bēn-mä-lā′).......P. I.	16.2 N	120.16 E
167	Binnaway (bĭn′ȧ-wā).......Austl.	31.34 S	149.26 E
145	Bintan (Rhio) (I.) (bĭn′tän) (rē′ō)....Neth. Ind.	1.3 N	104.20 E
160	Bintulu (bēn′tōō-lōō)........Sar.	3.5 N	113.7 E
158	Bira (bē′rä)............Sov. Un.	48.58 N	132.45 E
158	Bira R....................Sov. Un.	49.0 N	132.30 E
115	Bir Battifal (bēr bä-tē-fäl′)..Libya	28.31 N	22.0 E
72	Birch B. (bûrch) Wash. (Vancouver In.)	48.55 N	122.47 W
166	Birchip (bûrch′ĭp)..........Austl.	35.59 S	142.58 E
89	Bird Is.....La. (New Orleans In.)	29.21 N	89.17 W
143	Bird Is..................U. S. Afr.	33.51 S	26.18 E
89	Bird I. Sd. La. (New Orleans In.).	29.18 N	89.18 W
87	Bird Rock....................Can.	47.52 N	61.10 W
56	Birds Hill....Can. (Winnipeg In.)	49.58 N	97.0 W
164	Birdsville (bûrdz′vĭl).......Austl.	26.0 S	138.25 E
164	Birdum (bûrd′ŭm)............Austl.	15.42 S	133.20 E
113	Birecik (bē-rĕd-zhĕk′).......Tur.	37.5 N	38.2 E
139	Bir en Natrūn (bēr′ ĕn nä′trōōn) A. E. Sud.	18.12 N	26.45 E
135	Bireno, Djebel (Mt.) (jĕb′ĕl bē-rā′-nō). Tun. (In.)	35.27 N	8.49 E
114	Bir er Ressof (bēr ĕr rĕ-sôf′)..Alg.	32.18 N	7.57 E
139	Birhan, Mt. (bēr′hän)..It. E. Afr.	10.40 N	37.55 E
150	Birjand (bēr′jänd)..........Iran	33.2 N	59.29 E
116	Birkenhead (bûr′kĕn-hĕd).Gt. Brit.	53.25 N	3.0 W
170	Birkenhead............N. Z. (In.)	36.49 S	174.44 E
139	Birket Qarun (Pond) (bēr′kĕt ĕl kä-rōōn′).Eg.	29.30 N	30.30 E
82	Birmingham (bûr′mĭng-ȧm)...Ala.	33.30 N	86.50 W
73	Birmingham............Ala. (In.)		
116	Birmingham............Gt. Brit.	52.25 N	1.55 W
84	Birmingham..................Mich.	42.32 N	83.16 W
118	Birmingham Can.........Gt. Brit.	53.0 N	2.31 W
112	Birsk (bĭrsk)............Sov. Un.	55.25 N	55.32 E
118	Birstall (bûr′stôl).......Gt. Brit.	53.44 N	1.39 W
158	Birten, L. (bĭr′tĕn).........Manch.	43.57 N	128.55 E
131	Biryughii I. (bĭr-yōō′gĭ-ē) Sov. Un.	46.7 N	35.10 E
148	Biryusa (bĭr-yōō′sä)......Sov. Un.	55.40 N	97.27 E
148	Biryusa (Ona) R. (ō′nä) .Sov. Un.	56.30 N	98.35 E
121	Biržai (bēr-zhä′ē)............Lith.	56.10 N	24.45 E
131	Birzula (bĭr′zōō-lȧ)......Sov. Un.	47.49 N	29.28 E
75	Bisbee (bĭz′bē)...............Ariz.	31.27 N	109.55 W
124	Biscay, B. of, (bĭs′kā).....Atl. O.	45.0 N	2.30 W
83	Biscayne B. (bĭs-kān′)...Fla. (In.)	25.30 N	80.15 W
128	Bisceglie (bē-shā′lyä)........Ital.	41.14 N	16.30 E
125	Bischeim (bĭsh′hīm)...........Fr.	48.39 N	7.49 E
169	Bischoff, Mt. (bĭsh′ôf) Austl. (Tasmania In.)	41.26 S	145.34 E
46	Biscoe Is. (bĭs′kō).......Ant. O.	65.0 S	65.0 W
128	Biševo (I.) (bē′shĕ-vō).......Yugo.	42.58 N	16.1 E
74	Bishop (bĭsh′ŭp)..............Calif.	37.21 N	118.24 W
81	Bishop..........................Tex.	27.35 N	97.45 W
118	Bishop's Castle...........Gt. Brit.	52.29 N	2.57 W
83	Bishopville...................S. C.	34.13 N	80.13 W
138	Biskra (bĕs′krä)...............Alg.	34.50 N	5.45 E
163	Bislig B. (bĭs′lĭg).............P. I.	8.15 N	126.25 E
76	Bismarck, (bĭz′märk) ....N. D.	46.49 N	100.46 W
161	Bismarck Arch..........N. Gui. Ter.	4.0 S	151.30 E
161	Bismarck Ra............N. Gui. Ter.	5.45 S	145.0 E
160	Bisnulôk (bĭs-nōō-lōk′).........Thai.	16.52 N	100.10 E
138	Bissago Is. (bĭ-sä′gōō)..Port. Gui.	11.20 N	16.10 W
138	Bissau (bē-sä′ōō)........Port. Gui.	11.56 N	15.40 W
89	Bissell (bĭs′ĕl). Mo. (St. Louis In.)	38.45 N	90.13 W
81	Bistineau L. (bĭs-tĭ-nō′)........La.	32.20 N	93.26 W
123	Bistrița (bĭs′trĭt-sȧ)..........Rom.	47.9 N	24.29 E
113	Bistrița R......................Rom.	46.53 N	26.10 E
113	Bitlis (bĭt-lēs′).................Tur.	38.28 N	42.2 E
129	Bitolj (Monastir) (bē-tōl′y′).Yugo.	41.2 N	21.22 E
128	Bitonto (bē-tōn′tō)...............It.	41.6 N	16.42 E
71	Bitter Cr. (bĭt′ēr)...............Wyo.	41.41 N	108.50 W
122	Bitterfeld (bĭt′ēr-fĕlt)..........Ger.	51.39 N	12.18 E
142	Bitterfontein (bĭt′ēr-fŏn-tān′) U. S. Afr.	31.4 S	18.18 E
70	Bitter Root Mts. (bĭt′ēr-ōōt) Id.-Mont.	47.0 N	115.0 W
71	Bitterroot R..................Mont.	46.35 N	114.7 W
131	Bityug R. (bĭt′yōōg).....Sov. Un.	51.18 N	40.12 E
158	Biwa L. (bē′wä)...................Jap.	35.15 N	136.10 E
77	Biwabik (bē-wä′bĭk)...........Minn.	47.32 N	92.21 W
148	Biya R. (bĭ′yä)............Sov. Un.	52.25 N	87.0 E
143	Bizana (bē-zä′nä)..........U. S. Afr.	30.55 S	29.51 E
57	Bizard I. (bĭz′ērd) Can. (Montreal In.)	45.30 N	73.53 W
138	Bizerte (bē-zērt′).................Tun.	37.22 N	9.55 E
135	Bizerte, L. of,..............Tun. (In.)	37.10 N	9.50 E
129	Bjelopolje (byĕ-lō-pōl′yĕ)....Yugo.	43.2 N	19.45 E
128	Bjelovar (byĕ-lō′vär)............Yugo.	45.53 N	16.51 E
121	Björko (byûr′kō)....................Fin.	60.28 N	28.35 E
121	Björneborg (Pori) (byûr-nĕ-bōr′y′) (pō′rĭ).Fin.	61.30 N	21.48 E
120	Björne Fjord (byûr′nĕ fyōrd).Nor.	60.8 N	5.30 E
120	Blaavand, C. (blō′vänd).....Den.	55.34 N	8.5 E
165	Blackall (blăk′ŭl).............Austl.	24.25 S	145.35 E
77	Black B.............................Can.	48.40 N	88.28 W
89	Black B....La. (New Orleans In.)	29.37 N	89.37 W
170	Blackbridge (blăk′brĭj).N. Z. (In.)	41.12 S	174.56 E
169	Blackburn (blăk′bûrn) Austl. (Melbourne In.)	37.49 S	145.7 E
116	Blackburn...................Gt. Brit.	53.45 N	2.30 W
53	Blackburn, Mt.....................Alsk.	61.50 N	142.15 W
75	Black Canyon of the Gunnison Nat′l Mon...Colo.	38.35 N	107.45 W
116	Blackdown Hills (blăk′doun) Gt. Brit.	50.55 N	3.0 W
77	Blackduck (blăk′dŭk)............Minn.	47.42 N	94.32 W
71	Blackfoot (blăk′fōōt)..............Ida.	43.10 N	112.20 W
71	Blackfoot R.......................Mont.	46.56 N	113.40 W
71	Blackfoot R. Reservoir.........Ida.	42.55 N	111.35 W
122	Black For..........................Ger.	48.5 N	8.0 E
72	Black Hawk (blăk′ hôk) Colo (Denver In.)	39.48 N	105.29 W
171	Black Head...............N. Z. (In.)	45.56 S	170.28 E
76	Black Hills..................S. D.-Wyo.	44.5 N	104.0 W
72	Black Hollow..Colo. (Denver In.)	40.34 N	104.54 W
86	Black Lake.........................Can.	46.2 N	71.21 W
85	Black L..............................N. Y.	44.30 N	75.35 W
116	Blackpool (blăk′pōōl)....Gt. Brit.	53.50 N	3.0 W
79	Black R.......................Ark.-Mo.	36.30 N	90.25 W
96	Black R...............................Jam.	18.1 N	77.51 W
85	Black R..............................N. Y.	43.40 N	75.20 W
83	Black R..............................S. C.	33.52 N	80.0 W
77	Black R..............................Wis.	44.28 N	90.40 W
77	Black River Falls.................Wis.	44.18 N	90.50 W
70	Black Rock Desert...............Nev.	41.0 N	118.50 W
83	Blacksburg (blăks′bûrg)........S. C.	35.7 N	81.31 W
113	Black Sea.....................Eur.-Asia	43.30 N	35.0 E
71	Blacks Fork (R.).................Wyo.	41.22 N	110.15 W
83	Blackshear (blăk′shĭr)............Ga.	31.18 N	82.16 W
116	Blacksod B. (blăk′sŏd)...........Ire.	54.5 N	10.0 W
72	Blacksquirrel Cr. Colo. (Colo. Sprs. In.)	38.58 N	104.27 W
83	Blackstone (blăk′stōn)...........Va.	37.4 N	77.59 W
77	Black Sturgeon R. (blăk stûr′jŭn) Can.	49.0 N	88.30 W
169	Blacktown (blăk′toun) Austl. (Sydney In.)	33.46 S	150.54 E
143	Black Umberlusi R. (blăk ŭm-bĕr-lōō′sē).Swaz.	26.10 S	31.50 E
143	Black Umfolozi R. (blăk ŭm-fō-lō′zē).U. S. Afr.	28.0 S	31.30 E
86	Blackville (blăk′vĭl)..............Can.	46.45 N	65.51 W
83	Blackville..........................S. C.	33.21 N	81.18 W
138	Black Volta R. (vōl′tȧ) Fr. W. Afr.	10.0 N	2.45 W
82	Black Warrior R.................Ala.	33.0 N	87.47 W
116	Blackwater..........................Ire.	52.5 N	8.15 W
79	Blackwater R.......................Mo.	38.55 N	93.30 W
83	Blackwater R........................Va.	37.0 N	76.50 W
79	Blackwell (blăk′wĕl)...........Okla.	36.48 N	97.18 W
166	Blackwood (blăk′wōōd).....Austl.	37.29 S	144.12 E
72	Bladgett Pk. (blă′jĕt pēk) Colo. (Colo. Spgs. In.)	38.58 N	104.54 W
142	Bladgrond (blăd′grŭnd).U. S. Afr.	28.54 S	19.55 E
113	Blagodarnoe (blä′gō-där-nō′yĕ) .Sov. Un.	45.2 N	43.30 E
149	Blagoveshchensk (blä′gō-vyĕsh′-chĕnsk)...Sov. Un.	50.20 N	127.40 E
124	Blain (blăN)...........................Fr.	47.30 N	1.45 W
70	Blaine (blān)......................Wash.	48.59 N	122.44 W
85	Blaine............................W. Va.	39.24 N	79.12 W
76	Blair (blâr)........................Neb.	41.33 N	96.9 W
116	Blairgowrie (blâr-gou′rē).Gt. Brit.	56.35 N	3.20 W
85	Blairsville (blârs′vĭl)...............Pa.	40.27 N	79.14 W
82	Blakely (blāk′lē).....................Ga.	31.23 N	84.57 W
72	Blakeley I. Wash. (Vancouver In.)	48.33 N	122.48 W
99	Blanca, L. (blăŋ′kä) Chl. (Magallanes In.)	52.25 S	71.10 W
78	Blanca Pk. (blăŋ′kä)............Colo.	37.33 N	105.29 W
75	Blanca Pk., Sierra..............N. M.	33.21 N	105.48 W
163	Blanca Pt............................P. I.	8.30 N	123.3 E
80	Blanca, Sierra (Mts.) (sĭ-ĕr′ȧ-blăŋ′kȧ).Tex.	31.10 N	105.21 W
135	Blanc, Cape (blăN).....Tun. (In.)	37.14 N	9.50 E
125	Blanc, Mt. (môN blăN).............Fr.	45.50 N	6.50 E
142	Blanco (blăŋ′kō).........U. S. Afr.	33.58 S	22.22 E
104	Blanco, C. (blăŋ′kō)..............Arg.	47.10 S	65.45 W
94	Blanco, C..........................C. R.	9.33 N	85.7 W
138	Blanco, C....................Fr. W. Afr.	20.45 N	17.7 W
70	Blanco, C. (blăŋ′kō)...............Ore.	42.50 N	124.32 W
96	Blanco Cays (Is.) Cuba...........	23.15 N	81.0 W
95	Blanco, Pico (Mt.) (pē′kō blăŋ′-kō).C. R.	9.18 N	83.2 W
93	Blanco, R. (blăŋ′kō).............Mex.	18.43 N	96.30 W
92	Blanco, R...........................Mex.	24.9 N	99.20 W
143	Blaney (blā′nĭ)...............U. S. Afr.	32.51 S	27.31 E
119	Blankenburg (blăŋ′kĕn-bōōrgh) Ger. (Berlin In.)	52.36 N	13.27 E
122	Blankenburg..........................Ger.	51.48 N	10.57 E
93	Blanquilla I. (blän-kē′lyä)...Mex.	21.30 N	97.17 W
102	Blanquilla I.........................Ven.	11.50 N	64.45 W
140	Blantyre (blăn-tīr′)..................Nya.	15.50 S	35.3 E
128	Blato (blä′tō).......................Yugo.	42.55 N	16.47 E
124	Blaye-et-Ste.-Luce (blā′-ā-săNt-lüs′).Fr.	45.7 N	0.41 W
167	Blayney (blā′nĭ).................Austl.	33.31 S	149.15 E
123	Blazowa (bwä-zhō′vä)................Pol.	49.52 N	22.6 E
171	Blenheim (blĕn′ĕm)...............N. Z.	41.32 S	174.0 E
169	Blicks, R. (blĭks)........Austl. (In.)	30.5 S	152.45 E
138	Blida (blē′dä)........................Alg.	36.32 N	2.50 E
84	Blissfield (blĭs′fēld)..............Mich.	41.48 N	83.50 W
118	Blisworth (blĭz′wûrth).....Gt. Brit.	52.10 N	0.56 W
118	Blithe, R. (blīth).............Gt. Brit.	52.36 N	1.41 W
85	Block I. (blŏk).......................R. I.	41.20 N	71.35 W
82	Blocton (blŏk′tŭn)..................Ala.	33.6 N	87.7 W
143	Bloemfontein (blōōm′fŏn-tān) U. S. Afr.	29.6 S	26.11 E
143	Bloemhof (blōōm′hôf)...U. S. Afr.	27.37 S	25.37 E
124	Blois (blwä)..............................Fr.	47.35 N	1.21 E
123	Blonie (bwôn′yĕ)......................Pol.	52.11 N	20.39 E
77	Bloomer (blōōm′ēr)..................Wis.	45.8 N	91.30 W
84	Bloomfield (blōōm′fēld)..........Ind.	39.0 N	86.56 W
77	Bloomfield.............................Ia.	40.45 N	92.25 W
79	Bloomfield...........................Mo.	36.54 N	89.55 W
76	Bloomfield...........................Neb.	42.36 N	97.39 W
88	Bloomfield..........N. J. (N. Y. In.)	40.48 N	74.12 W
77	Blooming Prairie (blōōm′ĭng prā′rĭ). Minn.	43.53 N	93.3 W
73	Bloomington (blōōm′ĭng-tŭn) Calif. (Los Angeles In.)	34.4 N	117.24 W
79	Bloomington.........................Ill.	40.29 N	88.59 W

ng-sing; ŋ-baŋk; N-nasalized n nŏd; cŏmmit; ōld; ōbey; ôrder; fōōd; fŏŏt; ou-out; s-soft; sh-dish; th-thin; pūre; ûnite; ûrn; stŭd; circŭs; ü-as "y" in study; ′-indeterminate vowel.

Page	Name Pronunciation Region	Lat. °'	Long. °'
84	Bloomington Ind.	39.9 N	86.32 W
85	Bloomsburg (blo͞omz'bûrg) Pa.	40.48 N	76.28 W
73	Blossburg (blŏs'bûrg) Ala. (Birmingham In.)	33.38 N	86.58 W
85	Blossburg Pa.	41.43 N	77.1 W
82	Blountstown (blŭnts'tun) Fla.	30.26 N	85.3 W
122	Bludenz (blo͞o'dĕnts) Ger.	47.10 N	9.50 E
83	Bluefield (blo͞o'fēld) W. Va.	37.35 N	81.15 W
95	Bluefields (blo͞o'fēldz) Nic.	12.0 N	83.43 W
77	Blue Earth Minn.	43.38 N	94.5 W
77	Blue Earth R. Minn.	43.50 N	94.10 W
79	Blue Island Ill.	41.39 N	87.40 W
72	Blue Mt. Colo. (Colo. Spgs. In.)	38.42 N	104.55 W
87	Blue Mt. Newf.	50.20 N	57.11 W
96	Blue Mts. Jam.	18.2 N	76.33 W
70	Blue Mts. Ore.	45.30 N	118.20 W
164	Blue Mud B. Austl.	13.30 S	136.15 E
139	Blue Nile (Bahr el Azraq) (R.) (băr ĕl ăz-răk') A. E. Sud.-It. E. Afr.	13.0 N	34.0 E
167	Blue Plat. Austl.	33.40 S	149.40 E
79	Blue Rapids Kan.	39.40 N	96.41 W
59	Blue Ridge Mts. U. S.	36.30 N	80.30 W
171	Blueskin (blo͞o'skĭn) N. Z. (In.)	45.46 S	170.36 E
171	Blueskin B. N. Z. (In.)	45.44 S	170.36 E
73	Blue Spgs. Cr. Utah (Salt Lake City In.)	41.35 N	112.28 W
73	Blue Spgs. Hills Utah (Salt Lake City In.)	41.42 N	112.21 W
171	Bluff (blŭf) N. Z.	46.37 S	168.19 E
171	Bluff Har. N. Z.	46.33 S	168.22 E
171	Bluff, The N. Z.	46.33 S	168.15 E
84	Bluffton (blŭf'tŭn) Ind.	40.45 N	85.12 W
84	Bluffton Ohio	40.53 N	83.53 W
104	Blumenau (blo͞o'mĕn-ou) Braz.	26.50 S	49.2 W
119	Blundellsands (blŭn'dĕl-sănds) Gt. Brit. (Liverpool In.)	53.29 N	3.3 W
116	Blyth (blĭth) Gt. Brit.	55.5 N	1.32 W
74	Blythe Calif.	33.36 N	114.37 W
79	Blytheville (blīth'vĭl) Ark.	35.55 N	89.54 W
162	Boac (bō'āk) P. I.	13.27 N	121.50 E
94	Boaco (bō-ä'kō) Nic.	12.27 N	85.47 W
171	Boat Har. N. Z. (In.)	45.53 S	170.43 E
103	Bôa Vista (bō'ä vēsh'tä) Braz.	6.15 S	47.30 W
103	Boa Vista (Fordlandia) Bra.	3.50 S	55.25 W
103	Boa Vista do Rio Branco (bō'ä vēsh'tä do͞o rē'o͞o brän'ko͞o) Braz.	2.48 N	60.45 W
138	Boavista I. (bō-ä-vēsh'tä) C. V. Is. (In.)	16.0 N	22.50 W
122	Bober R. (bō'bēr) Ger.	51.20 N	15.33 E
125	Bobigny (bō-bē-nyē') Fr. (In.)	48.54 N	2.26 E
138	Bobo-Dioulasso (bō'bō-dyo͞o làs-sō') Fr. W. Afr.	11.15 N	4.15 W
162	Bobon (bō-bōn') P. I.	12.30 N	124.34 E
130	Bobr (bô'b'r) Sov. Un.	54.18 N	29.12 E
131	Bobrinets (bō-brĭ-nyĕts') Sov. Un.	48.4 N	32.8 E
123	Bóbrka (bo͞ob'r'kȧ) Pol.	49.37 N	24.17 E
131	Bobrov (bŏb'rôf) Sov. Un.	51.5 N	40.1 E
131	Bobrovitsa (bŏb'rō-vĕt-sȧ) Sov. Un.	50.43 N	31.25 E
130	Bobruisk (bŏ-bro͞o'ĭsk) Sov. Un.	53.6 N	29.12 E
93	Bocas (bō'kȧs) Mex.	22.31 N	101.0 W
95	BocasdelToro (bō'kȧsdĕl tō'rō) Pan.	9.20 N	82.16 W
161	Bocaue (bō-kä'wȧ) P.I. (Manila In.)	14.48 N	120.54 E
123	Bochnia (bôĸ'nyȧ) Pol.	49.58 N	20.28 E
122	Bochum (bō'ko͝om) Ger.	51.28 N	7.12 E
122	Böckingen (bûk'ĭng-ĕn) Ger.	49.9 N	9.11 E
149	Bodaibo (bō-dī'bō) Sov. Un.	57.55 N	114.20 E
139	Bodélé Depression (Reg.) (bō-dȧ-lā') Fr. Eq. Afr.-Fr. W. Afr.	17.0 N	17.0 E
122	Bodenbach (Podmokly) (bō'dĕn-bäk) (pôd'môk lĭ) Ger.	50.47 N	14.10 E
116	Boderg, L. (bō'dûrg) Ire.	53.50 N	7.55 W
141	Bodle (bŏd'lē) It. E. Afr.	5.5 N	42.53 E
116	Bodmin (bŏd'mĭn) Gt. Brit.	50.27 N	4.42 W
116	Bodmin Moor (bŏd'mĭn mo͞or) Gt. Brit.	50.35 N	4.30 W
110	Bodö (bôd'û) Nor.	67.13 N	14.20 E
161	Boela (bo͞o'lä) Neth. Ind.	3.12 S	130.30 E
124	Boën (bō-äɴ') Fr.	45.45 N	4.5 E
140	Boende (bō-ĕn'dȧ) Bel. Cong.	0.24 S	21.12 E
160	Boenjoe I. (bō-ĕn'jō-ē) Neth. Ind.	3.35 N	117.51 E
80	Boerne (bō'ērn) Tex.	29.47 N	98.44 W
161	Boeroe (I.) (bō-e'rō-ē) Neth. Ind.	3.30 S	126.40 E
	Boeton (bō'tŏn) I. Neth. Ind.	5.0 S	122.50 E
81	Boeuf R. (bĕf) La.	32.30 N	91.48 W
131	Boevo (bō'yĕ-vō) Sov. Un.	51.24 N	39.12 E
138	Boffa (bôf'ȧ) Fr. W. Afr.	10.12 N	14.8 W
159	Bofurnachi (bō'fo͞or-nä'chē) Jap.	34.3 N	131.37 E
81	Bogalusa (bō-gȧ-lo͞o'sȧ) La.	30.48 N	89.51 W
167	Bogan Gate (bō'gȧn) Austl.	33.8 S	147.48 E
167	Bogan R. Austl.	31.50 S	147.11 E
142	Bogenfels (bō'ghĕn-fĕls) S. W. Afr.	27.20 S	15.22 E
120	Bogense (bô'gĕn-sē) Den.	55.33 N	10.9 E
167	Boggabri (bŏg'ȧ-brĭ) Austl.	30.42 S	150.3 E
95	Boggy Pk. (bŏg'ĭ-pĕk) Le. Is. (In.)	17.3 N	61.51 W
114	Boghari (bō-gȧ-rē') (bō-gä'rē) Alg.	35.50 N	2.49 E
163	Bogo (bō-gō') P. I.	11.3 N	124.0 E
131	Bogodukhov (bŏ-gō-do͞o'ĸôf) Sov. Un.	50.10 N	35.31 E
167	Bogong, Mt. (bō'gông) Austl.	36.42 S	147.16 E
130	Bogoroditsk (bŏ-gŏ'rō-dĭtsk) Sov. Un.	53.47 N	38.7 E
148	Bogorodskoe (bŏ'gō-rŏd-skō'yĕ) Sov. Un.	56.40 N	84.20 E
102	Bogotá (bō-gō-tä') Col.	4.32 N	74.15 W
148	Bogotol (bŏ'gō-tŏl) Sov. Un.	56.10 N	89.30 E
131	Bogoyavlenskoe (bŏ'gō-yäf'lĕn-skō'yĕ) Sov. Un.	48.46 N	33.17 E
113	Boguchar (bō'go͞o-chär) Sov. Un.	49.42 N	41.0 E
123	Bogumin (Bohumín) (bō'go͞o mēn) (bo͞o'ho͞o-mēn) Pol.	49.55 N	18.21 E
131	Boguslav (bŏ'go͞o-släf) Sov. Un.	49.34 N	30.54 E
124	Bohain (bō-äɴ') Fr.	49.55 N	3.25 E
89	Bohemia La. (New Orleans In.)	29.33 N	89.45 W
122	Bohemia (Čechy) (Prov.) (bō-hē'mĭ-ȧ) (chĕĸ'ē) Czech.	49.44 N	14.15 E
122	Bohemian For. (bō-hē'mĭ-ȧn) Ger.-Czech.	49.15 N	12.55 E
122	Bohemian-Moravian Highlands (bō-hē'mĭ-ȧn-mō-rā'vĭ-ȧn) Czech.	49.20 N	15.40 E
122	Böhmisch Krumau, (Cesky Krumlov) (bû'mĭsh kro͞o'mou) (chĕs'kē kro͞om'lôf) Ger.	48.48 N	14.18 E
122	Böhmisch Leipa (Česká Lipa) (bû-mish lī'pȧ) (chĕs-kä lē'pȧ) Ger.	50.41 N	14.31 E
163	Bohol (I.) (bō-hôl') P. I.	9.50 N	124.15 E
163	Bohol Str. P. I.	9.50 N	123.35 E
141	Bohotleh (bō-hŏt'lē) Br. Som.	8.15 N	46.15 E
141	Bohotleh Yera (bō-hŏt'lē yē'rȧ) Br. Som.	8.55 N	45.57 E
	Bohumin, see Bogumin, Pol.		
86	Boiestown (boiz'toun) Can.	46.25 N	66.25 W
84	Bois Blanc I. (boi' blăɳk) Mich.	45.47 N	84.30 W
125	Bois de Boulogne (bwä dē bo͞o-lôn'-y') Fr. (In.)	48.51 N	2.15 E
70	Boise (boi'zȧ) Ida.	43.38 N	116.12 W
78	Boise City Okla.	36.43 N	102.28 W
70	Boise R. Ida.	43.41 N	116.30 W
54	Boissevain (bois'vān) Can.	49.17 N	100.2 W
125	Boissy (bwä-sē') Fr. (In.)	48.0 N	2.30 E
138	Bojador, C. (bō-hä-dōr') (bŏj-ȧ-dōr') R. de O.	26.15 N	14.30 W
162	Boieador, C. (bō-hä-ȧ-dōr') P. I.	18.30 N	120.33 E
161	Bokan Arch. (bō-kän') Neth. Ind.	2.0 S	123.40 E
138	Boké (bō-kā') Fr. W. Afr.	10.58 N	14.18 W
120	Bokn Fd. (bôk''n) Nor.	59.15 N	5.50 E
135	Boko Songo (bō'kō sŏɳ'gō) Fr. Eq. Afr. (Brazzaville In.)	4.22 S	13.37 E
143	Boksburg (bŏks'bûrg) U. S. Afr.	26.12 S	28.14 E
138	Bolama (bō-lä'mȧ) Port. Gui.	11.37 N	15.32 W
151	Bolan (bō-län') India	29.30 N	67.55 E
161	Bolan, Mt. (bō-län') N. Gui. Ter.	6.10 S	146.52 E
151	Bolan P. India	29.50 N	67.30 E
92	Bolaños (bō-län'yōs) Mex.	21.37 N	103.50 W
92	Bolaños, R. Mex.	21.40 N	103.55 W
124	Bolbec (bôl-bĕk') Fr.	49.35 N	0.30 E
162	Bolbok (bōl-bōk') P. I.	13.48 N	121.23 E
163	Bold Pt. (bōld) P. I.	10.3 N	119.12 E
138	Bole (bō'lȧ) G. C.	9.2 N	2.28 W
131	Bolgrad (bŏl-grät') Rom.	45.40 N	28.39 E
162	Bolinao (bō-lē-nä'ō) P. I.	16.22 N	119.53 E
162	Bolinao, C. P. I.	16.20 N	119.46 E
163	Bolipongpong I. (bō-lĭ-pông'pông) P. I.	5.40 N	120.50 E
104	Bolívar (bō-lē'vär) Arg.	36.20 S	61.10 W
102	Bolívar Col.	1.48 N	76.50 W
79	Bolivar (bŏl'ĭ-vȧr) Mo.	37.36 N	93.24 W
82	Bolivar Tenn.	35.44 N	88.59 W
81	Bolivar Pen. Tex.	29.27 N	94.37 W
102	Bolivia (bō-lĭv'ĭ-ȧ) S. A.	17.0 S	64.0 W
102	Bolivia, Plat. of Bol.	19.0 S	66.0 W
130	Bolkhov (bŏl-ĸôf') Sov. Un.	53.28 N	35.59 E
119	Bollin, R. (bŏl'ĭn) Gt. Brit. (Liverpool In.)	53.22 N	2.20 W
118	Bollin, R. Gt. Brit.	53.19 N	2.12 W
118	Bollington (bŏl'ĭng-tŭn) Gt. Brit.	53.18 N	2.6 W
120	Bollnäs (bŏl'nĕs) Swe.	61.22 N	16.20 E
126	Bollullos (bō-lyo͞ol'yōs) Sp.	37.20 N	6.32 W
120	Bolmen, L. (bŏl'mĕn) Swe.	56.55 N	13.40 E
131	Bolnovakna (bŏl-nō-väk'nȧ) Sov. Un.	47.32 N	37.30 E
140	Bolobo (bō'lō-bō) Bel. Cong.	2.12 S	16.20 E
128	Bologna (bō-lōn'yä) It.	44.30 N	11.21 E
130	Bologoe (bŏ-lō-gō'yĕ) Sov. Un.	57.52 N	34.4 E
96	Bolondrón (bō-lōn-drōn') Cuba	22.43 N	81.28 W
128	Bolseno, L. of (bōl-sā'nō) It.	42.35 N	11.56 E
131	Bolshaya Lepetikha (bŏl-shä'yȧ lyĕ'pyĕ-tē'kȧ) Sov. Un.	47.9 N	33.54 E
131	Bolshaya Vereka (bŏl-shä'yȧ vyĕr-yĕ'kȧ) Sov. Un.	49.27 N	36.9 E
131	Bolshaya Vradievka (bŏl-shä'yȧ vrä-dyĕf'kȧ) Sov. Un.	47.51 N	30.33 E
131	Bolshaya Znamenka (bŏl-shä'yȧ znä-myĕn'kȧ) Sov. Un.	47.26 N	34.18 E
149	Bolsheretskoe (bŏl-shyĕ'ryĕt-skō'yĕ) Sov. Un.	52.40 N	156.50 E
131	Bolshie Kopani (bŏl'shyĕ kō-pä'nĭ) Sov. Un.	46.27 N	32.55 E
131	Bolshie-Sorochintsy (bŏl'shyĕ-sō-rō-chĭnt'sĭ) Sov. Un.	49.59 N	33.55 E
131	Bolshie Viski (bŏl'shyĕ vĭs'kĭ) Sov. Un.	48.35 N	31.49 E
118	Bolsover (bŏl'zō-vēr) Gt. Brit.	53.14 N	1.17 W
73	Bolton (bōl'tŭn) Ga. (Atlanta In.)	33.49 N	84.28 W
116	Bolton Gt. Brit.	53.35 N	2.25 W
118	Bolton-on-Dearne (bōl'tŭn-ŏn-dûrn) Gt. Brit.	53.31 N	1.18 W
113	Bolu (bō'lo͞o) Tur.	40.46 N	31.46 E
130	Bolva R. (bôl'vȧ) Sov. Un.	53.55 N	34.22 E
113	Bolvadin (bŏl-vä-dēn') Tur.	38.45 N	31.0 E
128	Bolzano (bōl-tsä'nō) It.	46.31 N	11.23 E
140	Boma (bō'mȧ) Bel. Cong.	5.47 S	13.5 E
167	Bombala (bŏm-bä'lȧ) Austl.	36.54 S	149.15 E
151	Bombay (bŏm-bā') India	19.0 N	72.48 E
151	Bombay (Presidency) India	22.0 N	73.0 E
151	Bombay I. India (In.)	18.58 N	72.50 E
103	Bomfim (bôɴ-fēɴ') Braz.	10.29 S	40.2 W
103	Bomfim (bôɴ-fēɴ') Braz.	16.47 S	48.32 W
103	Bom Jardim (bôɴ zhär-dēɴ') Braz. (In.)	12.18 S	38.34 W
103	Bom Jesus do Rio de Contas (bôɴ zhä-zo͞osh do͞o rē'o͞o dä kôɴ'täzh) Braz.	13.5 S	41.59 W
104	Bom Jesus I. (bôɴ zhä'zo͞osh) Braz. (In.)	22.51 S	43.13 W
120	Bommel I. (bôm'mĕl) Nor.	59.48 N	5.15 E
102	Bonaire (I.) (bō-när') W. I.	12.5 N	68.20 W
127	Bonanza (bō-nän'thä) Sp. (In.)	36.48 N	6.20 W
126	Boñar (bō-nyär') Sp.	42.54 N	5.18 W
87	Bonavista (bŏ-nȧ-vĭs'tȧ) Newf.	48.36 N	53.8 W
87	Bonavista B. Newf.	48.40 N	53.40 W
135	Bon C. (bŏn) Tun. (In.)	37.5 N	10.50 E
78	Bond (bŏnd) Colo.	39.53 N	106.43 W
169	Bondi (bŏn'dē) Austl. (Sydney In.)	33.54 S	151.16 E
139	Bondo (bôn'dō) Bel. Cong.	3.50 N	23.45 E
162	Bondoc Pen. (bōn-dŏk') P. I.	13.30 N	122.30 E
162	Bondoc Pt. P. I.	13.10 N	122.35 E
138	Bondoukou (bōn-do͞o'ko͞o) Fr. W. Afr.	8.8 N	2.48 W
96	Bonds Cay (I.) (bŏnds kē) Ba. Is.	25.30 N	77.43 W
125	Bondy (bôɴ-dē') Fr. (In.)	48.54 N	2.28 E
138	Bône (bōn) Alg.	36.58 N	7.45 E
119	Bonea (bō'nä-ȧ) It. (Napoli In.)	40.40 N	14.27 E
79	Bonham (bŏn'ȧm) Tex.	33.35 N	96.11 W
124	Bonifacio (bō-nē-fä'chō) Cor. (In.)	41.25 N	9.10 E
128	Bonifacio, Str. of Cor.	41.20 N	9.20 E
82	Bonifay (bŏn-ĭ-fā') Fla.	30.47 N	85.42 W
160	Boni, G. of (bō'nē) Neth. Ind.	4.30 S	121.0 E
49	Bonita, Pt. (bō-nē'tȧ) Calif. (San Francisco In.)	37.48 N	122.32 W
103	Bonito (bō-nē tō) Braz.	8.28 S	35.40 W
122	Bonn (bŏn) Ger.	50.45 N	7.6 E
87	Bonne B. (bŏn) Newf.	49.35 N	58.0 W
70	Bonners Ferry (bŏn'ērz) Ida.	48.41 N	116.19 W
124	Bonnétable (bôn-ȧ-täb'l')) Fr.	48.11 N	0.25 E
79	Bonne Terre (bŏn târ') Mo.	37.55 N	90.33 W
166	Bonney, L. (bŏn'ē) Austl.	37.45 S	140.20 E
138	Bonny (bŏn'ē) Nig.	4.30 N	7.11 E
128	Bonorva (bō-nôr'vä) Sard.	40.26 N	8.46 E
160	Bonthain (bŏn-tīn') Neth. Ind.	5.29 S	119.58 E
162	Bontoc (bŏn-tŏk') P. I.	17.9 N	121.2 E
96	Booby Rocks (bo͞o'bĭ rŏks) Ba. Is.	23.58 N	77.2 W
166	Boolaboolka L. (bo͞o-lȧ-bo͞ol'kȧ) Austl.	32.38 S	143.13 E
77	Boone (bo͞on) Ia.	42.5 N	93.51 W
79	Booneville (bo͞on'vĭl) Ark.	35.8 N	93.53 W
84	Booneville Ky.	37.28 N	83.42 W
82	Booneville Miss.	34.37 N	88.36 W
70	Booneville Dam Ore.-Wash.	45.40 N	121.55 W
84	Boonville Ind.	38.3 N	87.14 W
79	Boonville Mo.	38.57 N	92.45 W
167	Boorowa (bo͞o-rō'wȧ) Austl.	34.26 S	148.44 E
86	Boothbay Harbor (bo͞oth'bā här'-bēr) Me.	43.52 N	69.38 W
55	Boothia, G. of, (bo͞o'thĭ-ȧ) Can.	68.30 N	87.0 W
54	Boothia Pen. Can.	70.30 N	95.0 W
116	Bootle (bo͞o't'l) Gt. Brit.	53.30 N	3.0 W
138	Boporo (bō-pō'rō) Lib.	7.10 N	10.42 W
122	Boppard (bōp'ärt) Ger.	50.14 N	7.35 E
139	Bor (bōr) A. E. Sud.	6.9 N	31.36 E
113	Bor (bōr) Tur.	37.58 N	34.35 E
71	Borah Peak (bō'rȧ) Idaho	44.12 N	113.41 W
120	Borås (bo͞o'rōs) Swe	57.43 N	12.57 E
150	Borazjan (bō-räz-jän') Iran	29.15 N	51.15 E
103	Borba (bôr'bȧ) Braz.	4.29 S	59.32 W
163	Borbon (bôr-bōn') P. I.	10.49 N	124.1 E
166	Borda, C. (bôr'dȧ) Austl.	35.43 S	136.38 E
124	Bordeaux (bôr-dō') Fr.	44.40 N	0.30 W
89	Bordeau, B. (bôr-dō') La. (New Orleans In.)	30.0 N	89.21 W
85	Bordentown (bôr'dĕn-toun) N. J.	40.7 N	74.43 W
166	Border Town Austl.	36.20 S	140.45 E
114	Bordj-bou-Arréridj (bôrj-bo͞o-ȧ-rȧ-rēj') Alg.	36.3 N	4.49 E
121	Borgå (Porvoo) (bôr'gō pôr'vō) Fin.	60.26 N	25.44 E
78	Borger (bôr'gēr) Tex.	35.39 N	101.22 W
117	Borgerhout (bôr'gēr-hout) Bel.	51.11 N	4.25 E
120	Borgholm (bôrg-hôlm') Swe.	56.53 N	16.41 E
81	Borgne, L. (bôrn'y') La.	30.0 N	89.40 W
128	Borgo (bôr'gō) It.	45.41 N	10.2 E
128	Borgomanero (bôr'gō-mä-nä'rō) It.	45.41 N	8.28 E
128	Borgo San Donnino (bôr-gō sän dôn-nē'nō) It.	44.45 N	10.8 E
128	Borgotaro (bôr-gō-tä'rō) It.	44.29 N	9.45 E
113	Borisoglebsk (bŏ-rē'sō-glyĕpsk') Sov. Un.	51.18 N	42.5 E
130	Borisov (bŏ-rē'sôf) Sov. Un.	54.14 N	28.34 E
131	Borisovka (bŏ-rē-sôf'kȧ) Sov. Un.	50.37 N	36.0 E
131	Borispol (bō-rĭs'pŏl) Sov. Un.	50.21 N	30.53 E
126	Borja (bôr'hä) Sp.	41.50 N	1.32 W
127	Borjas Blancas (bôr'häs bläɳ'-käs) Sp.	41.31 N	0.53 E
149	Borkhaya, C. (bŏr-ĸä'yȧ) Sov. Un.	71.50 N	133.20 E
149	Borkhaya B. Sov. Un.	71.25 N	131.0 E
139	Borkou (Reg.) (bôr-ko͞o') Fr. Eq. Afr.	18.0 N	19.30 E
122	Borkum (I.) (bôr'ko͞om) Neth.	53.36 N	6.45 E
120	Borlänge (bôr-lĕɳ'gē) Swe.	60.29 N	15.25 E
160	Borneo (I.) (bôr'nē-ō) E. Ind.	1.0 N	114.0 E
120	Bornholm (I.) (bôrn-hôlm') Den.	55.10 N	14.50 E
126	Bornos (bôr'nōs) Sp.	36.49 N	5.45 W
119	Bornstädt (bôrn'stĕt) Ger. (Berlin In.)	52.25 N	13.2 E
139	Bornu (Prov.) (bôr-no͞o') Nig.	11.30 N	13.0 E
131	Borodnevka (bŏ-rŏd-nyĕf'kȧ) Sov. Un.	48.44 N	34.6 E
131	Boromlya (bŏ-rôm''l-yȧ) Sov. Un.	50.35 N	34.56 E
113	Borona R. (bŏ'rō-nȧ) Sov. Un.	51.45 N	42.20 E
162	Borongan (bō-rōng'ăn) P. I.	11.36 N	125.27 E
118	Boroughbridge (bŭr'ō-brĭj) Gt. Brit.	54.5 N	1.23 W
129	Borovan (bŏ-rō-vän') Bul.	43.24 N	23.45 E
130	Borovichi (bŏ-rō-vē'chē) Sov. Un.	58.22 N	33.56 E
130	Borovsk (bŏ'rŏvsk) Sov. Un.	55.12 N	36.29 E
164	Borroloola (bŏr-rō-lo͞o'lȧ) Austl.	16.15 S	136.15 E
119	Borsbeck (bôrs'bĕk) Bel. (Anvers In.)	51.12 N	4.29 E

ăt; finăl; rāte; senāte; ärm; ȧsk; sofȧ; fâre; ch-choose; dh-as th in other; bē; ēvent; bĕt; recĕnt; cratēr; g-go; gh-gutteral g; bĭt; ĭ-short neutral; rīde; ĸ-gutteral k as ch in German ich;

Page	Name Pronunciation Region	Lat. °′	Long. °′
72	Borst (bôrst) Colo. (Colo. Sprs. In.)	39.4 N	104.52 W
119	Borstel (bôr′stĕl) Ger. (Hamburg In.)	53.32 N	9.42 E
123	Borszczów (bôrsh′chŏŏf) Pol.	48.48 N	26.4 E
124	Bort-es-Orgues (bôr-tĕs-ôrg′) Fr.	45.25 N	2.30 E
123	Boryslaw (bô′rĭs-wăf) Pol.	49.16 N	23.25 E
131	Borzna (bôrz′nȧ) Sov. Un.	51.15 N	32.22 E
149	Borzya (bôrz′yȧ) Sov. Un.	50.25 N	116.37 E
128	Bosa (bō′sä) Sard.	40.19 N	8.33 E
128	Bosanska Dubica (bō′sän-skä dōō′bĭt-sä) Yugo.	45.10 N	16.49 E
128	Bosanska Gradiška (bō′sän-skä grä-dĭsh′kä) Yugo.	45.7 N	17.17 E
128	Bosanski Novi (bō′sän-skĭ nō′vē) Yugo.	45.2 N	16.23 E
128	Bosanski Petrovac (bō′sän-skĭ pĕt′rō-väts) Yugo.	44.34 N	16.23 E
129	Bosanski Šamac (bō′sän-skĭ shä′-mäts) Yugo.	45.3 N	18.29 E
77	Boscobel (bŏs′kô-bĕl) Wis.	43.8 N	90.41 W
119	Boscoreale (bôs′kô-rā-ä′lā) It. (Napoli In.)	40.46 N	14.28 E
119	Boscotrecase (bŏs′kô-trā-kä′sā) It. (Napoli In.)	40.46 N	14.26 E
143	Boshof (bō′shŏf) U. S. Afr.	28.32 S	25.12 E
122	Boskovice (bŏs′kō-vē-tsĕ) Czech.	49.29 N	16.40 E
129	Bosna R. (bŏs′nȧ) Yugo.	44.30 N	18.10 E
128	Bosnia (Prov.) (bŏs′nĭ-ȧ) Yugo.	44.0 N	17.35 E
161	Bosoboso (bō-sô-bō′sô) P. I. (Manila In.)	14.39 N	121.15 E
113	Bosporus (Str.) (bŏs′pô-rŭs) Tur.	41.10 N	29.10 E
81	Bossier City (bŏsh′ēr) La.	32.32 N	93.41 W
82	Boston (bôs′tŭn) Ga.	30.47 N	83.50 W
116	Boston Gt. Brit.	53.0 N	0.0
86	Boston Mass.	42.15 N	71.7 W
87	Boston Mass. (In.)		
166	Boston B. Austl.	34.45 S	136.0 E
79	Boston Mts. Ark.	35.45 N	93.30 W
167	Botany B. (bŏt′ȧ-nĭ bā) Austl.	33.58 S	151.13 E
143	Bothaville (bō′tä-vĭl) U. S. Afr.	27.22 S	26.37 E
110	Bothnia, G. of (bŏth′nĭ-ȧ) Eur.	63.10 N	20.30 E
162	Botolan (bō-tō-län′) P. I.	15.17 N	120.1 E
123	Botoșani (bô-tô-shän′ĭ) Rom.	47.46 N	26.41 E
76	Bottineau (bŏt-ĭ-nō′) N. D.	48.50 N	100.27 W
87	Botwood Harbour (bŏt′wŏŏd) Newf.	49.6 N	55.22 W
138	Bouaflé (bōō-ȧ-flā′) Fr. W. Afr.	7.20 N	5.31 W
138	Bouaké (bōō-ȧ-kā′) Fr. W. Afr.	7.46 N	5.3 W
139	Bouara (bōō-ȧ-rä′) (bōō-är′ä) Fr. Eq. Afr.	5.59 N	15.33 E
57	Boucherville (bōō-shā-vēl′) Can. (Montreal In.)	45.37 N	73.26 W
119	Bouchout (bōō-shōō′) Bel. (Anvers In.)	51.10 N	4.29 E
138	Bou-Denib (bōō-dĕ-nēb′) Mor.	32.12 N	3.7 W
114	Bou Dia, C. (bōō dē′ȧ) Tun.	35.15 N	11.10 E
114	Boufarik (bōō-fȧ-rēk′) Alg.	36.35 N	2.55 E
161	Bougainville Trough (bōō-găɴ-vēl′) N. Gui. Ter.	7.0 S	151.0 E
138	Bougie (bōō-zhē′) Alg.	36.38 N	5.0 E
138	Bougouni (bōō-gōō-nē′) Fr. W. Afr.	11.22 N	7.30 W
127	Bouira (boo-ē′rȧ) Alg.	36.22 N	3.54 E
164	Boulder (bōl′dēr) Austl.	30.47 S	121.30 E
78	Boulder Colo.	40.2 N	105.18 W
74	Boulder City Nev.	36.1 N	114.53 W
72	Boulder Cr. Colo. (Denver In.)	40.8 N	104.58 W
70	Boulder Cr. Ida.	42.50 N	116.50 W
74	Boulder Dam Ariz.	36.4 N	114.45 W
71	Boulder Pk. Ida.	43.51 N	114.32 W
71	Boulder R. Mont.	46.10 N	112.0 W
138	Boulé R. (bōō-lā′) Fr. W. Afr.	11.30 N	7.20 W
125	Boullay-les Troux (bōō-lĕ′-lā trōō′) Fr. (In.)	48.41 N	2.3 E
124	Boulogne (bōō lôn′y′) Fr.	50.45 N	1.40 E
124	Boulogne-Billancourt (bōō-lôn′y′-bē-yäɴ-kōōr′) Fr.	48.50 N	2.20 E
138	Bouna (bōō-nä′) Fr. W. Afr.	9.18 N	2.57 W
72	Boundary B. (boun′dȧ-rĭ bā) Can. (Vancouver In.)	49.2 N	122.58 W
74	Boundary Pk. Nev.	37.51 N	118.21 W
71	Bountiful (boun′tĭ-fŏŏl) Utah	40.54 N	111.54 W
138	Bourem (bōō-răɴ′) Fr. W. Afr.	16.51 N	0.15 W
124	Bourg (bōōr) Fr.	46.15 N	5.15 E
124	Bourg-de-Péage (bōōr-dē-pā-äzh′) Fr.	45.0 N	5.5 E
124	Bourges (bōōrzh) Fr.	47.5 N	2.25 E
125	Bourgival (bōōr-zhē-vȧl′) Fr. (In.)	48.52 N	2.7 E
125	Bourg-la-Reine (bōōr-lȧ-rān′) Fr. (In.)	48.46 N	2.19 E
124	Bourgoin (bōōr-gwăɴ′) Fr.	45.35 N	5.20 E
124	Bourg-St. Andéol (bōōr′-săɴ tăɴ-dā-ôl′) Fr.	44.25 N	4.39 E
165	Bourke (bōrk) Austl.	30.14 S	145.59 E
118	Bourne (bōrn) Gt. Brit.	52.46 N	0.21 W
116	Bournemouth (bôrn′mŭth) Gt. Brit.	50.44 N	1.55 W
138	Bou-Saada (bōō-sä′dä) Alg.	35.12 N	4.7 E
139	Bousso (bōō-sô′) Fr. Eq. Afr.	10.30 N	16.42 E
138	Boutilimit (bōō-tê-lê-mē′) Fr. W. Afr.	17.30 N	14.52 W
46	Bouvet Is. (bōō-vĕ′) Ant. O.	54.0 S	5.0 E
128	Bovino (bō-vē′nō) It.	41.15 N	15.21 E
54	Bow R. (bō) Can.	51.15 N	114.0 W
118	Bow, R. Gt. Brit.	52.12 N	2.5 W
76	Bowbells (bō′bĕls) N. D.	48.47 N	102.1 W
76	Bowdle (bōd′′l) S. D.	45.28 N	99.37 W
165	Bowen (bō′ĕn) Austl.	20.0 S	148.8 E
72	Bowen I. Can. (Vancouver In.)	49.22 N	123.23 W
142	Bowesdorp (bōz′dôrp) U. S. Afr.	30.9 S	17.55 E
78	Bowie (bōō′ĭ) (bō′ê) Texas	33.33 N	97.50 W
82	Bowling Green (bō′lĭng grēn) Ky.	37.0 N	86.27 W
79	Bowling Green Mo.	39.19 N	91.12 W
84	Bowling Green Ohio	41.25 N	83.39 W
76	Bowman (bō′măn) N. D.	46.11 N	103.23 W
85	Bowmanville (bō′măn-vĭl) Can.	43.52 N	78.40 W
151	Bowringpet (bō′rĭng-pĕt′) India	13.5 N	78.5 E
72	Boxelder Cr. (bŏks′ĕl-dēr) Colo. (Denver In.)	40.10 N	104.37 W
71	Boxelder Cr. Mont.	47.20 N	108.43 W
71	Boxelder Cr. Mont.	45.30 N	104.36 W
73	Box Elder Pk. Utah (Salt Lake City In.)	41.38 N	112.1 W
76	Boyer R. (boi′ēr) Ia.	41.45 N	95.40 W
116	Boyle (boil) Ire.	53.55 N	8.20 W
73	Boyles (boilz) Ala. (Birmingham In.)	33.33 N	86.47 W
84	Boyne City (boin) Mich.	45.13 N	85.1 W
169	Boyne R. Austl. (In.)	26.25 S	151.20 E
116	Boyne, R. Ire.	53.40 N	6.40 W
129	Bozcaada (I.) (bōz-cä′dä) Tur.	39.47 N	26.2 E
129	Bozcaada (Tenedos) (bōz-cä′dä) Tur.	39.48 N	26.4 E
71	Bozeman (bōz′măn) Mont.	45.41 N	111.1 W
	Bozen, see Bolzano, It.		
128	Bra (brä) It.	44.41 N	7.52 E
128	Brač (I.) (brăch) Yugo.	43.18 N	16.40 E
128	Bracciano, L. of (brä-chä′nō) It.	42.7 N	12.15 E
85	Bracebridge (brās′brĭj) Can.	45.3 N	79.19 W
120	Bräcke (brĕk′kĕ) Swe.	62.44 N	15.26 E
80	Brackettville (brăk′ĕt-vĭl) Tex.	29.18 N	100.25 W
103	Braço Menor, (R.) (brä′sō mā-nôr′) Braz.	12.0 S	50.2 W
128	Bradano R. (brä-dä′nō) It.	40.40 N	16.20 E
85	Braddock (brăd′ŭk) Pa.	40.26 N	79.52 W
83	Bradenton (brā′dĕn-tŭn) Fla. (In.)	27.28 N	82.35 W
116	Bradford (brăd′fērd) Gt. Brit.	53.48 N	1.35 W
84	Bradford Ohio	40.10 N	84.28 W
85	Bradford Pa.	41.58 N	78.41 W
84	Bradley (brăd′lĭ) Ill.	41.10 N	87.52 W
80	Brady (brā′dĭ) Tex.	31.8 N	99.21 W
126	Braga (brä′gä) Port.	41.32 N	8.26 W
104	Bragado (brä-gä′dō) Arg.	35.18 S	60.30 W
103	Bragança (brä-gän′sä) Braz.	23.0 S	46.32 W
103	Bragança Braz.	2.1 S	46.58 W
126	Braganca Port.	41.47 N	6.48 W
152	Brahmaputra (Tsang Po) R. (brä′mȧ-pōō′trȧ) (tsäng′-pō′) Chn.-India	29.30 N	95.0 E
167	Braidwood (brād′wŏŏd) Austl.	35.27 S	149.48 E
129	Brăila (brē′ē-lȧ) Rom.	45.15 N	27.59 E
77	Brainerd (brān′ērd) Minn.	46.22 N	94.9 W
87	Braintree (brān′trē) Mass. (In.)	42.13 N	71.0 W
142	Brak R. (brăk) U. S. Afr.	29.50 S	23.10 E
143	Brakpan (brăk′păn) U. S. Afr.	26.12 S	28.21 E
119	Bramfeld (brăm′fĕlt) Ger. (Hamburg In.)	53.37 N	10.5 E
119	Bramhall (brăm′hôl) Gt. Brit. (Liverpool In.)	53.22 N	2.9 W
85	Brampton (brămp′tŭn) Can.	43.40 N	79.45 W
73	Branchville (brănch′vĭl) Ala. (Birmingham In.)	33.39 N	86.26 W
83	Branchville S. C.	33.16 N	80.49 W
103	Branco, R. (brăŋ′kō) Braz.	0.0	61.45 W
122	Brandenburg (brăn′dĕn-bŏŏrgh) Ger.	52.24 N	12.33 E
122	Brandenburg (Prov.) Ger.	52.12 N	13.55 E
54	Brandon (brăn′dŭn) Can.	49.50 N	99.59 W
86	Brandon Vt.	43.47 N	73.5 W
116	Brandon Hill Ire.	52.15 N	10.10 W
142	Brandvlei (brȧnd′vlȧ) U. S. Afr.	30.25 S	20.29 E
85	Branford (brăn′fērd) Conn.	41.16 N	72.50 W
95	Brangmans Bluff (brăng′mȧnz-blŭf) Nic.	14.5 N	83.20 W
123	Bránsk (brän′′sk) Pol.	52.44 N	22.53 E
85	Brantford (brănt′fērd) Can.	43.10 N	80.12 W
166	Branxholme (brănks′hōm) Austl.	37.52 S	141.49 E
87	Bras d' Or L. (brä-dôr′) Can.	45.53 N	60.58 W
123	Brașov (brä′shôf) Rom.	45.40 N	25.35 E
138	Brass (brăs) Nig.	4.26 N	6.27 E
119	Brasschaet (bräs′ᴋät) Bel. (Anvers In.)	51.18 N	4.29 E
128	Bratello P. (brä-tel′lō) It.	44.25 N	10.0 E
123	Bratislava (brä-tĭ-slä′vȧ) Czech.	48.8 N	17.7 E
148	Bratsk (brȧtsk) Sov. Un.	56.10 N	101.59 E
131	Bratslav (brät′slȧf) Sov. Un.	48.49 N	28.55 E
86	Brattleboro (brăt′′l-bŭr-ô) Vt.	42.50 N	72.35 W
122	Braunau (broun′ȧu) Ger.	48.15 N	13.2 E
122	Braunau (Broumov) (broun′ȧu) (brōō′môf) Ger.	50.31 N	16.10 E
123	Braunsberg (brouns′bĕrgh) Ger.	54.23 N	19.51 E
122	Braunschweig (State) (broun′shvīgh) Ger.	52.10 N	10.10 E
122	Braunschweig (Brunswick) (brŭnz′wĭk) Ger.	52.16 N	10.31 E
46	Braunsfield Str. (brounz′fēld) Ant. O.	63.0 S	60.0 W
141	Brava (brä′vä) It. E. Afr.	1.10 N	44.2 E
74	Brawley (brô′lĭ) Calif.	32.59 N	115.31 W
116	Bray (brā) Ire.	53.10 N	6.5 W
169	Braybrook (brā′brŏŏk) Austl. (Melbourne In.)	37.47 S	144.52 E
79	Braymer (brā′mēr) Mo.	39.34 N	93.47 W
81	Brays Bayou (brās′ bī′yōō) Texas (In.)	29.42 N	95.28 W
84	Brazil (brȧ-zĭl′) Ind.	39.32 N	87.7 W
102	Brazil S. A.	9.0 S	53.0 W
81	Brazos R. (brä′zōs) Tex.	30.50 N	96.40 W
80	Brazos R., Clear Fork of Tex.	33.0 N	99.15 W
78	Brazos R., Double Mt. Fork of Tex.	33.8 N	101.0 W
78	Brazos R., Salt Fork of Tex.	33.34 N	99.30 W
140	Brazzaville (brȧ-zȧ-vēl′) Fr. Eq. Afr.	4.10 S	15.18 E
129	Brčko (bĕrch′kô) Yugo.	44.53 N	18.46 E
123	Brda R. (bĕr-dä′) Pol.	53.30 N	17.53 E
73	Brea (brē′ȧ) Calif. (Los Angeles In.)	33.55 N	117.54 W
116	Brechin (brē′ᴋĭn) Gt. Brit.	56.45 N	2.40 W
119	Brecht (brĕᴋt) Bel. (Anvers In.)	51.21 N	4.38 E
76	Breckenridge (brĕk′ĕn-rĭj) Minn.	46.17 N	96.34 W
80	Breckenridge Tex.	32.45 N	98.54 W
99	Brecknock Pen. (brĕk′nŏk) Chl. (Magallanes In.)	54.30 S	71.20 W
	Breclav, see Lundenburg, Ger.		
116	Brecon Beacons (brĕk′ŭn bē′kŭns) Gt. Brit.	51.50 N	3.20 W
122	Breda (brā-dä′) Neth.	51.36 N	4.49 E
142	Bredasdorp (brā′das-dôrp) U. S. Afr.	34.32 S	20.2 E
72	Breed (brēd) Colo. (Colo. Spgs. In)	38.57 N	104.49 W
142	Breede R. (brēd) U. S. Afr.	33.49 S	19.50 E
122	Bregenz (brā′gĕnts) Ger.	47.31 N	9.46 E
129	Bregovo (brĕ-gō′vō) Bul.	44.8 N	22.40 E
110	Breidi Fd. (brā′dĭ) Ice.	65.10 N	23.0 W
125	Breil (brĕ′y′) Fr.	43.59 N	7.30 E
103	Brejo (brȧ′zhŏŏ) Braz.	3.37 S	42.48 W
120	Bremanger I. (brĕ′măŋ-gĕr) Nor.	61.50 N	5.5 E
122	Bremen (brā-mĕn) Ger.	53.5 N	8.49 E
84	Bremen (brē′mĕn) Ind.	41.27 N	86.8 W
122	Bremerhaven (brām-ēr-hä′fĕn) Ger.	53.34 N	8.34 E
143	Bremersdorp (brā′mērs-dôrp) Swaz.	26.32 S	31.21 E
70	Bremerton (brĕm′ēr-tŭn) Wash.	47.33 N	122.40 W
81	Bremond (brĕm′ŭnd) Tex.	31.10 N	96.40 W
81	Brenham (brĕn′ăm) Tex.	30.10 N	96.23 W
122	Brenner P. (brĕn′ēr) Ger.-It.	47.0 N	11.30 E
119	Brentford (brent′fērd) Gt. Brit. (London In.)	51.29 N	0.19 W
49	Brentwood (brĕnt′wŏŏd) Calif. (In.)	37.56 N	121.43 W
119	Brentwood Gt. Brit. (London In.)	51.38 N	0.18 E
85	Brentwood Md.	8.57 N	6.58 W
128	Brescia (brā′shä) It.	45.32 N	10.13 E
123	Breslau (brĕs′lou) Ger.	51.7 N	17.2 E
128	Bressanone (brĕs-sä-nō′nä) It.	46.44 N	11.37 E
124	Bressuire (brĕ-swēr′) Fr.	46.50 N	0.30 W
124	Brest (brĕst) Fr.	48.25 N	4.30 W
123	Brest-Litovsk (Brzesć nad Bugiem) (brĕst-lyē-tôfsk′) (bzhĕshch-näd-bŏŏ′gyĕm) Pol.	52.5 N	23.43 E
89	Breton I. (brĕt′ŭn) La. (New Orleans In.)	29.29 N	80.10 W
81	Breton Sd. La.	29.30 N	89.20 W
170	Brett C. (brĕt) N. Z.	35.10 S	174.20 E
83	Brevard (brê-värd′) N. C.	35.15 N	82.43 W
103	Breves (brā′vĕzh) Braz.	1.45 S	50.15 W
120	Brevik (brĕ′vêk) Nor.	59.4 N	9.41 E
165	Brewarrina (brōō-ēr-rē′nȧ) Austl.	30.0 S	146.48 E
86	Brewer (brōō′ēr) Me.	44.45 N	68.45 W
95	Brewster, Cerro (Mt.) (brōō′stēr) Pan.	9.20 N	79.15 W
82	Brewton (brōō′tŭn) Ala.	31.6 N	87.4 W
128	Brezice (brĕ′zhê-tsĕ) Yugo.	45.54 N	15.36 E
129	Breznik (brĕz′nêk) Bulg.	42.44 N	22.54 E
123	Brezno (brȧz′nô) Czech.	48.49 N	19.39 E
167	Briagolong (brē-ä′gō-lông) Austl.	37.49 S	147.5 E
125	Briançon (brē-äɴ-sôɴ′) Fr.	44.55 N	6.40 E
124	Briare (brē-är′) Fr.	47.40 N	2.48 E
169	Bribie (I.) (brī′bê) Austl. (In.)	26.55 S	153.7 E
49	Bridal Veil (brīd′ăl vāl) Ore. (Portland In.)	45.33 N	122.10 W
88	Bridgeburg (brĭj′bērg) Can. (Niagara Falls In.)	42.55 N	78.55 W
96	Bridge Pt. (brĭj) Ba. Is.	25.33 N	76.43 W
82	Bridgeport (brĭj′pōrt) Ala.	34.56 N	85.42 W
85	Bridgeport Conn.	41.12 N	73.12 W
84	Bridgeport Ill.	38.41 N	87.47 W
76	Bridgeport Neb.	41.40 N	103.7 W
84	Bridgeport Ohio	40.4 N	80.46 W
85	Bridgeport Pa.	40.7 N	75.22 W
79	Bridgeport Tex.	33.13 N	97.45 W
73	Bridgeton (brĭj′tŭn) Ala. (Birmingham In.)	33.28 N	86.38 W
85	Bridgeton N. J.	39.27 N	75.17 W
91	Bridgetown (brĭj′toun) Barb.	13.14 N	59.38 W
86	Bridgetown (brĭj′tŭn) Canada	44.52 N	65.19 W
89	Bridgeville (brĭj′vĭl) Pa. (Pittsburgh In.)	40.21 N	80.7 W
169	Bridgewater (brĭj′wô-tēr) Austl. (Tas. In.)	42.45 S	147.13 E
86	Bridgewater Can.	44.22 N	64.31 W
116	Bridgewater Gt. Brit.	51.10 N	3.0 W
166	Bridgewater C. Austl.	38.22 S	141.22 E
118	Bridgnorth (brĭj′nôrth) Gt. Brit.	52.32 N	2.25 W
86	Bridgton (brĭj′tŭn) Me.	44.3 N	70.45 W
116	Bridlington (brĭd′lĭng-tŭn) Gt. Brit.	54.5 N	0.15 W
118	Bridlington B. Gt. Brit.	54.3 N	0.9 W
169	Bridport (brĭd′pōrt) Austl. (Tas. In.)	41.1 S	147.24 E
123	Brieg (brēgh) Ger.	50.52 N	17.29 E
83	Brier Cr. (brī′ēr) Ga.	33.7 N	82.0 W
82	Brierfield (brī′ēr-fēld) Ala.	33.2 N	86.55 W
118	Brierfield Gt. Brit.	53.49 N	2.14 W
86	Brier I. (brī′ēr) Can.	44.15 N	66.25 W
118	Brierley Hill (brī′ēr-lê hĭl) Gt. Brit.	52.29 N	2.7 W
125	Briey (brē-ĕ′) Fr.	49.15 N	5.55 E
122	Brig (brēg) Switz.	46.18 N	7.59 E
118	Brigg (brĭg) Gt. Brit.	53.33 N	0.29 W
71	Brigham (brĭg′ăm) Utah	41.31 N	112.1 W
118	Brighouse (brĭg′hous) Gt. Brit.	53.42 N	1.47 W
167	Bright (brīt) Austl.	36.42 S	146.56 E
73	Brighton (brīt′ŭn) Ala. (Birmingham In.)	33.25 N	86.58 W
166	Brighton Austl.	37.56 S	144.59 E
169	Brighton (brī′tŭn) Austl. (Tas. In.)	42.41 S	147.17 E
78	Brighton Colo.	39.57 N	104.49 W
116	Brighton Gt. Brit.	50.50 N	0.10 W
77	Brighton Ia.	41.11 N	91.49 W
171	Brighton N. Z.	42.5 S	171.30 E
73	Brighton Utah (Salt Lake City In.)	40.37 N	111.36 W
125	Brignoles (brēn-yôl′) Fr.	43.25 N	6.5 E
87	Brigus (brĭg′ŭs) Newf.	47.30 N	53.14 W

ng-sing; ŋ-baŋk; ɴ-nasalized n; nŏd; cŏmmit; ōld; ôbey; ôrder; fōōd; fŏŏt; ou-out; s-soft; sh-dish; th-thin; pūre; ûnite; ûrn; stŭd; circŭs; ü-as "y" in study; ′-indeterminate vowel.

Page	Name Pronunciation Region	Lat. °′	Long. °′
126	Brihuega (brē-wä'gä) . . . . Sp.	40.47 N	2.52 W
129	Brindisi (brēn'dē-zē) . . . . It.	40.38 N	18.0 E
128	Brinje (brēn'yĕ) . . . . Yugo.	45.1 N	15.7 E
79	Brinkley (brĭŋk'lĭ) . . . . Ark.	34.54 N	91.11 W
166	Brinkworth (brĭnk'wērth) . . Austl.	33.40 S	138.23 E
49	Brinnon (brĭn'ŭn) Wash. (Seattle In.)	47.41 N	122.54 W
87	Brion I. (brē-ôN') . . . . Can.	47.47 N	61.30 W
124	Brioude (brē-ōōd') . . . . Fr.	45.18 N	3.21 E
165	Brisbane (brĭz'bān) . . . . Austl.	27.29 S	153.8 E
169	Brisbane R. . . . . Austl. (In.)	27.0 S	152.23 E
85	Bristol (brĭs'tŭl) . . . . Conn.	41.40 N	72.58 W
116	Bristol . . . . Gt. Brit.	51.25 N	2.40 W
85	Bristol . . . . Pa.	40.7 N	74.52 W
83	Bristol . . . . R. I.	41.38 N	71.18 W
83	Bristol . . . . Tenn.	36.35 N	82.10 W
86	Bristol . . . . Vt.	44.10 N	73.5 W
83	Bristol . . . . Va.	36.36 N	82.10 W
52	Bristol B. . . . . Alsk.	58.20 N	158.0 W
116	Bristol Chan. . . . . Gt. Brit.	51.20 N	4.0 W
79	Bristow (brĭs'tō) . . . . Okla.	35.50 N	96.25 W
54	British Columbia (Prov.) . . . . Can.	56.50 N	125.0 W
103	British Guiana (gē-ä'nà) . . . . . S. A.	5.0 N	59.0 W
94	British Honduras (hŏn-dōō'rás) Cen. Am. (In.)	17.10 N	88.40 W
160	British North Borneo (bôr'nē-ō) E. Ind.	5.30 N	117.0 E
141	British Somaliland (sō-mä'-lē-lănd) Afr. (In.)	9.30 N	46.0 E
142	Britstown (brĭts'toun) . . U. S. Afr.	30.35 S	23.32 E
77	Britt (brĭt) . . . . Ia.	43.5 N	93.47 W
124	Brittany, Hills of (brĭt'á-nĭ) . . . . Fr.	48.25 N	3.10 W
79	Britton (brĭt'ŭn) . . . . Okla.	35.34 N	97.33 W
76	Britton . . . . S. D.	45.48 N	97.44 W
119	Britz (brēts) . . . . . Ger. (Berlin In.)	52.27 N	13.27 E
124	Brive (brēv) . . . . Fr.	45.9 N	1.31 E
126	Briviesca (brē-vyās'kä) . . . . Sp.	42.33 N	3.20 W
122	Brno (Brünn) (b'r'nō) . . . . . Czech.	49.13 N	16.35 E
96	Broa B. (brō'á-bä) . . . . Cuba	22.32 N	81.55 W
165	Broad B. (brôd) . . . . Austl.	22.15 S	149.45 E
169	Broadmeadows (brôd'mĕd-ōz) Austl. (Melbourne In.)	37.40 S	144.56 E
72	Broadmoor (brôd'mōōr) Colo. (Colo. Sprs. In.)	38.48 N	104.51 W
82	Broad R. (brôd) . . . . Ga.	34.4 N	83.0 W
83	Broad R. . . . . S. C.	34.34 N	81.26 W
118	Brock R. (brŏk) . . . . Gt. Brit.	53.53 N	2.42 W
85	Brockport (brŏk'pōrt) . . . . . . N. Y.	43.13 N	77.57 W
86	Brockton (brŏk'tŭn) . . . . Mass.	42.5 N	71.0 W
51	Brockville (brŏk'vĭl) . . . . Can.	44.29 N	76.0 W
129	Brod (brōt) . . . . Yugo.	45.9 N	18.1 E
123	Brodnica (brôd'nĭt-sá) . . . . Pol.	53.16 N	19.26 E
123	Brody (brô'dĭ) . . . . Pol.	50.4 N	25.11 E
119	Broechem (brû'kĕm) Bel. (Anvers In.)	51.11 N	4.36 E
79	Broken Arrow . . . . Okla.	36.3 N	95.46 W
167	Broken B. . . . . Austl.	33.34 S	151.22 E
76	Broken Bow . . . . Neb.	41.24 N	99.38 W
79	Broken Bow . . . . Okla.	34.1 N	94.44 W
140	Broken Hill . . . . N. Rh.	14.25 S	28.27 E
165	Broken Hill . . . . Austl.	31.58 S	141.37 E
165	Broken Hill Plat. . . . . Austl.	30.45 S	142.30 E
166	Broken Hill (Willyama) (brōk'ĕn hĭl) (wĭl'yăm-á) . Austl.	31.57 S	141.28 E
119	Bromley (brŭm'lĭ) Gt. Brit. (London In.)	51.24 N	0.1 E
73	Brompton (brŏmp'tŭn) Ala. (Birmingham In.)	33.34 N	86.29 W
86	Bromptonville (brŭmp'tŭn-vĭl) Can.	45.38 N	71.59 W
118	Bromsgrove (brŏmz'grōv) Gt. Brit.	52.20 N	2.3 W
116	Bromwich, W. (brŭm'ĭch) Gt. Brit.	52.30 N	2.0 W
118	Bromyard (brŏm'yērd) . . Gt. Brit.	52.11 N	2.30 W
120	Brönderslev (brûn'dēr-slĕv) . . Den.	57.17 N	9.57 E
130	Bronnitsy (brô-nyĭ'tsĭ) . . . Sov. Un.	55.25 N	38.14 E
84	Bronson (brŏn'sŭn) . . . . Mich.	41.55 N	85.14 W
88	Bronx R. (brŏnks) N. Y. (New York In.)	40.53 N	73.52 W
163	Brookes Pt. (brōōks) . . . . P. I.	8.47 N	117.50 E
88	Brookfield (brōōk'fēld) Ill. (Chicago In.)	41.49 N	87.51 W
79	Brookfield . . . . Mo.	39.47 N	93.3 W
49	Brookfield . . . Wash. (Portland In.)	46.15 N	123.34 W
82	Brookhaven (brōōk'hāv'n) . . Miss.	31.35 N	90.28 W
76	Brookings (brōōk'ĭngs) . . . . . . S. D.	44.18 N	96.47 W
87	Brookline (brōōk'lĭn) . . Mass. (In.)	42.19 N	71.6 W
88	Brooklyn (brōōk'lĭn) . . N. Y. (In.)	40.40 N	73.58 W
170	Brooklyn . . . . N. Z. (In.)	36.58 S	174.37 E
73	Brookside (brōōk'sīd) Ala. (Birmingham In.)	33.38 N	86.55 W
53	Brooks Ra. (brōōks) . . . . Alsk.	68.20 N	150.0 W
83	Brooksville (brōōks'vĭl) . . Fla. (In.)	28.32 N	82.28 W
84	Brookville (brōōk'vĭl) . . . . Ind.	39.25 N	85.0 W
85	Brookville . . . . Pa.	41.10 N	79.3 W
82	Brookwood (brōōk'wōōd) . . . . . . Ala.	33.17 N	87.20 W
169	Brooloo (brōō'lōō) . . . . Austl. (In.)	26.28 S	152.39 E
116	Broom, L. (brōōm) . . . . . . Gt. Brit.	57.28 N	5.30 W
164	Broome (brōōm) . . . . Austl.	17.57 S	122.5 E
72	Broomfield (brōōm'fēld) Colo. (Denver In.)	39.55 N	105.5 W
57	Brosseau (brô-sō') Can. (Montreal In.)	45.27 N	73.27 W
88	Brother I. N. Y. (Niagara Falls In.)	43.5 N	79.4 W
96	Brothers (Is.) . . . . Ba. Is.	26.3 N	79.2 W
167	Broughton I. (brô'tŭn) . . . . . Austl.	32.38 S	152.22 E
166	Broughton R. . . . . Austl.	33.32 S	138.15 E
145	Brower Str. (brou'ēr) Neth. Ind.	1.30 N	102.0 E
97	Brown Bank . . . . Ba. Is.	21.30 N	74.32 W
78	Brownfield (broun'fēld) . . . . . . Tex.	33.11 N	102.15 W
118	Brownhills (broun'hĭlz) . . Gt. Brit.	52.38 N	1.55 W
73	Browning (broun'ĭng) Calif. (Los Angeles In.)	33.43 N	117.47 W
71	Browning . . . . Mont.	48.33 N	113.1 W
171	Brownings Pass . . . . N. Z.	42.57 S	171.22 E
56	Brown Pass Can. (Prince Rupert In.)	54.18 N	130.48 W
84	Brownstown (brounz'toun) . . . Ind.	38.51 N	86.2 W
82	Brownsville (brounz'vĭl) . . . . Tenn.	35.36 N	89.16 W
81	Brownsville . . . . Tex.	25.55 N	97.30 W
86	Brownville (broun'vĭl) . . . . Me.	45.19 N	69.2 W
80	Brownwood (broun'wōōd) . . . . Tex.	31.43 N	98.59 W
80	Brownwood L. . . . . Tex.	31.55 N	99.5 W
126	Brozas (brō'thäs) . . . . Sp.	39.37 N	6.47 W
164	Bruce, Mt. (brōōs) . . . . Austl.	22.40 S	118.5 E
82	Bruceton (brōōs'-tŭn) . . . . . . Tenn.	36.4 N	88.17 W
127	Bruch (brōōch) . . . . Sp. (In.)	41.35 N	1.48 E
57	Bruchesi (brōō-chĕ'sĭ) Can. (Montreal In.)	45.46 N	73.48 W
122	Bruchsal (brōōĸ'zäl) . . . . Ger.	49.8 N	8.42 E
122	Bruck (brōōk) . . . . Ger.	47.25 N	15.15 E
122	Bruck . . . . Ger.	48.2 N	16.44 E
117	Bruges (brōō'jĕz; brüzh) . . . . . Bel.	51.12 N	3.12 E
125	Brumath (brü-mät') . . . . Fr.	48.45 N	7.41 E
70	Bruneau R. (brōō-nō') . . . . Ida.	42.45 N	115.42 W
160	Brunei (brōō-nī') . . . . Bru.	5.0 N	115.0 E
160	Brunei . . . . E. Ind.	4.30 N	114.30 E
127	Brunete (brōō-nā'tā) . . . . . Sp. (In.)	40.24 N	4.0 W
164	Brunette Downs (brōō-nĕt' dounz') . Austl.	18.45 S	136.0 E
87	Brunette I. . . . . Newf.	47.18 N	55.55 W
169	Bruni I. (brōō'nē) Austl. (Tas. In.)	43.25 S	147.18 E
	Brünn, see Brno, Czech.		
119	Brunn am Gebirge (brōōn' äm gе-bĭr'gĕ) . Aus. (Wien In.)	48.7 N	16.17 E
171	Brunner (brŭn'ēr) . . . . N. Z.	42.27 S	171.22 E
171	Brunner L. . . . . N. Z.	42.38 S	171.28 E
125	Brunoy (brü-nwä') . . . . Fr. (In.)	48.42 N	2.30 E
	Brunswick, see Braunschweig, Ger.		
83	Brunswick (brŭnz'wĭk) . . . . Ga.	31.8 N	81.29 W
86	Brunswick . . . . Me.	43.55 N	69.59 W
85	Brunswick . . . . Md.	39.18 N	77.38 W
79	Brunswick . . . . Mo.	39.25 N	93.7 W
72	Brunswick, Mt. Can. (Vancouver In.)	49.29 N	123.12 W
99	Brunswick Pen. Chl. (Magallanes In.)	53.30 S	71.30 W
78	Brush (brŭsh) . . . . Colo.	40.14 N	103.38 W
167	Brush I. . . . . Austl.	35.33 S	150.26 E
49	Brush Prairie Wash. (Portland In.)	45.44 N	122.32 W
	Brussels, see Bruxelles, Bel.		
122	Brüx (Most) (brüks) (mōst) . . Ger.	50.32 N	13.38 E
117	Bruxelles (Brussels) (brü-sĕl'; brŭs'ĕls) . Bel.	50.52 N	4.22 E
84	Bryan (brī'ăn) . . . . Ohio	41.28 N	84.29 W
81	Bryan . . . . Tex.	30.40 N	96.22 W
130	Bryansk (b'r-yänsk') . . . . . Sov. Un.	53.12 N	34.21 E
130	Bryansk (Dist.) . . . . Sov. Un.	52.45 N	33.50 E
76	Bryant (brī'ănt) . . . . S. D.	44.36 N	97.26 W
89	Bryant L. Minn. (Minneapolis In.)	45.4 N	93.12 W
75	Bryce Canyon Natl. Park (brīs) Utah	37.38 N	112.10 W
82	Bryson City (brīs'ŭn) . . . . N. C.	35.26 N	83.27 W
131	Bryukhovetskaya (b'ryŭk'ō-vyĕt-skä'yä) . . . Sov. Un.	45.48 N	38.58 E
123	Brześć nad Bugiem (Brest-Litovsk) (bzhĕshch' nàd bōō'-gyĕm) (brĕst-lyē-tôfsk') . . . Pol.	52.5 N	23.43 E
123	Brzezany (bzhĕ-zhä'nĭ) . . . . Pol.	49.27 N	24.57 E
123	Brzeziny (bzhĕ-zhē'nĭ) . . . . Pol.	51.48 N	19.47 E
157	Buan (bōō'än') . . . . Cho.	35.44 N	126.44 E
163	Buayan (bōō-ä'yän) . . . . P. I.	6.3 N	125.15 E
138	Buba (bōō'bá) . . . . Port. Gui.	11.42 N	14.58 W
163	Bubuan I. (bōō-bwän') . . . . P. I.	5.24 N	120.35 E
141	Bububu (bōō-bōō-bōō') . . . . Zan.	6.5 S	39.16 E
102	Bucaramanga (bōō-kä'rä-mäŋ'gä) Col.	7.0 N	73.28 W
163	Bucas Grande I. (bōō'käs grän'dā) P. I.	9.40 N	125.58 E
162	Bucay (bōō-kī') . . . . P. I.	17.32 N	120.42 E
164	Buccaneer Arch. (bŭk-á-nēr') Austl.	16.15 S	123.15 E
138	Buchanan (bū-kăn'ăn) . . . . Lib.	6.0 N	10.6 W
84	Buchanan (bū-kăn'ăn) . . . . . . Mich.	41.49 N	86.25 W
165	Buchanan, L. . . . . Austl.	21.30 S	145.50 E
80	Buchanan Reservoir . . . . Tex.	30.45 N	98.25 W
129	Bucharest (Bucureşti) (bōō-kà-rĕst') (bōō-kōō-rĕsh'tĭ) . Rom.	44.25 N	26.7 E
85	Buckhannon (bŭk-hăn'ŭn) . W. Va.	39.0 N	80.14 W
116	Buckhaven (bŭk-hā'v'n) Gt. Brit.	56.10 N	3.0 W
72	Buckhorn Cr. (bŭk'hôrn) Colo. (Denver In.)	40.30 N	105.14 W
88	Buckhorn I. N. Y. (Niagara Falls In.)	43.4 N	79.0 W
119	Buckhurst Hill (bŭk'hûrst) Gt. Brit. (London In.)	51.38 N	0.2 E
116	Buckie (bŭk'ĭ) . . . . Gt. Brit.	57.40 N	3.0 W
118	Buckingham Co. (bŭk'ĭng-ăm) Gt. Brit.	52.7 N	0.45 W
165	Buckland Tableland (bŭk'lănd) Austl.	24.45	147.40 E
119	Buckow (bōōk'ou) Ger. (Berlin In.)	52.25 N	13.26 E
86	Bucksport (bŭks'pôrt) . . . . Me.	44.36 N	68.46 W
123	Bucovina (Reg) (bōō-kō-vē'nä) Rom.	48.7 N	25.35 E
86	Buctouche (bŭk-tōōsh') . . . . Can.	46.29 N	64.42 W
129	Bucureşti (Bucharest) (bōō-kōō-rĕsh'tĭ) (bōō-kà-rĕst') . Rom.	44.25 N	26.7 E
84	Bucyrus (bū-sī'rŭs) . . . . Ohio	40.50 N	82.48 W
123	Buczacz (bōō'chăch) . . . . Pol.	49.3 N	25.24 E
123	Budapest (bōō'dá-pĕsht') . . . . Hung.	47.30 N	19.5 E
131	Budenovsk (bōō'dĕ-nôfsk) Sov. Un.	50.38 N	38.22 E
	Budweis, see České Budějovice		
138	Buea (bōō-ā'ä) . . . . Nig.	4.12 N	9.15 E
102	Buenaventura (bwā'nä-vĕn-tōō'rä) . Col.	3.58 N	77.5 W
78	Buena Vista (bū'ná vĭs'tá) . . . Colo.	38.51 N	106.9 W
82	Buena Vista . . . . Ga.	32.16 N	84.31 W
85	Buena Vista . . . . Va.	37.44 N	79 21 W
96	Buenavista B. (bwā-nä-vēs'tä) Cuba	22.25 N	79.0 W
74	Buena Vista L. Reservoir, (bū'ná vĭs'tá) . Calif.	35.12 N	119.18 W
104	Buenos Aires (bwā'nōs ī'rās) . Arg.	34.35 S	58.22 W
99	Buenos Aires . . . . Arg. (In.)		
104	Buenos Aires (State) . . . . Arg.	36.30 S	60.0 W
104	Buenos Aires, L. . . . . Chl.-Arg.	46.32 S	72.0 W
93	Buey, Pt. (bōō-ā') . . . . Mex.	18.36 N	92.42 W
77	Buffalo (bŭf'á-lō) . . . . Minn.	45.10 N	93.50 W
85	Buffalo . . . . N. Y.	42.55 N	78.55 W
88	Buffalo . . . . N. Y. (In.)		
71	Buffalo . . . . Wyo.	44.21 N	106.41 W
81	Buffalo Bayou (bŭf'á-lō bī'ōō) Tex. (In.)	29.45 N	95.17 W
77	Buffalo Cr. . . . . Minn.	44.46 N	94.3 W
88	Buffalo Cr. N. Y. (Niagara Falls In.)	42.53 N	78.45 W
54	Buffalo L. . . . . Can.	56.0 N	109.0 W
79	Buffalo R. . . . . Ark.	35.57 N	92.50 W
76	Buffalo R. . . . . Minn.	46.52 N	96.20 W
82	Buffalo R. . . . . Tenn.	35.35 N	87.50 W
143	Buffalo R. . . . . U. S. Afr.	27.58 S	30.21 E
142	Buffels R. (bŭf'ĕls) . . . . . U. S. Afr.	29.35 S	17.30 E
82	Buford (bū'fērd) . . . . Ga.	34.6 N	84.1 W
75	Buford Lake . . . . N. M.	36.35 N	106.55 W
131	Bug R. (bōōg) . . . . . . Sov. Un.-Pol.	48.10 N	30.0 E
163	Bugasong (bōō-gä-sông') . . . . . . P. I.	11.2 N	122.4 E
128	Bugojno (bōō-gō'ī-nō) . . . . Yugo.	44.3 N	17.27 E
163	Bugsuk I. (bōōg-sōōk') . . . . . . P. I.	8.15 N	117.18 E
162	Buguey (bōō-gā') . . . . P. I.	18.16 N	121.51 E
162	Bugui Pt. (bōō'gē) . . . . P. I.	12.36 N	123.14 E
112	Bugulma (bōō-gōōl'mà) . . Sov. Un.	54.40 N	52.40 E
112	Buguruslan (bōō-gōō-rōōs-lán') Sov. Un.	53.33 N	52.28 E
162	Buhi (bōō'ē) . . . . P. I.	13.26 N	123.31 E
125	Buhl (bül) . . . . Fr.	47.45 N	7.11 E
70	Buhl (bŭl) . . . . Ida.	42.46 N	114.46 W
77	Buhl . . . . Minn.	47.29 N	92.49 W
130	Bui (bwē) . . . . Sov. Un.	58.27 N	41.32 E
99	Buin (bōō-ēn') Chl. (Valparaiso In.)	33.44 S	70.48 W
113	Buinaksk (bōō'ē-näksk) Sov. Un.	42.44 N	47.10 E
160	Buitenzorg (bûē'tĕn-zôrgh) Neth. Ind.	6.45 S	106.45 E
126	Bujalance (bōō-hä-län'thā) . . . . Sp.	37.53 N	4.22 W
103	Bujaru (bōō-hà-rōō') . . . Braz. (In.)	1.59 S	39.59 W
150	Bujnurd (bōōj-nōōrd') . . . . Iran	37.25 N	57.5 E
140	Bukama (bōō-kä'mä) . . Bel. Cong.	9.10 S	25.55 E
150	Bukhara (bōō-kä'rä) . . . . . Sov. Un.	39.50 N	64.15 E
148	Bukhtarma (bōōĸ-tär'mä) Sov.Un.	49.45 N	83.10 E
162	Bulacan (bōō-lä-kän') . . . . P. I.	14.47 N	120.53 E
161	Bulacan (Prov.) (bōō-lä-kän') P. I. (Manila In.)	14.54 N	121.0 E
161	Bulacan R. . . . . . P. I. (Manila In.)	14.47 N	120.48 E
163	Bulacaue Pt. (bōō-lä-kou'ä) . . P. I.	11.35 N	123.10 E
162	Bulalacao (bōō-lä-lä'kä-ō) . . . . P. I.	12.31 N	121.26 E
162	Bulan (bōō'län) . . . . P. I.	12.40 N	123.53 E
140	Bulawayo (bōō-lä-wä'yō) . . . S. Rh.	20.13 S	28.38 E
129	Bulgaria (bōōl-gā'rĭ-ă) . . . . Eur.	43.0 N	25.0 E
163	Buliluyan, C. (bōō-lē-lōō'yän) P. I.	8.20 N	117.11 E
169	Bulla (bōōl'á) Austl. (Melbourne In.)	37.39 S	144.49 E
126	Bullaque R. (bōō-lä'kä) . . . . Sp.	39.15 N	4.15 W
126	Bullas (bōōl'yäs) . . . . Sp.	38.5 N	1.40 W
75	Bulldog Cr. . . . . Utah	37.40 N	110.50 W
171	Buller R. (bōōl'ēr) . . . . N. Z.	41.50 S	172.10 E
96	Bull Head (Mt.) . . . . Jam.	18.9 N	77.17 W
167	Bulli (bōōl'ī) . . . . Austl.	34.19 S	150.55 E
166	Bullock Cr. (bōōl'ŭk) . . . . Austl.	36.15 S	144.10 E
165	Bulloo R. (bŭ-lōō') . . . . Austl.	27.30 S	144.0 E
170	Bulls . . . . N. Z.	40.8 S	175.25 E
141	Bulo Burti (bōō'lō-bōōr'tĭ) It. E. Afr.	3.55 N	45.28 E
166	Buloke, L. (bōō-lō'kē) . . . . . . Austl.	36.16 S	142.59 E
163	Buluan, L. (bōō-lōō'än) . . . . . . P. I.	6.40 N	124.48 E
149	Bulun (bōō-lōōn') . . . . Sov. Un.	70.40 N	127.10 E
140	Bulungu (bōō-lōōŋ'gōō) . Bel. Cong.	5.0 S	19.0 E
152	Bulun-Tokhoi (bōō-lōōn'-tō-ĸoi') Chn.	46.55 N	87.17 E
162	Bulusan (Vol.) (bōō-lōō'sän) . P. I.	12.46 N	124.4 E
143	Bulwer (bōōl'wēr) . . . . . . U. S. Afr.	29.48 S	29.45 E
139	Bumba (bōōm'bá) . . . . . Bel. Cong.	2.12 N	22.31 E
163	Bunawan (bōō-nä'wän) . . . . . . P. I.	8.11 N	125.57 E
165	Bundaberg (bŭn'dá-bûrg) . . . Austl.	24.45 S	152.10 E
162	Bunga Pt. (bōōng'ä) . . . . P. I.	12.12 N	125.30 E
115	Bu Ngem (bōō-'n-gĕm) . . . . . Libya	30.30 N	15.30 E
159	Bungo Str. (bōōŋ'gō) . . . . Jap.	33.10 N	132.10 E
166	Buninyong (bōōn'ĭn-yông) . . Austl.	37.39 S	143.52 E
81	Bunkie (bŭŋ'kĭ) . . . . La.	30.58 N	92.10 W
169	Bunya Mts. (bŭn'yá) . . Austl. (In.)	26.50 S	151.30 E
122	Bunzlau (bōōnts'lou) . . . . Ger.	51.15 N	15.35 E
150	Buraida (bōō-rī'dá) . . . . . . Sau. Ar.	26.28 N	44.15 E
89	Buras (bûr'ás) La. (New Orleans In.)	29.21 N	89.33 W
141	Burau (bōō-rä'ōō) . . . . Br. Som.	9.37 N	45.37 E
73	Burbank (bûr'bănk) Calif. (Los Angeles In.)	34.11 N	118.19 W
165	Burdekin R. (bûr'dē-kĭn) . . . Austl.	20.30 S	147.10 E
113	Burdur (bōōr-dōōr') . . . . Tur.	37.45 N	30.18 E
151	Burdwan (bōōrd-wän') . . . . . . India.	23.15 N	87.58 E
149	Bureya R. (bōō-rā'yä) . . . Sov. Un.	50.45 N	131.0 E
153	Burga Dist. (bōōr'gä) . . . . Chn.	50.0 N	120.0 E
141	Bur Gao (Porto Durnford) (bûr gä'ō) . It. E. Afr.	1.10 S	41.47 E
129	Burgas (bōōr-gäs') . . . . Bul.	42.29 N	27.29 E
129	Burgas, G. of, ... Bul.	42.30 N	27.40 E
83	Burgaw (bûr'gô) . . . . N. C.	34.33 N	77.56 W

ăt; finăl; rāte; senâte; ärm; àsk; sofá; fâre; ch-choose; dh-as th in other; bē; ēvent; bĕt; recĕnt; cratēr; g-go; gh-gutteral g; bĭt; ĭ-short neutral; rīde; ĸ-gutteral k as ch in German ich;

Page	Name Pronunciation Region	Lat. °′	Long. °′
122	Burgdorf (bo͝org'dôrf) Switz.	47.3 N	7.37 E
143	Burgerville (bûr'gẽr-vĭl) U. S. Afr.	30.42 S	24.21 E
169	Burgess (bûr'jĕs). Austl. (Tas. In.)	41.10 S	146.32 E
119	Burgh (bo͝org)...Bel. (Anvers In.)	51.12 N	4.20 E
143	Burghersdorp (bo͝or'gẽrs-dôrp) U. S. Afr.	31.2 S	26.19 E
139	Burgi (bo͞or'gē) Eth.	5.28 N	38.0 E
80	Burgos (bo͞or'gōs) Mex.	24.57 N	98.48 W
162	Burgos P. I.	16.3 N	119.52 E
126	Burgos Sp.	42.22 N	3.43 W
120	Burgsvik (bo͝orgs'vĭk) Swe.	57.3 N	18.20 E
151	Burhanpur (bo͞or'hän-po͞or)..India	21.15 N	76.15 E
162	Burias I. (bo͞o'rē-äs) P. I.	13.0 N	123.5 E
162	Burias Pass P. I.	13.0 N	123.15 E
95	Burica Pt. (bo͞o'rē-kä)...C. R.-Pan.	8.3 N	82.55 W
87	Burin (bûr'ĭn) Newf.	47.5 N	55.11 W
78	Burkburnett (bûrk-bûr'nĕt)..Tex.	34.5 N	98.34 W
86	Burke (bûrk) Vt.	44.38 N	71.59 W
164	Burketown (bûrk'toun) Austl.	17.48 S	139.30 E
71	Burley (bûr'lĭ) Ida.	42.31 N	113.48 W
49	Burley Wash. (Seattle In.)	47.24 N	122.38 W
74	Burlingame (bûr'lĭn-gām)...Calif.	37.34 N	122.24 W
79	Burlingame Kan.	38.45 N	95.49 W
78	Burlington (bûr'lĭng-tŭn) Colo.	39.17 N	102.26 W
77	Burlington Ia.	40.49 N	91.8 W
79	Burlington Kan.	38.12 N	95.45 W
89	Burlington...Ky. (Cincinnati In.)	39.2 N	84.44 W
85	Burlington N. J.	40.3 N	74.57 W
83	Burlington N. C.	36.5 N	79.26 W
86	Burlington Vt.	44.30 N	73.15 W
77	Burlington Wis.	42.41 N	88.18 W
72	Burlington Ditch Colo. (Denver In.)	39.53 N	104.55 W
135	Burlos, L. (bo͝or'lōs) Eg. (In.)	31.25 N	30.55 E
151	Burma (Prov.) (bûr'mȧ)...India	21.30 N	94.30 E
73	Burmester (bûr'mĕs-tẽr) Utah (Salt Lake City In.)	40.42 N	112.27 W
72	Burnaby L. (bûrn'ȧ-bĭ) Can. (Vancouver In.)	49.15 N	122.57 W
99	Burnay, Mt. (bo͞or-nī') Chl. (Magallanes In.)	52.19 S	73.20 W
80	Burnet (bûrn'ĕt) Tex.	30.45 N	98.15 W
19	Burnham-on-Crouch (bûrn'ăm-ŏn-krouch) Gt. Brit. (London In.)	51.38 N	0.48 E
69	Burnie (bûr'nē) Austl. (Tas. In.)	41.4 S	145.55 E
16	Burnley (bûrn'lē) Gt. Brit.	53.48 N	2.20 W
70	Burns (bûrnz) Ore.	43.35 N	119.4 W
82	Burnside (bûrn'sīd) Ky.	36.59 N	84.36 W
171	Burns Mt. N. Z.	45.40 S	167.28 E
86	Burnsville (bûrnz'vĭl) Can.	47.43 N	65.8 W
72	Burnt Mt. (bûrnt) Colo. (Denver In.)	40.4 N	105.29 W
70	Burnt R. Ore.	44.30 N	117.43 W
166	Burra (Kooringa) (bûr'ȧ) (ko͞o-rĭŋ'gȧ) Austl.	33.40 S	138.58 E
169	Burramba (bû-răm'bȧ) Austl. (In.)	28.38 S	150.36 E
72	Burrard Inlet (bûr'ȧrd) Can. (Vancouver In.)	49.18 N	123.13 W
72	Burrard Inlet, N. Arm Can. (Vancouver In.)	49.22 N	122.55 W
167	Burren Junction (bûr'ĕn)...Austl.	30.5 S	148.56 E
127	Burriana (bo͞or-rē-ä'nä) Sp.	39.54 N	0.5 W
167	Burrinjuck (bûr'ĭn-jŭk) Austl.	34.59 S	148.32 E
167	Burrinjuck Dam Austl.	34.59 S	148.50 E
113	Bursa (bo͞or'sȧ) Tur.	40.10 N	29.10 E
116	Burton (bûr'tŭn) Gt. Brit.	52.50 N	1.40 W
118	Burton Gt. Brit.	54.11 N	2.43 W
49	Burton Wash. (Seattle In.)	47.23 N	122.28 W
59	Burton Reservoir Ga.	34.45 N	83.30 W
119	Burtonwood (bûr'tŭn-wo͝od) Gt. Brit. (Liverpool In.)	53.26 N	2.39 W
84	Burts L. (bûrts) Mich.	45.27 N	84.40 W
163	Buruanga (bo͞o-ro͞o-äŋ'gä) P. I.	11.50 N	121.53 E
150	Burujird (bo͞o-ro͞o-jērd') Iran	33.50 N	49.0 E
162	Buruncan Pt. (bo͞o-ro͞on'kän). P. I.	12.13 N	121.13 E
76	Burwell (bûr'wĕl) Neb.	41.46 N	99.8 W
116	Bury (bĕr'ĭ) Gt. Brit.	53.35 N	2.20 W
149	Buryat-Mongol (Soviet Rep.) (bo͞or'yät'-mŏŋ'gŏl) Sov. Un.	53.0 N	110.0 E
117	Bury St. Edmunds (bĕr'ĭ-sānt ĕd'mŭndz Gt. Brit.	52.12 N	0.42 E
138	Busa (bo͞o'sä) Nig	10.12 N	4.30 E
139	Buseima (Well) (bo͞o-zä'mȧ).Libya	25.7 N	22.10 E
135	Bûsh (bo͞osh) Eg. (In.)	29.12 N	31.10 E
119	Bushey Heath (bo͝osh'ĭ hēth) Gt. Brit. (London In.)	51.39 N	0.22 W
150	Bushire (Bandar Abu Shehr) (bo͞o-shēr') (bŭn'dȧr-ä'bo͞o-shĕr') Per.	28.47 N	50.47 E
142	Bushman Land, Gt. (bo͝osh-mȧn lănd) U. S. Afr.	29.20 S	19.30 E
142	Bushman Land, Little...U. S. Afr.	29.30 S	18.33 E
143	Bushmans R. (bo͝osh'mȧnz) U. S. Afr.	33.30 S	26.30 E
79	Bushnell (bo͝osh'nĕl) Ill.	40.33 N	90.29 W
139	Businga (bo͞o-sĭŋ'gȧ)...Bel. Cong.	3.15 N	20.33 E
123	Busk (bo͝osk) Pol.	49.57 N	24.39 E
164	Busselton (bŭs''l-tŭn) Austl.	33.31 S	115.29 E
125	Bussy-St. Georges (bü-sē'-săN zhôrzh') Fr. (In.)	48.50 N	2.42 E
80	Bustamante (bo͞os-tä-män'tä) Mex.	26.34 N	100.30 W
49	Buster (bŭs'tẽr) Ore. (Portland In.)	45.54 N	123.24 W
88	Bustleton (bŭs''l-tŭn) Pa. (Philadelphia In.)	40.5 N	75.1 W
128	Busto Arsizio (bo͞os'tō är-sēd'zē-ō) It.	45.35 N	8.54 E
161	Bustos (bo͞os'tōs) P. I. (ManilaIn.)	14.58 N	120.53 E
162	Busuanga I. (bo͞o-swäŋ'gä)...P. I.	12.10 N	120.5 E
139	Buta (bo͞o'tä) Bel. Cong.	2.47 N	24.45 E
143	Buthabuthe (bo͞o-thä-bo͞o'thä)Bas.	28.46 S	28.15 E
84	Butler (bŭt'lẽr) Ind.	41.26 N	84.53 W
79	Butler Mo.	38.16 N	94.19 W
85	Butler Pa.	40.52 N	79.54 W
	Buton (I.) see, Boeton.		
123	Bütow (bü'tou) Ger.	54.9 N	17.30 E
82	Buttahatchie R. (bŭt-ȧ-hăch'ē) Miss.	33.54 N	88.10 W
71	Butte (būt) Mont.	46.0 N	112.31 W
143	Butterworth (bŭt'ẽr-wûrth) U. S. Afr.	32.19 S	28.8 E
72	Buttes (būts) Colo. (Colo. Spgs. In.)	38.36 N	104.40 W
143	Buttfontein (bo͞ot-fŏn-tān') U. S. Afr.	28.14 S	26.9 E
163	Butuan (bo͞o-to͞o'än) P. I.	8.56 N	125.32 E
163	Butuan B. P. I.	9.5 N	125.24 E
149	Butuntai R.(bo͞o-to͞on-tī').Sov. Un.	68.25 N	130.0 E
131	Buturlinovka (bo͞o-to͞or'lē-nôf'kȧ) Sov. Un.	50.47 N	40.38 E
119	Buxtehude (bo͝oks-tē-ho͞o'dē) Ger. (Hamburg In.)	53.29 N	9.43 E
118	Buxton (bŭks't'n) Gt. Brit.	53.15 N	1.55 W
49	Buxton Ore. (Portland In.)	45.41 N	123.11 W
153	Buyer Nor (L.) (bo͞o'yĕr nôr) Chn.	47.45 N	117.40 E
113	Buzachi Pen. (bo͞o-zä'chē) Sov. Un.	45.0 N	53.40 E
129	Buzău (bo͞o-zĕ'o͞o) Rom.	45.8 N	26.51 E
129	Buzău R. Rom.	45.5 N	27.0 E
113	Buzuluk (bo͞o-zo͞o-lo͝ok').Sov. Un.	52.45 N	52.15 E
140	Bwanamkubwa (bwä-näm-ko͞ob'wä) N. Rh.	13.10 S	28.45 E
141	Bweleo (bwä'lä-ō) Zan.	6.18 S	39.18 E
123	Bydgoszcz (bĭd'gôshch) Pol.	53.8 N	18.0 E
84	Byesville (bīz-vĭl) Ohio	39.58 N	81.33 W
120	Bygdin L. (bügh-dēn') Nor.	61.23 N	8.30 E
120	Byglandsfjord (bügh'länds-fyôr) Nor.	58.40 N	7.50 E
167	Byrock (bī'rŏk) Austl.	30.38 S	146.26 E
169	Byrun (bī'rŭn) Austl. (In.)	28.36 S	153.33 E
169	Byron B. Austl. (In.)	28.34 S	153.35 E
123	Bystrzyca R. (bĭst-zhĕt'sȧ)...Pol.	48.45 N	24.40 E
130	Bytosh (bĭ-tôsh') Sov. Un.	53.46 N	34.2 E
104	Caazapá (kä-zä-pä') Par.	26.10 S	56.28 W
163	Cabadbaran (kä'bȧd-bä-rän'). P. I.	9.6 N	125.33 E
162	Cabagan (kä-bä-gän') P. I.	17.26 N	121.46 E
162	Cabalete I. (kä-bä-lā'tā) P. I.	14.18 N	121.50 E
163	Cabalian (kä-bä-lē'än) P. I.	10.16 N	125.12 E
96	Caballones Cay (I.) (kä-bä-lyō'-nās). Cuba	20.51 N	79.0 W
96	Caballones Channel Cuba	20.48 N	78.57 W
162	Cabanatuan (kä-bä-nä-twän') P. I.	15.29 N	120.58 E
89	Cabaret I. (kă'bȧ-rĕt) Ill. (St. Louis In.)	38.43 N	90.11 W
162	Cabarruyan I. (kä-bä-ro͞o'yän) P. I.	16.17 N	119.58 E
161	Cabcabe (käb-kä'bä) P. I. (Manila In.)	14.27 N	120.30 E
103	Cabedelo (kä-bē-dā'lo͞o) Braz.	6.59 S	34.55 W
126	Cabeza del Buey (kä-bā'thä dĕl bwā'). Sp.	38.43 N	5.14 W
93	Cabeza Reefs (kä-bā'thä) Mex.	19.5 N	95.53 W
102	Cabija (kä-bē'hä) Bol.	11.1 S	68.59 W
140	Cabinda (kä-bĭn'dä) Ang.	5.40 S	12.12 E
140	Cabinda (Prov.) Ang.	5.0 S	12.15 E
163	Cabingaan I. (kä-bĭng-ä'än) ..P. I.	5.40 N	121.3 E
95	Cabo Gracias a Dias (kä'bō grä'sē-äs ä dyōs'). Nic.	14.57 N	83.17 W
169	Caboolture (kȧ-bo͞ol'tūr) Austl. (In.)	27.3 S	152.57 E
84	Cabot Head (C.) (kăb'ŭt) Can.	45.15 N	81.17 W
87	Cabot Str. Can.-Newf.	47.40 N	59.59 W
138	Cabo Yubi (cä'bō yo͞o'bē).R. de O.	27.55 N	12.46 W
126	Cabra (käb'rä) Sp.	37.28 N	4.26 W
162	Cabra I. P. I.	13.52 N	120.2 E
169	Cabramatta (kä-brȧ-măt'ȧ) Austl. (Sydney In.)	33.54 S	150.56 E
127	Cabrera I. (kä-brā'rä) Sp.	39.8 N	2.57 E
126	Cabriel R. (kä-brē-ĕl') Sp.	39.35 N	1.38 W
74	Cabrillo Natl. Mon. (kä-brēl'yō) Calif. (In.)	32.40 N	117.15 W
103	Cabrodó (kä-brō-dō') Braz.	8.47 S	38.59 W
163	Cabucan I. (kä-bo͞o'kän) P. I.	6.8 N	120.54 E
162	Cabugao (kä-bo͞o'gä-ō) P. I.	17.47 N	120.27 E
163	Cabulauan I. (kä-bo͞o-lä'wän). P. I.	11.22 N	120.7 E
129	Čačak (chä'chäk) Yugo.	43.51 N	20.22 E
126	Caceres (kä'thä-rās) Sp.	39.28 N	6.21 W
74	Cache Cr. (kăsh) Calif.	38.50 N	122.13 W
78	Cache Cr. Okla.	34.35 N	98.23 W
78	Cache la Poudre R. (kásh-lȧ-po͞od'r') Colo.	40.33 N	105.0 W
79	Cache R. Ark.	35.20 N	91.12 W
104	Cachinal (kä-chē-näl') Chl.	24.40 S	69.35 W
103	Cachoeira (kä-shō-ā'rä) Braz. (In.)	1.2 S	48.59 W
104	Cachoeira Braz.	30.1 S	53.0 W
103	Cachoeira Braz. (In.)	12.34 S	39.1 W
140	Caconda (kä-kōn'dä) Ang.	13.42 S	15.8 E
81	Caddo L. (kăd'ō) La.-Tex.	32.41 N	94.0 W
92	Cadereyta (kä-dä-rā'tä) Mex.	20.41 N	99.48 W
80	Cadereyta Jiménez (kä-dä-rā'tä hē-mā'nāz). Mex.	25.36 N	100.0 W
162	Cadig, Mt. (kä'dēg) P. I.	14.11 N	122.27 E
84	Cadillac (kăd'ĭ-lăk) Mich.	44.15 N	85.25 W
119	Cadishead (kăd'ĭs-hĕd) Gt. Brit. (Liverpool In.)	53.25 N	2.26 W
84	Cadiz (kă'dĭz) Ohio	40.18 N	81.0 W
163	Cadiz (kä'dēz) P. I.	10.57 N	123.19 E
127	Cadiz (kä'dhēth) Sp. (In.)	36.32 N	6.17 W
127	Cadiz (Prov.) Sp. (In.)	36.36 N	6.6 W
127	Cadiz B. Sp. (In.)	36.33 N	6.12 W
126	Cadiz, G. of Sp.	36.50 N	7.0 W
163	Caduruan Pt. (kä-do͞o-ro͞o-än') P. I.	11.43 N	124.4 E
124	Caen (käN) Fr.	49.10 N	0.20 W
145	Caesarea (sĕs-ȧ-rē'ȧ) Pal. (In.)	32.29 N	34.54 E
103	Caetité (kä-ā-tē-tā') Braz.	14.2 S	42.32 W
140	Cafima (kä-fē'mä) Ang.	16.52 S	16.25 E
104	Cagarras Is. (kä-gär'räs) Atl. O. (In.)	23.2 S	43.12 W
163	Cagayan (kä-gä-yän') P. I.	8.29 N	124.40 E
163	Cagayan Is. P. I.	9.35 N	121.15 E
162	Cagayan, L. P. I.	18.2 N	121.58 E
162	Cagayan R. P. I.	17.25 N	121.50 E
163	Cagayan Sulu I. (kä-gä-yän' so͞o'-lo͞o). P. I.	7.0 N	118.30 E
128	Cagli (käl'yē) It.	43.32 N	12.38 E
128	Cagliari (käl'yä-rē) Sard.	39.14 N	9.6 E
128	Cagliari, G. of Sard.	39.5 N	9.15 E
125	Cagnes-sur-Mer (kän'y'-sûr-mâr) Fr.	43.40 N	7.5 E
162	Cagraray I. (kä-grä-rī') P. I.	13.20 N	123.52 E
162	Cagua, Mt. (Vol.) (kä'gwä)...P. I.	18.13 N	122.7 E
91	Caguas (kä'gwäs) P. R. (In.)	18.10 N	66.0 W
73	Cahaba Mt. (kȧ-hô'bȧ) Ala. (Birmingham In.)	33.43 N	86.33 W
82	Cahaba R. Ala.	32.45 N	87.15 W
89	Cahokia (kȧ-hō'kĭ-ȧ) Ill. (St. Louis In.)	38.34 N	90.12 W
124	Cahors (kȧ-ôr') Fr.	44.28 N	1.30 E
95	Cahuita Pt. (kä-wē'tä) C. R.	9.45 N	82.50 W
131	Cahul (kä'ko͞ol) Rom.	45.48 N	28.16 E
161	Cahunchan, R. (kä-ho͞on'chän) P. I. (Manila In.)	13.47 N	121.5 E
140	Caiambo (kä-yäm'bō) Ang.	15.47 S	20.15 E
96	Caibarién (kī-bä-rē-ĕn') Cuba	22.29 N	79.31 W
163	Caibiran (kī-bē'rän) P. I.	11.33 N	124.34 E
97	Caicos Bank (kī'kōs) Ba. Is.	21.25 N	72.0 W
97	Caicos Passage Ba. Is.	22.0 N	72.40 W
81	Caillou B. (kȧ-yo͞o') La.	29.15 N	90.55 W
97	Caimanera (kī-mä-nā'rä) Cuba	19.58 N	75.10 W
162	Caiman Pt. (kī'män) P. I.	15.57 N	119.45 E
161	Cainta (kä-ēn-tä') P. I. (Manila In.)	14.35 N	121.7 E
46	Caird Land (Reg.) (kârd) Ant.	76.0 S	20.0 W
165	Cairns (kârnz) Austl.	17.0 S	145.47 E
139	Cairo (kī'rō) Eg.	30.2 N	31.21 E
141	Cairo, Eg. (In.)		
82	Cairo (kā'rō) Ga.	30.52 N	84.14 W
79	Cairo Ill.	37.0 N	89.10 W
99	Cairoçu Pt. (kī'rō-so͞o) Braz. (Rio de Janeiro In.)	23.22 S	44.35 W
141	Cairo, Old (Masr el Atiqa) (kī'rō) (mäz''r ĕl ȧ-tē'kä). Eg.	30.1 N	31.15 E
118	Caistor (kās'tẽr) Gt. Brit.	53.30 N	0.20 W
102	Cajamarca (kä-hä-mär'kä)...Peru	7.2 S	78.30 W
163	Cajidiocan (kä-hē dyō'kän)..P. I.	12.21 N	122.41 E
129	Cajniče (chī'nĭ-chĕ) Yugo.	43.32 N	19.5 E
73	Cajon (kȧ-hōn') Calif. (Los Angeles In.)	34.17 N	117.28 W
93	Cajones, R. (kä-hō'nās) Mex.	17.35 N	96.10 W
128	Čakovec (chä'kō-vĕts) Yugo.	46.25 N	16.27 E
143	Cala (kä'lä) U. S. Afr.	31.31 S	27.42 E
162	Calabanga (kä-lä-bäŋ'gä) P. I.	13.41 N	123.12 E
138	Calabar (kăl-ȧ-băr') Nig.	4.58 N	8.21 E
73	Calabasas (kă-lȧ-băs'ȧs) Calif. (Los Angeles In.)	34.9 N	118.40 W
102	Calabozo (kä-lä-bō'zō) Ven.	9.0 N	67.28 W
92	Calabozo, R. Mex.	21.30 N	98.24 W
128	Calabria (Prov.) (kä-lä'brē-ä) ..It.	39.20 N	16.30 E
161	Calaca (kä-lä'kä) P. I. (Manila In.)	13.57 N	120.46 E
129	Calafat (kȧ-lȧ-fät') Rom.	43.59 N	22.57 E
163	Calagnaan I. (kä-läg-nä-än') .P. I.	11.27 N	123.15 E
162	Calagua Is. (kä-läg'wä) P. I.	14.28 N	122.58 E
126	Calahorra (kä-lä-ôr'rä) Sp.	42.18 N	1.58 W
124	Calais (kȧ-lĕ') Fr.	50.55 N	1.50 E
86	Calais (kăl'ĭs) Me.	45.9 N	67.15 W
102	Calamar (kä-lä-mär') Col.	2.1 N	71.68 W
102	Calamar Col.	10.15 N	74.59 W
163	Calamba (kä-läm'bä) P. I.	14.13 N	121.9 E
162	Calamian Group (Is.) (kä-lä-myän'). P. I.	12.0 N	120.0 E
126	Calañas (kä-län'yäs) Sp.	37.41 N	6.52 W
127	Calanda (kä-län'dä) Sp.	40.57 N	0.14 W
162	Calapan (kä-lä-pän') P. I.	13.24 N	121.10 E
163	Calape (kä-lä'pä) P. I.	9.52 N	123.53 E
129	Călărași (kŭ-lŭ-rash'ĭ) Rom.	44.11 N	27.22 E
131	Călărași-Târg (kŭ-lŭ-rásh'ĭ-tărg) Rom.	47.14 N	28.12 E
126	Calasparra (kä-lä-spär'rä) Sp.	38.14 N	1.42 W
161	Calatagan (kä-lä-tä-gän') P. I. (Manila In.)	13.50 N	120.34 E
126	Calatayud (kä-lä-tä-yo͞odh') ...Sp.	41.23 N	1.38 W
162	Calauag (kä-lä-wäg') P. I.	13.58 N	122.17 E
162	Calauag B. P. I.	14.15 N	122.10 E
162	Calavite, C. (kä-lä-vē'tä) P. I.	13.27 N	120.18 E
161	Calawan (kä-lä'wän) P. I. (Manila In.)	14.10 N	121.21 E
162	Calayan I. (kä-lä-yän') P. I.	19.20 N	121.23 E
163	Calbayog (käl-bä'yōg) P. I.	12.4 N	124.37 E
163	Calbiga (käl-bē'gä) P. I.	11.37 N	125.1 E
81	Calcasieu L. (kăl'kȧ-shū) La.	29.55 N	93.17 W
81	Calcasieu R. La.	30.28 N	93.0 W
151	Calcutta (kăl-kŭt'ȧ) India	22.30 N	88.30 E
126	Caldas da Rainha (käl'däs dä rīn'yȧ). Port.	39.24 N	9.8 W
127	Caldas de Mombúy (käl'däs dä mōm-bo͞o'ē). Sp. (In.)	41.36 N	2.11 E
118	Calder, R. (kôl'dẽr) Gt. Brit.	53.40 N	1.36 W
104	Caldera (käl-dä'rä) Chl.	27.1 S	70.40 W
93	Caldera, Cerro (Mt.) (käl-dä'rä, sĕr'rō). Mex. (In.)	19.20 N	98.58 W
70	Caldwell (kôld'wĕl) Ida.	43.40 N	116.41 W
79	Caldwell Kan.	37.3 N	97.36 W
80	Caldwell Ohio	39.43 N	81.32 W
81	Caldwell Tex.	30.33 N	96.42 W
142	Caledon (kăl'ē-dŏn) U. S. Afr.	34.15 S	19.21 E
77	Caledonia (kăl-ē-dō'nĭ-ȧ) ...Minn.	43.38 N	91.30 W
116	Caledonian Canal Gt. Brit.	57.10 N	4.30 W

ng-sing; ŋ-baŋk; N-nasalized n; nŏd; cŏmmit; ōld; ôbey; ôrder; fo͞od; fo͝ot; ou-out; s-soft; sh-dish; th-thin; pūre; ûnite; ûrn; stŭd; circŭs; ü-as "y" in study; '-indeterminate vowel.

Page	Name Pronunciation Region	Lat. °′	Long. °′
143	Caledon R.........Bas.-U. S. Afr.	29.29 S	27.20 E
127	Calella (kä-lĕl′yä)...........Sp.	41.36 N	2.40 E
124	Calenzana (kä-lĕnt-sä′nä) Cor. (In.)	42.30 N	8.50 E
92	Calera (kä-lā′rä)...........Mex.	22.57 N	102.40 W
74	Calexico (kȧ-lĕk′sĭ-kō)......Calif.	32.40 N	115.30 W
54	Calgary (kăl′gȧ-rĭ)..........Can.	51.1 N	114.1 W
127	Calha Pt. (käl′yä).....Port. (In.)	38.40 N	9.16 W
82	Calhoun (kăl-hōōn′).........Ga.	34.30 N	84.57 W
89	Calhoun, L. Minn. (Minneapolis In.)	44.56 N	93.18 W
102	Cali (kä′lē).................Col.	3.20 N	76.33 W
113	Caliacra, C. (kä-lyä-krä′)....Rom.	43.28 N	28.30 E
89	Calibogue Sd. (kă-lĭ-bō′gū) S. C. (Savannah In.)	32.8 N	80.50 W
163	Calicoan I. (kä-lê-kō′än) ....P. I.	11.0 N	125.48 E
151	Calicut (kăl′ĭ-kŭt)..........India	11.15 N	75.47 E
75	Caliente (käl-yĕn′tä).........Nev.	37.38 N	114.29 W
79	California (kăl-ĭ-fôr′nĭ-ȧ).....Mo.	38.37 N	92.37 W
74	California (State)...........U. S.	37.5 N	119.50 W
89	California B. La. (New Orleans In.)	29.0 N	89.33 W
74	Calipatria (kăl-ĭ-pȧt′rĭ-ȧ)....Calif.	33.8 N	115.30 W
142	Calitzdorp (kä′lĭtz-dôrp) U. S. Afr.	33.31 S	21.40 E
93	Calkiní (käl-kê-nē′).........Mex.	20.23 N	90.3 W
72	Calkins L. (kô′kĭnz) Colo. (Denver In.)	40.11 N	105.3 W
102	Callao (käl-yä′ô) ....Peru	12.2 S	77.1 W
119	Calloo (kä-lōō′)..Bel. (Anvers In.)	51.15 N	4.17 E
73	Calls Fort (kôlz fôrt) Utah (Salt Lake City In.)	41.36 N	112.4 W
77	Calmar (kăl′mär).............Ia.	43.11 N	91.43 W
92	Calnali (käl-nä-lē′)..........Mex.	20.53 N	98.34 W
162	Calolbon (kä-lôl-bōn′).......P. I.	13.37 N	124.7 E
162	Caloocan (kä-lô-ō′kän)......P. I.	14.38 N	120.59 E
83	Caloosahatchee R. (kȧ-lōō-sȧ-hăch′ê).Fla. (In.)	26.40 N	81.50 W
169	Caloundria (kȧ-lōōn′drĭ-ȧ) Austl. (In.)	26.45 S	153.6 E
92	Calpulálpam (käl-pōō-läl′päm) Mex.	19.35 N	98.34 W
128	Caltagirone (käl-tä-jē-rō′nå)....It.	37.15 N	14.30 E
128	Caltanissetta (käl-tä-nê-sĕt′tä)..It.	37.29 N	14.2 E
124	Caluire (kȧ-lwēr′)............Fr.	45.50 N	4.50 E
140	Calumbo (kä-lōōm′bō)......Ang.	9.2 S	13.32 E
77	Calumet (kă-lū-mĕt′) ......Mich.	47.15 N	88.26 W
88	Calumet City....Ill. (Chicago In.)	41.38 N	87.32 W
88	Calumet Har....Ill. (Chicago In.)	41.44 N	87.31 W
88	Calumet, L......Ill. (Chicago In.)	41.41 N	87.35 W
88	Calumet Sag Chan. (Canal) Ill. (Chicago In.)	41.41 N	87.48 W
161	Calumpit (kä-lōōm-pēt′) P. I. (Manila In.)	14.57 N	120.42 E
163	Caluya (kä-lōō′yȧ)..........P. I.	11.56 N	121.33 E
163	Caluya I. ....P. I.	11.55 N	121.33 E
81	Calvert (kăl′vērt)............Tex.	30.58 N	96.40 W
54	Calvert I....................Can.	51.31 N	128.0 W
124	Calvi (käl′vē).........Cor. (In.)	42.30 N	8.42 E
92	Calvillo (käl-vēl′yō)........Mex.	21.53 N	102.48 W
142	Calvinia (kăl-vĭn′ĭ-ȧ)....U. S. Afr.	31.28 S	19.45 E
96	Camagüey (kä-mä-gwā′)....Cuba	21.21 N	77.59 W
96	Camagüey (State)...........Cuba	21.28 N	78.0 W
96	Camajuani (kä-mä-hwä′nê)..Cuba	22.25 N	79.46 W
162	Camalig (kä-mä′lêg).........P. I.	13.10 N	123.39 E
102	Camana (kä-mä′nä)..........Peru	16.32 S	72.47 W
49	Camano (kä-mä′nō) Wash. (Seattle In.)	48.10 N	122.31 W
49	Camano I.....Wash. (Seattle In.)	48.14 N	122.30 W
80	Camargo (kä-mär′gō).......Mex.	26.17 N	98.50 W
135	Camariñal, C. (kä-mä-rê-nyäl′) Sp. (Gibralter In.)	36.5 N	5.14 E
94	Camarón, C. (kä-mä-rōn′)..Hond.	15.58 N	85.8 W
127	Camarón, Pt............Sp. (In.)	36.44 N	6.27 W
70	Camas (kăm′ȧs)..........Wash.	45.35 N	122.25 W
49	Camas......Wash. (Portland In.)	45.35 N	122.25 W
71	Camas Cr....................Ida.	44.12 N	112.0 W
151	Cambay, G. of (kăm-bā′)....India	21.30 S	72.15 E
169	Camberwell (kăm′bēr-wĕl) Austl. (Melbourne In.)	37.50 S	145.4 E
160	Cambodia (State) (kăm-bō′dĭ-ȧ) Fr. In. Chn.	12.15 N	105.0 E
160	Cambodia Pt.........Fr. In. Chn.	8.37 N	104.38 E
116	Camborne (kăm′bôrn)...Gt. Brit.	50.15 N	5.15 W
124	Cambrai (käɴ-brĕ′)...........Fr.	50.10 N	3.11 E
57	Cambria (kăm′brĭ-ȧ) Can. (Montreal In.)	45.48 N	74.11 W
116	Cambrian Mts. (kăm′brĭ-ăn) Gt. Brit.	52.20 N	3.30 W
116	Cambridge (kām′brĭj)....Gt. Brit.	52.12 N	0.0
85	Cambridge..................Md.	38.34 N	76.7 W
86	Cambridge................Mass.	42.25 N	71.10 W
77	Cambridge................Minn.	45.35 N	93.12 W
78	Cambridge.................Neb.	40.17 N	100.11 W
170	Cambridge.................N. Z.	37.55 S	175.30 E
84	Cambridge.................Ohio	40.2 N	81.35 W
143	Cambridge............U. S. Afr.	32.59 S	27.52 E
84	Cambridge City.............Ind.	39.46 N	85.12 W
82	Camden (kăm′dĕn)...........Ala.	31.59 N	87.18 W
79	Camden....................Ark.	33.35 N	92.49 W
167	Camden..................Austl.	34.4 S	150.42 E
86	Camden....................Me.	44.12 N	69.4 W
85	Camden...................N. J.	39.53 N	75.9 W
83	Camden...................S. C.	34.15 N	80.37 W
167	Camden Haven............Austl.	31.38 S	152.51 E
99	Camden Is..Chl. (Magallanes In.)	54.45 S	72.0 W
79	Cameron (kăm′ēr-ŭn)........Mo.	39.45 N	94.14 W
81	Cameron...................Tex.	30.51 N	97.0 W
84	Cameron.................W. Va.	39.45 N	80.47 W
72	Cameron Cone Colo. (Colo. Sprs. In.)	38.50 N	104.57 W
170	Cameron Mt..........N. Z. (In.)	41.21 S	174.53 E
138	Cameroon Mts. (kăm-ēr-ōōn′) Nig.	4.15 N	9.6 E
138	Cameroons (kăm-ēr-ōōnz′)....Afr.	5.0 N	12.30 E
103	Cametá (kä-mȧ-tä′)........Braz.	2.15 S	44.30 W
162	Camiguin I. (kä-mê-gēn′)....P. I.	18.55 N	121.55 E
163	Camiguin I..................P. I.	9.10 N	124.43 E
162	Camiling (kä-mê-lĭng′) ......P. I.	15.41 N	120.24 E
82	Camilla (kȧ-mĭl′ȧ)...........Ga.	31.14 N	84.13 W
89	Caminada B. (kȧ-mĭ-nȧ′dȧ) La. (New Orleans In.)	29.15 N	90.3 W
126	Caminha (kä-mĭn′yȧ).......Port.	41.52 N	8.50 W
103	Camisão (kä-mē-souɴ′) Braz. (In.)	12.12 S	39.43 W
103	Cammamú (kăm-mȧ-mōō′) Braz. (In.)	13.57 S	39.9 W
103	Camocim (kä-mô-sēɴ′)......Braz.	2.59 S	40.58 W
164	Camooweal (kȧ′mōō-wēl)...Austl.	19.59 S	138.10 E
163	Camotes Is. (kä-mō′tās).....P. I.	10.40 N	124.25 E
163	Camotes Sea................P. I.	10.30 N	124.30 E
99	Campana (käm-pä′nä) Arg. (Buenos Aires In.)	34.9 S	59.0 W
104	Campaña I. (käm-pän′yä)....Chl.	48.28 S	75.20 W
126	Campanario (käm-pä-nä′rê ō)..Sp.	38.53 N	5.36 W
99	Campanhã (käm-pän-yăɴ′) Braz. (Rio de Janeiro In.)	21.49 S	45.20 W
128	Campania (Prov.) (käm-pän′yä) It.	40.45 N	15.0 E
166	Campaspe R. (kăm-păs′pĭ)..Austl.	36.18 S	144.40 E
161	Camp Avery (ā′vēr-ê) P. I. (Manila In.)	14.24 N	120.31 E
142	Campbell (kăm′bĕl)........Bech.	28.48 S	23.41 E
79	Campbell...................Mo.	36.28 N	90.5 W
171	Campbell C.................N. Z.	41.45 S	174.20 E
72	Campbell Cr. Can. (Vancouver In.)	49.3 N	122.42 W
46	Campbell I...............Ant. O.	52.30 S	169.0 E
169	Campbellfield (kăm′bĕl-fēld) Austl. (Melbourne In.)	37.41 S	144.57 E
82	Campbellsville (kăm′bĕlz-vĭl)..Ky.	37.20 N	85.20 W
55	Campbellton (kăm′bĕl-tŭn)..Can.	48.0 N	66.35 W
167	Campbelltown.............Austl.	34.5 S	150.48 E
169	Campbelltown (kăm′bĕl-toun) Austl. (Tas. In.)	41.56 S	147.31 E
116	Campbeltown...........Gt. Brit.	55.25 N	5.40 W
72	Camp Cr. (kămp) Colo. (Colo. Sprs. In.)	38.54 N	104.55 W
93	Campeche (käm-pā′chā).....Mex.	19.50 N	90.31 W
93	Campeche (State)..........Mex.	19.0 N	90.45 W
93	Campeche, B. of............Mex.	19.0 N	94.0 W
96	Campechuela (käm-pȧ-chwā′lä) Cuba	20.13 N	77.15 W
166	Camperdown (kăm-pēr-down′) Austl.	38.13 S	143.10 E
143	Camperdown..........U. S. Afr.	29.42 S	30.32 E
126	Campillo de Altobuey (käm-pēl′-yō dā äl-tō-bōō′ā).Sp.	39.37 N	1.48 W
129	Câmpina (kûm′pê-nä).......Rom.	45.7 N	25.45 E
103	Campina Grande (käm-pē′nä-(grän′dĕ.Braz.	7.10 S	35.50 W
103	Campinas (käm-pē′näzh)....Braz.	22.58 S	47.2 W
103	Campo (käm′pōō)..........Braz.	21.45 S	41.28 W
138	Campo (käm′pō)...........Cam.	2.28 N	9.58 E
128	Campobasso (käm′pô-bäs′sō)...It.	41.34 N	14.37 E
126	Campo de Criptana (käm′pō dā krēp-tä′nä).Sp.	39.25 N	3.7 W
103	Campo Largo (käm-pōō lär′gōō) Braz.	11.47 S	44.25 W
126	Campo Maior (käm-pōō-mä-yôr′) Port.	39.1 N	7.5 W
138	Campo R...................Cam.	2.30 N	10.30 E
127	Campo Real (käm′pō-rå-äl′) Sp. (In.)	40.21 N	3.23 W
119	Camposanto (käm′pō-sän′tō) It. (Napoli In.)	40.52 N	14.17 E
141	Camps B. (kămps)......U. S. Afr.	33.56 S	18.22 E
129	Câmpulung (kûm-pōō-lōōng′) Rom.	45.17 N	25.2 E
123	Câmpulungul (kûm-pōō-lōōŋ′gōōl) Rom.	47.32 N	25.37 E
80	Camp Wood................Tex.	29.42 N	100.0 W
116	Cam, R. (kăm).........Gt. Brit.	52.15 N	0.10 E
97	Camu R. (kä′mōō)..........Hai.	19.8 N	70.20 W
86	Canaan R. (kā′năn).........N. B.	45.55 N	65.45 W
54	Canada....................N. A.	55.0 N	95.0 W
78	Canadian (kȧ-nā′dĭ-ăn)......Tex.	35.54 N	100.23 W
79	Canadian R.................U. S.	35.0 N	97.22 W
79	Canadian R., Deep Fork of..Okla.	35.37 N	96.20 W
78	Canadian R., North........Okla.	35.20 N	97.0 W
85	Canajoharie (kăn-ȧ-jô-hăr′ê).N. Y.	42.55 N	74.32 W
113	Çanakkale (chä-näk-kä′lĕ)....Tur.	40.10 N	26.32 E
95	Canal Zone ....Cen. Am.	9.40 N	80.20 W
90	Canal Zone, Central America (In.)		
85	Canandaigua (kăn-ăn-dā′gwȧ) N. Y.	42.55 N	77.19 W
85	Canandaigua L............N. Y.	42.45 N	77.20 W
6	Canaries Mt. (kȧ-nā′rêz) St. Lucia (Martinique In.)	13.49 N	60.58 W
138	Canary Is. (kȧ-nā′rê)......Atl. O.	28.30 N	15.0 W
85	Canastota (kăn-ȧs-tō′tȧ)....N. Y.	43.3 N	75.45 W
80	Canatlan (kä-nät-län′)......Mex.	24.31 N	104.46 W
83	Canaveral, C. (kȧ-năv′ēr-ăl) Fla. (In.)	28.28 N	80.32 W
167	Canberra (kăn′bĕr-ȧ).......Austl.	35.28 S	149.9 E
165	Canberra.................Austl.	35.28 S	149.9 E
76	Canby (kăn′bĭ)............Minn.	44.43 N	96.15 W
124	Cancale (käɴ-kȧl′)............Fr.	48.40 N	1.50 W
93	Cancue (kän-kōō′å).........Mex.	16.53 N	92.28 W
162	Candelaria (kän-då-lä′rê-ä)...P. I.	15.38 N	119.55 E
161	Candelaria.....P. I. (Manila In.)	13.57 N	121.28 E
93	Candelaria, R.............Mex.	18.20 N	91.18 W
126	Candeleda (kän-dhå-lā′dhä)...Sp.	40.10 N	5.15 W
128	Candia (Erakleion) (kăn′dĭ-ȧ) (hê-răk′lĭ-ŏn).Grc. (In.)	35.19 N	25.8 E
52	Candle (kăn′d′l)...........Alsk.	65.50 N	162.0 W
76	Cando (kăn′dō)............N. D.	48.28 N	99.12 W
162	Candon (kän-dōn′)..........P. I.	17.12 N	120.27 E
127	Candor, Pt. (kän-dôr′)...Sp. (In.)	36.37 N	6.21 W
128	Canea (Khania) (kä-nĕ′ȧ) Grc. (In.)	35.27 N	24.4 E
102	Cañete (kän-yā′tå)..........Peru	13.2 S	76.28 W
119	Canewdon (kȧ-nū′dŭn)...Gt. Brit.	51.37 N	0.44 E
97	Caney (kä-nā′) (kā′nĭ)......Cuba	20.3 N	75.46 W
79	Caney.....................Kans.	37.1 N	95.57 W
79	Caney R...................Okla.	36.40 N	96.7 W
140	Canga (käŋ′gä).............Ang.	9.17 S	13.47 E
140	Cangamba (kän-gôm′bä).....Ang.	13.30 S	19.55 E
140	Canganza, Serra de (Mts.) (sĕr′rȧ dā kän-gän′zȧ).Ang.	7.45 S	15.30 E
126	Cangas (kän′gäs)..............Sp.	43.6 N	6.38 W
126	Cangas......................Sp.	42.6 N	8.47 W
126	Cangas de Onís (kaŋ′gäs dā ô-nēs′).Sp.	43.22 N	5.9 W
126	Canha R. (kän′yä).........Port.	38.45 N	8.35 W
128	Canicatti (kä-nê-kät′tē).......It.	37.22 N	13.51 E
163	Canigao Chan. (kä-nê-gä′ô)..P. I.	10.10 N	124.40 E
126	Caniles (kä-nē′lås)...........Sp.	37.27 N	2.42 W
127	Canillejas (kä-nē-lā′hås)..Sp. (In.)	40.27 N	3.37 W
113	Çankiri (chäŋ-kē′rē).........Tur.	40.40 N	33.35 E
163	Canlaon (Vol.) (kän-lä-ōn′)...P. I.	10.25 N	123.85 E
167	Canmain (kăn-mān′).......Austl.	34.49 S	147.0 E
116	Canna (I.) (kăn′nȧ).....Gt. Brit.	57.5 N	6.38 W
103	Cannavieiras (kä-nä-vyā′räzh) Braz.	15.30 S	39.1 W
84	Cannelton (kăn′ĕl-tŭn).......Ind.	37.55 N	86.45 W
125	Cannes (kȧn)................Fr.	43.35 N	7.0 E
86	Canning (kăn′ĭng)..........Can.	45.10 N	64.25 W
169	Canning R......Austl. (Perth In.)	32.1 S	115.54 E
169	Cannington (kăn′ĭng-tŭn) Austl. (Perth In.)	32.0 S	115.55 E
118	Cannock (kăn′ŭk).......Gt. Brit.	52.41 N	2.2 W
118	Cannock Chase (kăn′ŭk chās) Gt. Brit.	52.43 N	1.55 W
76	Cannonball R.............N. D.	46.21 N	102.0 W
77	Cannon R. (kăn′ŭn).......Minn.	44.20 N	93.14 W
85	Cannonsburg (kăn′ŭnz-bûrg)..Pa.	40.13 N	80.17 W
95	Cannouan I. (kä-nōō-äɴ′) Wind. Is. (In.)	12.42 N	61.20 W
95	Cano I. (kä′nō)............C. R.	8.40 N	83.53 W
73	Canoga (kä-nō′gȧ) Park.....Calif.	34.12 N	118.36 W
78	Cañon City (kăn′yŭn)......Colo.	38.27 N	105.15 W
83	Canoochee R. (kȧ-nōō′chē)....Ga.	32.20 N	82.5 W
128	Canosa (kä-nō′sä)............It.	41.13 N	16.4 E
167	Canowindra (kă-nō-wĭn′drȧ).Austl.	33.34 S	148.40 E
87	Canso (kăn′sō)..............Can.	45.19 N	61.0 W
87	Canso, C...................Can.	45.20 N	61.0 W
87	Canso, Str. of..............Can.	45.40 N	61.20 W
126	Cantabrian Mts. (kăn-tā′brĭ-ăn) Sp.	43.10 N	5.0 W
126	Cantanhede (kän-täɴ-yā′då) Port.	40.20 N	8.35 W
169	Canterbury (kăn′tēr-bēr-ê) Austl. (Sydney In.)	33.55 S	151.7 E
117	Canterbury............Gt. Brit.	51.15 N	1.0 E
171	Canterbury Bight..........N. Z.	44.10 S	172.0 E
171	Canterbury Plains.........N. Z.	43.50 S	171.30 E
163	Cantilan (kän-tē′län)........P. I.	9.20 N	125.58 E
96	Cantiles Cay (I.) (kän-tē′lås).Cuba	21.38 N	82.0 W
82	Canton (kăn′tŏn)............Ga.	34.14 N	84.29 W
79	Canton.....................Ill.	40.33 N	90.2 W
87	Canton............Mass. (In.)	42.9 N	71.8 W
82	Canton....................Miss.	32.46 N	90.3 W
79	Canton.....................Mo.	40.7 N	91.31 W
82	Canton....................N. C.	35.32 N	82.52 W
84	Canton....................Ohio	40.50 N	81.22 W
85	Canton.....................Pa.	41.43 N	76.43 W
76	Canton....................S. D.	43.18 N	96.35 W
154	Canton (Kwangchow) (kăn′tŏn′) (kwäng′chō′).Chn.	23.7 N	113.15 E
128	Cantù (kän-tōō′)..............It.	45.44 N	9.8 E
161	Canubang (kä-nōō-bäng′) P. I. (Manila In.)	14.15 N	121.8 E
78	Canyon (kăn′yŭn)...........Tex.	34.58 N	101.57 W
75	Canyon de Chelly (shĕl′lĭ) Nat. Mon...Ariz.	36.7 N	109.15 W
162	Capalonga (kä-pä-lôŋ′gä)....P. I.	14.20 N	122.30 E
128	Capannori (kä-pän′nô-rē)......It.	43.51 N	10.36 E
127	Caparica (kä-pä-rē′kä).Port. (In.)	38.40 N	9.12 W
86	Cap Chat (kȧp shä′)........Can.	49.6 N	66.42 W
86	Cap de la Madeleine (kȧp dē lȧ mȧ-d′lĕn′).Can.	46.23 N	72.29 W
124	Capdenac-Gare (kȧ-dē-näk-gär′) Fr.	44.35 N	2.5 E
169	Cape Barren I. (kāp băr′ĕn) Austl. (Tas. In.)	40.23 S	148.15 E
55	Cape Breton I. (kāp brĕt′ŭn).Can.	46.0 N	61.0 W
138	Cape Coast..................G. C.	5.10 N	1.15 W
85	Cape Cod B................Mass.	41.50 N	70.20 W
83	Cape Fear R...............N. C.	35.10 N	78.50 W
79	Cape Girardeau (jē-rär-dō′)...Mo.	37.17 N	89.33 W
49	Cape Horn..Wash. (Portland In.)	45.35 N	122.11 W
127	Capellades (kä-pȧl-yä′dās).Sp. (In.)	41.33 N	1.42 E
85	Cape May..................N. J.	38.56 N	74.56 W
85	Cape May C. H.............N. J.	39.4 N	74.53 W
142	Cape of Good Hope (Prov.) U. S. Afr.	31.35 S	24.0 E
138	Cape Palmas (Harper) (päl′mäs) (här′pēr).Lib.	4.30 N	7.54 W
124	Capestan (kȧ-pē-stäɴ′) ....Fr.	43.20 N	3.0 E
142	Capetown.............U. S. Afr.	33.55 S	18.22 E
141	Capetown........U. S. Afr. (In.)		
138	Cape Verde Is. (kāp vûrd) Atl. O. (In.)	16.0 N	24.0 W
165	Cape York Pen. (kāp yôrk).Austl.	13.0 S	142.30 E
97	Cap Haitien (kȧp ȧ-ē-syăɴ′) .Hai.	19.47 N	72.13 W
163	Cap I. (kăp)................P. I.	5.57 N	120.10 E
72	Capilano Cr. (kă-pĭ-lā′nō) Can. (Vancouver In.)	49.28 N	123.7 W
99	Capilla del Señor (kä-pēl′yä-dĕl sän-yôr′).Arg. (Buenos Aires In.)	34.16 S	59.8 W
78	Capitan Mts. (kä-pê-tän′)..N. M.	33.38 N	105.25 W
	Capitol Reef (kăp′ĭ-tŏl) Natl. Mon...Utah	38.15 N	111.30 W
163	Capiz (kä′pêz)..............P. I.	11.36 N	122.46 E
163	Capnoyan I. (kăp-nō′yän) ...P. I.	10.40 N	120.55 E

ăt; finăl; rāte; senâte; ärm; ȧsk; sofȧ; fâre; ch-choose; dh-as th in other; bē; êvent; bĕt; recĕnt; cratēr; g-go; gh-gutteral g; bĭt; ĭ-short neutral; rīde; ĸ-gutteral k as ch in German ich;

Page	Name Pronunciation Region	Lat. °′	Long. °′
165	Capoompeta (Mt.) (kȧ-pōōm-pē′tȧ). Austl.	29.20 S	152.10 E
128	Caporetto (kä-pô-rĕt′tō) .... It.	46.15 N	13.34 E
119	Cappellen (kä-pĕl′ĕn) Bel. (Anvers In.)	51.19 N	4.26 E
128	Capraia (I.) (kä-prä′yä) .... It.	43.3 N	9.48 E
128	Caprara Pt. (kä-prä′rä) ..... Sard.	41.8 N	8.22 E
128	Caprera (I.) (kä-prā′rä) ..... Sard.	41.15 N	9.25 E
128	Capri (I.) (kä′prē) .... It.	40.33 N	14.13 E
165	Capricorn Chan. (kăp′rĭ-kôrn) Austl.	22.30 S	151.30 E
86	Cap St. Ignace (kăp săN-tê-nyȧs′) (sānt ĭg′nȧs) Can.	47.2 N	70.26 W
128	Capua (kä′pwä) .... It.	41.7 N	14.12 E
163	Capual I. (kä-pwäl′) .... P. I.	6.3 N	121.25 E
138	Capuchinos (kä-pōō-chē′nōs) Az. Is. (In.)	38.34 N	28.48 W
162	Capul (kä-pŏŏl′) .... P. I.	12.25 N	124.10 E
92	Capulhuac (kä-pŏŏl-hwäk′) .. Mex.	19.28 N	99.32 W
78	Capulin Mountain Natl. Mon. (kȧ-pū′lĭn). N. M.	36.53 N	103.57 W
140	Caquengue (kä-kĕŋ′gĕ) ...... Ang.	12.20 S	22.28 E
102	Caquetá (Japura), R. (kä-kā-tä′) (hä-pōō′rȧ). Col.	1.0 S	72.2 W
127	Carabaña (kä-rä-bän′yä). Sp. (In.)	40.16 N	3.15 W
127	Carabanchel Alto (kä-rä-bän-chĕl′ äl′tō). Sp. (In.)	40.23 N	3.45 W
127	Carabanchel Bajo (kä-rä-bän-chĕl′ bä′hō). Sp. (In.)	40.23 N	3.45 W
163	Carabao I. (kä-rä-bä′ō) ...... P. I.	12.5 N	121.56 E
129	Caracál (kȧ-rȧ-kȧl′) .... Rom.	44.6 N	24.22 E
102	Caracas (kä-rä′käs) .... Ven.	10.30 N	66.58 W
92	Carácuaro (kä-rä′kwä-rō) .... Mex.	18.45 N	101.0 W
163	Caraga (kä-rä′gä) .... P. I.	7.19 N	126.34 E
163	Caraga B. .... P. I.	7.20 N	126.35 E
162	Caramoan (kä-rä-mō′än) .... P. I.	13.46 N	123.51 E
129	Caransebeş (kȧ-rȧn-sā′bĕsh). Rom.	45.24 N	22.13 E
104	Carapeguá (kä-rä-pâ-gwä′) ... Par.	25.40 S	57.15 W
86	Caraquet (kă-rȧ-kĕt′) .... Can.	47.47 N	64.56 W
95	Caratasca Lagoon (kä-rä-tās′kä). Hond.	15.30 N	83.40 W
126	Caravaca (kä-rä-vä′kä) .... Sp.	38.6 N	1.52 W
103	Caravelas (kä-rä-vĕl′äzh) .... Braz.	17.47 S	39.18 W
95	Caravelle Pen. (kä-rä-vĕl′) Mart. (In.)	14.50 N	60.50 W
126	Carballino (kär-bäl-yē′nō) ..... Sp.	42.36 N	8.5 W
126	Carballo (kär-bäl′yō) .... Sp.	43.13 N	8.42 W
95	Carbet Peaks (kär-bā′). Mart. (In.)	14.43 N	61.6 W
70	Carbonado (kär-bō-nā′dō) .. Wash.	47.4 N	122.3 W
128	Carbonara, C. (kär-bō-nä′rä). Sard.	39.7 N	9.31 E
79	Carbondale (kär′bŏn-dāl) ...... Ill.	37.44 N	89.13 W
85	Carbondale .... Pa.	41.32 N	75.30 W
87	Carbonear (kär-bô-nēr′) .... Newf.	47.42 N	53.15 W
92	Carbonera (kär-bō-nā′rä) .... Mex.	22.15 N	100.14 W
82	Carbon Hill (kär′bŏn) .... Ala.	33.53 N	87.33 W
82	Carbur (kär′bûr) .... Fla.	29.56 N	83.28 W
127	Carcagente (kär-kä-hĕn′tā) .... Sp.	39.7 N	0.28 W
163	Carcar (kär′kär) .... P. I.	10.7 N	123.39 E
99	Carcaraña, R. (kär-kä-rän′yä) Arg. (Buenos Aires In.)	33.0 S	61.25 W
124	Carcassone (kȧr-kȧ-sôn′) ...... Fr.	43.11 N	2.21 E
54	Carcross (kär′krôs) .... Can.	60.14 N	134.31 W
151	Cardamon Hills (kär′dȧ-mŭn) India (Cey. In.)	9.30 N	77.30 E
96	Cárdenas (kär′dâ-näs) ...... Cuba	23.1 N	81.11 W
93	Cárdenas .... Mex.	17.59 N	93.23 W
92	Cárdenas .... Mex.	22.0 N	99.38 W
96	Cárdenas B. .... Cuba	23.5 N	81.8 W
73	Cardiff (kär′dĭf) Ala. (Birmingham In.)	33.39 N	86.56 W
116	Cardiff .... Gt. Brit.	51.30 N	3.10 W
116	Cardigan (kär′dĭ-găn) .... Gt. Brit.	52.5 N	4.35 W
116	Cardigan B. .... Gt. Brit.	52.30 N	4.30 W
161	Cardona (kär-dō′nä) P. I. (Manila In.)	14.30 N	121.15 E
54	Cardston (kärds′tŭn) .... Can.	49.10 N	113.6 W
123	Careii (kä-rĕ′ê) .... Rom.	47.42 N	22.27 E
124	Carentan (kä-rôN-täN′) .... Fr.	49.18 N	1.11 W
84	Carey (kā′rê) .... Ohio	40.57 N	83.27 W
164	Carey, L. .... Austl.	29.0 S	122.25 E
167	Cargellico, L. (kär-jĕl′ĭ-kō).. Austl.	33.20 S	146.23 E
171	Cargill, Mt. (kär′gĭl) ... N. Z. (In.)	45.49 S	170.35 E
124	Carhaix (kär-ĕ′) .... Fr.	48.20 N	3.35 W
91	Caribbean S. (kăr-ĭ-bē′ăn) Cen. Am.	15.0 N	75.0 W
54	Cariboo Mts. (kă′rĭ-bōō) .... Can.	53.15 N	121.30 W
86	Caribou .... Me.	46.52 N	68.0 W
77	Caribou I. .... Can.	47.20 N	85.47 W
129	Caribrod (tsär′ĭ-brôd) ...... Yugo.	43.1 N	22.46 E
163	Carigara (kä-rê-gä′rä) .... P. I.	11.17 N	124.42 E
163	Carigara B. .... P. I.	11.20 N	124.40 E
103	Carinhanha (kä-rĭ-nyän′yä).. Braz.	14.32 S	43.58 W
128	Carini (kä-rē′nē) .... It.	38.8 N	13.10 E
85	Carleton Place (kärl′tŭn) .... Can.	45.7 N	76.7 W
169	Carlingford (kär′lĭng-fērd) Austl. (Sydney In.)	33.46 S	151.1 E
79	Carlinville (kär′lĭn-vĭl) .... Ill.	39.17 N	89.54 W
116	Carlisle (kär-līl′) .... Gt. Brit.	54.55 N	3.0 W
84	Carlisle .... Ky.	38.18 N	84.2 W
85	Carlisle .... Pa.	40.12 N	77.10 W
128	Carloforte (kär′lō-fôr-tȧ) .... Sard.	39.9 N	8.19 E
116	Carlow (kär′lō) .... Ire.	52.50 N	6.55 W
	Carlsbad, see Karlovy Vary, Czech.		
78	Carlsbad (kärlz′băd) .... N. M.	32.24 N	104.14 W
80	Carlsbad Caverns Nat. Pk.. N. M.	32.5 N	104.10 W
118	Carlton (kärl′tŭn) .... Gt. Brit.	52.58 N	1.5 W
77	Carlton .... Minn.	46.40 N	92.26 W
84	Carlton Center .... Mich.	42.47 N	85.18 W
79	Carlyle (kär-līl′) .... Ill.	38.36 N	89.22 W
128	Carmagnola (kär-mä-nyô′lä) ... It.	44.49 N	7.45 E
76	Carman (kär′mȧn) .... Can.	49.34 N	98.1 W
116	Carmarthen (kär-mär′thĕn) Gt. Brit.	51.50 N	4.20 W
116	Carmarthen B. .... Gt. Brit.	51.45 N	4.30 W
124	Carmaux (kȧr-mō′) .... Fr.	44.5 N	2.10 E
102	Carmen (kär′mĕn) .... Col.	9.45 N	75.30 W
93	Carmen .... Mex.	18.38 N	91.48 W
163	Carmen .... P. I.	10.34 N	124.1 E
99	Carmen de Areco (kär′mĕn′ dā ä-rā′kô) Arg. (Buenos Aires In.)	34.20 S	59.50 W
93	Carmen I. .... Mex.	18.41 N	91.40 W
93	Carmen, L. .... Mex.	18.16 N	93.47 W
46	Carmen Land (Reg.) .... Ant.	84.0 S	120.0 W
84	Carmi (kär′mī) .... Ill.	38.6 N	88.10 W
97	Carmichael (kär′mĭ-kāl) .... Ba. Is.	21.14 N	73.25 W
161	Carmona (kär-mō′nä) P. I. (Manila In.) ...	14.20 N	121.5 E
126	Carmona .... Sp.	37.28 N	5.38 W
164	Carnarvon (kär-när′vŭn) ... Austl.	24.47 S	113.40 E
116	Carnarvon .... Gt. Brit.	53.8 N	4.15 W
142	Carnarvon .... U. S. Afr.	30.59 S	22.9 E
116	Carnarvon B. .... Gt. Brit.	53.8 N	4.30 W
127	Carnaxide (kär-nä-shē′dĕ) Port. (In.)	38.43 N	9.15 W
116	Carndonagh (kärn-dō-nä′).. N. Ire.	55.15 N	7.15 W
78	Carnegie (kär-nĕg′ĭ) .... Okla.	35.6 N	98.36 W
89	Carnegie ..... Pa. (Pittsburgh In.)	40.24 N	80.5 W
88	Carnegie .... Wis. (Duluth In.)	46.38 N	92.11 W
164	Carnegie, L. .... Austl.	26.10 S	122.45 E
135	Carnero, Pt. (kär-nā′rō) Sp. (Gibraltar In.)	36.5 N	5.35 E
85	Carneys Point (kär′nêz) ..... N. J.	39.42 N	75.27 W
118	Carnforth (kärn′fûrth) ... Gt. Brit.	54.7 N	2.47 W
127	Carnot (kär-nō′) .... Alg.	36.16 N	1.41 E
139	Carnot .... Fr. Eq. Afr.	4.57 N	15.58 E
116	Carnoustie (kär-nōōs′tĭ) .. Gt. Brit.	56.30 N	2.40 W
116	Carnsore Pt. (kärn′sôr) .... Ire.	52.10 N	6.20 W
84	Caro (kâ′rō) .... Mich.	43.28 N	83.24 W
103	Carolina (kä-rô-lē′nä) .... Braz.	7.27 S	47.29 W
143	Carolina (kăr-ô-lī′nȧ) ... U. S. Afr.	26.5 S	30.9 E
7	Caroline Is. (kăr′ô-līn) .... Pac. O.	8.0 N	150.0 E
102	Caroni, R. (kä-rō′nē) .... Ven.	5.30 N	62.48 W
122	Carouge (kȧ-rōōzh′) .... Switz.	46.11 N	6.11 E
123	Carpathians (Mts.) (kär-pā′thĭ-ăn) Eur.	48.35 N	23.55 E
123	Carpathians, Little (Mts.).. Czech.	48.30 N	17.20 E
123	Carpathians, White (Mts.). Czech.	49.0 N	18.0 E
164	Carpentaria, G. of (kär-pĕn-târ′ĭȧ) Austl.	14 0 S	138.30 E
124	Carpentras (kȧr-päN-träs′) ..... Fr.	44.4 N	5.2 E
128	Carpi (kär′pē) .... It.	44.46 N	10.53 E
166	Carpolac (kär′pô-lȧk) ...... Austl.	36.43 S	141.15 E
82	Carrabelle (kăr′ȧ-bĕl) .... Fla.	29.52 N	84.40 W
128	Carrara (kä-rä′rä) .... It.	44.4 N	10.5 E
95	Carriacou (I.) (kăr-ê-ȧ-kōō′) Wind. Is. (In.)	12.30 N	61.26 W
116	Carrick (kăr′ĭk) .... Ire.	52.20 N	7.25 W
82	Carriere (kȧ-rēr′) .... Miss.	30.37 N	89.40 W
57	Carrier (kăr′ĭ-ēr) .. Can. (Que. In.)	46.44 N	71.6 W
79	Carriers Mills (kăr′ĭ-ērs) ...... Ill.	37.41 N	88.37 W
166	Carrieton (kăr′ĭ-tŭn) .... Austl.	32.26 S	138.31 E
76	Carrington (kăr′ĭng-tŭn) .... N. D.	47.26 N	99.8 W
49	Carr Inlet (kär) Wash. (Seattle In.)	47.17 N	122.43 W
96	Carrion Crow Har. (kăr′ĭ-ŭn krō) Ba. Is.	26.38 N	77.52 W
126	Carrión de los Condes (kär-rê-ōn′ dā lōs kōn′dâs) Sp.	42.21 N	4.35 W
126	Carrión R. (kär-rê-ōn′) .... Sp.	42.30 N	4.44 W
78	Carrizo Cr. (kär-rē′zō) ..... N. M.	36.14 N	103.10 W
80	Carrizo Springs .... Tex.	28.32 N	99.53 W
75	Carrizozo (kär-rê-zō′zō) .... N. M.	33.38 N	105.52 W
77	Carroll (kăr′ŭl) .... Ia.	42.3 N	94.50 W
49	Carrolls (kăr′ŭlz) Wash. (Portland In.)	46.4 N	122.52 W
82	Carrollton (kăr-ŭl-tŭn) .... Ga.	33.34 N	85.4 W
79	Carrollton .... Ill.	39.19 N	90.23 W
84	Carrollton .... Ky.	38.39 N	85.11 W
84	Carrollton .... Mich.	43.29 N	83.57 W
79	Carrollton .... Mo.	39.22 N	93.28 W
84	Carrollton .... Ohio	40.34 N	81.8 W
116	Carron, Loch (L.) (kȧ′rŭn, lŏK) Gt. Brit.	57.20 N	5.30 W
166	Carrum (kăr′ŭm) .... Austl.	38.5 S	145.6 E
169	Carrum Swamp Austl. (Melbourne In.)	38.2 S	145.7 E
113	Çarşamba (chär-shäm′bä) .... Tur.	41.10 N	36.50 E
74	Carson City (kär′sŭn) .... Nev.	39.10 N	119.45 W
74	Carson R. .... Nev.	39.12 N	119.35 W
74	Carson Sink .... Nev.	39.50 N	118.25 W
161	Carstensz, Mt. (kärs′tĕns) Neth. Ind.	3.57 S	137.3 E
102	Cartagena (kär-tä-hā′nä) ..... Col.	10.30 N	75.30 W
127	Cartagena .... Sp.	37.35 N	1.0 W
102	Cartago (kär-tä′gō) .... Col.	4.40 N	76.2 W
95	Cartago .... C. R.	9.52 N	83.51 W
126	Cartaxo (kär-tä′shō) .... Port.	39.10 N	8.48 W
126	Cartaya (kär-tä′yâ) .... Sp.	37.16 N	7.9 W
126	Cartelle (kär-tĕl′yâ) .... Sp.	42.15 N	8.4 W
124	Carteret (kär-tē-rĕ′) .... Fr.	49.25 N	1.45 W
82	Cartersville (kär′tērs-vĭl) ..... Ga.	34.10 N	84.48 W
171	Carterton (kär′tēr-tŭn) ...... N. Z.	41.2 S	175.32 E
79	Carthage (kär′thâj) .... Ill.	40.26 N	91.8 W
79	Carthage .... Mo.	37.10 N	94.19 W
85	Carthage .... N. Y.	3.59 N	75.39 W
83	Carthage .... N. C.	35.22 N	79.26 W
81	Carthage .... Tex.	32.9 N	94.20 W
138	Carthage (Ruins) .... Tun.	37.0 N	10.20 E
118	Cartmel (kärt′mĕl) ...... Gt. Brit.	54.12 N	2.57 W
55	Cartwright (kärt′rīt) .... Lab.	53.48 N	56.59 W
103	Caruarú (kä-rŏŏ-ȧ-rōō′) ..... Braz.	8.16 S	35.58 W
102	Carúpano (kä-rōō′pä-nō) ..... Ven.	10.33 N	63.28 W
79	Caruthersville (kȧ-rŭdh′ērz-vĭl) Mo.	36.11 N	89.39 W
73	Casa Blanca (kä′sä bläŋ′kä) Calif. (Los Angeles In.)	33.56 N	117.24 W
99	Casablanca (kä-sä-bläŋ′kä) Chl. (Valparaiso In.)	33.19 S	71.25 W
90	Casa Blanca... Cuba (Habana In.)	23.9 N	82.21 W
138	Casablanca .... Mor.	33.38 N	7.36 W
75	Casa Grande (kä′sä grän′dā). Ariz.	32.51 N	11.45 W
75	Casa Grande Natl. Mon. .... Ariz.	33.0 N	111.31 W
140	Casai R. (kä-sī′).. Bel. Cong.-Ang.	11.20 S	20.30 E
128	Casale (kä-sä′lā) .... It.	45.7 N	8.28 E
128	Casalmaggiore (kä-säl-mäd-jō′rā) It.	45.0 N	10.24 E
138	Casamance R. (kä-sä-mäNs′) Fr. W. Afr.	12.50 N	15.30 W
104	Casares (kä-sä′rĕs) .... Arg.	35.45 S	61.28 W
72	Cascade (kăs-kād′) Colo. (Colo. Sprs. In.	38.54 N	104.58 W
171	Cascade Pt. .... N. Z.	43.58 S	168.25 E
58	Cascade Range .... U. S.	42.0 N	122.0 W
70	Cascade Tunnel .... Wash.	47.43 N	121.0 W
104	Cascadura (käs-kä-dōō′rä) Braz. (In.)	22.53 S	43.20 W
127	Cascais (käs-kȧ-ēzh′) ... Port. (In.)	38.42 N	9.25 W
127	Cascais B. .... Port. (In.)	38.40 N	9.22 W
49	Case Inlet (kās) Wash. (Seattle In.)	47.15 N	122.51 W
104	Caseros (kä-sä′rôs) ..... Arg. (In.)	34.36 S	58.34 W
128	Caserta (kä-zĕr′tä) .... It.	41.4 N	14.19 E
84	Casey (kā′sĭ) .... Ill.	39.19 N	7.59 W
70	Cashmere (kăsh′mĭr) .... Wash.	47.30 N	120.29 W
162	Casiguran (kä-sē-gōō′rän) ... P. I.	12.52 N	124.2 E
162	Casiguran .... P. I.	16.16 N	122. 9 E
162	Casiguran Sd. .... P. I.	16.5 N	122.0 E
169	Casino (kȧ-sē′nō) ..... Austl. (In.)	28.52 S	153.2 E
102	Casiquiare, R. (kä-sê-kyä′rā). Ven.	2.0 N	66.30 W
122	Čáslav (chä′slȧf) .... Czech.	49.54 N	15.24 E
127	Caspe (käs′pâ) .... Sp.	41.15 N	0.2 W
71	Casper (kăs′pēr) .... Wyo.	42.51 N	106.18 W
113	Caspian Sea (kăs′pĭ-ăn) ... Eurasia	42.0 N	50.0 E
114	Casr Garian (kăs″r gä′rê-än) Libya	32.41 N	13.4 E
85	Cass (kăs) .... W. Va.	38.27 N	79.53 W
127	Cassá (käs-sä′) .... Sp.	41.53 N	2.52 E
140	Cassangi (kä-säŋ′gē) .... Ang.	9.15 S	17.45 E
84	Cass City (kăs) .... Mich.	43.36 N	83.10 W
76	Casselton (kăs″l-tŭn) .... N. D.	46.54 N	97.12 W
72	Cassidy (kăs′ĭ-dĭ) Can. (Vancouver In.)	49.4 N	123.52 W
140	Cassinga (kä-sĭŋ′gȧ) .... Ang.	15.8 S	16.12 E
128	Cassino (käs-sē′nō) .... It.	41.29 N	13.48 E
77	Cass Lake (kăs) .... Minn.	47.22 N	94.35 W
77	Cass L. .... Minn.	47.25 N	94.30 W
84	Cassopolis (kăs-ŏ′pô-lĭs) .... Mich.	41.56 N	86.0 W
171	Cass Pk. .... N. Z. (In.)	43.36 S	172.40 E
79	Cassville (kăs′vĭl) .... Mo.	36.41 N	93.53 W
73	Castaic (kăs-tā′ĭk) Calif. (Los Angeles In.)	34.26 N	118.37 W
103	Castanhal (käs-tä-nyäl′) Braz. (In.)	115.0 S	47.58 W
126	Castanheira (käs-tän-yā′rä) .. Port.	40.0 N	8.8 W
124	Casteljaloux (käs-tĕl-zhä-lōō′).. Fr.	44.20 N	0.5 E
128	Castellammare (käs-tĕl-läm-mä′rā) It.	40.42 N	14.28 E
127	Castellar (käs-tĕl-yär′) .. Sp. (In.)	41.36 N	2.5 E
127	Castellón de la Plana (kȧs-tĕl-lyōn′ dā lä plä′nä) Sp.	39.59 N	0.3 W
124	Castelnaudary (kȧs′tĕl-nō-dȧ-rē′) Fr.	43.20 N	1.58 E
126	Castelo Branco (käs-tā′lŏŏ bräŋ′ kŏŏ) Port.	39.49 N	7.29 W
126	Castelo de Vide (käs-tā′lŏŏ dĭ vē′dĭ) Port.	39.25 N	7.27 W
124	Castelsarraisin (kȧs′tĕl-sȧ-rȧ-zăN′) Fr.	44.1 N	1.10 E
128	Castelvetrano (käs′tĕl-vê-trä′nō) It.	37.43 N	12.47 E
166	Casterton (kăs′tēr-tŭn) ..... Austl.	37.35 S	141.26 E
126	Castilla la Nueva (New Castile) (Prov.) (käs-tē′lyä lä nwā′vȧ). Sp.	39.50 N	3.0 W
126	Castilla La Vieja (Old Castile) (Prov.) (käs-tēl′yä lä vyā′hä) . Sp.	41.40 N	3.40 W
116	Castlebar (kȧs″l-bär) .... Ire.	53.55 N	9.19 W
75	Castle Dale .... Utah	39.13 N	111.1 W
118	Castle Donington (dŏn′ĭng-tŭn) Gt. Brit.	52.50 N	1.21 W
118	Castleford (kȧs″l-fērd) ... Gt. Brit.	53.43 N	1.21 W
97	Castle I. (kȧs″l) .... Ba. Is.	22.8 N	74.19 W
166	Castlemaine (kȧs″l-mān) ... Austl.	37.4 S	144.13 E
171	Castle, Mt. .... N. Z.	44.50 S	167.50 E
78	Castle Pk. .... Colo.	39.0 N	106.51 W
171	Castle Pt. .... N. Z.	40.55 S	176.15 E
167	Castlereagh R. (kȧs″l-rā) (kȧs″l-rā′äK). Austl.	31.50 S	149.0 E
70	Castlerock (kȧs″l-rŏk) ..... Wash.	46.16 N	122.54 W
89	Castle Shannon (shăn′ŭn) ..... Pa.	40.22 N	80.1 W
79	Castor R. (kăs′tôr) .... Mo.	36.55 N	89.50 W
124	Castres (kȧs′tr′) .... Fr.	43.35 N	2.11 E
95	Castries (kȧs-trē′) ...... Wind. Is.	14.0 N	61.0 W
104	Castro (käs′trŏŏ) .... Braz.	24.50 S	50.0 W
104	Castro (käs′tro) .... Chl.	42.28 S	73.48 W
126	Castro .... Sp.	37.42 N	4.27 W
103	Castro Alves (käs′trŏŏ ȧl′vĕzh) Braz. (In.)	12.46 S	39.32 W
128	Castrogiovanni (käs′trō-jô-vän′nē) It.	37.35 N	14.16 E
126	Castro Daire (käs′trŏŏ dīr′ĭ) . Port.	40.56 N	7.58 W
126	Castro Marim (käs′trŏŏ mä-rĭN′) Port.	37.15 N	7.29 W
126	Castropol (käs-trō-pōl′) .... Sp.	43.30 N	7.5 W
126	Castro Urdiales (käs′trō ŏŏr-dyä′-lās). Sp.	43.23 N	3.13 W
126	Castro Verde (käs-trō vĕr′dĕ). Port.	37.44 N	8.4 W
128	Castrovillari (käs′trō-vēl-lyä′-rē) It.	39.47 N	16.13 E
126	Castuera (käs-tŏŏ-ā′rä) .... Sp.	38.43 N	5.32 W

ng-sing; ŋ-baŋk; N-nasalized n; nŏd; cŏmmit· ōld; ôbey; ôrder; fōōd; fŏŏt; ou-out; s-soft; sh-dish; th-thin; pūre; ûnite; ûrn; stŭd; circŭs; ŭ-as "y" in study; '-indeterminate vowel.

Page	Name Pronunciation Region	Lat. °′	Long. °′
81	Catahoula L. (kăt-ȧ-hōō′lȧ)...La.	31.30 N	92.8 W
163	Cataingan (kä-tä-ēŋ′gän).....P. I.	12.0 N	123.29 E
103	Catalão (kä-tä-louN′).......Braz.	18.10 S	47.59 W
97	Catalina I. (kä-tä-lē′nä).....Hai.	18.21 N	69.0 W
99	Catalina Punta Chl. (Magallanes In.)	52.32 S	68.45 W
127	Catalonia (Cataluña (Prov.) (kăt-ȧ-lō′nĭ-ȧ)(kä-tä-lōōn′yä).Sp.	41.30 N	1.0 E
104	Catamarca (State) (kä-tä-mär′-kä).Arg.	28.0 S	66.30 W
104	Catamarca..................Arg.	28.29 S	65.59 W
162	Catanauan (kä-tä-nä′wän)...P. I.	13.37 N	122.19 E
162	Catanduanes I. (kä-tän-dwä′näs) P. I.	13.45 N	124.15 E
128	Catania (kȧ-tä′nyä)...........It.	37.31 N	15.4 E
128	Catania, G. of................It.	37.25 N	15.15 E
128	Catanzaro (kä-tän-dzä′rō).....It.	38.53 N	16.36 E
162	Catarman (kä-tär-män′).....P. I.	12.29 N	124.39 E
127	Catarroja (kä-tär-rō′hä).......Sp.	39.24 N	0.25 W
166	Catastrophe, C. (kȧ-tăs′trô-fê) Austl.	34.59 S	136.3 E
83	Catawba R. (kȧ-tô′bȧ).N. C.-S. C.	35.0 N	81.0 W
163	Catbalogan (kät-bä-lō′gän)...P. I.	11.46 N	124.53 E
163	Cateel (kä-tä-ĕl′)...........P. I.	7.47 N	126.27 E
93	Catemaco (kä-tä-mä′kō).....Mex.	18.25 N	95.8 W
143	Cathcart (kăth′kärt)....U. S. Afr.	32.18 S	27.11 E
72	Cathedral Mt. (kȧ-thē′drăl) Can. (Vancouver In.)	49.28 N	12.31 W
80	Cathedral, Mt..............Tex.	30.9 N	103.45 W
139	Catherina, Mt. (kă-thĕr-ē′nä)..Eg.	28.32 N	33.52 E
143	Cathkin Pk. (kăth′kĭn)..U. S. Afr.	29.6 S	29.21 E
97	Cat I....................Ba. Is.	24.25 N	75.31 W
89	Cat I.....Miss. (New Orleans In.)	30.13 N	89.6 W
89	Cat Island Chan. La.-Miss. (New Orleans In.)	30.11 N	89.7 W
84	Catlettsburg (kăt′lĕts-bûrg)...Ky.	38.24 N	82.37 W
163	Catmon (kät-mōn′)..........P. I.	10.42 N	124.1 E
85	Catonsville (kā′tŭnz-vĭl).....Md.	39.16 N	76.42 W
92	Catorce (kä-tôr′sȧ).........Mex.	23.41 N	100.52 W
85	Catskill (kăts′kĭl)...........N. Y.	42.15 N	73.51 W
85	Catskill Mts...............N. Y.	42.15 N	74.35 W
143	Catuane (kä-twä′nĕ).........Moz.	26.49 S	32.13 E
140	Catumbella (kä′tŭm-bĕl′ȧ)...Ang.	12.30 S	13.40 E
166	Caturaundee Range (kă-tōō-rôn′-dē).Austl.	30.53 S	142.37 E
163	Cauayan (kou-ä′yän).........P. I.	9.58 N	122.38 E
162	Cauayan....................P. I.	16.57 N	121.46 E
102	Cauca, R. (kou′kä)..........Col.	7.30 N	75.30 W
113	Caucasus Mts. (kô′kȧ-sŭs) Sov. Un.	43.10 N	43.45 E
124	Caudebec-St. Pierre (kōd-bĕk′-săN pyâr′).Fr.	49.16 N	1.2 E
124	Caudéran (kō-dā-räN′)........Fr.	44.52 N	0.35 W
127	Caudete (kou-dā′tȧ)..........Sp.	38.43 N	0.59 W
124	Caudry (kō-drē′)..............Fr.	50.10 N	3.30 E
163	Cauit, Pt. (kä′wêt)..........P. I.	9.18 N	126.12 E
72	Caulfeild (kôl′fēld) Can. (Vancouver In.)	49.20 N	123.15 W
169	Caulfield (kôl′fēld) Austl. (Melbourne In.)	37.53 S	145.3 E
128	Caulonia (kou-lō′nyä).........It.	38.24 N	16.24 E
104	Cauquenes (kou-kā′nās)......Chl.	36.0 S	72.28 W
162	Cauralaningan (kou′rä-lä-nĭŋ′gän) P. I.	18.16 N	121.40 E
102	Caura, R. (kou′rä)..........Ven.	6.0 N	64.30 W
96	Cauto, R. (kou′tō)..........Cuba	20.33 N	76.30 W
126	Cavado, R. (kä-vä′dō)......Port.	41.40 N	8.11 W
140	Cavalaua (kä-vä-lou′ä)......Ang.	16.12 S	14.15 E
103	Cavalcante (kä-väl-kän′tā)..Braz.	13.47 S	47.30 W
76	Cavalier (kăv-ȧ-lēr′).......N. D.	48.47 N	97.37 W
116	Cavan (kăv′ăn)..............Ire.	54.0 N	7.20 W
129	Cavarna (kä-vär′nä)........Rom.	43.25 N	28.22 E
128	Cavarzere (kä-vär′dzȧ-rā)......It.	45.8 N	12.5 E
86	Cavendish (kăv′ĕn-dĭsh)......Vt.	43.25 N	72.35 W
103	Caviana I. (kä-vyä′nä)......Braz.	0.15 N	50.0 W
162	Cavite (kä-vē′tā)...........P. I.	14.29 N	120.54 E
161	Cavite (Prov.)..P. I. (Manila In.)	14.16 N	120.50 E
151	Cawnpore (kôn-pōr′)........India	26.29 N	80.20 E
118	Cawood (kā′wŏŏd)......Gt. Brit.	53.50 N	1.7 W
103	Caxias (kä′shê-äzh).........Braz.	4.50 S	43.18 W
104	Caxias.....................Braz.	29.14 S	51.15 W
140	Caxito (kä-shē′tōō)..........Ang.	8.22 S	13.33 E
80	Cayanosa Draw (kä-yä-nō′sȧ drô) Tex.	31.0 N	103.10 W
97	Cayemite Is. (kī-mēt′).......Hai.	18.38 N	73.46 W
103	Cayenne (kā-ĕn′).........Fr. Gu.	4.58 N	52.18 W
97	Cayes (kī′ĕs)................Hai.	18.12 N	73.46 W
102	Cay Grande (I.) (kī grän′dȧ).Ven.	11.56 N	66.42 W
96	Cayman Is. (kī-män′).......W. I.	19.30 N	80.0 W
96	Cayman Brac (I.) (kī-män′ bråk) W. I.	19.43 N	79.46 W
96	Cay Sal Bank...............W. I.	23.50 N	80.10 W
96	Cay Sal (I.) (kī säl)........W. I.	23.41 N	80.25 W
85	Cayuga L. (kā-yōō′gȧ)......N. Y.	42.45 N	76.43 W
88	Cayuga R. N. Y. (Niagara Falls In.)	43.6 N	78.57 W
126	Cazalla (kä-thäl′yä)...........Sp.	37.56 N	5.46 W
85	Cazenovia (kăz-ê-nō′vĭ-ă)...N. Y.	42.55 N	75.50 W
88	Cazenovia Cr. N. Y. (Niagara Falls In.)	42.50 N	78.47 W
128	Čazma (chäz′mä)..........Yugo.	45.45 N	16.38 E
96	Cazones B. (kä-zō′nâs)......Cuba	22.10 N	81.25 W
96	Cazones, G. of..............Cuba	21.55 N	81.10 W
93	Cazones, R..................Mex.	20.30 N	97.28 W
126	Cazorla (kä-thôr′lä)..........Sp.	37.55 N	3.0 W
128	Cazza (I.) (kät′sä)...........It.	42.46 N	16.31 E
126	Céa R. (thā′ä)...............Sp.	42.15 N	5.10 W
103	Ceará (State) (sā-ä-rä′).....Braz.	5.0 S	39.30 W
103	Ceará (Fortaleza) (fôr-tä-lā′zä) Braz.	3.40 S	38.32 W
95	Cebaco I. (sȧ-bä′kō)........Pan.	7.29 N	81.10 W
113	Cebelibereket (sĕ′bĕl-ĭ-bĕr′ĕ-kĕt) Tur.	37.5 N	37.30 E
75	Cebolla Cr. (sē-bōl′yä)......Colo.	38.20 N	107.5 W
126	Cebreros (thā-brā′rōs)........Sp.	40.28 N	4.28 W
163	Cebu (sā-bōō′)..............P. I.	10.18 N	123.53 E
163	Cebu (I.)...................P. I.	10.25 N	123.50 E
122	Čechy (Bohemia) (Prov.) (chĕ′ĸē).Czech.	49.44 N	14.15 E
169	Cecil Plains (sē′sĭl)....Austl. (In.)	27.31 S	151.11 E
81	Cedar Bayou (R.) (sē′dēr) Tex. (In.)	29.51 N	94.55 W
81	Cedar Bayou.........Tex. (In.)	29.45 N	94.55 W
142	Cedar Berg (Mt.).......U. S. Afr.	32.21 S	19.8 E
75	Cedar Breaks Natl. Mon.....Utah	37.38 N	112.45 W
77	Cedarburg..................Wis.	43.18 N	88.0 W
75	Cedar City.................Utah	37.41 N	113.3 W
76	Cedar Cr...................N. D.	46.3 N	102.0 W
77	Cedar Falls..................Ia.	42.32 N	92.25 W
81	Cedar Grove.................La.	32.25 N	93.46 W
82	Cedar Keys..................Fla.	29.7 N	83.3 W
54	Cedar L....................Can.	53.20 N	100.2 W
89	Cedar Lake Minn. (Minneapolis In.)	44.58 N	93.19 W
77	Cedar Rapids................Ia.	42.0 N	91.41 W
77	Cedar R.....................Ia.	42.25 N	92.12 W
77	Cedar R., West Fork of.......Ia.	42.45 N	92.58 W
57	Cedars.......Can. (Montreal In.)	45.21 N	74.6 W
57	Cedars Rapids.Can. (Montreal In.)	45.17 N	74.0 W
84	Cedar Springs.............Mich.	43.14 N	85.37 W
82	Cedartown...................Ga.	34.0 N	85.15 W
143	Cedarville............U. S. Afr.	30.25 S	29.3 E
92	Cedral (sā-dräl′)............Mex.	23.48 N	100.42 W
94	Cedros (sā′drōs)...........Hond.	14.35 N	87.25 W
164	Ceduna (sê-dōō′nȧ)........Austl.	32.5 S	133.50 E
128	Cefalù (chā-fä-lōō′)...........It.	38.2 N	14.1 E
126	Cega R. (thā′gä)..............Sp.	41.20 N	4.15 W
123	Cegléd (tsă′glād)..........Hung.	47.10 N	19.48 E
126	Cehegín (thā-â-hēn′).........Sp.	38.5 N	1.48 W
135	Cekhira (sĕ′ĸē-rä)......Tun. (In.)	34.17 N	10.5 E
92	Celaya (sā-lä′yä)............Mex.	20.32 N	100.49 W
160	Celebes (Is.) (sĕl′ê-bēz) (sĕl ā′bĕs).Neth. Ind.	2.30 S	120.30 E
160	Celebes Sea..........Neth. Ind.	3.0 N	122.0 E
84	Celina (sê-lī′nȧ).............Ohio	40.34 N	84.37 W
128	Celje (tsĕl′yĕ)..............Yugo.	46.14 N	15.15 E
122	Celle (tsĕl′ē)...............Ger.	52.37 N	10.4 E
78	Cement (sê-mĕnt′).........Okla.	34.55 N	98.7 W
128	Cenis, Mt. (sē-nē′)........It.-Fr.	45.15 N	6.53 E
125	Cenis Pass, Mt............Fr.-It.	45.15 N	6.50 E
124	Cenon (sē-nôN′)..............Fr.	44.50 N	0.30 W
81	Center (sĕn′tēr)..............Tex.	31.49 N	94.11 W
49	Centerville Calif. (San Francisco In.)	37.33 N	122.0 W
77	Centerville..................Ia.	40.42 N	92.51 W
85	Centerville.................Md.	39.2 N	76.5 W
85	Centerville.................Pa.	40.3 N	79.57 W
76	Centerville................S. D.	43.7 N	96.56 W
73	Centerville Utah (Salt Lake City In.)	40.55 N	111.53 W
94	Central America (ȧ-mĕr′ĭ-kȧ) N. A.		
72	Central City...Colo. (Denver In.)	39.48 N	105.31 W
84	Central City................Ky.	37.16 N	86 8 W
78	Central City...............Neb.	41.8 N	98 00 W
162	Central, Cordillera (Mts.) (sĕn′-trăl).P. I.	17.0 N	121.0 E
79	Centralia (sĕn-trā′lĭ-ȧ)........Ill.	38.31 N	89.8 W
79	Centralia...................Mo.	39.12 N	92.7 W
70	Centralia.................Wash.	46.42 N	122.58 W
151	Central India (Agency).....India	24.30 N	78.30 E
89	Central Junction Ga. (Savannah In.)	32.5 N	81.8 W
151	Central Provinces..........India	22.0 N	80.0 E
82	Century.....................Fla.	30.58 N	87.18 W
161	Ceram (I.) (sē′råm)....Neth. Ind.	3.0 S	129.0 E
124	Cerberus, C. (sûr′bēr-ŭs) (sĕr-bē-rüs′).Fr.	42.25 N	3.10 E
119	Cercola (chår′kō-lä) It. (Napoli In.)	40.51 N	14.21 E
142	Ceres (sē′rēz)..........U. S. Afr.	33.21 S	19.19 E
120	Céret (sā-rĕ′)................Fr.	42.29 N	2.46 E
128	Cerignola (chā-rê-nyô′lä)......It.	41.15 N	15.54 E
128	Cerknica (tsĕr′knê-tsȧ).....Yugo.	45.47 N	14.21 E
123	Cernăuţi (chĕr-nou′tsê).....Rom.	48.18 N	25.56 E
129	Cerna Vodă (chĕr-nȧ vō′dȧ).Rom.	44.21 N	28.4 E
125	Cernay (sĕr-nĕ′).............Fr.	47.50 N	7.10 E
125	Cernay-la-Ville (sĕr-nĕ′-lä-vēl′) Fr. (In.)	48.40 N	1.57 E
80	Cerralvo (sĕr-räl′vō)........Mex.	26.5 N	99.37 W
92	Cerritos (sĕr-rē′tôs).........Mex.	22.26 N	100.17 W
102	Cerro de Pasco (sĕr′rō dā päs′kō) Peru	10.45 S	76.15 W
92	Cerro La Gallina (Mt.) (gä′lē-nä) Mex.	22.18 N	101.30 W
92	Cerro Peña Nevada (Mt.) (pē′ŋȧ nĕ-vȧ′dä)..Mex.	23.45 N	99.53 W
162	Cervantes (sĕr-vän′tās)......P. I.	17.0 N	120.42 E
126	Cervantes (thĕr-vän′tās)......Sp.	42.53 N	7.4 W
126	Cervera del Río (thĕr-vā′rä dĕl rē′ō).Sp.	42.2 N	1.57 W
124	Cervione (sĕr-vê-ôn′) (chĕr-vê-ō′nä).Cor. (In.)	40.22 N	9.80 E
128	Cesena (chā-zā′nä)............It.	44.9 N	12.15 E
121	Cēsis (sā′sĭs)...............Lat.	57.18 N	25.19 E
	Česka Lipa, see Böhmisch Leipa, Ger.		
122	České Budějorice (chĕs-kā bōō′-dyĕ-yô-vēt-sĕ).Czech.	48.59 N	14.28 E
	Český Krumlov, see Böhmisch Krumau, Ger.		
129	Çeşme (chĕsh′mĕ)...........Tur	38.19 N	26.19 E
167	Cessnock (sĕs′nŏk).........Austl.	32.58 S	151.35 E
131	Cetatea Albă (chĕ tät′yȧ äl′bä) Rom.	46.10 N	30.18 E
129	Cetinje (tsĕt′in-yĕ)........Yugo.	42.24 N	18.56 E
138	Ceuta (thā-ōō′tä).......Sp. Mor.	35.58 N	5.23 W
124	Cévennes (Mts.) (sā-vĕn′).....Fr.	44.30 N	4.0 E
151	Ceylon (sê-lŏn′)........Asia (In.)	9.30 N	80.15 E
127	Cezimbra (sĕ-zēm′brȧ).Port. (In.)	38.27 N	9.6 W
99	Chacabuco (chä-kä-bōō′kō) Arg. (Buenos Aires In.)	34.31 S	60.27 W
92	Chacala R. (chä-kä′lä)......Mex.	19.16 N	104.20 W
93	Chacaltianguis (chä-käl-tê-äŋ′-gwês).Mex.	18.20 N	95.51 W
102	Chachapoyas (chä-chä-poi′yäs) Peru	6.15 S	77.45 W
75	Chaco Canyon Natl. Mon...N. M.	36.5 N	107.55 W
139	Chad (Colony) (chăd).Fr. Eq. Afr.	11.20 N	19.0 E
83	Chadbourn (chăd′bŭrn).....N. C.	34.18 N	78.54 W
139	Chad L. (chăd).............Afr.	13.30 N	14.30 E
76	Chadron (chăd′rŭn)........Neb.	42.50 N	103.0 W
126	Chafarina Is. (chä-fä-rē′nä)..Mor.	35.12 N	2.25 W
79	Chaffee (chăf′ê).............Mo.	27.10 N	89.38 W
124	Chagny (shä-nyē′)............Fr.	46.55 N	4.48 E
130	Chagodoshcha R. (chä-gō-dôsh-chä)...Sov. Un.	59.25 N	34.45 E
95	Chagres, R. (chä′grĕs).......C. Z.	9.10 N	79.40 W
153	Chahar (Prov.) (chä′här)....Chn.	44.15 N	115.0 E
150	Chahbar (chä′bär)..........Iran	25.20 N	60.45 E
140	Chai-Chai (Vila Nova de Gaza) chī-chī (vē-lä nō′vä dā gä′zä) Moz.	25.3 S	33.40 E
141	Chake Chake (chä′kĕ chä′kĕ).Zan.	5.17 S	39.46 E
139	Chala Mts. (chä′lä)...Fr. Eq. Afr.	9.30 N	23.20 E
158	Chalantun (chä′län-tōōn′).Manch.	47.59 N	122.45 E
94	Chalatenango (chäl-ä-tĕ-näŋ′gō) Sal.	14.6 N	89.0 W
139	Chalbe (Stefanie) L. (chäl′bĕ (stĕf-ȧ-nē′).Eth.	4.45 N	36.50 E
93	Chalcatongo (chäl-kä-tôŋ′gō) Mex.	17.2 N	97.34 W
93	Chalchicomula (chäl-chê-kō-mōō′-lä).Mex.	18.58 N	97.27 W
92	Chalchihuites (chäl-chê-wē′tâs) Mex.	23.30 N	103.54 W
94	Chalchuapa (chäl-chwä′pä)...Sal.	14.2 N	89.39 W
129	Chalcidice (Khalkidike) Pen. (kăl-sĭd′ĭ-sê) (ĸäl-kêd′ê-kĕ) Grc.	40.25 N	23.25 E
129	Chalcis (Khalkis) (kăl′sĭs) (ĸäl′kĭs).Grc.	38.27 N	23.38 E
93	Chalco (chäl-kō).......Mex. (In.)	19.16 N	98.54 W
55	Chaleur B. (shȧ-lûr′)........Can.	48.0 N	65.0 W
154	Chaling (chä′lĭng′)..........Chn.	26.47 N	113.17 E
171	Chalky Inlet (chôk′ĭ).......N. Z.	46.0 S	166.35 E
171	Chalmers, Mt. (chăl′mērs) N. Z. (In.)	45.47 S	170.38 E
124	Chalon-sur-Saône (shȧ-lôN′-sür-sōn′).Fr.	46.52 N	4.55 E
124	Chalons-sur-Marne (shȧ-lôN′-sür-märn).Fr.	48.55 N	4.20 E
92	Chamacuero de Comonfort (chä-mä-kwā′rô dā kô-môn-fôrt′) Mex.	20.42 N	100.44 W
124	Chamalières (shä-mä-lyâr′)....Fr.	45.45 N	3.1 E
151	Chaman (chŭm-än′).........India	30.50 N	66.40 E
75	Chama R. (chä′mä).........N. M.	36.22 N	106.36 W
127	Chamartín de la Rosa (chä-mär-tēn′dā lä rō′sä).Sp. (In.)	40.28 N	3.42 W
94	Chama, Sierra de (Mts.)....Guat.	15.45 N	90.0 W
151	Chambal R. (chŭm-bäl′).....India	26.00 N	77.0 E
76	Chamberlain (chām′bēr-lĭn)..S. D.	43.49 N	99.20 W
86	Chamberlain L...............Me.	46.13 N	69.20 W
85	Chambersburg (chām′bērz-bûrg) Pa.	39.57 N	77.41 W
166	Chambers Cr. (chām′bērz)..Austl.	31.5 S	139.10 E
125	Chambéry (shäm-bā-rē′).......Fr.	45.35 N	5.55 E
73	Chamblee (chăm-blē′) Ga. (Atlanta In.)	33.53 N	84.18 W
94	Chameleón, R. (kä-mȧ-lȧ-ōn′) Hond.	15.14 N	88.40 W
95	Chame Pt. (chä′mȧ).........Pan.	8.38 N	79.40 W
142	Chamgab R. (chäm′gäb) S. W. Afr.	28.2 S	17.50 E
139	Chamo, L. (chä′mō)....It. E. Afr.	5.50 N	37.35 E
125	Chamonix (shȧ-mô-nē′).......Fr.	45.55 N	6.50 E
125	Champagnole (chäN-pä-nyŭl′)..Fr.	46.45 N	5.52 E
79	Champaign (shăm-pān′).......Ill.	40.7 N	88.15 W
94	Champerico (chăm-pȧ-rē′kō) Guat.	14.18 N	91.56 W
125	Champigny-sur-Marne (shäN-pē-nyē′-sür-märn′).Fr. (In.)	48.48 N	2.31 E
77	Champion (chăm′pĭ-ŭn).....Mich.	46.31 N	87.59 W
86	Champlain L. (shăm-plān′) Vt.-N. Y.	44.35 N	73.20 W
125	Champlitte (shäN-plēt′).......Fr.	47.38 N	5.30 E
93	Champotón (chäm-pō-tōn′)..Mex.	19.21 N	90.43 W
93	Chamula (chä-mōō′lä).......Mex.	16.46 N	92.41 W
104	Chañaral (chän-yä-räl′).....Chl.	26.20 S	70.46 W
126	Chanca R. (chäŋ′kä)....Sp.-Port.	38.0 N	7.10 W
151	Chanda (chän′dŭ)..........India	19.59 N	79.29 E
160	Chandaburi (chän-dŭ-bōō′rê) Thai.	12.35 N	102.0 E
82	Chandeleur Is. (shăn-dē-lōōr′).La.	29.50 N	88.50 W
82	Chandeleur Sd.........G. of Mex.	29.54 N	89.6 W
151	Chandernagor (chŭn-dēr-nȧ-gōr′) India	22.45 N	88.20 E
86	Chandler (chăn′dlēr).........Can.	48.23 N	64.38 W
79	Chandler..................Okla.	35.41 N	96.52 W
154	Changan (chän′gän′)........Chn.	25.17 N	109.26 E
157	Chang Bak San (Mts.) (chäng′ bäk sän′).Cho.	40.8 N	127.20 E
154	Changchai (chäng′chī′)......Chn.	25.56 N	106.14 E
155	Changchow (chäng′chō′)....Chn.	24.30 N	117.36 E
154	Changchow.................Chn.	30.2 N	107.7 E
155	Changchow.................Chn.	31.45 N	119.55 E
153	Changchun (Hsinking) (chäng′chōōn′)..Manch.	44.2 N	123.29 E
155	Changhing (chäng′hĭng′).....Chn.	30.57 N	119.50 E
155	Changhwa (chäng′hwä′).....Chn.	30.16 N	119.18 E
156	Changi (chäng′ē′)...........Chn.	36.53 N	119.21 E
156	Changi.....................Chn.	36.53 N	119.21 E
156	Changko (chäng′kō′)........Chn.	34.13 N	113.55 E
156	Changku (chäng′kōō′).......Chn.	36.48 N	117.27 E
156	Changli (chäng′lē′)..........Chn.	39.46 N	119.11 E
155	Changlo (chäng′lō′).........Chn.	25.53 N	119.28 E
156	Changlo...................Chn.	36.44 N	118.53 E

ăt; finăl; rāte; senâte; ärm; ȧsk; sofȧ; fâre; ch-choose; dh-as th in other; bē; êvent; bĕt; recĕnt; cratēr; g-go; gh-gutteral g; bĭt; ĭ-short neutral; rīde; ĸ-gutteral k as ch in German ich;

Page	Name Pronunciation Region	Lat. °′	Long. °′
155	Changlok (chăng'lōk')........Chn.	24.1 N	115.24 E
155	Changning (chăng'nĭng').....Chn.	24.52 N	115.15 E
154	Changning.................Chn.	26.25 N	112.12 E
158	Chang Pai Shan (Mts.) (chăng' pī shăn') Manch.	42.15 N	128.15 E
153	Changpeh (chăng'pĕ')........Chn.	41.7 N	114.34 E
155	Changping (chăng'pĭng').....Chn.	25.18 N	117.23 E
155	Changpu (chăng-pōō')........Chn.	24.7 N	117.31 E
155	Chang R. (chăng) ....Chn.	29.24 N	116.58 E
154	Changsha (chăng'shä').......Chn.	28.12 N	112.45 E
156	Changshan (chăng'shăn')....Chn.	36.55 N	118.3 E
155	Changshu (chăng'shōō') .....Chn.	31.33 N	120.40 E
155	Changtai (chăng'tī') ....Chn.	24.36 N	117.42 E
157	Changtan (chăng'tăn').......Cho.	37.57 N	126.44 E
156	Changte (chăng'tĕ')..........Chn.	36.4 N	114.32 E
154	Changteh ....Chn.	29.0 N	111.22 E
155	Changtein.................Chn.	28.57 N	118.8 E
156	Changtsing (chăng'tsĭng')....Chn.	36.30 N	116.34 E
158	Changtu (chăng'tōō').....Manch.	43.0 N	123.59 E
154	Changyang (chăng'yăng')....Chn.	30.29 N	111.4 E
158	Changwu (chăng'wōō') ...Manch.	42.26 N	122.54 E
156	Changyüan (chăng'yü-ăn')...Chn.	35.9 N	114.58 E
157	Changyun (chăng'yōōn')......Cho.	38.17 N	125.3 E
158	Chan-Kwan-Tsai-Ling (Mts.) (chăn'kwăn'-ts]'lĭng') Manch.	44.30 N	128.30 E
124	Channel Is. (chăn'ĕl).....Gt. Brit.	49.35 N	2.30 W
126	Chantada (chăn-tä'dä)........Sp.	42.36 N	7.46 W
124	Chantilly (shăn-tē-yē')........Fr.	49.12 N	2.30 E
79	Chanute (shȧ-nōōt').........Kans.	37.41 N	95.28 W
148	Chany, L. (chä'nê)......Sov. Un.	54.45 N	77.30 E
156	Chanyangkwan (chăn'yăng'kwăn') Chn.	32.22 N	116.28 E
156	Chao L. (chä'ō).............Chn.	31.34 N	117.25 E
155	Chaoan (chä'ō-ăn') ....Chn.	23.45 N	117.0 E
155	Chaochow (chä'ō-chō') ......Chn.	23.41 N	116.25 E
156	Chaochow ....Chn.	37.50 N	114.50 E
155	Chaohsien (chä'ō-hsyĕn')....Chn.	31.38 N	117.48 E
154	Chaoping (chä'o-pĭng')......Chn.	24.7 N	110.46 E
152	Chaotung (chä'ō-tōōng).....Chn.	27.26 N	103.48 E
153	Chaoyang (chä'ō-yăng').....Chn.	41.35 N	120.25 E
155	Chaoyang (chä'ō-yăng') .....Chn.	23.18 N	116.20 E
158	Chaoyangchen (chou'yăng'chĕn') Manch.	42.45 N	126.2 E
156	Chaoyüan (chä'ō-yü-ăn') ....Chn.	37.20 N	120.23 E
92	Chapala (chä-pä'lä).........Mex.	20.18 N	103.11 W
92	Chapala L.................Mex.	20.15 N	103.0 W
153	Chapei (chä'pä'ê) Chn. (Shanghai In.)	31.11 N	121.25 E
119	Chapel-en-le-Frith (shȧ-pĕl'ôn-lē-frēt') (chăp''l-ĕn-lê-frĭth) Gt. Brit. (Liverpool In.)	53.20 N	1.54 W
83	Chapel Hill (chăp''l hĭl).....N. C.	35.55 N	79.3 W
72	Chapman Cr. (chăp'mȧn) Can. (Vancouver In.)	49.28 N	123.43 W
76	Chappell (chă-pĕl')..........Neb.	41.6 N	102.27 W
169	Chappell I.......Austl. (Tas. In.)	40.18 S	147.53 E
93	Chapultenango (chä-pŏŏl-tē-näŋ' gō) . Mex.	17.16 N	93.6 W
92	Charcas (chär'käs)..........Mex.	23.9 N	101.7 W
95	Charco Azul B. (chär'kō ä-zōōl') Pan.	8.15 N	82.40 W
46	Charcot I. (shȧr-kō') .....Ant. O.	70.0 S	74.0 W
124	Charente R. (shȧ-ränt').......Fr.	45.45 N	0.30 W
	(shȧ-rän-tôn'-lē-pôn') . Fr. (In.)	48.48 N	2.25 E
77	Chariton (chăr'ĭ-tŭn) ....Ia.	41.1 N	93.19 W
79	Chariton R..................Mo.	39.55 N	92.40 W
170	Chariu B. (chăr'yōō) ..N. Z. (In.)	41.13 S	174.44 E
117	Charleroi (shȧr-lē-rwä').......Bel.	50.25 N	4.31 E
85	Charleroi...................Pa.	40.18 N	79.55 W
85	Charles, C. (chärlz)..........Md.	37.5 N	75.58 W
77	Charles City.................Ia.	43.4 N	92.39 W
171	Charles, Mt..........N. Z. (In.)	45.52 S	170.44 E
84	Charleston (chärlz'tŭn) ....Ill.	39.30 N	88.12 W
82	Charleston................Miss.	34.0 N	90.3 W
79	Charleston..................Mo.	36.55 N	89.20 W
83	Charleston.................S. C.	32.47 N	79.57 W
49	Charleston....Wash. (Seattle In.)	47.33 N	122.41 W
84	Charleston................W. Va.	38.22 N	81.38 W
84	Charleston, South ....W. Va.	38.22 N	81.42 W
95	Charlestown..........Le. Is. (In.)	17.8 N	62.37 W
143	Charlestown...........U. S. Afr.	27.24 S	29.56 E
85	Charlestown..............W. Va.	39.15 N	77.55 W
119	Charlesworth Gt. Brit. (Liverpool In.)	53.26 N	1.59 W
165	Charleville (chär'lê-vĭl) .....Austl.	26.15 S	146.29 E
140	Charleville (shärl-vēl')..Bel. Cong.	5.25 S	21.0 E
124	Charleville....................Fr.	49.48 N	4.42 E
85	Charlevoix (shăr'lē-voi).....Mich.	45.18 N	85.17 W
89	Charley, L. Minn. (Minneapolis In.)	45.6 N	93.8 W
169	Charleys Cr..........Austl. (In.)	25.40 S	150.40 E
124	Charlieu (shar-lyû')..........Fr.	46.11 N	4.10 E
84	Charlotte (shär'lŏt)........Mich.	42.37 N	84.50 W
83	Charlotte..................N. C.	35.14 N	80.50 W
91	Charlotte Amalia (St. Thomas) (shär-lŏt'ĕ ä-mä'lĭ-ȧ) St. Thomas I. (In.)	18.20 N	64.54 W
83	Charlotte Har..........Fla. (In.)	26.50 N	82.5 W
120	Charlottenberg (shär-lŏt'ĕn-bĕrg) .Swe.	59.54 N	12.18 E
119	Charlottenburg (shär-lŏt'ĕn-bōōrgh) . Ger. (Berlin In.)	52.32 N	13.18 E
85	Charlottesville (shär'lŏtz-vĭl)..Va.	38.2 N	78.29 W
55	Charlottetown (shär'lŏt-toun) Can.	46.21 N	63.20 W
164	Charlotte Waters (shär'lŏt) ..Austl.	26.5 S	134.59 E
166	Charlton (chärl'tŭn).......Austl.	36.17 S	143.22 E
125	Charmes (shärm).............Fr.	48.25 N	6.15 E
118	Charnwood Forest (chärn'wōōd) . Gt. Brit.	52.42 N	1.15 W
151	Charsadda (chŭr-sä'dä) India (Peshawar In.)	34.8 N	71.43 E
165	Charters Towers (chär'tērz) Austl.	20.5 S	146.27 E
124	Chartres (shärt'r')............Fr.	48.25 N	1.30 E
104	Chascomus (chäs-kō-mōōs')...Arg.	35.40 S	58.2 W
83	Chase City (chās)............Va.	36.47 N	78.39 W
130	Chashniki (chăsh'nyê-kē) Sov. Un.	54.50 N	29.10 E
77	Chaska (chăs'kȧ)..........Minn.	44.48 N	93.33 W
124	Châteaubriant (shȧ-tō-brē-än')Fr.	47.42 N	1.21 W
124	Château-Chinon (chȧ-tō'-shē-nôn') . Fr.	47.5 N	3.57 E
124	Château-du-Loir(shȧtō'-dü-lwär') Fr.	47.40 N	0.27 E
124	Châteaudun (shä-tō-dăn') .....Fr.	48.5 N	1.20 E
125	Châteaufort (shȧ-tō-fôr')..Fr. (In.)	48.45 N	2.6 E
124	Château Gontier (chȧ-tō' gôn-tyā') . Fr.	47.50 N	0.49 W
57	Châteauguay (chȧ-tō-gā') Can. (Montreal In.)	45.23 N	73.46 W
124	Châteauneuf-sur-Loire shȧ-tō-nûf'-sür-lwär') . Fr.	47.52 N	2.11 E
124	Châteaurenault (shȧ-tō-rē-nō') . Fr.	47.35 N	1.0 E
57	Château Richer (shȧ-tō' rē-shā') Can. (Que. In.)	46.59 N	71.2 W
124	Châteauroux (shȧ-tō-rōō').....Fr.	46.48 N	1.40 E
124	Château-Thierry shȧ-tō'-tyĕr-rē') . Fr.	49.2 N	3.22 E
124	Châtellerault (shä-tĕl-rō')......Fr.	46.49 N	0.31 E
125	Châtenay (shăt-nĕ').....Fr. (In.)	48.46 N	2.17 E
77	Chatfield (chăt'fēld).......Minn.	43.51 N	92.10 W
55	Chatham (chăt'ȧm).........Can.	47.0 N	65.28 W
84	Chatham..................Can.	42.25 N	82.15 W
117	Chatham..............Gt. Brit.	51.20 N	0.35 E
6	Chatham Is. ....Pac. O.	4.0 S	176.0 W
56	Chatham Sd. Can. (Prince Rupert In.)	54.20 N	130.35 W
124	Châtillon-sur-Seine shä-tē-yôn'-sür-sân') . Fr.	47.50 N	4.35 E
169	Chatswood (chăts'wōōd) Austl. (Sydney In.)	33.47 S	151.11 E
73	Chatsworth Res............Calif.	34.18 N	118.29 W
73	Chatsworth (chătz'wûrth) Calif. (Los Angeles In.)	34.15 N	118.36 W
73	Chattahoochee (chăt-ȧ-hōō'chê) Ga. (Atlanta In.)	33.48 N	84.29 W
82	Chattahoochee R.........Ala.-Ga.	32.30 N	85.0 W
82	Chattanooga (chăt-ȧ-nōō'gȧ) Tenn.	35.2 N	85.18 W
82	Chattanooga, East ....Tenn.	35.5 N	85.14 W
82	Chattooga R. (chȧ-tōō'gȧ) Ga.-S. C.	34.50 N	83.17 W
57	Chaudière ....Can. (Que. In.)	46.42 N	71.18 W
86	Chaudière R................Can.	46.0 N	70.50 W
160	Chaudoc (shō-dôk')...Fr. In. Chn.	10.45 N	105.5 E
124	Chaumont (shō-môn') ....Fr.	48.9 N	5.9 E
149	Chaun B. (choun).......Sov. Un.	69.25 N	170.0 E
124	Chauny (shō-nē')............Fr.	49.39 N	3.10 E
130	Chausy (chou'sĭ)........Sov. Un.	53.48 N	31.0 E
85	Chautauqua L. (shȧ-tô'kwȧ) N. Y.	42.10 N	79.23 W
125	Chauvry (shō-vrē').......Fr. (In.)	49.3 N	2.17 E
125	Chavenay (shăv-nĕ').....Fr. (In.)	48.51 N	1.58 E
126	Chaves (chä'vĕzh)..........Port.	41.45 N	7.29 W
103	Chaves (I.) (chä'vĕs).........Ec.	0.40 S	90.15 W
124	Chazelles (shȧ-zĕl')...........Fr.	45.45 N	4.15 E
93	Chazumba (chä-zōōm'bä)....Mex.	18.13 N	97.39 W
18	Cheadle (chē'd'l).........Gt. Brit.	52.59 N	1.59 W
72	Cheam Pk. (chēm) Can. (Vancouver In.)	49.9 N	121.40 W
85	Cheat R. (chēt)...........W. Va.	39.30 N	79.38 W
...	Cheb, see Eger		
112	Cheboksari (chyĕ-bôk-sä'rê) Sov. Un.	56.8 N	47.12 E
84	Cheboygan (shê-boi'gȧn)....Mich.	45.38 N	84.29 W
113	Chechen I. (chyĕch'ĕn) ..Sov. Un.	44.0 N	47.45 E
79	Checotah (chê-kō'tȧ)........Okla.	35.27 N	95.32 W
87	Chedabucto B. (chĕd-ȧ-bŭk-tō) Can.	45.25 N	61.25 W
151	Cheduba (I.) (chê-dōō'bȧ)...India	18.45 N	93.45 E
156	Chefoo (chē-fōō')............Chn.	37.32 N	121.20 E
70	Chehalis (chê-hā'lĭs).......Wash.	46.39 N	122.58 W
72	Chehalis L...Can. (Vancouver In.)	49.25 N	122.2 W
72	Chehalis R...Can. (Vancouver In.)	49.22 N	122.0 W
70	Chehalis R................Wash.	46.55 N	123.18 W
155	Chekiang (Prov.) (chĕ'kyăng') Chn.	29.20 N	119.48 E
70	Chelan (chê-lăn')...........Wash.	47.48 N	119.59 W
70	Chelan, L..................Wash.	48.0 N	120.20 W
140	Chela, Serra da (Mts.) (sĕr'rȧ dā shā'lȧ) . Ang.	15.30 S	13.30 E
127	Cheleiros (shĕ-lā'rōzh)..Port. (In.)	38.53 N	9.20 W
150	Cheleken I. (chĕ-lyĕ-kĕn') Sov. Un.	39.30 N	53.15 E
114	Chelia, Jebel (Mt.) (jĕb'ĕl shâl'yȧ) . Alg.	35.29 N	6.35 E
114	Chelif (Touil) Wadi (R.) (wä'dê shȧ-lēf') (tōō-ēl') . Alg.	34.30 N	2.12 E
138	Chelif, Oued (wĕd) (R.)......Alg.	36.25 N	2.0 E
127	Cheliff, O. (shā-lēf')..........Alg.	35.30 N	2.30 E
148	Chelkar (chyĕl'kär)......Sov. Un.	48.0 N	59.40 E
113	Chelkar, L. ....Sov. Un.	50.30 N	51.35 E
148	Chelkar Tengiz, L. (tĕn'yēz) Sov. Un.	48.15 N	63.15 E
114	Chellala (chĕl-ȧ'lȧ)..........Alg.	35.5 N	2.22 E
125	Chelles (shĕl)............Fr. (In.)	48.52 N	2.35 E
123	Chelm (kĕlm) ....Pol.	51.7 N	23.30 E
123	Chelmno (kĕlm'nō) ....Pol.	53.20 N	18.26 E
117	Chelmsford (chĕmz'fērd) . Gt. Brit.	51.45 N	0.27 E
87	Chelmsford...........Mass. (In.)	42.36 N	71.21 W
123	Chelmza (kĕlm'zhȧ) ....Pol.	53.9 N	18.37 E
73	Chelsea (chĕl'sê) Ala. (Birmingham In.)	33.20 N	86.36 W
86	Chelsea..................Mass.	42.25 N	71.0 W
84	Chelsea..................Mich.	42.22 N	84.2 W
79	Chelsea...................Okla.	36.32 N	95.20 W
119	Chelsfield (chĕlz'fēld) Gt. Brit. (London In.)	51.21 N	0.8 E
169	Cheltenham (chĕlt'nȧm) Austl. (Melbourne In.)	37.58 S	145.3 E
116	Cheltenham.............Gt. Brit.	51.55 N	2.5 W
88	Cheltenham.Pa. (Philadelphia In.)	40.3 N	75.3 W
127	Chelva (chĕl'vä).............Sp.	39.44 N	0.58 W
148	Chelyabinsk (chĕl-yä-bênsk') Sov. Un.	55.15 N	61.30 E
149	Chelyuskin, C. (chĕl-yōōs'kĭn) Sov. Un.	77.35 N	105.0 E
72	Chemainus (chĕ-mā'nŭs) Can. (Vancouver In.)	48.55 N	123.43 W
148	Chemashevskoe (chĕm'ȧ-shyĕf-skō'yĕ)...Sov. Un.	62.55 N	65.10 E
124	Chemillé (shē-mê-yā').........Fr.	47.17 N	0.42 W
122	Chemnitz (kĕm'nĭts) ....Ger.	50.50 N	12.54 E
157	Chemulpo (Jinsen) (chê-mŭl'pō) (jĭn'sĕn') . Cho.	37.30 N	126.45 E
83	Chemung, R. (shê-mŭng')...N. Y.	42.20 N	77.29 W
53	Chena (chē'nȧ)............Alsk.	64.44 N	147.45 W
151	Chenab R. (chê-năb').......India	31.0 N	72.0 E
138	Chenachane (shē-nȧ-shân')...Alg.	26.8 N	4.10 W
154	Chenan (chĕn'ăn')..........Chn.	23.20 N	106.46 E
154	Chenchow (chĕn'chō').......Chn.	25.48 N	112.32 E
156	Chenchow..................Chn.	33.54 N	114.59 E
57	Chene, R. du (dü shân) Can. (Montreal In.)	45.35 N	74.0 W
70	Cheney (chē'nȧ)...........Wash.	47.29 N	117.34 W
154	Chengan (chĕŋ'găn')........Chn.	28.18 N	107.29 E
155	Chengan...................Chn.	28.45 N	115.2 E
156	Chengan...................Chn.	36.27 N	114.53 E
140	Chengane R. (chĕn-gä'nĕ)...Moz.	23.30 S	33.47 E
153	Chengchiatun (Liaoyuan) (chĕng'-chyä-tōōn') (lē-ou'yōō-ăn') Manch.	43.44 N	123.28 E
156	Chengchow (chĕng'chō').....Chn.	34.42 N	113.45 E
155	Chengho (chĕng'hō').........Chn.	26.23 N	118.40 E
154	Chengpu (chĕng-pōō').......Chn.	26.20 N	110.12 E
154	Chengsi (chĕng-sē')..........Chn.	23.10 N	106.23 E
153	Chengte (Jehol) (chĕng'te') Manch.	40.59 N	117.37 E
152	Chengtu (chĕng'tōō')........Chn.	30.40 N	104.15 E
157	Chengtzutung (chĕng'tsōō-tōōng) Kwang.	39.35 N	122.25 E
156	Chengwu (chĕng'wōō')......Chn.	34.59 N	115.58 E
156	Chengyang (chĕng'yăng')....Chn.	32.34 N	114.12 E
154	Chenki (chĕŋ-kē')...........Chn.	27.58 N	109.50 E
156	Chenliu (chĕn'lyōō')........Chn.	34.37 N	114.40 E
125	Chennevières-sur-Marne (shĕn-nē-vyâr'-sür-märn') . Fr. (In.)	48.47 N	2.32 E
155	Chenping (chĕn-pĭng').......Chn.	24.36 N	115.58 E
152	Chensi (Barköl) (chĕn'sē)(bär-kûl') . Chn.	43.32 N	93.0 E
156	Chenting (chĕn'tĭng) ....Chn.	38.12 N	114.35 E
154	Chenyüan (chĕn'yü-ăn')......Chn.	27.4 N	108.10 E
153	Chenzu (chĕn'zōō') Chn. (Shanghai In.)	31.11 N	121.21 E
95	Chepo (chā'pō).............Pan.	9.12 N	79.6 W
95	Chepo, R..................Pan.	9.10 N	78.44 W
92	Cherán (chā-răn')..........Mex.	19.41 N	101.55 W
83	Cheraw (chē'rô).............S. C.	34.40 N	79.52 W
135	Cherb, Djebel (Mts.) (jĕb'ĕl chĕrb) . Tun. (In.)	34.7 N	8.50 E
124	Cherbourg (shăr-bōōr').........Fr.	49.38 N	1.35 W
138	Cherchel (shĕr-shĕl').........Alg.	36.40 N	2.5 E
152	Cherchen (chĕr-chĕn').......Chn.	37.58 N	85.30 E
152	Cherchen Darya (R.) (chĕr-chĕn' där'yä) . Chn.	39.0 N	87.0 E
148	Cherdin (chĕr-dyēn').....Sov. Un.	60.30 N	56.30 E
148	Cheremkhovo (chĕr'yĕm-kô'vō) Sov. Un.	52.55 N	103.20 E
139	Cheren (chĕr'ĕn).......It. E. Afr.	15.41 N	38.30 E
148	Cherepanovo (chĕr'yĕ-pä-nô'vō) Sov. Un.	54.15 N	83.10 E
130	Cherepovets (chĕr-yĕ-pô'vyĕtz) Sov. Un.	59.7 N	37.56 E
130	Cherepovets (Dist.)......Sov. Un.	59.20 N	35.130 E
130	Chereya (chĕr-ā'yä)......Sov. Un.	54.36 N	29.16 E
114	Chergui, Chott ech (chĕr gē) .Alg.	34.15 N	0.30 E
160	Cheribon (chĕr-ĭ-bŏn') Neth. Ind.	6.47 S	108.36 E
130	Cherikov (chĕ'rē-kôf)....Sov. Un.	53.34 N	31.22 E
157	Cherin (chĕ'rĭn).............Cho.	41.25 N	127.35 E
131	Cherkassy (chĕr-kȧs'sĭ)...Sov. Un.	49.27 N	32.2 E
113	Cherkess (Adige) (Reg.) (chĕr-kĕs') (ä'dĭ-gā)...Sov. Un.	45.0 N	40.5 E
113	Cherkess (Karachai)(Auton. Reg.) (chĕr'kĕs) (kä-rȧ-chī') ..Sov. Un.	43.45 N	42.0 E
148	Cherlakovskoe Selo (chĕr-läk-ôf'-skô-yĕ syĕ'lô)...Sov. Un.	54.10 N	74.55 E
112	Chermozskii Zavod (chĕr môz'skĭ-yê zȧ-vôt')...Sov. Un.	58.50 N	56.5 E
130	Chern (chĕrn)............Sov. Un.	53.26 N	36.49 E
131	Chernigov (chĕr-nē'gôf) Sov. Un.	51.29 N	31.19 E
131	Chernigovka (chĕr-nê-gôf'kȧ) Sov. Un.	47.7 N	36.15 E
158	Chernigovsk (chĕr-nê'gôfsk) Sov. Un.	44.18 N	132.19 E
131	Chernobai (chĕr-nō-bī')..Sov. Un.	49.39 N	32.19 E
131	Chernobyl (chĕr-nō-bĭl')..Sov. Un.	51.17 N	30.11 E
131	Chernyanka (chĕrn-yäŋ'kä) Sov. Un.	50.57 N	37.48 E
76	Cherokee (chĕr-ô-kē').........Ia.	42.45 N	95.32 W
79	Cherokee..................Kan.	37.19 N	94.49 W
78	Cherokee..................Okla.	36.45 N	98.22 W
96	Cheroki Sd. (chĕr-ô-kē')....Ba. Is.	26.16 N	77.8 W
124	Cher R. (shâr)................Fr.	47.20 N	1.10 E
86	Cherrifield (chĕr'ĭ-fēld).......Me.	44.37 N	67.57 W
72	Cherry Cr. (chĕr'ĭ) Colo. (Denver In.)	39.34 N	104.46 W
85	Cherrydale..................Va.	38.56 N	77.8 W
169	Cherry Gully.........Austl. (In.)	28.29 S	151.58 E
79	Cherryvale.................Kan.	37.16 N	95.34 W
83	Cherryville.................N. C.	35.22 N	81.22 W
149	Cherski Mts. (chĕrs'kĭ)...Sov. Un.	64.35 N	149.0 E
128	Cherso (kĕr'sō)...............It.	44.58 N	14.23 E
128	Cherso (I.)...................It.	44.55 N	14.23 E
130	Cherven (chĕr'vyĕn).....Sov. Un.	53.42 N	28.28 E

ng-sing; ŋ-baŋk; n-nasalized n; nŏd; cŏmmit; ōld; ôbey; ôrder; fōōd; fŏŏt; ou-out; s-soft; sh-dish; th-thin; pūre; ûnite; ûrn; stŭd; circŭs; ü-as "y" in study; '-indeterminate vowel.

Page	Name Pronunciation Region	Lat. °′	Long. °′
118	Cherwell, R. (chär'wĕl)...Gt. Brit.	52.7 N	1.15 W
84	Chesaning (chĕs'ȧ-nĭng) ....Mich.	43.12 N	84.10 W
85	Chesapeake B. (chĕs'ȧ-pēk)...Md.	38.0 N	76.10 W
84	Cheshire (chĕsh'ĭr).........Mich.	42.30 N	85.58 W
118	Cheshire Co.............Gt. Brit.	53.15 N	2.30 W
112	Cheshskaya B. (chĕsh-skä'yȧ) So-. Un.	67.30 N	46.30 E
116	Chester (chĕs'tẽr).......Gt. Brit.	53.12 N	2.55 W
79	Chester......................Ill.	37.55 N	89.48 W
84	Chester....................Ohio	40.36 N	80.33 W
85	Chester......................Pa.	39.50 N	75.20 W
83	Chester....................S. C.	34.42 N	81.13 W
85	Chester......................Va.	37.21 N	77.27 W
88	Chester Cr....Minn. (Duluth In.)	46.49 N	92.6 W
116	Chesterfield.............Gt. Brit.	53.15 N	2.25 W
54	Chesterfield Inlet...........Can.	64.0 N	92.30 W
165	Chesterfield Is............Pac. O.	19.45 S	158.30 E
84	Chesterton..................Ind.	41.37 N	87.5 W
85	Chestertown.................Md.	39.12 N	76.5 W
86	Chesuncook L. (chĕs'ŭn-ko͝ok).Me.	46.2 N	69.22 W
77	Chetek (chĕ'tĕk)............Wis.	45.19 N	91.40 W
94	Chetumal B. (chĕt-o͞o-mäl') Br. Hond.-Mex. (In.)	18.20 N	88.0 W
75	Chevalon Cr. (shĕv'ȧ-lŏn) ...Ariz.	34.35 N	110.50 W
84	Cheviot (shĕv'ĭ-ŭt)..........Ohio	39.7 N	84.39 W
116	Cheviot Hills............Gt. Brit.	55.20 N	2.30 W
125	Chevreuse (shĕ-vrûz')....Fr. (In.)	48.42 N	2.3 E
70	Chewelah (chē-wē'lȧ).......Wash.	48.16 N	117.43 W
71	Cheyenne (shī-ĕn') ....Wyo.	41.9 N	104.48 W
72	Cheyenne Canon Colo. (Colo. Sprs. In.)	38.48 N	104.52 W
72	Cheyenne Cr.Colo. (Colo. Sprs. In.)	38.48 N	104.55 W
72	Cheyenne Mt. Colo. Colo.Sprs. In.)	38.44 N	104.52 W
76	Cheyenne R. ....S. D.	44.20 N	102.20 W
76	Cheyenne River Indian Res. .S. D.	44.55 N	101.0 W
78	Cheyenne Wells.............Colo.	38.47 N	102.21 W
152	Chiamdo (chē'äm'dō).......Chn.	30.52 N	96.33 E
	Chiangkiakow, see Kalgan, Chn.		
93	Chiapa de Corzo (chē-ä'pä dā kôr'-zō).Mex.	16.41 N	93.1 W
93	Chiapas (State) (chē-ä'päs) ..Mex.	16.35 N	92.0 W
93	Chiapas, Cordillera de (Mts.) (chē-ä'päs).Mex.	15.45 N	93.0 W
128	Chiari (kyä'rē)................It.	45.32 N	9.55 E
128	Chiasso (kyäs'sō).............It.	45.49 N	9.1 E
122	Chiasso.................Switz.	45.51 N	9.1 E
92	Chiautla (chyä-o͞ot'lȧ).......Mex.	18.16 N	98.36 W
128	Chiavara (kyä'vä-rē) ....It.	44.18 N	9.19 E
159	Chiba (chē'bȧ)..............Jap.	35.32 N	140.10 E
140	Chibi (chē'bē)............S. Rh.	20.17 S	30.17 E
86	Chibougamau L. (chē-bo͞o'gȧ-mou) Can.	49.50 N	74.15 W
140	Chibuto (chē-bo͞o'tō)........Moz.	24.40 S	33.35 E
84	Chicago (shĭ-kô'gō; chĭ-kȧ'gō)..Ill.	41.50 N	87.40 W
88	Chicago...............Ill. (In.)		
88	Chicago Drainage Can. Ill. (Chicago In.)	41.48 N	87.48 W
79	Chicago Hts..................Ill.	41.29 N	87.38 W
88	Chicago Ridge...Ill. (Chicago In.)	41.42 N	87.49 W
88	Chicago R., N....Ill. (Chicago In.)	42.0 N	87.47 W
126	Chica, Mar (sea) (mär chē'kä) Mor.	35.10 N	2.50 W
93	Chica, R. (chē'kä) .....Mex. (In.)	19.33 N	98.51 W
93	Chicbul (chĭk-bo͞ol')..........Mex.	18.45 N	90.56 W
53	Chichagof (I.) (chē-chä'gôf)..Alsk.	58.0 N	136.0 W
116	Chichester (chĭch'ĕs-tẽr) .Gt. Brit.	50.50 N	0.50 W
156	Chichow...................Chn.	38.31 N	115.17 E
52	Chickaloon (chĭk'ȧ-lo͞on) Alsk. (In.)	61.50 N	148.30 W
82	Chickamauga (chĭk-ȧ-mô'gȧ)..Ga.	34.53 N	85.18 W
82	Chickasawhay R. (chĭk-ȧ-sô'wā) Miss.	31.30 N	88.32 W
78	Chickasha (chĭk'ȧ-shā).......Okla.	35.3 N	97.58 W
127	Chiclana de la Frontera (chē-klä'nä dā lä frôn-tā'rä).Sp. (In.)	36.25 N	6.9 W
102	Chiclayo (chē-klä'yō)........Peru	6.45 S	79.58 W
74	Chico (chē'kō)..............Calif.	39.43 N	121.51 W
140	Chicoa (chē-kō'ä)...........Moz.	15.40 S	32.23 E
72	Chico Cr...Colo. (Colo. Spgs. In.)	38.43 N	104.27 W
93	Chicoloapan (chē-kō-lwä'pän) Mex. (In.)	19.25 N	98.54 W
93	Chiconahutla (chē-kō-nä-o͞o'tlȧ) Mex. (In.)	19.38 N	99.0 W
92	Chicontepec (chē-kōn'tĕ-pĕk') Mex.	20.58 N	98.9 W
86	Chicopee (chĭk'ō-pē).......Mass.	42.10 N	72.35 W
104	Chico, R....................Arg.	44.32 S	67.0 W
162	Chico, R....................P. I.	17.30 N	121.27 E
55	Chicoutimi (shē-ko͞o'tē-mē')..Can.	48.30 N	71.0 W
55	Chidley, C. (chĭd'lĭ).........Lab.	60.33 N	64.25 W
82	Chiefland (chēf'lănd).........Fla.	29.29 N	82.53 W
72	Chief Mt. (chēf) Colo. (Denver In.)	39.40 N	105.32 W
160	Chiengmai (chĭ-ĕng-mī') ....Thai.	18.45 N	98.55 E
160	Chiengrai (chĭ-ĕng-rī')......Thai.	19.50 N	99.45 E
128	Chieri (kyâ'rē)................It.	45.1 N	7.50 E
128	Chieti (kyĕ'tē)................It.	42.21 N	14.9 E
131	Chigirin (chē-gē'rēn).....Sov. Un.	49.2 N	32.38 E
92	Chignahuapan (chēn-yä-wä'pän) Mex.	19.50 N	98.2 W
86	Chignecto B. (shĭg-nĕk'tō) N.B.-N.S.	45.40 N	64.35 W
119	Chigwell (chĭg'wĕl) Gt. Brit. (London In.)	51.38 N	0.5 E
155	Chihchow (chĭ-chō).........Chn.	30.38 N	117.32 E
153	Chihfeng (chĭ'fûng).......Manch.	43.0 N	119.0 E
154	Chihing (chĭ'hĭng').........Chn.	25.7 N	113.38 E
154	Chihkiang (chĭ-kyăng')......Chn.	30.18 N	111.19 E
156	Chihsien (chĭ'hsyĕn')........Chn.	35.31 N	114.29 E
80	Chihuahua (chē-wä'wä)......Mex.	28.37 N	106.5 W
80	Chihuahua (State)..........Mex.	28.30 N	105.0 W
140	Chihuane (chē-wä'nä).......Moz.	20.47 S	34.52 E
153	Chikan (chē'kăn).........Manch.	52.15 N	120.57 E
140	Chikapa R. (chē-kä'pä)......Ang.	9.0 S	20.30 E
150	Chikishlyar (chē-kēsh-lyär')...Iran	37.46 N	54.2 E
92	Chilapa (chē-lä'pä).........Mex.	17.35 N	99.15 W
92	Chilchota (chēl-chō'tä)......Mex.	19.50 N	102.3 W
73	Childersburg (chĭl'dẽrz-bûrg) Ala. (Birmingham In.)	33.17 N	86.21 W
78	Childress (chīld'rĕs).........Tex.	34.25 N	100.12 W
119	Childwall (chīld'wȧl) Gt. Brit. (Liverpool In.)	53.24 N	2.53 W
104	Chile (chē'lā)..............S. A.	39.0 S	72.0 W
104	Chilecito (chē-lā-sē'tō).......Arg.	29.15 S	67.40 W
131	Chilia Nouă (kē'lyȧ nō'wă)..Rom.	45.27 N	29.19 E
153	Chilin (Kirin) (chĭl'ĭn') (kĭr'ĭn) Manch.	43.50 N	126.36 E
53	Chilko L. (chĭl'kō)..........Can.	51.0 N	124.15 W
53	Chilko R....................Can.	51.50 N	124.0 W
104	Chillán (chēl-yän')..........Chl.	36.35 S	72.5 W
79	Chillicothe (chĭl-ĭ-kŏth'ē)......Ill.	40.55 N	89.31 W
79	Chillicothe..................Mo.	39.47 N	93.33 W
84	Chillicothe.................Ohio	39.20 N	82.58 W
70	Chiliwack (chĭl'ĭ-wăk).......Can.	49.9 N	121.55 W
72	Chilliwack L. Can. (Vancouver In.)	49.3 N	121.25 W
104	Chiloé I. (chē-lō-ā')..........Chl.	42.30 S	73.45 W
92	Chilpancingo (chēl-pän-sēŋ'gō) Mex.	17.32 N	99.30 W
167	Chiltern (chĭl'tẽrn).........Austl.	36.10 S	146.36 E
77	Chilton (chĭl'tŭn)...........Wis.	44.2 N	88.11 W
93	Chiluca (chē-lo͞o'kä) ...Mex. (In.)	19.33 N	99.17 W
140	Chilwa, L. (chĭl'wä) ...Nya.-Moz.	15.15 S	35.45 E
49	Chimacum (chĭm'ä-kŭm) Wash. (Seattle In.)	48.0 N	122.46 W
93	Chimalhuacán (chē-mäl-wä-kän') Mex. (In.)	19.25 N	98.56 W
93	Chimalhuacán Cerro (Mt.) Mex. (In.)	19.24 N	98.57 W
93	Chimalpa (chē-mäl'pä). Mex. (In.)	19.14 N	98.56 W
93	Chimalpan (chē-mäl'pän) Mex. (In.)	19.26 N	99.20 W
93	Chimalpan Cerro (Mt.). Mex. (In.)	19.26 N	99.21 W
94	Chimaltenango (chē-mäl-tā-näŋ'-gō). Guat.	14.40 N	90.48 W
92	Chimaltitán (chēmäl-tē-tän').Mex.	21.33 N	103.50 W
150	Chimbai (chĭm-bī')......Sov. Un.	43.14 N	59.58 E
102	Chimborazo, Mt. (chēm-bō-rä'zō) Ec.	1.32 S	78.48 W
102	Chimbote (chēm-bō'tā)......Peru	9.1 S	78.31 W
148	Chimkent (chĭm-kĕnt) ...Sov. Un.	42.25 N	69.40 E
87	Chimney B................Newf.	50.45 N	56.15 W
94	Chinameca (chē-nä-mā'kä) ...Sal.	13.33 N	88.18 W
94	Chinandega (chē-nän-dā'gä)..Nic.	12.37 N	87.8 W
152	China (chī'nȧ)...............Asia	35.0 N	110.0 E
153	China Sea, E.................Asia	30.0 N	125.0 E
160	China Sea, S.................Asia	15.0 N	115.0 E
148	Chinaz (chĭn-äz')........Sov. Un.	40.55 N	68.55 E
102	Chincha Alta (chĭn'chä äl'tä). Peru	30.29 S	76.5 W
102	Chincha Is. (chĭn'chä).......Peru	11.28 S	77.45 W
169	Chinchilla (chĭn-chĭl'ȧ) Austl. (In.)	26.45 S	150.35 E
126	Chinchilla (chēn-chē'lyä) .....Sp.	38.55 N	1.44 W
153	Chinchow (chĭn'chō').....Manch.	41.4 N	120.58 E
140	Chinde (shēn'dĕ)...........Moz.	18.38 S	36.23 E
151	Chindwin R. (chĭn-dwĭn)....India	23.30 N	94.0 E
153	Chingkahang (chĭng'kä-häng') Chn. (Shanghai In.)	31.10 N	121.32 E
155	Ching San Yuen (Kinsha) (chĭng sän yo͞o'ĕn) (kēn-shä') ..Manch.	30.43 N	121.20 E
140	Chinguar (chĭng-gär)........Ang.	12.30 S	16.18 E
138	Chinguetti (chēŋ-gĕt'ē) Fr. W. Afr.	20.35 N	12.32 W
155	Chinhai (chĭn'hī') ....Chn.	29.58 N	121.45 E
156	Chinkiang (chĭn'kyăng') .....Chn.	32.11 N	119.28 E
157	Chinnampo (chĭn-nȧm'pō)...Cho.	38.50 N	125.27 E
73	Chino (chē'nō) Calif. (Los Angeles In.)	34.0 N	117.42 W
80	Chino......................Mex.	25.42 N	99.15 W
124	Chinon (shē-nôɴ')............Fr.	47.10 N	0.11 E
71	Chinook (shĭn-o͝ok') ....Mont.	48.35 N	109.15 W
49	Chinook.....Wash. (Portland In.)	46.17 N	123.56 W
152	Chinshui (chĭn'shwē').......Chn.	28.18 N	105.38 E
140	Chinteche (chĭn-tĕ'chĕ).......Nya.	11.47 S	34.8 E
157	Chinto (chĭn'tō).............Cho.	34.29 N	126.16 E
157	Chinto I....................Cho.	34.28 N	126.16 E
156	Chinwangtao (chĭn'wăng'tou') Chn.	39.55 N	119.36 E
154	Chinyang, R. (chĭn'yăng') ...Chn.	27.23 N	109.5 E
128	Chioggia (kyôd'jä)............It.	45.13 N	12.16 E
129	Chios (Khios) (kĭ'ōs)........Grc.	38.22 N	26.9 E
127	Chipiona (chē-pē-ō'nä)...Sp. (In.)	36.44 N	6.26 W
82	Chipley (chĭp'lĭ).............Fla.	30.45 N	85.32 W
86	Chipman (chĭp'măn)........Can.	46.11 N	65.53 W
82	Chipola R. (chĭ-pō'lȧ)........Fla.	30.30 N	85.10 W
77	Chippewa Falls (chĭp'ē-wä)...Wis.	44.53 N	91.54 W
76	Chippewa R...............Minn.	45.30 N	95.42 W
77	Chippewa R.................Wis.	45.0 N	91.21 W
86	Chiputneticook L. (chĭ-po͞ot-nĕt'ĭ-ko͝ok). Me.-N. B.	45.45 N	67.50 W
94	Chiquimula (chē-kē-mo͞o'lä).Guat.	14.47 N	89.32 W
102	Chiquinquirá (chē-kēŋ'kē-rä') Col.	5.29 N	74.2 W
104	Chiquita, Mar (L.) (mär chē-kē'tä).Arg.	31.50 S	62.35 W
154	Chi R. (chē)................Chn.	28.23 N	105.42 E
75	Chiracahua Natl. Mon. (chĭ-rä-cä'-hwä)..Ariz.	32.1 N	109.12 W
152	Chirgalantu (Kobdo) (chēr-gä-län'to͞o kôb'dō)..Chn.	49.0 N	91.0 E
95	Chiriquí (Vol.) (chē-rē-kē') ∴Pan.	8.47 N	82.37 W
95	Chiriquí Grande (grän'dā)...Pan.	9.57 N	82.8 W
95	Chiriquí, G. of ....Pan.	8.0 N	82.20 W
95	Chiriquí Lagoon............Pan.	9.5 N	82.0 W
158	Chirka (chĭr'kȧ).........Sov. Un.	48.23 N	134.58 E
140	Chiromo (chē-rō'mō)........Moz.	16.33 S	35.9 E
95	Chirripo, R. (chēr-rē'pō)....C. R.	9.50 N	83.24 W
95	Chirripo Grande (Mt.) (grän'dā).C. R.	9.28 N	83.32 W
145	Chishima (Kuril) Is. (chĭ'shē-mä ko͞o'rĭl) Jap.	46.0 N	150.0 E
77	Chisholm (chĭz'ŭm).........Minn.	47.29 N	92.51 W
141	Chisimaio (kē-sē-mī'ō)..It. E. Afr.	0.15 S	42.30 E
131	Chişinău (kē-shē-nû'o͞o).....Rom.	47.2 N	28.52 E
112	Chistopol (chis-tô'pôl-y').Sov. Un.	55.20 N	50.35 E
119	Chiswick (chĭz'ĭk) Gt. Brit. (London In.)	51.29 N	0.17 W
149	Chita (chē-tȧ')..........Sov. Un.	52.10 N	113.30 E
102	Chita, Sierra Nevada de (Mt.) (chē'tä).Col.	6.15 N	72.28 W
53	Chitina (chĭ-tē'nȧ)..........Alsk.	61.35 N	143.30 W
52	Chitina R.............Alsk. (In.)	61.20 N	144.0 W
151	Chitral (chē-träl')..........India	35.55 N	71.50 E
95	Chitre (chē'trā)...........Pan.	7.58 N	80.26 W
151	Chittagong (chĭt-ȧ-gông')....India	22.15 N	91.55 E
140	Chiumbe R. (chē-o͞om'bā)....Ang.	8.15 S	21.0 E
128	Chivasso (kē-väs'sō)..........It.	45.11 N	7.52 E
104	Chivilcoy (chē-vēl-koi')......Arg.	34.50 S	60.1 W
94	Chixoy, R. (chē-ᴋoi'). Guat.-Mex.	15.40 N	90.40 W
159	Chizu (chē-zo͞o')............Jap.	35.16 N	134.15 E
75	Chloride (klō'rīd)...........Ariz.	35.24 N	114.12 W
123	Chmielnik (ᴋmyĕl'nēk) ......Pol.	50.36 N	20.46 E
131	Chobanvasty (chō'bän-väs'tē) Sov. Un.	44.47 N	35.8 E
81	Chocolate Bayou ......Tex. (In.)	29.19 N	95.16 W
82	Choctawhatchee B. (chôk-tô-hăch'ē).Fla.	30.25 N	86.20 W
82	Choctawhatchee R...........Fla.	31.0 N	85.50 W
122	Chodziez (ᴋōj'yĕsh) ....Pol.	52.59 N	16.52 E
159	Chofu (chō'fo͞o')............Jap.	34.0 N	131.0 E
157	Cho I. (chō)...............Cho.	38.33 N	124.47 E
6	Choiseul (shwä-zûl') Sta. Luc. (In.)	13.44 N	61.0 W
165	Choiseul I....Solomon Is. (Prot.)	7.0 S	156.45 E
125	Choizy-le-Roi (shwä-zē'lû rwä') Fr. (In.)	48.46 N	2.25 E
123	Chojnice (ᴋoĭ-nē'tsĕ).........Pol.	53.41 N	17.34 E
124	Cholet (shō-lĕ')..............Fr.	47.5 N	0.56 W
160	Cholon (shō-lôɴ')....Fr. In. Chn.	10.45 N	106.31 E
92	Cholula (chō-lo͞o'lä).........Mex.	19.3 N	98.20 W
94	Choluteca (chō-lo͞o-tā'kä)...Hond.	13.18 N	87.12 W
94	Choluteca, R...............Hond.	13.30 N	87.0 W
	Chomutov, see Komotau, Ger.		
149	Chona R. (chō'nä) ......Sov. Un.	62.0 N	110.0 E
104	Chonos Arch. (chō'nōs)......Chl.	45.0 S	74.0 W
154	Cho R. (chō)...............Chn.	26.45 N	109.50 E
157	Choonchun (cho͝on-cho͞on')...Cho.	37.52 N	127.45 E
157	Choonghwa (cho͝ong'hwä')...Cho.	38.53 N	125.47 E
102	Chorillos (chō-rēl'yōs)..Peru (In.)	12.10 S	77.2 W
102	Chorillos Pt. ....Peru (In.)	12.10 S	77.3 W
118	Chorley (chôr'lĭ)........Gt. Brit.	53.39 N	2.38 W
95	Chorrera (chōr-rā'rä)........Pan.	8.54 N	79.49 W
157	Chosen (Korea) (chō'sĕn') (kō-rē'ȧ).Asia	38.0 N	127.0 E
157	Chosen (Korea) B...........Cho.	39.15 N	123.30 E
157	Chosen (Korea), G. of.......Cho.	39.40 N	128.0 E
157	Chosen (Korea), Arch........Cho.	34.11 N	126.45 E
158	Chosen (Korea) Str..........Asia	35.0 N	130.0 E
158	Choshi (chō'shē)............Jap.	35.40 N	140.48 E
71	Choteau (shō'tō)..........Mont.	47.50 N	112.10 W
83	Chowan R. (chō-wăn')......N. C.	36.10 N	76.45 W
158	Chowie R. (chō'wē-ĕ')....Manch.	47.0 N	122.0 E
156	Chowtsun (chō'tso͞on')........Chn.	36.50 N	117.49 E
171	Christchurch (krīst'chûrch) N. Z. (In.)	43.29 S	172.40 E
143	Christiana (krĭs-tyȧn'ȧ).U. S. Afr.	27.54 S	25.9 E
84	Christian I. (krĭs'chăn)......Can.	44.50 N	80.15 W
83	Christiansburg (krĭs'chănz-bûrg) Va.	37.8 N	80.26 W
160	Christmas I................Asia	11.0 S	105.35 E
6	Christmas I.............Pac. O.	1.55 N	157.20 W
79	Christopher (krĭs'tō-fẽr).......Ill.	37.57 N	89.4 W
122	Chrudim (ᴋro͞o'dyēm).....Czech.	49.57 N	15.48 E
123	Chrzanów (ᴋzhä'no͞of).......Pol.	50.8 N	19.24 E
155	Chuanchow (chwän'chō')....Chn.	24.55 N	118.35 E
154	Chüanchow (chü-än'chō')....Chn.	25.54 N	110.56 E
155	Chuanchow Har. (chwän'chō') Chn.	24.47 N	118.45 E
140	Chuane Pits (cho͞o-än'ĕ)....Bech.	23.57 S	21.50 E
156	Chüantsiao (chü-än'tsē-ou')..Chn.	32.7 N	118.17 E
140	Chuapa R. (chwä'pä)...Bel. Cong.	1.4 S	23.30 E
104	Chubut (State) (cho͞o-bo͞ot')..Arg.	44.0 S	69.0 W
104	Chubut R...................Arg.	43.50 S	68.28 W
156	Chucheng (cho͞o'chĕng')......Chn.	36.2 N	119.21 E
154	Chuchow (cho͞o'chō').........Chn.	27.51 N	112.52 E
155	Chuchow...................Chn.	28.24 N	119.50 E
156	Chuchow...................Chn.	32.18 N	118.19 E
155	Chüchow (chü'chō').........Chn.	29.3 N	119.2 E
156	Chüchow...................Chn.	35.34 N	118.46 E
95	Chucunaque R. (cho͞o-ko͞o-nä'kä) Pan.	8.35 N	77.50 W
130	Chudovo (cho͞o'dō-vō)....Sov. Un.	59.2 N	31.42 E
121	Chudskoe (cho͞ot'skō yĕ) (pī'psĭ) (Peipsi) L..Eur.	58.40 N	27.30 E
153	Chuerhkanho (cho͞o'ĕr-kän'hō) Manch.	52.15 N	120.57 E
52	Chugach Mts. (cho͞o'gȧch) Alsk. (In.)	61.10 N	146.0 W
148	Chuguchak (cho͞o'go͞o-chäk').Chn.	46.55 N	83.0 E
152	Chuguchak (Prov.)..........Chn.	46.0 N	85.0 E
152	Chuguchak (Tahcheng) (tä'-chĕng').Chn.	46.48 N	83.5 E
131	Chuguev (cho͞o'gwĕf).....Sov. Un.	49.50 N	36.41 E
71	Chugwater Cr. (chŭg'wô-tẽr) Wyo.	41.40 N	105.0 W
155	Chuki (cho͞o'kē)............Chn.	29.43 N	120.12 E
154	Chu Kiang (Pearl R.) (cho͞o' kyăng') (pẽrl).Chn.	22.38 N	113.38 E
149	Chukotski Pen. (cho͞o-kôtsk') Sov. Un.	66.0 N	175.0 W
74	Chula Vista (cho͞o'lȧ vĭs'tȧ) Calif. (In.)	32.37 N	117.5 W
148	Chulym R. (cho͞o-lĭm')...Sov. Un.	57.0 N	86.10 E
148	Chulkovo (cho͞ol'kō vō) Sov. Un.	62.40 N	88.30 E
153	Chultzuchien (Yenchi) (cho͞ol'-tzo͞o-chē-ĕn') (yĕn'kē') Manch.	43.0 N	129.32 E
156	Chulung R. (cho͞o'lo͞ong')....Chn.	38.45 N	116.4 E
156	Chumatien (cho͞o'mä-tyĕn')..Chn.	32.59 N	113.53 E
148	Chuna R. (cho͞o'nȧ)......Sov. Un.	57.0 N	99.10 E
155	Chungan (cho͝ong'än')........Chn.	27.44 N	117.47 E
154	Chungchow (cho͝ong'chō')....Chn.	30.26 N	108.6 E
157	Chungchun R. (cho͝ong'cho͞on') Cho.	39.50 N	126.0 E
156	Chunghing (cho͝ong'hĭng')...Chn.	33.42 N	118.47 E

ăt; finăl; rāte; senâte; ärm; ȧsk; sofȧ; fâre; ch-choose; dh-as th in other; bē; ēvent; bĕt; recĕnt; cratẽr; g-go; gh-guttural g; bĭt; ĭ-short neutral; rīde; ᴋ-gutteral k as ch in German ich;

Page	Name Pronunciation Region	Lat. °′	Long. °′
154	Chungking (chŏŏng'kĭng')....Chn.	29.46 N	106.34 E
	Chungming I., see Tsung Ming I.		
156	Chungmow (chŏŏng'mō')....Chn.	34.40 N	114.4 E
156	Chungsing I. (chŏŏng'sĭng')..Chn.	39.35 N	121.15 E
152	Chungwei (chŏŏng'wā)......Chn.	37.37 N	105.20 E
154	Chungye (chŏŏng'yĕ')......Chn.	25.53 N	113.52 E
154	Chun R. (chŏŏn)..........Chn.	26.8 N	112.20 E
148	Chunya R. (chŏŏn'yä')..Sov. Un.	61.35 N	100.0 E
104	Chuquicamata (chōō-kê-kä-mä'tä) Chl.	22.12 S	68.50 W
122	Chur (kōōr)..............Switz.	46.52 N	9.32 E
148	Chu R. (chŏŏ)..........Sov. Un.	44.45 N	72.0 E
54	Churchill (chûrch'ĭl)........Can.	58.50 N	94.0 W
54	Churchill R...............Can.	57.15 N	96.30 W
72	Church Pt...Can. (Vancouver In.)	48.19 N	123.32 W
118	Church Stretton (chûrch strĕt'ŭn) Gt. Brit.	52.32 N	2.49 W
152	Churgalantu (Kobdo) (chōōr-gä-län'tōō) (kôb'dô).Chn.	48.1 N	91.33 E
92	Churumuco (chōō-rōō-mōō'kō) Mex.	18.38 N	101.42 W
157	Chushu (chōō'shōō')........Cho.	37.1 N	127.58 E
112	Chusovaya R. (chōō-sô-vä'yȧ) Sov. Un.	58.0 N	58.30 E
148	Chusovskii (chōō-sôf'skĭ-yê) Sov. Un.	58.25 N	57.59 E
123	Chust (kŏŏst)............Czech.	48.11 N	23.18 E
148	Chust (chŏŏst)..........Sov. Un.	41.0 N	71.20 E
112	Chuvash (chōō'vȧsh)....Sov. Un.	55.30 N	47.0 E
80	Chuviscar R. (chōō-vês-kär') Mex.	28.40 N	106.0 W
141	Chwaka (chwä'kä).........Zan.	6.9 S	39.25 E
157	Chwangho (chwäng'hō')..Manch.	39.39 N	122.56 E
155	Chwansha (chwän'shä)......Chn.	31.8 N	121.46 E
97	Cibao Mts. (Gran Cordillera Cen.) (sê-bä'ô) (grän kôr-dēl-yā'rȧ sĕn-träl').Hai.	18.53 N	70.30 W
80	Cibolo Cr. (sē'bô-lō).........Tex.	29.30 N	98.10 W
79	Cicero (sĭs'ēr-ō).............Ill..	41.51 N	87.46 W
113	Cide (jē'dĕ)................Tur.	41.50 N	32.58 E
123	Ciechanów (tsyĕ-kä'nŏŏf).....Pol.	52.53 N	20.40 E
96	Ciego de Ávila (syā'gō dā ä'vê-lä) Cuba	21.50 N	78.46 W
126	Ciempozuelos (thyĕm-pô-thwā'lōs) Sp.	40.9 N	3.36 W
102	Cienaga (syā'nȧ-gä).........Col.	11.0 N	74.30 W
96	Cienfuegos (syĕn-fwā'gōs)...Cuba	22.8 N	80.28 W
96	Cienfuegos B..............Cuba	22.5 N	80.26 W
123	Cieszyn (tsyĕ'shĕn)..........Pol.	49.44 N	18.40 E
126	Cieza (thyā'thä).............Sp.	38.15 N	1.25 W
113	Cilician Gates (P.)(sĭ-lĭsh'ăn).Tur.	37.17 N	34.50 E
116	Cill Cainnig (Kilkenny) (kĭl' kä'nĭ) (kĭl-kĕn'ê).Ire.	52.39 N	7.15 W
116	Cill Mantainn (Wicklow) (kĭl män'tän) (wĭk'lō).Ire.	53.0 N	6.5 W
78	Cimarron R. (sĭm-ȧ-rōn') N. M.-Okla.	36.0 N	98.0 W
78	Cimarron R., N. Fork Colo.-Kan.-Okla.	37.25 N	101.5 W
127	Cinca R. (thēŋ'kä)...........Sp.	42.0 N	0.8 E
84	Cincinnati (sĭn-sĭ-nȧt'ĭ)......Ohio	39.6 N	84.30 W
89	Cincinnati...........Ohio (In.)		
96	Cinco Balas Cays (Is.) (thēŋ'kō bä'läs) Cuba	21.5 N	79.22 W
93	Cintalapa (sên-tä-lä'pä).....Mex.	16.41 N	93.45 W
124	Cinto Mt. (chēn'tō)....Cor. (In.)	42.25 N	8.55 E
53	Circle (sûr'k'l).............Alsk.	65.48 N	144.30 W
84	Circleville..................Ohio	39.36 N	82.57 W
169	Circular Hd......Austl. (Tas. In.)	40.42 S	145.16 E
139	Cirenaica (Prov.)..........Libya	31.30 N	22.0 E
135	Cires, Pt. (thē'räs) Sp. Mor. (Gib. In.)	35.54 N	5.31 E
125	Cirey (sē-rĕ')...............Fr.	48.35 N	6.55 E
129	Cirpan (chĭr-pȧn')...........Bul.	42.12 N	25.19 E
80	Cisco (sĭs'kō)...............Tex.	32.22 N	98.58 W
126	Cistierna (thês-tyĕr'nä).......Sp.	42.48 N	5.8 W
142	Citrusdal (sĭt'rŭs-dāl)...U. S. Afr.	32.36 S	19.2 E
128	Cittadella (chēt-tä-dĕl'lä)......It.	45.39 N	12.47 E
128	Città del Vaticano (Vatican City) (chēt-tä' dĕl vä-tê-kä'nō) (văt'ĭ-kăn sĭt'ê)............It.	41.53 N	12.28 E
128	Città di Castello (chēt-tä' dē käs-tĕl'lō) It.	43.27 N	12.17 E
88	City I. .... N. Y. (In.)	41.51 N	73.48 W
102	Ciuadad Bolivar (syōō-dhädh' bô-lē'vär) Ven.	8.1 N	63.32 W
80	Ciudad Camargo (Santa Rosalia) (syōō-dhädh' kä-mär'gō) Mex.	27.40 N	105.10 W
94	Ciudad Chetumal (Payo Obispo) (syōō-dhädh'chĕt-ōō-mäl) (pä'yō ō-bēs'pō)..Mex. (In.)	18.30 N	88.18 W
94	Ciudad Dario (syōō-dhädh'dä'rê-ō) Nic.	12.53 N	86.1 W
92	Ciudad del Maíz (syōō-dhädh' dĕl mä-ēz') Mex.	22.24 N	99.36 W
92	Ciudad de Valles (syōō-dhädh' dā vä'lyās) Mex.	21.59 N	99.1 W
127	Ciudadela (thyōō-dhä-dhä'lä)..Sp.	40.0 N	3.50 E
92	Ciudad Fernández (syōō-dhädh' fĕr-nän'dĕz) Mex.	21.57 N	100.1 W
92	Ciudad García (gär-sē'ä).....Mex.	22.42 N	103.2 W
92	Ciudad Gonzáles (gôn-zä'läs) Mex.	21.30 N	101.16 W
92	Ciudad Guzmán (gōōz-män') Mex.	19.41 N	103.25 W
80	Ciudad Juárez (hwä'räz)....Mex.	31.45 N	106.20 W
92	Ciudad Manuel Doblado (män-wäl' dō-blä'dō) Mex.	20.46 N	101.55 W
126	Ciudad Real (thyōō-dhädh' rā-äl') Sp.	38.59 N	3.55 W
126	Ciudad Rodrigo (thyōō-dhädh' rô-drē'gō) Sp.	40.37 N	6.32 W
97	Ciudad Trujillo (Santo Domingo) (trōō-hē'yō)..Dom. Rep.	18.28 N	69.53 W
92	Ciudad Victoria (syōō-dhädh' vêk-tō'rê-ä) Mex.	23.43 N	99.7 W
128	Cividale (chē-vê-dä'-lä).......It.	46.6 N	13.4 E
128	Civitavecchia (chē'vê-tä-vĕk'kyä) It.	42.6 N	11.48 E
113	Civril (jĭv-rĭl')..............Tur.	38.15 N	29.45 E
113	Cizre (jĭz'rĕ)................Tur.	37.20 N	42.0 E
119	Cladow (klä'dou).Ger. (Berlin In.)	52.27 N	13.9 E
85	Clairton (klâr'tŭn)............Pa.	40.18 N	79.54 W
125	Clamart (klȧ-mär')......Fr. (In.)	48.47 N	2.15 E
124	Clamecy (kläm-sē')...........Fr.	47.28 N	3.31 E
82	Clanton (klăn'tŭn)..........Ala.	32.50 N	86.38 W
142	Clanwilliam (klȧn-wĭl'yăm) U. S. Afr.	32.9 S	18.51 E
166	Clare (klâr)...............Austl.	33.49 S	138.37 E
84	Clare.....................Mich.	43.48 N	84.48 W
116	Clare I......................Ire.	53.50 N	9.50 W
169	Claremont......Austl. (Perth In.)	31.58 S	115.47 E
73	Claremont.Calif. (Los Angeles In.)	34.6 N	117.43 W
86	Claremont..................N. H.	43.23 N	72.22 W
141	Claremont.............U. S. Afr.	33.59 S	18.28 E
84	Claremont................W. Va.	37.57 N	81.3 W
79	Claremore.................Okla.	36.17 N	95.37 W
116	Claremorris (klâr-mŏr'ĭs).....Ire.	53.45 N	9.0 W
97	Clarence Har. (klăr'ĕns)....Ba. Is.	23.5 N	74.58 W
99	Clarence I...Chl. (Magallanes In.)	54.10 S	71.40 W
169	Clarence R...........Austl. (In.)	29.10 S	152.33 E
171	Clarence R.................N. Z.	42.20 S	173.15 E
164	Clarence Str...............Austl.	11.50 S	131.15 E
79	Clarendon (klăr'ĕn-dŭn)......Ark.	34.42 N	91.18 W
78	Clarendon...................Tex.	34.56 N	100.52 W
77	Clarinda (klȧ-rĭn'dȧ)..........Ia.	40.44 N	95.2 W
77	Clarion (klăr'ĭ-ŭn)............Ia.	42.44 N	93.43 W
85	Clarion.......................Pa.	41.10 N	79.23 W
76	Clark (klärk)...............S. D.	44.54 N	97.44 W
75	Clarkdale..................Ariz.	34.45 N	112.5 W
143	Clarkebury............U. S. Afr.	31.47 S	28.18 E
86	Clarke City.................Can.	50.13 N	66.41 W
169	Clarke I. (klărk) .Austl. (Tas. In.)	40.32 S	148.10 E
165	Clarke Ra..................Austl.	20.30 S	148.0 E
71	Clark Fork..........Mont.-Wyo.	45.0 N	109.0 W
70	Clark Fork (R.)............Mont.	47.47 N	115.30 W
171	Clark Mt...................N. Z.	41.50 S	173.5 E
84	Clark, Pt....................Can.	44.2 N	81.45 W
85	Clarksburg................W. Va.	39.16 N	80.21 W
82	Clarksdale.................Miss.	34.01 N	90.31 W
86	Clarks Har..................Can.	43.35 N	65.45 W
73	Clarkston.......Ga. (Atlanta In.)	33.48 N	88.14 W
70	Clarkston..................Wash.	46.25 N	117.3 W
79	Clarksville..................Ark.	35.28 N	93.28 W
82	Clarksville.................Tenn.	36.32 N	87.22 W
79	Clarksville..................Tex.	33.36 N	95.1 W
171	Clatha R. (klä'thȧ).........N. Z.	45.0 S	169.15 E
49	Clatskanie (klăt-skā'nê) Ore. (Portland In.)	46.6 N	123.13 W
122	Clausthal (klous'tăl).........Ger.	51.48 N	10.20 E
162	Claveria (klä-vȧ-rē'ä)........P. I.	18.37 N	121.6 E
56	Claxton (klăks'tŭn) Can. (Prince Rupert In.)	54.6 N	130.5 W
83	Claxton......................Ga.	32.7 N	81.55 W
84	Clay (klā)...................Ky.	37.29 N	87.50 W
72	Clayburn (klā'bûrn) Can. (Vancouver In.).	49.5 N	122.17 W
79	Clay Center................Kan.	39.24 N	97.8 W
84	Clay City....................Ky.	37.54 N	83.56 W
118	Clay Cross.............Gt. Brit.	53.10 N	1.25 W
125	Claye-Souilly (klā'-soo-yē') Fr. (In.)	48.56 N	2.42 E
73	Clays (klāz) Ala. (Birmingham In.)	33.41 N	86.36 W
82	Clayton (klā'tŭn)...........Ala.	31.52 N	85.28 W
169	Clayton...Austl. (Melbourne In.)	37.55 S	145.7 E
49	Clayton. Calif. (San Francisco In.)	37.56 N	121.56 W
118	Clayton................Gt. Brit.	53.47 N	1.49 W
89	Clayton......Mo. (St. Louis In.)	38.39 N	90.20 W
78	Clayton....................N. M.	36.26 N	103.11 W
83	Clayton....................N. C.	35.39 N	78.28 W
73	Clayton Pk. Utah (Salt Lake City In.)	40.36 N	111.34 W
79	Clear Boggy Cr. (klēr bŏg'ĭ krēk) Okla.	34.20 N	96.20 W
116	Clear, C. (klēr)..............Ire.	51.25 N	9.25 W
75	Clear Cr....................Ariz.	34.40 N	111.5 W
72	Clear Cr.......Colo. (Denver In.)	39.44 N	105.27 W
81	Clear Cr..............Tex. (In.)	29.34 N	95.12 W
70	Clear Cr....................Wyo.	44.35 N	106.30 W
85	Clearfield....................Pa.	41.0 N	78.27 W
73	Clearfield. Utah (Salt Lake City In.)	41.7 N	112.1 W
74	Clear L....................Calif.	39.5 N	122.50 W
54	Clear L.....................Can.	56.20 N	108.30 W
77	Clear L......................Ia.	43.9 N	93.21 W
76	Clear L....................S. D.	44.48 N	96.40 W
70	Clear Lake Reservoir.......Calif.	41.50 N	121.10 W
73	Clearwater.Calif. (Los Angeles In.)	33.54 N	118.10 W
82	Clearwater............Fla. (In.)	27.57 N	82.47 W
70	Clearwater Mts..............Ida.	45.55 N	115.10 W
70	Clearwater R................Ida.	46.30 N	116.43 W
70	Clearwater R., Middle Fork of. Ida.	46.8 N	115.50 W
70	Clearwater R., N. Fork of....Ida.	46.50 N	115.40 W
70	Clearwater R., S. Fork of....Ida.	45.45 N	115.50 W
81	Cleburne (klē'bŭrn).........Tex.	32.21 N	97.23 W
118	Clee Hill (klē)..........Gt. Brit.	52.24 N	2.38 W
70	Cle Elum (klē ĕl'ŭm)......Wash.	47.11 N	120.57 W
118	Cleobury Mortimer (klē'ô-bĕr'ĭ môr'tĭ-mēr) Gt. Brit.	52.22 N	2.28 W
163	Cleopatra Needle (Mt.) (klē-ô-pā'trȧ) P. I.	10.8 N	119.0 E
165	Clermont (klēr'mŏnt).......Austl.	22.58 S	147.38 E
124	Clermont-Ferrand (klĕr-môn'-fĕr-rän') Fr.	45.45 N	3.5 E
124	Clermont l'Herault (klĕr-môn' lā-rō') Fr.	43.38 N	3.22 E
122	Cleve (klā'vē)..............Ger.	51.48 N	6.8 E
169	Cleveland (klēv'lănd)..Austl. (In.)	27.31 S	153.16 E
82	Cleveland..................Miss.	33.45 N	90.42 W
84	Cleveland..................Ohio	41.30 N	81.42 W
89	Cleveland.............Ohio (In.)		
79	Cleveland..................Okla.	36.17 N	96.28 W
82	Cleveland..................Tenn.	35.8 N	84.52 W
81	Cleveland...................Tex.	30.20 N	95.5 W
84	Cleveland, East............Ohio	41.33 N	81.33 W
84	Cleveland Hts..............Ohio	41.30 N	81.34 W
116	Clew B. (klōō)...............Ire.	53.50 N	9.40 W
125	Clichy (klē-shē')........Fr. (In.)	48.53 N	2.18 E
116	Clifden (klĭf'dĕn)............Ire.	53.25 N	10.10 W
119	Cliffe (klĭf) .Gt. Brit. (London In.)	51.28 N	0.30 E
75	Clifton (klĭf'tŭn)...........Ariz.	33.3 N	109.19 W
169	Clifton ....Austl. (In.)	27.54 S	151.57 E
85	Clifton.....................N. J.	40.54 N	74.8 W
83	Clifton.....................S. C.	35.0 N	81.48 W
81	Clifton......................Tex.	31.45 N	97.32 W
49	Clifton.......Wash. (Seattle In.)	47.26 N	122.50 W
85	Clifton Forge.................Va.	37.50 N	79.50 W
96	Clifton Pt................Ba. Is.	25.1 N	77.36 W
82	Clinch R. (klĭnch)......Tenn.-Va.	36.25 N	83.0 W
119	Clinge (klĭŋ'gĕ) (klănzh) Neth. (Anvers In.)	51.16 N	4.5 E
82	Clingmans Dome (Mt.) (klĭng'măns-dōm) N. C.	35.33 N	83.30 W
79	Clinton (klĭn'tŭn)............Ill.	40.9 N	88.57 W
84	Clinton.....................Ind.	39.40 N	87.23 W
77	Clinton......................Ia.	41.50 N	90.11 W
79	Clinton......................Ky.	36.39 N	88.59 W
86	Clinton....................Mass.	42.25 N	71.41 W
79	Clinton......................Mo.	38.23 N	93.46 W
171	Clinton....................N. Z.	46.13 S	169.22 E
83	Clinton....................N. C.	34.59 N	78.18 W
78	Clinton....................Okla.	35.31 N	98.57 W
83	Clinton....................S. C.	34.28 N	81.53 W
82	Clinton....................Tenn.	36.6 N	84.9 W
54	Clinton-Colden L. (klĭn'tŭn-kōl'dĕn) Can.	64.0 N	107.30 W
77	Clintonville (klĭn'tŭn-vĭl)....Wis.	44.37 N	88.44 W
84	Clio (klē'ō)...............Mich.	43.10 N	83.3 W
6	Clipperton I. (klĭp'ēr-tŭn) .Pac. O.	11.0 N	109.20 W
118	Clitheroe (klĭdh'ēr-ō)....Gt. Brit.	53.53 N	2.23 W
164	Cloates, Pt. (klōts).........Austl.	22.45 S	113.40 E
116	Clonakilty B. (klŏn'ä-kĭl'tê)...Ire.	51.35 N	8.55 W
164	Cloncurry (klŏn-kŭr'ê).....Austl.	21.5 S	140.40 E
116	Clonmel (klŏn-mĕl')..........Ire.	52.20 N	7.45 W
77	Cloquet (klô-kā') ....Minn.	46.45 N	92.29 W
77	Cloquet R.................Minn.	47.2 N	92.5 W
71	Cloud Pk....................Wyo.	44.23 N	107.11 W
171	Cloudy B...................N. Z.	41.25 S	174.10 E
83	Clover (klō'vēr).............S. C.	35.7 N	81.12 W
74	Cloverdale.................Calif.	38.49 N	123.4 W
72	Cloverdale. .Can. (Vancouver In.)	49.6 N	122.45 W
72	Cloverly (klō'vēr-lê) Colo. (Denver In.)	40.27 N	104.38 W
84	Cloverport (klō'vēr-pôrt).....Ky.	37.48 N	86.39 W
78	Clovis (klō'vĭs)............N. M.	34.24 N	103.11 W
123	Cluj (klŏŏzh)...............Rom.	46.46 N	23.35 E
166	Clunes (klōō'nês)..........Austl.	37.18 S	143.48 E
118	Clun R. (klŭn)..........Gt. Brit.	52.24 N	2.53 W
124	Cluny (klü-nē')...............Fr.	46.28 N	4.42 E
171	Clutha R. (klōō'thȧ)........N. Z.	45.45 S	169.30 E
79	Clyde (klīd)................Kan.	39.35 N	97.23 W
84	Clyde.......................Ohio	41.17 N	82.59 W
116	Clydebank.............Gt. Brit.	55.55 N	4.20 W
116	Clyde, Firth of.........Gt. Brit.	55.30 N	5.0 W
169	Clyde R.........Austl. (Tas. In.)	42.25 S	147.0 E
116	Clyde, (R.) ....Gt. Brit.	55.40 N	4.0 W
93	Coacalco (kō-ä-käl'kō)..Mex. (In.)	19.38 N	99.6 W
92	Coahuay R., (kō-ä-wī')......Mex.	19.0 N	103.32 W
92	Coahuayutla (kō'ä-wī-yōōt'lȧ) Mex.	18.18 N	101.49 W
80	Coahuila (State) (kō-ä-wē'lä).Mex.	27.20 N	102.0 W
92	Coalcoman de Matamoros (kō-äl-kō-män' dā mä-tä-mō'rôs).Mex.	18.48 N	103.8 W
92	Coalcoman, Sierra de (mts.) (syĕr'rä dā kō-äl-kō-män').Mex.	18.30 N	103.0 W
72	Coal Creek....Colo. (Denver In.)	39.40 N	104.40 W
73	Coaldale...Ala. (Birmingham In.)	33.49 N	86.47 W
79	Coalgate...................Okla.	34.32 N	96.14 W
84	Coal Grove.................Ohio	38.29 N	82.39 W
74	Coalinga (kō-ȧ-lĭŋ'gȧ).......Calif.	36.9 N	120.22 W
169	Coal R...........Austl. (Tas. In.)	42.35 S	147.26 E
118	Coalville...............Gt. Brit.	52.43 N	1.21 W
91	Coamo (kō-ä'mō)......P. R. (In.)	18.4 N	66.22 W
93	Coanala (kō-ä-nä'lä)...Mex. (In.)	19.36 N	98.55 W
126	Coa R. (kō'ä)...............Port.	40.40 N	6.55 W
102	Coari (kō-är'ê).............Braz.	4.5 S	63.10 W
54	Coast Mts...................Can.	54.30 N	129.0 W
58	Coast Ranges..............U. S.	40.0 N	123.30 W
116	Coatbridge (kōt'brĭj)....Gt. Brit.	55.50 N	4.0 W
92	Coatepec (kō-ä-tä-pĕk').....Mex.	19.24 N	98.45 W
93	Coatepec....................Mex.	19.26 N	96.57 W
93	Coatepec, R..........Mex. (In.)	19.24 N	98.52 W
94	Coatepeque (kō-ä-tȧ-pā'kȧ) Guat.	14.41 N	91.53 W
94	Coatepeque..................Sal.	13.56 N	89.30 W
85	Coatesville (kōts'vĭl).........Pa.	39.59 N	75.49 W
92	Coatetelco (kō-ä-tȧ-tĕl'kō)...Mex.	18.43 N	99.19 W
86	Coaticook (kō'tĭ-kŏŏk)......Can.	45.9 N	71.50 W
55	Coats I. (kōts).............Can.	62.35 N	82.30 W
46	Coats Land (Reg.)..........Ant.	74.0 S	12.0 W
93	Coatzacoalcos R. (kô-ät'zä-kô-äl' kōs).Mex.	16.57 N	94.40 W
55	Cobalt (kō'bôlt)............Can.	47.12 N	79.47 W
94	Cobán (kō-bän')............Guat.	15.28 N	90.20 W
167	Cobar (kō'bär)............Austl.	31.28 S	145.50 E
167	Cobberas, Mt. (kŏb'ēr-ȧs)...Austl.	36.52 S	148.9 E
72	Cobble Hill (kŏb''l) Can. (Vancouver In.)	48.42 N	123.37 W
88	Cobbs Cr. (kŏbz) Pa. (Philadelphia In.)	39.57 N	75.15 W
86	Cobequid B. (kŏb'ê-kwĭd)....Can.	45.25 N	63.45 W
116	Cobh (kôv)...................Ire.	51.55 N	8.15 W
85	Cobourg (kō'bŏŏrgh)........Can.	43.57 N	78.4 W
167	Cobram (kō'brăm)..........Austl.	35.55 S	145.38 E
96	Cobre R. (kō'brā)...........Jam.	18.5 N	76.58 W

ng-sing; ŋ-baŋk; n-nasalized n; nŏd; cŏmmit; ōld; ôbey; ôrder; fōōd; fŏŏt; ou-out; s-soft; sh-dish; th-thin; pūre ûnite; ûrn; stŭd; circŭs; ü-as "y" in study; '-indeterminate vowel.

Page	Name Pronunciation Region	Lat. °′	Long. °′
169	Coburg (kō'bûrg) Austl. (Melbourne In.)	37.45 S	144.57 E
122	Coburg (kō'bo͞orgh) Ger.	50.16 N	10.57 E
164	Coburg Pen. Austl.	11.30 S	133.0 E
151	Cocanada (kō-kȧ-nä'dȧ) India	16.50 N	82.15 E
127	Cocentaina (kō-thān-tä-ē'nȧ) Sp.	38.44 N	0.25 W
102	Cochabamba (kō-chä-bäm'bä) Bol.	17.29 S	66.30 W
151	Cochin (kō-chĭn') India	9.58 N	76.14 E
160	Cochin-China (State) Fr. In. Chn.	10.0 N	105.30 E
97	Cochinos Banks (kō-chē'nōs) Ba. Is.	22.20 N	76.15 W
96	Cochinos B. Cuba	22.8 N	81.3 W
162	Cochinos Pt. P. I.	14.25 N	120.30 E
82	Cochran (kŏk'răn) Ga.	32.23 N	83.25 W
55	Cochrane Can.	49.0 N	80.55 W
166	Cockburn (kō'bŭrn) Austl.	32.6 S	140.59 E
99	Cockburn Canal Chl. (Magallanes In.)	54.20 S	71.30 W
84	Cockburn I. Can.	45.55 N	83.22 W
85	Cockeysville (kŏk'ĭz-vĭl) Md.	39.29 N	76.40 W
143	Cockscomb Mt. (kŏks'kōm) U. S. Afr.	33.35 S	24.46 E
83	Cocoa (kō'kō) Fla. (In.)	28.20 N	80.44 W
96	Coco Cay (I.) Cuba	22.28 N	78.22 W
83	Coconut Grove (kō'kō-nŭt grōv) Fla. (In.)	25.43 N	80.14 W
167	Cocoparra Ra. (kō-kō-pȧr'rȧ) Austl.	34.2 S	146.10 E
166	Coco Ra. Austl.	30.30 S	141.45 E
94	Coco, R. Hond.-Nic.	14.30 N	85.0 W
7	Cocos Is. Ind. O.	12.0 S	96.0 E
92	Cocula (kō-ko͞o'lä) Mex.	20.23 N	103.47 W
102	Codajaz (kō-dä-häzh') Braz.	3.56 S	62.2 W
86	Cod, C. (kŏd) Mass.	42.0 N	70.15 W
171	Codfish I. N. Z.	46.48 S	167.42 E
103	Codo (kō'dō) Braz.	4.32 S	43.38 W
128	Codogno (kō-dō'nyō) It.	45.9 N	9.42 E
95	Codrington (kŏd'rĭng-tŭn) Le. Is. (In.)	17.38 N	61.50 W
71	Cody (kō'dĭ) Wyo.	44.31 N	109.2 W
92	Coeneo de la Libertad (kō-ā'nā-ō dā lä lē-bēr-tädh') Mex.	19.47 N	101.32 W
70	Coeur d'Alene (kûr dȧ-lān') Ida.	47.41 N	116.48 W
70	Coeur d'Alene L. Ida.	47.30 N	116.40 W
70	Coeur d'Alene R. Ida.	47.28 N	116.32 W
79	Coffeyville (kŏf'ĭ-vĭl) Kan.	37.3 N	95.37 W
167	Coffs Harbour (kŏfs) Austl.	30.18 S	153.10 E
131	Cogalnic R. (kō-gäl'nĭk) Rom.	46.35 N	28.45 E
128	Coghinas R. (kō'gē-näs) Sard.	40.45 N	9.0 E
72	Coghlan (kŏg'lăn) Can. (Vancouver In.)	49.7 N	122.31 W
129	Coglie (kôl'yā) It.	40.48 N	17.31 E
124	Cognac (kōn-yȧk') Fr.	45.40 N	0.20 W
87	Cohasset (kō-hăs'ĕt) Mass. (In.)	42.14 N	70.48 W
85	Cohoes (kō-hōz') N. Y.	42.43 N	73.43 W
95	Coiba I. (kō-ē'bä) Pan.	7.25 N	81.45 W
104	Coile, R. (kō-ē'lä) Arg.	51.15 S	70.30 W
151	Coimbatore (kō-ēm-bȧ-tōr') India	11.0 N	76.59 E
126	Coimbra (kō-ēm'brä) Port.	40.13 N	8.26 W
126	Coín (kō-ēn') Sp.	36.39 N	4.45 W
127	Coina (kō-ē'nȧ) Port. (In.)	38.36 N	9.3 W
93	Coixtlahuaca (kō-ēs'tlä-wä'kä) Mex.	17.40 N	97.18 W
90	Cojimar (kō-hē-mär') Cuba (Habana In.)	23.10 N	82.19 W
94	Cojutepeque (kō-ho͞o-tē-pā'kā) Sal.	13.46 N	88.52 W
77	Cokato (kō-kā'tō) Minn.	45.5 N	94.11 W
151	Colaba Pt. (kō-lä'bä) India (Bombay In.)	18.53 N	72.50 E
166	Colac (kō-lȧk') Austl.	38.19 S	143.38 E
78	Colby (kōl'bĭ) Kan.	39.24 N	101.3 W
117	Colchester (kōl'chĕs-tēr) Gt. Brit.	51.52 N	0.52 E
78	Coldwater (kōld'wô-tēr) Kan.	37.14 N	99.19 W
84	Coldwater Mich.	41.56 N	85.0 W
78	Coldwater Cr. Okla.-Tex.	36.20 N	102.10 W
79	Coldwater R. Miss.	34.30 N	90.10 W
82	Coldwater R. Miss.	34.32 N	90.0 W
86	Cole Harbour (kōl) Can.	45.15 N	61.11 W
80	Coleman (kōl'măn) Tex.	31.48 N	99.26 W
143	Colenso (kō-lĕn'sō) U. S. Afr.	28.45 S	29.50 E
169	Colenton (kōl'ĕn-tŭn) Austl. (In.)	26.54 S	152.18 E
166	Coleraine (kōl-rān') Austl.	37.36 S	141.43 E
77	Coleraine Minn.	47.18 N	93.28 W
116	Coleraine Gt. Brit.	55.5 N	6.40 W
171	Coleridge L. (kōl'rĭj) N. Z.	43.15 S	171.32 E
143	Colesberg (kōlz'bērg) U. S. Afr.	30.45 S	25.5 E
118	Coleshill (kōlz'hĭl) Gt. Brit.	52.29 N	1.42 W
77	Colfax (kōl'făks) Ia.	41.41 N	93.14 W
81	Colfax La.	31.31 N	92.42 W
70	Colfax Wash.	46.52 N	117.12 W
104	Colhue, L. (kōl-wā') Arg.	45.28 S	69.0 W
143	Coligny (kō-lē-nyē') U. S. Afr.	26.8 S	26.14 E
92	Colima (kō-lē'mä) Mex.	19.13 N	103.44 W
92	Colima (State) Mex.	19.0 N	104.0 W
92	Colima, Vol. de Mex.	19.30 N	103.37 W
102	Collahuasi (kō-lyä-wä'sē) Chl.	20.58 S	68.58 W
127	Collares (kōl-lär'äzh) Port. (In.)	38.48 N	9.27 W
103	Collares (I.) Braz. (In.)	0.55 S	48.12 W
73	College Pk. Ga. (Atlanta In.)	33.39 N	84.27 W
88	College Pt. N. Y. (New York In.)	40.47 N	73.51 W
116	Coll (I.) (kōl) Gt. Brit.	56.35 N	6.30 W
164	Collie (kōl'ē) Austl.	33.12 S	116.12 E
164	Collier B. (kōl'yēr) Austl.	16.15 S	124.15 E
85	Collingswood (kŏl'ĭngz-wo͝od) N. J.	39.50 N	75.6 W
55	Collingwood (kŏl'ĭng-wo͝od) Can.	44.32 N	80.29 W
171	Collingwood N. Z.	40.40 S	172.40 E
82	Collins (kŏl'ĭns) Miss.	31.38 N	89.34 W
49	Collinsville (kŏl'ĭnz-vĭl) Calif. (San Francisco In.)	38.5 N	121.51 W
79	Collinsville Ill.	38.40 N	89.59 W
79	Collinsville Okla.	36.21 N	95.50 W

Page	Name Pronunciation Region	Lat. °′	Long. °′
138	Collo (kôl'ō) Alg.	37.0 N	6.30 E
129	Collonne, C. (kōl-lō'nä) It.	39.2 N	17.13 E
49	Colma (kōl'mȧ) Calif. (San Francisco In.)	37.40 N	122.28 W
125	Colmar (kōl'mär) Fr.	48.5 N	7.22 E
126	Colmenar de Oreja (kōl-mä-när' dā ō-rā'hä) Sp.	40.6 N	3.23 W
127	Colmenar Viejo (kōl-mä-när' vyā'-hō) Sp. (In.)	40.39 N	3.47 W
...	Cöln, see Köln, Ger.		
118	Colne (kōln) Gt. Brit.	53.52 N	2.10 W
167	Colo R. (kō'lō) Austl.	33.25 S	150.50 E
138	Colomb-Béchar (kō-lôɴ' bā-shär') Alg.	31.41 N	2.12 W
125	Colombes (kō-lôɴb') Fr. (In.)	48.56 N	2.17 E
102	Colombia (kō-lōm'bē-ȧ) S. A.	3.30 N	72.30 W
151	Colombo (kō-lōm'bō) Cey.	6.55 N	79.50 E
99	Colón (kō-lōn') Arg. (Buenos Aires In.)	33.50 S	61.8 W
102	Colon (Galapagos) Arch. (kō-lōn') (gä-lä-pä-gōs) Ec.	0.1 S	90.30 W
96	Colón Cuba	22.42 N	80.52 W
92	Colón Mex.	20.47 N	100.2 W
95	Colon Pan.	9.22 N	79.54 W
99	Colón Ur. (Buenos Aires In.)	34.47 S	56.10 W
104	Colonia (kō-lō'nē-ȧ) Ur.	34.30 S	57.45 W
80	Colonia Guadalupe (kō-lō'nē-ȧ gwä-dä-lo͞o'pä) Mex.	31.23 N	106.6 W
116	Colonsay (I.) (kŏl-ŏn-sā') Gt. Brit.	56.5 N	6.10 W
80	Colorado (kŏl-ō-rä'dō) Tex.	32.34 N	100.51 W
75	Colorado (State) U. S.	38.40 N	107.0 W
75	Colo. Natl. Mon. Colo.	39.3 N	108.42 W
104	Colorado R. Arg.	38.42 S	66.30 W
58	Colorado R. U. S.-Mex.	32.15 N	114.50 W
96	Colorados Rfs. (kō-lō-rä'dōs) Cuba	22.30 N	84.21 W
75	Colorado R. Ind. Res. Ariz.-Calif.	33.55 N	114.25 W
78	Colorado Springs Colo.	38.49 N	104.49 W
72	Colorado Springs Colo. (In.)		
93	Colotepec R. (kō-lō-tē-pĕk') Mex.	16.0 N	96.45 W
92	Colotlan (kō-lō-tlän') Mex.	22.11 N	103.17 W
92	Colotlan, R. Mex.	22.15 N	103.35 W
102	Colquechaca (kōl-kā-chä'kä) Bol.	18.47 S	66.0 W
73	Colton (kōl'tŭn) Calif. (Los Angeles In.)	34.4 N	117.20 W
166	Columa (kō-lo͞o'mȧ) Austl.	35.48 S	144.12 E
82	Columbia (kō-lŭm'bĭ-ȧ) Ky.	37.7 N	85.18 W
82	Columbia Miss.	31.15 N	89.50 W
79	Columbia Mo.	38.57 N	92.19 W
85	Columbia Pa.	40.2 N	76.30 W
83	Columbia S. C.	34.0 N	81.2 W
82	Columbia Tenn.	35.37 N	87.3 W
46	Columbia, C. Can.	83.0 N	70.0 W
84	Columbia City Ind.	41.9 N	85.30 W
89	Columbia Hts. Minn. (Minneapolis In.)	45.3 N	93.14 W
82	Columbiana (kō-lŭm-bĭ-ă'nȧ) Ala.	33.10 N	86.37 W
70	Columbia R. U. S.-Can.	45.52 N	121.40 W
82	Columbus (kō-lŭm'bŭs) Ga.	32.29 N	84.58 W
84	Columbus Ind.	39.13 N	85.56 W
79	Columbus Kan.	37.11 N	94.50 W
82	Columbus Miss.	33.29 N	88.26 W
71	Columbus Mont.	45.39 N	109.17 W
76	Columbus Neb.	41.25 N	97.21 W
75	Columbus N. M.	31.50 N	107.38 W
84	Columbus Ohio	39.56 N	83.0 W
81	Columbus Tex.	29.43 N	96.33 W
77	Columbus Wis.	43.21 N	89.0 W
97	Columbus Bank Ba. Is.	22.2 N	75.42 W
84	Columbus Grove Ohio	40.55 N	84.5 W
97	Columbus Pt. Ba. Is.	24.9 N	75.17 W
74	Colusa (kō-lū'sȧ) Calif.	39.13 N	122.2 W
70	Colville (kōl'vĭl) Wash.	48.33 N	117.53 W
52	Colville R. Alsk.	69.0 N	154.0 W
70	Colville R. Wash.	48.20 N	117.50 W
72	Colwood (kōl'wo͝od) Can. (Vancouver In.)	48.27 N	123.29 W
121	Comacchio (kō-mäk'kyō) It.	44.40 N	12.10 E
92	Comalá (kō-mä-lä') Mex.	19.16 N	103.45 W
93	Comalcalco (kō-mäl-käl'kō) Mex.	18.15 N	93.14 W
78	Comanche (kō-măn'chē) Okla.	34.21 N	97.58 W
80	Comanche Tex.	31.54 N	98.36 W
94	Comayagua (kō-mä-yä'gwä) Hond.	14.30 N	87.45 W
83	Combahee R. (kŏm-bȧ-hē') S. C.	32.40 N	80.40 W
119	Comberbach (kō'mēr-bȧk) Gt. Brit. (Liverpool In.)	53.17 N	2.32 W
167	Come by Chance (kŭm'bĭ chăns') Austl.	30.24 S	148.30 E
82	Comer (kŭm'ēr) Ga.	34.4 N	83.10 W
97	Comete C. (kō-mā'tȧ) Ba. Is.	21.43 N	71.28 W
151	Comilla (kō-mĭl'ȧ) India	23.29 N	91.15 E
128	Comino, C. (kō-mē'nō) Sard.	40.23 N	9.46 E
93	Comitán (kō-mē-tän') Mex.	16.15 N	92.8 W
124	Commentry (kō-mäɴ-trē') Fr.	46.15 N	2.15 E
82	Commerce (kŏm'ērs) Ga.	34.12 N	83.28 W
79	Commerce Okla.	36.56 N	94.54 W
80	Commerce Tex.	33.15 N	95.54 W
125	Commercy (kō-mēr-sē') Fr.	48.45 N	5.35 E
169	Como (kō'mō) Austl. (Sydney In.)	34.0 S	151.4 E
128	Como It.	45.47 N	9.5 E
104	Comodoro Rivadavia (kō-mō-dō'rō rē-vä-dä'vē-ä) Arg.	45.45 S	67.28 W
138	Comoé R. (kō-mō-ā') Fr. W. Afr.	7.0 N	4.50 W
128	Como, L. It.-Switz.	46.0 N	9.15 E
151	Comorin, C. (kŏ'mō-rĭn) India	7.37 N	77.28 E
143	Comoro Is. (kŏm'ō-rō) Ind. O.	12.10 S	44.15 E
55	Comox (kŭm'ŏks) Can.	49.40 N	129.1 W
143	Compass Berg (Mt.) (kŭm'pȧs bĕrg) U. S. Afr.	31.44 S	24.32 E
124	Compiegne (kôɴ-pyĕn'y') Fr.	49.25 N	2.50 E
143	Compies R. (kŏm'pēz) U. S. Afr.-Swaz.	26.45 S	30.50 E
127	Comporta (kōm-pōr'tȧ) Port. (In.)	38.24 N	8.49 W

Page	Name Pronunciation Region	Lat. °′	Long. °′
92	Compostela (kōm-pō-stā'lä) Mex.	21.15 N	104.54 W
119	Compstall (kŏmps'tôl) Gt. Brit. (Liverpool In.)	53.25 N	2.3 W
74	Compton (kŏmp'tŭn) Calif.	33.51 N	118.15 W
131	Comrat (kōm-rät') Rom.	46.17 N	28.39 E
138	Conakry (kō-nȧ-krē') Fr. W. Afr.	9.30 N	13.45 W
82	Conasauga (kō-nȧ-sô'gȧ) Ga.	34.52 N	84.50 W
124	Concarneau (kôɴ-kär-nō') Fr.	47.55 N	3.56 W
103	Concepción (kōn-sĕp-syōn') Bol.	15.58 S	61.28 W
104	Concepción Chl.	36.45 S	72.59 W
95	Concepción Pan.	8.31 N	82.38 W
104	Concepción Par.	23.28 S	57.29 W
162	Concepcion P. I.	15.19 N	120.39 E
94	Concepcion (Vol.) Nic.	11.33 N	85.38 W
94	Concepción del Mar (dĕl mär') Guat.	14.7 N	91.22 W
80	Concepción del Oro (dĕl ō'rō) Mex.	24.39 N	101.24 W
87	Conception B. (kŏn-sĕp'shŭn) Newf.	47.40 N	53.5 W
97	Conception I. Ba. Is.	23.50 N	75.7 W
74	Conception, Pt. Calif.	34.27 N	120.29 W
80	Concho R. (kŏn'chō) Tex.	31.31 N	100.0 W
80	Concho R., North Tex.	31.50 N	101.0 W
80	Conchos R. (kōn'chōs) Mex.	25.5 N	99.0 W
80	Conchos R. Mex.	28.0 N	105.15 W
49	Concord (kŏŋ'kŏrd) Calif. (San Francisco In.)	37.58 N	122.1 W
87	Concord Mass. (In.)	42.27 N	71.21 W
83	Concord N. C.	35.24 N	80.36 W
86	Concord N. H.	43.12 N	71.32 W
104	Concordia (kŏn-kôr'dĭ-ȧ) Arg.	31.28 S	58.1 W
79	Concordia Kan.	39.34 N	97.39 W
92	Concordia Mex.	23.17 N	106.5 W
142	Concordia (Mine) U. S. Afr.	29.30 S	17.58 E
70	Concrete (kŏn'krēt) Wash.	48.33 N	121.44 W
165	Condamine R. (kŏn'dȧ-mĭn) Austl.	27.0 S	150.0 E
76	Conde (kŏn-dē') S. D.	45.9 N	98.5 W
171	Conden (kŏn'dĕn) N. Z.	42.25 S	171.15 E
114	Condé-Smendou (kôɴ-dā' smäɴ-do͞o') Alg.	36.52 N	6.36 E
124	Condé-sur-Noireau (kôɴ dā' sür-nwä-rō') Fr.	45.50 N	0.32 W
103	Condeúba (kōn-dā-o͞o'bä) Braz.	14.57 S	41.58 W
167	Condobolin (kŏn'dō-bō-lĭn') Austl.	33.5 S	147.11 E
124	Condom (kôɴ-dôɴ') Fr.	43.38 N	0.22 E
70	Condon (kŏn'dŭn) Ore.	45.14 N	120.11 W
82	Conecuh R. (kō-nē'kŭ) Ala.	31.30 N	86.20 W
128	Conegliano (kō-nāl-yä'nō) It.	45.53 N	12.18 E
78	Conejos R. (kō-nā'hōs) Colo.	37.5 N	106.20 W
85	Conemaugh (kŏn'ē-mô) Pa.	40.22 N	78.50 W
88	Coney I. (kō'nĭ) N. Y. (In.)	40.34 N	73.58 W
124	Confalens (kôɴ-fä-läɴ') Fr.	46.1 N	0.40 E
125	Conflans (kôɴ-fläɴ') Fr.	49.10 N	5.50 E
125	Conflans-Ste. Honorine (kôɴ-fläɴ'-sāɴt'ō-nō-rēn') Fr. (In.)	48.58 N	2.5 E
83	Congaree R. (kŏŋ-gȧ-rē') S. C.	33.50 N	80.55 W
118	Congleton (kŏŋ'g'l-tŭn) Gt. Brit.	53.10 N	2.13 W
140	Congo (Dist.) (kŏŋ'gō) Ang.	6.30 S	15.15 E
135	Congo da Lemba (kōŋ'gō dȧ lĕm'-bȧ) Bel. Cong. (Brazzaville In.)	5.47 S	13.42 E
139	Congo R. (kŏŋ'gō) Afr.	2.15 N	22.0 E
135	Congo River Falls Bel. Cong. (Brazzaville In.)	4.50 S	14.30 E
72	Conifer (kŏ'nĭ-fēr) Colo. (Denver In.)	39.30 N	105.18 W
127	Conil (kō-nēl') Sp. (In.)	36.16 N	6.6 W
118	Conisborough (kŏn'ĭs-bŭr-ō) Gt. Brit.	53.29 N	1.13 W
151	Conjeeveram (kŏn-jē-vēr-ŭm') India	12.47 N	79.45 E
73	Conley (kŏn'lĭ) Ga. (Atlanta In.)	33.39 N	84.19 W
84	Conneaut (kŏn-ē-ôt') Ohio	41.57 N	80.34 W
85	Connecticut (State) (kŏ-nĕt'ĭ-kŭt) U. S.	41.30 N	72.40 W
86	Connecticut R. U. S.	43.50 N	72.30 W
73	Connellsville (kŏn'ĕlz-vĭl) Ala. (Birmingham In.)	33.21 N	87.11 W
85	Connellsville Pa.	40.2 N	79.36 W
116	Connemara, Mts. of (kŏn-nē-mȧ'-rȧ) Ire.	53.40 N	9.30 W
84	Connersville (kŏn'ērz-vĭl) Ind.	39.37 N	85.10 W
116	Conn, Lough (L.) (lŏĸ kŏn) Ire.	54.0 N	9.20 W
73	Connor (kŏn'ēr) Utah (Salt Lake City In.)	41.37 N	112.21 W
103	Conquista (kōn-kēs'tȧ) Braz.	15.10 S	40.45 W
71	Conrad (kŏn'răd) Mont.	48.10 N	111.48 W
81	Conroe (kŏn'rō) Tex.	30.18 N	95.28 W
85	Conshohocken (kŏn-shō-hŏk'ĕn) Pa.	40.5 N	75.20 W
96	Consolación del Sur (kōn-sō-lä-syōn' dĕl so͞or') Cuba	22.27 N	83.28 W
122	Constance, L. of (kŏn'stȧns) Switz.-Ger.	47.38 N	9.20 E
113	Constanța (kōn-stän'tsä) Rom.	44.12 N	28.38 E
126	Constantina (kōn-stän-tē'nä) Sp.	37.53 N	5.38 W
138	Constantine (kôɴ-stäɴ-tēn') Alg.	36.28 N	6.35 E
84	Constantine (kŏn'stȧn-tēn) Mich.	41.51 N	85.40 W
113	Constantinople (Istanbul) (kŏn-stăn-tĭ-nō'p'l) ('stän-bo͞ol') Tur.	41.2 N	29.0 E
104	Constitución (kōn'stĭ-to͞o-syōn') Chl.	35.28 S	72.30 W
72	Constitution, Mt. (kŏn-stĭ-tū'shŭn) Wash. (Vancouver In.)	48.41 N	122.50 W
126	Consuegra (kōn-swā'grä) Sp.	39.27 N	3.36 W
92	Contepec (kōn-tē-pĕk') Mex.	20.3 N	100.7 W
119	Contich (kŏn'tĭĸ) Bel. (Anvers In.)	51.7 N	4.27 E
79	Conway (kŏn'wā) Ark.	35.6 N	92.26 W
86	Conway N. H.	43.59 N	71.10 W
83	Conway S. C.	33.50 N	79.3 W
49	Conway Wash. (Seattle In.)	48.20 N	122.22 W
82	Conyers (kŏn'yērz) Ga.	33.42 N	84.4 W
169	Cogee (ko͞o-gē') Austl. (Sidney In.)	33.55 S	151.15 E
169	Cooke, Pt. Austl. (Melbourne In.)	37.56 S	144.48 E
82	Cookeville (ko͝ok'vĭl) Tenn.	36.9 N	85.31 W

Page	Name Pronunciation Region	Lat. °'	Long. °'
143	Cookhouse (kŏŏk'hous)..U. S. Afr.	32.47 S	25.47 E
53	Cook Inlet (kŏŏk).........Alsk.	60.0 N	152.30 W
6	Cook Is..................Pac. O.	19.30 S	158.30 W
171	Cook, Mt.................N. Z.	43.33 S	170.10 E
73	Cooks Sprs. Ala. (Birmingham In.)	33.35 N	86.24 W
171	Cook, Str..................N. Z.	41.0 S	174.30 E
165	Cooktown................Austl.	15.38 S	145.25 E
167	Coolah (kōō'lȧ)...........Austl.	31.48 S	149.43 E
167	Coolamon (kōō-lȧ-mŏn).....Austl.	34.50 S	147.14 E
169	Coolangatta (kōō-lăŋ-gă'tȧ) Austl. (In.)	28.9 S	153.27 E
83	Cooleemee (kōō-lē'mē) .....N. C.	35.49 N	80.31 W
164	Coolgardie (kōōl-gär'dē)...Austl.	30.52 S	121.15 E
119	Cooling (kōōl'ĭng) Gt. Brit. (London In.)	51.28 N	0.32 E
167	Cooma (kōō'mȧ)...........Austl.	36.15 S	149.18 E
167	Coonabarrabran (kōō'nȧ-băr'ȧ-brăn).Austl.	31.18 S	149.18 E
166	Coonalpyn (kōō-năl'pĭn).....Austl.	35.45 S	139.59 E
167	Coonamble (kōō-năm'b'l)...Austl.	30.56 S	148.22 E
79	Cooper (kōōp'ēr)...........Tex.	33.22 N	95.40 W
85	Cooperstown..............N. Y.	42.43 N	74.55 W
76	Cooperstown..............N. D.	47.27 N	98.6 W
166	Coorong, The (Pen.) (kōō'rŏng) Austl.	36.0 S	139.35 E
82	Coosa R. (kōō'sȧ)........Ala.-Ga.	34.0 N	86.0 W
82	Coosawattee R. (kōō-sȧ-wôt'ē) Ga.	34.35 N	84.40 W
70	Coos B. (kōōs)...............Ore.	43.20 N	124.20 W
167	Cootamundra (kōō-tȧ-mŭn'drȧ) Austl.	34.38 S	148.3 E
169	Cooyar (kōō'yär) .....Austl. (In.)	26.59 S	151.51 E
93	Copainalá (kō-pī-nä-lä').....Mex.	17.5 N	93.10 W
93	Copalita, R. (kō-pä-lē'tä)....Mex.	16.0 N	96.17 W
94	Copán (Ruins) (kō-pän')....Guat.	14.50 N	89.20 W
81	Copano B. (kō-pän'ō).........Tex.	28.8 N	97.5 W
...	Copenhagen, see København, Den.		
104	Copiapó (Cerro del Azufre) (Vol.) (kō-pyä-pō') (sĕr'rō dĕl ä-zōō'frā).Chl.	27.15 S	69.10 W
166	Copley (kŏp'lĭ)..............Austl.	30.33 S	138.26 E
128	Copparo (kôp-pä'rō)..........It.	44.54 N	11.49 E
53	Copper Center (kŏp'ēr).....Alsk.	61.57 N	145.18 W
82	Copperhill...............Tenn.	35.0 N	84.22 W
54	Coppermine R..............Can.	66.30 N	115.0 W
53	Copper R..................Alsk.	62.20 N	145.0 W
104	Coqueiros (kô-kā'rōzh) .Braz. (In.)	22.47 S	43.22 W
140	Coquilhatville (kô-kē'yȧ-vēl') Bel. Cong.	0.0	18.18 E
70	Coquille (kô-kēl')...........Ore.	43.10 N	124.11 W
104	Coquimbo (kō-kēm'bō)......Chl.	29.59 S	71.29 W
72	Coquitlam L. (kō-kwĭt-lăm) Can. (Vancouver In.)	49.24 N	122.46 W
129	Corabia (kô-rä'bĭ-ȧ)........Rom.	43.45 N	24.29 E
102	Coracora (kō'rä-kō'rä).......Peru	15.30 S	73.32 W
163	Coral B. (kŏr'ăl)............P. I.	8.25 N	117.25 E
83	Coral Gables...........Fla. (In.)	25.44 N	80.14 W
165	Coral Sea..................Austl.	15.0 S	155.0 E
166	Corangamite, L. (kō-răn'gȧ-mĭt) Austl.	38.10 S	143.25 E
89	Coraopolis (kō'rä-ŏp'ō-lĭs) Pa. (Pittsburgh In.)	40.31 N	80.10 W
128	Corato (kō'rä-tō).............It.	41.9 N	16.25 E
124	Corbeil (kôr-bĕ'y')...........Fr.	48.38 N	2.31 E
49	Corbett (kôr'bĕt) Wash. (Seattle In.)	45.32 N	122.17 W
124	Corbie (kôr-bē')..............Fr.	49.55 N	2.31 E
82	Corbin (kôr'bĭn).............Ky.	36.56 N	84.7 W
72	Corboia Cr. (kôr-boi'ȧ) Can. (Vancouver In.)	49.38 N	122.38 W
118	Corby (kôr'bĭ).........Gt. Brit.	52.50 N	0.32 W
104	Corcovado (Mt.) (kôr-kô-vä'dōō) Braz. (In.)	22.57 S	43.12 W
104	Corcovado G. (kôr-kô-vä'dhō) Chl.	43.30 S	73.30 W
169	Cordeaux, Mt. (kôr-dō') Austl. (In.)	27.59 S	152.23 E
82	Cordele (kôr-dēl')............Ga.	31.57 N	83.50 W
49	Cordelia (kôr-dē'lyȧ) Calif. (San Francisco In.)	38.11 N	122.10 W
78	Cordell (kôr-dĕl')..........Okla.	35.18 N	98.59 W
104	Córboba (kôr'dô-vä).........Arg.	31.28 S	64.10 W
104	Córdoba (State).............Arg.	31.0 S	64.0 W
93	Córdoba....................Mex.	18.55 N	96.55 W
126	Córdoba.....................Sp.	37.54 N	4.46 W
82	Cordova.....................Ala.	33.45 N	87.12 W
53	Cordova....................Alsk.	60.30 N	145.45 W
99	Cordova Pen. Chl. (Magallanes In.)	53.20 S	72.50 W
129	Corfu (I.) (kôr'fū)..........Grc.	39.35 N	19.52 E
129	Corfu (kerkyra) (kĕr'kē-rä) ..Grc.	39.35 N	19.55 E
128	Corigliano (kō-rē-lyä'nō).......It.	39.36 N	16.32 E
169	Corinna (Pieman) R. (kô-rĭn'ȧ) Austl. (Tas. In.)	41.45 S	145.20 E
73	Corinne (kô-rĕn') Utah (Salt Lake City In.)	41.32 N	112.6 W
82	Corinth (kŏr'ĭnth) ....Miss.	34.56 N	88.32 W
129	Corinth (Korinthos) (kô'rĭn-thôs) Grc.	37.55 N	22.55 E
129	Corinth, G. of...............Grc.	38.10 N	22.40 E
94	Corinto (kōr-ĭn'tō)...........Nic.	12.30 N	87.12 W
128	Corizia (kō-rēd'zē-ä)..........It.	45.57 N	13.37 E
116	Cork (kôrk)...................Ire.	51.55 N	8.30 W
116	Cork Har.....................Ire.	51.45 N	8.15 W
128	Corleone (kôr-lā-ō'nā)........It.	37.48 N	13.18 E
129	Çorlu (chŏr'lōō)..............Tur.	41.8 N	27.48 E
125	Cormeilles (kôr-mā'y')...Fr. (In.)	48.58 N	2.12 E
82	Cornelia (kôr-nē'lyȧ).........Ga.	34.32 N	83.33 W
143	Cornelia.............U. S. Afr.	27.15 S	28.52 E
77	Cornell (kôr-nĕl')............Wis.	45.10 N	91.10 W
167	Corner Inlet.................Austl.	38.45 S	146.15 E
169	Corners.........Austl. (Tas. In.)	41.50 S	147.23 E
49	Cornet (kôr'nĕt) Wash. (Seattle In.)	48.23 N	122.37 W
128	Corneto (Tarquinia) (kôr-nā'tō) (tär-kwē'nyä).It.	42.16 N	11.45 E
79	Corning (kôr'nĭng)..........Ark.	36.25 N	90.35 W
79	Corning.....................Ia.	40.59 N	94.42 W
85	Corning...................N. Y.	42.9 N	77.5 W
95	Corn I., Gt...............W. I.	12.12 N	83.2 W
95	Corn I., Little............W. I.	12.18 N	82.58 W
128	Corno, Mt. (kôr'nō)..........It.	42.27 N	13.33 E
55	Cornwall (kôrn'wôl)........Can.	45.3 N	74.45 W
170	Cornwallis (kôrn-wŏl'ĭs)N. Z. (In.)	37.0 S	174.37 E
102	Coro (kō'rō)................Ven.	11.28 N	69.32 W
102	Corocoro (kō-rō-kō'rō).......Bol.	17.15 S	68.31 W
170	Coromandel Chan. (kŏr-ô-măn'dĕl) N. Z.	36.25 S	175.30 E
151	Coromandel Coast..........India	13.0 N	80.30 E
163	Coron(kô-rōn')..............P. I.	12.1 N	120.13 E
82	Corona (kô-rō'nȧ)............Ala.	33.42 N	87.28 W
73	Corona....Calif. (Los Angeles In.)	33.53 N	117.34 W
92	Corona, R...................Mex.	24.0 N	99.10 W
95	Coronada B. (kô-rô-nä'dō)...C. R.	9.0 N	84.0 W
74	Coronado (kŏr-ô-nä'dō) Calif. (In.)	32.41 N	117.11 W
163	Coronado B..................P. I.	7.55 N	122.10 E
54	Coronation G. (kŏr-ô-nā'shŭn) Can.	68.0 N	112.30 W
163	Coron B. (kô-rōn')..........P. I.	11.55 N	120.10 E
104	Coronel (kō-rô-nĕl')..........Chl.	37.5 S	73.12 W
104	Coronel Suárez (swä'räs).....Arg.	37.32 S	62.5 W
163	Coron I.....................P. I.	11.55 N	120.15 E
102	Coropuna, Mt. (kô-rô-pōō'nä) Peru	15.58 S	72.2 W
167	Corowa (kôr'ô-wȧ).........Austl.	36.2 S	146.22 E
90	Corozal (kō-rô-zäl')....C. Z. (In.)	8.58 N	7.35 W
81	Corpus Christi (kôr'pŭs krĭs'tê) Tex.	27.48 N	97.24 W
81	Corpus Christi B............Tex.	27.50 N	97.15 W
80	Corpus Christi, L............Tex.	28.10 N	97.50 W
104	Corral (kô-räl')..............Chl.	39.59 S	73.28 W
126	Corral de Almaguer (kô-räl' dā äl-mä-gâr').Sp.	39.47 N	3.8 W
96	Corralillo (kô-rä-lē'lyō).....Cuba	22.58 N	80.38 W
162	Corregidor I. (kô-rā-hē-dōr'). P. I.	14.22 N	120.35 E
126	Correlia (kô-rĕl'yä)............Sp.	42.8 N	1.48 W
103	Correntina (kô-rĕn-tē'nȧ)....Braz.	13.45 S	44.45 W
116	Corrib, Lough (L.) (lŏk kŏr'ĭb) Ire.	53.30 N	9.10 W
104	Corrientes (kō-ryĕn'tās)......Arg.	27.28 S	58.45 W
104	Corrientes (State)...........Arg.	28.45 S	58.0 W
96	Corrientes B................Cuba	21.50 N	84.35 W
102	Corrientes, C................Col.	5.30 N	77.30 W
96	Corrientes, C...............Cuba	21.45 N	84.28 W
92	Corrientes, C................Mex.	20.22 N	105.43 W
85	Corry (kôr'ĭ).................Pa.	41.56 N	79.39 W
124	Corse, C. (kôrs).......Cor. (In.)	44.0 N	9.25 E
124	Corsica (I.) (kôr'sĭ-kȧ)...Fr. (In.)	42.0 N	9.0 E
81	Corsicana (kôr-sĭ-kăn'ȧ)......Tex.	32.6 N	96.28 W
92	Cortazar (kôr-tä-zär')........Mex.	20.28 N	100.57 W
124	Corte (kôr'tā).........Cor. (In.)	42.20 N	9.11 E
126	Cortegana (kôr-tȧ-gä'nä).......Sp.	37.55 N	6.49 W
126	Cortes (kôr-tās')..............Sp.	36.38 N	5.20 W
96	Cortes B....................Cuba	22.5 N	83.51 W
85	Cortland (kôrt'lănd).......N. Y.	42.36 N	76.9 W
128	Cortona (kôr-tō'nä)............It.	43.27 N	11.59 E
126	Coruche (kô-rōō'she)........Port.	38.57 N	8.32 W
113	Çoruh R. (chō-rōōκ')........Tur.	40.40 N	41.30 E
113	Çorum (chô-rōōm')..........Tur.	40.30 N	34.47 E
103	Corumbá (kō-rōōm-bä')......Braz.	19.0 S	57.45 W
84	Corunna (kô-rŭn'ȧ).........Mich.	42.57 N	84.8 W
103	Coruripe (kō-rōō-rē'pĭ)......Braz.	10.1 N	36.1 W
70	Corvallis (kŏr-văl'ĭs).........Ore.	44.34 N	123.17 W
118	Corve, R. (kôr'vê).......Gt. Brit.	52.28 N	2.42 W
138	Corvo I. (kôr'vōō)....Azores (In.)	39.40 N	31.8 W
84	Corydon (kŏr'ĭ-dŭn)..........Ind.	38.12 N	86.8 W
79	Corydon......................Ia.	40.49 N	93.21 W
84	Corydon.....................Ky.	37.45 N	87.42 W
93	Cosamaloápan (kô-sä-mä-lwä'pän) Mex.	18.21 N	95.49 W
93	Coscomatepec (kôs'kō-mä-tĕ-pĕk') Mex.	19.4 N	97.2 W
94	Coseguina (Vol.) (kô-sä-gē'nä) Nic.	12.58 N	87.34 W
118	Coseley (kōz'lĭ).........Gt. Brit.	52.33 N	2.5 W
128	Cosenza (kô-zĕnt'sä)............It.	39.15 N	16.16 E
84	Coshocton (kô-shŏk'tŭn).....Ohio	40.17 N	81.53 W
141	Cosmoledo Is. (kŏs-mō-lā'dō) Ind. O.	9.40 S	47.40 E
70	Cosmopolis (kŏz-mŏp'ō-lĭs) .Wash.	46.57 N	123.48 W
124	Cosne (kōn)..................Fr.	47.25 N	2.59 E
93	Cosamaloapan (kô-sä-mä-lwä'pän) Mex.	18.1 N	94.36 W
92	Cosoyoapa (kô-sô-yô-ä'pä)...Mex.	16.45 N	98.25 W
94	Costa Rica (kŏs'tȧ rē'kȧ)Cen. Am.	10.0 N	84.0 W
74	Cosumnes R. (kŏ-sŭm'nēz)...Calif.	38.20 N	121.15 W
102	Cotabambas (kō-tä-bäm'bäs) Peru	13.40 S	72.20 W
163	Cotabato (kō-tä-bä'tō).........P. I.	7.12 N	124.16 E
163	Cotabato Valley.............P. I.	7.0 N	124.30 E
93	Cotaxtla (kō-täs'tlä).........Mex.	18.48 N	96.23 W
93	Cotaxtla, R..................Mex.	18.50 N	96.23 W
124	Côte d'Or (kōt dôr')...........Fr.	47.10 N	4.50 E
92	Cotija de la Paz (kō-tē'hä dä lä päz) Mex.	19.45 N	102.38 W
138	Cotonou (kô-tô-nōō')..Fr. W. Afr.	6.28 N	2.28 E
102	Cotopaxi (Vol.) (kō-tô-päk'sê).Ec.	0.45 S	78.29 W
128	Cotrone (kô-trō'nä)............It.	39.4 N	17.5 E
116	Cotswold Hills (kŏtz'wōld) Gt. Brit.	51.40 N	2.10 W
70	Cottage Grove (kŏt'ăj grōv)..Ore.	43.47 N	123.5 W
169	Cottesloe (kŏt'ĕs-lō).........Austl.	32.0 S	115.46 E
74	Cottonwood Cr. (kŏt'ŭn-wŏŏd) Calif.	40.20 N	122.50 W
73	Cottonwood Cr. Utah (Salt Lake City In.)	41.10 N	111.41 W
76	Cottonwood R...............Minn.	44.12 N	95.0 W
97	Cotui (kō-twē')...............Hai.	19.4 N	70.11 W
80	Cotulla (kō-tŭl'lȧ)............Tex.	28.27 N	99.15 W
85	Coudersport (kou'dērz-pōrt)...Pa.	41.45 N	78.1 W
166	Couedie, Cape de (kōō-dē') Austl.	36.2 S	136.45 E
124	Couéron (kōō-ā-rôɴ')..........Fr.	45.15 N	1.41 W
142	Couga R. (kōō'gä)......U. S. Afr.	33.48 S	24.0 E
49	Cougar (kōō'gȧr) Wash. (Seattle In.)	46.3 N	122.17 W
46	Coulman I. (kōl'măn).......Ant.	73.30 S	170.30 E
124	Coulommiers (kōō-lô-myā')....Fr.	48.50 N	3.5 E
52	Council (koun'sĭl)..........Alsk.	64.55 N	163.30 W
79	Council Bluffs................Ia.	41.18 N	95.55 W
79	Council Grove..............Kan.	39.39 N	96.30 W
49	Coupeville (kōōp'vĭl) Wash. (Seattle In.)	48.12 N	122.41 W
103	Courantyne R. (kôr'ăn-tīn) Br. Gu.-Sur.	4.0 N	58.0 W
125	Courbevoie (kōōrb-vwȧ'). Fr. (In.)	48.54 N	2.16 E
125	Courdimanche (kōōr-dē-mäɴsh') Fr. (In.)	49.2 N	2.0 E
124	Coursan (kōōr'säɴ)...........Fr.	43.15 N	3.5 E
95	Courtown Cays (Is.) (kōōr'toun) W. I.	12.24 N	81.38 W
117	Courtrai (kōōr-trē')..........Bel.	50.49 N	3.15 E
81	Coushatta (kou-shăt'ȧ).......La.	32.2 N	93.21 W
124	Coutances (kōō-täɴs').........Fr.	49.4 N	1.28 W
124	Coutras (kōō-trä')............Fr.	45.2 N	0.9 W
116	Coventry (kŭv'ĕn-trĭ)....Gt. Brit.	52.25 N	1.35 W
126	Covilhã (kô-vēl'yăɴ).........Port.	40.18 N	7.31 W
73	Covina (kô-vē'nȧ) Calif. (Los Angeles In.)	34.5 N	117.54 W
82	Covington (kŭv'ĭng-tŭn)......Ga.	33.36 N	83.51 W
84	Covington...................Ind.	40.8 N	87.25 W
84	Covington...................Ky.	39.5 N	84.32 W
81	Covington...................La.	30.30 N	90.7 W
84	Covington..................Ohio	40.9 N	84.23 W
79	Covington..................Okla.	36.18 N	97.32 W
82	Covington..................Tenn.	35.34 N	89.40 W
85	Covington...................Va.	37.48 N	79.59 W
167	Cowal, L. (kou'ăl)..........Austl.	33.35 S	147.28 E
72	Cowan (kou'ăn)Colo. (Denver In.)	39.38 N	105.7 W
164	Cowan, L....................Austl.	31.45 S	121.47 E
70	Cow Cr.......................Ore.	42.45 N	123.30 W
166	Cowell (kou'ĕl)..............Austl.	33.40 S	136.55 E
116	Cowes (kouz)...........Gt. Brit.	50.45 N	1.20 W
72	Cowichan Station (kou-ĭch'ăn) Can. (Vancouver In.)	48.44 N	123.40 W
70	Cowlitz R. (kou'lĭts).......Wash.	46.30 N	122.40 W
166	Cowndilla L. (koun-dĭl'lä)..Austl.	32.28 S	142.15 E
167	Cowra (kou'rȧ)..............Austl.	33.51 S	148.42 E
103	Coxim (kō-shēɴ')...........Braz.	18.30 S	54.58 W
93	Coxquihui (kōz-kē-wē').....Mex.	20.11 N	97.34 W
80	Coyame (kō-yä'mä)..........Mex.	29.27 N	105.5 W
49	Coyle (koil)...Wash. (Seattle In.)	47.41 N	122.47 W
93	Coyoacán (kô-yô-ȧ-kän') Mex. (In.)	19.21 N	99.10 W
73	Coyote Cr. (kī-ō'tê) Calif. (Los Angeles In.)	33.50 N	118.4 W
74	Coyote R....................Calif.	37.26 N	121.58 W
92	Coyuca de Benítez (kō-yōō'kä dā bä-nē'tāz) Mex.	17.2 N	100.14 W
92	Coyuca de Catalán (dā kä-tä-län') Mex.	18.20 N	100.39 W
93	Coyutla (kō-yōō'tlä).........Mex.	20.14 N	97.39 W
78	Cozad (kō'zăd)...............Neb.	40.51 N	99.59 W
70	Crab Cr. (krăb)..............Wash.	47.20 N	118.50 W
169	Cradle Mt. (krā'd'l) Austl. (Tas. In.)	41.42 S	145.57 E
143	Cradock (krăd'ŭk)......U. S. Afr.	32.11 S	25.36 E
89	Crafton (krȧf'tŭn) Pa. (Pittsburgh In.)	40.26 N	80.4 W
72	Crags (krăgz).........Colo. (In.)	38.53 N	104.57 W
99	Craig (krāg) Arg. (Buenos Aires In.)	35.10 S	58.41 W
71	Craig.......................Colo.	40.33 N	107.33 W
57	Craigs Road (krāgz) Can. (Que. In.)	46.37 N	71.23 W
129	Craiova (krȧ-yō'vȧ)..........Rom.	44.18 N	23.49 E
85	Cranberry L. (krăn'bĕr-ĭ)...N. Y.	44.10 N	74.50 W
54	Cranbrook (krăn'brŏŏk).....Can.	49.28 N	115.32 W
77	Crandon (krăn'dŭn)..........Wis.	45.35 N	88.54 W
46	Crane Chan. (krān).......Ant. O.	67.0 S	68.0 W
124	Cransac (kräɴ-zăk')..........Fr.	44.28 N	2.20 E
85	Cranston (krăns'tŭn).........R. I.	41.45 N	71.27 W
70	Crater L. (krā'tēr)...........Ore.	42.55 N	122.7 W
70	Crater L. Natl. Pk...........Ore.	42.58 N	122.10 W
71	Craters of the Moon Natl. Mon. Ida.	43.25 N	113.30 W
103	Crateús (krä-tā-ōōzh')......Braz.	5.10 S	40.32 W
103	Crato (krä'tōō)..............Braz.	7.27 S	39.29 W
76	Crawford (krô'fērd)..........Neb.	42.41 N	103.25 W
163	Crawford Pt..................P. I.	11.20 N	119.25 E
84	Crawfordsville...............Ind.	40.2 N	86.55 W
81	Crawley (krô'lē).............La.	30.14 N	92.22 W
119	Crayford (krā'fērd) Gt. Brit. (London In.)	51.27 N	0.11 E
71	Crazy Mts..................Mont.	46.10 N	110.30 W
71	Crazy Woman Cr............Wyo.	44.10 N	106.26 W
73	Creek (krēk) Ala. (Birmingham In.)	33.39 N	87.6 W
54	Cree L. (krē)................Can.	57.35 N	107.0 W
76	Creighton (krā'tŭn)..........Neb.	42.27 N	97.54 W
143	Creighton.............U. S. Afr.	30.1 S	29.51 E
124	Creil (krĕ'y')..................Fr.	49.18 N	2.31 E
128	Crema (krā'mä)................It.	45.16 N	9.52 E
128	Cremona (krā-mō'nä)...........It.	45.8 N	10.1 E
72	Crescent (krĕs'ĕnt) Can. (Vancouver In.)	49.3 N	122.52 W
70	Crescent City...............Calif.	41.45 N	124.13 W
83	Crescent City................Fla.	29.26 N	81.33 W
56	Crescent L....Can. (Winnipeg In.)	49.58 N	98.18 W
83	Crescent L...................Fla.	29.25 N	81.30 W
70	Crescent L...................Ore.	43.28 N	122.0 W
89	Crescent Sprs.Ky. (Cincinnati In.)	39.3 N	84.35 W
77	Cresco (krĕs'kō)...............Ia.	43.23 N	92.7 W
124	Crest (krĕst)...................Fr.	44.42 N	5.1 E

ng-sing; ŋ-baŋk; ɴ-nasalized n; nŏd; cŏmmit; ōld; ôbey; ôrder; fōōd; fŏŏt; ou-ou; s-soft; sh-dish; th-thin; pūre; ûnite; ûrn; stŭd; circŭs; ü-as "y" in study; '-indeterminate vowel.

Page	Name Pronunciation Region	Lat. °′	Long. °′
78	Crested Butte (krĕst′ĕd būt) . Colo.	38.50 N	106.40 W
84	Crestline (krĕst-līn) .... Ohio	40.48 N	82.44 W
77	Creston (krĕs′tŭn) .... Ia.	41.3 N	94.21 W
82	Crestview (krĕst′vū) .... Fla.	30.46 N	86.34 W
166	Creswick (krĕs′wĭk) .... Austl.	37.23 S	143.52 E
79	Crete (krēt) .... Neb.	40.37 N	96.57 W
128	Crete (I.) .... Grc. (In.)	35.10 N	25.0 E
125	Créteil (krā-tē′y′) ...... Fr. (In.)	48.47 N	2.30 E
128	Crete, Sea of .... Grc.	35.40 N	24.55 E
127	Creus, C. (krā′o͞os) .... Sp.	42.18 N	3.18 E
124	Creuse R. (krûz) .... Fr.	46.45 N	0.50 E
125	Creutzwald (kroits′väld) ...... Fr.	49.11 N	6.41 E
127	Crevillente (krå-vē-lyĕn′tå) .... Sp.	38.14 N	0.49 W
116	Crewe (kro͞o) .... Gt. Brit.	53.15 N	2.30 W
83	Crewe .... Va.	37.10 N	78.8 W
72	Crews (kro͞os) Colo. (Colo. Sprs. In.)	38.43 N	104.43 W
122	Crimmitschau (krĭm′ĭt-shou) . . Ger.	50.49 N	12.22 E
78	Cripple Creek .... Colo.	38.45 N	105.12 W
85	Crisfield (krĭs-fēld) .... Md.	38.0 N	75.51 W
90	Cristobal (krēs-tô-bäl′) . C. Z. (In.)	9.21 N	79.54 W
123	Crişul Alb R. (krē′sho͞ol ălb) Rom.	46.20 N	22.10 E
129	Crnagora (Montenegro) (Prov.) (ts′r-ná-gō′rå) (mŏn-tå-nā′grō) (mŏn-tē-nē′grō) . Yugo.	42.45 N	19.25 E
129	Crna R. (ts′r′ná) .... Yugo.	41.10 N	21.47 E
128	Crnomelj (ch′r′nō-māl′) .... Yugo.	45.36 N	15.13 E
128	Croatia (Prov.) (krō-ā′shá) . . Yugo.	45.15 N	15.40 E
81	Crockett (krŏk′ĕt) .... Tex.	31.19 N	95.28 W
143	Crocodile R. (krŏk′ō-dīl) U. S. Afr.	25.25 S	31.0 E
119	Croft (krŏft) Gt. Brit. (Liverpool In.)	53.26 N	2.33 W
76	Crofton (krŏf′tŭn) .... Neb.	42.43 N	97.29 W
124	Croix (krwä) .... Fr.	50.40 N	3.19 E
164	Croker I. (krō′kĕr) .... Austl.	11.5 S	132.40 E
116	Cromarty (krŏm′ár-tĭ) . . . Gt. Brit.	57.40 N	4.0 W
171	Cromwell (krŏm′wĕl) .... N. Z.	45.2 S	169.15 E
119	Cronton (krŏn′tŭn) Gt. Brit. (Liverpool In.)	53.23 N	2.45 W
169	Cronulla (krō-nŭl′á) Austl. (Sydney In.)	34.4 S	151.9 E
79	Crooked Cr. (kro͝ok′ĕd) .... Ill.	40.15 N	90.45 W
78	Crooked Cr. .... Kan.	37.15 N	100.20 W
70	Crooked Cr. .... Ore.	42.35 N	118.0 W
97	Crooked I. .... Ba. Is.	22.45 N	74.12 W
97	Crooked I. Passage .... Ba. Is.	22.55 N	74.30 W
87	Crooked L. .... Newf.	48.25 N	56.15 W
70	Crooked R. .... Ore.	44.20 N	121.0 W
96	Crookston (kro͝oks′tŭn) .... Minn.	47.45 N	96.36 W
84	Crooksville (kro͝oks′vĭl) ...... Ohio	39.47 N	82.7 W
167	Crookwell (kro͝ok′wĕl) ...... Austl.	34.28 S	149.29 E
77	Crosby (krôz′bĭ) .... Minn.	46.30 N	93.58 W
76	Crosby .... N. D.	48.55 N	103.18 W
81	Crosby .... Tex. (In.)	30.0 N	95.3 W
79	Crossett (krôs′ĕt) .... Ark.	33.7 N	91.57 W
96	Cross Har. .... Ba. Is.	25.55 N	77.18 W
85	Cross L. .... Can.	44.55 N	76.50 W
54	Cross L. .... Can.	54.40 N	98.15 W
81	Cross L. .... La.	32.30 N	93.55 W
53	Cross Sd. .... Alsk.	58.20 N	136.30 W
84	Crosswell (krôz′wĕl) .... Mich.	43.15 N	82.36 W
119	Crouch, R. (krouch) Gt. Brit. (London In.)	51.37 N	0.48 E
78	Crow Cr. (krō) .... Wyo.-Colo.	40.40 N	104.20 W
76	Crow Creek Indian Res. ...... S. D.	44.10 N	99.23 W
119	Crowden (krō′dĕn) Gt. Brit. (Liverpool In.)	53.30 N	1.54 W
167	Crowdy B. (krou′dĭ) .... Austl.	31.50 S	152.48 E
167	Crowdy Hd. .... Austl.	31.52 S	152.48 E
166	Crowes (krōz) .... Austl.	38.41 S	143.22 E
77	Crow L. .... Can.	49.12 N	93.50 W
167	Crowl Cr. (kroul) .... Austl.	32.0 S	145.38 E
118	Crowle (kroul) .... Gt. Brit.	53.36 N	0.49 W
84	Crown Point (kroun point′) . . Ind.	41.25 N	81.22 W
85	Crown Point .... N. Y.	43.58 N	73.27 W
77	Crow R. .... Minn.	45.10 N	93.38 W
169	Crows Nest .... Austl. (In.)	27.15 S	152.3 E
77	Crow Wing R. .... Minn.	46.40 N	94.51 W
165	Croydon (kroi′dŭn) .... Austl.	18.8 S	142.5 E
116	Croydon .... Gt. Brit.	51.25 N	0.5 W
73	Croydon Utah (Salt Lake City In.)	41.4 N	111.31 W
7	Crozet Is. (krō-zĕ′) .... Ind. O.	46.20 S	51.30 E
74	Crucero (kro͞o-sĕ′rō) .... Calif.	35.3 N	116.11 W
96	Cruces (kro͞o′sås) .... Cuba	22.19 N	80.18 W
80	Cruillas (kro͞o-ēl′yås) .... Mex.	24.45 N	98.31 W
119	Cruybeke (kroi′bĕ-kĕ) Bel. (Anvers In.)	51.10 N	4.18 E
104	Cruz Alta (kro͞oz äl′tå) ..... Braz.	28.40 S	53.40 W
96	Cruz, C. (kro͞oz) .... Cuba	19.50 N	77.43 W
96	Cruz Cay (I.) (kro͞oz) .... Cuba	22.12 N	77.48 W
102	Cruzeiro do Sul (kro͞o-zā′ro͞o do͞o so͞ol) . Braz.	7.31 S	72.33 W
166	Crystal Brook .... Austl.	33.21 S	138.12 E
80	Crystal City .... Tex.	28.40 N	99.50 W
77	Crystal Falls .... Mich.	46.7 N	88.20 W
82	Crystal Sprs. .... Miss.	31.59 N	90.22 W
123	Csongrad (chŏn′grād) ...... Hung.	46.43 N	20.10 E
123	Csorna (chôr′nä) .... Hung.	47.40 N	17.11 E
150	Ctesiphon (Ruins) (tĕs′ĭ-fŏn) . . Iraq	33.0 N	44.45 E
93	Cuajimalpa (kwä-hē-mäl′pä) Mex. (In.)	19.21 N	99.18 W
94	Cuajiniquilapa (kwä′hē-nē-kē-lä′-pä) . Guat.	14.16 N	90.19 W
140	Cuamato (Dom Luiz) (kwä-mä′tō) Ang.	17.35 S	15.51 E
140	Cuando R. (kwän′dō) Ang.-N. Rho.	16.12 S	22.0 E
140	Cuango (kwäŋ′gō) .... Ang.	6.17 S	16.58 E
167	Cuangong (kwăŋ-gông′) .... Austl.	33.1 S	146.42 E
140	Cuanza (kwän′zä) .... Ang.	11.52 S	18.40 E
104	Cuareim, R. (kwä-rāɴ′) . Braz.-Ur.	30.30 S	56.30 W
104	Cuarto, R. (kwär′tō) .... Arg.	33.30 S	63.0 W
80	Cuatro Ciénegas (kwä′trō syā′nā-gäs) . Mex.	26.58 N	102.4 W
93	Cuauhtepec (kwä-o͞o-tĕ-pĕk′) Mex. (In.)	19.33 N	99.8 W
92	Cuautepec .... Mex.	16.44 N	99.3 W
92	Cuautepec .... Mex.	19.59 N	98.19 W
93	Cuautitlan, R. (kwä-o͞o-tēt-län′) Mex. (In.)	19.38 N	99.15 W
92	Cuautla (kwä-o͞ot′lå) .... Mex.	18.47 N	98.58 W
93	Cuautlalpan (kwä-o͞o-tläl-pän′) Mex. (In.)	19.26 N	98.54 W
96	Cuba (kū′bá) .... W. I.	22.0 N	79.0 W
126	Cuba (ko͞o′bå) .... Port.	38.10 N	7.54 W
140	Cubango (ko͞o-bäŋ′gō) .... Ang	14.35 S	16.33 E
72	Cub Mt. (kŭb) Colo. (Denver In.)	39.34 N	105.28 W
73	Cucamonga (ko͞o-ká-mŏŋ′gá) Calif. (Los Angeles In.)	34.6 N	117.34 W
140	Cuchi (ko͞o′chē) .... Ang.	14.47 S	16.55 E
97	Cuchillas de Toar (Mts.) (ko͞o-chē′lyäs dā twär′) . Cuba	20.30 N	75.0 W
80	Cuchillo Parado (ko͞o-chē′lyō pä-rä′dō) . Mex.	29.27 N	104.59 W
94	Cuchumatanes, Sierra de (Mts.) (ko͞o-cho͞o-mä-tä′nås) . Guat.	15.40 N	91 20 W
102	Cúcuta (ko͞o′ko͞o-tä) .... Col.	7.58 N	72.29 W
77	Cudahy (kŭd′á-hĭ) .... Wis.	42.57 N	87.52 W
151	Cuddalore (kŭd-á-lōr′) ...... India	11.35 N	79.45 E
151	Cuddapah (kŭd′á-pä) .... India	14.30 N	78.45 E
167	Cudgewa (kŭd-gū′wá) ...... Austl.	36.6 S	147.47 E
164	Cue (kū) .... Austl.	27.28 S	118.2 E
126	Cuellar (kwā-lyär′) .... Sp.	41.25 N	4.18 W
102	Cuenca (kwĕn′kä) .... Ec.	2.58 S	79.20 W
161	Cuenca .... P. I. (Manila In.)	13.56 N	121.3 E
126	Cuenca .... Sp.	40.5 N	2.8 W
80	Cuencamé (kwĕn kä-mā′) .... Mex.	24.52 N	103.40 W
92	Cuerámaro (kwā-rä′mä-rô) . . Mex.	20.35 N	101.41 W
92	Cuernavaca (kwĕr-nä-vä′kä) . Mex.	18.55 N	99.14 W
163	Cuernos of Negros (Mt.) (kwĕr′nōs) P. I.	9.15 N	123.12 E
81	Cuero (kwā′rō) .... Tex.	29.5 N	97.18 W
92	Cuetzalá (kwĕt-zä-lä′) .... Mex.	17.58 N	99.54 W
93	Cuetzalan del Progreso (kwĕt-zä-län′ dĕl prō-grā′sō) . Mex.	20.1 N	97.32 W
126	Cuevas de Vera (kwā′väs dā vā′rä) . Sp.	37.18 N	1.52 W
127	Cuevas de Vinromá (vēn-rō-mä′) Sp.	40.17 N	0.2 E
139	Cufra, Oases of (ko͞o′frä) .... Libya	25.0 N	22.0 E
128	Cuglieri (ko͞o-lyā′rē) .... Sard.	40.13 N	8.38 E
103	Cuiabá (ko͞o-yä-bä′) .... Braz.	15.30 S	56.10 W
93	Cuicatlán (kwē-kä-tlän′) .... Mex.	17.48 N	96.57 W
116	Cuillan Sd. (kool′ăn) .... Gt. Brit.	57.5 N	6.0 W
140	Cuito R. (ko͞o-ē′tō) .... Ang.	15.30 S	19.17 E
92	Cuitzeo (kwēt′zä-ō) .... Mex.	19.57 N	101.9 W
92	Cuitzeo, L. .... Mex.	19.55 N	101.0 W
163	Culasi (ko͞o-lä′sē) .... P. I.	11.25 N	122.4 E
167	Culcairn (kŭl-kârn′) .... Austl.	35.40 S	147.2 E
90	Culebra (ko͞o-lā′brä) ... C. Z. (In.)	9.2 N	79.40 W
94	Culebra, G. of .... C. R.	10.45 N	85.50 W
91	Culebra I. .... P. R. (In.)	18.19 N	65.17 W
165	Culgoa R. (kŭl-gō′á) .... Austl.	29.5 S	147.0 E
93	Culhuacán (ko͞ol-wä-kän′) Mex. (In.)	19.20 N	99.7 W
163	Culion (ko͞o-lē-ŏn′) .... P. I.	11.52 N	120.0 E
163	Culion I. .... P. I.	11.50 N	120.0 E
161	Culis (ko͞o′lēs) P. I. (Manila In.)	14.50 N	120.25 E
126	Cúllar (ko͞o′lyär) .... Sp.	37.36 N	2.35 W
127	Cullera (ko͞o-lyā′rä) .... Sp.	39.11 N	0.15 W
167	Cullerin Ra. (kŭl′ĕr-ĭn) .... Austl.	34.38 S	149.30 E
143	Cullinan (kŭl′ĭ-năn) .... U. S. Afr.	25.39 S	28.28 E
82	Cullman (kŭl′măn) .... Ala.	34.10 N	86.50 W
83	Culpeper (kŭl′pĕp-ĕr) .... Va.	38.30 N	7.58 W
102	Culpepper I. .... Ec.	1.45 N	92.0 W
56	Culross (kŭl′rôs) Can. (Winnipeg In.)	49.43 N	97.52 W
72	Cultus L. (kŭl′tŭs) Can. (Vancouver In.)	49.3 N	121.59 W
73	Culver (kŭl′vĕr) Calif. (Los Angeles In.)	34.1 N	118.25 W
84	Culver .... Ind.	41.16 N	86.27 W
102	Cumana (ko͞o-mä-nä′) .... Ven.	10.28 N	64.15 W
102	Cumarebo (ko͞o-mä′rē-bō) .... Ven.	11.28 N	69.20 W
85	Cumberland (kŭm′bĕr-lănd) . . Md.	39.40 N	78.44 W
77	Cumberland .... Wis.	45.31 N	92.1 W
165	Cumberland Is. .... Austl.	20.30 S	149.0 E
82	Cumberland Plat. .... Tenn.	35.55 N	85.0 W
82	Cumberland R. .... Ky.-Tenn.	36.20 N	86.10 W
55	Cumberland Sd. .... Can.	65.30 N	66.0 W
166	Cummins (kŭm′ĭns) .... Austl.	34.17 S	135.51 E
93	Cunduacán (ko͞on-do͞o-ä-kän′) Mex.	18.4 N	93.10 W
128	Cuneo (ko͞o′nā-ō) .... It.	44.23 N	7.32 E
165	Cunnamulla (kŭn-á-mŭl-á) . Austl.	28.0 S	145.58 E
92	Cuquio (ko͞o-kē′ō) .... Mex.	21.4 N	103.9 W
102	Curaçao (ko͞o-rä-sä′ō) .... W. I.	12.2 N	69.0 W
99	Curaumilla, Pt. (ko͞o-rou-mē′lyä) Chl. (Valparaiso In.)	33.5 S	71.46 W
104	Curicó (ko͞o-rē-kō′) .... Chl.	34.57 S	71.20 W
104	Curitiba (ko͞o-rē-tē′bä) ..... Braz.	25.20 S	49.15 W
96	Curly Cut Cays (Is.) ...... Ba. Is.	23.40 N	77.40 W
96	Current I. .... Ba. Is.	25.22 N	77.50 W
79	Current R. .... Ark.-Mo.	37.0 N	91.2 W
143	Currie, Mt. (kûr′ĭ) ..... U. S. Afr.	30.28 S	29.25 E
83	Currituck Sd. (kûr′ĭ-tŭk) ... N. C.	36.24 N	75.54 W
167	Currockbilly Ra. (kûr′rŏk-bĭl-ĭ) Austl.	35.30 S	150.2 E
129	Curtea de Arges (ko͝or′tē-á dĕ ár′-zhĕsh) . Rom.	45.8 N	24.39 E
76	Curtis (kûr′tĭs) .... Neb.	40.37 N	100.30 W
75	Curtis Cr. .... Utah	38.45 N	111.5 W
165	Curtis I. .... Austl.	23.45 S	151.28 E
103	Curuca (ko͞o-ro͞o′kä) . . Braz. (In.)	0.39 S	47.55 W
129	Ćurug (cho͞o′ro͞og) .... Yugo.	45.27 N	20.4 E
167	Curumbenya Ra. (ko͞o-ro͞om-bĕn′yá) . Austl.	33.0 S	148.20 E
102	Curupira, Serra (Mts.) (sĕr′rá ko͞o-ro͞o-pē′rá) . Braz.-Ven.	1.0 N	65.0 W
103	Cururupú (ko͞o-ro͞o-ro͞o-po͞o′) . Braz.	1.45 S	44.48 W
104	Curuzú Cuatiá (ko͞o-ro͞o-zo͞o′ kwä-tē-ä′) . Arg.	29.50 S	58.0 W
103	Curvêlo (ko͝or-vĕl′o͝o) .... Braz.	18.45 S	44.29 W
79	Cushing (kŭsh′ĭng) .... Okla.	35.58 N	96.47 W
124	Cusset (kü-sĕ′) .... Fr.	46.9 N	3.30 E
76	Custer (kŭs′tĕr) .... S. D.	43.46 N	103.36 W
72	Custer .... Wash. (Vancouver In.)	48.55 N	122.38 W
71	Cut Bank .... Mont.	48.38 N	112.19 W
150	Cutch (State) (kŭch) .... India	23.30 N	70.0 E
151	Cutch, Great Rann of (rŭn) . India	24.0 N	70.0 E
151	Cutch, G. of .... India	22.30 N	69.0 E
151	Cutch, Little Rann of .... India	23.30 N	72.00 E
82	Cuthbert (kŭth′bĕrt) .... Ga.	31.47 N	84.48 W
151	Cuttack (kŭ-tăk′) .... India	20.25 N	85.47 E
92	Cutzamalá (ko͞o-tzä-mä-lä′) . . Mex.	18.26 N	100.31 W
92	Cutzamalá, R. .... Mex.	19.0 N	100.20 W
170	Cuvier I. (kü-vyā′) .... N. Z.	36.27 S	175.50 E
140	Cuvo R. (ko͞o′vō) .... Ang.	11.15 S	14.45 E
122	Cuxhaven (ko͝oks′hä-fĕn) ..... Ger.	53.53 N	8.42 E
84	Cuyahoga Falls (kī-á-hō′gá) . . Ohio	41.8 N	81.27 W
89	Cuyahoga R. Ohio (Cleveland In.)	41.26 N	81.40 W
74	Cuyama R. (ko͞o-yä′má) .... Calif.	35.0 N	120.10 W
163	Cuyo (ko͞o′yō) .... P. I.	10.50 N	121.1 E
163	Cuyo East Pass .... P. I.	11.0 N	121.30 E
163	Cuyo I. .... P. I.	10.50 N	121.3 E
163	Cuyo Is. .... P. I.	11.5 N	121.0 E
94	Cuyotenango (ko͞o-yō-tē-näŋ′gō) Guat.	14.30 N	91.36 W
163	Cuyo West Pass .... P. I.	11.0 N	120.30 E
92	Cuyutlán (ko͞o-yo͞o-tlän′) ... Mex.	18.55 N	104.3 W
102	Cuzco (ko͞oz′kō) .... Peru	13.30 S	72.0 W
129	Cyclades (Is.) (sĭk′lá-dēz) .... Grc.	37.20 N	24.55 E
84	Cynthiana (sĭn-thĭ-ăn′á) ...... Ky.	38.22 N	84.18 W
81	Cypress Cr. (sī′prĕs) .... Tex.	32.50 N	94.43 W
72	Cypress I. . Wash. (Vancouver In.)	48.34 N	122.43 W
115	Cyprus (I.) (sī′prŭs) Mediterranean Sea	35.0 N	33.30 E
	Cyrenaica, see Cirenaica, Libya.		
139	Cyrene (Ruins) (sī-rē′nē) . . . Libya	32.55 N	21.50 E
122	Czechoslovakia (chĕĸ′ô-slô-vä′kĭ-á) . Eur.	49.5 N	18.35 E
123	Czersk (chĕrsk) .... Pol.	53.47 N	17.57 E
123	Częstochowa (chăɴ-stô-ĸô′vá) Pol.	50.49 N	19.8 E
123	Czortków (chôrt′ko͝of) .... Pol.	49.1 N	25.51 E
163	Daanbantayan (dä-ăn′băn-tä-yän′) P. I.	11.14 N	124.0 E
138	Dabakala (dä-bä-kä′lä) Fr. W. Afr.	8.21 N	4.30 W
49	Dabob (dä′bŏb) Wash. (Seattle In.)	47.51 N	122.49 W
49	Dabob B. ..... Wash. (Seattle In.)	47.43 N	122.51 W
123	Dąbrowa (dôɴ-brō′vá) .... Pol.	50.18 N	19.15 E
123	Dąbrowa .... Pol.	53.37 N	23.20 E
151	Dacca (dä′kä) (dăk′á) .... India	23.45 N	90.25 E
122	Dachau (dä′kou) .... Ger.	48.17 N	11.25 E
72	Dacono (dá-kō′nō) Colo. (Denver In.)	40.5 N	104.57 W
56	Dacotah (dá-kō′tå) Can. (Winnipeg In.)	49.53 N	97.38 W
83	Dade City (dād) .... Fla. (In.)	28.22 N	82.12 W
82	Dadeville (dād′vĭl) .... Ala.	32.49 N	85.47 W
162	Daet (dä′ăt) .... P. I.	14.7 N	122.59 E
138	Dagama (dä-gä′mä) Fr. W. Afr.	16.30 N	15.28 W
121	Dagda (däg′dä) .... Lat.	56.5 N	27.32 E
119	Dagenham (dăg′ĕn-ăm) Gt. Brit. (London In.)	51.32 N	0.10 E
74	Daggett (dăg′ĕt) .... Calif.	34.51 N	116.52 W
113	Daghestan (Soviet Republic) (dä-gĕs-tän′) . . . Sov. Un.	44.0 N	47.0 E
121	Dago (Hiiumaa) (I.) (dägh′ü) (hē′o͞o-mä) . Est.	58.50 N	22.40 E
162	Dagupan (dä-go͞o′pän) ...... P. I.	16.2 N	120.20 E
139	Dahlak Is. (dä-läk′) .... It. E. Afr.	15.45 N	40.15 E
150	Dahna (Great Sandy Desert) (dä′nä) . Asia	20.0 N	52.0 E
138	Dahomey (Colony) (dá-hō′mā) (dä-hō-mā′) . Fr. W. Afr.	9.0 N	2.0 E
157	Daidong R. (dī-dông′) .... Cho.	38.45 N	125.35 E
126	Daimiel (dī-myĕl′) .... Sp.	39.4 N	3.36 W
156	Dairen (dī′rĕn′) .... Kwan.	38.55 N	121.33 E
159	Daisen (Mt.) (dī′sĕn′) .... Jap.	35.21 N	133.2 E
97	Dajabon (dä-hä-bōn′) .... Hai.	19.34 N	71.42 W
164	Dajarra (dá-jăr′á) .... Austl.	21.40 S	139.28 E
138	Dakar (dá-kär′) ...... Fr. W. Afr.	14.40 N	17.28 W
151	Dakka (dăk′á) Afg. (Peshawar In.)	34.13 N	71.2 E
163	Dalaguete (dä-lä-gā′tā) ...... P. I.	9.45 N	123.32 E
153	Dalai Nor (L.) (dä-lī′ nōr) .... Chn.	49.0 N	117.40 E
163	Dalanganem Is. (dä-läŋ-gä′nĕm) P. I.	10.40 N	120.15 E
165	Dalby (dôl′bē) .... Austl.	27.8 S	151.10 E
120	Dale (dä′lĕ) .... Nor.	60.34 N	5.51 E
120	Dalen (dä′lĕn) .... Nor.	59.28 N	8.2 E
57	Dalesville (dālz′vĭl) Can. (Montreal In.)	45.43 N	74.24 W
167	Dalgety (dăl-gĕt′ĭ) .... Austl.	36.29 S	148.51 E
78	Dalhart (dăl′härt) .... Tex.	36.4 N	102.32 W
86	Dalhousie (dăl-ho͞o′zē) .... Can.	48.3 N	66.23 W
171	Dalhousie .... N. Z.	46.2 S	169.32 E
126	Dalías (dä-lē′äs) .... Sp.	36.50 N	2.51 W
73	Dallas (dăl′ás) Ga. (Atlanta In.)	33.55 N	84.51 W
70	Dallas .... Ore.	44.55 N	123.20 W
76	Dallas .... S. D.	43.14 N	99.33 W
81	Dallas .... Tex.	32.47 N	96.48 W
81	Dallas, L. .... Tex.	33.0 N	97.7 W
70	Dalles, The (dălz) .... Ore.	45.35 N	121.11 W
119	Dallgow (däl′go) . Ger. (Berlin In.)	52.32 N	13.5 E
139	Dallol Salt Pan (dä-lōl′) It. E. Afr.	13.45 N	40.30 E

ăt; fināl; rāte; senāte; ärm; åsk; sofá; fâre; ch-choose; dh-as th in other; bē; ēvent; bĕt; recĕnt; cratĕr; g-go; gh-gutteral g; bĭt; ĭ-short neutral; rīde; ĸ-gutteral k as ch in German ich;

Page	Name Pronunciation Region	Lat. °′	Long. °′
128	Dalmatia (Prov.) (dăl-mā'shĭ á) Yugo.	43.30 N	16.40 E
165	Dalrymple, Mt. (dăl'rĭm-p'l) Austl.	21.15 S	148.40 E
169	Dalrymple, Port..Austl. (Tas. In.)	41.4 S	146.46 E
82	Dalton (dôl'tŭn)...Ga.	34.46 N	84.59 W
143	Dalton...U. S. Afr.	29.21 S	30.38 E
162	Dalupiri I. (dä-lōō-pē'rē)....P. I.	19.4 N	121.13 E
162	Dalupiri I....P. I.	12.25 N	124.15 E
74	Daly City (dā'lē)...Calif.	37.40 N	122.30 W
164	Daly R....Austl.	14.15 S	131.30 E
164	Daly Waters...Austl.	16.19 S	133.28 E
103	Dam (däm)...Sur.	4.45 N	55.0 W
6	Dama (dä'mä)...Fiji Is. (In.)	16.52 S	178.39 E
139	Damanhûr (dä-män-hōōr')....Eg.	30.57 N	30.58 E
151	Damão (dä-mouN')...India	20.20 N	72.45 E
140	Damaraland (Dist.) (dá'má-rá-lănd).S. W. Afr.	22.15 S	17.30 E
161	Damar I. (dä'mär)....Neth. Ind.	7.5 S	128.45 E
96	Damas Cays (Is.) (dä'mäs)..W. I.	23.52 N	79.48 W
150	Damas (Damascus) (dá-mä') (dá-măs'kŭs).Syr.	33.35 N	36.28 E
140	Damba (däm'bä)...Ang.	6.48 S	15.22 E
129	Dâmbovita R. (dûm'bô-vē'tsà) Rom.	44.35 N	25.40 E
97	Dame Marie, C. (dām-må-rē')Hai.	18.36 N	74.26 W
150	Damghan (dām-gän')...Iran	35.50 N	54.29 E
139	Damietta (Dumiât) (dăm-ĭ-ĕt'á) (dōōm-yät').Eg.	31.27 N	31.48 E
125	Dammartin-en-Goële (däN-mär-tăN'-äN-gô-ĕl').Fr. (In.)	49.3 N	2.42 E
163	Dammi I. (däm'mē)...P. I.	5.48 N	120.26 E
164	Dampier Arch. (dăm'pēr)...Austl.	20.40 S	116.45 E
161	Dampier Str....Neth. Ind.	0.30 S	131.30 E
125	Dampierre (däN-pyår')...Fr. (In.)	48.43 N	1.58 E
74	Dana Mt. (dā'ná)...Calif.	37.53 N	119.12 W
163	Danao (dä-nä'ō)...P. I.	10.30 N	124.10 E
85	Danbury (dăn'bĕr-ĭ)...Conn.	41.24 N	73.27 W
81	Danbury...Tex. (In.)	29.13 N	95.21 W
161	Dancolao, R. (dän-kô-lä'ō) P. I. (Manila In.)	14.0 N	120.43 E
167	Dandenong (dăn'dē-nông)...Austl.	37.59 S	145.12 E
169	Dandenong Cr. Austl. (Melbourne In.)	38.0 S	145.12 E
158	Dandyo Is. (dän'dyō)...Jap.	32.0 N	128.20 E
118	Dane, R. (dān)...Gt. Brit.	53.11 N	2.15 W
86	Danforth (dăn'fûrth)...Me.	45.37 N	67.53 W
165	Danger, Pt....Austl.	28.10 S	153.35 E
166	Danger Pt....Austl.	38.25 S	141.40 E
142	Danger Pt....U. S. Afr.	34.38 S	19.15 E
83	Dania (dā'nĭ-á)...Fla. (In.)	26.2 N	8.8 W
142	Danielskuil (dăn'yĕlz-kûl)...Bech.	28.11 S	23.34 E
130	Danilov (dä'nē-lôf)...Sov. Un.	58.10 N	40.9 E
129	Danilovgrad (dá'nē-lôf-gräd) Yugo.	42.32 N	19.6 E
130	Dankov (däŋ'kôf)...Sov. Un.	53.16 N	39.7 E
94	Danli (dän'lē)...Hond.	13.57 N	86.29 W
85	Dannemora (dăn-ē-mō'rá)..N. Y.	44.44 N	43.47 W
170	Dannevirke (dăn'nĕ-vĭrk-ĕ)..N. Z.	40.15 S	176.3 E
143	Dannhauser (dän'hou-zēr) U. S. Afr.	28.2 S	30.50 E
83	Dan R. (dăn)...N. C.-Va.	36.30 N	79.40 W
163	Dansalan (dän-sä'län)...P. I.	8.1 N	124.19 E
85	Dansville (dănz'vĭl)...N. Y.	42.34 N	77.40 W
119	Danube Canal (dăn'ūb) Aust. (Wien In.)	48.13 N	16.22 E
129	Danube R....Eur.	45.0 N	27.50 E
87	Danvers (dăn'vērz)....Mass. (In.)	42.34 N	70.57 W
49	Danville (dăn'vĭl) Calif. (San Francisco In.)	37.49 N	121.59 W
84	Danville...Ill.	40.9 N	87.37 W
84	Danville...Ind.	39.45 N	86.30 W
84	Danville...Ky.	37.48 N	84.48 W
85	Danville...Pa.	40.57 N	76.37 W
83	Danville...Va.	36.36 N	79.23 W
123	Danzig, Free State of (dän'tsĭk) Eur.	54.10 N	18.50 E
123	Danzig, G. of...Baltic Sea	54.33 N	19.14 E
163	Dao (dä'ō)...P. I.	10.30 N	121.57 E
163	Dao...P. I.	11.23 N	122.41 E
163	Dapa (dä-pä')...P. I.	9.46 N	126.40 E
163	Dapiak, Mt. (däp-yäk')...P. I.	8.5 N	123.27 E
163	Dapitan (dä-pē'tän)...P. I.	8.38 N	123.27 E
123	Dărăbani (dĕ-rä-băn'ĭ)...Rom.	48.13 N	26.39 E
129	Dara-dere (dä'rä-dĕr'ĕ)...Bul.	41.23 N	25.20 E
163	Daram I. (dä-räm')...P. I.	11.35 N	124.48 E
135	Darâu (dá-rä'ōō)...Eg. (In.)	24.24 N	32.59 E
151	Darbhanga (dŭr-bŭŋ'gä)...India	26.10 N	85.59 E
88	Darby (där'bĭ) Pa. (Philadelphia In.)	39.55 N	75.16 W
88	Darby Cr...Pa. (Philadelphia In.)	39.55 N	75.16 W
97	Darby I....Ba. Is.	23.50 N	76.15 W
72	D'Arcy I. (dár'sē) Can. (Vancouver In.)	48.34 N	123.17 W
115	Dardanelles (Str.) (dár-dá-nĕlz').Tur.	40.15 N	26.40 E
169	Darebin Cr. (dă'rē-bĭn) Austl. (Melbourne In.)	37.42 S	145.20 E
119	Darenth (dăr'ĕnt) Gt. Brit. (London In.)	51.25 N	0.15 E
119	Daresbury (därz'bĕr-ĭ) Gt. Brit. (Liverpool In.)	53.20 N	2.38 W
141	Dar es Salaam (där ĕs sá-läm') Tan.	6.47 S	39.15 E
139	Darfur (Reg.) (där-fōōr') A. E. Sud.	13.30 N	24.30 E
167	Darg Plat. (därg)...Austl.	37.5 S	146.50 E
151	Dargai (dŭr-gä'ē)...India	34.44 N	71.28 E
170	Dargaville (där'gá-vĭl)...N. Z.	35.59 S	173.54 E
6	Daria (dä'rē-ä)...Fiji Is. (In.)	16.52 S	178.54 E
102	Darien, G. of (dā-rĭ-ĕn')...Col.	9.0 N	77.0 W
95	Darien, Serrania del (Mts.) (sĕr-ä-nē'ä dĕl dä-rē-ĕn').Pan.-Col.	8.40 N	77.30 W
151	Darjeeling (dŭr-jē'lĭng)...India	26.58 N	88.29 E
143	Darkton (därk'tŭn)...Swaz.	26.13 S	31.1 E
118	Darlaston (där'lás-tŭn)..Gt. Brit.	52.34 N	2.2 W
142	Darling (där'lĭng)...U. S. Afr.	33.21 S	18.20 E
165	Darling Downs (Reg.)...Austl.	27.45 S	150.0 E
166	Darling R....Austl.	31.30 S	144.0 E
164	Darling Scarp...Austl.	31.30 S	116.0 E
116	Darlington...Gt. Brit.	54.30 N	1.40 W
83	Darlington...S. C.	34.17 N	79.52 W
77	Darlington...Wis.	42.45 N	90.30 W
72	Darlow (där'lō).Colo. (Denver In.)	39.59 N	104.57 W
122	Darmstadt (därm'shtät)...Ger.	49.53 N	8.39 E
124	Darnétal (dár-nā-tál')...Fr.	49.25 N	1.10 E
126	Daroca (dä-rō'kä)...Sp.	41.8 N	1.25 W
119	Dartford (därt'fērd) Gt. Brit. (London In.)	51.27 N	0.13 E
116	Dartmoor (därt'mōōr)...Gt. Brit.	50.35 N	4.0 W
54	Dartmouth (därt'mŭth).Can. (In.)	44.40 N	63.34 W
116	Dartmouth...Gt. Brit.	50.20 N	3.30 W
161	Daru (dä'rōō)...Pap. Ter.	9.10 S	143.10 E
128	Daruvar (dä'rōō-vär)...Yugo.	45.35 N	17.17 E
160	Darvel B. (där'vĕl)...B. N. B.	4.45 N	118.30 E
118	Darwen (där'wĕn)...Gt. Brit.	53.41 N	2.28 W
118	Darwen, R....Gt. Brit.	53.46 N	2.36 W
164	Darwin (där'wĭn)...Austl.	12.20 S	130.59 E
99	Darwin, Cordillera (Mts.) Chl. (Magallanes In.)	54.40 S	69.40 W
99	Darwin, Mt..Chl. (Magallanes In.)	54.43 S	69.22 W
140	Darwin, Mt...S. Rh.	16.47 S	31.35 E
150	Darya-yi Namak (Des.) dăr'yä-yĭ ná-mák').Iran	34.45 N	51.45 E
150	Dasht-i-Kavir (Des.) (dŭsht-ê-kå vēr').Iran	34.30 N	55.0 E
150	Dasht-i-Lut (Des.) (dŭsht-ê-lōōt').Iran	31.30 N	58.30 E
150	Dasht R. (dŭsht)...India	26.0 N	63.30 E
161	Dasmarinas (däs-mä-rē'näs) P. I. (Manila In.)	14.20 N	120.55 E
162	Dasol B. (dä-sōl')...P. I.	15.53 N	119.50 E
142	Dassen I. (däs'ĕn)...U. S. Afr.	33.22 S	18.5 E
162	Data, Mt. (dä-tä')...P. I.	16.50 N	120.53 E
160	Datu, C. (dä-tōō')...Sar.	2.5 N	109.36 E
139	Daua R. (dá'wä)..It.E.Afr.-Kenya	4.45 N	40.0 E
127	Dauera (dá-wä'rä)...Alg.	36.41 N	2.58 E
89	Daufuskie I. (dô-fōō'skē) S. C. (Savannah In.)	32.7 N	80.52 W
121	Daugava R. (dá'ōō-gá-vá)...Lat.	56.38 N	24.45 E
121	Daugavpils (dá'ōō-gäv-pēls)..Lat.	55.53 N	26.32 E
163	Dauin (dä'wēn)...P. I.	9.11 N	123.16 E
163	Dauis (dä'wēs)...P. I.	9.37 N	123.52 E
54	Dauphin (dô'fĭn)...Can.	51.5 N	100.1 W
54	Dauphin, L....Can.	51.15 N	99.45 W
163	Davao (dä'vä-ô)...P. I.	7.4 N	125.37 E
163	Davao G....P. I.	6.35 N	125.45 E
77	Davenport (dăv'ĕnpōrt)...Ia.	41.31 N	90.33 W
70	Davenport...Wash.	47.38 N	118.9 W
118	Daventry (dăv'ĕn-trĭ)...Gt. Brit.	52.15 N	1.9 W
169	Davey R. (dā-vē).Austl. (Tas. In.)	43.0 S	145.58 E
169	Davey, Port....Austl. (Tas. In.)	43.20 S	145.55 E
95	David (dä-vēdh')...Pan.	8.27 N	82.27 W
76	David City (dā'vĭd)...Neb.	41.15 N	97.6 W
169	Davidson Pk. (dā'vĭd-sŭn) Austl. (Sydney In.)	33.45 S	151.12 E
79	Davis (dā'vĭs)...Okla.	34.33 N	97.8 W
85	Davis...W. Va.	39.10 N	79.28 W
73	Davis Cr...Ala. (Birmingham In.)	33.23 N	87.18 W
70	Davis L....Ore.	43.38 N	121.51 W
80	Davis Mts....Tex.	30.40 N	104.20 W
48	Davis Str....Can.	66.0 N	60.0 W
122	Davos (dä'vōs)...Switz.	46.48 N	9.59 E
158	Davunda (dá-vōōn'dá)...Sov. Un.	48.55 N	138.55 E
123	Dawidgródek (dá-vēd-grōō'dĕk) Pol.	52.2 N	27.14 E
118	Dawley (dô'lĭ)...Gt. Brit.	52.38 N	2.28 W
160	Dawna Ra. (dô'ná)....India-Siam	17.0 N	98.15 E
54	Dawson (dô'sŭn)...Can.	64.5 N	139.31 W
82	Dawson...Ga.	31.46 N	84.28 W
76	Dawson...Minn.	44.56 N	96.2 W
78	Dawson...N. M.	36.41 N	104.47 W
99	Dawson I....Chl. (Magallanes In.)	54.0 S	70.40 W
165	Dawson R....Austl.	25.0 S	150.0 E
82	Dawson Sprs....Ky.	37.10 N	87.41 W
124	Dax (däks)...Fr.	43.42 N	1.2 W
160	Dayak R., Gt. (dī'yăk) Neth. Ind.	2.15 S	113.58 E
160	Dayak R., Little...Neth. Ind.	2.0 S	114.15 E
166	Daylesford (dālz'fērd)...Austl.	37.18 S	114.8 E
89	Dayton (dā'tŭn) Ky. (Cincinnati In.)	39.7 N	84.28 W
78	Dayton...N. M.	32.44 N	104.22 W
84	Dayton...Ohio	39.45 N	84.12 W
82	Dayton...Tenn.	35.30 N	85.1 W
81	Dayton...Tex.	30.3 N	94.54 W
70	Dayton...Wash.	46.17 N	117.59 W
83	Daytona Beach (dā-tō'ná)....Fla.	29.12 N	81.12 W
85	Dayville (dā'vĭl)...Conn.	41.49 N	71.53 W
143	De Aar (dē-är')...U. S. Afr.	30.39 S	34.1 E
76	Dead L....Minn.	46.30 N	95.45 W
145	Dead Sea....Pal-Transj. (In.)	31.25 N	35.25 E
76	Deadwood...S. D.	44.23 N	103.42 W
143	Dealesville (dēlz'vĭl)....U. S. Afr.	28.38 S	25.40 E
85	Deal Island...Md.	38.10 N	75.57 W
84	Dearborn (dēr'bŭrn)...Mich.	42.20 N	83.13 W
54	Dease Str. (dēz)...Can.	68.40 N	108.30 W
74	Death Valley...Calif.	36.25 N	116.55 W
74	Death Valley Jc....Calif.	36.19 N	116.25 W
74	Death Valley Natl. Mon....Calif.	36.0 N	117.0 W
124	Deauville (dō-vēl')...Fr.	49.20 N	0.1 E
131	Debaltsevo (dyĕb'ál-tsyĕ'vô) Sov. Un.	48.16 N	38.25 E
114	Debdou (dĕb-dōō')...Mor.	34.0 N	2.58 W
123	Deblin (däN'blĭn)...Pol.	51.35 N	21.50 E
138	Debo Swamp (dā'bō)..Fr. W. Afr.	15.30 N	3.30 W
129	Debra (Dibra) (dā'brä)...Yugo.	41.31 N	20.32 E
139	Debra Marcos (dĕ'brá mär'kôs) It. E. Afr.	10.17 N	37.41 E
139	Debra Tabor (dĕ'brá tä'bôr) It. E. Afr.	11.58 N	38.6 E
123	Debrecen (dĕ'brĕ-tsĕn)...Hung.	47.32 N	21.38 E
82	Decatur (dē-kā'tŭr)...Ala.	34.35 N	87.0 W
82	Decatur...Ga.	33.47 N	84.17 W
79	Decatur...Ill.	39.51 N	88.58 W
84	Decatur...Ind.	40.47 N	84.57 W
84	Decatur...Mich.	42.11 N	85.58 W
79	Decatur...Tex.	33.14 N	97.34 W
72	Decatur I..Wash. (Vancouver In.)	48.30 N	122.48 W
124	Decazeville (dē-káz'vēl')...Fr.	44.32 N	2.17 E
151	Deccan, The (Plat.) (dĕk'ăn).India	15.45 N	77.0 E
46	Deception I....Ant. O.	63.0 S	61.0 W
	Děčín, see Tetschen, Ger.		
124	Decize (dē-sēz')...Fr.	46.55 N	3.30 E
77	Decorah (dē-kō'rá)...Ia.	43.18 N	91.48 W
129	Dedeagats (Alexandroupolis) (dĕ-dĕ-ä-gäts') (ä-lĕk-sän-drōō'pō-lĭs) Grc.	40.51 N	25.51 E
86	Dedham (dĕd'ăm)...Mass.	42.15 N	71.11 W
138	Dédougou (dā-dōō-gōō') Fr. W.Afr.	12.30 N	3.25 W
142	De Drift (dē drĕft')....U. S. Afr.	31.18 S	20.16 E
73	Deep Cr...Calif. (Los Angeles In.)	34.21 N	117.10 W
83	Deep R....N. C.	35.30 N	79.25 W
49	Deep R.....Wash. (Portland In.)	46.20 N	123.41 W
79	Deepwater...Mo.	38.15 N	93.46 W
164	Deep Well...Austl.	24.10 S	134.10 E
169	Dee R. (dē)...Austl. (Tas. In.)	42.20 S	146.39 E
116	Dee, R....Gt. Brit.	52.55 N	3.10 W
167	Deerema (dē-rē'mä)...Austl.	30.18 S	148.4 E
86	Deer I. (dēr)...Me.	44.15 N	68.40 W
95	Deer I....Nic.	11.56 N	83.40 W
49	Deer I.....Ore. (Portland In.)	45.56 N	122.51 W
87	Deer L....Newf.	49.8 N	57.25 W
71	Deer Lodge...Mont.	46.23 N	112.44 W
169	Deer Park..Austl. (Melbourne In.)	37.47 S	114.47 E
89	Deer Park...Ohio (Cincinnati In.)	39.12 N	84.24 W
70	Deer Park...Wash.	47.57 N	117.29 W
89	Deer Range.La. (New Orleans In.)	29.36 N	89.54 W
77	Deer R....Minn.	47.20 N	93.48 W
84	Defiance (dē-fī'ăns)...Ohio	41.17 N	84.21 W
82	De Funiak Springs (dē fū'nĭ-ăk) Fla.	30.42 N	86.7 W
122	Deggendorf (dĕ'ghĕn-dôrf)...Ger.	48.51 N	12.58 E
92	Degollado (dā-gô-lyä'dō)....Mex.	20.27 N	102.9 W
164	De Grey R. (dē grā')...Austl.	21.0 S	120.58 E
151	Dehra (dā'rŭ)...India	30.15 N	78.5 E
150	Deir-ez-zor (dā-ēr'-ĕz-zôr')...Syr.	35.25 N	40.14 E
123	Dej (däzh)...Rom.	47.8 N	23.53 E
77	De Kalb (dē kălb')...Ill.	41.55 N	88.43 W
140	Delagoa B. (dĕl-á-gō'á)...Moz.	26.0 S	32.45 E
78	Delagua (dĕl-á-gwä)...Colo.	37.19 N	104.40 W
83	De Land (dē lănd')...Fla.	29.2 N	81.18 W
74	Delano (dĕl'á-nō)...Calif.	35.46 N	119.17 W
75	Delano Mt....Utah	38.28 N	112.28 W
123	Delatyn (dĕ-lá'tĭn)...Pol.	48.31 N	24.38 E
77	Delavan (dĕl'á-văn)...Wis.	42.39 N	88.35 W
84	Delaware (dĕl'á-wâr)...Ohio	40.17 N	83.3 W
85	Delaware (State)...U. S.	39.0 N	75.20 W
85	Delaware B....Del.-N. J.	39.0 N	75.10 W
79	Delaware R....Kan.	39.30 N	95.34 W
85	Delaware R....U. S.	41.30 N	75.0 W
122	Delémont (dē-lā-môN')...Switz.	47.21 N	7.20 E
80	De Leon (dē lē-ŏn')...Tex.	32.7 N	98.32 W
117	Delft (dĕlft)...Neth.	52.0 N	4.21 E
141	Delgado, C. (dĕl-gä'dō)...Moz.	10.30 S	40.30 E
104	Delgado Pt....Arg.	42.50 S	63.40 W
139	Delgo (dĕl'gô)...A. E. Sud.	20.5 N	30.36 E
15	Delhi (dĕl'hī)...India	28.29 N	77.15 E
81	Delhi...La.	32.27 N	91.30 W
122	Delitzsch (dā'lĭch)...Ger.	51.32 N	12.17 E
113	Delizhan (dyĕ'lĭ-zhän')...Sov. Un.	40.47 N	45.0 E
120	Dellen L., N. (dĕl'ĕn)...Swe.	61.54 N	16.40 E
120	Dellen L., S....Swe.	61.48 N	16.32 E
76	Dell Rapids (dĕl)...S. D.	43.51 N	96.41 W
138	Dellys (dĕ-lēs')...Alg.	37.0 N	3.52 E
74	Del Mar (dĕl mär')....Calif. (In.)	32.57 N	117.16 W
122	Delmenhorst (dĕl'mĕn-hôrst).Ger.	53.2 N	8.38 E
78	Del Norte (dĕl nôrt')...Colo.	37.40 N	106.22 W
159	Delong Is. (dyĕ-lôŋ)...Sov. Un.	76.40 N	158.59 E
169	Deloraine (dĕl-ô-rān') Austl. (Tas. In.)	41.32 S	146.42 E
84	Delphi (dĕl'fī)...Ind.	40.36 N	86.41 W
84	Delphos (dĕl'fŏs)...Ohio	40.50 N	84.22 W
83	Delray Beach (dĕl-rā')..Fla. (In.)	26.27 N	80.4 W
80	Del Rio (dĕl rē'ō)...Tex.	29.21 N	100.54 W
75	Delta (dĕl'tá)...Colo.	38.44 N	108.5 W
75	Delta...Utah	39.21 N	112.35 W
56	Delta Station.Can. (Winnipeg In.)	50.10 N	98.21 W
139	Delvinë (dĕl'vē-nä)...Alb.	39.57 N	20.9 E
112	Dema R. (dyĕm'ä)...Sov. Un.	53.50 N	54.40 E
150	Demavend Mt.(dĕm-á-vĕnd') Iran	36.0 N	52.2 E
131	Demievka (dyĕm-yĕf'ká).Sov. Un.	50.24 N	30.30 E
75	Deming (dĕm'ĭng)...N. M.	32.16 N	107.46 W
72	Deming...Wash. (Vancouver In.)	48.50 N	122.13 W
122	Demmin (dĕ-mēn')...Ger.	53.55 N	13.2 E
138	Demnat (dĕm-nät')...Mor.	31.48 N	7.0 W
82	Demopolis (dē-mŏp'ō-lĭs)...Ala.	32.30 N	87.50 W
160	Dempo, Mt. (Vol.) (dĕm'pō) Neth. Ind.	3.47 S	103.7 E
148	Demyanka R. (dyĕm-yän'kä) Sov. Un.	59.0 N	72.0 E
130	Demyansk (dyĕm-yänsk') Sov. Un.	47.38 N	32.28 E
124	Denain (dē-năN')...Fr.	50.22 N	3.25 E
116	Denbigh (dĕn'bĭ)...Gt. Brit.	53.12 N	3.20 W

ng-sing; ŋ-baŋk; N-nasalized n; nŏd; cŏmmit; ōld; ôbey; ôrder; fōōd; fŏŏt; ou-out; s-soft; sh-dish; th-thin; pūre; ûnite; ûrn; stŭd; circŭs; ü-as "y" in study; '-indeterminate vowel.

Page	Name Pronunciation Region	Lat. °'	Long. °'
135	Dendara (dĕn'dȧ-rȧ).....Eg. (In.)	26.8 N	32.40 E
85	Dendron (dĕn'drŭn)..........Va.	37.2 N	76.52 W
148	Dengiz, L. (dĕŋ-gĭz')....Sov. Un.	50.30 N	64.0 E
122	Den Helder (dĕn hĕl'dĕr)...Neth.	52.57 N	4.45 E
127	Denia (dā'nyä)..........Sp.	38.50 N	0.5 E
166	Deniliquin (dĕ-nĭl'ĭ-kwĭn)...Austl.	35.35 S	144.59 E
76	Denison (dĕn'ĭ-sŭn)..........Ia.	42.1 N	95.20 W
79	Denison..........Tex.	33.45 N	96.32 W
113	Denizli (dĕn-ĭz-lē')..........Tur.	37.47 N	29.12 E
120	Denmark (dĕn'märk)........Eur.	56.0 N	10.10 E
83	Denmark..........S. C.	33.19 N	81.90 W
48	Denmark Str..........Grnld.	66.30 N	27.0 W
84	Dennison (dĕn'ĭ-sŭn)........Ohio	40.25 N	81.18 W
129	Denousa (I.) (dĕ-nōō'sȧ).....Grc.	37.5 N	25.50 E
89	Dent (dĕnt).Ohio (Cincinnati In.)	39.11 N	84.39 W
118	Denton (dĕn'tŭn).......Gt. Brit.	53.27 N	2.70 W
85	Denton..........Md.	38.54 N	75.50 W
81	Denton..........Tex.	33.11 N	97.8 W
78	Denver (dĕn'vẽr)..........Colo.	39.45 N	105.0 W
72	Denver..........Colo. (In.)		
104	Deodoro (dā-ōō-dō'rōō).Braz. (In.)	22.52 S	43.22 W
77	De Pere (dē pẽr')..........Wis.	42.26 N	88.2 W
85	Depew (dē-pū')..........N. Y.	42.56 N	78.42 W
79	De Queen (dē kwēn')........Ark.	34.2 N	94.21 W
81	De Quincy (dē kwĭn'sĭ).......La.	30.27 N	93.27 W
145	Déraa (dā-rä')..........Syr. (In.)	32.37 N	36.7 E
151	Dera Ghazi Khan (dā'rŭ gä-zē' ĸän').India	30.8 N	70.38 E
151	Dera Ismail Khan (dā'rŭ ĭs-mä-ēl' ĸän').India	31.59 N	70.59 E
113	Derbent (dĕr-bĕnt')......Sov. Un.	42.0 N	48.15 E
113	Derbeziye (dĕr-bä'zē-yȧ).....Tur.	37.10 N	40.1 E
164	Derby (där'bē) (dûr'bē).....Austl.	17.17 S	123.31 E
169	Derby..........Austl. (Tas. In.)	41.9 S	147.50 E
72	Derby (dûr'bē) Colo. (Denver In.)	39.49 N	104.55 W
85	Derby..........Conn.	41.20 N	73.6 W
116	Derby (där'bē)..........Gt. Brit.	52.55 N	1.30 W
118	Derby (Co.)..........Gt. Brit.	53.18 N	1.30 W
114	Derg (dĕrg)..........Libya	30.10 N	10.29 E
116	Dergh, Lough (L.) (lŏĸ dĕrg)..Ire.	52.55 N	8.20 W
81	De Ridder (dē rĭd'ẽr)..........La.	30.50 N	93.18 W
79	Dermott (dûr'mŏt)..........Ark.	33.32 N	91.25 W
139	Derna (dĕr'nä)..........Libya	32.45 N	22.32 E
72	Deroche (dē-rōsh') Can. (Vancouver In.)	49.11 N	122.4 W
116	Derravaragh, L. (dâr-rȧ-vä'rȧ) Ire.	53.40 N	7.20 W
129	Derventa (dăr'vĕn-tȧ)......Yugo.	44.58 N	17.55 E
169	Derwent R. (dûr'wĕnt) Austl. (Tas. In.)	42.33 S	146.45 E
118	Derwent, R..........Gt. Brit.	53.4 N	1.30 W
57	De Salaberry I. (dē sȧ-lȧ-bĕr'ĭ) Can. (Montreal In.)	45.16 N	74.8 W
79	Des Arc (dāz ärk')..........Ark.	34.58 N	91.31 W
139	Desbordeville (Impfondo) (dā-bōrd-vēl') (ĭmp-fōn'dō) Fr. Eq. Afr.	1.41 N	18.2 E
70	Deschutes R. (dā-shōōt')....Ore.	44.30 N	121.18 W
80	Desdemona (dĕz-dē-mō'nȧ)...Tex.	32.17 N	98.32 W
104	Deseado, R. (dā-sā-ä'dhō).....Arg.	47.0 S	68.0 W
7	Deserta Grande (R.) (dȧ-sĕr'tȧ grän'dā).Madeira Is. (In.)	32.28 N	16.30 W
95	Désirade (dā-zē-räd')..Guad. (In.)	16.20 N	61.3 W
76	De Smet (dē smĕt')..........S. D.	44.23 N	97.32 W
79	Des Moines (dē moin')........Ia.	41.32 N	93.32 W
78	Des Moines..........N. M.	36.44 N	103.47 W
79	Des Moines R..........Ia.	41.25 N	93.20 W
130	Desna R. (dyĕs-nȧ').....Sov. Un.	53.50 N	33.40 E
104	Desolation I..........Chl.	53.0 S	74.0 W
163	Desolation Pt..........P. I.	10.29 N	125.40 E
79	De Soto (dē sō'tō)..........Mo.	38.7 N	90.32 W
77	Des Plaines (dē plān'; dĕs plānz') Ill.	42.5 N	87.55 W
77	Des Plaines R..........Ill.	42.0 N	87.53 W
122	Dessau (dĕs'ou)..........Ger.	51.50 N	12.13 E
166	D'Estree B. (dĕs-trā').....Austl.	35.55 S	137.49 E
122	Detmold (dĕt'mōld)..........Ger.	51.56 N	8.53 E
84	Detroit (dē-troit')..........Mich.	42.20 N	83.0 W
89	Detroit..........Mich. (In.)		
79	Detroit..........Tex.	33.40 N	95.15 W
76	Detroit Lakes..........Minn.	46.50 N	95.50 W
89	Detroit R.....Mich. (Detroit In.)	42.20 N	83.2 W
130	Detskoe Selo (dyĕt'skō-yĕ syĕ-lō') Sov. Un.	59.45 N	30.20 E
123	Detva (dyĕt'vȧ)..........Czech.	48.34 N	19.23 E
119	Deurne (dûrn)...Bel. (Anvers In.)	51.14 N	4.27 E
123	Deutsch Eylau (doich ī'lou)..Ger.	53.36 N	19.36 E
122	Deutsch-Krone (doich-krō'nĕ) Ger.	53.16 N	16.27 E
129	Deva (dā'vä)..........Rom.	45.52 N	22.53 E
123	Dévaványa (dā'vô-vän-yô)..Hung.	47.2 N	20.57 E
113	Develi (dĕ'vȧ-lē)..........Tur.	38.25 N	35.15 E
122	Deventer (dĕv'ĕn-tĕr)......Neth.	52.15 N	6.10 E
103	Devils I..........Fr. Gu.	5.18 N	52.33 W
76	Devils L..........N. D.	48.3 N	99.0 W
76	Devils Lake..........N. D.	48.7 N	98.51 W
141	Devils Pk..........U. S. Afr.	33.57 S	18.27 E
74	Devil Postpile Natl. Mon....Calif.	37.40 N	119.6 W
80	Devils R..........Tex.	30.10 N	101.0 W
73	Devils Slide Utah (Salt Lake City In.)	41.4 N	111.33 W
71	Devils Tower Natl. Mon.....Wyo.	44.37 N	104.42 W
143	Devon (dĕv'ŭn)........U. S. Afr.	26.19 S	28.45 E
169	Devonport.......Austl. (Tas. In.)	41.10 S	146.11 E
170	Devonport..........N. Z. (In.)	36.51 S	174.48 E
73	Devore (dē-vôr') Calif. (Los Angeles In.)	34.14 N	117.27 W
81	Dewalt (dū'ălt)......Tex. (In.)	29.32 N	95.33 W
49	Dewatto (dē-wăt'ō) Wash. (Seattle In.)	47.27 N	123.3 W
72	Dewdney (dūd'nĭ) Can. (Vancouver In.)	49.0 N	122.12 W
143	Dewetsdorp (dē-vĕts'dôrp) U. S. Afr.	29.30 S	26.41 E
79	Dewey (dū'ĭ)..........Okla.	36.47 N	95.55 W
73	Deweyville (dū'ĭ-vĭl) Utah (Salt Lake City In.)	41.43 N	112.6 W
79	De Witt (dē wĭt')..........Ark.	34.16 N	91.21 W
77	De Witt..........Ia.	41.47 N	90.32 W
169	De Witt I.......Austl. (Tas. In.)	43.38 S	146.16 E
116	Dewsbury (dūz'bĕr-ĭ)....Gt. Brit.	53.45 N	1.40 W
86	Dexter (dĕks'tẽr)..........Me.	45.1 N	69.18 W
79	Dexter..........Mo.	36.47 N	89.57 W
83	Dexter L..........Fla.	29.7 N	81.25 W
52	Dezhneva, (East), C. (dāzh-nā'vȧ) Sov. Un.	66.0 N	170.0 W
151	Dhaulagiri, Mt. (dou-lȧ-gē'rē) Nep.	28.45 N	83.30 E
128	Dia (I.) (dē'ä)..........Grc.	35.26 N	25.13 E
49	Diablo, Mt. (dyä'blō) Calif. (San Francisco In.)	37.53 N	121.55 W
103	Diamantina (dyȧ-män-tē'nȧ) Braz.	18.12 S	43.32 W
164	Diamantina R. (dī'man-tē'nȧ) Austl.	25.42 S	140.0 E
103	Diamantino (dyȧ-män-tē'nōō) Braz.	14.28 S	56.30 W
70	Diamond Pk..........Ore.	43.32 N	122.10 W
160	Diamond Pt. (dī'mŭnd) Neth. Ind.	5.15 N	97.30 E
97	Diana Bank (dī-ăn'ȧ)......Ba. Is.	22.28 N	74.45 W
129	Dibra (Debra) (dē'brȧ) (dä'brȧ) Yugo.	41.31 N	20.32 E
152	Dichu (Yangtze Kiang) (R.) (dē'chōō') (yäng'tsĕ kyăng') Chn.	33.0 N	97.30 E
76	Dickinson (dĭk'ĭn-sŭn)......N. D.	46.52 N	102.48 W
81	Dickinson..........Tex. (In.)	29.27 N	95.2 W
81	Dickinson Bayou.......Tex. (In.)	29.27 N	95.3 W
85	Dickson (dĭk'sŭn)..........Pa.	41.26 N	75.41 W
82	Dickson..........Tenn.	36.4 N	87.23 W
113	Dicle R. (dĭj'lä)..........Tur.	37.50 N	41.0 E
119	Didsbury (dĭdz'bẽr-ĭ) Gt. Brit. (Liverpool In.)	53.25 N	2.13 W
129	Didymoteikhon (Dimotika) (dē-dü-mō'tā-ĸōn) (dē-mŏt'ĭ-kȧ) Grc.	41.20 N	26.28 E
125	Die (dē)..........Fr.	44.45 N	5.23 E
97	Diego de Ocampo, Pico (Pk.) (pē'kō dē ä'gō dä ō-käm'pō) Hai.	19.38 N	70.42 W
104	Diego Ramirez Is. (dē ä'gō rä-mē'rāz) Pac. O.	56.32 S	68.40 W
141	Diégo-Suarez (Antsirane) (dē ä'gō-swä'rāz) Madag.	12.10 S	49.13 E
124	Dieppe (dē-ĕp')..........Fr.	49.55 N	1.7 E
141	Diep R. (dē-ĕp')........U. S. Afr.	33.48 S	18.32 E
79	Dierks (dērks)..........Ark	34.7 N	94.1 W
86	Digby (dĭg'bĭ)..........Can.	44.38 N	65.45 W
169	Diggers Rest Austl. (Melbourne In.).	37.38 S	144.44 E
125	Digne (dēn'y')..........Fr.	44.6 N	6.18 E
124	Digoin (dē-gwăn')..........Fr.	46.28 N	4.9 E
161	Digul R. (dē-gōōl').....Neth. Ind.	6.30 S	140.22 E
157	Diisan (Mt.) (dē-ē-săn').....Cho.	35.20 N	127.44 E
124	Dijon (dē-zhôɴ')..........Fr.	47.20 N	5.4 E
131	Dikovka (dē-kôf'kȧ).....Sov. Un.	48.47 N	32.51 E
139	Dikwa (dē'kwȧ)..........Nig.	12.4 N	13.57 E
150	Dilam (dē-läm')........Sau. Ar.	23.59 N	47.8 E
162	Dilasac B. (dī-lȧ'săk)........P. I.	16.25 N	122.15 E
162	Dile Pt. (dē'lä)..........P. I.	17.34 N	120.20 E
161	Dili (dĭl'ē)..........Port. Tim.	8.37 S	125.34 E
135	Dillingât (dĭl-lĭŋ-gät')....Eg. (In.)	30.49 N	30.31 E
71	Dillon (dĭl'ŭn)..........Mont.	45.12 N	112.38 W
83	Dillon..........S. C.	34.24 N	79.22 W
140	Dilolo (dē-lō'lō).......Bel. Cong.	10.24 S	22.28 E
162	Dimasalang (dē-mä-sȧ-läng').P. I.	12.11 N	123.52 E
166	Dimboola (dĭm-bōō'lȧ)......Austl.	36.26 S	142.2 E
163	Dimiao (dē-mē-ä'ō)..........P. I.	9.37 N	124.10 E
129	Dimotika (Didymoteikhon) (dē-mŏt'ĭ-kȧ) (dē-dü-mō'tā-ĸōn) Grc.	41.20 N	26.28 E
163	Dinagat (dē-nä'gät)........P. I.	10.0 N	125.34 E
163	Dinagat I..........P. I.	10.10 N	125.35 E
163	Dinagat Sd..........P. I.	10.5 N	125.50 E
161	Dinalupihan (dē-nȧ-lōō-pē'hän) P. I. (Manila In.)	14.53 N	120.24 E
124	Dinan (dē-näɴ')..........Fr.	48.28 N	2.5 W
117	Dinant (dē-näɴ')..........Bel.	50.15 N	4.55 E
124	Dinard-St. Enogat (dē-när'săɴ-tē nō-gä') Fr.	48.35 N	2.0 W
160	Dindings (dĭn-dĭngz')....Strs. Sets.	4.30 N	100.45 E
162	Dingalan B. (dĭŋ-gä'län).....P. I.	15.18 N	121.25 E
116	Dingle (dĭng''l)..........Ire.	52.10 N	10.15 W
163	Dingle (dĭng'lä)..........P. I.	11.0 N	122.40 E
116	Dingle B. (dĭng''l)..........Ire.	52.0 N	10.20 W
165	Dingo (dĭŋ'gō)..........Austl.	23.44 S	149.27 E
162	Dingras (dĭn-gräs')..........P. I.	18.6 N	120.40 E
116	Dingwall (dĭng'wôl)......Gt. Brit.	57.35 N	4.25 W
71	Dinosaur Nat'l. Mon. (dī'nō-sôr) Utah-Colo.	40.30 N	109.0 W
74	Dinuba (dĭ-nū'bȧ)..........Calif.	36.32 N	119.22 W
138	Diorbivol (dē-ôr-bē-vōl') Fr. W. Afr.	16.8 N	13.20 W
96	Dios Cays (Is.) (dē-ōs')......Cuba	22.5 N	83.2 W
123	Diósgyör (dē'ōsh-dyûr).....Hung.	48.6 N	20.42 E
138	Diourbel (dē-ōōr-bĕl')..Fr. W. Afr.	14.36 N	16.20 W
163	Dipolog (dē-pō'lŏg)..........P. I.	8.34 N	123.23 E
95	Diquis, R. (dē-kēs')..........C. R.	8.57 N	83.25 W
139	Dire Daua (dē-rȧ-dä'wä) It. E. Afr.	9.34 N	41.48 E
94	Diriamba (dēr-yäm'bä)........Nic.	11.52 N	86.16 W
164	Dirk Hartog I. (dûrk här'tŏg) Austl.	25.50 S	113.0 E
165	Dirranbandi (dĭ-rȧ-băn'dē).Austl.	28.30 S	148.18 E
115	Dir Rissam (dēr rē-săm')...Libya	30.3 N	18.57 E
135	Dirût (dē-rōōt')..........Egypt	27.35 N	30.50 E
164	Disappointment, L..........Austl.	23.30 S	122.45 E
167	Disaster B..........Austl.	37.17 S	149.58 E
166	Discovery B..........Austl.	38.5 S	140.50 E
72	Discovery I.. Can. (Vancouver In.)	48.26 N	123.14 W
135	Dishna (dêsh'nȧ)........Eg. (In.)	26.6 N	32.28 E
48	Disko I. (dĭs'kō)..........Grnld.	70.0 N	54.0 W
83	Dismal Swamp..........Va.-N. C.	36.35 N	76.30 W
3	District of Columbia........U. S.	38.55 N	77.3 W
135	Disûq (dē-sōōk')........Eg. (In.)	31.6 N	30.40 E
163	Dit I. (dĭt)..........P. I.	11.15 N	120.56 E
151	Diu (dē'ōō)..........India	20.35 N	71.0 E
163	Diuata Mts. (dyōō-ä'tä).....P. I.	9.0 N	125.45 E
163	Diuata Pt..........P. I.	9.6 N	125.13 E
124	Dives (dēv)..........Fr.	49.18 N	0.0
72	Divide (dĭ-vĭd') Colo. (Colo. Sprs. In.)	38.57 N	105.9 W
162	Divilacan B. (dē-vē-lȧ'kän)...P. I.	17.24 N	122.17 E
103	Divisões, Serra das (Mts.) (sĕr'rȧ dăzh dē-vē-sôɴs') Braz.	18.0 S	53.0 W
113	Divrik (dĭv'rĭk)..........Tur.	39.28 N	38.10 E
73	Dixiana (dĭks-ĭ-ă'nȧ) Ala. (Birmingham In.)	33.45 N	86.42 W
77	Dixon (dĭks'ŭn)..........Ill.	41.51 N	89.29 W
54	Dixon Entrance..........Can.	54.30 N	133.30 W
113	Diyarbekir (dē-yär-bĕk'ĭr)....Tur.	38.0 N	40.10 E
150	Dizful (dēz-fōōl')..........Per.	32.20 N	48.31 E
129	Djakovica (dyä'kō-vē-tsä)..Yugo.	42.22 N	20.28 E
129	Djakovo (dyä'kō-vō).......Yugo.	45.18 N	18.25 E
160	Djambi (jăm'bē).......Neth. Ind.	1.40 S	103.32 E
150	Djebel Druse (Dist.) (jĕb'ĕl drōōz') (drüz) Syr.	32.48 N	37.0 E
138	Djelfa (jĕl'fä)..........Alg.	34.38 N	3.20 E
135	Djemmal (jĕm-mäl')...Tun. (In.)	35.38 N	10.40 E
138	Djenné (jĕn-nā')......Fr. W. Afr.	14.0 N	4.27 W
138	Djerid, Chott (L.) (jĕr'ĭd)....Tun.	33.45 N	8.30 E
135	Djezzine (jĕ-zēn')......Syr. (In.)	33.34 N	35.32 E
141	Djibouti (jē-bōō-tē').....Fr. Som.	11.30 N	43.3 E
114	Djidjelli (jē-jĕ-lē')..........Alg.	36.50 N	5.43 E
160	Djokjakarta (jōk-yä-kär'tä) Neth. Ind.	7.50 S	110.18 E
145	Djoubail (jōō-bī'y').....Syr. (In.)	34.8 N	35.40 E
145	Djounié (jōō-nyā')......Syr. (In.)	34.3 N	35.40 E
121	Djursholm (djōōrs'hōlm).....Swe.	59.23 N	18.1 E
131	Dmitriev (d'mē'trē-yĕf)..Sov. Un.	52.8 N	35.5 E
131	Dmitrievka (d'mē-trē-yĕf'kȧ) Sov. Un.	47.57 N	38.55 E
130	Dmitrov (d'mē'trôf)......Sov. Un.	56.20 N	37.31 E
130	Dmitrovsk (d'mē'trôfsk) Sov. Un.	52.30 N	35.8 E
131	Dnepr B (d'nyĕp''r).....Sov. Un.	46.31 N	31.49 E
131	Dnepr (Dnieper) R. (nē'pẽr) Sov. Un.	46.45 N	33.0 E
131	Dneprodzerzhinsk (Kamenskoe) (d'nyĕp'rō-zēr-shĭnsk kä-mĕn-skō'yĕ)..Sov. Un.	48.31 N	34.40 E
131	Dnepropetrovsk (Ekaterinoslav) (d'nyĕp'rō-pā-trôfsk) (yĕ-kä-tĕ-rē'nō-släf)....Sov. Un.	48.28 N	35.2 E
131	Dnestr B. (d'-nyĕst''r) Rom.-.Sov. Un.	45.15 N	30.15 E
131	Dnestr (Nistrul or Dniester) R. (nĕst'rōōl) (nēs'tẽr) Rom.-..Sov. Un.	47.35 N	29.8 E
131	Dnieper (Dnepr) R. (nē'pẽr) (dnyĕp'r)..Sov. Un.	50.10 N	31.0 E
131	Dniester (Dnestr or Nistrul) R. (nēs'tẽr) Rom.-..Sov. Un.	47.35 N	29.8 E
130	Dno (d'nô')..........Sov. Un.	57.48 N	29.59 E
164	Dobbyn (dŏb'ĭn)..........Austl.	19.50 S	139.58 E
121	Dobele (dō'bĕ-lĕ)..........Lat.	56.37 N	23.20 E
122	Döbeln (dû'bĕln)..........Ger.	51.7 N	13.4 E
161	Dobo (dō'bō)..........Neth. Ind.	5.57 S	134.16 E
129	Doboj (dō'boi)..........Yugo.	44.43 N	18.3 E
129	Dobrogea (Prov.) (dō'brō-jȧ) Rom.	44.25 N	28.10 E
123	Dobšiná (dôp'shē-nä)......Czech.	48.50 N	20.25 E
103	Doce, R. (dō'sȧ)..........Braz.	19.0 S	41.30 W
119	Dockenhuden (dŭk'ĕn-hōō-dĕn) Ger. (Hamburg In.)	53.34 N	9.49 E
73	Docray (dō'krä) Ala. (Birmingham In.)	33.14 N	87.12 W
92	Doctor Arroyo (dōk-tōr' är-rō'yō) Mex.	23.41 N	100.10 W
78	Dodge City (dŏj)..........Kan.	37.45 N	100.2 W
85	Dodgeville..........N. Y.	43.8 N	74.46 W
77	Dodgeville..........Wis.	42.58 N	90.8 W
140	Dodoma (dō'dō-mȧ)........Tan.	6.10 S	35.45 E
119	Doel (dōōl)....Bel. (Anvers In.)	51.19 N	4.15 E
77	Dog L..........Can.	48.44 N	89.30 W
96	Dog Rocks..........W. I.	24.3 N	79.51 W
150	Doha (Bida) (dō'hȧ) (bē'dȧ).Nejd	25.15 N	51.45 E
129	Doiran, L. (doi'rän)........Grc.	41.12 N	22.46 E
130	Dokszyce (dōk-shē'tsĕ).......Pol.	54.53 N	27.49 E
124	Dol (dōl)..........Fr.	48.35 N	1.42 W
125	Dôle (dōl)..........Fr.	47.8 N	5.30 E
49	Dole (dōl).....Wash. (Seattle In.)	45.47 N	122.20 W
131	Dolgaya, C. (dōl-gä'yȧ)..Sov. Un.	46.42 N	37.42 E
112	Dolgii I. (dôl'gĭ-ē)......Sov. Un.	69.10 N	59.0 E
123	Dolina (dō-lyē'nȧ)..........Pol.	48.57 N	24.2 E
96	Dollar Har..........Ba. Is.	25.28 N	79.15 W
139	Dolo (dō'lō)..........It. E. Afr.	4.2 N	42.4 E
73	Dolomite (dŏl'ō-mīt) Ala. (Birmingham In.)	33.28 N	86.58 W
128	Dolomites (Mts.)..........It.	46.25 N	11.50 E
104	Dolores (dō-lō'rĕs)..........Arg.	36.25 S	47.45 W
80	Dolores..........Tex.	27.40 N	99.43 W
162	Dolores..........P. I.	17.40 N	120.43 E
92	Dolores Hidalgo (ē-dăl'gō)...Mex.	21.9 N	100.45 W
75	Dolores R..........Colo.	38.30 N	109.0 W
163	Dolores R..........P. I.	12.6 N	125.16 E
54	Dolphin and Union Str. (dŏl'fĭn) Can.	69.0 N	115.0 W
129	Domanovići (dō'mȧ-no-vē'tyĭ) Yugo.	43.7 N	17.46 E
122	Domažlice (dō'mäzh-lē-tsĕ) Czech.	49.27 N	12.56 E
125	Dombasle (dôɴ-bäl')..........Fr.	48.38 N	6.20 E

ăt; finăl; rāte; senāte; ärm; ȧsk; sofȧ; fâre; ch-choose; dh-as th in other; bē; ēvent; bĕt; recĕnt; cratẽr; g-go; gh-gutteral g; bĭt; ĭ-short neutral; rīde; ĸ-gutteral k as ch in German ich;

Page	Name Pronunciation Region	Lat. °′	Long. °′
123	Dombóvár (dŏm′bō-vär)...Hung.	46.23 N	18.8 E
91	Dominica (I.) (dŏ-mĭ-nē′kȧ) Le. Is.	15.30 N	61.22 W
97	Dominican Republic (dô-mĭn′ĭ-kăn) W. I.	19.0 N	70.20 W
87	Dominion...Can.	46.12 N	60.5 W
140	Dom Luiz (Cwamato) (dōN lo͞o-ēzh′) (kwä-mä′tō) Ang.	17.3 S	15.15 E
141	Dom Luiz Filippe (Mtarica) (dōN lo͞o-ēzh′ fē-lē′pĕ) (′mtä′rĭ-kȧ) Moz.	12.45 S	36.40 E
125	Domont (dō môN′)...Fr. (In.)	49.1 N	2.20 E
116	Donaghadee (dŏn-ȧ-gȧ-dē′) Gt. Brit.	54.35 N	5.30 W
166	Donald (dŏn′ăld)...Austl.	36.21 S	143.1 E
81	Donaldsonville (dŏn′ăld-sun-vĭl) La.	30.5 N	91.0 W
82	Donalsonville (dŏn′ăl-sŭn-vĭl). Ga.	31.3 N	84.53 W
122	Donau (Danube) R. (dō′nou) (dăn′ūb). Eur.	48.47 N	12.0 E
122	Donawitz (dō′nȧ-vĭts)...Ger.	47.24 N	15.3 E
126	Don Benito (dōn′ bā-nē′tō)...Sp.	38.47 N	5.53 W
116	Doncaster (doŋ′kăs-tēr)..Gt. Brit.	53.30 N	1.10 W
140	Dondo (dōn′dō)...Ang.	9.38 S	14.30 E
140	Dondo...Moz.	19.43 S	34.47 E
151	Dondra Head (dŏn′drȧ)...Cey.	6.0 N	80.30 E
116	Donegal (dŏn-ê-gôl′)...Gt. Brit.	54.40 N	8.5 W
116	Donegal B...Gt. Brit.	54.35 N	8.20 W
116	Donegal, Mts. of...Gt. Brit.	54.50 N	8.10 W
131	Donets (Danube) R. (dō-nyĕts′) Eur.	50.10 N	36.50 E
164	Dongara (dôŋ-gä′ra)...Austl.	29.5 S	114.59 E
160	Donggala (dôŋ-gä′lä)..Neth. Ind.	0.38 S	119.41 E
160	Donghoi (dông-hô-ē′)..F. In. Chn.	17.38 N	106.29 E
140	Dongo (dôŋ′gō)...Ang.	14.43 S	15.50 E
139	Dongola (dŏŋ′gô-lȧ)...A. E. Sud.	19.12 N	30.27 E
162	Dongon Pt. (dŏng-ôn′)...P. I.	12.43 N	120.47 E
139	Dongou (dôŋ-go͞o′)...Bel. Cong.	2.32 N	18.27 E
166	Donington C. (dŏn′ĭng-tŭn). Austl.	34.45 S	136.3 E
79	Doniphan (dŏn′ĭ-făn)...Mo.	36.36 N	90.49 W
128	Donji Vakuf (dōn′yĭ väk′o͝of) Yugo.	44.8 N	17.26 E
70	Donner und Blitzen R. (dŏn′ēr o͝ont blĭ′tsĕn). Ore.	43.0 N	118.53 W
143	Donnybrook (dŏn′ĭ-bro͝ok) U. S. Afr.	29.55 S	29.50 E
118	Don, R. (dŏn)...Gt. Brit.	53.25 N	1.30 W
131	Don R. (dŏn)...Sov. Un.	50.54 N	39.50 E
162	Donsol (dōn-sôl′)...P. I.	12.54 N	123.36 E
142	Doorn R. (dōrn)...U. S. Afr.	31.52 S	19.0 E
89	Door Pt. (dōr) La. (New Orleans In.)	30.4 N	89.9 W
73	Dora (dō′rȧ) Ala. (Birmingham In.)	33.44 N	87.7 W
128	Dora Baltea R. (dō′rä bäl′tā-ä). It.	45.35 N	7.47 E
73	Doraville (dō′rȧ-vĭl) Ga. (Atlanta In.)	33.54 N	84.17 W
116	Dorchester (dôr′chĕs-tēr). Gt. Brit.	50.45 N	2.30 W
124	Dordogne R. (dôr-dôn′y′)...Fr.	44.50 N	0.30 E
117	Dordrecht (dôr′drĕKt)...Neth.	51.50 N	4.41 E
143	Dordrecht...U. S. Afr.	31.22 S	27.4 E
124	Dore, Mt. (dôr′)...Fr.	45.30 N	2.50 E
128	Dorgali (dôr′gä-lē)...Sard.	40.17 N	9.36 E
138	Dori (dô-rē′)...Fr. W. Afr.	14.0 N	0.0
99	Dorna (dôr′nä) Arg. (Buenos Aires In.)	35.35 S	58.50 W
119	Dornbach (dôrn′bäK) Aus. (Wien In.)	48.14 N	16.18 E
122	Dornbirn (dôrn′bĕrn)...Ger.	47.25 N	9.45 E
116	Dornoch (dôr′nŏK)...Gt. Brit.	57.55 N	4.4 W
116	Dornoch Firth (fûrth)...Gt. Brit.	57.50 N	4.0 W
130	Dorogobuzh (dô′rô′gô-bo͝ozh) Sov. Un.	54.56 N	33.20 E
123	Dorohoi (dō-rô-hoi′)...Rom.	47.58 N	26.27 E
121	Dorpat (Tartu) (dôr′pät) (tär′to͝o). Est.	58.24 N	26.48 E
164	Dorre I. (dôr)...Austl.	25.10 S	113.5 E
169	Dorrigo (dôr′ĭ-gō)...Austl.	30.17 S	152.41 E
122	Dortmund (dôrt′mo͝ont)...Ger.	51.31 N	7.28 E
113	Dörtyol (dûrt′yôl)...Tur.	36.50 N	36.15 E
139	Doria, Ganale (dôr′yȧ) (gȧ-nä′lȧ) It. E. Afr.	5.30 N	41.0 E
49	Dosewallips R. (dō-sê-wäl′ĭps) Wash. (Seattle In.)	47.43 N	123.7 W
126	Dos Hermanas (dō sĕr-mä′näs). Sp.	37.17 N	5.55 W
138	Dosso (dôs-ō′)...Fr. W. Afr.	13.2 N	3.8 E
82	Dothan (dō′thăn)...Ala.	31.13 N	85.23 W
78	Dotsero (dŏt-sēr′ō)...Colo.	39.37 N	107.5 W
124	Douai (do͞o-ā′)...Fr.	50.25 N	3.5 E
138	Douala (do͞o-ä′lä)...Cam.	4.2 N	9.40 E
124	Douarnenez (do͞o-är-nē-nĕs′)...Fr.	48.5 N	4.20 W
81	Double Bayou (dŭb′′l bī′yo͞o) Tex. (In.)	29.42 N	94.36 W
96	Double Headed Shot Cays (Is.) W. I.	23.57 N	80.25 W
80	Double Mountain R...Tex.	33.0 N	100.20 W
73	Double Oak Mt. Ala. (Birmingham In.)	33.24 N	86.38 W
125	Doubs R. (do͞o)...Fr.	47.0 N	5.30 E
171	Doubtful Sd...N. Z.	45.15 S	166.53 E
170	Doubtless B...N. Z.	34.55 S	173.30 E
124	Doué (do͞o-ā′)...Fr.	47.12 N	0.13 W
124	D'Ouessant I. (dwĕs-säN′)...Fr.	48.25 N	4.55 W
53	Douglas (dŭg′lăs)...Alsk.	58.12 N	134.30 W
75	Douglas...Ariz.	31.21 N	109.32 W
142	Douglas...Bech.	29.4 S	23.46 E
82	Douglas...Ga.	31.31 N	82.53 W
116	Douglas...Gt. Brit.	54.10 N	4.30 W
87	Douglas...Mass. (In.)	42.3 N	71.44 W
71	Douglas...Wyo.	42.47 N	105.22 W
118	Douglas, R...Gt. Brit.	53.39 N	2.49 W
82	Douglasville...Ga.	33.50 N	84.44 W
124	Doullens (do͞o-läN′)...Fr.	50.10 N	2.22 E
124	Doulon (do͞o-lôN′)...Fr.	47.15 N	1.30 W
145	Douma (do͞o′mä)...Syr. (In.)	33.34 N	36.24 E
139	Doumé (do͞o-mā′)...Cam.	4.18 N	13.30 E
118	Dove, R...Gt. Brit.	53.0 N	1.45 W
119	Dove-Elbe R. (dō′fē-ĕl′bē) Ger. (Hamburg In.)	53.28 N	10.7 E
85	Dover (dō′vēr)...Del.	39.9 N	75.33 W
117	Dover...Gt. Brit.	51.9 N	1.20 E
86	Dover...N. H.	43.12 N	70.52 W
85	Dover...N. J.	40.52 N	74.20 W
84	Dover...Ohio	40.33 N	81.30 W
86	Dover-Foxcroft (fŏks′krôft)...Me.	45.11 N	69.14 W
117	Dover, Str. of...Gt. Brit.-Fr.	51.0 N	1.40 E
112	Dovlekanovo (dŏv′lyĕk-ȧ-nô-vô) Sov. Un.	54.15 N	55.5 E
120	Dovre Fjeld (Plat.) (dŏv′rĕ fyĕl′) Nor.	62.5 N	8.30 E
84	Dowagiac (dô-wô′jăk)...Mich.	42.0 N	86.10 W
73	Downey (dou′nĭ)...Calif. (In.)	33.56 N	118.8 W
74	Downieville (dou′nĭ-vĭl)...Calif.	39.34 N	120.49 W
116	Downpatrick (doun-păt′rĭk) Gt. Brit.	54.20 N	5.45 W
117	Downs (dounz)...Gt. Brit.	51.15 N	0.50 E
78	Downs...Kan.	39.30 N	98.34 W
138	Draa, Wad (R.) (wäd drä′)..Mor.	29.0 N	8.15 W
131	Drabovo (drä′bô-vô)...Sov. Un.	49.58 N	32.10 E
87	Dracut (drā′kŭt)...Mass. (In.)	42.40 N	71.20 W
129	Draganovo (drä-gä-nō′vô)...Bulg.	43.12 N	25.43 E
129	Dragaşani (drä-gä-shän′ĭ)...Rom.	44.39 N	24.18 E
142	Draghoender (drȧ′ghûn-dĕr) U. S. Afr.	29.22 S	22.9 E
125	Draguignan (drä-gên-yäN′)...Fr.	43.35 N	6.29 E
72	Drake (drāk)...Colo. (Denver In.)	40.26 N	105.21 W
143	Drakensberg (Mts.) (drä′kĕnz-bĕrgh). U. S. Afr.	29.0 S	29.0 E
129	Drama (drā′mä)...Grc.	41.8 N	24.10 E
122	Dramburg (dräm′bo͝orgh)...Ger.	53.31 N	15.49 E
120	Drammen (dräm′ĕn)...Nor.	59.45 N	10.15 E
125	Drancy (dräN-sē′)...Fr. (In.)	48.55 N	2.27 E
73	Draper (drāp′ēr)...Utah (In.)	40.32 N	111.52 W
122	Drau R. (drou)...Ger.	46.48 N	13.30 E
122	Drava R. (drä′vä)...Eur.	46.30 N	17.0 E
125	Drave R. (dräv)...Fr.	45.0 N	5.45 E
125	Draveil (drä-vĕ′y′)...Fr. (In.)	48.41 N	2.25 E
72	Drayton Har. (drā′tŭn) Wash. (Vancouver In.)	48.59 N	122.46 W
72	Drennan (drĕn′ăn) Colo. (Colo. Sprs. In.)	38.45 N	104.28 W
129	Drepanon, C. (drĕp′ä-nōn)...Grc.	39.55 N	23.56 E
122	Dresden (drās′dĕn)...Ger.	51.3 N	13.45 E
124	Dreux (drû)...Fr.	48.42 N	1.25 E
118	Driffield (drĭ′fēld)...Gt. Brit.	54.0 N	0.26 W
129	Drina R. (drē′nä)...Yugo.	43.40 N	19.0 E
129	Drin R. (drēn)...Alb.	41.50 N	20.20 E
130	Drissa (drĭs′sä)...Sov. Un.	55.47 N	27.59 E
130	Drissa R...Sov. Un.	55.41 N	28.25 E
120	Dröbak (drû′bäk)...Nor.	59.40 N	10.37 E
116	Drogheda (drŏ′hê-dȧ)...Ire.	53.42 N	6.22 W
123	Drohiczyn (drō-hē′chĭn)...Pol.	52.11 N	25.12 E
123	Drohobycz (drô-hô′bĭch)...Pol.	49.21 N	23.31 E
118	Droitwich (droit′wĭch)...Gt. Brit.	52.16 N	2.8 W
124	Drôme R. (drōm)...Fr.	44.45 N	5.0 E
118	Dronfield (drōn′fēld)...Gt. Brit.	53.18 N	1.28 W
122	Druja (dro͞o′yȧ)...Pol.	55.46 N	27.29 E
89	Drum B....La. (New Orleans In.)	29.54 N	89.15 W
84	Drummond I. (drŭm′ŭnd)...Mich.	46.0 N	83.40 W
86	Drummondville...Can.	45.53 N	72.31 W
79	Drumright (drŭm′rīt)...Okla.	35.50 N	96.37 W
130	Drut R. (dro͞ot)...Sov. Un.	53.48 N	29.48 E
123	Drweca R. (d′r-văN′tsȧ) Pol.-Ger.	53.10 N	19.15 E
169	Dry Cr....Austl. (Adelaide In.)	34.50 S	138.35 E
71	Dry Cr...Mont.	47.22 N	106.30 W
46	Drygalski I. (drĭ-gäl′skĭ)...Ant. O.	65.30 S	93.0 E
143	Dry Hart (drī-härt)...Bech.	27.20 S	24.44 E
83	Dry Tortugas (Is.) (tôr-to͞o′gäz) Fla. (In.)	24.40 N	82.55 W
138	Dschang (dshäng)...Cam.	5.34 N	10.6 E
73	Duarte (do͞o-är′tȧ) Calif. (Los Angeles In.)	34.9 N	117.58 W
54	Dubawnt L. (do͞o-bônt′)...Can.	63.15 N	101.30 W
54	Dubawnt R...Can.	61.30 N	103.35 W
167	Dubbo (dŭb′ō)...Austl.	32.15 S	148.38 E
82	Dublin (dŭb′lĭn)...Ga.	32.32 N	82.56 W
80	Dublin...Tex.	32.5 N	98.20 W
116	Dublin (Baile Atha Cliath) (dŭb′lĭn) (bŏ′lĕ ô′hŏ klē′ŏh)...Ire.	53.20 N	6.15 W
123	Dubno (do͝ob′nô)...Pol.	50.25 N	25.45 E
85	Du Bois (do͝o-bois′)...Pa.	41.9 N	78.46 W
131	Dubossari (do͝o-bŏ-sä′rĭ)..Sov. Un.	47.16 N	29.10 E
113	Dubovka (do͝o-bôf′kȧ)...Sov. Un.	49.5 N	44.45 E
130	Dubovoye (do͝ob′ô-vō-yĕ). Sov. Un.	53.4 N	49.0 E
130	Dubrovna (do͞o-brôf′nȧ)..Sov. Un.	54.38 N	30.52 E
129	Dubrovnik (Ragusa) (do͝o′brôv-nêk) (rä-go͞o′sä). Yugo.	42.39 N	18.9 E
77	Dubuque (do͝o-būk′)...Ia.	42.30 N	90.40 W
75	Duchesne R. (do͝o-shān′)...Utah	40.20 N	110.45 W
164	Duchess (dŭch′ĕs)...Austl.	21.28 S	139.50 E
6	Ducie I. (dü-sē′)...Pac. O.	24.40 S	124.48 W
49	Duckabush (dŭk′ȧ-bo͝osh) Wash. (Seattle In.)	47.38 N	122.56 W
49	Duckabush R..Wash. (Seattle In.)	47.40 N	123.5 W
84	Duck I...Can.	45.38 N	82.55 W
82	Duck R...Tenn.	35.35 N	87.0 W
82	Ducktown (dŭk′toun)...Tenn.	35.5 N	84.21 W
70	Duck Valley Ind. Res...Ida.-Nev.	42.0 N	116.10 W
148	Dudinskoe (do͝o′dên-skô-yĕ) Sov. Un.	69.25 N	86.10 E
116	Dudley (dŭd′lĭ)...Gt. Brit.	52.30 N	2.10 W
88	Dudley...Pa. (Philadelphia In.)	39.57 N	75.4 W
163	Duero (dwā′rō)...P. I.	9.41 N	124.23 E
126	Duero R...Sp.	41.30 N	5.30 W
88	Dufferin Is. (dŭf′ēr-ĭn) Can. (Niagara Falls In.)	43.4 N	79.4 W
169	Dugandan (do͞o-găn′dăn) Austl. (In.)	28.2 S	152.40 E
169	Du Gane Ra. (dû gān′) Austl. (Tas. In.)	41.50 S	146.0 E
84	Dugger (dŭg′ēr)...Ind.	39.3 N	87.7 W
128	Dugi (I.) (do͞o′gê)...Yugo.	44.2 N	15.0 E
122	Duisburg-Hamborn (do͞o′ĭs-bo͝orgh häm′bôrn). Ger.	51.26 N	6.45 E
157	Dukchun (do͝ok′cho͝on′)...Cho.	39.46 N	126.19 E
130	Dukhovshchina (do͞o-Kôfsh′chē-nȧ). Sov. Un.	55.11 N	32.24 E
118	Dukinfield (dŭk′ĭn-fēld)..Gt. Brit.	53.28 N	2.4 W
123	Dukla P. (do͞o′klä)...Pol.-Czech.	49.25 N	21.42 E
157	Duk Yu San (Mts.) (do͝ok′ yo͞o sän′). Cho.	35.55 N	127.47 E
163	Dulag (do͞o′läg)...P. I.	10.58 N	125.2 E
94	Dulce, Golfo (L. Izabal) do͞ol′sā, gōl′fô (ē-zä-bäl′). Guat.	15.30 N	89.10 W
95	Dulce, G. of...C. R.	8.30 N	83.15 W
129	Dulcigno (Ulcinj) (do͞ol-chēn′yō) (o͞ol′tsēn-y′). Yugo.	41.56 N	19.12 E
77	Duluth (do͝o-lo͞oth′)...Minn.	46.49 N	92.5 W
88	Duluth...Minn. (In.)		
163	Dumaguete (do͞o-mä-gā′tā)...P. I.	9.18 N	123.19 E
163	Dumalag (do͞o-mä′läg)...P. I.	11.17 N	122.38 E
162	Dumali Pt. (do͞o mä′lē)...P. I.	13.7 N	121.33 E
163	Dumangas (do͞o-män′gäs)...P. I.	10.48 N	122.43 E
163	Dumanjug (do͞o-män-ho͞og′)..P. I.	10.3 N	123.27 E
163	Dumanquilas B. (do͞o-män-kē′läs) P. I.	7.30 N	123.5 E
158	Duman R. (do͞o′män′)...Chn.	42.30 N	129.40 E
163	Dumaran (do͞o-mä-rän′)...P. I.	10.31 N	119.46 E
163	Dumaran I...P. I.	10.35 N	119.42 E
169	Dumaresq R. (do͞o-mȧ-rĕsk′) Austl. (In.)	28.50 S	151.10 E
116	Dumfries (dŭm-frēs′)...Gt. Brit.	55.5 N	3.35 W
139	Dumiât (Damietta) (do͝om-yät′) (dăm-ĭ-ĕt′ȧ). Eg.	31.27 N	31.48 E
131	Dunaevtsy (do͞o′nä-yĕf′tsĭ) Sov. Un.	48.55 N	26.50 E
123	Dunaföldvár (do͝o′nô-fûld′vär) Hung.	46.47 N	18.54 E
123	Duna (Danube) R. (do͝o′nä). Eur.	47.53 N	17.26 E
123	Dunajec R. (do͝o-nä′yĕts)...Pol.	49.50 N	20.45 E
166	Dunally (dŭ-năl′ĭ)...Austl.	36.52 S	143.45 E
57	Dunany (do͞o-nā′nĭ) Can. (Montreal In.)	45.45 N	74.16 W
123	Dunapatoj (doo′nô-pô-toi)..Hung.	46.42 N	19.2 E
129	Dunărea (Danube) R. (do͞o-nă′rā-ä). Eur.	43.45 N	24.0 E
129	Dunav (Danube) R. (do͞o′näv) Eur.	43.45 N	24.0 E
116	Dunbar (dŭn′bär)...Gt. Brit.	56.0 N	2.30 W
84	Dunbar...W. Va.	38.22 N	81.46 W
116	Dunbarton (dŭn′bär-tŭn). Gt. Brit.	55.55 N	4.30 W
164	Dunbury (dŭn′bĕr-ê)...Austl.	33.20 S	115.40 E
78	Duncan (dŭŋ′kăn)...Okla.	34.29 N	97.58 W
116	Duncansby Hd. (dŭn′kănz-bĭ) Gt. Brit. (In.)	58.35 N	3.0 W
116	Dundalk (dŭn′dôk)...Ire.	54.0 N	6.25 W
116	Dundalk B...Ire.	53.55 N	6.20 W
169	Dundas (dŭn-dăs′) Austl. (Tas. In.)	41.45 S	145.27 E
85	Dundas...Can.	43.16 N	80.57 W
164	Dundas, L...Austl.	32.30 S	121.55 E
164	Dundas Str...Austl.	11.30 S	13.45 E
116	Dundee (dŭn-dē′)...Gt. Brit.	56.30 N	2.55 W
143	Dundee...U. S. Afr.	28.10 S	30.15 E
116	Dundrum B. (dŭn-drŭm′) Gt. Brit.	54.10 N	5.50 W
82	Dunedin (dŭn-ē′dĭn)...Fla. (In.)	28.0 N	82.45 W
171	Dunedin...N. Z. (In.)	45.52 S	170.32 E
116	Dunfermline (dŭn-fērm′lĭn) Gt. Brit.	56.5 N	3.25 W
116	Dungarvan (dŭn-gär′văn)...Ire.	52.5 N	7.30 W
116	Dungarvan Har...Ire.	52.5 N	7.35 W
49	Dungeness (dŭnj-nĕs′) Wash. (Seattle In.)	48.8 N	123.7 W
99	Dungeness, Pt. Arg. (Magallanes In.)	52.24 S	68.25 W
49	Dungeness...Wash. (Seattle In.)	47.52 N	123.7 W
167	Dungog (dŭn-gôg′)...Austl.	32.27 S	151.47 E
139	Dungu (do͝oŋ-go͞o′)...Bel. Cong.	3.44 N	28.32 E
124	Dunkerque (dŭN-kĕrk′)...Fr.	51.0 N	2.15 E
	Dunkirk, see Dunkerque, Fr.		
84	Dunkirk (dŭn′kûrk)...Ind.	40.21 N	85.23 W
85	Dunkirk...N. Y.	42.30 N	79.20 W
116	Dun Laoghaire (dŭn-lā′rĕ)...Ire.	53.15 N	6.10 W
76	Dunlap (dŭn′lăp)...Ia.	41.53 N	95.34 W
82	Dunlap...Tenn.	35.24 N	85.24 W
85	Dunmore (dŭn′mōr)...Pa.	41.24 N	75.39 W
83	Dunn (dŭn)...N. C.	35.18 N	78.36 W
73	Dunnavant (dŭn′ȧ-vănt) Ala. (Birmingham In.)	33.30 N	86.33 W
83	Dunnellon (dŭn-ĕl′ŏn)...Fla.	29.5 N	82.27 W
116	Dunnet Hd. (dŭn′ĕt)...Gt. Brit.	58.50 N	3.20 W
85	Dunnville (dŭn′vĭl)...Can.	42.56 N	79.38 W
116	Dunoon (dŭn-o͞on′)...Gt. Brit.	55.55 N	4.55 W
70	Dunsmuir (dŭnz′mūr)...Calif.	41.11 N	122.18 W
171	Dunstan Mts. (dŭns′tăn)...N. Z.	44.55 S	169.30 E
88	Dunton (dŭn′tŏn)...N. Y. (In.)	40.41 N	73.49 W
54	Dunvegan (dŭn-vē′găn)...Can.	56.1 N	118.28 W
73	Dunwoody (dŭn-wo͝od′ĭ) Ga. (Atlanta In.)	33.57 N	84.20 W
162	Dupax (do͞o′päks)...P. I.	16.17 N	121.5 E
129	Dupnica (do͞op′nê-tsȧ)...Bul.	42.15 N	23.6 E
89	Dupo (dū′pō)...Ill. (St. Louis In.)	38.33 N	90.12 W
49	Du Pont (dû pŏnt′) Wash. (Seattle In.)	47.5 N	122.37 W
140	Duque de Bragança (do͞o′kā dā brä-gäN′sä). Ang.	9.0 S	16.12 E
85	Duquesne (do͝o-kān′)...Pa.	40.22 N	79.52 W
79	Duquoin (do͝o-kwoin′)...Ill.	38.1 N	89.14 W
125	Durance R. (dū-räNs′)...Fr.	43.50 N	5.50 E
84	Durand (dû-rănd′)...Mich.	42.53 N	83.57 W

ng-sing; ŋ-baŋk; N-nasalized n; nŏd; cŏmmit; ōld; ôbey; ôrder; fo͞od; fo͝ot; ou-out; s-soft; sh-dish; th-thin; pūre; ûnite; ûrn; stŭd; circŭs; ü-as "y" in study; ′-indeterminate vowel.

Page	Name Pronunciation Region	Lat. °′	Long. °′
77	Durand .... Wis.	44.38 N	91.58 W
75	Durango (dōō-răŋ′gō) .... Colo.	37.17 N	107.51 W
92	Durango (State) (dōō-räŋ′gō) Mex.	23.40 N	105.0 W
80	Durango .... Mex.	24.1 N	104.40 W
82	Durant (dû-rănt′) .... Miss.	33.3 N	89.51 W
79	Durant .... Okla.	33.58 N	96.24 W
126	Duratón (dōō-rä-tōn′) .... Sp.	41.30 N	4.0 W
104	Durazno (dōō-räz′nō) .... Ur.	33.25 S	56.35 W
129	Durazzo (Durrsi) (dōō-rät′sō) (dōōr′sĭ). Alb.	41.19 N	19.28 E
143	Durban (dûr′băn) .... U. S. Afr.	29.51 S	31.0 E
121	Durbe (dōōr′bĕ) .... Lat.	56.35 N	21.28 E
122	Düren (dü′rĕn) .... Ger.	50.49 N	6.29 E
152	Durga Nor (L.) (dōōr′gȧ nôr). Chn.	48.0 N	93.15 E
116	Durham (dûr′ăm) .... Gt. Brit.	54.45 N	1.40 W
83	Durham .... N. C.	36.0 N	78.55 W
122	Durlach (dōōr′läк) .... Ger.	49.1 N	8.29 E
129	Durrës (Durazzo) (dōōr′ĕs) (dōō-rät′sō) Alb.	41.19 N	19.28 E
171	D'Urville I. (dûr′vĭl) .... N. Z.	40.50 S	173.55 E
85	Duryea (dōōr-yā′) .... Pa.	41.22 N	75.47 W
149	Dushkachany (dōōsh-kȧ-chän′y′) Sov. Un.	55.50 N	109.50 E
171	Dusky Sd. .... N. Z.	45.45 S	166.30 E
122	Düsseldorf (düs′ĕl-dôrf) .... Ger.	51.14 N	6.48 E
52	Dutch Harbor (dŭch här′bẽr). Alsk.	53.54 N	166.35 W
122	Dux (Duchcov) (dōōks) (dōōk′tsôf) Ger.	40.37 N	13.45 E
150	Duzdab (Zahedan) (dōōz-däb′) (zä-hĕ-dän′)... Iran	29.32 N	60.34 E
130	Dvina R. (dvē-nä′) .... Sov. Un.	55.20 N	30.26 E
112	Dvina, N. (Severnaya Dvina) R. (syĕ′bĕr-nä′yä dvē-nȧ′).. Sov. Un.	62.30 N	43.45 E
112	Dvinsk, G. of (dvēnsk) .. Sov. Un.	64.50 N	39.30 E
122	Dvůr Králové (dvōōr′ krä′lô-vā). Czech.	50.28 N	15.50 E
142	Dwequa R. (dwĕk′wȧ) .. U. S. Afr.	32.45 S	19.42 E
79	Dwight (dwīt) .... Ill.	41.5 N	88.26 W
130	Dyatkovo (dyät′kō-vō)... Sov. Un.	53.34 N	34.18 E
142	Dyer Is. (dī′ẽr) .... U. S. Afr.	34.42 S	19.22 E
82	Dyersburg (dī′ẽrz-bûrg) .... Tenn.	36.2 N	89.24 W
81	Dyersdale (dī′ẽrz-dāl)... Tex. (In.)	29.54 N	95.15 W
77	Dyersville (dī′ẽrz-vĭl) .... Ia.	42.28 N	91.8 W
157	Dyungpyung (dyōōng′pyōōng′) Cho.	39.48 N	127.22 E
148	Dyushambe (Stalinabad) (dyōō-shăm′bĕ) (stä-lē′nȧ-bȧd) Sov. Un.	38.45 N	68.50 E
141	Dzaoudzi (dzou′dzĭ)... Comoro Is.	12.40 S	45.15 E
152	Dzapkhin R. (dzȧp′кĕn′) .... Chn.	47.45 N	95.0 E
149	Dzhalinda (Reinova) (dzhȧ′lĕn-dȧ) (rȧ′ĕ-nô′vȧ). Sov. Un.	53.30 N	124.0 E
148	Dzhalyal Abad (dzhäl′yäl ä′bäd) Sov. Un.	41.10 N	73.30 E
113	Dzhambeitinskaya Stavka (dzhȧm-byĕ-ē′tĭn-skä′yä stäf′kȧ). Sov. Un.	50.12 N	52.40 E
131	Dzhankoi (dzhän′koi) .... Sov. Un.	45.42 N	34.24 E
148	Dzharkent (dzhär′kĕnt) .. Sov. Un.	44.15 N	79.59 E
148	Dzhizak (dzhē′zäk) .... Sov. Un.	40.15 N	67.55 E
123	Dzialoszyce (jyä-wō-shē′tsĕ) .. Pol.	50.21 N	20.23 E
122	Dzisna (dzēs′nȧ) .... Pol.	55.33 N	28.10 E
122	Dzisna R. .... Pol.	55.18 N	27.10 E
93	Dzitbalché (dzēt-bäl-chā′)... Mex.	20.18 N	90.3 W
152	Dzungaria (Reg.) (dzōōŋ-gä′rĭ-ȧ) Chn.	44.30 N	88.0 E
53	Eagle (ē′g′l) .... Alsk.	64.40 N	141.25 W
81	Eagle .... Tex. (In.)	29.40 N	94.40 W
84	Eagle .... W. Va.	38.9 N	81.21 W
49	Eaglecliff .... Wash. (Portland In.)	46.10 N	123.15 W
77	Eagle Grove .... Ia.	41.41 N	93.53 W
166	Eaglehawk .... Austl.	36.42 S	144.14 E
70	Eagle L. .... Calif.	40.40 N	120.30 W
86	Eagle L. .... Me.	47.5 N	68.38 W
81	Eagle L. .... Tex.	29.37 N	96.20 W
80	Eagle Mt. .... Tex.	30.55 N	105.5 W
81	Eagle Mountain, Lake .... Tex.	33.0 N	97.30 W
80	Eagle Pass .... Tex.	28.42 N	100.30 W
70	Eagle Peak .... Calif.	41.16 N	120.11 W
75	Eagle R. .... Colo.	39.36 N	106.55 W
119	Ealing (ē′lĭng) Gt. Brit. (London In.)	51.31 N	0.19 W
79	Earl (ûrl) .... Ark.	35.15 N	90.28 W
84	Earlington (ûr′lĭng-tŭn) .... Ky.	37.15 N	87.32 W
171	Earnslaw, Mt. (ûrnz′lô) .... N. Z.	44.37 S	168.25 E
118	Easingwold (ē′zĭng-wôld) Gt. Brit.	54.7 N	1.10 W
83	Easley (ēz′lĭ) .... S. C.	34.50 N	82.36 W
73	Easonville (ē′zŭn-vĭl) Ala. (Birmingham In.)	33.31 N	86.19 W
86	East Angus (ēst ăŋ′gŭs) .... Can.	45.30 N	71.40 W
46	East Antarctica (Reg.) (ănt-ärk′tĭ-kȧ). Ant.	76.0 S	80.0 E
89	East B. .... La.	29.3 N	89.15 W
81	East B. .... Tex. (In.)	29.30 N	94.40 W
83	East Bernstadt (bûrn′stȧt) .... Ky.	37.11 N	84.9 W
117	Eastbourne (ēst′bôrn) .... Gt. Brit.	50.49 N	0.20 E
170	Eastbourne .... N. Z. (In.)	41.18 S	174.54 E
97	East Caicos I. (kī′kōs) .... Ba. Is.	21.40 N	71.30 W
88	East Camden (kăm′dĕn) N. J. (Philadelphia In.)	39.57 N	75.6 W
73	East Canyon Cr. (kăn′yŭn) Utah (Salt Lake City In.)	40.55 N	111.38 W
83	East C. .... Fla. (In.)	25.7 N	81.5 W
170	East C. .... N. Z.	37.35 S	178.35 E
89	East Carondelet (kȧ-rŏn′dĕ-lĕt) Ill. (St. Louis In.)	38.32 N	90.14 W
84	East Chicago .... Ind.	41.38 N	87.26 W
155	East China Sea .... Chn.	28.30 N	122.0 E
89	East Cleveland Ohio (Cleveland In.)	41.32 N	81.34 W
81	East Cote Blanche B. (kōt blänsh′). La.	29.35 N	91.35 W

Page	Name Pronunciation Region	Lat. °′	Long. °′
77	East Des Moines R. (dē moin′). Ia.	43.10 N	94.10 W
89	East Detroit (dē-troit′) Mich. (Detroit In.)	42.29 N	82.56 W
6	Easter I. (Rapa Nui) (ēs′tẽr) (rä′pä nōō′ē). Pac. O.	29.0 S	109.30 W
165	Eastern Highlands .... Austl.	22.30 S	146.0 E
76	East Grand Forks .... Minn.	47.56 N	97.0 W
116	East Ham .... Gt. Brit.	51.30 N	0.10 E
119	Eastham (ēst′ăm) .... Gt. Brit.	53.19 N	2.57 W
86	Easthampton (ēst-hămp′tŭn) Mass.	42.15 N	72.41 W
85	East Hartford (härt′fẽrd)... Conn.	41.46 N	72.38 W
71	East Helena (hĕl′ē-nȧ) .... Mont.	46.35 N	111.55 W
73	East Highlands Calif. (Los Angeles In.)	34.7 N	117.9 W
119	East Horndon (hôrn′dŭn) Gt. Brit.	51.36 N	0.22 E
84	East Jordan (jôr′dăn) .... Mich.	45.6 N	85.4 W
82	East Lake .... Ala.	33.34 N	86.40 W
72	Eastlake (ēst′lāk) Colo. (Denver In.)	39.55 N	104.58 W
73	East Lake .... Ga. (Atlanta In.)	33.44 N	84.16 W
80	Eastland (ēst′lănd) .... Tex.	32.23 N	98.49 W
84	East Lansing .... Mich.	42.47 N	84.30 W
78	East Las Vegas (läs vā′gȧs). N. M.	35.36 N	105.12 W
84	East Liverpool (lĭv′ẽr-pōōl) .. Ohio	40.38 N	80.35 W
143	East London (lŭn′dŭn) .. U. S. Afr.	33.1 S	27.56 E
55	Eastmain R. (ēst′mān) .... Can.	52.30 N	76.0 W
82	Eastman (ēst-măn) .... Ga.	32.12 N	83.12 W
119	East Molesey (mōlz′ĭ) Gt. Brit. (London In.)	51.24 N	0.22 W
79	East Moline (mō-lēn′) .... Ill.	41.32 N	90.26 W
167	East Molong (mō-lông′) .... Austl.	33.5 S	148.53 E
77	East Nishnabotna R. (nĭsh-nȧ-bŏt′nȧ). Ia.	41.20 N	95.10 W
72	East Oil Cr. Colo. (Colo. Sprs. In.)	38.50 N	105.15 W
49	East Olympia (ō-lĭm′pĭ-ȧ) Wash. (Seattle In.)	46.58 N	122.51 W
85	Easton (ēst′ŭn) .... Md.	38.47 N	76.5 W
85	Easton .... Pa.	40.42 N	75.11 W
72	Eastonville. Colo. (Colo. Sprs. In.)	39.4 N	104.34 W
85	East Orange .... N. J.	40.46 N	74.13 W
96	East Pt. .... Isle of Pines	21.35 N	82.25 W
82	East Point .... Ga.	33.40 N	84.28 W
86	Eastport .... Me.	44.54 N	67.0 W
85	Eastport .... Md.	38.57 N	76.30 W
85	East Providence .... R. I.	41.48 N	71.24 W
123	East Prussia (Prov.) .... Ger.	54.10 N	21.0 E
118	East Riding (Borough) (rīd′ĭng) Gt. Brit.	54.3 N	0.30 W
88	East R. .... N. Y. (In.)	40.48 N	73.54 W
85	East Rochester .... N. Y.	43.8 N	77.30 W
79	East St. Louis (sānt lōō′ĭs; lōō-ĭ). Ill.	38.36 N	90.9 W
117	East Scheldt R. .... Neth.	51.40 N	3.50 E
72	Eastsound. Wash. (Vancouver In.)	48.42 N	122.55 W
85	East Stroudsburg .... Pa.	41.0 N	75.12 W
85	East Syracuse .... N. Y.	43.4 N	76.4 W
84	East Tawas (tô′wăs) .... Mich.	44.18 N	83.29 W
74	East Walker R. (wôk′ẽr) Calif.-Nev.	38.30 N	118.35 W
89	East Windsor (wĭn′zẽr) Mich. (Detroit In.)	42.20 N	82.58 W
169	Eastwood .... Austl. (Sydney In.)	33.46 S	151.5 E
78	Eaton (ē′tŭn) .... Colo.	40.31 N	104.43 W
84	Eaton .... Ohio	39.46 N	84.39 W
72	Eaton Ditch... Colo. (Denver In.)	40.33 N	104.55 W
84	Eaton Rapids .... Mich.	42.29 N	84.40 W
82	Eatonton (ē′tŭn-tŭn) .... Ga.	33.20 N	83.24 W
77	Eau Claire (ō klâr′) .... Wis.	44.48 N	91.30 W
138	Ebelowa (ĕ-bē-lō′wä) .... Cam.	2.56 N	11.5 E
120	Ebeltoft (ĕ′bĕl-tŭft) .... Den.	56.11 N	10.41 E
88	Ebenezer (ĕb-ĕn-ē′zẽr) N. Y. (Niagara Falls In.)	42.50 N	78.45 W
122	Eberswalde (ā-bĕrs-väl′dĕ)... Ger.	52.51 N	13.48 E
122	Ebingen (ā′bĭng-ĕn) .... Ger.	48.13 N	9.3 E
152	Ebi Nor (L.) (ā′bē nōr′) .... Chn.	45.0 N	82.45 E
128	Eboli (ĕb′ō-lē) .... It.	40.37 N	15.3 E
126	Ebro R. (ā′brō) .... Sp.	42.30 N	2.30 W
118	Eccles (ĕk″lz) .... Gt. Brit.	53.29 N	2.21 W
84	Eccles .... W. Va.	37.46 N	81.12 W
118	Eccleshall (ĕk″lz-hôl) .... Gt. Brit.	52.52 N	2.15 W
162	Echague (ā-chä′gwä) .... P. I.	16.42 N	121.40 E
73	Echo City (ĕk′ō) Utah (Salt Lake City In.)	40.58 N	111.27 W
169	Echo, L. .... Austl. (Tas. In.)	42.10 S	146.39 E
125	Echternach (ĕк′tẽr-näк) .... Lux.	49.48 N	6.25 E
166	Echuca (ē-chōō′kȧ) .... Austl.	36.9 S	144.46 E
126	Écija (ā′thē-hä) .... Sp.	37.32 N	5.5 W
122	Eckernförde (ĕk′ẽrn-fûr-dē)... Ger.	54.27 N	9.52 E
49	Ecola (ē-kō′lȧ). Ore. (Portland In.)	45.53 N	123.57 W
84	Ecorse (ē-kôrs′) .... Mich.	42.14 N	83.9 W
125	Ecouen (ā-kōō-äɴ′) .... Fr. (In.)	49.1 N	2.23 E
102	Ecuador (ĕk′wȧ-dôr) .... S. A.	78.3 W	0.0
139	Ed Dāmer (ĕd dä′mĕr) .. A. E. Sud.	17.37 N	33.58 E
139	Ed Debba (ĕd dĕb′ȧ)... A. E. Sud.	18.3 N	30.57 E
139	Ed Dirr (ĕd dẽr′) .... Eg.	22.45 N	32.10 E
139	Ed Dueim (ĕd dōō-ām′). A. E. Sud.	14.0 N	32.22 E
82	Eddyville (ĕd′ĭ-vĭl) .... Ky.	37.3 N	88.4 W
138	Edéa (ĕ-dā′ä) .... Cam.	3.50 N	10.10 E
119	Edeghem (ĕ′dĕ-gĕm) Bel. (Anvers In.)	51.9 N	4.27 E
73	Eden (ē′d′n) Ala. (Birmingham In.)	33.35 N	86.19 W
167	Eden .... Austl.	37.3 S	149.53 E
73	Eden... Utah (Salt Lake City In.)	41.18 N	111.49 W
143	Edenburg (ē′d′n-bûrg) .. U. S. Afr.	29.42 S	25.59 E
171	Edendale (ē′d′n-dāl) .... N. Z.	46.20 S	168.48 E
118	Edenham (ē′d′n-ăm) .... Gt. Brit.	52.46 N	0.25 W
170	Eden, Mt. .... N. Z. (In.)	36.52 S	174.46 E
116	Eden, R. .... Gt. Brit.	54.40 N	2.35 W
83	Edenton (ē′dĕn-tŭn) .... N. C.	36.3 N	76.36 W
166	Edeowie (ēd-ō′wē) .... Austl.	31.28 S	138.26 E
152	Eder R. (ē′dẽr) .... Chn.	48.45 N	98.0 E
122	Eder R. (ā′dẽr) .... Ger.	51.7 N	8.50 E
129	Edessa (ē-dĕs′ȧ) .... Grc.	40.47 N	22.4 E

Page	Name Pronunciation Region	Lat. °′	Long. °′
138	Edeyen (Dunes) (ĕ-dā′yĕn) Libya-Alg.	27.30 N	11.0 E
49	Edgecomb (ĕj′kŭm) Wash. (Seattle In.)	48.8 N	122.8 W
83	Edgefield (ĕj′fēld) .... S. C.	33.48 N	81.56 W
76	Edgeley (ĕj′lĭ) .... N. D.	46.22 N	98.41 W
76	Edgemont (ĕj′mŏnt) .... S. D.	43.18 N	103.49 W
72	Edgerton (ĕj′ẽr-tŭn) Colo. (Colo. Sprs. In.)	38.58 N	104.50 W
77	Edgerton .... Wis.	42.51 N	89.5 W
72	Edgewater (ĕj′wô-tẽr) Colo. (Denver In.)	39.46 N	105.4 W
119	Edgware (ĕj′wâr) Gt. Brit. (London In.)	51.37 N	0.18 W
89	Edina (ē-dī′nȧ) Minn. (Minneapolis In.)	44.55 N	93.20 W
79	Edina .... Mo.	40.8 N	92.12 W
84	Edinburg (ĕd″n-bûrg) .... Ind.	39.20 N	85.58 W
80	Edinburg .... Tex.	26.18 N	98.10 W
116	Edinburgh (ĕd″n-bŭr-ō). Gt. Brit.	55.55 N	3.10 W
113	Edirne (Adrianople) (ĕ-dĭr′nĕ) (ā-drĭ-ăn-ō′p′l). Tur.	41.40 N	26.35 E
83	Edisto I. (ĕd′ĭs-tō) .... S. C.	32.34 N	80.18 W
83	Edisto R. .... S. C.	33.0 N	80.25 W
83	Edisto R., North Fork .... S. C.	33.35 N	81.0 W
83	Edisto R., South Fork .... S. C.	33.30 N	81.25 W
166	Edithburgh (ē′dĭth-bŭr-ō)... Austl.	35.6 S	137.44 E
49	Ediz Hook (ē′dĭz) Wash. (Seattle In.)	48.8 N	123.25 W
135	Edku, L. (ĕd′kōō) .... Eg. (In.)	31.15 N	30.20 E
72	Edlowe (ĕd′lō) Colo. (Colo. Sprs. In.)	38.58 N	105.5 W
79	Edmond (ĕd′mŭnd) .... Okla.	35.38 N	97.29 W
49	Edmonds (ĕd′mŭndz) Wash. (Seattle In.)	47.48 N	122.22 W
54	Edmonton (ĕd′mŭn-tŭn) .... Can.	53.45 N	113.30 W
119	Edmonton.. Gt. Brit. (London In.)	51.37 N	0.9 W
55	Edmundston (ĕd′mŭn-stŭn) .. Can.	47.27 N	68.8 W
81	Edna (ĕd′nȧ) .... Tex.	28.58 N	96.38 W
113	Edremit (ĕd-rĕ-mēt′) .... Tur.	39.40 N	27.2 E
129	Edremit, G. of .... Tur.	39.25 N	26.40 E
152	Edsin Gol (ĕd′sĕn gôl) .... Chn.	40.45 N	100.0 E
166	Edunda (ē-dŭn′dȧ) .... Austl.	34.11 S	139.6 E
77	Edward I. (ĕd′wẽrd) .... Can.	48.23 N	88.37 W
140	Edward, L. .... Afr.	0.20 S	29.40 E
166	Edward R. .... Austl.	35.18 S	144.30 E
80	Edwards Plat. (ĕd′wẽrdz) .... Tex.	30.30 N	100.30 W
79	Edwardsville .... Ill.	38.48 N	89.58 W
119	Eeckeren (āk′ẽr-ĕn) Bel. (Anvers In.)	51.17 N	4.25 E
70	Eel R. (ēl) .... Calif.	40.35 N	124.10 W
84	Eel R. .... Ind.	40.52 N	86.0 W
74	Eel R., South Fork .... Calif.	40.0 N	123.48 W
165	Efate (Sandwich) I. (ā-fä′tä) (sand-wich). New Hebr.	17.50 S	168.15 E
79	Effingham (ĕf′ĭng-hăm) .... Ill.	39.5 N	88.32 W
130	Efremov (yĕf′rĕ-môf) .... Sov. Un.	53.8 N	38.5 E
128	Egadi (Aegadian) Is. (ĕ′gä-dē) (ē-gā′dĭ-ăn). It.	38.55 N	12.20 E
73	Egan (ē′găn) .... Ga. (Atlanta In.)	33.40 N	84.26 W
126	Ega R. (ā′gä) .... Sp.	42.40 N	2.0 W
126	Egéa de los Caballeros (ā-кā′ȧ dā lōs kä-bäl-yā′rôs). Sp.	42.8 N	1.7 W
123	Eger (ĕ′gĕr) .... Hung.	47.54 N	20.23 E
122	Eger (Cheb) (ā′gẽr) (Kĕb) .... Ger.	50.4 N	12.23 E
122	Eger (Ohře) R. (ā′gĕr) (ōr′zhĕ) Ger.	50.23 N	13.15 E
120	Egersund (ĕ′ghĕr-sōōn′) .... Nor.	58.29 N	6.1 E
122	Eggenberg (ĕg′ĕn-bĕrgh) .... Ger.	47.6 N	15.22 E
85	Egg Harbor (City) .... N. J.	39.32 N	74.40 W
152	Egin R. (ā-gēn′) .... Chn.	49.40 N	102.30 E
49	Eglon (ĕg′lŭn). Wash. (Seattle In.)	47.53 N	122.31 W
170	Egmont, C. (ĕg′mŏnt) .... N. Z.	39.17 S	173.45 E
170	Egmont, Mt. .... N. Z.	39.18 S	174.2 E
130	Egor'evsk (yĕ′gôr-yĕfsk). Sov. Un.	55.21 N	39.1 E
139	Egypt (ē′jĭpt) .... Afr.	28.0 N	30.0 E
126	Eibar (ā′ē-bär) .... Sp.	43.11 N	2.22 W
122	Eichstatt (īк′shtät) .... Ger.	48.55 N	11.13 E
120	Eid (īdh) .... Nor.	61.55 N	6.0 E
119	Eidelstedt (ī′dĕl-shtĕt) Ger. (Hamburg In.)	53.36 N	9.54 E
120	Eidfjord (īdh′fyôr′) .... Nor.	60.29 N	7.5 E
120	Eidsberg (īdhs′bĕrgh) .... Nor.	59.31 N	11.16 E
120	Eidsvold (īdhs′vôl) .... Nor.	60.20 N	11.15 E
122	Eifel (Reg.) (ī′fĕl) .... Ger.	50.7 N	6.40 E
116	Eigg (I.) (ĕg) .... Gt. Brit.	56.55 N	6.5 W
72	Eightmile Cr. (āt′mīl) Colo. (Colo. Sprs. In.)	38.37 N	105.8 W
164	Eighty Mile Beach .... Austl.	19.25 S	121.15 E
122	Eilenburg (ī′lĕn-bōōrgh) .... Ger.	51.27 N	12.37 E
122	Einbeck (īn′bĕk) .... Ger.	51.48 N	9.52 E
122	Eindhoven (īnd′hō-vĕn) .... Neth.	51.26 N	5.28 E
145	Ein Gannim (Jenin) (ān gȧ-nēm′) (jĕ-nēn′). Pal. (In.)	32.22 N	35.18 E
122	Eisenach (ī′zĕn-äк) .... Ger.	50.59 N	10.18 E
131	Eisk (yĕ′ēsk) .... Sov. Un.	46.42 N	38.18 E
122	Eisleben (īs′lā′bĕn) .... Ger.	51.32 N	11.32 E
157	Eisyung (ā′syōōng′) .... Cho.	36.22 N	128.43 E
119	Eiszendorf (īs′ĕn-dôrf) Ger. (Hamburg In.)	53.28 N	9.57 E
93	Ejutla de Crespo (ā-hōōt′lä dā krās′pō). Mex.	16.33 N	96.43 W
...	Ekaterinburg, see Sverdlovsk, Sov. Un.		
...	Ekaterinodar, see Krasnodar, Sov. Un.		
131	Ekaterinoslav (Dnepropetrovsk) (yĕ-kȧ-tyĕ-rē′nô-släf′) (d′nyĕp′-rō-pyĕ-trôfsk′)... Sov. Un.	48.28 N	35.2 E
121	Ekenäs (Tammisaari) (ĕ′kĕ-nâs tȧm′ĭ-sä′rĭ).. Fin.	59.58 N	23.28 E
171	Eketahuna (ĕk-ē-tȧ-hōō′nȧ).. N. Z.	40.35 S	175.43 E
56	Ekhart (ĕk′ärt) Can. (Winnepeg In.)	50.10 N	97.26 W
120	Eksjö (ĕk′shû) .... Swe.	57.41 N	14.59 E
112	Elabuga (yĕ-lä′bōō-gȧ)... Sov. Un.	55.45 N	52.5 E
127	El Affraun (ĕl ȧf-frouɴ′) .... Alg.	36.28 N	2.38 E
113	Elan (yĕ-län′) .... Sov. Un.	50.50 N	43.58 E

ăt; finăl; rāte; senâte; ärm; ȧsk; sofȧ; fâre; ch-choose; dh-as th in other; bē; ēvent; bĕt; recĕnt; cratẽr; g-go; gh-gutteral g; bĭt; ĭ-short neutral; rīde; к-gutteral k as ch in German ich;

Page	Name Pronunciation Region	Lat. °′	Long. °′
142	Elands Berg (Mt.) (ā'lānts bĕrgh) U. S. Afr.	31.15 S	22.22 E
126	El Arahal (ĕl ä-rä-äl') Sp.	37.16 N	5.33 W
145	El Auja (äl ou'jà) Pal. (In.)	30.52 N	34.25 E
113	Elâziz (ĕl-ä'zēz) Tur.	38.35 N	39.12 E
114	El Azizia (ĕl ä-zē'zē-ä) Libya	32.40 N	13.12 E
82	Elba (ĕl'bȧ) Ala.	31.36 N	86.4 W
89	Elba I. Ga. (Savannah In.)	32.5 N	81.0 W
128	Elba (I.) It.	42.45 N	10.18 E
126	El Barco (ĕl bär'kō) Sp.	42.25 N	6.59 W
129	Elbasan (ĕl-bä-sän'') Alb.	41.7 N	20.4 E
122	Elbe (Labe) R. (ĕl'bē) (läb'ĕ) Eur.	50.10 N	15.0 E
78	Elbert, Mt. (ĕl'bērt) Colo.	39.7 N	106.27 W
82	Elberton (ĕl'bēr-tŭn) Ga.	34.6 N	82.53 W
123	Elbing (ĕl'bĭng) Ger.	54.10 N	19.24 E
113	Elbistan (ĕl-bē-stän') Tur.	38.15 N	37.15 E
124	Elboeuf (ĕl-bûf') Fr.	49.17 N	1.0 E
126	El Bonillo (ĕl bō-nēl'yō) Sp.	38.58 N	2.32 W
96	Elbow Cay Ba. Is.	26.30 N	77.0 W
76	Elbow Lake Minn.	45.59 N	95.58 W
113	Elbrus, Mt. (ĕl'brōōs) Sov. Un.	43.28 N	42.30 E
150	Elburz Mts. (ĕl'bōōrz') Iran	36.15 N	52.0 E
81	El Campo (ĕl kăm'pō) Tex.	29.12 N	96.17 W
97	El Can (ĕl kän) Dom. Rep.	17.57 N	71.15 W
80	El Capitan (Mt.) (ĕl kä-pē-tän') Tex.	31.58 N	104.55 W
73	El Casco (ĕl käs'kō) Calif. (Los Angeles In.)	33.59 N	117.6 W
74	El Centro (ĕl sĕn'trō) Calif.	32.48 N	115.32 W
104	El Chaco (State) (chä'kō) Arg.	26.30 S	61.0 W
115	El Chadder (ĕl chȧd'ĕr) Libya	28.48 N	19.24 E
127	Elche (ĕl'chā) Sp.	38.16 N	0.41 W
127	Elda (ĕl'dä) Sp.	38.29 N	0.46 W
141	Eldanane (ĕl-dä-nä'nä) It. E. Afr.	6.30 N	49.0 E
122	Elde R. (ĕl'dē) Ger.	53.25 N	11.34 E
135	El Djem (ĕl jĕm') Tun.	35.18 N	10.35 E
138	El Djouf (Salt) Desert (ĕl jōōf) Fr. W. Afr.	22.0 N	6.0 W
77	Eldon (ĕl-dŭn) Ia.	40.55 N	92.12 W
79	Eldon Mo.	38.19 N	92.35 W
49	Eldon Wash. (Seattle In.)	47.32 N	123.3 W
77	Eldora (ĕl-dō'rȧ) Ia.	42.21 N	93.5 W
79	El Dorado (ĕl dō-rä'dō) Ark.	33.13 N	92.38 W
79	Eldorado Ill.	37.49 N	88.25 W
79	El Dorado Kan.	37.48 N	96.51 W
79	Eldorado Springs Mo.	37.52 N	94.2 W
139	Eldoret (ĕl-dō-rĕt') Kenya	0.32 S	35.18 E
92	El Ebano (ĕl ā-bä'nō) Mex.	22.13 N	98.25 W
78	Electra (ē-lĕk'trȧ) Tex.	34.2 N	98.55 W
71	Electric Pk. Mont.	45.1 N	110.52 W
75	Elephant Butte Reservoir N. M.	33.25 N	107.10 W
89	Elephant Pass La. (New Orleans In.)	30.0 N	89.9 W
130	Elets (yĕ-lyĕts') Sov. Un.	52.38 N	38.30 E
97	Eleuthera I. (ē-lū'thēr-ȧ) Ba. Is.	25.10 N	76.12 W
97	Eleuthera Pt. Ba. Is.	24.40 N	76.10 W
79	Eleven Point R. Mo.-Ark.	36.40 N	91.12 W
139	El Fäsher (ĕl fä'shĕr) A. E. Sud.	13.42 N	25.22 E
126	El Ferrol (ĕl fä-rōl') Sp.	43.29 N	8.14 W
139	El Gara Oasis (ĕl gä'rä) Eg.	29.30 N	26.30 E
135	El Garbi (R.) (ĕl gär'bē) Eg. (In.)	31.0 N	30.43 E
139	El Gheria (ĕl gä'rē ä) Libya	30.27 N	13.21 E
145	El Ghor (ĕl gôr) Pal.-Transj. (In.)	30.55 N	35.23 E
116	Elgin (ĕl'jĭn) Gt. Brit.	57.40 N	3.20 W
77	Elgin Ill.	42.2 N	88.18 W
76	Elgin Neb.	41.59 N	98.4 W
70	Elgin Ore.	45.34 N	117.54 W
81	Elgin Tex.	30.20 N	97.22 W
138	El Goléa (ĕl gō-lā-ä') Alg.	30.38 N	2.51 E
139	Elgon, Mt. (ĕl'gŏn) Kenya	1.5 N	34.35 E
114	El Hamada (Plat.) (ĕl häm'ä-dä) Alg.	31.45 N	0.30 W
135	El Hatob, Oued (R.) (ĕl hä'tōb) Tun. (In.)	35.30 N	9.30 E
56	Elie (ē'lē) Can. (Winnipeg In.)	49.54 N	97.47 W
140	Elila R. (ē-lē'lä) Bel. Cong.	3.28 S	27.30 E
142	Elim (ē'lĭm) U. S. Afr.	34.36 S	19.44 E
121	Elisenvaara (ā-lē'sĕn-vä'rä) Fin.	61.29 N	29.40 E
81	Elizabeth (ē-lĭz'ȧ-bĕth) La.	30.53 N	92.48 W
85	Elizabeth N. J.	40.40 N	74.12 W
149	Elizabeth, C. Sov. Un.	54.30 N	142.50 E
83	Elizabeth City N. C.	36.17 N	76.14 W
89	Elizabeth R. Va. (Norfolk In.)	36.52 N	76.19 W
89	Elizabeth R. South Branch Va. (Norfolk In.)	36.49 N	76.17 W
89	Elizabeth R. Western Branch Va. (Norfolk In.)	36.51 N	76.21 W
83	Elizabethton Tenn.	36.20 N	82.12 W
84	Elizabethtown Ky.	37.42 N	85.54 W
140	Elizabethville Bel. Cong.	11.40 S	27.28 E
148	Elizarovskoe (yĕ-lē-zȧ-rôf'skō-yĕ) Sov. Un.	61.25 N	68.15 E
...	Elisavetgrad, see Zinovievsk, Sov. Un.		
126	Elizonda (Baztán) (ā-lē-thōn'dä) (bäth-tän') Sp.	43.11 N	1.32 W
126	Elja R. (ĕl'zhä) Port.-Sp.	40.0 N	6.53 W
97	El Jovero (ĕl hō-vä'rō) Hai.	18.59 N	69.4 W
139	El Kamlīn (ĕl käm-lēn') A. E. Sud.	15.3 N	33.10 E
115	El Kanais, C. (ĕl kä'nīs) Eg.	31.25 N	27.25 E
78	Elk City (ĕlk) Okla.	35.24 N	99.23 W
78	Elk Cr. Colo. (Denver In.)	39.29 N	105.27 W
88	Elk Grove Ill. Chicago (In.)	42.1 N	87.58 W
139	El Khandaq (ĕl kän-däk') A. E. Sud.	18.36 N	30.30 E
84	Elkhart (ĕlk'härt) Ind.	41.41 N	85.57 W
78	Elkhart Kan.	37.1 N	101.54 W
81	Elkhart Tex.	31.38 N	95.33 W
145	El Khelasa (Haluza) (ĕl kĕ-lä'sä) (hä-lōō'zä) Pal. (In.)	31.6 N	34.37 E
77	Elkhorn (ĕlk'hôrn) Wis.	42.40 N	88.30 W
76	Elkhorn R. Neb.	42.0 N	97.0 W
83	Elkin (ĕl'kĭn) N. C.	36.15 N	80.50 W
85	Elkins (ĕl'kĭnz) W. Va.	38.54 N	79.50 W
70	Elko (ĕl'kō) Nev.	40.50 N	115.45 W
76	Elk Point S. D.	42.42 N	96.40 W
84	Elk Rapids Mich	44.53 N	85.25 W
88	Elkridge Md. (Baltimore In.)	39.12 N	76.43 W
82	Elk R. Ala.-Tenn.	35.5 N	86.45 W
70	Elk R. Ida.	46.47 N	116.11 W
77	Elk R. Minn.	45.18 N	93.32 W
84	Elk R W. Va	38.30 N	81.15 W
72	Elkton Colo. (Colo. Sprs. In.)	38.43 N	105.9 W
82	Elkton Ky.	36.50 N	87.10 W
85	Elkton Md.	39.36 N	75.52 W
76	Elkton S. D.	44.16 N	96.27 W
135	El Kubri (ĕl kōō'brē) Eg. (Suez Can. In.)	30.2 N	32.35 E
52	Ellamar (ĕl'ȧ-mär) Alsk. (In.)	60.56 N	146.40 W
118	Elland (el'ănd) Gt. Brit.	53.40 N	1.50 W
76	Ellendale (ĕl'ĕn-dāl) N. D.	46.0 N	98.31 W
70	Ellensburg (ĕl'ĕnz-bûrg) Wash.	47.0 N	120.33 W
85	Ellenville (ĕl'ĕn-vĭl) N. Y.	41.38 N	74.27 W
73	Ellenwood (ĕl'ĕn-wōōd) Ga. (Atlanta In.)	33.37 N	84.17 W
167	Ellery, Mt. (ĕl'ēr-ĭ) Austl.	37.27 S	148.49 E
118	Ellesmere (ĕlz'mēr) Gt. Brit.	52.55 N	2.54 W
48	Ellesmere I. Can.	81.0 N	80.0 W
171	Ellesmere, L. N. Z.	43.45 S	172.30 E
118	Ellesmere Port Gt. Brit.	53.17 N	2.54 W
7	Ellice Is. (ĕl'lēs) Pac. O.	8.31 S	179.8 E
143	Elliot (ĕl'ĭ-ŭt) U. S. Afr.	31.20 S	27.53 E
143	Elliotdale U. S. Afr.	31.58 S	28.41 E
169	Elliott Cove Austl. (Tas. In.)	43.3 S	145.35 E
78	Ellis (ĕl'ĭs) Kan.	38.56 N	99.34 W
82	Ellisville Miss.	31.36 N	89.12 W
151	Ellore (ĕl-lōr') India	16.38 N	81.5 E
78	Ellsworth (ĕlz'wûrth) Kan.	38.34 N	98.14 W
86	Ellsworth Me.	44.33 N	68.25 W
49	Ellsworth Wash. (Portland In.)	45.36 N	122.34 W
122	Ellwangen (ĕl'väŋ-gĕn) Ger.	48.58 N	10.8 E
88	Ellwood Park (ĕl'wōōd) N. Y. (Niagara Falls In.)	42.58 N	78.51 W
72	Elm (ĕlm) Colo. (Denver In.)	40.22 N	104.46 W
70	Elma (ĕl'mȧ) Wash.	47.1 N	123.20 W
114	El Maadid (ĕl mä-ä-dēd') Mor.	31.30 N	4.31 W
79	Elm Cr. Tex.	33.20 N	97.3 W
56	Elm Cr. Can. (In.)	49.42 N	97.59 W
135	El Menar (ĕl mä-när') Sp. Mor. (Gibraltar In.)	35.47 N	5.17 E
166	Elmhurst (ĕlm'hûrst) Austl.	37.11 S	143.16 E
88	Elmhurst Ill.	41.59 N	87.59 W
85	Elmira (ĕl-mī'rȧ) N. Y.	42.6 N	76.50 W
85	Elmira Heights N. Y.	42.9 N	76.49 W
73	El Modeno (ĕl mō-dē'nō) Calif. (Los Angeles In.)	33.46 N	117.49 W
73	El Monte (ĕl mōn'tā) Calif. (Los Angeles In.)	34.5 N	118.2 W
75	El Morro Natl. Mon. (ĕl môr'rō) N. M.	35.3 N	108.21 W
76	Elm R. S. D.	45.50 N	98.24 W
122	Elmshorn (ĕlms'hôrn) Ger.	53.46 N	10.38 E
115	El Mugtaa (Muctar) (ĕl mōōg'tä) (mōōk'tär) Libya	30.25 N	18.42 E
88	Elmwood Park (ĕlm'wōōd) Ill. (Chicago In.)	41.55 N	87.50 W
124	Elne (ĕln) Fr.	42.37 N	3.0 E
130	Elnya (yĕl'nyä) Sov. Un.	54.33 N	33.12 E
139	El Obeid (ĕl ō-bād') A. E. Sud.	13.12 N	30.15 E
139	El Odaiya (ĕl ō-dī'yä) A. E. Sud.	12.6 N	28.17 E
89	Eloi B. (ē'loi) La. (New Orleans In.)	29.43 N	89.23 W
49	Elokomin R. (ē-lō'kō-mĭn) Wash. (Seattle In.)	46.15 N	123.18 W
92	El Oro de Hidalgo (ĕl ō'rō dā ē-dăl'gō) Mex.	19.48 N	100.5 W
138	El Oued (ĕl wĕd') Alg.	33.28 N	6.52 E
149	Elovka (Yelovka) (yĕ-lôf'kä) Sov. Un.	56.59 N	160.45 E
127	El Panadés (ĕl pä-nä-dās') Sp. (In.)	41.17 N	1.42 E
127	El Pardo (ĕl pär'dō) Sp. (In.)	40.31 N	3.47 W
80	El Paso (ĕl päs'ō) Tex.	31.46 N	106.28 W
95	El Porvenir (ĕl pōr-vä-nēr') Pan.	9.35 N	78.55 W
92	El Pueblito (ĕl pwĕ-blē'tō) Mex.	20.32 N	100.25 W
127	El Puerto de Sta. María (ĕl pwĕr' tō dä sän'tä mä-rē'ä) Sp. (In.)	36.36 N	6.13 W
145	El Qasaima (ĕl kä-sä'ē-mȧ) Eg. (In.)	30.41 N	34.21 E
145	El Qatrani (ĕl kä-trä'nē) Transj. (In.)	31.9 N	35.59 E
139	El Qedāref (ĕl kȧ-dȧ'rĕf) A. E. Sud.	14.5 N	35.26 E
135	El Qurna (ĕl kōōr'nȧ) Eg. (In.)	25.42 N	32.38 E
95	El Real (ĕl rā-äl) Pan.	8.7 N	77.42 W
92	El Refugio (ĕl rā-fōō'hē-ō) Mex.	23.3 N	100.28 W
78	El Reno (ĕl rē'nō) Okla.	35.32 N	97.58 W
77	Elroy (ĕl'roi) Wis.	43.44 N	90.16 W
126	Elsa R. (ĕl'sä) Sp.	42.10 N	5.33 W
92	El Salto (ĕl säl'tō) Mex.	23.48 N	105.20 W
80	El Sauz (ĕl sous') Mex.	29.3 N	106.14 W
79	Elsberry (ĕlz'bĕr-ĭ) Mo.	39.9 N	90.45 W
73	El Segundo (ĕl sĕgŭn'dō) Calif. (Los Angeles In.)	33.55 N	118.25 W
97	El Seibo (ĕl sā'bō) Hai.	18.45 N	69.2 W
139	El Sheb (ĕl shĕb) Eg.	22.30 N	29.57 E
49	Elsie (ĕl'sē) Ore. (Portland In.)	45.51 N	123.35 W
82	Elsiecoal (ĕl'sē-kōl) Ky.	37.8 N	82.56 W
	Elsinore, see Helsingör, Den.		
74	Elsinore (ĕl'sĭ-nôr) Calif.	33.40 N	117.20 W
73	Elsinore L. Calif. (Los Angeles In.)	33.40 N	117.20 W
73	Elsinore Mts. Calif. (Los Angeles In.)	33.39 N	117.25 W
72	Elsmere (ĕlz'mēr) Colo. (Colo. Sprs. In.)	38.52 N	104.43 W
169	Eltham (ĕl'thȧm) Austl. (Melbourne In.)	37.43 S	145.9 E
170	Eltham N. Z.	39.25 S	174.15 E
113	Eltonskoe, L. (yĕl-tôn'skō-yĕ) Sov. Un.	49.5 N	46.45 E
73	El Toro (ĕl tō'rō) Calif. (Los Angeles In.)	33.37 N	117.41 W
94	El Triumfo (ĕl trē-ōōm'fō) Sal.	13.16 N	88.32 W
75	El Vado Reservoir (ĕl vä'dō) N. M.	36.35 N	106.45 W
126	Elvas (ĕl'väzh) Port.	38.54 N	7.10 W
120	Elverum (ĕl'vĕ-rōōm) Nor.	60.54 N	11.32 E
92	El Vieja (Taxco) (ĕl vyā'hȧ) (täs'kō) Mex.	18.32 N	99.36 W
79	Elvins (ĕl'vĭnz) Mo.	37.47 N	90.32 W
139	El Wak (ĕl wäk') Kenya	2.58 N	40.58 E
84	Elwood (ĕl'wōōd) Ind.	40.17 N	85.51 W
73	Elwood Utah (Salt Lake City In.)	41.40 N	112.11 W
116	Ely (ē'lĭ) Gt. Brit.	52.25 N	0.20 E
77	Ely Minn.	47.54 N	91.52 W
74	Ely Nev.	39.15 N	114.53 W
84	Elyria (ē-lĭr'ĭ-ȧ) Ohio	41.22 N	82.7 W
121	Ema R. (ā'mȧ) Est.	58.25 N	27.0 E
113	Emba R. (yĕm'bȧ) Sov. Un.	47.0 N	55.0 E
84	Embarras R. (ĕm-băr'ăs) Ill.	39.20 N	88.10 W
119	Emblehem (ĕm'blĕ-hĕm) Bel. (Anvers In.)	51.10 N	4.36 E
125	Embrun (äN-brăN') Fr.	44.35 N	6.30 E
122	Emden (ĕm'dĕn) Ger.	53.22 N	7.12 E
165	Emerald (ĕm'ēr-ăld) Austl.	23.35 S	148.0 E
54	Emerson (ĕm'ēr-sŭn) Can.	49.1 N	97.1 W
112	Emetsk (yĕ-myĕtsk') Sov. Un.	63.30 N	41.45 E
139	Emi Koussi (Vol.) (ā'mē kōō-sē') Fr. Eq. Afr.	19.50 N	18.30 E
128	Emilia (Prov.) (ā-mēl'yä) It.	44.40 N	11.0 E
84	Eminence (ĕm'ĭ-nĕns) Ky.	38.25 N	85.11 W
161	Emirau (I.) (ā-mē-rä'ōō) N. Gui. Ter.	1.45 S	150.0 E
143	Emmaus (ĕ-mä'ŭs) U. S. Afr.	29.2 S	25.19 E
122	Emmen (ĕm'ĕn) Neth.	52.47 N	6.57 E
122	Emmerich (ĕm'ēr-ĭk) Ger.	51.51 N	6.13 E
77	Emmetsburg (ĕm'ĕts-bûrg) Ia.	43.5 N	94.40 W
70	Emmett (ĕm'ĕt) Ida.	43.52 N	116.30 W
71	Emmons, Mt. (ĕm'ŭnz) Utah	40.44 N	110.19 W
92	Empalme de Cañitas (ĕm-päl'mā dā kä-nyē'tȧs) Mex.	23.33 N	102.37 W
73	Empire (ĕm'pīr) Ala. (Birmingham In.)	33.48 N	86.59 W
90	Empire C. Z. (In.)	9.3 N	79.41 W
128	Empoli (äm'pō-lē) It.	43.43 N	10.57 E
79	Emporia (ĕm-pō'rĭ-ȧ) Kan.	38.24 N	96.11 W
83	Emporia Va.	36.41 N	77.33 W
85	Emporium (ĕm-pō'rĭ-ŭm) Pa.	41.28 N	78.14 W
120	Em R. (ĕm) Swe.	57.25 N	15.50 E
122	Emsdetten (ĕms'dĕt-ĕn) Ger.	52.10 N	7.30 E
122	Ems R. (ĕms) Ger.	52.30 N	7.18 E
	Enakievo, see Ordzhonikidze, Sov. Un.		
120	Enånger (ĕn-ôŋ'gĕr) Swe.	61.35 N	16.59 E
162	Encanto Pt. (ĕn-kän'tō) P. I.	15.44 N	121.38 E
104	Encarnación (ĕn-kär-nä-syōn') Par.	27.15 S	55.59 W
92	Encarnación de Díaz (ĕn-kär-nä-syōn dā dē'äz) Mex.	21.31 N	102.14 W
80	Encinal (ĕn'sĭ-nōl) Tex.	28.3 N	99.21 W
140	Encoge (ĕn-kō'zhä) Ang.	7.42 S	15.2 E
104	Encontrados (ĕn-kōn-trä'dōs) Ven.	9.0 N	75.0 W
166	Encounter B. (ĕn-koun'tēr) Austl.	35.38 S	138.42 E
73	Enda (ĕn'dȧ) Utah (Salt Lake City In.)	41.28 N	112.4 W
46	Enderby Land (Reg.) (ĕn'dēr-bĭ) Ant.	69.0 S	46.0 E
76	Enderlin (ĕn'dēr-lĭn) N. D.	46.38 N	97.36 W
85	Endicott (ĕn'dĭ-kŏt) N. Y.	42.7 N	76.4 W
163	End Pk. P. I.	9.19 N	118.12 E
135	Enfidaville (äN-fē-dȧ-vēl') Tun. (In.)	36.8 N	10.18 E
85	Enfield (ĕn'fēld) Conn.	41.55 N	72.35 W
116	Enfield Gt. Brit.	51.35 N	0.10 W
83	Enfield N. C.	36.12 N	77.41 W
97	Engaño, C. (ĕn-gän'yō) Hai.	18.38 N	68.20 W
162	Engaño, C. P. I.	18.31 N	122.15 E
139	Engare Uaso Nyiro R. (ĕn-gä'rä wä'sō nyē'rō) Kenya	0.48 N	38.0 E
143	Engcobo (ĕng-kō'bō) U. S. Afr.	31.41 S	28.2 E
113	Engels (ĕŋ'gĕls) Sov. Un.	51.25 N	46.10 E
160	Enggano (Telanjang I.) (ĕng-gä'nō) (tē-lăn-yăng') Neth. Ind.	5.25 S	102.15 E
79	England (ĭŋ'glȧnd) Ark.	34.33 N	91.58 W
116	England Gt. Brit.	52.40 N	1.0 W
78	Englewood (ĕn'g'l-wōōd) Colo.	39.38 N	105.0 W
88	Englewood Ill. (Chicago In.)	41.47 N	87.38 W
88	Englewood N. J. (N. Y. In.)	40.54 N	73.58 W
84	English (ĭn'glĭsh) Ind.	38.18 N	86.26 W
96	English Cays (Is.) Cuba	21.55 N	82.25 W
116	English Chan. Gt. Brit.	50.20 N	2.0 W
55	English R. Can.	50.35 N	94.0 W
127	Énguera (än'gārä) Sp.	38.58 N	0.41 W
156	Enhsien (ĕn'hsyĕn') Chn.	37.9 N	116.14 E
78	Enid (ē'nĭd) Okla.	36.24 N	97.54 W
148	Enisei (Yenisei) R. (yĕ-nē-sē'ē) Sov. Un.	61.30 N	90.0 E
148	Eniseisk (yĕ-nĭ-sä'ĭsk) Sov. Un.	58.30 N	92.10 E
140	Enkeldoorn (ĕŋ'k'l-dōōrn) S. Rh.	19.5 S	30.50 E
120	Enköping (ĕn'kû-pĭng) Swe.	59.38 N	17.5 E
139	En Nahud (ĕn nä'hōōd) A. E. Sud.	12.41 N	28.26 E
139	Ennedi (Reg.) (ĕn-nĕd'ē) Fr. Eq. Afr.	16.45 N	23.0 E
116	Ennell, L. (ĕn'ĕl) Ire.	53.25 N	7.25 W
116	Ennis (ĕn'ĭs) Ire.	52.55 N	9.0 W
81	Ennis Tex.	32.20 N	96.38 W
116	Enniscorthy (ĕn-ĭs-kôr'thĭ) Ire.	52.40 N	6.40 W
116	Enniskillen (ĕn-ĭs-kĭl'ĕn) N. Ire.	54.20 N	7.40 W
122	Enns R. (ĕns) Ger.	47.36 N	14.30 E
72	Eno (ē'nō) Colo. (Denver In.)	39.52 N	104.52 W
83	Enoree (ē-nō'rē) S. C.	34.39 N	81.58 W
83	Enoree R. S. C.	34.35 N	81.50 W
129	Enos (Inoz) (ā'nōs) (ē'nōz) Tur.	40.42 N	46.3 E
49	Enright (ĕn'rĭt) Ore. (Portland In.)	45.43 N	123.31 W

ng-sing; ŋ-baŋk; N-nasalized n; nŏd; cŏmmit; ōld; ōbey; ôrder; fōōd; fōōt; ou-out; s-soft; sh-dish; th-thin; pūre; ûnite; ûrn; stŭd; circŭs; ŭ-as "y" in study; '-indeterminate vowel.

Page	Name Pronunciation Region	Lat. °′	Long. °′
97	Enriquillo L. (ĕn-rē-kēl'yō) Hai.	18.25 N	71.35 W
122	Enschede (ĕns'ĸā-dĕ) Neth.	52.13 N	6.53 E
143	Enseleni (ĕn-sĕ-lē'nĭ) U. S. Afr.	28.42 S	32.1 E
74	Ensenada (ĕn-sĕ-nä'dä) Mex.	31.50 N	116.38 W
82	Ensley (ĕnz'lĭ) Ala.	33.32 N	86.51 W
139	Entebbe (ĕn-tĕb'ĕ) Ug.	0.2 N	32.28 E
82	Enterprise (ĕn'tēr-prīz) Ala.	31.19 N	85.52 W
70	Enterprise Ore.	45.25 N	117.17 W
167	Entrance, L. (ĕn'trăns) Austl.	37.55 S	147.45 E
124	Entraygues (ĕɴ-trĕg') Fr.	44.39 N	2.35 E
169	Entrecasteaux Chan., D' (däɴ-tr'-kȧs-tō'). Austl. (Tas. In.)	43.25 S	147.5 E
161	Entrecasteaux Is. d' Pap. Ter.	9.30 S	150.45 E
164	Entrecasteaux Pt. d' Austl.	34.48 S	116.0 E
104	Entre Rios (State) (ĕn'trä-rē'ōs). Arg.	31.30 S	59.0 W
103	Entre Rios (ĕn'trä-rē'ōōzh) Braz. (In.)	11.55 S	38.1 W
138	Enugu (ĕ-nōō'gōō) Nig.	6.38 N	7.22 E
70	Enumclaw (ĕn'ŭm-klô) Wash.	47.11 N	121.59 W
150	Enzeli (Pahlevi) (ĕn'zĕ-lē) (pȧ'lĕ-vē). Per.	37.30 N	29.29 E
124	Epernay (ā-pĕr-nĕ') Fr.	49.3 N	3.55 E
75	Ephraim (ē'frā-ĭm) Utah	39.22 N	111.35 W
165	Epi I. (ā'pē) New Hebr.	16.45 S	168.15 E
126	Épila (ā'pē-lä) Sp.	41.38 N	1.16 W
125	Épinal (ā-pē-näl') Fr.	48.11 N	6.28 E
125	Épinay (ā-pē-nĕ') Fr. (In.)	48.57 N	2.18 E
129	Epirus (Prov.) (ē-pī'rŭs) Grc.	39.30 N	20.50 E
169	Epping (ĕp'ĭng) Austl.	37.39 S	145.2 E
118	Epworth (ĕp'wûrth) Gt. Brit.	53.31 N	0.50 W
124	Équeurdreville (ā-kûr-dr'-vēl'). Fr.	49.39 N	1.38 W
128	Erakleion (Candia) (hē-răk'lĭ-ŏn) (kăn'dĭ-ȧ). Grc. (In.)	35.19 N	25.8 E
163	Eran B. (ä'rän) P. I.	9.6 N	117.42 E
139	Erba, Mt. (ĕr'bȧ) A. E. Sud.	20.48 N	36.48 E
129	Ercegnovi (ĕr-tsĕg-nō'vē) Yugo.	42.27 N	18.32 E
73	Erda (ĕr'dä) Utah (Salt Lake City In.)	40.37 N	112.15 W
129	Erdek (ĕr'dĕk) Tur.	40.24 N	27.47 E
46	Erebus, Mt. (ĕr'ē-bŭs) Ant.	77.0 S	168.0 E
113	Ereğli (ĕ-rā'ĭ-lē) Tur.	37.32 N	34.0 E
113	Ereğli Tur.	41.20 N	31.30 E
131	Eremeevka (yĕ'rĕ-mĕ-yĕf'kȧ) Sov. Un.	49.23 N	32.31 E
122	Erfurt (ĕr'fōōrt) Ger.	50.59 N	11.1 E
129	Ergene R. (ĕr'gĕ-nĕ) Tur.	41.21 N	27.0 E
129	Ergeri (Gjinocastro) (ĕr-gĕ-rē') (jē-nō-kȧs'trō). Alb.	40.4 N	20.8 E
126	Eria R. (ā-rē'ä) Sp.	42.11 N	6.10 W
78	Erick (âr'ĭk) Okla.	35.13 N	99.52 W
72	Erie (ē'rĭ) Colo. (Denver In.)	40.3 N	105.3 W
79	Erie Kan.	37.35 N	95.17 W
85	Erie Pa.	42.6 N	80.4 W
84	Erie, L. U. S.-Can.	42.0 N	81.0 W
158	Erimo C. (ā'rē-mō) Jap.	42.0 N	143.5 E
119	Erith (ē'rĭth). Gt. Brit. (London In.)	51.29 N	0.11 E
139	Eritrea (ā-rē-trä'ȧ) (Division) It. E. Afr.	13.30 N	39.0 E
113	Erivan (ĕr-ē-vän') Sov. Un.	40.10 N	44.32 E
122	Erlangen (ĕr'läng-ĕn) Ger.	49.37 N	11.1 E
89	Erlanger (ĕr'lăng-ēr) Ky. (Cincinnati In.)	39.1 N	84.36 W
112	Ermak I. (yĕr-măk') Sov. Un.	66.40 N	71.15 E
143	Ermelo (ĕr'mĕ-lō) U. S. Afr.	26.32 S	29.59 E
125	Ermont (ĕr-môɴ') Fr. (In.)	48.58 N	2.16 E
124	Ernée (ĕr-nā') Fr.	48.19 N	0.51 W
116	Erne, Lough (L.) (lŏĸ ûrn) N. Ire.	54.30 N	7.50 W
81	Eros (ē'rōs) La.	32.23 N	92.27 W
145	Er Ramle (Ramla) (ĕr răm'lĕ) (răm'lȧ) Pal. (In.)	31.55 N	34.51 E
139	Er Renk (ĕr rĕnk') A. E. Sud.	11.47 N	32.50 E
116	Errigal, Mt. (ĕr-ĭ-gôl') N. Ire.	55.0 N	8.5 W
115	Er Rik (ĕr rĕk') Libya	29.7 N	22.22 E
116	Erris Head (ĕr'ĭs) Ire.	54.20 N	10.0 W
165	Erromanga I. (ĕr-ô-măŋ'gȧ) New Hebr.	18.45 S	169.15 E
139	Er Roseires (ĕr rō-sā'rĕs) A. E. Sud.	12.2 N	32.51 E
123	Ersekújvar (Nove'Zamky) (ĕr'shĕk-ōō'y'-vär) (nô'văzäm'kē) Hung.	47.59 N	18.10 E
167	Erskine R. (ĕr'skĭn) Austl.	32.8 S	149.10 E
125	Erstein (ĕr'shtīn) Fr.	48.25 N	7.42 E
83	Erwin (ûr'wĭn) N. C.	35.16 N	78.40 W
83	Erwin Tenn.	36.8 N	82.25 W
113	Erzincan (ĕr-zĭn-jän') Tur.	39.45 N	39.30 E
113	Erzurum (ĕrz'-rōōm') Tur.	39.55 N	41.15 E
158	Esashi (ĕs'ȧ-shē) Jap.	41.52 N	140.10 E
120	Esbjerg (ĕs'byĕrgh) Den.	55.28 N	8.27 E
121	Esbo (ĕs'bō) Fin.	60.14 N	24.45 E
163	Escalante (ĕs-kä-län'tä) P. I.	10.48 N	123.33 E
75	Escalante (ĕs-kȧ-lăn'tē) Utah	37.47 N	111.37 W
75	Escalante R. Utah	37.40 N	111.15 W
82	Escambia R. (ĕs-kăm'bĭ-ȧ) Fla.	30.45 N	87.19 W
77	Escanaba (ĕs-kȧ-nô'bȧ) Mich.	45.45 N	87.5 W
77	Escanaba R. Mich.	45.48 N	87.30 W
95	Escarpado, Pt. (ĕs-kär-pä'dō) Pan.	8.5 N	78.30 W
125	Esch (ĕsh) Lux.	49.30 N	6.0 E
122	Eschwege (ĕsh'vā-gĕ) Ger.	51.11 N	10.2 E
122	Eschweiler (ĕsh'vī-lēr) Ger.	50.49 N	6.16 E
7	Escobonal (ĕs-kō-bō-näl') Can. Is. (Tenerife In.)	28.17 N	16.24 W
97	Escocesa B. (ĕs-kō-sä'sä) Hai.	19.20 N	69.40 W
74	Escondido (ĕs-kŏn-dē'dō) Calif.	33.6 N	117.7 W
95	Escondido (ĕs-kōn-dē'dō) R. Nic.	12.7 N	84.6 W
127	Escorial (ĕs-kō-rē-äl') Sp. (In.)	40.35 N	4.8 W
95	Escuda de Veraguas (I.) (ĕs-kōō'dä dā vä-rä'gwäs) Pan.	0.5 N	81.33 W
92	Escuinapa (ĕs-kwē-nä'pä) Mex.	22.51 N	105.46 W
94	Escuintla (ĕs-kwēn'tlä) Guat.	14.16 N	90.48 W
93	Escuintla Mex.	15.18 N	92.41 W
138	Eséka (ĕ-sā'kȧ) Cam.	3.45 N	11.2 E
126	Esgueva R. (ĕs-gā'vä) Sp.	41.50 N	4.0 W
119	Esher (ĕsh'ēr) Gt. Brit. (London In.)	51.22 N	0.23 W
143	Eshowe (ĕsh'ō-wē) U. S. Afr.	28.51 S	31.30 E
145	Esh Shobek (ĕsh shō-bĕk') Transj. (In.)	30.31 N	35.32 E
169	Esk (ĕsk) Austl. (In.)	27.13 S	152.25 E
52	Eska (ĕs'kȧ) Alsk. (In.)	61.49 N	148.56 W
84	Eskdale (ĕsk'dāl) W. Va.	38.7 N	81.27 W
129	Eski-Džumaya (ĕs'kē-dzhōō-mä'yȧ) Bul.	43.14 N	26.33 E
110	Eskifjördur (ĕs'kē-fyûr'dōōr) Ice.	65.4 N	13.50 W
120	Eskilstuna (ā'shĕl-stü-nȧ) Swe.	59.21 N	16.29 E
113	Eskişehir (ĕs-kē-shĕ'h'r) Tur.	39.45 N	30.30 E
169	Esk R. Austl. (Tas. In.)	41.45 S	147.27 E
93	Eslava, R. de (ĕs-lä'vä, rē'ō dā) Mex. (In.)	19.17 N	99.14 W
120	Eslöv (ĕs'lûv) Swe.	55.50 N	13.19 E
102	Esmeraldas (ĕs-mä-rāl'däs) Col.	0.59 N	79.45 W
97	Espada Pt. (ĕs-pä'dä) Hai.	18.22 N	68.28 W
127	Esparraguera (ĕs-pär-rä-gā'rä) Sp. (In.)	41.32 N	1.52 E
95	Esparta (ĕs-pär'tä) C. R.	9.59 N	84.40 W
164	Esperance (ĕs'pē-răns) Austl.	33.40 S	121.58 E
96	Esperanza (ĕs-pā-ränd'zä) Cuba	22.26 N	80.7 W
127	Espichel, C. (ĕs-pē-shĕl') Port. (In.)	38.25 N	9.13 W
102	Espinal (ĕs-pē-näl') Col.	3.58 N	75.10 W
103	Espirito Santo (State) Braz.	20.0 S	41.0 W
162	Espiritu Santo, C. (ĕs-pē'rē-tōō sänt'ō) P. I.	12.35 N	125.9 E
165	Espiritu Santo I. (ĕs-pē'rē-tōō sän'tō) New Hebr.	15.15 S	167.0 E
126	Esposende (ĕs-pō-zĕn'dä) Port.	41.32 N	8.48 W
70	Esquimalt (ĕs-kwī'mōlt) Can.	48.25 N	123.35 W
145	Es Safiye (ĕs sȧ'fē-yĕ) Transj. (In.)	31.6 N	35.29 E
122	Essen (ĕs'ĕn) Ger.	51.28 N	7.0 E
169	Essendon (ĕs'ĕn-dŭn) Austl. (Melbourne In.).	37.45 S	144.55 E
113	Essentuki (yĕs'ĕn-tōō'kē) Sov. Un.	44.5 N	42.45 E
103	Essequibo R. (ĕs-ä-kē'bō). Br. Gu.	3.0 N	58.15 W
87	Essex (ĕs'ĕks) Mass. (In.)	42.38 N	70.47 W
86	Essex Jc. Vt.	44.31 N	73.8 W
84	Essexville (ĕs'ĕks-vĭl) Mich.	43.36 N	83.49 W
56	Essington (ĕs'ĭng-tŭn) Can. (Prince Rupert In.)	54.9 N	129.58 W
115	Es Sultan (ĕs sōōl-tän') Libya	31.2 N	17.17 E
138	Es Suweira (Mogador) (ĕs sōō-wā'rȧ) (mō-gȧ-dōr') Mor.	31.32 N	9.42 W
72	Estabrook (ĕs'tȧ-brŏŏk) Colo. (Denver In.)	39.24 N	105.22 W
103	Estancia (ĕs-tän'sĭ-ȧ) Braz.	11.27 S	37.28 W
92	Estanzuela (ĕs-tän-zwā'lȧ) Mex.	21.17 N	103.31 W
126	Estarreja (ĕs-tär-rā'zhȧ) Port.	40.45 N	8.39 W
143	Estcourt (ĕst-kôrt) U. S. Afr.	29.0 S	29.52 E
128	Este (ĕs'tā) It.	45.14 N	11.38 E
94	Estelí (ĕs-tā-lē') Nic.	13.14 N	86.17 W
126	Estella (ĕs-täl'yä) Sp.	42.41 N	2.1 W
126	Estepa (ĕs-tā'pä) Sp.	37.18 N	4.53 W
126	Estepona (ĕs-tā-pō'nä) Sp.	36.26 N	5.9 W
119	Este R. (ĕs'tĕ) Ger. (Hamburg In.)	53.29 N	9.42 E
74	Esteros B. (ĕs-tā'rōs) Calif.	35.25 N	120.55 W
72	Estes Park (ĕs'tĭz) Colo. (Denver In.)	40.23 N	105.32 W
76	Estevan (ē-stē'vŏn) Can.	49.10 N	103.0 W
77	Estherville (ĕs'tēr-vĭl) Ia.	43.25 N	94.49 W
83	Estill (ĕs'tĭl) S. C.	32.45 N	81.15 W
143	Eston (ĕs'tŭn) U. S. Afr.	29.52 S	30.31 E
121	Estonia (ĕs-tō'nĭ-ȧ) Eur.	58.45 N	25.20 E
126	Estrella, Serra da (Mts.) (sĕr'rä dä ĕs-trā'lȧ) Port.	40.25 N	7.45 W
126	Estremadura (Prov.) (ĕs-trā-mä-dōō'rȧ) Port.	39.0 N	8.30 W
126	Estremoz (ĕs-trā-mōzh') Port.	38.50 N	7.35 W
103	Estrondo, Serra do (Mts.) (sĕr'rȧ dōō ĕs-trôn'dōō) Braz.	8.0 S	49.0 W
122	Eszlingen (ĕs'lĭng-ĕn) Ger.	48.46 N	9.19 E
123	Esztergom (ĕs'tĕr-gōm) Hung.	47.45 N	18.44 E
48	Etah (ē'tȧ) Grnld.	78.20 N	72.42 W
124	Étampes (ā-täɴp') Fr.	48.25 N	2.9 E
124	Étang de Carcans (L.) (ā-täɴ dē kär-käɴ') Fr.	45.5 N	1.5 W
124	Étang de Cazau (L.) (ā-täɴ' dē kä-zō') Fr.	44.30 N	1.10 W
124	Étaples (ā-täp'l') Fr.	50.31 N	1.41 E
57	Etchemin R. (ĕch'ĕ-mĭn) Can. (Quebec In.)	46.42 N	71.5 W
102	Eten (ā-tän') Peru	7.0 S	79.45 W
	Ethiopia (Abyssinia), see Italian East Africa		
93	Etlatongo (San Mateo) (ĕt-lä-tôŋ'-gō) (sän-mä-tā'ō) Mex.	17.1 N	97.1 W
89	Etna (ĕt'nȧ) Pa. (Pittsburgh In.)	40.30 N	79.57 W
49	Etna Wash. (Portland In.)	45.55 N	122.37 W
128	Etna (Mt.) It.	37.44 N	14.59 E
140	Etosha Pan (Dry L.) (ĕtō'shȧ) S. W. Afr.	18.50 S	16.20 E
82	Etowah (ĕt'ô-wä) Tenn.	35.18 N	84.32 W
82	Etowah, R. Ga.	34.15 N	84.30 W
145	Et Taiyibe (ĕt tī-yē'bĕ) Transj. (In.)	32.29 N	35.44 E
117	Etterbeek (ĕt'ĕr-bāk) Bel.	50.50 N	4.20 E
92	Etzatlán (ĕt-zä-tlän') Mex.	20.45 N	104.4 W
124	Eu (û) Fr.	50.1 N	1.29 E
129	Euboea (I.) (û-bē'ȧ) Grc.	38.30 N	23.55 E
164	Eucla (ū'klȧ) Austl.	31.40 S	128.46 E
84	Euclid (ū'klĭd) Ohio	41.36 N	81.29 W
79	Eudora (û-dō'rȧ) Ark.	33.5 N	91.17 W
82	Eufaula (û-fô'lȧ) Ala.	31.54 N	85.9 W
79	Eufaula Okla.	35.16 N	95.34 W
70	Eugene (û-jēn') Ore.	44.3 N	123.6 W
167	Euglo (ū'glō) Austl.	33.25 S	147.14 E
167	Eugowra (û-gou'rȧ) Austl.	33.24 S	148.22 E
81	Eunice (ū'nĭs) La.	30.30 N	92.25 W
117	Eupen (oi'pĕn) Bel.	50.35 N	6.5 E
150	Euphrates (Firat) R. (û-frā'tēz) (fĭ-rät') Asia	38.0 N	39.5 E
70	Eureka (û-rē'kȧ) Calif.	40.47 N	124.10 W
79	Eureka Kan.	37.48 N	96.17 W
70	Eureka Mont.	48.52 N	115.3 W
70	Eureka Nev.	39.33 N	115.58 W
76	Eureka S. D.	45.47 N	99.38 W
81	Eureka Tex. (In.)	29.48 N	95.23 W
75	Eureka Utah	39.56 N	112.8 W
79	Eureka Springs Ark.	36.24 N	93.44 W
124	Eure R. (ûr) Fr.	49.1 N	1.10 E
167	Euroa (û-rō'ȧ) Austl.	36.44 S	145.36 E
141	Europa I. (û-rō'pȧ) Ind. O.	22.20 S	40.25 E
106	Europe (ū'rŭp)		
122	Euskirchen (ois'kĭrĸ-ĕn) Ger.	50.40 N	6.48 E
83	Eustis (ūs'tĭs) Fla.	28.51 N	81.41 W
166	Euston (ūs'tŭn) Austl.	34.33 S	142.43 E
82	Eutaw (ū'tô) Ala.	32.49 N	87.53 W
169	Evandale (ĕv'ăn-dāl) Austl.	41.35 S	147.17 E
120	Evanger (ĕ-väŋ'gĕr) Nor.	60.39 N	6.8 E
72	Evans (ĕv'ănz) Colo. (Denver In.)	40.22 N	104.41 W
170	Evans B. N. Z. (In.)	41.18 S	174.49 E
6	Evans, Mt. Fiji Is. (In.)	17.38 S	177.34 E
77	Evanston Ill.	42.2 N	87.42 W
71	Evanston Wyo.	41.16 N	110.58 W
84	Evansville Ind.	38.0 N	87.33 W
77	Evansville Wis.	42.38 N	89.18 W
84	Evart (ĕv'ērt) Mich.	43.57 N	85.10 W
77	Eveleth (ĕv'ĕ-lĕth) Minn.	47.26 N	92.32 W
164	Everard, L. (ĕv'ēr-ärd) Austl.	31.15 S	135.5 E
164	Everard Ranges (Mts.) Austl.	27.15 S	132.30 E
151	Everest, Mt. (ĕv'ēr-ĕst) Nep.	27.58 N	87.5 E
87	Everett (ĕv'ēr-ĕt) Mass. (In.)	42.24 N	71.3 W
70	Everett Wash.	47.59 N	122.12 W
83	Everglades, The (Swamp) (ĕv'ēr-glādz). Fla. (In.)	26.0 N	80.40 W
82	Evergreen (ĕv'ēr-grēn) Ala.	31.36 N	86.58 W
72	Evergreen Colo. (Denver In.)	39.38 N	105.20 W
72	Everson (ĕv'ēr-sŭn) Wash. (Vancouver In.)	48.55 N	122.20 W
118	Evesham (ēv'shȧm) Gt. Brit.	52.5 N	1.56 W
126	Évora (ĕv'ō-rä) Port.	38.34 N	7.55 W
131	Evpatoriya (Guesleve) (yĕf-pä-tō'-rē-yȧ) (gwĕs'lyĕ-vĕ) Sov. Un.	45.11 N	32.22 E
124	Évreux (ā-vrû') Fr.	49.1 N	1.10 E
129	Evros (Maritsa) R. (ĕv'rōs) (mä'-rēt-sȧ). Tur.	41.0 N	26.21 E
129	Evrotas R. (ĕv-rō'tȧs) Grc.	37.0 N	22.30 E
129	Evstratios (I.) (ĕv-strä'tĭ-ōs) Grc.	39.30 N	25.0 E
173	Ewa (ē'wä) Haw.	21.18 N	158.2 W
79	Excelsior Springs (ĕk-sĕl'sĭ-ŏr). Mo.	39.20 N	94.13 W
116	Exe (R.) (ĕks) Gt. Brit.	51.5 N	3.30 W
74	Exeter (ĕk'sē-tēr) Calif.	36.17 N	119.9 W
116	Exeter Gt. Brit.	50.45 N	3.30 W
86	Exeter N. H.	42.55 N	70.58 W
116	Exmoor (ĕks'mōōr) Gt. Brit.	51.10 N	3.45 W
116	Exmouth (ĕks'mŭth) Gt. Brit.	50.40 N	3.22 E
164	Exmouth G. Austl.	22.0 S	114.15 E
87	Exploits R. (ĕks-ploits') Newf.	48.45 N	56.25 W
126	Extremadura (Prov.) (ĕks-trä-mä-doo'rä). Sp.	39.0 N	6.20 W
97	Exuma (ĕk-sōō'mȧ) Ba. Is.	24.15 N	76.5 W
131	Eya R. (ĕ-yä') Sov. Un.	46.38 N	38.54 E
142	Eyasi, L. (ā-yä'sē) Tan.	3.38 S	35.0 E
110	Eyla Fjord (ī'lȧ) Ice.	66.0 N	18.15 W
119	Eynsford (ānz'fērd) Gt. Brit. (London In.)	51.22 N	0.13 E
121	Ezel (Saaremaa) (I.) (ā'zĕl) (sä'-rĕ-mä'). Est.	58.26 N	22.36 E
121	Ežerenai (Zarasai) (ā-zhā'rĕ-nī') (zä-rä-sī'). Lith.	55.44 N	26.17 E
129	Ezine (ā'zĭ-nȧ) Tur.	39.46 N	26.20 E
164	Eyre (âr) Austl.	32.10 S	126.10 E
164	Eyre, L. Austl.	28.30 S	137.15 E
164	Eyre's Pen. (ârz) Austl.	33.28 S	136.40 E
145	Ezraa (ĕz-rä') Syr. (In.)	32.53 N	36.8 E
138	Ezu (ĕ-zōō') Nig.	6.40 N	10.3 E
120	Faaborg (fô'bôrg) Den.	55.5 N	10.18 E
80	Fabens (fā'bĕnz) Tex.	31.30 N	106.8 W
128	Fabriano (fä-brē-ä'nō) It.	43.19 N	12.55 E
139	Fada (fä'dä) Fr. Eq. Afr.	17.3 N	21.20 E
138	Fada N'Gourma (fä'dȧ 'n gōōr'mȧ) Fr. W. Afr.	12.12 N	0.23 E
149	Faddeevski (Thaddeus) I. (fȧ-dyā'-yĕf-skĭ) (thăd-ē-ŭs) Sov. Un.	75.20 N	144.0 E
120	Faemund L. (fā'mōōn') Nor.	62.10 N	11.54 E
128	Faenza (fä-ĕnd'zä) It.	44.27 N	11.52 E
110	Faeroes, The (Is.) (fā'rōz) Atl. O.	61.55 N	6.45 W
126	Fafe (fä'fä) Port.	41.30 N	8.10 W
123	Făgăraş (fä-gä'räsh) Rom.	45.50 N	24.58 E
120	Fagernes (fä'ghēr-nĕs) Nor.	61.0 N	9.15 E
138	Faguibine, L. (fä-gē-bē'nȧ) Fr. W. Afr.	16.50 N	4.0 W
141	Fah (fä) It. E. Afr.	4.58 N	48.3 E
160	Faifo (fī'fō') Fr. In. Chn.	15.58 N	108.10 E
56	Fairbank (fâr'bănk) Can. (In.)	43.42 N	79.28 W
53	Fairbanks (fâr'bănks) Alsk.	64.44 N	147.39 W
73	Fairbûrn (fâr'bûrn) Ga. (Atlanta In.)	33.34 N	84.35 W
79	Fairbury (fâr'bĕr-ĭ) Ill.	40.43 N	88.30 W
79	Fairbury Neb.	40.8 N	97.11 W
77	Fairfax (fâr'făks) Minn.	44.31 N	94.42 W
83	Fairfax S. C.	32.57 N	81.15 W
82	Fairfield (fâr'fēld) Ala.	33.29 N	86.57 W
169	Fairfield (fâr'fēld) Austl.	33.52 S	150.57 E
79	Fairfield Ill.	38.23 N	88.22 W

ăt; finȧl; rāte; senāte; ärm; ȧsk; sofȧ; fâre; ch-choose; dh-as th in other; bē; ēvent; bĕt; recĕnt; cratēr; g-go; gh-gutteral g; bĭt; ĭ-short neutral; rīde; ĸ-gutteral k as ch in German ich;

Page	Name Pronunciation	Region	Lat. °′	Long. °′
77	Fairfield	Ia.	41.0 N	91.58 W
86	Fairfield	Me.	44.36 N	69.37 W
85	Fairhaven (fâr-hā′vĕn)	Mass.	41.35 N	70.57 W
86	Fair Haven	Vt.	43.37 N	73.15 W
116	Fair I. (fâr)	Gt. Brit. (In.)	59.30 N	1.30 W
84	Fairmont (fâr′mŏnt)	Ind.	40.26 N	85.42 W
76	Fairmont	Minn.	43.39 N	94.25 W
49	Fairmont	Wash. (Seattle In.)	47.59 N	122.51 W
85	Fairmont	W. Va.	39.29 N	80.11 W
85	Fairport (fâr′pōrt)	N. Y.	43.7 N	77.26 W
84	Fairport Har.	Ohio	41.44 N	81.16 W
89	Fairview (fâr′vū)	Ohio (Cleveland In.)	41.27 N	81.50 W
78	Fairview	Okla.	36.16 N	98.29 W
75	Fairview	Utah	39.38 N	111.28 W
72	Fairview Pk.	Colo. (Denver In.)	40.8 N	105.21 W
86	Fairville (fâr′vĭl)	Can.	45.16 N	66.7 W
53	Fairweather, Mt. (fâr-wĕdh′ẽr)	Alsk.	59.0 N	134.30 W
76	Faith (fāth)	S. D.	45.1 N	102. 2 W
151	Faizabad (fī-zä-băd′)	Afg.	37.15 N	70.31 E
139	Fajao (fä-jä′ō)	Ug.	2.9 N	31.41 E
124	Falaise (fȧ-lâz′)	Fr.	48.56 N	0.11 W
72	Falcon (fô′k′n)	Colo. (Colo. Sprs. In.)	38.56 N	104.36 W
85	Falconer (fô′k′n-ẽr)	N. Y.	42.7 N	79.11 W
138	Falémé R. (fȧ-lā-mā′)	Fr. W. Afr.	13.30 N	12.0 E
123	Fălesti (fŭ-lȧsh′tĭ)	Rom.	47.33 N	27.43 E
80	Falfurrias (făl-fo͞o-rē′ȧs)	Tex.	27.13 N	98.9 W
120	Falkenberg (fäl′kĕn-bĕrgh)	Swe.	56.55 N	12.29 E
119	Falkenhagen (fäl′kĕn-hä-gĕn)	Ger. (Berlin In.)	52.34 N	13.7 E
116	Falkirk (fôl′kûrk)	Gt. Brit.	55.59 N	3.45 W
104	Falkland Is. (fôk′lănd)	Atl. O.	51.45 S	59.0 W
6	Falkland Is. Dependencies	Antarct. O.	65.0 S	50.0 W
120	Falköping (fäl′chûp-ĭng)	Swe.	58.9 N	13.32 E
89	Falling (fôl′ĭng)	Ill. (St. Louis In.)	38.33 N	90.10 W
74	Fallon (făl′ŭn)	Nev.	39.29 N	118.47 W
85	Fall River	Mass.	41.40 N	71.10 W
79	Falls City	Neb.	40.3 N	95.36 W
169	Falmouth (făl′mŭth)	Austl. (Tas. In.)	41.31 S	148.16 E
116	Falmouth	Gr. Brit.	50.10 N	5.5 W
96	Falmouth	Jam.	18.31 N	77.41 W
84	Falmouth	Ky.	38.40 N	84.22 W
142	False B.	U. S. Afr.	34.10 S	18.40 E
97	False C.	Hai.	17.45 N	71.40 W
120	Falster (I.) (fäls′tĕr)	Den.	54.50 N	12.0 E
123	Fălticeni (fŭl-tê-chȧn′y′)	Rom.	47.28 N	26.17 E
120	Falun (fä-lo͞on′)	Swe.	60.38 N	15.38 E
115	Famagusta (fä-mä-go͞os′tä)	Cyp.	35.18 N	34.0 E
139	Famaka (fä-mä′kä)	A. E. Sud.	11.24 N	34.47 E
161	Famy (fä′mê)	P. I. (Manila In.)	14.30 N	121.30 E
156	Fangshan (fäng′shän′)	Chn.	39.42 N	115.52 E
6	Fanning I. (făn′ĭng)	Pac. O.	3.51 N	159.21 W
56	Fannystelle (făn′ĭ-stĕl)	Can. (Winnipeg In.)	49.45 N	97.45 W
128	Fano (fä′nō)	It.	43.50 N	13.1 E
120	Fanö (I.) (fän′û)	Den.	55.22 N	8.25 E
141	Farafangana (fä-rä-fäŋ-gä′nä)	Madag.	22.47 S	47.50 E
139	Farafra, Oases of (fä-rä′frä)	Eg.	27.8 N	28.2 E
150	Farah (fä-rä′)	Afg.	32.20 N	62.12 E
150	Farah R.	Afg.	32.45 N	63.0 E
92	Farallón, Pt. (fä-rä-lōn′)	Mex.	19.23 N	105.3 W
138	Faranah (fä-rä′nä)	Fr. W. Afr.	10.2 N	10.37 W
150	Farasan Is. (fä-rȧ-sän′)	Asia	16.45 N	41.45 E
149	Far East Area	Sov. Un.	60.0 N	145.0 E
115	Faregh Wadi (R.) (wä′dê fä-rĕg′)	Libya	30.3 N	20.0 E
48	Farewell, C. (fâr-wĕl′)	Grnld.	60.0 N	44.0 W
171	Farewell C.	N. Z.	40.32 S	172.32 E
76	Fargo (fär′gō)	N. D.	46.53 N	96.47 W
121	Får. I. (fôr)	Swe.	57.54 N	19.10 E
77	Faribault (fâ′rĭ-bō)	Minn.	44.18 N	93.15 W
135	Farigh, Wadi el (R.) (wädê ĕl fä-rēg′)	Eg. (In.)	30.0 N	30.20 E
126	Farilhões Is. (fä-rê-lyôɴzh′)	Port.	39.28 N	9.32 W
164	Farina (fȧ-rē′nȧ)	Austl.	30.2 S	138.27 E
135	Fariskûr (fä-rês-ko͞or′)	Eg. (In.)	31.19 N	31.45 E
84	Farmersburg (fär′mẽrz-bûrg)	Ind.	39.15 N	87.25 W
79	Farmersville	Tex.	33.11 N	96.38 W
87	Farmingham	Mass. (In.)	42.17 N	71.25 W
79	Farmington	Ill.	40.41 N	90.1 W
86	Farmington	Me.	44.49 N	70.18 W
77	Farmington	Minn.	44.38 N	93.4 W
79	Farmington	Mo.	37.46 N	90.26 W
75	Farmington	N. M.	36.41 N	108.10 W
71	Farmington	Utah	41.0 N	111.55 W
83	Farmville	N. C.	35.36 N	77.36 W
83	Farmville	Va.	37.17 N	78.25 W
119	Farnborough (färn′bŭr-ô)	Gt. Brit. (London In.)	51.21 N	0.4 E
116	Farne Is. (färn)	Gt. Brit.	55.39 N	1.35 W
86	Farnham (fär′năm)	Can.	45.15 N	72.55 W
118	Farnworth (färn′wŭrth)	Gt. Brit.	53.33 N	2.23 W
103	Faro (fä′ro͝o)	Braz.	2.15 S	56.45 W
126	Faro	Port.	37.1 N	7.57 W
164	Farquhar C. (fär′kwȧr)	Austl.	23.45 S	113.28 E
84	Farrell (făr′ĕl)	Ohio	41.12 N	80.30 W
151	Farukhabad (fŭ-ro͝ok-hä-băd′)	India	27.15 N	79.38 E
120	Farsund (fär′so͝on)	Nor.	58.5 N	6.50 E
150	Fartak, C. (fär-täk′)	Aden	15.40 N	52.15 E
78	Farwell (fär′wĕl)	Tex.	34.24 N	103.1 W
150	Fasa (fŭ-sä′)	Iran	29.0 N	53.59 E
129	Fasano (fä-zä′nō)	It.	40.50 N	17.21 E
135	Fashn (fäsh′n)	Eg. (In.)	28.48 N	30.55 E
116	Fastnet Light House (făst′nĕt)	Ire.	51.22 N	9.35 W
131	Fastov (fäs′tôf)	Sov. Un.	50.4 N	29.55 E
131	Fatezh (fät′yĕzh)	Sov. Un.	52.5 N	35.53 E
113	Fatsa (fät′sä)	Tus.	40.58 N	37.32 E
154	Fatshan (fät′shän′)	Chn.	23.5 N	113.3 E
125	Faucilles, Monts (Mts.) (môɴ′ fō-sēl′)	Fr.	48.10 N	6.0 E
143	Fauresmith (four′smĭth)	U. S. Afr.	29.41 S	25.20 E
128	Favara (fä-vä′rä)	It.	37.19 N	13.39 E
119	Fawkham (fôk′ăm)	Gt. Brit. (London In.)	51.23 N	0.18 W
110	Faxa Fjord (fäk′sä fyôr′)	Ice.	64.27 N	23.0 W
139	Faya (fȧ-yä′)	Fr. Eq. Afr.	17.47 N	19.30 E
7	Fayal I. (fä-yäl′)	Az. Is. (In.)	38.33 N	28.42 W
138	Fayal I.	Az. Is. (In.)	38.30 N	28.40 W
82	Fayette (fȧ-yĕt′)	Ala.	33.40 N	87.50 W
77	Fayette	Ia.	42.51 N	91.49 W
82	Fayette	Miss.	31.42 N	91.4 W
79	Fayette	Mo.	39.8 N	92.40 W
79	Fayetteville	Ark.	36.3 N	94.9 W
73	Fayetteville	Ga. (Atlanta In.)	33.27 N	84.27 W
83	Fayetteville	N. C.	35.3 N	78.55 W
82	Fayetteville	Tenn.	35.10 N	86.32 W
135	Fâyid (fä-yēd′)	Eg. (Suez Can. In.)	30.20 N	32.19 E
139	Fayûm (fä-ê-o͞om′)	Eg.	29.21 N	30.47 E
154	Fayünhsing (fä′yün′hsĭng′)	Chn.	23.29 N	113.12 E
83	Fear, C.	S. C.	33.50 N	77.58 W
119	Fearnhead (fẽrn′hĕd)	Gt. Brit. (Liverpool In.)	53.24 N	2.34 W
74	Feather R. (fĕth′ẽr)	Calif.	38.55 N	121.37 W
74	Feather R. Middle Fk.	Calif.	39.47 N	121.15 W
74	Feather R. N. Fk.	Calif.	39.50 N	121.30 W
118	Featherstone (fĕdh′ẽr-stŭn)	Gt. Brit.	53.40 N	1.21 W
171	Featherstone	N. Z.	41.7 S	175.20 E
167	Feathertop, Mt. (fĕdh′ẽr-tŏp)	Austl.	36.51 S	147.6 E
124	Fécamp (fā-käɴ′)	Fr.	49.45 N	0.21 E
103	Federal Dist.	Braz.	48.15 W	16.15 S
92	Federal Dist.	Mex.	19.15 N	99.10 W
160	Federated Malay States	Asia	3.30 N	102.30 E
135	Fedjadj, Chott el (L.) (shŏt ĕl fä′jäj)	Tun. (In.)	33.55 N	9.20 E
131	Fedorovka (fyĕ-dô-rôf′kȧ)	Sov. Un.	47.3 N	35.19 E
122	Fehmarn (I.) (fā′märn)	Ger.	54.27 N	11.5 E
156	Feihsien (fā′ê-hsyĕn′)	Chn.	35.12 N	117.44 E
170	Feilding (fēld′ĭng)	N. Z.	40.12 S	175.40 E
126	Feira (fĕ′ê-rä)	Port.	40.57 N	8.32 W
103	Feira de Sant-Anna (dā-sänt-än′ä)	Braz. (In.)	12.15 S	38.55 W
127	Felanitx (fā-lȧ-nēch′)	Sp.	39.38 N	3.9 E
122	Feldkirch (fĕlt′kĭrκ)	Ger.	47.15 N	9.38 E
49	Felida (fĕ-lē′dȧ)	Wash. (Portland In.)	45.42 N	122.42 W
123	Felsögalla (fĕl′shû-gäl′lä)	Hung.	47.33 N	18.26 E
126	Feltre (fĕl′trā)	It.	46.2 N	11.53 E
153	Fenchow (fûn′chō′)	Chn.	37.4 N	111.40 E
141	Fénérive (fȧ-nȧ-rēv′)	Madag.	17.17 S	49.25 E
153	Fengchen (fûng′chĕn′)	Chn.	40.30 N	113.28 E
155	Fengcheng (fûng′chûng′)	Chn.	28.7 N	115.37 E
156	Fenghsien (fûng′hsyĕn′)	Chn.	34.39 N	116.47 E
155	Fenghwa (fûng′hwä′)	Chn.	29.38 N	121.27 E
154	Fenghwang (fûng′hwäng′)	Chn.	27.52 N	109.18 E
157	Fenghwangcheng (fûng-hwäng′-chĕng′)	Manch.	40.21 N	123.58 E
156	Fengjen (fûng′jûn′)	Chn.	39.48 N	118.2 E
155	Fengkin Ling (Mts.) (fûng′-kĭn′ lĭng′)	Chn.	28.15 N	118.32 E
156	Fengkiu (fûng′kyo͞o′)	Chn.	34.58 N	114.38 E
155	Fengshui (fûng′shwê)	Chn.	29.59 E	119.31 E
152	Fengsiang (fûng′syäng′)	Chn.	34.32 N	107.21 E
156	Fengtai (fûng′tī′)	Chn.	32.45 N	116.39 E
156	Fengtai	Chn.	39.45 N	116.19 E
152	Fengtien (Prov.) (fûng′tiĕn)	Manch.	42.30 N	124.0 E
154	Fengtu (fûng′to͞o′)	Chn.	30.2 N	107.48 E
156	Fengyang (fûng′yäng′)	Chn.	32.53 N	117.32 E
154	Fengyi (fûng′yê)′	Chn.	23.43 N	107.0 E
155	Feni (fû-nĭ′)	Chn.	27.43 N	114.42 E
84	Fenton (fĕn′tŭn)	Mich.	42.48 N	83.41 W
169	Fenton, L.	Austl. (Tas. In.)	42.37 S	146.39 E
131	Feodosiya (Kefe) (fĕ-ô-dō′sē′yȧ) (kyĕ′fĕ)	Sov. Un.	45.1 N	35.23 E
129	Ferdinand (fûr′dĭ-nănd)	Bul.	43.24 N	23.13 E
138	Fernando Po (I.) (fẽr-nän′dō pō′) (fĕr-nän′dō-pō′ō)	Sp. Gui.	3.30 N	8.40 E
128	Ferentino (fā-rĕn-tē′nō)	It.	41.41 N	13.15 E
76	Fergus Falls (fûr′gŭs)	Minn.	46.17 N	96.4 W
89	Ferguson (fûr-gŭ-sŭn)	Mo. (St. Louis In.)	38.45 N	90.18 W
73	Fermin, Pt. (fẽr′mĭn)	Calif. (Los Angles In.)	33.43 N	118.17 W
128	Fermo (fĕr′mō)	It.	43.10 N	13.41 E
126	Fermoselle (fĕr-mō-säl′yȧ)	Sp.	41.20 N	6.22 W
116	Fermoy (fẽr-moi′)	Ire.	52.5 N	8.15 W
83	Fernandina (fûr-năn-dē′nȧ)	Fla.	30.39 N	81.29 W
103	Fernando Noronha, I. (fĕr-nȧn′-do͝o nô-rō′nyä)	Braz.	3.58 S	32.30 W
126	Fernan-Nuñez (fĕr-nän′ no͞on′-yȧth)	Sp.	37.41 N	4.42 W
70	Ferndale (fûrn′dāl)	Calif.	40.35 N	124.15 W
72	Ferndale	Wash. (Vancouver In.)	48.52 N	122.36 W
54	Fernie (fûr′nĭ)	Can.	49.27 N	115.5 W
72	Fern Ridge (fûrn)	Can. (Vancouver In.)	49.3 N	122.39 W
87	Ferolle, Pt. (fē-rōl′)	Newf.	51.0 N	57.0 W
151	Ferozepore (fê-rōz-pōr′)	India	30.59 N	74.31 E
128	Ferrara (fĕr-rä′rä)	It.	44.50 N	11.37 E
127	Ferrat, C. (fĕr-rät′)	Alg.	35.54 N	0.28 W
126	Ferreira do Alentejo (fĕr-rĕ′ê-rä do͝o ä-lĕɴ-tā′zho͝o)	Port.	38.3 N	8.8 W
126	Ferreira do Zezere (do͝o zâ-zā′rĕ)	Port.	39.44 N	8.17 W
81	Feriday (fĕr′ĭ-dā)	La.	31.37 N	91.33 W
138	Ferro (I.) (fĕr′rō)	Can. Is.	27.45 N	18.0 W
87	Ferryland (fĕr′ê-lănd)	Newf.	47.5 N	52.58 W
135	Ferryville (fĕr-ê-vēl′)	Tun. (In.)	37.8 N	9.48 E
76	Fertile (fûr′tĭl)	Minn.	47.32 N	96.18 W
128	Fertilia (fĕr-tē′lē-a)	Sard.	40.38 N	8.19 E
138	Fès (Fez) (fĕs) (fĕz)	Mor.	34.10 N	4.59 W
76	Fessenden (fĕs′ĕn-dĕn)	N. D.	47.35 N	99.37 W
116	Festiniog (fĕs-tĭn′ĭ-ŏg)	Gt. Brit.	52.57 N	3.55 W
79	Festus (fĕst′ŭs)	Mo.	38.13 N	90.23 W
113	Fethiye (fĕt-hē′yĕ)	Tur.	36.42 N	29.10 E
125	Feucherolles (fû-shē-rōl′)	Fr. (Paris In.)	48.53 N	1.58 E
122	Feuerbach (foi′ẽr-bäκ)	Ger.	48.49 N	9.11 E
124	Feurs (fûr)	Fr.	45.45 N	4.15 E
139	Fezzan (Reg.) (fĕz-zän′)	Libya	26.30 N	15.30 E
139	Fezzan, Oases of	Libya	25.30 N	15.0 E
141	Fianarantsoa (fyȧ-nä′rȧn-tsō′ȧ)	Madag.	21.25 S	47.8 E
143	Ficksburg (fĭks′bûrg)	U. S. Afr.	28.51 S	27.52 E
54	Field (fēld)	Can.	51.28 N	116.35 W
70	Fieldbrook (fēld′bro͝ok)	Calif.	40.59 N	124.2 W
169	Field East, Mt.	Austl. (Tas. In.)	42.36 S	146.49 E
169	Field West, Mt.	Austl. (Tas. In.)	42.38 S	146.30 E
129	Fier (fyĕr)	Alb.	40.43 N	19.33 E
140	Fife (fīf)	N. Rh.	9.22 S	32.32 E
116	Fife Ness (fīf′nes′)	Gt. Brit.	56.15 N	2.25 W
124	Figeac (fē-zhȧk′)	Fr.	44.38 N	2.1 E
120	Figeholm (fē-ghē-hōlm)	Swe.	57.23 N	16.36 E
126	Figueira da Foz (fē′gĕ-ê′rä dä fōzh)	Port.	40.9 N	8.51 W
127	Figueras (fê-gā′räs)	Sp.	42.17 N	2.57 E
138	Figuig (fē-gēg′)	Mor.	32.12 N	1.20 W
6	Fiji Is. (fē′jē)	Pac. O. (In.)	18.0 S	178.0 W
95	Filadelfia (fĭl-ȧ-dĕl′fĭ-a)	C. R.	10.27 N	85.37 W
83	Filbert (fĭl′bẽrt)	W. Va.	37.17 N	81.33 W
46	Filchner Shelf Ice (fĭlκ′nẽr)	Ant. O.	76.0 S	38.0 W
118	Filey (fī′lĭ)	Gt. Brit.	54.13 N	0.17 W
118	Filey Bay	Gt. Brit.	54.12 N	0.15 W
128	Filicudi, (I.) (fē′lê-ko͞o′dē)	It.	38.34 N	14.33 E
120	Filipstad (fĭl′ĭps-städh)	Swe.	59.41 N	14.9 E
75	Fillmore (fĭl′môr)	Utah	38.59 N	112.20 W
113	Filyas (fĭl′yȧs)	Tur.	41.32 N	32.8 E
113	Filyas R.	Tur.	41.12 N	32.45 E
119	Finchley (fĭnsh′lĭ)	Gt. Brit. (London In.)	51.35 N	0.10 W
84	Findlay (fĭnd′lȧ)	Ohio	41.5 N	83.29 W
169	Fingal (fĭŋ′găl)	Austl. (Tas. In.)	41.38 S	148.2 E
140	Fini R. (fê-nē′)	Bel. Cong.	2.45 S	17.45 E
126	Finisterre C. (fĭn-ĭs-târ′)	Sp.	42.52 N	9.18 W
119	Finkenwärder (fĭŋ′kĕn-vĕr-dẽr)	Ger. (Hamburg In.)	53.32 N	9.52 E
164	Finke R. (fĭŋ′kê)	Austl.	26.0 S	135.30 E
121	Finland (fĭn′lănd)	Eur.	62.20 N	27.0 E
121	Finland, G. of	Eur.	60.0 N	27.0 E
54	Finlay R. (fĭn′lȧ)	Can.	57.30 N	125.30 W
167	Finley (fĭn′lĭ)	Austl.	35.38 S	145.35 E
122	Finsterwalde (fĭn′stẽr-väl-dĕ)	Ger.	51.37 N	13.42 E
104	Fiorito (fyô-rē′tô)	Arg. (In.)	34.43 S	58.26 W
49	Fir (fûr)	Wash. (Seattle In.)	48.21 N	122.20 W
113	Firat (Euphrates) (R.) (fē rät′) (û-frā′tēz)	Asia	38.0 N	39.5 E
135	Firdân (fêr-dän′)	Eg. (Suez Can. In.)	30.42 N	32.21 E
150	Firdaus (fēr-dä′o͞os)	Per.	34.5 N	58.14 E
128	Firenze (Florence) (fê-rĕnt′sā)	It.	43.47 N	11.15 E
128	Firenzuola (fē-rĕnt-swô′lä)	It.	44.6 N	11.24 E
169	Fires, B. of	Aust. (Tas. In.)	41.2 S	148.20 E
72	Firestone (fīr′stôn)	Colo. (Denver In.)	40.8 N	104.57 W
124	Firminy (fēr-mê-nē′)	Fr.	45.22 N	4.15 E
119	Fischbeck (fĭsh′bĕk)	Ger. (Hamburg In.)	53.28 N	9.50 E
142	Fish B.	U. S. Afr.	34.15 S	21.55 E
97	Fish Cays (Is.)	Ba. Is.	22.30 N	74.15 W
81	Fisher (fĭsh′ẽr)	La.	31.28 N	93.30 W
54	Fisher Str.	Can.	62.45 N	84.15 W
86	Fish L.	Me.	46.48 N	68.48 W
142	Fish R.	U. S. Afr.	31.50 S	20.20 E
142	Fishwater (fĭsh′wô-tẽr)	U. S. Afr.	31.41 S	18.12 E
86	Fitchburg (fĭch′bûrg)	Mass.	42.35 N	71.50 W
169	Fitzgerald (fĭts-jĕr′ăld)	Austl. (Tas. In.)	42.47 S	146.36 E
82	Fitzgerald	Ga.	31.42 N	83.18 W
164	Fitzroy (fĭts-roi′)	Austl.	18.0 S	125.45 E
170	Fitzroy B.	N. Z. (In.)	41.23 S	174.53 E
104	Fitzroy, Mt.	Arg.	49.15 S	73.0 W
164	Fitzroy R.	Austl.	18.30 S	125.0 E
84	Fitzwilliam I. (fĭts-wĭl′yŭm)	Can.	45.30 N	81.45 W
128	Fiume (fyo͞o′mā)	It.	45.20 N	14.26 E
73	Five Points	Utah (Salt Lake City In.)	41.17 N	111.57 W
120	Fjällbacka (fyĕl′băk-ȧ)	Swe.	58.36 N	11.18 E
120	Flaam (flôm)	Nor.	60.52 N	7.9 E
75	Flagstaff	Ariz.	35.12 N	111.39 W
143	Flagstaff	U. S. Afr.	31.5 S	29.30 E
77	Flambeau R. (flăm-bō′)	Wis.	45.42 N	90.48 W
116	Flamborough Hd. (flăm′bŭr-ô)	Gt. Brit.	54.10 N	0.0
97	Flamingo Cay (I.) (flȧ-mĭŋ′gô)	Ba. Is.	22.53 N	75.51 W
91	Flamingo Pt.	St. Thomas (In.)	18.19 N	64.58 W
76	Flandreau (flăn′drō)	S. D.	44.2 N	96.34 W
143	Flands R. (flăndz)	U. S. Afr.	28.25 S	28.52 E
116	Flannan (Is.) (flăn′ăn)	Gt. Brit.	58.15 N	7.35 W
110	Flatey (I.) (flät′ȧ)	Ice.	65.18 N	22.45 W
71	Flathead L. (flăt′hĕd)	Mont.	47.57 N	114.6 W
71	Flathead R.	Mont.	48.40 N	114.10 W
71	Flathead R., Middle Fork	Mont.	48.20 N	113.40 W
71	Flathead R., South Fork	Mont.	48.50 N	113.50 W
171	Flat Pt.	N. Z.	41.13 S	176.0 E
70	Flattery, C. (flăt′ẽr-ĭ)	Wash.	48.23 N	124.44 W
71	Flat Willow Cr.	Mont.	46.45 N	108.43 W
163	Flecha Pt. (flā′chȧ)	P. I.	7.21 N	123.26 E
163	Flechas Pt. (flā′chȧs)	P. I.	10.22 N	119.34 E
118	Fleetwood (flēt′wo͝od)	Gt. Brit.	53.55 N	3.1 W
120	Flekkefjord (flĕk′kē-fyôr)	Nor.	58.18 N	6.40 E

ng-sing; ŋ-bank; ɴ-nasalized n; nŏd; cŏmmit; ōld; ôbey; ôrder; fo͞od; fo͝ot; ou-out; s-soft; sh-dish; th-thin; pūre; ûnite; ûrn; stŭd; circŭs; ü-as "y" in study; ′-indeterminate vowel.

Page	Name Pronunciation Region	Lat. °'	Long. °'
84	Flemingsburg (flĕm'ĭngz-bûrg) Ky.	38.26 N	83.48 W
122	Flensburg (flĕns'bo͝orgh) Ger.	54.44 N	9.25 E
124	Flers (flâr) Fr.	48.43 N	0.35 W
166	Fleurieu Pen. (flû-ryû') Austl.	35.32 S	138.22 E
165	Flinders I. (flĭn'dẽrz) Austl.	40.0 S	148.0 E
165	Flinders-Murray Reg. (mûr'ĭ) Austl.	34.0 S	142.0 E
166	Flinders Ra. (flĭn'dẽrz) Austl.	31.25 S	138.48 E
165	Flinders Rts. Austl.	17.45 S	148.30 E
118	Flint (flĭnt) Gt. Brit.	53.15 N	3.7 W
84	Flint Mich.	43.2 N	83.40 W
118	Flint Co. Gt. Brit.	53.12 N	3.0 W
82	Flint R. Ga.	30.52 N	84.0 W
73	Flippen (flĭp'ĕn) Ga. (Atlanta In.)	33.30 N	84.11 W
120	Flisen (flē'sĕn) Nor.	60.35 N	12.3 E
119	Flixton (flĭks'tŭn) Gt. Brit. (Liverpool In.)	53.26 N	2.24 W
79	Flora (flō'rȧ) Ill.	38.39 N	88.29 W
84	Flora Ind.	40.32 N	86.30 W
82	Florala (flŏr-ăl'ȧ) Ala.	31.1 N	86.19 W
82	Florence (flŏr'ĕns) Ala.	34.47 N	87.40 W
75	Florence Ariz.	33.3 N	111.23 W
73	Florence .. Calif. (Los Angeles In.)	33.58 N	118.14 W
78	Florence Colo.	38.23 N	105.8 W
128	Florence (Firenze) It.	43.47 N	11.15 E
79	Florence Kan.	38.14 N	96.56 W
83	Florence S. C.	34.11 N	79.46 W
102	Florencia (flō-rĕn'sē-ȧ) Col.	1.45 N	75.15 W
99	Florencia Varela (flō-rĕn'sē-ä vä-rā'lä). Arg. (Buenos Aires In.)	34.51 S	58.14 W
103	Flores (flō'rĕzh) Braz.	7.58 S	37.58 W
94	Flores (flō'rĕs) Guat. (In.)	16.53 N	89.54 W
138	Flores I. (flō'rĕzh) Az. Is. (In.)	39.30 N	31.10 W
160	Flores (I.) (flō'rĕs) Neth. Ind.	8.40 S	121.30 E
160	Flores Sea Neth. Ind.	7.15 S	122.30 E
80	Floresville Tex.	29.8 N	98.9 W
103	Floriano (flō-rē-ä'no͞o) Braz.	6.47 S	43.1 W
104	Florianópolis (flō-rē-ȧ-nō'pō-lēs) Braz.	27.35 S	48.30 W
104	Florida (flō-rē'dhä) Arg. (In.)	34.32 S	58.30 W
104	Florida Ur.	34.10 S	56.25 W
82	Florida (State) (flŏr'ĭ-dȧ) U. S.	30.20 N	84.0 W
83	Florida B. Fla. (In.)	24.55 N	81.0 W
161	Floridablanca (flō-rē'dä-blän'kä) P. I. (Manila In.)	14.59 N	120.26 E
165	Florida (I.) Solomon I. (Prot.)	9.5 S	160.8 E
83	Florida Keys Fla. (In.)	24.40 N	81.10 W
80	Florido, R. (flō-rē'dō) Mex.	27.0 N	105.0 W
119	Floridsdorf (flō'rĭds-dôrf) Aus. (Wien In.)	48.16 N	16.24 E
129	Florina (flō-rē'nä) Grc.	40.47 N	21.24 E
72	Florissant (flŏr'ĭ-sănt) Colo. (Colo. Sprs. In.)	38.57 N	105.17 W
120	Florö (flôr'û) Nor.	61.36 N	5.2 E
73	Floyd (floid) Ga. (Atlanta In.)	33.51 N	84.33 W
78	Floydada (floi-dā'dȧ) Tex.	33.59 N	101.19 W
96	Floyd R. Ia.	42.50 N	96.10 W
128	Flumendosa R. (flo͞o-mĕn-dō'sä) Sard.	39.40 N	9.18 E
	Flushing, see Vlissingen, Neth.		
84	Flushing (flŭsh'ĭng) Mich.	43.4 N	83.52 W
88	Flushing N. Y. (In.)	40.45 N	73.50 W
88	Flushing B. N. Y. (In.)	40.46 N	73.51 W
161	Fly R. Neth. N. Guin.-Pap. Ter.	7.0 S	141.0 E
129	Foča (fō'chä) Yugo.	43.29 N	18.48 E
123	Focşani (fōk-shä'nē) Rom.	45.41 N	27.13 E
128	Foggia (fôd'jä) It.	41.27 N	15.33 E
87	Fogo (fō'gō) Newf.	49.38 N	54.12 W
138	Fogo I. (fō'gō) C. V. Is. (In.)	14.55 N	24.25 W
87	Fogo I. Newf.	49.35 N	54.10 W
122	Fohnsdorf (fōns'dôrf) Ger.	47.13 N	14.41 E
122	Föhr (I.) (fûr) Ger.	54.53 N	8.30 E
124	Foix (fwä) Fr.	42.59 N	1.38 E
128	Foligno (fō-lēn'yō) It.	42.57 N	12.41 E
117	Folkestone (fōk'stŭn) Gt. Brit.	51.5 N	1.8 E
118	Folkingham (fō'kĭng-ăm) Gt. Brit.	52.53 N	0.24 W
78	Folsom (fŏl'sŭm) N. M.	36.49 N	103.55 W
74	Folsom City Calif.	38.39 N	121.10 W
77	Fonda (fŏn'dȧ) Ia.	42.35 N	94.51 W
77	Fond du Lac (fŏn dŭ lăk') Wis.	43.48 N	88.28 W
128	Fondi (fōn'dē) It.	41.23 N	13.27 E
126	Fonsagrada (fōn-sä-grä'dhä) Sp.	43.7 N	7.6 W
94	Fonseca, G. of (fōn-sā'kä) Cen. Am.	13.0 N	87.50 W
124	Fontainebleau (fôn-tĕn-blō') Fr.	48.25 N	2.45 E
73	Fontana (fŏn-tă'nȧ) Calif. (Los Angeles In.)	34.6 N	117.28 W
102	Fonte Boa (fōn'tä bō'ȧ) Braz.	2.31 S	66.2 W
125	Fontenay-en-Parisis (fônt-nĕ' äN pä-rē-sē') Fr. (In.)	49.3 N	2.27 E
124	Fontenay-le-Comte (fônt-nĕ' lē kônt') Fr.	46.28 N	0.50 W
155	Foochow (fo͞o'chō') Chn.	26.5 N	119.12 E
169	Footscray (fo͝ots'krā) Austl. (Melbourne In.)	37.49 S	144.53 E
154	Foo Yong R. (fo͞o-yông') Chn.	28.25 N	107.34 E
53	Foraker, Mt. (fôr-ȧ-kẽr) Alsk.	63.0 N	151.30 W
125	Forbach (fôr'bäk) Fr.	49.11 N	6.55 E
165	Forbes (fôrbz) Austl.	33.28 S	148.0 E
167	Forbes Austl.	33.22 S	148.2 E
138	Forcados (fôr-kä'dōs) Nig.	5.21 N	5.28 E
125	Forcalquier (fôr-kál-kyā') Fr.	43.38 N	5.49 E
122	Forchheim (fôrk'hīm) Ger.	49.43 N	11.3 E
79	Fordyce (fôr'dīs) Ark.	33.47 N	92.25 W
138	Forecariah (fōr-kä-rē'ä') Fr. W. Afr.	9.32 N	13.12 W
117	Forest (fō-rā') (fôrst) Bel.	50.45 N	4.20 E
82	Forest (fŏr'ĕst) Miss.	32.22 N	89.28 W
77	Forest City Ia.	43.15 N	93.56 W
83	Forest City N. C.	35.20 N	81.52 W
85	Forest City Pa.	41.35 N	75.30 W
70	Forest Grove Ore.	45.30 N	123.6 W
73	Forest Park Ga. (Atlanta In.)	33.37 N	84.21 W
76	Forest R. N. D.	48.10 N	97.40 W

Page	Name Pronunciation Region	Lat. °'	Long. °'
48	Foret, Mt. (fō-rā') Grnld.	65.50 N	37.41 W
124	Forez Mts. (fō-rā') Fr.	45.55 N	3.45 E
116	Forfar (fôr'fȧr) Gt. Brit.	56.35 N	2.51 W
82	Forked Deer R. Tenn.	35.56 N	89.30 W
82	Forked Deer R., North Fork. Tenn.	35.52 N	89.0 W
82	Forked Deer R., South Fork. Tenn.	35.30 N	88.44 W
88	Forks ... N. Y. (Niagara Falls In.)	42.54 N	78.46 W
72	Forks Creek .. Colo. (Denver In.)	39.45 N	105.24 W
128	Forli (fôr-lē') It.	44.14 N	12.2 E
118	Formby (fôrm'bē) Gt. Brit.	53.33 N	3.3 W
118	Formby Pt. Gt. Brit.	53.33 N	3.7 W
127	Formentera I. (fôr-mĕn-tā'rä) Sp.	38.45 N	1.25 E
97	Formigas Bk. (fôr-mē'gäs) W. I.	18.32 N	75.42 W
104	Formosa (State) (fôr-mō'sä) Arg.	24.45 S	60.0 W
104	Formosa Arg.	26.10 S	58.14 W
103	Formosa Braz.	15.28 S	47.15 W
158	Formosa (Taiwan) (Prov.) (fôr-mō'sȧ) (tī-wän') Jap. (In.)	24.0 N	121.0 E
158	Formosa (Taiwan) Str. Tai. (In.)	25.0 N	120.0 E
166	Forrest (fŏr'ĕst) Austl.	38.31 S	143.44 E
79	Forrest City Ark.	35.1 N	90.46 W
165	Forsayth (fôr-sīth') Austl.	18.29 S	143.35 E
120	Forshaga (fôrs'hä'gä) Swe.	59.32 N	13.29 E
122	Forst (fôrst) Ger.	51.45 N	14.38 E
82	Forsyth (fôr-sīth') Ga.	33.3 N	83.57 W
71	Forsyth Mont.	46.15 N	106.40 W
103	Fortaleza (Ceará) (fôr-tä-lā'zȧ) (sā-ä-rä') Braz.	3.40 S	38.32 W
150	Fort Aleksandrovsk (Ft. Uritskogo) (o͞o'rĭts-kō-gō) Sov. Un.	44.30 N	50.15 E
75	Fort Apache Ind. Res. (ȧ-păch'ē) Ariz.	34.0 N	110.15 W
139	Fort Archambault (fôr är-chäN-bō') Fr. Eq. Afr.	9.7 N	18.21 E
77	Fort Atkinson (ăt'kĭn-sŭn) Wis.	42.55 N	88.50 W
160	Fort Bayard (fôr bȧ-yär') Fr. In. Chn.	21.15 N	110.15 E
143	Fort Beaufort (bō'fẽrt) U. S. Afr.	32.47 S	26.40 E
71	Fort Benton (bĕn'tŭn) Mont.	47.50 N	110.40 W
76	Fort Berthold Ind. Res. (bẽrth'ōld) N. D.	47.40 N	102.30 W
74	Fort Bragg (fôr brăg) Calif.	39.27 N	123.48 W
84	Fort Branch (fôr brănch) Ind.	38.16 N	87.34 W
138	Fort Charlet (fôr shȧr-lĕ') Alg.	24.37 N	9.36 E
78	Fort Collins (fôr kŏl'ĭns) Colo.	40.35 N	105.6 W
139	Fort Crampel (fôr kräm-pĕl') Fr. Eq. Afr.	7.6 N	19.10 E
141	Fort Dauphin (fôr dō-făN') Madag.	25.0 S	46.58 E
91	Fort de France (fôr dē fräNs) Mart.	14.40 N	61.8 W
6	Fort de France B. Mart. (In.)	14.33 N	61.3 W
138	Fort Delion (Haci Inifel) (fôr dē-lē-ôN) (hä'sē ē-nē-fĕl') Alg.	29.47 N	3.57 E
139	Fort de Possel (dē pō-sĕl') Fr. Eq. Afr.	5.2 N	19.11 E
164	Fortescue R. (fôr'tĕs-kū) Austl.	22.0 S	118.0 E
77	Fort Dodge (dŏj) Ia.	42.30 N	94.10 W
85	Fort Edward (ĕd'wẽrd) N. Y.	43.16 N	73.35 W
88	Fort Erie (ē'rĭ) Can. (Niagara Falls In.)	42.54 N	78.55 W
85	Fort Eustis (ūs'tĭs) Va.	37.10 N	76.35 W
86	Fort Fairfield (fâr'fēld) Me.	46.47 N	68.5 W
138	Fort Flatters (fôr flȧ-târ') Alg.	28.4 N	6.31 E
77	Fort Frances (frăn'cĕz) Can.	48.35 N	93.25 W
82	Fort Gaines (gānz) Ga.	31.36 N	85.3 W
55	Fort George R. (jôrj) Can.	54.0 N	78.0 W
79	Fort Gibson (gĭb'sŭn) Okla.	35.47 N	95.15 W
116	Forth, Firth of (fûrth ŭv fôrth') Gt. Brit.	56.10 N	2.40 W
169	Forth R. (fôrth) .. Austl. (Tas. In.)	41.25 S	146.10 E
141	Fort Hall (hôl) Kenya	0.40 S	37.3 E
71	Fort Hall Ind. Res. Ida.	43.0 N	112.30 W
139	Fort Harrington (Moyale) (hăr'ĭng-tŭn) Kenya	3.28 N	39.6 E
75	Fort Huachuca (wä-cho͞o'kä) Ariz.	31.32 N	110.21 W
56	Fortier (fôr-tyā') Can. (Winnipeg In.)	49.56 N	97.55 W
140	Fort Jameson (jăm'sŭn) ... N. Rh.	13.39 S	32.39 E
140	Fort Johnston Nya.	14.21 S	35.12 E
86	Fort Kent (kĕnt) Me.	47.14 N	68.37 W
138	Fort Lallemand (fôr lȧ-lē-mäN') Alg.	31.17 N	6.12 E
139	Fort Lamy (fôr lȧ-mē'). Fr. Eq. Afr.	12.12 N	15.3 E
72	Fort Langley (lăng'lĭ) Can. (Vancouver In.)	49.10 N	122.34 W
138	Fort Lapperrine (fôr lȧ-pē-rēn') Alg.	22.45 N	5.45 E
83	Fort Lauderdale (lô'dẽr-dāl) Fla. (In.)	26.8 N	80.9 W
79	Fort Leavenworth (lĕv'ĕn-wûrth) Kan.	39.21 N	94.55 W
88	Fort Lee .... N. J. (New York In.)	40.51 N	73.48 W
97	Fort Liberte (lē-bĕr-tā') Hai.	19.40 N	71.52 W
72	Fort Logan (lō'găn) Colo. (Denver In.)	39.38 N	105.3 W
78	Fort Lupton (lŭp'tăn) Colo.	40.4 N	104.48 W
138	Fort Mac Mahon (fôr măk mȧ-ôN') Alg.	29.50 N	1.48 E
79	Fort Madison (măd'ĭ-sŭn) Ia.	40.38 N	91.19 W
140	Fort Manning (măn'ĭng) Nya.	13.45 S	32.58 E
83	Fort Meade (mēd) Fla. (In.)	27.45 N	81.47 W
83	Fort Mill S. C.	35.2 N	80.58 W
161	Fort Mills (mĭlz) P. I. (Manila In.)	14.24 N	120.30 E
114	Fort Miribel (fôr mē-rē-bĕl') .. Alg.	28.58 N	2.57 E
74	Fort Mohave Ind. Res. (mō-hä'vä) Ariz.-Nev.	35.0 N	114.38 W
85	Fort Monroe (mŏn-rō') Va.	37.0 N	76.22 W
78	Fort Morgan (môr'găn) Colo.	40.13 N	103.48 W
83	Fort Myers (mī'ẽrz) Fla. (In.)	26.37 N	81.51 W
114	Fort National (fôr nȧ-syō-nȧl') Alg.	36.43 N	4.15 E
54	Fort Nelson (nĕl'sŭn) Can.	58.46 N	123.20 W
54	Fort Nelson R. Can.	59.0 N	123.0 W
82	Fort Payne (pān) Ala.	34.36 N	85.42 W
71	Fort Peck (pĕk) Mont.	47.58 N	106.30 W

Page	Name Pronunciation Region	Lat. °'	Long. °'
71	Fort Peck Dam Site Mont.	47.58 N	106.25 W
83	Fort Pierce (pērs) Fla. (In.)	27.26 N	80.20 W
138	Fort Polignac (fôr pō-lē-nyăk') Alg.	26.30 N	8.35 E
139	Fort Portal (pōr'tăl) Ug.	0.40 N	30.17 E
90	Fort Randolph (răn'dŏlf) C. Z. (In.)	9.23 N	79.53 W
89	Fortress Monroe, Va. (Norfolk In.)	37.0 N	76.19 W
79	Fort Riley (rī'lĭ) Kan.	39.4 N	96.46 W
140	Fort Rosebery (rōz'bẽr-ĭ) .. N. Rh.	11.12 S	28.52 E
140	Fort Rousset (fôr ro͞o-sĕ') Fr. Eq. Afr.	0.29 S	15.46 E
54	Fort St. John Can.	56.18 N	120.50 W
151	Fort Sandeman (săn'dā-măn) Ind.	31.15 N	69.29 E
79	Fort Scott (skŏt) Kan.	37.51 N	94.42 W
55	Fort Severn (sĕv'ẽrn) Can.	55.58 N	87.35 W
77	Fort Sheridan (shẽr'ĭ-dăn) Ill.	42.14 N	87.49 W
139	Fort Sibut (fôr sē-bü') Fr. Eq. Afr.	5.45 N	19.3 E
78	Fort Sill (sĭl) Okla.	34.38 N	98.23 W
79	Fort Smith Ark.	35.23 N	94.24 W
89	Fort Snelling (snĕl'ĭng) Minn. (Minneapolis In.)	44.53 N	93.12 W
49	Fort Stevens (stē-vĕnz) Ore. (Portland In.)	46.12 N	123.57 W
80	Fort Stockton (stŏk'tŭn) Tex.	30.54 N	102.53 W
78	Fort Sumner (sŭm'nẽr) N. M.	34.29 N	104.15 W
89	Fort Thomas (tŏm'ăs) Ky. (Cincinnati In.)	39.4 N	84.27 W
141	Fort Tura (Ruins) (to͞o'rä) Eg.	29.56 N	31.17 E
70	Fortuna (fôr-tü'nȧ) Calif.	40.36 N	124.8 W
87	Fortune B. (fôr'tŭn) Newf.	47.25 N	55.25 W
97	Fortune I. Ba. Is.	22.38 N	74.20 W
82	Fort Valley (văl'ĭ) Ga.	32.33 N	83.53 W
54	Fort Vermilion (vẽr-mĭl'yŭn) Can.	58.28 N	115.44 W
84	Fortville Ind.	39.38 N	85.48 W
84	Fort Wayne (wān) Ind.	41.4 N	85.10 W
56	Fort Whyte (whīt) Can. (Winnipeg In.)	49.46 N	97.14 W
55	Fort William (wĭl'yŭm) Can.	48.20 N	89.15 W
116	Fort William Gt. Brit.	56.48 N	5.5 W
81	Fort Worth (wûrth) Tex.	32.45 N	97.18 W
53	Fortymile (fôr'tĭ-mīl) Can.	64.20 N	140.35 W
53	Fort Yukon (yo͞o'kŏn) Alsk.	66.28 N	145.15 W
128	Fossano (fōs-sä'nō) It.	44.33 N	7.43 E
76	Fossil Cycad Natl. Mon. (fŏs-ĭl sī'kăd) S. D.	43.23 N	103.42 W
128	Fossombrone (fōs-sôm-brō'nä) .. It.	43.42 N	12.47 E
76	Fosston (fŏs'tŭn) Minn.	47.35 N	95.42 W
84	Fostoria (fŏs-tō'rĭ-ȧ) Ohio	41.10 N	83.24 W
124	Fougères (fo͞o-zhâr') Fr.	48.22 N	1.11 W
116	Foula (I.) (fou'lȧ) .. Gt. Brit. (In.)	60.5 N	2.5 W
119	Foulness (foul-nĕs') Gt. Brit. (London In.)	51.36 N	0.52 E
171	Foulwind C. (foul'wĭnd) N. Z.	41.45 S	171.35 E
138	Foumban (fo͞om-bän') Cam.	5.48 N	10.48 E
72	Fountain (foun'tĭn) Colo. (Colo. Sprs. In.)	38.41 N	104.42 W
78	Fountain Cr. Colo.	38.40 N	104.43 W
124	Fourchambaut (fo͞or-shäN-bō') . Fr.	47.0 N	3.9 E
79	Fourche la Fave R. (fo͞orsh lȧ fāv') Ark.	34.57 N	93.20 W
143	Fouriesburg (fo͞o'rēz-bûrg) U. S. Afr.	28.37 S	28.14 E
124	Fourmies (fo͞or-mē') Fr.	50.0 N	4.5 E
72	Fourmile Cr. (fōr'mīl) Colo. (Colo. Sprs. In.)	38.47 N	105.20 W
72	Fourmile Cr. .. Colo. (Denver In.)	40.3 N	105.30 W
88	Four Mile Cr. N. Y. (Niagara Falls In.)	43.14 N	79.2 W
138	Fouta Djalon Mts. (fo͞o'tä shä-lôn) Fr. W. Afr.	11.30 N	17.0 W
171	Foveaux Str. (fô-vō') N. Z.	40.40 S	168.0 E
156	Fowcheng (fō'chĕng') Chn.	37.59 N	116.4 E
154	Fowchow (fō-chō') Chn.	29.47 N	107.24 E
78	Fowler (foul'ẽr) Colo.	38.6 N	104.3 W
84	Fowler Ind.	40.38 N	87.21 W
80	Fowlerton Tex.	28.27 N	98.50 W
156	Fowning (fō'nĭng') Chn.	33.43 N	119.49 E
87	Foxboro (fŏks'bŭr-ô) .. Mass. (In.)	42.4 N	71.15 W
55	Foxe Channel (fŏks) Can.	66.10 N	81.0 W
55	Foxe Land Can.	65.30 N	77.0 W
84	Fox I. Mich.	45.25 N	85.50 W
49	Fox I. Wash. (Seattle In.)	47.14 N	122.37 W
52	Fox Is. Alsk.	54.0 N	166.0 W
77	Fox R. Wis.	44.0 N	88.3 W
77	Fox R. Ill.	41.50 N	88.18 W
72	Foxton Colo. (Denver In.)	39.25 N	105.15 W
170	Foxton N. Z.	40.25 S	175.18 E
116	Foyle Lough (L.) (lŏk foil') Gt. Brit.	55.5 N	7.10 W
127	Fraga (frä'gä) Sp.	41.32 N	0.21 E
96	Fragoso Cay (I.) (frä-gō'sō) . Cuba	22.40 N	79.25 W
161	Fraile I. (frä-ē'lä) P. I. (Manila In.)	14.18 N	120.34 E
46	Framheim (Little America) (främ'hĭm) Ant.	78.30 S	161.30 W
129	Francavilla (fräŋ-kä-vēl'lä) It.	40.31 N	17.36 E
124	France (fräns) Eur.	48.0 N	2.0 E
73	Frances (frăn'sĕz) Calif. (Los Angeles In.)	33.42 N	117.45 W
96	Frances C. Cuba	21.52 N	83.55 W
96	Frances, Pt. Isle of Pines	21.38 N	83.10 W
97	Frances Viejo, C. (frän'sȧs vyā'hō) Dom. Rep.	19.37 N	69.51 W
140	Franceville (fräNs-vēl') Fr. Eq. Afr.	1.40 S	13.36 E
140	Francistown (frăn'sĭs-toun) .. Bech.	21.15 S	27.28 E
6	Francois (fräN-swȧ') Mart. (St. Lucia In.)	14.37 N	60.54 W
125	Franconville (fräN-kôN-vēl') Fr. (In.)	48.58 N	2.13 E
122	Frankenstein (fräŋk'ĕn-shtīn) Ger.	50.45 N	16.47 E
122	Frankenthal (fräŋk'ĕn-täl) .. Ger.	49.32 N	8.22 E
88	Frankford (fräŋk'fŭrd) Pa. (Philadelphia In.)	40.1 N	75.5 W

ăt; finăl; rāte; senāte; ärm; ȧsk; sofȧ; fâre; ch-choose; dh-as th in other; bē; ēvent; bĕt; recĕnt; cratẽr; g-go; gh-gutteral g; bĭt; ĭ-short neutral; rīde K-gutteral k as ch in German ich;

Page	Name Pronunciation Region	Lat. °′	Long. °′
88	Frankford Cr.Pa.(Philadelphia In.)	40.4 N	75.6 W
84	Frankfort (frăŋk'fẽrt)........Ind.	40.15 N	86.32 W
79	Frankfort..................Kan.	39.41 N	96.21 W
84	Frankfort..................Ky.	38.11 N	84.55 W
84	Frankfort..................Mich.	44.39 N	86.13 W
85	Frankfort..................N. Y.	43.6 N	75.6 W
143	Frankfort.............U. S. Afr.	27.16 S	28.31 E
49	Frankfort...Wash. (Portland In.)	46.16 N	123.45 W
122	Frankfurt (frăŋk'fŏŏrt)......Ger.	52.20 N	14.30 E
122	Frankfurt..................Ger.	50.7 N	8.41 E
169	Franklin (frăŋk'lĭn) Austl. (Tas. In.)	43.4 S	147.0 E
84	Franklin..................Ind.	39.37 N	86.3 W
82	Franklin..................Ky.	36.44 N	86.34 W
81	Franklin..................La.	29.46 N	91.30 W
87	Franklin.............Mass. (In.)	42.5 N	71.23 W
78	Franklin..................Neb.	40.5 N	98.58 W
86	Franklin..................N. H.	43.25 N	71.40 W
84	Franklin..................Ohio	39.34 N	84.19 W
85	Franklin..................Pa.	41.25 N	79.50 W
82	Franklin..................Tenn.	35.55 N	86.55 W
143	Franklin..............U. S. Afr.	30.24 S	29.28 E
83	Franklin..................Va.	36.40 N	76.57 W
55	Franklin Dist. of...........Can.	69.0 N	84.0 W
74	Franklin L..................Nev.	40.25 N	115.20 W
171	Franklin, Mt...............N. Z.	42.2 S	172.48 E
166	Franklin Har...............Austl.	33.45 S	136.55 E
88	Franklin Park...Ill. (Chicago, Ill.)	41.56 N	87.52 W
169	Franklin R.......Austl. (Tas. In.)	42.20 S	145.47 E
81	Franklinton................La.	30.51 N	90.9 W
142	Franschhoek (frănsh'hŏŏk) U. S. Afr.	33.55 S	19.5 E
	Franz Josef Land, see Fridtjof Nansen Land, Arc. O.		
128	Frascati (frăs-kä'tē)..........It.	41.48 N	12.41 E
142	Fraserburg (frā'zẽr-bûrg).U. S. Afr.	31.55 S	21.31 E
116	Fraserburgh............Gt. Brit.	57.40 N	2.0 W
165	Fraser (Great Sandy) I. (frā'zẽr) Austl.	25.0 S	153.5 E
70	Fraser R..................Can.	49.10 N	122.20 W
72	Fraser R. North Arm Can. (Vancouver In.)	49.12 N	123.6 W
72	Fraser R. North Arm, North Fork.Can. (Vancouver In.)	49.13 N	123.12 W
72	Fraser R. North Arm, South Fork Can. (Vancouver In.)	49.10 N	123.12 W
55	Fraserville (frā'zẽr-vĭl)......Can.	48.59 N	69.10 W
115	Fras, Wadi (R.)(wä'dē fräs')Libya	30.24 N	17.30 E
122	Fraustadt (frou'shtät).......Ger.	51.47 N	16.19 E
104	Fray Bentos (frī bĕn'tōs)......Ur.	33.15 S	58.15 W
76	Frazee (frā-zē')...........Minn.	46.42 N	95.44 W
120	Fredericia (frĕdh-ĕ-rē'tsē-ȧ)..Den.	55.33 N	9.45 E
72	Frederick (frĕd'ẽr-ĭk) Colo. (Denver In.)	40.6 N	104.56 W
85	Frederick..................Md.	39.26 N	77.27 W
78	Frederick..................Okla.	34.23 N	99.0 W
80	Fredericksburg.............Tex.	30.16 N	98.52 W
85	Fredericksburg.............Va.	38.18 N	77.38 W
79	Fredericktown..............Mo.	37.32 N	90.17 W
55	Fredericton (frĕd'ẽr-ĭk-tŭn)..Can.	45.46 N	66.35 W
161	Frederik Hendrik I. (hĕn'drĕk) Neth. Ind.	7.40 S	138.20 E
120	Frederikshavn (frĕdh'ĕ-rêks-houn) Den.	57.28 N	10.31 E
120	Frederikssund (frĕdh'ĕ-rêks-sōōn).Den.	55.49 N	12.2 E
143	Frederikstad (frā'dē-rĭk-städ) U. S. Afr.	26.31 S	27.8 E
91	Frederiksted (frĕd'rĭk-stĕd) St. Croix I. (P. R. In.)	17.44 N	64.54 W
79	Fredonia (frē-dō'nĭ-ȧ).......Kan.	37.32 N	95.49 W
85	Fredonia..................N. Y.	42.27 N	79.20 W
	Fredrikshald, see Halden, Nor.		
120	Fredrikstad (frådh'rêks-städ).Nor.	59.12 N	10.59 E
120	Fredriksvaern (frådh'rêks-vĕrn) Nor.	58.59 N	10.1 E
85	Freehold (frē'hōld).........N. J.	40.16 N	74.15 W
85	Freeland (frē'lănd)..........Pa.	41.0 N	75.52 W
87	Freels, C. (frēlz)..........Newf.	49.15 N	52.25 W
77	Freeport (frē'pōrt)..........Ill.	42.18 N	89.37 W
85	Freeport..................N. Y.	40.41 N	73.36 W
81	Freeport..................Tex.	28.56 N	95.22 W
138	Freetown (frē'toun).........S. L.	8.32 N	13.15 W
126	Fregenal de la Sierra (frā-hȧ-näl' dā lä syĕr'rä).Sp.	38.11 N	6.39 W
122	Freiberg (frī'bĕrgh)........Ger.	50.56 N	13.19 E
122	Freiburg (frī'bŏŏrgh)........Ger.	48.0 N	7.50 E
122	Freiburg..................Ger.	50.52 N	16.17 E
122	Freienwalde (frī'ĕn-väl-dĕ)....Ger.	52.48 N	14.2 E
122	Freiwaldau (Frývaldov), (frī-väl'dou) (frē'väl-dôf).Ger.	50.13 N	17.13 E
104	Freirina (frā-ĭ-rē'nä)..........Chl.	28.29 S	71.25 W
122	Freising (frī'zĭng)...........Ger.	48.24 N	11.44 E
125	Frejus (frā-zhüs')............Fr.	43.28 N	6.45 E
164	Fremantle (frē'măn-t'l)....Austl.	32.0 S	115.47 E
84	Fremont (frē-mŏnt')........Mich.	43.27 N	85.58 W
78	Fremont..................Neb.	41.27 N	96.29 W
84	Fremont..................Ohio	41.20 N	83.6 W
73	Fremont I.Utah(Salt Lake City In.)	41.9 N	112.22 W
71	Fremont Peak..............Wyo.	43.5 N	109.36 W
75	Fremont R.................Utah	38.23 N	111.0 W
82	French Broad R......Tenn.-N. C.	35.55 N	83.0 W
139	French Equatorial Africa......Afr.	10.0 N	19.0 E
138	French Guinea (Colony) (gĭ'nē) Fr. W. Afr.	10.30 N	11.0 W
103	French Guiana (gē-ä'nȧ)........	4.50 N	52.30 W
167	French I..................Austl.	38.20 S	145.20 E
160	French Indo-China..........Asia	15.0 N	107.0 E
84	French Lick................Ind.	38.35 N	86.37 W
78	Frenchman Cr.........Colo.-Neb.	40.24 N	101.30 W
71	Frenchman Cr...............Mont.	48.50 N	107.15 W
169	Frenchmans Cap (Mt.) Austl. (Tas. In.)	42.17 S	145.53 E

Page	Name Pronunciation Region	Lat. °′	Long. °′
139	French Somaliland...........Afr.	12.0 N	42.30 E
138	French Sudan (Colony) (sōō-dăn') Fr. W. Afr.	16.0 N	5.0 W
138	French West Africa..........Afr.	17.0 N	2.0 W
92	Fresnillo (frās-nēl'yō).......Mex.	23.12 N	102.50 W
74	Fresno (frĕz'nō)............Calif.	36.44 N	119.48 W
74	Fresno R...................Calif.	36.58 N	120.15 W
74	Fresno Slough..............Calif.	36.35 N	120.10 W
122	Freudenstadt (froi'dĕn-shtät).Ger.	48.27 N	8.25 E
124	Frévent (frā-väN')............Fr.	50.18 N	2.21 E
169	Freycinet Pen. (frā-sē-nĕ'). Austl. (Tas. In.)	42.10 S	148.21 E
122	Fribourg (frē-bōōr')........Switz.	46.48 N	7.9 E
72	Friday Harbor Wash. (Vancouver In.)	48.32 N	123.1 W
89	Fridley (frĭd'lĭ) Minn. (Minneapolis In.)	45.5 N	93.17 W
46	Fridtjof Nansen Land (frĕt'yôf nän'sĕn).Arc. O.	80.0 N	50.0 E
122	Friedberg (frēd'bĕrgh).........Ger.	50.20 N	8.46 E
122	Friedland (Frýdlant) (frēt'länt) (frēd'länt).Ger.	50.56 N	15.6 E
123	Friedland (frēd'länt).........Ger.	54.27 N	21.1 E
122	Friedland..................Ger.	53.40 N	13.33 E
122	Friedrichshafen (frē-drĭks-häf'-ĕn).Ger.	47.39 N	9.29 E
79	Friend (frĕnd)..............Neb.	40.38 N	97.16 W
81	Friendswood..........Tex. (In.)	29.31 N	95.11 W
119	Friern Barnet (frī'ẽrn bär'nĕt) Gt. Brit. (London In.)	51.37 N	0.11 W
83	Fries (frēz)..................Va.	36.43 N	80.58 W
90	Frijoles (frē-hō'lås) Canal Zone (In.)	9.11 N	79.49 W
103	Frio, C. (frē'ō)............Braz.	22.50 S	42.0 W
140	Frio, C..............S. W. Afr.	18.30 S	12.5 E
126	Friol (frē-ōl')................Sp.	43.2 N	7.47 W
80	Frio R.....................Tex.	28.30 N	98.55 W
123	Frisches Haff (Sea) (frĭsh'ĕs häf) Ger.	54.30 N	19.50 E
122	Frisian Is., East (frē'zhăn)..Neth.	53.40 N	7.0 E
122	Frisian Is., North...........Ger.	54.40 N	8.30 E
122	Frisian Is., West...........Neth.	53.22 N	4.57 E
55	Frobisher B. (frŏb'ĭsh-ẽr)....Can.	63.0 N	67.0 W
118	Frodingham (frŏd'ĭng-ăm) Gt. Brit.	53.36 N	0.38 W
118	Frodsham (frŏdz'ăm)....Gt. Brit.	53.18 N	2.43 W
166	Frome, L. (frōōm)........Austl.	30.45 S	139.50 E
118	Frome, R...............Gt. Brit.	52.7 N	2.29 W
79	Frontenac (frŏn'tē-năk).....Kan.	37.27 N	94.40 W
93	Frontera (Alvaro Obregon) (frôn-tā'rä) (äl'vä-rō ō-brā-gōn').Mex.	18.32 N	92.38 W
124	Frontignan (frôN-te-nyäN').....Fr.	43.36 N	3.47 E
102	Fronton I. (frôn-tōn')...Peru (In.)	12.7 S	77.12 W
58	Front Range.........Wyo.-Colo.	41.0 N	105.15 W
85	Front Royal.................Va.	38.56 N	78.11 W
128	Frosinone (frō-zē-nō'nä).......It.	41.37 N	13.22 E
85	Frostburg (frôst'bûrg)........Md.	39.41 N	78.57 W
125	Frouard (frōō-är')............Fr.	48.45 N	6.9 E
99	Froward, C. (frō'wẽrd) Chl. (Magallanes In.)	53.55 S	71.10 W
75	Fruita (frōōt-ȧ)............Colo.	39.8 N	108.45 W
148	Frunze (frōōn'zĕ)........Sov. Un.	42.45 N	74.40 E
123	Frýdek (frē'dĕk)..........Czech.	49.42 N	18.23 E
155	Fu R. (fōō)..................Chn.	28.7 N	115.55 E
156	Fu R........................Chn.	39.4 N	116.5 E
155	Fuan (fōō'än')...............Chn.	27.5 N	119.33 E
153	Fuchin (fōō'chĭn')........Manch.	47.10 N	131.59 E
155	Fuchow (fōō'chō')............Chn.	27.55 N	116.15 E
156	Fuchow..................Manch.	39.45 N	121.41 E
154	Fuchüan (fōō'chü-än').......Chn.	24.41 N	111.14 E
159	Fuda (fōō'dä)....Jap. (Tokyo In.)	35.36 N	139.37 E
94	Fuego (Vol.) (fwā'gō).......Guat.	14.27 N	90.53 W
127	Fuencarral (fuän-kär-räl') Sp. (In.)	40.29 N	3.41 W
126	Fuensalida (fwān-sä-lē'dä)....Sp.	40.4 N	4.15 W
126	Fuente Álamo (fwĕn'tä ä'lä-mō)Sp.	37.45 N	1.14 W
126	Fuente de Cantos (dā kän'tōs) Sp.	38.14 N	6.18 W
127	Fuente el Saz (ĕl säth')...Sp. (In.)	40.38 N	3.30 W
126	Fuente Ovejuna (ōvä-hōō'nä)..Sp.	38.15 N	5.25 W
126	Fuentesaúco (fwĕn-tä-sä-ōō'kō) Sp.	41.14 N	5.28 W
103	Fuerte Olimpo (fwĕr'tä ô lēmpō) Par.	21.0 S	58.0 W
95	Fuerte San Carlos (fwĕr'tä sän kär'lōs).Nic.	11.8 N	84.48 W
138	Fuerteventura (I.) (fwĕr'tä-vĕn-tōō'rä).Can. Is.	28.30 N	14.0 W
162	Fuga I. (fōō'gä)............P. I.	18.52 N	121.22 E
119	Fuhlsbüttel (fōōls'büt-ĕl) Ger. (Hamburg In.)	53.38 N	10.1 E
159	Fujikawa, R. (fōō'jē-kä'wä)..Jap.	35.30 N	138.27 E
159	Fuji, Mt. (fōō'jē)............Jap.	35.18 N	138.45 E
159	Fukae (I.) (fōō'kä-ē).........Jap.	32.44 N	128.45 E
154	Fukang (fōō'käng')...........Chn.	23.51 N	113.16 E
155	Fukien (Prov.) (fōō'kyĕn')...Chn.	25.58 N	117.38 E
159	Fukuchiyama (fōō'kōō-chē-yä'mä) Jap.	35.17 N	135.7 E
159	Fukui (fōō'kōō-ē)............Jap.	36.5 N	136.15 E
159	Fukuoka (fōō'kōō-ō'kä).......Jap.	33.31 N	130.29 E
158	Fukushima (fōō'kōō-shē'mä)..Jap.	37.46 N	140.29 E
159	Fukuyama (fōō'kōō-yä'mä)...Jap.	34.29 N	133.21 E
122	Fulda (fōōl'dä)..............Ger.	50.34 N	9.42 E
122	Fulda R.....................Ger.	50.50 N	9.41 E
73	Fullerton (fōōl'ẽr-tŭn) Calif. (Los Angeles In.)	33.52 N	117.55 W
81	Fullerton...................La.	31.0 N	93.0 W
88	Fullerton ....Md. (Baltimore In.)	39.22 N	76.31 W
78	Fullerton...................Neb.	41.22 N	97.59 W
82	Fulton......................Ky.	36.31 N	88.53 W
79	Fulton......................Mo.	38.51 N	91.56 W
85	Fulton.....................N. Y.	43.18 N	76.26 W
135	Fumu Zabi (fū-mū' zä-bē') (fōō'-mōō zä'bē).Fr. Eq. Afr. (Brazzaville In.)	4.47 S	14.50 E
159	Funabashi (fōō'nä-bä'shē)....Jap.	35.43 N	140.0 E

Page	Name Pronunciation Region	Lat. °′	Long. °′
138	Funchal (fōōn-shäl')..Madeira Is.	32.36 N	16.58 W
126	Fundão (fōōn-douN')........Port.	40.8 N	7.30 W
55	Fundy, B. of (fŭn'dĭ)..........Can.	45.10 N	65.30 W
154	Fungchun (fōōng'chōōn')....Chn.	23.21 N	111.27 E
155	Fungshun (fōōng'shōōn')....Chn.	23.53 N	116.3 E
155	Funing (fōō'nĭng')...........Chn.	26.55 N	119.54 E
156	Funing......................Chn.	39.58 N	119.19 E
156	Fuping (fōō'pĭng')...........Chn.	38.52 N	114.5 E
93	Furbero (fōōr-bā'rō).........Mex.	20.25 N	97.32 W
169	Furneaux Group (Is.) (fûr'nō) Austl. (Tas. In.)	40.0 S	148.0 E
72	Furry Cr. (fûr'ĭ)............Can.	49.35 N	123.10 W
122	Fürstenburg (für'stĕn-bōōrgh) Ger.	52.8 N	14.39 E
122	Fürstenfeld (für'stĕn-fĕlt)....Ger.	47.3 N	16.3 E
122	Fürstenwalde (für'stĕn-väl-dĕ)Ger.	52.22 N	14.4 E
122	Fürth (fürt)................Ger.	49.28 N	10.59 E
159	Furuichi (fōō'rōō-ē'chē) Jap. (Osaka In.)	34.53 N	135.6 E
157	Fusan (fōō'sän')............Cho.	35.10 N	129.0 E
159	Fushiki (fōō'shē-kē)..........Jap.	36.47 N	137.1 E
159	Fushimi (fōō'shē-mē)..........Jap.	34.57 N	135.45 E
153	Fushun (fōō'shōōn')......Manch.	42.0 N	124.5 E
155	Futing (fōō'tĭng')............Chn.	27.16 N	120.4 E
155	Futo L. (fōō'tō')............Chn.	29.57 N	114.18 E
159	Futtsu (fōōt'tsōō') Jap. (Tokyo In.)	35.19 N	139.48 E
135	Fūwa (fōō'wä)..........Eg. (In.)	31.11 N	30.33 E
153	Fuyu (fōō'yōō')..........Manch.	45.18 N	125.4 E
157	Fuyu (fōō'yōō')..............Cho.	36.18 N	126.57 E
120	Fyn (I.) (fü'n)..............Den.	55.20 N	10.30 E
116	Fyne (L.) (fīn).........Gt. Brit.	56.10 N	5.10 W
120	Fyresdal L. (fü'rĕs-däl).......Nor.	59.2 N	8.15 E
151	Fyzabad (fī-zä-bäd')........India	26.38 N	82.10 E
140	Gaberones (gä-bē-rō'nĕz)...Bech.	24.40 S	25.55 E
138	Gabés (gä'bĕs)..............Tun.	33.58 N	10.3 E
138	Gabés, G. of................Tun.	34.15 N	10.45 E
123	Gąbin (gôN'bĕn)..............Pol.	52.23 N	19.48 E
122	Gablonz (Jablonec) (gä'blônts) (yab'lô-nyĕts).Ger.	50.42 N	15.11 E
140	Gabon (Colony) (gȧ-bôN') Fr. Eq. Afr.	1.30 S	12.15 E
72	Gabriola I. (gä-brĭ-ō'lȧ) Can. (Vancouver In.)	49.10 N	123.45 W
129	Gabrovo (gäb'rō-vō)..........Bul.	42.50 N	25.20 E
102	Gacheta (gä-chā'tä)..........Col.	4.55 N	73.58 W
129	Gacko (gäts'kō).............Yugo.	43.10 N	18.32 E
138	Gadames (gä-dä'mĕs) ......Libya	30.3 N	9.30 E
82	Gadsden (gădz'dĕn)..........Ala.	34.1 N	86.1 W
131	Gadyach (gäd-yäch')....Sov. Un.	50.21 N	33.59 E
129	Gaeşti (gä-yĕsh'tē)..........Rom.	44.43 N	25.21 E
128	Gaeta (gä-ā'tä)..............It.	41.13 N	13.34 E
128	Gaeta, G. of.................It.	41.12 N	13.40 E
83	Gaffney (găf'nĭ).............S. C.	35.4 N	81.39 W
138	Gafsa (gäf'sä)...............Tun.	34.24 N	8.40 E
86	Gagetown (gāj'toun)..........Can.	45.47 N	66.8 W
125	Gagny (gȧ-nyē')........Fr. (In.)	48.53 N	2.32 E
103	Gaiba (gä-ē'bä)..............Bol.	18.0 S	57.45 W
128	Gaidaronisi (I.) (gä'ē-dä-rō-nē'sē) Grc. (Crete In.)	34.52 N	25.42 E
124	Gaillac (gȧ-yȧk')............Fr.	43.55 N	1.51 E
116	Gaillimh (Galway) (gōl'lĭv) (gôl'-wā).Ire.	53.15 N	9.0 W
83	Gainesville (gānz'vĭl) ....Fla.	29.38 N	82.18 W
82	Gainesville..................Ga.	34.17 N	83.48 W
79	Gainesville..................Tex.	33.37 N	97.8 W
116	Gainsborough (gānz'bŭr-ō) Gt.Brit.	53.25 N	0.45 W
164	Gairdner, L. (gârd'nẽr)....Austl.	31.30 S	136.0 E
131	Gaisin (gä'ĭ-sēn)........Sov. Un.	48.47 N	29.22 E
131	Gaivoron (gä'ĭ-vō-rôn')..Sov. Un.	47.39 N	30.11 E
102	Galápagos (Colon) Arch. (gä-lä'pä-gōs) (kō-lōn')...........Ec.	0.1 S	90.30 W
127	Galapagar (gä-lä-pä-gär') Sp. (In.)	40.35 N	3.59 W
116	Galashiels (găl-ȧ-shēlz)...Gt. Brit.	55.35 N	1.50 W
129	Galaţi (gȧ-lätz'ĭ)............Rom.	45.25 N	28.1 E
128	Galatina (gä-lä-tē'nä)..........It.	40.11 N	18.11 E
83	Galax (gā'lăks)...............Va.	36.40 N	80.56 W
129	Galaxeidion (gä-läks-ē'dĭ-ōn).Grc.	38.22 N	22.22 E
120	Galdhöpig (Mt.) (gäl-hû-pēgh') Nor.	61.38 N	8.15 E
80	Galeana (gä-lå-ä'nä)..........Mex.	24.50 N	100.4 W
77	Galena (gȧ-lē'nȧ)..............Ill.	42.25 N	90.16 W
79	Galena.......................Kan.	37.5 N	94.38 W
7	Galera Pt. (gä-lā'rä)...Trin. (In.)	10.51 N	60.56 W
79	Galesburg (gālz'bûrg)..........Ill.	40.56 N	90.22 W
77	Galesville (gālz'vĭl)...........Wis.	44.5 N	91.22 W
72	Galeton(gāl'tŭn)Colo.(Denver In.)	40.31 N	104.35 W
85	Galeton.......................Pa.	41.44 N	77.40 W
72	Galiano (gä-lĭ-ä'nō) Can. (Vancouver In.)	48.52 N	123.22 W
130	Galich (gäl'ĭch)........Sov. Un.	58.21 N	42.21 E
123	Galicia (Prov.) (gȧ-lĭsh'ĭ-ȧ)....Pol.	49.37 N	22.20 E
126	Galicia (Prov.) (gä-lē'thyä)....Sp.	42.50 N	7.50 W
165	Galilee, L. (găl'ĭ-le).........Austl.	22.30 S	145.45 E
145	Galilee, Sea of.....Pal.-Syria (In.)	32.50 N	35.35 E
96	Galina Pt. (gä-lē'nä)..........Jam.	18.25 N	76.55 W
84	Galion (găl'ĭ-ŭn).............Ohio	40.44 N	82.46 W
139	Galla (gäl'lä) (Division).It. E. Afr.	7.30 N	36.0 E
139	Gallabat (Qallabat) (gäl'ȧ-băt) (kȧ-lȧ-băt).A. E. Sud.	12.58 N	36.6 E
141	Gallacaio (gäl-lä-kī'ō)...It. E. Afr.	7.0 N	47.22 E
128	Gallarate (gäl-lä-rä'tä) ....It.	45.39 N	8.49 E
79	Gallatin (găl'ȧ-tĭn)..........Mo.	39.55 N	93.58 W
82	Gallatin......................Tenn.	36.24 N	86.26 W
71	Gallatin R...................Mont.	45.15 N	111.15 W
151	Galle (gäl)...................Cey.	6.10 N	80.12 E
127	Gallego R. (gäl-yā'gō).........Sp.	42.0 N	0.46 W
102	Gallinas, Pt. (gä-lyē'näs) .....Col.	12.15 N	71.45 W
128	Gallipoli (gäl-lē'pō-lē)..........It.	40.43 N	17.58 E
129	Gallipoli (Gelibolu) (gäl-lĭp'ō-lē) (gĕ-lĭb'ō-lōō).Tur.	40.25 N	26.40 E
129	Gallipoli Pen.................Tur.	40.20 N	26.30 E
84	Gallipolis (găl-ĭ-pō-lēs')......Ohio	38.50 N	82.15 W
78	Galisteo (gä-lĭst'ē-ō).........N. M.	35.23 N	105.58 W
110	Gällivare (yĕl-ĭ-vär'ĕ) ....Swe.	20.28 N	67.5 E

ng-sing; ŋ-baŋk; N-nasalized n; nŏd; cŏmmit; ōld; ōbey; ôrder; fōōd; fŏŏt; ou-out; s-soft; sh-dish; th-thin; pūre; ûnite; ûrn; stŭd; circŭs; ü-as "y" in study; '-indeterminate vowel.

Page	Name Pronunciation Region	Lat. °′	Long. °′
129	Gallo, C. (gäl′lō)............Grc.	36.33 N	21.54 E
126	Gallo R. (gäl′yō)............Sp.	40.46 N	1.45 W
75	Gallup (găl′ŭp)............N. M.	35.31 N	108.45 W
167	Galong (gȧ-lông′)..........Austl.	34.38 S	148.33 E
85	Galt (gôlt)...............Can.	43.18 N	80.18 W
116	Galtee Mts. (gôl′tē).........Ire.	52.20 N	8.15 W
79	Galva (găl′vȧ)..............Ill.	41.10 N	90.2 W
81	Galveston.................Tex.	29.19 N	94.49 W
81	Galveston B...........Tex. (In.)	29.30 N	94.50 W
81	Galveston I...........Tex. (In.)	29.15 N	94.54 W
116	Galway B. (gôl′wā)..........Ire.	53.10 N	9.10 W
138	Gambaga (găm-bä′gä)......G. C.	10.33 N	0.25 W
139	Gambela (găm-bā′lȧ)...It. E. Afr.	8.16 N	34.34 E
138	Gambia (găm′bē-ȧ)..........Afr.	13.30 N	16.0 W
138	Gambia R.......Fr. W. Afr.-Gam.	13.30 N	13.45 W
72	Gambier I. (găm′bēr) Can. (Vancouver In.)	49.30 N	123.24 W
166	Gambier Is...............Austl.	35.8 S	136.30 E
6	Gambier Is..............Pac. O.	23.8 S	134.58 W
166	Gambier, Mt.............Austl.	37.51 S	140.44 E
90	Gamboa (găm-bō′ȧ) Canal Zone (In.)	9.7 N	79.43 W
140	Gamboma (gäm-bō′mä) Fr. Eq. Afr.	2.10 S	16.3 E
142	Gamka R. (gȧm′kä)....U. S. Afr.	33.0 S	22.0 E
120	Gamleby (gäm′lĕ-bü).........Swe.	57.54 N	16.21 E
143	Gamtoos R. (gȧm′tōs) ..U. S. Afr.	33.50 S	24.50 E
162	Gamu (gä-mōō′).............P. I.	17.4 N	121.50 E
117	Gand (Ghent) (gäɴ) (gĕnt)....Bel.	51.5 N	3.41 W
163	Gandara (gän-dä′rä) ....P. I.	12.1 N	124.49 E
87	Gander L. (găn′dēr)........Newf.	48.55 N	54.45 W
87	Gander R.................Newf.	48.45 N	55.15 W
127	Gandía (gän-dē′ä)............Sp.	38.58 N	0.11 W
113	Gandzha (gänd′zhȧ).....Sov. Un.	40.40 N	46.25 E
124	Ganges (gäɴzh)..............Fr.	43.55 N	3.42 E
151	Ganges R. (găn′jēz) ....India	26.0 N	80.15 E
128	Gangi (gän′jē)...............It.	37.47 N	14.12 E
124	Gannat (gän-nä′)............Fr.	46.5 N	3.11 E
170	Gannet I. (găn′ĕt)..........N. Z.	37.57 S	174.40 E
71	Gannett Peak.............Wyo.	43.10 N	109.39 W
166	Gantheaume, C. (gȧn-tōm′) Austl.	36.3 S	137.29 E
138	Gao (gä′ō)...........Fr. W. Afr.	16.20 N	0.0
138	Gaoua (gȧ-ōō-ȧ′)......Fr. W. Afr.	10.20 N	3.8 W
125	Gap (gȧp)....................Fr.	44.35 N	6.6 E
162	Gapan (gä-pän′).............P. I.	15.18 N	120.57 E
95	Garachine (gä-rä-chē′nȧ) ....Pan.	8.3 N	78.21 W
123	Garam (Hron) R. (gŏ′rŏm) (hrōn) Czech-Hung.	48.35 N	18.40 E
158	Garambi C. (gä-räm′bē) .Tai. (In.)	22.0 N	120.45 E
103	Garanhuns (gä-rän-yōōɴsh′) . Braz.	8.48 S	36.31 W
79	Garber (gȧr′bēr)...........Okla.	36.26 N	97.32 W
80	Garcia (gär-sē′ä) ....Mex.	25.49 N	100.36 W
128	Garda, L. of (gär′dä).........It.	45.45 N	10.45 E
125	Gardanne (gȧr-dȧn′) ....Fr.	43.27 N	5.28 E
122	Gardelegen (gär-dē-lȧ′ghĕn)...Ger.	52.32 N	11.21 E
73	Gardena (gär-dē′nȧ) Calif. (Los Angeles In.)	33.54 N	118.17 W
78	Garden City..............Kan.	37.57 N	100.53 W
84	Garden I. (gär′d′n).........Mich.	45.48 N	85.40 W
89	Garden Island B. La. (New Orleans In.)	29.5 N	89.9 W
88	Gardenville N. Y. (Niagara Falls In.)	42.51 N	78.45 W
86	Gardiner (gärd′nēr)..........Me.	44.13 N	69.47 W
71	Gardiner.................Mont.	45.4 N	110.45 W
78	Gardiner.................N. M.	36.52 N	104.30 W
86	Gardner.................Mass.	42.35 N	72.0 W
88	Garfield (gär′fēld) N. J. (New York In.)	40.52 N	74.6 W
73	Garfield.Utah (Salt Lake City In.)	40.44 N	112.11 W
89	Garfield Heights Ohio (Cleveland In.)	41.24 N	81.36 W
129	Gargalianoi (gär-gä-lyä′nē)...Grc.	37.4 N	21.39 E
121	Gargždai (gärgzh′dī).......Lith.	55.42 N	21.23 E
142	Garies (gâr′ēz).........U. S. Afr.	30.32 S	17.58 E
71	Garland (gär′lănd)..........Utah	41.45 N	112.12 W
79	Garnett (gär′nĕt)...........Kan.	38.16 N	95.15 W
124	Garonne R. (gȧ-rôn′).........Fr.	44.32 N	0.0
139	Garoua (gär′wä)...........Cam.	9.20 N	13.28 E
84	Garrett (găr′ĕt).............Ind.	41.22 N	85.8 W
76	Garrison (găr′ĭ-sŭn)........N. D.	47.38 N	101.25 W
126	Garrovillas (gä-rô-vēl′yäs).....Sp.	39.42 N	6.32 W
54	Garry, L. (găr′ĭ)............Can.	66.10 N	100.30 W
118	Garstang (gȧr′stăng).....Gt. Brit.	53.55 N	2.47 W
119	Garston (gȧrs′tŭn) Gt. Brit. (Liverpool In.)	53.21 N	2.54 W
152	Gartok (gär-tŏk′)...........Chn.	32.0 N	80.27 E
171	Garvie Mts. (gär′vĭ)........N. Z.	45.20 S	169.0 E
123	Garwolin (gär-vō′lēn)........Pol.	51.56 N	21.38 E
84	Gary (gā′rĭ)................Ind.	41.35 N	87.20 W
102	Garzón (gär-thōn′)..........Col.	2.30 N	75.29 W
162	Gasan (gä-sän′).............P. I.	13.19 N	121.52 E
84	Gas City..................Ind.	40.30 N	85.42 W
79	Gasconade R. (găs-kô-nād′)...Mo.	38.0 N	91.58 W
164	Gascoyne R. (găs-koin′)....Austl.	25.0 S	116.28 E
138	Gashiga (gä-shē′gä).........Nig.	7.30 N	11.27 E
141	Gasi (gä′sē)...............Kenya	4.25 S	39.31 E
167	Gaso I. (gä′sô).............Austl.	37.35 S	149.55 E
97	Gaspar Hernández (gäs-pär′ ĕr-nän′däth) . Hai.	19.38 N	70.15 W
86	Gaspé (gȧs′pā) (gȧs-pā′).....Can.	48.51 N	64.31 W
86	Gaspé B...................Can.	48.45 N	64.15 W
86	Gaspé, C...................Can.	48.45 N	64.10 W
86	Gaspé Pen.................Can.	48.48 N	65.30 W
84	Gassaway (găs′ȧ-wā)......W. Va.	38.40 N	80.48 W
83	Gastonia (găs-tô′nĭ-ȧ).......N. C.	35.16 N	81.12 W
138	Gat (gät).................Libya	24.57 N	10.18 E
126	Gata, C. de (gä′tä)...........Sp.	36.44 N	2.8 W
115	Gatar, Wadi (R.) (wä′dē gä′tär) Libya	29.43 N	18.30 E
126	Gata, Sierra de (Mt.) (syĕr′rȧ dā gȧ′tä) . Sp.	40.20 N	6.30 W
116	Gateshead (gāts′hĕd)....Gt. Brit.	54.55 N	1.35 W
81	Gatesville (gāts′vĭl).........Tex.	31.26 N	97.45 W
54	Gatin (gȧt′ĭn).........Can. (In.)	45.31 N	75.42 W
85	Gatineau R. (gȧ′tē-nō)......Can.	45.40 N	75.55 W
140	Gatooma (gä-tōō′mä)......S. Rh.	18.27 S	29.50 E
119	Gatow (gä′tō)....Ger. (Berlin In.)	52.29 N	13.11 E
162	Gattaran (gä-tä-rän′) ....P. I.	18.3 N	121.39 E
90	Gatun (gä-tōōn′) Canal Zone (In.)	9.17 N	79.55 W
95	Gatun L...................Pan.	9.5 N	80.0 W
121	Gauja R. (gou′yȧ)..........Lat.	57.36 N	25.40 E
161	Gautier Mts. (gō-tyā′) Neth. Ind.	2.30 S	139.0 E
127	Gavá (gä-vä′)...........Sp. (In.)	41.18 N	2.1 E
116	Gava, Lough (L.) (lŏĸ gä′vȧ) Ire.	53.55 N	8.30 W
128	Gavdos (I.) (gäv′dôs)........Grc.	34.48 N	24.5 E
124	Gave de Pau R. (gäv′ dē pō′)..Fr.	43.35 N	0.50 W
124	Gave d′Ossau R. (gȧv′ dôs-sō′) Fr.	43.20 N	0.50 W
150	Gavkhaneh (Marsh) (gäv-ĸä′nā) Iran	31.45 N	53.30 E
120	Gävle (yĕv′lĕ)..............Swe.	60.40 N	17.8 E
120	Gävle B...................Swe.	60.43 N	17.20 E
130	Gavrilov (gȧ-vrē-lôf′)....Sov. Un.	57.13 N	39.49 E
131	Gavrilovka (gȧ′vrē-lôf′ka) Sov. Un.	48.4 N	36.24 E
130	Gavrilov Posad (pô-sȧt) Sov. Un.	56.33 N	40.9 E
166	Gawler (gô′lēr)............Austl.	34.35 S	138.45 E
164	Gawler Ranges............Austl.	32.30 S	136.0 E
151	Gaya (gŭ′yä) (gī′ȧ).........India	24.45 N	84.58 E
138	Gaya (gä′yä)...............Nig.	12.0 N	9.10 E
84	Gaylord (gā′lôrd)..........Mich.	45.1 N	84.46 W
145	Gaza (gä′zȧ)...........Pal. (In.)	31.29 N	34.27 E
113	Gazi-Ayintap (gä-zĭ ȧ-yĭn-tȧp′) Tur.	37.5 N	37.32 E
130	Gdov (g′dôf)...........Sov. Un.	58.44 N	27.51 E
123	Gdynia (g′dēn′yȧ)...........Pol.	54.28 N	18.32 E
49	Gearhart (gēr′hȧrt) Ore. (Portland In.)	46.1 N	123.55 W
78	Geary (gē′rĭ)..............Okla.	35.36 N	98 18 W
71	Gebo (gĕb′ō)..............Wyo.	43.47 N	108.15 W
81	Ged (gĕd)....................La.	30.8 N	93.35 W
166	Geelong (jē-lông′).........Austl.	38.8 S	144.18 E
161	Geelvink B. (gāl′vĭŋk) Neth. Ind.	2.30 S	135.30 E
142	Geel Vloer (L.) (gāl vlōōr) U. S. Afr.	29.28 S	20.8 E
164	Geikie Range (gē′kē).......Austl.	18.15 S	126.45 E
142	Geinab R. (gā′nȧb)....S. W. Afr.	27.50 S	19.35 E
122	Geislingen (gīs′lĭng-ĕn).......Ger.	48.37 N	9.52 E
129	Gelibolu (Gallipoli) (gĕ-lĭb′ô-lōō) Tur.	40.25 N	26.40 E
127	Gelida (hā-lē′dȧ)........Sp. (In.)	41.26 N	1.53 E
131	Gelmyazova (gyĕl′myä-zō′vȧ) Sov. Un.	49.49 N	31.50 E
122	Gelsenkirchen-Buer (gĕl′zĕn-kĭrĸ-ĕn-bōōr) . Ger.	51.38 N	7.6 E
145	Gemas (jĕm′ȧs) Fed. Mal. States (In.)	2.33 N	102.37 E
167	Gembrook (jĕm′brŏŏk).....Austl.	37.58 S	145.35 E
113	Gemlik (gĕm′lĭk)............Tur.	40.30 N	29.12 E
135	Geneffa, Jebel (Mts.) (jĕ-nĕf′ȧ) Eg. (Suez Canal In.)	30.16 N	32.20 E
74	General Grant Natl. Park...Calif.	36.44 N	118.58 W
99	General Pinto (gā-nȧ-räl′ pēn′tō) Arg. (Buenos Aires In.)	34.44 S	61.57 W
99	General Rodriguez (rô-drē′gāz) Arg. (Buenos Aires In.)	34.37 S	58.58 W
80	General Zepeda (zȧ-pā′dä)...Mex.	25.25 N	101.30 W
80	General Zuazua (zwä′zwä)...Mex.	25.55 N	100.8 W
143	Genesa (jē-nē′sȧ)..........Bech.	26.35 S	24.12 E
85	Genesee R. (jĕn-ē-sē′)......N. Y.	42.30 N	77.55 W
79	Geneseo (jĕn-ē-sē′ō)..........Ill.	41.26 N	90.9 W
82	Geneva (jē-nē′vȧ)...........Ala.	31.2 N	85.52 W
79	Geneva...................Neb.	40.33 N	97.35 W
85	Geneva...................N. Y.	42.52 N	77.0 W
84	Geneva...................Ohio	41.57 N	80.47 W
122	Geneva (Génève) (zhȧ-nĕv′) Switz.	46.13 N	6.11 E
122	Geneva, L...............Switz.	46.25 N	6.40 E
122	Génève (Geneva) (zhā-nĕv′) Switz.	46.13 N	6.11 E
131	Genichesk (gȧ′nē-chyĕsk′) Sov. Un.	46.11 N	34.49 E
126	Genil R. (hȧ-nēl′)............Sp.	37.15 N	4.30 W
129	Genitsa (yĕ-nēt′sȧ)..........Grc.	40.46 N	22.25 E
125	Gennevilliers (zhĕn-vē-yā′) Fr. (In.)	48.56 N	2.17 E
76	Genoa (jĕn′ô-ȧ).............Neb.	41.28 N	97.42 W
81	Genoa..............Tex. (In.)	29.37 N	95.11 W
128	Genoa (Genova) (jĕn′ō-vä).....It.	44.24 N	8.55 E
128	Genoa, G. of.................It.	44.10 N	9.0 E
128	Genova (Genoa) (jĕn′ō-vä) (jen′ô-ȧ) . It.	44.24 N	8.55 E
157	Gensan (Wonsan) (jĕn′sän′) (wōn′sän′) . Cho.	39.11 N	127.38 E
122	Genthin (gĕn-tēn′) ....Ger.	52.24 N	12.10 E
125	Gentilly (zhäɴ-tē-yē′)....Fr. (In.)	48.48 N	2.21 E
164	Geographe B. (jē-ô-grăf′)...Austl.	33.25 S	115.15 E
164	Geographe Chan...........Austl.	24.45 S	113.15 E
113	Geokchai (gĕ-ôk′chī).....Sov. Un.	40.40 N	47.45 E
142	George...............U. S. Afr.	33.57 S	22.27 E
87	George B..................Can.	45.45 N	61.40 W
54	George Dawson, Mt. (dô′sŭn) Can.	51.27 N	124.32 W
167	George, L................Austl.	35.5 S	149.25 E
166	George, L................Austl.	37.25 S	140.0 E
83	George, L...................Fla.	29.17 N	81.37 W
85	George, L.................N. Y.	43.40 N	73.30 W
171	George Sd.................N. Z.	44.50 S	167.25 E
169	Georges R.....Austl. (Sydney In.)	33.57 S	150.58 E
7	Georgetown....Ascension I. (In.)	7.56 S	14.24 W
169	Georgetown......Austl. (Tas. In.)	41.5 S	146.50 E
103	Georgetown............Br. Gu.	6.45 N	58.15 W
87	Georgetown...............Can.	46.10 N	62.30 W
85	Georgetown...............Del.	38.42 N	75.22 W
84	Georgetown.................Ill.	39.59 N	87.39 W
96	Georgetown....Grand Cayman I.	19.18 N	81.24 W
84	Georgetown................Ky.	38.12 N	84.34 W
85	Georgetown................Md.	39.23 N	75.53 W
87	Georgetown.........Mass. (In.)	42.43 N	71.0 W
83	Georgetown...............S. C.	33.23 N	79.18 W
160	Georgetown..........Strs. Sets.	5.21 N	100.15 E
81	Georgetown...............Tex.	30.37 N	97.40 W
82	Georgia (State)............U. S.	32.40 N	83.20 W
113	Georgia (Soviet Rep.)....Sov. Un.	41.50 N	44.0 E
82	Georgiana..................Ala.	31.38 N	86.44 W
55	Georgian B.................Can.	45.30 N	81.0 W
70	Georgia, Str. of............Can.	49.0 N	123.25 W
113	Georgievsk (gyôr-gyĕfsk′) Sov. Un.	44.8 N	43.30 E
164	Georgina R. (jôr-jē′nȧ).....Austl.	22.0 S	138.30 E
122	Gera (gā′rä)...............Ger.	50.53 N	12.4 E
171	Geraldine (jĕr′ăl-dēn).......N. Z.	44.4 S	171.17 E
164	Geraldton (jĕr′ăld-tŭn).....Austl.	28.32 S	114.31 E
104	Geral, Serra (Mts.) (sĕr′rȧ zhȧ-räl′) Braz.	28.0 S	49.30 W
119	Gerasdorf (gā′räs-dôrf)......Ger.	48.18 N	16.28 E
126	Gérgal (gĕr′gäl).............Sp.	37.8 N	2.29 W
76	Gering (gē′rĭng)............Neb.	41.49 N	103.40 W
167	Geringong (gē′rĭŋ-gông′) ...Austl.	34.45 S	150.48 E
84	Germantown (jûr′mȧn-toun) Ohio	39.38 N	84.23 W
122	Germany (jûr′mȧ-nĭ) ....Eur.	51.0 N	13.0 E
143	Germiston (jûr′mĭs-tŭn) U. S. Afr.	26.13 S	28.11 E
162	Gerona (hā-rō′nä)...........P. I.	15.36 N	120.36 E
127	Gerona....................Sp.	41.57 N	2.49 E
89	Gervais L. (jûr′vās) Minn. (Minneapolis In.)	45.1 N	93.4 W
114	Géryville (zhā-rē-vēl′).......Alg.	33.42 N	1.2 E
139	Gesira (Well) (jĕ′zē-rä). ...Libya	25.45 N	21.28 E
127	Getafe (hā-tä′fȧ)........Sp. (In.)	40.19 N	3.44 W
85	Gettysburg (gĕt′ĭs-bûrg)......Pa.	39.52 N	77.13 W
76	Gettysburg................S. D.	45.1 N	99.59 W
49	Gettysburg....Wash. (Seattle In.)	48.9 N	123.50 W
143	Geysdorp (Mt.) (gīz′dôrp) U. S. Afr.	26.35 S	25.20 E
138	Ghardaïa (gär-dä′ē-ä)........Alg.	32.30 N	3.35 E
151	Ghats, Eastern (Mts.)......India	17.0 N	80.30 E
151	Ghats, Western (Mts.)......India	16.30 N	74.15 E
151	Ghazni (gŭz′nē).............Afg.	33.32 N	68.30 E
115	Ghemines (gȧ-mē′nȧs)......Libya	31.35 N	20.0 E
117	Ghent (Gand) (gĕnt) (gäɴ)...Bel.	51.5 N	3.41 W
123	Gheorgheni (gyôr-gān′ĭ).....Rom.	46.49 N	25.31 E
123	Gherla (gĕr′lä).............Rom.	47.2 N	23.55 E
139	Ghigner (gēn-yĕr′).....It. E. Afr.	7.7 N	40.35 E
139	Giado (jä′dō)..............Libya	31.58 N	12.2 W
139	Giaghbub (Giarabub) (jäg′bōōb) (jä′rä-bōōb) Libya	29.47 N	24.32 E
139	Gialo, Oasis (jä′lō).........Libya	29.15 N	22.5 E
128	Giannutri (I.) (jän-nōō′trē)....It.	42.15 N	11.7 E
143	Giants Castle (Mt.).....U. S. Afr.	29.21 S	29.29 E
139	Giarabub (Giaghbub) (jä′rä-bōōb) (jäg′bōōb) Libya	29.47 N	24.32 E
97	Gibara (hē-bä′rä)..........Cuba	21.6 N	76.10 W
140	Gibeon (gĭb′ē-ŭn)......S. W. Afr.	25.13 S	17.35 E
126	Gibraleón (hē-brä-lȧ-ōn′)......Sp.	37.24 N	6.59 W
126	Gibraltar (jĭ-brôl′tēr)........Gib.	36.8 N	5.40 W
135	Gibraltar..................(In.)		
79	Gibson City (gĭb′sŭn).........Ill.	40.27 N	88.21 W
164	Gibson Desert (gĭb′sŭn)....Austl.	24.45 S	125.0 E
72	Gibsons Landing Can. (Vancouver In.)	49.24 N	123.31 W
148	Gida R. (gē′dȧ).........Sov. Un.	70.35 N	79.0 E
81	Giddings (gĭd′ĭngz)..........Tex.	30.11 N	96.57 W
79	Gideon (gĭd′ē-ŭn)...........Mo.	36.26 N	89.57 W
124	Gien (zhē-ăɴ′)...............Fr.	47.42 N	2.38 E
122	Gieszen (gēs′ĕn).............Ger.	50.35 N	8.40 E
125	Gif (zhēf)..............Fr. (In.)	48.42 N	2.8 E
159	Gifu (gē′fōō)...............Jap.	35.30 N	136.45 E
80	Gigantes, L. (hē-gän′tȧs)....Mex.	27.55 N	104.35 W
163	Gigaquit (hē-gä′kēt)........P. I.	9.35 N	125.42 E
141	Giggiga (jē-jē′gȧ)......It. E. Afr.	9.28 N	42.48 E
49	Gig Harbor (gĭg) Wash. (Seattle In.)	47.20 N	122.36 W
128	Giglio (Il) (jēl′yō).............It.	42.22 N	10.55 E
126	Giguela R. (hē-gā′lä).........Sp.	39.40 N	3.4 W
163	Gihulñgan (hē-ōōl′ny′gän)....P. I.	10.8 N	123.16 E
126	Gijon (hē-hōn′)..............Sp.	43 32 N	5.38 W
75	Gila Bend Ind. Res..........Ariz.	33.0 N	112.50 W
75	Gila Cliff Dwellings Nat′l Mon. ....N. M.	33.14 N	108.16 W
75	Gila R. (hē′lȧ)..............Ariz.	33.5 N	111.15 W
139	Gila R. (gē′lä).........It. E. Afr.	7.45 N	34.0 E
75	Gila River Ind. Res.........Ariz.	33.10 N	112.0 W
77	Gilbert (gĭl′bērt)...........Minn.	47.28 N	92.28 W
7	Gilbert Is...............Pac. O.	1.0 S	175.0 E
52	Gilbert, Mt...........Alsk. (In.)	61.12 N	148.20 W
165	Gilbert R.................Austl.	17.18 S	142.0 E
143	Gilboa, Mt. (gĭl-bō′ȧ)...U. S. Afr.	29.19 S	30.18 E
72	Gilcrest (gĭl′krĕst) Colo. (Denver In.)	40.17 N	104.46 W
99	Giles (hē′lȧs) Arg. (Buenos Aires In.)	34.23 S	59.29 W
167	Gilgandra (gĭl-găn′drȧ).....Austl.	31.42 S	148.38 E
151	Gilgit (gĭl′gĭt)..............India	35.59 N	74.14 E
131	Giligul R...............Sov. Un.	47.25 N	30.30 E
72	Gill (jĭl) ....Colo. (Denver In.)	40.27 N	104.32 W
166	Gilles, L. (jĭl′ēz) ....Austl.	32.50 S	136.45 E
79	Gillett (jĭ-lĕt′)..............Ark.	34.7 N	91.23 W
72	Gillett......Colo. (Colo. Sprs. In.)	38.47 N	105.7 W
71	Gillette...................Wyo.	44.18 N	105.29 W
117	Gillingham (gĭl′ĭng-ăm)..Gt. Brit.	51.20 N	0.35 E
164	Gillon, L. (gĭl′ŭn)...........Austl.	26.10 S	124.45 E
117	Gilly (zhē-yē′)..............Bel.	50.25 N	4.35 E
79	Gilman (gĭl′măn).............Ill.	40.46 N	88.0 W
81	Gilmer (gĭl′mēr).............Tex.	32.43 N	94.58 W
74	Gilroy (gĭl-roi′)............Calif.	37.0 N	121.33 W
124	Gimone R. (zhē-mōn′)........Fr.	43.35 N	0.45 E

ăt; finăl; rāte; senâte; ärm; ȧsk; sofȧ; fâre; ch-choose; dh-as th in other; bē; ēvent; bĕt; recĕnt; cratēr; g-go; gh-gutteral g; bĭt; ĭ-short neutral; rīde; ĸ-gutteral k as ch in German ich;

Page	Name Pronunciation Region	Lat. °′	Long. °′
135	Gineifa (jê-nā'fä) Eg. (Suez Can. In.)	30.12 N	32.26 E
167	Gin Gin (jĭn' jĭn)....Austl.	31.56 S	148.8 E
163	Gingoog B. (hēn-gō'ôg)....P. I.	9.0 N	125.5 E
128	Ginosa (jê-nō'zä)....It.	40.34 N	16.46 E
126	Ginzo (hēn-thō')....Sp.	42.4 N	7.45 W
139	Giof (jôf)....Libya	24.15 N	23.36 E
139	Giofra, Oasis of (jôf'rä)....Libya	29.0 N	15.30 E
128	Gioja del Colle (jô'yä dĕl kôl'lā). It.	40.47 N	16.57 E
167	Gippsland (Reg.) (gĭps'lănd) Austl.	37.45 S	147.27 E
169	Gipps Town (gĭps' toun) Austl. (Sydney In.)	33.52 S	151.8 E
158	Giran (gē'rän)....Tai. (In.)	24.45 N	121.45 E
82	Girard (jĭ-rärd')....Ala.	32.26 N	85.1 W
79	Girard....Kan.	37.31 N	94.51 W
102	Girardot (hē-rär-dōt')....Col.	4.15 N	69.59 W
113	Giresun (ghĕr'ĕ-sōōn')....Tur.	40.55 N	38.28 E
135	Girga (jĕr'gȧ)....Eg. (In.)	26.20 N	31.53 E
128	Girgenti (jĕr-jĕn'tē)....It.	37.19 N	13.34 E
151	Giridih (jē'rê-dê)....India	24.8 N	86.7 E
125	Giromagny (zhē-rô-mȧn-yē')..Fr.	47.45 N	6.59 E
124	Gironde R. (zhē-rônd')....Fr.	45.25 N	0.50 W
116	Girvan (gûr'vȧn)....Gt. Brit.	55.15 N	4.50 W
170	Gisborne (gĭz'bŭrn)....N. Z.	38.40 S	178.3 E
157	Gishu (gē'shōō')....Cho.	40.14 N	124.31 E
124	Gisors (zhē-zôr')....Fr.	49.18 N	1.49 E
129	Giura (I.) (yōō'rä)....Grc.	39.22 N	24.10 E
129	Giurgiu (jōōr'jōō)....Rom.	43.53 N	25.57 E
117	Givet (zhē-vĕ')....Bel.	51.8 N	4.49 E
124	Givors (zhē-vôr')....Fr.	45.35 N	4.48 E
141	Gîza (gē'zȧ)....Eg.	30.1 N	31.13 E
141	Gîza Pyramids....Eg.	29.59 N	31.7 E
149	Gizhiga (gē'zhĭ-gȧ)....Sov. Un.	61.55 N	160.30 E
129	Gjinocastër (Ergeri) (gyĕ-nô-käs'tĕr) (ĕr-gē-rē') Alb.	40.5 N	20.8 E
120	Gjövik (gyû'vĕk)....Nor.	60.48 N	10.40 E
128	Gjurgjevac (dyōōr'dyĕ-väts) Yugo.	46.2 N	17.3 E
87	Glace B. (glȧs)....Can.	46.15 N	59.57 W
54	Glacier (glā'shẽr)....Can.	51.10 N	117.16 W
72	Glacier....Wash. (Vancouver In.)	48.54 N	121.57 W
54	Glacier Natl. Park....Can.	51.15 N	117.15 W
71	Glacier Natl. Park (Waterton-Glacier Internat'l Peace Park) Mont.	48.50 N	114.0 W
70	Glacier Peak....Wash.	48.7 N	121.8 W
122	Gladbach-Rheydt (glät'bäk-rīt') Ger.	51.13 N	6.27 E
165	Gladstone (glăd'stōn)....Austl.	23.50 S	151.15 E
166	Gladstone....Austl.	33.16 S	138.21 E
77	Gladstone....Mich.	45.51 N	87.1 W
89	Gladstone. Minn. (Minneapolis In.)	45.0 N	93.2 W
171	Gladstone....N. Z.	44.35 S	169.23 E
84	Gladwin (glăd'wĭn)....Mich.	43.59 N	84.27 W
128	Glamoč (gläm'ôch)....Yugo.	44.2 N	16.51 E
163	Glan (glän)....P. I.	5.46 N	125.12 E
169	Glanville (glăn'vĭl) Austl. (Adelaide In.)	34.50 S	138.29 E
122	Glarus (glä'rōōs)....Switz.	47.2 N	9.2 E
116	Glasgow (glȧs'gō)....Gt. Brit.	55.50 N	4.15 W
82	Glasgow....Ky.	37.1 N	85.56 W
79	Glasgow....Mo.	39.14 N	92.48 W
71	Glasgow....Mont.	48.13 N	106.39 W
89	Glassport (glȧs'pōrt) Pa. (Pittsburgh In.)	40.19 N	79.54 W
122	Glatz (gläts)....Ger.	50.27 N	16.38 E
122	Glauchau (glou'kou)....Ger.	50.49 N	12.34 E
119	Glazebury (glāz'bẽr-ĭ) Gt. Brit. (Liverpool In.)	53.28 N	2.30 W
112	Glazov (glä'zôf)....Sov. Un.	58.5 N	52.45 E
122	Głębokie (gwăN-bôk'yĕ)....Pol.	55.8 N	27.44 E
122	Gleiwitz (glī'wĭts)....Ger.	50.17 N	18.41 E
125	Glénans, Iles de (Is.) (glā-näN') Fr.	47.40 N	4.0 W
166	Glencoe (glĕn'kō)....Austl.	37.42 S	140.32 E
77	Glencoe....Minn.	44.46 N	94.8 W
143	Glencoe....U. S. Afr.	28.10 S	30.11 E
75	Glendale (glĕn'dāl)....Ariz.	33.31 N	112.12 W
74	Glendale....Calif.	34.9 N	118.18 W
71	Glendive (glĕn'dīv)....Mont.	47.7 N	104.41 W
73	Glendora (glĕn-dō'rȧ) Calif. (Los Angeles In.)	34.9 N	117.52 W
170	Gleneden (glĕn-ē'dĕn)..N. Z. (In.)	36.55 S	174.40 E
166	Glenelg (glĕn-ĕlg')....Austl.	34.59 S	138.32 E
166	Glenelg R....Austl.	37.55 S	141.25 E
169	Glenfield (glĕn'fēld) Austl. (Sydney In.)	33.58 S	150.53 E
167	Glengarry (glĕn-găr'ĭ)....Austl.	38.7 S	146.33 E
167	Glen Innes (glĕn ĭn'ĕs)....Austl.	29.45 S	151.45 E
81	Glenmora (glĕn-mō'rȧ)....La.	30.58 N	92.35 W
70	Glenns Ferry (glĕnz fĕr'ĭ)....Ida.	42.59 N	115.18 W
83	Glennville (glĕn'vĭl)....Ga.	31.55 N	81.56 W
88	Glen Olden (glĕn ōl'd'n) Pa. (Philadelphia In.)	39.54 N	75.17 W
118	Glen, R. (glĕn)....Gt. Brit.	52.44 N	0.18 W
167	Glenreagh (glĕn-rā')....Austl.	30.2 S	153.1 E
71	Glenrock (glĕn'rŏk)....Wyo.	42.52 N	105.51 W
169	Glenroy (glĕn-roi') Austl. (Melbourne In.)	37.42 S	144.55 E
85	Glens Falls (glĕnz)....N. Y.	43.18 N	73.38 W
89	Glenshaw (glĕn'shô) Pa. (Pittsburgh In.)	40.32 N	79.57 W
76	Glen Ullin (glĕn ŭl'ĭn)....N. D.	46.48 N	101.49 W
88	Glenview (glĕn'vū) Ill. (Chicago In.)	42.4 N	87.48 W
79	Glenwood (glĕn'wŏŏd)....Ia.	41.3 N	95.41 W
76	Glenwood....Minn.	45.39 N	95.21 W
87	Glenwood....Newf.	48.58 N	54.50 W
75	Glenwood Springs....Colo.	39.33 N	107.19 W
75	Globe (glōb)....Ariz.	33.23 N	110.47 W
131	Globino (glôb'ē-nô)....Sov. Un.	49.19 N	33.12 E
131	Glodosti (glô-dôst'yĭ)....Sov. Un.	48.28 N	31.16 E
122	Glogau (glō'gou)....Ger.	51.40 N	16.3 E
120	Glommen R. (glôm'ĕn)....Nor.	61.10 N	11.20 E
141	Glorious Is....Ind. O.	11.30 S	47.20 E
73	Gloryetta (glô-rĭ-et'ȧ) Calif. (Los Angeles In.)	33.42 N	117.51 W
118	Glossop (glŏs'ŭp)....Gt. Brit.	53.27 N	1.57 W
82	Gloster (glŏs'tẽr)....Miss.	31.11 N	91.3 W
167	Gloucester (glŏs'tẽr)....Austl.	32.1 S	151.57 E
116	Gloucester....Gt. Brit.	51.55 N	2.15 W
86	Gloucester....Mass.	42.35 N	70.40 W
84	Gloucester....Ohio	39.35 N	82.58 W
85	Gloucester City....N. J.	39.52 N	75.10 W
118	Gloucester County....Gt. Brit.	52.6 N	1.48 W
85	Gloversville (glŭv'ẽrz-vĭl)...N. Y.	43.4 N	74.20 W
131	Glukhov (glōō'kôf')....Sov. Un.	51.42 N	33.52 E
131	Glushkovo (glōōsh'kô-vô) Sov. Un.	51.21 N	34.42 E
130	Glusk (glōōsk)....Sov. Un.	52.55 N	28.39 E
122	Gmünd (g'mŭnt)....Ger.	48.48 N	9.49 E
122	Gmunden (g'mōōn'dĕn)....Ger.	47.57 N	13.48 E
123	Gniezno (g'nyăz'nô)....Pol.	52.32 N	17.35 E
129	Gnjilane (gnyē'là-nĕ)....Yugo.	42.27 N	21.27 E
151	Goa (gō'ȧ)....India	15.15 N	74.0 E
162	Goa (gō'ä)....P. I.	13.41 N	123.29 E
102	Goajira Pen. (gō-ä-kē'rȧ)....Col.	11.30 N	72.45 W
94	Goascoran (gō-äs'kō-rän')....Hond.	13.39 N	87.46 W
88	Goat Is..N. Y. (Niagara Falls In.)	43.5 N	79.4 W
143	Goba (gō'bä)....Moz.	26.9 S	32.12 E
140	Gobabis (gō-bä'bĭs)....S. W. Afr.	22.32 S	18.58 E
152	Gobi, The (Shamo) (Desert) (gō'bē) Chn.	43.0 N	130.0 E
49	Goble (gō'b'l)..Ore. (Portland In.)	45.1 N	122.53 W
122	Goch (gōk)....Ger.	51.42 N	6.12 E
151	Godavari R. (gô-dä'vŭ-rē)...India	19.0 N	79.0 E
164	Goddards Cr. (gŏd'ȧrdz)....Austl.	31.18 S	124.15 E
84	Goderich (gŏd'rĭch)....Can.	43.44 N	81.42 W
48	Godhavn (gōdh'hävn)....Grnld.	69.15 N	53.30 W
171	Godley Head (gŏd'lĭ)...N. Z. (In.)	43.35 S	172.50 E
54	Gods L. (gŏdz)....Can.	54.20 N	95.0 W
48	Godthaab (gŏt'hōōb)....Grnld.	64.10 N	51.32 W
151	Godwin Austen, Mt. (gŏd'wĭn ôs'tĕn). India	35.58 N	76.30 E
117	Goedereede (I.) (kōō'dē-rā-dĕ) Neth.	51.45 N	4.10 E
73	Goethite (gō'thīt) Ala. (Birmingham In.)	33.16 N	87.6 W
74	Goffs (gôfs)....Calif.	34.56 N	115.4 W
159	Gogawa, R. (gō-gä'wä)....Jap.	34.50 N	132.40 E
77	Gogebic L. (gō-gē'bĭk)....Mich.	46.30 N	89.34 W
92	Gogorrón (gō-gô-rōn')....Mex.	21.50 N	100.54 W
151	Gogra R. (gŏg'rä)....India	26.15 N	83.0 E
103	Goiaz (State) (gô'yäzh')....Braz.	14.0 S	49.0 W
103	Goiaz....Braz.	15.58 S	50.5 W
113	Gokcha, L. (gôk'chä) (gûk'chȧ) Sov. Un.	40.25 N	46.15 E
113	Gök Su (R.) (gûk'sōō')....Tur.	37.0 N	33.0 E
120	Göl (gûl)....Nor.	60.44 N	9.1 E
119	Golborne (gŏl'bŭrn) Gt. Brit. (Liverpool In.)	53.28 N	2.36 W
118	Golcar (gŏl'kȧr)....Gt. Brit.	53.38 N	1.52 W
79	Golconda (gŏl-kŏn'dȧ)....Ill.	37.22 N	88.29 W
151	Golconda....India	17.15 N	78.15 E
123	Goldap (gôl'däp)....Ger.	54.17 N	22.18 E
138	Gold Coast....Afr.	8.0 N	1.30 W
75	Golden....Colo.	39.45 N	105.13 W
171	Golden B....N. Z.	40.40 S	172.50 E
70	Goldendale....Wash.	45.48 N	120.50 W
49	Golden Gate Calif. (San Francisco In.)	37.47 N	122.28 W
72	Goldfield...Colo. (Colo. Sprs. In.)	38.43 N	105.7 W
74	Goldfield....Nev.	37.42 N	117.13 W
90	Gold Hill (Mt.)....C. Z. (In.)	9.3 N	79.38 W
83	Goldsboro....N. C.	35.23 N	77.59 W
72	Goldstream..Can. (Vancouver In.)	48.27 N	123.34 W
80	Goldthwaite (gōld'thwāt)....Tex.	31.27 N	98.33 W
129	Golemo-Konare (gō'lȧ-mō-kō'-nȧ-rĕ). Bul.	42.16 N	24.31 E
81	Goliad (gō-lĭ-ăd')....Tex.	28.40 N	97.22 W
170	Gollans R. (gŏl'ȧns)....N. Z. (In.)	41.22 S	174.53 E
122	Gollnow (gŏl'nō)....Ger.	53.33 N	14.51 E
131	Golodaevka (gô'lô-dä-yĕf'kȧ) Sov. Un.	47.51 N	38.53 E
162	Golo I. (gō'lō)....P. I.	13.39 N	120.22 E
131	Golovchino (gō-lôf'chē-nō) Sov. Un.	50.31 N	35.51 E
140	Golungo Alto (gô-lōōŋ'gô äl'tō) Ang.	9.10 S	14.40 E
130	Gomel (gō'mĕl')....Sov. Un.	52.25 N	31.1 E
138	Gomera I. (gô-mä'rä)...Canary Is.	28.10 N	17.15 W
125	Gometz-le-Châtel (gō-mĕts'-lē-shä-tĕl'). Fr. (In.)	48.41 N	2.8 E
80	Gómez Farias (gō'mäz fȧ-rē'äs) Mex.	24.59 N	101.2 W
99	Gómez, L. de (gō'mäz) Arg. (Buenos Aires In.)	34.35 S	61.5 W
80	Gómez Palacio (gō'mäz pä-lä'syō) Mex.	25.34 N	103.30 W
97	Gonaïves (gō-nȧ-ēv')....Hai.	19.27 N	72.42 W
97	Gonaïves, G. of....Hai.	19.20 N	73.10 W
129	Gönan (gû'nän)....Tur.	40.6 N	27.41 E
97	Gonave Chan. (gō-nȧv')....Hai.	18.40 N	73.10 W
97	Gonave I....Hai.	18.50 N	73.5 W
139	Gondar (gŏn'dȧr)....It. E. Afr.	12.36 N	37.28 E
125	Gonesse (gô-nĕs')....Fr. (In.)	48.58 N	2.28 E
141	Gonja (gŏn'jȧ)....Tan.	4.16 S	38.4 E
56	Gonor (gŏ'nôr) Can. (Winnipeg In.)	50.3 N	96.54 W
81	Gonzales (gŏn-zä'lĕz)....Tex.	29.31 N	97.27 W
73	Goodes (gŏŏdz)..Ga. (Atlanta In.)	33.32 N	84.44 W
54	Good Hope....Can.	66.9 N	128.35 W
142	Good Hope, C. of....U. S. Afr.	34.21 S	18.25 E
70	Gooding (gŏŏd'ĭng)....Ida.	42.56 N	114.44 W
84	Goodland (gŏŏd'lănd)....Ind.	40.52 N	87.14 W
78	Goodland....Kan.	39.20 N	101.42 W
73	Goodsprings (gŏŏd'sprĭngz) Ala. (Birmingham In.)	33.39 N	87.14 W
169	Goodwood (gŏŏd'wŏŏd) Austl. (Adelaide In.)	34.57 S	138.36 E
118	Goole (gōōl)....Gt. Brit.	53.42 N	0.52 W
169	Goondiwindi (gōōn-dē-wĭn'dê) Austl. (In.)	28.33 S	150.22 E
71	Gooseberry Cr....Wyo.	44.1 N	108.30 W
71	Goose Cr....Nev.-Ida.	42.0 N	114.0 W
81	Goose Creek....Tex.	29.42 W	95.0 W
70	Goose L....Calif.	41.56 N	120.25 W
76	Goose R....N. D.	47.30 N	97.20 W
122	Göppingen (gûp'ĭng-ĕn)....Ger.	48.43 N	9.40 E
123	Góra-Kalwarja (gōō'rȧ-käl-vär'yȧ). Pol.	51.58 N	21.13 E
151	Gorakhpur (gō'rŭk-pōōr)....India	26.35 N	83.29 E
161	Goram Is. (gō'räm)....Neth. Ind.	4.0 S	131.29 E
96	Gorda Cay (I.) (gôr'dä)....Ba. Is.	26.5 N	77.33 W
96	Gorda Pt....Cuba	22.23 N	82.5 W
169	Gordon (gôr'dŭn). Austl. (Tas. In.)	43.16 S	147.13 E
56	Gordon....Can. (Winnipeg In.)	50.0 N	97.21 W
76	Gordon....Neb.	42.48 N	102.11 W
169	Gordon R....Austl. (Tas. In.)	42.40 S	145.58 E
169	Gordons B....Austl. (Sydney In.)	33.56 S	151.16 E
139	Gore (gō'rĕ)....It. E. Afr.	8.12 N	35.32 E
171	Gore (gōr)....N. Z.	46.5 S	168.55 E
171	Gore, Mt....N. Z.	42.17 S	172.0 E
138	Gorgeram (gôr'gȧ-räm)....Nig.	12.40 N	10.45 E
128	Gorgona (I.) (gôr-gō'nä)....It.	43.27 N	9.53 E
113	Gori (gō'rē)....Sov. Un.	42.0 N	44.5 E
122	Gorinchem (gō'rĭn-kĕm)....Neth.	51.50 N	5.0 E
111	Gorki (Nizhni Novgorod) (gôr'kĭ) (nĕzh'nĭ-ê nôv'gō-rŏt)...Sov. Un.	56.15 N	43.58 E
123	Gorlice (gôr-lēt'sĕ)....Pol.	49.39 N	21.10 E
122	Görlitz (gûr'lĭts)....Ger.	51.9 N	15.1 E
131	Gorlovka (gôr'lôf-kȧ)....Sov. Un.	48.18 N	38.2 E
80	Gorman (gôr'mȧn)....Tex.	32.13 N	98.40 W
129	Gorna-Džumaya (gôr'nȧ-dzhōō-mä'yȧ). Bul.	42.1 N	23.5 E
129	Gorna-Orekhovica (gôr'nȧ-ôr-yĕk'ô-vē-tsȧ). Bul.	43.7 N	25.41 E
129	Gornji-Milanovac (gôrn'yē-mē'lȧ-nô-väts). Yugo.	44.2 N	20.29 E
112	Gorodets (gôr'ô-dyĕts)...Sov. Un.	56.40 N	43.30 E
131	Gorodnya (gô-rôd''nyȧ)..Sov. Un.	51.53 N	31.31 E
130	Gorodok (gō-rô-dôk')....Sov. Un.	55.27 N	29.58 E
166	Goroke (gō-rō'kē)....Austl.	36.43 S	141.27 E
131	Gorokhovka (gô'rô-kôf'kȧ) Sov. Un.	50.7 N	40.5 E
160	Gorontalo (gō-rōn-tä'lō). Neth. Ind.	0.51 N	123.0 E
160	Gorontalo (Tomini) G. of (tō-mē'nê) Neth. Ind.	0.0	122.0 E
119	Gorton (gôr'tŭn) Gt. Brit. (Liverpool In.)	53.28 N	2.8 W
167	Gosford (gŏz'fŭrd)....Austl.	33.24 S	151.21 E
84	Goshen (gō'shĕn)....Ind.	41.36 N	85.49 W
72	Goshen....Wash. (Vancouver In.)	48.51 N	122.20 W
75	Goshute Ind. Res. (gō-shōōt') Utah	39.50 N	114.0 W
122	Goslar (gŏs'lär)....Ger.	51.55 N	10.25 E
128	Gospić (gôs'pĭch)....Yugo.	44.32 N	15.23 E
129	Gostivar (gôs'tē-vär)....Yugo.	41.46 N	20.57 E
123	Gostyń (gôs'tĭn-y')....Pol.	51.52 N	17.1 E
123	Gostynin (gôs-tē'nĭn)....Pol.	52.25 N	19.31 E
120	Götaälv (R.) (yû'tȧ-ĕlv)....Swe.	58.10 N	12.8 E
120	Göta Canal (yû'tȧ)....Swe.	58.38 N	15.25 E
120	Göteborg (yû'tĕ-bôrgh)....Swe.	57.41 N	11.58 E
94	Gotera (San Francisco) (gō-tā'rä) Sal.	13.47 N	88.7 W
122	Gotha (gō'tȧ)....Ger.	50.57 N	10.42 E
78	Gothenburg (gŏth'ĕn-bûrg)...Neb.	40.56 N	100.9 W
159	Gotō Is. (gō'tō)....Jap.	32.50 N	128.50 E
121	Gotska Sand I. (gŏt'skȧ sänd') Swe.	58.23 N	19.15 E
122	Göttingen (gût'ĭng-ĕn)....Ger.	51.32 N	9.55 E
120	Gottland (I.) (gŏt'lănd)....Swe.	57.30 N	18.30 E
117	Gouda (gou'dä)....Neth.	52.0 N	4.45 E
6	Gough I. (gŏf)....Atl. O.	39.20 S	11.10 W
167	Goulburn (gōl'bŭrn)....Austl.	34.46 S	149.42 E
167	Goulburn R....Austl.	36.45 S	145.10 E
138	Goumbou (gōōm-bōō')..Fr. W. Afr.	15.2 N	7.34 W
138	Goundam (gōōn-däN')..Fr. W. Afr.	16.30 N	3.40 W
138	Gouré (gōō-rā')....Fr. W. Afr.	13.57 N	10.40 E
142	Gouritz R. (gou'rĭts)....U. S. Afr.	33.50 S	21.40 E
124	Gournay (gōōr-nĕ')....Fr.	49.28 N	1.45 E
167	Gourock Range (gōōr'ŏk)...Austl.	35.50 S	149.30 E
85	Gouverneur (gŭv-ẽr-nōōr')..N. Y.	44.20 N	75.28 W
104	Governor's I. (gŭv'ẽr-nẽrz) Braz. (In.)	22.48 S	43.12 W
88	Governors I....N. Y. (N. Y. In.)	40.41 N	74.1 W
72	Gowanda (gô-wŏn'dȧ) Colo. (Denver In.)	40.12 N	104.55 W
85	Gowanda....N. Y.	42.30 N	78.56 W
116	Gowna, L. (gō'nȧ)....Ire.	53.50 N	7.35 W
169	Gowrie (gour'rē)....Austl. (In.)	27.28 S	151.53 E
104	Goya (gō'yä)....Arg.	29.10 S	59.15 W
118	Goyt, R. (goit)....Gt. Brit.	53.21 N	2.0 W
7	Gozo (I.) (gŏt'sō) Medit. Sea (Maltese Is. In.)	36.3 N	14.15 E
143	Graaff-Reinet (gräf'-rī'nĕt) U. S. Afr.	32.14 S	24.32 E
119	Graauw (grou). Neth. (Anvers In.)	51.20 N	4.6 E
128	Gračac (grä'chäts)....Yugo.	44.17 N	15.51 E
129	Gračanica (grä-chän'ĭ-tsä)...Yugo.	44.42 N	18.20 E
76	Graceville (grās'vĭl)....Minn.	45.33 N	96.27 W
82	Graceville....Fla.	30.59 N	85.32 W
94	Gracias (grä'syäs)....Hond.	14.32 N	88.44 W
95	Gracias a Dios, C....Nic.	15.0 N	83.0 W
138	Graciosa I. (grä-sê-ō'zȧ) Az. Is. (In.)	39.0 N	28.0 W
7	Graciosa I....Az. Is. (In.)	39.3 N	28.0 W
129	Gradačac (grȧ-dä'chats)....Yugo.	44.52 N	18.28 E
126	Gradefes (grä-dhä'fäs')....Sp.	42.38 N	5.16 W
131	Gradizhsk (grä-dēzhsk')..Sov. Un.	49.11 N	33.2 E
126	Grado (grä'dō)....Sp.	43.23 N	6.3 W
167	Grafton (gräf'tŭn)....Austl.	29.42 S	152.58 E
87	Grafton....Mass. (In.)	42.12 N	71.41 W
76	Grafton....N. D.	48.25 N	97.23 W
85	Grafton....W. Va.	39.19 N	80.1 W

ng-sing; ŋ-baŋk; N-nasalized n; nŏd; cŏmmit; ōld; ôbey; ôrder; fōōd; fŏŏt; ou-out; s-soft; sh-dish; th-thin; pūre; ûnite; ûrn; stŭd; circŭs; ü-as "y" in study; '-indeterminate vowel.

Page	Name Pronunciation Region	Lat. °′	Long. °′
99	Grafton Is... Chl. (Magallanes In.)	54.10 S	73.20 W
83	Graham (grā'ăm)...N. C.	36.4 N	79.24 W
78	Graham...Tex.	33.8 N	98.35 W
83	Graham...Va.	37.34 N	81.18 W
49	Graham...Wash. (Seattle In.)	47.3 N	122.16 W
54	Graham I....Can.	53.30 N	130.15 W
143	Grahamstown...U. S. Afr.	33.19 S	26.31 E
128	Graian Alps (Mts.) (grā'yăn) It.-Fr.	45.28 N	7.15 E
131	Graivoron (grä'ĭ-vô-rōn'). Sov. Un.	50.28 N	35.41 E
103	Grajahu (grá-zhä'ōō)...Braz.	5.58 S	43.29 W
103	Grajahu, R....Braz.	5.0 S	46.0 W
123	Grajewo (grä-yā'vō)...Pol.	53.38 N	22.27 E
129	Gramada (grä'mä-dä)...Bul.	43.46 N	22.41 E
128	Grammichele (gräm-mê-kĕ'lā)...It.	37.14 N	14.37 E
166	Grampians (grăm'pĭ-ănz)...Austl.	37.4 S	142.32 E
116	Grampians (Mts.)...Gt. Brit.	56.50 N	4.20 W
166	Grampians (Mts.), The...Austl.	37.15 S	142.25 E
94	Granada (grä-nä'dhä)...Nic.	11.56 N	85.58 W
126	Granada...Sp.	37.11 N	3.36 W
81	Granbury (grăn'bĕr-ĭ)...Tex.	32.27 N	97.46 W
86	Granby (grăn'bĭ)...Can.	45.25 N	72.45 W
79	Granby...Mo.	36.55 N	94.15 W
138	Gran Canaria (I.) (grän' kä-nä'rê-ä). Can. Is.	28.0 N	15.30 W
103	Gran Chaco (Mts.) (grän chä'kō) Par.	22.0 S	61.45 W
97	Gran Cordillera Central (Cibao Mts.) (grän côr-dêl-yā'rȧ sĕn-träl') (sê-bä'ō). Hai.	18.53 N	70.30 W
86	Grande Baie (gränd bā')...Can.	48.17 N	70.51 W
87	Grand Bank...Newf.	47.5 N	55.45 W
138	Grand Bassam (grän bȧ-sän') Fr. W. Afr.	5.15 N	3.47 W
95	Grand Bourg (grän bōōr') Guad. (In.)	15.54 N	61.19 W
97	Grand Caicos I. (grănd kä-ē'kōs) Ba. Is.	21.48 N	71.44 W
156	Grand Canal (Yun R.) (yōōn) Chn.	35.50 N	116.10 E
75	Grand Canyon...Ariz.	36.3 N	112.8 W
75	Grand Canyon Natl. Mon....Ariz.	36.20 N	112.55 W
75	Grand Canyon Natl. Park...Ariz.	36.15 N	112.20 W
96	Grand Cayman (I.) (kā'măn) W. I.	19.18 N	81.15 W
96	Grande Cay (I.) (grän'dā)...Cuba	20.59 N	79.11 W
70	Grand Coulee Dam (kōō'lē). Wash.	47.58 N	118.58 W
93	Grande de Chiapas, R. (grän'dā dā chê-ä'päs) (chê-äp'ä) Mex.	16.40 N	93.0 W
94	Grande de Otoro (grän'dȧ dā ô-tō'rô). Hond.	14.36 N	88.14 W
103	Grande, R. (grän'dĕ)...Braz.	20.0 S	48.0 W
99	Grande, R. (grän'dā) Chl.-Arg. (Magallanes In.)	53.55 S	68.40 W
58	Grande, R....U. S.-Mex.	30.0 N	104.45 W
138	Grand Erg Occidental (ûrg)...Alg.	30.0 N	1.0 E
138	Grand Erg Oriental...Alg.	30.0 N	7.0 E
97	Grande Rivière du Nord (gränd' rē-vyâr' dü nôr'). Hai.	19.35 N	72.10 W
70	Grande Ronde R. (grănd rŏnd') Ore.	45.45 N	117.45 W
95	Grande Terre (I.) (gränd têr') Guad. (In.)	16.20 N	61.28 W
89	Grande Terre I. La. (New Orleans In.)	29.18 N	89.51 W
95	Grande Vigie Point (Gränd vē-gē'). Guad. (In.)	16.30 N	61.28 W
86	Grand Falls...Can.	47.0 N	67.47 W
87	Grand Falls...Newf.	48.58 N	55.39 W
83	Grandfather Mt....N. C.	36.6 N	81.49 W
78	Grandfield (grănd'fēld)...Okla.	34.14 N	98.41 W
70	Grand Forks...Can.	49.3 N	118.28 W
76	Grand Forks...N. D.	47.55 N	97.2 W
124	Grand-Fougeray (grän-fōōzh'-rĕ'). Fr.	47.44 N	1.41 W
84	Grand Haven (grănd hā'v'n) Mich.	43.3 N	86.14 W
89	Grand I. (grănd) La. (New Orleans In.)	30.9 N	89.26 W
77	Grand I....Mich.	46.30 N	86.40 W
78	Grand Island...Neb.	40.56 N	98.20 W
88	Grand I... N. Y. (Niagara Falls In.)	43.1 N	78.57 W
88	Grand Island N. Y. (Niagara Falls In.)	42.59 N	78.57 W
89	Grand I. Pass La.-Miss. (New Orleans In.)	30.10 N	89.26 W
89	Grand Isle.. La. (New Orleans In.)	29.14 N	89.57 W
75	Grand Junction...Colo.	39.3 N	108.32 W
138	Grand Lahou (grän lȧ-ōō') Fr. W. Afr.	58.0 N	5.0 W
86	Grand L....Can.	45.58 N	66.2 W
89	Grand L.... La. (New Orleans In.)	29.45 N	89.51 W
81	Grand L....La.	29.55 N	92.45 W
81	Grand L....La.	30.0 N	91.30 W
86	Grand L....Me.	45.15 N	67.52 W
87	Grand L....Newf.	48.50 N	57.35 W
84	Grand Ledge...Mich.	42.45 N	84.47 W
124	Grand-Lieu, L. de (grän'-lyû)..Fr.	47.5 N	1.40 W
86	Grand Manan I. (mă-năn)...Can.	44.45 N	66.48 W
86	Grand Mère (grän mâr')...Can.	46.34 N	72.41 W
126	Grândola (grän'dô-lȧ)...Port.	38.11 N	8.36 W
89	Grand Pass. La. (New Orleans In.)	29.16 N	89.54 W
56	Grand Pointe (grănd point') Can. (Winnipeg In.)	49.47 N	97.2 W
138	Grand-Popo (grän'-pô-pô') Fr. W. Afr.	6.28 N	1.56 E
84	Grand Rapids (răp'ĭdz)...Mich.	43.0 N	85.42 W
77	Grand Rapids...Minn.	47.15 N	93.32 W
85	Grand R....Can.	43.7 N	80.0 W
77	Grand R....Ia.	41.0 N	94.5 W
84	Grand R....Mich.	43.0 N	85.0 W
79	Grand R....Mo.	39.44 N	93.30 W
94	Grand, R. (Matagalpa) (mä-tä-gäl'pä). Nic.	13.0 N	84.10 W
76	Grand R....S. D.	45.40 N	101.20 W
76	Grand R., North Fork...S. D.	45.56 N	102.50 W
76	Grand R., South Fork...S. D.	45.40 N	102.50 W
71	Grand Teton Mt. (grănd tē'tŏn) Wyo.	43.45 N	110.48 W
71	Grand Teton Natl. Park...Wyo.	43.45 N	110.48 W
84	Grand Traverse B. (trăv'ērs.) Mich.	45.0 N	85.30 W
97	Grand Turk I. (tûrk)...Ba. Is.	21.28 N	71.8 W
118	Grange-over-Sands (grānj) Gt. Brit.	54.11 N	2.55 W
169	Grange, The.. Austl. (Adelaide In.)	34.54 S	138.30 E
71	Granger (grān'jēr)...Wyo.	41.37 N	109.59 W
70	Grangeville (grānj'vĭl)...Ida.	45.56 N	116.9 W
79	Granite City...Ill.	38.43 N	90.9 W
76	Granite Falls...Minn.	44.48 N	95.32 W
83	Granite Falls...N. C.	35.48 N	81.25 W
71	Granite Peak (grăn'ĭt)...Mont.	45.12 N	109.46 W
83	Graniteville...S. C.	33.33 N	81.49 W
103	Granito (grä-nē'tō)...Braz.	7.38 S	39.45 W
126	Granja de Torrehermosa (grän'hä dā tôr'rā-ĕr-mō'sä)..Sp.	38.21 N	5.35 W
120	Grānna (grĕn'ȧ)...Swe.	58.1 N	14.28 E
127	Granollérs (grä-nôl-yĕrs')...Sp.	41.37 N	2.28 E
75	Gran Quivira Natl. Mon. (grän kê-vē'rä). N. M.	34.11 N	106.5 W
116	Grantham (grăn'tăm)...Gt. Brit.	52.55 N	0.40 W
46	Grant Land (Reg.) (grănt)...Can.	82.0 N	80.0 W
70	Grants Pass...Ore.	42.27 N	123.20 W
73	Grantsville Utah (Salt Lake City In.)	40.36 N	112.28 W
125	Granvillars (grän-vē-yär')...Fr.	47.35 N	7.0 E
124	Granville (grän-vēl')...Fr.	48.51 N	1.32 W
85	Granville (grăn'vĭl)...N. Y.	43.26 N	73.18 W
54	Granville L....Can.	56.30 N	100.30 W
103	Grão Mogol (groun' mōō-gôl') Braz.	16.32 S	42.48 W
49	Grapeview (grāp'vu) Wash. (Seattle In.)	47.20 N	122.50 W
120	Gräs I. (grĕs)...Swe.	60.24 N	18.25 E
122	Graslitz (Kraslice) (gräs'lĭts) (kräs'lê-tsĕ). Ger.	50.19 N	12.29 E
91	Grass Cay (I.)... St. Thomas (In.)	18.22 N	64.50 W
125	Grasse (gräs)...Fr.	43.40 N	6.55 E
73	Grasselli (grä-sĕl'ĭ) Ala. (Birmingham In.)	33.27 N	86.54 W
89	Grass L... Minn. (Minneapolis In.)	44.53 N	93.15 W
85	Grass R....N. Y.	44.40 N	75.10 W
74	Grass Valley...Calif.	39.12 N	121.4 W
87	Grates Pt. (grāts)...Newf.	48.10 N	52.55 W
124	Graulhet (grō-lĕ')...Fr.	43.45 N	1.59 E
119	Gravenwezel (Kräv'ĕn-vā'zĕl) Bel. (Anvers In.)	51.16 N	4.33 E
169	Gravesend (grāvz'ĕnd)...Austl.	29.35 S	150.22 E
117	Gravesend...Gt. Brit.	51.25 N	0.20 E
88	Gravesend B.. N.Y. (New York In.)	40.35 N	74.0 W
128	Gravina (grä-vē'nä)...It.	40.48 N	16.27 E
97	Gravois, Pt. (grȧ-vwä')...Hai.	18.2 N	73.53 W
125	Gray (grȧ)...Fr.	47.27 N	5.37 E
84	Grayling (grā'lĭng)...Mich.	44.40 N	84.40 W
87	Gray (Little) R....Newf.	48.0 N	56.55 W
119	Grays (grāz) Gt. Brit. (London In.)	51.28 N	0.20 E
70	Grays Harbor...Wash.	46.55 N	124.10 W
71	Grays L....Ida.	43.3 E	111.25 W
73	Grayson (grā'sŭn) Ga. (Atlanta In.)	33.55 N	83.58 W
78	Grays Peak (grāz)...Colo.	39.30 N	105.52 W
49	Grays River. Wash. (Portland In.)	46.21 N	123.36 W
73	Graysville.. Ala. (Birmingham In.)	33.37 N	86.59 W
122	Graz (grāts)...Ger.	47.4 N	15.25 E
96	Great Abaco I. (ä'bä-kō)...Ba. Is.	26.20 N	77.10 W
164	Great Australian Bight...Austl.	33.30 S	130.0 E
96	Great Bahama Bank (bȧ-hā'mȧ) Atl. O.	24.0 N	78.40 W
170	Great Barrier I. (băr'ĭ-ēr)...N. Z.	36.12 S	175.25 E
165	Great Barrier Reef...Austl.	18.0 S	147.30 E
58	Great Basin...Nev.	39.0 N	116.30 W
54	Great Bear L....Can.	66.0 N	120.30 W
120	Great Belt (Str.)...Den.	55.25 N	10.55 E
78	Great Bend...Kan.	38.21 N	98.47 W
142	Great Berg R. (bĕrg)... U. S. Afr.	33.0 S	18.56 E
135	Great Bitter L. Eg. (Suez Canal In.)	30.21 N	32.24 E
116	Great Blasket I. (blăs'kĕt)...Ire.	52.5 N	10.35 W
116	Great Britain (brĭt''n)...Eur.	54.0 N	2.0 W
119	Great Budworth (bŭd'wûrth) Gt. Brit. (Liverpool In.)	53.18 N	2.30 W
140	Great Cataract (Waterfall) (căt'ȧ-răkt) S. W. Afr.	17.18 S	14.30 E
85	Great Chazy R. (shā-sē')...N. Y.	44.55 N	73.40 W
141	Great Comoro I. (kŏm'ô-rō). Ind. O.	11.40 S	43.15 E
119	Great Crosby (krôz'bĭ) Gt. Brit. (Liverpool In.)	53.30 N	3.1 W
138	Great Eastern Dunes, The (El Erg)...Alg.	30.0 N	7.0 E
135	Great Europa Pt. (û-rō'pȧ) Gib. (In.)	36.7 N	5.40 E
97	Great Exuma I. (ĕk-sōō'mä) Ba. Is.	23.35 N	75.55 W
71	Great Falls...Mont.	47.31 N	111.18 W
83	Great Falls...S. C.	34.33 N	80.54 W
6	Great Fiji (Viti Levu) (I.) (fē'jē) (vē'tê lā'vōō). Fiji Is. (In.)	17.48 S	178.0 E
143	Great Fish Pt....U. S. Afr.	33.30 S	27.10 E
143	Great Fish R....U. S. Afr.	33.4 S	26.0 E
142	Great Fish R....S. W. Afr.	27.20 S	17.41 E
167	Great Glennie Is. (glĕn'ĭ)...Austl.	39.5 S	146.15 E
97	Great Guana Cay (I.) (gwä'nä) Ba. Is.	24.3 N	76.22 W
96	Great Harbor Cay (I.)...Ba. Is.	25.45 N	77.53 W
97	Great Inagua I. (ê-nä'gwä). Ba. Is.	21.5 N	73.20 W
96	Great Isaac I. (ī'zȧk)...Ba. Is.	26.3 N	79.6 W
142	Great Karaz Mts. (kär'ȧz) S. W. Afr.	27.15 S	18.40 E
143	Great Kei R. (kī)...U. S. Afr.	32.18 S	27.40 E
88	Great Kills (Inlet) N. Y. (New York In.)	40.33 N	74.8 W
169	Great L....Austl. (Tas. In.)	41.54 S	146.46 E
140	Great Makari Kari Salt Pan (Dry L.) (mä-kä'rê kä'rê). Bech.	20.45 S	26.15 E
170	Great Mercury I. (mûr'kû-rĭ) N. Z.	36.35 S	175.50 E
87	Great Miquelon I. (mĭk-ē-lôn') N. A.	47.5 N	56.20 W
142	Great Namaqualand (Reg.) (nä-mä'kwä-lănd). S. W. Afr.	26.15 S	18.0 E
160	Great Paternoster (Tenga) Is. (pā'tēr-nŏs-tēr) (tĕŋ'gȧ) Neth. Ind.	7.35 S	117.30 E
97	Great Ragged I....Ba. Is.	22.11 N	75.44 W
128	Great St. Bernard Pass (sānt bēr-närd'). It.	45.50 N	7.10 E
96	Great Sale Cay (I.)...Ba. Is.	27.1 N	78.11 W
71	Great Salt L....Utah	41.15 N	112.40 W
71	Great Salt Lake Des....Utah	41.20 N	113.30 W
75	Great Sand Dunes Natl. Mon. Colo.	37.45 N	105.45 W
164	Great Sandy Des....Austl.	21.30 S	125.0 E
150	Great Sandy Des. (Dahna or Rub al Khali) (dä'nä; rōōb äl Kä'lê). Asia	20.0 N	52.0 E
165	Great Sandy (Fraser) I. (frā'zēr) Austl.	25.0 S	153.5 E
127	Great Sebkha (Basin) (sĕb'Kȧ) Alg.	35.35 N	0.50 W
54	Great Slave L....Can.	61.30 N	114.30 W
82	Great Smoky Mountains Natl. Park...N. C.	35.35 N	83.30 W
96	Great Stirrup Cay (I.) (stĭr'ŭp) Ba. Is.	25.49 N	77.55 W
164	Great Victoria Des. (vĭk-tō'rĭ-ȧ) Austl.	29.30 S	127.0 E
119	Great Wakering (wāk'ēr-ĭng) Gt. Brit. (London In.)	51.35 N	0.48 E
153	Great Wall...Chn.	41.0 N	115.30 E
119	Great Warley (wôr'lĭ) Gr. Brit. (London In.)	51.36 N	0.17 E
138	Great Western Dunes, The (El Erg) (ĕl ĕrg')...Alg.	30.0 N	1.0 E
169	Great Western Range Austl. (Tas. In.)	41.50 S	147.0 E
55	Great Whale R....Can.	55.15 N	7.6 W
118	Great Whernside (Mt.) (whērn'sīd). Gt. Brit.	54.11 N	1.59 W
117	Great Yarmouth (yär'mŭth) Gt. Brit.	52.35 N	1.45 E
120	Grebbestad (grĕb-bĕ-städh)...Swe.	58.42 N	11.14 E
126	Gredos, Sierra de (Mt.) (syĕr'rä dā grā'dōs). Sp.	40.15 N	5.10 W
129	Greece (grēs)...Eur.	39.30 N	22.30 E
73	Greeley (grē'lĭ) Ala. (Birmingham In.)	33.17 N	87.8 W
78	Greeley...Colo.	40.26 N	104.43 W
77	Green B....Wis.-Mich.	45.0 N	87.30 W
77	Green Bay...Wis.	44.31 N	88.1 W
81	Green Bayou...Tex. (In.)	29.48 N	95.12 W
96	Green Cay (I.)...Ba. Is.	24.1 N	77.12 W
84	Greencastle...Ind.	39.38 N	86.49 W
83	Green Cove Springs...Fla.	29.57 N	81.41 W
82	Greeneville...Tenn.	36.9 N	82.52 W
119	Greenfield. Gt. Brit. (Liverpool In.)	53.18 N	31.9 W
84	Greenfield...Ind.	39.46 N	85.42 W
77	Greenfield...Ia.	41.15 N	94.29 W
86	Greenfield...Mass.	42.35 N	72.38 W
79	Greenfield...Mo.	37.24 N	93.49 W
84	Greenfield...Ohio	39.20 N	83.26 W
82	Greenfield...Tenn.	36.8 N	88.48 W
171	Green I....N. Z. (In.)	45.54 S	170.25 E
163	Green Island B....P. I.	10.15 N	119.22 E
48	Greenland (grēn'lănd)...N. A.	74.0 N	40.0 W
48	Greenland Sea...Grnld.	75.30 N	10.0 W
87	Greenly I. (grēn'lê)...Newf.	51.22 N	57.5 W
72	Green Mt.... Colo. (Denver In.)	39.43 N	105.11 W
72	Green Mountain Falls Colo. (Colo. Sprs. In.)	38.56 N	105.1 W
86	Green Mts....Vt.	44.10 N	72.50 W
116	Greenock (grēn'ŭk)...Gt. Brit.	55.55 N	4.45 W
116	Greenore Pt. (grē-nôr')...Ire.	52.15 N	6.20 W
169	Green Pt....Austl. (Tas. In.)	40.53 S	144.40 E
141	Green Point...U. S. Afr.	33.53 S	18.24 E
73	Green Pond. Ala. (Birmingham In.)	33.14 N	87.8 W
82	Green R....Ky.	37.15 N	86.0 W
76	Green R....N. D.	47.0 N	103.0 W
58	Green R....U. S.	40.0 N	109.45 W
71	Green R....Wash.	47.15 N	121.40 W
75	Greenriver...Utah	38.59 N	110.9 W
71	Green River...Wyo.	41.33 N	109.28 W
82	Greensboro...Ala.	32.42 N	87.36 W
82	Greensboro...Ga.	33.34 N	83.12 W
83	Greensboro...N. C.	36.4 N	79.46 W
84	Greensburg...Ind.	39.18 N	85.30 W
78	Greensburg...Kan.	37.36 N	99.18 W
85	Greensburg...Pa.	40.18 N	79.32 W
82	Greenville...Ala.	31.49 N	86.39 W
79	Greenville...Ill.	38.53 N	89.24 W
82	Greenville...Ky.	37.13 N	87.12 W
138	Greenville...Lib.	5.3 N	8.45 W
86	Greenville...Me.	45.27 N	69.36 W
84	Greenville...Mich.	43.11 N	85.22 W
82	Greenville...Miss.	33.25 N	91.3 W
83	Greenville...N. C.	35.35 N	77.22 W
84	Greenville...Ohio	40.7 N	84.39 W
84	Greenville...Pa.	41.26 N	80.26 W
83	Greenville...S. C.	34.51 N	82.24 W
79	Greenville...Tex.	33.09 N	96.07 W
119	Greenwich (grēn'wĭch) (grĕn'ĭch) Gt. Brit. (London In.)	51.29 N	0.0
79	Greenwood...Ark.	35.13 N	94.15 W
83	Greenwood...Ga.	34.11 N	82.9 W
84	Greenwood...Ind.	39.37 N	86.8 W
82	Greenwood...Miss.	33.30 N	90.10 W
83	Greer (grēr)...S. C.	34.56 N	82.12 W
76	Gregory (grĕg'ô-rĭ)...S. D.	43.13 N	99.26 W
164	Gregory, L. (grĕg'ô-rê)...Austl.	29.15 S	139.30 E
165	Gregory Range...Austl.	19.15 S	143.15 E
122	Greifenberg (grīf'ĕn-bĕrgh)...Ger.	53.55 N	15.11 E
122	Greifenhagen (grīf'ĕn-hä-gĕn). Ger.	53.14 N	14.30 E
122	Greifswald (grīfs'vält)...Ger.	54.6 N	13.22 E
122	Greiz (grīts)...Ger.	50.40 N	12.13 E
120	Grenaa (grēn'ô)...Den.	56.24 N	10.51 E

ăt; finăl; rāte; senâte; ärm; ȧsk; sofȧ; fâre; ch-choose; dh-as th in other; bē; êvent; bĕt; recĕnt; cratēr; g-go; gh-gutteral g; bĭt; ĭ-short neutral; rīde; K-gutteral k as ch in German ich;

Page	Name Pronunciation Region	Lat. °′	Long. °′
82	Grenada (grê-nā'da)........Miss.	33.46 N	89.48 W
91	Grenada (I.)...........Wind. Is.	12.10 N	61.40 W
124	Grenade (grē-nȧd')..............Fr.	43.46 N	1.18 E
95	Grenadines, The (I.) (grĕn'ȧ-dēnz) Wind. Is. (In.)	12.45 N	61.30 W
167	Grenfell (grĕn'fĕl)..........Austl.	33.52 S	148.11 E
125	Grenoble (grē-nō'bl')..........Fr.	45.15 N	5.45 E
76	Grenora (grê-nō'rȧ)........N. D.	48.36 N	103.55 W
85	Grenville (grĕn'vĭl)..........Can.	45.37 N	74.35 W
95	Grenville.............Wind. Is.	12.7 N	61.38 W
70	Gresham (grĕsh'ăm).........Ore.	45.30 N	122.24 W
167	Greta (grē'tȧ)..............Austl.	32.42 S	151.22 E
118	Greta R..............Gt. Brit.	54.10 N	2.27 W
81	Gretna (grĕt'nȧ)..............La.	29.55 N	90.4 W
129	Grevena (grĕ'vȧ-nȧ).........Grc.	40.1 N	21.30 E
71	Greybull (grā'bŏŏl)..........Wyo.	44.30 N	108.5 W
71	Greybull R..............Wyo.	44.10 N	108.52 W
143	Greylingstad (grā'lĭng-stȧd) U. S. Afr.	26.49 S	28.46 E
171	Greymouth (grā'mouth).....N. Z.	42.28 S	171.15 E
165	Grey Range (grā).........Austl.	27.30 S	143.30 E
171	Grey R..................N. Z.	42.22 S	171.30 E
142	Greyton (grā'tŭn)......U. S. Afr.	34.4 S	19.36 E
171	Greytown (grā'toun).........N. Z.	41.7 S	175.28 E
95	Greytown (San Juan del Norte) Nic.	10.56 N	83.46 W
143	Greytown............U. S. Afr.	29.55 S	30.35 E
74	Gridley (grĭd'lĭ)............Calif.	39.22 N	121.42 W
82	Griffin (grĭf'ĭn)..............Ga.	33.15 N	84.17 W
167	Griffith (grĭf'ĭth)...........Austl.	34.14 S	146.4 E
131	Grigorievka (grĭ'gôr-ĭ-yĕf'kȧ) Sov. Un.	48.7 N	36.4 E
131	Grigoriopol (grĭ'gôr-ĭ-ô'pôl) Sov. Un.	47.8 N	29.18 E
93	Grijalva, R. (grē-hăl'vȧ)....Mex.	18.0 N	92.50 W
160	Grim, C. (grĭm)..Austl. (Tas. In.)	40.39 S	144.43 E
122	Grimma (grĭm'ȧ)............Ger.	51.14 N	12.43 E
116	Grimsby (grĭmz'bĭ)......Gt. Brit.	53.32 N	0.5 W
110	Grimsey (I.) (grĭms'ȧ)........Ice.	66.42 N	18.0 W
120	Grimstad (grĭm-stȧdh).........Nor.	58.21 N	8.32 E
77	Grinnell (grĭ-nĕl')..............Ia.	41.45 N	92.42 W
119	Grinzing (grĕntz'ĭng) Aus. (Wien In.)	48.15 N	16.20 E
142	Griqualand West (Reg.) (grēk'-wȧ-lănd).Bech.	28.35 S	23.0 E
142	Griquatown (grē'kwȧ-toun).Bech.	28.50 S	23.18 E
131	Grishino (grĕsh'ê-nō).....Sov. Un.	48.19 N	37.4 E
77	Griswold (grĭz'wŭld)..........Ia.	41.13 N	95.5 W
121	Griva (grē'vȧ)...............Lat.	55.52 N	26.32 E
87	Groats I. (grōts)...........Newf.	50.55 N	55.35 W
121	Grobini (grō'bĭ-nê)...........Lat.	56.32 N	21.13 E
123	Gródek Jagiellonsk (grōō'dĕk yȧ-gyĕ-lôn'sk').Pol.	49.46 N	23.40 E
123	Grodno (grôd'nō)..............Pol.	53.40 N	23.50 E
123	Grodzisk (grô'jĕsk)............Pol.	52.6 N	20.40 E
122	Grodzisk.....................Pol.	52.14 N	16.22 E
142	Groen R. (grōōn).......U. S. Afr.	30.45 S	17.50 E
142	Groen Water R...........Bech.	28.38 S	22.50 E
81	Groesbeck (grōs'bĕk)..........Tex.	31.32 N	96.31 W
124	Groix, I. de (ēl dē grwȧ')......Fr.	47.39 N	3.30 W
123	Grójec (grōō'yĕts)..............Pol.	51.52 N	20.52 E
135	Grombalia (grôm-bȧ'lē-ȧ) Tun. (In.)	36.35 N	10.25 E
122	Gronau (grō'nou)............Ger.	52.12 N	7.2 E
122	Groningen (grō'nĭng-ĕn)....Neth.	53.12 N	6.35 E
142	Grootdrink (grōt'drĭnk).U. S. Afr.	28.32 S	21.44 E
164	Groote Eylandt (I.) (grō'tē ī'lȧnt) Austl.	14.0 S	136.45 E
143	Groote R. (grō'tē)......U. S. Afr.	33.20 S	24.20 E
143	Groote River Heights...U. S. Afr.	33.13 S	24.25 E
140	Grootfontein (grōt'fŏn-tān') S. W. Afr.	19.40 S	18.12 E
143	Grootvlei (grōt'vlĭ).....U. S. Afr.	26.52 S	28.38 E
142	Groot Vloer (L.) (grōt' vlōōr') U. S. Afr.	29.55 S	20.45 E
142	Groot Zwartberg (grōt zvȧrt'bĕrg) U. S. Afr.	33.21 S	22.20 E
125	Groslay (grō-lĕ').........Fr. (In.)	48.58 N	2.21 E
87	Gros Morne, Mt.(grō môrn') Newf.	49.35 N	57.45 W
56	Grosse Isle (grōs il') Can. (Winnipeg In.)	50.3 N	97.26 W
84	Grosse Pointe (grōs point')..Mich.	42.24 N	82.57 W
128	Grosseto (grôs-sā'tō)............It.	42.46 N	10.8 E
119	Grossflottbek (grōs-flôt'bĕk) Ger. (Hamburg In.)	53.34 N	9.53 E
119	Gross Ziethen (tsē'tĕn) Ger. (Berlin In.)	52.24 N	13.27 E
71	Gros Ventre R. (grōvĕn't'r)..Wyo.	43.38 N	110.30 W
122	Groszenhain (grōs'ĕn-hīn)....Ger.	51.17 N	13.32 E
119	Groszglienicke (grōs'glē'nĭ-kē) Ger. (Berlin In.)	52.28 N	13.7 E
122	Grosz Glockner (Mt.) (grōs glôk'nĕr).Aus.	47.4 N	12.43 E
123	Groszstrehlitz (grōs'shtrā'lĭts).Ger.	50.30 N	18.20 E
85	Groton (grôt'ŭn)...........Conn.	41.20 N	72.4 W
87	Groton..............Mass. (In.)	42.37 N	71.34 W
76	Groton....................S. D.	45.27 N	98.5 W
129	Grottaglie (grōt-tȧl'yȧ)........It.	40.32 N	17.26 E
87	Groveland (grōv'lănd).Mass. (In.)	42.46 N	71.1 W
86	Groveton (grōv'tŭn)........N. H.	44.35 N	71.32 W
81	Groveton....................Tex.	31.4 N	95.8 W
113	Grozny (grôz'nĭ)..........Sov. Un.	43.20 N	45.42 E
123	Grudziadz (grōō'jyônts)........Pol.	53.29 N	18.48 E
122	Grünberg (grün'bĕrgh)..........Ger.	51.57 N	15.31 E
77	Grundy Center (grŭn'dĭ).......Ia.	42.21 N	92.35 W
119	Grünendeich (grü'nĕn-dīk) Ger. (Hamburg In.)	53.34 N	9.37 E
92	Gruñidora (grōō-nyê-dô'rō)..Mex.	24.5 N	101.54 W
130	Gryazi (gryȧ'zĭ)..........Sov. Un.	52.30 N	39.57 E
130	Gryazovaya (gryȧz'ô-vȧ-yȧ) Sov. Un.	58.52 N	40.12 E
95	Guabito (gwȧ-bē'tô)...........Pan.	9.30 N	82.37 W
96	Guacanayabo, G. of (gwȧ-kȧ-nȧ-yȧ'bō).Cuba	20.30 N	77.35 W
126	Guadajira R. (gwȧ-dhȧ-kē'rȧ)..Sp.	38.30 N	6.30 W
92	Guadalajara (gwȧ-dhȧ-lȧ-hȧ'rȧ) Mex.	20.40 N	103.20 W
126	Guadalajara..................Sp.	40.38 N	3.10 W
126	Guadalaviar R. (gwȧ'dhȧ-lȧ-vê-ȧr').Sp.	40.0 N	1.16 W
126	Guadalcanal (gwȧ-dhȧl-kȧ-nȧl')Sp.	38.5 N	5.49 W
165	Guadal Cañal (I.) (gwȧ-dhȧl' kȧ-nyȧr').Solomon Is.	9.38 S	160.0 E
92	Guadalcázar (gwȧ-dhȧl-kȧ'zȧr) Mex.	22.38 N	100.22 W
126	Guadalete R. (gwȧ-dhȧ-lā'tȧ)..Sp.	36.45 N	5.48 W
126	Guadalhorce R. (gwȧ-dhȧl-ôr'thȧ) Sp.	37.0 N	4.45 W
126	Guadalimar R. (gwȧ-dhȧ-lē-mȧr') Sp.	38.10 N	3.10 W
126	Guadalquivir R. (gwȧ-dhȧl-kê-vēr').Sp.	38.2 N	4.0 W
92	Guadalupe (gwȧ-dhȧ-lōō'pȧ).Mex.	22.45 N	102.30 W
93	Guadalupe Hidalgo (ē-dȧl'gō) Mex. (In.)	19.29 N	99.7 W
6	Guadalupe I. (gwȧ-dȧ-lōō'pȧ) Pac. O.	29.0 N	120.0 E
80	Guadalupe Mts..............Tex.	31.40 N	104.40 W
127	Guadalupe R.................Sp.	40.50 N	0.15 W
80	Guadalupe R..................Tex.	29.53 N	98.30 W
93	Guadalupe, Sierra de (Mts.) Mex. (In.)	19.36 N	99.7 W
126	Guadalupe, Sierra de (Mts.) (syĕr'rȧ dȧ gwȧ-dhȧ-lōō'pȧ).Sp.	39.30 N	5.15 W
127	Guadarrama R. (gwȧ-dhȧr-rȧ'mȧ) Sp. (In.)	40.30 N	3.57 W
126	Guadarrama, Sierra de (Mts.).Sp.	40.50 N	4.0 W
91	Guadeloupe (I.) (gwȧ-dē-lōōp') W. I.	16.15 N	61.30 W
126	Guadiana alto (R.) (gwȧ-dhē-ȧ'nȧ ȧl'tō).Sp.	39.4 N	3.0 W
96	Guadiana B.................Cuba	22.6 N	84.23 W
126	Guadiana Menor R. (mā'nôr)..Sp.	37.40 N	3.0 W
126	Guadiana R...............Sp.-Port.	39.20 N	5.0 W
126	Guadiaro R. (gwȧ-dhê-ȧ'rō)....Sp.	36.30 N	5.24 W
126	Guadiato R. (gwȧ-dhê-ȧ'tō)....Sp.	38.10 N	5.15 W
126	Guadiela R. (gwȧ-dhê-ȧ'lȧ)....Sp.	40.25 N	2.30 W
126	Guadix (gwȧ-dhēsh')...........Sp.	37.18 N	3.8 W
94	Guagnali Mts. (gwȧ-nyȧ'lê)...Nic.	13.15 N	85.40 W
162	Guagua (gwȧ'gwȧ)...........P. I.	14.58 N	120.27 E
96	Guajaba Cay (I.) (gwȧ-hȧ'bȧ)Cuba	21.51 N	77.30 W
102	Guajará Falls (gwȧ-zhȧ-rȧ').Braz.	10.45 S	65.20 W
102	Guajará Mirim (mē-rēN')....Braz.	10.57 S	65.17 W
94	Gualan (gwȧ-lȧn').........Guat.	15.7 N	89.21 W
99	Gualeguay (gwȧ-lȧ-gwī') Arg. (Buenos Aires In.)	33.3 S	59.20 W
99	Gualeguay, R. Arg. (Buenos Aires In.)	33.10 S	59.20 W
104	Gualeguaychú (gwȧ-lȧ-gwī-chōō') Arg.	33.1 S	58.30 W
103	Guamá, R. (gwȧ-mȧ')..Braz. (In.)	1.30 S	48.0 W
6	Guam (I.) (gwȧm). Pac. O. (Guam. In.)	13.27 N	144.45 E
104	Guamini (gwȧ-mê-nē')........Arg.	37.8 S	62.20 W
96	Guanabacoa (gwȧ-nȧ-bȧ-kō'ȧ) Cuba	23.7 N	82.18 W
104	Guanabara B. (gwȧ-nȧ-bȧ'rȧ) Braz. (In.)	22.47 S	43.8 W
94	Guanacaste, Cordillera (Mts.) (gwȧ-nȧ-kȧs'tȧ).C. R.	10.45 N	85.10 W
96	Guanahacabibes Pen. (gwȧ'nȧ-hȧ-kȧ-bē'bȧs).Cuba	21.55 N	84.30 W
96	Guanajay (gwȧ-nȧ-hī')........Cuba	22.55 N	82.41 W
92	Guanajuato (gwȧ-nȧ-hwȧ'tō).Mex.	21.2 N	101.15 W
92	Guanajuato (State)..........Mex.	21.10 N	101.0 W
102	Guanare (gwȧ-nȧ'rȧ)........Ven.	8.59 N	69.45 W
96	Guane (gwȧ'nȧ)..............Cuba	22.10 N	84.2 W
97	Guantánamo (gwȧn-tȧ'nȧ-mô) Cuba	20.7 N	75.12 W
97	Guantánamo B...............Cuba	19.58 N	75.8 W
102	Guaporé R. (gwȧ-pô-rȧ')Bol.-Braz.	13.30 S	62.0 W
102	Guaqui (guȧ'kē)..............Bol.	16.31 S	68.45 W
103	Guarabira (gwȧ-rȧ-bē'rȧ)....Braz.	6.57 S	35.29 W
103	Guarapari (gwȧ-rȧ-pȧ'rê)....Braz.	20.31 S	40.31 W
104	Guarapuava (gwȧ-rȧ-pwȧ'vȧ)Braz.	25.20 S	51.30 W
99	Guaratinguetá (guȧ-rȧ-tĭN-gȧ-tȧ').Braz. (Rio de Janeiro In.)	22.51 S	45.12 W
126	Guarda (gwȧr'dȧ).............Port.	40.33 N	7.18 W
141	Guardafui, C. (gwȧr-dȧ-fwē') It. E. Afr.	11.50 N	51.10 E
126	Guareña (gwȧ-rā'nyȧ)..........Sp.	38.53 N	6.7 W
96	Guasipati (gwȧ-sê-pȧ'tē).....Ven.	7.15 N	61.58 W
128	Guastalla (gwȧs-tȧl'lȧ)..........It.	44.54 N	10.39 E
94	Guatemala (guȧ-tȧ-mȧ'lȧ) Cen. Am.	15.10 N	90.30 W
94	Guatemala..................Guat.	14.37 N	90.31 W
102	Guaviare, R. (gwȧ-vē-ȧ'rȧ)...Col.	3.0 N	70.30 W
104	Guaxindiba (gwȧ-shēn-dē'bȧ) Braz. (In.)	22.47 S	42.59 W
97	Guayajayuco R. (gwȧ-yȧ-hȧ-yōō'kō).Hai.	18.59 N	71.38 W
91	Guayama (gwȧ-yȧ'mȧ).P. R. (In.)	18.0 N	66.7 W
97	Guayamuco R. (gwȧ-yȧ-mōō'kō) Hai.	19.10 N	72.5 W
102	Guayaquil (gwī-ȧ-kēl')........Ec.	2.32 S	79.78 W
102	Guayaquil, G. of...............Ec.	3.0 S	80.30 W
97	Guayubin (gwī-yōō-bēn')......Hai.	19.41 N	71.26 W
94	Guazacapán (gwȧ-zȧ-kȧ-pȧn') Guat.	14.3 N	90.26 W
162	Gubat (gōō'bȧt)................P. I.	12.57 N	124.7 E
128	Gubbio (gōōb'byō)...............It.	43.12 N	12.36 E
122	Guben (gōō'bĕn)...............Ger.	51.57 N	14.43 E
127	Gúdar, Sierra de (Mts.) (syĕr'rȧ dȧ gōō'dhȧr).Sp.	40.20 N	0.40 W
120	Guden R. (gōō'dhĕn)...........Den.	56.24 N	9.30 E
120	Gudvangen (gōōdh'văŋ-gĕn)..Nor.	60.52 N	6.50 E
125	Guebwiller (gĕb-vê-lȧr')........Fr.	47.55 N	7.15 E
126	Guecho (gā'chō)...............Sp.	43.20 N	3.0 W
138	Guelma (gwĕl'mȧ)............Alg.	36.31 N	7.23 E
55	Guelph (gwĕlf)...............Can.	43.28 N	80.27 W
114	Guemar (gē-mȧr')............Alg.	33.25 N	6.4 E
124	Guéret (gā-rĕ')..................Fr.	46.10 N	1.52 E
126	Guernica y Luno (gȧr-nē'kȧ ē lōō'nō).Sp.	43.18 N	2.41 W
124	Guernsey (I.) (gûrn'zĭ) Channel Is.	49.30 N	2.35 W
114	Guerrara (gĕr-rȧ'rȧ).........Alg.	32.48 N	4.27 E
92	Guerrero (State) (gĕr-rā'rō)..Mex.	17.40 N	100.0 W
92	Guerrero.....................Mex.	22.0 N	98.46 W
80	Guerrero.....................Mex.	26.47 N	99.20 W
80	Guerrero.....................Mex.	28.20 N	100.24 W
131	Guesleve (Evpatoriya) (gwĕs-lĕf'ĕ) (yĕf-pȧ-tô'rê-yȧ)...Sov. Un.	45.11 N	33.22 E
135	Guettar, Chott el (L.) (shŏt ĕl gwĕt'tȧr).Tun. (In.)	34.17 N	9.3 E
124	Gueugnon (gû-nyôN')..........Fr.	46.35 N	4.5 E
81	Gueydan (gā'dăn)...............La.	30.2 N	92.30 W
166	Guicheu B. (gwê-chȧ'ōō).....Aus.	37.9 S	139.45 E
93	Güichicovi (San Juan) (gwē-chê-kō'vê).Mex.	16.59 N	95.5 W
128	Guidania (gwē-dȧ'nyȧ)..........It.	41.59 N	12.45 E
161	Guiguinto (gê-gēn'tō) P. I. (Manila In.)	14.50 N	120.52 E
94	Guija, L. (gē'hȧ)..............Sal.	14.16 N	89.30 W
116	Guildford (gĭl'fērd)......Gt. Brit.	51.15 N	0.35 W
124	Guilvenec (gēl-vē-nĕk')........Fr.	47.50 N	4.18 W
126	Guimarães (gē-mȧ-rȧNsh')...Port.	41.26 N	8.21 W
163	Guimaras I. (gē-mȧ-rȧs')....P. I.	10.35 N	122.37 E
163	Guimaras Str.................P. I.	10.40 N	122.50 E
163	Guimbal (gēm-bȧl')...........P. I.	10.40 N	122.19 E
163	Guindulman (gēn-dōōl'mȧn) .P. I.	9.46 N	124.30 E
96	Güines (gwē'nȧs)..............Cuba	22.51 N	82.4 W
124	Guingamp (găN-găN')...........Fr.	48.35 N	3.10 W
162	Guinobatan (gē-nô-bȧ'tȧn)..P. I.	13.12 N	123.36 E
96	Güira de Melena (gwē'rȧ dȧ mȧ-lā'nȧ).Cuba	22.47 N	82.31 W
114	Guir, Wadi (R.) (wȧ'dê gwer') Mor.-Alg.	31.48 N	3.0 W
124	Guise (guēz)...................Fr.	49.55 N	3.38 E
94	Guisisil (Vol.) (gê-sê-sēl').....Nic.	12.37 N	86.17 W
163	Guiuan (gē'wȧn).................P. I.	11.3 N	125.44 E
124	Gujan-Mestras (gü-zhȧN' mĕs-trȧ') Fr.	44.38 N	1.0 W
120	Gula (R.) (gōō'lȧ)............Nor.	63.2 N	10.20 E
120	Guldinge Fjord (gōōl'dĭng-ĕ).Swe.	57.46 N	16.36 E
82	Gulfport (gŭlf'pōrt).........Miss.	30.23 N	89.6 W
151	Gul Koh (Mts.) (gōōl'kō')....Afg.	33.12 N	67.57 E
171	Gull Rocks (gŭl).......N. Z. (In.)	45.55 S	170.41 E
131	Gulyai-Pole (gōōl-yȧ'ĭ-pôl''ĕ) ..Sov. Un.	47.39 N	36.10 E
162	Gumaca (gōō-mȧ-kȧ')........P. I.	13.55 N	122.5 E
139	Gumbari (gōōm-bȧ'rê)..Bel. Cong.	2.36 N	29.2 E
123	Gumbinnen (gōōm-bĭn'ĕn)....Ger.	54.35 N	22.12 E
122	Gummersbach (gōōm'ĕrs-bȧk) Ger.	51.3 N	7.33 E
96	Gun Cay (I.)...............Ba. Is.	25.36 N	79.20 W
167	Gundagai (gŭn'dȧ-gī)......Austl.	35.5 S	148.7 E
167	Gunnedah (gŭn'ē-dȧ).......Austl.	31.0 S	150.17 E
75	Gunnison (gŭn'ĭ-sŭn)..........Colo.	38.32 N	106.56 W
75	Gunnison....................Utah	39.7 N	111.50 W
75	Gunnison R..................Colo.	38.47 N	108.10 W
82	Guntersville (gŭn'tērz-vĭl)....Ala.	34.20 N	86.18 W
151	Guntur (gōōn'tōōr)............India	16.5 N	80.29 E
161	Gunung Api (I.) (gōō'nōōng-ȧ'pê) ...Neth. Ind.	6.38 S	126.37 E
123	Gura-Humorului (gōō'rȧ-hōō-mô'rōō-lōō-ē).Rom.	47.34 N	25.57 E
79	Gurdon (gûr'dŭn)..............Ark.	33.56 N	93.9 W
142	Gurib R. (gōō'rĭb).......S. W. Afr.	26.45 S	17.20 E
113	Gur'ev (gōōr'yĕf)........Sov. Un.	47.10 N	51.57 E
120	Gursk I. (gōōrsk).............Nor.	62 16 N	5.40 E
103	Gurupá (gōō-rōō-pȧ')........Braz.	1.30 S	51.30 W
103	Gurupi, R. (gōō-rōō-pē')....Braz.	3.0 S	46.50 W
138	Gusau (gōō-zȧ'ōō)..............Nig.	12.10 N	6.38 E
129	Gusinje (gōō-sēn'yĕ)..........Yugo.	42.34 N	19.52 E
130	Gus-Khrustalny (gōōs-krōō-stȧl'ny')...Sov. Un.	55.38 N	40.41 E
130	Gus R. (gōōs)..............Sov. Un.	55.25 N	40.45 E
122	Güstrow (güs'trō)..............Ger.	53.48 N	12.11 E
123	Gúta (gōō'tȧ)................Hung.	47.55 N	18.0 E
122	Gütersloh (gü'tērs-lō)..........Ger.	51.54 N	8.23 E
79	Guthrie (gŭth'rĭ)..............Okla.	35.52 N	97.25 W
77	Guthrie Center..................Ia.	41.40 N	94.30 W
92	Gutiérrez (gōō-tĭ-ȧr'rȧz).......Mex.	16.45 N	93.5 W
93	Gutiérrez Zamora (zȧ-mō'rȧ).Mex.	20.27 N	97.5 W
77	Guttenberg (gŭt'ĕn-bûrg)........Ia.	42.48 N	91.8 W
78	Guymon (gī'mŏn)..............Okla.	36.41 N	101.29 W
87	Guysborough (gīz'bŭr-ō).......Can.	45.22 N	61.30 W
150	Gwadar (gwȧ'dŭr)..............India	25.15 N	62.30 E
138	Gwando (gwȧn'dō)...............Nig.	12.33 N	4.42 E
139	Gwane (gwȧn)...........Bel. Cong.	4.41 N	25.45 E
140	Gwelo (gwā'lō)...............S. Rh.	19.25 S	29.45 E
77	Gwinn (gwĭn)..................Mich.	46.17 N	87.29 W
169	Gwydir R. (gwē'dēr)..Austl. (In.)	29.50 S	150.33 E
152	Gyangtse (gyȧng'tsĕ')...........Chn.	28.56 N	89.32 E
129	Gyaros (yē'ȧ-rôs)...............Grc.	37.37 N	24.44 E
165	Gympie (gĭm'pê)...............Austl.	26.25 S	152.44 E
	Gymri, see Leninakan, Sov. Un.		
123	Gyöngyös (dyûn'dyûsh).....Hung.	47.47 N	19.55 E
123	Györ (dyûr)....................Hung.	47.40 N	17.38 E
122	Györ R.........................Hung.	47.20 N	17.0 E
159	Gyotoku (gyō'tô-kōō') Jap. (Tokyo In.)	35.42 N	139.54 E
129	Gytheion (yē'thĭ-ôn)...........Grc.	36.35 N	22.34 E
123	Gyula (dyōō'lȧ)...............Hung.	46.39 N	21.18 E
130	Gzhatsk (g'zhȧtsk)......Sov. Un.	55.32 N	34.59 E
142	Haakshain Pan (Salt Pan) (hȧks'hȧn).Bech.	26.55 S	20.15 E
121	Haapamäki (hȧp'ȧ-mĕ-kē)....Fin.	62.15 N	24.30 E
121	Haapsalu (hȧp'sȧ-lōō).........Est.	58.56 N	23.32 E

ng-sing; ŋ-baŋk; N-nasalized n; nŏd; cŏmmit ;ōld; ôbey; ôrder; fōōd; fŏŏt; ou-out; s-soft; sh-dish; th-thin; pūre; ûnite; ûrn; stŭd; circŭs; ü-as "y" in study; '-indeterminate vowel.

Page	Name Pronunciation Region	Lat. °′	Long. °′
117	Haarlem (här'lĕm) .... Neth.	52.21 N	4.40 E
142	Haarlem .... U. S. Afr.	33.44 S	23.20 E
96	Habana (State) (hä-vä'nä) .. Cuba	22.55 N	82.10 W
96	Habana .... Cuba	23.8 N	82.23 W
90	Habana .... Cuba (In.)		
127	Habibas I. (hä-bē'bäs) ...... Alg.	35.45 N	0.53 W
159	Habu (hä'bōō) .. Jap. (Osaka In.)	35.3 N	135.27 E
158	Hachinoche (hä'chē-nō'chĕ) .. Jap.	40.30 N	141.29 E
159	Hachioji (hä'chē-ō'jē) ...... Jap.	35.44 N	139.20 E
85	Hackensack (hăk'ĕn-săk) .... N. J.	40.53 N	74.3 W
88	Hackensack R. N. J. (New York In.)	40.52 N	74.2 W
150	Hadd, C. el (ĕl häd') .... Oman	22.35 N	59.48 E
88	Haddonfield (hăd'ŭn-fēld) Pa. (Philadelphia In.)	39.54 N	75.2 W
88	Haddon Heights Pa. (Philadelphia In.)	39.53 N	75.3 W
138	Hadeija (hä-dā'jä) .... Nig.	12.32 N	10.3 E
119	Hadersdorf (hä'dērs-dōrf) Aus. (Wien In.)	48.13 N	16.14 E
120	Haderslev (hä'dhĕrs-lĕv) ..... Den.	55.16 N	9.28 E
150	Hadhramaut (Reg.) (hä-drä-mōt') Aden	16.0 N	51.0 E
119	Hadleigh (hăd'lĭ) Gt. Brit. (London In.)	51.34 N	0.36 E
157	Hadong (hä'dông') .... Cho.	35.6 N	127.47 E
119	Haesdonck (häs'dŏnk) Bel. (Anvers In.)	51.11 N	4.14 E
110	Hafnafjördur (häf'nä-fyûr-dōōr) Ice.	64.2 N	21.55 W
141	Hafun (hä-fōōn') .. It. E. Afr. (In.)	10.30 N	51.15 E
122	Hagen (hä'gĕn) .... Ger.	51.22 N	7.27 E
84	Hagerstown (hā'gērz-toun) ... Ind.	39.54 N	85.11 W
85	Hagerstown .... Md.	39.39 N	77.45 W
159	Hagi (hä'gĭ) .... Jap.	34.25 N	131.45 E
162	Hagonoy (hä-gō-noi') .... P. I.	14.49 N	120.43 E
124	Hague, C. de la (dē lȧ äg') .... Fr.	49.45 N	1.55 W
125	Haguenau (äg'nō') .... Fr.	48.48 N	7.49 E
159	Haibara (hä'ē-bä'rä) .... Jap.	34.28 N	135.57 E
156	Haichow (Tunghai) (hä'ē-chō') (tōōng'hī') . Chn.	34.32 N	119.13 E
113	Haidar Paşa (hī'dȧr pä-shä') . Tur.	40.58 N	29.15 E
145	Haifa (hä'ē-fä) .... Pa. (In.)	32.48 N	34.59 E
156	Haifeng (hä'ē-fĕng') .... Chn.	37.52 N	117.31 E
155	Haifung (hī'fōōng') .... Chn.	23.0 N	115.13 E
157	Haikeumkang (hä'ē-kē-ōōm'käng') Cho.	38.42 N	128.17 E
150	Hail (hāl) .... Sau. Ar.	27.45 N	41.55 E
153	Hailar (Hulun) (hä-ē-lär') (hōō'lōōn') Manch.	49.8 N	119.34 E
71	Hailey (hā'lĭ) .... Ida.	43.31 N	114.19 W
79	Haileyville (hā'lĭ-vĭl) .... Okla.	34.53 N	95.34 W
158	Hailin (hä'ē-lēn') .... Manch.	44.35 N	129.15 E
158	Hailun (hä'ē-lōōn') .... Manch.	47.44 N	127.0 E
158	Hailung (hä'ē-lōōng') ..... Manch.	42.40 N	125.53 E
156	Haimen (hä'ē-mĕn') .... Chn.	31.51 N	121.6 E
160	Hainan (I.) (hä'e-nän') ...... Chn.	19.0 N	110.0 E
122	Hainburg (hīn'bōōrgh) .... Ger.	48.8 N	16.54 E
53	Haines (hānz) .... Alsk.	59.20 N	135.30 W
83	Haines City .... Fla. (In.)	28.7 N	81.37 W
155	Haining (hī'nĭng') .... Chn.	30.24 N	120.32 E
160	Haiphong (hä'ē-fông') (hä'ē-p'hŏng') . Fr. In. Chn.	20.58 N	106.40 E
155	Haitan I. (hī'tän') .... Chn.	25.26 N	119.58 E
97	Haiti (Hispaniola) (I.) (hā'tĭ) W. I.	19.10 N	72.10 W
97	Haiti .... W. I.	19.0 N	73.0 W
156	Haiyang (hä'ē-yäng') .... Chn.	36.44 N	121.11 E
157	Haiyang I. .... Kwan.	39.5 N	123.5 E
155	Haiyen (hī'yĕn') .... Chn.	30.31 N	120.53 E
123	Hajdubószörmény (hôl'dōō-bû'sûr-män') . Hung.	47.42 N	21.32 E
123	Hajduhadház (hô'ĭ-dōō-hôd'häz) . Hung.	47.42 N	21.43 E
123	Hajdunánás (hô'ĭ-dōō-nä'näsh) . Hung.	47.51 N	21.28 E
123	Hajduszoboszló (hô'ĭ-dōō-sō'bôs-lō) . Hung.	47.27 N	21.25 E
158	Hakodate (hä-kō-dä'tä) ...... Jap.	41.46 N	140.46 E
159	Hakusan (Mt.) (hä'kōō-sän') .. Jap.	36.7 N	136.46 E
93	Halachó (ä-lä-chō') .... Mex.	20.20 N	90.4 W
139	Halaib (hä-lä'ēb) .... Eg.	22.2 N	36.10 E
173	Halawa (hä-lä'wä) .... Haw.	21.10 N	156.45 W
122	Halberstadt (häl'bēr-shtät) ... Ger.	51.54 N	11.4 E
162	Halcon, Mt. (häl-kōn') ...... P. I.	13.17 N	121.0 E
120	Halden (häl'dĕn) .... Nor.	59.9 N	11.20 E
118	Hale (hāl) .... Gt. Brit.	53.23 N	2.21 W
173	Haleakala, Crater of (hä'lā-ä'kä-lä') . Haw.	20.43 N	156.14 W
118	Halesowen (hālz'ō-wĕn) .. Gt. Brit.	52.27 N	2.3 W
119	Halewood (hāl'wŏŏd) Gt. Brit. (Liverpool In.)	53.22 N	2.49 W
82	Haleyville (hā'lĭ-vĭl) .... Ala.	34.13 N	87.37 W
49	Halfmoon B. (hăf'mōōn) Calif. (San Francisco In.)	37.28 N	122.26 W
55	Halifax (hăl'ĭ-făks) .... Can.	44.8 N	63.47 W
54	Halifax .... Can. (In.)		
116	Halifax .... Gt. Brit.	53.45 N	1.55 W
165	Halifax B. .... Austl.	19.0 S	146.50 E
86	Halifax Harbor .... Can.	44.40 N	63.45 W
122	Hall (hôl) .... Ger.	47.18 N	11.30 E
122	Hall .... Ger.	49.7 N	9.44 E
122	Halle (häl'ĕ) .... Ger.	51.30 N	11.57 E
122	Hallein (häl-līn') .... Ger.	47.41 N	13.3 E
81	Halletsville (hăl'ĕts-vĭl) ...... Tex.	29.27 N	96.55 W
76	Hallock (hăl'ŭk) .... Minn.	48.48 N	96.55 W
81	Halls Bayou .... Tex. (In.)	29.52 N	95.20 W
120	Hallsberg (häls'bĕrgh) ...... Swe.	59.3 N	15.5 E
164	Halls Creek (hôlz) .... Austl.	18.15 S	127.45 E
86	Halls Stream (R.) .... N. H.-Can.	45.10 N	71.30 W
124	Halluin (äl-lü-ăN') .... Fr.	50.48 N	3.9 E
161	Halmahera (I.) (häl-mä-hā'rä) Neth. Ind.	0.40 N	128.0 E
120	Halmstad (hälm'städ) .... Swe.	56.40 N	12.49 E
129	Halonnesos (I.) (ä-lô-nä'sôs) . Grc.	39.10 N	23.55 E
142	Hal R. (häl) .... U. S. Afr.	31.30 S	18.30 E
120	Halse Fjord (häl'sĕ) .... Nor.	63.0 N	8.12 E
163	Halsey Harbor (hôl'zĭ) ...... P. I.	11.47 N	119.55 E
120	Hälsingborg (hĕl'sĭng-bôrgh) .. Swe.	56.3 N	12.41 E
79	Halstead (hôl'stĕd) .... Kan.	38.3 N	97.31 W
119	Halstenbek (häl'stĕn-bĕk) Ger. (Hamburg In.)	53.38 N	9.51 E
153	Halunarshan .... Manch.	47.30 N	119.50 E
145	Haluza (El Khelasa) (hä-lōō'zä) (ĕl-kē-lä'zä) . Pal. (In.)	31.6 N	34.37 E
169	Haly, Mt. (hā'lē) ..... Austl. (In.)	26.46 S	151.31 E
150	Hama (hä'mä) .... Syr.	35.15 N	36.50 E
159	Hamada (hä-mä'dä) .... Jap.	34.50 N	132.2 E
150	Hamadan (hŭ-mŭ-dän') ..... Iran	34.45 N	48.15 E
159	Hamamatsu (hä'mä-mät'sōō) . Jap.	34.45 N	137.45 E
157	Haman (häm'än') .... Cho.	35.16 N	128.27 E
120	Hamar (hä'mär) .... Nor.	60.49 N	11.5 E
159	Hamasaka (hä'mä-sä'kä) ..... Jap.	35.37 N	134.28 E
118	Hambledon Hills (hăm'b'l-dŭn) Gt. Brit.	54.15 N	1.18 W
79	Hamburg (hăm'bûrg) .... Ark.	33.14 N	91.48 W
122	Hamburg (häm'bōōrgh) ...... Ger.	53.33 N	10.2 E
119	Hamburg .... Ger. (In.)		
79	Hamburg (hăm'bûrg) .... Ia.	40.35 N	95.40 W
85	Hamburg .... N. Y.	42.47 N	78.52 W
143	Hamburg (häm'bōōrgh) . U. S. Afr.	33.18 S	27.28 E
85	Hamden (hăm'dĕn) .... Conn.	41.22 N	72.58 W
121	Hämeenlinna (hĕ'mān-lĭn-nä) . Fin.	61.1 N	24.30 E
122	Hameln (hä'mĕln) .... Ger.	52.6 N	9.23 E
164	Hamersley Plat. (hăm'ērz-lē) Austl.	22.15 S	118.15 E
157	Hamheung (Kanko) (häm'hē-ōōng') (kän'kō') . Cho.	39.58 N	127.32 E
152	Hami (Qomul) (hä'mē) (kō-mōōl') Chn.	42.47 N	93.29 E
166	Hamilton (hăm'ĭl-tŭn) ...... Austl.	37.45 S	142.8 E
55	Hamilton .... Can.	43.13 N	79.48 W
116	Hamilton .... Gt. Brit.	56.45 N	4.5 W
87	Hamilton .... Mass. (In.)	42.37 N	70.51 W
71	Hamilton .... Mont.	46.15 N	114.10 W
79	Hamilton .... Mo.	39.45 N	94.0 W
170	Hamilton .... N. Z.	37.46 S	175.22 E
84	Hamilton .... Ohio	39.24 N	84.36 W
80	Hamilton .... Tex.	31.41 N	98.8 W
77	Hamilton .... Wis.	43.43 N	88.28 W
55	Hamilton Inlet .... Lab.	54.30 N	56.45 W
55	Hamilton R. .... Lab.	53.0 N	62.0 W
121	Hamina (hä'mē-nä) .... Fin.	60.35 N	27.18 E
83	Hamlet (hăm'lĕt) .... N. C.	34.52 N	79.42 W
49	Hamlet .... Ore. (Portland In.)	45.50 N	123.41 W
80	Hamlin (hăm'lĭn) .... Tex.	32.52 N	100.8 W
122	Hamm (häm) .... Ger.	51.40 N	7.50 E
138	Hammada-el-Homra (Red Stony Desert) (häm'ä-dä-ĕl-hôm'rä) Libya	29.30 N	12.0 E
135	Hammamet (hä-mä-mĕt') Tun. (In.)	36.22 N	10.30 E
135	Hammamet, G. of .... Tun. (In.)	36.10 N	10.40 E
110	Hammerfest (häm'mēr-fĕst) .. Nor.	70.38 N	23.38 E
169	Hammock I. ..... Austl. (Tas. In.)	40.4 S	147.45 E
84	Hammond (hăm'ŭnd) .... Ind.	41.37 N	87.28 W
81	Hammond .... La.	30.31 N	90.28 W
70	Hammond .... Ore.	46.10 N	123.58 W
85	Hammonton (hăm'ŭn-tŭn) ... N. J.	39.37 N	74.46 W
86	Hampden (hăm'dĕn) .... Me.	44.45 N	68.51 W
171	Hampden .... N. Z.	45.19 S	170.52 E
116	Hampshire Downs (hămp'shĭr dounz) . Gt. Brit.	51.5 N	1.0 W
86	Hampton (hămp'tŭn) .... Can.	45.32 N	65.50 W
73	Hampton ...... Ga. (Atlanta In.)	33.23 N	84.17 W
77	Hampton .... Ia.	42.45 N	93.12 W
85	Hampton .... Va.	37.0 N	76.22 W
89	Hampton Roads (Inlet) Va. (Norfolk In.)	36.58 N	76.21 W
157	Ham Pyung (häm' pyōōng) .. Cho.	35.7 N	126.32 E
142	Ham R. (hăm) .... S. W. Afr.	28.15 S	19.15 E
120	Hamrånge (häm'rông'ĕ) ...... Swe.	60.58 N	17.1 E
71	Hams Fork (R.) (hămz) ..... Wyo.	42.0 N	110.40 W
84	Hamtramck (hăm-trăm'ĭk) .. Mich.	42.22 N	83.2 W
150	Hamun-i-Helmand (L.) (hä-mōōn'ē-hĕl'mŭnd) . Iran-Afg.	31.0 N	61.15 E
151	Hamun-i Mashkel (L.) (hä-mōōn'ē mäsh-kĕl') . Ind.	28.15 N	63.5 E
157	Hamyang (häm'yäng') .... Cho.	35.35 N	127.46 E
154	Han R. (hän) .... Chn.	30.55 N	112.35 E
154	Han R. .... Cho.	37.30 N	127.30 E
173	Hana (hä'nä) .... Haw.	20.43 N	155.59 W
96	Hanabana, R. (hä-nä-bä'nä) Cuba	22.30 N	80.35 W
173	Hanalei B. (hä-nä-lā'ē) ..... Haw.	22.12 N	159.33 W
151	Hanamkonda (hŭ-näm-kōn'dŭ) India	18.5 N	79.38 E
122	Hanau (hä'nou) .... Ger.	50.9 N	8.57 E
118	Hanbury (hăn'bĕr-ĭ) .... Gt. Brit.	52.17 N	2.4 W
154	Hanchwan (hän'chwän') ..... Chn.	30.38 N	113.40 E
77	Hancock (hăn'kŏk) .... Mich.	47.8 N	88.35 W
140	Handa (hän'dä) .... Ang.	15.52 S	15.55 E
141	Handeni (hän-dā'nē) .... Tan.	5.27 S	38.4 E
119	Handforth (hăn'fērth) Gt. Brit. (Liverpool In.)	53.21 N	2.13 W
74	Hanford (hăn'fērd) .... Calif.	36.19 N	119.39 W
155	Hangchow (häng'chō') ...... Chn.	30.15 N	120.10 E
155	Hangchow B. .... Chn.	30.32 N	121.30 E
167	Hanging Rock (Mt.) .... Austl.	31.28 S	151.15 E
143	Hanglip, C. (hăng'lĭp) ... U. S. Afr.	34.22 S	18.47 E
121	Hangö (häng'gû) .... Fin.	59.50 N	22.57 E
81	Hankamer (hăŋ'kȧ-mēr) . Tex. (In.)	29.52 N	94.37 W
143	Hankey (hăŋ'kĭ) ...... U. S. Afr.	33.51 S	24.52 E
76	Hankinson (hăŋ'kĭn-sŭn) .... N. D.	46.5 N	96.54 W
155	Hankow (hän'kō') .... Chn.	30.35 N	114.8 E
71	Hanna (hăn'ȧ) .... Wyo.	41.52 N	106.34 W
76	Hannah .... N. D.	48.58 N	98.42 W
157	Hannasan (Mt.) (hän'nä-sän') Jap.	33.28 N	126.31 E
79	Hannibal (hăn'ĭ-băl) .... Mo.	39.42 N	91.21 W
164	Hann, Mt. (hăn) .... Austl.	16.0 S	125.47 E
122	Hannover (hän-ō'vēr) .... Ger.	52.29 N	9.20 E
122	Hannover (Prov.) .... Ger.	52.50 N	9.20 E
120	Hanö B. (hän'û) .... Swe.	55.54 N	15.0 E
160	Hanoi (hä-noi') ...... Fr. In. Chn.	21.0 N	105.51 E
84	Hanover (hăn'ō-vēr) .... Can.	40.10 N	81.4 W
87	Hanover .... Mass. (In.)	42.7 N	70.48 W
86	Hanover .... N. H.	43.42 N	72.18 W
85	Hanover .... Pa.	39.48 N	76.59 W
143	Hanover .... U. S. Afr.	31.4 S	24.26 E
104	Hanover I. .... Chl.	51.0 S	74.30 W
156	Hanshan (hän'shän') .... Chn.	31.45 N	118.3 E
154	Hanshow (hän'shō') .... Chn.	28.53 N	111.39 E
91	Hans Lollick I. (häns' lŏl'ĭk) St. Thomas (In.)	18.24 N	64.55 W
87	Hanson (hăn'sŭn) ..... Mass. (In.)	42.3 N	70.53 W
142	Hantams Bergen (Mts.) (hän'tàms bĕr'ghen) . U. S. Afr.	31.20 S	19.50 E
142	Hantams R. (hăn'tȧmz) . U. S. Afr.	31.13 S	19.20 E
156	Hantan (hän'tän') .... Chn.	36.36 N	114.38 E
86	Hantsport (hănts'pōrt) ...... Can.	45.5 N	64.12 W
155	Hanyang (hän'yäng') .... Chn.	30.32 N	114.6 E
110	Haparanda (hä-pä-rän'dä) ... Swe.	65.55 N	24.0 E
73	Hapeville (hāp'vĭl) Ga. (Atlanta In.)	33.39 N	84.24 W
89	Happy Jack, La. (New Orleans In.)	29.30 N	89.45 W
153	Harbin (Pinkiang) (här-bēn') (pĭn'kyäng') Manch.	45.40 N	126.31 E
84	Harbor Beach .... Mich.	43.50 N	82.40 W
87	Harbor Grace .... Newf.	47.39 N	53.15 W
96	Harbor I. .... Ba. Is.	25.26 N	76.35 W
84	Harbor Springs .... Mich.	45.27 N	85.0 W
87	Harbour au Bouche (här'bēr ō bōōsh') . Can.	45.39 N	61.31 W
87	Harbour Breton (brĕt'ŭn) (brē-tôN') . Newf.	47.28 N	55.51 W
122	Harburg-Wilhelmsburg (här'bōōrgh-vĕl'hĕlms-bōōrgh) . Ger.	53.27 N	9.57 E
86	Harcourt (här'cōrt) (ȧr-kōōr') Can.	46.28 N	65.15 W
120	Hardanger Fjeld (Plat.) (här-däng'ĕr fyĕl') . Nor.	60.15 N	7.0 E
120	Hardanger Fd. .... Nor.	59.58 N	5.57 E
120	Hardanger Jökulen (Mt.) (yû'kōōl-ĕn) . Nor.	60.32 N	7.25 E
167	Harden (här'dĕn) .... Austl.	34.33 S	148.23 E
72	Hardin (här'dĭn) Colo. (Denver In.)	40.21 N	104.26 W
71	Hardin .... Mont.	45.45 N	107.37 W
143	Harding (här'dĭng) ..... U. S. Afr.	30.35 S	29.51 W
74	Hardy, R. (här'dĭ) .... Mex.	32.0 N	115.12 W
87	Hare B. (hâr) .... Newf.	51.15 N	55.55 W
124	Harfleur (ȧr-flûr') .... Fr.	49.31 N	0.11 E
141	Hargeisa (här-gā'ē-sä) .... Br. Som.	9.35 N	43.55 E
123	Harghitei Mts. (här-gē'tā) ... Rom.	46.26 N	25.40 E
159	Harima Sea (hä'rē-mä) .... Jap.	34.33 N	134.36 E
150	Hari Rud (R.) (hŭ'rē rōōd') .. Afg.	34.20 N	63.0 E
57	Harlaka (här'lä-kä) Can. (Quebec In.)	46.49 N	71.8 W
76	Harlan (här'lăn) .... Ia.	41.40 N	95.19 W
82	Harlan .... Ky.	36.53 N	83.19 W
71	Harlem (här'lĕm) .... Mont.	48.32 N	108.50 W
88	Harlem R. .. N. Y. (New York In.)	40.50 N	73.56 W
122	Harlingen (här'lĭng-ĕn) ..... Neth.	53.10 N	5.27 E
81	Harlingen .... Tex.	26.12 N	97.41 W
71	Harlowton (här'lō-tŭn) ..... Mont.	46.27 N	109.50 W
84	Harmony (här'mō-nĭ) .... Ind.	39.33 N	87.3 W
70	Harney Basin (här'nĭ) .... Ore.	43.25 N	120.0 W
70	Harney L. .... Ore.	43.15 N	119.10 W
76	Harney Peak .... S. D.	43.52 N	103.30 W
120	Härnösand (hĕr-nû-sänd) ..... Swe.	62.39 N	18.0 E
126	Haro (ä'rō) .... Sp.	42.35 N	2.50 W
72	Haro, Canal de Can. (Vancouver In.)	49.5 N	123.35 W
72	Haro Str. (hä'rō) Wash.-Can. (Vancouver In.)	48.37 N	123.14 W
78	Harper (här'pēr) .... Kan.	37.18 N	98.2 W
49	Harper ...... Wash. (Seattle In.)	47.30 N	122.31 W
138	Harper (Cape Palmas) (päl'mȧs) . Lib.	4.30 N	7.54 W
85	Harpers Ferry .... W. Va.	39.18 N	77.47 W
73	Harpersville Ala. (Birmingham In.)	33.21 N	86.27 W
113	Harput (kär-pōōt') .... Tur.	38.45 N	39.15 E
141	Harrania (hä-rä'nyä) .... Eg.	29.58 N	31.10 E
141	Harrar (hȧ-rär') (Division) It. E. Afr.	8.30 N	42.0 E
139	Harrar (hȧ-rär') ...... It. E. Afr.	9.17 N	42.3 E
89	Harriet, L. (hăr'ĭ-ĕt) Minn. (Minneapolis In.)	44.55 N	93.18 W
82	Harriman (hăr'ĭ-măn) ...... Tenn.	35.56 N	84.33 W
85	Harrington (hăr'ĭng-tŭn) ..... Del.	38.55 N	75.37 W
79	Harrisburg (hăr'ĭs-bûrg) ...... Ill.	37.45 N	88.32 W
85	Harrisburg .... Pa.	40.16 N	76.50 W
81	Harrisburg .... Tex. (In.)	29.43 N	95.16 W
116	Harris (I.) .... Gt. Brit.	57.48 N	7.0 W
83	Harris, L. .... Fla. (In.)	28.46 N	81.50 W
143	Harrismith .... U. S. Afr.	28.13 S	29.9 E
79	Harrison .... Ark.	36.14 N	93.5 W
88	Harrison .... N. J. (New York In.)	40.45 N	74.10 W
85	Harrisonburg .... Va.	38.28 N	78.52 W
72	Harrison Hot Springs Can. (Vancouver In.)	49.18 N	121.47 W
72	Harrison L. . Can. (Vancouver In.)	49.35 N	121.50 W
72	Harrison Mills Can. (Vancouver In.)	49.14 N	121.56 W
79	Harrisonville .... Mo.	38.39 N	94.20 W
73	Harrisville Utah (Salt Lake City In.)	41.17 N	112.0 W
84	Harrisville .... W. Va.	39.11 N	81.3 W
84	Harrodsburg (hăr'ŭdz-bûrg) ... Ky	37.42 N	84.50 W
118	Harrogate (hăr'ō-gāt) .... Gt. Brit.	53.59 N	1.33 W
118	Harrold (hăr'ŭld) .... Gt. Brit.	52.12 N	0.37 W

ăt; finȧl; rāte; senȧte; ärm ȧsk; sofȧ; fâre; ch-choose; dh-as th in other; bē; ēvent; bĕt; recĕnt; cratēr; g-go; gh-gutteral g; bĭt; ĭ-short neutral; ride; K-gutteral k as ch in German ich·

Page	Name Pronunciation Region	Lat. °′	Long. °′
119	Harrow (hăr'ō) Gt. Brit. (London In.)	51.35 N	0.21 W
129	Hârsova (kär-sō'vȧ)........Rom.	44.41 N	27.58 E
110	Harstad (här'städh)........Nor.	68.45 N	16.27 E
49	Harstine I. (hăr'stĭn Wash.) (Seattle In.)	47.14 N	122.54 W
84	Hart (härt)..............Mich.	43.41 N	86.23 W
142	Hartebeest R. (härt'bēst) U. S. Afr.	29.0 S	20.45 E
142	Hartebeestkuil (härt'bēst-kûl) U. S. Afr.	32.56 S	23.33 E
82	Hartford (härt'fẽrd).........Ala.	31.5 N	85.42 W
79	Hartford..................Ark.	35.3 N	94.22 W
85	Hartford.................Conn.	41.45 N	72.40 W
84	Hartford..................Ky.	37.27 N	86.53 W
84	Hartford.................Mich.	42.16 N	86.16 W
77	Hartford..................Wis.	43.19 N	88.22 W
84	Hartford City..............Ind.	40.30 N	40.27 W
88	Hart I...............N. Y. (In.)	40.51 N	73.46 W
118	Hartington (härt'ĭng-tŭn) Gt. Brit.	53.8 N	1.48 W
76	Hartington................Neb.	42.38 N	97.17 W
166	Hart, L...................Austl.	31.8 S	136.25 E
86	Hartland (härt'lănd).........Can.	46.19 N	67.31 W
116	Hartland Pt...........Gt. Brit.	51.5 N	4.35 W
116	Hartlepool (här't'l-pōōl)..Gt. Brit.	54.40 N	1.12 W
76	Hartley (härt'lĭ)..............Ia.	43.11 N	95.28 W
140	Hartley.................S. Rh.	18.12 S	30.9 E
82	Hartselle (härt'sĕl)..........Ala.	34.37 N	86.57 W
79	Hartshorne (härts'hôrn).....Okla.	34.51 N	95.33 W
143	Harts R. (härts)..U. S. Afr.-Bech.	27.15 S	25.12 E
83	Hartsville (härts'vĭl).........S. C.	34.21 N	80.3 W
82	Hartwell (härt'wĕl)..........Ga.	34.21 N	82.57 W
77	Harvard (här'vȧrd)...........Ill.	42.25 N	88.38 W
87	Harvard............Mass. (In.)	42.30 N	71.35 W
78	Harvard..................Neb.	40.36 N	98.5 W
78	Harvard, Mt...............Colo.	38.56 N	106.21 W
84	Harvey (här'vĭ)..............Ill.	41.42 N	87.36 W
76	Harvey...................N. D.	47.47 N	99.56 W
165	Harvey Creek.............Austl.	17.27 N	146.5 E
72	Harvey Mt..Can. (Vancouver In.)	49.28 N	123.14 W
117	Harwich (här'wĭch)......Gt. Brit.	51.55 N	1.15 E
122	Harz Mts. (härts)............Ger.	51.43 N	10.55 E
145	Hasbaya (häs'bä'yȧ) ...Syr. (In.)	33.27 N	35.42 E
88	Hasbrouck Heights (hăz'brŏŏk) N. J. (N. Y. In.)	40.52 N	74.4 W
119	Haselau (häs'ē-lou) Ger. (Hamburg In.)	53.40 N	9.37 E
119	Haseldorf (häs'ĕl-dôrf) Ger. (Hamburg In.)	53.38 N	9.36 E
159	Hashimoto (hä'shē-mō'tō)....Jap.	34.20 N	135.37 E
121	Häsijarvi (L.) (hĕ'sē-yĕr'vĕ)..Fin.	61.40 N	23.50 E
79	Haskell (hăs'kĕl)............Okla.	35.49 N	95.39 W
78	Haskell....................Tex.	33.9 N	99.45 W
118	Haslingden (hăz'lĭng-dĕn).Gt. Brit.	53.42 N	2.20 W
120	Hassela (häs'ĕl-ō)..........Swe.	62.6 N	16.49 E
117	Hasselt (häs'ĕlt).............Bel.	50.59 N	5.25 E
120	Hässjö (hĕs'shû)............Swe.	62.36 N	17.31 E
120	Hassleholm (häs'lĕ-hōlm)....Swe.	56.10 N	13.45 E
93	Hastahuacán (ä-stä-hwä-kän') Mex. (In.)	19.21 N	99.2 W
117	Hastings (hās'tĭngz).....Gt. Brit.	50.51 N	0.35 E
84	Hastings..................Mich.	42.42 N	85.20 W
77	Hastings..................Minn.	44.45 N	92.51 W
78	Hastings...................Neb.	50.35 N	98.24 W
170	Hastings..................N. Z.	39.40 S	176.52 E
167	Hastings Range............Austl.	31.10 S	152.11 E
167	Hastings R................Austl.	31.25 S	152.32 E
82	Hatchie R. (hăch'ē)........Tenn.	35.25 N	89.5 W
129	Hațeg (kät-säg') ....Rom.	45.36 N	22.57 E
96	Hatiguanico R. (ä-tē-gwä-nē'kō) Cuba	22.22 N	81.20 W
83	Hatteras, C. (hăt'ẽr-ȧs).....N. C.	35.15 N	75.32 W
82	Hattiesburg (hăt'ĭz-bûrg)....Miss.	31.19 N	89.19 W
123	Hatvan (hôt'vôn)...........Hung.	47.39 N	19.43 E
120	Haugesund (hou'gē-sōōn')....Nor.	59.27 N	5.20 E
170	Hauhangaroa Ra. (hä'ōō-hăŋ-gä-rō'ȧ).N. Z.	38.40 S	175.30 E
121	Haukivesi (L.) (hou'kē-vē'sē).Fin.	62.2 N	28.35 E
170	Hauraki G. (hä-ōō-rä'kē)....N. Z.	36.25 S	175.5 E
171	Haurangi Ra. (hä-ōō-răŋ'gē) N. Z.	41.25 S	175.25 E
171	Hauroko L. (hä-ōō-rō'kō)....N. Z.	46.0 S	167.20 E
121	Hausjärvi (hä'ōōs-yĕr'vē) ....Fin.	60.46 N	24.48 E
145	Hauta (hou'tä).........Aden (In.)	13.3 N	44.54 E
150	Hauta..................Sau. Ar.	23.35 N	46.35 E
124	Hautmont (ō-môN')............Fr.	50.15 N	3.52 E
79	Havana (hȧ-vä'nȧ)............Ill.	40.17 N	90.2 W
79	Havelock (hăv'lŏk)..........Neb.	40.51 N	96.38 W
86	Havelock..................Can.	45.59 N	65.20 W
171	Havelock..................N. Z.	41.15 S	173.48 E
122	Havel R. (hä'fĕl)............Ger.	53.0 N	13.20 E
86	Haverhill (hā'vẽr-hĭl)........Mass.	42.47 N	71.5 W
86	Haverhill..................N. H.	44.1 N	72.5 W
119	Havering (hā'vẽr-ĭng) Gt. Brit. (London In.)	51.37 N	0.11 E
85	Haverstraw (hā'vẽr-strô)....N. Y.	41.12 N	73.59 W
71	Havre (hăv'ẽr)..............Mont.	48.33 N	109.41 W
85	Havre de Grace (hăv'ẽr dē gräs') Md.	39.33 N	76.7 W
173	Hawaiian Is. (hä-wī'ăn)...Pac. O.	21.0 N	157.0 W
173	Hawaii (I.) (hä-wī'ē).........Haw.	19.30 N	155.30 W
173	Hawaii (Ter.)..............Pac. O.	21.0 N	157.0 W
141	Hawamdiya (hȧ'wăm-dē-yȧ)..Eg.	29.54 N	31.15 E
76	Hawarden (hā'wär-dĕn).........Ia.	43.0 N	96.5 W
166	Hawdon, L. (hô'dŭn)........Austl.	37.10 S	139.55 E
171	Hawea L. (hä'wē-ȧ)..........N. Z.	44.30 S	169.22 E
170	Hawera (hä'wȧ-rȧ)...........N. Z.	39.35 S	174.15 E
84	Hawesville (hôz'vĭl)..........Ky.	37.53 N	86.46 W
173	Hawi (hä'wē)...............Haw.	20.15 N	155.48 W
116	Hawick (hô'ĭk).........Gt. Brit.	55.25 N	2.50 W
170	Hawke B. (hôk)..............N. Z.	39.20 S	177.30 E
167	Hawke, C...................Austl.	32.13 S	152.33 E
166	Hawker (hôk'ẽr)............Austl.	31.52 S	138.26 E
85	Hawkesbury (hôks'bẽr-ĭ)......Can.	45.35 N	74.37 W
82	Hawkinsville (hô'kĭnz-vĭl).....Ga.	32.17 N	83.29 W
167	Hawksbury R. (hôks'bẽr-ĭ)..Austl.	33.30 S	150.58 E
97	Hawks Nest Pt...........Ba. Is.	24.9 N	75.33 W
76	Hawley (hô'lĭ)..............Minn.	46.54 N	96.18 W
118	Haworth (hô'wŭrth).......Gt. Brit.	53.50 N	1.57 W
83	Haw River (hô)..............N. C.	35.55 N	79.18 W
142	Hawston (hôs'tŭn)......U. S. Afr.	34.21 S	19.6 E
73	Hawthorne (hô'thôrn) Calif. (Los Angeles In.)	33.55 N	118.21 W
54	Hawthorne............Can. (In.)	45.23 N	75.36 W
74	Hawthorne..................Nev.	38.31 N	118.38 W
78	Haxtun (hăks'tŭn)...........Colo.	40.37 N	102.38 W
166	Hay........................Austl.	34.28 S	144.52 E
125	Hayange (hȧ-yäNzh')..........Fr.	49.20 N	6.5 E
75	Hayden (hā'dĕn).............Ariz.	33.1 N	110.49 W
169	Hayden..............Austl. (In.)	27.14 S	151.52 E
119	Haydock (hā'dŏk) Gt. Brit. (Liverpool In.)	53.28 N	2.39 W
119	Hayes (hāz) Gt. Brit. (London In.)	51.22 N	0.1 E
53	Hayes, Mt..................Alsk.	63.40 N	146.30 W
54	Hayes R....................Can.	55.30 N	94.0 W
119	Hayfield..Gt. Brit. (Liverpool In.)	53.22 N	1.56 W
77	Hay L......................Mich.	46.22 N	84.12 W
122	Haynau (hī'nou)..............Ger.	51.16 N	15.56 E
79	Haynesville (hānz'vĭl).........Ark.	32.59 N	93.8 W
81	Haynesville..................La.	32.57 N	93.10 W
164	Hay R......................Austl.	23.30 S	137.10 E
54	Hay River..................Can.	60.58 N	116.19 W
78	Hays.......................Kan.	38.52 N	99.20 W
77	Hayward (hā'wẽrd)...........Wis.	46.1 N	91.29 W
171	Hayward Pt..........N. Z. (In.)	45.46 S	170.43 E
49	Haywards Calif. (San Francisco In.)	37.40 N	122.5 W
56	Haywood....Can. (Winnipeg In.)	49.40 N	98.14 W
82	Hazard (hăz'ȧrd)..............Ky.	37.15 N	83.12 W
159	Haze (hä'zē)....Jap. (Osaka In.)	34.45 N	135.47 E
124	Hazebrouck (ȧz-brōōk').......Fr.	50.45 N	2.35 E
119	Hazel Grove (hā'z'l) Gt. Brit. (Liverpool In.)	53.23 N	2.8 W
83	Hazelhurst (hā'z'l-hûrst)......Ga.	31.51 N	82.36 W
82	Hazlehurst...................Miss.	31.52 N	90.24 W
85	Hazleton (hā'z'l-tŭn)..........Pa.	40.58 N	75.58 W
142	Hazuur (hȧ-zōōr')......S. W. Afr.	26.36 S	19.50 E
56	Headingly (hĕd'ĭng-lĭ) Can. (Winnipeg In.)	49.53 N	97.22 W
82	Headland (hĕd'lănd).........Ala.	31.21 N	85.32 W
74	Healdsburg (hĕldz'bûrg)......Calif.	38.37 N	122.53 W
79	Healdton (hĕld'tŭn).........Okla.	34.14 N	97.29 W
167	Healesville (hēlz'vĭl).........Austl.	37.40 S	145.33 E
118	Heanor (hĕn'ŏr)..........Gt. Brit.	53.1 N	1.22 W
7	Heard I. (hûrd)..........Ind. O.	53.10 S	74.35 E
81	Hearne (hûrn)...............Tex.	30.52 N	96.36 W
46	Hearst Land (Reg.) (hûrst)...Ant.	72.0 S	64.0 W
76	Heart R. (härt)..............N. D.	46.38 N	102.0 W
87	Hearts Content..............Newf.	47.52 N	53.22 W
169	Heathcote (hĕth'kŏt) Austl. (Sydney In.)	34.5 S	151.1 E
171	Heathcote R.................N. Z.	43.33 S	172.37 E
87	Heath Pt. (hēth)..............Can.	49.5 N	61.45 W
79	Heavener (hēv'nẽr)..........Okla.	34.53 N	94.36 W
80	Hebbronville (hē'brŭn-vĭl)....Tex.	27.18 N	98.41 W
75	Heber (hē'bẽr)..............Utah	40.41 N	111.27 W
79	Heber Springs...............Ark.	35.28 N	91.59 W
71	Hebgen Reservoir (hĕb'gĕn).Mont.	44.48 N	111.15 W
116	Hebrides, G. of the (hĕb'-rĭ-dēz) Gt. Brit.	56.50 N	6.50 W
55	Hebron (hē'brŭn).............Lab.	58.10 N	62.45 W
79	Hebron......................Neb.	40.10 N	97.35 W
76	Hebron......................N. D.	46.54 N	102.3 W
145	Hebron...............Pal. (In.)	31.32 N	35.5 E
145	Hebron (Beit Jibrin) (bāt' zhē-brēn').Pal. (In.)	31.37 N	34.57 E
120	Heby (hĭ'bü)................Swe.	59.57 N	16.50 E
54	Hecate Str. (hĕk'ȧ-tē).........Can.	53.15 N	131.0 W
93	Hecelchakán (ā-sĕl-chä-kän').Mex.	20.11 N	90.7 W
120	Hedemora (hĭ-dē-mō'rȧ).....Swe.	60.17 N	15.55 E
120	Hedesunda Fjörd (hĭ-dē-sōōn'dȧ) Swe.	60.26 N	17.10 E
118	Hedon (hĕd'ŭn)...........Gt. Brit.	53.44 N	0.12 W
157	Heechun (hē'ē-chōōn')........Cho.	40.13 N	126.19 E
117	Heerlen (hār'lĕn)............Neth.	50.54 N	5.57 E
82	Heflin (hĕf'lĭn)..............Ala.	33.39 N	85.36 W
122	Heide (hī'dē)................Ger.	54.12 N	9.6 E
169	Heidelberg (hī'dĕl-bûrg) Austl. (Melbourne In.)	37.45 S	145.4 E
122	Heidelberg (hī'dĕl-bĕrgh).....Ger.	49.25 N	8.43 E
143	Heidelberg............U. S. Afr.	26.32 S	28.25 E
142	Heidelberg............U. S. Afr.	34.4 S	20.58 E
122	Heidenheim (hī'dĕn-hīm).....Ger.	48.42 N	10.9 E
158	Heijo (Pyengyang) (hā'jō') (pyĕng'yăng').Cho.	39.6 N	125.46 E
143	Heilbron (hĭl'brōn).....U. S. Afr.	27.18 S	27.58 E
122	Heilbronn...................Ger.	49.9 N	9.14 E
119	Heiligenstadt (hī'lĭ-gĕn-shtät) Aus. (Wien In.)	48.15 N	16.22 E
122	Heiligenstadt................Ger.	51.22 N	10.0 E
123	Heilsberg (hīls'bĕrgh)........Ger.	54.8 N	20.37 E
153	Heilungkiang (Prov.) (hā-lōōng'kyăng') Manch.	48.10 N	122.0 E
121	Heinola (hā-nō'lȧ)...........Fin.	61.14 N	26.4 E
49	Heisson (hī'sŭn) Wash. (Portland In.)	45.49 N	122.28 W
119	Heist (hīst)...Ger. (Hamburg In.)	53.39 N	9.40 E
150	Hejaz (State) (hĕ-jăz') (hĕ-zhăz') Sau. Ar.	25.0 N	38.0 E
110	Hekla, Mt. (Vol.) (hĕk'lȧ)....Ice.	64.0 N	19.45 W
123	Hel (hāl)....................Pol.	54.36 N	18.48 E
73	Helena (hĕl'ē-nȧ) Ala. (Birmingham In.)	33.18 N	86.50 W
79	Helena......................Ark.	34.32 N	90.36 W
71	Helena.....................Mont.	46.36 N	112.1 W
116	Helensburgh (hĕl'ĕnz-bŭr-ō) Gt. Brit.	56.0 N	4.40 W
170	Helensville (hĕl'ĕnz-vĭl).....N. Z.	36.40 S	174.27 E
120	Helge R. (hĕl'gĕ).............Swe.	56.20 N	14.2 E
122	Helgoland (I.) (hĕl'gō-lănd) North Sea	54.12 N	7.53 E
169	Helidon (hĕl'ĭ-dŏn)....Austl. (In.)	27.31 S	152.8 E
141	Heliopolis (Ruins) (hē-lĭ-ŏp'ō-lĭs).Eg.	30.6 N	31.20 E
145	Heliopolis (Baalbeck) (bäl'bĕk) Syr. (In.)	33.59 N	36.9 E
119	Hellbrok (hĕl'brŏk) Ger. (Hamburg In.)	53.36 N	10.4 E
83	Hellier (hĕl'yẽr)..............Ky.	37.17 N	82.29 W
126	Hellin (ĕl-yēn')...............Sp.	38.31 N	1.41 W
150	Helmand R. (hĕl'mŭnd).......Afg.	31.0 N	64.0 E
122	Helmond (hĕl'mŏnt) (ĕl'môN') Neth.	51.30 N	5.42 E
118	Helmsley (hĕlmz'lĭ)......Gt. Brit.	54.15 N	1.3 W
122	Helmstedt (hĕlm'shtĕt).......Ger.	52.14 N	11.1 E
75	Helper (hĕlp'ẽr)..............Utah	39.41 N	110.55 W
143	Helpmakaar (hĕlp-mȧ-kär') U. S. Afr.	28.28 S	30.26 E
121	Helsingfors (Helsinki) (hĕl-sĭng-fôrs') (hĕl-sĕn-kē).Fin.	60.10 N	24.58 E
120	Helsingör (hĕl-sĭng-ûr').......Den.	56.3 N	12.35 E
121	Helsinki (Helsingfors) (hĕl'sĕn-kē).Fin.	60.10 N	23.58 E
143	Helvellyn (Mt.) (hĕl-vĕl'ĭn) U. S. Afr.	30.42 S	27.15 E
141	Helwan (hĕl'wăn).............Eg.	29.50 N	31.19 E
73	Hemet (hĕm'ĕt) Calif. (Los Angeles In.)	33.45 N	116.58 W
76	Hemingford (hĕm'ĭng-fẽrd)...Neb.	42.19 N	103.2 W
119	Hemixem (hĕm'ĭk-sĕm) Bel. (Anvers In.)	51.9 N	4.20 E
81	Hemphill (hĕmp'hĭl)..........Tex.	31.20 N	93.49 W
81	Hempstead (hĕmp'stĕd).......Tex.	30.7 N	96.5 W
120	Hemse (hĕm'sē)...............Swe.	57.16 N	18.28 E
120	Hems I. (hĕms)...............Swe.	62.45 N	18.5 E
120	Hen (hĭn)....................Nor.	60.15 N	10.13 E
170	Hen and Chickens Is.........N. Z.	36.0 S	174.45 E
126	Henares R. (ā-nä'rȧs).........Sp.	40.40 N	3.10 W
124	Hendaye (äN-dä')..............Fr.	43.25 N	1.38 W
72	Henderson (hĕn'dẽr-sŭn) Colo. (Denver In.)	39.55 N	104.51 W
84	Henderson....................Ky.	37.50 N	87.33 W
170	Henderson...................N. Z.	36.53 S	174.38 E
83	Henderson...................N. C.	36.18 N	78.22 W
82	Henderson...................Tenn.	35.27 N	88.40 W
81	Henderson....................Tex.	32.9 N	94.49 W
83	Hendersonville...............N. C.	35.18 N	82.28 W
169	Hendon (hĕn'dŭn)....Austl. (In.)	28.5 S	151.59 E
116	Hendon...................Gt. Brit.	51.35 N	0.15 W
73	Henefer (hĕn'ē-fẽr) Utah (Salt Lake City In.)	41.2 N	111.30 W
154	Hengchow (hĕng'chō').......Chn.	26.56 N	112.30 E
122	Hengelo (hĕng'ē-lō)..........Neth.	52.16 N	6.47 E
156	Heng R. (hĕng)...............Chn.	31.56 N	114.50 E
154	Hengshan (hĕng'shän').......Chn.	27.10 N	112.32 E
154	Heng Shan (Nan Yueh) (Mts.) (nän'yōō-ā').Chn.	26.55 N	111.48 E
156	Hengshui (hĕng'shōō-ē').....Chn.	37.51 N	115.46 E
124	Hénin-Liétard (ā-näN'lyā-tär').Fr.	50.25 N	2.59 E
169	Henley Beach (hĕn'lē) Austl. (Adelaide In.)	34.56 S	138.30 E
118	Henley-in-Arden (hĕn'lĭ-ĭn-är'dĕn) Gt. Brit.	52.17 N	1.47 W
85	Henlopen, C. (hĕn-lō'pĕn)....Del.	38.48 N	75.6 W
124	Hennebont (ĕn-bôN')..........Fr.	47.48 N	3.15 W
119	Hennersdorf (hĕn'ĕrs-dōrf) Aus. (Wien In.)	48.7 N	16.22 E
78	Hennessey (hĕn'ĕ-sĭ).........Okla.	36.6 N	97.53 W
78	Henrietta (hĕn-rĭ-ĕt'ȧ).........Tex.	33.47 N	98.13 W
85	Henry, C. (hĕn'rĭ)............Va.	36.53 N	76.0 W
79	Henryetta.....................Okla.	35.26 N	95.58 W
71	Henrys Fork (R.)..............Ida.	43.50 N	111.55 W
167	Henty (hĕn'tĭ)................Austl.	35.31 S	147.3 E
70	Heppner (hĕp'nẽr)............Ore.	45.22 N	119.33 W
150	Herat (hĕ-rät')...............Afg.	34.30 N	62.15 E
171	Herbert (hẽr'bẽrt)............N. Z.	45.15 S	170.50 E
142	Herbertsdale (hẽr'bẽrts-dāl) U. S. Afr.	34.1 S	21.45 E
125	Herblay (ĕr-blĕ')........Fr. (In.)	49.0 N	2.10 E
128	Hercegovina (Prov.) (hĕr-tsĕ-gō'vē-nȧ).Yugo.	43.20 N	18.10 E
119	Herculaneum (hẽr-kōō-lā'nē-ōōm) (hûr-kū-lā'nē-ŭm).It. (Napoli In.)	40.48 N	14.20 E
92	Hércules (ĕr'kōō-lȧs).........Mex.	20.38 N	100.19 W
169	Herdsmans L. (hûrdz'mănz) Austl. (Perth In.)	31.55 S	115.48 E
95	Heredia (ā-rā'dhē-ä)..........C. R.	10.3 N	84.7 W
116	Hereford (hĕr'ē-fẽrd).....Gt. Brit.	52.5 N	2.45 W
78	Hereford.....................Tex.	34.47 N	102.25 W
118	Hereford Co..............Gt. Brit.	52.12 N	2.45 W
126	Herencia (ā-rān'thē-ä).........Sp.	39.23 N	3.21 W
122	Herford (hĕr'fōrt)............Ger.	52.7 N	8.40 E
125	Héricourt (ā-rē-kōōr')..........Fr.	47.35 N	6.45 E
79	Herington (hĕr'ĭng-tŭn).....Kan.	38.41 N	96.47 W
122	Herisau (hā'rē-zou)..........Switz.	47.23 N	9.17 E
85	Herkimer (hûr'kĭ-mẽr)......N. Y.	43.3 N	74.58 W
116	Herma Ness (hûr'mȧ-nĕs) Gt. Brit. (In.)	60.50 N	1.0 W
79	Hermann (hûr'măn)...........Mo.	38.41 N	91.27 W
145	Hermel (hûr'mĕl).......Syr. (In.)	34.24 N	36.22 E
167	Hermidon (hûr'mĭ-dŏn).....Austl.	30.48 S	147.14 E
87	Hermitage B. (hûr'mĭ-tĕj)...Newf.	47.40 N	56.0 W
161	Hermit Is. (hûr'mĭt)..N. Gui. Ter.	1.30 S	145.0 E
145	Hermon, Mt. (hûr'mŭn).Syr. (In.)	33.25 N	35.48 E
161	Hermosa (ĕr-mō'sä) P. I. (Manila In.)	14.48 N	120.27 E
73	Hermosa Beach (hẽr-mō'sȧ) Calif. (Los Angeles In.)	33.52 N	118.25 W
129	Hermoupolis (ĕr-mōō'pō-lyĕs).Grc.	37.28 N	24.55 E
120	Herning (hĕr'nĭng)...........Dan.	56.8 N	8.59 E

ŋ-sing; ŋ-baŋk; N-nasalized n; nŏd; cŏmmit; ōld; ōbey; ôrder; fōōd; fŏŏt; ou-out; s-soft; sh-dish; th-thin; pūre; ūnite; ûrn; stŭd; circŭs; ü-as "y" in study; '-indeterminate vowel

Page	Name Pronunciation Region	Lat. °′	Long. °′
55	Heron Bay (hĕr'ŭn) Can.	48.35 N	86.0 W
76	Heron Lake Minn.	43.45 N	95.15 W
169	Herries Ra. (hĕr'ēz) Austl. (In.)	28.23 S	151.47 E
79	Herrin (hĕr'ĭn) Ill.	37.47 N	89.1 W
143	Herschel (hĕr'shĕl) U. S. Afr.	30.38 S	27.10 E
122	Hersfeld (hĕrs'fĕlt) Ger.	50.54 N	9.42 E
117	Herstal (hĕr'stäl) Bel.	50.40 N	5.40 E
116	Hertford (hûrt'fērd) Gt. Brit.	51.50 N	0.10 W
83	Hertford N. C.	36.11 N	76.28 W
126	Hervas (ĕr'väs) Sp.	40.17 N	5.51 W
165	Hervey B. (hûr'vê) Austl.	25.0 S	152.45 E
73	Hesperia (hĕs-pē'rĭ-à) Calif. (Los Angeles In.)	34.25 N	117.19 W
122	Hessen (State) (hĕs'ĕn) Ger.	50.20 N	8.46 E
119	Heswall (hĕz'wôl) Gt. Brit. (Liverpool In.)	53.21 N	3.8 W
119	Hetlingen (hĕt'lĭng-ĕn) Ger. (Hamburg In.)	53.37 N	9.38 E
158	Heto C. (hē'tō') Ryukyu Is. (In.)	26.48 N	128.15 E
76	Hettinger (hĕt'ĭn-jēr) N. D.	46.6 N	102.38 W
164	Heughlin, Mt. (hoi'glĭn) Austl.	23.5 S	133.59 E
158	Heunghai (Poko) (hyŏŏng'hī') Cho.	36.1 N	129.20 E
157	Heungyang (hĕŏŏng'yăng') Cho.	34.38 N	127.18 E
118	Heysham (hā'shăm) Gt. Brit.	54.2 N	2.54 W
166	Heywood (hā'wŏŏd) Austl.	38.9 S	141.39 E
118	Heywood Gt. Brit.	53.35 N	2.12 W
154	Hiakiang (hyä'kyäng') Chn.	25.45 N	108.42 E
154	Hiakiang Chn.	25.23 N	107.44 E
79	Hiawatha (hī-à-wô'thà) Kan.	39.51 N	95.34 W
75	Hiawatha Utah	39.29 N	111.4 W
77	Hibbing (hĭb'ĭng) Minn.	47.27 N	92.55 W
169	Hibbs, Pt. (hĭbz) Austl. (Tas. In.)	42.37 S	145.14 E
82	Hickman (hĭk'măn) Ky.	36.33 N	98.10 W
83	Hickory (hĭk'ô-rĭ) N. C.	35.43 N	81.21 W
84	Hicksville (hĭks'vĭl) Ohio	41.17 N	84.46 W
8	Hico (hī'kō) Tex.	34.0 N	98.2 W
92	Hidalgo (State) (ē-dhäl'gō) Mex.	20.25 N	99.0 W
92	Hidalgo Mex.	24.13 N	99.27 W
80	Hidalgo Mex.	27.48 N	99.53 W
128	Hierapetra (yā'rä-pā'trä) Grc. (Crete In.)	35.1 N	25.45 E
84	Higgins L. (hĭg'ĭnz) Mich.	44.28 N	84.42 W
79	Higginsville (hĭg'ĭnz-vĭl) Mo.	39.4 N	93.44 W
119	Higham (hĭg'ăm) Gt. Brit. (London In.)	51.26 N	0.29 E
118	Higham Ferrers (fĕr'ērz) Gt. Brit.	52.19 N	0.34 W
56	High Bluff Can. (Winnipeg In.)	50.2 N	98.10 W
96	Highborn Cay (I.) (hī'bôrn) Ba. Is.	24.42 N	76.50 W
72	High Cr. Colo. (Colo. Sprs. In.)	38.43 N	105.20 W
73	Highgrove Calif. (Los Angeles In.)	34.1 N	117.20 W
84	High I. Mich.	45.44 N	85.42 W
81	High Island Tex. (In.)	29.34 N	94.25 W
73	Highland Calif. (Los Angeles In.)	34.8 N	117.13 W
72	Highland Colo. (Denver In.)	40.15 N	105.5 W
79	Highland Ill.	38.45 N	89.39 W
77	Highland Park Ill.	42.11 N	87.47 W
84	Highland Park Ky.	38.12 N	85.50 W
84	Highland Park Mich.	42.23 N	83.5 W
73	High Level Ala. (Birmingham In.)	33.39 N	87.12 W
76	Highmore S. D.	44.31 N	99.27 W
162	High Peak P. I.	15.30 N	120.7 E
83	High Point N. C.	35.57 N	80.0 W
83	High Springs Fla.	29.51 N	82.37 W
85	Hightstown (hīts'toun) N. J.	40.15 N	74.32 W
143	High Veld (Plain) (vĕlt) U. S. Afr.	26.55 S	26.0 E
97	Higüey (ē-gwā') Hai.	18.37 N	68.42 W
121	Hiiumaa (Dago) (I.) (hē'ōōm-ô) (däg'ō) Est.	58.50 N	22.40 E
121	Hiitola (hē-ē'tô-lä) Fin.	61.15 N	29.35 E
159	Hikone (hē'kô-nĕ) Jap.	35.15 N	136.14 E
170	Hikurangi (hē-kōō-räŋ'gē) N. Z.	35.37 S	174.20 E
118	Hilbre Pt. (hĭl'brē) Gt. Brit.	53.23 N	3.11 W
122	Hildburghausen (hĭld'bŏŏrg-hou-zĕn) Ger.	50.26 N	10.44 E
122	Hildesheim (hĭl'dĕs-hīm) Ger.	52.9 N	9.56 E
95	Hillaby, Mt. (hĭl'à-bĭ) Barb. (In.)	13.14 N	59.36 W
78	Hill City Kan.	39.22 N	99.55 W
77	Hill City Minn.	46.59 N	93.35 W
167	Hill End Austl.	33.3 S	149.28 E
120	Hillerød (hĕ'lĕ-rûdh) Den.	55.55 N	12.19 E
139	Hillet Abbas (hĕl'ĕt à-bäs') A. E. Sud.	13.6 N	32.41 E
49	Hillhurst (hĭl'hûrst) Wash. (Seattle In.)	47.5 N	122.31 W
79	Hillsboro (hĭlz'bŭr-ō) Ill.	39.8 N	89.28 W
79	Hillsboro Kan.	38.22 N	97.11 W
86	Hillsboro N. H.	43.5 N	71.55 W
76	Hillsboro N. D.	47.24 N	97.3 W
84	Hillsboro Ohio	39.11 N	83.40 W
70	Hillsboro Ore.	45.31 N	122.59 W
81	Hillsboro Tex.	32.1 N	97.7 W
77	Hillsboro Wis.	43.38 N	90.20 W
84	Hillsdale Mich.	41.55 N	84.37 W
167	Hillston Austl.	33.31 S	145.32 E
72	Hill Top Colo. (Denver In.)	39.28 N	104.41 W
70	Hillyard (hĭl'yärd) Wash.	47.42 N	117.22 W
173	Hilo (hē'lō) Haw.	19.42 N	155.3 W
163	Hilonghilong, Mt. (hē-lông-hē'-lông) P. I.	9.7 N	125.43 E
163	Hilongos (hē-lôŋ'gōs) P. I.	10.22 N	124.46 E
122	Hilversum (hĭl'vēr-sŭm) Neth.	52.12 N	5.10 E
151	Himalaya Mts. (hĭ-mä'là-yà) Asia	28.0 N	81.0 E
163	Himamaylan (hē-mä-mī'län) P. I.	10.7 N	122.53 E
159	Himeji (hē'mà-jē) Jap.	34.45 N	134.46 E
163	Hinatuan (hē-nä-tōō'än) P. I.	8.22 N	126.20 E
97	Hinche (hēn'chä) (ăNsh) Hai.	19.9 N	72.0 W
52	Hinchinbrook I. (hĭn'chĭn-brŏŏk) Alsk. (In.)	60.20 N	146.25 W
165	Hinchinbrook I. Austl.	18.15 S	146.15 E
118	Hinckley (hĭnk'lĭ) Gt. Brit.	52.32 N	1.21 W
163	Hindang (hēn-däng') P. I.	10.27 N	124.44 E
123	Hindenburg (hĭn'dĕn-bŏŏrgh) Ger.	50.18 N	18.48 E
119	Hindley (hīnd'lĭ) Gt. Brit. (Liverpool In.)	53.32 N	2.34 W
118	Hindley Gt. Brit.	53.32 N	2.36 W
166	Hindmarsh, L. (hīnd'märsh) Austl.	36.4 S	141.55 E
169	Hindmarsh Austl.	34.54 S	138.34 E
151	Hindu Kush Mts. (hĭn'dōō kōōsh') Asia	35.45 N	70.30 E
152	Hingan (hĭn'gän') Chn.	32.42 N	109.29 E
154	Hingan Chn.	25.32 N	110.32 E
155	Hingan Chn.	27.37 N	117.39 E
87	Hingham (hĭng'ăm) Mass. (In.)	42.14 N	70.54 W
155	Hinghwa (hĭng'hwä') Chn.	25.26 N	118.58 E
156	Hinghwa Chn.	32.55 N	119.50 E
155	Hinghwa Sound Chn.	25.18 N	119.18 E
155	Hingkwo (hĭng'kwō) Chn.	29.46 N	115.8 E
155	Hingkwo Chn.	26.18 N	115.1 E
155	Hingning (hĭng'nĭng') Chn.	24.4 N	115.32 E
163	Hinigaran (hē-nē-gä'rän) P. I.	10.16 N	122.52 E
126	Hinojosa (ē-nō-hō'sä) Sp.	38.30 N	5.9 W
88	Hinsdale (hĭnz'dāl) Ill. (Chicago In.)	41.48 N	87.54 W
119	Hinterbrühl (hĭn'tēr-brül) Aus. (Wien In.)	48.4 N	16.14 E
119	Hintersdorf (hĭn'tērs-dôrf) Aus. (In.)	48.18 N	16.13 E
84	Hinton (hĭn'tŭn) W. Va.	37.42 N	80.55 W
163	Hinunangan (hē-nōō-nän'gän) P. I.	10.24 N	125.12 E
163	Hinundayan (hē-nōōn-dä'yän) P. I.	10.21 N	125.15 E
158	Hirado (I.) (hē'rä-dō) Jap.	33.16 N	129.30 E
73	Hiram (hī'răm) Ga. (Atlanta In.)	33.52 N	84.46 W
159	Hirano (hē'rä-nō) Jap. (Osaka In.)	34.37 N	135.33 E
159	Hirasaki (hē'rä-sä'kē) Jap. (Tokyo In.)	35.15 N	139.38 E
158	Hirosaki (hē'rô-sä'kē) Jap.	40.33 N	140.30 E
159	Hirose (hē'rô-sä) Jap.	35.20 N	133.10 E
159	Hiroshima (hē-rô-shē'mà) Jap.	32.29 N	132.28 E
122	Hirschberg (hĭrsh'bĕrgh) Ger.	50.53 N	15.43 E
125	Hirson (ēr-sôN') Fr.	4.8 E	49.53 W
97	Hispaniola (Haiti) (I.) (hĭ'spăn-ĭ-ō-lä) W. I.	19.10 N	72.10 W
148	Hissar (hĭ-sär') Sov. Un.	38.35 N	68.40 E
150	Hit (hĭt) Iraq	33.38 N	42.45 E
81	Hitchcock (hĭch'kŏk) Tex. (In.)	29.21 N	95.1 W
159	Hitoyoshi (hē'tô-yō'shē) Jap.	32.14 N	130.44 E
120	Hitteren (I.) (hē'tēr-ĕn) Nor.	53.30 N	8.40 E
159	Hiwasa (hē'wà-sä) Jap.	33.45 N	134.30 E
82	Hiwassee R. (hī-wŏs'sē) Tenn.	35.20 N	84.50 W
120	Hjälmar, L. (yĕl'mär) Swe.	59.16 N	15.45 E
120	Hjo (yō) Swe.	58.19 N	14.13 E
120	Hjørring (jûr'ĭng) Den.	57.27 N	10.0 E
143	Hlabisa (hlä-bē'sä) U. S. Afr.	28.10 S	31.51 E
143	Hlakanelo (hlä-kä-nä'lō) Bas.	29.42 S	28.49 E
143	Hlatikulu (hlä-tĭ-kōō'lōō) Swaz.	26.57 S	31.20 E
143	Hlobane (hlō-bä'nē) U. S. Afr.	27.44 S	30.56 E
123	Hlohovec (hlō'hô-vĕts) Czech.	48.25 N	17.48 E
143	Hlotse (Leribe) (hlôt'sĕ) (lĕ'rē-bĕ) Bas.	28.51 S	28.3 E
143	Hluti (hlōō'tĭ) Swaz.	27.12 S	31.38 E
169	Hobart (hō'bărt) Austl. (Tas. In.)	42.52 S	147.19 E
84	Hobart Ind.	41.34 N	87.17 W
78	Hobart Okla.	35.1 N	99.6 W
117	Hoboken (hō'bō-kĕn) Bel.	51.11 N	4.21 E
88	Hoboken N. J. (N. Y. In.)	40.45 N	74.2 W
120	Hobro (hô-brô') Den.	56.38 N	9.47 E
169	Hobsons B. (hŏb'sŭnz) Austl.	37.51 S	144.55 E
170	Hobsonville N. Z. (In.)	36.48 S	174.40 E
154	Hochih (hō'chē') Chn.	24.40 N	107.52 E
154	Hochow (hō'chō') Chn.	30.10 N	106.22 E
155	Hochow Chn.	31.40 N	118.18 E
156	Hochow Chn.	31.38 N	118.17 E
122	Höchst (hûKst) Ger.	50.7 N	8.32 E
171	Hochstetter Dome Mt. (hōK'stĕt-ēr) N. Z.	42.30 S	172.12 E
118	Hodder, R. (hŏd'ēr) Gt. Brit.	53.56 N	2.30 W
150	Hodeida (hô-dā'ē-dä) Yemen	14.45 N	43.0 E
82	Hodgenville (hŏj'ĕn-vĭl) Ky.	37.33 N	85.46 W
87	Hodges Hill (hŏj'ĕz) Newf.	49.0 N	55.55 W
123	Hodmezövasarhely (hōd'mĕ-zû-vô'shôr-hĕl-y') Hung.	46.25 N	20.20 E
114	Hodna, Chott el (L.) (shŏt ĕl hŏd'nà) Alg.	35.25 N	4.45 E
159	Hodogawa R. (hŏ'dô-gä'wä) Jap. (Tokyo In.)	35.24 N	139.36 E
123	Hodonín (hŏ'dô-nēn) Czech.	48.51 N	17.6 E
142	Hoetjes Bay (hōōt'yĕz) U. S. Afr.	32.59 S	17.55 E
119	Hoevenen (hoo'vĕ-nĕn) Bel. (Anvers In.)	51.18 N	4.24 E
122	Hof (hōf) Ger.	50.19 N	11.54 E
154	Hofeng (hō'fĕng') Chn.	29.54 N	109.42 E
89	Hoffman Cr. (hŏf'măn) Ohio (Cleveland In.)	41.26 N	81.45 W
143	Hofmeyr (hŏf'mī-ēr) U. S. Afr.	31.39 S	25.46 E
110	Hofs-Jökull (Glacier) (hôfs'yû'kŏŏl) Ice.	64.50 N	17.30 W
150	Hofuf (hô-fōōf') Sau. Ar.	25.25 N	49.45 E
82	Hogansville (hō'gănz-vĭl) Ga.	33.11 N	84.55 W
97	Hog Cay (I.) Ba. Is.	23.23 N	75.30 W
96	Hog I. Ba. Is.	25.5 N	77.22 W
89	Hog I. La. (New Orleans In.)	29.27 N	89.26 W
84	Hog I. Mich.	45.48 N	85.22 W
121	Hogland (I.) Fin.	60.5 N	27.0 E
97	Hogsty Reef Ba. Is.	21.42 N	73.50 W
122	Hohenelbe (Vrchlabi) (hō'ĕn-ĕl'bĕ) (v'r'Klä-bē) Ger.	50.37 N	15.37 E
122	Hohe Tauern (Mts.) (hō'ĕtou'ērn) Ger.	47.10 N	12.20 E
154	Hohsien (hō'syĕn') Chn.	24.19 N	111.28 E
154	Hoikin (hoi'kĭn') Chn.	23.52 N	111.23 E
157	Hoingsung (hō'ĭng-sŏŏng') Cho.	37.27 N	127.58 E
154	Hoiping (hoi'pĭng') Chn.	22.36 N	112.22 E
78	Hoisington (hoi'zĭng-tŭn) Kan.	38.31 N	98.46 W
157	Hoivang (hoi'yăng') Cho.	38.44 N	127.40 E
159	Hojo (hō'jō) Jap.	33.58 N	132.49 E
159	Hojo Jap.	35.0 N	139.53 E
154	Hokiang (hō'kyäng') Chn.	28.49 N	105.45 E
170	Hokianga R. (hō-kē-äŋ'gä) N. Z.	35.30 S	173.20 E
156	Hokien (hō'kē-ĕn') Chn.	38.34 N	116.2 E
171	Hokitika (hō-kĭ-tē'kä) N. Z.	42.42 S	171.3 E
158	Hokkaido I. (hŏk'kī-dō) Jap.	43.30 N	143.0 E
155	Hokow (hō'kō') Chn.	28.19 N	117.42 E
154	Hokshan (hōk'shän') Chn.	22.45 N	112.36 E
120	Holbaek (hôl'bĕk) Den.	55.41 N	11.42 E
75	Holbrook (hōl'brŏŏk) Ariz.	34.54 N	110.11 W
167	Holbrook Austl.	35.44 S	147.19 E
87	Holbrook Mass. (In.)	42.9 N	71.1 W
49	Holbrook Ore. (Portland In.)	45.39 N	122.51 W
87	Holden (hōl'dĕn) Mass. (In.)	42.21 N	71.56 W
79	Holden Mo.	38.42 N	94.0 W
84	Holden W. Va.	37.48 N	82.5 W
79	Holdenville Okla.	35.4 N	96.25 W
78	Holdrege (hōl'drĕj) Neb.	40.25 N	99.24 W
120	Hölen (hûl'ĕn) Nor.	59.33 N	10.41 E
97	Holguin (ôl-gēn') Cuba	20.53 N	76.18 W
84	Holland (hŏl'ănd) Mich.	42.46 N	86.8 W
	Holland, see Netherlands.		
85	Hollidaysburg (hŏl'ĭ-dāz-bûrg) Pa.	40.28 N	78.26 W
78	Hollis (hŏl'ĭs) Okla.	34.40 N	99.55 W
74	Hollister (hŏl'ĭs-tēr) Calif.	36.51 N	121.24 W
87	Holliston (hŏl'ĭs-tŭn) Mass. (In.)	42.15 N	71.25 W
78	Holly (hŏl'ĭ) Colo.	38.3 N	102.7 W
84	Holly Mich.	42.49 N	83.33 W
49	Holly Wash. (Seattle In.)	47.33 N	122.58 W
82	Holly Springs Miss.	34.46 N	89.28 W
73	Hollywood (hŏl'ĭ-wŏŏd) Calif. (Los Angeles In.)	34.8 N	118.20 W
83	Hollywood Fla. (In.)	26.1 N	80.10 W
119	Holm (hōlm) Ger. (Hamburg In.)	53.37 N	9.41 E
165	Holmes Reefs (hōmz) Austl.	16.50 S	148.0 E
72	Holmes Colo. (Colo. Sprs. In.)	38.38 N	104.42 W
88	Holmesburg (hōmz'bûrg) Pa. (Philadelphia In.)	40.3 N	75.3 W
120	Holmestrand (hôl'mĕ-strän) Nor.	59.29 N	10.18 E
120	Holm I. (hôlm) Swe.	62.26 N	15.20 E
120	Holmsbu (hôlms'bōō) Nor.	59.36 N	10.30 E
120	Holstebro (hôl'stĕ-brô') Den.	56.22 N	8.40 E
82	Holston R. (hōl'stăn) Tenn.	36.10 N	83.30 W
118	Holt (hōlt) Gt. Brit.	53.4 N	2.53 W
79	Holton (hōl'tŭn) Kan.	39.28 N	95.44 W
74	Holtville Calif.	32.49 N	115.24 W
52	Holy Cross Alsk.	62.10 N	160.0 W
116	Holyhead (hŏl'ē-hĕd) Gt. Brit.	53.19 N	4.35 W
116	Holyhead I. Gt. Brit.	53.15 N	4.45 W
116	Holy I. (hō'lĭ) Gt. Brit.	55.42 N	1.50 W
78	Holyoke (hōl'yōk) Colo.	40.36 N	102.19 W
86	Holyoke Mass.	42.12 N	72.40 W
122	Holzminden (hôlts'mĭn-dĕn) Ger.	51.51 N	9.27 E
122	Homburg (hŏm'bŏŏrgh) Ger.	50.14 N	8.37 E
125	Homécourt (ô-mā-kōōr') Fr.	49.14 N	5.59 E
81	Homer (hō'mēr) La.	32.47 N	93.5 W
83	Homestead (hōm'stĕd) Fla. (In.)	25.27 N	80.28 W
85	Homestead Pa.	40.24 N	79.54 W
79	Hominy (hŏm'ĭ-nĭ) Okla.	36.25 N	96.24 W
82	Homochitto R. (hō-mō-chĭt'ō) Miss.	31.20 N	91.0 W
163	Homonhon I. (hō-môn-hōn') P. I.	10.43 N	125.43 E
150	Homs (hōms) Syr.	34.45 N	36.50 E
139	Homs (Lebda) (lĕb'dä) Libya	32.36 N	14.12 E
154	Honam (hō'näm') Chn.	23.4 N	113.15 E
155	Honan (Prov.) (hō'năn') Chn.	31.33 N	115.12 E
153	Honanfu (hō'năn-fōō') Chn.	34.44 N	112.26 E
102	Honda (hŏn'dä) Col.	5.12 N	74.58 W
96	Honda B. Cuba	22.58 N	83.9 W
163	Honda B. P. I.	9.55 N	118.48 E
142	Hondeklip B. (hŏn'dĕ-klĭp) U. S. Afr.	30.18 S	17.16 E
80	Hondo (hŏn'dō) Tex.	29.20 N	99.9 W
94	Hondo R. Br. Hond.-Mex. (In.)	18.10 N	88.40 W
73	Hondo, R. Calif. (Los Angeles In.)	34.2 N	118.4 W
93	Hondo, R. Mex. (In.)	19.26 N	99.15 W
78	Hondo, R. N. M.	33.20 N	105.0 W
94	Honduras (hŏn-dōō'räs) Cen. Am.	14.50 N	87.10 W
94	Honduras, G. of Cen. Am.	16.10 N	88.0 W
83	Honea Path (hŭn'ĭ păth) S. C.	34.24 N	82.27 W
120	Hønefoss (hû'nĕ-fôs) Nor.	60.10 N	10.13 E
85	Honesdale (hōnz'dāl) Pa.	41.30 N	75.16 W
79	Honey Grove Tex.	33.35 N	95.55 W
74	Honey L. Calif.	40.15 N	120.20 W
73	Honeyville Utah (Salt Lake City In.)	41.38 N	112.5 W
124	Honfleur (ôN-flûr') Fr.	49.25 N	0.15 E
157	Hongchun (hŏng'chōōn') Cho.	37.40 N	127.53 E
155	Honghai B. (hŏng'hī') Chn.	22.43 N	115.2 E
154	Hong Kong (I.) (hŏng' kŏng') Chn.	22.16 N	114.12 E
153	Hongkow Cr. (hŏng'kō') Chn. (Shanghai In.)	31.13 N	121.26 E
159	Hongo (hōŋ'gō) Jap. (Tokyo In.)	35.9 N	139.51 E
157	Hongwon (hŏng'wŏn') Cho.	40.4 N	127.57 E
173	Honolulu (hŏn-ō-lōō'lōō) Haw.	21.18 N	157.51 W
173	Honomu (hŏn'ō-mōō) Haw.	19.51 N	155.4 W
158	Honshu I. (hŏn'shōō) Jap.	36.0 N	138.0 E
70	Hood Canal (hŏŏd) Wash.	47.30 N	123.3 W
70	Hood, Mt. Ore.	45.22 N	121.42 W
70	Hood River Ore.	45.43 N	121.30 W
49	Hoodsport (hŏŏdz'pōrt) Wash. (Seattle In.)	47.25 N	123.8 W
151	Hooghly R. (hōōg'lĭ) India	21.30 N	88.0 E
119	Hook (hŏŏk) Gt. Brit. (London In.)	51.22 N	0.19 W
78	Hooker (hŏŏk'ēr) Okla.	36.51 N	101.13 W
173	Hookeng (hō-ô-kĕng') Haw.	19.22 N	155.51 W
70	Hoopa Valley Ind. Res. (hōō'pà) Calif.	41.5 N	123.40 W
76	Hooper (hŏŏp'ēr) Neb.	41.37 N	96.31 W
73	Hooper Utah (Salt Lake City In.)	41.10 N	112.8 W
171	Hoopers Inlet N. Z. (In.)	45.51 S	170.42 E
84	Hoopeston (hōōps'tŭn) Ill.	40.35 N	87.40 W

ăt; fināl; rāte; senāte; ärm; àsk; sofà; fâre; ch-choose; dh-as th in other; bē; ēvent; bĕt; recĕnt; cratēr; g-go; gh-gutteral g; bĭt; ĭ-short neutral; rīde; K-gutteral k as ch in German ich;

Page	Name Pronunciation Region	Lat. °′	Long. °′
143	Hoopstad (hŏŏp'städ)...U. S. Afr.	27.47 S	25.56 E
122	Hoorn (hōrn)...Neth.	52.38 N	5.4 E
85	Hoosick Falls (hōō'sĭk)...N. Y.	42.55 N	73.20 W
74	Hoover Dam (hōō'vẽr) .Ariz. Nev.	36.4 N	114.45 W
53	Hope (hōp)...Alsk.	60.45 N	144.30 W
79	Hope...Ark.	33.39 N	93.35 W
72	Hope...Can. (Vancouver In.)	49.23 N	121.27 W
76	Hope...N. D.	47.18 N	97.46 W
55	Hopedale (hōp'dāl)...Lab.	55.29 N	60.32 W
87	Hopedale...Mass. (In.)	42.7 N	71.32 W
167	Hopefield (hōp'fēld)...Austl.	35.55 S	146.25 E
142	Hopefield...U. S. Afr.	33.3 S	18.19 E
156	Hopeh (Prov.) (hō'pā')...Chn.	38.20 N	116.0 E
164	Hopetoun (hōp'toun)...Austl.	33.45 S	120.10 E
166	Hopetown...Austl.	35.46 S	142.22 E
143	Hopetown...U. S. Afr.	29.35 S	24.5 E
85	Hopewell (hōp'wĕl)...Va.	37.16 N	77.13 W
75	Hopi Ind. Res. (hō'pē)...Ariz.	36.18 N	110.30 W
155	Hoping (hō'pĭng')...Chn.	24.23 N	114.53 E
166	Hopkins R. (hŏp'kĭnz)...Austl.	38.3 S	142.40 E
82	Hopkinsville...Ky.	36.53 N	87.28 W
87	Hopkinton...Mass. (In.)	42.13 N	71.31 W
70	Hoquiam (hō'kwĭ-ăm)...Wash.	46.59 N	123.52 W
120	Hörby (hûr'bü)...Swe.	55.50 N	13.39 E
122	Horgen (hôr'gĕn)...Switz.	47.15 N	8.34 E
77	Horicon (hŏr'ĭ-kŏn)...Wis.	43.29 N	88.38 W
150	Hormuz, Str. of (hôr'mŭz)...Asia	26.30 N	56.30 E
104	Horn, C. (hôrn)...S. A.	56.0 S	67.30 W
110	Horna Water (L.) (hôr'nä)...Swe.	66.0 N	17.50 E
171	Hornby (hôrn'bē)...N. Z. (In.)	43.32 S	172.32 E
119	Hornchurch (hôrn'chûrch) Gt. Brit. (London In.)	51.34 N	0.13 E
119	Horneburg (hôr'nē-bōōrgh) Ger. (Hamburg In.)	53.31 N	9.35 E
85	Hornell (hôr-nĕl')...N. Y.	42.21 N	77.40 W
165	Horn I....Pap. Ter.	10.42 S	142.30 E
161	Hornos, Pt. (ôr'nōs) P. I. (Manila In.)	14.25 N	120.25 E
167	Hornsby (hôrnz'bĭ)...Austl.	33.43 S	151.6 E
118	Hornsea (hôrn'zē)...Gt. Brit.	53.55 N	0.10 W
116	Hornsey...Gt. Brit.	51.35 N	0.10 W
120	Hornsland (Pen.) (hōrns'lănd) Swe.	61.40 N	17.28 E
123	Horodenka (hō-rô-dĕŋ'kä)...Pol.	48.41 N	25.31 E
102	Horrodada I. (hôr-rä-dhä'dhä) Peru (In.)	12.8 S	77.8 W
78	Horse Cr. (hôrs)...Colo.	38.30 N	103.40 W
71	Horse Cr....Wyo.	41.25 N	105.10 W
120	Horsens (hôrs'ĕns)...Den.	55.50 N	9.50 E
72	Horsetooth (Mt.) (hôrs'tōōth) Colo. (Denver In.)	40.33 N	105.12 W
118	Horsforth (hôrs'fŭrth)...Gt. Brit.	53.50 N	1.39 W
165	Horsham (hôr'shăm) (hôrs'ăm) Austl.	36.35 S	142.15 E
7	Horta (ôr'tä)...Az. (In.)	38.32 N	28.40 W
120	Horten (hôr'tĕn)...Nor.	59.25 N	10.30 E
79	Horton (hôr'tŭn)...Kan.	39.38 N	95.32 W
119	Horton Kirby (kûr'bĭ) Gt. Brit. (London In.)	51.23 N	0.15 E
118	Horwich (hŏr'ĭch)...Gt. Brit.	53.35 N	2.33 W
123	Horyń R. (hō'rēn')...Pol.	51.20 N	26.22 E
156	Hoshun (hō'shōōn')...Chn.	37.19 N	113.32 E
81	Hoskins (hŏs'kĭnz)...Tex. (In.)	29.8 N	95.12 W
158	Hososhima (hō'sō-shē'mä)...Jap.	32.29 N	131.40 E
127	Hospitalet (ōs-pē-tä-lĕt')..Sp. (In.)	41.22 N	2.6 E
104	Hoste I. (ōs'tā)...Chl.	55.15 S	69.0 W
92	Hostotipaquillo (ōs-tō'tĭ-pä-kēl'yō) Mex.	21.11 N	104.4 W
167	Hotham, Mt. (hŏ'thăm)...Austl.	36.57 S	147.8 E
152	Hotien (Khotan) (hō'tyĕn') (kō-tän') Chn.	37.2 N	79.52 E
123	Hotin (hô'tēn)...Rom.	48.31 N	26.30 E
53	Hot Springs...Alsk.	65.0 N	150.35 W
79	Hot Springs...Ark.	34.30 N	93.2 W
75	Hot Springs...N. M.	33.8 N	107.19 W
76	Hot Springs...S. D.	43.26 N	103.30 W
73	Hot Springs Utah (Salt Lake City In.)	41.20 N	112.2 W
85	Hot Springs...Va.	38.0 N	79.52 W
79	Hot Springs Natl. Park...Ark.	34.30 N	93.0 W
77	Houghton (hō'tŭn)...Mich.	47.6 N	88.32 W
84	Houghton L....Mich.	44.20 N	84.45 W
125	Houilles (ōō-yĕs')...Fr. (In.)	48.55 N	5.11 E
86	Houlton (hōl'tŭn)...Me.	46.8 N	67.50 W
81	Houma (hōō'mȧ)...La.	29.35 N	90.43 W
142	Houmoed (hou'mōōd)...U. S. Afr.	29.19 S	19.31 E
142	Houm R. (houm)...S. W. Afr.	28.20 S	18.40 E
135	Houmt Souk (hōōmt sōōk') Tun. (In.)	33.53 N	10.43 E
119	Hounslow (hounz'lō) Gt. Brit. (London In.)	51.28 N	0.23 W
85	Housatonic R. (hōō-sȧ-tŏn'ĭk) Conn.-Mass.	42.0 N	73.23 W
82	Houston (hūs'tŭn)...Miss.	33.54 N	89.2 W
81	Houston...Tex.	29.45 N	95.22 W
81	Houston...Tex. (In.)		
81	Houston Ship Channel..Tex. (In.)	29.35 N	94.56 W
164	Houtman Rocks (hout'măn) Austl.	28.5 S	112.28 E
142	Houwater (hou'v-ätẽr)..U. S. Afr.	30.18 S	23.16 E
119	Hove (hō'vĕ) Bel. (Anvers In.)	51.9 N	4.28 E
116	Hove (hōv)...Gt. Brit.	50.50 N	0.10 W
75	Hovenweep Natl. Mon. (hō'v'n-wēp) Utah	37.22 N	109.5 W
79	Howard (hou'ård)...Kan.	37.26 N	96.14 W
76	Howard...S. D.	44.2 N	97.31 W
167	Howe, C. (hou)...Austl.	37.30 S	149.56 E
118	Howeden (hou'dĕn)...Gt. Brit.	53.45 N	0.52 W
84	Howell (hou'ĕl)...Mich.	42.40 N	83.57 W
72	Howe Sound Can. (Vancouver In.)	49.25 N	123.25 W
170	Howick (hou'ĭk)...N. Z.	36.54 S	174.56 E
143	Howick...U. S. Afr.	29.30 S	30.12 E
167	Howitt, Mt. (hou'ĭt)...Austl.	37.10 S	146.38 E
6	Howland I. (hou'lănd)...Pac. O.	11.3 S	171.5 W
151	Howrah (hou'rä)...India	22.30 N	88.25 E
116	Howth (hōth)...Ire.	53.20 N	6.5 W
79	Hoxie (hŏk'sĭ)...Ark.	36.3 N	91.0 W
122	Hoyerswerda (hoi'ērs-vĕr'dä) Ger.	51.27 N	14.13 E
116	Hoy (I.) (hoi)...Gt. Brit. (In.)	58.50 N	3.15 W
118	Hoylake (hoi-lāk')...Gt. Brit.	53.23 N	3.10 W
127	Hoyo, Sierra del (Mt.) (syĕr'rä dĕl hō'yō).Sp. (In.)	40.38 N	3.55 W
155	Hoyün (hō'yün')...Chn.	23.40 N	114.37 E
122	Hradec Králové (hrä'dĕts krä'lō-vā).Czech.	50.12 N	15.51 E
123	Hranice (hrän'yē-tsĕ)...Czech.	49.33 N	17.44 E
123	Hriňová (hrēn'yō-vä)...Czech.	48.36 N	19.33 E
123	Hrubieszów (hrōō-byā'shōōf)..Pol.	50.47 N	23.53 E
151	Hsawnghsup (sông'sŭp')...India	24.25 N	94.40 E
154	Hsiang R. (hsē'äng')...Chn.	26.38 N	112.10 E
154	Hsiaokan (hsē-ä'ō-kän')...Chn.	30.54 N	113.47 E
158	Hsifeng (Taulu) (hsē'fĕng') (tou'lōō') Chn.	43.26 N	124.15 E
153	Hsingan (Prov.) (hsĭng'ăn) Manch.	50.0 N	120.0 E
153	Hsinking (Changchun) (hsĭn-kĭng) Manch.	44.2 N	123.29 E
154	Hsingwei (hsĭng'wā')...Chn.	22.53 N	109.59 E
156	Hsüchow (hsü'chō')...Chn.	34.4 N	113.56 E
153	Hsuhang (hsōō'hăng') Chn. (Shanghai In.)	31.9 N	121.28 E
102	Huacas Pt. (wä'käs)...Peru	13.45 S	76.30 W
102	Huacho (wä'chō)...Peru	11.10 S	77.31 W
92	Huajicori (wä-jē-kō'rē)...Mex.	22.39 N	105.22 W
92	Huajuápam de León (wäj-wä'pȧm dä lā-ōn').Mex.	17.48 N	97.47 W
102	Huallaga R. (wäl-yä'gä)...Peru	8.30 S	76.0 W
75	Hualpai Ind. Res. (wäl'pī)...Ariz.	35.45 N	113.35 W
102	Huamachuco (wä-mä-chōō'kō) Peru	7.32 S	78.2 W
93	Huamantla (wä-män'tlä)...Mex.	19.19 N	97.55 W
140	Huambo (Nova Lisboa) (wăm'bō) (nō'vȧ lēzh-bō'ȧ).Ang.	12.45 S	15.47 E
92	Huamuxtitlán (wä-mōōs-tē-tlän') Mex.	17.49 N	98.36 W
102	Huancavelica (wän'kä-vä-lē'kä) Peru	12.58 S	75.0 W
102	Huancayo (wän-kä'yō)...Peru	12.2 S	75.3 W
102	Huanchaca (wän-chä'kä)...Bol.	20.15 S	66.40 W
92	Huango de Morelos (wäŋ'gō dä mō-rä'lōs).Mex.	19.55 N	101.25 W
102	Huanuco (wä-nōō'kō)...Peru	9.57 S	76.12 W
92	Huaquechula (wä-kä-chōō'lä) Mex.	18.44 N	98.36 W
102	Huaráz (wä-räz')...Peru	9.30 S	77.30 W
92	Huaritura, L.(wä-rē-tōō'rä)..Mex.	22.15 N	105.30 W
102	Huascarán, Mt. (wäs-kä-rän') Peru	9.0 S	77.40 W
104	Huasco (wäs'kō)...Chl.	28.35 S	71.5 W
92	Huatlatlauca (wä'tlä-tlä-ōō'kä) Mex.	18.40 N	98.4 W
93	Huatusco (wä-tōōs'kō)...Mex.	19.8 N	96.58 W
92	Huauchinango (wä-ōō-chē-näŋ'gō) Mex.	20.10 N	98.3 W
93	Huautla (wä-ōō'tlä)...Mex.	18.9 N	96.51 W
92	Huautla...Mex.	21.1 N	98.18 W
92	Huaycatenango (wī'kä-tē-näŋ'gō) Mex.	17.30 N	99.4 W
93	Huazolotlitlán (Sta. María) (wä'zō-lō-tlē-tlän').Mex.	16.18 N	97.54 W
81	Hubbard (hŭb'ẽrd)...Tex.	31.51 N	96.47 W
84	Hubbard L....Mich.	44.50 N	83.30 W
53	Hubbard, Mt....Can.	60.20 N	139.0 W
151	Hubli (hōō'blē)...India	15.20 N	75.12 E
155	Huchow (hōō'chō')...Chn.	30.50 N	120.3 E
118	Hucknall (hŭk'năl)...Gt. Brit.	53.2 N	1.12 W
116	Huddersfield (hŭd'ẽrz-fēld) Gt. Brit.	53.40 N	1.50 W
120	Hudiksvall (hōō'dĭks-väl)...Swe.	61.46 N	17.5 E
57	Hudson (hŭd'sŭn) Can. (Montreal In.)	45.28 N	74.9 W
72	Hudson...Colo. (Denver In.)	40.4 N	104.39 W
87	Hudson...Mass. (In.)	42.24 N	71.33 W
84	Hudson...Mich.	41.50 N	84.19 W
85	Hudson...N. Y.	42.27 N	73.47 W
77	Hudson...Wis.	44.59 N	92.45 W
55	Hudson B....Can.	60.30 N	85.30 W
85	Hudson Falls...N. Y.	43.19 N	73.32 W
85	Hudson R....N. Y.	42.0 N	73.55 W
55	Hudson Str....Can.	62.50 N	73.0 W
160	Hué (ü-ā')...Fr. In. Chn.	16.29 N	107.28 E
94	Huehuetenango (wā-wā-tā-näŋ'gō) Guat.	15.20 N	91.26 W
92	Huejotzingo (wā-hō-tzĭŋ'gō)..Mex.	19.9 N	98.25 W
92	Huejúcar (wā-hōō'kär)...Mex.	22.26 N	103.22 W
92	Huejutla (wā-hōō'tlä)...Mex.	21.8 N	98.25 W
92	Huejuquilla el Alto (wā-hōō-kēl'-yä ĕl äl'tō).Mex.	22.41 N	103.55 W
126	Huelma (wĕl'mä)...Sp.	37.39 N	3.26 W
126	Huelva (wĕl'vä)...Sp.	37.16 N	6.56 W
126	Huercal-Overa (wĕr-käl' ō-vä'rä) Sp.	37.23 N	1.57 W
78	Huerfano R. (wâr'fȧ-nō)...Colo.	37.45 N	104.50 W
126	Huerva R. (wĕr'vä)...Sp.	41.20 N	1.5 W
127	Huesca (wĕs'kä)...Sp.	42.8 N	0.25 W
126	Huéscan (wās'kän)...Sp.	37.49 N	2.32 W
93	Huesos I. (wä'sōs)...Mex.	22.43 N	97.52 W
92	Huetamo de Múñez (wā-tä'mō dä mōōn'yäz).Mex.	18.33 N	100.52 W
126	Huete (wā'tā)...Sp.	40.8 N	2.41 W
93	Huexotla (wāks-ō'tlä)..Mex. (In.)	19.29 N	98.52 W
93	Hueytlalpan (wā'ĭ-tlăl'pän)..Mex.	20.4 N	97.40 W
73	Huffman (hŭf'măn) Ala. (Birmingham In.)	33.36 N	86.39 W
169	Hugel, Mt. (hŭg'ĕl) Austl.(Tas. In.)	42.6 S	146.8 E
165	Hughenden (hū'ĕn-dĕn)...Austl.	20.45 S	144.8 E
53	Hughes (hūz)...Alsk.	66.0 N	154.0 W
164	Hughes...Austl.	30.32 S	129.30 E
79	Hugo (hū'gō)...Okla.	34.1 N	95.31 W
78	Hugoton (hū'gō-tŭn)...Kan.	37.11 N	101.26 W
170	Huiarau Ra. (hwē'ä-rä'ōō)...N. Z.	38.45 S	176.50 E
92	Huichapan (wē-chä-pän')...Mex.	20.22 N	99.38 W
102	Huila, Mt. (Vol.) (wē'lä)...Col.	3.0 N	77.0 W
93	Huimanguillo (wē-män-gēl'yō) Mex.	17.50 N	93.24 W
93	Huitepec (Sta. Margarita) (wē-tä-pĕk').Mex.	16.54 N	95.43 W
92	Huitzitziling (wē-tsē-tzē-lĭng') Mex.	21.10 N	98.41 W
92	Huitzuco (wē-tzōō'kō)...Mex.	18.19 N	99.18 W
93	Huixtla (wēs'tlä)...Mex.	15.12 N	92.26 W
158	Hukae I. (hōō'kä-ā)...Jap.	32.40 N	128.45 E
155	Hukow (hōō'kō')...Chn.	29.46 N	116.15 E
153	Hulan (hōō'län')...Manch.	45.58 N	126.28 E
158	Hulan R....Manch.	46.52 N	126.30 E
158	Hulin (hōō'lĭn')...Manch.	46.0 N	133.30 E
85	Hull (hŭl)...Can.	45.27 N	75.56 W
116	Hull...Gt. Brit.	53.45 N	0.25 W
87	Hull...Mass. (In.)	42.18 N	70.54 W
118	Hull, R....Gt. Brit.	53.51 N	0.23 W
119	Hulst (hōōlst)..Neth. (Anvers In.)	51.17 N	4.3 E
153	Hulun (Hailar) (hōō'lōōn') (hī-lär').Manch.	49.8 N	119.34 E
156	Hulutao (hōō'lōō-tä'ō)...Manch.	40.44 N	120.48 E
91	Humacao (ōō-mä-kä'ō) .P. R. (In.)	18.8 N	65.50 W
102	Humaitá (ōō-mä-ē-tä')...Braz.	7.30 S	63.0 W
104	Humaitá...Par.	27.1 S	58.30 W
143	Humansdorp (hōō'mäns-dôrp) U. S. Afr.	34.2 S	24.47 E
140	Humbe (hōōm'bȧ)...Ang.	16.52 S	14.55 E
87	Humbermouth (hŭm'bẽr-mŭth) Newf.	48.57 N	57.50 W
116	Humber (R.) (hŭm'bẽr)..Gt. Brit.	53.35 N	0.20 W
81	Humble (hŭm'b'l)...Tex.	30.0 N	95.15 W
77	Humbolt (hŭm'bōlt)...Ia.	42.45 N	94.11 W
77	Humboldt...Kan.	37.47 N	95.27 W
79	Humboldt...Neb.	40.9 N	95.57 W
82	Humboldt...Tenn.	35.48 N	88.56 W
70	Humboldt B....Calif.	40.45 N	124.15 W
161	Humboldt B....Neth. Ind.	2.32 S	140.45 E
74	Humboldt R....Nev.	40.20 N	118.25 W
70	Humboldt R., East Fork...Nev.	41.0 N	115.25 W
70	Humboldt R., North Fork...Nev.	41.25 N	115.48 W
74	Humboldt Salt Marsh...Nev.	39.50 N	118.0 W
74	Humboldt Sink...Nev.	40.0 N	118.35 W
167	Hume Dam (hūm)...Austl.	36.3 S	147.0 E
167	Hume Ra....Austl.	37.32 S	145.35 E
171	Hump, The Mt. (hŭmp) N. Z. (In.)	45.46 S	170.37 E
75	Humphrey Peak (hŭm'frĭ)...Ariz.	35.20 N	111.40 W
73	Humphreys (hŭm'frĭz) Calif. (Los Angeles In.)	34.25 N	118.26 W
122	Humpolec (hōōm'pō-lĕts)...Czech.	49.33 N	15.22 E
169	Humpy Bang (hŭm'pē băng') Austl. (In.)	27.13 S	153.3 E
167	Humula (hōō'mōō-lä)...Austl.	35.31 S	147.46 E
94	Humuya, R. (ōō-mōō'yä)...Hond.	14.35 N	87.40 W
110	Húnaflói (Fjord) (hōō'nä-flō'ĭ) Ice.	65.45 N	21.0 W
154	Hunan (Prov.) (hōō'nän')...Chn.	27.24 N	111.14 E
153	Hunchun (hōōn'chōōn')...Manch.	42.50 N	130.22 E
129	Hunedoara (kōō'nĕd-wä'rä).Rom.	45.45 N	22.53 E
122	Hungary (hŭŋ'gȧ-rĭ)...Eur.	47.0 N	19.15 E
165	Hungerford (hŭŋ'gẽr-fẽrd)..Austl.	28.55 S	144.35 E
154	Hung L. (hōōng)...Chn.	29.45 N	112.58 E
154	Hung R....Chn.	25.8 N	106.50 E
156	Hungtze L. (hōōng'tzĕ')...Chn.	33.15 N	118.35 E
118	Hunmanby (hŭn'măn-bĭ).Gt. Brit.	54.11 N	0.19 W
156	Hun R. (Yungting R.) (hōōn) (yōōng'tĭng').Chn.	39.40 N	116.10 E
122	Hunsrück (Mts.) (hōōns'rük).Ger.	49.55 N	7.13 E
122	Hunte R. (hōōn'tē)...Ger.	52.50 N	8.29 E
169	Hunter I....Austl. (Tas. In.)	40.30 S	144.46 E
167	Hunter Range...Austl.	32.48 S	150.38 E
167	Hunter R....Austl.	32.10 S	150.55 E
169	Hunters Is....Austl. (Tas. In.)	40.27 S	144.50 E
84	Huntingburg...Ind.	38.16 N	86.56 W
72	Huntingdon. Can. (Vancouver In.)	49.0 N	122.16 W
85	Huntingdon...Pa.	40.32 N	78.2 W
82	Huntingdon...Tenn.	36.1 N	88.25 W
118	Huntingdon County...Gt. Brit.	52.27 N	0.20 W
85	Huntington...Can.	45.6 N	74.4 W
84	Huntington...Ind.	40.55 N	84.28 W
84	Huntington...W. Va.	38.25 N	82.25 W
74	Huntington Beach...Calif.	33.40 N	118.0 W
74	Huntington Park...Calif.	33.58 N	118.15 W
170	Huntly...N. Z.	37.32 S	175.12 E
82	Huntsville...Ala.	34.44 N	86.36 W
85	Huntsville...Can.	45.21 N	79.14 W
79	Huntsville...Mo.	39.25 N	92.31 W
81	Huntsville...Tex.	30.45 N	95.34 W
71	Huntsville...Utah	41.16 N	111.46 W
93	Hunucmá (hōō-nōōk-mä')...Mex.	20.58 N	89.56 W
155	Hunyüan (hōōn'yü-än')...Chn.	39.40 N	113.47 E
161	Huon G. (hōō'ŏn)...N. Gui. Ter.	7.0 S	147.30 E
169	Huon R....Austl. (Tas. In.)	43.0 S	146.50 E
156	Hupeh (Prov.) (hōō'pā')...Chn.	31.25 N	114.20 E
55	Hurd, C. (hûrd)...Can.	45.10 N	81.12 W
77	Hurley (hûr'lĭ)...Wis.	46.27 N	90.11 W
84	Huron (hū'rŏn)...Ohio	41.23 N	82.36 W
76	Huron...S. D.	44.21 N	98.12 W
59	Huron, L....U. S.-Can.	45.0 N	82.30 W
75	Hurricane (hŭr'ĭ-kān)...Utah	37.11 N	113.20 W
96	Hurricane Flats...Ba. Is.	23.35 N	78.25 W
167	Hurstbridge (hûrst'brĭj)...Austl.	37.38 S	145.14 E
171	Hurunui R. (hōō-rōō-nōō'ē) .N. Z.	42.45 S	172.30 E
131	Huşi (hōōsh')...Rom.	46.39 N	28.2 E
120	Huskvarna (hōōsk-vär'nȧ)...Swe.	57.48 N	14.15 E
72	Husted (hū'stĕd) Colo. (Colo. Spgs. In.)	39.1 N	104.50 W
122	Husum (hōō'zōōm)...Ger.	54.28 N	9.3 E
78	Hutchinson (hŭch'ĭn-sŭn)...Kan.	38.2 N	97.56 W
77	Hutchinson...Minn.	44.54 N	94.21 W
89	Hutchinsons I..Ga. (Savannah In.)	32.6 N	81.6 W

ng-sing; ŋ-baŋk; N-nasalized n; nŏd; cŏmmit; ōld; ôbey; ôrder; fōōd; fŏŏt; ou-out; s-soft; sh-dish; th-thin; pūre; ûnite; ûrn; stŭd; circŭs; ü-as "y" in study; '-indeterminate vowel.

Page	Name Pronunciation Region	Lat. °'	Long. °'
156	Huto R. (hōō'tō') .... Chn.	38.10 N	115.55 E
119	Hütteldorf (hüt''l-dôrf) Aus. (Wien In.)	48.12 N	16.15 E
170	Hutt R. (hŭt) .... N. Z. (In.)	41.12 S	174.57 E
142	Huxley, Mt. (hŭks'lĭ) .... Bech.	28.5 S	23.12 E
171	Huxley Mt. .... N. Z.	44.2 S	169.45 E
117	Huy (ü-e') (hŭ'ē) .... Bel.	50.31 N	5.15 E
119	Huyton (hoi'tŭn) .... Gt. Brit.	53.24 N	2.51 W
128	Hvar (I.) (ĸhvär) .... Yugo.	43.8 N	16.40 E
156	Hwahsien (hwä'hsyĕn') .... Chn.	35.32 N	114.52 E
156	Hwaian (hwä'ē-än') .... Chn.	33.38 N	119.12 E
156	Hwaijen (hwä'ē-jĕn') .... Chn.	39.44 N	113.14 E
156	Hwaiking (hwä'ē-kĭng') ...... Chn.	35.6 N	112.59 E
156	Hwailu (hwä'ē-lōō') .... Chn.	38.10 N	114.19 E
156	Hwai R. (hwä'ē) .... Chn.	33.52 N	119.0 E
155	Hwaiyang Shan (Mts.) (hwī'yäng' shän'). Chn.	31.30 N	114.35 E
156	Hwaiyin (hwä'ē-yĭn') .... Chn.	33.33 N	119.4 E
156	Hwaiyüan (hwä'ē-yü-än') .... Chn.	32.57 N	117.8 E
154	Hwajung (hwä'jōōng') .... Chn.	29.32 N	112.17 E
155	Hwangan (hwăng'än') .... Chn.	31.18 N	114.33 E
154	Hwangchow (hwäng'chō') ... Chn.	27.20 N	108.47 E
155	Hwangchow .... Chn.	30.27 N	114.48 E
157	Hwang Hai (Yellow Sea) (hwäng' hä'ē). Chn.	36.0 N	123.0 E
152	Hwang Ho (R.) (hwäng'hō'). Chn.	37.30 N	105.0 E
156	Hwanghsien (hwäng'hsyĕn') .. Chn.	37.36 N	120.31 E
158	Hwangju (hwäng'jōō') .... Cho.	38.44 N	125.48 E
157	Hwangkan (hwäng'kän') ..... Cho.	36.9 N	127.2 E
154	Hwang L. (hwäng) .... Chn.	29.37 N	113.28 E
155	Hwangmei (hwäng'mā') ..... Chn.	30.4 N	115.50 E
155	Hwangpei (hwäng'pā') ...... Chn.	30.52 N	114.11 E
154	Hwangping (hwäng'pĭng') ... Chn.	26.49 N	107.44 E
155	Hwangpo R. (hwäng'pō) ..... Chn.	30.50 N	121.10 E
155	Hwang Shan (Mts.) (hwäng' shän') Chn.	30.8 N	118.6 E
155	Hwangsha Shan (Mts.) (hwäng'-shä' shän'). Chn.	26.12 N	115.12 E
155	Hwangyen (hwäng'yĕn') ..... Chn.	28.37 N	121.13 E
152	Hwan Ho (R.) (hwän' hō') .... Chn.	36.0 N	107.52 E
158	Hwanjen (hwän'jĕn') ..... Manch.	41.16 N	125.29 E
156	Hweichang (hwā'chäng') ..... Chn.	25.28 N	115.30 E
155	Hweichow (hwā'chō') .... Chn.	29.52 N	118.23 E
156	Hweilai (hwā'lī') .... Chn.	23.3 N	116.5 E
152	Hweili (hwā'ē-lĭ') .... Chn	26.45 N	102.16 E
154	Hweitung (hwā'tōōng') .... Chn.	26.50 N	109.26 E
156	Hwokia (hwō'kyä') .... Chn.	35.15 N	113.51 E
156	Hwokiu (hwō'kyōō') .... Chn.	32.20 N	116.11 E
118	Hyde (hīd) .... Gt. Brit.	52.27 N	2.4 W
119	Hyde Pk. .. Gt. Brit. (London In.)	51.30 N	0.10 W
151	Hyderabad (hī-dēr-ȧ-băd') .. India	17.15 N	78.30 E
151	Hyderabad .... India	25.28 N	68.35 E
151	Hyderabad (State) .... India	18.15 N	78.0 E
129	Hydra (I.) (ēdh'rä) .... Grc.	37.20 N	23.30 E
125	Hyères (ē-âr') .... Fr.	43.9 N	6.9 E
125	Hyères, Iles d' (Is.) (ēl'dē yâr'). Fr.	43.0 N	6.10 E
72	Hygiene (hī-jĭ-ēn') Colo. (Denver In.)	40.11 N	105.10 W
169	Hyland, Mt. (hī'lănd). Austl. (In.)	30.10 S	152.25 E
84	Hymera (hī-mē'rȧ) .... Ind.	39.13 N	87.19 W
71	Hyndman Peak (hīnd'măn) ... Ida.	43.47 N	114.3 W
73	Hyrum (hī'rŭm) Utah (Salt Lake City In.)	41.38 N	111.52 W
129	Ialomița R. (yä-lō-mēt'sȧ) ... Rom.	44.40 N	26.40 E
123	Iasi (Jassy) (yä'shē) .... Rom.	47.12 N	27.35 E
162	Iba (ē'bä) .... P. I.	15.20 N	119.59 E
138	Ibadan (ē-bä'dän) .... Nig.	7.28 N	3.56 E
102	Ibagué (ē-bä'gā') .... Col.	4.52 N	75.28 W
161	Ibahan (ē-bä'än') P. I. (Manila In.)	13.51 N	121.7 E
163	Ibajay (ē-bȧ-hī') .... P. I.	11.48 N	122.11 E
159	Ibaraki (ē'bȧ-rä'kē) Jap. (Osaka In.)	34.49 N	135.34 E
129	Ibar R. (ē'bär) .... Yugo.	43.4 N	20.53 E
102	Ibarra (ē-bär'rä) .... Ec.	0.20 N	78.2 W
86	Iberville (ē-bär-vēl') (ī'bēr-vĭl). Can.	45.19 N	73.15 W
138	Ibi (ē'bē) .... Nig.	8.12 N	9.45 E
103	Ibitinga (ē-bē-tĭŋ'gȧ) .... Braz.	21.40 S	48.58 W
127	Ibiza (ē-bē'thä) .... Sp.	38.55 N	1.25 E
127	Ibiza I. .... Sp.	39.0 N	1.25 E
141	Ibo (ē'bō) .... Moz.	12.15 S	40.40 E
102	Ica (ē'kä) .... Peru	14.2 S	75.32 W
7	Icacos Pt. (ē'kä'kōs) ... Trin. (In.)	10.4 N	61.56 W
113	Içel (ē-chĕl') .... Tur.	36.28 N	34.0 E
110	Iceland (īs'lănd) .... Atl. O.	65.0 N	19.0 W
154	Ichang (ē'chäng') .... Chn.	25.28 N	112.40 E
154	Ichang .... Chn.	30.43 N	111.10 E
156	Icheng (ē'chĕng) .... Chn.	32.17 N	119.11 E
159	Ichibusayama (Mt.) (ē'chē-bōō'sȧ-yä'mä). Jap.	32.18 N	131.4 E
159	Ichikawa (ē'chē-kä'wä) Jap. (Tokyo In.)	35.43 N	139.54 E
158	Ichinomiya (ē'chē-nō-mē'yȧ). Jap.	35.25 N	140.22 E
159	Ichinomiya .... Jap.	35.19 N	136.49 E
131	Ichnya (ĭch'nyȧ) .... Sov. Un.	50.52 N	32.21 E
156	Ichow (ē'chō') .... Chn.	35.5 N	118.16 E
103	Icó (ē-kō') .... Braz.	6.28 S	38.58 W
102	Icutú, Mt. (ē-kōō-tōō') .... Ven.	6.33 N	65.29 W
79	Idabel (ī'dȧ-bĕl) .... Okla.	33.53 N	94.48 W
76	Idagrove (ī'dȧ-grōv) .... Ia.	42.22 N	95.28 W
138	Idah (ē'dä) .... Nig.	7.7 N	6.42 E
70	Idaho (State) (ī'dȧ-hō) ...... U. S.	45.0 N	115.10 W
71	Idaho Falls .... Ida.	43.30 N	112.1 W
75	Idaho Sprs. .... Colo.	39.44 N	105.31 W
126	Idanha-a-Nova (ē-dän'yȧ-ȧ-nō'vȧ) Port.	39.58 N	7.13 W
139	Idfû (ĕd'fōō) .... Eg.	24.59 N	32.46 E
160	Idi (ē'dē) .... Neth. Ind.	4.59 N	97.46 E
135	Idkû (ĕd'kōō) .... Eg. (In.)	31.18 N	30.20 E
118	Idle, R. (īd''l) .... Gt. Brit.	53.23 N	0.56 W
128	Idria (ē'drē-ä) .... It.	46.1 N	14.1 E
143	Idutywa (ē-dōō-tī'wȧ) .. U. S. Afr.	32.6 S	28.18 E

Page	Name Pronunciation Region	Lat. °'	Long. °'
128	Iesi (yā'sē) .... It.	43.35 N	13.19 E
138	Iferouane (ēf'rōō-än') .. F. W. Afr.	19.30 N	8.30 E
138	Ifni (ēf'nē) .... Afr.	29.25 N	10.18 W
103	Igarapé-Mirim (ē-gä-rä-pā' mē-rēɴ'). Braz. (In.)	1.55 S	48.55 W
114	Igharghar, Wadi (R.) (wä'dē ē-gär'-gär). Alg.	32.30 N	6.5 E
138	Igidi (Sand Dunes) (ē-gē'dē) .. Alg.	26.30 N	5.30 W
128	Iglesias (ē-glā'zē-äs) .... Sard.	39.19 N	8.34 E
138	Igli (ē-glē') .... Alg.	30.30 N	2.15 W
103	Igrapiuna (ē-grä-pē-ōō'nȧ) Braz. (In.)	13.45 S	39.12 W
113	Igridir (ē-ghrē-dēr') .... Tur.	37.50 N	30.50 E
113	Igridir, L. .... Tur.	38.10 N	30.48 E
92	Iguala (ē-gwä'lä) .... Mex.	18.18 N	99.33 W
127	Igualada (ē-gwä-lä'dä) ... Sp. (In.)	41.35 N	1.37 E
104	Iguassú, R. (ē-gwȧ-sōō') Arg.-Braz.	26.0 S	52.0 W
104	Iguassú Falls .... Arg.-Braz.	25.30 S	54.0 W
103	Iguatú (ē-gwȧ-tōō') .... Braz.	6.28 S	39.28 W
162	Iguig (ē-gēg') .... P. I.	17.46 N	121.43 E
155	Ihing (ē'hĭng') .... Chn.	31.21 N	119.47 E
155	Ihwang (ē'hwäng') .... Chn.	27.28 N	116.3 E
159	Iida (ē'ē-dȧ) .... Jap.	35.38 N	137.52 E
112	Ii Joki (R.) (ē'yō'kĭ) .... Fin.	65.28 N	27.0 E
138	Ijebu Ode (ē-jĕ'bōō ō'dȧ) .... Nig.	6.47 N	4.2 E
122	Ijsel Sea .... Neth.	54.15 N	5.0 E
121	Ikaalinen (ē'kȧ-lĭ-nĕn) .... Fin.	61.48 N	22.58 E
129	Ikaria (I.) (ē-kä'ryȧ) .... Grc.	37.35 N	26.10 E
159	Ikedi (ē'kȧ-dē) ... Jap. (Osaka In.)	34.50 N	135.25 E
129	Ikhtiman (ēk'tē-män) .... Bul.	42.26 N	23.49 E
159	Iki I. (ē'kē) .... Jap.	33.45 N	129.45 E
140	Ikoma (ē-kō'mä) .... Tan.	2.12 S	34.47 E
162	Ilagan (ē-lä'gän) .... P. I.	17.8 N	121.53 E
153	Ilan (ī-län') .... Manch.	46.14 N	129.32 E
86	Ile-aux-Coudres, I. (ēl'-ō-kōōd'r') Can.	47.25 N	70.25 W
56	Ile des Chênes (ēl' dā shân') Can. (Winnipeg In.)	49.41 N	96.57 W
113	Ilek R. .... Sov. Un.	51.0 N	54.10 E
113	Iletskaya Zashchita (ēl'yĕt-skä'yȧ) Sov. Un.	51.8 N	55.5 E
119	Ilford (ĭl'fērd) Gt. Brit. (London In.)	51.34 N	0.4 E
116	Ilfracombe (ĭl-frȧ-kōōm'). Gt. Brit.	51.10 N	4.10 W
99	Ilha Grande B. (ēl'yȧ grän'dē) Braz. (Rio de Janeiro In.)	23.12 S	44.30 W
99	Ilha Grande (I.) Braz. (Rio de Janeiro In.)	23.10 S	44.15 W
126	Ilhavo (ēl'yȧ-vō) .... Port.	40.36 N	8.40 W
103	Ilhéos (ēl-yā'ōzh) .... Braz.	14.28 S	39.2 W
152	Ili (Qulja) (ē-lē') (kōōl'jä) ... Chn.	43.55 N	81.0 E
53	Iliamna (ē-lē-ăm'nä) .... Alsk.	59.45 N	154.0 W
52	Iliamna L. .... Alsk.	59.30 N	155.0 W
53	Iliamna Vol. .... Alsk.	60.10 N	153.0 W
112	Ilich R. (ē'l'ĭch) .... Sov. Un.	62.35 N	57.30 E
163	Iligan B. (ē-lē'gän) .... P. I.	8.25 N	124.5 E
162	Iligan Pt. .... P. I.	18.20 N	122.20 E
140	Ilim R. (ē-lyĕm') .... Sov. Un.	57.0 N	103.30 E
148	Ilimsk (ē-lyĕmsk') ...... Sov. Un.	56.45 N	103.45 E
162	Ilin I. (ē-lēn') .... P. I.	12.15 N	121.5 E
131	Ilintsy (ē-lyĕnt'sĭ) ...... Sov. Un.	49.7 N	29.11 E
85	Ilion (ĭl'ĭ-ŭn) .... N. Y.	43.0 N	75.2 W
148	Ili R. (ē'l'ē) .... Sov. Un.	44.0 N	77.0 E
116	Ilkeston (ĭl'kĕs-tŭn) ..... Gt. Brit.	52.55 N	2.20 W
118	Ilkley (ĭlk'lĭ) .... Gt. Brit.	53.55 N	1.49 W
102	Illampú (Mt.) (ēl-yäm-pōō') .. Bol.	15.58 S	68.30 W
163	Illana B. (ēl-yä'nä) .... P. I.	7.30 N	123.35 E
104	Illapeh (ēl-yä'pä) .... Chl.	31.45 S	70.15 W
167	Illawara L. (ĭl-ȧ-wăr'ȧ) ..... Austl.	34.32 S	150.52 E
122	Iller R. (ĭl'er) .... Ger.	47.50 N	10.12 E
141	Illig (ēl'lĕg) .... It. E. Afr.	7.50 N	49.42 E
102	Illimani (Mt.) (ēl-yē-mä'nē) .. Bol.	16.45 S	67.42 W
79	Illinois (State) (ĭl-ĭ-noi') (ĭl-ĭ-noiz') U. S.	39.40 N	90.0 W
88	Illinois and Michigan Canal Ill. (Chicago In.)	41.46 N	87.50 W
79	Illinois and Mississippi Canal .. Ill.	41.25 N	89.40 W
79	Illinois R. .... Ill.	40.0 N	90.0 W
125	Illkirch (ēl'kĭrĸ) .... Fr.	48.32 N	7.45 E
126	Illora (ēl'yō-rä) .... Sp.	37.17 N	3.53 W
122	Ilmenau (ēl'mē-nou) .... Ger.	50.42 N	10.56 E
130	Ilmen, L. (ēl''män'') (ĭl'mĕn) Sov. Un.	58.20 N	31.22 E
138	Ilo (ē'lō) .... Nig.	11.32 N	3.41 E
102	Ilo .... Peru	17.42 S	71.15 W
94	Ilobasco (ē-lō-bäs'kō) .... Sal.	13.57 N	88.47 W
163	Iloc I. (ē-lōk) .... P. I.	11.18 N	119.42 E
163	Iloilo (ē-lō-ē'lō) .... P. I.	10.41 N	122.34 E
163	Iloilo Str. .... P. I.	10.30 N	122.20 E
94	Ilopango, L. (ē-lō-päŋ'gō) .... Sal.	13.40 N	89.0 W
138	Ilorin (ē-lō-rēn') .... Nig.	8.33 N	4.32 E
130	Ilovai-Dmitrievsk (ē'lō-vī-d'mē'trē-ĕfsk) Sov. Un.	53.8 N	40.15 E
131	Ilskaya (ēl'skȧ-yȧ) ...... Sov. Un.	44.52 N	38.32 E
121	Ilukste (ē-lōōk'shtä) .... Lat.	55.59 N	26.20 E
70	Ilwaco (ĭl-wä'kō) .... Wash.	46.18 N	124.2 W
159	Imabaru (ē'mȧ-bä'rōō) .... Jap.	34.1 N	132.59 E
159	Imachi (ē'mȧ-chē) .... Jap.	35.16 N	132.55 E
140	Iman (ē-män') .... Sov. Un.	45.59 N	133.35 E
112	Imandra, L. (ē-män'drȧ) .. Sov. Un.	67.40 N	32.30 E
158	Iman R. (ē-män') .... Sov. Un.	45.52 N	135.0 E
141	Imbâba (ēm-bä'bȧ) .... Eg.	30.5 N	31.13 E
158	Imianpo (ēm'yän-pō') ...... Manch.	45.0 N	128.1 E
84	Imlay City (ĭm'lā) .... Mich.	43.0 N	83.6 W
119	Immenbeck (ĭm'ĕn-bĕk) Ger. (Hamburg In.)	53.27 N	9.43 E
122	Immenstadt (ĭm'ĕn-shtät) .... Ger.	47.34 N	10.13 E
128	Imola (ē'mō-lä) .... It.	44.21 N	11.41 E
128	Imotski (ē-mōts'kē) .... Yugo.	43.27 N	17.14 E
163	Impasugong (ēm-pȧ-sōō'gōng) P. I.	8.15 N	125.0 E
143	Impendhle (ĭm-pĕnd'lȧ) . U. S. Afr.	29.37 S	29.51 E

Page	Name Pronunciation Region	Lat. °'	Long. °'
128	Imperia (ēm-pä'rē-ä) .... It.	43.53 N	8.1 E
74	Imperial Beach (ĭm-pē'rĭ-ăl). Calif.	82.33 N	117.7 W
74	Imperial Valley .... Calif.	32.58 N	115.30 W
139	Impfondo (Desborderville) (ĭmp-fōn'dō) (dā-bord'vēl') Fr. Eq. Afr.	1.41 N	18.2 E
151	Imphal (ĭmp'hŭl) .... India	24.45 N	93.58 E
129	Imroz (I.) (ĭm'rōz) .... Tur.	40.8 N	25.50 E
163	Imuruan B. (ē-mōō-rōō'än) .. P. I.	10.40 N	119.10 E
162	Imus (ē'mōōs) .... P. I.	14.25 N	120.57 E
143	Imvani (ēm-vä'nē) ..... U. S. Afr.	32.2 S	27.5 E
143	Imvusi Swamp (ēm-vōō'zē) U. S. Afr.	27.0 S	32.30 E
163	Inabanga (ē-nä-bäŋ'gä) ...... P. I.	10.1 N	124.4 E
74	Inaja Ind. Res. (ē-nä'hä) .... Calif.	32.55 N	116.45 W
138	In-Azaoua (ēn-ä-zou'ä) .... Alg.	20.52 N	7.30 E
127	Inca (ēŋ'kä) .... Sp.	39.42 N	2.55 E
104	Incahuasi (Mt.) (ēŋ-kȧ-wä'sē) Arg.-Chl.	26.59 S	68.29 W
119	Ince (Ins). Gt. Brit. (Liverpool In.)	53.32 N	2.36 W
113	Ince, C. (ĭn'jä) .... Tur.	42.5 N	35.0 E
124	Incudine (Mt.) (ēn-kōō-dē'nä) (äɴ-kü-dēn') Cor. (In.)	41.55 N	9.15 E
120	Indals R. (ĭn'däls) .... Swe.	63.10 N	15.30 E
162	Indan (ēn-dän') .... P. I.	14.15 N	122.53 E
162	Indang (ēn'däng') .... P. I.	14.12 N	120.53 E
80	Inde (ēn'dā) .... Mex.	25.53 N	105.14 W
77	Independence (ĭn-dē-pĕn'dĕns). Ia.	42.28 N	91.52 W
79	Independence .... Kan.	37.14 N	95.42 W
79	Independence .... Mo.	39.5 N	94.24 W
70	Independence .... Ore.	44.50 N	123.10 W
113	Inderskoe, L. (ēn-dyĕr'skō-yĕ) Sov. Un.	48.30 N	52.0 E
151	India (ĭn'dĭ-ȧ) .... Asia	24.0 N	80.0 E
85	Indiana (ĭn-dĭ-ăn'ȧ) .... Pa.	40.38 N	79.10 W
84	Indiana (State) .... U. S.	40.0 N	86.0 W
84	Indianapolis (ĭn-dĭ-ăn-ăp'ō-lĭs) Ind.	39.45 N	86.10 W
96	Indian Cays (Is.) .... Cuba	21.49 N	83.8 W
7	Indian O.	10.0 S	80.0 E
77	Indianola (ĭn-dĭ-ăn-ō'lȧ) .... Ia.	41.21 N	93.32 W
82	Indianola .... Miss.	33.27 N	90.39 W
74	Indian Peak (Paiute) Ind. Res. (pī-ōōt') Utah	38.15 N	113.50 W
72	Indian R. ... Can. (Vancouver In.)	49.36 N	122.56 W
83	Indian R. .... Fla. (In.)	28.25 N	80.53 W
85	Indian R. .... N. Y.	44.10 N	75.40 E
149	Indigirka R. (ēn-dē-gēr'kä) Sov. Un.	68.0 N	146.20 E
151	Indore (ĭn-dōr') .... India	22.40 N	75.58 E
160	Indragiri R. (ĭn-drȧ-jē'rē) Neth. Ind.	0.30 S	102.30 E
151	Indravari R. (ĭn-drŭ-vä'rē) .. India	19.5 N	81.30 E
124	Indre (ăɴ'dr') .... Fr.	47.15 N	1.40 W
120	Indre Sullen (I.) (ĭn'dhrĕ sōōl'ĕn) Nor.	61.8 N	4.56 E
151	Indus R. (ĭn'dŭs) .... India	33.0 N	71.30 E
143	Indwe (ĭnd'wä) .... U. S. Afr.	31.26 S	27.17 E
113	Inebolu (ē-nä-bō'lōō) .... Tur.	41.58 N	33.45 E
113	Inegöl (ē'nȧ-gōl) .... Tur.	40.2 N	29.20 E
162	Infanta (ēn-fän'tä) .... P. I.	15.49 N	119.54 E
162	Infanta .... P. I.	14.44 N	121.39 E
142	Infanta, C. .... U. S. Afr.	34.28 S	21.51 E
126	Infantes (ēn-fän'tâs) .... Sp.	38.45 N	3.1 W
93	Inferior, L. (ēn-fȧ-rē-ōr') .... Mex.	16.17 N	94.44 W
84	Ingersoll (ĭn'gēr-sŏl) .... Can.	43.5 N	80.56 W
165	Ingham (ĭng'ăm) .... Austl.	18.45 S	146.5 E
73	Inglenook (ĭŋ'g'l-nōōk) Ala. (Birmingham In.)	33.34 N	86.46 W
163	Inglesia Pt. (ēŋ-glä'sē-ȧ) ..... P. I.	8.30 N	117.30 E
118	Ingleton (ĭŋ'g'l-tŭn) ..... Gt. Brit.	54.9 N	2.27 W
166	Inglewood (ĭŋ'g'l-wŏŏd) ..... Austl.	36.33 S	143.52 E
169	Inglewood .... Austl. (In.)	28.26 S	151.8 E
74	Inglewood .... Calif.	33.55 N	118.22 W
170	Inglewood .... N. Z.	39.9 S	174.15 E
149	Ingoda R. (ēn-gō'dȧ) ..... Sov. Un.	51.45 N	113.0 E
122	Ingolstadt (ĭŋ'gōl-shtät) ...... Ger.	48.47 N	11.26 E
131	Ingul R. (ēn-gōōl') .... Sov. Un.	47.15 N	32.15 E
131	Ingulets R. (ēn-gōōl'yĕts') Sov. Un.	47.10 N	33.0 E
131	Ingulskaya Kamenka (ēn-gōōl'-skȧ-yȧ kȧ-mĕn'kȧ) ... Sov. Un.	48.16 N	32.30 E
113	Ingur R. (ēn-gōōr') ...... Sov. Un.	42.45 N	42.0 E
143	Ingwavuma (ĭŋ-gwȧ-vōō'mȧ) U. S. Afr.	27.8 S	32.1 E
140	Inhambane (ēn-yäm-bä'nȧ) .. Moz.	23.52 S	35.20 E
103	Inhambupe (ēn-yäm-bōō'pȧ) Braz. (In.)	11.50 S	38.15 W
140	Inharrime (ēn-yär-rē'mä) .... Moz.	24.28 S	35.2 E
103	Inhaúma (ēn-yȧ-ōō'mä) Braz. (In.)	22.52 S	43.17 W
126	Iniesta (ēn-yäs'tä) .... Sp.	39.27 N	1.44 W
154	Ining (ē'nĭng') .... Chn.	25.19 N	109.59 E
102	Inini (ē-nē-nē') .... S. Am.	4.0 N	53.0 W
102	Inirida, R. (ē-nē-rē'dä) .... Col.	2.30 N	69.30 W
116	Inishbofin (I.) (ĭn'ĭsh-bō-fĭn') .. Ire.	53.39 N	10.10 W
116	Inishtrahull (I.) (ĭn'ĭsh-trȧ'hŭl) Gt. Brit.	55.25 N	7.10 W
116	Inishturk (I.) (ĭn'ĭsh-tûrk') .... Ire.	53.45 N	10.5 W
163	Initao (ē-nē-tä'ō) .... P. I.	8.29 N	124.20 E
127	Inkermann (ĭn-kĕr-män) ...... Alg.	35.58 N	0.56 E
121	Inkeroinen (ĭn'kĕr-oi-nĕn) ..... Fin.	60.45 N	26.55 E
135	Inkisi R. (ēn-kē'sē) Bel. Cong. (Brazzaville In.)	5.20 S	15.20 E
143	Inkwelo Mt. (ĭn-kwĕl'ō) U. S. Afr.	27.32 S	29.48 E
88	Inland (ĭn'lănd) N. Y. (Niagara Falls In.)	43.2 N	78.58 W
91	Inner Bras (I.) (ĭn'ēr-brä') St. Thomas (In.)	18.23 N	64.58 W
116	Inner Sd. (ĭn'ēr) .... Gt. Brit.	57.25 N	6.5 W
122	Inn R. (ĭn) .... Eur.	47.30 N	12.0 E
122	Innsbruck (ĭns'brŏŏk) .... Ger.	47.16 N	11.24 E
159	Ino (ē'nō) .... Jap.	33.33 N	133.24 E
140	Inongo (ē-nôŋ'gō) ...... Bel. Cong.	1.50 S	18.32 E

ăt; finăl; rāte; senāte; ärm; ȧsk; sofȧ; fâre; ch-choose; dh-as th in other; bē; ēvent; bĕt; recĕnt; cratēr g-go; gh-guttural g; bĭt; ĭ-short neutral; rīde; ĸ-gutteral k as ch in German ich;

Page	Name Pronunciation	Region	Lat. °'	Long. °'
123	Inowroclaw (ē-nô-vrŏts'läf)	Pol.	52.47 N	18.15 E
129	Inoz (Enos) (ĕn'ŏz) (ā'nôs)	Tur.	40.42 N	46.3 E
138	In-Salah (ēn-sȧ-lä')	Alg.	27.18 N	2.25 E
75	Inscription House Ruin	Ariz.	36.45 N	110.48 W
123	Insterburg (ĭn'stēr-bŏŏrgh)	Ger.	54.38 N	21.49 E
77	International Falls	Minn.	48.35 N	94.23 W
159	Inuyama (ē'nōō-yä'mä)	Jap.	35.23 N	136.58 E
171	Invercargill (ĭn-vēr-kär'gĭl)	N. Z.	46.25 S	168.22 E
167	Inverell (ĭn-vēr-ĕl')	Austl.	29.49 S	151.17 E
89	Invergrove(ĭn'vēr-grōv)	Minn. (Minneapolis In.)	44.51 N	93.1 W
83	Inverness (ĭn-vēr-nĕs')	Fla. (In.)	28.50 N	82.20 W
116	Inverness	Gt. Brit.	57.30 N	4.10 W
87	Inverness	Can.	46.12 N	61.19 W
166	Investigator Str. (ĭn-vĕs'tĭ-gā-tēr)	Austl.	35.23 S	137.15 E
140	Inyangani (Mt.) (ên-yăn-gä'nê)	S. Rh.	18.17 S	32.47 E
74	Inyo Mts. (ĭn'yō)	Calif.	36.55 N	118.8 W
119	Inzersdorf (ĭnt'sērs-dôrf)	Aus. (Wien In.)	48.9 N	16.21 E
138	In Zize (Well) (ēn-zē'zĕ)	Alg.	23.29 N	2.30 E
129	Ioannina (Yannina) (yô-ä'nê-nȧ) (yä'nê-nȧ)	Grc.	39.38 N	20.53 E
79	Iola (ī-ō'lȧ)	Kan.	37.55 N	95.24 W
72	Ione (ī-ō'nê)	Colo. (Denver In.)	40.8 N	104.49 W
84	Ionia (ī-ō'nĭ-ȧ)	Mich.	43.0 N	85.5 W
129	Ionian Is. (ī-ō'nĭ-ăn)	Grc.	38.45 N	20.50 E
129	Ionian Sea	It.-Grc.	39.0 N	19.0 E
129	Ios (I.) (ī'ŏs)	Grc.	36.45 N	25.18 E
112	Ioshkar Ola (Krasnokokshaisk) (yŏsh'kär ō'lä)	Sov. Un.	56.35 N	47.50 E
77	Iowa (State) (ī'ô-wȧ)	U. S.	42.10 N	93.20 W
77	Iowa City	Ia.	41.39 N	91.32 W
77	Iowa Falls	Ia.	42.32 N	93.15 W
78	Iowa Park	Tex.	33.57 N	98.38 W
77	Iowa R.	Ia.	41.56 N	92.30 W
103	Ipameri (ē-pä-mȧ-rē')	Braz.	17.45 S	48.10 W
154	Ipe (ē'pĕ)	Chn.	25.13 N	108.19 E
102	Ipiales (ē-pê-ä'lās)	Col.	0.50 N	77.48 W
160	Ipoh (ī'pō)	Strs. Sets.	6.25 N	101.0 E
123	Ipoly R. (ē'pôl-y')	Hung.	48.6 N	19.20 E
165	Ipswich (ĭps'wĭch)	Austl.	27.40 S	152.59 E
117	Ipswich	Gt. Brit.	52.5 N	1.10 E
87	Ipswich	Mass. (In.)	42.41 N	70.50 W
76	Ipswich	S. D.	45.27 N	99.0 W
130	Iput R. (ê-pŏŏt')	Sov. Un.	52.40 N	31.46 E
102	Iquique (ê-kē'kā)	Chl.	20.5 S	70.1 W
102	Iquitos (ê-kē'tōs)	Peru	3.45 S	73.0 W
104	Irajá (ê-rȧ-hä')	Braz. (In.)	22.51 S	43.19 W
150	Iran (Persia) (ē-rän)	Asia	33.0 N	55.0 E
160	Iran Mts.(ī'răn)(ē-rän')	Neth. Ind.	2.30 N	114.45 E
150	Iran, Plateau of (ē'rän')	Iran	32.0 N	59.0 E
150	Iranshahr (ē-rän-shär')	Iran	28.55 N	58.55 E
92	Irapuato (ē-rä-pwä'tō)	Mex.	20.40 N	101.20 W
150	Iraq (ē-räk')	Asia	32.0 N	43.30 E
103	Irará (ē-rȧ-rä')	Braz. (In.)	12.8 S	38.33 W
95	Irazú (Vol.) (ē-rä-zōō')	C. R.	9.59 N	83.53 W
145	Irbid (êr-bēd')	Transj. (In.)	32.33 N	35.49 E
148	Irbit (êr-bêt')	Sov. Un.	57.40 N	63.10 E
140	Irebu (ē-rā'bōō)	Bel. Cong.	0.35 S	17.47 E
143	Irene (ī-rēn')	U. S. Afr.	25.51 S	28.15 E
148	Irgiz (ĭr-gēz')	Sov. Un.	48.35 N	61.15 E
148	Irgiz R.	Sov. Un.	49.30 N	60.20 E
162	Iriga (ê-rē'gä)	P. I.	13.25 N	123.24 E
140	Iringa (ê-rĭŋ'gä)	Tan.	7.45 S	35.38 E
94	Iriona (ê-rê-ō'nä)	Hond.	15.57 N	85.7 W
103	Iriri, R. (ê-rē'rē)	Braz.	5.0 S	54.28 W
116	Irish Free State	Eur.	53.0 N	8.0 W
116	Irish Sea (ī'rĭsh)	Eur.	53.40 N	5.0 W
148	Irkutsk (ĭr-kŏŏtsk')	Sov. Un.	52.30 N	104.20 E
119	Irlam(ûr'lăm)	Gt.Brit.LiverpoolIn.	53.26 N	2.25 W
118	Irlam	Gt. Brit.	53.26 N	2.26 W
159	Iro C. (ē'rō)	Jap.	34.32 N	138.58 E
166	Iron Baron	Austl.	33.2 S	137.5 E
73	Irondale	Ala. (Birmingham In.)	33.33 N	86.43 W
166	Iron Knob	Austl.	32.43 S	137.8 E
73	Iron Mt.	Calif. (Los Angeles In.)	34.21 N	118.14 W
77	Iron Mountain	Mich.	45.50 N	88.4 W
75	Iron Mountain	Utah	37.37 N	113.17 W
77	Iron River	Mich.	46.6 N	88.38 W
54	Ironside	Can. (In.)	45.30 N	75.44 W
84	Ironton	Ohio	38.32 N	82.42 W
77	Ironwood	Mich.	46.27 N	90.9 W
84	Iroquois R. (ĭr'ô-kwoi)	Ill.-Ind.	40.50 N	87.30 W
162	Irosin (ē-rô-sēn')	P. I.	12.42 N	124.2 E
131	Irpen R. (ĭr-pĕn')	Sov. Un.	50.20 N	30.10 E
151	Irrawaddy R. (ĭr-ȧ-wäd'ê)	India	23.30 N	96.0 E
148	Irtysh R. (ĭr-tĭsh')	Sov. Un.	57.35 N	73.0 E
139	Irumu (ê-rōō'mōō)	Bel. Cong.	1.29 N	29.51 E
126	Irún (ê-rōōn')	Sp.	43.20 N	1.48 W
73	Irvine (ûr'vĭn)	Calif. (Los Angeles In.)	33.40 N	117.45 W
116	Irvine	Gt. Brit.	55.35 N	4.40 W
84	Irvine	Ky.	37.40 N	83.58 W
49	Irvington	Calif. (San Francisco In.)	37.32 N	121.57 W
88	Irvington	N. J. (New York In.)	40.44 N	74.15 W
119	Irwell R. (ûr'wĕl)	Gt. Brit. (Liverpool In.)	53.32 N	2.17 W
163	Isabela (ē-sä-bā'lä)	P. I.	6.42 N	121.59 E
163	Isabela	P. I.	10.11 N	123.0 E
97	Isabela, C.	Hai.	19.55 N	71.0 W
182	Isabela (I.)	Ec.	0.30 S	91.0 W
92	Isabel I. (ē-sä-bĕl')	Mex.	21.53 N	105.55 W
94	Isabella, Cordillera (Mts.)	Nic.	13.50 N	84.50 W
131	Isaccea (ê-säk'chä)	Rom.	45.16 N	28.28 E
110	Isafjördur (ēs'ȧ-fyûr-dŏŏr)	Ice.	66.8 N	23.15 W
139	Isangi (ê-säŋ'gē)	Bel. Cong.	0.51 N	24.13 E
135	Isangila (ê-säŋ-gê-lä')	Bel. Cong. (Brazzaville In.)	5.22 S	13.31 E
128	Isarco R. (ê-sär'kō)	It.	46.35 N	11.30 E
162	Isarog Vol. (ē-sä-rôg')	P. I.	13.40 N	123.22 E
122	Isar R. (ē'zär)	Ger.	48.30 N	12.0 E
128	Ischia (I.) (ēs'kyä)	It.	40.44 N	13.54 E
157	Isen (ē'sĕn)	Cho.	38.30 N	126.52 E
128	Iseo, L. of (ê-zĕ'ō)	It.	45.42 N	10.4 E
125	Isère R. (ê-zâr')	Fr.	45.15 N	5.25 E
128	Isernia (ê-zĕr'nyä)	It.	41.37 N	14.32 E
150	Isfahan (ĭs-fȧ-hän')	Iran	32.44 N	51.45 E
129	Ishëm (ēsh''m)	Alb.	41.32 N	19.36 E
148	Ishim (ĭsh-êm')	Sov. Un.	56.10 N	69.15 E
148	Ishim R.	Sov. Un.	54.0 N	67.40 E
158	Ishnomaki (ĭsh-nō-mä'kē)	Jap.	38.28 N	141.15 E
158	Ishnomaki B.	Jap.	38.15 N	141.15 E
77	Ishpeming (ĭsh'pê-mĭng)	Mich.	46.30 N	87.40 W
143	Isihlengeni (ê'sê-lĕn-gä'nê)	U. S. Afr.	27.51 S	31.15 E
143	Isipingo (ê-sê-pĭŋ'gô)	U. S. Afr.	29.59 S	30.55 E
143	Isitegi (ê-sê-tä'gê)	Swaz.	26.34 S	31.59 E
129	Isker R. (ĭs'k'r)	Bul.	43.10 N	24.0 E
113	Iskilip (ĕs'kĭ-lêp')	Tur.	40.45 N	34.35 E
126	Isla-Cristina (ĭs'lä-krê-stē'nä)	Sp.	37.14 N	7.21 W
163	Island B. (ī'lănd bā)	P. I.	9.6 N	118.10 E
55	Island L.	Can.	53.30 N	94.30 W
166	Island Lagoon	Austl.	31.28 S	136.42 E
87	Islands, B. of	Newf.	48.58 N	57.55 W
87	Islands, B. of	Newf.	49.15 N	58.20 W
170	Islands, B. of	N. Z.	35.12 S	174.10 E
52	Islands of the Four Mts.	Alsk.	52.30 N	170.30 W
116	Islay (I.) (ī'lā)	Gt. Brit.	55.45 N	6.25 W
86	Isle au Haut (I.) (ēl ô ō')	Me.	44.2 N	68.38 W
116	Isle of Man	Gt. Brit.	54.10 N	4.40 W
124	Isle R. (ēl)	Fr.	45.0 N	0.10 E
77	Isle Royale (ēl' roi-ăl')	Mich.	48.0 N	88.50 W
89	Isles, Lake of the (īlz)	Minn. (Minneapolis In.)	44.57 N	93.19 W
75	Isleta (ês-lā'tä) (ī-lē'tȧ)	N. M.	34.57 N	106.45 W
86	Isle Verte (ēl vĕrt')	Can.	48.1 N	69.19 W
131	Ismail (ēs-mȧ-ēl')	Rom.	45.21 N	28.51 E
135	Ismailia (ēs-mȧ-ēl'ê-ȧ)	Eg. (Suez Can. In.)	30.35 N	32.18 E
135	Ismailia Canal	Eg. (In.)	30.25 N	31.40 E
135	Isna (ês'nȧ)	Eg. (In.)	25.18 N	32.32 E
113	Isparta (ê-spär'tȧ)	Tur.	37.45 N	30.32 E
148	Issiq Kul (L.) (ĭ'sĭk kûl)	Sov. Un.	42.25 N	77.30 E
124	Issoire (ē-swȧr')	Fr.	45.31 N	3.15 E
124	Issoudun (ē-sōō-dăN')	Fr.	45.55 N	2.0 E
125	Issy-les-Moulineaux (ê-sē'-lȧ-mōō-lê-nō')	Fr. (In.)	48.48 N	2.16 E
113	Istanbul (Constantinople) (ê-stän-bŏŏl')	Tur.	41.2 N	29.0 E
129	Istiaia (ĭs-tyī'yä)	Grc.	38.57 N	23.11 E
83	Istokpoga,L.(ĭs-tŏk-pō'gȧ)	Fla.(In.)	27.23 N	81.15 W
131	Istovnoe (ĭs-tôf'nō-yĕ)	Sov. Un.	51.10 N	38.39 E
129	Istranca Mts. (ĭ-strän'jȧ)	Tur.	41.40 N	27.50 E
124	Istres (ēs'tr')	Fr.	43.30 N	4.59 E
128	Istrian Pen. (ĭs'trĭ-ăn)	It.	45.15 N	14.0 E
159	Itabashi (ē'tȧ-bä'shē)	Jap. (Tokyo In.)	35.45 N	139.42 E
99	Itaborahi (ē'tȧ-bō-rä'ê)	Braz. (Rio de Janeiro In.)	22.48 S	42.49 W
103	Itacoatiara (ē-tȧ-kwȧ-tyä'rȧ)	Braz.	3.5 S	58.28 W
104	Itaipu, L. de (ē-tī'pōō)	Braz. (In.)	22.57 S	43.2 W
103	Itaituba (ê-tä'ī-tōō'bȧ)	Braz.	4.15 S	55.31 W
104	Itajahí (ē'tȧ-zhä-ē')	Braz.	26.52 S	48.40 W
141	Itala (ê-tä'lā)	It. E. Afr.	2.45 N	46.12 E
139	Italian East Africa (Ethiopia)	Afr.	9.0 N	38.0 E
	Italian Somaliland, see Italian East Africa.			
128	Italy (ĭt'ȧ-lĭ)	Eur.	42.50 N	12.50 E
81	Italy	Tex.	32.10 N	96.52 W
103	Itaparica (ê-tȧ-pȧ-rē'kȧ)	Braz.(In.)	12.53 S	38.40 W
103	ItapicurúR.(ê-tȧ'pê-kōō-rōō')	Braz.	4.0 S	44.12 W
103	Itapicurú-Mirim (me-reN')	Braz.	3.28 S	44.12 W
103	Itaperuna (ē-tȧ-pȧ-rōō'nä)	Braz.	21.5 S	41.48 W
103	Itapira (ē-tȧ-pē'rȧ)	Braz.	20.30 S	51.18 W
104	Itararé (ē-tȧ-rȧ-rā')	Braz.	24.8 S	49.15 W
81	Itasca (ī-tăs'kȧ)	Tex.	32.9 N	97.10 W
77	Itasca, L.	Minn.	47.14 N	95.11 W
99	Itatiaya Mt. (ê-tä-tê-ä'yä)	Braz.	22.29 S	44.47 W
162	Itbayat (ēt-bä-yăt')	P. I. (In.)	20.45 N	121.52 E
84	Ithaca (ĭth'ȧ-kȧ)	Mich.	43.19 N	84.36 W
85	Ithaca	N. Y.	42.27 N	76.31 W
129	Ithake (I.) (ē'thä-kĕ)	Grc.	38.25 N	20.42 E
138	Itobe (ê-tō'bā)	Nig.	7.29 N	6.46 E
140	Itoko (ê-tō'kō)	Bel. Cong.	1.15 S	22.10 E
102	Itönama, R. (ê-tō-nä'mä)	Bol.	15.0 S	63.0 W
135	Itsa (êt'sȧ)	Eg. (In.)	29.12 N	30.48 E
99	Itú(ê-tōō')	Braz.(Rio de Janeiro In.)	23.18 S	47.18 W
154	Itu (ē'tōō')	Chn.	30.25 N	111.18 E
102	Ituango (ê-twäŋ'gō)	Col.	6.59 N	76.2 W
93	Itundujia (Santa Cruz) (ê-tōōn-dōō-hē'ȧ)	Mex.	16.51 N	97.39 W
153	Itung (ē'tŏŏng')	Manch.	43.28 N	125.27 E
93	Iturbide (ē-tōōr-bē'dhā)	Mex.	18.25 N	92.54 W
92	Iturbide	Mex.	21.0 N	100.23 W
122	Itzehoe (ĭt'sē-hō)	Ger.	53.56 N	9.31 E
122	Itzling (ĭts'lĭng)	Ger.	47 50 N	13.2 E
82	Iuka (ī-ū'kȧ)	Miss.	34.48 N	88.11 W
166	Ivanhoe (ī'văn-hō)	Austl.	32.52 S	144.20 E
130	Ivanovo (ê-vä'nô-vō)	Sov. Un.	57.1 N	40.59 E
130	Ivanovo Indust. Ter. (Aut. Area)	Sov. Un.	56.48 N	40.40 E
130	Ivertsa R. (ē-vĕrt'sȧ)	Sov. Un.	57.20 N	34.50 E
138	Ivindo R. (ê-vĭn'dō)	Fr. Eq. Afr.	1.0 N	13.0 E
141	Ivohibe (ê-vô-hê-bā')	Madag.	22.15 S	46.52 E
89	Ivory (ī'vô-rĭ)	Mo. (St. Louis In.)	38.32 N	90.17 W
138	Ivory Coast (Colony)	Fr. W. Afr.	7.0 N	6.0 W
128	Ivrea (ê-vrĕ'ä)	It.	45.27 N	7.52 E
158	Iwateyama (Mt.) (ē-wä-tē-yä'mä)	Jap.	39.52 N	140.52 E
159	Iwaya (ē'wȧ-yȧ)	Jap. (Osaka In.)	34.36 N	135.2 E
159	Iwo, I. (ē'wô)	Jap.	30.47 N	130.16 E
92	Ixcateopán (ēs-kä-tȧ-ō-pän')	Mex.	18.23 N	99.52 W
93	Ixhuatán (San Francisco) (ēs-hwä-tän')	Mex.	16.22 N	94.28 W
92	Ixhuatlán (ēs-wȧt-län')	Mex.	20.40 N	98.0 W
92	Ixmiquilpan (ēs-mê-kēl'pän)	Mex.	20.28 N	99.12 W
143	Ixopo (ĭks-ō'pō)	U. S. Afr.	30.10 S	30.5 E
93	Ixtacalco (ēs-tȧ-käl'kō)	Mex. (In.)	19.23 N	99.7 W
92	Ixtaccihuatl, Cerro (Mt.) (ēs-täk-sē'hwät'l)	Mex.	19.10 N	98.37 W
93	Ixtaltapec (Asunción) (ēs-täl-tĕ-pĕk')	Mex.	16.30 N	95.1 W
93	Ixtapalapa (ēs'tä-pä-lä'pä)	Mex. (In.)	19.22 N	99.6 W
93	Ixtapaluca (ēs'tä-pä-lōō'kä)	Mex. (In)	19.19 N	98.53 W
93	Ixtapan, R. (ēs-tä'pän')	Mex. (In.)	19.35 N	98.57 W
93	Ixtenco (ēs-tĕŋ'kō)	Mex.	19.14 N	97.53 W
93	Ixtepec (San Jerónimo) (ēs-tĕ-pĕk') (sän hȧ-rō'nē-mō)	Mex.	16.35 N	95.5 W
92	Ixtlahuaca (ēs-tlä-wä'kä)	Mex.	19.32 N	99.44 W
93	Ixtlán de Juárez (Villa Juárez) (ēs-tlän' dā hwä'rȧz)	Mex.	17.20 N	96.30 W
92	Ixtlán del Rio(ēs-tlän'dĕl rē'ō)	Mex.	21.4 N	104.22 W
155	Iyang (ē'yäng')	Chn.	28.33 N	117.28 E
148	Iya R. (ē'yä)	Sov. Un.	53.55 N	100.0 E
159	Iyo Sea (ē'yō)	Jap.	33.30 N	132.0 E
94	Izabal (ē'zä-bäl')	Guat.	15.24 N	89.11 W
94	Izabal, L. (Golfo Dulce) gôl'fō dōōl'sȧ)	Guat.	15.30 N	89.10 W
94	Izalco (ē-zäl'kō)	Sal.	13.49 N	89.40 W
112	Izhevsk (ê-zhyĕfsk')	Sov. Un.	56.48 N	53.10 E
112	Izhma (ĭzh'mȧ)	Sov. Un.	65.0 N	54.0 E
112	Izhma R.	Sov. Un.	64.15 N	53.30 E
124	Izieux (ē-zyû')	Fr.	45.28 N	4.25 E
113	Izmir (Smyrna) (ĭz-mēr') (smûr'nȧ)	Tur.	38.25 N	27.10 E
129	Izmir, G. of	Tur.	38.30 N	26.50 E
113	Izmit (ĭz-mêt')	Tur.	40.47 N	29.59 E
128	Izonzo, R. (ē-zōn'zô)	It.	46.0 N	13.36 E
159	Izuhara (ē'zōō-hä'rä)	Jap.	34.12 N	129.16 E
159	Izu Shichitō Is.) (ē'zōō shĭ-chê'tô)	Jap.	34.0 N	139.30 E
131	Izyaslavl (ē'zyȧ-släv'l)	Sov. Un.	50.8 N	26.51 E
131	Izyum (ê-zyŏŏm')	Sov. Un.	49.9 N	37.18 E
121	Jaakkima (yä'kē-mȧ)	Fin.	61.35 N	30.15 E
126	Jabalón R. (hä-bä-lōn')	Sp.	38.45 N	3.35 W
	Jablonec, see Gablonz, Ger.			
123	Jablonicka (Jablonica) Pass (yä-bwô-nē'tskȧ) (yä-blô-nē'tsȧ)	Pol.-Czech.	48.22 N	24.23 E
123	Jablunkov Pass (yäb'lŏŏn-kôf)	Czech.-Pol.	49.30 N	18.47 E
163	Jabonga (hä-bôŋ'gȧ)	P. I.	9.20 N	125.32 E
127	Jaca (hä'kä)	Sp.	42.35 N	0.31 W
94	Jacaltenango (hä-kȧl-tĕ-näŋ'gō)	Guat.	15.39 N	91.41 W
99	Jacarépaguá (zhä-kä-rȧ'pä-gwä')	Braz. (Rio de Janeiro In.)	22.58 S	43.24 W
	Jáchymov, see Sankt Joachimsthal, Ger.			
81	Jacinto R. (hä-sên'tō) (jȧ-sĭn'tō)	Tex. (In.)	29.50 N	95.5 W
78	Jacksboro (jăks'bŭr-ô)	Tex.	33.13 N	98.10 W
82	Jackson (jăk'sŭn)	Ala.	31.30 N	87.54 W
74	Jackson	Calif.	38.21 N	120.47 W
82	Jackson	Ga.	33.18 N	83.56 W
84	Jackson	Ky.	37.34 N	83.25 W
81	Jackson	La.	30.50 N	91.12 W
84	Jackson	Mich.	42.17 N	84.27 W
77	Jackson	Minn.	43.38 N	94.59 W
82	Jackson	Miss.	32.17 N	90.12 W
84	Jackson	Ohio	39.4 N	82.42 W
82	Jackson	Tenn.	35.37 N	88.50 W
71	Jackson L.	Wyo.	43.55 N	110.40 W
171	Jacksons B.	N. Z.	43.55 S	168.45 E
82	Jacksonville	Ala.	33.53 N	85.47 W
83	Jacksonville	Fla.	30.20 N	81.40 W
79	Jacksonville	Ill.	39.44 N	90.13 W
81	Jacksonville	Tex.	31.58 N	95.18 W
83	Jacksonville Beach	Fla.	30.17 N	81.25 W
83	Jacksonville, South	Fla.	30.17 N	81.39 W
97	Jacmel (zhȧk-mĕl')	Hai.	18.13 N	72.33 W
103	Jacobina (zhä-kô-bē'nȧ)	Braz.	11.12 S	40.12 W
143	Jacobsdal (yä'kôps-däl)	U. S. Afr.	29.5 S	24.49 E
80	Jaco L. (hä'kō)	Mex.	27.50 N	103.55 W
86	Jacques Cartier (Tabletop), Mt. (zhȧk' kär-tyā')	Can.	48.58 N	66.2 W
86	Jacquet R. (zhȧ-kĕ') (jăk'ĕt)	Can.	47.57 N	66.0 W
103	Jacuhpey, R. (zhä-kōō-hē'pĕ)	Braz. (In.)	12.0 S	39.30 W
102	Jaén (hä-ān')	Ec.	5.32 S	78.45 W
126	Jaén	Sp.	37.46 N	3.48 W
145	Jaffa (yä'fä)	Pal.	32.2 N	34.46 E
166	Jaffa, C. (jăf'ȧ)	Austl.	37.0 S	139.41 E
151	Jaffna (jăf'nȧ)	Cey. (In.)	9.45 N	80.0 E
123	Jägerndorf (Krnov) (yā-gĕrn-dôrf') (k'r'nôf)	Ger.	50.4 N	17.41 E
143	Jägersfontein (yā'gērs-fŏn-tān)	U. S. Afr.	29.41 S	25.25 E
163	Jagna (häg'nä)	P. I.	9.39 N	124.22 E
99	Jaguari, R. (zhä-gwä'rē)	Braz. (Rio de Janeiro In.)	22.42 S	47.30 W
103	Jaguaripe(zhä-gwä-rē'pä)	Braz.(In.)	13.8 S	38.54 W
96	Jaguey Grande (hä'gwā grän'dā)	Cuba	22.31 N	81.6 W
103	Jahú (zhä-hōō')	Braz.	22.15 S	48.31 W
97	Jaibo, R. (hä-ē'bō)	Cuba	20.8 N	75.15 W
151	Jaipur (jī'pŏŏr)	India	26.50 N	75.45 E
157	Jairyung (jä'êr-yŏŏng')	Cho.	38.24 N	125.36 E
128	Jajce (yī'tsĕ)	Yugo.	44.20 N	17.18 E
151	Jajpur (jī'pŏŏr)	India	20.45 N	86.28 E
161	Jako, Pulo (I.) (pōō'lō yä'kō)	Port. Tim.	8.31 S	127.29 E
112	Jakobstad (Pietarsaari) (yȧ'kôb-städh)	Fin.	63.40 N	22.45 E
92	Jala (hä'lä)	Mex.	21.7 N	104.24 W
93	Jalacingo (hä-lä-sĭŋ'gō)	Mex.	19.48 N	97.16 W

ng-sing; ŋ-baŋk; N-nasalized n; nŏd; cŏmmit; ōld; ôbey; ôrder; fōōd; fŏŏt; ou-out; s-soft; sh-dish; th-thin; pūre; ûnite; ûrn; stŭd; circŭs; ü-as "y" in study; '-indeterminate vowel.

Page	Name Pronunciation Region	Lat. °'	Long. °'
161	Jalajala (hä-lä-hä'lä) P. I. (Manila In.)	14.22 N	121.22 E
151	Jalalabad (jŭ-l-älä-bäd') Afg. (Peshawar In.)	34.26 N	70.27 E
94	Jalan, R. (hä-län') .... Hond.	14.20 N	86.20 W
94	Jalapa (hä-lä'pä) .... Guat.	14.38 N	89.58 W
93	Jalapa de Díaz (San Felipe) (hä-lä'pä dä dē'äz) (sän fä-lē'pä) Mex.	18.3 N	96.55 W
93	Jalapa del Marqués (hä-lä'pä děl mär-käs') Mex.	16.30 N	95.28 W
93	Jalapa Enríquez (hä-lä'pä ěn-rē'kāz) Mex.	19.32 N	96.55 W
92	Jalisco (hä-lēs'kō) .... Mex.	21.26 N	104.55 W
92	Jalisco (State) .... Mex.	20.30 N	103.20 W
125	Jallieu (zhä-lyû') .... Fr.	45.35 N	5.20 E
126	Jalón R. (hä-lōn') .... Sp.	41.30 N	1.30 W
92	Jalostotitlán (hä-lōs-tē-tlän') Mex.	21.14 N	102.26 W
93	Jalpa (häl'pä) .... Mex.	18.12 N	93.3 W
92	Jalpa .... Mex.	21.41 N	103.6 W
92	Jalpan (häl'pän) .... Mex.	21.14 N	99.30 W
92	Jaltepec, R. (häl-tå-pěk') .... Mex.	17.22 N	95.20 W
93	Jaltipan (häl-tē-pän') .... Mex.	17.58 N	94.42 W
93	Jaltocan (häl-tō-kän') .... Mex.	21.9 N	98.31 W
88	Jamaica (jȧ-mā'kȧ) N. Y. (New York In.)	40.42 N	73.46 W
96	Jamaica .... W. I.	18.10 N	77.10 W
88	Jamaica B. . N. Y. (New York In.)	40.38 N	73.50 W
92	Jamay (hä-mī') .... Mex.	20.16 N	102.42 W
139	Jamba (jäm-bä) .... Bel. Cong.	3.3 N	24.5 E
129	Jambol (yäm'bôl) .... Bul.	42.27 N	26.30 E
103	Jambú Assú (zhäm-bōō' ä-sōō') Braz. (In.)	1.4 S	47.41 W
55	James B. (jāmz) .... Can.	53.30 N	80.30 W
72	James Cr. ..... Colo. (Denver In.)	40.7 N	105.23 W
72	James I. .... Can. (Vancouver In.)	48.37 N	123.22 W
83	James, L. .... N. C.	35.35 N	81.55 W
97	James Pt. .... Ba. Is.	25.21 N	76.23 W
79	James R. .... Mo.	37.0 N	93.22 W
76	James R. .... S. D.-N. D.	44.55 N	98.28 W
85	James R. .... Va.	37.37 N	78.0 W
164	James Range .... Austl.	24.15 S	133.30 E
46	James Ross I. .... Ant. O.	64.30 S	57.30 W
166	Jameston .... Austl.	33.12 S	138.36 E
72	Jamestown . . . Colo. (Denver In.)	40.7 N	105.24 W
85	Jamestown .... N. Y.	42.7 N	79.15 W
76	Jamestown .... N. D.	46.55 N	98.41 W
7	Jamestown .... St. Helena (In.)	15.56 S	5.41 W
143	Jamestown .... U. S. Afr.	31.9 S	26.46 E
93	Jamiltepec (hä-mēl-tå-pěk) .. Mex.	16.17 N	97.50 W
163	Jamindan (hä-mēn-dän') ...... P. I.	11.25 N	122.30 E
151	Jamnagar (Navanagar) (jäm-nŭ'-gŭr) .. India	22.15 N	70.5 E
151	Jamrud (jäm'rōōd) Afg. (Peshawar In.)	34.0 N	71.21 E
103	Jamunda, R. (zhä-mōōn'dä) . Braz.	1.30 S	58.30 W
127	Janda, Laguna de la (L.) (lä-gōō-nä dā lä hän'dä) Sp. (In.)	36.17 N	5.51 W
169	Jandowae (jăn-dō-wä'ē) Austl. (In.)	26.46 S	151.6 E
126	Jándula R. (hän'dōō-lȧ) .... Sp.	38.30 N	3.55 W
77	Janesville (jānz'vĭl) .... Wis.	42.41 N	89.0 E
...	Janica, see Genitsa, Grc.		
163	Janiuay (hä-nē-wī') .... P. I.	10.57 N	122.30 E
48	Jan Mayen (I.) (yän mī'ěn) Grnld. Sea	71.0 N	8.0 W
120	Jannelund (yän'ě-lōōnd) ..... Swe.	59.13 N	14.24 E
123	Jánoshalma (yä'nôsh-hôl-mô) Hung.	46.17 N	19.20 E
123	Janów (yä'nōōf) .... Pol.	50.41 N	22 23 E
143	Jansenville (jăn'sěn-vĭl) . U. S. Afr.	32.55 S	24.41 E
103	Januaria (zhä-nwä'rē-ä) ..... Braz.	15.28 S	44.28 W
156	Jaoyang (jä'ō-yäng') .... Chn.	38.25 N	115.42 E
158	Japan (jȧ-păn') .... Asia	36.0 N	138.0 E
158	Japan, Sea of .... Asia	40.0 N	134.0 E
161	Japen I. (yä'pěn) ...... Neth. Ind.	1.45 S	136.0 E
102	Japurá (Caquetá) R. (hä-pōō-rä') (kä-kä-tä') Col.	1.0 S	72.2 W
102	Japurá, R. (zhä-pōō-rä') ..... Braz.	1.4 S	68.0 W
151	Japvo, Mt. (jäp'vō) .... India	25.35 N	94.15 E
89	Jaques, B. (zhäk) (jāks) La. (New Orleans In.)	29.14 N	89.30 W
139	Ja R. (yä) .... Cam.	2.30 N	14.15 E
97	Jarabacoa (hä-rä-bä-kō'ä) .... Hai.	19.5 N	70.40 W
92	Jaral del Progreso (hä-räl děl prō-grā'sō) Mex.	20.21 N	101.4 W
126	Jarama R. (hä-rä'mä) .... Sp.	40.30 N	3.34 W
152	Jara, Mt. (jä'rä) .... Chn.	30.29 N	101.50 E
103	Jardim (zhär-dēn') .... Braz.	6.42 S	36.42 W
96	Jardines Bank (här-dē'näs) .. Cuba	21.40 N	81.30 W
124	Jarnac (zhär-nák') .... Fr.	45.0 N	0.9 W
163	Jaro (hä'rō) .... P. I.	10.43 N	122.32 E
163	Jaro .... P. I.	11.9 N	124.44 E
123	Jarocin (yä-rō'tsyēn) .... Pol.	51.48 N	17.32 E
130	Jaroslavl (Yaroslavl) (yá-rô-släv''l) Sov. Un.	57.37 N	39.51 E
130	Jaroslavl (Yaroslavl) (Dist.) Sov. Un.	58.10 N	39.10 E
123	Jaroslaw (yá-rôs'wäf) .... Pol.	50.1 N	22.41 E
116	Jarrow (jă'rō) .... Gt. Brit.	54.55 N	1.30 W
6	Jarvis I. (jär'vĭs) .... Pac. O.	0.23 S	160.3 W
103	Jary, R. (zhä'rē) .... Braz.	0.0	53.0 W
123	Jasiña (yá'sē-nyá) .... Czech.	48.17 N	24.22 E
123	Jasiolda R. (yä-syôl'dä) ...... Pol.	52.15 N	25.55 E
150	Jask (jäsk) .... Iran	25.40 N	57.57 E
123	Jaslo (yäs'wō) .... Pol.	49.44 N	21.28 E
84	Jasonville (jā'sŭn-vĭl) .... Ind.	39.12 N	87.13 W
82	Jasper (jăs'pēr) .... Ala.	33.50 N	87.18 W
82	Jasper .... Fla.	30.32 N	82.56 W
84	Jasper .... Ind.	38.23 N	86.56 W
76	Jasper .... Minn.	43.52 N	96.20 W
81	Jasper .... Tex.	30.55 N	93.58 W
	Jassy, see Iași, Rom.		
123	Jászapáti (yäs'ô-pä-tē) ..... Hung.	47.30 N	20.10 E
123	Jászberény (yäs'bě-rān') .... Hung.	47.30 N	19.55 E
123	Jaszuny (yá'shōōn') .... Pol.	54.27 N	25.20 E
93	Jatate, R. (hä-tä-tā') .... Mex.	16.40 N	91.40 W
96	Jatibonico (hä-tē-bō-nē'kō) .. Cuba	21.55 N	79.11 W
127	Játiva (hä'tē-vä) .... Sp.	38.58 N	0.31 W
122	Jauer (you'ěr) .... Ger.	51.3 N	16.12 E
150	Jauf (jouf) .... Sau. Ar.	29.40 N	39.15 E
102	Jauja (zhä-ōō'zhä) .... Peru	11.42 S	75.18 W
92	Jaumave (hou-mä'vå) .... Mex.	23.23 N	99.24 W
121	Jaunjelgava (youn'yěl'gá-vá) . Lat.	56.36 N	25.6 E
121	Jaunlatgale (youn'lät-gä-lě) ... Lat	57.4 N	27.52 E
160	Java (I.) (jä'vȧ) (jä'vä) . Neth. Ind.	7.30 S	110.0 E
102	Javary, R. (zhä-vä'rē) . Braz.-Peru	5.0 S	72.30 W
160	Java Sea .... Neth. Ind.	5.0 S	112.30 E
127	Javea (hä-vā'ä) .... Sp.	38.46 N	0.8 E
123	Jaworów (yä-vô'rōōf) .... Pol.	49.56 N	23.23 E
123	Jaworzno (yä-vôzh'nō) .... Pol.	50.11 N	19.18 E
81	Jeanerette (jěn-ēr-et')(zhän-rět') La.	29.54 N	91.40 W
126	Jebala (Prov.) (jě-bä'lä) ..... Mor.	35.25 N	5.30 W
138	Jebba (jěb'ȧ) .... Nig.	9.10 N	4.48 E
150	Jebel Anaiza (Mt.) (jěb'ěl á-nī'zá) Iraq	32.15 N	39.0 E
139	Jebel-es-Soda (Mts.) (jěb'ěl-ěs-sō'dä) Lib.	28.30 N	15.0 E
150	Jebel Hada (Mt.) (jěb'ěl hä'dä) Yem.	15.38 N	43.50 E
114	Jedi, Wadi (R.) (wä'dē jē'dē) . Alg.	34.20 N	4.30 E
119	Jedlersdorf, Gross (yěd'lērz-dōrf) Aus. (Wien In.)	48.17 N	16.25 E
123	Jedrzejów (yăN-dzhā'yōōf) .... Pol.	50.38 N	20.18 E
82	Jefferson (jěf'ēr-sŭn) .... Ga.	34.6 N	83.37 W
77	Jefferson .... Ia.	42.2 N	94.21 W
81	Jefferson .... Tex.	32.46 N	94.20 W
77	Jefferson .... Wis.	43.0 N	88.48 W
89	Jefferson Barracks Mo. (St. Louis In.)	38.30 N	90.17 E
79	Jefferson City .... Mo.	38.35 N	92.12 W
70	Jefferson, Mt. .... Ore.	44.42 N	121.48 W
71	Jefferson R. .... Mont.	45.40 N	112.16 W
84	Jeffersonville .... Ind.	38.18 N	85.55 W
143	Jeffreys B. (jěf'rĭz) ..... U. S. Afr.	34.1 S	24.55 E
153	Jehol (Chengte) (rē-hōl') (chěng'-tě') Manch.	40.59 N	117.57 E
145	Jeib, Wadi el (R.) (wä'dē ěl jāb') Pal.-Transj. (In.)	30.45 N	35.18 E
121	Jekabpils (yěk'áb-pĭls) .... Lat.	56.28 N	25.50 E
121	Jelgava (yěl'gá-vá) .... Lat.	56.38 N	23.43 E
82	Jellico (jěl'ĭ-kō) .... Tenn.	36.34 N	84.8 W
75	Jemez Indian Res. (hā'māz) N. M.	35.35 N	106.50 W
114	Jemmapes (zhē-màp') .... Alg.	36.55 N	6.50 E
122	Jena (yā'nä) .... Ger.	50.56 N	11.35 E
119	Jenfeld (yěn'fělt) Ger. (Hamburg In.)	53.34 N	10.8 E
127	Jenhwai (jěn'hwī') .... Chn.	27.47 N	106.0 E
145	Jenin (Ein Gannim) (jě-nēn') (ān ghä-nēm') Pal. (In.)	32.22 N	35.18 E
83	Jenkins (jěŋ'kĭnz) .... Ky.	37.10 N	82.38 W
88	Jenkintown (jěŋ'kĭn-toun) Pa. (Philadelphia In.)	40.6 N	75.8 W
156	Jenkiu (jěn'kyōō') .... Chn.	38.50 N	115.57 E
154	Jenlung (jěn'lōōng') .... Chn.	23.38 N	107.12 E
81	Jennings (jěn'ĭngz) .... La.	30.14 N	92.39 W
84	Jennings .... Mich.	44.22 N	85.18 W
89	Jennings ...... Mo. (St. Louis In.)	38.43 N	90.15 W
154	Jenyang (jěn'yäng') .... Chn.	23.47 N	106.50 E
103	Jequirica, R. (zhě-kē-rē-sä') Braz. (In.)	13.15 S	39.50 W
103	Jequirissá (zhě-kē-rē-sä') Braz. (In.)	13.12 S	39.28 W
103	Jequitinhonha, R. (zhě-kē-tēn-yōn'yä) Braz.	16.30 S	41.15 W
135	Jerba I. (jěr'bä) .... Tun. (In.)	33.50 N	10.45 E
97	Jérémie (zhā-rā-mē') .... Hai.	18.38 N	74.7 W
103	Jeremoabo (zhě-rä-mō-ä'bō) . Braz.	10.2 S	38.28 W
127	Jerez de la Frontera (kē-räth' dā lä frōn-tā'rä) Sp. (In.)	36.41 N	6.8 W
126	Jerez de los Caballeros (kē-räth' dā lōs kä-väl-yä'rōs) Sp.	38.19 N	6.46 W
93	Jerez, Pt. (kē-rāz') .... Mex.	23.3 N	97.45 W
165	Jericho (jěr'ĭ-kō) .... Austl.	23.38 S	146.8 E
145	Jericho .... Pal. (In.)	31.51 N	35.29 E
167	Jerilderie (jě-rĭl-dě-rē) ...... Austl.	35.22 S	145.42 E
75	Jerome (jě-rōm') .... Ariz.	34.44 N	112.8 W
71	Jerome .... Ida.	42.43 N	114.31 W
85	Jersey City (jûr'zĭ) .... N. J.	40.40 N	74.10 W
124	Jersey (I.) .... Gt. Brit.	49.15 N	2.10 W
85	Jersey Shore .... Pa.	41.11 N	77.14 W
79	Jerseyville .... Ill.	39.6 N	90.19 W
145	Jerusalem (jē-rōō'sȧ-lěm) . Pal. (In.)	31.46 N	35.14 E
167	Jervis B. (jûr'vĭs) .... Austl.	35.5 S	150.45 E
166	Jervis, C. .... Austl.	35.35 S	138.10 E
160	Jesselton Town (jěs'ěl-tŭn) B. N. B.	5.57 N	116.5 E
89	Jesuit Bend (jěz'ū-ĭt) La. (New Orleans In.)	29.45 N	90.3 W
83	Jesup (jěs'ŭp) .... Ga.	31.36 N	81.53 W
57	Jesus, Isle (jē'zŭs) Can. (Montreal In.)	45.35 N	73.45 W
49	Jewell (jū'ěl) .. Ore. (Portland In.)	45.56 N	123.31 W
76	Jewel Cave Natl. Mon. ...... S. D.	43.44 N	103.51 W
151	Jhalrapatan (jäl'rŭ-pä'tŭn) . India	24.29 N	76.15 E
151	Jhansi (jän'sē) .... India	25.30 N	78.44 E
151	Jhelum (jā'lŭm) .... India	32.55 N	73.37 E
151	Jhelum R. .... India	32.0 N	72.16 E
75	Jicarilla Apache Indian Res. (kē-kä-rēl'yä) . N. M.	36.40 N	107.0 W
95	Jicaron I. (kē-kä-rōn') ...... Pan.	7.15 N	81.47 W
122	Jičín (yē'chēn) .... Czech.	50.26 N	15.22 E
150	Jidda (jĭd'dä) .... Sau. Ar.	21.35 N	39.10 E
141	Jidhaleh (jĭd-ä'lä) .... Br. Som.	8.58 N	47.15 E
164	Jigalong (jĭg'ȧ-lông) .... Austl.	22.32 S	120.30 E
97	Jiguaní (kē-gwä-nē') .... Cuba	20.21 N	76.28 W
91	Jiguero Pt. (kē-gä'rō) . P. R. (In.)	18.22 N	67.30 W
96	Jiguey B. (kē'gwā) .... Cuba	22.10 N	78.5 W
156	Jihchao (jĭ'chä'ō) .... Chn.	35.33 N	119.26 E
122	Jihlava (yē'hlä-vä) .... Czech.	49.23 N	15.34 E
123	Jijia R. (zhĭ'zhyȧ) .... Rom.	47.30 N	27.22 E
	Jijiga, It. E. Afr., see Giggiga.		
127	Jijona (kē-hō'nä) .... Sp.	38.31 N	0.29 W
126	Jiloca R. (kē-lō'kä) .... Sp.	41.10 N	1.30 W
161	Jilolo Str. (jĭ-lō'lō) ..... Neth. Ind.	0.0	129.15 E
163	Jimalalud (kē-mä-lä-lōōd') ... P. I.	10.0 N	123.12 E
123	Jimbolea (zhĭm-bō-lyä) ..... Rom.	45.47 N	20.42 E
126	Jimena (kē-mā'nä) .... Sp.	36.26 N	5.27 W
93	Jiménez (kē-mā'nāz) .... Mex.	18.4 N	96.35 W
92	Jiménez .... Mex.	24.12 N	98.30 W
80	Jiménez .... Mex.	27.7 N	104.55 W
80	Jiménez .... Mex.	29.2 N	100.42 W
163	Jiménez .... P. I.	8.20 N	123.51 E
72	Jimmy Camp Cr. Colo. (Colo. Sprs. In.)	38.45 N	104.38 W
122	Jindřichuv Hradec (yēn'd'r-zhĭ-kōōf hrä'děts) . Czech.	49.9 N	15.1 E
139	Jinja (jĭn'jä) .... Ug.	0.32 N	33.11 E
159	Jintsu R. (jĭn'tsōō) .... Jap.	36.34 N	137.12 E
94	Jinotega (kē-nō-tā'gä) .... Nic.	13.18 N	85.50 W
94	Jinotepe (kē-nō-tā'pä) .... Nic.	11.51 N	86.12 W
157	Jinsen (Chemulpo) (jĭn'sěn') (chě-mŭl'pō) . Cho.	37.30 N	126.45 E
163	Jintotolo Chan. (kēn-tō-tō'lō) . P. I.	11.50 N	123.0 E
102	Jipijapa (kē-pē-hä'pä) .... Ec.	1.43 S	80.44 W
92	Jiquilpan de Juárez (kē-kēl'pän dähwä'räz) . Mex.	19.59 N	102.42 W
139	Jiran (jē'răn) .... It. E. Afr.	7.36 N	36.57 E
93	Jitotol (kē-tō-tōl') .... Mex.	17.4 N	92.52 W
129	Jiul R. (zhē'ōōl) .... Rom.	44.24 N	23.40 E
150	Jizan (jē'zăn) .... Sau. Ar.	16.59 N	42.38 E
167	Joadju Cr. (jō-äd'jōō) ...... Austl.	34.25 S	150.12 E
103	João Pessoa (Parahiba) (zhô-ouN'pě-sō'ȧ) (pä-rä-ē'bȧ) Braz.	7.3 S	34.55 W
103	Joazeiro (zhō-á-zā'rōō) ...... Braz.	9.28 S	40.28 W
96	Jobabo R. (hō-bä'bä) .... Cuba	20.55 N	77.21 W
92	Jocotepec (hō-kō-tå-pěk') .... Mex.	20.17 N	103.25 W
126	Jódar (hō'där) .... Sp.	37.53 N	3.20 W
151	Jodhpur (jōd'pōōr) .... India	26.15 N	73.0 E
121	Joensuu (yō'ěn-sōō) .... Fin.	62.34 N	29.45 E
121	Jõesuu, N. (yō'ě-sōō) .... Est.	59.26 N	28.4 E
125	Joeuf (zhûf) .... Fr.	49.14 N	6.1 E
121	Jõgeva (yō'gě-vä) .... Est.	58.45 N	26.26 E
86	Joggin Mines (jŏg'ĭn) .... Can.	45.42 N	64.25 W
143	Johannesburg (yō-hän'ěs-bōōrgh) U. S. Afr.	26.12 S	28.4 E
70	John Day R. .... Ore.	44.50 N	119.47 W
70	John Day R., Middle Fork ... Ore.	44.50 N	119.3 W
70	John Day R., North Fork .... Ore.	44.50 N	120.0 W
73	Johns ...... Ala. (Birmingham In.)	33.22 N	87.7 W
85	Johnsonburg (jŏn'sŭn-bûrg) ... Pa.	41.30 N	78.40 W
85	Johnson City .... N. Y.	42.18 N	75.58 W
83	Johnson City .... Tenn.	36.18 N	82.22 W
170	Johnsonville .... N. Z. (In.)	41.14 S	174.49 E
6	Johnston I. (jŏn'stŭn) ..... Pac. O.	17.0 N	168.30 W
54	Johnston, L. .... Can.	50.10 N	106.0 W
72	Johnstown (jonz'toun) Colo. (Denver In.)	40.20 N	104.55 W
85	Johnstown .... N. Y.	43.0 N	74.22 W
85	Johnstown .... Pa.	40.22 N	78.52 W
160	Johore (State) (jō-hōr') Non-fed. Mal. St.	2.0 N	103.0 E
160	Johore Bahru (jō-hōr' bä-rōō') Strs. Sets.	1.35 N	103.44 E
121	Jõhvi (yō'vĭ) .... Est.	59.19 N	27.25 E
124	Joigny (zhwän-yē') .... Fr.	47.58 N	3.25 E
104	Joinville (zhwäN-vēl') .... Braz.	26.20 S	48.50 W
124	Joinville .... Fr.	48.28 N	5.5 E
46	Joinville I. .... Ant. O.	61.30 S	56.0 W
92	Jojutla (hō-hōō'tlä) .... Mex.	18.36 N	99.12 W
110	Jökullså (R.) (yû'kōōls-ô) ..... Ice.	65.30 N	16.10 W
79	Joliet (jō'lĭ-ět) .... Ill.	41.47 N	88.5 W
55	Joliette (zhō-lyět') .... Can.	46.5 N	73.25 W
163	Jolo (hō-lō') .... P. I.	6.2 N	121.0 E
163	Jolo I. .... P. I.	6.0 N	121.10 E
162	Jomalig I. (hō-mä'lēg) ...... P. I.	14.42 N	122.23 E
92	Jomulco (hō-mōōl'kō) .... Mex.	21.7 N	104.22 W
92	Jonacatepec (hō-nä-kä-tå-pěk') Mex	18.39 N	98.47 W
121	Jonava (yō-nä'vä) .... Lith.	55.4 N	24.11 E
120	Jondal (yōn'däl) .... Nor.	60.15 N	6.18 E
162	Jones (jōnz) .... P. I.	12.57 N	122.4 E
162	Jones .... P. I.	16.30 N	121.39 E
79	Jonesboro .... Ark.	35.50 N	90.42 W
82	Jonesboro .... Ga. (Atlanta In.)	33.31 N	84.21 W
81	Jonesboro .... La.	32.14 N	92.42 W
89	Jones I. ...... S. C. (Savannah In.)	32.4 N	80.56 W
81	Jonesville .... La.	31.36 N	91.50 W
84	Jonesville .... Mich.	41.59 N	84.43 W
121	Joniškis (yō'nĭsh-kĭs) .... Lith.	56.13 N	23.38 E
120	Jönköping (yûn'chē-pĭng) .... Swe.	57.47 N	14.10 E
86	Jonquière (zhôN-kyâr') ...... Can.	48.24 N	17.15 W
93	Jonuta (hō-nōō'tä) .... Mex.	18.8 N	92.8 W
124	Jonzac (zhôN-zák') .... Fr.	45.25 N	0.25 W
79	Joplin (jŏp'lĭn) .... Mo.	37.5 N	94.31 W
163	Jordan (jôr'dăn) .... P. I.	10.38 N	122.36 E
70	Jordan Cr. .... Ore.	42.55 N	117.30 W
145	Jordan R. .... Pal.-Transj. (In.)	32.25 N	35.34 E
73	Jordan R. Utah (Salt Lake City In.)	40.34 N	111.55 W
151	Jorhat (jôr-hät') .... India	26.40 N	94.15 E
119	Jork (yôrk) ... Ger. (Hamburg In.)	53.32 N	9.41 E
92	Jorullo, Vol. de (hō-rōōl'yō) .. Mex.	18.52 N	101.33 W
138	Jos (jōs) .... Nig.	9.52 N	9.0 E
143	Josana (jō-sä'na) .... Swaz.	26.25 S	31.50 E
164	Joseph Bonaparte G. (djō'sěf bō'ná-pàrt) .. Austl.	14.15 S	128.50 E
158	Joshin (jō'shĭn') .... Cho.	40.30 N	128.55 E
74	Joshua Tree Natl. Mon. ..... Calif.	34.0 N	116.0 W
120	Jostedal Glacier (yôs'tē-däl) .. Nor.	61.40 N	6.50 E

ăt; finăl; rāte; senåte; ärm; åsk; sofȧ; fâre; ch-choose; dh-as th in other; bē; ēvent; bět; recěnt; cratēr; g-go; gh-gutteral g; bĭt; ĭ-short neutral; rīde; K-gutteral k as ch in German ich;

Page	Name Pronunciation Region	Lat. °'	Long. °'
120	Jotun Fjeld (Plat.) (yō'tōōn-fyĕl') . Nor.	61.42 N	8.20 E
125	Jouars-Pontchartrain (zhōō-är'-pôN-shär-trăN') .. Fr. (In.)	48.47 N	1.55 E
96	Joulter's Cays (Is.) (jōl'tērz) Ba. Is.	25.15 N	78.9 W
125	Jouy-en-Josas (zhōō-ē'äN-zhō-zä') Fr. (In.)	48.46 N	2.10 E
125	Jouy-le-Moutier (zhōō-ē'lē-mōō-tyā') .. Fr. (In.)	49.1 N	2.3 E
96	Jovellanos (hō-vĕl-yä'nōs) ... Cuba	22.47 N	81.11 W
70	Juan de Fuca Str. (hwän' dā fōō'kä) .. Can.-U. S.	48.25 N	124.0 W
54	Juan de Fuca, Str. of ... Can.	48.15 N	124.0 W
98	Juan Fernández Is. (hwän' fĕr-năn-dāth) . Pac. O.	33.30 S	79.0 W
96	Juan Luis Cays (Is.) (hwän lōō-ēs') . Cuba	22.08 N	81.50 W
162	Juban (hōō-bän') ... P. I.	12.51 N	124.0 E
141	Juba R. (jōō'bȧ) ... It. E. Afr.	2.30 N	42.20 E
96	Júcaro (hōō'kä-rō) ... Cuba	21.36 N	78.52 W
126	Júcar R. (hōō'kär) ... Sp.	39.13 N	1.20 W
92	Juchipila (hōō-chē-pē'lä) ... Mex.	21.25 N	103.15 W
93	Juchitán de Zaragoza (hōō-chē-tän' dā thä-rä-gō'thä) .. Mex.	16.26 N	95.0 W
92	Juchitlán (hōō-chē-tlän') ... Mex.	20.6 N	104.4 W
122	Judenburg (jōō'dĕn-bûrg) ... Ger.	47.10 N	14.40 E
71	Judith R. (jōō'dĭth) ... Mont.	47.5 N	109.44 W
121	Jūgala R. (yü'gà-lȧ) ... Est.	59.25 N	25.22 E
155	Juian (jwĭ'än') ... Chn.	27.43 N	120.36 E
155	Juichang (jwĭ'chäng') ... Chn.	29.37 N	115.36 E
155	Juichow (jwĭ'chō') ... Chn.	28.18 N	115.9 E
94	Juigalpa (hwē-gäl'pä) ... Nic.	12.2 N	85.25 W
155	Juikin (jwĭ'kĭn') ... Chn.	25.47 N	115.51 E
103	Juiz de Fóra (zhōō-ēzh' dā fō'rä) Braz.	21.49 S	43.29 W
104	Jujuy (State) (hōō-hwē') ... Arg.	23.0 S	65.30 W
104	Jujuy ... Arg.	24.10 S	65.15 W
78	Julesburg (jōōlz'bûrg) ... Colo.	40.59 N	102.17 W
102	Juliaca (hōō-lē-ä'kä) ... Peru	15.29 S	70.2 W
48	Julianehaab ... Grnld.	60.45 N	46.2 W
143	Jumbla (Mt.) (jŭm'blȧ) . U. S. Afr.	30.30 S	28.54 E
97	Jumentos Cays (Is.) (hōō-mĕn'tōs) . Ba. Is.	23.5 N	75.40 W
117	Jumet (zhü-mĕ') ... Bel.	50.28 N	4.31 E
126	Jumilla (hōō-mēl'yä) ... Sp.	38.28 N	1.19 W
77	Jump R. (jŭmp) ... Wis.	45.26 N	91.40 W
80	Junction (jŭŋk'shŭn) ... Tex.	30.29 N	99.48 W
79	Junction City ... Kans.	39.3 N	96.49 W
99	Jundiahi (zhōōn-dē-ä'ē) Braz. (Rio de Janeiro In.)	23.13 S	46.54 W
53	Juneau (jōō'nō) ... Alsk.	58.20 N	134.35 W
157	Junee (jōō-nē') ... Austl.	34.51 S	147.35 E
122	Jungfrau (Mt.) (yŏŏng'frou) Switz.	46.32 N	7.57 E
154	Jungyun (jŏŏng'yōōn) ... Chn.	22.57 N	110.26 E
85	Juniata (jōō-nĭ-ăt'ȧ) ... Pa.	40.36 N	78.24 W
104	Junín (hōō-nēn') ... Arg.	34.35 S	61.0 W
102	Junín ... Chl.	19.43 S	70.2 W
110	Junkeren (Mt.) (yōōn'kĕ-rĕn) . Nor.	66.17 N	14.48 E
87	Jupiter R. (jōō'pĭ-tēr) ... Can.	49.30 N	63.25 W
156	Ju R. (jōō) ... Chn.	32.47 N	114.30 E
165	Juanda (jōō-ăn'dȧ) ... Austl.	26.12 S	149.58 E
138	Juba R. (jōō'bȧ) ... It. E. Afr.	3.0 N	42.30 E
151	Jubbulpore (jŭb-ŭl-pōr') ... India	23.15 N	79.55 E
156	Jukao (jōō'kä'ō) ... Chn.	32.20 N	120.30 E
151	Jullundur (jŭl'ŭn-dŭr) ... India	31.27 N	75.28 E
151	Jumna R. (jŭm'nŭ) ... India	26.0 N	80.10 E
157	Jungcheng (jŏŏng'chĕng') ... Chn.	37.22 N	122.28 E
156	Jungcheng ... Chn.	39.8 N	115.43 E
157	Jungsun (jŏŏng'sōōn') ... Cho.	37.27 N	128.38 E
156	Jungtseh (jŏŏng'tsĕ') ... Chn.	34.53 N	113.38 E
157	Jungup (jōōn'gōōp') ... Cho.	35.36 N	126.52 E
156	Jungyang (jŏŏng'yäng') ... Chn.	34.45 N	113.26 E
156	Juning (jōō'nĭng') ... Chn.	33.2 N	114.18 E
116	Jura (I.) (jōō'rȧ) ... Gt. Brit.	56.0 N	6.0 W
122	Jura Mts. (zhü-rȧ') ... Fr.-Switz.	47.0 N	6.30 E
116	Jura, Sd. of (jōō'rȧ) ... Gt. Brit.	56.0 N	5.40 W
121	Jurbarkas (yōōr-bär'käs) ... Lith.	55.5 N	22.48 E
102	Juruá, R. (zhōō-rōō-ä') ... Braz.	6.0 S	67.45 W
139	Jur R. (jōōr) ... A. E. Sud.	7.0 N	28.0 E
156	Jushui R. (jōō'shōō-ē') ... Chn.	32.50 N	114.55 E
122	Jüterbog (yü'tēr-bōgh) ... Ger.	51.59 N	13.4 E
94	Jutiapa (hōō-tē-ä'pä) ... Guat.	14.16 N	89.55 W
94	Juticalpa (hōō-tē-käl'pä) ... Hond.	14.39 N	86.14 W
125	Juvisy sur Orge (zhü-vē-sē'sür ôrzh') . Fr. (In.)	48.41 N	2.22 E
92	Juxtlahuaca (Santiago) (hōōs-tlä-hwä'kä) . Mex.	17.18 N	98.2 W
7	Jyunju (Zenshu) (jōōn'jōō') .. Cho.	35.52 N	127.5 E
121	Jyväskylä (yü'vĕs-kü-lĕ) ... Fin.	62.14 N	25.46 E
143	Kaalfontein (käl'fŏn-tān) U. S. Afr.	26.3 S	28.15 E
143	Kaapmuiden (käp'mû-dĕn) U. S. Afr.	25.32 S	31.20 E
142	Kaap Plateau (käp) ... Bech.	28.30 S	24.0 E
143	Kaapsche Hoop, de (dē käp'shē hōp') . U. S. Afr.	25.39 S	30.42 E
160	Kabaena (I.) (kä-bä-ä'nä) Neth. Ind.	5.15 S	122.0 E
140	Kabalo (kä-bä'lō) ... Bel. Cong.	6.5 S	26.50 E
140	Kabambare (kä-bäm-bä'rä) Bel. Cong.	4.52 S	27.45 E
131	Kabane (kȧ-bä'nyĕ) ... Sov. Un.	49.12 N	38.9 E
113	Kabardino-Balkaria (Reg. (kä'bär-dē'nō bäl-kä'rĭ-ȧ) . Sov. Un.	43.45 N	43.30 E
163	Kabasalan (kä-bä-sä-län') ... P. I.	7.47 N	122.47 E
159	Kabe (kä'bĕ) ... Jap.	34.32 N	132.29 E
145	Kabinda (kä-bēN'dä) ... Bel. Cong.	6.10 S	24.20 E
145	Kabir I. (kȧ-bēr') ... Red Sea (In.)	13.45 N	42.45 E
142	Kabiskow, (Mt.) (kȧ-bĭs'kôf) U. S. Afr.	30.49 S	19.15 E
142	Kabiskow Ra ... U. S. Afr.	30.50 S	19.52 E
140	Kabompo R. (kȧ-bôm'pō) .. N. Rh.	13.50 S	24.0 E
140	Kabongo (kȧ-bông'ō) ... Bel. Cong.	7.50 S	25.22 E

Page	Name Pronunciation Region	Lat. °'	Long. °'
162	Kabugao (kä-bōō'gä-ō) ... P. I.	18.3 N	121.10 E
151	Kabul (kä'bōōl) ... Afg.	34.31 N	69.0 E
151	Kabul R ... Afg.-India	34.30 N	70.30 E
151	Kachin Hills (Mts.) (kä'chĕn) India	26.15 N	96.0 E
131	Kadievka (kȧ-dĭ-yĕf'kȧ) .. Sov. Un.	48.28 N	38.31 E
166	Kadina (kȧ-dī'nȧ) ... Austl.	33.58 S	137.41 E
148	Kadin (Nadym) R. (kä-dēn') Sov. Un.	65.20 N	73.20 E
112	Kadnikov (käd'nē-kôf) ... Sov. Un.	59.32 N	40.20 E
138	Kaduna (kä-dōō'nä) ... Nig.	10.30 N	7.30 E
138	Kaédi (kä-ā-dē') ... Fr. W. Afr.	16.25 N	13.32 W
173	Kaena Pt. (kä'ā-nä) ... Hawaii	21.33 N	158.19 W
143	Kaffir R. (kăf'ĕr) ... U. S. Afr.	29.25 S	26.0 E
139	Kafia Kingi (kä'fē-ȧ kĭŋ'gē) A. E. Sud.	9.21 N	24.30 E
140	Kafue (kä'fōō-ȧ) ... N. Rh.	15.45 S	28.13 E
131	Kagalnik, R. (kȧ-gäl''nĕk) Sov. Un.	47.2 N	39.25 E
140	Kagera, R. (kä-gä'rȧ) ... Tan.-Ug.	1.15 S	31.15 E
158	Kagi (kä'gē) ... Tai. (In.)	23.32 N	120.30 E
159	Kago (kä'gō) ... Jap.	31.18 N	130.18 E
159	Kagoshima (kä'gō-shē'mȧ) ... Jap.	31.32 N	130.30 E
159	Kagoshima B ... Jap.	31.15 N	130.40 E
119	Kagran (kä'grän) . Aus. (Wien In.)	48.15 N	16.27 E
77	Kahnipiminanikok L. (kȧ-nĭ-pĭ'mĭ-nȧ'nĭ-kôk) . Can.	48.23 N	91.15 W
79	Kahoka (kȧ-hō'kȧ) ... Mo.	40.26 N	91.42 W
173	Kahoolawe (I.) (kä'hōō-lä'wē) Hawaii	20.33 N	156.35 W
173	Kahuku Pt. (kä-hōō'kōō) .. Hawaii	21.43 N	157.58 W
171	Kaiapoi (kä'ē-ȧ-pō'ē) ... N. Z.	43.23 S	172.42 E
75	Kaibab Ind. Res. (kä'ē-băb) . Ariz.	36.58 N	112.40 W
154	Kaichow (kī'chō') ... Chn.	27.0 N	106.46 E
156	Kaichow ... Chn.	35.41 N	115.21 E
113	Kaidak G. (kī-dăk') ... Sov. Un.	45.0 N	53.30 E
103	Kaieteur Falls (kī-ĕ-tōōr') . Br. Gu.	5.0 N	58.47 W
156	Kaifeng (kī'fĕng') ... Chn.	34.45 N	114.29 E
158	Kaiho (kī-hō') ... Manch.	43.32 N	129.36 E
155	Kaihwa (kī'hwä') ... Chn.	29.10 N	118.35 E
152	Kaihwa ... Chn.	23.28 N	104.32 E
157	Kaijo (Songdo) (kī'jō') (sông'dō') Cho.	38.1 N	126.30 E
170	Kaikohe (kä'ē-kō'hĕ) ... N. Z.	35.25 S	173.50 E
171	Kaikoura (kä-ē-kōō'rȧ) ... N. Z.	42.24 S	173.42 E
171	Kaikoura Ra ... N. Z.	42.0 S	173.35 E
129	Kailaria (kī-lä'rĭ-ȧ) ... Grc.	40.30 N	21.42 E
172	Kailua (kä'ē-lōō'ä) ... Haw.	19.38 N	155.59 W
170	Kaimanawa Ra. (kä'ē-'mȧ-nä'wȧ) N. Z.	39.0 S	176.0 E
157	Kainan (kä'ē-nän') ... Cho.	34.35 N	126.36 E
148	Kainsk (kä-ēnsk') ... Sov. Un.	55.30 N	78.10 E
173	Kai o Kalohi (Chan.) (kä'ē ō' kȧ-lō'hē) . Haw.	20.58 N	157.10 W
170	Kaipara Har. (kä'ē-pä'rä) ... N. Z.	36.25 S	174.30 E
157	Kaiping (kī-pĭng') ... Chn.	39.44 N	118.7 E
138	Kairouan (kĕr-ōō-äN') ... Tun.	35.43 N	10.2 E
131	Kairy Zapadnie (kīr'yē zä-päd''n-yĕ) ... Sov. Un.	46.57 N	33.42 E
...	Kaisarieh, see Kayseri, Tur.		
157	Kaisen (kī'sĕn') ... Cho.	39.40 N	125.58 E
119	Kaiser-Ebersdorf (kī'zĕr-ā'bĕrs-dôrf) . Aus. (Wien In.)	48.10 N	16.28 E
122	Kaiserslautern (kī-zĕrs-lou'tĕrn) Ger.	49.27 N	7.47 E
46	Kaiser Wilhelm II Land, (kī'sĕr vĕl'hĕlm) . Ant.	68.0 S	90.0 E
156	Kaishow (kī'shō') ... Chn.	32.59 N	119.26 E
157	Kaishu ... Cho.	38.2 N	125.42 E
170	Kaitaia (kä-ē-tä'ē-ȧ) ... N. Z.	35.7 S	173.20 E
171	Kaitangata (kī-täŋ-gä'tȧ) ... N. Z.	46.18 S	169.53 E
171	Kaitarau, Mt. (kä'ē-tä-rä'ōō) N. Z.	42.10 S	173.4 E
173	Kaiwi Chan. (kä'ē-wē) ... Hawaii	21.15 N	157.35 W
158	Kaiyuan (kī'yōō-än') ... Manch.	42.52 N	123.58 E
52	Kaiyuh Mts. (kī-yōō') ... Alsk.	64.20 N	157.30 W
121	Kajaani (kä'yȧ-nĕ) ... Fin.	64.12 N	27.40 E
159	Kajiki (kä'jē-kĕ) ... Jap.	31.45 N	130.40 E
142	Kakamas (kä-kä'mäs) ... U. S. Afr.	28.42 S	20.34 E
131	Kakhovka (kȧ-kôf'kȧ) ... Sov. Un.	46.48 N	33.27 E
139	Kakindu (kä-kĭn'dōō) ... Ug.	1.2 N	33.1 E
121	Käkisalmi (kĕ'kĭ-säl-mē) ... Fin.	61.3 N	30.6 E
135	Kalaa-kebira (kȧ-lä-ȧ-kĕ-bē'rȧ) Tun. (In.)	35.52 N	10.25 E
114	Kalaat (kȧ-lȧ-ăt') ... Tun.	35.50 N	8.23 E
138	Kalaba (kȧ-lä'bȧ) ... S. L.	9.52 N	11.27 W
113	Kalach (kȧ-lăch') ... Sov. Un.	50.15 N	41.0 E
173	Ka Lae Pt. (kä-lä'ȧ) ... Hawaii	18.55 N	155.38 W
140	Kalahari Des. (kä-lä-hä'rē) .. Bech.	23.15 S	21.45 E
70	Kalama (kȧ-lăm-ȧ) ... Wash.	46.1 N	122.51 W
129	Kalamai (kä-lä-mĭ') ... Grc.	37.3 N	22.7 E
70	Kalama R .. Wash. (Portland In.)	46.3 N	122.40 W
84	Kalamazoo (kăl-ȧ-mȧ-zōō') .. Mich.	42.20 N	85.38 W
84	Kalamazoo R ... Mich.	42.30 N	85.50 W
131	Kalanchak (kȧ-lăn-chăk') Sov. Un.	46.16 N	33.13 E
173	Kalapana (kä-lä-pä'nä) ... Haw.	19.21 N	154.58 W
151	Kalat (kŭ-lät') ... India	29.5 N	66.40 E
160	Kalautowa (kä-lä'ōō-tō'wä) Neth. Ind.	7.28 S	121.45 E
153	Kalgan (Chiangkiakow) (kăl-găn') (chäng'kyä'kō') . Chn.	40.53 N	114.54 E
164	Kalgoorlie (kăl-gōōr'lē) ... Austl.	30.45 S	121.29 E
163	Kalian Pt. (käl-yän') ... P. I.	6.6 N	125.44 E
130	Kalikino (kȧ-lĭ-kē'nō) ... Sov. Un.	52.56 N	39.48 E
130	Kalinin (Iver) (kȧ'lē-nēn) Sov. Un.	56.51 N	35.57 E
112	Kalininsk (kȧ-lē-nēnsk') .. Sov. Un	61.45 N	34.20 E
131	Kalinkovichi (kȧ-lēn-kō-vē'chē) Sov. Un.	52.7 N	20.20 E
70	Kalispel Ind. Res. (kăl-ĭ-spĕl') Wash.	48.25 N	117.17 W
71	Kalispell ... Mont	48.12 N	114.20 W
123	Kalisz (kä'lēsh) ... Pol.	51.45 N	18.4 E

Page	Name Pronunciation Region	Lat. °'	Long. °'
131	Kalitva R. (kȧ-lēt'vȧ) ... Sov. Un.	50.20 N	39.10 E
110	Kalix R. (kä'lĕks) ... Swe.	66.50 N	22.45 E
140	Kalkfeld (kälk'fĕlt) ... S. W. Afr.	21.2 S	16.7 E
142	Kalkfontein (kälk'fŏn-tān) S. W. Afr.	28.2 S	18.45 E
110	Kalkholmen (kälk'hôlm-ĕn) .. Swe.	64.42 N	21.15 E
119	Kalksburg (kälks'bōōrgh) Aus. (Wien In.)	48.8 N	16.15 E
120	Kalmar (käl'mär) ... Swe.	56.40 N	16.20 E
120	Kalmar Sd ... Swe.	56.40 N	16.25 E
131	Kalmius R. (käl'myōōs) .. Sov. Un.	47.15 N	37.50 E
113	Kalmyk (Aut. Area) (käl''mōōk) (käl'mŭk) ... Sov. Un.	46.0 N	46.0 E
123	Kalocsa (kō'lō-chō) ... Hung.	46.32 N	18.58 E
140	Kalomo (kä-lō'mō) ... N. Rh.	17.8 S	26.18 E
119	Kaltenleutgeben (käl'tĕn-loit'gä-bĕn) . Aus. (Wien In.)	48.7 N	16.12 E
130	Kaluga (kȧ-lōō'gȧ) ... Sov. Un.	54.30 N	36.16 E
130	Kaluga (Dist.) ... Sov. Un.	54.36 N	35.4 E
120	Kalundborg (kȧ-lōōn''bôr') ... Den.	55.40 N	11.6 E
123	Kalusz (kä'wōōsh) ... Pol.	49.2 N	24.23 E
123	Kaluszyn (kä-wōōsh'ĕn) ... Pol.	52.12 N	21.53 E
121	Kalvarija (käl-vä-rē'yȧ) ... Lith.	54.23 N	23.12 E
166	Kalwin (käl'wĭn) ... Austl.	35.3 S	142.41 E
130	Kalyazin (kȧl-yȧ'zĕn) ... Sov. Un.	57.13 N	37.52 E
138	Kamabai (kä-mȧ-bä'ē) ... S. L.	9.15 N	11.57 W
159	Kamakura (kä'mȧ-kōō'rȧ) ... Jap.	35.19 N	139.34 E
148	Kama R. (kä'mȧ) ... Sov. Un.	55.28 N	51.0 E
140	Kambove (käm-bō'vĕ) .. Bel. Cong.	10.52 S	26.42 E
149	Kamchatka Mts. (käm-chät'kȧ) Sov. Un.	60.0 N	165.0 E
149	Kamchatka Pen ... Sov. Un.	56.0 N	160.0 E
129	Kamčik R. (käm'chĕk) ... Bul.	42.50 N	27.5 E
148	Kamen (kȧ'mĕn) ... Sov. Un.	53.50 N	81.20 E
	Kamenskoe, see Dneprodzerzhinsk, Sov. Un.		
131	Kamenka (kȧ-mĕn'kȧ) ... Sov. Un.	48.3 N	28.41 E
131	Kamensk (kȧ'mĕnsk) ... Sov. Un.	48.22 N	40.15 E
131	Kamenskoe, see Dneprodzerzhinsk, Sov. Un.		
122	Kamenz (kä'mĕnts) ... Ger.	51.15 N	14.5 E
159	Kameoka (kä'mä-ō'kä) Jap. (Osaka In.)	35.1 N	135.36 E
142	Kamies Berg (Mt.) (kä'mēz bûrg) . U. S. Afr.	30.20 S	18.8 E
49	Kamilehe (kȧ-mĭ-lē'hē) Wash. (Seattle In.)	47.7 N	123.5 W
77	Kaministikwia R. (kȧ-mĭ-nĭ-stĭk'wĭ-ȧ) . Can.	48.22 N	89.30 W
123	Kamionka Strumilowa (kȧ-myôŋ'-kȧ strōō-mē-lō'vȧ) . Pol.	50.6 N	24.22 E
148	Kamishlov (kȧ-mēsh'lôf) Sov. Un.	56.50 N	62.40 E
159	Kami Suwa (kä'mē sōō'wä) ... Jap.	36.3 N	138.8 E
54	Kamloops (kăm'lōōps) ... Can.	50.42 N	120.22 W
122	Kammin (kä-mēn') ... Ger.	53.57 N	14.48 E
170	Kamo (kä'mō) ... N. Z.	35.42 S	174.17 E
139	Kampala (käm-pä'lä) ... Ug.	0.12 N	32.32 E
160	Kampar R. (käm'pär) Neth. Ind.	0.25 N	101.30 E
122	Kampen (kämp'ĕn) ... Neth.	52.32 N	5.54 E
160	Kampot (käm'pōt) ... Fr. In. Chn.	10.37 N	104.10 E
122	Kamp R. (kämp) ... Ger.	48.35 N	15.23 E
173	Kamuela (kä-mōō-ā'lä) ... Haw.	19.58 N	155.30 W
158	Kamui C. (kä'mwē) ... Jap.	43.15 N	140.20 E
131	Kamyshevatskaya (kȧ-mēsh'ĕ-vȧt-skȧ'yȧ) .. Sov. Un.	46.24 N	37.54 E
113	Kamyshin (kȧ-mēsh'ĭn) .. Sov. Un.	50.5 N	45.20 E
131	Kamyshnya (kȧ-mēsh''n-yȧ) Sov. Un.	50.7 N	33.40 E
75	Kanab (kăn'ăb) ... Utah	37.2 N	112.31 W
159	Kanagawa (kä'nä-gä'wä) Jap. (Tokyo In.)	35.28 N	139.38 E
72	Kanaka Cr. (kȧ-năk'ȧ) Can. (Vancouver In.)	49.15 N	122.25 W
159	Kanawa I. (kä'nȧ-wä) ... Jap.	33.30 N	139.20 E
84	Kanawha R. (kȧ-nô'wȧ) ... W. Va.	38.20 N	81.35 W
159	Kanazawa (kä'nȧ-zä'wä) ... Jap.	36.30 N	136.37 E
159	Kanazawa ... Jap. (Tokyo In.)	35.20 N	139.38 E
155	Kanchow (kän'chō) ... Chn.	25.52 N	114.25 E
152	Kanchow ... Chn.	38.45 N	100.58 E
151	Kandahar (kŭn-dȧ-här') ... Afg.	31.44 N	65.45 E
140	Kanda Kanda (kän'dȧ kän'dȧ) Bel. Cong.	5.40 S	23.32 E
112	Kandalaksha (kȧn-dȧ-lȧk'shȧ) Sov. Un.	67.12 N	32.34 E
112	Kandalaksha B ... Sov. Un.	66.25 N	34.30 E
121	Kandava (kän'dȧ-vȧ) ... Lat.	57.3 N	22.46 E
138	Kandi (kän'dē) ... Fr. W. Afr.	11.5 N	3.2 E
151	Kandy (kăn'dē) ... Cey. (In.)	7.25 N	80.38 E
85	Kane (kān) ... Pa.	41.40 N	78.48 W
173	Kaneohe B. (kä-nā-ō'hä) ... Haw.	21.27 N	157.47 W
131	Kanev (kä-nyôf') ... Sov. Un.	49.45 N	31.26 E
150	Kangavar (kŭŋ'gär') ... Iran	34.40 N	47.50 E
166	Kangaroo I. (kăŋ-gȧ-rōō') ... Austl.	35.50 S	137.10 E
160	Kangean Is. (käŋ'gȧ-än) Neth. Ind.	7.0 S	115.45 E
157	Kangjin (käng'jĭn') ... Cho.	34.37 N	126.47 E
158	Kangkay (käng'kī') ... Cho.	40.59 N	126.40 E
157	Kangheung (käng'nĕ-ōōng') ... Cho.	37.48 N	128.46 E
140	Kango (kän'gō) ... Fr. Eq. Afr.	0.12 N	10.6 E
157	Kangsyu (käng'syōō') ... Cho.	38.59 N	125.28 E
157	Kangtong (käng'tông') ... Cho.	39.9 N	126.9 E
157	Kangwa (käng'wä') ... Cho.	37.45 N	126.27 E
158	Kangwa I ... Cho.	37.45 N	126.28 E
55	Kaniapiskau L. (kä-nĭ-ăp'ĭs-kô) Can.	54.15 N	69.15 W
55	Kaniapiskau R ... Can.	56.30 N	68.30 W
112	Kanin Pen. (kȧ-nē') ... Sov. Un.	68.10 N	45.0 E
79	Kankakee (kăŋ-kȧ kē') ... Ill.	41.6 N	87.52 W
79	Kankakee R ... Ill.	41.12 N	88.0 W
138	Kankan (käN-käN') (kän-kän') Fr. W. Afr.	10.22 N	9.17 W

ng-sing; ŋ-baŋk; N-nasalized n; nŏd; cŏmmit; ōld; ôbey; ôrder; fōōd; fŏŏt; ou-out; s-soft; sh-dish; th-thin; pūre; ûnite; ûrn; stŭd; circŭs; ü-as "y" in study; '-indeterminate vowel.

Page	Name Pronunciation Region	Lat. °′	Long. °′
157	Kanko (Hamheung) (kăŋ'kō) (hăm'hĕ-ōōng') Cho.	39.58 N	127.32 E
83	Kannapolis (kăn-ăp'ô-lĭs) . . . N. C.	35.30 N	80.38 W
159	Kannoura (kä'nō-ōō'rä) . . . . . . Jap.	33.34 N	134.17 E
138	Kano (kä'nō) . . . . Nig.	12.3 N	8.32 E
155	Kan R. (kän) . . . . Chn.	27.38 N	115.18 E
148	Kan R. . . . . Sov. Un.	56.15 N	95.0 E
142	Kansaap R. (kän-säp') . . U. S. Afr.	30.10 S	18.40 E
78	Kansas (State) (kăn'zȧs) . . . . U. S.	39.0 N	98.0 W
79	Kansas City . . . . Kan.	39.6 N	94.39 W
79	Kansas City . . . . Mo.	39.5 N	94.35 W
79	Kansas R. . . . . Kan.	39.5 N	95.40 W
152	Kansu (Prov.) (kän'sōō') . . . . Chn.	38.0 N	101.0 E
157	Kansung (kän-sōōng') . . . . Cho.	38.38 N	128.29 E
160	Kantang (kän'täng') . . . . Thai.	7.27 N	99.30 E
142	Kanus (kän'ŭs) . . . . S. W. Afr.	27.50 S	18.35 E
156	Kanyü (kän'yü') . . . . Chn.	34.50 N	119.8 E
159	Kanzaki (kän'zȧ-kê) Jap. (Osaka In.)	34.45 N	135.27 E
156	Kaocheng (kä'ō-chĕng') . . . . . Chn.	38.4 N	114.48 E
138	Kaolak (kä-ô-läk') . . . . Fr. W. Afr.	14.10 N	16.8 W
156	Kaotang (kä'ō-täng') . . . . Chn.	36.49 N	116.10 E
161	Kaouyao (kä'ô-ōō-yä'ō) P. I. (Manila In.)	14.17 N	121.9 E
156	Kaoyang (kä'ō-yäng') . . . . Chn.	38.49 N	115.42 E
156	Kaoyi (kä'ō-yē') . . . . Chn.	37.39 N	114.39 E
156	Kaoyu (kä'ō-yōō') . . . . Chn.	32.48 N	119.27 E
156	Kaoyuan (kä'ō-yōō-än') . . . . . Chn.	37.8 N	118.7 E
156	Kaoyu L. . . . . Chn.	32.50 N	118.58 E
128	Kapela (Mts.) (kä-pä'lȧ) . . . Yugo.	44.55 N	15.33 E
122	Kapfenberg (käp'fĕn-bĕrgh) . . Ger.	47.26 N	15.18 E
171	Kapiti I. (kȧ-pē'tê) . . . . N. Z.	40.50 S	174.55 E
123	Kaposvár (kô'pôsh-vär) . . . . Hung.	46.22 N	17.47 E
49	Kapowsin (kă'pô-sĭn) Wash. (Seattle In.)	46.59 N	122.14 W
158	Kapsan (käp'sän') . . . . Cho.	41.2 N	128.28 E
160	Kapuas Mts., Upper (kä'pōō-äs) Sar.-Neth. Ind.	1.30 N	112.15 E
160	Kapuas (R.) . . . . Neth. Ind.	0.30 N	112.0 E
166	Kapunda (kä-pōōn'dä) . . . . . Austl.	34.18 S	138.55 E
113	Kapustin Yar (kä'pōōs-tên-yär') Sov. Un.	48.35 N	45.50 E
123	Kapuvár (kô'pōō-vär) . . . . . . Hung.	47.35 N	17.2 E
123	Kapyczyńce (kȧ-pû-chûn''tsĕ) Pol.	49.6 N	25.55 E
130	Karabanovo (kä'rȧ-bȧ-nō'vô) Sov. Un.	56.18 N	38.41 E
140	Karabib (kȧr'ȧ-bĭb) . . . . S. W. Afr.	21.50 S	15.50 E
113	Karachai (Cherkess) (Aut. Reg.) (kä'rȧ-chī) (chĕr'kĕs) . . . Sov. Un.	43.45 N	42.0 E
130	Karachev (kȧ-rȧ-chôf') . . . Sov. Un.	53.7 N	34.58 E
151	Karachi (kŭ-rä'chê) . . . . India	24.55 N	67.0 E
158	Karafuto (I.) (kä-rä-fōō'tō) . . . Jap.	48 0 N	142.30 E
148	Karagandinski . . . . Sov. Un.	49.30 N	73.30 E
149	Karaginski I. (kä-rä-gēn') Sov. Un.	59.0 N	164.0 E
	Karahissar, see Afyon-Karahisar, Tur.		
113	Kara Khobda R. (kä-rȧ ᴋôb'dô) Sov. Un.	50.30 N	55.15 E
113	Kara Kichu G. (kä'rȧ kē'chōō) Sov. Un.	44.25 N	53.0 E
148	Karakol (kä-rä-kôl') . . . . . . Sov. Un.	42.25 N	78.15 E
152	Kara Korum (Ruins) (kä'rä kō'rōōm) . Chn.	47.20 N	102.27 E
151	Karakorum Pass . . . . India	35.30 N	77.58 E
151	Karakorum Ra. . . . . India	35.45 N	77.0 E
113	Karaköse (kä-rä-kû'sĕ) . . . . Tur.	39.45 N	43.2 E
150	Kara Kum (Qara Qum) Des (kä'rȧ kōōm) . . Sov. Un.	47.0 N	63.15 E
113	Karaman (kä-rä-män') . . . . Tur.	37.8 N	33.5 E
171	Karamea Bight (kȧ-rȧ-mē'ȧ bīt) N. Z.	41.20 S	172.0 E
171	Karamea R. . . . . N. Z.	41.12 S	172.20 E
129	Kara Mts. (kä'rȧ) . . . . Yugo.	42.20 N	21.40 E
152	Kara Nor (L.) (kä'rä-nōr') . . . Chn.	40.37 N	94.34 E
152	Kara Nor (L.) . . . . Chn.	48.0 N	92.0 E
112	Kara R. . . . . Sov. Un.	68.45 N	65.30 E
148	Kara Sea . . . . Sov. Un.	72.30 N	62.0 E
148	Kara Str. . . . . Sov. Un.	70.30 N	58.0 E
95	Karata Lagoon (kä-rä'tȧ) . . . . . Nic.	13.55 N	83.30 W
159	Karatsu (kä'rȧ-tsōō) . . . . Jap.	33.27 N	129.58 E
122	Karawankas (Mts.) (kä-rä-väŋ'kȧs) . Ger.	46.28 N	14.20 E
150	Karbala (kŭr'bȧ-lä) . . . . Iraq.	32.45 N	44.5 E
123	Karcag (kôr'tsôg) . . . . Hung.	47.18 N	20.57 E
129	Karditsa (kär'dê-tsȧ) . . . . Grc.	39.22 N	21.57 E
121	Kärdla (kĕrd'lȧ) . . . . Est.	59.0 N	22.46 E
139	Kareima (kä-rā'mȧ) . . . . A. E. Sud.	18.34 N	31.50 E
112	Karelian (Soviet Rep.) (kȧ-rē'lĭ-ȧ) Sov. Un.	64.10 N	33.30 E
140	Karema (kä-rā'mȧ) . . . . Tan.	6.45 S	30.24 E
148	Kargat (kär-gät') . . . . Sov. Un.	55.25 N	80.15 E
112	Kargopol (kär-gō-pōl'') . . . Sov. Un.	61.30 N	39.0 E
142	Kariega R. (kȧ-rĭ-ā'gȧ) . . U. S. Afr.	32.30 S	23.30 E
151	Karikal (kä-rê-käl') . . . . India	10.50 N	79.50 E
138	Karimama (kä-rê-mä'mȧ) Fr. W. Afr.	12.10 N	3.7 E
160	Karimata Arch. (kä-rê-mä'tȧ) Neth. Ind.	1.30 S	109.0 E
160	Karimata, Str. . . . . Neth. Ind.	2.0 S	108.30 E
160	Karimunjawa Is. (kä'rê-mōōn-yä'vä) . . . . Neth. Ind.	5.55 S	110.25 E
141	Karin (kȧr'ĭn) . . . . Br. Som.	10.50 N	45.45 E
150	Karind (kŭ-rĭnd') . . . . Iran	34.15 N	46.29 E
148	Karkaralinsk (kär-kär-ȧ-lēnsk') Sov. Un.	49.30 N	75.30 E
161	Karkar I. (kär'kär) . . . N. Gui. Ter.	4.38 S	145.55 E
150	Karkheh R. (kär'kĕ) . . . . Iran	33.0 N	48.0 E
131	Karkinitskii B. (kär-kê-nēt'skĭ-ê) Sov. Un.	45.50 N	32.59 E
129	Karla, L. (kär'lä) . . . . Grc.	39.28 N	22.47 E
128	Karlovac (kär'lô-vȧts) . . . . . . Yugo.	45.30 N	15.33 E
128	Karlobag (kär-lō-bäg') . . . . . . Yugo.	44.32 N	15.6 E
129	Karlovci (kär'lôv-tsê) . . . . . . Yugo.	45.11 N	19.58 E
131	Karlovka (kȧr'lôv-kȧ) . . . . Sov. Un.	49.28 N	35.5 E
129	Karlovo (kär'lō-vō) . . . . Bul.	42.47 N	24.48 E
122	Karlsbad (Karlovy Vary) (kärls'bȧd) (kär'lô-vê vä'rê) . Ger.	50.13 N	12.52 E
120	Karlshamn (kärls'häm) . . . . . . Swe.	56.11 N	14.51 E
120	Karlskrona (kärls'krô-nä) . . . . Swe.	56.10 N	15.35 E
122	Karlsruhe (kärls'rōō-ē) . . . . Ger.	49.1 N	8.22 E
120	Karlstad (kärl'ståd) . . . . Swe.	59.24 N	13.30 E
	Karlstadt, see Karlovac, Yugo.		
53	Karluk (kär'lŭk) . . . . Alsk.	57.30 N	154.30 W
120	Karm I. (kärm) . . . . Nor.	59.14 N	5.15 E
135	Karnak (Ruins) (kär'nȧk) Eg. (In.)	25.41 N	32.40 E
129	Karnobat (kär-nô'bät) . . . . Bul.	42.38 N	26.59 E
122	Kärnten (Prov.) (kĕrn'tĕn) . . . Ger.	46.58 N	13.48 E
140	Karonga (kȧ-rôŋ'gȧ) . . . . Nyas.	9.55 S	33.48 E
166	Karoonda (kȧ-rōōn'dȧ) . . . . . Austl.	35.5 S	139.52 E
170	Karori (kȧ-rō'rê) . . . . . . N. Z. (In.)	41.17 S	174.45 E
170	Karori R. . . . . N. Z. (In.)	41.20 S	174.43 E
142	Karree Bergen (Mts.) (kȧ-rē' bĕrg'ĕn) . U. S. Afr.	30.50 S	22.10 E
142	Karroo, Great (Reg.) (kȧ-rōō') U. S. Afr.	32.40 S	22.50 E
113	Kars (kärs) . . . . Tur.	40.42 N	43.5 E
121	Karsava (kär'sä-vä) . . . . Lat.	56.48 N	27.40 E
148	Kartali (kȧr'tȧ-lê) . . . . Sov. Un.	53.0 N	60.30 E
150	Karun R. (kŭ-rōōn') . . . . Iran	31.45 N	50.0 E
123	Karwin (Karvinná), (kär'vên) (kȧr'vên-nä) . Pol.	49.49 N	18.29 E
129	Karyai (kär'ê-ī) . . . . Grc.	40.14 N	24.15 E
113	Kasaba (kä'sȧ-bä) . . . . Tur.	38.28 N	27.45 E
140	Kasama (kȧ-sä'mȧ) . . . . N. Rh.	10.15 S	31.12 E
140	Kasanga (kȧ-säŋ'gȧ) . . . . Tan.	8.25 S	31.6 E
159	Kasaoka (kä'sȧ-ō'kȧ) . . . . Jap.	34.34 N	133.30 E
158	Kasari C. (kä'sä-rē) . . . . Jap.	28.30 N	129.45 E
138	Kasba-Tadla (käs'bȧ-täd'lȧ) . . Mor.	32.34 N	5.21 W
157	Kaseda (kä'sȧ-dȧ) . . . . Jap.	31.25 N	130.21 E
140	Kasempa (kȧ-sĕm'pȧ) . . . . . N. Rh.	13.20 S	25.45 E
140	Kasenga (kȧ-seŋ'gȧ) . . . . Bel. Cong.	10.23 S	28.39 E
155	Kashan (kä'shän') . . . . Chn.	30.46 N	120.55 E
150	Kashan (kä-shän') . . . . Per.	33.55 N	51.20 E
152	Kashgar Darya (R.) (käsh-gär där'yȧ) . Chn.	39.30 N	76.30 E
152	Kashgar (Shufu) (shōō'fōō') . . Chn.	39.28 N	76.2 E
130	Kashin (kä-shēn') . . . . Sov. Un.	57.21 N	37.38 E
155	Kashing (kä'shĭng') . . . . Chn.	30.43 N	120.45 E
130	Kashira (kä-shē'rȧ) . . . . . . Sov. Un.	54.50 N	38.8 E
113	Kashirinsk (kä-shê-rēnsk') Sov. Un.	52.25 N	55.28 E
151	Kashmir (State) (kȧsh-mēr') . India	35.0 N	76.30 E
150	Kash R. (kŭsh) . . . . Afg.	31.45 N	63.15 E
130	Kasimov (kȧ-sē'môf) . . . . . Sov. Un.	54.58 N	41.25 E
79	Kaskaskia R. (kăs-kăs'kĭ-ȧ) . . . . Ill.	38.50 N	89.10 W
	Kaskinen, see Kaskö, Fin.		
121	Kaskö (Kaskinen) (käs'kû käs'kē-nĕn) . . Fin.	62.24 N	21.14 E
140	Kasongo (kä-sôŋ'gō) . . . Bel. Cong.	4.28 S	26.36 E
123	Kassa (Košice) (kä'sä) (kō'shê-tsĕ) Hung.	48.43 N	21.15 E
139	Kassala (kä-sä'lä) . . . . . . A. E. Sud.	15.28 N	36.28 E
129	Kassandra, G. of (kȧ-sän'drȧ) Grc.	40.5 N	23.35 E
122	Kassel (käs'ĕl) . . . . Ger.	51.19 N	9.30 E
77	Kasson (kăs'ŭn) . . . . Minn.	44.2 N	92.42 W
113	Kastamonu (kä-stȧ-mō'nōō) . . Tur.	41.25 N	33.47 E
129	Kastoria (kȧs-tō'rĭ-ȧ) . . . . Grc.	40.28 N	21.17 E
129	Kastron (kȧs-trōn') . . . . Grc.	39.52 N	25.3 E
129	Kastron . . . . Tur.	40.13 N	25.53 E
86	Katahdin, Mt. (kȧ-tä'dĭn) . . . . Me.	45.57 N	68.59 W
52	Katalla (kȧ-tô'lȧ) . . . . . . Alsk. (In.)	60.10 N	144.30 W
145	Katana (kä-tä'nä) . . . . . . Syr. (In.)	33.26 N	36.2 E
140	Katanga (Dist.) (kȧ-täŋ'gȧ) Bel. Cong.	8.45 S	25.15 E
163	Katanglad Mts. (kȧ-täŋ-glȧd') . P. I.	8.7 N	124.53 E
164	Katanning (kȧ-tăn'ĭng) . . . . . Austl.	33.37 S	117.31 E
129	Katerinē (kȧ-tĕ-rē'nä) . . . . Grc.	40.17 N	22.34 E
164	Katherine (kăth'ēr-ĭn) . . . . . . Austl.	14.28 S	132.20 E
151	Kathiawar Pen. (kä'tê-ȧ-wär') India	21.30 N	71.0 E
142	Kathu (kä-thōō') . . . . Bech.	27.40 S	23.0 E
155	Kating (kä'tĭng') . . . . Chn.	31.20 N	121.10 E
52	Katmai Nat'l. Mon. (kăt'mī) Alsk.	58.20 N	155.0 W
151	Katmandu (kät-män-dōō') . . . Nep.	27.45 N	85.25 E
151	Katni (kät'nê) . . . . India	23.31 N	80.10 E
167	Katoomba (kȧ-tōōm'bȧ) . . . . Austl.	33.42 S	150.19 E
142	Katop Hills (kä'tŭp) . . . . U. S. Afr.	30.10 S	19.55 E
123	Katowice (kä-tô-vē'tsĕ) . . . . . . Pol.	50.16 N	19.3 E
120	Katrineholm (kȧ-trē'nĕ-hōlm) Swe.	59.1 N	16.10 E
138	Katsina (kät'sê-nȧ) . . . . Nig.	13.5 N	7.36 E
138	Katsina Ala (kät'sê-nȧ ä'lä) . . Nig.	7.19 N	9.19 E
148	Kattakurgan (kȧ-tȧ-kōōr-gän') Sov. Un.	39.50 N	66.30 E
120	Kattegat (Str.) (kăt'ĕ-gät) . . . . Eur.	57.0 N	11.20 E
148	Katun R. (kȧ-tōōn') . . . . . Sov. Un.	5.25 N	86.0 E
173	Kauai Chan. (kä-ōō-ä'ê) . . . . . Haw.	21.50 N	158.40 W
173	Kauai (I.) . . . . Haw.	22.0 N	159.30 W
122	Kaufbeuren (kouf'boi-rĕn) . . . . Ger.	47.53 N	10.38 E
81	Kaufman (kôf'măn) . . . . Tex.	32.35 N	96.18 W
77	Kaukauna (kô-kô'nȧ) . . . . Wis.	44.17 N	88.16 W
140	Kaukau Veld (Prairie) (kô'kô) S. W. Afr.-Bech.	20.0 S	21.0 E
173	Kaulakahi Chan. (kä'ōō-lȧ-kä'hê) Haw.	22.0 N	160.0 W
173	Kaunakakai (kä'ōō-nȧ-kä'kī) . Haw.	21.5 N	157.1 W
121	Kaunas (Kovno) (kou'nȧs) (kôv'nô) . Lith.	54.53 N	23.54 E
129	Kavajë (kȧ-vä'yȧ) . . . . Alb.	41.11 N	19.34 E
129	Kavaklü (kä-väk'lê) . . . . Bul.	42.5 N	26.19 E
129	Kavalla (kä-vä'lä) . . . . Grc.	40.56 N	24.23 E
129	Kavalla, G. of . . . . Grc.	40.45 N	24.25 E
138	Kavalli Pt. (kȧ-väl'ê) . . . . Lib.	6.0 N	7.45 W
161	Kavieng (kä-vê-ĕng') . N. Gui. Ter.	2.35 S	150.55 E
148	Kavinsk (kȧ-vēnsk') . . . . . Sov. Un.	58.30 N	100.18 E
159	Kawagoe (kä-wä-gō'å) . . . . Jap.	35.55 N	139.29 E
159	Kawai (kä-wä'ê) . . . . Jap.	35.3 N	137.39 E
170	Kawakawa (kô'wȧ-kô'wȧ) . . . N. Z.	35.20 S	174.5 E
158	Kawasaki (kä-wä-sä'kê) . . . . . . Jap.	35.29 N	139.44 E
56	Kawende (kô-wĕn'dê) Can. (Winnipeg In.)	49.55 N	98.0 W
170	Kawhia Harbor (kä'hwê-ȧ) . . N. Z.	38.5 S	174.55 E
161	Kawit (kä-wēt') . P. I. (Manila In.)	14.27 N	120.53 E
138	Kaya (kä'yä) . . . . Fr. W. Afr.	13.0 N	1.25 W
52	Kayak I. (kī-yȧk') . . . . . Alsk. (In.)	60.0 N	144.25 W
160	Kayan R. (kä'yän) . . . . . Neth. Ind.	2.0 N	116.0 E
71	Kaycee (kā-sē') . . . . Wyo.	43.44 N	106.38 W
138	Kayes (kāz) . . . . Fr. W. Afr.	14.28 N	11.31 W
155	Kaying (kä'yĭng') . . . . Chn.	24.12 N	115.59 E
113	Kayseri (kī'sĕ-rē) . . . . Tur.	38.42 N	35.28 E
73	Kaysville, (kāz'vĭl) Utah (Salt Lake City In.)	41.2 N	111.57 W
148	Kazak (Aut. Rep.) (kȧ-zäk') Sov. Un.	49.30 N	70.0 E
148	Kazalinsk (kä-zȧ-lēnsk') . . Sov. Un.	45.45 N	62.10 E
112	Kazan (kȧ-zän') . . . . Sov. Un.	55.48 N	49.10 E
150	Kazanin (kȧ-zȧ-nēn') . . . . Iran	29.31 N	51.58 E
131	Kazanka (kȧ-zän'kȧ) . . . . . Sov. Un.	47.49 N	32.46 E
129	Kazanlek (kȧ-zȧn-lĕᴋ') . . . . Bul.	42.36 N	25.23 E
131	Kazatin (kȧ-zȧ-tēn') . . . . . Sov. Un.	49.42 N	28.51 E
131	Kazatskoe (kȧ-zȧt'skô-yĕ) Sov. Un.	49.8 N	31.10 E
113	Kazbek, Mt. (kȧz-byĕk') Sov. Un.	42.45 N	44.32 E
148	Kazim R. (kä-zēm') . . . . . . Sov. Un.	63.45 N	69.0 E
112	Kazlinskii Zavod (kȧz-lĭn'skê zȧ-vôt') . . . Sov. Un.	55.52 N	60.45 E
150	Kazvin (käz-vēn') . . . . Iran	36.14 N	50.0 E
173	Kealaikahiki Channel (kā-ä'lä-ê-kä-hē'kē) . Haw.	20.40 N	156.50 W
76	Kearney (kär'nĭ) . . . . Neb.	40.42 N	99.2 W
49	Keasey (kēz'ĭ) . Ore. (Portland In.)	45.50 N	123.20 W
72	Keats I. (kēts) Can. (Vancouver In.)	49.23 N	123.28 W
135	Kebili (kĕ-bē'lê) . . . . Tun. (In.)	33.40 N	9.8 E
110	Kebnekaise (Mt.) (kĕp'nĕ-kȧ-ēs'ĕ) Swe.	67.53 N	18.32 E
123	Kecskemét (kĕch'kĕ-māt) . . . Hung.	46.52 N	19.42 E
160	Kedah (State) (kä'dä) Non-fed. Mal. St.	6.0 N	100.30 E
121	Kedainiai (kē-dī'nĭ-ī) . . . . Lith.	55.16 N	23.59 E
86	Kedgwick (kĕdj'wĭk) . . . . Can.	47.40 N	67.25 W
158	Keelung (Kiirun) (kē'lōōng) (kē'ê-rōōn') . Tai. (In.)	25.6 N	121.45 E
86	Keene (kēn) . . . . N. H.	42.55 N	72.18 W
72	Keenesburg (kēnz'bûrg) Colo. (Denver In.)	40.7 N	104.31 W
142	Keetmanshoop (kāt'mȧns-hōp) S. W. Afr.	26.32 S	18.9 E
77	Keewatin (kē-wä'tĭn) . . . . . . Minn.	47.34 N	93.1 W
54	Keewatin, Dist. of . . . . Can.	61.15 N	85.0 E
131	Kefe (Feodosiya) (kyĕf'ĕ) (fā-ô-dō'sê-yȧ) . . . Sov. Un.	45.1 N	35.23 E
138	Keffi (kĕf'ê) . . . . Nig.	8.54 N	7.52 E
118	Keighley (kē'lĭ) . . . . Gt. Brit.	53.50 N	1.55 W
161	Kei Is. (kī) . . . . Neth. Ind.	5.45 S	132.45 E
157	Keijo (Seoul) (kā'jô) (sĕ-ōōl) . . Cho.	37.38 N	127.0 E
121	Keila (kā'lȧ) . . . . Est.	59.18 N	24.28 E
142	Keimoes (kī'mōōs) . . . . Bech.	28.39 S	20.59 E
143	Keimouth (kī'mŭth) . . . . U. S. Afr.	32.41 S	28.20 E
143	Kei Road (kī) . . . . U. S. Afr.	32.44 S	27.31 E
157	Keishu (kī'shōō') . . . . Cho.	35.52 N	129.10 E
143	Keis Kama R. (kīs kä'mä) . U. S. Afr.	33.3 S	27.20 E
121	Keitele, L. (kā'tĕ-lĕ) . . . . Fin.	62.50 N	26.0 E
160	Kelantan (State) (kĕ-län-tän') Non-fed. Mal. St.	5.30 N	102.0 E
135	Kelbia, Sebkha (L.) (sĕb'ᴋȧ kĕl'bê-ȧ) . Tun. (In.)	35.50 N	10.15 E
135	Kelibia (kĕ-lē'bê-ȧ) . . . . . Tun. (In.)	36.51 N	10.53 E
72	Kelker (kĕl'kēr) Colo. (Colo. Sprs. In.)	38.47 N	104.47 W
73	Kellerman (kĕl'ēr-mȧn) Ala. (Birmingham In.)	33.20 N	87.19 W
70	Kellogg (kĕl'ŏg) . . . . Ida.	47.33 N	116.8 W
73	Kelly Cr. (kĕl'ĭ) Ala. (Birmingham In.)	33.30 N	86.25 W
121	Kelme (kăl-mā') . . . . Lith.	55.35 N	22.55 E
70	Kelso (kĕl'sō) . . . . Wash.	46.9 N	122.55 W
112	Kem (kĕm) . . . . Sov. Un.	64.59 N	34.40 E
81	Kemah (kē'mȧ) . . . . Tex. (In.)	29.32 N	95.1 W
139	Kemboma (kĕm-bō'mä) Fr. Eq. Afr.	0.40 N	13.33 E
112	Kemi (kā'mê) . . . . Fin.	65.48 N	24.45 E
159	Kemigawa (kĕ'mê-gä'wä) Jap. (Tokyo In.)	35.39 N	140.3 E
112	Kemi, L. (kā'mê) . . . . Fin.	66.40 N	28.30 E
112	Kemi R. . . . . Fin.	66.15 N	25.30 E
112	Kemijärvi (kā'mê-yĕr-vē) . . . . . Fin.	66.40 N	27.30 E
71	Kemmerer (kĕm'ēr-ēr) . . . . . . Wyo.	41.47 N	110.34 W
78	Kemp, L. (kĕmp) . . . . Tex.	33.45 N	99.15 W
46	Kemp Land (kĕmp) . . . . Ant.	68.0 S	58.0 E
165	Kempsey (kĕmp'sê) . . . . Austl.	31.10 S	152.45 E
89	Kempsville (kĕmps'vĭl) Va. (Norfolk In.)	36.50 N	76.10 W
122	Kempten (kĕmp'tĕn) . . . . Ger.	47.44 N	10.17 E
86	Kempt L. (kĕmpt) . . . . Can.	47.25 N	74.15 W
119	Kemseke (kĕm'sĕ-kȧ) Bel. (Anvers In.)	51.12 N	4.4 E
53	Kenai (kĕ-nī') . . . . Alsk.	60.30 N	151.15 W
53	Kenai Mts. . . . . Alsk.	60.0 N	150.0 W
53	Kenai Pen. . . . . Alsk.	60.20 N	150.30 W
116	Kendal (kĕn'dăl) . . . . Gt. Brit.	54.20 N	2.45 W
143	Kendal . . . . U. S. Afr.	26.3 S	28.58 E
72	Kendall (kĕn'dăl) Wash. (Vancouver In.)	48.55 N	122.8 W
84	Kendallville (kĕn'dăl-vĭl) . . . . . Ind.	41.28 N	85.18 W
80	Kenedy (kĕn'ĕ-dĭ) . . . . Tex.	28.48 N	97.50 W
142	Kenhardt (kĕn'hȧrt) . . . . U. S. Afr.	29.18 S	21.9 E
118	Kenilworth (kĕn'ĭl-wûrth) Gt. Brit.	52.21 N	1.34 W
88	Kenilworth . . . . . . Ill. (Chicago In.)	42.6 N	87.42 W
141	Kenilworth . . . . U. S. Afr.	33.59 S	18.28 E
143	Kenira R. (kĕ-nē'rȧ) . . . . U. S. Afr.	30.35 S	28.45 E
138	Kenitra (Port-Lyautey) (kĕ-nē'-trȧ) Mor.	34.22 N	6.31 W
116	Kenmare (kĕn-mâr') . . . . Ire.	51.55 N	9.39 W

ăt; finăl; rāte; senâte; ärm; ȧsk; sofȧ; fâre; ch-choose; dh-as th in other; bē; êvent; bĕt; recĕnt; cratēr g-go; gh-gutteral g; bĭt; ĭ-short neutral; rīde; ᴋ-gutteral k as ch in German ich;

Page	Name Pronunciation Region	Lat. °'	Long. °'
76	Kenmare ....N. D.	48.41 N	102.5 W
116	Kenmare R. ....Ire.	51.30 N	10.0 W
88	Kenmore (kĕn'mōr) N. Y. (Niagara Falls In.)	42.58 N	78.52 W
84	Kenmore ....Ohio	41.3 N	81.37 W
86	Kennebec R. (kĕn-ê-bĕk') ..... Me.	44.50 N	69.50 W
86	Kennebunk (kĕn-ê-bŭŋk') .... Me.	43.25 N	70.32 W
81	Kenner (kĕn'ēr) ....La.	29.59 N	90.16 W
79	Kennett (kĕn'ĕt) ....Mo.	36.14 N	90.3 W
70	Kennewick (kĕn'ê-wĭk) ..... Wash.	46.12 N	119.8 W
86	Kenogami (kĕn-ô'gä-mê) ..... Can.	48.26 N	71.14 W
55	Kenora (kê-nō'rȧ) ....Can.	49.48 N	94.20 W
77	Kenosha (kê-nō'shȧ) ....Wis.	42.35 N	87.50 W
84	Kenova (kê-nō'vȧ) ....W. Va.	38.22 N	82.34 W
169	Kensington (kĕn'zĭng-tŭn) Austl. (Adelaide In.)	34.55 S	138.39 E
84	Kent (kĕnt) ....Ohio	41.8 N	81.23 W
49	Kent ....Wash. (Seattle In.)	47.22 N	122.15 W
152	Kentai Shan (Mts.) (kĕn'tī' shän') Chn.	49.10 N	108.30 E
153	Kentani (kĕn-tä'nê) .... U. S. Afr.	32.31 S	28.19 E
152	Kentei Alin (Mts.) (kĕn'tā' ä-lēn') Manch.	45.45 N	131.30 E
84	Kentland (kĕnt'lănd) ....Ind.	40.48 N	87.26 W
84	Kenton (kĕn'tŭn) ....Ohio	40.40 N	83.36 W
118	Kent, R. ....Gt. Brit.	54.12 N	2.54 W
84	Kentucky (State (kĕn-tŭk'ĭ) . U. S.	37.0 N	85.0 W
84	Kentucky R. ....Ky.	38.30 N	84.53 W
86	Kentville (kĕnt'vĭl) ....Can.	45.5 N	64.30 W
81	Kentwood (kĕnt'wŏŏd) ....La.	30.57 N	90.31 W
73	Kenwood (kĕn'wŏŏd) Ga. (Atlanta In.)	33.30 N	84.26 W
139	Kenya (kēn'yȧ) ....Afr.	2.0 N	38.0 E
139	Kenya, Mt. ....Kenya	0.3 S	37.25 E
77	Kenyon (kĕn'yŭn) ....Minn.	44.15 N	92.58 W
77	Keokuk (kē'ô-kŭk) ....Ia.	40.25 N	91.25 W
129	Keos (I.) (kĕ'ôs) ....Grc.	37.37 N	24.20 E
129	Kephallenia (I.) (kyĕ-fä-lē-nyä') Grc.	38.15 N	20.35 E
123	Kępno (kăŋ'pnō) ....Pol.	51.16 N	17.59 E
145	Kerak (kĕ'räk) ...... Transj. (In.)	31.10 N	35.42 E
165	Kerang (kê-răng') ....Austl.	35.45 S	143.52 E
166	Kerang ....Austl.	35.44 S	143.55 E
	Kerassunde, see Giresun, Tur.		
131	Kerch (kĕrch) ....Sov. Un.	45.19 N	36.29 E
131	Kerch Str. ....Sov. Un.	45.12 N	36.35 E
135	Kerd, Oued el (R.) (wĕd-ĕl-kûrd) Tun. (In.)	35.40 N	9.40 E
54	Keremeos (kĕr-ê-mē'ŏz) ...... Can.	49.13 N	119.40 W
7	Kerguelen I. (kĕr'gȧ-lĕn) ... Ind. O.	49.50 S	69.30 E
152	Keriya (Yutien) (yōō'tyĕn') .. Chn.	36.32 N	81.20 E
152	Keriya Darya (R.) (kĕ'rê-yȧ där'yȧ) . Chn.	37.30 N	81.33 E
138	Kerkennah I. (kĕr'kĕn-nä) ... Tun.	34.45 N	11.15 E
151	Kerki (kĕr'kê) ....Sov. Un.	37.50 N	65.12 E
129	Kerkyra (Corfu) (kĕr'kü-rȧ) (kŏr-fōō') . Grc.	39.36 N	19.55 E
6	Kermadec Is. (kĕr-măd'ĕk) . Pac. O.	30.0 S	178.0 W
150	Kerman (kĕr-män') ....Iran	30.29 N	57.12 E
150	Kermanshah (kĕr-män-shä') .. Iran	34.14 N	47.10 E
74	Kern R. (kûrn) ....Calif.	35.30 N	118.40 W
74	Kern R., South Fork ....Calif.	35.38 N	118.18 W
80	Kerrville (kûr'vĭl) ....Tex.	30.2 N	99.7 W
116	Kerry, Mts. of (kĕr'ĭ) ....Ire.	51.55 N	9.40 W
72	Kersey (kûr'sĭ) . Colo. (Denver In.)	40.23 N	104.34 W
153	Kerulen R. (kĕr'ŏŏ-lĕn) ....Chn.	48.30 N	116.30 E
153	Kerulen (San-Beisa-Urgo) (sän'-bā'sȧ-ōōr'gō) . Chn.	48.12 N	114.34 E
129	Keşan (kĕ'shän) ....Tur.	40.51 N	26.38 E
119	Kessel (kĕs'ĕl) ...Bel. (Anvers In.)	51.8 N	4.38 E
118	Kesteven (Borough) (kĕs'tê-vĕn) Gt. Brit.	53.0 N	0.37 W
123	Keszthely (kĕst'hĕl-lĭ) ....Hung.	46.46 N	17.13 E
160	Ketapang (kê-tȧ-päng') Neth. Ind.	1.52 S	110.0 E
53	Ketchikan (kĕch-ĭ-kăn') ......Alsk.	55.20 N	131.35 W
73	Ketona (kê-tō'nȧ) Ala. (Birmingham In.)	33.36 N	86.46 W
148	Ket R. (kyĕt) ....Sov. Un.	58.30 N	86.0 E
118	Kettering (kĕt'ēr-ĭng) .... Gt. Brit.	52.24 N	0.43 W
77	Kettle R. (kĕt''l) ....Minn.	46.20 N	92.50 W
119	Kettleshulme (kĕt''lz-hōm) Gt. Brit. (Liverpool In.)	53.18 N	2.1 W
123	Kety (kăŋ'tĭ) ....Pol.	49.54 N	19.15 E
85	Keuka L. (kê-ū'kȧ) ....N. Y.	42.30 N	77.10 W
157	Keum R. (kĕ'ōōm') ....Cho.	36.7 N	126.53 E
79	Kewanee (kê-wä'nê) ....Ill.	41.15 N	89.55 W
77	Kewaunee (kê-wô'nê) ....Wis.	44.28 N	87.31 W
77	Keweenaw B. (kē'wê-nô) ....Mich.	47.0 N	88.20 W
	Kexholm, see Käkisalmi, Fin.		
76	Keya Paha R. (kē-yȧ-pä'hä) S. D.-Neb.	43.6 N	100.0 W
83	Key Largo ....Fla. (In.)	25.10 N	80.20 W
116	Key, Lough (L.) (lŏĸ kē') ..... Ire.	54.0 N	8.15 W
88	Keyport (kē'pōrt). N. J. (N. Y. In.)	40.26 N	74.12 W
85	Keyser (kī'zēr) ....W. Va.	39.27 N	79.0 W
83	Key West (kē wĕst') .....Fla. (In.)	24.33 N	81.47 W
123	Kežmarok (kĕzh'mȧ-rôk) ... Czech.	49.8 N	20.27 E
142	Kgokgole R. (k'gŏk-gō'lȧ) .. Bech.	26.28 S	23.20 E
149	Khabarovsk (kä-bä'rôfsk) Sov. Un.	48.30 N	135.0 E
150	Khabis (ĸä-bēs') ....Iran	30.40 N	57.59 E
150	Khaburah (ĸä-bōō'rȧ) .... Oman	23.52 N	57.30 E
150	Khaibar (ĸī'bär) ....Sau. Ar.	25.45 N	39.29 E
152	Khaidik Gol (R.) (ĸī'dĕk gōl) Chn.	42.15 N	85.0 E
129	Khalkidike (Chalcidice) Pen. (kăl-ĸēd'ê-kĕ) (kăl-sĭd'ĭ-sê) . Grc.	40.25 N	23.25 E
129	Khalkis (Chalcis) (kăl'kĭs) (kăl'sĭs) . Grc.	38.27 N	23.38 E
112	Khalturin (ĸäl'tōō-rēn) ... Sov. Un.	58.32 N	48.58 E
145	Khan ez Zebib (ĸän ĕz zē-bēb') Transj. (In.)	31.29 N	36.2 E
128	Khania (Canea) (kä-nē'ä) (kä-nē'ä) . Grc. (In.)	35.27 N	24.4 E
128	Khania, G. of ....Grc.	35.35 N	24.0 E

Page	Name Pronunciation Region	Lat. °'	Long. °'
149	Khanka, L. (ĸän'kȧ) .... Sov. Un.	44.0 N	132.30 E
113	Khanskaya Stavka (Urda) (ĸän'skȧ'yȧ stäf'kȧ) (ōōr'dȧ) Sov. Un.	48.48 N	47.40 E
131	Kharkov (kär'kôf) ...... Sov. Un.	49.58 N	36.11 E
129	Kharmanlii (ĸȧr-män'lē) ..... Bul.	41.54 N	25.53 E
139	Khartoum (kär-tōōm') . A. E. Sud.	15.35 N	32.32 E
139	Khartoum North ...... A. E. Sud.	15.40 N	32.34 E
129	Khaskovo (ĸäs'kô-vô) ....Bul.	41.56 N	25.32 E
149	Khatanga (ĸȧ-täŋ'gȧ) ... Sov. Un.	71.50 N	102.0 E
149	Khatanga R. .... Sov. Un.	72.0 N	102.30 E
149	Khatangski G. ....Sov. Un.	74.0 N	110.0 E
152	Khem Belder (Krasny) (kĕm' bĕl-dĕr')(kräs'nĭ) . . Sov. Un.	51.40 N	94.5 E
131	Kherson (kĕr-sôn') ...... Sov. Un.	46.38 N	32.36 E
148	Kheta R. (ĸĕ'tȧ) .... Sov. Un.	71.0 N	99.0 E
149	Khilok R. (ĸê-lôk') .... Sov. Un.	51.10 N	109.0 E
153	Khingan Mts., Great (ĸĭn-gän') Chn.	48.30 N	120.0 E
153	Khingan Mts., Little ..... Manch.	49.0 N	127.30 E
129	Khios (Chios) (kē'ôs) (kī'ŏs) .. Grc.	38.22 N	26.9 E
129	Khios (I.) ....Grc.	38.23 N	26.5 E
150	Khiva (ĸē'vȧ) ....Sov. Un.	41.31 N	60.28 E
131	Khmelnik (ĸmyĕl'nĭk) ... Sov. Un.	49.34 N	27.58 E
131	Khodorkov (ĸô-dôr'kôf) Sov. Un.	50.3 N	29.12 E
148	Khodzhent, see Leninabad, Sov. Un.		
150	Khoi (kōr) ....Iran	38.35 N	45.5 E
131	Khoiniki (koi-nē'kê) ...... Sov. Un.	51.55 N	29.59 E
130	Kholm (kôlm) .... Sov. Un.	57.9 N	31.8 E
160	Khong (kŏng) .... Fr. In. Chn.	14.4 N	105.37 E
113	Khoni (ĸô'nê) .... Sov. Un.	42.20 N	42.30 E
160	Khonkaen (ĸŏŋ'kä-ĕn') ..... Thai.	16.35 N	102.46 E
113	Khoper R. (ĸô'pĕr) ...... Sov. Un.	51.45 N	43.15 E
129	Khora (kō'rȧ) ....Grc.	37.44 N	26.55 E
128	Khora Sphakion (kō'rȧ sfȧ-kĭ-ŏn') . Grc.	35.13 N	24.9 E
151	Khorog (kôr'ôg) .... Sov. Un.	37.29 N	71.40 E
131	Khorol (kô'rôl) .... Sov. Un.	49.48 N	33.18 E
131	Khorol R. .... Sov. Un.	49.50 N	33.30 E
150	Khorramshahr (Mohammorah) (kô-räm'shär mō'häm-mō'rä) Iran	30.31 N	48.17 E
152	Khotan (Hotien) (ĸō-tän') (hō'tyĕn') . Chn.	37.2 N	79.52 E
152	Khotan Darya (R.) (ĸō-tän' där'yȧ) . Chn.	38.30 N	80.50 E
150	Khurma (ĸōōr'mȧ) ...... Sau. Ar.	21.40 N	41.45 E
150	Khurramabad (kōō-rȧ-mȧ-bȧd') Iran	36.59 N	50.31 E
113	Khvalinsk (ĸvȧ-lĭnsk') ... Sov. Un.	52.28 N	48.0 E
151	Khyber Pass (kī'bēr) ... Afg.-India	34.9 N	71.10 E
154	Kiahwa (kyä'hwä') ....Chn.	25.30 N	112.4 E
152	Kialing (R.) (kyä'lĭng') ....Chn.	32.30 N	105.32 E
167	Kiama (kê-äm'ȧ) ....Austl.	34.41 S	150.51 E
140	Kiambi (kyäm'bê) ..... Bel. Cong.	7.28 S	27.58 E
79	Kiamichi R. (kyȧ-mē'chê) .. Okla.	34.30 N	95.30 W
158	Kiamusze (Chiamussu) .... Manch.	46.50 N	130.20 E
155	Kian (kyän) ....Chn.	27.3 N	114.43 E
162	Kiangan (kyăŋ'găn) .... P. I.	16.47 N	121.9 E
154	Kianghwa (kyăng'hwä') ...... Chn.	25.18 N	111.30 E
155	Kiangning (Nanking) (kyăng'nĭng') (nän'kĭng') Chn.	32.4 N	118.45 E
152	Kiangpei (kyäng'pā') ....Chn.	29.45 N	106.35 E
156	Kiangpu (kyäng'pōō') ....Chn.	32.2 N	118.33 E
155	Kiangshan (kyäng'shän') ......Chn.	28.47 N	118.45 E
155	Kiangsi (Prov.) (kyäng'sē') .. Chn.	27.52 N	115.38 E
155	Kiangsu (Prov.) (kyäng'sōō') . Chn.	31.30 N	120.5 E
155	Kiangtsin (kyäng'tsēn') ....Chn.	29.12 N	106.18 E
155	Kiangyin (kyäng'yēn') ....Chn.	31.50 N	120.16 E
112	Kianta, L. (kyän'tȧ) ....Fin.	65.0 N	28.15 E
156	Kiaochow (kyou'chō') ....Chn.	36.18 N	120.2 E
156	Kiaochow B. ....Chn.	36.8 N	120.11 E
156	Kiaomi (kyou'mē') ....Chn.	36.22 N	119.47 E
156	Kiao R. (kyou) ....Chn.	36.50 N	119.34 E
152	Kiating (kyä'tĭng') ....Chn.	29.31 N	103.51 E
154	Kiayu (kyä'yōō') ....Chn.	29.56 N	113.45 E
129	Kičevo (kē'chȧ-vô) ....Yugo.	41.30 N	20.59 E
156	Kichow (kē'chō') ....Chn.	30.2 N	115.19 E
156	Kichow ....Chn.	40.2 N	117.21 E
156	Kichow ....Chn.	37.42 N	115.37 E
77	Kickapoo R. (kĭk'ȧ-pōō) ....Wis.	43.20 N	90.50 W
138	Kidal (kê-däl') .... Fr. W. Afr.	18.36 N	1.0 E
116	Kidderminster (kĭd'ēr-mĭn-stēr) Gt. Brit.	52.25 N	2.15 W
170	Kidnappers C. (kĭd'năp-ērz) . N. Z.	39.40 S	177.7 E
118	Kidsgrove (kĭdz'grōv) .... Gt. Brit.	53.5 N	2.15 W
122	Kiel (kēl) ....Ger.	54.19 N	10.10 E
77	Kiel ....Wis.	43.52 N	88.3 W
122	Kiel B. ....Ger.	54.30 N	10.30 E
122	Kiel Canal ....Ger.	54.13 N	9.33 E
123	Kielce (kyĕl'tsĕ) ....Pol.	50.51 N	20.40 E
119	Kieldrecht (kēld'rĕĸt) Bel. (Anvers In.)	51.18 N	4.10 E
155	Kienchang (kyĕn'chăng') ..... Chn.	27.32 N	116.33 E
155	Kienchang ....Chn.	29.9 N	115.32 E
154	Kienchow (kyĕn'chō') ....Chn.	28.10 N	109.20 E
154	Kienli (kyĕn'lē') ....Chn.	29.48 N	112.42 E
155	Kienning (kyĕn'nĭng') ....Chn.	27.4 N	118.15 E
155	Kienping (kyĕn'pĭng') ....Chn.	31.10 N	119.11 E
155	Kien R. (kyĕn) ....Chn.	26.40 N	117.8 E
155	Kienshih (kyĕn'shē') ....Chn.	30.35 N	109.16 E
154	Kiensi (kyĕn'sē') ....Chn.	27.0 N	105.52 E
155	Kienteh (kyĕn'tä') ....Chn.	30.7 N	117.9 E
154	Kienyang (kyĕn'yăng') ....Chn.	27.9 N	109.33 E
155	Kienyang ....Chn.	27.22 N	117.53 E
131	Kiev (kē'yĕf) ....Sov. Un.	50.28 N	30.31 E
138	Kiffa (kēf'ä) ....Fr. W. Afr.	16.53 N	10.47 W
140	Kigali (kê-gä'lê) ....Bel. Cong.	1.58 S	30.2 E
140	Kigoma (kê-gō'mä) ....Tan.	4.45 S	29.40 E
121	Kihnu I. (kē'nōō) ....Est.	58.8 N	24.0 E
156	Kihsien (kē'hsyĕn') ....Chn.	34.31 N	114.54 E
140	Kihurio (kê-hōō'rê-ō) ....Tan.	4.28 S	38.5 E
159	Kii Chan. (kē'ê) ....Jap.	34.0 N	134.48 E

Page	Name Pronunciation Region	Lat. °'	Long. °'
158	Kiirun (Keelung) (kē'ê-rōōn') (kē'lōōng') . Taiwan (In.)	25.6 N	121.45 E
141	Kijungu (kê-jōōn'gōō) ....Tan.	5.23 S	37.18 E
154	Kikiang (kē'kyăng') ....Chn.	28.56 N	106.38 E
143	Kikvorsch Berg (Mt.) (kĕk'vôrsh) . U. S. Afr.	31.12 S	25.15 E
140	Kikwit (kē'kwĕt) ......Bel. Cong.	5.20 S	18.55 E
120	Kil (kêl) ....Swe.	59.29 N	13.16 E
173	Kilauea (kē-lȧ-ōō-ā'ä) ....Haw.	22.11 N	159.28 W
173	Kilauea Crater ....Haw.	19.27 N	155.15 W
84	Kilbourn (Wisconsin Dells) (kĭl'bŏŏrn) .. Wis.	43.37 N	89.45 W
169	Kilcoy (kĭl'koi) ....Austl. (In.)	26.54 S	152.34 E
116	Kildare (kĭl-dâr') ....Ire.	53.5 N	6.55 W
141	Kilimanjaro Mt. (kĭl-ê-män-jä'rō) Tan.	3.5 S	37.15 E
140	Kilimatinde (kĭl-ê-mȧ-tĭn'dȧ) . Tan.	5.47 S	34.55 E
141	Kilindini (kĭl-ĕn-dē'nê) ..... Kenya	4.5 S	39.36 E
121	Kilingi-Nomme (kē'lĭŋ-gê-nŏm'mĕ) . Est.	58.8 N	25.2 E
113	Kilis (kê'lēs) ....Tur.	36.45 N	37.15 E
116	Kilkenny (Cill Cainning) (kĭl-kĕn'ê) (kĭl ĸä'nĭg) ..... Ire.	52.39 N	7.15 W
129	Kilkis (kĭl'kĭs) ....Grc.	40.58 N	22.53 E
116	Killala (kĭ-lä'lȧ) ....Ire.	54.15 N	9.15 W
169	Killarney (kĭ-lär'nê) ... Austl. (In.)	28.19 S	152.18 E
116	Killarney ....Ire.	52.5 N	9.35 W
76	Killdeer (kĭl'dēr) ....N. D.	47.21 N	102.43 W
88	Kill van Kul (Inlet) (kĭl văn kŭl') N. J.-N. Y. (In.)	40.39 N	74.6 W
116	Kilmarnock (kĭl mär'nŭk) Gt. Brit.	55.35 N	4.40 W
166	Kilmore (kĭl'mōr) ....Austl.	37.18 S	144.56 E
167	Kilmorie (kĭl-mō'rê) ....Austl.	37.44 S	147.49 E
135	Kiloango (kĭ-lô-äŋ'gō) Ang. (Brazzaville In.)	6.0 S	15.29 E
141	Kilosa (kē-lō'sȧ) ....Tan.	6.49 S	37.3 E
164	Kilroy Downs (kĭl'roi dounz') Austl.	19.15 S	136.5 E
116	Kilrush (kĭl'rŭsh) ....Ire.	52.40 N	9.30 W
141	Kilwa (kēl'wä) ....Tan.	8.40 S	39.22 E
166	Kimba (kĭm'bȧ) ....Austl.	33.8 S	136.25 E
76	Kimball (kĭm'bȧl) ....Neb.	41.11 N	103.40 W
76	Kimball ....S. D.	43.45 N	98.58 W
143	Kimberley (kĭm'bēr-lĭ) .. U. S. Afr.	28.42 S	24.46 E
164	Kimberleys (Reg.) (kĭm'bēr-lêz) Austl.	17.0 S	126.30 E
73	Kimberly .. Ala. (Birmingham In.)	33.47 N	86.49 W
118	Kimbolton (kĭm'bŭl-tŭn) . Gt. Brit.	52.19 N	0.23 W
73	Kimbrel (kĭm'brĕl) Ala. (Birmingham In.)	33.18 N	87.3 W
155	Kimen (kē'mĕn') ....Chn.	29.52 N	117.45 E
129	Kimolos (I.) (kē'mô-lôs) ......Grc.	36.48 N	24.35 E
135	Kimpanzou (kĭm-pän-zōō') Fr. Eq. Afr. (Brazzaville In.)	4.23 S	15.10 E
130	Kimry (kĭm'rê) ....Sov. Un.	56.53 N	37.21 E
163	Kinabatangan R. (kē-nȧ-bȧ-täŋ'gän) . B. N. B.	5.27 N	118.0 E
163	Kinapusan Is. (kê-nȧ-pōō-sän') P.I.	5.12 N	120.26 E
84	Kincardine (kĭn-kär'dĭn) ...... Can.	44.8 N	81.40 W
151	Kinchinjunga, Mt. (kĭn-chĭn-jōōŋ'gȧ) . Nep.	27.38 N	88.15 E
156	Kinchow (kĭn'chō') ....Kwan.	39.8 N	121.38 E
81	Kinder (kĭn'dēr) ....La.	30.30 N	92.50 W
138	Kindia (kĭn'dê-ȧ) .... Fr. W. Afr.	10.1 N	12.58 W
140	Kindu (kĕn-dōō') .... Bel. Cong.	2.58 S	25.50 E
112	Kinel R. (kê-nĕl'') .... Sov. Un.	53.25 N	51.2 E
112	Kinel-Cherkesskaya (kê-nĕl''-chĕr-kĕs-kä'yȧ) .. Sov. Un.	53.32 N	51.32 E
130	Kineshma (kê-nĕsh'mȧ) .. Sov. Un.	57.26 N	42.10 E
141	Kingani R. (kĭŋ-gä'nê) .... Tan.	6.40 S	38.45 E
154	Kingchow (kĭng'chō') ....Chn.	30.21 N	112.0 E
74	King City ....Calif.	36.12 N	121.8 W
78	Kingfisher (kĭng'fĭsh-ēr) ..... Okla.	35.42 N	97.56 W
46	King George V Land (Reg.) .. Ant.	66.0 S	150.0 E
164	King George Sd. ....Austl.	35.0 S	118.0 E
165	King I. ....Austl.	39.45 S	143.55 E
130	Kingisepp (kĭŋ-gê-sĕp') .. Sov. Un.	59.21 N	28.39 E
164	King Leopold Ra. (lē'ô-pōld) Austl.	16.45 S	125.0 E
75	Kingman (kĭng'măn) ....Ariz.	35.11 N	114.3 W
78	Kingman ....Kan.	37.37 N	98.8 W
154	Kingmen (kĭng'mĕn') ....Chn.	31.2 N	111.55 E
155	Kingning (kĭng'nĭng') ....Chn.	27.51 N	119.42 E
169	King R. .... Austl. (Tas. In.)	42.10 S	145.40 E
154	Kingshan (kĭng'shän') ....Chn.	31.2 N	112.57 E
143	Kingsley (kĭngz'lĭ) ...... U. S. Afr.	27.59 S	30.32 E
117	Kings Lynn (kĭngz lĭn') .. Gt. Brit.	52.45 N	0.25 E
83	Kings Mountain ....N. C.	35.11 N	81.29 W
118	Kings Norton (nôr'tŭn) .. Gt. Brit.	52.25 N	1.55 W
164	King Sd. ....Austl.	16.42 S	123.30 E
71	Kings Peaks ....Utah	40.47 N	110.25 W
83	Kingsport (kĭngz'pōrt) ....Tenn.	36.33 N	82.36 W
74	Kings R. ....Calif.	36.27 N	119.45 W
166	Kingston (kĭngz'tŭn) ....Austl.	36.51 S	139.51 E
55	Kingston ....Can.	44.10 N	76.44 W
116	Kingston ....Gt. Brit.	51.25 N	0.19 W
96	Kingston ....Jam.	17.59 N	76.49 W
85	Kingston ....N. Y.	41.56 N	74.0 W
171	Kingston ....N. Z.	45.18 S	168.45 E
85	Kingston ....Pa.	41.16 N	75.52 W
49	Kingston ...... Wash. (Seattle In.)	47.47 N	122.30 W
91	Kingston (kĭngz'toun) . St. Vincent	13.14 N	61.12 W
83	Kingstree (kĭngz'trē) ....S. C.	33.38 N	79.50 W
80	Kingsville (kĭngz'vĭl) ....Tex.	27.32 N	97.52 W
155	Kingtehchen (kĭng'tĕ-chĕn') .. Chn.	29.26 N	117.7 E
116	Kingussie (kĭn-yōōs'ĭ) .... Gt. Brit.	57.5 N	4.5 W
54	King William I. ....Can.	69.10 N	98.0 W
143	Kingwilliamstown (kĭng-wĭl'-yŭmz-toun) . U. S. Afr.	32.52 S	27.24 E
152	Kingyang (kĭng'yăng') ....Chn.	36.2 N	107.55 E
154	Kingyuan (kĭng'yōō-än') ....Chn.	24.29 N	108.48 E
155	Kingyüan (kĭng'yü-än') ....Chn.	27.38 N	118.43 E
156	Kingyün (kĭng'yün') ....Chn.	37.53 N	117.13 E
155	Kinhwa (kēn'hwä') ....Chn.	29.8 N	119.42 E

ng-sing; ŋ-baŋk; ĸ-nasalized n; nŏd; cŏmmit; ōld; ôbey; ôrder; fōōd; fŏŏt; ou-out; s-soft; sh-dish; th-thin; pūre; ûnite; ûrn; stŭd; circŭs; ü-as "y" in study; '-indeterminate vowel.

Page	Name Pronunciation Region	Lat. °′	Long. °′
160	Kinibalu, Mt. (kē-nē-bȧ'lōō) B. N. B.	6.0 N	116.35 E
155	Kinki (kēn'kē') .... Chn.	27.56 N	116.44 E
156	Kinkiakow (kĭn'kyä-kō') ..... Chn.	36.33 N	120.49 E
89	Kinlock Park (kĭn'lŏk) Mo. (St. Louis In.)	38.45 N	90.20 W
116	Kinnaird Hd. (kĭn-ârd') .. Gt. Brit.	57.40 N	1.50 W
159	Kinomoto (kē'nō-mō'tō) ..... Jap.	33.53 N	136.5 E
159	Kinosaki (kē'nō-sȧ'kē) .... Jap.	35.37 N	134.47 E
155	Kin R. (kēn) .... Chn.	28.10 N	114.58 E
116	Kinsale (kĭn-sāl') .... Ire.	51.40 N	8.30 W
116	Kinsale Harbor .... Ire.	51.35 N	8.30 W
116	Kinsale, Old Head of .... Ire.	51.35 N	8.30 W
157	Kinsen (kĭn'sĕn') .... Cho.	36.7 N	128.8 E
156	Kinsha (kĭn'shä') .... Chn.	32.7 N	120.59 E
156	Kinsiang (kĭn'syäng') .... Chn.	35.4 N	116.17 E
78	Kinsley (kĭnz'lĭ) .... Kans.	37.55 N	99.25 W
83	Kinston (kĭnz'tŭn) .... N. C.	35.16 N	77.36 W
152	Kinta (kĭn'tä') .... Chn.	40.4 N	99.0 E
138	Kintampo (kĕn-tȧm'pō) ..... G. C.	8.4 N	1.38 W
135	Kinzila (kēn-zē'lȧ) ... Fr. Eq. Afr.	4.36 S	15.0 E
139	Kioga, L. (kē-ō'gȧ) .... Ug.	1.30 N	33.0 E
156	Kioshan (kyō'shän') .... Chn.	32.51 N	113.53 E
78	Kiowa (kī'ô-wȧ) .... Kans.	37.1 N	98.29 W
79	Kiowa .... Okla.	34.43 N	95.54 W
140	Kipembawe (kê-pĕm-bä'wȧ) .. Tan.	7.45 S	33.23 E
81	Kirbyville (kûr'bĭ-vĭl) .... Tex.	30.39 N	93.55 W
119	Kirchbach (kĭrK'bäK) Aust. (Wien In.)	48.17 N	16.13 E
119	Kirchsteinbek (kĭrK'shtīn-bĕk) Ger. (Hamburg In.)	53.32 N	10.8 E
141	Kirdâsa (kĭr-dä'sȧ) .... Eg.	30.3 N	31.6 E
149	Kirenga R. (kê-rĕṇ'gȧ) ... Sov. Un.	56.0 N	107.30 E
149	Kirensk (kē-rĕnsk') ...... Sov. Un.	57.45 N	108.15 E
148	Kirghiz (Aut. Rep.) (kĭr-gēz') Sov. Un.	48.0 N	68.0 E
113	Kirghiz Steppe .... Sov. Un.	48.45 N	56.0 E
152	Kirgis Nor (L.) (kĭr'gĭs nōr') . Chn.	49.10 N	93.15 E
153	Kirin (Chilin) (chĭ-lĭn') ... Manch.	43.50 N	126.36 E
159	Kirishima (Mt.) (kē'rē-shē'mȧ) Jap.	31.55 N	130.50 E
119	Kirkby (kûrk'bē) Gt. Brit. (Liverpool In.)	53.29 N	2.54 W
118	Kirkby-in-Ashfield (ăsh'fēld) Gt. Brit.	53.6 N	1.16 W
118	Kirkby Lonsdale (lŏnz'dāl) Gt. Brit.	54.12 N	2.36 W
116	Kirkcaldy (kĕr-kô'dĭ) ... Gt. Brit.	56.5 N	3.10 W
118	Kirkham (kûrk'ăm) ..... Gt. Brit.	53.47 N	2.53 W
49	Kirkland (kûrk'lănd) Wash. (Seattle In.)	47.41 N	122.12 W
113	Kirklareli (kĕrk'lȧr-ĕ'lē) ..... Tur.	41.45 N	27.12 E
79	Kirksville (kûrks'vĭl) .... Mo.	40.12 N	92.35 W
150	Kirkuk (kĭr-kōōk') .... Iraq	35.29 N	44.29 E
79	Kirkwood (kûrk'wŏŏd) .... Mo.	38.34 N	90.25 W
122	Kirn (kĕrn) .... Ger.	49.47 N	7.23 E
151	Kirthar Ra. (Mts.) (kĭr-tŭr) . India	26.15 N	67.0 E
118	Kirton (kûr'tŭn) .... Gt. Brit.	53.29 N	0.35 W
55	Kirkland Lake (kûrk'lănd) .. Can.	48.10 N	80.0 W
116	Kirkwall (kûrk'wôl). Gt. Brit. (In.)	59.0 N	2.55 W
73	Kirkwood (kûrk'wŏŏd) Ga. (Atlanta In.)	33.46 N	84.18 W
143	Kirkwood .... U. S. Afr..	33.22 S	25.28 E
131	Kirovo (Zinove'vsk) (kĕr'ō-vō zē-nō'vyĕfsk) .. Sov. Un.	48.31 N	32.15 E
113	Kirsanov (kêr-sȧ'nôf) .... Sov. Un.	52.40 N	42.40 E
113	Kirşehir (kêr-shĕ'hĕr) .... Tur.	39.5 N	34.0 E
140	Kiru, L. (kē-rōō') ...... Bel. Cong.	2.0 S	29.0 E
110	Kiruna (kē-rōō'nȧ) .... Swe.	67.50 N	20.15 E
158	Kiryu (kē'rĭ-ōō) .... Jap.	36.20 N	139.20 E
130	Kirzhach (kêr-zhäK') ..... Sov. Un.	56.8 N	38.52 E
159	Kisabe (kē'sȧ-bā). Jap. (Osaka In.)	34.48 N	135.42 E
141	Kisaki (kē-sȧ'kē) .... Tan.	7.28 S	37.40 E
141	Kisanga Mts. (kē-säṇ'gȧ) .... Moz.	12.30 S	38.30 E
159	Kisarazu (kē'sȧ-rȧ'zōō) Jap. (Tokyo In.)	35.24 N	139.55 E
140	Kisenyi (kē-sĕn'yē) ... Bel. Cong.	1.38 S	29.15 E
141	Kiserawe (kê-sȧ-rô'wā) .... Tan.	6.53 S	39.4 E
	Kishinev, see Chişinău, Rom.		
159	Kishiwada (kē'shē-wȧ'dȧ) .... Jap.	34.24 N	135.18 E
112	Kishtim (kēsh-tēm') ..... Sov. Un.	55.45 N	60.40 E
155	Kishui (kĭsh'wē') .... Chn.	27.10 N	115.0 E
155	Kishui .... Chn.	30.27 N	115.10 E
112	Kişinskii Zavod (kê-sĭn'skê zȧ-vôt') ... Sov. Un.	55.18 N	59.30 E
141	Kisiwani (kê-sê-wȧ'nê) ...... Tan.	4.6 S	37.59 E
52	Kiska I. (kĭs'kȧ) .... Alsk.	52.20 N	175.45 E
123	Kiskōrōs (kĭsh'kû-rûsh) ..... Hung.	46.37 N	19.17 E
123	Kiskunfélegyháza (kĭsh'kŏŏn-fā'-lĕd-y'hȧ-zô). Hung.	46.43 N	19.51 E
123	Kiskunhalas (kĭsh'kŏŏn-hô'lôs) Hung.	46.25 N	19.29 E
123	Kiskunmajsa (kĭsh'kŏŏn-mī'shô) Hung.	46.30 N	19.45 E
113	Kislovodsk (kês-lô-vôtsk') Sov. Un.	43.58 N	42.43 E
159	Kisogawa, R. (kē'sō-gȧ'wȧ) .. Jap.	35.28 N	137.15 E
123	Kispest (kĭsh'pĕsht') .... Hung.	47.28 N	19.12 E
128	Kissamos Kastelli (kē-sȧ'mōs kȧs-tĕl'ē). Grc.	35.28 N	23.39 E
158	Kisshu (kĭs'shōō') .... Cho.	41.0 N	129.28 E
138	Kissidougou (kē'sē-dōō'gōō) Fr. W. Afr.	9.20 N	10.15 W
83	Kissimmee (kĭ-sĭm'ē) .... Fla. (In.)	28.17 N	81.23 W
83	Kissimmee, L. .... Fla. (In.)	27.55 N	81.17 W
151	Kistna R. (kĕst'nȧ) .... India	16.15 N	76.0 E
110	Kistrand (kē'strănd) .... or.	70.30 N	25.5 E
123	Kisújszállás (kĭsh'ōō'y'-sä-lȧsh) Hung.	47.12 N	20.46 E
139	Kisumu (kē'sōō-mōō) .... Kenya	0.3 S	34.51 E
138	Kita (kē'tȧ) .... Fr. W. Afr.	13.9 N	9.30 W
152	Kitai (Kuchengtze) (kē'tā') (kōō'chĕng'tzē') . Chn.	44.3 N	89.22 E
158	Kita-Nayoshi (kē'tȧ-nȧ-yō'shē) Kar.	145.29 N	142.12 E
84	Kitchener (kĭch'ĕ-nĕr) .... Can.	43.25 N	80.35 W
55	Kitchioh (kĭt'chĭ-ō') .... Chn.	22.50 N	115.40 E
140	Kitega (kē-tā'gȧ) ...... Bel. Cong.	3.20 S	30.5 E
139	Kitgum (kĭt'gŏŏm) .... Ug.	3.22 N	33.2 E
75	Kitsil Ruin (kĭt'sĭl) .... Ariz.	36.46 N	110.32 W
85	Kittaning (kĭ-tăn'ĭng) .... Pa.	40.50 N	79.32 W
86	Kittery (kĭt'ĕr-ĭ) .... Me.	43.5 N	70.45 W
155	Kityang (kĭt'yäng') .... Chn.	23.33 N	116.9 E
122	Kitzingen (kĭt'zĭng-ĕn) .... Ger.	49.45 N	10.8 E
155	Kiukiang (kyōō'kyäng') ..... Chn.	29.40 N	115.52 E
158	Kiuliencheng (kyōō'lyĕn-chĕng') Manch.	40.15 N	124.29 E
155	Kiulung R. (kyōō'lōōng') ... Chn.	25.0 N	117.24 E
160	Kiungchow (kyōōng'chō') .... Chn.	19.59 N	110.15 E
141	Kivale (kē-vä'lē) .... Kenya	4.11 S	39.28 E
154	Kiyang (kē'yäng') .... Chn.	26.28 N	111.46 E
148	Kizel (kē'zĕl) .... Sov. Un.	59.10 N	57.40 E
113	Kizil Irmak(R.) (kĭz'ĭl-ĭr-măk') Tur.	40.28 N	33.45 E
113	Kizlyar (kĭz-lyär') .... Sov. Un.	43.58 N	46.45 E
159	Kizu (kē'zōō) .... Jap.	34.44 N	135.46 E
159	Kizuki (kē'zōō-kē) .... Jap.	35.24 N	132.40 E
110	Kjölen Mts. (chû'lĕn) Swe.-Nor...	63.00 N	12.00 E
142	Klaarstroom (klär'strōm) U. S. Afr.	33.19 S	22.31 E
122	Kladno (kläd'nō) .... Czech.	50.9 N	14.6 E
122	Klagenfurt (klä'gĕn-fōōrt) .... Ger.	46.38 N	14.18 E
121	Klaipéda (Memel) (klī-pā'dȧ) Lith.	55.42 N	21.10 E
70	Klamath Falls (klăm'ȧth) .... Ore.	42.12 N	121.48 W
70	Klamath L., Lower .... Ore.-Calif.	41.59 N	121.49 W
70	Klamath L., Upper .... Ore.	42.20 N	121.30 W
70	Klamath Mts. .... Ore.-Calif.	42.0 N	123.20 W
70	Klamath R. .... Ore.-Calif.	41.30 N	124.3 W
120	Klar R. (klär) .... Swe.	60.38 N	13.0 E
49	Klaskunine Cr. (klăs'kû-nĭn) Ore. (Portland In.)	46.3 N	123.5 W
49	Klaskunine R. . Ore. (Portland In.)	46.2 N	123.42 W
122	Klatovy (klȧ'tō-vē) .... Czech.	49.24 N	13.17 E
	Klausenberg, see Cluj, Rom.		
123	Kleck (klĕtsk) .... Pol.	53.2 N	26.40 E
142	Kleinkaras (klĭn-kär'ȧs).S. W. Afr.	27.35 S	18.5 E
119	Klein-Machnow (klīn-mäK'nō) Ger. (Berlin In.)	52.24 N	13.14 E
142	Klein Roggeveld (Mts.) (klīn rō'gĕ-vĕlt) . U. S. Afr.	33.0 S	20.30 E
142	Klein Zwartberg (Mts.) (klīn zvärt'bĕrg) . U. S. Afr.	33.20 S	21.20 E
143	Klerksdorp (klĕrks'dōrp) U. S. Afr.	26.52 S	26.39 E
130	Kletnya (klyĕt'nyȧ) ...... Sov. Un.	53.18 N	33.11 E
70	Klickitat R. (klĭk'ĭ-tăt) ...... Wash.	45.50 N	121.5 W
130	Klimovichi (klē-mô-vē'chē) Sov. Un.	53.36 N	31.58 E
130	Klin (klēn) .... Sov. Un.	56.18 N	36.43 E
163	Kling (klĭng) .... P. I.	5.58 N	124.42 E
120	Klintehamn (klĭn'tē-häm) ... Swe.	57.24 N	18.12 E
130	Klintsy (klēn'tsĭ) .... Sov. Un.	52.45 N	32.12 E
143	Klipplaat (klĭp'lät) ..... U. S. Afr.	33.2 S	24.22 E
143	Klip R. (klĭp) .... U. S. Afr.	27.15 S	29.25 E
128	Kljuĉ (klyōōch) .... Yugo.	44.33 N	16.47 E
123	Klobuck (kwō'bōōtsk) .... Pol.	50.53 N	18.58 E
110	Klofa-Jōkull (Vatna-Jōkull) (Glacier) (klō'fȧ-yû-kōōl) (vät-nȧ-yû'kōōl) . Ice.	64.30 N	16.45 W
53	Klondike R. (klŏn'dīk) ...... Can.	64.0 N	138.30 W
54	Klondike Reg. .... Can.	64.0 N	140.0 W
122	Klosterneuberg (klōs-tĕr-noi'-bōōrgh) . Ger.	48.18 N	16.17 E
53	Kluane L. (klōō-än') .... Can.	61.15 N	139.0 W
52	Klutina L. (klōō-tē'nȧ) . Alsk. (In.)	61.40 N	146.7 W
130	Klyazma R. (klyäz'mȧ) .. Sov. Un.	56.1 N	40.10 E
149	Klyuchevskaya (Vol.) (klyōō-chĕf-skȧ'yȧ) ... Sov. Un.	56.10 N	160.55 E
49	Knappa (năp'ȧ) Ore. (Portland In.)	46.11 N	123.35 W
118	Knaresborough (nârz'bŭr-ô) Gt. Brit.	54.1 N	1.28 W
135	Kneïss I. (knē-ēs') .... Tun. (In.)	34.22 N	10.17 E
129	Kneža (knyā'zhȧ) .... Bul.	43.27 N	24.3 E
76	Knife R. .... N. D.	47.11 N	102.0 W
52	Knight I. .... Alsk. (In.)	60.20 N	147.50 W
84	Knightstown (nīts'town) ...... Ind.	39.45 N	85.32 W
140	Kwilu R. (kwē'lōō) Fr. Eq. Afr.-Bel. Cong.	3.30 S	12.30 E
123	Knihinin (knê-hē'nĕn) .... Pol.	48.57 N	24.45 E
128	Knin (knēn) .... Yugo.	44.3 N	16.14 E
122	Knittelfeld (knĭt''l-fĕlt) ...... Ger.	47.14 N	14.49 E
171	Knobbs, The (Mt.) .... N. Z. (In.)	43.39 S	172.38 E
162	Knob Pk. (nŏb) .... P. I.	12.28 N	121.20 E
116	Knockmealdown Mts. (nŏk-mēl'doun) . Ire.	52.15 N	8.0 W
118	Knottingley (nŏt'ĭng-lĭ) .. Gt. Brit.	53.42 N	1.14 W
119	Knowsley (nōz'lĭ) Gt. Brit. (Liverpool In.)	53.28 N	2.51 W
84	Knox (nŏks) .... Ind.	41.18 N	86.40 W
77	Knoxville (nŏks'vĭl) .... Ia.	41.18 N	93.5 W
82	Knoxville .... Tenn.	35.58 N	83.57 W
118	Knutsford (nŭts'fērd) .... Gt. Brit.	53.18 N	2.22 W
130	Knyaz, L. (knyäz) .... Sov. Un.	52.25 N	27.59 E
142	Knysna (knĭs'nȧ) .... U. S. Afr.	34.3 S	23.4 E
123	Knyszyn (knē'shēn) .... Pol.	53.16 N	22.58 E
142	Koa Vallei R. (kō-ȧ vȧ'lā) U.S.Afr.	29.15 S	18.40 E
152	Kobdo R., see Chirgalantu, Chn.		
159	Kobe (kō'bĕ) .... Jap.	34.40 N	135.10 E
131	Kobelyaki (kō-bĕl-yȧ'kē) . Sov. Un.	49.8 N	34.12 E
120	Köbenhavn (kû-b'n-houn') ... Den.	55.40 N	12.34 E
122	Koblenz (kō'blĕntz) .... Ger.	50.22 N	7.35 E
130	Kobozha R. (kō-bō'zhȧ) . Sov. Un.	58.44 N	34.59 E
123	Kobryń (kō'brĕn') .... Pol.	52.13 N	24.23 E
52	Kobuk R. (kō'bŭk) .... Alsk.	67.0 N	160.0 W
113	Kobuleti (kô-bōō-lyä'tē) . Sov. Un.	41.50 N	41.45 E
129	Kočane (kō'chȧ-nĕ) .... Yugo.	41.54 N	22.24 E
128	Kočevje (kō'chäv-yĕ) .... Yugo.	45.38 N	14.50 E
152	Kocha (Kuche) (kō'chä') (kōō'chē') . Chn.	41.32 N	82.58 E
157	Kochang (kō'chäng) .... Cho.	35.44 N	127.56 E
122	Kocher R. (kôK'ĕr) .... Ger.	49.10 N	9.45 E
159	Kochi (kō'chē) .... Jap.	33.35 N	133.30 E
53	Kodiak (kō'dyăk) .... Alsk.	57.40 N	152.30 W
53	Kodiak I. .... Alsk.	57.20 N	153.30 W
139	Kodok (ko'dŏk) .... A. E. Sud.	9.57 N	32.2 E
142	Koedoes Mts. (kōō'dōōs) U. S. Afr.	32.40 S	20.13 E
72	Koenig (kû'nĕg) Colo. (Denver In.)	40.23 N	104.57 W
161	Koepang (kōō-pänḡ) .. Neth. Ind.	10.15 S	123.42 E
122	Koesfeld (kûs'fĕlt) .... Ger.	51.56 N	7.10 E
160	Koetaradja (kōō'tȧ-räd'jȧ) Neth. Ind.	5.29 N	95.23 E
142	Koez (kûz) .... S. W. Afr.	25.59 S	19.6 E
143	Koffyfontein (kô-fĭ-fŏn-tān') U. S. Afr.	29.22 S	25.2 E
138	Koforidua (kō-fô-rĭ-dōō'ȧ) ... G. C.	6.4 N	0.15 W
159	Kofu (kō'fōō') .... Jap.	35.41 N	138.32 E
169	Kogarah (kōgō-ȧ-rȧ) Austl. (Sydney In.)	33.58 S	151.8 E
120	Köge (kû'gĕ) .... Den.	55.27 N	12.10 E
159	Kohana (kō-hȧ-nȧ) Jap. (Osaka In.)	34.49 N	135.21 E
151	Kohima (kō-ē'mȧ) .... India	25.45 N	94.15 E
170	Kohukohu (kô-hōō-kô-hōō') .. N. Z.	35.20 S	173.30 E
130	Koidanovo (koi'dȧ-nô'vô) Sov. Un.	53.40 N	27.8 E
129	Koinare (kō'ĭ-nȧ-rĕ) .... Bul.	43.22 N	24.8 E
157	Koisan (kō'ē-sän') .... Cho.	36.47 N	127.50 E
159	Koitoi (kō'e-tô'ē) .... Jap.	45.21 N	141.46 E
157	Kōje I. (kû'jĕ) .... Cho.	34.50 N	128.35 E
123	Kojetín (kô'yĕ-tyĕn) .... Czech.	49.21 N	17.19 E
158	Kojo (kō'jō') .... Cho.	38.50 N	128.20 E
148	Kokand (kô-känt') .... Sov. Un.	40.30 N	70.50 E
148	Kokchetav (kôk'chĕ-tȧf) Sov. Un.	53.25 N	69.20 E
121	Kokemäen R. (kô'kē-mȧ'ĕn) .. Fin.	61.20 N	22.9 E
142	Kokenap (kō'kĕ-năp) ... U. S. Afr.	31.28 S	18.28 E
130	Kokhma (kôK'mȧ) ...... Sov. Un.	56.56 N	41.9 E
112	Kokkola (kôk'kō-lȧ) .... Fin.	63.50 N	23.10 E
84	Kokomo (kō'kō-mô) .... Ind.	40.30 N	86.9 W
152	Koko Nor (L.) .... Chn.	37.0 N	100.0 E
161	Kokopo (kô-kō'pō) ... N. Gui. Ter.	4.22 S	152.27 E
148	Kokpektinskaya (kôk'pĕk-tēn'skȧ-yȧ) ... Sov. Un.	48.55 N	82.15 E
72	Koksilah R. (kôk'sē-lȧ) Can. (Vancouver In.)	48.39 N	123.45 W
55	Koksoak R. (kôk'sō-ăk) ..... Can.	58.0 N	69.0 W
143	Kokstad (kôk'shtät) .... U. S. Afr.	30.34 S	29.25 E
157	Koksung (kôk'sōōng') .... Cho.	35.18 N	127.19 E
159	Kokuba (kō'kōō-bȧ) .... Jap.	31.42 N	130.48 E
159	Kokubu (kō'kōō-bōō) Jap. (Osaka In.)	34.34 N	135.39 E
159	Kokura (kō'kōō-rȧ) .... Jap.	33.47 N	130.52 E
157	Kokusan (kō-kōō-sän') .... Cho.	38.47 N	126.39 E
157	Kokwa (bay) .... Cho.	37.30 N	126.30 E
112	Kola (kō'lȧ) .... Sov. Un.	68.58 N	33.10 E
138	Kolahun (kō-lä'hōōn) .... Lib.	8.30 N	10.8 W
112	Kola Pen. .... Sov. Un.	67.30 N	37.0 E
151	Kolar (kō-lär') .... India	13.15 N	77.59 E
122	Kolberg (kôl'bergh) .... Ger.	54.9 N	15.35 E
130	Kolchugino (kôl-chōō'gē-nô) Sov. Un.	56.16 N	39.28 E
120	Kolding (kôl'dĭng) .... Den.	55.28 N	9.26 E
140	Kole (kō'lȧ) .... Bel. Cong.	3.20 S	22.43 E
112	Kolguev I. (kôl-gōō'yĕf) . Sov. Un.	69.15 N	49.0 E
151	Kolhapur (kōl'hȧ-pōōr) .... India	16.45 N	74.2 E
122	Kolin (kō'lēn) .... Czech.	50.1 N	15.12 E
139	Kollo, Mt. (kŏl'ō) ...... It. E. Afr.	11.5 N	39.15 E
142	Kolmanskop (kōl'măns-kōp) S. W. Afr.	26.41 S	15.15 E
122	Köln (kûln) .... Ger.	50.57 N	6.57 E
123	Kolno (kôw'nô) .... Pol.	53.25 N	21.57 E
123	Kolo (kô'wô) .... Pol.	52.11 N	18.37 E
130	Kolomna (kȧl-ôm'nȧ) ..... Sov. Un.	55.5 N	38.49 E
123	Kolomyja (kō'lô-mē'yȧ) ...... Pol.	48.32 N	25.2 E
131	Kolosovka (kō-lô-sôf'kȧ) . Sov. Un.	47.17 N	30.59 E
130	Kolpino (kôl'pē-nô) ..... Sov. Un.	59.45 N	30.39 E
130	Kolpny (kôlp'nē) .... Sov. Un.	52.12 N	36.52 E
130	Kolp R. (kôlp) .... Sov. Un.	59.25 N	35.40 E
149	Kolyma R. (kô-lē-mȧ') ... Sov. Un.	66.0 N	151.30 E
149	Kolymski Ridge (kô-lēm'skē) Sov. Un.	61.30 N	150.0 E
148	Kolyvan (kôl-ē-vän') ..... Sov. Un.	55.25 N	82.50 E
145	Komandorskie Is. .... Sov. Un.	55.0 N	172.0 W
	Komarno (kō'mär-nō), see Komárom, Hung.		
123	Komárno (kō'mär-nō) .... Pol.	49.37 N	23.43 E
123	Komárom (Komárno) (kō'mä-rŏm) (kō'mär-no) . Hung.	47.44 N	18.6 E
143	Komati R. (kō-mä'tē) ... U. S. Afr.	26.3 S	31.0 E
143	Komatipoort (kō-mȧ'tē-pōrt) U. S. Afr.	25.25 S	31.55 E
122	Komotau (Chomutov) (kō'mō-tou) (kō'mōō-taf) . Ger.	50.27 N	13.25 E
159	Komatsu (kō-măt'sōō) .... Jap.	36.20 N	136.30 E
141	Kôm Bira (kôm' bē'rȧ) .... Eg.	30.5 N	31.8 E
143	Komgha (kōm'gȧ) .... U. S. Afr.	32.36 S	27.54 E
112	Komi (Zyryan) (Aut. Ter.) (kô'mē) (zĭr'ĭ-ăn) ... Sov. Un.	64.0 N	55.0 E
138	Komodugu-Yobe R. (kō-mô-dōō'gōō-yō'bā) . Nig.	12.52 N	11.0 E
129	Komotēnē (kō-mō-tē'nē) ...... Grc.	41.7 N	25.23 E
160	Kompongthom (kôm'pŏng-tōm) Fr. In. Chn.	12.38 N	104.41 E
142	Koms Berg (Mts.) (kōms' bĕrgh) U. S. Afr.	32.35 S	21.0 E
149	Komsomol'tsa G. (kôm-sô-môl'tsȧ) Sov. Un.	45.30 N	54.15 E
152	Konche Darya (R.) (kōn'chĕ där'yȧ) . Chn.	40.45 N	87.30 E
112	Konda R. (kôn'dȧ) .... Sov. Un.	60.25 N	63.50 E
140	Kondoa Irangi (kōn-dō'ȧ ē-räṇ'gē) . Tan	4.50 S	35.55 E
131	Konevskaya (kô-nyôf'skȧ-yȧ) Sov. Un.	46.5 N	38.56 E
138	Kong (kŏng) .... Fr. W. Afr.	9.7 N	4.36 W
138	Kong (Prov.) .... Fr. W. Afr.	9.30 N	4.30 W
141	Konge (kōṇ'gȧ) .... Tan.	5.51 S	37.53 E
154	Kongmoon (kông'mōōn') ..... Chn.	22.34 N	113.0 E

ăt; finăl; rāte; senāte; ärm; ȧsk; sofȧ; fâre; ch-choose; dh-as th in other; bē; ēvent; bĕt; recĕnt; cratēr; g-go; gh-gutteral g; bĭt; ĭ-short neutral; rīde; K-gutteral k as ch in German ich;

Page	Name Pronunciation Region	Lat. °′	Long. °′
154	Kongmoon City............Chn.	22.30 N	112.59 E
157	Kongo, Mt. (kôŋ′gō)........Cho.	38.30 N	128.0 E
140	Kongolo (kôŋ-gō′lō)....Bel. Cong.	5.18 S	26.57 E
120	Kongsberg (kôngs′bĕrg)......Nor.	59.40 N	9.39 E
120	Kongsvinger (kôngs′vĭŋ-gēr)..Nor.	60.12 N	12.0 E
123	Königsberg (kû′nēks-bĕrgh)...Ger.	54.42 N	20.31 E
140	Koni Hill (kō′nē)......Bel. Cong.	10.34 S	27.22 E
123	Konin (kô′nyĕn)............Pol.	52.11 N	18.15 E
129	Konitsa (kô′nyē′tsȧ).........Grc.	40.4 N	20.45 E
129	Konjic (kôn′yēts)..........Yugo.	43.38 N	17.59 E
142	Konkib R. (kōn′kêb)...S. W. Afr.	27.0 S	17.15 E
131	Konotop (kô-nô-tôp′)....Sov. Un.	51.13 N	33.13 E
123	Konskie (koin″skyĕ).........Pol.	51.11 N	20.26 E
131	Konstantinov (kôn-stȧn-tē′nôf) Sov. Un.	49.46 N	27.12 E
131	Konstantinovka (kôn-stȧn-tê-nôf′kȧ) Sov. Un.	47.49 N	31.11 E
131	Konstantinovka-Dmitrievka (kôn-stȧn-tê-nôf′kȧ-dmē′trê-yĕf′kȧ) Sov. Un.	48.33 N	37.39 E
122	Konstanz (Constance) (kôn′shtänts) (kŏn′stȧns) Switz.	47.39 N	9.11 E
138	Kontagora (kōn-tȧ-gō′rä)....Nig.	10.30 N	5.30 E
138	Kontcha (kōn′chȧ).........Cam.	8.0 N	12.20 E
113	Konya (kōn′yȧ).............Tur.	37.52 N	32.30 E
142	Kooigoed Flats (kō′ē-gōōd) U. S. Afr.	30.20 S	18.50 E
166	Koondrook (kŏŏn-drŏŏk′)...Austl.	35.40 S	144.10 E
169	Koonyum Range (kō-ôn-yōōm′) Austl. (In.)	28.30 S	153.12 E
143	Koopmansfontein (kōp′mäns-fŏn-tān′) Bech.	28.15 S	24.5 E
167	Koorawatha (kō-ô-rȧ-wä′thȧ) Austl.	34.2 S	148.33 E
166	Kooringa (Burra) (kō-ô-rĭŋ′gȧ) (bōōr′ȧ) Austl.	33.40 S	138.58 E
54	Kootenay L. (kōō′tê-nȧ).....Can.	49.50 N	116.30 W
70	Kootenay Landing..........Can.	49.15 N	116.42 W
70	Kootenay R...........U. S.-Can.	48.50 N	116.20 W
167	Koo Wee Rup (kō′ô wē′ rŭp) Austl.	38.11 S	145.28 E
148	Kopal (kô-päl′).........Sov. Un.	45.20 N	79.0 E
120	Kopervik (kô′pĕr-vêk).......Nor.	59.18 N	5.20 E
120	Köping (chû′pĭng)..........Swe.	59.31 N	15.59 E
120	Kopparberg (kŏp′pȧr-bĕrgh)..Swe.	59.52 N	15.0 E
128	Koprivnica (kô′prēv-nê′tsȧ) Yugo.	46.9 N	16.51 E
167	Koramburra (kō-räm-bōō′rȧ) Austl.	38.25 S	145.49 E
143	Korannafontein (kô-rä′nä-fŏn-tān′) U. S. Afr.	26.50 S	26.0 E
129	Korcë (Korica) (kôr′chĕ) (kô′rêt-sȧ) Alb.	40.36 N	20.49 E
128	Korčula (I.) (kôr′chōō-lȧ) ..Yugo.	42.55 N	16.55 E
139	Kordofan Plat. (kôr-dô-fän′) A. E. Sud.	11.30 N	30.30 E
157	Korea (Chosen) (kô-rē′ȧ)....Asia	38.0 N	127.0 E
157	Korea B. (Chosen)..........Cho.	39.15 N	123.30 E
157	Korea, G. of (Chosen).......Cho.	39.40 N	128.0 E
157	Korean Arch. (Chosen)......Cho.	34.11 N	126.45 E
158	Korea Str. (Chosen).........Asia	35.0 N	130.0 E
157	Korea Str. (Chosen).........Cho.	34.35 N	129.0 E
138	Korhogo (kôr-hō′gō)...Fr. W. Afr.	9.28 N	5.18 W
129	Korica (Korcë) (kô-rêt′sȧ) (kôr′chĕ) Alb.	40.36 N	20.49 E
160	Korinchi, Mt. (kô-rēn′chê) Neth. Ind.	1.45 S	101.21 E
129	Korinthos (Corinth) (kô-rên′thôs) (kŏr′ĭnth) Grc.	37.55 N	22.55 E
159	Koriyama (kō′rê-yä′mä).....Jap.	34.37 N	135.43 E
158	Koriyama..................Jap.	37.20 N	140.20 E
149	Korkodon R. (kôr′kô-dōn′) Sov. Un.	63.30 N	153.0 E
122	Körmend (kûr′mĕnt).......Hung.	47.2 N	16.35 E
128	Kornat (I.) (kôr-nät′)......Yugo.	43.45 N	15.20 E
143	Kornet Spruit (R.) (kōr′nĕt sprût′) Bas.	30.0 S	27.30 E
122	Korneuburg (kôr′noi-bŏŏrgh).Ger.	48.22 N	16.20 E
131	Korocha (kô-rō′chȧ).....Sov. Un.	50.50 N	37.11 E
141	Korogwe (kô-rō′gwĕ)........Tan.	5.8 S	38.38 E
6	Koro (I.) (kō′rô).....Fiji Is. (In.)	17.21 S	179.24 E
166	Koroit (kō′rô-ĭt)...........Austl.	38.16 S	142.21 E
163	Koronadal (kô′rô-nȧ-däl′)....P. I.	6.7 N	125.2 E
131	Korop (kō′rôp)..........Sov. Un.	51.32 N	32.53 E
161	Koror (kō′rôr) ....Pelew Is.	7.16 N	134.32 E
169	Kororoit Cr. (kō′rō-rō′êt) Austl. (Melbourne In.)	37.47 S	144.48 E
131	Korosten (kô′rôs-tĕn)....Sov. Un.	50.58 N	28.40 E
131	Korostishev (kô-rôs′tê-shôf) Sov. Un.	50.20 N	29.0 E
131	Korotoyak (kô′rô-tô-yȧk′) Sov. Un.	50.59 N	39.5 E
121	Korsnäs (kôrs′nĕs)...........Fin.	62.45 N	21.10 E
120	Korsör (kôrs′ûr′)...........Den.	55.18 N	11.7 E
139	Korti (kôr′tê).........A. E. Sud.	18.10 N	31.33 E
131	Koryukovka (kôr-yōō-kôf′kȧ) Sov. Un.	51.45 N	32.22 E
123	Korzec (kō′zhĕts)............Pol.	50.35 N	27.12 E
122	Kóscian (kôsh′tsyȧn).........Pol.	52.5 N	16.37 E
123	Kościerzyna (kôsh-tsyĕ-zhû-ē′nȧ) Pol.	54.7 N	17.59 E
82	Kosciusko (kŏs-ĭ-ŭs′kō).....Miss.	33.3 N	89.37 W
167	Kosciusko, Mt..............Austl.	36.28 S	148.16 E
167	Kosciusko Plat.............Austl.	36.10 S	148.20 E
123	Kosel (kō′zĕl)...............Ger.	50.19 N	18.9 E
139	Kosha (kō′shä)........A. E. Sud.	20.55 N	30.33 E
153	Koshan (kō′shän′) ....Manch.	48.20 N	126.0 E
159	Koshiki Is. (kō-shē′kê).......Jap.	31.45 N	129.45 E
157	Koshu (kō′shōō′)...........Cho.	35.12 N	126.55 E
157	Koshu.....................Cho.	36.28 N	127.2 E
	Košice, see Kassa, Hung.		
143	Kosi, L. (kô′sē)........U. S. Afr.	27.10 S	32.45 E
122	Kōslin (kûs′lên)............Ger.	54.11 N	16.10 E
152	Koso Gol (L.) (kô′sô gôl′)...Chn.	51.0 N	100.30 E

Page	Name Pronunciation Region	Lat. °′	Long. °′
123	Kossów (kôs′sŏŏf)...........Pol.	52.45 N	25.12 E
128	Kostajnica (kôs′tä-ê-nē′tsȧ).Yugo.	45.14 N	16.33 E
139	Kosti (kôs′tê).........A. E. Sud.	13.8 N	32.35 E
130	Kostroma (kôs-trô-mȧ′)..Sov. Un.	57.46 N	40.59 E
130	Kostroma (Dist.)........Sov. Un.	58.12 N	41.50 E
130	Kostroma R.............Sov. Un.	58.18 N	41.10 E
157	Kosung (kō′sōōng′).........Cho.	35.0 N	128.19 E
158	Kosung....................Cho.	38.45 N	128.15 E
122	Köszeg (kû′sĕg)...........Hung.	47.22 N	16.31 E
160	Kotabaro (kō′tȧ-bä′rō).Neth. Ind.	3.20 S	116.10 E
159	Kotachi (kō′tȧ-chê) Jap. (Osaka In.)	34.38 N	135.39 E
140	Kota Kota (kō-tȧ kō′tȧ).....Nya.	12.50 S	34.13 E
139	Kota R. (kō′tȧ)......Fr. Eq. Afr.	6.0 N	22.0 E
129	Kotel (kō-tĕl′)..............Bul.	42.53 N	26.26 E
131	Kotelevka (kô′tĕ-lyĕf′kȧ) Sov. Un.	50.2 N	34.42 E
149	Kotelni I. (kô-tyĕl′nê)...Sov. Un.	75.10 N	140.0 E
112	Kotelnich (kô-tyĕl′nêch) .Sov. Un.	58.20 N	48.20 E
122	Köthen (kû′tĕn)............Ger.	51.46 N	11.58 E
142	Kotjeskolk (kôt′yĕs-kôlk) U. S. Afr.	31.18 S	20.19 E
121	Kotka (kŏt′kȧ)..............Fin.	60.28 N	27.0 E
112	Kotlas (kôt′lȧs).........Sov. Un.	61.15 N	46.45 E
128	Kotor (kō′tôr).............Yugo.	42.25 N	18.48 E
130	Kotorost R. (kō-tôr-ôst′) Sov. Un.	57.16 N	39.40 E
122	Kottbus (kôt′bōōs)..........Ger.	51.47 N	14.20 E
148	Kotul R. (kô-tōōl′)......Sov. Un.	68.0 N	102.0 E
52	Kotzebue (kôt′sē-bōō).......Alsk.	66.40 N	162.30 W
53	Kotzebue Sd...............Alsk.	66.30 N	163.0 W
138	Kouandé (kwän-dā′)...Fr. W. Afr.	10.25 N	1.40 E
143	Koudeveld Berg (Mts.) (kou′dē-vĕlt).U. S. Afr.	32.5 S	24.15 E
138	Koudougou (kōō-dōō′gōō) Fr. W. Afr.	12.7 N	2.15 W
138	Koulikoro (kōō-lê-kō′rô) Fr. W. Afr.	13.0 N	7.30 W
138	Koumbia (kōōm′bĭ-ȧ)..Fr. W. Afr.	11.36 N	13.3 W
139	Koundé (kōōn-dā′)...Fr. Eq. Afr.	6.3 N	14.34 E
138	Kouroussa (kōō-rōō′sä) Fr. W. Afr.	10.42 N	10.0 W
138	Koutiala (kōō-tê-ä′lä).Fr. W. Afr.	12.30 N	5.22 W
121	Kouvola (kō′ŏŏ-vô-lä)........Fin.	60.45 N	26.45 E
112	Kovda, L. (kôv′dȧ)......Sov. Un.	66.45 N	32.0 E
121	Kovno (Kaunas) (kôv′nô)...Lith.	54.53 N	23.54 E
130	Kovrov (kôv-rôf′).......Sov. Un.	56.22 N	41.20 E
123	Kowel (kō′vĕl)..............Pol.	51.12 N	24.43 E
154	Kowloon (kō′lōōn′).........Chn.	22.22 N	114.6 E
157	Kowon (kō′ôn′).............Cho.	39.28 N	127.12 E
159	Koya (kō′yȧ)....Jap. (Osaka In.)	34.47 N	135.23 E
52	Koyukuk R. (kô-yōō′kŏŏk)...Alsk.	66.0 N	156.0 W
129	Kozanē (kô-zhä′nā)..........Grc.	40.17 N	21.50 E
131	Kozelets (kô′zĕ-lyĕts)....Sov. Un.	50.53 N	31.5 E
130	Kozelsk (kô-zĕlsk′)......Sov. Un.	54.2 N	35.51 E
123	Kozienice (kō-zyĕ-nē′tsĕ).....Pol.	51.34 N	21.34 E
149	Kozlovskaya (kôz-lôf′skȧ′yȧ) Sov. Un.	47.0 N	134.0 E
129	Kozloduі (kôz′lō-dōōē).......Bul.	43.46 N	23.42 E
159	Kozushima (Seven Is.) (kō′zōō-shē′mȧ).Jap.	34.12 N	139.8 E
143	Kraai R. (krä′ê)........U. S. Afr.	30.57 S	27.15 E
160	Kra Bin (krȧ bēn) ....Thai.	13.52 N	101.37 E
120	Kragerö (krä′gēr-û).........Nor.	58.53 N	9.25 E
129	Kragujevac (krä′gōō-yĕ-vȧts) Yugo.	44.1 N	20.56 E
123	Kraków (krȧ′kŏŏf)..........Pol.	50.5 N	19.59 E
129	Kraljevo (krȧl-yĕ′vō).......Yugo.	43.42 N	20.43 E
131	Kramatorskaya (krȧ-mȧ-tôr′skȧ-yȧ)...Sov. Un.	48.45 N	37.32 E
120	Kramfors (kräm′fôrs)........Swe.	62.55 N	17.50 E
128	Kranj (krän′)..............Yugo.	46.15 N	14.23 E
143	Krantzkop (kränts′kôp) U. S. Afr.	28.59 S	30.52 E
131	Krasilov (krä′sê-lôf).....Sov. Un.	49.41 N	27.1 E
121	Kràslava (kräs′lä-vä)........Lat.	55.52 N	27.12 E
...	Kraslice, see Graslitz, Ger.		
123	Krasnik (kräs′nêk)..........Pol.	50.54 N	22.14 E
131	Krasnoarmeisk (Yalta) (krȧs′nô-ȧr-mā′ēsk) (yäl′tä)....Sov. Un.	44.29 N	34.10 E
113	Krasnoarmeiskoe (krȧs′nô-ar-mȧ′-ê-skō′yĕ)...Sov. Un.	48.30 N	44.30 E
131	Krasnodar (krȧs′nô-dȧr) .Sov. Un.	45.3 N	39.0 E
149	Krasnoe (krȧs′nô-yĕ).....Sov. Un.	67.25 N	122.59 E
149	Krasnoe, L..............Sov. Un.	64.0 N	173.30 E
131	Krasnograd (krȧs′nô-grät) Sov. Un.	49.23 N	35.28 E
131	Krasnogrigorievka (krȧs′nô-grê-gô-rê-yĕf′kā)...Sov. Un.	47.40 N	34.31 E
130	Krasnogvardeisk (Trotsk) (krȧs′nô-vär-dēsk trôtsk)Sov. Un.	59.38 N	30.6 E
131	Krasnokutsk (krȧs′nô-kōōtsk) Sov. Un.	50.2 N	35.5 E
113	Krasno-Polyanskoe (krȧs′nô-pôlí-yȧn-skō′yĕ)...Sov. Un.	43.45 N	40.15 E
131	Krasnoselie (krȧs′nô-sĕl′ê-yĕ) Sov. Un.	48.54 N	32.21 E
112	Krasnoslobodsk (krȧs′nô-slô-bôtsk′)...Sov. Un.	54.20 N	43.45 E
113	Krasnovodsk (krȧs-nô-vôtsk′) Sov. Un.	40.0 N	53.10 E
148	Krasnoyarsk (krȧs′nô-yȧrsk′) Sov. Un.	56.10 N	93.0 E
130	Krasny (krȧs′nê)........Sov. Un.	59.44 N	30.6 E
152	Krasny (Khem Belder) (krȧs′nê) (ᴋĕm′ bĕl-dĕr′).Chn.	31.40 N	94.5 E
130	Krasny Kholm (krȧs′nê ᴋōlm) Sov. Un.	58.3 N	37.8 E
113	Krasnykut (krȧs′nê-kōōt′) Sov. Un.	50.58 N	47.5 E
123	Krasnystaw (kräs′nê-stȧf)....Pol.	50.58 N	23.10 E
113	Krasny Sulin (krȧs′nê-sōō-lēn′) ..Sov. Un.	47.58 N	40.10 E

Page	Name Pronunciation Region	Lat. °′	Long. °′
160	Kratiē (krȧ-tā′)......Fr. In. Chn.	12.29 N	106.2 E
129	Kratovo (krȧ-tô′vô) ....Yugo.	42.4 N	22.11 E
129	Krdžali (k′rd′zhȧ-lê).........Bul.	41.38 N	25.21 E
122	Krefeld-Uerdingen (krā′fĕlt-ür′-dĭng-ĕn).Ger.	51.20 N	6.34 E
131	Kremenchug (krĕm′ĕn-chōōgh′) Sov. Un.	49.4 N	33.29 E
131	Kremennoe (krĕ′mĕ-nô′yĕ) Sov. Un.	49.3 N	38.9 E
122	Krems (krĕms)..............Ger.	48.26 N	15.35 E
130	Kresttsi (kråst′sê).......Sov. Un.	58.12 N	32.24 E
121	Kretinga (krĕ-tĭŋ′gȧ)........Lith.	55.55 N	21.20 E
123	Kreuzburg (kroits′bŏŏrgh)....Ger.	50.58 N	18.13 E
138	Kribi (krē′bê).............Cam.	3.0 N	9.57 E
130	Krichev (krê′chôf).......Sov. Un.	53.41 N	31.41 E
129	Kriekhankhi (krĭ-ĕ-ᴋäŋ′hê)...Grc.	38.13 N	23.17 E
120	Kristiansand (krĭs-tyȧn-sän″).Nor.	58.9 N	7.59 E
120	Kristianstad (krĭs-tyȧn-städ′).Swe.	56.2 N	14.9 E
120	Kristiansund (krĭs-tyȧn-sŏŏn″).Nor.	63.8 N	7.45 E
121	Kristiina (Kristinestad) (krĭs′tē-nȧ) Fin.	62.16 N	21.25 E
120	Kristinehamn (krês-tē′nĕ-häm′) Swe.	59.18 N	14.7 E
121	Kristinestad (Kristiina).......Fin.	62.16 N	21.25 E
129	Kriva-Palanka (krē-vȧ-pȧ-läŋ′kȧ).Yugo.	42.12 N	22.19 E
131	Krivoe Ozero (krē′vô-yĕ ô′zĕr-ô) Sov. Un.	47.58 N	30.17 E
131	Krivoi Rog (krê-vô′ê rôgh′) Sov. Un.	47.56 N	33.21 E
128	Križevci (krē′zhĕv-tsê).....Yugo.	46.2 N	16.32 E
128	Krk (I.) (k′rk)............Yugo.	45.5 N	14.35 E
	Krnov, see Jägerndorf, Ger.		
120	Kröderen (krû′dĕ-rĕn).......Nor.	60.8 N	9.50 E
131	Krolevets (krô-lyā′vyĕts) Sov. Un.	51.32 N	33.22 E
123	Królewska Huta (krŏŏ-lĕf′skȧ hōō′tȧ).Pol.	50.17 N	18.58 E
123	Kroměříž (krô′myĕr-zhēzh) Czech.	49.17 N	17.23 E
130	Kromi (krô′mê).........Sov. Un.	52.44 N	35.41 E
142	Kromme R. (krôm′mĕ)..U. S. Afr.	31.0 S	19.0 E
149	Kronotskii, C. (krô′nôt′skĭ-ê) Sov. Un.	54.50 N	162.0 E
130	Kronshtadt (krôn′shtät) Sov. Un.	59.59 N	29.49 E
143	Kroonstad (krōn′shtät)..U. S. Afr.	27.42 S	27.19 E
113	Kropotkin (krȧ-pôt′kên) Sov. Un.	45.28 N	40.35 E
123	Krosno (krôs′nô)............Pol.	49.42 N	21.47 E
123	Krotoszyn (krô-tō′shên)......Pol.	51.42 N	17.26 E
128	Krško (k′rsh′kô)............Yugo.	45.58 N	15.29 E
129	Kruë (krōō′ĕ)...............Alb.	41.31 N	19.49 E
140	Kruger Natl. Park (krōō′gĕr) (krü′gĕr).U. S. Afr.	23.45 S	31.30 E
143	Krugersdorp (krōō′gĕrz-dôrp) U. S. Afr.	26.6 S	27.45 E
129	Kruševać (krŏŏ′shĕ-vȧts)...Yugo.	43.34 N	21.20 E
129	Kruševo (krŏŏ′shĕ-vô)......Yugo.	41.20 N	21.16 E
121	Krustpils (krŏŏst′pêls).......Lat.	56.30 N	25.51 E
120	Krylbo (krül′bô)............Swe.	60.7 N	16.13 E
131	Krym (Sov. Rep.) (krĭm).Sov. Un.	45.20 N	34.24 E
131	Krymskaya (krĭm′skȧ-yȧ) Sov. Un.	44.58 N	37.57 E
123	Krynki (krên′kê)............Pol.	53.15 N	23.46 E
131	Kryukov (k′r′yōō-kôf′) Sov. Un.	49.2 N	33.25 E
123	Krzemieniec (kzhĕ-myā′nyĕts) Pol.	50.6 N	25.44 E
138	Ksar Smeidi (k′sär smā′ê-dê) Fr. W. Afr.	22.52 N	3.30 W
135	Ksour (k′sōōr).........Tun. (In.)	35.53 N	9.0 E
135	Ksour Mts...........Tun. (In.)	33.25 N	9.55 E
114	Ksour, Mts. of the..........Alg.	33.15 N	9.2 E
160	Kuala Lumpur (kwä′lä lŏŏm-pōōr′).Strs. Sets.	3.12 N	101.38 E
145	Kuala Pilah (pē′lȧ) Fed. Mal. States (In.)	2.46 N	102.15 E
145	Kuala Sembrong (sĕm′brŏng) Fed. Mal. States (In.)	2.29 N	103.35 E
156	Kuan (kōō′än′).............Chn.	39.28 N	116.14 E
113	Kuba (kōō′bȧ)..........Sov. Un.	41.10 N	48.32 E
113	Kuban R. (kŏŏ-bȧn″)....Sov. Un.	45.25 N	40.0 E
152	Kuche (Kocha) (kōō′chĕ′) (kō′chä′).Chn.	41.32 N	82.58 E
156	Kuchen (kōō′chĕn′).........Chn.	33.19 N	117.14 E
156	Kucheng (kōō′chĕng′).......Chn.	37.33 N	116.6 E
152	Kuchengtze (Kitai) (kōō′chĕng′-tzĕ′) (kĭ-tī′)	44.3 N	89.22 E
160	Kuching (kōō′chĭng).........Sar.	1.30 N	116.26 E
159	Kuchi No Erabo (I.) (kōō′chê nō ĕr′ȧ-bō).Jap.	30.36 N	130.14 E
154	Kuchow (kōō′chō′)..........Chn.	25.53 N	108.28 E
159	Kudamatsu (kōō′dȧ-mä′tsōō).Jap.	34.1 N	131.52 E
160	Kudat (kōō-dät′)........B. N. B.	7.0 N	116.46 E
122	Küddow (kü′dō).............Ger.	53.30 N	16.55 E
112	Kudenskoe, L. (kŏŏ′dĕn-skō′yĕ) Sov. Un.	59.45 N	39.30 E
156	Kuen Lun Shan (Mts.) (kōō′ĕn lōōn′ shän′).Chn.	37.6 N	121.20 E
152	Kuerhlei (Kurla) (kōō′ĕr-lā′ê) (kōōr′lä).Chn.	41.30 N	86.10 E
156	Kufow (kōō′fō′)............Chn.	35.46 N	117.2 E
122	Kufstein (kōōf′shtīn)........Ger.	47.34 N	12.11 E
142	Kuibis (kwĭ′bĭs).......S. W. Afr.	26.42 S	16.47 E
112	Kuibishev (Samara) (kōō-ĭ′bĭ-shĕf) Sov. Un.	53.10 N	50.10 E
157	Kuisyung (kōō′ĭ-syŏŏng).....Cho.	40.0 N	125.16 E
159	Kujusan (Mt.) (kōō′jōō-sän′).Jap.	33.5 N	131.15 E
139	Kukawa (kōō-kä′wä)........Nig.	12.58 N	13.38 E
129	Kukës (kōō′kĕs).............Alb.	42.2 N	20.25 E
129	Kula (kōō′lȧ)...............Bul.	43.52 N	22.31 E
113	Kula......................Tur.	38.35 N	28.40 E
149	Kular Mts. (kŏŏ-lär′)....Sov. Un.	69.25 N	131.0 E

ng-sing; ŋ-bank; ɴ-nasalized n; nŏd; cŏmmit; ōld; ôbey; ôrder; fōōd; fŏŏt; ou-out; s-soft; sh-dish; th-thin; pūre; ûnite; ûrn; stŭd; circŭs; ü-as "y" in study; ′-indeterminate vowel.

Page	Name Pronunciation Region	Lat. °′	Long. °′
121	Kuldiga (ko͝ol′dê-gȧ) . . . . Lat.	56.58 N	21.58 E
112	Kulebaki (ko͞o-lĕ-băk′ĭ) . . Sov. Un.	55.28 N	42.35 E
151	Kulhakangri, Mt. (ko͞ol-hä-käŋ′grê) Bhu.	27.59 N	90.15 E
130	Kulikovo (ko͞o-lê-kô′vô) Sov. Un.	52.16 N	39.32 E
122	Kulmbach (ko͝olm′bäκ) . . . . . . Ger.	50.6 N	11.27 E
128	Kulpa R. (ko͝ol′pȧ) . . . . Yugo.	45.32 N	15.40 E
149	Kulskoe (ko͞ol′skô-yĕ) Sov. Un.	52.15 N	109.30 E
156	Kulu (ko͞o′lo͞o′) . . . . Chn.	37.14 N	115.6 E
148	Kulunda (ko͞o-lo͞on′dȧ) Sov. Un.	52.36 N	78.55 E
148	Kulundinski, L. (ko͝o-lo͞on-dyên′skĭ) Sov. Un.	53.0 N	79.30 E
159	Kuma (ko͞o′mä) . . . . Jap.	33.21 N	130.55 E
159	Kumamoto (ko͞o′mä-mō′tô) . . . Jap.	32.51 N	130.40 E
159	Kumano Sea (ko͞o-mä′nō) . . . . Jap.	33.40 N	136.30 E
129	Kumanovo (ko͝o-mä′nô-vô) . . Yugo.	42.8 N	21.40 E
113	Kuma R. (ko͞o′mä) . . . . . . Sov. Un.	45.0 N	46.0 E
171	Kumara (ko͞o-mä′rä) . . . . N. Z.	42.38 S	171.15 E
138	Kumasi (ko͞o-mä′sê) . . . . G. C.	6.48 N	1.33 W
138	Kumba (ko͝om′bȧ) . . . . Nig.	4.35 N	9.30 E
151	Kumbakonam (ko͝om′bŭ-kō′nŭm) India	10.50 N	79.28 E
157	Kumchon (ko͞om′chōn′) . . . . . . Cho.	38.13 N	126.27 E
157	Kumsan (ko͞om′sän′) . . . . Cho.	36.6 N	127.29 E
157	Kumsung (ko͞om′so͝ong′) . . . . . Cho.	38.27 N	127.36 E
157	Kumte (ko͞om′tĕ′) . . . . Cho.	35.49 N	126.52 E
143	Kunana (ko͞o-nä′nä) . . . . U. S. Afr.	26.21 S	25 19 E
143	Kunap R. (ko͞o′năp) . . . . U. S. Afr.	32.45 S	26.18 E
158	Kunashiri I. (ko͞o′nä-shē′rê) . . Jap.	44.15 N	145.50 E
121	Kunda (ko͝on′dȧ) . . . . Est.	59.31 N	26.35 E
145	Kuneĭtra (ko͞o-nȧ-ē′trȧ) . . . Syr. (In.)	33.5 N	36.9 E
140	Kunene R. (ko͝o-nā′nĕ) Ang.-S. W. Afr.	16.30 S	15.15 E
120	Kungälv (ko͝ong′ĕlf) . . . . Swe.	57.53 N	12.0 E
154	Kungan (ko͞on′găn′) . . . . Chn.	29.56 N	111.54 E
152	Kungchang (ko͝ong′chăng) . . . Chn.	34.52 N	105.32 E
154	Kungcheng (ko͝ong′chĕng′) . . . Chn.	24.48 N	110.44 E
156	Kunghsien (ko͝ong′hsyĕn′) . . . Chn.	34.42 N	112.56 E
155	Kung R. (ko͝ong) . . . . Chn.	25.47 N	114.52 E
150	Kungrad (ko͝on-grăt′) . . . . Sov. Un.	43.15 N	59.5 E
120	Kungsbacka (ko͝ongs′bä-kȧ) . . Swe.	57.31 N	12.2 E
148	Kungur (ko͝oŋ-go͞or′) . . . . . Sov. Un.	57.30 N	57.0 E
165	Kunie (Isle of Pines) (ko͞on′yĕ) (kü-nyā′) . New Cal.	22.30 S	167.30 E
152	Kunlun Mts. (ko͝on′lo͞on′) . . . . Chn.	36.0 N	90.0 E
157	Kunsan (ko͞on′sän′) . . . . Cho.	36.0 N	126.45 E
155	Kunshan (ko͞on′shän′) . . . . Chn.	31.18 N	120.51 E
123	Kunszentmárton (ko͝on′sĕnt-mär′ tōn) Hung.	46.49 N	20.19 E
130	Kuntsevo (ko͝on′tsĕ-vō) . . Sov. Un.	55.43 N	37.25 E
130	Kunya R. (ko͝on′yȧ) . . . . . Sov. Un.	56.25 N	30.48 E
112	Kuopio (ko͝o-ŏ′pê-ŏ) . . . . Fin.	62.50 N	27.35 E
72	Kuper I. (ko͞o′pẽr) Can. (Vancouver In.)	48.58 N	123.38 W
148	Kupino (Opalikha) (ko͝o-pĭ′nô ô-pä-lēk′hä) . . Sov. Un.	54.10 N	76.59 E
121	Kupiškis (ko͝o-pĭsh′kĭs) . . . . . . Lith.	55.49 N	24.58 E
131	Kupyansk (ko͝op-yänsk′) Sov. Un.	49.42 N	37.37 E
113	Kura R. (ko͞o′rȧ) . . . . Sov. Un.	41.20 N	45.40 E
159	Kurayoshi (ko͞o′rä-yō′shê) . . . . Jap.	35.26 N	133.50 E
113	Kurdakly (ko͝ord′ȧ-klê) Sov. Un.	49.10 N	54.40 E
113	Kurdistan (Reg.) (kûrd′ĭ-stăn) Asia	37.40 N	43.50 E
157	Kure (ko͞o′rȧ) . . . . Cho.	35.14 N	127.28 E
159	Kure . . . . Jap.	34.15 N	132.32 E
131	Kuressaare (ko͝o′rĕ-sä′rĕ) . . . . . Est.	58.16 N	22.30 E
148	Kurgan (ko͝or-găn′) . . . . . . Sov. Un.	55.25 N	65.15 E
148	Kurgan Tyube (ko͝or-găn′ tyo͞o′bĕ) Sov. Un.	37.45 N	68.55 E
145	Kuril Is., see Chishima Is., Jap.		
149	Kuril Str. (ko͞o′rĭl) . . Sov. Un.-Jap.	50.50 N	156.40 E
123	Kurisches Haff (Sea) (ko͝o′rĭsh-ĕs häf′) . Ger.	55.5 N	21.0 E
151	Kurla (ko͝or′lȧ) India (Bombay In.)	19.4 N	72.53 E
152	Kurla (Kuerhlei) (kwĕr′lā′) . . Chn.	41.30 N	86.10 E
139	Kurmuk (ko͝or′mo͞ok) . . A. E. Sud.	10.35 N	34.15 E
151	Kurnool (ko͝or-no͞ol′) . . . . India	15.45 N	78.0 E
159	Kuro I. (ko͞o′rô) . . . . Jap.	30.50 N	129.55 E
171	Kurow (ko͞o′rou) . . . . N. Z.	44.44 S	170.30 E
121	Kuršenai (ko͝or′shȧ-nī) . . . . . . Lith.	56.0 N	22.58 E
129	Kuršumlija (ko͝or-sho͝om′lĭ-yȧ) Yugo.	43.6 N	21.15 E
159	Kururi (ko͞o′ro͞o-rê) Jap. (Tokyo In.)	35.18 N	140.6 E
139	Kurusku (ko͞o-ro͞os-ko͞o′) . . . . . . Eg.	22.32 N	32.21 E
131	Kushchevskaya (ko͝osh-chôf′skä-yä) . . . Sov. Un.	46.33 N	39.36 E
130	Kurshinovo (ko͝or-shê-nô′vô) Sov. Un.	56.59 N	34.9 E
131	Kursk (ko͝orsk) . . . . Sov. Un.	51.45 N	36.9 E
131	Kursk (Dist.) . . . . Sov. Un.	51.25 N	36.0 E
142	Kuruman (ko͞o′ro͞o-män) . . . . Bech.	27.25 S	23.25 E
142	Kuruman Hills . . . . Bech.	27.35 S	23.20 E
159	Kurume (ko͞o′ro͞o-mĕ) . . . . Jap.	33.27 N	130.30 E
148	Kushevatskoe (ko͝o-shĕ-väts′-kô-yĕ) . . . Sov. Un.	65.10 N	65.30 E
156	Kushih (ko͞o′shĭ′) . . . . Chn.	32.14 N	115.33 E
159	Kushimoto (ko͞o′shĭ-mō′tō) . . . Jap.	33.29 N	135.47 E
158	Kushiro (ko͞o′shē-rō) . . . . Jap.	43.1 N	144.22 E
150	Kushka (ko͝osh′kȧ) . . . . . . Sov. Un.	33.15 N	62.37 E
113	Kushum R. (ko͝o-sho͝om′) Sov. Un.	50.30 N	50.32 E
158	Kushun-nai (ko͞o′sho͞on-nī′) . . . Kar.	47.59 N	142.15 E
148	Kushva (ko͝osh′vȧ) . . . . . . Sov. Un.	58.25 N	59.55 E
52	Kuskokwim B. (kŭs′kô-kwĭm) Alsk.	59.40 N	162.0 W
52	Kuskokwim R. . . . . Alsk.	61.20 N	160.0 W
148	Kustanai (ko͝os-tȧ-nī′) . . . . Sov. Un.	53.20 N	63.40 E
	Kustendje, see Constanta. Rom.		
122	Küstrin (küstrēn′) . . . . Ger.	52.35 N	14.39 E
159	Kusuki (ko͞o′so͝o-kê) . . . . Jap.	33.24 N	131.35 E
113	Kütahya (kü-tä′hyȧ) . . . . Tur.	39.28 N	29.48 E
113	Kutais (ko͝o-tȧ-ês′) . . . . . . Sov. Un.	42.15 N	42.40 E
145	Kuteïfé (ko͞o-tĕ-ê-fā′) . . . . Syr. (In.)	33.54 N	36.40 E
155	Kutien (kü′tyĕn′) . . . . Chn.	26.37 N	118.42 E
128	Kutina (ko͞o′tê-nȧ) . . . . Yugo.	45.27 N	16.49 E
122	Kutná Hora (ko͝ot′nä hô′rȧ) Czech.	49.57 N	15.16 E
123	Kutno (ko͝ot′nô) . . . . Pol.	52.13 N	19.23 E
112	Kutno, L. . . . . Sov. Un.	65.15 N	31.30 E
123	Kuty (ko͞o′tê) . . . . Pol.	48.15 N	25.11 E
112	Kuusamo (ko͞o′sȧ-mô) . . . . Fin.	65.55 N	29.15 E
150	Kuwait (ko͞o-wīt′) . . . . Asia	29.30 N	47.45 E
159	Kuwana (ko͞o′wȧ-nȧ) . . . . Jap.	35.2 N	136.40 E
156	Küyang (kü′yäng) . . . . Chn.	38.41 N	114.36 E
156	Kuyeh (ko͞o′yĕ′) . . . . Chn.	35.24 N	116.8 E
148	Kuzkii I. (ko͝oz′kĭ-ê) . . . . . Sov. Un.	72.45 N	79.0 E
113	Kuznetsk (ko͝oz-nyĕtsk′) . . Sov. Un.	53.0 N	46.32 E
130	Kuznetsovo (ko͝oz′nyĕt′sô′vô) . . Sov. Un.	56.38 N	36.52 E
156	Kwachow (kwä′chō′) . . . . Chn.	32.15 N	119.21 E
158	Kwainei (kwī′nä) . . . . Cho.	42.30 N	129.40 E
154	Kwangan (kwän′găn′) . . . . Chn.	30.33 N	106.34 E
156	Kwangchang (kwäng′chăng′) Chn.	39.26 N	114.32 E
156	Kwangchow (kwäng′chō′) . . . . Chn.	32.13 N	114.59 E
154	Kwangchow (Canton) (kăn-tŏn′) Chn.	23.7 N	113.15 E
160	Kwangchowan (kwäng′chō′-wän′) Fr. In. Chn.	21.15 N	110.30 E
155	Kwangfeng (kwȧng′fĕng′) . . . . Chn.	28.28 N	118.17 E
156	Kwangling (kwäng′lĭng′) . . . . . Chn.	39.48 N	114.6 E
140	Kwango R. (kwäng′ō′) Bel. Cong.-Ang.	8.0 S	17.40 E
156	Kwangping (kwäng′pĭng′) . . . Chn.	36.44 N	114.53 E
156	Kwangshan (kwäng′shän′) . . . Chn.	32.3 N	114.54 E
154	Kwangshun (kwäng′sho͞on′) . . Chn.	25.22 N	106.30 E
154	Kwangsi (Prov.) (kwäng′sē′) . Chn.	24.8 N	108.56 E
155	Kwangsin (kwäng′sĭn′) . . . . . . Chn.	28.29 N	118.0 E
155	Kwangteh (kwäng′tĕ′) . . . . . . Chn.	30.54 N	119.26 E
155	Kwangtseh (kwäng′tsĕ′) . . . . . Chn.	27.28 N	116.58 E
155	Kwangtsi (kwäng′tsē′) . . . . . . Chn.	30.6 N	115.32 E
156	Kwangtsung (kwäng′tso͝ong′) Chn.	37.7 N	115.16 E
154	Kwangtung (Prov.) (kwäng′to͝ong′) Chn.	22.30 N	109.30 E
156	Kwantao (kwän′tä′ō) . . . . Chn.	36.35 N	115.38 E
156	Kwantung (kwän′to͝ong′) . . . . . Asia	39.10 N	121.40 E
154	Kwanyang (kwän′yäng′) . . . . . Chn.	25.27 N	110.58 E
157	Kwanyang . . . . Chn.	35.0 N	127.36 E
156	Kwanyun (kwän′yo͞on′) . . . . . Chn.	34.25 N	119.20 E
158	Kwarenko (kwȧ-rĕn′kô) . . Tai. (In.)	24.1 N	121.31 E
154	Kweichow (kwā′chō′) . . . . Chn.	31.1 N	110.37 E
154	Kweichow (Prov.) . . . . Chn.	26.58 N	106.54 E
154	Kweihsien (kwā′hsyĕn′) . . . . . Chn.	23.10 N	109.42 E
155	Kweihwa (kwā′hwä′) . . . . Chn.	26.15 N	117.4 E
155	Kweiki (kwā′kē′) . . . . Chn.	27.50 N	117.4 E
154	Kweilhwa (kwāl′hwä′) . . . . Chn.	25.42 N	105.58 E
154	Kweilin (kwā′lĕn′) . . . . Chn.	25.13 N	110.12 E
155	Kweimoy I. (kwā′moi′) . . . . . . Chn.	24.28 N	118.34 E
156	Kwei R. (kwā) . . . . Chn.	33.30 N	116.53 E
153	Kweisui (gwā′soi′) . . . . Chn.	40.55 N	111.45 E
156	Kweiteh (kwā′tĕ′) . . . . Chn.	34.27 N	115.47 E
154	Kweiting (kwā′tĭng′) . . . . Chn.	26.31 N	107.5 E
152	Kweitun (Wusu) (kwā′to͞on′) (wo͞o′so͞o′) Chn.	44.29 N	84.28 E
154	Kweiyang (kwā′yäng′) . . . . Chn.	25.48 N	112.20 E
154	Kweiyang . . . . Chn.	26.33 N	106.33 E
140	Kwenge R. (kwĕŋ′gĕ) Bel. Cong.-Ang.	7.0 S	18.45 E
140	Kwilu-Juma R. (kwē′lo͞o-jo͞o′mȧ) Bel. Cong.	6.30 S	19.15 E
138	Kwitta (kwĭt′ȧ) . . . . G. C.	5.57 N	0.58 E
154	Kwoi R. (kwoi) . . . . Chn.	24.20 N	110.46 E
154	Kwongning (kwông′nĭng′) . . . . Chn.	23.45 N	112.20 E
156	Kwo R. (kwō) . . . . Chn.	33.47 N	115.50 E
156	Kwoyang (kwō′yăng′) . . . . Chn.	33.30 N	116.12 E
166	Kyabram (kī′ȧ-brăm) . . . . . . Austl.	36.19 S	145.2 E
151	Kyaukpyu (chouk′pyo͞o′) . . . . India	19.15 N	93.35 E
121	Kybartai (kē′bär-tī′) . . . . Lith.	54.40 N	22.45 E
129	Kyme (kē′mȧ) . . . . Grc.	38.37 N	24.5 E
166	Kyneton (kĭn′tŭn) . . . . Austl.	37.14 S	144.24 E
165	Kynuna (kī-no͞o′nȧ) . . . . Austl.	21.38 S	141.46 E
159	Kyogami C. (kyō-gä′mê) . . . . . Jap.	35.45 N	135.10 E
159	Kyoto (kyō′tō′) . . . . Jap.	35.2 N	135.45 E
129	Kyparissia (kê-pä-rēs′sê-ȧ) . . . Grc.	37.16 N	21.42 E
129	Kyparissia, G. of . . . . Grc.	37.25 N	21.30 E
129	Kyra Panagia (I.) (kē′rȧ pȧ-nä′jê-ȧ) Grc.	39.16 N	24.5 E
121	Kyro R. (kü′rô) . . . . Fin.	63.0 N	22.20 E
129	Kythnos (I.) (kēth′nōs) . . . . . Grc.	37.25 N	24.25 E
157	Kyungsan (kyo͝ong′sän′) . . . . . Cho.	35.49 N	128.44 E
159	Kyushu I. (kyo͞o′sho͞o′) . . . . . . Jap.	32.30 N	131.0 E
129	Kyustendil (kyo͝os-tĕn-dĭl′) . . . Bul.	42.17 N	22.40 E
148	Kyzyl Kum (Qizi lQum) Des. (kĭ′zĭl ko͞om) . . Sov. Un.	44.0 N	64.0 E
148	Kzyl-Orda (Ak-Mechet) (kzêl-ôr′dȧ) (ȧk′-mȧch′ĕt) . . Sov. Un.	44.50 N	65.30 E
122	Laa (lä) . . . . Ger.	48.44 N	16.23 E
120	Laagen R. (lô′ghĕn) . . . . Nor.	61.30 N	10.18 E
126	La′Almunia de Doña Godina (lä-äl-mo͞o′nê′ä dā dō′nyä gō-dē′nä) Sp.	41.31 N	1.21 W
119	Laamswarde (läms′vär-dĕ) Neth. (Anvers In.)	51.21 N	4.3 E
102	La Asuncion (lä ä-so͞on-syōn′) Ven.	11.0 N	64.0 W
104	La Banda (lä bän′dä) . . . . Arg.	27.45 S	64.12 W
92	La Barca (lä bär′kȧ) . . . . Mex.	20.17 N	102.32 W
138	Labé (lȧ-bā′) . . Fr. W. Afr.	11.20 N	12.18 W
122	Labe (Elbe) R. (lä′bĕ) (ĕl′bĕ) Czech.	50.10 N	15.0 E
54	Laberge, L. (lȧ-bẽrj′) . . . . Can.	61.10 N	135.15 W
96	Laberinto de las Doce Leguas (Is.) (lä-bâ-rēn′tô dā läs dō′sâ-lā′gwäs) Cuba	20.40 N	78.35 W
126	Labiana (lä-vê-ä′nä) . . . . Sp.	43.16 N	5.32 W
123	Labiau (lȧ′bê-ou) . . . . Ger.	54.51 N	21.7 E
113	Labinskaya (lä-bên-skä′yä) Sov. Un.	44.35 N	40.45 E
145	Labis (lăb′ĭs) Non-fed. Mal. St. (In.)	2.23 N	103.4 E
127	La Bisbal (lä bēs-bäl′) . . . . Sp.	41.56 N	3.2 E
162	Labo (lä′bô) . . . . P. I.	14.11 N	122.49 E
162	Labo, Mt. . . . . P. I.	14.0 N	122.47 E
124	Labouheyre (lȧ-bo͞o-âr′) . . . . Fr.	44.15 N	0.55 W
55	Labrador (lăb-rȧ-dôr′) . . . . . . N. A.	54.0 N	61.0 W
102	Labréa (lä-brā′ä) . . . . Braz.	7.26 S	64.45 W
160	Labuan (I.) (lä-bo͝o-ȧn′) Strs. Sets.	5.28 N	115.10 E
163	Labuk B. (lȧ-bo͝ok′) . . . . . . B. N. B.	6.10 N	117.50 E
57	L′Acadie (lȧ-kȧ-dē′) Can. (Montreal In.)	45.19 N	73.19 W
135	La Calle (lȧ kȧl′) . . Alg. (Tun. In.)	36.53 N	8.40 E
126	La Calzada de Calatrava (lä käl-thä′dhä dā κä-lä-trä′vä) Sp.	38.42 N	3.47 W
73	La Cañada (lä kän-yä′dä) Calif. (Los Angeles In.)	34.13 N	118.12 W
93	Lacantuil, R. (lä-kän-twēl′) . . Mex.	16.20 N	90.50 W
163	La Carlota (lä kär-lō′tä) . . . . . P. I.	10.26 N	122.55 E
126	La Carolina (lä kä-rô-lē′nä) . . . Sp.	38.16 N	3.37 W
151	Laccadive Is. (lăk′ȧ-dīv) . . . . India	11.30 N	72.45 E
77	Lac Court Oreille Ind. Res. (lăk′ kôrt-ô-rēl′) (lȧk ko͞or tô-rā′y′) Wis.	45.50 N	91.20 W
77	Lac des Mille Lacs (L.) (lȧk dā mē′y′ lȧk) Can.	48.55 N	90.30 W
77	Lac du Flambeau Ind. Res. (lȧk dü fläɴ-bō′) (lăk′ flăm-bō′) . . . . Wis.	46.0 N	89.52 W
94	La Ceiba (lȧ sēbä) . . . . Hond.	15.45 N	86.53 W
49	La Center (lȧ sĕn′tẽr) Wash. (Portland In.)	45.51 N	122.40 W
166	Lacepede B. (lȧ′sê-pēd) . . . . . Austl.	36.45 S	139.50 E
49	Lacey (lā′sĭ) . . . Wash. (Seattle In.)	47.2 N	122.48 W
112	Lacha, L. (lȧ′chä) . . . . Sov. Un.	61.15 N	38.50 E
124	La Charité (lȧ shȧ-rê-tā′) . . . . . . Fr.	47.11 N	3.5 E
124	La Châtre (lȧ shät′r′) . . . . Fr.	46.35 N	1.58 E
122	La Chaux-de-Fonds (lȧ shō dē fôɴ′) Switz.	47.6 N	6.50 E
125	La Chesnay (lē shĕ-nâ′) . . Fr. (In.)	48.50 N	2.7 E
55	Lachine (lȧ-shēn′) . . . . Can.	45.32 N	73.50 W
57	Lachine Rapids, Can. (Montreal In.)	45.25 N	73.37 W
167	Lachlan Ra. (lăk′lăn) . . . . . . Austl.	33.35 S	145.58 E
167	Lachlan R. . . . . Austl.	33.25 S	146.0 E
57	Lachute (lȧ-sho͞ot′) Can. (Montreal In.)	45.40 N	74.20 W
125	La Ciotat (lȧ syô-tȧ′) . . . . Fr.	43.12 N	5.37 E
85	Lackawanna (lăk-ȧ-wŏn′ȧ) . . N. Y.	42.52 N	78.52 W
77	Lac la Croix (L.) (lȧk lȧ krwä) Can.-U. S.	48.20 N	92.5 W
119	La Clinge (lȧ klăɴzh) Bel. (Anvers In.)	51.15 N	4.5 E
93	La Concordia (lä kôn-kôr′dê-ȧ) Mex.	16.5 N	92.39 W
86	Laconia (lȧ-kō′nĭ-ȧ) . . . . N. H.	43.30 N	71.30 W
129	Laconia, G. of . . . . Grc.	36.35 N	22.45 E
126	La Coruña (lä kô-ro͞on′yä) . . . . . Sp.	43.21 N	8.26 W
128	Lacosta (I.) (lä-kôs′tȧ) . . . . It.	42.45 N	16.53 E
78	La Cross (lȧ-krôs′) . . . . Kan.	38.31 N	99.20 W
77	La Crosse . . . . Wis.	43.49 N	91.15 W
102	La Cruz (lȧ-kro͞oz′) . . . . Colo.	2.1 N	66.59 W
76	Lacs, R. des (rê vyâr′ dā lȧk′) N. D.	48.30 N	101.50 W
79	Lacygne (lȧ-sēn′y′) (lȧ-sēn′) . . Kan.	38.20 N	94.47 W
119	Ladekop (lä′dē-kôp) Ger. (Hamburg In.)	53.31 N	9.40 E
142	Ladismith (lā′dĭ-smĭth) . . U. S. Afr.	33.29 S	21.15 E
72	Ladner (lăd′nẽr) Can. (Vancouver In.)	49.5 N	123.5 W
121	Ladoga L. (lȧ′dô-gȧ) . . . . Eur.	61.0 N	31.30 E
102	La Dorada (lä dô-rä′dȧ) . . . . . . Col.	5.28 N	74.48 W
143	Ladybrand (lā′dĭ-brănd) U. S. Afr.	29.11 S	27.28 E
143	Lady Frere (lā′dĭ frēr′) . U. S. Afr.	31.42 S	27.14 E
143	Lady Grey (grā′) . . . . U. S. Afr.	30.43 S	27.11 E
70	Ladysmith (lā′dĭ-smĭth) . . . . . Can.	48.59 N	123.49 W
143	Ladysmith . . . . U. S. Afr.	28.32 S	29.48 E
77	Ladysmith . . . . Wis.	45.27 N	91.5 W
120	Laerdal (lâr′dȧl) . . . . Nor.	61.2 N	7.30 E
120	Laerdalsören (lâr′dȧls-û′rĕn) . Nor.	61.7 N	7.29 E
120	Laesö (I.) (lâs′û) . . . . Den.	157.6 N	11.0 E
94	La Esperanza (lä ĕs-pâ-rän′zä) Hond.	14.17 N	88.27 W
126	La Estrada (lä ĕs-trä′dä) . . . . . . Sp.	42.41 N	8.30 W
158	Lafa (lä′fä) . . . . Manch.	43.50 N	127.15 E
82	Lafayette (lä-fâ-yĕt′) . . . . Ala.	32.54 N	85.24 W
72	Lafayette . . . . . . Colo. (Denver In.)	40.0 N	105.5 W
82	La Fayette . . . . Ga.	34.42 N	85.18 W
84	La Fayette . . . . Ind.	40.26 N	86.53 W
81	Lafayette . . . . La.	30.15 N	92.1 W
104	Laferrere (lä-fĕ-rā′rĕ) . . . Arg. (In.)	34.44 S	58.33 W
124	La Ferté-Bernard (lȧ fĕr-tā′-bĕr-nȧr′) . Fr.	48.12 N	0.40 E
124	La Ferté Macé (lȧ fĕr-tā′ mȧ-sā′) Fr.	48.35 N	0.20 W
124	La Ferté-sous-Jouarre (lȧ fĕr-tā′-so͞o-zho͞o-är′) . Fr.	48.55 N	3.10 E
124	La Flèche (lȧ flăsh′) . . . . Fr.	47.42 N	0.2 W
124	La Flotte (lȧ-flôt) . . . . Fr.	46.11 N	1.18 W
82	Lafollette (lä-fŏl′ĕt) . . . . Tenn.	36.22 N	84.9 W
89	La Fortuna, Pt. (lä fôr-to͞o′nä) La. (New Orleans In.)	29.38 N	89.24 W
81	Lafourche, Bayou (bä-yo͞o′ lȧ-fo͝orsh′) . La.	29.30 N	90.20 W
114	La Galite I. (lȧ gȧ-lēt′) . Medit. Sea	37.34 N	8.57 E
116	Lagan, R. (lā′găn) . . . . . . Gt. Brit.	54.30 N	6.0 W
104	Lageado (lä-zhȧ-ä′do͝o) . . . . . . Braz.	29.29 S	51.59 W

ăt; finăl; rāte; senâte; ärm; ȧsk; sofȧ; fâre; ch-choose; dh-as th in other; bē; êvent; bĕt; recĕnt; cratẽr; g-go; gh-gutteral g; bĭt ĭ-short neutral; rīde; κ-gutteral k as ch in German ich;

Page	Name Pronunciation Region	Lat. °′	Long. °′
127	Lage Pt. (lä-zhĕ) ......Port. (In.)	38.40 N	9.20 W
104	Lages (lä′gäzh) ....Braz.	27.40 S	50.20 W
138	Laghouat (lä-gwät′).........Alg.	33.48 N	2.53 E
124	Lagny (län-yē′)..............Fr.	48.52 N	2.45 E
126	Lagoa (lä′gō-ȧ)..............Port.	37.9 N	8.25 W
162	Lagonoy (lä-gō-noi′)..........P. I.	13.44 N	123.31 E
162	Lagonoy G..................P. I.	13.30 N	124.0 E
138	Lagos (lä′gōs)..............Nig.	6.31 N	3.21 E
126	Lagos (lä′gōzh)..............Port.	37.7 N	8.41 W
92	Lagos de Moreno (lä′gōs dā mō-rā′nō).Mex.	21.21 N	101.56 W
135	La Goulette (lȧ gōō-lĕt′)Tun. (In.)	36.50 N	10.15 E
127	La Granada (lä grä-nä′dä) Sp. (In.)	41.21 N	1.43 E
124	La Grand′ Combe (lȧ grän kônb′) Fr.	44.12 N	4.5 E
70	La Grande (lȧ grănd′)........Ore.	45.20 N	118.7 W
82	Lagrange (lȧ-grānj′)..........Ga.	33.2 N	85.2 W
88	La Grange......Ill. (Chicago In.)	41.49 N	87.52 W
84	Lagrange...................Ind.	41.40 N	85.26 W
84	La Grange...................Ky.	38.26 N	85.24 W
79	La Grange...................Mo.	40. 2 N	91.30 W
81	Lagrange....................Tex.	29.55 N	96.51 W
102	La Grita (lä grē′tä).........Ven.	8.2 N	72.0 W
102	La Guaira (lä gwä′ē-rä) ......Ven.	10.31 N	66.58 W
126	La Guardia (lä gwär′dē-ä) .....Sp.	41.54 N	8.51 W
104	Laguna (lä-gōō′nä) ....Braz.	28.29 S	48.45 W
161	Laguna (Prov.) (lä-gōō′nä) P. I. (Manila In.)	14.10 N	121.30 E
169	Laguna B. (lä-gōō′nȧ) .Austl. (In.)	26.18 S	153.4 E
96	Lagune Cays (Is.)...........Cuba	22.10 N	82.40 W
162	Laguna de Bay (B.) (lä-gōō′nä dā bä′ē).P. I.	14.25 N	121.20 E
75	Laguna Ind. Res. (lȧ′gōō′nȧ) N. M.	35.7 N	107.27 W
102	Lagunillas (lä-gōō-nēl′yäs)....Bol.	19.32 S	63.44 W
92	Lagunillas..................Mex.	21.35 N	99.34 W
158	Laha (lä-hä) ....Manch.	48.7 N	124.24 E
73	La Habra (lȧ hăb′rȧ) Calif. (Los Angeles In.)	33.55 N	117.57 W
163	Lahad Datu(lä′häd dä′tōō)B. N. B.	5.3 N	118.19 E
173	Lahaina (lä-hä′ē-nä)........Haw.	20.52 N	156.41 W
124	La Haye-Descartes (lȧ ā-dā-kärt′) Fr.	46.59 N	0.41 E
122	Lahn R. (län)...............Ger.	50.30 N	8.15 E
120	Laholm (lä′hōlm)............Swe.	56.31 N	13.3 E
151	Lahore (lȧ-hōr′)............India	31.37 N	74.18 E
97	La Hotte Mts. (lȧ ôt′).......Hai.	18.25 N	73.53 W
122	Lahr (lär)..................Ger.	48.21 N	7.52 E
121	Lahti (lä′tē)...............Fin.	61.0 N	25.40 E
156	Laian (lī′än′)..............Chn.	32.27 N	118.25 E
	Laibach, see Ljubljana, Yugo.		
156	Laichow (lī′chō)............Chn.	37.13 N	119.55 E
156	Laichow B...................Chn.	37.12 N	119.30 E
169	Laidley (lăd′lē)......Austl. (In.)	27.35 S	152.23 E
154	Laifeng (lī′fĕng′)...........Chn.	29.28 N	109. 2 E
124	Laigle (lĕ′gl′)..............Fr.	48.45 N	0.38 E
150	Laila (lä′ē-lȧ)..........Sau. Ar.	22.44 N	46.29 E
119	Laindon (lān′dŭn) Gt. Brit. (London In.)	51.34 N	0.26 E
142	Laingsburg (lăngz′bûrg).U. S. Afr.	33.11 S	20.51 E
110	Lainio R. (lī′nĭ-ō)..........Swe.	68.0 N	22.0 E
154	Laipin (lī′pĭn′).............Chn.	23.45 N	109.25 E
154	Laipo (lī′pō′)...............Chn.	24.26 N	110.20 E
156	Laiwu (lī′wōō′).............Chn.	36.15 N	117.44 E
96	Lajas (lä′häs)..............Cuba	22.22 N	80.19 W
74	La Jolla (lȧ hōl′yȧ)....Calif. (In.)	32.50 N	117.17 W
74	La Jolla Ind. Res............Calif.	33.20 N	116.35 W
78	La Junta (lȧ hōōn′tȧ).......Colo.	37.58 N	103.34 W
139	Lak Dera (R.) (läk dä′rä) Kenya-It. E. Afr.	0.40 N	41.0 E
81	Lake Arthur (lāk är′thŭr)......La.	30.6 N	92.39 W
49	Lakebay (lāk-bā′) Wash. (Seattle In.)	47.15 N	122.45 W
76	Lake Benton (lāk bĕn′tŭn) . Minn.	44.15 N	96.16 W
164	Lake Brown..................Austl.	30.59 S	118.29 E
81	Lake Charles (lāk chärlz′).......La.	30.15 N	93.13 W
83	Lake City....................Fla.	30.10 N	82.38 W
77	Lake City....................Ia.	42.16 N	94.42 W
77	Lake City...................Minn.	44.26 N	92.18 W
83	Lake City...................S. C.	33.52 N	79.44 W
49	Lake City.....Wash. (Seattle In.)	47.8 N	122.33 W
77	Lake Crystal (lāk krĭs′tăl)..Minn.	44.7 N	94.12 W
116	Lake District..............Gt. Brit.	54.25 N	2.55 W
77	Lake Forest (lāk fŏr′ĕst) ......Ill.	42.15 N	87.50 W
75	Lake Fork (R.)..............Utah	40.25 N	110.23 W
77	Lake Geneva (lāk jĕ-nē′vȧ)...Wis.	42.37 N	88.25 W
72	Lake George (lāk jôrj) Colo. (Colo. Sprs. In.)	38.58 N	105.22 W
83	Lakeland (lāk′lănd).....Fla. (In.)	28.2 N	81.58 W
82	Lakeland......................Ga.	31.3 N	83.3 W
77	Lake Linden (lāk lĭn′dĕn)...Mich.	47.12 N	88.24 W
77	Lake Mills (lāk mĭlz′)...........Ia.	43.27 N	93.30 W
84	Lake Odessa (lāk ō-dĕs′ȧ)...Mich.	42.50 N	85.12 W
73	Lake Point Utah (Salt Lake City In.)	40.43 N	112.14 W
74	Lake Port (lāk′ pōrt)........Calif.	39.3 N	122.56 W
76	Lake Preston (lāk prĕs′tŭn)..S. D.	44.21 N	97.20 W
81	Lake Providence (lāk prŏv′ĭ-dĕns) La.	32.47 N	91.11 W
74	Lakeside (lāk′sīd).....Calif. (In.)	32.51 N	116.56 W
73	Lakeview (lāk-vū′) Calif. (Los Angeles In.)	33.50 N	117.7 W
70	Lakeview....................Ore.	42.11 N	120.21 W
49	Lakeview.....Wash. (Seattle In.)	47.9 N	122.30 W
71	Lake Walcott Reservoir (wôl′kŏt) Ida.	42.43 N	113.38 W
83	Lake Wales (lāk′ wālz) ..Fla. (In.)	27.55 N	81.34 W
85	Lakewood (lāk′wŏŏd).......N. J.	40.4 N	74.11 W
84	Lakewood....................Ohio	41.28 N	81.48 W
49	Lakewood.....Wash. (Seattle In.)	48.8 N	122.12 W
83	Lake Worth (lāk-wûrth′) Fla. (In.)	26.37 N	80.3 W
76	Lakota (lȧ-kō′tȧ)...........N. D.	48.3 N	98.20 W
94	La Libertad (lä lē-bĕr-tädh′) Guat. (In.)	16.46 N	90.14 W
94	La Libertad..................Sal.	13.30 N	89.20 W
99	La Ligua (lä lē′gwä) Chl. (Valparaiso In.)	32.30 S	71.15 W
158	Lalín (lä′lēn′)..........Manch.	45.18 N	126.56 E
126	Lalín........................Sp.	42.39 N	8.8 W
126	La Linea (lä lē′nā-ä)..........Sp.	36.10 N	5.21 W
127	La Llacuna (lä lyä-kōō′nä) Sp. (In.)	41.27 N	1.34 E
114	Lalla-Maghnia (lȧ′lȧ-măg′nē-ȧ) Alg.	34.50 N	1.45 W
162	Lal-lo (läl-lō′)..............P. I.	18.11 N	121.40 E
127	L′Alma (lȧl′mȧ)..............Alg.	36.45 N	3.25 E
117	La Louvière (lȧ lōō-vyâr′)....Bel.	50.30 N	4.0 E
92	La Luz (lä lōōz′)............Mex.	21.4 N	101.20 W
124	La Machine (lȧ mȧ-shēn′).....Fr.	46.54 N	3.29 E
86	La Malbaie (lȧ mȧl-bâ′).....Can.	47.38 N	70.11 W
126	La Mancha (Reg.) (lä män′chä) Sp.	39.0 N	2.50 W
78	Lamar (lȧ-mär′).............Colo.	38.4 N	102.38 W
79	Lamar.......................Mo.	37.27 N	94.16 W
54	La Martre, Lac. (L.) (lȧk lȧ mär′-tr′) Can.	62.58 N	119.30 W
124	Lamballe (län-bȧl′)..........Fr.	48.30 N	2.31 W
140	Lambaréné (län-bȧ-rȧ-nā′) Fr. Eq. Afr.	0.45 S	10.10 E
102	Lambayeque (läm-bä-yā′kā) .Peru	6.30 S	79.59 W
82	Lambert (lăm′bērt).........Miss.	34.13 N	90.18 W
142	Lambert′s B..........U. S. Afr.	32.5 S	18.18 E
85	Lambertville (lăm′bērt-vĭl)..N. J.	40.22 N	74.56 W
163	Lambunao (läm-bōō′nä-ō)...P. I.	11.3 N	122.28 E
71	Lame Deer (lām dēr′) .....Mont.	45.37 N	106.40 W
126	Lamego (lä-mā′gō)..........Port.	41.6 N	7.38 W
74	La Mesa (lä-mā′sä)....Calif. (In.)	32.47 N	117.2 W
80	Lamesa......................Tex.	32.44 N	101.55 W
125	La Mesnil-Amelot (lē mā-nēl′-ȧ-mē-lō′).Fr. (In.)	49.1 N	2.36 E
129	Lamia (lȧ-mē′ȧ)..............Grc.	38.54 N	22.26 E
163	Lamitan (lä-mē′tän)........P. I.	6.40 N	122.10 E
162	Lamon B. (lä-mōn′) ....P. I.	14.30 N	122.0 E
77	Lamoni (lȧ-mō′nĭ)............Ia.	40.35 N	93.55 W
127	La Morella (Mts.) (lä mō-rāl′yä) Sp. (In.)	41.17 N	1.56 E
76	La Moure (lȧ mōōr′).......N. D.	46.23 N	98.16 W
80	Lampasas (lăm-păs′ȧs).......Tex.	31.4 N	98.10 W
80	Lampasas R..................Tex.	31.20 N	98.10 W
80	Lampazos (läm-pä′zōs)......Mex.	27.2 N	100.30 W
114	Lampedusa (I.) (läm-pȧ-dōō′sä) It.	35.56 N	12.52 E
73	Lampo (lăm′pō) Utah (Salt Lake City In.)	41.40 N	112.27 W
141	Lamu (lä′mōō).............Kenya	2.15 S	41.0 E
125	La Mure (lȧ mür′)............Fr.	44.55 N	5.50 E
135	Lamy (lȧ-mē′)........Tun. (In.)	36.30 N	8.25 E
173	Lanai (I.) (lä-nä′ē)..........Haw.	20.50 N	156.55 W
163	Lanao, L. (lä-nä′ō).........P. I.	7.50 N	124.15 E
116	Lanark (lăn′ȧrk).........Gt. Brit.	55.40 N	3.45 W
118	LancashireCo.(lăŋ′kȧ-shĭr)Gt.Brit.	53.39 N	2.30 W
116	Lancaster (lăŋ′kȧs-tēr)...Gt. Brit.	54.5 N	2.50 W
84	Lancaster...................Ky.	37.36 N	84.34 W
87	Lancaster............Mass. (In.)	42.27 N	71.40 W
86	Lancaster..................N. H.	44.30 N	71.35 W
85	Lancaster..................N. Y.	42.57 N	78.40 W
84	Lancaster...................Ohio	39.42 N	82.36 W
85	Lancaster....................Pa.	40.3 N	76.20 W
83	Lancaster..................S. C.	34.42 N	80.46 W
77	Lancaster...................Wis.	42.52 N	90.42 W
155	Lanchi (län′chē′)............Chn.	29.10 N	119.35 E
152	Lanchow (län′chō′)...........Chn.	36.6 N	103.50 E
140	Landana (län-dä′nä)..........Ang.	5.15 S	12.10 E
122	Landau (län′dou)..............Ger.	49.13 N	8.6 E
71	Lander (lăn′dēr).............Wyo.	42.49 N	108.43 W
124	Landerneau (län-dĕr-nō′)......Fr.	48.28 N	4.12 W
122	Landeshut (län′dĕs-hōōt)......Ger.	50.47 N	16.2 E
124	Landes, The (Moorland) (länd)Fr.	44.30 N	1.0 W
124	Landevisau (länd′-vē-syō′).....Fr.	48.35 N	4.5 W
122	Landsberg (länts′bĕrgh).......Ger.	48.3 N	10.54 E
122	Lansberg.....................Ger.	52.44 N	15.13 E
116	Lands End...............Gt. Brit.	50.5 N	5.45 W
122	Lanshut (länts′hōōt)..........Ger.	48.32 N	12.8 E
120	Landskrona (läns-krōō′nä)...Swe.	55.51 N	12.49 E
82	Lanett (lȧ-nĕt′)..............Ala.	32.51 N	85.12 W
156	Lanfeng (län′fĕng′)..........Chn.	34.45 N	115.4 E
129	Langadia (läŋ-gä′dē-ȧ).......Grc.	37.41 N	22.2 E
110	Langanes (Pt.) (läŋ′gä-nĕs)...Ice.	66.25 N	14.30 W
76	Langdon (lăng′dŭn)..........N. D.	48.45 N	98.22 W
124	Langeac (län-zhȧk′)...........Fr.	45.5 N	3.30 E
142	Langeberg (läng′ĕ-bĕrgh).....Bech.	27.52 S	22.45 E
142	Lange Berg (Mt.)......U. S. Afr.	30.40 S	18.45 E
142	Lange Bergen (Mts.)... U. S. Afr.	33.59 S	20.50 E
57	L′Ange Gardien (länzh gȧr-dyăn′) Can. (Quebec In.)	46.55 N	71.7 W
122	Langenbielau (läng-ĕn-bē′lou)..Ger.	50.41 N	16.34 E
119	Langenhorn (läng′ĕn-hôrn) Ger. (Hamburg In.)	53.39 N	10.0 E
122	Langensalza (läng-ĕn-zäl′tsä)..Ger.	51.7 N	10.40 E
120	Langesund (läng′ĕ-sōōn′).....Nor.	58.59 N	9.2 E
120	Lang Fjord (läng′ fyōr′).....Nor.	62.43 N	7.50 E
110	Lang-Jökull (Glacier) (läng-yû′-kōōl).Ice.	64.45 N	20.30 W
83	Langley (lăng′lĭ)............S. C.	33.30 N	81.52 W
49	Langley......Wash. (Seattle In.)	48.2 N	122.25 W
72	Langley Prairie Can. (Vancouver In.)	49.6 N	122.40 W
122	Langnau (läng′nou).........Switz.	46.57 N	7.47 E
124	Langogne (län-gōn′y′).........Fr.	44.43 N	3.51 E
124	Langon (län-gôn′)..............Fr.	44.32 N	0.15 W
124	Langres (län′gr′)..............Fr.	47.53 N	5.20 E
125	Langres, Plat. of..............Fr.	47.50 N	5.30 E
160	Langsa (läng′sä).........Neth. Ind	4.38 N	97.58 E
79	L′Anguille, R. (län-gē′y′).....Ark.	35.15 N	90.55 W
54	Lanigan (lăn′ĭ-gȧn)...........Can.	51.55 N	105.10 W
129	Lankhada (län-kä′dä).........Grc.	40.43 N	23.6 E
124	Lannion (lȧ-nē-ôn′)...........Fr.	48.45 N	3.25 W
153	Lan R. (län)..................Chn.	41.30 N	117.10 E
123	Lan R........................Pol.	52.33 N	27.12 E
85	Lansdale (lănz′dāl)...........Pa.	40.17 N	75.18 W
88	Lansdowne (lănz′doun) Pa. (Philadelphia In.)	39.57 N	75.16 W
77	L′Anse (läns)...............Mich.	46.45 N	88.25 W
77	L′Anse Ind. Res.............Mich.	46.45 N	88.22 W
85	Lansford (lănz′fērd)..........Pa.	40.47 N	75.48 W
154	Lanshan (län′shän′)..........Chn.	25.17 N	111.55 E
77	Lansing (lăn′sĭng)............Ia.	43.22 N	91.15 W
84	Lansing.....................Mich.	42.45 N	84.35 W
104	Lanús (lä-nōōs′)........Arg. (In.)	34.42 S	58.23 W
128	Lanuse (lȧ-nōō′sȧ)..........Sard.	39.52 N	9.33 E
163	Lanuza B. (lä-nōō′zä).......P. I.	9.20 N	126.5 E
138	Lanzarote (I.) (län-zä-rō′tä) Can. Is.	29.10 N	13.45 W
162	Laoag (lä-wäg′)..............P. I.	18.11 N	120.36 E
162	Laoang (lä-wäng′)...........P. I.	12.35 N	125.0 E
156	Lao-Chang R. (lä′ō chäng′)..Chn.	37.30 N	115.52 E
160	Laoet (Laut) I. (lȧ′ōōt).Neth. Ind.	3.30 S	116.8 E
152	Lao Kay (lä′ō kä′ē)..Fr. In. Chn.	22.30 N	103.53 E
124	Laon (län)....................Fr.	49.35 N	3.35 E
160	Laos (State) (lä′ōz) (lȧ-ōz′) Fr. In. Chn.	18.30 N	104.30 E
163	Lapac I. (lä-päk′)..........P. I.	5.32 N	120.47 E
126	La Palma....................Sp.	37.25 N	6.33 W
104	La Pampa (päm′pä).........Arg.	37.0 S	66.0 W
163	Laparan I. (lä′pä-rän).......P. I.	5.55 N	120.0 E
92	La Parrilla (lä pä-rēl′yä)....Mex.	23.42 N	104.8 W
104	La Paz (lä päz′).............Arg.	30.52 S	59.35 W
102	La Paz.......................Bol.	16.29 S	68.3 W
94	La Paz.....................Hond.	14.20 N	87.48 W
162	La Paz.......................P. I.	17.40 N	120.40 E
84	Lapeer (lȧ-pēr′)............Mich.	43.5 N	83.15 W
89	La Petit Pass I. (lȧ pē-tē′ pȧs′) La. (New Orleans In.)	30.6 N	89.24 W
92	La Piedad de Cabadas (lä pyä-dhädh′ dā kä-bä′dhäs).Mex.	20.20 N	102.1 W
57	La Plaine (lȧ-plān′) Can. (Montreal In.)	45.48 N	73.45 W
112	Lapland (lăp′lănd)..........Eur.	68.30 N	27.0 E
104	La Plata (lä plä′tä)........Arg.	34.59 S	58.0 W
79	La Plata....................Mo.	40.2 N	92.28 W
78	La Plata Pk.................Colo.	39.0 N	106.27 W
90	La Playa (lä plä′yȧ) Cuba (Habana In.)	23.6 N	82.28 W
156	Lapo (lä′pō′)..............Kwan.	39.24 N	121.31 E
127	La Pobla de Claramunt (lä pōb′-lä dā klärä-mōōnt′).Sp.	41.33 N	1.42 E
162	Lapog (lä-pōg′).............P. I.	17.45 N	120.28 E
87	La Poile B. (lȧ pwȧl′).......Newf.	47.45 N	58.20 W
77	La Pointe Ind. Res. (lȧ pwănt′) Wis.	46.30 N	90.40 W
126	La Pola (lä pō′lä)............Sp.	42.51 N	5.40 W
84	La Porte (lȧ pōrt′)..........Ind.	41.37 N	86.44 W
81	La Porte............Tex. (In.)	29.40 N	95.1 W
77	La Porte City.................Ia.	42.19 N	92.11 W
121	Lappeenranta (lä′pēn-rän′tä) Fin.	61.5 N	28.6 E
57	Laprairie (lȧ-prȧ-rē′) Can. (Montreal In.)	45.25 N	73.29 W
129	Lapsaki (läp′sȧ-kē)..........Tur.	40.19 N	26.42 E
127	La Puebla (lä pwä′blä).......Sp.	39.46 N	3.1 E
126	La Puebla de Montalbán (lä pwā′-blä dā mōnt-äl-bän′).Sp.	39.52 N	4.21 W
102	La Punta (lä pōōn′tä)...Peru (In.)	12.5 S	77.0 W
123	Lapuşul R. (lä′pōō-shōōl)...Rom.	47.27 N	23.45 E
104	La Quiaca (lä kē-ä′kä).......Arg.	22.0 S	65.35 W
150	Lar (lär)....................Iran	27.44 N	54.15 E
138	Larache (lä-rä′chā)..........Mor.	35.9 N	6.5 W
71	Laramie (lăr′ȧ-mĭ)..........Wyo.	41.19 N	105.35 W
71	Laramie R.........Wyo.-Colo.	41.15 N	105.40 W
127	L′Arba (lȧr′bȧ)..............Alg.	36.35 N	3.10 E
88	Larchmont (lärch′mŏnt) N. Y. (New York In.)	40.55 N	73.45 W
126	Laredo (lȧ-rā′dhō)...........Sp.	43.24 N	3.25 W
80	Laredo (lȧ-rā′dō)............Tex.	27.30 N	99.30 W
163	Larena (lä-rā′nä)............P. I.	9.14 N	123.36 E
124	La Réole (lȧ rȧ-ōl′) ....Fr.	44.35 N	0.1 W
124	Largentière (lȧr-zhän-tyâr′)....Fr.	44.35 N	4.18 E
96	Largo Cay (I.) (lär′gō)......Cuba	21.38 N	81.30 W
124	La Ricamarie (lȧ rē-kȧ-mȧ-rē′).Fr.	45.25 N	4.20 E
76	Larimore (lăr′ĭ-mōr)........N. D.	47.54 N	97.37 W
128	Larino (lä-rē′nō).............It.	41.47 N	14.53 E
104	La Rioja (lä rē-ō′hä).........Arg.	29.25 S	66.58 W
104	La Rioja (State)..............Arg.	29.30 S	67.30 W
129	Larisa (lä′rĭ-sȧ)..............Grc.	39.36 N	22.25 E
73	Lark (lärk) Utah (Salt Lake City In.)	40.32 N	112.5 W
171	Larkins, Mt. (lär′kĭns)......N. Z.	44.52 S	168.38 E
115	Larnaca (lär′nȧ-kä)..........Cyp.	34.54 N	33.35 E
78	Larned (lär′nĕd).............Kan.	38.11 N	99.7 W
126	La Robla (lä rōb′lä)..........Sp.	42.48 N	5.36 W
127	La Roca (lä rō′kä)......Sp. (In.)	41.35 N	2.20 E
124	La Rochelle (lȧ rō-shĕl′).......Fr.	46.11 N	1.9 W
124	La Roche-sur-Yon (lȧ rōsh′-sür-yôn′) Fr.	46.40 N	1.25 W
126	La Roda (lä rō′dä)............Sp.	39.12 N	2.9 W
97	La Romana (lä rō-mä′nä).....Hai.	18.25 N	68.59 W
54	La Ronge, Lac (L.) (lȧk lȧ rônzh′) Can.	55.12 N	105.0 W
164	Larrey, Pt. (lăr′ē)...........Austl.	20.0 S	119.0 E
72	Larson (lär′sŭn) Wash. (Vancouver In.)	48.45 N	122.25 W
124	Laruns (lȧ-răns′)..............Fr.	42.58 N	0.28 W
120	Larvik (lär′vēk)..............Nor.	59.5 N	10.2 E
126	La Sagra (Mt.) (lä sä′grä).....Sp.	37.57 N	2.32 W
72	La Salle (lȧ săl′).Colo.(Denver In.)	40.21 N	104.42 W
79	La Salle......................Ill.	41.18 N	89.5 W
85	La Salle....................N. Y.	43.5 N	78.57 W
78	Las Animas (läs ȧ′nē-mȧs)....Colo.	38.4 N	103.16 W
97	Las Cahobas (läs kä-ō′bäs)...Hai.	18.48 N	71.57 W
94	Las Cañas (läs kän′yäs).....C. R.	10.27 N	85.7 W
90	Las Cascadas (läs käs-kä′däs) C. Z. (In.)	9.6 N	79.42 W
75	Las Cruces (läs krōō′sĕs)...N. M.	32.20 N	107.49 W
141	Las Dureh (läs dōō′rä) Br. Som.	10.7 N	45.55 E

ng-sing; ŋ-bank; n-nasalized n; nŏd; cŏmmit; ōld; ōbey; ôrder; fōōd; fŏŏt; ou-out; s-soft; sh-dish; th-thin; pūre; ûnite; ûrn; stŭd; circŭs; ü-as "y" in study; ′-indeterminate vowel.

Page	Name Pronunciation Region	Lat. °′	Long. °′
97	La Selle Mts. (lȧ sĕl′)........Hai.	18.22 N	72.3 W
125	La Seyne-sur-Mer (la sân′sür mĕr′) Fr.	43.8 N	5.50 E
104	Las Flores (läs flō′rês).......Arg.	36.5 S	59.2 W
99	Las Heras (läs ā′räs) Arg. (Buenos Aires In.)	34.54 S	58.54 W
152	Lashio (lăsh′ē-ō)..........India	22.56 N	97.56 E
151	Lashkar (lŭsh′kŭr).........India	26.10 N	78.15 E
141	Las Khoreh (läs kō′rä)...Br. Som.	11.10 N	48.15 E
126	Las Marismas (Reg.) (mȧ-rēs′-mȧs).Sp.	37.5 N	6.15 W
126	La Solano (lä sō-lä′nō)..........Sp.	38.56 N	3.14 W
138	Las Palmas (läs päl′mȧs)..Can. Is.	28.8 N	15.25 W
95	Las Palmas..............Pan.	8.5 N	81.23 W
95	Las Perlas (Pearl Lagoon) (läs pĕr′läs).Nic.	12.20 N	83.41 W
161	Las Piñas (läs pē′nȧs) P. I. (Manila In.)	14.29 N	120.58 E
93	Las Rosas (Pinola) (läs rō′säs) (pē-nō′lä).Mex.	16.24 N	92.26 W
127	Las Rozas de Madrid (läs rō′thäs dē mä-drēdh′).Sp.	40.29 N	3.53 W
141	Lassarat (lä-sȧ-rät′).........Eth.	10.45 N	42.25 E
74	Lassen Pk. (lăs′ĕn)........Calif.	40.30 N	121.39 W
74	Lassen Vol. Nat. Pk........Calif.	40.30 N	121.20 W
95	Las Tablas (läs tä′bläs)........Pan.	7.47 N	80.17 W
140	Lastoursville (lȧs-tōōr-vēl′) Fr. Eq. Afr.	0.50 S	12.48 E
74	Las Vegas (läs vā′gȧs).......Nev.	36.11 N	115.9 W
78	Las Vegas................N. M.	35.35 N	105.15 W
93	Las Vigas (läs vē′gȧs).......Mex.	19.37 N	97.3 W
102	Latacunga (lä-tä-kōōŋ′gä).....Ec.	0.59 S	78.32 W
150	Latakia (Lattaquie) (lä-tä-kē′ä) (lȧ-tȧ-kē′).Syr.	35.35 N	35.59 E
115	Latakia (Rep.)..............Syr.	35.10 N	36.0 E
124	La Teste (lȧ tĕst′)...........Fr.	44.40 N	1.8 W
79	Lathrop (lā′thrŭp)..........Mo.	39.33 N	94.20 W
128	Latium (Prov.) (lä′shĭ-ŭm).....It.	41.45 N	13.0 E
84	Latonia (lȧ-tō′nĭ-ȧ)...........Ky.	39.4 N	84.32 W
123	Latoreza (Latorica) R. (lä′tô-r-ĕzä) (lä′tô rê-tsä).Hung.-Czech.	48.30 N	22.40 E
52	Latouche (lȧ-tōōsh′)...Alsk. (In.)	60.5 N	148.0 W
125	La Tour du Pin (lȧ tōōr′dü păN′)Fr.	45.33 N	5.27 E
124	La Tremblade (lȧ trăN-blȧd′)..Fr.	45.45 N	1.9 W
93	La Trinitaria (Zapaluta) (lä trē-nē-tä′rē-ä) (zä-pä-lōō′tä).Mex.	16.7 N	92.2 W
169	Latrobe (lȧ-trōb′) Austl. (Tas. In.)	41.12 S	146.25 E
85	Latrobe....................Pa.	40.22 N	79.18 W
167	Latrobe (R.)..............Austl.	38.10 S	146.20 E
150	Lattaquie (Latakia) (lä-tȧ-kē′) (lä-tä-kē′ä) Syr.	35.35 N	35.59 E
55	La Tuque (lȧ tük′)..........Can.	47.25 N	72.58 W
121	Latvia (lăt′vĭ-ȧ)............Eur.	57.0 N	24.30 E
163	Laua-an (lä′wä-än′).........P. I.	11.8 N	122.3 E
122	Lauban (lou′bän)...........Ger.	51.7 N	15.17 E
123	Lauenburg (lou′ĕn-bōōrgh)...Ger.	54.32 N	17.45 E
169	Launceston (lôn′sĕs-tŭn) Austl. (Tas. In.)	41.26 S	147.10 E
92	La Unión (lä ōōn-nyōn′).....Mex.	17.58 N	101.49 W
94	La Unión ....Sal.	13.18 N	87.50 W
127	La Unión...................Sp.	37.37 N	0.51 W
173	Laupahoehoe (lä′ōō-pä-hō′ē-hō-ē) Haw.	19.59 N	155.13 W
166	Laura (lô′rȧ)..............Austl.	33.11 S	138.19 E
121	Laura (lou′rȧ)...............Est.	57.36 N	27.31 E
85	Laurel (lô′rĕl)..............Del.	38.33 N	75.39 W
85	Laurel.....................Md.	39.5 N	76.52 W
82	Laurel....................Miss.	31.41 N	89.8 W
71	Laurel....................Mont.	45.40 N	108.47 W
83	Laurens (lô′rĕnz)............S. C.	34.29 N	82.2 W
86	Laurentides Park (lô′rĕn-tĭdz) Can.	47.40 N	71.20 W
128	Lauria (lou′rē-ä)..............It.	40.2 N	15.50 E
83	Laurinburg (lô′rĭn-bûrg)....N. C.	34.46 N	79.28 W
77	Laurium (lô′rĭ-ŭm).........Mich.	47.14 N	88.25 W
122	Lausanne (lō-zȧn′).........Switz.	46.32 N	6.40 E
104	Lautaro (lou-tä′rō)..........Chl.	38.30 S	72.29 W
160	Laut I., see Laoet I., Neth. Ind.		
160	Laut Is., Little........Neth. Ind.	4.51 S	115.45 E
70	Lava Beds Nat. Mon.........Calif.	41.45 N	121.30 W
81	Lavaca R. (lȧ-văk′ȧ).........Tex.	29.15 N	96.50 W
126	Lavadores (lä-vä-dō′räs).......Sp.	42.14 N	8.46 W
71	Lava Hot Springs...........Ida.	42.37 N	112.1 W
57	Laval (lȧ-văl′)..Can. (Quebec In.)	47.1 N	71.13 W
124	Laval......................Fr.	48.5 N	0.45 W
121	Lavansaari I. (lä-vän-sä′rē)...Fin.	60.0 N	27.50 E
124	Lavaur (lȧ-vōr′)..............Fr.	43.40 N	1.50 E
124	Lavaveix-les-Mines (lȧ-vȧ-vĕ′ lā mēn′) Fr.	46.5 N	2.5 E
149	Lavdon R. (lȧv-dōn′)....Sov. Un.	63.0 N	151.0 E
97	La Vega (lä vā′gä)..........Hai.	19.13 N	70.31 W
124	Lavelanet (lȧ-vē-lȧ-nĕ′).........Fr.	42.56 N	1.51 E
128	Lavello (lä-vĕl′lō)..............It.	41.4 N	15.47 E
124	La Verdon (lē vĕr-dôN′).........Fr.	45.33 N	1.5 W
73	La Verne (lȧ vûrn′) Calif. (Los Angeles In.)	34.6 N	117.46 W
164	Laverton (lā′vēr-tŭn).......Austl.	28.38 S	122.28 E
80	La Vibora (lä vē-bō′rä).......Mex.	27.8 N	103.0 W
102	La Victoria (lä vēk-tō′rē-ä)...Ven.	10.15 N	67.12 W
161	Lavongai (I.) (lȧ-vŏŋ-gä′ē) N. Gui. Ter.	2.30 S	150.15 E
82	Lavonia (lȧ-vō′nĭ-ȧ).........Ga.	34.37 N	83.7 W
103	Lavras (lä′vräzh)...........Braz.	6.45 S	39.0 W
129	Lavrion (läv′rĭ-ŏn)............Grc.	37.44 N	24.3 E
79	Lawrence (lô′rĕns).........Kans.	38.58 N	95.14 W
86	Lawrence.................Mass.	42.41 N	71.11 W
171	Lawrence.................N. Z.	45.55 S	169.42 E
72	Lawrence..Wash. (Vancouver In.)	48.52 N	122.17 W
84	Lawrenceburg (lô′rĕns-bûrg)...Ind.	39.7 N	84.53 W
84	Lawrenceburg...............Ky.	38.2 N	84.56 W
82	Lawrenceburg..............Tenn.	35.14 N	87.20 W
82	Lawrenceville (lô-rĕns-vĭl)....Ga.	33.37 N	83.58 W
84	Lawrenceville................Ill.	38.45 N	87.44 W
83	Lawrenceville...............Va.	36.46 N	77.52 W
85	Lawsonia (lô-sō′nĭ-ȧ)........Md.	37.58 N	75.50 W
78	Lawton (lô′tŭn)..............Okla.	34.35 N	98.24 W
145	Layang Layang (lȧ-yäng′ lȧ-yäng′) Non-fed. Mal. St. (In.).	1.49 N	103.33 E
56	Layland (lā′lȧnd) Can. (Winnipeg In.)	49.49 N	98.11 W
73	Layton (lā′tŭn) Utah (Salt Lake City In.)	41.4 N	111.59 W
121	Laždijai (läzh′dē-yī′)........Lith.	54.12 N	23.30 E
163	Lazi (lä′zē).................P. I.	9.8 N	123.39 E
119	Lea, R. (lē) Gt. Brit. (London In.)	51.32 N	0.2 W
76	Lead (lēd)..................S. D.	44.21 N	103.46 W
78	Leadville (lĕd′vĭl)..........Colo.	39.14 N	106.19 W
55	Leaf R. (lēf)...............Can.	58.0 N	72.0 W
82	Leaf R....................Miss.	31.25 N	89.20 W
81	League City (lēg)........Tex. (In.)	29.31 N	95.5 W
84	Leamington (lĕm′ĭng-tŭn)....Can.	42.5 N	82.37 W
116	Leamington.............Gt. Brit.	52.15 N	1.30 W
170	Leamington...............N. Z.	37.57 S	175.30 E
118	Leam, R. (lĕm).........Gt. Brit.	52.19 N	1.18 W
54	Leaside (lē′sīd).........Can. (In.)	43.42 N	79.22 W
79	Leavenworth (lĕv′ĕn-wûrth) Kans.	39.18 N	94.55 W
70	Leavenworth...............Wash.	47.35 N	120.40 W
123	Leba (lä′bȧ)................Ger.	54.44 N	17.34 E
84	Lebanon (lĕb′ȧ-nŏn).........Ind.	40.1 N	86.31 W
84	Lebanon....................Ky.	37.36 N	85.16 W
79	Lebanon....................Mo.	37.41 N	92.44 W
86	Lebanon..................N. H.	43.39 N	72.15 W
84	Lebanon...................Ohio	39.25 N	84.12 W
70	Lebanon....................Ore.	44.31 N	122.55 W
85	Lebanon.....................Pa.	40.20 N	76.25 W
82	Lebanon...................Tenn.	36.12 N	86.17 W
115	Lebanon Mts.................Syr.	34.10 N	35.50 E
115	Lebanon, Rep. of.............Syr.	33.45 N	35.45 E
139	Lebda (Homs) (lĕb′dȧ) (hōms) Libya	32.36 N	14.12 E
131	Lebedin (lyĕ′bĕ-dēn).....Sov. Un.	48.57 N	31.35 E
130	Lebedyan (lyĕ′bĕ-dyän′).Sov. Un.	53.3 N	39.8 E
124	Le Blanc (lē bläN′)............Fr.	46.38 N	1.1 E
124	Le Boncau (lē bôN-kō′).........Fr.	43.32 N	1.25 W
97	Le Borgne (lē bōrn′y′).......Hai.	19.51 N	72.30 W
125	Le Bourget (lē bōōr-zhĕ′).Fr. (In.)	48.56 N	2.25 E
124	Le Bouscat (lē bōōs-kȧ′).........Fr.	44.52 N	0.35 W
126	Lebrija (lȧ-brē′hä)...........Sp.	36.55 N	6.5 W
104	Lebu (lā-bōō′)...............Chl.	37.35 S	73.31 W
135	Le Cap (lē kȧp)Eg. (Suez Canal In.)	30.56 N	32.20 E
124	Le Cateau (lē kȧ-tō′)..........Fr.	50.5 N	3.35 E
129	Lecce (lĕt′chā)...............It.	40.21 N	18.10 E
128	Lecco (lĕk′kō)...............It.	45.50 N	9.25 E
124	Le Chambon-Feugerolles (lē shäN-bôN′fû-zhē-rôl′) Fr.	45.25 N	4.20 E
93	Lechería (lä-chä-rē′ä)...Mex. (In.)	19.37 N	99.11 W
122	Lech R. (lĕk)................Ger.	48.15 N	10.55 E
81	Lecomte (lē-kôNt′)............La.	31.6 N	92.25 W
124	Le Coteau (lē kō-tō′)..........Fr.	46.2 N	4.8 E
124	Le Creusot (lē krû-zō′).........Fr.	46.49 N	4.25 E
124	Le Croisic (lē krwȧ-zēk′).......Fr.	47.18 N	2.30 W
123	Łęczyca (wăŋ-chü′-tsä).......Pol.	52.3 N	19.13 E
126	Ledesma (lȧ-dĕs′mä)...........Sp.	41.4 N	5.59 W
89	Lee (lē)....La. (New Orleans In.)	30.1 N	89.57 W
77	Leech L. (lēch)..............Minn.	47.10 N	94.20 W
82	Leeds (lēdz)..................Ala.	33.33 N	86.31 W
116	Leeds.....................Gt Brit.	53.45 N	1.30 W
76	Leeds.....................N. D.	48.17 N	99.25 W
118	Leeds and Liverpool Can.Gt. Brit.	53.54 N	2.10 W
118	Leek (lēk).............Gt. Brit.	53.6 N	2.1 W
122	Leer (lār).....................Ger.	53.13 N	7.27 E
116	Lee, R. (lē).....................Ire.	51.55 N	8.35 W
83	Leesburg (lēz′bûrg)...........Fla.	28.49 N	81.53 W
85	Leesburg......................Va.	39.7 N	77.35 W
79	Lees Summit (lēz).............Mo.	38.54 N	94.22 W
97	Lee Stocking I............Ba. Is.	23.48 N	76.8 W
81	Leesville (lēz′vĭl)..............La.	31.8 N	93.18 W
167	Leeton (lē′tŭn)...............Austl.	34.22 S	146.57 E
84	Leetonia (lē-tō′nĭ-ȧ)..........Ohio	40.55 N	80.46 W
122	Leeuwarden (lā′wär-dĕn)....Neth.	53.11 N	5.47 E
143	Leeuwfontein (Mt.) (lā′ōō-fŏn-tān′) U. S. Afr.	26.40 S	36.14 E
164	Leeuwin, C. (lōō′wĭn)......Austl.	34.15 S	115.10 E
95	Leeward Is. (lē′wērd)..W. I. (In.)		
91	Leeward Is....................W. I.	17.0 N	62.0 W
169	Lefevres Pen. (lē-fĕ′vēr) Austl. (Adelaide In.)	34.48 S	138.30 E
164	Lefroy, L. (lē-froi′)........Austl.	31.15 S	121.45 E
127	Leganes (lā-gä′nās)......Sp. (In.)	40.20 N	3.46 W
162	Legaspi (lā-gäs′pē)............P. I.	13.9 N	123.44 E
128	Leghorn (Livorno) (lĕg′hôrn) (lē-vôr′nō) It.	43.33 N	10.20 E
128	Legnano (lā-nyä′nō)............It.	45.35 N	8.55 E
151	Leh (lā)......................India	34.8 N	77.35 E
124	Le Havre (lē ȧv′r′)............Fr.	49.30 N	0.5 E
75	Lehi (lē′hī)...................Utah	40.23 N	111.51 W
75	Lehman Caves Nat. Mon. (lē′mȧn) Nev.	39.0 N	114.13 W
122	Lehrte (lār′tē)................Ger.	52.22 N	9.58 E
173	Lehua (I.) (lā′hōō-ä).........Haw.	22.2 N	160.7 W
116	Leicester (lĕs′tēr)......Gt. Brit.	52.40 N	1.10 W
118	Leicester Co............Gt. Brit.	52.41 N	1.15 W
164	Leichhardt R. (lĭk′härt).....Austl.	18.30 S	139.57 E
117	Leiden (lī′dĕn)...............Neth.	52.10 N	4.30 E
118	Leigh....................Gt. Brit.	53.30 N	2.32 W
119	Leigh-on-Sea Gt. Brit. (London In.)	51.32 N	0.38 E
120	Leikanger (lī′käŋ′gēr)........Nor.	61.10 N	6.54 E
122	Leine R. (lī′nē)................Ger.	52.30 N	9.28 E
84	Leipsic (lĭp′sĭk).............Ohio	41.7 N	84.3 W
122	Leipzig (lĭp′tsĭk).............Ger.	51.20 N	12.20 E
126	Leiria (lā-rē′ȧ).................Port.	39.44 N	8.49 W
84	Leitchfield (lēch′fēld).........Ky.	37.29 N	86.18 W
122	Leitmeritz (Litoměřice) (lĭt′mēr-ĭts) (lē′tō-myĕr′zhĕt-sĕ).Ger.	50.33 N	14.9 E
126	Leixoes (Matozinhos) (lā-shôŋzh′) (mä-tō-zēn′yōzh) Port.	41.11 N	8.41 W
154	Leiyang (lā′yäng′)..............Chn.	26.30 N	112.38 E
135	Le Kef (lē kĕf′)........Tun. (In.)	36.10 N	8.53 E
122	Lek R. (lĕk)................Neth.	51.57 N	5.20 E
120	Leksand (lĕk′sänd)..........Swe.	60.45 N	15.0 E
82	Leland (lē′lȧnd)............Miss.	33.25 N	90.55 W
49	Leland........ Wash. (Seattle In.)	47.53 N	122.53 W
122	Le Locle (lē lô′kl′).........Switz.	47.3 N	6.46 E
124	le Lude (lē lüd′)...............Fr.	47.38 N	0.10 E
104	La Maire Str. (lē mâr′)......Arg.	55.0 S	65.0 W
124	Le Mans (lē mäN′)............Fr.	48.1 N	0.10 E
76	Le Mars (lē märz′)............Ia.	42.48 N	96.10 W
123	Lemberg (Lwów) (lĕm′bĕrgh) (lvōōf).Pol.	49.49 N	24.2 E
162	Lemery (lā-mȧ-rē′)............P. I.	13.52 N	120.55 E
122	Lemgo (lĕm′gō)................Ger.	52.1 N	8.54 E
71	Lemhi R. (lĕm′hī)..............Ida.	45.0 N	113.40 W
71	Lemhi Ra.......................Ida.	44.30 N	113.30 W
76	Lemmon (lĕm′ŭn)..............S. D.	45.56 N	102.8 W
129	Lemnos (I.) (lĕm′nŏs).........Grc.	39.55 N	25.15 E
97	Le Mole (lē mōl′)..............Hai.	19.49 N	73.22 W
74	Lemongrove (lĕm′ŭn-grōv) Calif. (In.)	32.44 N	117.2 W
95	Le Moule (lē mōōl′)...Guad. (In.)	16.20 N	61.22 W
94	Lempa, R. (lĕm′pä)............Sal.	13.30 N	88.40 W
120	Lemvig (lĕm′vēgh)............Den.	56.32 N	8.20 E
126	Lena (lā′nä)....................Sp.	43.11 N	5.51 W
120	Lena (lē′nä)....................Swe.	60.0 N	17.42 E
149	Lena R. (lyĕ′nä)........Sov. Un.	60.0 N	119.0 E
103	Lençóes (lĕN-sôNs′)..........Braz.	12.31 S	41.31 W
103	Lençóes.......................Braz.	22.50 S	49.1 W
113	Leninakan(lyĕ-nē-nȧ-kän′)Sov. Un.	40.45 N	43.50 E
148	Leninabad (Khodzhent) (lyĕ-nē-nȧ-bȧd′)..Sov. Un.	40.20 N	69.40 E
130	Leningrad (lyĕ-nēn-grȧt′) Sov. Un.	59.55 N	30.20 E
121	Leninsk (lyĕ-nēnsk′).....Sov. Un.	59.53 N	29.55 E
130	Leninsk...................Sov. Un.	56.43 N	37.32 E
148	Leninsk Kuznetski (lyĕ-nēnsk′ kōōz-nyĕt′skĭ-ē)..Sov. Un.	54.30 N	86.40 E
150	Leninsk-Turkmenskii (lyĕ′nĕnsk-tōōrk-mĕn′skĭ-ē)...Sov. Un.	39.5 N	63.40 E
113	Lenkoran (lĕŋ-kô-rän′)...Sov. Un.	38.48 N	48.50 E
76	Lennox (lĕn′ŭks)............S. D.	43.22 N	96.52 W
83	Lenoir (lē-nōr′)............N. C.	35.55 N	81.33 W
82	Lenoir City................Tenn.	35.47 N	84.17 W
77	Lenox (lĕn′ŭks)................Ia.	40.52 N	94.32 W
124	Lens (läNs)....................Fr.	50.28 N	2.50 E
122	Leoben (lā-ō′bĕn)............Ger.	47.23 N	15.9 E
123	Leobschütz (lā′ōp-shüts).....Ger.	50.12 N	17.48 E
97	Léogane (lā-ô-gän′)..........Hai.	18.31 N	72.38 W
76	Leola (lē-ō′lȧ)...............S. D.	45.43 N	98.55 W
116	Leominster (lĕm′stēr) (lĕm′ĭn-stēr).Gt. Brit.	52.13 N	2.44 W
86	Leominster (lĕm′ĭn-stēr)....Mass.	42.31 N	71.49 W
77	Leon (lē′ŏn)....................Ia.	40.42 N	93.45 W
92	León (lȧ-ōn′)................Mex.	21.8 N	101.41 W
94	León.........................Nic.	12.27 N	86.53 W
163	Leon (lā′ōn′)................P. I.	10.46 N	122.23 E
126	León..........................Sp.	42.36 N	5.34 W
126	León (Prov.)..................Sp.	41.30 N	5.50 W
135	Leona, Pt. (lā-ō′nä) Sp. Mor. (Gib. In.)	35.54 N	5.37 E
128	Leonforte (lā-ōn-fôr′tä)........It.	37.38 N	14.24 E
80	Leon R. (lē′ŏn)...............Tex.	31.50 N	98.15 W
140	Leopold II, L. (lā′ō-pōld) (lē′ō-pōld).Bel. Cong.	2.0 S	18.20 E
103	Leopoldina (lā-ō-pōl-dē′nä)..Braz.	21.30 S	42.44 W
119	Leopoldsdorf (lā′ō-pōlts-dôrf′) Aus. (Wien In.)	48.7 N	16.24 E
140	Léopoldville (lā-ō-pōld-vēl′) (lē-ō-pōld-vĭl).Bel. Cong.	4.18 S	15.17 E
131	Leova (lȧ-ō′vä)...............Rom.	46.30 N	28.13 E
126	Lepe (lā′pä)....................Sp.	37.14 N	7.11 W
130	Lepel (lyĕ-pĕl′)...........Sov. Un.	54.51 N	28.43 E
125	Le Perreux (lē pē-rû′)...Fr. (In.)	48.50 N	2.30 E
57	L'Epiphanie (lā pē-fȧ-nē′) Can. (Montreal In.)	45.51 N	73.29 W
122	Lepontine Alps (lē-pŏn′tĭn).Switz.	46.27 N	8.54 E
124	Le Portel (lē pōr-tĕl′)...........Fr.	50.41 N	1.35 E
86	Lepreau (lē-prō′)............Can.	45.8 N	66.28 W
148	Lepsinsk (lyĕp-sēnsk′) ...Sov. Un.	45.30 N	80.30 E
124	Le Puy (lē pü-ē′)..............Fr.	45.0 N	3.55 E
125	Le Raincy (lē răN-sē′) ...Fr. (In.)	48.53 N	2.31 E
128	Lercara (lĕr-kä′rä)..............It.	37.42 N	12.34 E
80	Lerdo (lĕr′dō)................Mex.	25.34 N	103.30 W
139	Léré (lā-rā′)..........Fr. Eq. Afr.	9.40 N	14.18 E
143	Leribe (Hlotse) (lē-rē′bē) (hlōt′sē) Bas.	28.51 S	28.3 E
127	Lérida (lā′rē-dhä)..............Sp.	41.38 N	0.36 E
93	Lerma (lĕr′mä)...............Mex.	19.50 N	90.35 W
126	Lerma..........................Sp.	42.1 N	3.45 W
92	Lerma, R.....................Mex.	20.13 N	100.40 W
85	Le Roy (lē roi′)..............N. Y.	43.0 N	78.0 W
116	Lerwick (lĕr′ĭk) (lûr′wĭk) Gt. Brit. (In.)	60.10 N	1.10 W
124	Les Andelys (lā zäN-dē-lē′).....Fr.	49.15 N	1.30 E
125	Les Clayes (lā klā′).......Fr. (In.)	48.48 N	1.58 E
125	Les Essarts (lā zĕs-sär′)...Fr. (In.)	48.44 N	1.54 E
129	Leshe (Alessio) (lĕshē) (ȧ-lā′sē-ō) Alb.	41.47 N	19.40 E
128	Lesina, L. of (lĕ′zē-nä).........It.	41.52 N	15.25 E
129	Leskovac (lĕs′kō-väts).......Yugo.	42.59 N	21.57 E
129	Leskovec (lĕs′kō-vyĕts).........Bul.	43.5 N	25.42 E
79	Leslie (lĕz′lĭ).................Ark.	35.49 N	92.32 W
125	Les Mesnil (lā mȧ-nēl′)..Fr. (In.)	48.0 N	1.57 E
124	Lesparre (lē-spär′)............Fr.	45.20 N	0.58 W
124	Les Sables d' Olonne (lā sä′bl′ dō-lôn′).Fr.	46.30 N	1.48 E
95	Les Saintes Is. (lā-săNt′)Guad. (In.)	15.52 N	61.38 W
91	Lesser Antilles (I.) (lĕs′ēr ăn-tĭl′ēz) W. I.	15.0 N	62.0 W
54	Lesser Slave L..............Can.	55.28 N	115.45 W
143	Lesseyton (lĕs′ĭ-tŭn)....U. S. Afr.	31.49 S	26.48 E
88	Lester R. (lĕs′tēr) Minn. (Duluth In.)	46.50 N	92.5 W

ăt; finăl; rāte; senăte; ärm; ȧsk; sofȧ; fâre; ch-choose; dh-as th in other; bē; ēvent; bĕt; recĕnt; cratēr; g-go; gh-gutteral g; bĭt; ĭ-short neutral; rīde; K-gutteral k as ch in German ich;

Page	Name Pronunciation Region	Lat. °′	Long. °′
77	Le Sueur (lē sōōr') Minn.	44.27 N	93.54 W
122	Leszno (lĕsh'nô) Pol.	51.50 N	16.32 E
124	Le Teil (lē tā'y') Fr.	44.35 N	4.48 E
54	Lethbridge (lĕth'brĭj) Can.	49.45 N	112.50 W
131	Letichev (lyĕ-tē-chĕf') Sov. Un.	49.22 N	27.39 E
124	Le Tréport (lē trā-pôr') Fr.	50.2 N	1.25 E
123	Léva (Levice) (lā'vŏ) (lā'vêt-sĕ) Hung.	48.13 N	18.37 E
129	Levadeia (lyē-vá-dhē'á) Grc.	38.26 N	22.51 E
125	Levallois-Perret (lā-vàl-wà'-pĕ-rĕ') Fr. (In.)	48.53 N	2.17 E
128	Levana (Mts.) (lĕ-vä'nä) It.	45.21 N	7.10 E
110	Levanger (lĕ'väŋ-gĕr) Nor.	63.38 N	11.8 E
116	Leven (lĕ'vĕn) Gt. Brit.	56.15 N	3.0 W
118	Leven, R. Gt. Brit.	54.12 N	3.3 W
164	Leveque, C. (lē-vĕk') Austl.	16.20 S	122.47 E
140	Leverville (lĕ-vā-vēl') Bel. Cong.	5.15 S	18.45 E
...	Levice, see Léva, Hung.		
128	Levico (lā'vē-kō) It.	46.2 N	11.19 E
124	Lévie (lā-vē') Cor.	41.40 N	9.10 E
124	Le Vigan (lĕ vē-gäN') Fr.	43.39 N	3.38 E
171	Levin (lĕv'ĭn) N. Z.	40.32 S	175.17 E
55	Lévis (lā-vē') (lĕ'vĭs) Can.	46.50 N	71.13 W
129	Levkas (lyĕf-kàs') Grc.	38.48 N	20.43 E
129	Levkas (I.) Grc.	38.45 N	20.40 E
123	Levoča (lā'vô-chá) Czech.	49.2 N	20.39 E
6	Levuka (lâ-vōō'kà) Fiji Is. (In.)	17.41 S	178.48 E
83	Levy L. (lĕ'vĭ) Fla.	29.31 N	82.20 W
89	Levy L. La. (New Orleans In.)	29.48 N	89.48 W
85	Lewes (lū'ĭs) Del.	38.46 N	75.12 W
116	Lewes Gt. Brit.	50.55 N	0.0
54	Lewes R. Can.	62.25 N	136.30 W
88	Lewis (lū'ĭs) N. Y. (Niagara Falls In.)	42.59 N	78.51 W
71	Lewis and Clark Cavern Nat'l Mon. Mont.	45.50 N	111.42 W
49	Lewis and Clark R. Ore. (Portland In.)	46.6 N	123.53 W
82	Lewisburg (lū'ĭs-bûrg) Tenn.	35.27 N	86.48 W
85	Lewisburg W. Va.	37.50 N	80.25 W
116	Lewis, Butt of (C.) Gt. Brit.	58.30 N	6.15 W
116	Lewis (I.) Gt. Brit.	58.0 N	6.50 W
87	Lewisporte (lū'ĭs-pōrt) Newf.	49.15 N	55.2 W
71	Lewis Ra. Mont.	48.10 N	113.10 W
70	Lewis R. Wash.	46.3 N	122.10 W
70	Lewiston (lū'ĭs-tŭn) Ida.	46.25 N	117.1 W
86	Lewiston Me.	44.5 N	70.11 W
85	Lewiston N. Y.	43.10 N	79.0 W
79	Lewistown (lū'ĭs-toun) Ill.	40.24 N	90.9 W
71	Lewistown Mont.	47.5 N	109.27 W
85	Lewistown Pa.	40.37 N	77.30 W
84	Lexington (lĕk'sĭng-tŭn) Ky.	38.2 N	84.31 W
87	Lexington Mass. (In.)	42.27 N	71.13 W
82	Lexington Miss.	33.7 N	90.3 W
79	Lexington Mo.	39.10 N	93.52 W
78	Lexington Neb.	40.45 N	99.45 W
83	Lexington N. C.	35.48 N	80.16 W
82	Lexington Tenn.	35.37 N	88.25 W
85	Lexington Va.	37.47 N	79.27 W
72	Leyden (lā'dĕn) Colo. (Denver In.)	39.50 N	105.11 W
163	Leyte (lā'tā) P. I.	11.22 N	124.30 E
163	Leyte G. P. I.	10.50 N	125.28 E
163	Leyte (I.) P. I.	10.50 N	124.50 E
116	Leyton (lā'tŭn) Gt. Brit.	51.32 N	0.0
123	Lezajsk (lĕ'zhä-ĭsk) Pol.	50.14 N	22.25 E
124	Lézignan (lā-zē-nyäN') Fr.	43.15 N	2.48 E
127	Lezirias (Reg.) (lā-zē-rē'äzh) Port. (In.)	38.54 N	8.57 W
131	Lgov (lgôf) Sov. Un.	51.42 N	35.20 E
152	Lhasa (läs'ä) Chn.	29.48 N	91.2 E
125	L'Hay (lā-ĕ') Fr. (In.)	48.47 N	2.22 E
161	Lian (lē-än') P. I. (Manila In.)	14.5 N	120.34 E
163	Lianga (lē-äŋ-gä') P. I.	8.38 N	126.6 E
163	Lianga B. P. I.	8.36 N	126.10 E
152	Liangchow (lyäng'chō') Chn.	38.0 N	102.32 E
154	Liangshan (lyäng'shän') Chn.	30.47 N	107.55 E
161	Lian, R. P. I. (Manila In.)	14.5 N	120.37 E
156	Liaochow (lyä'ō'chō') Chn.	37.6 N	113.24 E
153	Liao R. (lyä'ō) Manch.	43.0 N	123.30 E
157	Liaotung Pen. Asia	40.10 N	122.50 E
153	Liaoyang (lyä'ō-yäng') Manch.	41.17 N	123.10 E
153	Liaoyüan (Chengchiatun) (lyä'ō-yü-än') (chĕng'chyä'tōōn') Chn.	43.44 N	123.28 E
54	Liard (lē-är') Can.	60.13 N	123.32 W
54	Liard R. Can.	59.30 N	125.0 W
163	Libacao (lē-bä-kä'ō) P. I.	11.29 N	122.28 E
70	Libby (lĭb'ē) Mont.	48.23 N	115.32 W
139	Libenge (lē-bĕŋ'gä) Bel. Cong.	3.33 N	18.36 E
78	Liberal (lĭb'ēr-ăl) Kan.	37.3 N	100.56 W
...	Liberec, see Reichenberg, Ger.		
138	Liberia (lī-bē'rĭ-ȧ) Afr.	6.30 N	9.30 W
94	Liberia C. R.	10.39 N	85.27 W
99	Libertad (lē-bĕr-tädh') Ur. (Buenos Aires In.)	34.36 S	56.37 W
84	Liberty (lĭb'ēr-tĭ) Ind.	39.37 N	84.55 W
79	Liberty Mo.	39.16 N	94.24 W
83	Liberty S. C.	34.48 N	82.40 W
81	Liberty Tex.	30.4 N	94.48 W
73	Liberty Utah (Salt Lake City In.)	41.19 N	111.51 W
77	Libertyville (lĭb'ēr-tĭ-vĭl) Ill.	42.18 N	87.59 W
161	Libigan, R. (lē-bē'-gän) P. I. (Manila In.)	13.56 N	121.24 E
162	Libmanan (lĭb-mä'nän) P. I.	13.41 N	123.3 E
143	Libode (lĭ-bō'dĕ) U. S. Afr.	31.30 S	29.2 E
124	Libourne (lē-bōōrn') Fr.	44.55 N	0.15 W
93	Libres (lē'brās) Mex.	19.27 N	97.41 W
138	Libreville (lē-br'vēl') Fr. Eq. Afr.	0.30 N	9.30 E
163	Libuganon R. (lēbōō'gä-nōn') P. I.	7.40 N	125.34 E
139	Libya (lĭb'ē-ä) Afr.	28.0 N	18.0 E
139	Libyan Des. (lĭb'ē-ăn) Eg.-Libya	28.0 N	25.0 E
115	Libyan Plat. Eg.	30.30 N	26.30 E
104	Licancábur (Vol.) (lē-kän-kä'-bōōr) Chl.	22.38 S	67.50 W
128	Licata (lē-kä'tä) It.	37.7 N	13.55 E
118	Lichfield (lĭch'fēld) Gt. Brit.	52.41 N	1.49 W
154	Lichow (lē'chō') Chn.	29.36 N	111.24 E
119	Lichtenberg (lĭk'tĕn-bĕrgh) Ger. (Berlin In.)	52.31 N	13.28 E
143	Lichtenburg (lĭk'tĕn-bōōrgh) U. S. Afr.	26.10 S	26.10 E
119	Lichtenrade (lĭk'tĕn-rä-dĕ) Ger. (Berlin In.)	52.23 N	13.25 E
119	Lichterfelde, Gr. (lĭk'tēr-fĕl-tĕ) Ger. (Berlin In.)	52.26 N	13.18 E
154	Lichwan (lĭch'wän') Chn.	30.16 N	108.34 E
84	Licking R. (lĭk'ĭng) Ky.	38.25 N	84.0 W
128	Licosa (lē-kō'sä) It.	40.15 N	14.53 E
141	Licungo R. (lē-kooŋ'gō) Moz.	16.30 S	37.0 E
123	Lida (lē'dȧ) Pol.	53.53 N	25.18 E
76	Lida L. Minn.	46.36 N	95.59 W
169	Lidcombe (lĭd'kŭm) Austl. (Sydney In.)	33.52 S	151.3 E
76	Lidgerwood (lĭj'ēr-wood) N. D.	46.5 N	97.9 W
120	Lidköping (lēt'chû-pĭng) Swe.	58.30 N	13.8 E
122	Liechtenstein (lĕk'tĕn-shtīn) Eur.	47.7 N	9.33 E
117	Liége (lē-āzh') Bel.	50.39 N	5.35 E
122	Liegnitz (lēgh'nĭtz) Ger.	51.12 N	16.10 E
154	Lienhwa (lyĕn'hwä') Chn.	27.10 N	113.40 E
155	Lienkong (lyĕn'kŏng') Chn.	26.11 N	119.28 E
154	Lien R. (lyĕn) Chn.	27.38 N	112.12 E
122	Lienz (lē-ĕnts') Ger.	46.50 N	12.45 E
121	Liepāja (lē'pä-yä') Lat.	56.30 N	21.0 E
117	Lierre (lyâr) Bel.	51.8 N	4.30 E
122	Liesing (lē'sĭng) Ger.	48.9 N	16.16 E
122	Liestal (lēs'täl) Switz.	47.28 N	7.45 E
124	Liévin (lyā-văN') Fr.	50.25 N	2.45 E
116	Liffey, R. (lĭf'ĭ) Ire.	53.15 N	6.40 W
116	Lifford (lĭf'ērd) Gt. Brit.	54.50 N	7.25 W
165	Lifu (I.) (lē-fōō') N. Cal.	21.0 S	167.15 E
162	Ligao (lē-gä'ō) P. I.	13.15 N	123.32 E
141	Ligonha R. (lē-gō'nyȧ) Moz.	16.0 S	38.42 E
84	Ligonier (lĭg-ô-nēr') Ind.	41.30 N	85.34 W
163	Liguasan Marsh (lĭ-gwä'sän) P. I.	7.0 N	124.45 E
128	Liguria (Prov.) (lē-gōō-rē-ä) It.	44.30 N	9.0 E
128	Ligurian Sea (lĭ-gū'rĭ-ăn) It.	43.30 N	9.0 E
165	Lihou Reefs and Cays (lē-hōō') Austl.	17.0 S	152.0 E
156	Lihsien (lē'hsyĕn') Chn.	38.38 N	115.34 E
173	Lihue (lē-hōō'ā) Haw.	21.59 N	159.24 W
121	Lihula (lē'hōō-lä) Est.	58.41 N	23.50 E
140	Likasi (lē-kä'sē) Bel. Cong.	11.13 S	26.47 E
130	Likhoslavl (lyē'kô-slä'v'l) Sov. Un.	57.7 N	35.29 E
131	Likhovka (lyē-kôf'kȧ) Sov. Un.	48.41 N	33.57 E
130	Likhvin (lyēk-vēn') Sov. Un.	54.5 N	36.14 E
152	Likiang (lē'kyäng') Chn.	26.58 N	100.27 E
73	Lilburn (lĭl'bûrn) Ga. (Atlanta In.)	33.53 N	84.9 W
124	l'Ile Rousse (lēl rōōs') Cor. (In.)	42.40 N	9.0 E
154	Liling (lē'lĭng') Chn.	27.41 N	113.14 E
161	Lilio (lē-lē'ō) P. I. (Manila In.)	14.8 N	121.29 E
124	Lille (lēl) Fr.	50.38 N	3.0 E
120	Lillehammer (lēl'ĕ-häm'mĕr) Nor.	61.8 N	10.28 E
120	Lillesand (lēl'ĕ-sän') Nor.	58.16 N	8.22 E
120	Lilleström (lēl'ĕ-strûm) Nor.	59.57 N	11.4 E
163	Liloan P. I.	10.24 N	123.59 E
140	Lilongwe (lē-lôŋ'gwā) Nyasaland	13.58 S	33.45 E
84	Lima (lī'mȧ) Ohio	40.44 N	84.7 W
103	Lima Peru (In.)		
103	Lima (lē'mä) Peru	12.0 S	77.0 W
89	Limaburg (lī-mȧ-bûrg) Ky. (Cincinnati In.)	39.1 N	84.41 W
99	Limache (lē-mä'chä) Chl. (Valparaiso In.)	33.2 S	71.15 W
113	Liman, Bolshoi (Manych Sea) (bôl'shô-ē lē-män) (mȧ-nĭch') Sov. Un.	46.20 N	42.45 E
126	Lima R. (lē'mä) Port.-Sp.	41.50 N	8.19 W
71	Lima Reservoir (lī'mȧ) Mont.	44.38 N	112.20 W
115	Limasol (lē-mȧ-sōl') Cyp.	34.42 N	32.57 E
161	Limay (lē-mä'ē) P. I. (Manila In.)	14.31 N	120.31 E
104	Limay, R. Arg.	39.50 S	69.30 W
121	Limbazi (lēm'bä-zĭ) Lat.	57.31 N	24.45 E
161	Limbones I. (lēm-bō'näs) P. I. (Manila In.)	14.15 N	120.31 E
122	Limburg (lĭm'bûrg) Ger.	50.22 N	8.3 E
120	Limedsforsen (lē'mĕs-förs'ĕn) Swe.	60.55 N	13.24 E
116	Limerick (Luimneach) (lĭm'ēr-ĭk) (lĭm'nȧk) Ire.	52.38 N	8.38 W
120	Lim Fjord (lēm fyôr') Den.	56.58 N	10.15 E
161	Limit, Pt. (lē-mēt') P. I. (Manila In.)	14.17 N	120.34 E
164	Limmen Bight (lĭm'ĕn) Austl.	14.40 S	136.0 E
129	Limnē (lēm'nē) Grc.	38.45 N	23.22 E
124	Limoges (lē-mōzh') Fr.	45.50 N	1.15 E
78	Limon (lī'mŏn) Colo.	39.16 N	103.40 W
95	Limón (lē-mōn') C. R.	10.1 N	83.3 W
90	Limon B. C. Z. (In.)	9.21 N	79.56 W
97	Limón L. Hai.	18.20 N	71.35 W
161	Limon, R. P. I. (Manila In.)	14.20 N	120.51 E
124	Limousin Plat. (lē-mōō-zăN') Fr.	46.0 N	1.0 E
124	Limoux (lē-mōō') Fr.	43.5 N	2.15 E
140	Limpopo R. (lĭm-pō'pō) Afr.	22.15 S	30.15 E
155	Linan (lē'nän') Chn.	30.16 N	119.48 E
163	Linao B. (lē-nä'ō) P. I.	6.45 N	124.0 E
163	Linao Pt. P. I.	6.46 N	123.58 E
163	Linapacan I. (lē-nä-pä'kän) P. I.	11.25 N	119.50 E
163	Linapacan Str. P. I.	11.35 N	119.50 E
104	Linares (lē-nä'räs) Chl.	35.50 S	71.45 W
80	Linares Mex.	24.53 N	99.34 W
126	Linares Sp.	38.7 N	3.47 W
128	Linara, C. (lē-nä'rō) It.	40.2 N	11.50 E
156	Linchang (lĭn'chäng') Chn.	36.17 N	114.50 E
156	Lincheng (lĭn'chĕng') Chn.	37.31 N	114.37 E
154	Linchow (lĭn'chō') Chn.	24.47 N	112.12 E
156	Linchu (lĭn'chōō') Chn.	36.29 N	118.37 E
104	Lincoln (lĭŋ'kŭn) Arg.	34.50 S	61.32 W
74	Lincoln Calif.	38.52 N	121.19 W
116	Lincoln Gt. Brit.	53.15 N	0.33 W
79	Lincoln Ill.	40.9 N	89.21 W
78	Lincoln Kan.	39.3 N	98.9 W
86	Lincoln Me.	45.23 N	68.30 W
87	Lincoln Mass. (In.)	42.26 N	71.18 W
76	Lincoln Neb.	40.50 N	96.41 W
78	Lincoln N. M.	33.28 N	105.25 W
171	Lincoln N. Z. (In.)	43.37 S	172.30 E
118	Lincoln County Gt. Brit.	53.10 N	0.33 W
78	Lincoln, Mt. Colo.	39.25 N	106.5 W
118	Lincoln Heights Gt. Brit.	53.9 N	0.36 W
85	Lincoln Park N. Y.	43.8 N	77.38 W
48	Lincoln Sea Grnld.	83.30 N	55.0 W
83	Lincolnton (lĭŋ'kŭn-tŭn) N. C.	35.28 N	81.15 W
116	Lincoln Wolds (lĭŋ'kŭn wōldz') Gt. Brit.	53.20 N	0.0
82	Lindale (lĭn'dāl) Ga.	34.11 N	85.10 W
122	Lindau (lĭn'dou) Ger.	47.34 N	9.40 E
74	Linda Vista (lĭn'dȧ vĭs'tȧ) Calif. (In.)	32.52 N	117.10 W
88	Linden (lĭn'dĕn) N. J. (New York In.)	40.38 N	74.15 W
120	Lindesberg (lĭn'dĕs-bĕrgh) Swe.	59.37 N	15.15 E
120	Lindesnes (The Naze) (lĭn''ĕs-nĕs) Nor.	58.0 N	7.6 E
141	Lindi (lĭn'dē) Tan.	9.55 S	39.37 E
139	Lindi R. Bel. Cong.	1.30 N	26.30 E
143	Lindley (lĭn'lĭ) U. S. Afr.	27.50 S	28.0 E
143	Lindley Road U. S. Afr.	27.59 S	27.47 E
55	Lindsay (lĭn'zē) Can.	44.18 N	79.2 W
79	Lindsay Okla.	34.52 N	97.38 W
46	Lindsay I. Ant. O.	54.30 S	3.0 E
165	Lindsay Mt. Austl.	28.20 S	152.55 E
79	Lindsborg (lĭnz'bôrg) Kan.	38.34 N	97.41 W
118	Lindsey (Borough) (lĭn'zĭ) Gt. Brit.	53.22 N	0.30 W
73	Line Cr. (līn) Ga. (Atlanta In.)	33.24 N	84.37 W
82	Lineville (līn'vĭl) Ala.	33.18 N	85.46 W
162	Lingayen (lĭŋ-gä-yän') P. I.	16.1 N	120.13 E
162	Lingayen G. P. I.	16.12 N	120.15 E
154	Lingchwan (lĭng'chwän') Chn.	25.23 N	110.17 E
150	Lingeh (lĭŋ'gĕ) Iran	26.45 N	54.55 E
122	Lingen (lĭŋ'gĕn) Ger.	52.31 N	7.20 E
160	Lingga Arch. (lĭng-gä') Neth. Ind.	0.20 S	104.30 E
154	Linghsien (lĭng'hsyĕn') Chn.	26.29 N	113.24 E
156	Lingkiu (lĭng'kyōō') Chn.	39.27 N	114.9 E
156	Lingpi (lĭng'pī') Chn.	33.33 N	117.30 E
138	Linguere (lĭŋ-gĕr') Fr. W. Afr.	15.25 N	15.5 W
156	Linhsien (lĭn'hsyĕn') Chn.	36.2 N	113.56 E
155	Linkiang (lĭn'kyäng') Chn.	27.55 N	115.22 E
120	Linköping (lĭn'chû-pĭng) Swe.	58.24 N	15.38 E
158	Linkou (lĭn'kō') Manch.	45.16 N	130.10 E
116	Linnhe (L.) (lĭn'ē) Gt. Brit.	56.35 N	5.15 W
49	Linnton (lĭn'tŭn) Ore. (Portland In.)	45.36 N	122.49 W
155	Linping (lĭn'pĭng') Chn.	24.20 N	114.19 E
154	Linshan (lĭn'shän') Chn.	24.48 N	111.58 E
154	Linshui (lĭn'shwē') Chn.	30.24 N	106.50 E
154	Linsiang (lĭn'syäng') Chn.	29.34 N	113.27 E
88	Linthicum (lĭn'thĭ-kŭm) Md. (Baltimore In.)	39.12 N	76.39 W
84	Linton (lĭn'tŭn) Ind.	39.7 N	87.13 W
76	Linton N. D.	46.16 N	100.15 W
156	Lintsing (lĭn'tsĭng') Chn.	36.46 N	115.48 E
154	Linwu (lĭn'woo') Chn.	25.11 N	112.12 E
156	Linyi (lĭn'yĭ') Chn.	37.11 N	116.44 E
156	Linying (lĭn'yĭng') Chn.	33.49 N	113.59 E
122	Linz (lĭnts) Ger.	48.18 N	14.17 E
124	Lions, G. of (lī'ŭnz) Fr.	43.0 N	4.0 E
141	Lions Head (Mt.) U. S. Afr.	33.56 S	18.23 E
162	Lipa (lē-pä') P. I.	13.56 N	121.10 E
128	Lipari (lē'pä-rē) It.	38.28 N	14.56 E
128	Lipari (I.) It.	38.30 N	14.55 E
128	Lipari Is. It.	38.34 N	14.50 E
130	Lipetsk (lyē'pĕtsk) Sov. Un.	52.39 N	39.38 E
104	Lipez, Mt. (lē-päz') Arg.-Bol.	21.50 S	67.15 W
154	Liping (lē'pĭng') Chn.	26.9 N	108.59 E
123	Lipno (lēp'nô) Pol.	52.49 N	19.12 E
131	Lipnyazhka (lēp-nyäzh'kȧ) Sov. Un.	48.23 N	31.3 E
122	Lippe (State) (lĭp'ĕ) Ger.	52.7 N	9.0 E
122	Lippstadt (lĭp'shtät) Ger.	51.40 N	8.20 E
167	Liptrap, C. (lĭp'trăp) Austl.	38.53 S	145.55 E
131	Liptsi (lyēp'tsē) Sov. Un.	50.10 N	36.22 E
154	Li R. (lē) Chn.	29.23 N	111.2 E
127	Liria (lē'rē-ä) Sp.	39.37 N	0.34 W
127	Lirio R. (lē'rē-ō) Sp. (In.)	36.25 N	6.6 W
128	Liri R. (lē'rē) It.	41.40 N	13.33 E
139	Lisala (lē-sä'lä) Bel. Cong.	2.12 N	21.35 E
127	Lisboa (Prov.) (lēzh-bō'ä) Port. (In.)	38.42 N	9.11 W
127	Lisboa (Lisbon) (lēzh-bō'a) (lĭz'-bŭn) Port. (In.)	38.44 N	9.9 W
86	Lisbon Me.	44.0 N	70.0 W
76	Lisbon N. D.	46.27 N	97.42 W
84	Lisbon Ohio	40.58 N	80.49 W
116	Lisburn (lĭs'bŭrn) Gt. Brit.	54.35 N	6.5 W
52	Lisburne, C. (lĭz'bŭrn) Alsk.	68.40 N	166.9 W
119	Liscard (lĭs'kärd) Gt. Brit. (Liverpool In.)	53.25 N	3.5 W
155	Lishui (lē'shwē') Chn.	31.38 N	119.0 E
124	Lisieux (lē-zyû') Fr.	49.10 N	0.12 E
131	Liski (lyĕs'kē) Sov. Un.	50.57 N	39.29 E
166	Lismore (lĭz'mōr) Austl.	37.56 S	143.21 E
112	Lisvinskii Zavod (lēz-vĕn'skĭ-ē zȧ-vôt') Sov. Un.	58.12 N	57.45 E
131	Lisya Gora (lē'zyȧ gô'rȧ) Sov. Un.	48.7 N	31.6 E
79	Litchfield (lĭch'fēld) Ill.	39.9 N	89.38 W
77	Litchfield Minn.	45.8 N	94.30 W
167	Lithgow (lĭth'gō) Austl.	33.29 S	150.10 E
73	Lithia Springs (lĭth'ĭ-ȧ sprĭngz) Ga. (Atlanta In.)	33.47 N	84.37 W
128	Lithinon, C. (lē'thē-nōn) Grc.	34.54 N	24.56 E

ng-sing; ŋ-baŋk; N-nasalized n; nŏd; cŏmmit; ōld; ōbey; ôrder; fōōd; fŏŏt; ou-out; s-soft; sh-dish; th-thin; pūre; ûnite; ûrn; stŭd; circŭs; ü-as "y" in study; '-indeterminate vowel.

Page	Name Pronunciation Region	Lat. °′	Long. °′
73	Lithonia (lĭ-thō′nĭ-ȧ) Ga. (Atlanta In.)	33.42 N	84.6 W
121	Lithuania (lĭth-ů-ā′nĭ-ȧ)......Eur.	55.3 N	24.0 E
131	Litin (lê-tēn′)..........Sov. Un.	49.17 N	28.8 E
129	Litokhoron (lĕ′tô-ḳō′rŏn)....Grc.	40.4 N	22.30 E
	Litoměřice, see Leitmeritz, Ger.		
122	Litomyšl (lē′tô-mēsh′l).....Czech.	49.52 N	16.14 E
96	Little Abaco I. (ă′bā-kō)...Ba. Is.	26.55 N	77.45 W
46	Little America (Framheim) (främ′hām) Ant.	78.30 S	161.30 W
96	Little Bahama Bank (bȧ-hā′mȧ) Ba. Is.	26.50 N	78.40 W
170	Little Barrier I. (băr′ĭ-ēr)...N. Z.	36.12 S	175.7 E
73	Little Bear R. Utah (Salt Lake City In.)	41.38 N	111.52 W
73	Little Bear R., Blacksmith Fork Utah (Salt Lake City In.)	41.38 N	111.43 W
73	Little Bear R., East Fork Utah (Salt Lake City In.)	41.30 N	111.40 W
73	Little Bear R., South Fork Utah (Salt Lake City In.)	41.28 N	111.50 W
120	Little Belt (Str.)............Den.	55.0 N	10.0 E
71	Little Belt Mts..............Mont.	47.0 N	110.40 W
89	Little Bird I. La. (New Orleans In.)	29.25 N	89.29 W
135	Little Bitter L.Eg. (Suez Can. In.)	30.14 N	32.33 E
70	Little Bitterroot R.........Mont.	47.50 N	114.40 W
79	Little Blue R..........Neb.-Kan.	40.10 N	97.14 W
118	Littleborough (lĭt′′l-bŭr-ô) Gt.Brit.	53.39 N	2.6 W
73	Little Cahaba R. (kȧ-hô′bȧ) Ala. (Birmingham In.)	33.30 N	86.35 W
96	Little Cayman (I.) (kā′mȧn).W. I.	19.42 N	80.3 W
75	Little Colorado R. (kŏl-ô-rä′dō) Ariz.	35.50 N	111.20 W
97	Little Exuma I. (ĕk-sōō′mȧ) Ba. Is.	23.28 N	75.40 W
77	Little Falls...............Minn.	45.58 N	94.22 W
85	Little Falls................N. Y.	43.3 N	74.52 W
78	Littlefield (lĭt′′l-fēld)........Tex.	33.56 N	102.18 W
143	Little Fish R...........U. S. Afr.	32.50 S	25.35 E
72	Little Fountain Cr. (foun′tĭn) Colo. (Colo. Sprs. In.)	38.40 N	104.47 W
91	Little Hans Lollick I. St. Thomas (In.)	18.25 N	64.55 W
70	Little Horn R..............Mont.	45.10 N	107.23 W
119	Little Hulton (hŭl′t′n) Gt. Brit. (Liverpool In.)	53.32 N	2.25 W
70	Little Humboldt R. (hŭm′bōlt) Nev.	41.15 N	117.35 W
97	Little Inagua I. (ē-nä′gwä)..Ba. Is.	21.30 N	73.0 W
96	Little Isaac I. (ī′zȧk)......Ba. Is.	25.58 N	78.55 W
84	Little Kanawha R. (kȧ-nô′wȧ) W. Va.	38.55 N	81.0 W
142	Little Karroo (Reg.) (kȧ-rōō′) U. S. Afr.	33.45 S	21.20 E
77	Little Fork R...............Minn.	48.10 N	93.30 W
89	Little L.....La. (New Orleans In.)	29.30 N	90.9 W
89	Little Miami R. (mī-ăm′ĭ) Ohio (Cincinnati In.)	39.7 N	84.23 W
116	Little Minch (Chan.) (mĭnsh) Gt. Brit.	57.30 N	6.50 W
87	Little Miquelon I. (mē-k′lôɴ′) (mĭk-ē-lŏn′)N. A.	46.60 N	56.20 W
79	Little Missouri R. (mĭ-sōō′rĭ) .Ark.	33.55 N	93.30 W
76	Little Missouri R...........N. D.	46.40 N	103.30 W
73	Little Mountain Utah (Salt Lake City In.)	41.15 N	112.15 W
142	Little Namaland (nä′mä-lănd) U. S. Afr.	29.0 S	17.20 E
88	Little Neck B. N. Y. (New York In.)	40.47 N	73.46 W
83	Little Peedee R. (pē-dē′)....S. C.	34.25 N	79.20 W
71	Little Powder R. (pou′dēr) Wyo.-Mont.	45.0 N	105.20 W
79	Little Red R...............Ark.	35.30 N	92.0 W
87	Little (Gray) R...........Newf.	48.0 N	56.55 W
79	Little R..............Ark.-Okla.	33.55 N	94.30 W
79	Little R....................Mo.	36.30 N	89.40 W
81	Little R...................Tex.	30.50 N	97.10 W
83	Little River..........Fla. (In.)	25.51 N	80.11 W
79	Little Rock................Ark.	34.43 N	92.16 W
128	Little St. Bernard P. (sȧnt bēr-närd′) (săɴ bĕr-när′) It-Fr.	45.40 N	6.53 E
97	Little San Salvador I. (săn săl′vȧ-dôr′) Ba. Is.	24.36 N	75.57 W
83	Little Saltila R. (sȧ-tĭl′ȧ).....Ga.	31.35 N	82.20 W
76	Little Sioux R. (sōō).........Ia.	42.40 N	95.35 W
71	Little Snake R........Colo.-Wyo.	40.40 N	108.17 W
119	Little Sutton (sŭt′′n) Gt. Brit. (Liverpool In.)	53.17 N	2.57 W
83	Little Tennessee R. (tĕn-ĕ-sē′) Tenn.-N. C.	35.26 N	83.40 W
72	Little Thompson R. (tŏmp′sŭn) Colo. (Denver In.)	40.15 N	105.10 W
73	Littleton (lĭt′′l-tŭn) Ala. (Birmingham In.)	33.42 N	87.0 W
78	Littleton..................Colo.	39.36 N	105.1 W
87	Littleton............Mass. (In.)	42.32 N	71.28 W
86	Littleton..................N. H.	44.18 N	71.48 W
79	Little Wabash R. (wô′băsh)...Ill.	39.0 N	88.35 W
72	Little West Cr. Colo. (Colo. Sprs. In.)	39.5 N	105.13 W
76	Little White R.............S. D.	43.10 N	101.0 W
71	Little Wood R...............Ida.	43.10 N	114.3 W
156	Litsing (lĭ′tsĭng′)...........Chn.	37.32 N	118.15 E
156	Liuan (lyōō′än′).............Chn.	31.45 N	116.16 E
154	Liucheng (lyōō′chĕng′)......Chn.	24.32 N	109.20 E
154	Liuchow (Luchow) (lōō′chō)..Chn.	24.22 N	109.30 E
155	Liuho (lyōō′hō′).............Chn.	31.28 N	121.20 E
154	Liu R. (lyōō)................Chn.	25.42 N	109.23 E
154	Liuyang (lyōō′yäng′)........Chn.	28.12 N	113.20 E
121	Livani (lē′vȧ-nē)............Lat.	56.23 N	26.8 E
53	Livengood (lĭv′ĕn-gōōd).....Alsk.	65.7 N	149.8 W
82	Live Oak (lĭv′ōk)............Fla.	30.17 N	82.59 W
74	Livermore (lĭv′ēr-mōr).......Calif.	37.41 N	121.46 W
84	Livermore...................Ky.	37.30 N	87.8 W
86	Liverpool (lĭv′ēr-pōōl).......Can.	44.2 N	64.42 W
119	Liverpool ....Gt. Brit. (In.)		
116	Liverpool ....Gt. Brit.	53.25 N	3.0 W
81	Liverpool............Tex. (In.)	29.17 N	95.17 W
53	Liverpool B..................Can.	70.0 N	128.30 W
167	Liverpool Ra...............Austl.	31.48 S	150.30 E
82	Livingston (lĭv′ĭng-stŭn)......Ala.	32.35 N	88.10 W
94	Livingston.................Guat.	15.48 N	88.46 W
71	Livingston.................Mont.	45.40 N	110.35 W
82	Livingston.................Tenn.	36.23 N	85.20 W
140	Livingstone (lĭv′ĭng-stōn)..N. Rh.	17.50 S	25.47 E
140	Livingstonia (lĭv-ĭng-stō′nĭ-ȧ) Nya	10.42 S	34.3 E
46	Livingston I..............Ant. O.	62.30 S	60.0 W
128	Livno (lēv′nō)..............Yugo.	43.50 N	17.1 E
130	Livny (lēv′nê)...........Sov. Un.	52.27 N	37.38 E
128	Livorno (Leghorn) (lê-vôr′nō) (lĕg′hôrn) It.	43.33 N	10.20 E
125	Livry (lē-vrē′)..........Fr. (In.)	48.55 N	2.33 E
155	Liyang (lē′yäng′)............Chn.	31.22 N	119.30 E
116	Lizard Hd. (lĭz′ȧrd)......Gt. Brit.	49.55 N	5.10 W
128	Ljubljana (lyōō′blyä-nȧ)....Yugo.	46.2 N	14.30 E
128	Ljubuški (lyōō′bōōsh-kê)...Yugo.	43.12 N	17.31 E
120	Ljunga R. (lyōōng′ȧ)........Swe.	62.30 N	14.55 E
120	Ljungby (lyōōng′bü).........Swe.	56.50 N	13.54 E
120	Ljusdal (lyōōs′däl)..........Swe.	61.51 N	16.10 E
120	Ljusna R. (lyōōs′nō)........Swe.	62.5 N	14.0 E
116	Llandudno (lăn-dŭd′nō)..Gt. Brit.	53.19 N	3.45 W
116	Llanelly (lȧ-nĕth′lĭ) (lȧ-nĕl′ĭ) Gt. Brit.	51.42 N	4.10 W
126	Llanes (lyä′näs)...............Sp.	43.26 N	4.45 W
80	Llano (lä′nō) (lyä′nō).........Tex.	30.45 N	98.40 W
78	Llano Estacado (Plain) (lä′nô ĕs-tȧ-kä′dō) N. M.-Tex.	33.45 N	103.0 W
80	Llano R.....................Tex.	30.40 N	99.5 W
92	Llera (lyā′rä)...............Mex.	23.19 N	99.2 W
92	Llera, R....................Mex.	23.18 N	99.0 W
126	Llerena (lyā-rā′nȧ)...........Sp.	38.15 N	6.1 W
116	Lleyn Pen. (lĭn)..........Gt. Brit.	52.55 N	4.45 W
127	Llobregat R. (lyô-brē-gät′)....Sp.	41.55 N	1.55 E
163	Llorente (lyō-rĕn′tā)..........P. I.	11.24 N	125.32 E
127	Lluchmayor (lyōōch-mä-yôr′)..Sp.	39.28 N	2.54 E
104	Llullaillaco (Vol.) (lyōō-lyī-lyä′kō) Arg.-Chl.	24.45 S	68.40 W
155	Loan (lō′än′)...............Chn.	27.16 N	115.36 E
140	Loange R. (lô-äŋ′gä)...Bel.Cong.	6.15 S	19.45 E
140	Loango (lô-äŋ′gō)....Fr. Eq. Afr.	4.40 S	11.58 E
155	Lo-an R.....................Chn.	28.56 N	116.48 E
104	Loa, R. (lō′ȧ)...............Chl.	22.25 S	69.0 W
163	Loay (lô-ī′)..................P. I.	9.36 N	124.2 E
122	Löbau (lû′bou)..............Ger.	51.7 N	14.41 E
140	Lobito (lô-bē′tō)............Ang.	12.15 S	13.37 E
162	Lobo (lō′bō).................P. I.	13.38 N	121.12 E
163	Loboc (lō′bōk)...............P. I.	9.38 N	124.2 E
99	Lobos (lō′bōs) Arg. (Buenos Aires In.)	35.7 S	59.5 W
96	Lobos Cay (I.)...............W. I.	22.21 N	77.36 W
93	Lobos I.....................Mex.	21.26 N	97.13 W
102	Lobos Is. ....Peru	6.30 S	79.59 W
122	Locarno (lô-kär′nō).........Switz.	46.11 N	8.46 E
154	Locheng (lō′chĕng′)..........Chn.	24.45 N	108.56 E
124	Loches (lōsh)..................Fr.	47.9 N	1.0 E
83	Lochloosa, L. (lŏḳ-lō′sȧ)......Fla.	29.32 N	82.10 W
70	Lochsa R. (lŏḳ′sȧ)...........Ida.	46.24 N	115.12 W
116	Lochy, Loch (L.) (lŏḳ lŏḳ′ĭ) Gt. Brit.	56.55 N	5.0 W
86	Lockeport (lŏk′pōrt)..........Can.	43.45 N	65.5 W
167	Lockhart (lŏk′härt)........Austl.	35.14 S	146.44 E
83	Lockhart...................S. C.	34.46 N	81.28 W
81	Lockhart....................Tex.	29.53 N	97.40 W
85	Lock Haven (lŏk′ hā-vĕn) .....Pa.	41.6 N	77.37 W
84	Lockport (lŏk′pōrt)...........Ill.	41.36 N	88.2 W
85	Lockport...................N. Y.	43.11 N	78.41 W
82	Locust Fork (R.) (lō′kŭst)....Ala.	33.55 N	86.40 W
166	Loddon R. (lŏd′ŭn)........Austl.	37.0 S	143.40 E
112	Lodeinoe Pole (lô′dä-nô-yĕ pôl′yĕ) Sov. Un.	60.45 N	33.30 E
124	Lodève (lô-dĕv′)...............Fr.	43.42 N	3.17 E
78	Lodge Pole Cr. (lŏj′pōl) Neb.-Wyo.	41.12 N	103.40 W
74	Lodi (lō′dī)................Calif.	38.7 N	121.18 W
128	Lodi (lô′dē)....................It..	45.17 N	9.30 E
123	Lódz (wōōdzh)...............Pol.	51.46 N	19.30 E
127	Loeches (lô-āch′ĕs).......Sp. (In.)	40.23 N	3.26 W
142	Loeriesfontein (lōō′rēz-fŏn-tān′) U. S. Afr.	30.59 S	19.28 E
110	Lofoten Is. (lô′fō-tĕn).........Nor.	68.10 N	14.0 E
169	Loftus (lŏf′tŭs)Austl. (Sydney In.)	34.3 S	151.3 E
166	Lofty, Mt. (lŏf′tĭ)..........Austl.	34.59 S	138.45 E
169	Logan (lō′gȧn)........Austl. (In.)	27.45 S	153.6 E
84	Logan......................Ohio	39.34 N	82.24 W
71	Logan......................Utah	41.45 N	111.51 W
84	Logan......................W. Va.	37.50 N	82.0 W
54	Logan, Mt...................Can.	60.48 N	140.28 W
73	Logan Pk. Utah (Salt Lake City In.)	41.43 N	111.43 W
169	Logan R..............Austl. (In.)	28.0 S	152.59 E
73	Logan R..Utah (Salt Lake City In.)	41.44 N	111.48 W
84	Logansport...................Ind.	40.47 N	86.25 W
73	Loganville.......Ga. (Atlanta In.)	33.50 N	83.54 W
139	Logone R. (lō-gō′nä) (lô-gôn′) Fr. Eq. Afr.	10.0 N	15.40 E
138	Logoualé (lô-gwȧ-lä′)..Fr. W. Afr.	7.21 N	7.33 W
126	Logroño (lô-grō′nyō)...........Sp.	42.27 N	2.25 W
126	Logrosán (lô-grô-sän′).........Sp.	39.22 N	5.29 W
120	Løgstør (lŭgh-stûr′).........Den.	56.57 N	9.19 E
119	Lohe-Tonndorf (lō′hē-tŏn′dôrf) Ger. (Hamburg In.)	53.35 N	10.8 E
124	Loire R. (lwȧr)................Fr.	47.55 N	2.0 E
124	Loir R. (lwȧr).................Fr.	47.40 N	0.25 E
102	Loja (lō′hä)....................Ec.	4.2 S	79.3 W
126	Loja..........................Sp.	37.10 N	4.9 W
154	Lokchong (lŏk′chŏng′).......Chn.	25.13 N	112.50 E
131	Lokhvitsa (lôḳ-vēt′sȧ)....Sov. Un.	50.21 N	33.19 E
138	Lokoja (lô-kō′yä)............Nig.	7.57 N	6.41 E
119	Lokstedt (lŏk′shtĕt) Ger. (Hamburg In.)	53.36 N	9.57 E
156	Loling (lō′lĭng′)............Chn.	37.55 N	117.1 E
120	Lolland (I.) (lŏl′än′)........Den.	54.45 N	11.30 E
138	Lolo (lō′lō)................Cam.	3.15 N	10.38 E
139	Lol R. (lŏl)...........A. E. Sud.	9.0 N	28.0 E
129	Lom (lŏm)..................Bul.	43.48 N	23.12 E
140	Lomami R. (lô-mä′mê).Bel. Cong.	5.0 S	25.3 E
99	Lomas B. (lō′mäs) Chl. (Magallanes In.)	52.35 S	69.0 W
104	Lomas de Zamora (lō′mäs dā zä-mō′rä).Arg. (In.)	34.45 S	58.23 W
143	Lomati R. (lô-mä′tē)....U. S. Afr.	25.40 S	31.32 E
128	Lombardy (Prov.) (lŏm′bȧr-dĭ) It.	45.15 N	9.30 E
161	Lomblen (I.) (lŏm-blĕn′) Neth. Ind.	8.20 S	123.45 E
160	Lombok (I.)(lŏm-bŏk′)..Neth.Ind.	8.45 S	116.20 E
160	Lombok Str...........Neth. Ind.	8.30 S	115.45 E
138	Lomé (lō-mā′) (lō′mā).Fr. W. Afr.	6.11 N	1.12 E
140	Lomela (lō-mā′lȧ)......Bel. Cong.	2.20 S	23.40 E
140	Lomela R..............Bel. Cong.	1.12 S	22.0 E
80	Lometa (lô-mē′tȧ)............Tex.	31.10 N	98.25 W
139	Lomié (lō-mê-ā′).............Cam.	3.12 N	13.35 E
116	Lomond, Loch (L.) (lŏḳ lō′mŭnd) Gt. Brit.	56.10 N	4.40 W
74	Lompoc (lŏm-pōk′).........Calif.	34.38 N	120.30 W
123	Lomza (lôm′zhȧ)..............Pol.	53.9 N	22.3 E
85	Lonaconing (lō-nȧ-kō′nĭng)...Md.	39.34 N	79.0 W
55	London (lŭn′dŭn)............Can.	43.2 N	81.30 W
119	London, Gr. Brit. (In.)		
116	London................Gt. Brit.	51.25 N	0.20 E
82	London......................Ky.	37.7 N	84.7 W
84	London.....................Ohio	39.52 N	83.29 W
86	Londonderry (lŭn′dŭn-dĕr-ĭ) .Can.	45.29 N	63.37 W
116	Londonderry..........Gt.Brit.	55.0 N	7.20 E
164	Londonderry, C.............Austl.	13.45 S	127.0 E
85	Lonely I....................Can.	45.34 N	81.26 W
72	Lonetree Res. (lōn′trē′) Colo. (Denver In.)	40.20 N	105.7 W
140	Longa R. (lôŋ′gȧ)............Ang.	10.20 S	15.0 E
74	Long Beach.................Calif.	33.47 N	118.11 W
85	Long Branch................N. J.	40.20 N	74.0 W
49	Long Branch..Wash. (Seattle In.)	47.11 N	122.46 W
118	Long Eaton (ē′tŭn)......Gt. Brit.	52.54 N	1.17 W
119	Longfield (lông′fēld)......Gt. Brit.	51.24 N	0.18 E
169	Longford (lông′fērd) Austl. (Tas. In.)	41.37 S	147.7 E
116	Longford.....................Ire.	53.40 N	7.47 W
97	Long I....................Ba. Is.	23.20 N	75.9 W
86	Long I.......................Can.	44.30 N	66.20 W
161	Long I................N. Gui. Ter.	5.20 S	147.5 E
85	Long Is.....................N. Y.	39.50 N	73.0 W
171	Long I......................N. Z.	47.13 S	167.28 E
88	Long Island City.......N. Y. (In.)	40.46 N	73.54 W
85	Long Island Sd.........Conn.-N. Y.	41.10 N	72.30 W
125	Longjumeau (lôɴ-zhü-mō′) Fr. (In.)	48.41 N	2.20 E
76	Longlake....................S. D.	45.53 N	99.10 W
56	Long L.......Can. (Winnipeg In.)	50.6 N	97.57 W
86	Long L......................Me.	47.12 N	68.16 W
76	Long L......................N. D.	46.45 N	100.5 W
78	Longmont (lông′mŏnt).......Colo.	40.10 N	105.8 W
118	Longnor (lông′nôr)........Gt. Brit.	53.11 N	1.52 W
161	Longos (lôŋ′gōs).P. I. (Manila In.)	14.20 N	121.33 E
76	Long Pine...................Neb.	42.32 N	99.41 W
85	Long Pt.....................Can.	42.33 N	80.5 W
87	Long Pt.....................Newf.	48.47 N	58.45 W
163	Long Pt......................P. I.	9.38 N	118.20 E
85	Long Point B................Can.	42.40 N	80.10 W
77	Long Prairie................Minn.	45.56 N	94.50 W
87	Long Ra....................Newf.	50.5 N	57.30 W
165	Longreach (lông′rēch).......Austl.	23.30 S	144.15 E
86	Long Reach (B.).............N. B.	45.30 N	66.0 W
118	Longridge (lông′rĭj).......Gt. Brit.	53.50 N	2.37 W
78	Longs Peak..................Colo.	40.16 N	105.36 W
118	Longton (lông′tŭn).......Gt. Brit.	52.59 N	2.8 W
86	Longueuil (lôɴ-gû′y′)........Can.	45.32 N	73.39 W
125	Longuyon (lôɴ-gwē-yôɴ′).......Fr.	49.30 N	5.38 E
73	Longview (lông′vū) Ala. (Birmingham In.)	33.13 N	86.46 W
81	Longview....................Tex.	32.29 N	94.45 W
70	Longview...................Wash.	46.8 N	122.56 W
81	Longville (lông′vĭl)...........La.	30.36 N	93.15 W
125	Longwy (lôɴ-wē′)..............Fr.	49.35 N	5.45 E
79	Lonoke (lō′nōk)..............Ark.	34.47 N	91.52 W
125	Lons-le-Saunier (lôɴ-lē-sō-nyā′) Fr.	46.40 N	5.30 E
162	Looc (lô-ōk′).................P. I.	12.16 N	122.0 E
161	Looc B...........P. I. (Manila In.)	14.15 N	120.33 E
84	Loogootie (lō-gō′tē)..........Ind.	38.42 N	86.57 W
83	Lookout, C. (lŏŏk′out).......N. C.	34.36 N	76.33 W
169	Lookout, Mt.........Austl. (In.)	30.25 S	152.35 E
163	Loon (lô-ōn′).................P. I.	9.47 N	123.49 E
116	Loop Hd.......................Ire.	52.35 N	9.55 W
124	Loos (lō-ōs′)...................Fr.	50.37 N	3.0 E
83	Loosahatchie R. (lōz-ȧ-hă′chē) Tenn.	35.18 N	89.40 W
149	Lopatka, C. (lô-pät′kȧ)...Sov. Un.	50.50 N	156.50 E
162	Lopez (lō′päz)................P. I.	13.53 N	122.15 E
72	Lopez.....Wash. (Vancouver In.)	48.32 N	122.55 W
162	Lopez B.......................P. I.	14.0 N	122.5 E
72	Lopez I....Wash. (Vancouver In.)	48.30 N	122.54 W
155	Loping (lō′pĭng′)............Chn.	29.2 N	117.6 E
152	Lop Nor (L.) (lŏp nōr′)......Chn.	40.0 N	90.0 E
139	Lopori R. (lō-pō′rē)....Bel. Cong.	1.30 N	21.0 E
126	Lora (lō′rä)...................Sp.	37.40 N	5.3 W
84	Lorain (lô-rān′)..............Ohio	41.27 N	82.9 W

ăt; finȧl; rāte; senâte; ärm; ȧsk; sofȧ; fâre; ch-choose; dh-as th in other; bē; ēvent; bĕt; recĕnt; cratēr; g-go; gh-guttural g; bĭt; ĭ-short neutral; rīde; ḳ-guttural k as ch in German ich;

Page	Name Pronunciation Region	Lat. °′	Long. °′
151	Loralai (lō-rŭ-lī')..........India	30.30 N	68.38 E
126	Lorca (lôr'kä)..........Sp.	37.40 N	1.41 W
165	Lord Howe I. (hou).......Pac. O.	31.46 S	159.8 E
75	Lordsburg (lôrdz'bûrg).....N. M.	32.22 N	108.43 W
99	Lorena (lō-rā'nȧ) Braz. (Rio de Janeiro In.)	22.46 S	45.7 W
103	Loreta (lō-rā'tō)..........Braz.	7.2 S	45.20 W
57	Lorette (lō-rĕt') Can. (Quebec In.)	46.48 N	71.21 W
102	Lorica (lō-rē'kä)..........Col.	9.5 N	75.45 W
124	Lorient (lō-rē'äɴ')..........Fr.	47.48 N	3.12 W
116	Lorne, Firth of (lôrn)....Gt. Brit.	56.15 N	5.50 W
166	Lorquon (lôr'kôn)..........Austl.	36.8 S	141.49 E
122	Lörrach (lûr'äĸ)..........Ger.	47.37 N	7.40 E
73	Los Alamitos (lōs ăl-ȧ-mē'tōs) Calif. (Los Angeles In.)	33.49 N	118.4 W
104	Los Andes (State) (lōs än'dās) Arg.	25.0 S	67.30 W
99	Los Andes...Chl. (Valparaiso In.)	32.50 S	70.38 W
73	Los Angeles (lōs ăŋ'gĕl-ĕs) (lōs ăn'jĕl-ĕs) (lōs äŋ'hā-lās) Calif. (Los Angeles In.)	34.3 N	118.15 W
74	Los Angeles..........Calif.	34.5 N	118.20 W
104	Los Angeles (lōs äŋ'hā-lās)...Chl.	37.20 S	72.29 W
74	Los Angeles Aqueduct......Calif.	35.0 N	118.12 W
73	Los Angeles R. Calif. (Los Angeles In.)	33.53 N	118.13 W
161	Los Baños (lōs bä'nyōs) P. I. (Manila In.)	14.12 N	121.15 E
126	Los Barrios (lōs bär'rē-ōs).....Sp.	36.11 N	5.29 W
160	Loser, Mt. (lōs'ĕr).....Neth. Ind.	3.42 N	97.20 E
74	Los Gatos (lōs gä'tōs)........Calif.	37.13 N	121.59 W
156	Loshan (lō'shän')..........Chn.	32.15 N	114.25 E
80	Los Herreros (lōs ĕr-rā-rōs)..Mex.	25.55 N	99.23 W
130	Losinoostrovskaya (lô'sē-nō-ōs'-trôf-skä'yä)...Sov. Un.	55.51 N	37.41 E
97	Los Llanos (lōs lyä'nōs)......Hai.	18.36 N	69.30 W
73	Los Nietos (lōs nyā'tōs) Calif. (Los Angeles In.)	33.57 N	118.5 W
123	Losoncz (Lučenec) (lō'shônts) (lōō'chā-nyĕts).Hung.	48.19 N	19.42 E
96	Los Organos Mts. (lōs ôr'gä-nōs) Cuba	22.40 N	83.12 W
96	Los Palacios (lōs pä-lä'sē-ōs) Cuba	22.32 N	83.14 W
75	Los Pinos R. (lōs pē'nōs) Colo.-N. M.	37.0 N	107.35 W
92	Los Reyes (lōs rā'yĕs).......Mex.	19.29 N	102.29 W
95	Los Santos (lōs sän'tōs).......Pan.	7.56 N	80.24 W
126	Los Santos..........Sp.	38.28 N	6.21 W
73	Lost Cr. Utah (Salt Lake City In.)	41.7 N	111.30 W
99	Los Toldos (lōs tōl'dōs) Arg. (Buenos Aires In.)	35.1 S	61.3 W
71	Los R..........Ida.	44.3 N	113.50 W
70	Lost R..........Ore.	42.7 N	121.30 W
71	Lost River Mts..........Ida.	44.20 N	113.50 W
104	Los Vilos (lōs vē'lōs).....Chl.	31.59 S	71.32 W
104	Lota (lō'tä)..........Chl.	37.15 S	73.10 W
155	Lotien (lō'tyĕn')..........Chn.	30.48 N	115.20 E
154	Loting (lō'tĭng')..........Chn.	22.48 N	111.23 E
97	Lo Torro (Pk.) (lō tôr'rō)....Hai.	18.48 N	72.57 W
124	Lot R. (lō)..........Fr.	44.30 N	0.55 E
122	Lötschen Tunnel (lût'shĕn).Switz.	46.25 N	7.45 E
123	Lötzen (lût'sĕn)..........Ger.	54.3 N	21.49 E
160	Louangprabang (lōō-äng'-prä-bäng').Fr. Ind. Chn.	19.50 N	102.5 E
124	Loudon (lōō-dôɴ')..........Fr.	47.2 N	0.1 E
82	Loudon (lou'dŭn)..........Tenn.	35.44 N	84.23 W
84	Loudonville (lou'dŭn-vĭl).....Ohio	40.40 N	82.16 W
138	Louga (lōō'gä).......Fr. W. Afr.	15.33 N	16.20 W
116	Loughborough (lŭf'bŭr-ō) Gt. Brit.	52.45 N	1.15 W
119	Loughton (lou'tŭn) Gt. Brit. (London In.)	51.39 N	0.3 E
57	Louisa (lōō-ē'zȧ) Can. (Montreal In.)	45.47 N	74.22 W
84	Louisa..........Ky.	38.5 N	82.37 W
87	Louisburg..........Can.	45.55 N	60.0 W
83	Louisburg (lōō'ĭs-bûrg)....N. C.	36.6 N	78.18 W
165	Louisiade Arch. (lōō-ē-zē-äd') Pap. Ter.	11.0 S	153.30 E
79	Louisiana (lōō-ē-zē-ăn'ȧ).....Mo.	39.26 N	91.3 W
81	Louisiana (State)..........U. S.	31.0 N	92.0 W
140	Louis Trichardt (lōō'ĭs trĭch'ärt) U. S. Afr.	22.58 S	29.58 E
78	Louisville (lōō'ĭs-vĭl) (lōō'ē-vĭl) Colo.	39.57 N	105.9 W
83	Louisville..........Ga.	33.0 N	82.25 W
84	Louisville..........Ky.	38.15 N	85.45 W
82	Louisville..........Miss.	33.7 N	89.3 W
126	Loulé (lō-lā')..........Port.	37.8 N	8.2 W
122	Louny (lō'nē)..........Czech.	50.20 N	13.47 E
76	Loup City..........Neb.	41.17 N	98.58 W
76	Loup R. (lōōp)..........Neb.	41.20 N	98.0 W
76	Loup R., North..........Neb.	41.50 N	99.30 W
124	Lourdes (lōōrd)..........Fr.	43.7 N	0.3 W
140	Lourenço Marques (lō-rĕn'sō mär'kĕs).Moz.	25.50 S	32.33 E
127	Loures (lō'rĕzh)........Port. (In.)	38.49 N	9.10 W
126	Lousa (lō'zȧ)..........Port.	40.6 N	8.15 W
116	Louth (louth)..........Gt. Brit.	53.20 N	0.0
117	Louvain (lōō-väɴ')..........Bel.	50.51 N	4.40 E
72	Louviers (lōō-vyā') (lōō-vērz') Colo. (Denver In.)	39.29 N	105.0 W
124	Louviers (lōō-vyā')..........Fr.	49.15 N	1.11 E
125	Louvres (lōōv'r')........Fr. (In.)	49.2 N	2.30 E
143	Louwsburg (lous'bŏŏrgh) U. S. Afr.	27.32 S	31.15 E
130	Lovat R. (lō-vät'y')....Sov. Un.	57.4 N	30.55 E
129	Loveč (lō'vĕts)..........Bul.	43.8 N	24.40 E
73	Lovejoy (lŭv'joi) Ga. (Atlanta In.)	33.27 N	84.18 W
78	Loveland (lŭv'lănd)..........Colo.	40.24 N	105.6 W
72	Loveland and Greeley Ditch Colo. (Denver In.)	40.23 N	104.55 W
71	Lovell (lŭv'ĕl)..........Wyo.	44.51 N	108.23 W
74	Lovelock (lŭv'lŏk)..........Nev.	40.11 N	118.28 W
121	Loviisa (lō'vē-sȧ)..........Fin.	60.28 N	26.11 E
6	Low (Tuamotou) Arch. (lō) (tōō-ä-mō'tōō).Pac. O.	17.0 S	145.0 W
140	Lowa R. (lō'wä).......Bel. Cong.	1.15 S	27.15 E
75	Lowell (lō'ĕl)..........Ariz.	31.26 N	109.53 W
84	Lowell..........Ind.	41.17 N	87.25 W
86	Lowell..........Mass.	42.40 N	71.20 W
84	Lowell..........Mich.	42.57 N	85.20 W
73	Lowe, Mt. (lō) Calif. (Los Angeles In.)	34.14 N	118.7 W
142	Lowen R. (lō'vĕn).....S. W. Afr.	27.0 S	17.52 E
54	Lower Arrow L..........Can.	49.50 N	118.1 W
76	Lower Brule Indian Res. (brū'lā) S. D.	44.7 N	99.58 W
170	Lower Hutt (hŭt).....N. Z. (In.)	41.12 S	174.55 E
70	Lower Klamath L. (klăm'ăth) Ore.-Calif.	41.59 N	121.49 W
70	Lower L..........Calif.-Nev.	41.15 N	120.3 W
74	Lower Otay Reservoir (ō'tā) Calif. (In.)	32.37 N	116.53 W
77	Lower Red L..........Minn.	47.57 N	95.0 W
117	Lowestoft (lō'stŏft)......Gt. Brit.	52.30 N	1.42 E
123	Lowicz (lô'vĭch)..........Pol.	52.5 N	19.57 E
119	Lowton (lō'tŭn) Gt. Brit. (Liverpool In.)	53.28 N	2.34 W
85	Lowville (lou'vĭl)..........N. Y.	43.47 N	75.28 W
93	Loxicha (San Agustin) (lō-zē'chä) (sän ä-gōōs-tēn').Mex.	16.3 N	96.46 W
166	Loxton (lŏks'tŭn)..........Austl.	34.26 S	140.35 E
165	Loyalty Is. (loi'ăl-tē).....N. Cal.	21.0 S	167.30 E
154	Loyung (lō'yōōng')..........Chn.	24.26 N	109.42 E
129	Loznica (lōz'nē-tsȧ)..........Yugo.	44.31 N	19.15 E
131	Lozovatka (lō-zō-vät'kä) Sov. Un.	48.3 N	33.16 E
131	Lozovaya (lō-zō-vä'yä)..Sov. Un.	48.54 N	36.18 E
131	Lozovaya-Pavlovka (päv-lôf'kä) Sov. Un.	48.26 N	38.47 E
127	Lozoya, Can. of (Aqueduct) (lō-thō-yä).Sp. (In.)	40.33 N	3.42 W
140	Lualaba-Congo R.......Bel. Cong.	4.30 S	26.30 E
140	Lualaba R. (lōō-ȧ-lä'bä) Bel. Cong.	9.12 S	25.38 E
140	Luama R. (lōō-ä'mä)...Bel. Cong.	4.30 S	28.15 E
140	Luanda (Dist.) (lōō-än'dä)...Ang.	9.15 S	15.45 E
140	Luanda (lōō-än'dȧ)..........Ang.	8.47 S	13.15 E
140	Luanginga R. (lōō-än-gĭŋ'gȧ) Ang.-N. Rh.	14.10 S	22.0 E
140	Luangwa R. (lōō-äŋ'gwȧ)..N. Rh.	12.47 S	32.0 E
140	Luapula R. (lōō-ä-pōō'lȧ) Bel. Cong.-N. Rh.	12.15 S	29.0 E
126	Luarca (lwär'kä)..........Sp.	43.34 N	6.35 W
123	Lubaczów (lōō-bä'chōōf).....Pol.	50.8 N	23.8 E
121	Lubanas, L. (lōō'bȧ-näs)......Lat.	56.46 N	26.55 E
162	Lubang (lōō-bäng')..........P. I.	13.50 N	120.7 E
162	Lubang I..........P. I.	13.45 N	120.10 E
162	Lubang Is..........P. I.	13.45 N	120.25 E
162	Lubao (lōō-bä'ō)..........P. I.	14.56 N	120.36 E
123	Lubartów (lōō-bär'tōōf)......Pol.	51.27 N	22.36 E
123	Lubawa (lōō-bä'vä)..........Pol.	53.31 N	19.48 E
78	Lubbock (lŭb'ŭk)..........Tex.	33.35 N	101.51 W
86	Lubec (lū'bĕk)..........Me.	44.50 N	67.2 W
122	Lübben (lüb'ĕn)..........Ger.	51.57 N	13.52 E
122	Lübeck (lü'bĕk)..........Ger.	53.53 N	101.41 E
122	Lübeck B..........Ger.	54.5 N	11.10 E
122	Lüben (lü'bĕn)..........Ger.	51.24 N	16.13 E
140	Lubilash R. (lōō-bē-läsh') Bel. Cong.	7.30 S	23.58 E
123	Lublin (lyōō'blēn')..........Pol.	51.13 N	22.32 E
131	Lubny (lōōb'nē).........Sov. Un.	50.1 N	33.1 E
126	Lubrín (lōō-brēn')..........Sp.	37.14 N	2.4 W
140	Lubudi R. (lōō-bōō'dē).Bel. Cong.	9.30 S	25.0 E
162	Lubungan (lōō-bōōŋ'gän)....P. I.	17.21 N	121.11 E
163	Lubungan (lōō-bōōŋ-gän)....P. I.	8.30 N	123.19 E
128	Lucca (lōōk'kä)..........It.	43.51 N	10.30 E
116	Luce B. (lūs)..........Gt. Brit.	54.45 N	4.40 W
162	Lucena (lōō-sä'nä)..........P. I.	13.56 N	121.37 E
126	Lucena (lōō-thā'nä)..........Sp.	37.25 N	4.29 W
127	Lucena de Cid (lōō-thā'nä-dā-thēdh').Sp.	40.8 N	0.19 W
...	Lučenec, see Losoncz, Hung.		
128	Lucera (lōō-châ'rä)..........It.	41.30 N	15.21 E
72	Lucerne (lû-sûrn') Colo. (Denver In.)	40.28 N	104.42 W
	Lucerne, see Luzern, Switz.		
	Lucerne, L. of (lü-sĕrn') (lōō-tsĕrn').Switz.	46.59 N	8.30 E
156	Lucheng (lōō'chĕng')..........Chn.	36.30 N	113.24 E
152	Luchow (lōō'chō')..........Chn.	20.0 N	105.20 E
154	Luchow (Liuchow)..........Chn.	24.22 N	109.30 E
156	Lüchow (lü'chō')..........Chn.	31.51 N	117.9 E
71	Lucin (lû-sēn')..........Utah	41.22 N	113.54 W
161	Lucipara Is. (lōō-sē-pä'rä) Neth. Ind.	5.30 S	127.45 E
123	Luck (wōōtsk)..........Pol.	50.45 N	25.20 E
122	Luckenwalde (lōōk-ĕn-väl'dē).Ger.	52.6 N	13.9 E
143	Luckhoff (lōōk'hôf)......U. S. Afr.	29.41 S	24.49 E
151	Lucknow (lŭk'nou)..........India	26.46 N	80.59 E
124	Luçon (lü-sôɴ')..........Fr.	46.28 N	1.11 W
94	Lucrecia Pt. (lōō-krā'sē-ä)...Cuba	21.4 N	75.36 W
122	Lüdenscheid (lü'dĕn-shīt).....Ger.	51.13 N	7.37 E
142	Lüderitz (lü'dĕr-ĭts) (lōō'dĕr-ĭts) S. W. Afr.	26.38 S	15.12 E
140	Lüderitz B..........S. W. Afr.	26.30 S	15.5 E
84	Ludington (lŭd'ĭng-tŭn).....Mich.	44.0 N	86.28 W
118	Ludlow (lŭd'lō).........Gt. Brit.	52.22 N	2.43 W
89	Ludlow......Ky. (Cincinnati In.)	39.6 N	84.33 W
120	Ludvika (lōōdh-vē'kä)........Swe.	60.10 N	15.11 E
122	Ludwigsburg (lōōt'vēks-bōōrgh) Ger.	48.54 N	9.13 E
122	Ludwigshafen (lōōt'vēks-hä'fĕn) Ger.	49.28 N	8.25 E
122	Ludwigslust (lōōt'vēks-lōōst)..Ger.	53.19 N	11.30 E
121	Ludza (lōōd'zä)..........Lat.	56.31 N	27.42 E
140	Luebo (lōō-ā'bō).......Bel. Cong.	5.20 S	21.20 E
140	Lufira R. (lōō-fē'rä)....Bel. Cong.	10.0 S	27.12 E
81	Lufkin (lŭf'kĭn)..........Tex.	31.21 N	94.45 W
130	Luga (lōō'gä).........Sov. Un.	58.42 N	29.52 E
122	Lugano (lōō-gä'nō)........Switz.	46.1 N	8.56 E
...	Lugansk, see Vorichilovgrad Sov. Un.		
130	Luga R..........Sov. Un.	59.4 N	29.20 E
118	Lugg R. (lŭg)..........Gt. Brit.	52.9 N	2.42 W
141	Lugh (lōōg)..........It. E. Afr.	3.47 N	42.38 E
128	Lugo (lōō'gō)..........It.	44.25 N	11.54 E
126	Lugo (lōō'gō)..........Sp.	43.1 N	7.33 W
129	Lugos (lōō'gōsh)..........Rom.	45.41 N	21.56 E
119	Lühe R. (lü'ĕ) Ger. (Hamburg In.)	53.30 N	9.33 E
156	Luho (lōō'hō')..........Chn.	32.22 N	118.48 E
140	Luilaka R. (lōō-ē-lä'kä).Bel. Cong.	1.52 S	21.0 E
154	Lui R. (lwē)..........Chn.	25.55 N	111.35 E
116	Luimneach (Limerick) (lĭm'năk) Ire.	52.38 N	8.58 W
161	Luisiana (lōō-ē-sē-ä'nä) P. I. (Manila In.)	14.12 N	121.35 E
46	Luitpold Land (lût'pôld).....Ant.	78.0 S	20.0 W
99	Luján (lōō-hän') Arg. (Buenos Aires In.)	34.32 S	59.9 W
141	Lujenda R. (lōō-zhĕn'dȧ)....Moz.	12.15 S	37.30 E
140	Lukanga Swamp lōō-käŋ'gȧ) N. Rh.	14.15 S	27.45 E
140	Lukenie R. (lōō-kā'nyā) Bel. Cong.	3.12 S	20.0 E
155	Lukfung (lōōk'fōōng')..........Chn.	22.56 N	115.30 E
154	Luki (lōō'kē')..........Chn.	28.11 N	109.48 E
155	Lukiang (lōō'kyăng')..........Chn.	31.15 N	117.19 E
141	Lukigura (R.) (.ōō-kē-gōō'rȧ).Tan.	6.0 S	37.54 E
140	Lukolele (lōō-kō-lā'lä)..Bel. Cong.	1.12 S	17.18 E
129	Lukovit (lōō'kō-vēt')..........Bul.	43.12 N	24.9 E
123	Luków (wōō'kōōf)..........Pol.	51.56 N	22.23 E
140	Lukuga R. (lōō-kōō'gȧ).Bel. Cong.	5.55 S	28.15 E
110	Luleå (lōō'lĕ-ō)..........Swe.	65.38 N	22.0 E
129	Lüleburgaz (lü'lĕ-bōōr-gäs')..Tur.	41.24 N	27.22 E
141	Luli (Lúrio) (lōō'lē) (lōō'rē-ō).Moz.	14.9 S	38.0 E
81	Luling (lū'lĭng)..........Tex.	29.41 N	97.38 W
140	Luluabourg (lōō'lōō-ȧ-bōōrg') Bel. Cong.	6.15 S	22.25 E
140	Lulua R. (lōō'lōō-ȧ)....Bel. Cong.	7.0 S	22.30 E
72	Lulu I. (lū'lōō) Can. (Vancouver In.)	49.9 N	123.11 W
161	Lumban (lōōm-bän') P. I. (Manila In.)	14.17 N	121.32 E
83	Lumber R..........N. C.	34.50 N	79.20 W
82	Lumberton (lŭm'bĕr-tŭn)...Miss.	31.0 N	89.27 W
83	Lumberton..........N. C.	34.36 N	78.59 W
140	Lumbira (lōōm-bē'rȧ)........Tan.	9.32 S	34.10 E
72	Lummi I. (lŭm'ĭ) Wash. (Vancouver In.)	48.41 N	122.40 W
162	Luna (lōō'nä)..........P. I.	16.51 N	120.23 E
120	Lund (lŭnd)..........Swe.	55.42 N	13.10 E
140	Lunda (Dist.) (lōōn'dä)......Ang.	9.15 S	20.15 E
122	Lundenburg (Břeclav) (lōōn'dĕn-bōōrk) (brzhĕl'läf).Ger.	48.47 N	16.53 E
140	Lundi R. (lōōn'dē).......S. Rho.	20.52 S	31.0 E
116	Lundy (I.) (lŭn'dē)....Gt. Brit.	51.10 N	4.40 W
122	Lüneburg (lü'nē-bōōrgh).....Ger.	53.16 N	10.23 E
122	Lüneburger Heide (Moorlands) (lü'nē-bōōr-gĕr hī'dē).Ger.	53.0 N	10.2 E
124	Lunel (lü-nĕl')..........Fr.	43.40 N	4.9 E
86	Lunenburg (lōō'nĕn-bûrg)....Can.	44.25 N	64.15 W
87	Lunenburg..........Mass. (In.)	42.36 N	71.43 W
118	Lune, R. (lūn)..........Gt. Brit.	54.6 N	2.39 W
125	Luneville (lü-nä-vēl')..........Fr.	48.38 N	6.30 E
154	Lungan (looŋ'gän')..........Chn.	23.12 N	107.48 E
140	Lunga R. (lōōŋ'gä).......N. Rho.	13.0 S	26.30 E
158	Lungchen (lōōng'chĕn)....Manch.	48.45 N	126.50 E
158	Lungchingtsun (lōōng'chĭng'tsōōn') Manch.	42.47 N	129.27 E
154	Lungchow (lōōng'chō')........Chn.	22.27 N	106.49 E
154	Lungchuan (lōōng'chōō-än').Chn.	26.38 N	113.54 E
154	Lungchüan (lōōng'chü-än').Chn.	27.51 N	107.48 E
155	Lungchun (lōōng'chōōn')....Chn.	24.4 N	115.0 E
140	Lunge Bungo R. (lŭn'gä bŭn'gō) Ang.-N. Rho.	13.20 S	22.0 E
152	Lungein-Bulan (lōōŋ-gän'-bōō-län').Chn.	47.42 N	105.4 E
155	Lungkang L. (lōōng'käng')...Chn.	29.55 N	116.8 E
153	Lungkiang (Tsitsihar) (lōōng'-kyäng') (tsĕt-sē-här').Manch.	47.28 N	123.57 E
156	Lungkow (lōōng'kō')........Chn.	37.42 N	120.15 E
154	Lungli (lōōng'lē')..........Chn.	26.25 N	106.49 E
154	Lungmoon (lōōng'mōōn')....Chn.	23.46 N	114.12 E
155	Lungnan (lōōng'nän')........Chn.	24.47 N	114.15 E
156	Lungping (lōōng'pĭng')........Chn.	37.26 N	114.54 E
154	Lung R. (lōōng)..........Chn.	24.35 N	108.20 E
154	Lungshan (lōōng'shän')......Chn.	29.22 N	109.3 E
155	Lungyen (lōōng'yĕn')........Chn.	25.10 N	116.50 E
155	Lungyu (lōōng'yōō')..........Chn.	29.2 N	119.17 E
123	Luniniec (wōō-nēn'yĕts)......Pol.	52.14 N	26.49 E
163	Lun R. (lōōn)..........P. I.	6.5 N	125.28 E
171	Lunsden (lŭnz'dĕn)........N. Z.	45.43 S	168.28 E
135	Luozi (lōō-ō'zē) Bel. Cong. (Brazzaville In.)	4.55 S	14.7 E
153	Lupei (lōō'pē)..........Manch.	44.35 N	121.0 E
153	Lupin (Manchouli) (lōō'pĭn') (män-chōō'lē).Chn.	49.34 N	117.28 E
139	Luqsor (lŭk'sôr)..........Eg.	25.40 N	32.40 E
104	Luque (lōō'kä)..........Par.	25.15 S	57.30 W
85	Luray (lū-rā')..........Va.	38.39 N	78.28 W
125	Lure (lür)..........Fr.	47.43 N	6.29 E
116	Lurgan (lûr'găn)..........Gt. Brit.	54.25 N	6.25 W
102	Lurigancho (lōō-rē-gän'chō) Peru (In.)	12.1 S	77.0 W
141	Lúrio (Luli) R. (lōō'rē-ō) (lōō'lē) Moz.	14.9 S	38.0 E
119	Lurup (lōō-rōōp') Ger. (Hamburg In.)	53.35 N	9.52 E
140	Lusaka (lōō-sä'kȧ)........N. Rh.	15.27 S	28.17 E
140	Lusambo (lōō-säm'bō).Bel. Cong.	4.52 S	23.30 E
141	Lushoto (lōō-shō'tō)..........Tan.	4.47 S	38.17 E
156	Lushun (Riojun) (Port Arthur) (lōō'shŭn)..Kwan.	38.51 N	121.7 E
143	Lusikisiki (lōō-sē-kē-sē'kē) U. S. Afr.	31.21 S	29.32 E
76	Lusk (lŭsk)..........Wyo.	42.47 N	104.28 W
128	Lussino (L.) (lōōs-sē'nō).......It.	44.35 N	14.24 E
128	Lussinpiccolo (lōōs-sēn'pĕk'kō-lō) It.	44.31 N	14.29 E

ng-sing; ŋ-baŋk; ɴ-nasalized n; nŏd; cŏmmit; ōld; ôbey; ôrder; fōōd; fŏŏt; ou-out; s-soft; sh-dish; th-thin; pūre; ûnite; ûrn; stŭd; circŭs; ü-as "y" in study; '-indeterminate vowel.

Page	Name Pronunciation	Region	Lat. °′	Long. °′
81	Lutcher (lŭch'ẽr)	La.	30.3 N	90.42 W
122	Lutherstadt (Wittenberg) (lo͞o'tĕr-stät) (vĭt'ĕn bĕrk)	Ger.	51.53 N	12.40 E
116	Luton (lū'tŭn)	Gt. Brit.	51.55 N	0.20 W
82	Luverne (lû-vûrn')	Ala.	31.42 N	86.16 W
76	Luverne	Minn.	43.39 N	96.3 W
140	Luvua R. (lo͞o'vo͞o-ȧ)	Bel. Cong.	7.45 S	28.0 E
140	Luvungi (lo͞o-vo͞oŋ'gē)	Bel. Cong.	2.53 S	28.58 E
82	Luxapallila R. (lŭk-sȧ-pôl'ĭ-lȧ)	Ala.	33.35 N	88.0 W
125	Luxembourg (lŭk-sĕm-bûrg) (lük-säɴ-bo͞or') (lo͝ok'sĕm-bo͝orgh)	Eur.	49.50 N	6.0 E
125	Luxeuil (lük-sû'y')	Fr.	47.50 N	6.20 E
90	Luyanó (lo͞o-yä-nō')	Cuba (Habana In.)	23.7 N	82.20 W
90	Luyanó R.	Cuba (Habana In.)	23.6 N	82.20 W
112	Luza R. (lo͞o'zä)	Sov. Un.	60.40 N	47.30 E
122	Luzern (lo͞o-tsĕrn') (City and Lake)	Switz.	47.3 N	8.17 E
162	Luzon (I.) (lo͞o-zŏn')	P. I.	15.35 N	120.45 E
156	Lwancheng (lwän'chĕng')	Chn.	37.57 N	114.42 E
156	Lwanchow (lwän'chō')	Chn.	39.50 N	118.43 E
123	Lwów (Lemberg) (lvo͝of) (lĕm'bĕrgh)	Pol.	49.49 N	24.2 E
149	Lyakhovskie (Is.) (lyȧ'kôf-skē)	Sov. Un.	73.30 N	142.0 E
170	Lyall B. (lī'ăl)	N. Z. (In.)	41.20 S	174.49 E
123	Lyck (lĭk)	Ger.	53.50 N	22.22 E
145	Lydda (lĭd'ȧ)	Pal. (In.)	31.58 N	34.54 E
143	Lydenburg (lī'dĕn-bûrg)	U. S. Afr.	25.8 S	30.25 E
119	Lydgate (lĭd'gāt)	Gt. Brit. (Liverpool In.)	53.32 N	2.57 W
169	Lyell, Mt. (lī'ĕl)	Austl. (Tas. In.)	42.1 S	145.39 E
74	Lyell, Mt.	Calif.	37.44 N	119.17 W
85	Lykens (lī'kĕnz)	Pa.	40.32 N	76.45 W
911	Lymm (lĭm)	Gt. Brit. (Liverpool In.)	53.22 N	2.28 W
82	Lynch (lĭnch)	Ky.	36.57 N	82.56 W
85	Lynchburg (lĭnch'bûrg)	Va.	37.25 N	79.10 W
83	Lynches R. (lĭn'chĕz)	S. C.	34.10 N	80.10 W
70	Lynden (lĭn'dĕn)	Wash.	48.56 N	122.28 W
166	Lyndhurst (lĭnd'hûrst)	Austl.	30.19 S	138.21 E
86	Lyndonville (lĭn'dŭn-vĭl)	Vt.	44.32 N	72.0 W
86	Lynn (lĭn)	Mass.	42.29 N	70.59 W
124	Lyon (lē-ôɴ)	Fr.	45.45 N	4.50 E
72	Lyons (lī'ŭnz)	Colo. (Denver In.)	40.14 N	105.17 W
83	Lyons	Ga.	32.8 N	82.17 W
88	Lyons	Ill. (Chicago In.)	41.49 N	87.48 W
78	Lyons	Kan.	38.21 N	98.12 W
76	Lyons	Neb.	41.57 N	96.28 W
85	Lyons	N. Y.	43.5 N	76.58 W
55	Lyon Str. (lī'ŭn)	Can.	62.48 N	81.30 W
120	Lyse Fjord (lü'sĕ fyōr')	Nor.	59.0 N	6.18 E
120	Lysekil (lü'sĕ-kēl)	Swe.	58.17 N	11.22 E
123	Lysogóry (Mts.) (wē-sō-go͞o'rē)	Pol.	50.56 N	21.0 E
118	Lytham (lĭth'ăm)	Gt. Brit.	53.44 N	2.58 W
171	Lyttelton (lĭt''l-tŭn)	N. Z. (In.)	43.35 S	172.44 E
171	Lyttelton, Port	N. Z. (In.)	43.35 S	172.46 E
54	Lytton (lĭt'ŭn)	Can.	50.9 N	121.25 W
130	Lyuban (lyo͞o'bȧn)	Sov. Un.	59.20 N	31.18 E
131	Lyubar (lyo͞o'bär)	Sov. Un.	49.56 N	27.46 E
130	Lyubertsi (lyo͞o'bĕr-tsē)	Sov. Un.	55.41 N	37.58 E
130	Lyubim (lyo͞o-bêm')	Sov. Un.	58.21 N	40.41 E
130	Lyudinovo (lyo͞o-dē-nô'vō)	Sov. Un.	53.51 N	34.24 E
50	Ma'an (mä-än')	Transj.	30.15 N	35.45 E
121	Maarianhamina (Mariehamn) (mä're-ȧn-hä-mē-nȧ) (mä-rē'ĕ-häm''n)	Fin.	60.8 N	19.58 E
120	Maarvand (L.) (môr'vän)	Nor.	60.10 N	8.15 E
163	Maasin (mä-ä'sĭn)	P. I.	10.8 N	124.51 E
117	Maastricht (mäs'trĭkt)	Bel.	50.50 N	5.40 E
81	Mabank (mā'bănk)	Tex.	32.22 N	96.7 W
161	Mabatan (mä-bä-tän')	P. I. (Manila In.)	14.43 N	120.28 E
162	Mabini (mä-bē'nē)	P. I.	13.44 N	120.56 E
163	Mabini	P. I.	9.51 N	124.31 E
161	Mabitao (mä-bē-tä'ō)	P. I. (Manila In.)	14.27 N	121.30 E
73	Mableton (mā'b'l-tŭn)	Ga. (Atlanta In.)	33.48 N	84.35 W
114	Mabrouk (mȧ-bro͞ok')	Alg.	29.20 N	0.20 E
138	Mabrouk	Fr. W. Afr.	19.30 N	1.15 W
143	Mabula (mä-bo͞o'lȧ)	Bech.	25.47 S	24.34 E
161	Macabebe (mä-kä-bā'bā)	P. I. (Manila In.)	14.54 N	120.38 E
86	McAdam (măk-ăd'ăm)	Can.	45.36 N	67.21 W
103	Macaé (mä-kä-ā')	Braz.	22.18 S	41.50 W
163	Macajalar B. (mä-kä-hä-lär')	P. I.	8.35 N	124.40 E
162	Macalelon (mä-kä-lā-lōn')	P. I.	13.45 N	122.8 E
79	Mc Alester (măk ăl'ĕs-tẽr)	Okla.	34.56 N	95.45 W
169	Macalister (măk-ăl'ĭs-tẽr)	Austl. (In.)	27.4 S	151.3 E
139	Macalle (mä'kȧ-lā)	It. E. Afr.	13.30 N	39.30 E
80	McAllen (măk-ăl'ĕn)	Tex.	26.12 N	98.14 W
167	Macallister R. (măk-ăl'ĭs-tẽr)	Austl.	37.52 S	146.45 E
103	Macapá (mä-kä-pä')	Braz.	0.1 S	51.1 W
160	Macassar Str. (Makasser) (mȧ-käs'ȧr)	Neth. Ind.	2.0 S	118.30 E
80	McCamey (mă-kā'mĭ)	Tex.	31.7 N	102.15 W
154	Macau (mȧ-kä'o͞o)	Chn.	22.7 N	113.10 E
103	Macau	Braz.	5.5 S	36.31 W
154	Macau	Macau	22.7 N	113.10 E
82	McCaysville (mă-kāz'vĭl)	Ga.	34.57 N	84.21 W
116	Macclesfield (măk''lz-fēld)	Gt. Brit.	53.15 N	2.10 W
118	Macclesfield Can.	Gt. Brit.	53.15 N	2.7 W
161	MacCluer G. (mȧ-klo͞or')	Neth. Ind.	2.15 S	132.30 E
83	McColl (mȧ-kôl')	S. C.	34.38 N	79.32 W
82	McComb (mȧ-kōm')	Miss.	31.14 N	90.29 W
78	McCook (mȧ-ko͝ok')	Neb.	40.13 N	100.38 W
83	McCormick (mȧ-kôr'mĭk)	S. C.	33.55 N	82.18 W
164	Macdonald, L. (măk-dŏn'ăld)	Austl.	23.30 S	128.30 E
164	Macdonnell Ranges (măk-dŏn'ĕl)	Austl.	23.30 S	133.0 E
73	McDonough (măk-dŏn'ô)	Ga. (Atlanta In.)	33.27 N	84.9 W
54	Macdougall, L. (măk-do͞o'găl)	Can.	66.10 N	98.45 W
166	Macedon, Mt. (măs'ê-dŏn)	Austl.	37.20 S	144.33 E
129	Macedonia (Prov.) (măs-ê-dō'nĭ-ȧ)	Grc.	41.0 N	22.50 E
103	Maceió (mä-sȧ-yō')	Braz.	9.31 S	35.45 W
140	Macequece (mä-sȧ-kā'sȧ)	Moz.	19.2 S	32.45 E
128	Macerata (mä-chȧ-rä'tȧ)	It.	43.17 N	13.27 E
166	Macfarlane, L. (măk-fär'lȧn)	Austl.	31.55 S	136.45 E
79	McGehee (mȧ-gē')	Ark.	33.37 N	91.24 W
74	McGill (mȧ-gĭl')	Nev.	39.25 N	114.47 W
77	McGregor (măk-grĕg'ẽr)	Ia.	43.0 N	91.11 W
81	McGregor	Tex.	31.25 N	97.24 W
142	McGregor	U. S. Afr.	33.58 S	19.50 E
143	Machache Mt. (mä-chä'chȧ)	Bas.	29.21 S	27.54 E
143	Machadodorp (mä-chä'dô-dôrp)	U. S. Afr.	25.41 S	30.15 E
156	Machang (mä'chäng')	Chn.	39.47 N	121.47 E
102	Machola (mä-chä'lä)	Ec.	6.32 N	79.58 W
155	Macheng (mä'chĕng')	Chn.	31.10 N	114.56 E
86	Machias (mȧ-chī'ȧs)	Me.	44.42 N	67.27 W
129	Măcin (mȧ-chēn')	Rom.	45.14 N	28.9 E
76	McIntosh (măk'ĭn-tŏsh)	S. D.	45.55 N	101.21 W
169	Macintyre Cr. (măk'ĭn-tīr)	Austl. (In.)	28.25 S	151.15 E
169	Macintyre R.	Austl. (In.)	29.0 S	150.50 E
165	Mackay (mă-kī')	Austl.	21.7 S	149.5 E
71	Mackay	Ida.	43.55 N	113.36 W
54	Mackay, L.	Can.	64.5 N	113.32 W
85	McKeesport (mȧ-kēz'pōrt)	Pa.	40.20 N	79.50 W
85	McKees Rocks (mȧ-kēz' rŏks)	Pa.	40.26 N	80.3 W
82	McKenzie (mȧ-kĕn'zĭ)	Tenn.	36.8 N	88.31 W
53	Mackenzie B.	Can.	69.20 N	136.30 W
54	Mackenzie, Dist. of	Can.	63.35 N	115.0 W
53	Mackenzie Mts.	Can.	62.0 N	127.0 W
54	Mackenzie R.	Can.	65.0 N	126.28 W
70	McKenzie R.	Ore.	44.7 N	122.40 W
77	Mackinac, Str. of (măk'ĭ-nô) (măk'ĭ-năk)	Mich.	45.50 N	84.40 W
84	Mackinaw (măk'ĭ-nô)	Mich.	45.46 N	84.41 W
79	Mackinaw R.	Ill.	40.38 N	89.0 W
53	McKinley, Mt. (mȧ-kĭn'lĭ)	Alsk.	63.0 N	151.0 W
48	McKinley Sea	Grnld.	84.0 N	15.0 W
79	McKinney (mȧ-kĭn'ĭ)	Tex.	33.10 N	96.21 W
54	Macklin (măk'lĭn)	Can.	52.18 N	109.48 W
167	Macksville (măks'vĭl)	Austl.	30.38 S	152.58 E
76	McLaughlin (măk-lŏf'lĭn)	S. D.	45.49 N	100.47 W
79	McLeansboro (mȧ-klānz'bŭr-ô)	Ill.	38.6 N	88.31 W
143	Maclear (mȧ-klēr')	U. S. Afr.	31.4 S	28.21 E
167	Macleay R. (mă-klā')	Austl. (In.)	30.50 S	152.30 E
54	Macleod (mȧ-kloud')	Can.	49.42 N	113.28 W
70	McLoughlin, Mt. (mȧk-lŏk'lĭn)	Ore.	42.27 N	122.21 W
78	McMillan, L. (măk-mĭl'ȧn)	N. M.	32.40 N	104.17 W
49	McMillin (măk-mĭl'ĭn)	Wash. (Seattle In.)	47.8 N	122.15 W
70	McMinnville (măk-mĭn'vĭl)	Ore.	45.13 N	123.11 W
82	McMinnville	Tenn.	35.41 N	85.47 W
54	McMurray (măk-mŭr'ĭ)	Can.	56.42 N	11.19 W
49	McMurray	Wash. (Seattle In.)	48.19 N	122.14 W
81	McNary (măk-nâr'ē)	La.	31.0 N	92.33 W
49	McNeil I. (măk-nēl')	Wash. (Seattle In.)	47.12 N	122.40 W
79	Macomb (mȧ-ko͞om')	Ill.	40.26 N	90.39 W
82	Macon (mā'kŏn)	Ga.	32.49 N	83.39 W
82	Macon	Miss.	33.7 N	88.33 W
124	Mâcon (mä-kôɴ')	Fr.	46.20 N	4.50 E
79	Macon (mā'kŏn)	Mo.	39.44 N	92.29 W
54	McPherson (măk-fûr's'n)	Can.	67.12 N	134.32 W
79	McPherson	Kans.	38.22 N	97.40 W
169	MacPhersons Range (măk-fûr's'nz)	Austl. (In.)	28.23 S	153.0 E
169	Macquarie Har. (mȧ-kwŏr'ē)	Austl. (Tas. In.)	42.15 S	145.20 E
46	Macquarie I.	Ant. O.	53.30 S	159.0 E
67	Macquarie, L.	Austl.	33.5 S	151.37 E
167	Macquarie Range	Austl.	33.56 S	149.44 E
165	Macquarie R.	Austl.	31.30 S	147.38 E
140	Macquival (mä-kē-väl')	Moz.	17.45 S	36.45 E
82	McRae (măk-rā')	Ga.	32.3 N	82.57 W
83	McRoberts (măk-rŏb'ẽrts)	Ky.	37.13 N	82.39 W
74	Macuato, L. (mä-kwä'tô)	Mex.	32.25 N	115.25 W
141	Madagascar (măd-ȧ-găs'kȧr)	Ind. O.	19.0 S	46.45 E
87	Madame I.	Can.	45.29 N	60.55 W
161	Madang (mä-däng')	N. Gui. Ter.	5.12 S	145.42 E
138	Madaoua (mȧ-dou'ȧ)	Fr. W. Afr.	14.3 N	6.0 E
85	Madawaska R. (măd-ȧ-wôs'kȧ)	Can.	45.10 N	77.6 W
102	Madeira Falls. (mä-dā'rä)	Braz.	9.15 S	64.45 W
7	Madeira I.	Madeira Is. (In.)	32.45 N	17.0 W
138	Madeira Is.	Atl. O.	33.0 N	16.30 W
7	Madeira Is.	Atl. O. (In.)		
102	Madeira, R.	Braz.	6.30 S	62.25 W
86	Madeleine, C. (măd'lĕn')	Can.	49.16 N	65.10 W
77	Madelia (mȧ-dē'lĭ-ȧ)	Minn.	44.4 N	94.22 W
77	Madeline I. (măd'ĕ-lĭn)	Wis.	46.50 N	90.40 W
74	Madera (mȧ-dā'rȧ)	Calif.	36.56 N	120.3 W
94	Madera (Vol.)	Nic.	11.27 N	85.32 W
143	Madibamatso R. (mä-dē-bä-mät'sô)	Bas.	29.0 S	28.35 E
79	Madill (mȧ-dĭl')	Okla.	34.4 N	96.46 W
135	Madimba (mä-dēm'bä)	Bel. Cong. (Brazzaville In.)	4.52 S	15.19 E
82	Madison (măd'ĭ-sŭn)	Fla.	30.27 N	83.55 W
82	Madison	Ga.	33.36 N	83.29 W
89	Madison	Ill. (St. Louis In.)	38.41 N	90.10 W
84	Madison	Ind.	38.45 N	85.24 W
79	Madison	Kan.	38.7 N	96.8 W
86	Madison	Me.	44.46 N	69.52 W
76	Madison	Minn.	45.0 N	96.12 W
76	Madison	Neb.	41.50 N	97.27 W
83	Madison	N. C.	36.13 N	79.59 W
76	Madison	S. D.	44.1 N	97.6 W
77	Madison	Wis.	43.5 N	89.22 W
71	Madison Reservoir	Mont.	45.25 N	111.41 W
71	Madison R.	Mont.	45.10 N	111.44 W
84	Madisonville (măd'ĭ-sŭn-vĭl)	Ky.	37.20 N	87.30 W
81	Madisonville	La.	30.27 N	90.11 W
81	Madisonville	Tex.	30.57 N	95.54 W
160	Madoera (Madura) (I.) (mä-do͞o'rä)	Neth. Ind.	71.10 S	113.25 E
121	Madona (mȧ'dō'nȧ)	Lat.	56.51 N	20.12 E
70	Mad R.	Calif.	40.39 N	123.45 W
150	Madraka, C. (mä-dräk'ä)	Oman	18.58 N	57.45 E
73	Madras (mȧ-drȧs')	Ga. (Atlanta In.)	33.26 N	84.43 W
151	Madras (Presidency) (mŭ-drŭs') (mȧ-drȧs')	India	15.30 N	80.0 E
151	Madras	India	13.5 N	80.15 E
104	Madre de Dios Arch. (mä'drȧ dā dē-ōs')	Chl.	50.30 S	75.0 W
102	Madre de Dios, R.	Bol.	12.0 S	68.0 W
92	Madre del Sur, Sierra (Mts.) (mä'drā dĕl so͞or')	Mex.	17.10 N	98.0 W
81	Madre, Laguna (L.) (lä-go͞o'nä mä'drȧ)	U. S.-Mex.	25.0 N	97.35 W
162	Madre, Sierra (Mts.)	P. I.	17.0 N	122.15 E
92	Madre Occidental, Sierra (Mts.) (ôk-sē-dĕn-täl')	Mex.	22.0 N	104.35 W
92	Madre Oriental, Sierra (Mts.) (ō-rē-ĕn-täl')	Mex.	22.0 N	99.30 W
77	Madrid (măd'rĭd)	Ia.	41.54 N	93.48 W
127	Madrid (mä-drēdh')	Sp. (In.)	40.26 N	3.42 W
127	Madrid (Prov.)	Sp. (In.)	40.30 N	3.45 W
126	Madridejos (mä-drē-dhā'hōs)	Sp.	39.28 N	3.31 W
73	Madsen (măd'sĕn)	Utah (Salt Lake City In.)	41.40 N	112.6 W
151	Madura (mŭd'o͞o-rŭ) (mȧ-do͞o'rȧ)	India	9.55 N	78.15 E
160	Madura (Madoera) (I.) (mä-do͞o'rä)	Neth. Ind.	7.10 S	113.25 E
104	Madureira (mä-do͞o-rā'rȧ)	Braz. (In.)	22.53 S	43.20 W
159	Maebashi (mä-ĕ-bä'shē)	Jap.	36.25 N	139.2 E
127	Maella (mä-āl'yä)	Sp.	41.11 N	0.7 E
96	Maestra, Sierra (Mts.) (mä-ās'trä)	Cuba	20.5 N	76.30 W
140	Mafeking (mȧf'ē-kĭng)	U. S. Afr.	25.46 S	25.36 E
143	Mafeteng (mä'fē-tĕng)	Bas.	29.49 S	27.14 E
141	Mafia I. (mä-fē'ä)	Afr.	7.45 S	39.45 E
161	Mafor (I.) (mä-fōr')	Neth. Ind.	0.45 S	135.30 E
127	Mafra (mäf'rȧ)	Port. (In.)	38.56 N	9.20 W
141	Magadi, L. (mȧ-gä'dē)	Kenya	1.50 S	36.15 E
140	Magadi (Natron) (nä'trōn)	Tan.	2.15 S	36.0 E
143	Magalies Bergen (Mts.) (mä-gä'lyĕs bĕr'gĕn)	U. S. Afr.	25.47 S	27.30 E
143	Magaliesburg	U. S. Afr.	25.59 S	27.30 E
99	Magallanes (mä-gäl-yä'näs)	Chl. (In.)		
104	Magallanes	Chl.	53.10 S	71.0 W
162	Magallanes	P. I.	12.49 N	123.50 E
161	Magallanes	P. I. (Manila In.)	14.13 N	120.42 E
102	Magangue (mä-gän'kā)	Col.	9.15 N	74.45 W
162	Magat R. (mä-gät')	P. I.	16.50 N	121.30 E
139	Magdala (mäg'dȧ-lä)	It. E. Afr.	11.23 N	39.29 E
99	Magdalena (mäg-dä-lā'nä)	Arg. (Buenos Aires In.)	35.5 S	57.32 W
102	Magdalena	Bol.	13.30 N	63.45 W
93	Magdalena	Mex. (In.)	19.22 N	98.57 W
75	Magdalena	N. M.	34.7 N	107.16 W
102	Magdalena	Peru (In.)	12.5 S	77.4 W
161	Magdalena	P. I. (Manila In.)	14.13 N	121.30 E
102	Magdalena del Mar (dĕl mär')	Peru (In.)	12.6 S	77.5 W
104	Magdalena I.	Chl.	44.30 S	73.0 W
92	Magdalena, L.	Mex.	20.50 N	104.0 W
102	Magdalena, R.	Col.	10.0 N	74.45 W
93	Magdalena, R.	Mex. (In.)	19.30 N	98.50 W
55	Magdalen Is. (măg'dȧ-lĕn)	Can.	47.30 N	61.45 W
122	Magdeburg (mäg'dē-bo͝orgh)	Ger.	52.6 N	11.38 E
99	Magé (mä-zhā')	Braz. (Rio de Janeiro In.)	22.40 S	43.3 W
159	Mage I. (mä'gĕ)	Jap.	30.44 N	130.48 E
104	Magellan, Str. of (mȧ-jĕl'ăn)	Chl.	52.30 S	74.0 W
128	Magenta (mȧ-jĕn'tȧ)	It.	45.26 N	8.53 E
110	Magerö (I.) (mä'gẽr-û)	Nor.	70.58 N	24.0 E
128	Maggiore, L. of (mäd-jō'rä)	It.-Switz.	46.5 N	8.30 E
92	Magiscatzin (mä-kēs-kät-zēn')	Mex.	22.49 N	98.41 W
129	Maglaj (mȧ'glä-ē)	Yugo.	44.32 N	18.10 E
129	Maglic (mäg'lēch)	Yugo.	43.34 N	20.33 E
129	Maglie (mäl'yā)	It.	40.6 N	18.19 E
73	Magna (măg'nȧ)	Utah (Salt Lake City In.)	40.43 N	112.6 W
112	Magnitogorsk (mȧg-nyē'tô-gôrsk)	Sov. Un.	53.10 N	59.10 E
79	Magnolia (măg-nō'lĭ-ȧ)	Ark.	33.15 N	93.14 W
82	Magnolia	Miss.	31.8 N	90.28 W
86	Magog (mȧ-gŏg')	Can.	45.15 N	72.10 W
86	Magpie L. (măg'pī)	Can.	51.0 N	64.43 W
86	Magpie R.	Can.	50.30 N	64.34 W
77	Magpie R.	Can.	48.12 N	84.40 W
145	Magra, Jebel El (Mts.) (jĕb'ĕl ĕl mäg'rä)	Pal. (In.)	30.35 N	35.0 E
140	Magude (mä-go͞o'dȧ)	Moz.	25.3 S	32.37 E
151	Magwe (mŭg-wā')	India	20.8 N	94.58 E
123	Magyaróvár (môd'yôr-ō-vär)	Hung.	47.50 N	17.17 E
141	Mahaddei (mä-häd'ä-ē)	It. E. Afr.	2.55 N	45.28 E
139	Mahagi (mä-hä'gē)	Bel. Cong.	2.11 N	31.6 E
135	Mahalla (mȧ-häl'ȧ)	Eg. (In.)	30.59 N	31.10 E
141	Mahaly (mȧ-hȧl-ē')	Madag.	23.55 S	46.13 E
151	Mahanadi R. (mŭ-hä-nŭd'ē)	India	21.30 N	84.0 E
141	Mahanoro (mȧ-hȧ-nô'rō)	Madag.	19.45 S	48.43 E
85	Mahanoy City (mä-hȧ-noi')	Pa.	40.48 N	76.10 W
141	Mahavavy R. (mä-hä-vä'vē)	Madag.	17.0 S	46.5 E
139	Mahadera Maryam (mä'dȧ-rä mär'yȧm)	It. E. Afr.	11.40 N	38.2 E
135	Mahdia (mä-dē'ȧ) (mä'dē-ȧ)	Tun. (In.)	35.31 N	10.52 E

ăt; finăl; rāte; senâte; ärm; åsk; sofȧ; fâre; ch-choose; dh-as th in other; bē; êvent; bĕt; recĕnt; cratẽr; g-go; gh-gutteral g; bĭt; ĭ-short neutral; rīde; k-gutteral k as ch in German ich;

Page	Name Pronunciation Region	Lat. °'	Long. °'
151	Mahé (mä-ā') India	11.45 N	75.29 E
6	Mahébourg (mà-ā'bōōrg) Mauritius I. (In.)	20.24 S	57.41 E
141	Mahenge (mä-hĕŋ'gā) Tan.	8.38 S	36.38 E
170	Mahia Pen. (mä'yà) N. Z.	39.10 S	177.55 E
143	Mahlabatini (mä'lä-bà-tē'nē) U. S. Afr.	28.18 S	31.31 E
76	Mahnomen (mô-nō'mĕn) Minn.	47.19 N	95.58 W
143	Mahoeng (mä'ō-ĕng) Bas.	29.56 S	28.50 E
127	Mahón (mä-ōn') Sp.	39.55 N	4.15 E
86	Mahone B. Can.	44.28 N	64.15 W
86	Mahone Bay (mȧ-hōn') Can.	44.27 N	64.22 W
123	Mährisch Schönberg (Šumperk) (mâ'rĭsh shûn'bĕrk) (shŏŏm'pĕrk) Ger.	49.58 N	17.0 E
151	Mahul (mŭ'hōōl) India (Bombay In.)	19.0 N	72.54 E
139	Maidaguri (mä'ē-dà-gōō'rē) Nig.	11.58 N	13.12 E
150	Maidan-i-Naftun (mŭ-ē-dän'ēnäf-tōōn') Per.	31.45 N	49.28 E
129	Maidos (Aci Abad) (mī'dōs) (ä'jē ä-bäd') Tur.	40.11 N	26.21 E
117	Maidstone (mād'stŭn) Gt. Brit.	51.15 N	0.31 E
159	Maiko (mī'kō') Jap. (Osaka In.)	34.39 N	135.3 E
113	Maikop (mī'kôp) Sov. Un.	44.35 N	40.8 E
150	Maimana (mī-mà-nä') Afg.	35.58 N	64.47 E
166	Main Barrier (Stanley Ra.) (stăn'lĭ) Austl.	31.20 S	141.27 E
86	Maine (State) (mān) U. S.	45.8 N	69.25 W
170	Main Entrance (Chan.) N. Z. (In.)	41.21 S	174.51 E
163	Mainit, L. (mä-ē'nēt) P. I.	9.27 N	125.32 E
116	Mainland (I.) Gt. Brit. (In.)	60.15 N	1.20 W
89	Main Pass. La. (New Orleans In.)	29.15 N	89.15 W
122	Main R. (mīn) Ger.	50.0 N	10.0 E
141	Maintirano (mä'ēn-tē-rä'nō) Madag.	18.3 S	44.3 E
122	Mainz (mīnts) Ger.	50.0 N	8.13 E
138	Maio I. (mä'yō) Cape Verde Is. (In.)	15.15 N	23.15 W
99	Maipo, R. (mī'pō) Chl. (Valparaiso In.)	33.40 S	70.40 W
104	Maipo (Vol.) Arg.-Chl.	34.10 S	69.50 W
102	Maipures (mī-pōō'räs) Ven.	5.15 N	67.32 W
162	Mairaira Pt. (mī-rī'rä) P. I.	18.39 N	120.50 E
97	Maisí, C. (mī-sē') Cuba	20.15 N	74.10 W
125	Maisons-Alfort (mā-zôN' ăl-fôr') Fr. (In.)	48.47 N	2.26 E
125	Maisons-Laffitte (mā'zôN' là-fēt') Fr. (In.)	48.56 N	2.9 E
141	Mait I. (māt) Afr.	11.15 N	47.12 E
167	Maitland (māt'lănd) Austl.	32.45 S	151.38 E
141	Maitland U. S. Afr.	33.55 S	18.30 E
84	Maitland R. Can.	43.50 N	81.28 W
159	Maizuru (mä-ĭ'zōō-rōō) Jap.	35.25 N	135.15 E
139	Maji (mä'jē) It. E. Afr.	6.9 N	35.33 E
127	Majorca (I.) (mȧ-jôr'kȧ) Sp.	39.35 N	3.0 E
135	Majoura, Djebel (Mt.) (jĕb'ĕl mä-jōō'rä) Tun. (In.)	34.40 N	9.20 E
141	Majunga (mȧ-jŭŋ'gȧ) Madag.	15.40 S	46.20 E
70	Makah Indian Res. (mȧ-kô') Wash.	48.20 N	124.38 W
170	Makai (mȧ-kī') N. Z.	38.32 S	175.55 E
	Makale, It. E. Afr., see Macalle.		
141	Makanya (mä-kän'yä) Tan.	4.23 S	37.50 E
170	Makara R. (mä'kà-rä) N. Z. (In.)	41.15 S	174.44 E
112	Makariev (mä'kär-yĕf) Sov. Un.	57.55 N	43.48 E
128	Makarska (mä'kär-skä) Yugo.	43.17 N	17.4 E
160	Makasser (mȧ-kăs'ăr) Neth. Ind.	5.9 S	119.30 E
160	Makasser (Macassar) Str. Neth. Ind.	2.0 S	118.30 E
161	Makati (mä-kä'tē) P. I. (Manila In.)	14.34 N	121.2 E
131	Makeevka (Dmitrievsk) (mä-kee-f'kä) (d'mē'trē-yĕfsk) Sov. Un.	48.2 N	37.55 E
113	Makhach-Kala (mäk'äch-kä'lä) Sov. Un.	43.0 N	47.30 E
129	Makhlata (mäK'lä-tä) Bul.	43.27 N	24.16 E
131	Makhnovka (mäK-nôf'kä) Sov. Un.	49.42 N	28.41 E
156	Makia R. (mä'kyä') Chn.	37.50 N	117.6 E
123	Makó (mô'kō) Hung.	46.13 N	20.31 E
138	Makokou (mä-kô-kōō') Fr. Eq. Afr.	0.40 N	12.40 E
123	Maków (mä'kōōf) Pol.	52.52 N	21.7 E
151	Makri (mŭ-kĭ') India	19.45 N	81.59 E
135	Maktar (mäk-tär') Tun. (In.)	35.53 N	9.20 E
148	Makushino (mȧ-kōō-shē'nô) Sov. Un.	55.15 N	67.30 E
159	Makuwari (mä'kōō-wä'rē) Jap. (Tokyo In.)	35.40 N	140.3 E
141	Makuyuni (mä-kōō-yōō'nē) Tan.	4.17 S	37.50 E
151	Malabar Coast (mäl'ȧ-băr) India	11.0 N	75.30 E
135	Malabata, Pt. (mä'lä-bä'tä) Sp. Mor. (Gib. In.)	35.48 N	5.16 E
162	Malabon (mä-lä-bōn') P. I.	14.24 N	120.58 E
163	Malabuyoc (mä-lä-bōō'yŏk) P. I.	9.40 N	123.21 E
160	Malacca (mȧ-läk'ȧ) Strs. Sets.	2.17 N	102.16 E
160	Malacca (State) Strs. Sets.	2.30 N	102.0 E
160	Malacca, Str. of Neth. Ind.	2.30 N	101.30 E
71	Malad (mȧ-lăd') Ida.	42.11 N	112.16 W
127	Maladetta (Reg.) (mä-lä-dĕt'tä) Sp.	42.32 N	0.45 E
126	Málaga (mä'lä-gä) Sp.	36.43 N	4.25 W
126	Málaga B. Sp.	36.38 N	4.15 W
142	Malagas (mă'lȧ-gȧs) U. S. Afr.	34.19 S	20.32 E
126	Malagon (mä-lä-gōn') Sp.	39.12 N	3.51 W
165	Malaita I. (mȧ-lä'ē-tȧ) Solomon Is.	9.0 S	161.0 E
139	Malakal (mȧ-lȧ-käl') A. E. Sud.	9.38 N	31.47 E
125	Malakoff (mȧ-lȧ-kôf') Fr. (In.)	48.48 N	2.18 E
163	Malampaya Sd. (mä-läm-pä'yä) P. I.	10.57 N	119.15 E
163	Malanao I. (mä-lä-nä'ō) P. I.	9.28 N	118.37 E
140	Malanje (mä-läŋ'gä) Ang.	9.28 S	16.22 E
163	Malanut B. (mä-lä-nōōt') P. I.	9.18 N	118.0 E
95	Mala, Pt. (mä'lä) Pan.	7.30 N	80.0 W
161	Malaraya Mt. (mä-lä-rä'yä) P. I. (Manila In.)	14.0 N	121.18 E
120	Mälar L. (mâ'lär) Swe.	59.30 N	17.4 E
113	Malatya (mȧ-lä'ty-ȧ) Tur.	38.25 N	38.18 E
130	Malaya Vishera (mȧ-lä'yȧ vē-shā'rä) Sov. Un.	58.50 N	32.11 E
163	Malaybalay (mä-lī-bä'lī) P. I.	8.3 N	125.7 E
160	Malay Pen. (mȧ-lā') (mā'lā) Asia	7.0 N	100.0 E
160	Malay States Asia	5.0 N	102.0 W
116	Mal B. (măl) Ire.	52.50 N	9.30 W
164	Malbon (măl'bŭn) Austl.	21.15 S	140.30 E
163	Malbul R. (mäl-bōōl') P. I.	6.33 N	124.50 E
127	Malcabran R. (mäl-kä-brän') Port. (In.)	38.51 N	8.48 W
119	Malchow (mäl'Kō) Ger. (Berlin In.)	52.35 N	13.28 E
96	Malcolm B. (măl'kŭm) Jam.	17.59 N	77.52 W
86	Malden (môl'dĕn) Mass.	42.28 N	71.5 W
79	Malden Mo.	36.32 N	89.57 W
6	Malden I. Pac. O.	4.3 N	154.59 W
144	Maldive Is. (măl'dīv) Ind. O.	5.0 N	73.0 E
104	Maldonado Ur.	34.50 S	54.59 W
92	Maldonado, Pt. Mex.	16.19 N	98.35 W
165	Malekula (Malikolo) I. (mä-lā-kōō'lä) (mäl-ē-kō'lō) New Hebr.	16.20 S	167.30 E
124	Malesherbes (mål'zĕrb') Fr.	48.19 N	2.25 E
70	Malheur L. (mȧ-lōōr') Ore.	43.19 N	118.47 W
70	Malheur R. Ore.	43.47 N	118.0 W
129	Malia, C. (mä'lĭ-ȧ) Grc.	36.17 N	23.12 E
131	Malie Viski (mäl'ĭ-yĕ vēs'kē) Sov. Un.	48.39 N	31.38 E
163	Maligay B. (mä-lē'-gī) P. I.	7.30 N	123.15 E
165	Malikolo (Malekula) I. (mäl-ē-kō'lō) (mä-lā-kōō'lä) New Hebr.	16.20 S	167.30 E
131	Malin (mȧ-lēn') Sov. Un.	50.46 N	29.11 E
92	Malinalco (mä-lē-näl'kō) Mex.	18.58 N	99.29 W
92	Malinaltepec (mä-lē-näl-tȧ-pĕk') Mex.	17.11 N	98.23 W
116	Malin Hd. (mă'lĭn) Gt. Brit.	55.25 N	7.30 W
163	Malinao (mä-lē'-nä-ō) P. I.	11.38 N	122.18 E
141	Malindi (mä-lēn'dē) Kenya	3.10 S	40.7 E
123	Malineč (mä'lē-nyĕts') Czech.	48.30 N	19.41 E
117	Malines (mȧ-lēn') Bel.	51.0 N	4.25 E
116	Malinmore Hd. (mă'lĭn-mōr) Ire.	54.40 N	8.50 W
131	Malinovka (mȧ-lē-nôf'kȧ) Sov. Un.	49.47 N	36.40 E
92	Malintzin, Cerro (Mt.) (mȧ-lēnt-zēn') Mex.	19.13 N	98.1 W
163	Malita (mä-lē'tä) P. I.	6.23 N	125.37 E
163	Malitbog (mä-lēt'bōg) P. I.	10.9 N	125.0 E
163	Malitobug R. (mä-lē'tō-bōōg) P. I.	7.20 N	124.40 E
129	Malkara (mäl'kȧ-rä) Tur.	40.54 N	26.54 E
129	Malko-Trnova (mäl'kō-t'r'nō-vō) Bul.	41.57 N	27.29 E
167	Mallacoota Inlet (mô-lȧ-kōō'tȧ) Austl.	37.35 S	149.45 E
116	Mallaig (măl'āg) Gt. Brit.	57.0 N	5.45 W
163	Mallawalle I. (mä-lä-wä'lä) B. N. B.	7.3 N	117.19 E
135	Mallawi (mȧ-lä'wē) Eg. (In.)	27.45 N	30.50 E
116	Mallow (măl'ō) Ire.	52.5 N	8.40 W
117	Malmédy (mȧl-mā-dē') Bel.	50.25 N	6.0 E
142	Malmesbury (mämz'bēr-ĭ) U. S. Afr.	33.27 S	18.40 E
120	Malmköping (mȧlm'chû'pĭng) Swe.	59.8 N	16.40 E
120	Malmö (mälm'û) Swe.	55.35 N	13.0 E
166	Malmsbury (mämz'bēr-ĭ) Austl.	37.11 S	144.19 E
149	Malmyzh (mȧl-mēzh') Sov. Un.	49.55 N	136.50 E
112	Malmyzh Sov. Un.	56.30 N	50.45 E
130	Maloarkhangelsk (mä'lô-är-käŋ'gĕlsk) Sov. Un.	52.26 N	36.30 E
162	Malolos (mä-lô'lōs) P. I.	14.50 N	120.49 E
85	Malone (mȧ-lōn) N. Y.	44.52 N	74.20 W
130	Maloyaroslavets (mä'lō-yä-rō-slä-vyĕts') Sov. Un.	55.1 N	36.29 E
118	Malpas (măl'pȧz) Gt. Brit.	53.1 N	2.46 W
102	Malpelo I. (mäl-pä'lō) Col.	4.1 N	81.30 W
86	Malpeque B. (môl-pĕk') Can.	46.35 N	63.45 W
7	Malta (môl'tȧ) Medit. Sea	35.55 N	14.27 E
71	Malta Mont.	48.21 N	107.50 W
140	Maltahohe (mäl'tä-hō'ē) S. W. Afr.	24.55 S	16.45 E
49	Maltby (môlt'bē) Wash. (Seattle In.)	47.47 N	122.7 W
118	Malton (môl'tŭn) Gt. Brit.	54.8 N	0.47 W
93	Maltrata (mäl-trä'tä) Mex.	18.49 N	97.15 W
163	Maluko (mä-lōō'kō) P. I.	8.20 N	125.0 E
79	Malvern (măl'vērn) Ark.	34.23 N	92.48 W
118	Malvern Gt. Brit.	52.7 N	2.19 W
149	Maly Is. (mä'lĭ) Sov. Un.	74.0 N	141.0 E
93	Mamantel (mä-män-täl') Mex.	18.31 N	91.5 W
163	Mambajao (mäm-bä'hä-ō) P. I.	9.14 N	124.43 E
161	Mamberamo (R.) (mäm-bȧ-rä'mō) Neth. Ind.	2.30 S	138.20 E
141	Mamboya (mäm-bō'yä) Tan.	6.16 S	37.15 E
162	Mamburao (mäm-bōō'rä-ō) P. I.	13.13 N	120.35 E
163	Mambusao (mäm-bōō'sä-ō) P. I.	11.26 N	122.36 E
124	Mamers (mȧ-mā') Fr.	48.21 N	0.21 E
138	Mamfe (mäm'fē) Nig.	5.51 N	9.9 E
159	Mamibara (mä'mē-bä-rä) Jap.	32.41 N	131.11 E
82	Mammoth Cave (măm'ŏth) Ky.	37.12 N	86.5 W
82	Mammoth Cave Natl. Mon. Ky.	37.12 N	86.8 W
71	Mammoth Hot Sprs. Wyo.	44.57 N	110.50 W
102	Mamoré, R. (mä-mō-rā') Bol.	14.0 S	65.0 W
138	Mamou (mȧ-mōō') Fr. W. Afr.	10.28 N	12.10 W
135	Mamoura, Ras (C.) (räs mä'mōō-rä') Tun. (In.)	36.26 N	10.40 E
142	Mamre (măm'rä) U. S. Afr.	33.29 S	18.26 E
150	Manama (mŭ-nä'mȧ) Bahrein I.	26.10 N	50.40 E
151	Manar (Mannar) (mŭ-när') Cey. (In.)	9.5 N	79.50 E
152	Manas R. (mȧ-näs') Chn.	44.45 S	86.0 E
127	Manacor (mä-nä-kôr') Sp.	39.34 N	3.12 E
94	Managua (mä-nä'gwä) Nic.	12.10 N	86.16 W
94	Managua, L. Nic.	12.20 N	86.20 W
170	Manaia (mä-nī'ä) N. Z.	39.32 S	174.8 E
163	Manamoc I. (mä-nä-môk') P. I.	11.18 N	120.41 E
141	Mananara R. (mä-nä-nä'rä) Madag.	23.0 S	47.15 E
166	Manangatang (mä-näŋ-gä-tăng') Austl.	35.1 S	142.51 E
141	Mananjari (mä-nän-zhä'rē) Madag.	21.15 S	48.18 E
103	Manáos (Manaus) (mä-nä'ōs) (mä-nä'ōōzh) Braz.	3.1 S	60.0 W
163	Manapla (mä-näp'lä) P. I.	10.57 N	123.8 E
171	Manapowri L. (mä-nä-pou'rē) N. Z.	45.28 S	167.30 E
85	Manassas (mȧ-năs'ȧs) Va.	38.45 N	77.30 W
83	Manatee (măn-ȧ-tē') Fla. (In.)	27.29 N	82.34 W
103	Manaus (Manáos) (mä-nä'ōōzh) Braz.	3.1 S	60.0 W
141	Manawât (mä-nä-wät') Eg.	29.55 N	31.14 E
170	Manawatu R. (mä-nä-wä'tōō) N. Z.	40.25 S	175.15 E
163	Manay (mä-nī') P. I.	7.11 N	126.32 E
116	Man, Calf of (I.) Gt. Brit.	54.5 N	4.50 W
84	Mancelona (măn-sē-lō'nȧ) Mich.	44.50 N	85.7 W
126	Mancha Real (män'chä rā-äl') Sp.	37.47 N	3.36 W
143	Manch Berg (Mt.) (mänK' bĕrgh) U. S. Afr.	25.10 S	30.32 E
156	Mancheng (män'chĕng') Chn.	39.3 N	115.13 E
85	Manchester (măn'chĕs-tēr) Conn.	41.46 N	72.28 W
82	Manchester Ga.	32.51 N	84.37 W
116	Manchester Gt. Brit.	53.30 N	2.15 W
77	Manchester Ia.	42.30 N	91.29 W
83	Manchester Ky.	38.42 N	83.38 W
87	Manchester Mass. (In.)	42.34 N	70.46 W
86	Manchester N. H.	43.0 N	71.30 W
118	Manchester Ship Canal Gt. Brit.	53.22 N	2.33 W
153	Manchouli (Lupin) (män-chōō'lē) (lōō'pĭn') Chn.	49.34 N	117.28 E
153	Manchukuo (măn-chōō'kwō) Asia	47.30 N	126.0 E
140	Manda (män'dä) Tan.	10.28 S	34.33 E
120	Mandal (män'däl) Nor.	58.2 N	7.28 E
151	Mandalay (măn'dȧ-lā) (män-dȧ-lā') India	21.59 N	95.59 E
120	Mandals R. (män'däls) Nor.	58.20 N	7.30 E
76	Mandan (măn'dăn) N. D.	46.51 N	100.55 W
139	Mandara Mts. (män-dä'rä) Cam.	10.30 N	14.30 E
163	Mandaue (män-dä'wā) P. I.	10.19 N	123.56 E
141	Mandera (män-dā'rä) Tan.	6.13 S	38.24 E
95	Mandinga (män-dĭŋ'gä) Pan.	9.32 N	79.4 W
143	Mandini (män-dē'nē) U. S. Afr.	29.10 S	31.25 E
129	Mandra (män'drä) Grc.	38.5 N	23.31 E
141	Mandritsara (män-drēt-sä'rä) Madag.	15.40 S	48.45 E
150	Mand Rud (R.) (mŭnd' rōōd') Iran	28.15 N	52.30 E
99	Manduba Pt. (män-dōō'bȧ) Braz. (Rio de Janeiro In.)	24.2 S	46.17 W
129	Manduria (män-dōō'rē-ä) It.	40.23 N	17.39 E
151	Mandvi (mŭnd'vē) India	22.45 N	69.25 E
135	Manfalût (män-fȧ-lōōt') Eg. (In.)	27.19 N	30.57 E
128	Manfredonia (män-frȧ-dô'nyä) It.	41.37 N	15.53 E
128	Manfredonia, G. of It.	41.30 N	16.0 E
103	Mangabeiras, Serra das (Mts.) (sĕr'rȧ däzh mäŋ-gä-bā'ē-räzh) Braz.	9.30 S	46.30 W
151	Mangalore (mŭŋ-gŭ-lōr') India	12.50 N	74.45 E
170	Mangari (män-gä'rē) N. Z. (In.)	36.57 S	174.48 E
162	Mangatarem (män'gȧ-tä'rĕm) P. I.	15.47 N	120.18 E
160	Mangkalihat, C. (mäng'kȧ-lē-hät') Neth. Ind.	1.2 N	119.2 E
96	Mangles Is. (mäŋ'gläs) (măŋ'g'lz) Cuba	22.5 N	82.35 W
141	Mangoky R. (män-gō'kē) Madag.	21.30 S	45.30 E
157	Mangsan (mäng'sän') Cho.	39.41 N	126.30 E
126	Mangualde (män-gwäl'dē) Port.	40.37 N	7.45 W
104	Mangueira, L. da (män-gā'ē-rȧ) Braz.	33.15 S	52.40 W
161	Mangulli (I.) (män-gōō-lē') Neth. Ind.	1.50 S	126.0 E
78	Mangum (măŋ'gŭm) Okla.	34.52 N	99.31 W
79	Manhattan (măn-hăt'ăn) Kan.	39.11 N	96.34 W
73	Manhattan Beach Calif. (Los Angeles In.)	33.54 N	118.25 W
88	Manhattan (I.) N. Y. (New York In.)	40.48 N	73.58 W
141	Mania R. (män'yä) Madag.	20.0 S	46.20 E
103	Manicoré (mä-nē-kō-rā') Braz.	5.45 S	61.15 W
6	Manihiki I. (mä'nē-hē'kē) Pac. O.	10.23 S	161.1 W
55	Manikuagan R. (măn-ē-kwä'gȧn) Can.	51.30 N	68.30 W
161	Manila (mȧ-nĭl'ȧ) P. I. (In.)		
162	Manila P. I.	14.35 N	121.0 E
162	Manila B. P. I.	14.40 N	120.50 E
167	Manilla Austl.	30.45 S	150.45 E
113	Manisa (mä'nē-sä) Tur.	38.40 N	27.29 E
116	Man, Isle of Gt. Brit.	54.10 N	4.40 W
84	Manistee (măn-ĭs-tē') Mich.	44.4 N	86.20 W
84	Manistee R. Mich.	44.30 N	85.30 W
77	Manistique (măn-ĭs-tēk') Mich.	45.58 N	86.15 W
77	Manistique L. Mich.	46.15 N	85.45 W
77	Manistique R. Mich.	46.13 N	85.59 W
54	Manitoba (Prov.) (măn-ĭ-tō'bȧ) Can.	55.10 N	98.0 W
54	Manitoba, L. Can.	50.45 N	98.30 W
78	Manitou (măn'ĭ-tōō) Colo.	38.53 N	104.56 W
77	Manitou I. Mich.	47.25 N	87.38 W
84	Manitou Is. Mich.	45.5 N	86.0 W
77	Manitou L. Can.	49.15 N	93.0 W
55	Manitoulin I. (măn-ĭ-tōō'lĭn) Can.	45.45 N	82.30 W
77	Manitowoc (măn-ĭ-tō-wŏk') Wis.	44.5 N	87.39 W
102	Manizales (mä-nē-zä'läs) Col.	5.2 N	75.45 W
140	Manjacaze (man'yä-kä'zē) Moz.	24.45 S	34.0 E
150	Manjil (mŭn-jēl') Iran	36.32 N	49.32 E
163	Manjuyod (män-hōō'yōdh) P. I.	9.40 N	123.9 E
78	Mankato (măn-kā'tō) Kan.	39.47 N	98.13 W
77	Mankato Minn.	44.10 N	93.59 W
167	Manly (măn'lĭ) Austl.	33.48 S	15.18 E
127	Manlleu (män-lyä'ōō) Sp.	42.0 N	2.17 E

ng-sing; ŋ-baŋk; N-nasalized n; nŏd; cŏmmit; ōld; ôbey; ôrder; fōōd; fŏŏt; ou-out; s-soft; sh-dish; th-thin; pūre; ûnite; ûrn; stŭd; circŭs; ü-as "y" in study; '-indeterminate vowel.

Page	Name Pronunciation Region	Lat. °′	Long. °′
162	Manmanoc, Mt. (män-mä-nôk′) P. I.	17.40 N	121.5 E
166	Manna Hill (măn′ȧ) . . . . Austl.	32.25 S	139.59 E
151	Mannar (Manar) (mȧ-när′) Cey. (In.)	9.5 N	79.50 E
122	Mannheim (män′hīm) . . . . Ger.	49.30 N	8.28 E
77	Manning (măn′ĭng) . . . . Ia.	41.54 N	95.3 W
83	Manning . . . . S. C.	33.41 N	80.12 W
167	Manning R. . . . . Austl.	31.53 S	152.8 E
85	Mannington (măn′ĭng-tŭn) . W. Va.	39.33 N	80.26 W
143	Mannoca (mä-nō′kȧ) . . . . Moz.	26.48 S	32.35 E
169	Mann R. (măn) . . . . . . Austl. (In.)	29.42 S	152.5 E
97	Man of War B. . . . . Ba. Is.	21.3 N	73.40 W
97	Man of War Chan. . . . . Ba. Is.	22.45 N	75.51 W
161	Manokwari (mȧ-nŏk-wä′rē) Neth. Ind.	0.50 S	134.5 E
125	Manosque (mȧ-nôsk′) . . . . Fr.	43.51 N	5.50 E
127	Manresa (män-rā′sä) . . . . Sp.	41.44 N	1.50 E
55	Mansel I. (măn′sĕl) . . . . Can.	62.10 N	80.10 W
167	Mansfield (mănz′fēld) . . . . . . Austl.	37.4 S	146.4 E
116	Mansfield . . . . Gt. Brit.	53.10 N	1.10 W
81	Mansfield . . . . La.	32.2 N	93.43 W
84	Mansfield . . . . Ohio	40.47 N	82.32 W
70	Mansfield . . . . Wash.	47.46 N	119.39 W
86	Mansfield Mt. . . . . Vt.	44.34 N	72.52 W
118	Mansfield Woodhouse . . . Gt. Brit.	53.10 N	1.11 W
139	Mansûra (mȧn-sōō′rȧ) . . . . Eg.	31.2 N	31.11 E
102	Manta (män′tä) . . . . Ec.	1.0 S	80.33 W
163	Mantalingajan, Mt. (män-tä-lēŋ-gä′hän) . P. I.	8.49 N	117.39 E
163	Mantangule I. (män-täŋ-gōō′lȧ) P. I.	8.10 N	117.10 E
124	Mantes (mäɴt′) . . . . Fr.	49.0 N	1.42 E
75	Manti (măn′tī) . . . . Utah	39.16 N	111.39 W
99	Mantiqueira, Serra da (Mts.) (sĕr′rä dä män-tē-kā′ē-rȧ) Braz. (Rio de Janeiro In.)	22.40 S	45.20 W
128	Mantova (Mantua) (män′tô-vä) (măn′tū-ȧ) . It.	45.8 N	10.46 E
96	Mantua (män-tōō′ȧ) . . . . Cuba	22.17 N	84.16 W
128	Mantua (Mantova) (măn′tū-ȧ) (män′tô-vä) . It.	45.8 N	10.46 E
73	Mantua (măn′tū-ȧ) Utah (Salt Lake City In.)	41.30 N	111.56 W
86	Manuan L. (mä-nōō′ăn) . . . . . Can.	50.40 N	70.40 W
86	Manuan R. . . . . Can.	50.0 N	70.40 W
99	Manuel Rodriguez I. (mä-nōō-ĕl′ rô-drē′gĕz) . Chl. (Magallanes In.)	52.35 S	73.50 W
160	Manui Is. (mä-nōō′ē) . . Neth. Ind.	3.30 S	123.10 E
170	Manukau Entrance (mä-nōō-kä′ōō) . N. Z. (In.)	37.3 S	174.33 E
170	Manukau Har. . . . . N. Z. (In.)	37.1 S	174.42 E
161	Manus (I.) (mä′nōōs) . N. Gui. Ter.	2.0 S	146.45 E
81	Manvel (măn′vĕl) . . . . . . Tex. (In.)	29.27 N	95.22 W
141	Manyal Shiha (män-yäl′ shē′hȧ) Eg.	29.57 N	31.13 E
135	Manyanga (män-yäŋ′gä) Bel. Cong. (Brazzaville In.)	4.55 S	14.28 E
113	Manych R. (mȧ-nĭch′) . . . Sov. Un.	47.15 N	41.0 E
113	Manych Sea (Bolshoi Liman) (mȧ-nĭchȧ′) (bôl′shô-ē lē′măn) Sov. Un.	46.20	42.45 E
135	Manzala (măn′zȧ-lȧ) . . . . Eg. (In.)	31.9 N	32.4 E
126	Manzanares (män-thä-nä′räs) . . Sp.	39.0 N	3.23 W
127	Manzanares Canal . . . . . . Sp. (In.)	40.18 N	3.36 W
127	Manzanares R. . . . . Sp. (In.)	40.33 N	3.48 W
96	Manzanillo (män′zä-nēl′yō) . . Cuba	20.21 N	77.9 W
92	Manzanillo . . . . Mex.	19.2 N	104.20 W
97	Manzanillo B. . . . . Hai.	19.42 N	71.52 W
92	Manzanillo B. . . . . Mex.	19.4 N	104.23 W
139	Mao (mä′ō) . . . . Fr. Eq. Afr.	14.9 N	15.12 E
93	Mapastepec (mä-päs-tä-pĕk′) Mex.	15.25 N	92.55 W
161	Mapia Is. (mä′pē-ȧ) . . . Neth. Ind.	1.0 N	134.25 E
80	Mapimi (mä-pē-mē′) . . . . Mex.	25.49 N	103.50 W
80	Mapimi, Bolson de (Depression) (bôl-sōn′ dä mä-pē-mē′) . . Mex.	28.0 N	104.30 W
72	Maple Falls (mā′p′l) Wash. (Vancouver In.)	48.55 N	122.5 W
89	Maple Heights Ohio (Cleveland In.)	41.25 N	81.34 W
79	Maplewood (mā′p′l-wŏŏd) . . . . Mo.	38.37 N	90.19 W
119	Maplin Sands (măp′lĭn) Gt. Brit. (London In.)	51.35 N	0.55 E
143	Mapumulo (mä-pä-mōō′lō) U. S. Afr.	29.15 S	31.2 E
143	Maputa (Usutu) R. (mȧ-pōō′tȧ) (ōō-sōō′tōō) . Moz.	26.30 S	32.35 E
163	Maqueda B. (mä-kā′dä) . . . . . P. I.	11.30 N	125.0 E
162	Maqueda Chan. . . . . P. I.	13.45 N	124.4 E
140	Maquela do Zombo (mȧ-kā′lȧ dŏŏ zŏm′bŏŏ) . Ang.	6.2 S	15.13 E
77	Maquoketa (mȧ-kō-kē-tȧ) . . . . . Ia.	42.4 N	90.39 W
77	Maquoketa R. . . . . Ia.	42.20 N	91.16 W
103	Maracá I. (mä-rȧ-kä′) . . . . Braz.	2.0 N	50.28 W
102	Maracaibo (mä-rä-kī′bō) . . . . . Ven.	10.32 N	71.43 W
102	Maracaibo L. . . . . Ven.	9.30 N	71.30 W
7	Maracas, Mt. (mä-rä′käs) Trin. (In.)	10.42 N	61.24 W
138	Maradi (mȧ-rȧ-dē′) . . . Fr. W. Afr.	13.33 N	7.10 E
135	Marâgha (mȧ-rä′gȧ) . . . . . Eg. (In.)	26.42 N	31.37 E
103	Maragojipe (mä′rȧ-gō-zhē′pĕ) Braz. (In.)	12.46 S	38.55 W
161	Maragondon (mä′rä-gōn-dōn′) P. I.	14.18 N	120.42 E
103	Marajó I. (mä-rä-zhō′) . . . . . . Braz.	1.0 S	50.30 W
163	Maramag (mä-rä′mäg) . . . . P. I.	7.44 N	125.1 E
141	Maramba (mä-räm′bä) . . . . Tang.	4.52 S	38.50 E
140	Marandellas (mä-rän-dăl′äs) S. Rh.	18.15 S	13.30 E
103	Maranguape (mä-räŋ-gwä′pĕ) Braz.	3.58 S	38.43 W
103	Maranhão (Sao Luiz) (mä-rän-youɴ (souɴ-lōō-ezh′) . Braz.	2.30 S	44.12 W

Page	Name Pronunciation Region	Lat. °′	Long. °′
103	Maranhão (State) . . . . Braz.	5.0 S	45.0 W
165	Maranoa R. (mä-rȧ-nō′ȧ) . . . Austl.	26.30 S	147.51 E
102	Marañon, R. (mä-rä-nyōn′) Ec.-Peru	5.0 S	76.0 W
124	Marans (mä-räɴ′) . . . . Fr.	46.20 N	1.0 W
163	Maraob (mä′rä-ôb′) . . . . . . B. N. B.	5.25 N	119.0 E
103	Marapanim (mä-rȧ-päɴ-ēɴ′) . Braz.	0.45 S	47.45 W
113	Maras (mä-räsh′) . . . . Tur.	37.40 N	36.55 E
160	Maratoea (Maratus) I. (mȧ-rä′tōō mȧ-rä′tōōs) Neth. Ind.	2.15 N	118.35 E
160	Maratus I., see Maratoea, Neth. Ind.		
92	Maravatio (mä-rȧ-vä′tē-ō) . . . Mex.	19.53 N	100.24 W
126	Marbella (mär-bâl′yä) . . . . Sp.	36.32 N	4.52 W
164	Marble Bar . . . . Austl.	21.15 S	119.30 E
87	Marblehead (mär′b′l-hĕd) Mass. (In.)	42.30 N	70.51 W
122	Marburg (mär′bŏŏrgh) . . . . Ger.	50.48 N	8.46 E
79	Marceline (mär-sē-lēn′) . . . . Mo.	39.44 N	92.56 W
117	Marche (märsh) . . . . Bel.	50.15 N	5.19 E
128	Marche (Prov.) (mär′kä) . . . . . . It.	43.30 N	13.0 E
126	Marchena (mär-chā′nä) . . . . Sp.	37.21 N	5.25 W
102	Marcheno (I.) (mär-chā′nō) . . . Ec.	0.28 N	90.30 W
163	Marchesa B. (mär-chā′sȧ) B. N. B.	6.33 N	117.35 E
99	Marcos Paz (mär-kōs′ päz) Arg. (Buenos Aires In.)	34.43 S	58.50 W
85	Marcus Hook (mär′kŭs hŏŏk) . Pa.	39.47 N	75.27 W
85	Marcy, Mt. (mär′sē) . . . . N. Y.	44.8 N	73.57 W
104	Mar del Plata (mär dĕl plä′tä) Arg.	38.1 S	57.31 W
113	Mardin (mär-dēn′) . . . . Tur.	37.28 N	40.35 E
116	Maree, Loch (L.) (mȧ-rē′) Gt. Brit.	57.35 N	5.40 W
165	Maré I. (mä-rä′) . . . . N. Cal.	21.40 S	168.5 E
77	Marengo (mȧ-rĕŋ′gō) . . . . Ia.	41.47 N	92.3 W
124	Marennes (mȧ-rĕn′) . . . . Fr.	45.48 N	1.5 W
135	Mareotis, L. (mär-ē-ō′tĭs) Eg. (In.)	31.5 N	29.55 E
143	Maretsano R. (mä-rĕt-sä′nē) . Bech.	26.2 S	25.10 E
80	Marfa (mär′fȧ) . . . . Tex.	30.18 N	104.2 W
73	Margaret (mär′gȧ-rĕt) Ala. (Birmingham In.)	33.39 N	86.30 W
102	Margarita I. (mär-gȧ-rē′tȧ) . . Ven.	11.0 N	54.0 W
117	Margate (mär′gāt) . . . . . . Gt. Brit.	51.21 N	1.21 E
148	Margelan (mär-gĕ′län′) . . Sov. Un.	20.20 N	71.50 E
123	Marggrabowa (mär-grȧ-bō′va) Ger.	54.2 N	22.30 E
163	Margosatubig (mär′gô-sȧ-tōō′bĕg) P. I.	7.33 N	123.10 E
112	Mari (Aut. Ter.) (mä′rē) . Sov. Un.	56.35 N	48.20 E
86	Maria (mȧ-rē′ȧ) . . . . Can.	48.10 N	66.3 W
163	Maria (mä-rē′ȧ) . . . . P. I.	9.11 N	123.40 E
96	María Aguilar, Pt. (mä-rē′ä ä-gē-lär′) . Cuba	21.45 N	80.0 W
92	María Cleofas I. (mä-rē′ä klā′ô-fäs) . Mex.	21.17 N	106.13 W
120	Mariager (mä′rē-ägh′ĕr) . . . . . Den.	56.38 N	10.0 E
120	Mariager Fjord . . . . Den.	56.42 N	10.15 E
169	Maria I. (mȧ-rī′ȧ) . Austl. (Tas. In.)	42.37 S	148.6 E
92	María Madre I. (mä-rē′ä mä′drȧ) . Mex.	21.35 N	106.32 W
92	Maria Magdalena I. (mä-rē′ä mäg-dä-lā′nä) . Mex.	21.25 N	106.24 W
121	Mariampole (mä-rē-äm′pôl-y′) Lith.	54.32 N	23.21 E
96	Marianao (mä-rē-ä-nä′ō) . . . . Cuba	23.4 N	82.28 W
90	Marianao, R. . . Cuba (Habana In.)	23.4 N	82.27 W
7	Marianas Is. (mä-rē-ä′näs) Pac. O.	16.0 N	145.0 E
79	Marianna (mā-rī-ăn′ȧ) . . . . Ark.	34.46 N	90.46 W
82	Marianna . . . . Fla.	30.46 N	85.16 W
	Mariánské Lázně, see Marienbad, Ger.		
71	Marias R. (mȧ-rī′ȧz) . . . . Mont.	48.25 N	111.50 W
95	Mariato Pt. (mä-rē-ä′tō) . . . . . Pan.	7.16 N	80.57 W
170	Maria van Diemer, C. (mȧ-rē′ȧ văn dē′mĕr) . N. Z.	34.27 S	172.36 E
120	Maribo (mä′rē-bō) . . . . Den.	54.47 N	11.28 E
163	Maribojoc (mä′rē-bô-yōk′) . . . P. I.	9.44 N	123.51 E
128	Maribor (mä′rē-bôr) . . . . Yugo.	46.34 N	15.36 E
129	Marica R. (mä′rēt-sä) . . . . Bul.	42.3 N	25.30 E
162	Maricaban I. (mä-rē-kä-bän′) P. I.	13.38 N	120.54 E
46	Marie Byrd Land (mȧ-rē′ bûrd′) Ant.	78.0 S	140.0 W
120	Mariefred (mä-rē′ĕ frĕd) . . . . . Swe.	59.15 N	17.10 E
95	Marie Galante (I.) (mȧ-rē′ gȧ-läɴt′) . Guad. (In.)	15.57 N	61.17 W
121	Mariehamn (Maarianhamina) (mȧ-rē′ĕ-häm″n) (mä′rē-än-hä′mē-nä) . Fin.	60.8 N	19.58 E
122	Marienbad (Mariánské Lázně) (mä-rē′ĕn-bät) (mär′yȧn-skĕ′ läz′nyĕ) . Ger.	49.58 N	12.42 E
123	Marienburg (mä-rē′ĕn-bŏŏrgh) Ger.	54.2 N	19.3 E
119	Mariendorf (mä-rē′ĕn-dôrf) Ger. (Berlin In.)	52.26 N	13.24 E
119	Marienfelde (mä-rē′ĕn-fĕl′dĕ) Ger. (Berlin In.)	52.25 N	13.22 E
123	Marienwerder (mä-rē′ĕn-vĕr′dĕr) Ger.	53.44 N	18.57 E
120	Mariestad (mä-rē′ĕ-städ′) . . . . Swe.	58.41 N	13.48 E
82	Marietta (mā-rĭ-ĕt′ȧ) . . . . Ga.	33.57 N	84.34 W
84	Marietta . . . . Ohio	39.24 N	81.30 W
79	Marietta . . . . Okla.	33.54 N	97.8 W
72	Marietta . . . Wash. (Vancouver In.)	48.48 N	122.35 W
97	Mariguana I. (mä-rē-gwä′nä) Ba. Is.	22.25 N	72.55 W
97	Mariguana Passage . . . . Ba. Is.	22.22 N	73.20 W
149	Mariinsk (mä-rē′ĭnsk) . . . . Sov. Un.	51.45 N	140.20 E
148	Mariinsk . . . . Sov. Un.	55.50 N	87.40 E
161	Marikina (mä-rē-kē′nȧ) P. I. (Manila In.)	14.38 N	121.6 E
161	Marilao (mä-rē-lä′ō) P. I. (Manila In.)	14.46 N	120.56 E
6	Marin (mȧ-răɴ′) . . . . . . Mart. (In.)	14.29 N	60.52 W
126	Marin (mä-rēn′) . . . . Sp.	42.23 N	8.41 W
162	Marinduque I. (mä-rên-dōō′kä) P. I.	13.20 N	122.0 E
84	Marine City (mȧ-rēn′) . . . . . Mich.	42.45 N	82.30 W
77	Marinette (mär-ĭ-nĕt′) . . . . . . Wis.	45.5 N	87.37 W
139	Maringa R. (mä-rĭŋ′gä) . Bel. Cong.	1.0 N	20.30 E

Page	Name Pronunciation Region	Lat. °′	Long. °′
126	Marinha Grande (mä-rēn′yȧ grän′dĕ) . Port.	39.45 N	8.53 W
82	Marion (mär′ĭ-ŭn) . . . . Ala.	32.37 N	87.19 W
79	Marion . . . . Ill.	37.44 N	88.56 W
84	Marion . . . . Ind.	40.34 N	85.43 W
77	Marion . . . . Ia.	42.2 N	91.36 W
79	Marion . . . . Kan.	38.20 N	97.2 W
84	Marion . . . . Ky.	37.20 N	88.5 W
83	Marion . . . . N. C.	35.40 N	82.1 W
76	Marion . . . . N. D.	46.37 N	98.20 W
84	Marion . . . . Ohio	40.37 N	83.7 W
83	Marion . . . . S. C.	34.10 N	79.13 W
83	Marion . . . . Va.	36.50 N	81.32 W
169	Marion B. . . . . Austl. (Tas. In.)	42.45 S	147.55 E
165	Marion Reef . . . . Austl.	18.59 S	152.29 E
161	Mariquina R. (mä-rē-kē′nä) P. I. (Manila In.)	14.45 N	121.11 E
103	Maripanim (mä-rē-päɴ-ĕɴ′) Braz. (In.)	0.40 S	47.40 W
163	Maripipi I. (mä-rē-pē-pē′) . . . . P. I.	11.47 N	124.20 E
74	Mariposa R. (măr-ĭ-pō′sȧ) . . . Calif.	37.13 N	120.35 W
129	Maritsa (Evros) R. (mȧ′rē-tsȧ) (ĕv′rôs) . Tur.	41.0 N	26.21 E
131	Mariupol (mä′rē-ōō-pôl′y′) Sov. Un.	47.6 N	37.34 E
162	Mariveles (mä-rê-vā′lās) . . . . . P. I.	14.27 N	120.29 E
161	Mariveles Mts. (mä-rê-vā′lās) P. I. (Manila In.)	14.31 N	120.23 E
120	Markaryd (mar′kä-rüd) . . . . . . Swe.	56.30 N	13.37 E
79	Marked Tree . . . . Ark.	35.31 N	90.26 W
118	Market Bosworth (bŏz′wûrth) Gt. Brit.	52.37 N	1.23 W
118	Market Deeping (dēp′ĭng) Gt. Brit.	52.40 N	0.18 W
118	Market Drayton (drā′tŭn) Gt. Brit.	52.54 N	2.29 W
118	Market Harborough (här′bŭr-ô) Gt. Brit.	52.28 N	0.55 W
118	Market Rasen (rā′zĕn) . . . Gt. Brit.	53.23 N	0.21 W
118	Market Weighton (wā′tŭn) Gt. Brit.	53.52 N	0.40 W
149	Markha R. (mär′ĸȧ) . . . . . Sov. Un.	64.50 N	115.0 E
149	Markhakhanskoe (mär-ĸȧ-ĸän′-skô-yĕ) . Sov. Un.	60.40 N	123.40 E
131	Markova (mär′kô-vȧ) . . . . Sov. Un.	49.31 N	39.32 E
149	Markovo (mär′kô-vô) . . . . Sov. Un.	64.35 N	170.35 E
113	Marksshtadt (märks′shtät) Sov. Un.	51.40 N	46.48 E
81	Marksville (märks′vĭl) . . . . La.	31.7 N	92.5 W
122	Marktredwitz (märkt-rĕd′vĕts) Ger.	50.1 N	12.5 E
86	Marlboro (märl′bŭr-ô) . . . . . . Mass.	42.20 N	71.32 W
84	Marlette (mär-lĕt′) . . . . Mich.	43.20 N	83.4 W
54	Marlile I. (mär′lĭl) . . . . Can.	62.42 N	91.30 W
81	Marlin (mär′lĭn) . . . . Tex.	31.18 N	96.54 W
85	Marlinton (mär′lĭn-tŭn) . . . W. Va.	38.14 N	80.10 W
78	Marlow (mär′lō) . . . . Okla.	34.39 N	97.57 W
125	Marly-le-Roi (mär-lē′lē rwä′) Fr. (In.)	48.51 N	2.6 E
124	Marmande (mȧr-mäɴd′) . . . . . . Fr.	44.30 N	0.10 E
129	Marmara I. (mär′mȧ-rȧ) . . . . . Tur.	40.35 N	27.40 E
113	Marmara, Sea of . . . . Tur.	40.45 N	28.30 E
76	Marmarth (mär′mȧrth) . . . . . . N. D.	46.18 N	103.57 W
127	Mar Menor (L.) (mär-mä-nôr′) Sp.	37.45 N	0.45 W
128	Marmora (Mt.) (mär′mō-rä) . Sard.	40.0 N	9.19 E
93	Mar Muerto (L.) (mär mwĕr′tō) Mex.	16.10 N	94.12 W
124	Marne R. (märn) . . . . Fr.	49.0 N	3.30 E
166	Marnoo (mär-nōō′) . . . . Austl.	36.40 S	142.52 E
139	Maroua (mär′wä) . . . . Cam.	10.33 N	14.21 E
102	Maroa (mä-rō′ä) . . . . Ven.	2.33 N	67.29 W
142	Maroantsetra (mȧ-rō-äŋ-tsä′trȧ) Madag.	15.20 S	49.48 E
125	Marolles (mȧ-rōl′) . . . . Fr. (In.)	48.41 N	2.36 E
103	Maroni R. (mȧ-rō′nē) Fr. Gui.-Sur.	4.0 N	53.15 W
166	Maroona (mȧ-rōō-nȧ) . . . . Austl.	37.26 S	142.51 E
118	Marple (mär′p′l) . . . . Gt. Brit.	53.24 N	2.4 W
92	Marqués, R. del (rē′ō dĕl mär-kās′) . Mex.	18.51 N	102.30 W
6	Marquesas Is. (mär-kā′sȧs) Pac. O	9.0 S	140.0 W
83	Marquesas Keys (Is.) . . . Fla. (In.)	23.45 N	82.10 W
56	Marquette (mär-kĕt′) Can. (Winnipeg In.)	50.4 N	97.45 W
77	Marquette . . . . Mich.	46.32 N	87.23 W
84	Marquette R. . . . . Mich.	43.55 N	86.0 W
81	Marquez (mär-käz′) . . . . Mex.	29.0 N	105.7 W
81	Marquez . . . . Tex.	31.14 N	96.15 W
124	Marquise (mȧr-kēz′) . . . . Fr.	50.49 N	1.41 E
167	Marra Cr. (măr′rȧ) . . . . Austl.	30.55 S	147.15 E
139	Marra, Jebel (Mts.) (jĕb′ĕl mär′ä) . A. E. Sud.	13.15 N	24.30 E
138	Marrakech (mȧr-rä′kĕsh) . . . . Mor.	31.50 N	8.0 W
169	Marrawah (mär′rȧ-wä) Austl. (Tas. In.)	40.54 S	144.43 E
164	Marre (măr′rē) . . . . Austl.	29.32 S	138.0 E
126	Marroqui, Pt. (mä-rō-kē′) . . . . . . Sp.	36.2 N	5.35 W
128	Marsala (mär-sä′lä) . . . . It.	37.48 N	12.28 E
115	Marsa Matrouh (mär′sa mȧ-trōō′) Eg.	31.20 N	27.12 E
104	Mar, Serra do (Mts.) (sĕr′rȧ dōō mär′) . Braz.	25.0 S	48.30 W
118	Marsden (märz′dĕn) . . . . . Gt. Brit.	53.36 N	155.0 W
124	Marseillan (mȧr-sȧ-yäɴ′) . . . . . . Fr.	43.20 N	3.30 E
125	Marseille (mȧr-sâ′y′) . . . . Fr.	43.20 N	5.20 E
143	Marseilles (mȧr-sālz′) . . . U. S. Afr.	29.8 S	27.16 E
72	Marshall (mär′shȧl) Colo. (Denver In.)	39.57 N	105.14 W
84	Marshall . . . . Ill.	39.25 N	87.40 W
84	Marshall . . . . Mich.	42.18 N	84.56 W
76	Marshall . . . . Minn.	44.28 N	95.48 W
79	Marshall . . . . Mo.	39.6 N	93.11 W
81	Marshall . . . . Tex.	32.33 N	94.21 W
7	Marshall Is. . . . . Pac. O.	10.0 N	171.0 E
77	Marshalltown (mär′shȧl-toun) . . Ia.	42.3 N	92.52 W
82	Marshallville (mär′shȧl-vĭl) . . . Ga.	32.28 N	83.58 W

ăt; finȧl; rāte; senâte; ärm; ȧsk; sofȧ; fâre; ch-choose dh-as th in other; bē; êvent; bĕt; recĕnt; cratẽr; g-go; gh-gutteral g; bĭt; ĭ-short neutral; rīde; ĸ-gutteral k as ch in German ich.

Page	Name Pronunciation Region	Lat. °′	Long. °′
87	Marshfield (märsh'fēld) Mass. (In.)	42.6 N	70.43 W
79	Marshfield Mo.	37.20 N	92.54 W
70	Marshfield Ore.	43.21 N	124.14 W
77	Marshfield Wis.	44.40 N	90.9 W
81	Marsh I. (märsh) La.	29.35 N	91.50 W
86	Mars Hill (märz' hĭl') Me.	46.32 N	67.55 W
49	Marshland (märsh'lănd) Ore. (Portland In.)	46.7 N	123.16 W
120	Marstrand (mär'strănd) Swe.	57.55 N	11.34 E
81	Mart (märt) Tex.	31.33 N	96.50 W
160	Martaban, G. of (mär-tŭ-bän') Ind.	16.0 N	96.45 E
160	Martapoera (mär-tä-pōō'rä) Neth. Ind.	3.20 S	114.50 E
85	Marthas Vineyard I. (mär'thȧz vĭn'yȧrd) Mass.	41.25 N	70.40 W
96	Marti (mär-tē') Cuba	22.58 N	80.55 W
122	Martigny (mȧr-tē-nyē') Switz.	46.6 N	7.3 E
124	Martigues (mȧr-tēg') Fr.	43.24 N	5.0 E
82	Martin (mär'tĭn) Tenn.	36.20 N	88.47 W
129	Martina (mär-tē'nä) It.	40.42 N	17.20 E
49	Martinez (mär-tē'nĕz) Calif. (San Francisco In.)	38.1 N	122.7 W
55	Martin Falls (mär'tĭn) Can.	51.35 N	86.20 W
91	Martinique (mȧr-tē-nēk') W. I.	14.45 N	61.0 W
49	Martins Bluff (mär'tĭnz) Wash. (Portland In.)	45.57 N	122.47 W
85	Martinsburg (mär'tĭnz-bûrg) W. Va.	39.27 N	77.58 W
84	Martins Ferry Ohio	40.5 N	80.45 W
84	Martinsville (mär'tĭnz-vĭl) Ind.	39.25 N	86.27 W
83	Martinsville Va.	36.42 N	79.54 W
170	Marton (mär'tŭn) N. Z.	40.5 S	175.25 E
127	Martorell (mär-tō-rĕl') Sp. (In.)	41.28 N	1.55 E
126	Martos (mär'tōs) Sp.	37.43 N	3.57 W
131	Martovaya (mär'tō-vä'yȧ) Sov. Un.	49.57 N	36.55 E
159	Marugame (mä'rōō-gä'mā) Jap.	34.14 N	133.48 E
124	Marvejols (mȧr-vē-zhōl') Fr.	44.34 N	3.15 E
131	Maryanovskaya (mär'yȧ-nôf-skä'-yȧ) Sov. Un.	45.5 N	38.38 E
166	Maryboro (mā'rĭ-bŭr-ō) Austl.	37.3 S	143.44 E
165	Maryboro Austl.	25.44 S	152.44 E
85	Maryland (State) (mĕr'ĭ-lănd) U. S.	39.0 N	76.30 W
116	Maryport (mā'rĭ-pōrt) Gt. Brit.	54.45 N	3.25 W
70	Marys R. (mā'rĭz) Nev.	41.25 N	115.14 W
74	Marysville (mā'rĭz-vĭl) Calif.	39.8 N	121.36 W
86	Marysville Can.	45.59 N	66.38 W
79	Marysville Kan.	39.51 N	96.37 W
84	Marysville Ohio	40.13 N	83.23 W
49	Marysville Wash. (Seattle In.)	48.3 N	122.11 W
169	Maryvale (mā'rĭ-vāl) Austl. (In.)	28.4 S	152.14 E
79	Maryville (mā'rĭ-vĭl) Mo.	40.21 N	94.51 W
82	Maryville Tenn.	35.35 N	83.58 W
157	Masan (mä-sän') Cho.	35.12 N	128.29 E
161	Masantol (mä-sän-tōl') P. I. (Manila In.)	14.53 N	120.38 E
141	Mâ sara Station (mä"sȧ-rä) Eg.	29.54 N	31.17 E
141	Masasi (mä-sä'sē) Tan.	10.25 S	38.0 E
94	Masaya (mä-sä'yä) Nic.	11.58 N	86.5 W
162	Masbate (mäs-bä'tä) P. I.	12.21 N	123.38 E
162	Masbate I. P. I.	12.20 N	123.30 E
138	Mascara (mäs'kä-rä) (mȧs-kȧ-rȧ') Alg.	35.30 N	0.5 E
82	Mascot (măs'kŏt) Tenn.	36.6 N	83.47 W
92	Mascota (mäs-kō'tä) Mex.	20.33 N	104.46 W
92	Mascota, R. de Mex.	20.35 N	104.50 W
57	Mascouche R. (mȧs-kōōsh') Can. (Montreal In.)	45.45 N	73.41 W
143	Maseru (măz'ēr-ōō) Bas.	29.19 S	27.30 E
118	Masham (măsh'ȧm) Gt. Brit.	54.13 N	1.39 W
150	Mashhad (mŭsh-hŭd') Iran	36.20 N	59.30 E
142	Mashowing R. (mȧ-shō'ĭng) Bech.	26.45 S	23.20 E
139	Masindi (mä-sēn'dē) Ug.	1.42 N	31.40 E
116	Mask, Lough (L.) (lŏk măsk) Ire.	53.40 N	9.20 W
127	Masnow (mäs'nō) Sp. (In.)	41.29 N	2.19 E
84	Mason (mā'sŭn) Mich.	42.34 N	84.28 W
80	Mason Tex.	30.45 N	99.14 W
77	Mason City Ia.	43.9 N	93.21 W
160	Ma Song (R.) (sŏng' mä') Fr. In. Chn.	20.30 N	105.0 E
49	Mason L. Wash. (Seattle In.)	47.20 N	122.57 W
72	Masonville (mā'sŭn-vĭl) Colo. (Denver In.)	40.30 N	105.14 W
150	Masqat (Muscat) (mŭs-kăt') (mŭs-kăt') Oman	23.35 N	58.38 E
127	Masquefa (mäs-kā'fä) Sp. (In.)	41.29 N	1.51 E
141	Masr el Atîga (Old Cairo) (măz"r ĕl ȧ-tē'kȧ) Eg.	30.1 N	31.15 E
128	Massa (mäs'sä) It.	44.2 N	10.8 E
86	Massachusetts (State) (măs-ȧ-chōō'sĕts) U. S.	42.28 N	72.0 W
86	Massachusetts B. U. S.	42.25 N	70.15 W
128	Massafra (mäs-sä'frä) It.	40.35 N	17.6 E
128	Massa Maritima (mäs'sä mä rē'tē-mä) It.	43.3 N	10.54 E
139	Massaua (mäs-sä'wä) It. E. Afr.	15.36 N	14.28 E
85	Massena (mă-sē'nȧ) N. Y.	44.57 N	74.54 W
119	Massenhoven (mäs'ĕn-hō'vĕn) Bel. (Anvers In.)	51.12 N	4.38 E
139	Massenya (mä-sĕn'yä) Fr. Eq. Afr.	11.28 N	16.10 E
54	Masset (măs'ĕt) Can.	54. 2 N	132.4 W
124	Massif Central (Plat.) (mȧ-sēf' säN-trȧl') Fr.	44.50 N	3.30 E
84	Massillon (măs'ĭ-lŏn) Ohio	40.50 N	81.32 W
140	Massinga (mä-sĭn'gȧ) Moz.	23.20 S	35.18 E
78	Massive, Mt. (măs'ĭv) Colo.	39.10 N	106.29 W
125	Massy (mȧ-sē') Fr. (In.)	48.45 N	2.17 E
169	Mastermans Range (măs'tēr-mȧnz) Austl. (In.)	20.10 S	150.50 E
171	Masterton (mȧs'tēr-tŭn) N. Z.	40.58 S	175.42 E
96	Mastic Pt. (măs'tĭk) Ba. Is.	25.5 N	78.0 W
159	Masude (mä-sōō'dä) Jap.	34.44 N	131.55 E
151	Masulipatam (mŭ-sōō'lē-pŭ-tŭm') India	16.8 N	81.8 E
123	Masuria (Reg.) (mȧ-zōō'rĭ-ȧ) Ger.	53.45 N	21.25 E
140	Matadi (mȧ-tä'dē) Bel. Cong.	5.47 S	13.35 E
103	Mata do São João (mä-tä dōō souN zhô-ouN) Braz. (In.)	12.30 S	38.17 W
94	Matagalpa (mä-tä-gäl'pä) Nic.	13.9 N	85.41 W
81	Matagorda B. (măt-ȧ-gôr'dȧ) Tex.	28.35 N	96.30 W
81	Matagorda I. Tex.	28.15 N	96.35 W
163	Matalom (mȧ-tä-lŏm') P. I.	10.18 N	124.48 E
138	Matam (mȧ-tăm') Fr. W. Afr.	15.42 N	13.21 W
170	Matamata (mä-tȧ-mä'tȧ) N. Z.	37.47 S	176.4 E
80	Matamoros (mä-tä-mō'rōs) Mex.	25.32 N	103.14 W
81	Matamoros Mex.	25.52 N	97.30 W
92	Matamoros de Izúcar (mä-tä-mō'-rôs dā ē'zōō'kär) Mex.	18.34 N	98.27 W
163	Matanal Pt. (mä-tä-näl') P. I.	6.37 N	122.19 E
55	Matane (mȧ-tăn') Can.	48.45 N	67.28 W
140	Matanga (mä-täŋ'gä) Ang.	7.32 S	17.28 E
53	Matanuska (mä-tä-nōōs'kȧ) Alsk.	61.38 N	149.0 W
52	Matanuska R. Alsk. (In.)	61.50 N	148.15 W
104	Matanza (mä-tän'zä) Arg. (In.)	34.42 S	58.32 W
96	Matanzas Cuba	23.1 N	81.39 W
97	Matanzas Hai.	19.19 N	69.47 W
96	Matanzas (State) (mä-tän'zäs) Cuba	22.47 N	81.10 W
96	Matanzas B. Cuba	23.5 N	81.34 W
104	Matanzas, R. Arg. (In.)	34.42 S	58.27 W
95	Matapalo, C. (mä-tä-pä'lō) C. R.	8.22 N	83.19 W
129	Matapan, C. (mȧ-tȧ-păn') Grc.	36.22 N	22.30 E
86	Matapedia (mă-tȧ-pē'dĭ-ȧ) Can.	48.0 N	66.56 W
86	Matapedia, L. Can.	48.34 N	67.35 W
86	Matapedia R. Can.	48.16 N	67.18 W
151	Matara (mä-tä'rä) Cey. (In.)	6.0 N	80.35 E
163	Matarinao B. (mä-tä-rē-nä'ō) P. I.	11.14 N	125.35 E
127	Mataró (mä-tä-rō') Sp. (In.)	41.33 N	2.27 E
170	Matata (mä-tä'tä) N. Z.	37.52 S	176.47 E
143	Matatiela (mä-tä-tyā'lä) U. S. Afr.	30.21 S	28.46 E
163	Matatindoc Pt. (mä-tä-tēn-dŏk') P. I.	9.40 N	122.24 E
171	Mataura (mȧ-tou'rȧ) N. Z.	46.12 S	168.52 E
171	Mataura R. N. Z.	45.40 S	168.42 E
6	Matautu (mä-tou'tōō) Sam. (In.)	13.29 S	172.22 W
92	Matehuala (mä-tä-wä'lä) Mex.	23.38 N	100.38 W
128	Matera (mä-tā'rä) It.	40.40 N	16.36 E
135	Mateur (mȧ-tûr') Tun. (In.)	37.2 N	9.41 E
55	Matheson (măth'ē-sŭn) Can.	48.29 N	80.27 W
97	Mathewtown (măth'ū-toun) Ba. Is.	20.58 N	73.40 W
163	Mati (mä'tē) P. I.	6.58 N	126.14 E
72	Matia Is. (mȧ'tyȧ) Wash. (Vancouver In.)	48.45 N	122.50 W
163	Matiguid I. (mä-tē-gēd') P. I.	11.3 N	119.35 E
95	Matina (mä-tē'nä) C. R.	10.4 N	83.16 W
121	Matisi (mä'tē-sē) Lat.	57.43 N	25.10 E
143	Matiwana Range (mä-tē-wä'nä) U. S. Afr.	31.20 S	28.30 E
142	Matjesfontein (măt'yĕs-fŏn-tān') U. S. Afr.	33.13 S	20.32 E
118	Matlock (măt'lŏk) Gt. Brit.	53.8 N	1.33 W
118	Matlock Bath Gt. Brit.	53.6 N	1.34 W
142	Matlowina R. (mät-lō-wē'nȧ) Bech.	27.12 S	23.30 E
135	Matmata (mȧt-mȧ'tȧ) Tun. (In.)	33.33 N	9.58 E
103	Mato Grosso (State) (mät'ōō grōs'-ōō) Braz.	15.0 S	55.0 W
103	Mato Grosso, Plat. of Braz.	15.0 S	54.0 W
126	Matozinhos (Leixoes) (mä-tō-zēn'yōzh) Port.	41.11 N	8.41 W
150	Matrah (mȧ'trä') Oman.	23.35 N	58.36 E
131	Matrenki (mä-trĕŋ'kē) Sov. Un.	51.27 N	38.39 E
72	Matsqui (măts'kē) Can. (Vancouver In.)	49.6 N	122.17 W
159	Matsudo (mät'sōō-dō) Jap. (Tokyo In.)	35.45 N	139.54 E
159	Matsué (mät'sōō-ĕ) Jap.	35.29 N	133.2 E
159	Matsukaichi (mät'sōō-kä'ē-chē) Jap.	34.22 N	132.19 E
159	Matsumoto (mät'sōō-mō'tō) Jap.	36.14 N	138.0 E
159	Matsuyama (mät'sōō-yä'mä) Jap.	33.48 N	132.45 E
55	Mattagami L. (mȧ-tȧ-gä'mē) Can.	50.0 N	77.28 W
85	Mattaponi R. (măt'ȧ-pō-nī') Va.	37.45 N	76.35 W
55	Mattawa (măt'ȧ-wȧ) Can.	46.16 N	78.13 W
86	Mattawin R. (măt'ȧ-wĭn) Can.	46.55 N	73.30 W
122	Matterhorn (Mt.) (mät'ēr-hôrn) Switz.	45.58 N	7.38 E
79	Mattoon (mă-tōōn') Ill.	39.27 N	88.22 W
102	Maturín (mä-tōō-rēn') Ven.	9.45 N	63.15 W
163	Matutum, Mt. (mä-tōō'tōōm) P. I.	6.20 N	125.7 E
159	Matzuzaka (mät'zōō-zä'kä) Jap.	34.34 N	136.33 E
104	Maua (mä'ōō-ä) Braz. (In.)	22.45 S	43.10 W
162	Mauban (mä'ōō-bän') P. I.	14.11 N	121.43 E
124	Maubeuge (mō-bûzh') Fr.	50.20 N	3.50 E
85	Mauch Chunk (môk' chŭnk') Pa.	40.52 N	75.45 W
119	Mauer (mou'ēr) Aus. (Wien In.)	48.9 N	16.16 E
123	Mauer L. Ger.	54.7 N	21.43 E
103	Maués (mä-ōō-āzh') Braz.	3.31 S	57.32 W
173	Maui (I.) (mä'ōō-ē) Haw.	20.45 N	156.20 W
158	Mauka (mä'ōō-kä') Kar.	47.2 N	142.2 E
124	Mauléon-Licharre (mō-lā-ôN'-lē-shär') Fr.	43.10 N	0.50 W
84	Maumee (mô-mē') Ohio	41.35 N	83.39 W
84	Maumee B. Mich.-Ohio	41.45 N	83.15 W
84	Maumee R. Ind.-Ohio	41.23 N	84.0 W
173	Mauna Kea (Vol.) (mä'ōō-nä kā'ä) Haw.	19.55 N	155.28 W
173	Mauna Loa (Vol.) (mä'ōō-nä lō'ä) Haw.	19.29 N	155.36 W
125	Maurecourt (mōr'kōōr') Fr. (In.)	48.59 N	2.4 E
81	Maurepas L. (mō-rē-pä') La.	30.15 N	90.30 W
138	Mauritania (Colony) (mô-rē-tā'-nĭ-ȧ) Fr. W. Afr.	19.0 N	12.0 W
6	Mauritius (I.) (mô-rĭsh'ĭ-ŭs) Ind. O. (In.)	20.18 S	57.36 E
49	Maury I. (mô'rĭ) Wash. (Seattle In.)	47.22 N	122.27 W
77	Mauston (môs'tŭn) Wis.	43.45 N	90.5 W
93	Maxcanú (mäs-kä-nōō') Mex.	20.36 N	89.59 W
112	Maxim Gorki, see Gorki Sov. Un.		
116	Maxwelltown (măks'wĕl-toun) Gt. Brit.	55.5 N	3.35 W
91	Mayagüez (mä-yä-gwāz') P.R. (In.)	18.10 N	67.15 W
154	Mayang (mä'yäng') Chn.	27.36 N	109.15 E
149	Maya R. (mä'yä) Sov. Un.	58.0 N	135.20 E
97	Mayarí (mä-yä-rē') Cuba	20.40 N	75.41 W
97	Mayarí, R. Cuba	20.32 N	75.40 W
122	Mayen (mī'ĕn) Ger.	50.18 N	7.13 E
124	Mayenne (mȧ-yĕn') Fr.	48.20 N	0.30 W
124	Mayenne R. Fr.	48.20 N	0.35 W
88	Mayfair (mā'fâr) Ill. (Chicago In.)	41.58 N	87.45 W
82	Mayfield (mā'fēld) Ky.	36.46 N	88.35 W
82	Mayfield Cr. Ky.	36.55 N	88.50 W
49	Mayger (mā'gēr) Ore. (Portland In.)	46.9 N	123.6 W
169	Maylands (mā'lăndz) Austl. (Perth In.)	31.55 S	115.54 E
73	Maylene (mā-lēn') Ala. (Birmingham In.)	33.13 N	86.54 W
152	Maymyo (mī'myō') India	22.25 N	96.30 E
87	Maynard (mā'nȧrd) Mass. (In.)	42.26 N	71.26 W
72	Mayne I. (mān) Can. (Vancouver In.)	48.52 N	123.17 W
163	Mayo B. (mä'yō) P. I.	6.56 N	126.20 E
83	Mayodan (mā-yō'dȧn) N. C.	36.25 N	79.59 W
53	Mayo L. (mā'ō) Can.	63.45 N	135.0 W
54	Mayo Landing Can.	63.59 N	135.31 W
116	Mayo, Mts. of Ire.	54.10 N	9.40 W
163	Mayon Vol. (mä-yōn') P. I.	13.15 N	123.40 E
170	Mayor I. (mā'ēr) N. Z.	37.17 S	176.15 E
141	Mayotte I. (mȧ-yŏt') Ind. O.	12.45 S	45.10 E
140	Mayoumba (mȧ-yōōm'bȧ) Fr. Eq. Afr.	3.13 S	10.42 E
80	Mayran, L. (mī-rän') Mex.	25.45 N	102.45 W
84	Maysville (māz'vĭl) Ky.	38.38 N	83.46 W
85	Mayville (mā'vĭl) N. Y.	42.14 N	79.30 W
76	Mayville N. D.	47.31 N	97.18 W
77	Mayville Wis.	43.31 N	88.32 W
89	Maywood (mā'wŏŏd) Ill. (Chicago In.)	41.53 N	87.50 W
140	Mazabuka (mä-zä-bōō'kä) N.. Rh.	16.0 S	27.48 E
138	Mazagan (mȧ-zȧ-gän') Mor.	33.21 N	8.30 W
103	Mazaganópolis (mä-zä-gä-nō'pō-lēzh) Braz.	0.10 S	51.29 W
124	Mazamet (mȧ-zȧ-mĕ') Fr.	43.30 N	2.20 E
80	Mazapil (mä-zä-pēl') Mex.	24.40 N	101.30 W
151	Mazar-i-Sharif (mä-zär'-ē-shä-rēf') Afg.	36.44 N	67.28 E
126	Mazarón (mä-thä-rōn') Sp.	37.36 N	1.18 W
103	Mazaruni R. (mä-zä-rōō'nē) Br. Gu.	6.0 N	59.30 W
94	Mazatenango (mä-zä-tā-näŋ'gō) Guat.	14.31 N	91.31 W
92	Mazatlán (mä-zä-tlän') Mex.	23.12 N	106.25 W
93	Mazatlán (San Juan) (sän'hwän') Mex.	17.3 N	95.27 W
121	Mažeikiai (mȧ'zhā-kē-ī') Lith.	56.19 N	22.25 E
128	Mazzara del Vallo (mät-sä'rä dĕl väl'lō) It.	37.39 N	12.37 E
128	Mazzarino (mät-sä-rē'nō) It.	37.18 N	14.12 E
143	Mbabane (m'bä-bä'nē) Swaz.	26.22 S	31.12 E
139	M'Baiki (m'bȧ-ē'kē) Fr. Eq. Afr.	3.58 N	17.58 E
140	M'Bigou (m-bē-gōō') Fr. Eq. Afr.	2.5 S	12.8 E
139	M'Bomu R. (m'bō'mōō) Bel. Cong.-Fr. Eq. Afr.	4.50 N	25.0 E
140	Mboukou (m-bōō-kōō') Fr. Eq. Afr.	4.28 S	12.12 E
138	M'Bout (m'bōō') Fr. W. Afr.	16.2 N	12.32 W
141	Mbweni (m-bwä'nē) Tan.	6.37 S	39.9 E
72	Mead (mēd) Colo. (Denver In.)	40.14 N	105.0 W
74	Mead, L. (mēd) Nev.	36.10 N	114.40 W
78	Meade (mēd) Kan.	37.17 N	100.21 W
71	Meade Peak Ida.	42.28 N	111.17 W
49	Meadowdale (mĕd'ō-dāl) Wash. (Seattle In.)	47.50 N	122.20 W
56	Meadows (mĕd'ōz) Can. (Winnipeg In.)	50.2 N	97.37 W
85	Meadville (mēd'vĭl) Pa.	41.40 N	80.10 W
84	Meaford (mē'fērd) Can.	44.36 N	80.39 W
165	Meandarra (mē-ăn-dä'rȧ) Austl.	27.20 S	149.29 E
124	Meaux (mō) Fr.	49.0 N	2.52 E
93	Mecapalapa (mā-kä-pä-lä'pä) Mex.	20.30 N	97.54 W
87	Mecatina I. (mā-kȧ-tē'nȧ) Can.	50.48 N	58.60 W
87	Mecatina R. Can.	50.50 N	59.50 W
150	Mecca (mĕk'ȧ) Sau. Ar	21.29 N	39.45 E
86	Mechanic Falls (mē-kăn'ĭk) Me.	44.5 N	70.25 W
85	Mechanicsburg (mē-kăn'ĭks-bûrg) Pa.	40.15 N	77.2 W
85	Mechanicsville (mē-kăn'ĭks-vĭl) N. Y.	42.56 N	73.46 W
114	Mécheria (mā-shē-rē'ä) Alg.	33.29 N	0.18 W
122	Mecklenburg (State) (mĕk'lĕn-bōōrgh) Ger.	53.35 N	12.5 E
160	Medan (mā-dän') Neth. Ind.	3.37 N	98.38 E
118	Medden, R. (mĕd'ĕn) Gt. Brit.	53.15 N	1.6 E
138	Médéa (mā-dā'ä) Alg.	36.24 N	2.35 E
102	Medellín (mā-dhĕl-yēn') Col.	6.1 N	75.47 W
93	Medellín Mex.	19.2 N	96.10 W
163	Medellín P. I.	11.8 N	123.59 E
135	Médenine (mā-dē-nēn') Tun. (In.)	33.23 N	10.25 E
87	Medfield (mĕd'fēld) Mass. (In.)	42.11 N	71.18 W
87	Medford (mĕd'fērd) Mass. (In.)	42.25 N	71.6 W
78	Medford Okla.	36.46 N	97.43 W
70	Medford Ore.	42.20 N	122.43 W
77	Medford Wis.	45.9 N	90.20 W
123	Medias (mĕd-yäsh') Rom.	46.10 N	24.22 E
70	Medical Lake (mĕd'ĭ-kăl) Wash.	47.34 N	117.40 W
71	Medicine L. (mĕd'ĭ-sĭn) Mont.	48.27 N	104.25 W
71	Medicine Bow Ra. (bō) Wyo.-Colo.	41.0 N	106.8 W
71	Medicine Bow R. Wyo.	42.0 N	106.30 W
54	Medicine Hat Can.	50.2 N	110.40 W

ng-sing; ŋ-baŋk; N-nasalized n; nŏd; cŏmmit; ōld; ōbey; ôrder; fōōd; fŏŏt; ou-out; s-soft; sh-dish; th-thin; pūre; ûnite; ûrn; stŭd; circŭs; ü-as "y" in study; '-indeterminate vowel.

Page	Name Pronunciation Region	Lat. °′	Long. °′
78	Medicine Lodge............Kan.	37.16 N	98.35 W
78	Medicine Lodge R.....Kan.-Okla.	37.10 N	98.34 W
150	Medina (må-dē′nä ......Sau. Ar.	24.30 N	39.45 E
85	Medina (mê-dī′nȧ).........N. Y.	43.16 N	78.23 W
84	Medina....................Ohio	41.8 N	81.51 W
126	Medina del Campo (må-dē′nä dĕl käm′pō).Sp.	41.17 N	4.55 W
126	Medina de Rioseco (må-dē′nä dā rê-ô-sā′kō).Sp.	41.53 N	5.4 W
80	Medina R. (må-dē′nä).......Tex.	29.30 N	98.55 W
127	Medina-Sidonia (må-dē′nä sê-dō′-nyä).Sp. (In.)	36.28 N	5.44 W
128	Mediterranean Sea (mĕd-ĭ-tĕr-ā′-nê-ăn).Eur.-Afr.-Asia	34.50 N	25.0 E
135	Medjerda Mts. (mĕ-jĕr′dȧ) Tun. (In.)	36.35 N	8.40 E
135	Medjerda, Oued (R.) (wĕd mĕ-jĕr′-dȧ).Tun. (In.)	36.32 N	9.0 E
135	Medjez-el-Bab (mĕ-jĕz′ĕl-bȧb′) Tun. (In.)	36.38 N	9.39 E
130	Medveditsa R. (måd-vyĕ′dê-tsȧ) Sov. Un.	50.30 N	44.30 E
131	Medvedovskaya (måd-vyĕ′dôf-skä′yä)...Sov. Un.	45.28 N	38.58 E
149	Medvezhi Is. (måd-vyĕ′zhê) Sov. Un.	70.40 N	161.0 E
113	Medvezhie (måd-vyĕ′zhĕ-yĕ) Sov. Un.	45.45 N	41.28 E
131	Medvin (måd-vên′)......Sov. Un.	49.22 N	30.48 E
87	Medway (mĕd′wā)....Mass. (In.)	42.8 N	71.23 W
119	Medway, R..Gt. Brit. (London In.)	51.22 N	0.29 E
130	Medyn (må-dēn′).......Sov. Un.	54.58 N	35.54 E
131	Medzhibozh (måd′zhê-bōzh′) Sov. Un.	49.25 N	27.25 E
164	Meekatharra (mē-kȧ-thăr′ȧ) Austl.	26.28 S	118.30 E
75	Meeker (mēk′ĕr)............Colo.	40.4 N	107.55 W
87	Meelpaeg L. (mēl′pȧ-ĕg)....Newf.	48.15 N	56.35 W
122	Meerane (mā-rä′nē).........Ger.	50.52 N	12.27 E
119	Meerdonck (mār′dônk) Bel. (Anvers In.)	51.16 N	4.9 E
151	Meerut (mē′ro͝ot) ....India	28.50 N	77.45 E
129	Megalopolis (mĕg-ȧ-lŏ′pô-lĭs) .Grc.	37.22 N	22.8 E
55	Megantic (mê-găn′tĭk) ......Can.	45.40 N	70.50 W
129	Megara (mĕg′ȧ-rȧ)...........Grc.	37.59 N	23.20 E
83	Meggett (mĕg′ĕt)...........S. C.	32.44 N	80.16 W
49	Megler (mĕg′lēr) Wash. (Portland In.)	46.15 N	123.51 W
130	Meglino, L. (må-glē′nô)..Sov. Un.	58.25 N	35.25 E
83	Meherrin R. (mê-hĕr′ĭn)......Va.	36.40 N	77.30 W
124	Mehun (mē-ŭɴ′).............Fr.	47.10 N	2.15 E
119	Meiendorf (mī′ĕn-dôrf) Ger. (Hamburg In.)	53.37 N	10.9 E
154	Mei Ling (mā′lĭng′).........Chn.	25.27 N	113.35 E
122	Meiningen (mī′nĭng-ĕn)......Ger.	50.34 N	10.25 E
155	Mei R. (mā′ē)..............Chn.	23.45 N	115.35 E
122	Meiringen (mī′rĭng-ĕn) .....Switz.	46.44 N	8.12 E
119	Meirreit (mī′rĭt).Bel. (Anvers In.)	51.21 N	4.35 E
122	Meiszen (mī′sĕn)...........Ger.	51.10 N	13.27 E
154	Meitan (mā′tän′)...........Chn.	37.45 N	107.37 E
154	Meitsi Ling (Mts.) (mā′tsē-lĭng′) Chn.	25.7 N	112.7 E
104	Mejillones (må-ĸê-lyō′nås) ...Chl.	23.1 S	70.30 W
138	Meknés (mĕk′nĕs) (mĕk-nĕs′) Mor.	34.0 N	5.33 W
160	Mekong R......Fr. In. Chn.-Siam	16.0 N	105.0 E
143	Melanies Kop (Mt.) (mĕ′lȧ-nēz kŏp′).U. S. Afr.	28.4 S	29.40 E
169	Melbourne (mĕl′bŭrn) Austl. (In.)		
166	Melbourne.................Austl.	37.47 S	144.58 E
83	Melbourne.............Fla. (In.)	28.3 N	80.37 W
118	Melbourne.............Gt. Brit.	52.49 N	1.26 W
79	Melcher (mĕl′chēr) ....Ia.	41.02 N	93.16 W
112	Melekess (mål′yĕ-kĕs′)...Sov. Un.	54.15 N	49.35 E
130	Melenki (må-lyĕŋ′kê)....Sov. Un.	55.20 N	41.41 E
128	Melfi (mĕl′fē)...............It.	40.58 N	15.38 E
103	Melgaço (mĕl-gä′so͞o) ....Braz.	16.30 S	56.0 W
139	Melik, Wadel (R.) (wäd-ĕl mĕ-lēk′).A. E. Sud.	17.0 N	30.0 E
138	Melilla (mā-lēl′yä)......Sp. Mor.	35.23 N	3.0 W
99	Melincué (må-lên-kwā′) Arg. (Buenos Aires In.)	33.39 S	61.26 W
99	Melipilla (må-lê-pē′lyä) Chl. (Valparaiso In.)	33.41 S	71.16 W
131	Melitopol (mā-lê-tô′pôl-y′) Sov. Un.	46.49 N	35.22 E
135	Mellègue, O. (R.) (wäd mē-lĕg′) Tun. (In.)	36.10 N	8.45 E
77	Mellen (mĕl′ĕn).............Wis.	46.19 N	90.39 W
120	Mellerud (mål′ĕ-ro͞odh)......Swe.	58.42 N	12.27 E
143	Melmoth (mĕl′môth) ...U. S. Afr.	28.35 S	31.24 E
104	Melo (mā′lō)................Ur.	32.28 S	54.10 W
129	Melos (Milo) (I.) (mē′lŏs) (mē′lō) Grc.	36.42 N	24.27 E
114	Melrir, Chott (mĕl′rēr).......Alg.	34.30 N	6.30 E
87	Melrose (mĕl′rōz).....Mass. (In.)	42.27 N	71.4 W
77	Melrose..................Minn.	45.40 N	94.48 W
170	Melrose..............N. Z. (In.)	41.20 S	174.47 E
88	Melrose Park ...Ill. (Chicago In.)	41.53 N	87.51 W
119	Melsele (mĕl′sĕ-lē)Bel. (Anvers In.)	51.13 N	4.16 E
140	Melsetter (mĕl-sĕt′ēr)......S. Rh.	19.50 S	32.47 E
118	Meltham (mĕl′thăm) ....Gt. Brit.	53.35 N	1.51 W
118	Melton Mowbray (mĕl′tŭn mō′brå) Gt. Brit.	52.46 N	0.52 W
124	Melin (mē-lŭɴ′)..............Fr.	48.35 N	2.41 E
135	Melusa (mā-lo͞o′sä) Sp. Mor. (Gibraltar In.)	35.42 N	5.23 E
139	Melut (må-lo͞ot′).......A. E. Sud.	10.30 N	32.11 E
81	Melville (mĕl′vĭl)............La.	30.41 N	91.45 W
49	Melville.......Ore. (Portland In.)	46.2 N	123.51 W
165	Melville, C...............Austl.	14.8 S	144.38 E
163	Melville, C.................P. I.	7.48 N	117.0 E
164	Melville I.................Austl.	11.30 S	131.0 E
55	Melville, L.................Lab.	54.2 N	59.0 W
55	Melville Pen................Can.	67.50 N	84.30 W

Page	Name Pronunciation Region	Lat. °′	Long. °′
48	Melville Sd.................Can.	73.30 N	10.50 W
169	Melville Water (L.) Austl. (Perth In.)	31.59 S	115.50 E
72	Melvin (mĕl′vĭn)Colo. (Denver In.)	39.37 N	104.50 W
123	Mélykút (mā′l′ ko͞ot)......Hung.	46.13 N	19.23 E
141	Memba (mĕm′bȧ)..........Moz.	14.13 S	40.28 E
121	Memel (Klaipēda) (klī′pĕ-dȧ) Lith.	55.42 N	21.10 E
123	Memel R. (mā′mĕl) ....Ger.-Lith.	55.7 N	21.45 E
122	Memmingen (mĕm′ĭng-ĕn)....Ger.	47.49 N	10.11 E
135	Memphis (Ruins)(mĕm′fĭs)Eg.(In.)	29.50 N	31.15 E
79	Memphis....................Mo.	40.27 N	92.11 W
82	Memphis..................Tenn.	35.7 N	90.5 W
78	Memphis...................Tex.	34.43 N	100.32 W
86	Memphremagog L. (mĕm′frê-mā′-gŏg).Can.	45.5 N	72.10 E
79	Mena (mē′nȧ)...............Ark.	34.35 N	94.10 W
131	Mena (mā-nȧ′) ....Sov. Un.	51.31 N	32.11 E
161	Menado (må-nä′do)....Neth. Ind.	1.30 N	124.53 E
160	Menam Chao Bhraya (R.) (må-näm′ chä′ō brä′yȧ).Siam	15.0 N	100.17 E
160	Menam Nan (R.) (må-näm′ nän′) Siam	18.0 N	100.30 E
80	Menard (mê-närd′)..........Tex.	30.56 N	99.48 W
77	Menasha (mê-năsh′ȧ)........Wis.	44.12 N	88.26 W
124	Mende (mäɴd)...............Fr.	44.30 N	3.30 E
113	Menderes (R.) (mĕn′dĕr-ĕs) ..Tur.	38.10 N	29.0 E
161	Mendez Nuñez (mĕn′dĕz no͞on′yĕz) P. I. (Manila In.)	14.11 N	120.53 E
116	Mendip Hills (mĕn′dĭp) ..Gt. Brit.	51.10 N	2.30 W
70	Mendocino, C. (mĕn′dô-sē′nō) Calif.	40.28 N	124.8 W
73	Mendon (mĕn′dŭn) Utah (Salt Lake City In.)	41.43 N	11.58 W
79	Mendota (mĕn-dō′tȧ).........Ill.	41.34 N	89.6 W
89	Mendota. Minn. (Minneapolis In.)	44.53 N	93.10 W
77	Mendota, L.................Wis.	43.5 N	89.25 W
104	Mendoza (mĕn-dō′sä)........Arg.	32.50 S	68.45 W
104	Mendoza (State)............Arg.	35.15 S	68.30 W
156	Mengcheng (mĕng′chĕng′)...Chn.	33.17 N	116.29 E
156	Meng Shan (Mts.) (mĕng′ shän′) Chn.	35.40 N	117.50 E
152	Mengtze (mĕng′tzĕ′)........Chn.	23.15 N	103.6 E
156	Mengyin (mĕng′yĭn′).........Chn.	35.47 N	117.54 E
166	Menindee (mĕn-ĭn′dê)......Austl.	32.24 S	142.25 E
166	Menindee, L...............Austl.	32.20 S	142.20 E
166	Meningie (mĕn-ĭn′gê).......Austl.	35.40 S	139.20 E
76	Menno (mĕn′ô)..............S. D.	43.14 N	97.33 W
77	Menominee (mê-nŏm′ĭ-nē)..Mich.	45.9 N	87.38 W
77	Menominee Ind. Res.........Wis.	45.0 N	88.40 W
77	Menominee R.........Mich.-Wis.	45.40 N	87.50 W
77	Menomonie.................Wis.	44.54 N	91.55 W
171	Menowai L. (mĕ-nô-wī′).....N. Z.	45.50 S	167.25 E
160	Mentawai Is. (mĕn-tä-vī′) Neth. Ind.	2.0 S	99.30 E
125	Menton (mäɴ-tôɴ′)...........Fr.	43.45 N	7.31 E
169	Mentone (mĕn-tō′nê) Austl. (Melbourne In.)	37.59 S	145.4 E
73	Mentone..Calif. (Los Angeles In.)	34.5 N	117.8 W
135	Menzala, L. (mĕn-zä′lȧ)..Eg. (In.)	31.15 N	32.0 E
112	Menzelinsk (mĕn′zyĕ-lênsk′) Sov. Un.	55.45 N	53.2 E
164	Menzies (mĕn′zēz)........Austl.	29.47 S	121.10 E
119	Meopham (mê-ŏp′ăm) Gt. Brit. (London In.)	51.22 N	0.22 E
80	Meoqui (må-ō′kê)..........Mex.	28.15 N	105.26 W
122	Meppel (mĕp′ĕl)...........Neth.	52.41 N	6.11 E
122	Meppen (mĕp′ĕn)...........Ger.	52.41 N	7.17 E
128	Merabelo, G. of (må-rä-bå-lô). Grc.	35.15 N	25.55 E
79	Meramec R. (mĕr′ȧ-mĕk)....Mo.	38.20 N	90.50 W
128	Merano (må-rä′nō)...........It.	46.40 N	11.10 E
87	Merasheen I. (mē′rȧ-shēn)..Newf.	47.30 N	54.15 W
161	Merauke (må-rou′kā)..Neth. Ind.	8.31 S	140.29 E
141	Merca (mĕr′kä)........It. E. Afr.	1.56 N	44.48 E
74	Merced (mēr-sĕd′)..........Calif.	37.17 N	120.30 W
104	Mercedario, Mt. (mĕr-så-dhä′-rê-ō).Arg.	31.58 S	70.15 W
104	Mercedes (mĕr-sā′dhās)......Arg.	29.15 S	58.10 W
104	Mercedes....................Ur.	33.28 S	58.0 W
80	Mercedes (mĕr-sā′dĕs).......Tex.	26.8 N	97.55 W
74	Merced R...................Calif.	37.23 N	120.40 W
170	Mercer (mûr′sēr)...........N. Z.	37.18 S	175.8 E
49	Mercer I......Wash. (Seattle In.)	47.33 N	122.13 W
88	Merchantville (mûr′chănt-vĭl) Pa. (Philadelphia In.)	39.57 N	75.3 W
57	Mercier (mĕr-syā)′.....Can. (In.)	46.47 N	70.28 W
127	Mercier-Lacombe (mĕr-syā′-lȧ-kôɴb′) Alg.	35.15 N	0.12 W
145	Merdjeioun (mĕr-jå-o͞on′) Syr. (In.)	33.23 N	35.33 E
123	Mereczanka R. (må′rå-chăŋ-kä) Pol.	54.26 N	25.10 E
86	Meredith (mĕr′ê-dĭth)......N. H.	43.35 N	71.35 W
131	Merefa (må-rĕf′ȧ).......Sov. Un.	49.48 N	36.3 E
94	Merendon, Sierra de (Mts.) (syår′-ä dā må-rĕn-dōn′).Cen. Am.	15.15 N	88.55 W
153	Mergen (Nünkiang) (mĕr′gĕn) (nün′kyäng′).Manch.	49.20 N	125.27 E
160	Mergui (mĕr-gē′)...........India	12.28 N	98.40 E
160	Mergui Arch...............India	11.30 N	98.15 E
93	Mérida (mā′rê-dhä).........Mex.	20.57 N	89.37 W
163	Mérida......................P. I.	10.54 N	124.32 E
126	Mérida.......................Sp.	38.55 N	6.20 W
102	Mérida......................Ven.	8.31 N	71.1 W
85	Meriden (mĕr′ĭ-dĕn)........Conn.	41.32 N	72.48 W
82	Meridian (mê-rĭd′ĭ-ăn)......Miss.	32.22 N	88.42 W
81	Meridian....................Tex.	31.55 N	97.38 W
166	Meringer (mĕ′rĭn-jēr)......Austl.	34.15 S	141.11 E
104	Meriti (må-rē′tê)......Braz. (In.)	22.47 S	43.17 W
121	Merikarvia (mā′rē-kȧr-vê-ȧ)..Fin.	62.45 N	21.30 E
80	Merkel (mûr′kĕl)............Tex.	32.28 N	100.2 W
121	Merkine (mĕr′kĭ-nē) ....Lith.	54.11 N	24.10 E
139	Merowi (mā-rô-wē′)....A. E. Sud.	18.30 N	31.55 E
77	Merrill (mĕr′ĭl).............Wis.	45.11 N	89.40 W

Page	Name Pronunciaton Region	Lat. °′	Long. °′
87	Merrimac (mĕr′ĭ-măk).Mass. (In.)	42.50 N	71.5 W
86	Merrimack R........Mass.-N. H.	43.10 N	71.30 W
169	Merri Merri Cr. (mĕr′ê mĕr′ê) Austl. (Melbourne In.)	37.42 S	144.59 E
167	Merriwa (mĕr′ĭ-wȧ)........Austl.	32.10 S	150.22 E
167	Merrygoen (mĕr-rê-gō′ĕn)...Austl.	31.51 S	149.13 E
81	Merryville (mĕr′ĭ-vĭl).........La.	30.46 N	93.35 W
122	Merseburg (mĕr′zē-bo͝orgh)...Ger.	51.21 N	11.59 E
169	Mersey R. (mûr′zê) Austl. (Tas. In.)	41.30 S	146.30 E
116	Mersey R...............Gt. Brit.	53.15 N	2.50 W
113	Mersin (mĕr-sēn′)...........Tur.	36.50 N	34.40 E
116	Merthyr Tydfil (mûr′thēr tĭd′vĭl).Gt. Brit.	51.45 N	3.25 W
126	Mértola (mĕr′tô-lȧ).........Port.	37.38 N	7.42 W
48	Mertz Glacier (mĕrts).......Ant.	67.0 S	145.0 E
124	Méru (mā-rü′)...............Fr.	49.15 N	2.9 E
139	Meru (mā′ro͞o)............Kenya	0.2 N	37.36 E
150	Merv (mĕrf)...........Sov. Un.	37.50 N	61.40 E
117	Merxem (mĕrk′sĕm).........Bel.	51.15 N	4.25 E
113	Merzifon (mĕr′zê-fōn).......Tur.	40.50 N	35.32 E
75	Mesa (mā′sȧ)...............Ariz.	33.24 N	111.51 W
72	Mesa.........Colo. (Denver In.)	39.45 N	104.43 W
77	Mesabi Range.............Minn.	47.32 N	92.30 W
129	Mesagne (mā-sän′yā).........It.	40.34 N	17.49 E
75	Mesa Verde Natl. Park (mā′sä vâr′dā).Colo.	37.15 N	108.30 W
78	Mescalero Apache Ind. Res. (mĕs-kä-lā′rō).N. M.	33.10 N	105.30 W
122	Meseritz (mĕ-zĕ-rēts′).......Ger.	52.27 N	15.35 E
130	Meshchevsk (myĕsh′chĕfsk) Sov. Un.	54.18 N	35.19 E
	Meshed, see Mashhad, Iran.		
139	Meshraer Reg. (mĕsh′rȧ-ĕr) A. E. Sud.	8.28 N	29.19 E
75	Mesilla (må-sē′yä).........N. M.	32.18 N	106.49 W
129	Mesolongion (mē-sô-lôŋ′gê-ôn) Grc.	38.23 N	21.27 E
...	Mesopotamia, see Iraq		
129	Messene (mĕ-sē′nê)..........Grc.	37.3 N	22.0 E
129	Messene, G. of..............Grc.	36.35 N	22.5 E
128	Messina (mĕ-sē′nȧ)...........It.	38.13 N	15.13 E
140	Messina...............U. S. Afr.	22.20 S	30.10 E
128	Messina, Str. of..............It.	38.15 N	15.37 E
125	Messy (mē-sē′)..........Fr. (In.)	48.58 N	2.43 E
129	Mesta R. (mĕ-stȧ′)..........Bul.	41.40 N	23.43 E
128	Mestre (mĕs′trā).............It.	45.29 N	12.14 E
119	Meta (mā′tä) It. (Napoli In.)	40.38 N	14.23 E
86	Metabetchouan R. (mĕ-tȧ-bĕt-cho͞o-än′).Can.	48.0 N	72.0 W
112	Metallist (må-tä-lêst′)....Sov. Un.	55.59 N	43.5 E
94	Metapa (Ciudad Dario) (må-tä′pä) (syo͞o-dhädh′ dä′rê-ō).Nic.	12.53 N	86.1 W
94	Metapán (må-tä-pän′)........Sal.	14.21 N	89.27 W
102	Meta, R. (mā′tä).......Ven.-Col.	6.0 N	69.30 W
92	Metepec (må-tĕ-pĕk′).......Mex.	18.56 N	98.29 W
92	Metepec ....Mex.	19.16 N	99.35 W
70	Methow R. (mĕt′hou) (mĕt hou′) Wash.	48.25 N	120.10 W
87	Methuen (mê-thū′ĕn)..Mass. (In.)	42.43 N	71.11 W
55	Métis (må-tē′) (mā-tĭs′).....Can.	48.32 N	68.0 W
86	Métis Beach................Can.	48.39 N	68.3 W
129	Metković (mĕt′kô-vĭch)....Yugo.	43.3 N	17.40 E
56	Metlakatla (mĕt-lȧ-kăt′lȧ) Can. (Prince Rupert In.)	54.21 N	130.28 W
79	Metropolis (mê-trŏp′ô-lĭs).....Ill.	37.9 N	88.42 W
70	Metropolis.................Nev.	41.13 N	115.9 W
121	Metsäpirtti (mĕt′sĕ-pēr′tĭ)....Fin.	60.35 N	30.34 E
83	Metter (mĕt′ēr)..............Ga.	32.20 N	82.3 W
125	Metz (mĕtz)..................Fr.	49.9 N	6.10 E
92	Metztitlán (mĕtz-têt-län′)...Mex.	20.35 N	98.45 W
125	Meudon (mû-dôɴ′)......Fr. (In.)	48.48 N	2.14 E
125	Meulan (mû-läɴ′).......Fr. (In.)	49.0 N	1.54 E
124	Meung (măɴ′)................Fr.	47.52 N	1.49 E
117	Meuse, R. (mûz) (mūz)......Eur.	50.30 N	5.0 E
118	Mexborough (mĕks′bŭr-ô)Gt. Brit.	53.30 N	1.17 W
92	Mexcala, R. (mĕs-kä′lä).....Mex.	17.55 N	99.0 W
81	Mexia (må-hē′ä).............Tex.	31.41 N	96.28 W
74	Mexicali (må-hē-kä′lê)......Mex.	32.38 N	115.30 W
86	Mexico (mĕk′sĭ-kō)..........Me.	44.35 N	70.31 W
93	Mexico D. F..........Mex. (In.)		
92	Mexico (State), (måk′sê-kō). Mex.	19.0 N	100.0 W
93	Mexico, D. F.........Mex. (In.)	19.26 N	99.7 W
79	Mexico (mĕk′sĭ-kō)..........Mo.	39.9 N	91.51 W
48	Mexico, G. of..............N. A.	25.0 N	90.0 W
92	Mexico, Plat. of............Mex.	22.0 N	102.0 W
92	Mexticacán (mĕs′tê-kä-kän′).Mex.	21.15 N	102.45 W
161	Meycauayán (mā′ê-kou-ä-yän′) P. I. (Manila In.)	14.45 N	120.56 E
85	Meyersdale (mī′ērz-dāl).......Pa.	39.52 N	79.2 W
143	Meyerton (mī′ēr-tŭn)...U. S. Afr.	26.35 S	28.2 E
124	Méze (mâz)..................Fr.	43.25 N	3.35 E
112	Mezen (må-zĕn′y′)......Sov. Un.	65.50 N	44.25 E
112	Mezen R...............Sov. Un.	65.0 N	46.0 E
130	Mezha R. (myā′zhȧ).....Sov. Un.	55.50 N	32.15 E
131	Mezherichi (må-zhĕ-rē′chê) Sov. Un.	50.42 N	34.29 E
124	Mézières (mā-zyâr′)..........Fr.	49.45 N	4.45 E
123	Mezōkōvesd (mĕ′zû-kû′vĕsht) Hung.	47.48 N	20.35 E
123	Mezōtúr (mĕ′zû-to͞or)......Hung.	47.0 N	20.36 E
92	Mezquital (måz-kê-täl′).....Mex.	23.28 N	104.23 W
92	Mezquital, R................Mex.	23.33 N	104.20 W
92	Mezquitic (måz-kê-tēk′).....Mex.	22.31 N	103.46 W
141	Mgera (m′gā′rä) ....Tan.	5.23 S	37.33 E
130	Mglin (m′glên′).........Sov. Un.	53.2 N	32.51 E
141	Mhonda (m′hôn′dȧ).........Tan.	6.8 S	37.40 E
92	Miacatlán (mē′ä-kä-tlän′)...Mex.	18.45 N	99.21 W
163	Miagao (mē-ä-gä′ō) ....P. I.	10.38 N	122.14 E
93	Miahuatlán (San Andrés) (mē′ä-wä-tlän′) Mex.	16.20 N	96.30 W
126	Miajadas (mê-ä-hä′däs).......Sp.	39.10 N	5.52 W

ăt; finăl; rāte; senâte; ārm; ȧsk; sofȧ; fâre; ch-choose; dh-as th in other; bē; êvent; bĕt; recĕnt; cratēr; g-go; gh-gutteral g; bĭt; ĭ-short neutral; rīde; ĸ-gutteral k as ch in German ich;

Page	Name Pronunciation Region	Lat. °′	Long. °′
75	Miami (mī-ăm′ĭ)...........Ariz.	33.23 N	110.54 W
83	Miami...............Fla. (In.)	25.46 N	80.12 W
79	Miami...................Okla.	36.53 N	94.51 W
78	Miami.....................Tex.	35.41 N	100.38 W
83	Miami Beach..........Fla. (In.)	25.47 N	80.7 W
84	Miami R...................Ohio	39.20 N	84.38 W
84	Miamisburg (mī-ăm′ĭz-bûrg).Ohio	39.40 N	84.18 W
156	Miau-Tao I. (mē′ou′-tä′ō)...Chn.	38.12 N	120.40 E
123	Michalovce (mē′kȧ-lôf′tsĕ).Czech.	48.45 N	21.55 E
87	Michel L.(mē-shĕl′)(mĭch′ĕl)Newf.	50.20 N	56.55 W
84	Michigan (State) (mĭsh′ĭ-găn)U. S.	44.0 N	85.0 W
84	Michigan City.............Ind.	41.42 N	86.54 W
84	Michigan, L...............U. S.	44.0 N	87.0 W
77	Michipicoten Har. (mĕ-shĭ-pĭ-kō′tĕn).Can.	47.59 N	84.51 W
55	Michipicoten I.............Can.	47.50 N	85.32 W
77	Michipicoten R.............Can.	47.56 N	84.28 W
92	Michoacán (State) (mē-chō-ä-kän′) Mex.	19.0 N	102.0 W
130	Michurinsk (mĭ-chōō-rĭnsk′) Sov. Un.	52.54 N	40.31 E
70	Midas (mī′dȧs).............Nev.	41.15 N	116.48 W
117	Middleburg (mĭd′ĕl-bûrg)...Neth.	51.32 N	3.35 E
120	Middelfart (mĕd′′l-fŏrt).....Den.	55.30 N	9.44 E
96	Middle Bight (bĭt)........Ba. Is.	24.20 N	77.40 W
143	Middleburg (mĭd′′l-bûrg)U. S. Afr.	25.45 S	29.25 E
143	Middelburg............U. S. Afr.	31.30 S	24.58 E
86	Middlebury (mĭd′′l-bĕr-ĭ).....Vt.	44.0 N	73.11 W
56	Middlechurch (mĭd′′l-chûrch) Can. (Winnipeg In.)	49.58 N	97.4 W
80	Middle Concho R. (kŏn′chō) .Tex.	31.22 N	101.0 W
140	Middle Congo (State) (kŏŋ′gō) Fr. Eq. Afr.	2.30 S	13.45 E
97	Middle Ground...........Ba. Is.	22.50 N	76.8 W
96	Middle Ground...........Ba. Is.	24.55 N	77.3 W
70	Middle L.............Calif.-Nev.	41.25 N	120.3 W
76	Middle Loup R. (lōōp)......Neb.	41.20 N	99.5 W
84	Middleport (mĭd′′l-pōrt).....Ohio	39.0 N	82.5 W
82	Middlesboro (mĭd′′lz-bŭr-ō)...Ky.	36.37 N	83.43 W
116	Middlesborough (mĭd′′lz-brŭ) Gt. Brit.	54.35 N	1.15 W
86	Middleton (mĭd′′l-tŭn)......Can.	44.57 N	65.5 W
118	Middleton..............Gt. Brit.	53.33 N	2.11 W
87	Middleton...........Mass. (In.)	42.36 N	71.1 W
53	Middleton I................Alsk.	59.25 N	145.30 W
85	Middletown (mĭd′′l-toun)...Conn.	41.33 N	72.40 W
85	Middletown.................Del.	39.27 N	75.43 W
85	Middletown................N. Y.	41.27 N	74.27 W
84	Middletown.................Ohio	39.30 N	84.27 W
118	Middlewich (mĭd′′l-wĭch) Gt. Brit.	53.11 N	2.27 W
124	Midi d'Ossau, Pic du (Mt.) (pĕk dü mē-dē′ dŏs-sō′.Fr.	42.50 N	0.35 W
143	Mid Illovo (mĭd ĭl′ō-vō).U. S. Afr.	29.59 S	30.32 E
85	Midland (mĭd′lȧnd)..........Can.	44.43 N	79.54 W
72	Midland...Colo. (Colo. Sprs. In.)	38.52 N	105.10 W
84	Midland....................Mich.	43.40 N	84.18 W
80	Midland.....................Tex.	32.0 N	102.4 W
75	Midvale (mĭd′vāl)...........Utah	40.35 N	111.56 W
73	Midway (mĭd′wā) Utah (Salt Lake City In.)	40.31 N	111.29 W
6	Midway I.................Pac. O.	28.13 N	177.21 W
71	Midwest (mĭd-wĕst′)........Wyo.	43.37 N	106.15 W
113	Midye (mēd′yĕ)..............Tur.	41.35 N	28.8 E
141	Mie (mē′ā)...........It. E. Afr.	9.54 N	49.30 E
123	Miechów (myĕ′kōōf)..........Pol.	50.22 N	20.2 E
122	Miedzychód (myăN-dzŭ′kōōt).Pol.	52.36 N	15.54 E
123	Międzyrzec (myăN-dzē′zhĕts).Pol.	51.58 N	22.47 E
123	Mielec (myā′lĕts)............Pol.	50.16 N	21.26 E
154	Mienyang (myĕn′yăng′)......Chn.	30.11 N	113.4 E
80	Mier (myâr)................Mex.	26.27 N	99.10 W
126	Mieres (myā′rās)..............Sp.	43.15 N	5.45 W
142	Miers Kloof (Mt.) (mī′ĕrz klōōf) U. S. Afr.	31.28 S	19.55 E
92	Miery Noriega (myâr e nō-rē-ā′gä) Mex.	23.25 N	100.9 W
82	Mignon (mĭn′yŏn)...........Ala.	33.4 N	86.15 W
156	Mihsien (mē′hysĕn′)........Chn.	34.29 N	133.20 E
159	Mi I. (mē)...................Jap.	34.48 N	131.8 E
127	Mijares R. (mē-hä′rās).......Sp.	40.10 N	0.48 W
97	Mijo, Mt. (mē′hō)...........Hai.	18.58 N	71.9 W
159	Mikage(mē′kȧ-gȧ) Jap. (Osaka In.)	34.43 N	135.15 E
159	Mikawa, B. (mē′kȧ-wȧ).......Jap.	34.45 N	137.10 E
141	Mikese (mē-kā′sȧ)...........Tan.	6.48 S	37.56 E
113	Mikhailov (mē-kȧ′ē-lôf)..Sov. Un.	50.5 N	43.15 E
130	Mikhailov...............Sov. Un.	54.12 N	39.3 E
131	Mikhailovka (mē-kȧ-ē-lôf′kȧ) Sov. Un.	47.14 N	35.8 E
150	Mikhlaf (mĕk-läf′)........Sau. Ar.	17.37 N	45.16 E
159	Miki (mē′kē)....Jap. (Osaka In.)	34.49 N	134.59 E
141	Mikindani (mē-kĕn-dä′nē)...Tan.	10.15 S	40.5 E
121	Mikkeli (mēk′ĕ-lĭ)............Fin.	61.44 N	27.16 E
	Mikulov, see Nikolsburg, Ger.		
159	Mikuni (mē′kōō-nē)..........Jap.	36.16 N	136.12 E
138	Mila (mē′lä)..................Alg.	36.30 N	6.15 E
77	Milaca (mē-lăk′ȧ)...........Minn.	45.46 N	93.39 W
162	Milagros (mē-lä′grōs)........P. I.	12.14 N	123.31 E
128	Milan (Milano) (mĭl′ăn) (mē-lä′nō) It.	45.27 N	9.10 E
79	Milan (mī′lăn)...............Mo.	40.13 N	93.6 W
84	Milan.......................Mich.	42.5 N	83.40 W
82	Milan.......................Tenn.	35.55 N	88.47 W
128	Milano (Milan) (mē-lä′nō) (mĭl′ăn) It.	45.27 N	9.10 E
166	Milang (mĭ-lăng′)..........Austl.	35.22 S	138.59 E
113	Milas (mē′läs)................Tur.	37.20 N	27.45 E
128	Milazzo (mē-lät′sō)...........It.	38.13 N	15.15 E
76	Milbank (mĭl′băŋk)..........S. D.	45.14 N	96.38 W
166	Mildura (mĭl-dū′rȧ).........Austl.	34.11 S	142.9 E
71	Miles City (mīlz)...........Mont.	46.25 N	105.49 W
85	Milford (mĭl′fērd)..........Conn.	41.12 N	73.5 W
85	Milford......................Del.	38.55 N	75.26 W
86	Milford.....................Mass.	42.9 N	71.32 W
86	Milford.....................N. H.	42.50 N	71.40 W
75	Milford.....................Utah	38.25 N	113.1 W
116	Milford Haven..........Gt. Brit.	51.42 N	5.0 W
171	Milford Sd..................N. Z.	44.35 S	167.52 E
114	Miliana (mēl-yä′nä).........Alg.	36.20 N	2.7 E
164	Miling (mĭl′ĭng)...........Austl.	30.25 S	116.32 E
71	Milk R...............Alta.-Mont.	48.28 N	108.30 W
86	Mill........................Can.	44.10 N	64.39 W
124	Millau (mē-yō′)...............Fr.	44.5 N	3.5 E
49	Millbrae (mĭl′brā) Calif. (San Francisco In.)	37.35 N	122.23 W
119	Millbrook (mĭl′brŏŏk) Gt. Brit. (Liverpool In.)	53.30 N	2.3 W
87	Millbury (mĭl′bĕr-ĭ)...Mass. (In.)	42.12 N	71.45 W
74	Mill Cr......................Calif.	40.9 N	121.55 W
82	Milledgeville (mĭl′ĕj-vĭl)......Ga.	33.5 N	83.15 W
57	Mille Iles, R. des (rē-vyâr dā mē′y′ēl′) Can. (Montreal In.)	45.40 N	73.45 W
77	Mille Lacs L. (mĭl lăk′).....Minn.	46.75 N	93.40 W
83	Millen (mĭl′ĕn)...............Ga.	32.48 N	81.57 W
76	Miller (mĭl′ēr)..............S. D.	44.32 N	98.59 W
88	Miller Cr......Minn. (Duluth In.)	46.47 N	92.9 W
131	Millerovo (mēl-ĕ-rô′vô)..Sov. Un.	48.56 N	40.24 E
84	Millersburg (mĭl′ērz-bûrg)....Ky.	38.18 N	84.10 W
84	Millersburg.................Ohio	40.38 N	81.56 W
85	Millersburg...................Pa.	40.34 N	76.58 W
86	Millerton (mĭl′ēr-tŭn).......Can.	46.55 N	65.37 W
87	Millertown (mĭl′ēr-toun)....Newf.	48.48 N	56.30 W
166	Millicent (mĭl′ĭ-sĕnt).......Austl.	37.34 S	140 19 E
72	Milliken (mĭl′ĭ-kĕn) Colo. (Denver In.)	40.19 N	104.52 W
86	Millinocket (mĭl-ĭ-nŏk′ĕt).....Me.	45.40 N	68.43 W
87	Millis (mĭl′ĭs)........Mass. (In.)	42.10 N	71.23 W
164	Millstream (mĭl′strēm).....Austl.	21.40 S	117.0 E
86	Milltown (mĭl′toun).........Can.	45.10 N	67.19 W
49	Milltown......Wash. (Seattle In.)	48.18 N	122.21 W
49	Mill Valley Calif. (San Francisco In.)	37.53 N	122.31 W
79	Millville (mĭl′vĭl)...........Ark.	33.43 N	92.36 W
82	Millville......................Fla.	30.8 N	85.37 W
85	Millville.....................N. J.	39.26 N	75.2 W
73	Millville. Utah (Salt Lake City In.)	41.41 N	111.49 W
169	Milmerran (mĭl′mē-rȧn)Austl.(In.)	27.56 S	151.21 E
141	Milnerton (mĭl′nēr-tŭn).U. S. Afr.	33.53 S	18.29 E
76	Milnor (mĭl′nēr)............N. D.	46.17 N	97.26 W
86	Milo (mī′lō)..................Me.	45.17 N	69.0 W
129	Milo (Melos) (I.) (mī′lō) (mē′-lŏs).Grc.	36.45 N	24.28 E
49	Milpitas (mĭl′pĭ-tȧs) Calif. (San Francisco In.)	37.26 N	121.55 W
167	Milton (mĭl′tŭn)............Austl.	35.19 S	150.25 E
82	Milton........................Fla.	30.37 N	87.3 W
119	Milton.....Gt. Brit. (London In.)	51.21 S	0.43 E
87	Milton..............Mass. (In.)	42.16 N	71.3 W
171	Milton.......................N. Z.	46.9 S	169.58 E
70	Milton........................Ore.	45.56 N	118.25 W
85	Milton.........................Pa.	41.0 N	76.50 W
49	Milton........Wash. (Seattle In.)	47.15 N	122.20 W
77	Milwaukee (mĭl-wô′kē).......Wis.	43.2 N	87.55 W
127	Mina, Wadi (R.) (mē′nȧ)......Alg.	35.30 N	0.40 E
159	Minakuchi (mē′nȧ-kōō′chē)...Jap.	34.58 N	136.7 E
104	Minas (mē′nȧs)................Ur.	34.28 S	55.15 W
86	Minas Basin (mī′nȧs).........Can.	45.15 N	64.15 W
86	Minas Chan...................Can.	45.15 N	64.45 W
126	Minas de Ríotinto (mē′nās dā rē-ō-tēn′tō).Sp.	37.42 N	6.35 W
103	Minas Geraes (State) (mē′näzh zhā-rä′ăzh).Braz.	19.0 S	45.0 W
103	Minas Novas (mē′näzh nō′väzh) Braz.	17.20 S	42.32 W
94	Minas, Sierra de las (Mts.) (syĕr′rä dā läs mē′näs).Guat.	15.10 N	89.50 W
76	Minatare, L. (mĭn′ȧ-târ).....Neb.	41.54 N	103.15 W
93	Minatitlán (mē-nä-tē-tlän′)...Mex.	18.0 N	94.31 W
92	Minatitlán....................Mex.	19.22 N	104.3 W
159	Minato (mē′nȧ-tō)............Jap.	35.13 N	139.52 E
53	Minchumina L. (mĭn-chōō-mē′nȧ) Alsk.	63.55 N	151.30 W
163	Mindanao (I.) (mĭn-dä-nä′ō).P. I.	8.0 N	124.30 E
163	Mindanao R...................P. I.	7.2 N	124.30 E
163	Mindanao Sea.................P. I.	9.20 N	124.30 E
135	Mindauli (mĕn-dou′lē) Fr. Eq. Afr. (Brazzaville In.)	4.11 S	14.27 E
122	Minden (mĭn′dĕn)............Ger.	52.17 N	8.55 E
81	Minden........................La.	32.36 N	93.19 W
78	Minden.......................Neb.	40.31 N	98.59 W
162	Mindoro (I.) (mēn-dō′rō).....P. I.	12.55 N	121.10 E
162	Mindoro Str...................P. I.	12.30 N	120.30 E
85	Mineola (mĭn-ē-ō′lȧ)........N. Y.	40.45 N	73.37 W
81	Mineola......................Tex.	32.40 N	95.30 W
92	Mineral del Chico (mē-nȧ-räl′ dĕl chē′kō).Mex.	20.12 N	98.46 W
92	Mineral del Monte (mōn′tā).Mex.	20.8 N	98.38 W
113	Mineralnie Vodi (mē-nĕ-räl′nĕ-ē vô′dē).Sov. Un.	44.12 N	43.12 E
77	Mineral Pt. (mĭn′ēr-ăl)......Wis.	42.52 N	90.10 W
80	Mineral Wells................Tex.	32.48 N	98.7 W
84	Minerva (mĭ-nûr′vȧ).........Ohio	40.46 N	81.11 W
128	Minervino (mē-nĕr-vē′nō).......It.	41.5 N	16.5 E
159	Mineyama (mē-nĕ-yä′mä).....Jap.	35.38 N	135.4 E
86	Mingan (mĭŋ′găn)............Can.	50.18 N	64.3 W
166	Mingary Cr. (mĭŋ′gȧ-rĭ).....Austl.	32.0 S	140.46 E
164	Mingenew (mĭn′gĕ-nû).......Austl.	29.3 S	115.40 E
84	Mingo Junction (mĭŋ′gō).....Ohio	40.20 N	80.38 W
131	Mingrelskaya (mĕn-grĕl-skä′yȧ) Sov. Un.	45.1 N	38.18 E
154	Mingshan (mĭng′shän′).......Chn.	24.8 N	110.30 E
126	Minho (Prov.) (mēn′yōō)....Port.	41.30 N	8.20 W
96	Minho R......................Jam.	18.0 N	77.12 W
126	Minho R..................Port.-Sp.	42.5 N	8.30 W
139	Minia (mēn′ē-ä)...............Eg.	28.3 N	30.41 E
155	Minkiang Estuary (mĭn′kyăng′) Chn.	26.2 N	119.48 E
138	Minna (mĭn′ä).................Nig.	9.41 N	6.32 E
79	Minneapolis (mĭn-ē-ăp′ō-lĭs).Kan.	39.7 N	97.41 W
89	Minneapolis..........Minn. (In.)		
77	Minneapolis...................Minn.	44.57 N	93.15 W
54	Minnedosa (mĭn-ē-dō′sȧ).....Can.	50.15 N	99.44 W
76	Minneota (mĭn-ē-ō′tȧ)......Minn.	44.35 N	95.55 W
77	Minnesota (State) (mĭn-ē-sō′tȧ) U. S.	46.0 N	94.40 W
77	Minnesota R.................Minn.	44.12 N	94.10 W
77	Minnetonka L. (mĭn-ē-tôŋ′kȧ) Minn.	44.55 N	93.35 W
75	Minnie Maud Cr. (mĭn′ĭ môd′)Utah	39.50 N	110.20 W
126	Miño R. (mē′nyō)..............Sp.	42.40 N	7.42 W
127	Minorca (I.) (mē-nôr′kȧ)......Sp.	40.0 N	4.0 E
76	Minot (mī′nŏt)...............N. D.	48.14 N	101.17 W
155	Min R. (mĭn).................Chn.	27.34 N	118.8 E
135	Minshā (mēn-shä′).....Eg. (In.)	26.32 N	31.49 E
141	Minshâtel Bakkâri (mĭn-shät′ ăl bä-kä′rē).Eg.	30.2 N	31.8 E
130	Minsk (mēnsk)............Sov. Un.	53.55 N	27.35 E
123	Minsk-Mazówiecki(mēnsk′mä′zōōf) Pol.	52.11 N	21.33 E
119	Minster (mĭn′stēr) Gt. Brit. (London In.)	51.25 N	0.49 E
86	Minto (mĭn′tō)...............Can.	46.3 N	66.5 W
55	Minto, L.....................Can.	57.20 N	75.30 W
155	Mintsing (mĭn′tsĭng)........Chn.	26.15 N	118.46 E
128	Minturno (mēn-tōōr′nō).......It.	41.17 N	13.43 E
135	Minûf (mē-nōōf′)........Eg. (In.)	30.28 N	30.55 E
148	Minusinsk(mē-nōō-sēnsk′)Sov. Un.	53.50 N	91.40 E
152	Minya Konka, Mt. (mēn′yȧ kôŋ′kȧ).Chn.	29.50 N	101.50 E
158	Miohiangsan (Mt.) (myō′hyăng′-sän′).Cho.	40.1 N	126.28 E
87	Miquelon (Is.) (mĭ′kē-lŏn) (mē-k′-lôN′).N. A.	47.0 N	56.20 W
92	Miquihuana (mē-kē-wä′nä)..Mex.	23.34 N	99.47 W
154	Mi R. (mē)...................Chn.	26.56 N	112.45 E
123	Mir (mēr).....................Pol.	53.29 N	26.29 E
126	Mira (mē′rȧ).................Port.	40.25 N	8.45 W
103	Mirador (mē-rä-dōr′).......Braz.	6.27 S	44.31 W
102	Miraflores (mē-rä-flō′rās).....Col.	5.10 N	73.28 W
102	Miraflores............Peru (In.)	12.7 S	77.2 W
90	Miraflores Locks......C. Z. (In.)	9.0 N	79.36 W
97	Miragoane (mē-rȧ-gwän′)....Hai.	18.27 N	73.7 W
151	Miraj (mē-rŭj′)..............India	16.45 N	74.35 E
161	Miralip (mē-rä-lēp′) P. I. (Manila In.)	14.59 N	120.39 E
90	Miramar (mē-rä-mär′) Cuba (Habana In.)	23.7 N	82.25 W
170	Miramar (mĭr′ȧ-mär)..N. Z. (In.)	41.19 S	174.50 E
124	Miramas (mē-rȧ-mȧ′)...........Fr.	43.35 N	5.0 E
86	Miramichi B. (mĭr′ȧ-mē′shē).Can.	47.8 N	65.10 W
86	Miramichi R.................Can.	46.35 N	66.15 W
126	Miranda de Ebro (mē-rän′dä dä ā′brō).Sp.	42.41 N	2.58 W
126	Miranda do Douro (dōō dō′rōō) Port.	41.29 N	6.18 W
126	Mirandela (mē-rän-dä′lȧ)....Port.	41.28 N	7.11 W
80	Mirando City (mĭr-ăn′dō)....Tex.	27.27 N	99.5 W
97	Mira Por Vos Islets (mē′rä pôr vōs′).Ba. Is.	22.6 N	74.30 W
97	Mira Por Vos Pass........Ba. Is.	22.5 N	74.22 W
126	Mira R......................Port.	37.30 N	8.30 W
97	Mirebalais (mēr-bȧ-lĕ′).......Hai.	18.49 N	72.8 W
125	Mirecourt (mēr-kōōr′)..........Fr.	48.20 N	6.10 E
124	Mirepoix (mēr-pwä′)...........Fr.	43.5 N	1.53 E
118	Mirfield (mûr′fēld)......Gt. Brit.	53.40 N	1.42 W
131	Mirgorod (mēr′gō-rôt)...Sov. Un.	49.58 N	33.40 E
160	Miri (mē′rē)...................Sar.	4.20 N	114.10 E
138	Mirik, C. (mē-rēk′)...Fr. W. Afr.	19.30 N	16.30 W
104	Mirim, L. (mē-rēN′)..........Braz.	32.45 S	52.50 W
131	Miropolie (mē-rô-pôl′yĕ).Sov. Un.	51.1 N	35.12 E
148	Mirsoyan (Aulie Ata) (mēr-sô-yän′).Sov. Un.	42.55 N	71.25 E
151	Mirzapur (mēr′zä-pōōr)......India	25.5 N	82.35 E
138	Misa (mē′sa).........Fr. W. Afr.	7.0 N	0.33 E
159	Misaki (mē′sȧ-kē) Jap. (Tokyo In.)	35.9 N	139.37 E
163	Misamis (mē-sä′mĭs)..........P. I.	8.9 N	123.51 E
93	Misantla (mē-sän′tlä)........Mex.	19.56 N	96.51 W
86	Miscou I. (mĭs′kō)...........Can.	47.58 N	64.32 W
86	Miscou Pt...................Can.	48.2 N	64.33 W
119	Miseno, C. (mē-zĕ′nō) It. (Napoli In.)	40.46 N	14.5 E
95	Misery, Mt. (mĭz′ēr-ĭ).Le. Is. (In.)	17.22 N	62.48 W
158	Mishan.....................Manch.	45.30 N	132.25 E
84	Mishawaka (mĭsh-ȧ-wôk′ȧ)...Ind.	41.40 N	86.14 W
55	Mishikamau, L. (mĭsh-ē-kȧ-mô′) Lab.	54.15 N	64.0 W
159	Mishima (mē′shē-mȧ)........Jap.	35.9 N	138.55 E
104	Misiones (State) (mē-syō′nās).Arg.	27.0 S	54.30 W
123	Miskolc (mĭsh′kōlts).........Hung.	48.6 N	20.48 E
145	Mismié (mēs-myā′).....Syr. (In.)	33.14 N	36.21 E
161	Misol (I.) (mē-sōl′).....Neth. Ind.	1.50 S	130.0 E
55	Missinaibi R. (mĭs′ĭn-ä′ē-bē).Can.	50.15 N	83.0 W
164	Mission (mĭsh′ŭn)...........Austl.	23.38 S	133.32 E
80	Mission......................Tex.	26.13 N	98.20 W
72	Mission City.Can.(Vancouver In.)	49.8 N	122.18 W
49	Mission San Jose (mĭsh′ŭn sän hō-sā′).Calif. (San Francisco In.)	37.31 N	121.55 W
84	Mississinewa R. (mĭs-ĭ-sĭn′ē-wä) Ind.	40.30 N	85.40 W
82	Mississippi (State) (mĭs-ĭ-sĭp′ē)U.S.	32.55 N	89.40 W
85	Mississippi L................Can.	45.5 N	76.10 W
85	Mississippi R...............Can.	45.15 N	76.15 W
59	Mississippi R...............U. S.	31.0 N	91.30 W
82	Mississippi Sd...............Miss.	30.20 N	89.0 W
71	Missoula (mĭ-zōō′lȧ).........Mont.	46.52 N	114.0 W
79	Missouri (State) (mĭ-sōō′rē).U. S.	38.30 N	93.0 W
81	Missouri City..........Tex. (In.)	29.37 N	95.31 W
59	Missouri R.....................Mo.	40.15 N	95.30 W
76	Missouri Valley................Ia.	41.32 N	95.50 W
49	Mist (mĭst)....Ore. (Portland In.)	46.0 N	123.15 W
86	Mistassibi R. (mĭs-tȧ-sē′bē)..Can.	49.30 N	72.6 W

ng-sing; ŋ-baŋk; N-nasalized n; nŏd; cŏmmit; ōld; ôbey; ôrder; fōōd; fŏŏt; ou-out; s-soft; sh-dish; th-thin pūre; ûnite; ûrn; stŭd; circŭs; ü-as "y" in study; ′-indeterminate vowel.

Page	Name Pronunciation Region	Lat. °′	Long. °′
55	Mistassini (mĭs-tȧ-sĭ-nē′).....Can.	48.57 N	72.10 W
55	Mistassini, L. (mĭs-tȧ-sĕ′nē)..Can.	51.10 N	73.30 W
55	Mistassini R................Can.	50.0 N	72.30 W
122	Mistelback (mĭs′tĕl bäκ).....Ger.	48.34 N	16.32 E
102	Misti (Vol.) (mēs′tē)........Peru	16.15 S	70.58 W
128	Mistretta (mė-strĕt′tä)........It.	37.56 N	14.21 E
139	Misurata (mē-so͞o-rä′tä)....Libya	32.26 N	15.2 E
114	Misurata Marina (mä-rē′nä) Libya	32.28 N	15.13 E
92	Mita Pt. (mē′tä)...........Mex.	20.45 N	105.34 W
141	Mit Aqaba (mĭt äk′ȧ-bȧ)......Eg.	30.4 N	31.12 E
169	Mitcham (mĭch′ăm) Austl. (Adelaide In.)	34.59 S	138.38 E
119	Mitcham..Gt. Brit. (London In.)	51.24 N	0.10 W
89	Mitchell (mĭch′ĕl) Ill.(St.Louis In.)	38.46 N	90.5 W
84	Mitchell...................Ind.	38.44 N	86.28 W
76	Mitchell...................Neb.	41.56 N	103.48 W
76	Mitchell...................S. D.	43.43 N	98.1 W
84	Mitchell, L. (mĭch′ĕl).......Mich.	44.15 N	85.25 W
83	Mitchell, Mt..............N. C.	35.46 N	82.15 W
165	Mitchell R................Austl.	16.5 S	142.30 E
130	Mitishchi (mė-tēsh′chĭ)..Sov. Un.	55.56 N	37.48 E
158	Mito (mē′tō′)..............Jap.	36.22 N	140.30 E
129	Mitrovica (mē′trô-vėt-sȧ)...Yugo.	44.59 N	19.39 E
129	Mitrovica.................Yugo.	42.51 N	20.51 E
125	Mitry-Mori (mė-trē′-mô-rē′) Fr. (In.)	48.58 N	2.37 E
159	Mitsu (mēt′so͞o.............Jap.)	34.21 N	132.49 E
159	Mitsugahama (mēt′so͞o-gȧ-hä′mä) Jap.	33.51 N	132.45 E
167	Mittagong (mĭt′ȧ-gông) ....Austl.	34.26 S	150.29 E
167	Mitta Mitta R. (mĭt′ȧ mĭt′å) Austl.	36.28 S	147.20 E
122	Mittelland Canal (mĭt′ĕl länd) Ger.	52.18 N	11.0 E
122	Mittweida (mĭt-vī′dä)........Ger.	50.59 N	12.57 E
131	Mius R. (mė-o͞os′).......Sov. Un.	47.25 N	38.55 E
94	Mixco (mēs′kō)............Guat.	14.38 N	90.37 W
93	Mixcoac (mēs-kô-äk′)..Mex. (In.)	19.22 N	99.11 W
92	Mixquiahuala (mēs-kė-wä′lä) Mex.	20.13 N	99.12 W
92	Mixteco R. (mės-tā′kō) .....Mex.	17.40 N	98.6 W
159	Miyadi (mē-yȧ′dē)...........Jap.	32.55 N	131.10 E
159	Miyakejima (I.) (mē′yȧ-kå-jē′mä) Jap.	34.5 N	139.22 E
159	Miyakonojo (mē′yȧ-kô-nō′jō).Jap.	31.41 N	131.2 E
150	Miyanej (mė-yän′ĕj).........Iran	37.25 N	47.44 E
159	Miyazaki (mē′yä-zä′kė)......Jap.	31.59 N	131.29 E
159	Miyoshi (mē′yô-shė).........Jap.	34.50 N	132.45 E
114	Mizda (mēz′dä)............Libya	31.27 N	13.0 E
129	Mizil (mē′zėl)..............Rom.	45.0 N	26.28 E
120	Mjölby (myûl′bü)............Swe.	58.19 N	15.10 E
141	Mjonga R. (m-jôŋ′gȧ).......Tan.	5.50 S	37.35 E
120	Mjös, L. (myûs)............Nor.	60.40 N	11.5 E
140	Mkalamo (m′kä-lä′mō).......Tan.	4.5 S	34.35 E
141	Mkata R. (m′kä′tä)..........Tan.	6.33 S	37.30 E
141	Mkoani (m′kô-ä′nė).........Zan.	5.22 S	39.39 E
141	Mkokotoni (m′kō-kô-tō′nė) ..Zan.	5.53 S	39.15 E
141	Mkomazi (m′kô-mä′zė)......Tan.	4.37 S	38.6 E
141	Mkomazi R.................Tan.	4.35 S	38.4 E
141	Mkunduchi (m′ko͝on-do͞o′chė) Zan.	6.23 S	39.33 E
141	Mkuzi Katani (m′ko͞o′zė-kä-tä′nė) Tan.	5.21 S	38.58 E
141	Mkwaja (m′kwä′jä).........Tan.	5.47 S	38.51 E
122	Mladá Boleslav (mlȧ′dä bô′lå-släf) Czech.	50.26 N	14.53 E
141	Mlalo (m′lä′lō).............Tan.	4.34 S	38.20 E
123	Mlawa (mwä′vȧ).............Pol.	53.7 N	20.24 E
128	Mljet (I.) (mlyĕt)..........Yugo.	42.45 N	17.35 E
141	Mnyusi (m′nyo͞o′sė).........Tan.	5.13 S	38.35 E
141	Moa (mō′ä).................Tan.	4.45 S	39.10 E
161	Moa (I.) ....Neth. Ind.	8.15 S	128.0 E
75	Moab (mō′ăb)..............Utah	38.33 N	109.31 W
163	Moalboal (mô-äl-bō′äl′)......P. I.	9.57 N	123.24 E
166	Moama (mō-äm′ȧ)..........Austl.	36.6 S	144.45 E
143	Moamba (mō-äm′bȧ).......Moz.	25.37 S	32.12 E
74	Moapa River Ind. Res. (mō-ȧp′ȧ) Nev.	36.40 N	114.40 W
139	Mobaye (mô-bä′y′)...Fr. Eq. Afr.	4.28 N	21.8 E
119	Mobberley (mô′bēr-lĭ) Gt. Brit. (Liverpool In.)	53.19 N	2.19 W
79	Moberly....................Mo.	39.25 N	92.25 W
82	Mobile (mô-bēl′)............Ala.	30.42 N	88.4 W
82	Mobile B...................Ala.	30.30 N	88.0 W
82	Mobile R...................Ala.	31.0 N	88.0 W
76	Mobridge (mō′brĭj)..........S. D.	45.33 N	100.26 W
97	Moca (mō′kä)...............Hai.	19.23 N	70.31 W
141	Moçambique (mō-säɴ-bē′kĕ).Moz.	15.3 S	40.42 E
145	Mocha (mō′κä)........Yem. (In.)	13.19 N	43.16 E
92	Mochitlán (mō-chė-tlän′)....Mex.	17.32 N	99.21 W
140	Mochudi (mō-cho͞o′dė)......Bech.	24.20 S	26.7 E
92	Moctezuma (môk′tå-zo͞o′mä) Mex.	22.44 N	101.4 W
92	Moctezuma, R..............Mex.	21.34 N	98.40 W
143	Modder R. (mŏd′ēr)....U. S. Afr.	28.50 S	25.50 E
143	Modder River..............Bech.	29.2 S	24.37 E
88	Modeltown (mŏd″l-toun) N. Y. (Niagara Falls In.)	43.11 N	78.59 W
128	Modena (mô′då-nä)...........It.	44.37 N	10.54 E
74	Modesto (mô-dĕs′tō).......Calif.	37.38 N	121.0 W
122	Mödling (mûd′lĭng)..........Ger.	48.5 N	16.16 E
167	Moe (mō)..................Austl.	38.11 S	146.18 E
120	Möen (I.) (mû′ĕn)..........Den.	54.58 N	12.30 E
78	Moffat Tunnel (mŏf′ăt).....Colo.	39.55 N	105.40 W
141	Mogadiscio (mô-gå-dē′shō) It. E. Afr.	2.0 N	45.17 E
138	Mogador (Es Suweira) (môg-ȧ-dōr′) (ĕs′so͞o-wā′rȧ).Mor.	31.22 N	9.42 W
152	Mogaung (mô-gä′o͝ong)......India	25.27 N	96.56 E
123	Mogielnica (mô-gyĕl-nēt′sȧ) ..Pol.	51.42 N	20.44 E
131	Mogilev (mô-gė-lyôf′) ...Sov. Un.	48.26 N	27.51 E
130	Mogilev................Sov. Un.	53.54 N	30.20 E
123	Mogilno (mô-gēl′nô).........Pol.	52.38 N	17.57 E
152	Mogok (mô-gōk′)...........India	22.58 N	96.28 E
75	Mogollon (mō-gô′yōn′).....N. M.	33.24 N	108.48 W
162	Mogpog (môg-pôg′).........P. I.	13.28 N	121.52 E
126	Moguer (mô-gĕr′)............Sp.	37.17 N	6.50 W
123	Mohács (mô′häch) ....Hung.	45.59 N	18.41 E

Page	Name Pronunciation Region	Lat. °′	Long. °′
170	Mohaka R. (mō-hä′kä)......N. Z.	39.10 S	176.40 E
143	Mohaleshoek (mō-hä′lĕs-ho͝ok)Bas.	30.10 S	27.28 E
70	Mohall (mō′hôl)...........N. D.	48.47 N	101.30 W
150	Mohammerah, see Khorramshahr Iran		
74	Mohave Des. (mô-hä′vā)....Calif.	34.55 N	117.45 W
74	Mohave R.................Calif.	34.40 N	117.18 W
85	Mohawk R. (mō′hôk)......N. Y.	43.10 N	75.20 W
141	Moheli I.(mô-ā-lē′)(mô-hā′lė)Ind.O.	12.18 S	43.40 E
153	Moho (mō′hō′)...........Manch.	53.22 N	122.27 E
124	Mohon (mô-ôɴ′).............Fr.	49.45 N	4.49 E
121	Moisaküla (mĕĕ′sȧ-kü-lȧ).....Est.	58.6 N	25.12 E
162	Moises, Mt. (mō-ė-sås′)......P. I.	17.12 N	122.15 E
55	Moisie R. (mwȧ-zē′).........Can.	51.40 N	66.0 W
124	Moissac (mwä-sȧk′)...........Fr.	44.7 N	1.6 E
125	Moisseles (mwä-sĕl′).....Fr. (In.)	49.3 N	2.20 E
127	Moita (mô-ē′tȧ).......Port. (In.)	38.39 N	9.0 W
80	Mojada, Sierra (Mts.) (mô-hä′dä) Mex.	27.16 N	103.41 W
159	Moji (mō′jė)................Jap.	33.52 N	131.0 E
99	Mojidas Cruzes(mō′zhė däzh kro͞o′-zėzh).Braz. (Rio de Janeiro In.)	23.33 S	46.10 W
99	Moji Guassú, Rio (mō′zhė gwä-so͞o′) Braz. (Rio de Janeiro In.)	22.20 S	47.10 W
99	Moji-Mirim (mō′zhė-mė-rēɴ′) Braz. (Rio de Janeiro In.)	22.29 S	46.58 W
160	Mojo (I.) (mō′yō)....Neth. Ind.	8.20 S	117.35 E
103	Moju (mô-zho͞o′)......Braz. (In.)	1.55 S	48.40 W
103	Mojú, R.............Braz. (In.)	1.50 S	48.38 W
170	Mokau R. (mō-kä′o͞o).......N. Z.	38.40 S	174.55 E
74	Mokelumne R. (mō-kė-lŭm′nė) Calif.	38.10 N	121.10 W
171	Mokihinui (mô-kė-hē′no͞o-ė).N. Z.	41.42 S	171.55 E
140	Mokopon (mō′kô-pōn)......Bech.	25.20 S	22.58 E
157	Mokpo (Mokuho) (môk′pō′) (mō-ko͞o′hō).Cho.	34.50 N	126.29 E
112	Moksha R. (môk-shä′)...Sov. Un.	54.45 N	43.10 E
157	Mokuho (môk′pō′).........Cho.	34.50 N	126.29 E
128	Mola (mô′lä).................It.	41.3 N	17.5 E
131	Moldavian (Dist.) (mŏl-dā′vĭ-ăn) Sov. Un.	47.35 N	29.25 E
123	Moldavia (Moldova) (Prov.).Rom.	47.8 N	27.22 E
120	Molde (môl′dĕ)..............Nor.	62.45 N	7.10 E
120	Molde Fjord................Nor.	62.40 N	7.0 E
123	Moldova (Moldavia) (Prov.) (môl-dô′vȧ) (mŏl-dā′vĭ-ȧ).Rom.	47.8 N	27.22 E
123	Moldova R..................Rom.	47.20 N	26.24 E
140	Molepolole (mō-lå-pô-lō′lå)..Bech.	24.25 S	25.35 E
128	Molfetta (môl-fĕt′tä)..........It.	41.10 N	16.36 E
126	Molina (mô-lē′nä).............Sp.	38.5 N	1.12 W
126	Molina......................Sp.	40.52 N	1.53 W
79	Moline (mô-lēn′)..............Ill.	41.30 N	90.34 W
127	Molíns de Rey (mô-lēns′ dā rā′ė) Sp. (In.)	41.24 N	2.2 E
128	Moliterno (mōl-ė-tĕr′nō).......It.	40.44 N	15.52 E
102	Mollendo (mô-lyĕn′dō)......Peru	17.0 S	72.1 W
127	Mollet (môl-yåt′)........Sp. (In.)	41.31 N	2.12 E
120	Mölndal (mûln′däl).........Swe.	57.38 N	12.0 E
131	Molochnoe, L. (mô′lôch-nō′yĕ) Sov. Un.	46.35 N	35.22 E
131	Molochnoe R..........Sov. Un.	46.55 N	35.29 E
123	Molodeczno (mô-wô-dåch′nô).Pol.	54.19 N	26.52 E
130	Mologa (mô-lô′gȧ) ......Sov. Un.	58.11 N	38.24 E
73	Molokai (I.) (mō-lô-kä′ė)....Haw.	21.8 N	157.0 W
142	Molopo R. (mō-lō′pô) ......Bech.	26.40 S	22.0 E
143	Molteno (môl-tā′nô)....U. S. Afr.	31.23 S	26.22 E
161	Molucca Passage (mô-lŭk′ȧ) Neth. Ind.	1.45 N	126.15 E
128	Moluccas (Spice Is.) (mô-lŭk′ăz) Neth. Ind.	1.0 S	128.0 E
161	Molucca Sea.........Neth. Ind.	0.15 N	126.0 E
171	Molyneux (mŭl′ĭ-no͞oks).....N. Z.	46.23 S	169.45 E
141	Mombasa (mōm-bä′sä) ....Kenya	4.0 S	39.40 E
158	Mombets (môm′bĕts′).......Jap.	44.27 N	143.4 E
141	Mombo (mōm′bô)...........Tan.	4.52 S	38.18 E
84	Momence (mô-mĕns′).........Ill.	41.10 N	87.38 W
6	Momi (mō′mė).......Fiji Is. (In.)	17.56 S	177.20 E
94	Momostenango (mô-mōs-tā-näŋ′-gō).Guat.	15.1 N	91.24 W
162	Mompog Pass (mōm-pōg′)...P. I.	13.30 N	122.15 E
102	Mompas (mōm-pōs′)..........Col.	9.45 N	74.15 W
125	Monaco (mŏn′ȧ-kō).........Eur.	43.44 N	7.24 E
128	Monaco.....................Fr.	43.44 N	7.24 E
116	Monaghan (mŏn′ȧ găn).......Ire.	54.15 N	7.0 W
97	Mona Passage (mō′nä)......W. I.	18.0 N	68.45 W
167	Monaro Range (mō-nä′rō)..Austl.	36.15 S	149.0 E
135	Monastir (mōn-ȧs-tēr).Tun. (In.)	35.47 N	10.42 E
129	Monastir (Bitolj) (mŏn′ȧs-tēr′) (bė′tôl-y′).Yugo.	41.2 N	21.22 E
131	Monastyrishche (mô-nȧ-stė-ēsh′-chå).Sov. Un.	48.58 N	29.49 E
130	Monastyrishche........Sov. Un.	54.18 N	31.50 E
162	Moncada (mōn-kä′dä).......P. I.	15.43 N	120.34 E
127	Moncada y Reixach (mōnkā′dä ē rå-ėks-äch′).Sp. (In.)	41.28 N	2.11 E
103	Monção (moŋ-souɴ′).......Braz.	3.28 S	45.12 W
126	Moncayo (Mt.) (môn-kä′yō) ..Sp.	41.46 N	1.49 W
126	Monchique (môn-chē′kĕ)....Port.	37.19 N	8.34 W
126	Monchique, Serra de (Mts.) (sĕr′rä dā môn-chē′kĕ).Port.	37.20 N	8.35 W
80	Monclova (môn-klō′vä) .....Mex.	26.54 N	101.25 W
55	Moncton (mŭŋk′tŭn)........Can.	46.3 N	64.48 W
126	Mondego, C. (môn-dā′go͝o)..Port.	40.12 N	8.55 W
126	Mondego R................Port.	40.25 N	8.0 W
140	Mondombe (môn-dôm′bå) Bel. Cong.	0.45 S	23.6 E
126	Mondoñedo (môn-dô-nyā′dō)..Sp.	43.26 N	7.25 W
128	Mondovi (mōn-dô′vē′).........It.	44.22 N	7.49 E
77	Mondovi (mŏn-dō′vĭ)........Wis.	44.35 N	91.40 W
149	Monero R. (mô-nyĕr′ô)..Sov. Un.	67.30 N	104.0 E
79	Monett (mô-nĕt′)............Mo.	36.56 N	93.56 W
128	Monfalcone (mōn-fäl-kō′nā) ...It.	45.59 N	13.31 E
124	Monfort (môɴ-fôr′)...........Fr.	48.10 N	2.0 W

Page	Name Pronunciation Region	Lat. °′	Long. °
126	Monforte (môn-fôr′tā)........Sp.	42.32 N	7.31 W
139	Mongala R. (mŏn-gȧl′ȧ) Bel. Cong.	2.30 N	20.30 E
139	Mongalla............A. E. Sud.	5.7 N	31.45 E
151	Monghyr (mŏn-gēr′)........India	25.15 N	87.0 E
152	Mongolia (Dependency) (mŏŋ-gō′lĭ-ȧ).Chn.	46.30 N	105.0 E
139	Mongoumba (mŏŋ-go͞om′bȧ) Fr. Eq. Afr.	3.36 N	18.30 E
158	Mongpai C. (môŋg′pī′)......Cho.	40.58 N	129.40 E
140	Mongu (mŏŋ-go͞o′)........N. Rh.	15.15 S	23.3 E
163	Monkayo (môn-kä′yō).......P. I.	7.49 N	126.0 E
95	Monkey Pt. (mŭŋ′kĭ)........Nic.	11.38 N	83.40 W
94	Monkey River.........Br. Hond.	16.21 N	88.32 W
140	Monkoto (môn-kō′tô)..Bel. Cong.	1.50 S	20.55 E
73	Monmouth (mŏn′mŭth) Ala. (Birmingham In.)	33.44 N	86.45 W
116	Monmouth.............Gt. Brit.	51.50 N	3.0 W
79	Monmouth..................Ill.	40.54 N	90.38 W
74	Mono L. (mō′nō)..........Calif.	38.0 N	119.0 W
84	Monon (mō′nŏn)............Ind.	40.52 N	86.53 W
85	Monongah (mô-nŏŋ′gȧ) ...W. Va.	39.26 N	80.13 W
85	Monongahela (mô-nŏŋ-gȧ-hē′lȧ) Pa.	40.12 N	79.58 W
85	Monongahela R..........W. Va.	39.30 N	80.10 W
129	Monopoli (mô-nô′pô-lė).......It.	40.56 N	17.17 E
127	Monóvar (mô-nō′vär).........Sp.	38.26 N	0.50 W
128	Monreale (mōn-rå-ä′lā)........It.	38.4 N	13.17 E
82	Monroe (mŭn-rō′)............Ga.	33.48 N	83.43 W
81	Monroe....................La.	32.30 N	92.7 W
84	Monroe...................Mich.	41.56 N	83.24 W
83	Monroe...................N. C.	34.39 N	80.33 W
75	Monroe...................Utah	38.38 N	112.10 W
70	Monroe..................Wash.	47.51 N	121.57 W
77	Monroe....................Wis.	42.35 N	89.39 W
79	Monroe City...............Mo.	39.38 N	91.42 W
83	Monroe, L.................Fla.	28.50 N	81.16 W
82	Monroeville (mŭn-rō′vĭl).....Ala.	31.32 N	87.20 W
74	Monrovia (mŏn-rō′vĭ-ȧ).....Calif.	34.9 N	118.1 W
138	Monrovia..................Lib.	6.27 N	10.58 W
117	Mons (môɴ′)................Bel.	50.29 N	3.55 E
103	Monsaraz (môŋ-sȧ-räzh′) Braz. (In.)	0.55 S	48.35 W
86	Monson (mŏn′sŭn)...........Me.	45.17 N	69.28 W
120	Mönsterås (mûn′stĕr-ôs′)....Swe.	57.3 N	16.24 E
142	Montagu (mŏn′tȧ-gū)...U. S. Afr.	33.45 S	20.6 E
84	Montague................Mich.	43.27 N	86.22 W
53	Montague I................Alsk.	60.0 N	147.30 W
167	Montague I...............Austl.	36.17 S	150.11 E
162	Montalban (mōnt-äl-bän′)...P. I.	14.44 N	121.10 E
126	Montalegre (mōn-tä-lā′grė)..Port.	41.50 N	7.48 W
71	Montana (State) (mŏn-tăn′ȧ) U. S.	46.48 N	109.10 W
126	Montánchez (môn-tän′chåth)..Sp.	39.13 N	6.9 W
128	Montane R. (môn-tä′nā) ......It.	43.52 N	11.40 E
124	Montargis (môɴ-tȧr-zhē′).....Fr.	47.59 N	2.42 E
124	Montataire (môɴ-tȧ-târ)......Fr.	49.18 N	2.28 E
124	Montauban (môɴ-tô-bäɴ′) ....Fr.	44.1 N	1.22 E
85	Montauk Pt. (mŏn-tôk′)....N. Y.	41.5 N	71.52 W
125	Montbéliard (môɴ-bā-lyȧr′)...Fr.	47.32 N	6.48 E
81	Mont Belvieu (mŏnt bĕl′vū) Tex. (In.)	29.51 N	94.54 W
127	Montblanch (mōnt-blänch′)...Sp.	41.21 N	1.7 E
124	Montbrison (môɴ-brė-zôɴ′)....Fr.	45.35 N	4.9 E
124	Montcalm, Pic de (Mt.) (pēk dē môɴ-kȧm′).Fr.	42.45 N	1.25 E
124	Montceau-les-Mines (môɴ-sō′lā-mēn′).Fr.	46.40 N	4.22 E
124	Montchanin-les-Mines (môɴ-shȧ-năɴ′lā mēn′).Fr.	46.45 N	4.30 E
88	Montclair (mŏnt-klâr′) N. J. (New York In.)	40.49 N	74.13 W
124	Mont-de-Marsan (môɴ-dē-mȧr-säɴ′) Fr.	43.55 N	0.30 W
123	Montdidier (môɴ-dē-dyā′).....Fr.	49.41 N	2.35 E
102	Monteagudo (mōn′tå-ä-go͞o′dhō) Bol.	19.48 S	64.2 W
103	Monte Alegre (mōn-tĕ ȧ-lā′grĕ) Braz. (In.)	11.45 S	40.5 W
73	Montebello (mŏn-tė-bĕl′ō) Calif. (Los Angeles In.)	34.0 N	118.7 W
164	Monte Bello Is............Austl.	20.30 S	115.35 E
97	Monte Cristi (mōn′tå krēs′tē)Hai.	19.51 N	71.40 W
97	Monte Cristi Mts............Hai.	19.40 N	70.50 W
93	Montecristo (mōn′tå-krēs′tō) Mex.	17.44 N	91.45 W
128	Montecristo (I.)..............It.	42.20 N	10.19 E
92	Monte Escobedo (mōn′tå ĕs-kô-bā′dhō).Mex.	22.23 N	103.39 W
126	Montefrío (mōn-tå-frē′ō)......Sp.	37.20 N	4.1 W
96	Montego B. (mŏn-tē′gō).....Jam.	18.30 N	77.56 W
127	Montelavar (mōn-tĕ-lȧ-vär′) Port (In.)	38.51 N	9.20 W
28	Monteleone (mōn′tå-lå-ō′nā)...It.	38.41 N	16.7 E
24	Montélimar (môɴ-tā-lē-mär′)..Fr.	44.35 N	4.46 E
90	Monte Lirio (mōn′tå lē′rė-ō) C. Z. (In.)	9 14 N	79.52 W
126	Montellano (mōn-tå-lyä′nō)...Sp.	37.0 N	5.34 W
77	Montello (mŏn-tĕl′ō).......Wis.	43.48 N	89.19 W
80	Montemorelos (mōn′tå-mô-rā′lōs) Mex.	25.13 N	99.50 W
126	Montemor-o-Novo (mōɴ-tĕ-môr′-o͝o-nô′vo͝o).Port.	38.39 N	8.12 W
129	Montenegro (Crnagora) (Prov.) (môn-tå-nā′grō) (mŏn-tė-nē′grō) (tsĕr′nä-gô-rä).Yugo.	42.45 N	19.25 E
128	Montepulciano (môn′tå-po͞ol-chä′nō).It	43.18 N	11.47 E
124	Montereau-faut-Yonne (môɴt′rō′fō-yôn′).Fr.	48.25 N	3.0 E
74	Monterey (mŏn-tĕ-rā′)......Calif.	36.35 N	121.52 W
82	Monterey.................Tenn.	36.8 N	85.18 W
74	Monterey B...............Calif.	36.50 N	122.5 W
102	Montería (mōn-tå-rē′ä) ......Col.	8.30 N	76.0 W
80	Monterrey (mōn-tĕr-rā′).....Mex.	25.42 N	100.20 W
128	Monte San Guiliano (mōn′tå sän jo͞ol-yä′nō).It.	38.2 N	12.36 E
70	Montesano (mŏn-tė-sä′nō)..Wash.	46.59 N	123.36 W

ăt; finăl; rāte; senåte; ärm; ȧsk; sofȧ; fâre; ch-choose; dh-as th in other; bē; ėvent; bĕt; recĕnt; cratēr; g-go; gh-gutteral g; bĭt; ĭ-short neutral; rīde; κ-gutteral k as ch in German ich;

Page	Name Pronunciation Region	Lat. °′	Long. °′
128	Monte Sant' Angelo (mōn′tȧ sän-tän′ jȧ-lō) It.	41.42 N	15.59 E
125	Montesson (môN-tě-sôN′). Fr. (In.)	48.54 N	2.8 E
128	Montevarchi (mōn-tȧ-vär′kē) . . It.	43.32 N	11.34 E
76	Montevideo (mŏn-tê-vĭd′ê-ō) Minn.	44.52 N	95.41 W
104	Montevideo (mōn′tȧ-vê-dhā′ō) Ur.	34.40 S	56.15 W
78	Monte Vista (mŏn′tê vĭs′tȧ). Colo.	37.34 N	106.9 W
83	Montezuma (mŏn-tê-zōō′mȧ) . . Ga.	32.18 N	84.1 W
75	Montezuma Castle Natl. Mon. Ariz.	34.37 N	111.51 W
125	Montfermeil (môN-fěr-mā′y′) Fr. (In.)	48.53 N	2.35 E
125	Montgeron (môN-gē-rôN′) Fr. (In.)	48.42 N	2.27 E
82	Montgomery (mŏnt-gŭm′ẽr-ĭ). Ala.	32.21 N	86.18 W
169	Montgomery . . . . . Austl. (Tas. In.)	42.44 S	145.28 E
89	Montgomery Ohio (Cincinnati In.)	39.14 N	84.21 W
84	Montgomery . . . . W. Va.	38.11 N	81.23 W
79	Montgomery City . . . . Mo.	38.58 N	91.30 W
124	Montbard (môN-bȧr′) . . . . Fr.	47.40 N	4.20 E
125	Monthyon (môN-tê-ôN′) . . Fr. (In.)	49.0 N	2.47 E
79	Monticello (mŏn-tê-sĕl′ō) . . . . Ark.	33.36 N	91.48 W
82	Monticello . . . . Fla.	30.33 N	83.53 W
82	Monticello . . . . Ga.	33.19 N	83.43 W
84	Monticello . . . . Ind.	40.43 N	86.48 W
77	Monticello . . . . Ia.	42.16 N	91.11 E
82	Monticello . . . . Ky.	36.48 N	84.51 W
86	Monticello . . . . Me.	46.28 N	67.54 W
77	Monticello . . . . Minn.	45.17 N	93.49 W
85	Monticello . . . . N. Y.	41.36 N	74.38 W
75	Monticello . . . . Utah	37.53 N	109.21 W
125	Montigny-les-Metz (môN-tēn-yē′-lȧ-mĕts′) Fr.	49.5 N	6.9 E
126	Montijo (môn-tē′hō) . . . . Sp.	38.55 N	6.36 W
95	Montijo, G. of . . . . Pan.	7.35 N	81.10 W
126	Montilla (môn-tēl′yä) . . . . Sp.	37.36 N	4.38 W
124	Montivilliers (môN-tē-vē-yā′) . . Fr.	49.35 N	0.11 E
86	Mont Joli (môN zhô-lē′) . . . . . Can.	48.36 N	68.11 W
124	Montluçon (môN-lü-sôN′) . . . . . . Fr.	46.19 N	2.38 E
55	Montmagny (môN-mȧn-yē′) . . Can.	46.58 N	70.33 W
57	Montmorency Falls (mŏnt-mô-rĕn′sĭ) . . Can. (Quebec In.)	46.53 N	71.10 W
125	Montmorency (môN′mô-räN-sē′) Fr. (In.)	48.58 N	2.19 E
57	Montmorency R. (mŏnt-mô-rĕn′sĭ) Can. (Quebec In.)	47.0 N	71.12 W
124	Montmorillon (môN′mô-rê-yôN′) Fr.	46.25 N	0.50 E
126	Montoro (môn-tō′rō) . . . . Sp.	38.1 N	4.22 W
71	Montpelier (mŏnt-pēl′yẽr) . . . . Ida.	42.19 N	11.18 W
84	Montpelier . . . . Ind.	40.35 N	85.20 W
84	Montpelier . . . . Ohio	41.36 N	84.36 W
86	Montpelier . . . . Vt.	44.16 N	72.36 W
124	Montpellier (môN-pĕ-lyā′) . . . . . Fr.	43.38 N	3.53 E
57	Montreal . . . . Can. (In.)		
55	Montreal (mŏn-trê-ôl′) . . . . . . Can.	45.33 N	73.35 W
57	Montreal, I. of, Can. (Montreal In.)	45.30 N	73.40 W
124	Montreuil (môN-trû′y′) . . . . Fr.	50.29 N	1.49 E
125	Montreuil-sous-Bois (môN-trû′y′-sōō-bwä′) Fr. (In.)	48.51 N	2.30 E
122	Montreux (môN-trû′) . . . . . . Switz.	46.26 N	6.56 E
75	Montrose (mŏn-trōz′) . . . . Colo.	38.28 N	107.52 W
116	Montrose . . . . Gt. Brit.	56.45 N	2.30 W
85	Montrose (mŏnt-rōz′) . . . . Pa.	41.49 N	75.48 W
125	Montrouge (môN-rōōzh′). Fr. (In.)	48.48 N	2.18 E
95	Montserrat (I.) (mŏnt-sĕ-răt′) Le. Is. (In.)	16.45 N	162.12 W
86	Monts, Pointe des (pwăNt′ dā môN′) Can.	49.19 N	67.22 W
72	Monument (mŏn′û-mĕnt) Colo. (Colo. Sprs. In.)	39.5 N	104.52 W
72	Monument Cr. Colo. (Colo. Sprs. In.)	39.0 N	104.50 W
151	Monywa (mŏn′yōō-wȧ) . . . . . India	21.55 N	95.12 E
128	Monza (mōn′tsä) . . . . It.	45.35 N	9.15 E
127	Monzón (mōn-thōn′) . . . . Sp.	41.54 N	0.10 E
81	Moody (mōō′dĭ) . . . . Tex.	31.19 N	97.20 W
143	Mooi R. (mōō′ĭ) . . . . U. S. Afr.	29.5 S	30.15 E
143	Mooi River . . . . U. S. Afr.	29.12 S	29.59 E
157	Mooju (mōō′jōō′) . . . . Chn.	36.2 N	127.42 E
167	Mooki R. (mōō′kĭ) . . . . Austl.	31.20 S	150.27 E
157	Moonchun (mōōn′chōōn′) . . . Cho.	39.17 N	127.17 E
169	Moonie R. (mōōn′ê) . . Austl. (In.)	27.30 S	150.28 E
157	Moonkyung (mŏŏnk′yŏŏng′) . Cho.	36.45 N	128.6 E
89	Moon Run . . . Pa. (Pittsburgh In.)	40.27 N	80.8 W
166	Moonta (mōōn′tȧ) . . . . Austl.	34.4 S	137.35 E
164	Moora (mŏŏr′ȧ) . . . . Austl.	30.32 S	116.2 E
119	Moorburg (môr′bŏŏrgh) Ger. (Hamburg In.)	53.29 N	9.56 E
71	Moorcroft (mōr′krôft) . . . . . . Wyo.	44.27 N	104.58 W
119	Moore (mōr) Gt. Brit. (Liverpool In.)	53.21 N	2.38 W
164	Moore, L. . . . . Austl.	29.50 S	117.40 E
89	Moore L. . Minn. (Minneapolis In.)	45.5 N	93.14 W
84	Mooresville (mōrz′vĭl) . . . . Ind.	39.36 N	86.26 W
83	Mooresville . . . . N. C.	35.34 N	80.48 W
119	Moorfleth (môr′flĕt) Ger. (Hamburg In.)	53.31 N	10.4 E
76	Moorhead (mōr′hĕd) . . . . Minn.	46.52 N	96.45 W
82	Moorhead . . . . Miss.	33.27 N	90.32 W
169	Moorina (mŏŏ-rē′nȧ) Austl. (Tas. In.)	41.6 S	147.58 E
142	Moorreesburg (mō′rāz-bŏŏrg) U. S. Afr.	33.8 S	18.36 E
119	Moorrege (mōr′ĕ-gĕ) Ger. (Hamburg In.)	53.40 N	9.40 E
157	Moosan (mōō′sän′) . . . . Cho.	37.53 N	126.44 E
86	Moosehead L. (mōōs′hĕd) . . . . Me.	45.33 N	69.38 W
54	Moose Jaw (mōōs jô) . . . . Can.	50.28 N	105.35 W
54	Moose L. (mōōs) . . . . Can.	54.0 N	100.15 W
86	Mooselookmeguntic L. (mōō-sĕ-lŏŏk-mê-gŭn′tĭk). Me.	44.55 N	70.45 W
55	Moose R. . . . . Can.	51.0 N	81.0 W
55	Moosonee . . . . Can.	51.20 N	80.44 W
138	Mopti (mŏp′tê) . . . . Fr. W. Afr.	14.30 N	4.3 W
52	Moquawkie (mô-kwô′kē) Alsk. (In.)	61.5 N	151.18 W
102	Moquegua (mô-kā′gwä) . . . . . Peru	17.15 S	71.0 W
123	Mor (mōr) . . . . Hung.	47.22 N	18.12 E
77	Mora (mō′rȧ) . . . . Minn.	45.53 N	93.17 W
78	Mora . . . . N. M.	35.57 N	105.17 W
126	Mora . . . . Sp.	39.43 N	3.45 W
127	Mora . . . . Sp.	41.6 N	0.37 E
151	Moradabad (mô-rä-dä-bäd′) . India	28.45 N	78.30 E
72	Moraine, L. (mô-rān′) Colo. (Colo. Spgs. In.)	38.48 N	104.59 W
141	Moramanga (mō-rä-hwŋ′gä) Madag.	18.45 S	48.10 E
97	Morant Pt. (mô-rănt′) . . . . Jam.	17.55 N	76.11 W
120	Morastrand (mō′rä-strônd) . . . Swe.	61.0 N	14.32 E
127	Morata de Tajuña (mô-rä′tä dā tä-hōō′nyä). Sp. (In.)	40.13 N	3.27 W
126	Moratalla (mō-rä-täl′yä) . . . . . . Sp.	38.15 N	1.54 W
122	Morava R. (mô′rä-vä) . . . . . Czech.	49.15 N	17.29 E
129	Morava R. . . . . Yugo.	43.30 N	21.45 E
122	Morava (Moravia) (Prov.) (mô′-rä-vä) (mô-rā′vĭ-ȧ). Czech.	49.25 N	17.15 E
123	Moravská Ostrava (mô′rȧf-skä ôs′trȧ-vȧ). Czech.	49.49 N	18.17 E
103	Morawhanna (mô-rȧ-hwä′nȧ) Br. Gu.	8.12 N	59.32 W
116	Moray Firth (mŭr′â) . . . . Gt. Brit.	57.40 N	3.40 W
120	Mörbylånga (mûr′bü-lôŋ′gȧ) . Swe.	56 32 N	16.24 E
124	Morcenx (môr-săNs′) . . . . Fr.	44.1 N	0.51 W
76	Morden (môr′dĕn) . . . . Can.	49.15 N	98.4 W
166	Mordialloc (môr-dĭ-ăl′ŏk) . . . Austl.	38.0 S	145.5 E
76	Moreau R. (mô-rō′) . . . . S. D.	45.12 N	102.0 W
118	Morecambe (mōr′kăm) . . . Gt. Brit.	54.4 N	2.52 W
116	Morecambe B. . . . . Gt. Brit.	54.5 N	3.0 W
165	Moree (mō′rē) . . . . Austl.	29.20 S	149.45 E
84	Morehead (mōr′hĕd) . . . . Ky.	38.12 N	83.30 W
83	Morehead City . . . . N. C.	34.43 N	76.43 W
79	Morehouse (mōr′hous) . . . . Mo.	36.50 N	89.40 W
92	Morelia (mô-rā′lyä) . . . . Mex.	19.42 N	101.11 W
127	Morella (mô-rāl′yä) . . . . Sp.	40.37 N	0.7 W
92	Morelos (State) (mô-rā′lōs) . . Mex.	18.40 N	99.0 W
92	Morelos . . . . Mex.	22.49 N	102.27 W
80	Morelos . . . . Mex.	28.25 N	100.52 W
126	Morena, Sierra (Mts.) (syĕr′rä mô-rā′nä). Sp.	38.25 N	5.0 W
75	Morenci (mô-rĕn′sĭ) . . . . Ariz.	33.5 N	109.23 W
84	Morenci . . . . Mich.	41.44 N	84.8 W
54	Moresby I. (mōrz′bĭ) . . . . Can.	52.30 N	132.0 W
72	Moresby I. . . Can. (Vancouver In.)	48.43 N	123.18 W
96	Mores I. (mōrz) . . . . Ba. Is.	26.18 N	77.35 W
169	Moreton B. (môr′tŭn). Austl. (In.)	27.12 S	153.12 E
169	Moreton I. . . . . Austl. (In.)	27.10 S	153.23 E
167	Morewell (mōr′wĕl) . . . . Austl.	38.14 S	146.22 E
125	Morez (mô-rĕ′) . . . . Fr.	46.30 N	6.1 E
166	Morgan (môr′găn) . . . . Austl.	34.3 S	139.40 E
71	Morgan . . . . Utah	41.10 N	111.41 W
81	Morgan City . . . . La.	29.40 N	91.10 W
84	Morganfield (môr′găn-fēld) . . . Ky.	37.40 N	87.54 W
89	Morgan Har. . La. (New Orleans In.)	29.50 N	89.15 W
165	Morgan, Mt. . . . . Austl.	23.45 S	150.27 E
88	Morgan Park . . . . Ill. (Chicago In.)	41.42 N	87.40 W
83	Morganton (môr′găn-tŭn) . . . N. C.	35.45 N	81.42 W
85	Morgantown (môr′găn-toun) W. Va.	39.38 N	79.57 W
143	Morgenzon (môr′gĕn-zōn′) U.S.Afr.	26.45 S	29.37 E
159	Mori (mô′rē) . . . . Jap.	33.25 N	131.8 E
145	Morib (mô-rēb′) Fed. Mal. St. (In.)	2.47 N	101.27 E
159	Moriguchi (mō′rê-gōō′chê) Jap. (Osaka In.)	34.45 N	135.33 E
143	Morija (mô-rē′yä) . . . . Bas.	29.38 S	27.31 E
158	Morioka (mō′rê-ō′kȧ) . . . . Jap.	39.45 N	141.13 E
149	Morkoka R. (môr-kô′kȧ) . Sov. Un.	65.0 N	112.0 E
124	Morlaix (môr-lĕ′) . . . . Fr.	48.37 N	3.50 W
151	Mormugão (mōr-mōō-gouN′). India	15.28 N	73.58 E
95	Morne Diablotin (Mt.) (môrn dê-ȧ-blô-tăN′). Le. Is. (In.)	15.30 N	61.26 W
95	Morne Gimie (Mt.) (môrn′ zhê-mē′) Wind. Is.	13.52 N	61.2 W
166	Mornington (môr′nĭng-tŭn). Austl.	38.13 S	145.3 E
161	Morobe (mô-rō′bā) . . . N. Gui. Ter.	7.53 S	147.32 E
138	Morocco (mô-rŏk′ō) . . . . Afr.	32.0 N	6.0 W
138	Morocco, Spanish . . . . Afr.	35.0 N	5.0 W
130	Moroch R. (mô-rôch′) Pol.-Sov. Un.	52.45 N	27.5 E
163	Moro G. (mō′rō) . . . . P. I.	7.0 N	123.0 E
141	Morogoro (mō-rô-gō′rō) . . . . . . Tan.	6.47 S	37.43 E
142	Morokwen (mō′rô-kwĕn) . . . . Bech.	26.8 S	23.46 E
92	Moroleón (mô-rō-lā-ōn′) . . . . . Mex.	20.7 N	101.12 W
96	Morón (mô-rōn′) . . . . Cuba	22.5 N	78.36 W
141	Morondava (mô-rōn-dȧ′vȧ) Madag.	20.15 S	44.18 E
126	Morón de la Frontera (mô-rōn′ dā lā frôn-tā′rā). Sp.	37.7 N	5.26 W
162	Morong (mō′rông) . . . . P. I.	14.30 N	121.14 E
74	Morongo Indian Res. (mō-rôŋ′gō) Calif.	33.57 N	116.50 W
75	Moroni (mô-rō′nĭ) . . . . Utah	39.33 N	11.39 W
96	Morón Lagoon (mô-rōn′) . . . . Cuba	22.10 N	78.37 W
161	Morotai (I.) (mō-rô-tā′ê) Neth. Ind.	2.15 N	128.30 E
113	Morozovskaya (mô′rô-zôf-skȧ′yȧ) Sov. Un.	48.18 N	41.55 E
167	Morpeth (môr′pĕth) . . . . Austl.	32.44 S	151.39 E
76	Morrill (mŏr′ĭl) . . . . Neb.	41.58 N	103.53 W
79	Morrilton (mŏr′ĭl-tŭn) . . . . Ark.	35.9 N	91.42 W
103	Morrinhos (mô-rēn′yōzh) . . . . Braz.	17.45 S	49.12 W
170	Morrinsville (mŏr′ĭnz-vĭl) . . . . N. Z.	37.38 S	175.37 E
73	Morris (mŏr′ĭs) Ala. (Birmingham In.)	33.45 N	86.48 W
76	Morris . . . . Can.	49.20 N	97.30 W
79	Morris . . . . Ill.	41.22 N	88.25 W
76	Morris . . . . Minn.	45.36 N	95.52 W
73	Morris . . Utah (Salt Lake City In.)	40.40 N	112.16 W
88	Morris Can. . . . . . N. J. (N Y. In.)	40.52 N	74.11 W
77	Morrison (mŏr′ĭ-sŭn) . . . . Ill.	41.48 N	89.57 W
72	Morrison, Mt. . Colo. (Denver In.)	39.40 N	105.13 W
82	Morristown (mŏr′ĭs-toun) . . . Tenn.	36.12 N	83.18 W
86	Morrisville (mŏr′ĭs-vĭl) . . . . Vt.	44.32 N	72.36 W
90	Morro Castle (môr′ō) Cuba (Habana In.)	23.9 N	82.21 W
103	Morro do Champéo (môr-ŏŏ dŏŏ chăm-pā′ŏŏ). Braz.	11.32 S	41.12 W
73	Morrow (mŏr′ō). Ga. (Atlanta In.)	33.34 N	84.20 W
113	Morshansk (môr-shȧnsk′) Sov. Un.	53.10 N	41.55 E
120	Mors (I.) (môrs) . . . . Den.	56.48 N	8.45 E
124	Mortagne (môr-tän′y′) . . . . Fr.	48.32 N	0.35 E
128	Mortara (môr-tä′rä) . . . . It.	45.15 N	8.45 E
125	Morteau (môr-tō′) . . . . Fr.	47.5 N	6.38 E
166	Mortlake (môrt′lāk) . . . . Austl.	38.5 S	142.49 E
88	Morton Grove (môr′tŭn grōv) Ill. (Chicago In.)	42.2 N	87.47 W
119	Mortsel (môr-sĕl′) Bel. (Anvers In.)	51.10 N	4.28 E
167	Moruya (mō-rōō′yä) . . . . Austl.	35.46 S	150.4 E
124	Morvan Mts. (môr-văN′) . . . . . . Fr.	47.10 N	4.10 E
112	Morzhovets I. (môr′zhô-vyĕts′) Sov. Un.	66.40 N	42.35 E
130	Mosalsk (mō-zȧlsk′) . . . . . Sov. Un.	54.28 N	34.58 E
158	Mosan (mō′săn′) . . . . Cho.	42.14 N	129.15 E
70	Moscow (mŏs′kō) . . . . Ida.	46.44 N	117.0 W
130	Moscow (Moskva) (mŏs-kvȧ′) Sov. Un.	55.45 N	37.36 E
130	Moscow (mŏs′kō) Sea . . . . Sov. Un.	56.47 N	37.0 E
150	Moseirah (I.) (mô-sā′rä) . . . . Oman	20.30 N	58.48 E
122	Mosel R. (mō′sĕl (mô-zĕl′) . . . . Ger.	50.0 N	7.7 E
125	Moselle R. (mô-zĕl′) . . . . Fr.	49.0 N	6.10 E
70	Moses L. (mō′zĕz) . . . . Wash.	47.9 N	119.10 W
171	Mosgiel (môs′gēl) . . . . . . N. Z. (In.)	45.53 S	170.22 E
141	Moshi (mō′shê) . . . . Tan.	3.17 S	37.18 E
143	Mosita (mô-zē′tȧ) . . . . Bech.	26.9 S	24.48 E
130	Moskva (Aut. Area) (mŏs-kvȧ′) Sov. Un.	55.32 N	37.0 E
130	Moskva (Moscow) . . . . Sov. Un.	55.45 N	37.36 E
130	Moskva R. . . . . Sov. Un.	55.38 N	36.25 E
103	Mosqueiro I. (môs-kā′rŏŏ) Braz. (In.)	1.7 S	48.25 W
95	Mosquito Cays (Is.) (mŏs-kē′tō) W. I.	14.35 N	82.40 W
95	Mosquito Coast (Reg.) . . . . Nic.	12.40 N	83.45 W
95	Mosquito G. . . . . Pan.	9.20 N	81.10 W
120	Moss (môs) . . . . Nor.	59.28 N	10.40 E
140	Mossámedes (mô-sä′mȧ-dĕs) . Ang.	15.12 S	12.12 E
140	Mossámedes (Dist.) . . . . Ang.	15.30 S	12.30 E
142	Mossel B. (mŏs′ĕl) . . . . . U. S. Afr.	34.5 S	22.12 E
142	Mossel Bay . . . . U. S. Afr.	34.10 S	22.8 E
118	Mossley (môs′lĭ) . . . . Gt. Brit.	53.31 N	2.3 W
103	Mossoró (mō-sô-rŏŏ′) . . . . Braz.	5.10 S	37.28 W
82	Moss Point (môs) . . . . Miss.	30.25 N	88.33 W
167	Most Vale . . . . Austl.	34.34 S	150.21 E
. . .	Most, see Brüx, Ger.		
138	Mostaganem (mŏs′tä-gȧ-nĕm′) Alg.	36.0 N	0.6 E
129	Mostar (môs′tär) . . . . Yugo.	43.20 N	17.50 E
127	Mostoles (môs-tō′lās) . . . . Sp. (In.)	40.19 N	3.52 W
119	Mostyn (mŏs′tĭn) Gt. Brit. (Liverpool In.)	53.19 N	3.17 W
150	Mosul (mō-sōōl′) . . . . Iraq	36.1 N	43.0 E
154	Mosün (mō′sün′) . . . . Chn.	23.37 N	109.49 E
94	Motagua, R. (mô-tä′gwä) . . . Guat.	15.10 N	89.20 W
120	Motala (mô-tô′lä) . . . . Swe.	58.33 N	15.2 E
89	Mother L. (mŭdh′ẽr) Minn. (Minneapolis In.)	44.54 N	93.14 W
116	Motherwell (mŭdh′ẽr-wĕl) Gt. Brit.	55.48 N	4.0 W
170	Motiti I. (mô-tē′tê) . . . . N. Z.	37.35 S	176.27 E
148	Motovilikha (mô′tô-vē′lê-Kȧ) Sov. Un.	58.0 N	56.25 E
126	Motril (mô-trēl′) . . . . Sp.	36.45 N	3.30 W
171	Motueka (mô-tōō-ā′kȧ) . . . . . N. Z.	41.7 S	173.0 E
170	Motukorehu Chan. (mō-tōō-kô-rē′hû). N. Z. (In.)	36.50 S	174.53 E
170	Motukorehu I. . . . . N. Z. (In.)	36.50 S	174.54 E
97	Mouchoir Bank (mōō-chwȧr′) Ba. Is.	21.0 N	70.45 W
97	Mouchoir Passage . . . . Ba. Is.	21.9 N	70.55 W
166	Moulamein (mōl-ȧ-mān′) . . . Austl.	35.5 S	144.1 E
166	Moulamein Cr. . . . . Austl.	35.18 S	145.0 E
124	Moulins (mōō-lăN′) . . . . Fr.	46.35 N	3.20 E
160	Moulmein (mōl-mān′) . . . . India	16.29 N	97.35 E
138	Moulouya R. (mōō-lōō′yȧ) . . . Mor.	34.0 N	3.40 W
82	Moultrie (mōl′trĭ) . . . . Ga.	31.10 N	83.48 W
79	Mound City (mound) . . . . Ill.	37.6 N	89.10 W
79	Mound City . . . . Mo.	40.6 N	95.14 W
84	Moundsville (moundz′vĭl) . . W. Va.	39.57 N	80.55 W
125	Mounier, Mt. (mōō-nyā′) . . . . . . Fr.	44.10 N	6.57 E
148	Mountain Badakhshan (Gorno Badakshan) (Aut. Ter.) (gôr′nô bȧ-dȧk′shȧn) . . Sov. Un.	38.50 N	73.0 E
79	Mountain Grove . . . . Mo.	37.6 N	92.17 W
70	Mountain Home . . . . Ida.	43.7 N	115.42 W
139	Mountain Nile (Bahr el Jebel) (R.) (bär-ĕl jĕb′ĕl). Afr.	7.0 N	31.0 E
49	Mountain View Calif. (San Francisco In.)	37.24 N	122.5 W
79	Mountain View . . . . Mo.	37.0 N	91.47 W
83	Mount Airy (mount âr′ĭ) . . . . N. C.	36.30 N	80.37 W
129	Mount Athos (Pen.) (ăth′ŏs). Grc.	40.15 N	24.15 E
143	Mount Ayliff (ā′lĭf) . . . . . U. S. Afr.	30.51 S	29.20 E
77	Mount Ayr (âr) . . . . Ia.	40.43 N	94.12 W
84	Mount Carmel (kär′mĕl) . . . . . . Ill.	38.26 N	87.45 W
85	Mount Carmel . . . . Pa.	40.48 N	76.25 W
84	Mount Clemens (klĕm′ĕnz) . . Mich.	42.35 N	82.53 W
54	Mount Denis (dĕn′ĭs) . . . Can. (In.)	43.41 N	79.30 W
86	Mount Desert I. (dê-zûrt′) . . . Me.	44.20 N	68.25 W
83	Mount Dora (dō′rȧ) . . . . Fla.	28.46 N	81.38 W
166	Mount Emu Cr. (ē′mū) . . . . Austl.	37.55 S	143.5 E
143	Mount Fletcher (flĕch′ẽr) U. S. Afr.	30.42 S	28.32 E
84	Mount Forest . . . . Can.	43.38 N	80.46 W
143	Mount Frere (frēr) . . . . . U. S. Afr.	30.56 S	28.58 E
166	Mount Gambier (găm′bēr). Austl.	37.49 S	140.46 E
84	Mount Gilead (gĭl′ê-ăd) . . . . . . Ohio	40.34 N	82.53 W

ng-sing; ŋ-baŋk; N-nasalized n; nŏd; cŏmmit; ōld; ôbey; ôrder; fōōd; fŏŏt; ou-out; s-soft; sh-dish; th-thin; pūre; ûnite; ûrn; stŭd; circŭs; ü-as "y" in study; ′-indeterminate vowel.

Page	Name Pronunciation Region	Lat. °′	Long. °′
89	Mount Healthy Ohio (Cincinnati In.)	39.14 N	84.33 W
84	Mount Hope.............W. Va.	37.55 N	81.12 W
164	Mount Isa (ī′zȧ)...........Austl.	20.59 S	139.35 E
72	Mount Lehman (lā′mȧn) Can. (Vancouver In.)	49.7 N	122.23 W
166	Mount Lofty Ra. (lŏf′tĭ)....Austl.	34.45 S	139.10 E
53	Mount McKinley Natl. Pk. (mȧ-kĭn′lĭ).Alsk.	63.20 N	150.0 W
84	Mount Morris (mŏr′ĭs).....Mich.	43.6 N	83.42 W
85	Mount Morris...........N. Y.	42.46 N	77.50 W
83	Mount Olive (ŏl′ĭv).........N. C.	35.12 N	78.4 W
70	Mount Olympic Natl. Park (ô lĭm′pĭk).Wash.	47.55 N	123.30 W
73	Mount Pinson (pĭn′zŭn) Ala. (Birmingham In.)	33.41 N	86.42 W
77	Mount Pleasant (plĕz′ănt).....Ia.	40.58 N	91.33 W
84	Mount Pleasant ....Mich.	43.37 N	84.47 W
83	Mount Pleasant............S. C.	32.47 N	79.52 W
82	Mountpleasant............Tenn.	35.32 N	87.12 W
81	Mount Pleasant............Tex.	33.8 N	95.0 W
75	Mount Pleasant............Utah	39.33 N	111.26 W
88	Mount Prospect (prŏs′pĕkt) Ill. (Chicago In.)	42.4 N	87.56 W
70	Mount Rainier Natl. Park (rȧ-nēr′). Wash.	46.50 N	121.20 W
167	Mount Royal Ra...........Austl.	32.0 S	151.20 E
85	Mount Savage (săv′âj).......Md.	39.43 N	78.53 W
70	Mount Shasta (shăs′tȧ).....Calif.	41.17 N	122.15 W
79	Mount Sterling (stûr′lĭng).....Ill.	39.59 N	90.44 W
84	Mount Sterling..............Ky.	38.4 N	83.58 W
85	Mount Union...............Pa.	40.25 N	77.53 W
79	Mount Vernon (vûr′nŭn)......Ill.	38.17 N	88.55 W
84	Mount Vernon..............Ind.	37.56 N	87.53 W
79	Mount Vernon..............Mo.	37.7 N	93.46 W
85	Mount Vernon.............N. Y.	40.56 N	73.50 W
84	Mount Vernon.............Ohio	40.26 N	82.30 W
85	Mount Vernon..............Va.	38.43 N	77.5 W
70	Mount Vernon............Wash.	48.24 N	122.20 W
167	Mount Victoria (vĭk-tō′rĭ-ȧ).Austl.	33.37 S	150.17 E
103	Moura (mō′rȧ)..............Braz.	1.32 S	61.33 W
126	Moura.....................Port.	38.7 N	7.27 W
116	Mourne Mts. (môrn)....Gt. Brit.	54.10 N	6.5 W
125	Moutières (mōō-tyâr′).........Fr.	45.30 N	6.35 E
141	Mowbray (mō′brȧ).....U. S. Afr.	33.56 S	18.28 E
169	Mowbullan, Mt. (mō′bōō-lȧn) Austl. (In.)	26.54 S	151.36 E
170	Mowlom Mt. (mō′lŏm) N. Z. (In.)	41.15 S	174.58 E
92	Moyahua (mô-yä′wä).......Mex.	21.19 N	103.17 W
139	Moyale (Fort Harrington) (mô-yä′ lä) (fōrt hăr′ĭng-tŭn).Kenya	3.28 N	39.6 E
138	Moyamba (mô-yäm′bä).....S. L.	8.11 N	12.30 W
143	Moyeni (mô-yā′nê)..........Bas.	30.25 S	27.44 E
125	Moyeuvre (mô-yûv′r′).........Fr.	49.17 N	6.5 E
70	Moyie R. (moi′yê)...........Ida.	49.0 N	116.12 W
102	Moyobamba (mō-yô-bäm′bä).Peru	6.2 S	76.58 W
154	Moyün (mō′yün′)...........Chn.	23.30 N	108.26 E
140	Mozambique (Portuguese East Africa) (mō-zăm-bēk′).Afr.	18.15 S	35.0 E
140	Mozambique Chan........Ind. O.	18.0 S	41.0 E
113	Mozdok (môz-dôk′)......Sov. Un.	43.48 N	44.35 E
130	Mozhaisk (mô-zhȧ-ēsk′) Sov. Un.	55.31 N	36.3 E
131	Mozir (mô-zēr) ....Sov. Un.	52.3 N	29.15 E
141	Mpera (′m-pā′rä) ....Tan.	6.50 S	38.43 E
143	Mpofana (′m-pô-fā′nä).. U. S. Afr.	28.51 S	30.28 E
140	Mponda (′m-pōn′dä) ....Nya.	14.22 S	35.8 E
140	Mporokoso (′m-pō-rô-kō′sō).N.Rh.	9.31 S	30.12 E
141	Mpwapwa (′m-pwä′pwä) ....Tan.	6.15 S	36.33 E
143	Mquanduli (′m-kän′dōō-lê) U. S. Afr.	31.49 S	28.45 E
141	Msangazi R. (′m-säŋ-gä′zê) ..Tan.	5.43 S	38.40 E
138	M′sila (m′sē′lȧ) ....Alg.	35.45 N	4.32 E
130	Msta R. (m′stȧ′) ....Sov. Un.	58.29 N	32.25 E
130	Mstislavi (m′stē-släv″l) Sov. Un.	54.1 N	31.42 E
115	Msus (′m-sōōs)............Libya	31.22 N	21.13 E
141	Mtai (′m-tī′)...............Tan.	4.29 S	38.14 E
141	Mtangata (m-täŋ-gä′tä).....Tan.	5.14 S	39.3 E
141	Mtariça (Dom Luiz Filippe) (′m-tȧ-rē′sȧ) (dōɴ lōō-ēzh′ fê-lēp′ĕ).Moz.	12.45 S	36.40 E
140	Mtengula (′m-tĕŋ-gōō′lȧ)....Moz.	12.40 S	34.50 E
140	Mtetwe Pan (Basin) (′m-tĕt′wĕ) Bech.	20.40 S	25.30 E
130	Mtsensk (m′tsĕnsk)......Sov. Un.	53.16 N	36.35 E
103	Muaná (mōō-ȧ-nä′) ...Braz. (In.)	1.30 S	49.20 W
6	Muanivatu, Mt. (mwä-nê-vä′tōō) Fiji Is. (In.)	17.49 S	177.57 E
118	Much Wenlock (mŭch wĕn′lŏk) Gt. Brit.	52.35 N	2.33 W
116	Muck (I.) (mŭk)........Gt. Brit.	56.45 N	6.10 W
115	Muctar (El Mugtaa) (mōōk-tär′) (ĕl mōōg-tä′ä).Libya	30.25 N	18.42 E
103	Mucujé (mōō-kōō-zhā′).....Braz.	13.2 S	41.28 W
158	Mudan R. (mōō′dän′).....Manch.	45.0 N	129.33 E
79	Muddy Boggy Cr. (bôg′ĭ)...Okla.	34.30 N	96.12 W
74	Muddy R. (mŭd′ĭ)..........Nev.	36.55 N	114.45 W
167	Mudgee (mŭ-jē′)...........Austl.	32.37 S	149.33 E
77	Mud L......................Mich.	46.12 N	84.10 W
89	Mud L... Minn. (Minneapolis In.)	44.53 N	93.16 W
70	Mud L.......................Nev.	40.31 N	119.20 W
126	Mugía (mōō-ĸē′ä)............Sp.	43.5 N	9.14 W
115	Muğla (mōōg′lä).............Tur.	37.15 N	28.25 E
122	Mühldorf (mül-dôrf).........Ger.	48.16 N	12.32 E
122	Mühlhausen (mül′hou-zĕn)...Ger.	51.13 N	10.25 E
121	Muhu (I.) (mōō′hōō).........Est.	58.36 N	23.15 E
49	Muir (mūr)................Calif.	37.59 N	122.7 W
74	Muir Woods Nat. Mon. (mūr) Calif.	37.53 N	122.35 W
142	Muizenberg (mū′zĕn-bûrg) U. S. Afr.	34.5 S	18.25 E
	Mukačevo, see Munkács, Hung.		
150	Mukalla (mŭ-kä′lä).........Aden	14.28 N	49.5 E
153	Mukden (Shenyang) (mōōk′dĕn) (shĕn′yäng′).Manch.	42.1 N	123.28 E
149	Mukhtuya (mōōĸ-tōō′yȧ) Sov. Un.	60.40 N	114.50 E
135	Mukimbungu (mōō′kēm-bōōŋ-gōō) Bel. Cong. (Brazzaville In.)	5.9 S	14.1 E
159	Mukogawa R. (mōō′kô-gä′wä) Jap. (Osaka In.)	34.52 N	135.18 E
159	Mukomachi (mōō′kô-mä′chê) Jap. (Osaka In.)	34.57 N	135.42 E
126	Mula (mōō′lä)................Sp.	38.3 N	1.28 W
128	Mulat (I.) (mōō′lät).......Yugo.	44.15 N	14.50 E
82	Mulberry Fork (R.) (mŭl′bĕr-ĭ) Ala.	33.52 N	87.0 W
122	Mulde R. (mōōl′dē)..........Ger.	51.10 N	12.47 E
142	Muldersvlei (mōōl′dērs-vlī) U. S. Afr.	33.50 S	18.45 E
92	Muleros (mōō-lā′rōs)........Mex.	23.45 N	103.59 W
87	Mulgrave (mŭl′grāv)........Can.	45.37 N	61.22 W
165	Mulgrave I.............Pap. Ter.	10.10 S	142.8 E
126	Mulhacén (Mt.) (mōōl-ä-thān′) Sp.	37.3 N	3.19 W
122	Mülheim (mül′hīm).........Ger.	51.26 N	6.54 E
125	Mulhouse (mü-lōōz′) ....Fr.	47.45 N	7.20 E
70	Mullan (mŭl′ăn)............Ida.	47.27 N	115.47 W
160	Müller Mts. (mül′ēr)...Neth. Ind.	0.38 N	113.30 E
84	Mullet L. (mŭl′ĕt).........Mich.	45.30 N	84.23 W
116	Mullets Pen..................Ire.	54.10 N	10.0 W
116	Mull (I.) (mŭl).........Gt. Brit.	56.30 N	6.0 W
116	Mullingar (mŭl-ĭn-gär′).......Ire.	53.30 N	7.20 W
83	Mullins (mŭl′ĭnz)...........S. C.	34.12 N	79.14 W
94	Mullins River.....Br. Hond. (In.)	17.7 N	88.17 W
151	Multan (mōōl-tän′).........India	30.15 N	71.31 E
79	Mulvane (mŭl-vān′).........Kan.	37.27 N	97.13 W
140	Mumbwa (mōōm′bwä)....N. Rh.	15.0 S	27.5 E
141	Muna el Amîr (mōō′nä ĕl ȧ-mēr′).Eg.	29.55 N	31.15 E
122	München (Munich) (mün′ĸĕn) Ger.	48.8 N	11.35 E
84	Muncie (mŭn′sĭ).............Ind.	40.10 N	85.25 W
122	Münden (mün′dĕn)...........Ger.	51.26 N	9.39 E
167	Mundoonan Ra. (mŭn-dōō′nȧn) Austl.	34.38 S	148.50 E
166	Mundoora (mŭn-dōō′rȧ)....Austl.	33.35 S	138.7 E
165	Mungana (mŭn-găn′ȧ).....Austl.	17.8 S	144.15 E
165	Mungindi (mŭn-gĭn′dê).....Austl.	29.0 S	149.0 E
140	Munhanga (mōōn-häŋ′gȧ)....Ang.	12.8 S	18.58 E
138	Muni (Prov.) (mōō′nê)...Sp. Gui.	1.30 N	10.30 E
122	Munich (münchen) (mū′nĭk) (mün-ĸĕn).Ger.	48.8 N	11.35 E
77	Munising (mū′nĭ-sĭng)......Mich.	46.24 N	86.39 W
123	Munkács (Mukačevo) (mōōn′käch) (mōō′kȧ-chĕ′vô).Hung.	48.26 N	22.42 E
148	Munku Sardik (Mt.) (mōōn′kōō-sär-dĭk′)...Sov. Un.	51.40 N	100.30 E
162	Muñoz (mōō-nyōth′)........P. I.	15.43 N	120.54 E
99	Muñoz Gamero Pen.(mōōn′yôz gä-mā′rō) Chl. (Magallanes In.).	52.40 S	73.10 W
125	Munster (mûn′stēr)..........Fr.	48.1 N	7.5 E
122	Münster (mün′stēr)..........Ger.	51.58 N	7.38 E
129	Muntenia (Prov.) (mōōn-tȧ′nĭ-ȧ) Rom.	45.0 N	26.0 E
161	Muntinglupa (mōōn-tĭng-lōō′pä) P. I. (Manila In.)	14.25 N	121.3 E
160	Muntok (mōōn-tŏk′) Neth. Ind.	2.5 S	105.10 E
160	Muongsing (mōō′ŏng-sĭng′) Fr. In. Chn.	21.5 N	101.14 E
113	Muradiye (mōō-rä′dê-yĕ).....Tur.	38.58 N	43.45 E
131	Murafa (mōō-rȧ′fȧ)......Sov. Un.	50.1 N	35.17 E
128	Mura R. (mōō′rä).....Yugo.-Ger.	46.45 N	15.50 E
124	Murat (mü-rä′)...............Fr.	45.5 N	2.59 E
113	Murat R. (mōō-rȧt′)..........Tur.	38.45 N	40.45 E
139	Murchison Falls(mûr′chĭ-sŭn) .Ug.	2.15 N	31.46 E
164	Murchison R...............Austl.	26.30 S	116.30 E
126	Murcia (mōōr′thyä)..........Sp.	38.0 N	1.8 W
126	Murcia (Prov.)...............Sp.	38.30 N	1.45 W
76	Murdo (mûr′dô)............S. D.	43.54 N	100.41 W
158	Muren R. (mōō′rĕn) .....Manch.	45.13 N	131.0 E
123	Mureşul R. (mōō′rĕsh-ōōl) ..Rom.	46.20 N	23.43 E
124	Muret (mü-rĕ′)...............Fr.	43.28 N	1.19 E
82	Murfreesboro (mûr′-frêz-bŭr-ô) Tenn.	35.51 N	86.24 W
150	Murgohab R. (mōōr-gäb′) Sov. Un.	37.0 N	62.30 E
169	Murgon (mûr′gŭn).........Austl.	26.13 S	151.54 E
122	Müritz (mür′ĭts).............Ger.	53.24 N	12.55 E
122	Müritz L...................Ger.	53.25 N	12.42 E
112	Murmansk (mōōr-mänsk′) Sov. Un.	68.50 N	33.10 E
112	Murom (mōō′rôm)......Sov. Un.	55.30 N	42.0 E
158	Muroran (mōō′rô-rȧn) ....Jap.	42.22 N	140.59 E
126	Muros (mōō′rōs).............Sp.	42.47 N	9.5 W
159	Muroto C. (mōō′rô-tō) ......Jap.	33.16 N	134.10 E
72	Murphy (mŭr′fĭ) Colo. (Colo. Sprs. In.)	38.54 N	105.10 W
82	Murphy...................N. C.	35.6 N	84.2 W
79	Murphysboro (mŭr′fĭz-bŭr-ô)..Ill.	37.46 N	89.21 W
122	Mur R. (mōōr).......Aus.-Hung.	47.24 N	15.10 E
140	Murraça (mōōr-rä′sȧ).......Moz.	17.52 S	35.12 E
82	Murray (mŭr′ĭ)..............Ky.	36.40 N	88.18 W
71	Murray...................Utah	40.40 N	111.54 W
55	Murray B..................Can.	47.47 N	70.17 W
166	Murray Bridge.............Austl.	35.8 S	139.15 E
167	Murray Ra................Austl.	35.42 S	148.0 E
59	Murray, L.................S. C.	34.15 N	81.45 W
166	Murray R..................Austl.	34.10 S	142.10 E
142	Murraysburg (mŭr′ĭz-bûrg) U. S. Afr.	31.57 S	23.47 E
166	Murrayville (mŭr′ĭ-vĭl).....Austl.	35.21 S	141.17 E
72	Murrayville. Can. (Vancouver In.)	49.5 N	122.37 W
166	Murrumbidgee R. (mŭr-ŭm-bĭd′jê) Austl.	34.30 S	145.42 E
167	Murrurundi (mŭr′rōō-rōōn′dê) Austl.	31.46 S	150.51 E
151	Murshidabad (mōōr′shê-dä-bäd′) India	24.5 N	88.29 E
166	Murtoa (mŭr-tō′ȧ).........Austl.	36.38 S	142.30 E
161	Murua (Woodlark) (I.) (mōō′rōō-ȧ) (wōōd′lärk).Pap.Ter	9.0 S	152.45 E
169	Murvillumbah (mŭr-wĭl-lŭm′bȧ) Austl (In.)	28.19 S	153.21 E
122	Mürz R. (mürts)............Ger.	47.47 N	15.40 E
139	Murzuch (mōōr-zōōĸ′).....Libya	25.58 N	14.12 E
139	Murzuch (Dunes)..........Libya	24.30 N	14.0 E
122	Mürzzuschlag (mürts′tsōō-shlägh) Ger.	47.37 N	15.41 E
113	Muş (mōōsh)................Tur.	38.48 N	41.28 E
145	Musa (mōō′sȧ)........Yem. (In.)	13.42 N	43.19 E
150	Muscat (Masqat) (mŭs-kăt′) (măs-kät′).Oman	23.31 N	58.38 E
77	Muscatine (mŭs-kȧ-tēn′).......Ia.	41.24 N	91.2 W
82	Muscle Shoals (mŭs″l shōlz′). Ala.	34.46 N	87.38 W
145	Musemir (mōō-sȧ-mēr′) Aden (In.)	13.29 N	44.49 E
164	Musgrave R. (mŭs′grāv)....Austl.	26.10 S	131.45 E
140	Mushie (mŭsh′ê).......Bel. Cong.	3.2 S	16.48 E
160	Musi R. (mōō′sê)......Neth. Ind.	2.55 S	104.0 E
84	Muskegon (mŭs-kē′gŭn)....Mich.	43.14 N	86.15 W
84	Muskegon Heights.........Mich.	43.10 N	86.18 W
84	Muskegon R...............Mich.	43.20 N	86.0 W
84	Muskingum R. (mŭs-kĭŋ′gŭm) Ohio	39.55 N	82.0 W
79	Muskogee (mŭs-kō′gê)......Okla.	35.44 N	95.22 W
85	Muskoka, L. (mŭs-kō′kȧ)....Can.	45.5 N	79.30 W
87	Muskwaro L. (mŭsk-wă′rô)...Can.	50.25 N	61.0 W
161	Mussau Is. (mōō-sä′ōō) N. Gui. Ter.	1.30 S	149.35 E
116	Musselburgh (mŭs″l-bŭr-ô) Gt. Brit.	55.55 N	3.0 W
71	Musselshell R (mŭs″l-shĕl).Mont.	46.30 N	108.20 W
128	Mussolinia (mōōs′sô-lē′nē-ȧ).Sard.	40.45 N	8.32 E
167	Musswellbrook (mŭz′wĕl-brōōk) Austl.	32.18 S	150.55 E
113	Mustafakemalpaşa (mōō-stä′fȧ-kĕm′ȧl′-pȧ-shä).Tur.	40.5 N	28.30 E
152	Mustagh Ata (Mt.) (mōōs-täĸ′ä-tä′).Chn.	38.22 N	75.0 E
81	Mustang Bayou (mŭs′tăng) Tex. (In.)	29.25 N	95.12 W
78	Mustang Cr.................Tex.	36.0 N	102.30 W
81	Mustang I..................Tex.	27.45 N	97.5 W
104	Musters, L. (mŭs′tērz) (mōōs-tĕrs′) Arg.	45.30 S	68.30 W
95	Mustique I. (mūs-tēk′) Wind. Is. (In.)	12.52 N	61.12 W
121	Mustvee (mōōst′vĕ-ĕ)........Est.	58.50 N	26.56 E
140	Mutombo Mukulu (mōō-tôm′bō mōō-kōō′lōō).Bel. Cong.	8.0 S	23.58 E
104	Mutondo (mōō-tōn′dōō) Braz. (In.)	22.50 S	43.1 W
158	Mutsu B. (mōōt′sōō)........Jap.	41.2 N	140.50 E
87	Mutton B. (mŭt″n).........Can.	50.45 N	59.5 W
151	Muttra (mōōt′trä)..........India	27.25 N	77.45 E
159	Muya (mōō′yä)..............Jap.	34.13 N	134.34 E
148	Muyun Kum Desert (mōō-yōōn′ kōōm′).Sov. Un.	44.40 N	72.0 E
80	Múzquiz (mōōz′kēz)........Mex.	27.53 N	101.30 W
140	Mwanza (mwän′zä)...........Tan.	2.30 S	32.52 E
141	Mwatate (mwä-tä′tä)......Kenya	3.22 S	38.18 E
140	Mwaya (mwä′yä)............Tan.	9.35 S	33.52 E
140	Mweru, L. (mwā′rōō) ..Bel. Cong.	9.0 S	28.45 E
158	Myakonojo (myȧ′kô-nō′jô)....Jap.	31.45 N	131.2 E
167	Myall L. (mī′ôl)...........Austl.	32.28 S	152.22 E
114	Mya, Wadi (R.) (wä′dê myä′).Alg.	29.45 N	3.30 E
151	Myingyan (myĕng-yŭn′) ....India	21.15 N	95.28 E
152	Myitkyina (mēch′ē-nä) .....India	25.29 N	97.21 E
123	Myjava (mûê′-yȧ-vä)......Czech.	48.45 N	17.33 E
129	Mykonos (I.) (mē′kô-nôs)....Grc.	37.27 N	25.23 E
151	Mymensingh (mî-mŭn-sĭnĸ′).India	24.45 N	90.20 E
116	Mynydd Bach (mŭ-nŭdh′ bäĸ) Gt. Brit.	52.10 N	3.40 W
110	Myrdals-Jökull (glacier) (mür′däls-yû′kōōl).Ice.	63.35 N	18.15 W
70	Myrtle Point (mûr′t′l)........Ore.	43.4 N	124.8 W
130	Myshkin (mêsh′kên).....Sov. Un.	57.47 N	38.25 E
151	Mysore....................India	12.17 N	76.32 E
151	Mysore (State) (mī-sōr′).....India	13.45 N	77.0 E
77	Mystic (mĭs′tĭk)...............Ia.	40.46 N	92.56 W
129	Mytilēnē (mĭt-ĭ-lē′nê) (mĭt-ĭ-lyē′-nyê).Grc.	39.6 N	26.34 E
113	Mytilene (I.)..........Aegean S.	39.15 N	26.20 E
140	Mzimba (′m-zĭm′bä) ....Nya.	11.50 S	33.38 E
122	Naab R. (näp)...............Ger.	49.32 N	12.10 E
138	Naama (nä′ä-mä)............Lib.	7.21 N	9.30 W
121	Naantali (nän′tȧ-lê) ....Fin.	60.30 N	22.1 E
143	Naauwpoort (nou′pōrt). U. S. Afr.	31.10 S	24.56 E
163	Nabas (nä′bäs)..............P. I.	11.49 N	122.4 E
164	Nabberoo, L. (năb′ēr-ōō) ...Austl.	25.45 S	120.45 E
138	Nabeul (nä-bûl′).............Tun.	36.32 N	10.40 E
145	Nablus (Shekhem) (nä-blōōs′) (shĕ′ĸĕm).Pal. (In.)	32.13 N	35.10 E
162	Nabua (nä′bwä).............P. I.	13.24 N	123.22 E
94	Nacaome (nä-kä-ō′mȧ).....Hond.	13.32 N	87.27 W
152	Na Cham (nä chäm′).Fr. In. Chn.	22.3 N	106.17 E
66	Naches R. (năch′ĕz).......Wash.	46.50 N	120.50 W
122	Náchod (näĸ′ôt)..........Czech.	50.25 N	16.9 E
74	Nacimiento R. (nȧ-sĭ-myĕn′tô) Calif.	35.45 N	121.15 W
81	Nacogdoches (năk′ô-dō′chĕz) .Tex.	31.37 N	94.40 W
80	Nadadoreś (nä-dä-dō′rās)....Mex.	27.3 N	101.36 W
158	Nadan-Khatala-Alin (Mts.) (nä′-dän-ĸä′tä-lä-ä-lēn′).Manch.	46.30 N	133.0 E
148	Nadezhdinsk (nä′dyĕzh-dênsk) Sov. Un.	59.40 N	60.40 E
157	Nadju Is. (näd′jōō′) ....Cho.	34.45 N	126.0 E

ăt; finăl; rāte; senâte; ärm; ȧsk; sofȧ; fâre; ch-choose; dh-as th in other; bē; êvent; bĕt; recĕnt; cratēr; g-go; gh-gutteral g; bĭt; ĭ-short neutral; rīde; ĸ-gutteral k as ch in German ich;

Page	Name Pronunciation Region	Lat. °′	Long. °′
123	Nădlac (năd-lȧk′)..........Rom.	46.9 N	20.45 E
123	Nadwórna (nȧ-dvŏŏr′nȧ).....Pol.	48.36 N	24.36 E
148	Nadym (Kadin) R. (nȧ′dĭm kȧ′dĭn) Sov. Un.	65.20 N	73.20 E
120	Naestved (nĕst′vĭdh)........Den.	55.11 N	11.46 E
162	Naga (nä′gä)...............P. I.	13.37 N	123.12 E
163	Naga......................P. I.	10.13 N	123.45 E
159	Nagahama (nä′gä-hä′mä).....Jap.	33.32 N	132.28 E
159	Nagahama..................Jap.	35.25 N	136.15 E
159	Naga I. (nä′gä).............Jap.	32.9 N	130.8 E
159	Nagano (na′gä-nô)..........Jap.	36.44 N	138.3 E
158	Nagaoka (nä′gȧ-ō′kȧ)........Jap.	37.25 N	138.59 E
159	Nagasaki (nä′gȧ-sä′kê).......Jap.	32.45 N	129.50 E
159	Nagasu (nä′gäs-ōō)..........Jap.	33.31 N	131.22 E
162	Nagcarlan (näg-kär-län′)....P. I.	14.8 N	121.25 E
135	Nag Hamâdi (näg′ hä-mä′dê) Eg. (In.)	26.2 N	32.12 E
113	Nagornogokarabakh (Aut. Area) (nȧ′gôr-nô′gô-kȧ-rȧ-bäK′)...Sov. Un.	40.0 N	47.0 E
60	Nagor Rajasima (Korat) (nä-gōr′ rä-jä-sē′mä) (kō-rät′). Thai.	14.55 N	102.12 E
160	Nagor Sridharmarâj (nä-gōr′ srē-dar′mŭ-räj′). Thai.	8.27 N	100.0 E
159	Nagoya (nä′gō′yȧ)...........Jap.	35.11 N	136.58 E
151	Nagpur (näg′pōōr)..........India	21.15 N	79.12 E
162	Naguilian (nä-gwê-lē′än).....P. I.	16.31 N	120.24 E
123	Nagykanizsa (nôd′y′kô′nê-shô) Hung.	46.28 N	17.0 E
123	Nagykörös (nôd′y′kû′rûsh) .Hung.	47.2 N	19.47 E
123	Nagysurány (Šurany) (nŏd′y′-shōō′rȧ-nûê)(shōō′rȧ-nûê) Hung.	48.5 N	18.12 E
158	Naha (nä′hä)....Ryūkyū Is. (In.)	26.10 N	127.44 E
160	Nahakam R. (nä′hä-käm) Neth. Ind.	0.20 S	116.0 E
87	Nahant (nȧ-hănt′)....Mass. (In.)	42.25 N	70.55 W
	Näho, see Noho, Manch.		
127	Nahr-Ouassel(R.)(när′-wä-sĕl′)Alg.	35.35 N	2.0 E
104	NahuelHuapi,L.(nä′wâlwä′pê)Arg.	41.0 S	71.30 W
94	Nahuizalco (nä-wê-zäl′kō)....Sal.	13.49 N	89.43 W
141	Nahya (nä′hyȧ)..............Eg.	30.3 N	31.8 E
158	Naibuchi (nī-bōō′chê).......Kar.	47.20 N	142.45 E
162	Naic (nä′ēk)...............P. I.	14.20 N	120.47 E
80	Naica (nä-ē′kä).............Mex.	27.53 N	105.29 W
55	Nain (nīn)..................Lab.	56.32 N	61.59 W
116	Nairn (nârn)............Gt. Brit.	57.35 N	3.50 W
141	Nairobi (nī-rō′bê)..........Kenya	1.15 S	36.45 E
121	Naissaare (I.) (nī′sä-rĕ)......Est.	59.32 N	24.32 E
141	Naivasha (nī-vä′shȧ).......Kenya	0.43 S	36.23 E
96	Najasa R. (nä-hä′sä).......Cuba	20.58 N	78.0 W
150	Najran (nŭj-rän′) (Reg.)....Nejd	17.15 N	45.30 E
157	Naju (nä′jōō′)..............Cho.	35.2 N	126.40 E
157	Nakadori I. (nä′kä-dō′rê).....Jap.	32.56 N	129.4 E
159	Na Kaido (nä′ kä′ê-dō) Jap. (Osaka In.)	34.42 N	135.39 E
159	Nakatsu (nä′käts-ōō)........Jap.	33.31 N	131.12 E
157	Nakdong R. (näk′dông′)....Cho.	36.0 N	128.25 E
113	Nakhichevan (nȧ-Kē-chĕ-vȧn′) Sov. Un.	39.12 N	45.28 E
131	Nakhichevan...........Sov. Un.	47.14 N	39.48 E
123	Naklo (nȧk′wô)..............Pol.	53.7 N	17.37 E
142	Nakop (näk′ŏp)........S. W. Afr.	28.5 S	19.41 E
120	Nakskov (näk′skou).........Den.	54.50 N	11.7 E
113	Nalchik (nȧl-chēk′)......Sov. Un.	43.32 N	43.35 E
126	Nalon R. (nä-lōn′)............Sp.	43.20 N	5.50 W
114	Nalut (nä-lōōt′)...........Libya	32.3 N	11.5 E
143	Namaàcha (nä′mȧ-äch′ȧ)....Moz.	25.59 N	32.2 E
77	Namakan L. (nă′mȧ-kăn)...Minn.	48.27 N	92.35 W
150	Namakzar (Des.) (nŭ-mŭk-zär′) Iran	30.15 N	58.45 E
148	Namangan (nȧ-mȧn-gän′) Sov. Un.	41.10 N	71.50 E
161	Namatanai (nä′mä-tȧ-nä′ê) N. Gui. Ter.	3.38 S	152.30 E
159	Namaze (nä′mȧ-zä) Jap. (Osaka In.)	34.49 N	135.19 E
75	Nambe Pueblo Ind. Res. (näm′bȧ pwĕb′lô). N. M.	35.53 N	106.0 W
160	Namdinh (näm′dēnK′) .Fr. In. Chn.	20.29 N	106.10 E
157	Namhai (näm′hī′)...........Cho.	34.51 N	127.53 E
157	Namhai I...................Cho.	34.48 N	127.55 E
154	Namheung (näm′hĕ-ōōng′) ..Chn.	22.49 N	109.26 E
140	Namib (Reg.) (nä-mēb′)S. W. Afr.	24.30 S	14.45 E
155	Namkwan (näm′kwän′).....Chn.	27.12 N	120.20 E
155	Namoa I. (nä′mō-ȧ)..........Chn.	23.23 N	116.48 E
167	Namoi R. (năm′oi)........Austl.	30.25 S	149.53 E
6	Namosi, Mt. (nȧ-mō′sê) FijiIs.(In.)	18.3 S	178.7 E
114	Namous, Wadi en (R.) (wä′dê ĕn nȧ-mōōs′). Alg.	31.30 N	0.27 W
70	Nampa (năm′pȧ).............Ida.	43.35 N	116.34 W
110	Namsos (näm′sôs)...........Nor.	64.30 N	11.28 E
154	Namtow (näm′tō′)...........Chn.	22.35 N	113.50 E
152	Nam Tso (Tengri Nor) (L.) (näm′ tsô (tĕŋ′grê nôr′). Chn.	30.45 N	90.39 E
117	Namur (nȧ-mür′)............Bel.	50.28 N	4.50 E
140	Namutoni (nȧ-mōō-tō′nê) S.W.Afr.	18.55 S	17.2 E
154	Namyung (näm′yōōng′).....Chn.	25.15 N	113.58 E
70	Nanaimo (nȧ-nī′mō)........Can.	49.8 N	123.58 W
154	Nanan (nä′nän′)............Chn.	25.31 N	113.52 E
169	Nanango (nȧ-năŋ′gô)..Austl. (In.)	26.38 S	152.2 E
159	Nanao (nä′nä-ō)............Jap.	37.0 N	136.59 E
155	Nanchang (nän′chäng′)......Chn.	28.37 N	115.46 E
155	Nanching (nän′chĭng′)......Chn.	24.34 N	117.27 E
154	Nanchow (nän′chō′).........Chn.	29.22 N	112.11 E
154	Nanchwan (nän′chwän′).....Chn.	29.9 N	107.6 E
125	Nancy (näN-sē′)..............Fr.	48.41 N	6.10 E
151	Nanda Devi (nän′dä′dā′vē′) Mts. Chn.	30.27 N	80.20 E
166	Nandaly (năn′dȧ-lĭ)........Austl.	35.17 S	142.43 E
167	Nandewar Range (năn′dĕ-wȧr) Austl.	30.28 S	150.55 E
158	Nanfaisan (Mt.) (nän′fī′sän)..Jap.	36.45 N	139.31 E
155	Nanfeng (nän′fĕng′).........Chn.	27.11 N	116.17 E
163	Nangalao I. (näŋ-gä-lä′ō)....P. I.	11.27 N	120.11 E
157	Nangan.....................Cho.	35.27 N	127.23 E
163	Nangtud, Mt. (näng-tōōd′)...P. I.	11.14 N	122.12 E
155	Nankang (nän′käng′)........Chn.	25.38 N	114.15 E
155	Nankang....................Chn.	29.23 N	115.54 E
155	Nanking (Kiangning) (nän′kĭng′) (kyäng′nĭng′). Chn.	32.4 N	118.45 E
155	Nankodai-San (nän′kō′dī′ sän) Mt.. Tai. (In.)	24.25 N	121.29 E
156	Nankung (nän′kōōng′)......Chn.	37.26 N	115.25 E
156	Nanlo (nän′lō′).............Chn.	36.5 N	115.28 E
164	Nannine (nă-nēn′)..........Austl.	26.47 S	118.20 E
154	Nanning (nän′nĭng′).........Chn.	22.55 N	108.32 E
155	Nanning....................Chn.	30.56 N	118.20 E
156	Nanpi (nän′pĭ′).............Chn.	38.12 N	116.30 E
89	Nansemond R. (năn′sê-mŭnd) Va. (Norfolk In.)	36.53 N	76.29 W
154	Nan Shan (Mts.) (nän′shän′) Chn.	24.58 N	111.18 E
152	Nan Shan (Mts.)...........Chn.	38.30 N	98.30 E
155	Nansiang (nän′syäng′)......Chn.	31.13 N	121.21 E
159	Nantaisan (Mt.) (nän′tī-sän′). Jap.	36.47 N	139.30 E
154	Nantan (nän′tän′)...........Chn.	24.57 N	107.30 E
125	Nanterre (näN-târ′)......Fr. (In.)	48.53 N	2.12 E
124	Nantes (näNt′)...............Fr.	47.13 N	1.33 W
85	Nanticoke (năn′tĭ-kōk).......Pa.	41.22 N	76.0 W
125	Nantua (näN′tü-ȧ)............Fr.	46.10 N	5.38 E
85	Nantucket (I.) (năn-tŭk′ĕt). Mass.	41.15 N	70.5 W
155	Nantung (nän′tōōng′).......Chn.	32.0 N	120.53 E
118	Nantwich (nănt′wĭch)....Gt. Brit.	53.4 N	2.31 W
154	Nan Yuek (Heng Shan) (Mts.) (nän′ yōō-ek′) (hĕng′ shän). Chn.	26.55 N	111.48 E
127	Nao C. (nä′ō)................Sp.	38.45 N	0.13 E
93	Naolinco (nä-ō-lēŋ′kō)......Mex.	19.40 N	96.51 W
129	Naousa (nä′ōō-sȧ)...........Grc.	40.38 N	22.5 E
74	Napa (năp′ȧ)...............Calif.	38.19 N	122.19 W
85	Napanee (năp′ȧ-nē).........Can.	44.15 N	77.0 W
170	Napier (nā′pĭ-ēr)...........N. Z.	39.30 S	176.55 E
142	Napier................U. S. Afr.	34.29 S	19.54 E
128	Naples (Napoli) (nā′p′lz) (nä′pô-lē) It.	40.51 N	14.26 E
128	Naples, B. of.................It.	40.45 N	14.15 E
84	Napoleon (nȧ-pō′lē-ŭn)......Ohio	41.24 N	84.10 W
81	Napoleonville (nȧ-pō′lê-ŭn-vĭl) .La.	29.55 N	91.3 W
119	Napoli (Naples) ....It. (In.)		
128	Napoli (Naples) (nä′pô-lē).....It.	40.51 N	14.26 E
102	Napo R. (nä′pō)..............Ec.	2.0 S	75.0 W
84	Nappanee (năp′ȧ-nē)........Ind.	41.26 N	86.2 W
138	Nara (nä′rä)..........Fr. W. Afr.	15.7 N	7.30 W
159	Nara........................Jap.	34.44 N	135.46 E
166	Naracoorte (nȧ-rȧ-kōōn′tê) .Austl.	36.59 S	140.42 E
167	Naradham (nă′răd-ăm).....Austl.	33.38 S	146.22 E
130	Nara R..................Sov. Un.	55.12 N	36.58 E
159	Narawa(nä′rȧ-wä) Jap. (Tokyo In.)	35.26 N	139.57 E
151	Narbada R. (nŭr-bŭd′ä)....India	22.15 N	76.0 E
88	Narberth (när′bûrth) Pa. (Philadelphia In.)	40.0 N	75.16 W
124	Narbonne (nȧr-bôn′)..........Fr.	43.11 N	3.0 E
129	Nardò (när-dô′)...............It.	40.11 N	18.1 E
148	Nareny (nȧ-rĕn′y′)......Sov. Un.	53.15 N	102.59 E
123	Narew R. (nä′rĕf)...........Pol.	53.13 N	22.24 E
148	Narin (nȧ-rên′).........Sov. Un.	41.25 N	76.0 E
163	Nariz Pt. (nä-rēth′).........P. I.	8.53 N	118.0 E
130	Narocz, L. (nä′rôch)..........Pol.	54.50 N	26.50 E
112	Narodnaya (nȧ-rôd′nȧ-yȧ)Sov. Un.	65.20 N	61.00 E
130	Naro-Fominsk (nȧ′rô-fô-mēnsk′) Sov. Un.	55.23 N	36.45 E
126	Narón (nä-rōn′)..............Sp.	43.31 N	8.9 W
161	Narotas(nä-rō′täs)P.I.(Manila In.)	14.40 N	120.56 E
169	Narrabeen (năr-ȧ-bĭn)......Austl.	33.43 S	151.18 E
167	Narrabri (nä-rä′brê).......Austl.	30.18 S	149.48 E
167	Narrabri West.............Austl.	30.21 S	149.45 E
85	NarragansettB.(năr-ȧ-găn′sĕt)R.I.	41.20 N	71.20 W
167	Narrandera (nȧ-rȧn-dē′rȧ)..Austl.	34.44 S	146.32 E
164	Narrogin (năr′ô-gĭn).......Austl.	32.59 S	117.3 E
167	Narromine (năr′ō-mīn).....Austl.	32.15 S	148.16 E
88	Narrows, The (Inlet) (năr′ōz) N. Y. (N. Y. In.)	40.37 N	74.3 W
166	Narrung (när-rōōng′).......Austl.	34.45 S	143.13 E
121	Narva (nȧr′vȧ)...............Est.	59.22 N	28.8 E
162	Narvacan (när-vä-kän′)......P. I.	17.25 N	120.29 E
110	Narvik (när′vêk).............Nor.	68.20 N	17.35 E
148	Narym (nä-rēm′)........Sov. Un.	58.50 N	81.59 E
148	Narymskoe, Bolshoi (Sea) (bŏl′shôĭ-nä-rĭm-skô′yĕ)...Sov. Un.	49.15 N	84.35 E
148	Naryn R..................Sov. Un.	41.35 N	73.0 E
118	Naseby (nāz′bĭ)..........Gt. Brit.	52.23 N	0.59 W
171	Naseby.....................N. Z.	45.2 S	170.10 E
86	Nashua (năsh′ū-ȧ)..........N. H.	42.45 N	71.30 W
79	Nashville (năsh′vĭl)..........Ark.	33.56 N	93.51 W
82	Nashville....................Ga.	31.13 N	83.17 W
79	Nashville....................Ill.	38.21 N	89.23 W
84	Nashville..................Mich.	42.37 N	85.4 W
82	Nashville..................Tenn.	36.10 N	86.49 W
77	Nashwauk (năsh′wôk)......Minn.	47.22 N	93.10 W
129	Našice (nȧ-shē′tsĕ)..........Yugo.	45.29 N	18.6 E
123	Nasielsk (nä′shĕlsk)..........Pol.	52.36 N	20.51 E
151	Nasik (nä′sĭk)..............India	19.59 N	73.45 E
139	Nasir (nä-zēr′).........A. E. Sud.	8.32 N	33.2 E
55	Naskaupi (năs′kô-pī)........Lab.	54.0 N	61.30 W
163	Naso Pt. (nä′sō).............P. I.	10.25 N	121.58 E
96	Nassau (năs′ô)............Ba. Is.	25.4 N	77.22 W
161	Nassau Ra. (năs′ô) (nä′sou) Neth. Ind.	4.5 S	137.0 E
120	Nässjö (nĕs′shû).............Swe.	57.39 N	14.41 E
162	Nasugbu (nȧ-sōōg-bōō′).....P. I.	14.5 N	120.38 E
80	Nasworthy, L................Tex.	31.45 N	100.35 W
103	Natal (nä-täl′)..............Braz.	5.45 S	35.15 W
143	Natal (Prov.) (nȧ-täl′)..U. S. Afr.	29.0 S	30.30 E
87	Natashkwan (nä-täsh′kwän)..Can.	50.10 N	61.47 W
82	Natchez (năch′ĕz)...........Miss.	31.32 N	91.24 W
81	Natchitoches (năk′ĭ-tŏsh) (nȧch-ĭ-tōsh′). La.	31.45 N	93.5 W
87	Natick (nā′tĭk).......Mass. (In.)	42.17 N	71.21 W
166	Natimuk (năt′ĭ-mŭk).......Austl.	36.45 S	141.54 E
71	National Bison Ra.........Mont.	47.20 N	114.20 W
74	National City........Calif. (In.)	32.40 N	117.7 W
167	National Park.............Austl.	34.6 S	151.5 E
103	Natividade (nä-tê-vê-dä′dĕ)..Braz.	11.32 S	47.32 W
93	Natívitas (nä-tē′vê-täs). Mex. (In.)	19.15 N	99.5 W
160	Natoena (Natuna) I., Great (nä-tōō′nä)..Neth. Ind.	4.0 N	108.0 E
160	Natoena (Natuna) Is...Neth. Ind.	3.0 N	108.30 E
160	Natoena (Natuna) Is., South Neth. Ind.	2.30 N	108.45 E
140	Natron (Magad) L. (nä′trŏn) (mä-gäd′). Tan.	2.15 S	36.0 E
135	Natrun, Wadi en (R.) (wä-dê ĕn nä′trōōn). Eg. (In.)	30.25 N	30.20 E
75	Natural Bridges Natl. Mon. .Utah	37.21 N	109.48 W
164	Naturaliste,C.(năt-û-rȧ-lĭst′)Austl.	33.29 S	115.3 E
122	Nauen (nou′ĕn).............Ger.	52.36 N	12.52 E
85	Naugatuck (nô′gȧ-tŭk).....Conn.	41.27 N	73.6 W
93	Nauhcampatepen, Cerro (Mt.) (sĕr′ô nä′ōō-käm′pä-tā′pĕn). Mex.	19.28 N	97.8 W
162	Naujan (nä-ōō-hän′)........P. I.	13.18 N	121.17 E
162	Naujan, L...................P. I.	13.9 N	121.20 E
122	Naumburg (noum′bōōrgh)....Ger.	51.8 N	11.48 E
121	Naumiestis (nä-ōō-myĕs′tĭs)..Lith.	54.52 N	22.58 E
129	Nauplion (näf′plyê-ôn).......Grc.	37.33 N	22.49 E
7	Nauru (I.) (nä′ōō-rōō).....Pac. O.	0.25 S	166.57 E
6	Nausori Mill (nä-ōō-sō′rê) Fiji Is. (In.)	18.2 S	178.33 E
93	Nautla (nä-ōōt′lä)..........Mex.	20.13 N	96.47 W
80	Nava (nä′vä)...............Mex.	28.25 N	100.45 W
126	Nava del Rey (nä-vä dĕl rā′ê) .Sp.	41.21 N	5.4 W
126	Navahermosa (nä′vä-ĕr-mō′sä).Sp.	39.38 N	4.28 W
96	Navajas (nä-vä′häs)........Cuba	22.41 N	81.19 W
75	Navajo Indian Reservation, (năv′ȧ-hō). Ariz.-N. Mex.	36.0 N	110.0 W
75	Navajo Indian Reservation Ariz.-Utah	37.8 N	100.40 W
75	Navajo Natl. Mon.(năv′ȧ-hō) Ariz.	36.43 N	10.40 W
126	Nava, L......................Sp.	42.4 N	4.40 W
127	Navalcarnero (nä-väl′kär-nā′rō) Sp. (In.)	40.18 N	4.2 W
126	Navalmoral de la Mata (nä-väl′mō-räl′ dē lä mä′tä).Sp.	39.53 N	5.31 W
116	Navan (nă′vȧn)..............Ire.	53.40 N	6.42 W
151	Navanagar, see Jamnagar, India		
104	Navarin I. (nä-vä-rēn′)......Arg.	55.10 S	67.40 W
126	Navarra (Prov.) (nä-vär′rä)...Sp.	42.40 N	1.30 W
166	Navarre (nȧ-vär′)..........Austl.	36.53 S	143.8 E
81	Navasota (năv-ȧ-sō′tȧ).......Tex.	30.24 N	96.5 W
81	Navasota R..................Tex.	31.0 N	96.15 W
97	Navassa I. (nȧ-vȧs′ȧ)........W. I.	18.25 N	75.2 W
126	Navia R. (nä-vē′ä)...........Sp.	43.10 N	6.55 W
97	Navidad Bank (nä-vê-dädh′).W. I.	20.0 N	68.53 W
6	Naviti (I.) (nä-vē′tê). Fiji Is. (In.)	17.9 S	177.21 E
6	Navua Mill (nä′vōō-ä)Fiji Is. (In.)	18.13 S	178.11 E
88	Navy I. (nā′vĭ) Can. (Niagara Falls In.)	43.3 N	79.1 W
151	Nawagai (nŭ-wŭ-gī′) India (Peshawar In.)	34.38 N	71.15 E
129	Naxos (I.) (nȧk′sôs).........Grc.	37.5 N	25.30 E
92	Nayarit (State) (nä-yä-rēt′)..Mex.	21.40 N	104.40 W
92	Nayarit, Sierra de (Mts.)....Mex.	23.0 N	105.0 W
126	Nazaré (nä-zä-rā′)..........Port.	39.36 N	9.5 W
103	Nazareth (nä-zä-rĕt′).......Braz.	7.45 S	35.15 W
103	Nazareth.............Braz. (In.)	13.0 S	39.1 W
145	Nazareth (năz′ȧ-rĕth)...Pal. (In.)	32.42 N	35.16 E
80	Nazas (nä′zäs)..............Mex.	25.13 N	104.8 W
80	Nazas, R....................Mex.	25.10 N	104.30 W
120	Naze, The (Lindesnes) (nāz) (lĭn′dĕs-nĕs). Nor.	58.0 N	7.6 E
113	Nazilli (nȧ-zĭ-lē′)...........Tur.	37.50 N	28.25 E
148	Nazimovo (nä-zê′mô-fô)..Sov. Un.	59.15 N	91.25 E
139	N′Délé (n′dā-lā′).....Fr. Eq. Afr.	8.25 N	20.36 E
140	N′Djolé (n′dzhô-lā′)..Fr. Eq. Afr.	0.12 S	10.45 E
140	Ndola (n′dō′lä)...........N. Rh.	13.0 S	28.43 E
116	Neagh, Lough (L.) (lŏK nā) (lŏK nā′äK). Gt. Brit.	54.40 N	6.30 W
165	Neandara (nē-ȧn-dă′rȧ).....Austl.	27.20 S	149.29 E
129	Neapolis (nȧ-ŏp′ô-lĭs)........Grc.	36.21 N	23.4 E
52	Near Is. (nēr)..............Alsk.	52.40 N	173.0 E
116	Neath (nēth)............Gt. Brit.	51.38 N	3.49 W
145	Nebik (nĕb′êk).........Syr. (In.)	34.4 N	36.45 E
78	Nebraska(State) (nê-brăs′kȧ). U.S.	40.45 N	99.0 W
76	Nebraska City.............Neb.	40.42 N	95.52 W
49	Necanicum (nê-kăn′ĭ-kŭm) Ore. (Portland In.)	45.53 N	123.47 W
81	Neches R. (nĕch′ĕz).........Tex.	31.25 N	95.0 W
122	Neckar R. (nĕk′är)..........Ger.	49.8 N	9.10 E
104	Necochea (nā-kô-chā′ä)......Arg.	38.30 S	58.40 W
99	Necol (nȧ-kōl′) Arg. (Buenos Aires In.)	35.3 S	62.11 W
72	Nederland (nĕ′dēr-lănd) Colo. (Denver In.)	39.57 N	105.31 W
131	Nedrigailov(nȧ-drĭ-gä′ĭ-lôf)Sov.Un.	50.49 N	33.50 E
87	Needham (nēd′ăm)....Mass. (In.)	42.17 N	71.14 W
74	Needles (nē′d′lz)...........Calif.	34.50 N	114.36 W
170	Neekes I. (Paketutu) (nēks) (pä-kā-tōō′tōō). N. Z. (In.)	36.58 S	174.45 E
77	Neenah (nē′nȧ)..............Wis.	44.10 N	88.28 W
150	Nefud (nĕ-fōōd′).........Sau. Ar.	28.45 N	41.0 E
151	Negapatam (neg′ȧ-pȧ-tăm′)..India	10.38 N	79.50 E
77	Negaunee (nê-gô′nê).......Mich.	46.31 N	87.35 W
129	Negoi (Mts.) (nā-goi′)......Rom.	45.32 N	24.35 E
129	Negotin (nā′gô-tên)........Yugo.	44.13 N	22.34 E
151	Negrais (nĕ-grä′ês).........India	16.0 N	94.10 E
126	Negreira (nā-grȧ-ē′rā).........Sp.	42.55 N	8.45 W
145	Negri Sembilan (State) (nā′grê sĕm-bê-län′). Fed. Mal. States (In.)	2.45 N	102.0 E
126	Negro, C. (nā′grô)..........Mor.	35.41 N	5.18 W
95	Negro, Cumbre (Mt.).......Pan.	8.45 N	80.37 W
135	Negro, Mt. Sp. Mor.(Gibraltar In.)	35.39 N	5.43 E
104	Negro, R....................Arg.	40.0 S	65.0 W
102	Negro R. (nā′grōō)..........Braz.	1.30 S	62.0 W
104	Negro, R.................Braz.-Ur.	32.32 S	56.0 W
94	Negro, R. (nā′grô).....Hond.-Nic.	13.0 N	87.0 W

ng-sing; ŋ-baŋk; N-nasalized n; nŏd; cŏmmit; ōld; ôbey; ôrder; fōōd; fŏŏt; ou-out; s-soft; sh-dish; th-thin; pūre; ûnite; ûrn; stŭd; circŭs; ü-as "y" in study; ′-indeterminate vowel.

Page	Name Pronunciation Region	Lat. °′	Long. °′
163	Negros (I.) (nā'grōs)........P. I.	10.0 N	123.0 E
163	Negros, Cuernos de (Mt.) (kwěr'nôs dā nā'grôs).P. I.	9.15 N	123.12 E
70	Nehalem R. (nê-hăl'ĕm)......Ore.	45.60 N	123.30 W
49	Nehalem R....Ore. (Portland In.)	45.45 N	123.18 W
97	Neiba (nâ-ē'bä).......Dom. Rep.	18.28 N	71.22 W
97	Neiba B.............Dom. Rep.	18.15 N	71.3 W
97	Neiba, Mts. of........Dom. Rep.	18.38 N	71.33 W
123	Neidenburg (nī'dĕn-bŏŏrgh)..Ger.	53.22 N	20.30 E
71	Neihart (nī'härt)..........Mont.	46.55 N	110.41 W
156	Neihwang (nā'hwäng')......Chn.	35.54 N	115.10 E
77	Neillsville (nēlz'vĭl).........Wis.	44.35 N	90.35 W
122	Neisze R. (nīs'ē)...........Ger.	51.30 N	14.50 E
123	Neisze.....................Ger.	50.28 N	17.20 E
102	Neiva (nâ-ē'vä) (nā'vä)......Col.	32.0 N	75.15 W
150	Nejd, see Saudi Arabia.		
135	Nejila, Jebel (Mts.) (jĕb'ĕl nĕj'ĭ-lȧ).Eg. (In.)	26.40 N	32.30 E
77	Nekoosa (nê-kōō'sȧ).........Wis.	44.19 N	89.53 W
120	Neksö (nĕk'sû).............Den.	55.3 N	15.8 E
76	Neligh (nē'lĭg)..............Neb.	42.8 N	98.1 W
149	Nelkan (nĕl-kän')........Sov. Un.	57.45 N	136.15 E
54	Nelson (nĕl'sŭn)............Can.	49.30 N	117.2 W
118	Nelson................Gt. Brit.	53.50 N	2.13 W
171	Nelson....................N. Z.	41.15 S	173.20 E
73	Nelson..Utah (Salt Lake City In.)	41.40 N	112.19 W
166	Nelson, C..................Austl.	38.25 S	141.34 E
74	Nelson Cr...................Nev.	40.20 N	114.40 W
53	Nelson I...................Alsk.	60.30 N	164.30 W
54	Nelson R...................Can.	56.0 N	96.48 W
84	Nelsonville (nĕl'sŭn-vĭl)......Ohio	39.30 N	82.14 W
143	Nelspruit (nĕl'sprût)....U. S. Afr.	25.29 S	30.58 E
138	Néma (nā'mä)........Fr. W. Afr.	16.45 N	7.0 W
88	Nemadji R. (nĕ-măd'jê) Wis. (Duluth In.)	46.40 N	92.4 W
122	Německý Brod (nyĕ'mĕt-skē brōd') Czech.	49.37 N	15.34 E
131	Nemirov (nyȧ-mê'rôf)....Sov. Un.	48.58 N	28.49 E
138	Nemours (nē-mōōr').........Alg.	35.1 N	1.58 W
124	Nemours.....................Fr.	48.17 N	2.40 E
121	Nemunas R. (nĕ'mōō-nȧs)...Lith.	55.8 N	23.5 E
123	Nemunas (Niemen) R........Eur.	53.39 N	22.10 E
158	Nemuro Str. (nā'mōō-rō).....Jap.	44.15 N	145.30 E
118	Nen, R. (nĕn)...........Gt. Brit.	52.18 N	0.39 W
116	Nenagh (nē'nȧ)..............Ire.	52.50 N	8.10 W
53	Nenana (nȧ-nä'nȧ)..........Alsk.	64.30 N	149.0 W
157	Nengpyun (nĕng'pyōōn').....Cho.	39.50 N	125.49 E
140	Neno (nā'nô)...............Nya.	15.27 S	34.40 E
79	Neodesha (nē'ô-dê-shô').....Kan.	37.25 N	95.41 W
79	Neosho (nê-ō'shō)...........Mo.	36.53 N	94.23 W
79	Neosho R...................Okla.	37.30 N	95.10 W
151	Nepal (nĕ-pôl')..............Asia	28.0 N	84.0 E
166	Nepean B. (nê-pē'ăn)......Austl.	35.40 S	137.40 E
166	Nepean, Pt.................Austl.	38.18 S	144.38 E
75	Nephi (nē'fī)................Utah	39.43 N	111.50 W
124	Nérac (nā-rȧk')...............Fr.	44.8 N	0.20 E
169	Nerang (nĕ-răng').....Austl. (In.)	27.58 S	153.22 E
128	Nera R. (nā'rä)...............It.	42.40 N	12.47 E
149	Nerchinsk (nyĕr'chênsk) .Sov. Un.	51.50 N	116.15 E
149	Nerchinski-Zavod (nyĕr'chên-skĭ-ê-zȧ-vôt')...Sov. Un.	51.30 N	119.45 E
149	Nerchinski Mts. ....Sov. Un.	52.0 N	119.0 E
130	Nerekhta (nyĕ-rĕĸ'tȧ)...Sov. Un.	57.28 N	40.34 E
129	Neretva R. (nā'rĕt-vȧ).....Yugo.	43.40 N	17.50 E
126	Nerja (nĕr'hä)................Sp.	36.45 N	3.53 W
130	Nerl R. (nyĕrl)..........Sov. Un.	56.55 N	38.5 E
130	Nero, L. (nyĕ'rô)........Sov. Un.	57.6 N	39.25 E
130	Nerusa R. (nyȧ-rōō'sȧ)...Sov. Un.	52.25 N	34.15 E
126	Nerva (nĕr'vä)................Sp.	37.42 N	6.33 W
78	Ness City (nĕs).............Kan.	38.26 N	99.55 W
116	Ness, Loch (lŏĸ nĕs).....Gt. Brit.	57.15 N	4.25 W
119	Neston (nĕs'tŭn)...Gt. Brit. (In.)	53.18 N	3.4 W
129	Nestos R. (nās'tōs)..........Grc.	41.15 N	24.30 E
122	Netherlands (nĕdh'ēr-lăndz)..Eur.	52.20 N	5.50 E
160	Netherlands (Borneo) (Prov.) (nĕdh'ēr-lăndz bôr'nê-ō) Neth. Ind.	1.0 S	114.0 E
103	Netherlands Guiana (Surinam) (gē-ăn'ȧ) S. A.	4.0 N	56.0 W
160	Netherlands Indies (ĭn'dēz)...Asia	5.30 N	114.0
161	Netherlands New Guinea (gĭn'ê) Neth. Ind.	4.0 S	138.0 E
161	Netherlands Timor (tê-mōr') Neth. Ind.	9.30 S	124.45 E
55	Netsalik L. (nĕt'sȧ-lĭk')......Can.	66.30 N	71.30 W
122	Netze R. (nĕt'zē)...........Ger.	52.53 N	16.5 E
122	Neubrandenburg (noi-brän'dĕn-bŏŏrgh).Ger.	53.33 N	13.15 E
122	Neuburg (noi'bŏŏrgh).......Ger.	48.43 N	11.11 E
122	Neuchâtel (nû-shȧ-tĕl').....Switz.	46.49 N	7.54 E
122	Neuchâtel, L.............Switz.	46.54 N	6.51 E
122	Neudamm (noi'däm)........Ger.	52.44 N	14.43 E
119	Neuengamme (noi'ĕn-gäm'ĕ) Ger. (Hamburg In.)	53.27 N	10.13 E
123	Neufahrwasser (noi-fär'väs-ēr) Dan.	54.24 N	18.40 E
125	Neufchâteau (nû'shȧ-tō)......Fr.	48.25 N	5.42 E
124	Neufchâtel (nû-shȧ-tĕl').......Fr.	49.42 N	1.28 E
119	Neugraben (noi'grä-bĕn) Ger. (Hamburg In.)	53.28 N	9.52 E
122	Neuhaldensleben (noi-häl'dĕns-lā'bĕn).Ger.	52.17 N	11.23 E
125	Neuilly (nû-yē')..........Fr. (In.)	48.52 N	2.17 E
119	Neukloster (noi'klŏs-tēr) Ger. (Hamburg In.)	53.29 N	9.37 E
119	Neukölln (noi'kûln) Ger. (Berlin In.)	52.28 N	13.27 E
122	Neumarkt (noi'märkt)......Ger.	49.17 N	11.29 E
122	Neumünster (noi'münstēr)...Ger.	54.4 N	9.59 E
122	Neunkirchen (noin'kĭrĸ-ĕn)...Ger.	47.43 N	16.4 E
104	Neuquén (nā-ōō-kān').......Arg.	38.59 S	68.1 W
104	Neuquén (Ter.).............Arg.	39.0 S	70.30 W
104	Neuquén, R.................Arg.	38.28 S	69.0 W
119	Neu-Rahlstedt (noi'-räl'shtĕt) Ger. (Hamburg In.)	53.36 N	10.9 E
122	Neu Ruppin (noi' rōō-pēn')..Ger.	52.56 N	12.47 E
122	Neusalz (noi-zälts')..........Ger.	51.49 N	15.41 E
83	Neuse R. (nūz)............N. C.	35.20 N	78.0 W
122	Neusiedler L. (noi-zēd'lēr) Ger.-Hung.	47.46 N	16.41 E
122	Neustadt (noi'shtăt).........Ger.	50.20 N	11.8 E
122	Neustadt....................Ger.	54.7 N	10.48 E
122	Neustadt....................Ger.	49.22 N	8.8 E
123	Neustadt....................Ger.	50.19 N	17.33 E
122	Neustettin (noi-shtĕ-tēn')....Ger.	53.42 N	16.42 E
123	Neu Titschein (Nový Jičín) (noi tĭt'shīn) (nô'vē yê'chēn) Pol.	49.36 N	18.1 E
122	Neustrelitz (noi-strā'lĭts).....Ger.	53.22 N	13.3 E
122	Neu Ulm (noi ŏŏlm')........Ger.	48.23 N	10.2 E
122	Neuwied (noi'vēdt)..........Ger.	50.26 N	7.28 E
117	Neuzen (noi'sĕn)...........Neth.	51.20 N	3.50 E
77	Nevada (nê-vä'dȧ)............Ia.	42.1 N	93.25 W
79	Nevada.....................Mo.	37.50 N	94.21 W
74	Nevada (State)............U. S.	39.8 N	117.0 W
74	Nevada City..............Calif.	39.16 N	121.3 W
102	Nevada de Mérida, Sierra (Mts.) (syĕr'rä nȧ-vä'dhä dā mā'rê-dhä).Ven.	9.0 N	70.0 W
74	Nevada, Sierra (Mts.) (nê-vä'dȧ) Calif	37.20 N	118.40 W
126	Nevada, Sierra (Mts.) (syĕr'rä nā-vä'dhä).Sp.	37.0 N	3.10 W
104	Nevado de Cachi (Mt.) (nā-vä'dho dā kä'chê).Arg.	24.29 S	66.32 W
92	Nevado de Colima (Mt.) (nȧ-vä'dhô dā kô-lē'mä).Mex.	19.35 N	103.40 W
92	Nevado de Toluca (Mt.) (tô-lōō'kä).Mex.	19.8 N	99.41 W
130	Neva R. (nyĕ-vä')......Sov. Un.	59.45 N	30.45 E
130	Nevel (nyĕ'vĕl)........Sov. Un	56.4 N	29.54 E
119	Nevendon (nĕv'ĕn-dŭn) Gt. Brit. (London In.)	51.36 N	0.30 E
124	Nevers (nē-vâr')..............Fr.	47.0 N	3.10 E
167	Nevertire (nĕv'ēr-tīr).......Austl.	31.50 S	147.42 E
104	Neves (nā'vĕzh).......Braz. (In.)	22.52 S	43.6 W
129	Nevesinje (nĕ-vā'sēn-yĕ)....Yugo.	43.15 N	18.8 E
95	Nevis (I.) (nē'vĭs)....Le. Is. (In.)	17.10 N	62.35 W
95	Nevis Pk...........Le. Is. (In.)	17.10 N	62.34 W
129	Nevrokop (nĕv'rō-kôp')......Bul.	41.34 N	23.45 E
113	Nevşehir (nĕv-shĕ'hêr).......Tur	38.35 N	34.40 E
148	Nevyansk (nĕv-yänsk')...Sov Un.	57.25 N	60.10 E
84	Newago (nê-wä'gō).........Mich.	43.25 N	85.50 W
84	New Albany (nû ôl'bȧ-nĭ)....Ind.	38.18 N	85.50 W
82	New Albany................Miss.	34.28 N	89.0 W
103	New Amsterdam (ăm'stēr-dăm) Br. Gu.	6.15 N	57.30 W
7	New Amsterdam I........Ind. O.	37.51 S	77.32 E
49	Newark (nū'ērk) Calif. (San Francisco In.)	37.32 N	122.2 W
85	Newark.....................Del.	39.41 N	75.47 W
116	Newark................Gt. Brit.	53.5 N	0.50 W
85	Newark....................N. J.	40.45 N	74.10 W
85	Newark....................N. Y.	43.5 N	77.5 W
84	Newark....................Ohio	40.5 N	82.25 W
119	New Barnet (bär'nĕt) Gt. Brit. (London In.)	51.39 N	0.11 W
88	Newark B.......N. J. (N. Y. In.)	40.41 N	74.8 W
85	New Bedford (bĕd'fērd)....Mass.	41.37 N	71.0 W
70	Newberg (nū'bûrg)..........Ore.	45.18 N	122.59 W
83	New Bern (bûrn)..........N. C.	35.6 N	77.3 W
82	Newbern..................Tenn.	36.7 N	89.16 W
77	Newberry (bĕr-ĭ)..........Mich.	46.22 N	85.30 W
83	Newberry..................S. C.	34.16 N	81.40 W
143	New Bethseda (bê-thĕz'dȧ) U. S. Afr.	31.54 S	24.34 E
84	New Boston (bôs'tŭn).......Ohio	38.47 N	82.56 W
80	New Braunfels (broun'fĕlz)...Tex.	29.42 N	98.8 W
119	New Brighton (brī'tŭn) Gt. Brit. (Liverpool In.)	53.27 N	3.3 W
89	New Brighton Minn. (Minneapolis In.)	45.4 N	93.11 W
88	New Brighton.........N. Y. (In.)	40.39 N	74.5 W
171	New Brighton.........N. Z. (In.)	43.30 S	172.45 E
85	New Brighton................Pa.	40.46 N	80.20 W
85	New Britain (brĭt''n).......Conn.	41.40 N	72.48 W
161	New Britain (I.) (brĭt''n) N. Gui. Ter.	5.45 S	150.30 E
55	New Brunswick (Prov.) (brŭnz'wĭk).Can.	47.50 N	66.30 W
85	New Brunswick............N. J.	40.28 N	74.28 W
84	Newburg (nū'bûrg)..........Ind.	37.58 N	87.26 W
79	Newburg....................Mo.	37.54 N	91.53 W
85	Newburgh.................N. Y.	41.30 N	74.0 W
116	Newbury (nū'bēr-ĭ)......Gt. Brit.	51.25 N	1.20 W
87	Newbury...................Mass.	42.48 N	70.52 W
86	Newburyport...............Mass.	42.49 N	70.55 W
165	New Caledonia (I.) (kăl-ê-dō'nĭ-a).New Cal.	21.30 S	165.30 E
86	New Carlisle (kär-līl').......Can.	48.1 N	65.21 W
126	New Castile (Castilla La Nueva) (Prov.) (kăs-tēl') (käs-tēl'yä lä nwā'vä).Sp.	39.50 N	3.0 W
73	Newcastle (nū'kȧs'l) Ala. (Birmingham In.)	33.39 N	86.46 W
167	Newcastle.................Austl.	32.59 S	151.47 E
55	Newcastle..................Can.	47.8 N	65.32 W
85	New Castle.................Del.	39.38 N	75.36 W
118	Newcastle.............Gt. Brit.	53.1 N	2.14 W
116	Newcastle.............Gr. Brit.	54.55 N	1.37 W
84	New Castle.................Ind.	39.55 N	85.22 W
171	Newcastle..................N. Z.	44.42 S	169.15 E
84	New Castle.................Ohio	40.20 N	82.10 W
85	New Castle...................Pa.	41.0 N	80.22 W
78	Newcastle...................Tex.	33.12 N	98.45 W
143	Newcastle.............U. S. Afr.	27.47 S	29.55 E
76	Newcastle..................Wyo.	43.52 N	104.12 W
164	Newcastle Waters..........Austl.	17.12 S	133.14 E
119	Newchurch (nū'chûrch) Gt Brit. (Liverpool In.)	53.27 N	2.31 W
84	Newcomerstown (nū'kŭm-ērz-toun).Ohio	40.17 N	81.37 W
145	New Delhi (dĕl'hī)........ India	28.19 N	77.15 E
8	New Dorp (dōrp).....N. Y. (In.)	40.35 N	74.8 W
76	Newell (nū'ĕl)..............S. D.	44.43 N	103.26 W
165	New England Plat..........Austl.	30.0 S	152.0 E
167	New England Ra. (nû ĭŋ'glănd) Austl.	30.15 S	151.35 E
87	Newfoundland (nû-fŭn'-lănd') (nū'fŭnd-lănd) (nû-found-lănd').N. A.	48.30 N	56.20 W
165	New Georgia I. (jôr'jĭ-ȧ) Solomon Is.	8.15 S	157.30 E
87	New Glasgow (glȧs'gō)......Can.	45.35 N	62.40 W
161	New Guinea, N. E. (Ter.) (gĭn'ê) N. Gui. Ter.	5.0 S	144.0 E
161	New Guinea (Papua) (I.) (pä'pōō-ȧ).Pac. O.	6.0 S	142.0 E
161	New Guinea, Ter. of......Pac. O.	4.0 S	146.0 E
73	Newhall (nū'hôl) Calif. (Los Angeles In.)	34.22 N	118.32 W
86	New Hampshire (State) (hămp'shĭr).U. S.	43.30 N	71.45 W
77	New Hampton (hămp'tŭn)....Ia.	43.4 N	92.19 W
143	New Hanover (hăn'ô-vēr) U. S. Afr.	29.21 S	30.31 E
84	New Harmony (här'mô-nĭ)...Ind.	38.9 N	87.56 W
169	New Haven (hāv''n) Austl. (Adelaide In.)	34.49 S	138.31 E
85	New Haven...............Conn.	41.18 N	72.58 W
84	New Haven.................Ind.	41.4 N	85.1 W
171	Newhaven..................N. Z.	46.27 S	169.43 E
165	New Hebrides (Is.) (hĕb'rĭ-dēz) Pac. O.	17.0 S	169.0 E
118	New Holland (hŏl'ănd)...Gt. Brit.	53.42 N	0.21 W
83	New Holland..............N. C.	35.27 N	76.15 W
81	New Iberia (ī-bē'rĭ-ȧ).........La.	30.0 N	91.50 W
119	Newington (nū-ĭng-tŭn) Gt. Brit. (London In.)	51.21 N	0.39 E
161	New Ireland (I.) (īr'lănd) N. Gui. Ter.	3.20 S	152.0 E
85	New Jersey (State) (jûr'zĭ)...U. S.	40.0 N	74.30 W
85	New Kensington (kĕn'zĭng-tŭn) Pa.	40.35 N	79.45 W
79	Newkirk (nū'kûrk).........Okla.	36.53 N	97.3 W
148	New Land (Novaya Zemlya) (nô'vä-yä zĕm-lyȧ')....Sov. Un.	74.0 N	57.0 E
84	New Lexington (lĕk'sĭng-tŭn) Ohio	39.45 N	82.12 W
77	New Lisbon (lĭz'bŭn)........Wis.	43.54 N	90.10 W
85	New London (lŭn'dŭn).....Conn.	41.20 N	72.8 W
79	New London................Wis.	44.24 N	88.42 W
170	New Lynn (lĭn).......N. Z. (In.)	36.55 S	174.41 E
79	New Madrid (măd'rĭd).......Mo.	36.35 N	89.32 W
119	New Malden (môl'dĕn) Gt. Brit. (London In.)	51.24 N	0.16 W
76	Newman Grove............Neb.	41.46 N	97.45 W
83	Newman L. (nū'măn)........Fla.	29.40 N	82.14 W
85	Newmarket (nū'mär-kĕt)....Can.	44.3 N	79.28 W
84	New Martinsville (mär'tĭnz-vĭl) W. Va.	39.47 N	80.52 W
75	New Mexico (State) (mĕk'sĭ-kō) U. S.	34.45 N	107.30 W
118	New Mills..............Gt. Brit.	53.22 N	2.0 W
82	Newnan (nū'năn)............Ga.	33.22 N	84.48 W
167	Newnes (nūnz).............Austl.	33.12 S	150.15 E
169	New Norfolk (nôr'fŏk) Austl. (Tas. In.)	42.46 S	147.5 E
89	New Orleans...........La. (In.)		
81	New Orleans (ôr'lê-ănz).......La.	30.0 N	90.5 W
84	New Philadelphia (fĭl-ȧ-dĕl'fĭ-ȧ) Ohio	40.30 N	81.27 W
170	New Plymouth (plĭm'ŭth)...N. Z.	39.5 S	174.5 E
79	Newport (nū'pōrt)..........Ark.	35.35 N	91.16 W
169	Newport...................Austl.	37.51 S	144.53 E
116	Newport...............Gt. Brit.	50.40 N	1.20 W
116	Newport...............Gt. Brit.	51.35 N	3.0 W
118	Newport...............Gt. Brit.	52.46 N	2.22 W
84	Newport.....................Ky.	39.4 N	84.30 W
86	Newport.....................Me.	44.50 N	69.18 W
89	Newport .Minn. (Minneapolis In.)	44.52 N	93.0 W
86	Newport...................N. H.	43.25 N	72.10 W
85	Newport....................R. I.	41.27 N	71.20 W
82	Newport...................Tenn.	35.56 N	83.12 W
86	Newport.....................Vt.	44.57 N	72.16 W
70	Newport...................Wash.	48.11 N	117.2 W
74	Newport Beach............Calif.	33.37 N	117.56 W
85	Newport News...............Va.	36.57 N	76.26 W
118	Newport Pagnell(păg'nĕl)Gt. Brit.	52.5 N	0.43 W
77	New Prague (prāg)........Minn.	44.31 N	93.32 W
96	New Providence (I.) (prŏv'ĭ-dĕns) Ba. Is.	25.2 N	77.25 W
83	New R. (nū).................Va.	36.50 N	80.58 W
84	New Richmond (rĭch'mŭnd). Ohio	38.57 N	84.17 W
77	New Richmond..............Wis.	45.8 N	92.31 W
81	New Roads...................La.	30.42 N	91.26 W
85	New Rochelle (rô-shĕl')......N. Y.	40.55 N	73.47 W
76	New Rockford (rŏk'fērd)...N. D.	47.41 N	99.9 W
116	New Ross (rôs)...............Ire.	52.25 N	6.55 W
149	New Siberian Is. (sī-bē'rĭ-ăn) Sov. Un.	75.30 N	145.0 E
83	New Smyrna (smûr'nȧ)......Fla.	29.2 N	80.56 W
166	New South Wales (State)...Austl.	33.0 S	146.0 E
84	Newton (nū'tŭn).............Ill.	39.0 N	88.10 W
77	Newton.......................Ia.	41.42 N	93.1 W
79	Newton.....................Kan.	38.3 N	97.21 W
87	Newton..............Mass. (In.)	42.20 N	71.12 W
82	Newton....................Miss.	32.18 N	89.10 W
85	Newton....................N. J.	41.5 N	74.48 W
83	Newton....................N. C.	35.40 N	81.13 W
81	Newton.....................Tex.	30.50 N	93.46 W

ăt; finăl; rāte; senâte; ärm; ȧsk; sofȧ; fâre; ch-choose; dh-as th in other; bē; êvent; bĕt; recĕnt; cratēr; g-go; gh-gutteral g; bĭt; -short neutral; rīde; ĸ-gutteral k as ch in German ich;

Page	Name Pronunciation Region	Lat. °′	Long. °′
118	Newton-in-Makerfield (nū′tŭn-ĭn-māk′ēr-fēld) Gt. Brit.	53.27 N	2.37 W
56	Newton Siding Can. (Winnipeg In.)	49.55 N	98.2 W
116	Newtownards (nū-t′n-ärdz′) Gt. Brit.	54.35 N	5.40 W
77	New Ulm (ŭlm)..........Minn.	44.19 N	94.25 W
163	New Washington (wŏsh′ĭng-tŭn) P. I.	11.39 N	122.25 E
87	New Waterford (wô′tēr-fērd) Can.	46.15 N	60.5 W
54	New Westminster (wĕst′mĭn-stēr) Can.	49.12 N	122.54 W
88	New York (yôrk).....N. Y. (In.)		
85	New York...............N. Y.	40.40 N	73.50 W
85	New York (State)..........U. S.	43.0 N	76.0 W
170	New Zealand (zē′lȧnd)....Pac. O.	42.0 S	174.0 E
92	Nexapa, R. (nĕks-ä′pä)......Mex.	18.45 N	98.26 W
93	Nexquipayac (nĕs-kē-pä-yäk′) Mex. (In.)	19.35 N	98.56 W
149	Nezametny (nyĕ′zȧ-mĕt′nḗ) Sov. Un.	58.45 N	125.20 E
131	Nezhin (nyĕ-zhên′)......Sov. Un.	51.4 N	31.53 E
70	Nez Perce (nā′pĕr sā′).......Ida.	46.15 N	116.15 W
170	Ngakauranga ('n-gä-kou-räŋ′gȧ) N. Z. (In.)	41.15 S	174.49 E
140	Ngami, L. ('n-gä′mḗ).......Bech.	20.30 S	22.40 E
139	Ngaoundéré (n′gōn-dȧ-rā′)..Cam.	7.21 N	13.33 E
170	Ngaruawahia ('n-gä-rōō′ȧ-wä′hḗ-ä) N. Z.	37.40 S	175.13 E
170	Ngaruroro R. ('n-gä′rōō-rō′rô) N. Z.	39.30 S	176.22 E
6	Ngau (I.) ('n-gou′)...Fiji Is. (In.)	18.3 S	179.18 E
170	Ngaurohoe (Vol.) ('n-gou-rō′hô-ĕ) N. Z.	39.10 S	175.38 E
135	Ngolo ('n-gō′lô) Fr. Eq. Afr. (Brazzaville In.)	4.47 S	14.30 E
141	Ngomeni ('n-gô-mā′nḗ)......Tan.	5.8 S	38.53 E
141	Ngong ('n-gông)..........Kenya	1.18 S	36.35 E
143	Ngqeleni ('ng-kĕ-lā′nē)..U. S. Afr.	31.40 S	29.2 E
139	N'Guigmi ('n-gēg′mḗ).Fr. W. Afr.	14.18 N	13.3 E
138	Nguru ('n-gōō′rä)...........Nig.	12.55 N	10.28 E
160	Nhatrang (nyä-träng′)Fr. In. Chn.	12.14 N	109.5 E
166	Nhill (nyĭl)..............Austl.	36.19 S	141.39 E
138	Niafunke (nē-ȧ-fŏŏn′kĕ) Fr. W. Afr.	15.58 N	4.15 W
77	Niagara (nī-ăg′ȧ-rȧ).........Wis.	45.46 N	88.3 W
88	Niagara Falls.........N. Y. (In.)		
55	Niagara Falls.............Can.	43.10 N	79.12 W
85	Niagara Falls.............N. Y.	43.5 N	79.2 W
88	Niagara-on-the-Lake Can. (Niagara Falls In.)	43.14 N	79.4 W
85	Niagara R.................N. Y.	43.5 N	79.2 W
138	Niamey (nē-ä-mȧ′)....Fr. W. Afr.	13.40 N	2.3 E
139	Niangara (nē-äŋ-gä′rȧ).Bel. Cong.	3.34 N	27.59 E
79	Niangua R. (nī-ăŋ′gwȧ)......Mo.	37.50 N	92.50 W
135	Niari R. (nḗ-ä′rḗ) Fr. Eq. Afr. (Brazzaville In.)	4.10 S	13.50 E
160	Nias I. (nē-äs′)........Neth. Ind.	1.0 N	97.40 E
120	Nibe (nē′bĕ)...............Den.	56.58 N	9.39 E
94	Nicaragua (nĭk-ȧ-rä′gwȧ)Cen. Am.	12.50 N	85.0 W
94	Nicaragua, L...............Nic.	11.30 N	85.30 W
128	Nicastro (nḗ-käs′trō)..........It.	38.58 N	16.19 E
125	Nice (nēs)..................Fr.	43.41 N	7.18 E
55	Nichikun L. (nĭch′ĭ-kŭn).....Can.	53.15 N	70.40 W
96	Nicholas Chan. (nĭk′ô-lȧs)...W. I.	23.20 N	80.0 W
84	Nicholasville................Ky.	37.55 N	84.35 W
160	Nicobar, Great (I.) (nĭk-ô-bär′) India	7.0 N	93.45 E
160	Nicobar Is.................India	7.45 N	93.30 E
131	Nicoreşti (nḗ-kô-rĕsht″).....Rom.	45.59 N	27.14 E
115	Nicosia (nē-kô-sē′ȧ).........Cyp.	35.12 N	33.22 E
94	Nicoya (nē-kō′yä)..........C. R.	10.7 N	85.27 W
94	Nicoya, G. of..............C. R.	10.0 N	85.0 W
94	Nicoya Pen.................C. R.	10.0 N	86.0 W
99	Nictheroy (Niteroi) (nĭk-tē-roi′) (nē-tĕ-rō′ĭ) Braz. (Rio de Janeiro In.)	22.54 S	43.6 W
120	Nidaros (Trondheim) (nē′dȧ-rôs) (trôn′hâm) Nor.	63.26 N	10.21 E
118	Nidd, R. (nĭd)..........Gt. Brit.	54.3 N	1.42 W
123	Niemen (Nemunas) R. (nē′mĕn) Eur.	53.39 N	22.10 E
122	Nienburg (nē′ĕn-bŏŏrgh).....Ger.	52.38 N	9.14 E
152	Nienchen Tangla (Mts.) (nyĕn′chĕn tän′glā).Chn.	30.0 N	90.0 E
119	Niendorf (nē′ĕn-dôrf) Ger. (Hamburg In.)	53.37 N	9.57 E
153	Nienkachow (nyĕn′kȁ-chō′) Chn. (Shanghai In.)	31.9 N	121.29 E
119	Nienstedten (nēn′shtĕt-ĕn) Ger. (Hamburg In.)	53.33 N	9.51 E
123	Nieświez (nyēsh′vyĕsh)......Pol.	53.12 N	26.41 E
169	Nietta (nē-ĕt′ȧ)..Austl. (Tas. In.)	41.21 S	146.4 E
142	Nieuwerust (nē′ōō-vē-rŏŏst) U. S. Afr.	31.9 S	18.18 E
142	Nieuwhoutville (nḗ-ōō′hout-vḗl) U. S. Afr.	31.22 S	19.9 E
119	Nieuwkerken Waes (nē′ŏŏ-kĕr-kĕn vä′ĕs).Bel. (Anvers In.)	51.12 N	4.10 E
103	Nieuw Nickerie (nḗ′ōō nḗk-ēr-ē′) Sur.	5.45 N	57.0 W
142	Nieuwveld Mts. (nḗ-ōō′vĕlt) U. S. Afr.	32.5 S	22.0 E
92	Nieves (nyā′vȧs)...........Mex.	24.2 N	102.56 W
135	Nifîsha (nḗ-fēs′hȧ) Eg. (Suez Can. In.)	30.34 N	32.17 E
113	Nigde (nĭg′dĕ)..............Tur.	37.58 N	34.38 E
138	Nigeria (nī-jē′rĭ-ȧ)..........Afr.	9.0 N	8.0 E
138	Niger R. (nī′jēr).Fr. W. Afr.-Nig.	14.0 N	1.30 E
138	Niger, Ter. of the.....Fr. W. Afr.	16.0 N	7.0 E
171	Nightcaps (nīt′kăps).........N. Z.	45.57 S	168.3 E
158	Niigata (nē′ê-gä′tȧ).........Jap.	37.50 N	139.7 E
173	Niihau (I.) (nē′ê-hä′ōō).....Haw.	21.55 N	160.10 W
159	Niijima (I.) (nē′ê-jē′mä).....Jap.	34.25 N	139.15 E
159	Niimi (nē′ê-mḗ).............Jap.	34.59 N	133.29 E
158	Niitaka (Mt.) (nē′ê-tä-kä) Tai. (In.)	23.29 N	120.53 E
126	Níjar (nē′här)...............Sp.	36.56 N	2.11 W
122	Nijmegen (nī′mā-gĕn)......Neth.	51.50 N	5.52 E
159	Nikaido (nĭk′ȧ-ē′dō) Jap. (Osaka In.)	34.37 N	135.48 E
130	Nikitinka (nḗ-kḗtēŋ′kȧ)..Sov. Un.	55.33 N	33.22 E
159	Nikko (nĭk′kō).............Jap.	36.45 N	139.38 E
131	Nikolaev (nē-kô-lā′yĕf)..Sov. Un.	46.58 N	32.1 E
113	Nikolaevsk (nē-kô-lä′yĕfsk) Sov. Un.	50.2 N	45.30 E
149	Nikolaevsk.............Sov. Un.	53.20 N	140.35 E
122	Nikolsburg (Mikulov) (nē′kôls-bŏŏrk) (mĭ′kŏŏ-lôf).Ger.	48.47 N	16.38 E
112	Nikolsk (nē′kôlsk).......Sov. Un.	59.30 N	45.30 E
148	Nikolskoe (nē′kôl-skō′yĕ) Sov. Un.	69.40 N	60.30 E
149	Nikolsk Ussuriiski (nē′kôlsk ōō′-sōō-rḗ-ēs′kĭ-ḗ)...Sov. Un.	43.45 N	131.59 E
129	Nikopol (nḗ-kô′pŏl).........Bul.	43.40 N	24.51 E
131	Nikopol.................Sov. Un.	47.35 N	34.25 E
129	Nikšić (nēk′shḗch).........Yugo.	42.46 N	18.59 E
159	Nikura (nē′kŏŏ-rä)..........Jap.	33.52 N	139.36 E
139	Nile R. (nīl)...............Afr.	22.40 N	32.0 E
49	Niles (nīlz) Calif. (San Francisco In.)	37.35 N	121.59 W
88	Niles..........Ill. (Chicago In.)	42.1 N	87.48 W
84	Niles.....................Mich.	41.50 N	86.17 W
84	Niles.....................Ohio	41.13 N	80.47 W
88	Niles Center.....Ill. (Chicago In.)	42.2 N	87.45 W
169	Nilumbik (nī-lŭm′bĭk) Austl. (Melbourne In.)	37.40 S	145.10 E
138	Nimba, Mt. (nĭm′bȧ)..Fr. W. Afr.	7.45 N	8.30 W
124	Nimes (nēm)................Fr.	43.50 N	4.22 E
167	Nimmitabel (nĭm′ĭ-tȧ-bĕl′)...Aus.	36.30 S	149.18 E
139	Nimule (nḗ-mōō′lȁ)....A. E. Sud.	3.40 N	32.9 E
160	Ninbinh (nēn-bēnᴋ′).Fr. In. Chn.	20.15 N	106.5 E
167	Ninety Mile Beach........Austl.	38.18 S	147.18 E
150	Ninevah (Ruins) (nĭn′ê-vĕ)...Iraq	36.8 N	43.15 E
153	Ningan (nĭŋ-găn).........Manch.	44.25 N	129.36 E
155	Ninghai (nĭng′hī′).........Chn.	29.18 N	121.26 E
156	Ninghai...................Chn.	37.24 N	121.34 E
156	Ningho (nĭng′hō′)..........Chn.	39.26 N	117.33 E
155	Ninghwa (nĭng′hwā′)........Chn.	26.9 N	116.30 E
155	Ningkwo (nĭng′kwô′)........Chn.	30.58 N	118.43 E
155	Ningkwohsien (nĭng′kwô-syĕn′) Chn.	30.37 N	118.59 E
152	Ninghsia (nĭng′syā′)........Chn.	38.27 N	106.6 E
152	Ninghsia (Prov.)...........Chn.	40.15 N	102.30 E
156	Ningling (nĭng′lĭng′)........Chn.	34.33 N	115.33 E
155	Ningpo (nĭng-pō′)..........Chn.	29.53 N	121.34 E
154	Ningsiang (nĭng′syăng′).....Chn.	28.17 N	112.12 E
156	Ningtsin (nĭng′tsĭn′)........Chn.	37.42 N	114.57 E
156	Ningtsin...................Chn.	37.50 N	116.39 E
156	Ningtsin L.................Chn.	37.40 N	115.20 E
155	Ningtu (nĭng′tōō′)..........Chn.	26.27 N	115.44 E
153	Ningwu (nĭng′wōō′).........Chn.	39.15 N	112.10 E
155	Ningyang (nĭng′yăng′)......Chn.	25.34 N	117.15 E
154	Ningyüan (nĭng′yü-ăn′).....Chn.	25.37 N	111.47 E
152	Ningyüan..................Chn.	27.57 N	102.21 E
161	Ninigo Is. (nḗ-nē′gō).N. Gui. Ter.	1.20 S	144.15 E
119	Ninkop (nēn′kŭp) Ger. (Hamburg In.)	53.31 N	9.47 E
78	Ninnescah R. (nĭn′ĕs-kä)....Kan.	37.36 N	98.0 W
46	Ninnis Glacier (nĭn′ĭs) ......Ant.	67.0 S	147.0 E
103	Nioaqua (nḗ-ô-ä′kwā).......Braz.	21.2 S	55.45 W
76	Niobrara R. (nī-ô-brâr′ȧ)....Neb.	42.47 N	101.0 W
138	Nioro (nḗ-ō′rō).......Fr. W. Afr.	15.23 N	9.27 W
124	Niort (nḗ-ôr′)...............Fr.	46.20 N	0.28 W
97	Nipe B. (nē′pā).............Cuba	20.48 N	75.40 W
97	Nipe, Sierra de (Mts.)......Cuba	20.28 N	75.48 W
55	Nipigon (nĭp′ĭ-gŏn).........Can.	49.0 N	88.5 W
77	Nipigon B..................Can.	48.55 N	88.0 W
55	Nipigon L..................Can.	49.50 N	88.30 W
77	Nipigon R..................Can.	49.12 N	88.20 W
86	Nipisiquit R. (nĭ-pĭ′sĭ-kwĭt)..Can.	47.25 N	66.20 W
55	Nipissing, L. (nĭp′ĭ-sĭng).....Can.	46.15 N	79.48 W
96	Niquero (nḗ-kā′rō).........Cuba	20.1 N	77.36 W
150	Niriz, L. (nḗ-rēz′)..........Iran	29.30 N	53.40 E
129	Niš (nḗsh)................Yugo.	43.17 N	21.53 E
126	Nisa (nē′sȧ)...............Port.	39.32 N	7.42 W
129	Nišava R. (nē′shȧ-vȧ)......Yugo.	43.13 N	22.20 E
150	Nishapur (nĭsh-ȧ-pōōr′)......Iran	36.14 N	58.40 E
159	Nishikata (nē′shḗ-kā′tā).....Jap.	31.54 N	130.15 E
159	Nishino I. (nēsh′ê-nô)......Jap.	36.5 N	133.5 E
159	Nishinomiya (nēsh′ê-nô-mē′yā) Jap. (Osaka In.)	34.45 N	135.20 E
159	Nishinoomote (nēsh-ê-nô-ô-mō′tō) Jap.	30.44 N	131.0 E
158	Nishi Notoro C. (nē′shḗ nō′tô-rō) Kar.	45.59 N	142.2 E
159	Nishio (nēsh′ê-ô)...........Jap.	34.51 N	137.3 E
79	Nishnabotna R. (nĭsh-nȧ-bŏt′nȧ) Ia.-Mo.	40.30 N	95.36 W
79	Nishnabotna R., East.........Ia.	41.05 N	95.15 W
79	Nishnabotna R., West........Ia.	41.10 N	95.15 W
119	Nisida I. (nē′zḗ-dä) It. (Napoli In.)	40.47 N	14.10 E
123	Nisko (nēs′kô)..............Pol.	50.30 N	22.7 E
49	Nisqually (nĭs-kwôl′ĭ) Wash. (Seattle In.)	47.4 N	122.41 W
70	Nisqually R...............Wash.	46.50 N	122.20 W
120	Nissa R. (nĭs-sȧ)...........Swe.	56.58 N	13.10 E
120	Nisser L. (nĭs′ēr)...........Nor.	59.14 N	8.29 E
131	Nistrul (Dnester, Dniester) R. (nēst′rŏŏl).Rom.-..Sov. Un.	47.35 N	29.8 E
103	Niteroi (nē-tĕ-rō′ĭ).........Braz.	22.59 S	43.1 W
116	Nith (R.) (nĭth).........Gt. Brit.	55.10 N	3.50 W
123	Nitra (nē′trȧ)..............Czech.	48.18 N	18.4 E
123	Nitra R...................Czech.	48.25 N	18.8 E
84	Nitro (nī′trô).............W. Va.	38.24 N	81.51 W
112	Nitva (nēt′vȧ)..........Sov. Un.	58.2 N	55.15 E
153	Niuchwangcheng, see Yingkow, Manch.		
117	Nivelles (nē′vĕl′)...........Bel.	51.37 N	4.20 E
124	Nivernais, Hills of the (nē-vĕr-nĕ′) Fr.	47.10 N	3.30 E
72	Niwot (nī′wŏt).Colo. (Denver In.)	40.7 N	105.10 W
81	Nixon (nĭk′sŭn).............Tex.	29.17 N	97.45 W
113	Nizhne Chirskaya (nḗzh′nyĕ chêr-skä′yȧ)...Sov. Un.	48.20 N	43.2 E
149	Nizhne Kamchatsk (kăm-chätsk′) Sov. Un.	56.20 N	161.40 E
149	Nizhne Kolymsk (kô-lêmsk′) Sov. Un.	68.35 N	160.59 E
112	Nizhne-Saldinski Zavod (sȧl-dēn-skĭ-ê zȧ-vôt′)...Sov. Un.	58.8 N	60.30 E
112	Nizhne-Serginskii Zavod (sĕr-jēn′-skĭ-ê zȧ-vôt′)...Sov. Un.	56.35 N	59.25 E
148	Nizhneudinsk (nḗzh′nyĕ-ōō-dēnsk′)...Sov. Un.	54.55 N	99.15 E
131	Nizhnie Mayachki (nḗzh′nḗ-yĕ mȧ-yäch′kĭ)...Sov. Un.	46.29 N	33.5 E
131	Nizhnie Serogazi (sā′rô-gä′zē) Sov. Un.	46.51 N	34.22 E
112	Nizhni-Novgorod, see Gorki, Sov. Un.		
148	Nizhni Tagil (nḗzh′niḗ tā′gḗl) Sov. Un.	57.50 N	59.55 E
120	Njurunda (nyōō-rŏŏn′dȧ)....Swe.	62.16 N	17.20 E
143	Nkande ('n-kăn′dȁ).....U. S. Afr.	27.58 S	30.37 E
143	Nkandhla ('n-känd′lä)..U. S. Afr.	28.38 S	31.5 E
52	Noatak R. (nô-ȧ′tȧk).......Alsk.	68.0 N	159.30 W
159	Nobeoka (nō-bȁ-ō′kȧ)........Jap.	32.36 N	131.40 E
84	Noblesville (nō′bl′z-vĭl)......Ind.	40.2 N	86.2 W
92	Nochistlán (nô-chēs-tlän′)...Mex.	21.25 N	102.57 W
93	Nochixtlán (Asunción) (ä-sŏŏn-syōn′).Mex.	17.27 N	97.13 W
79	Nodaway R. (nŏd′ȧ-wā)...Mo.-Ia.	40.30 N	95.4 W
131	Nogaisk (nō′gȧ-êsk)......Sov. Un.	46.42 N	36.17 E
75	Nogales (nô-gä′lĕs)..........Ariz.	31.21 N	110.56 W
93	Nogales...................Mex.	18.49 N	97.8 W
124	Nogent-en-Bassigny nô-zhäɴ′äɴ-bȧ-sḗ-nyē′).Fr.	48.0 N	5.25 E
124	Nogent-le-Retrou (lē-rē-trōō′)..Fr.	48.21 N	0.50 E
125	Nogent-sur-Marne (sür-märn′) Fr. (In.)	48.50 N	2.28 E
124	Nogent-sur-Seine (sür-sān′)....Fr.	48.30 N	3.30 E
130	Noginsk (nô-gēnsk′).....Sov. Un.	55.50 N	38.25 E
126	Nogueira (nô-gā′rä)..........Sp.	42.26 N	7.44 E
127	Nogueira Pallarisa R. (pä-lyä-rā′sä).Sp.	42.15 N	1.0 E
158	Noho (Bordo chan) (nô′hô′) (bôr′dô′chän′).Manch.	48.30 N	124.44 E
124	Noire Mts. (nwȧr)...........Fr.	48.5 N	3.50 W
124	Noirmoutier, Ile de (I.) (nwȧr-mōō-tyā′).Fr.	47.0 N	2.15 W
125	Noisiel (nwȧ-zyĕl′).......Fr. (In.)	48.51 N	2.37 E
125	Noisy-le-Grand (nwȧ-zē′-lē-gräɴ′) Fr. (In.).	48.50 N	2.33 E
125	Noisy-le Sec (nwä′sḗ lē sĕk′) Fr. (In.)	48.53 N	2.27 E
159	Nojimi, C. (nō′jḗ-mē)........Jap.	34.55 N	139.55 E
142	Nokanna R. (nô-kä′mä).....Bech.	28.28 S	22.25 E
54	Nokomis (nô-kō′mĭs)........Can.	51.31 N	105.10 W
79	Nokomis...................Ill.	39.17 N	89.16 W
128	Nola (nô′lä)..................It.	40.55 N	14.33 E
83	Nolichucky R. (nŏl-ĭ-chŭk′ĭ).Tenn.	36.10 N	82.30 W
112	Nolinsk (nô-lênsk′)......Sov. Un.	57.30 N	49.55 E
77	Nomakagon R. (nō-mȧ-kā′gŏn) Wis.	45.55 N	91 50 W
159	Nomami C. (nō′mä-mḗ) .....Jap.	31.28 N	130.15 E
52	Nome (nōm)...............Alsk.	64.25 N	165.30 W
160	Nong-Khây (nŏng-ᴋä′ê) ....Thai.	17.58 N	102.52 E
143	Nongoma (nŏn-gō′mȧ)..U. S. Afr.	27.52 S	31.40 E
153	Nonni R. (nŏn′ê).........Manch.	47.30 N	123.57 E
143	Noodsberg (nōdz′bĕrgh).U. S. Afr.	29.27 S	30.47 E
72	Nooksack (nŏŏk′săk) Wash. (Vancouver In.)	48.56 N	122.19 W
72	Nooksack R. Wash. (Vancouver In.)	48.53 N	122.33 W
169	Noosa Hd. (nōō′sȧ)....Austl. (In.)	26.20 S	153.6 E
54	Nootka I. (nōōt′kȧ)........Can.	49.40 N	126.50 W
140	Nogui (nô-kē′).............Ang.	6.0 S	13.35 E
120	Nora (nô′rä)...............Swe.	59.31 N	14.59 E
55	Noranda (nô-rȧn′dȧ)........Can.	48.25 N	79.10 W
79	Norborne (nôr′bôrn).........Mo.	39.16 N	93.38 W
73	Norco (nôr′kô) Calif. (Los Angeles In.)	33.56 N	117.34 W
73	Norcross (nôr′krôs) Ga. (Atlanta In.)	33.57 N	84.13 W
122	Norden (nôr-dĕn)...........Ger.	53.36 N	7.12 E
149	Nordenskjöld Sea (nôr′dĕn-shûl) Sov. Un.	74.30 N	126.0 E
122	Norderney (I.) (nôr′dēr-nī)..Neth.	53.43 N	7.15 E
120	Nord Fjord (nôr′ fyôr).......Nor.	61.55 N	5.35 E
122	Nordhausen (nôrt-hau′zĕn)...Ger.	51.30 N	10.47 E
122	Nordhorn (nôrt′hôrn)........Ger.	52.26 N	7.3 E
49	Nordland (nôrd′lȧnd) Wash. (Seattle In.)	48.2 N	122.42 W
122	Nördlingen (nûrt′lĭng-ĕn).....Ger.	48.52 N	10.29 E
116	Nore, R. (nōr)...............Ire.	52.30 N	7.10 W
82	Norfield (nôr′fēld)..........Miss.	31.24 N	90.18 W
87	Norfolk (nôr′fŏk)......Mass. (In.)	42.7 N	71.19 W
76	Norfolk...................Neb.	42.2 N	97.24 W
89	Norfolk...............Va. (In.)		
85	Norfolk....................Va.	36.50 N	76.18 W
165	Norfolk I...............Pac. O.	29.8 S	168.8 E
92	Noria (nō′rê-ȧ).............Mex.	23.31 N	106.15 W
79	Normal (nôr′mȧl).............Ill.	40.31 N	88.59 W
54	Norman (nôr′mȧn)..........Can.	64.50 N	125.20 W
79	Norman...................Okla.	35.13 N	97.26 W
170	Normanby................N. Z.	39.33 S	174.15 E
87	Norman, C...............Newf.	51.47 N	55.55 W
124	Normandy, Hills of (nôr′mȧn-dḗ) Fr.	48.40 N	0.10 W
165	Norman R. (nôr′măn)......Austl.	18.30 S	141.20 E
165	Normanton (nôr′mȧn-tŭn)..Austl.	17.38 S	141.0 E
118	Normanton.............Gt. Brit.	53.41 N	1.25 W
164	Nornalup (nôr-năl′ŭp)......Austl.	34.45 S	116.47 E
158	Nor R. (nōr)...............Chn.	47.2 N	133.0 E
120	Nörresundby (nû-rĕ-sŏŏn′bü).Den.	57.4 N	9.55 E

ng-sing; ŋ-baŋk; ɴ-nasalized n; nŏd; cŏmmit; ōld; ôbey; ôrder; fōōd; fŏŏt; ou-out; s-soft; sh-dish; th-thin; pūre; ûnite; ûrn; stŭd; circŭs; ü-as "y" in study; ′-indeterminate vowel.

Page	Name Pronunciation Region	Lat. °′	Long. °′
59	Norris L. . . . . Tenn.	36.15 N	83.30 W
85	Norristown (nŏr′ĭs-town) . . . . . . Pa.	40.8 N	75.20 W
120	Norrköping (nôr′chûp-ĭng) . . . Swe.	58.36 N	16.11 E
120	Norrköping B. . . . . Swe.	58.35 N	16.55 E
120	Norrtälje (nôr-tĕl′yĕ). . . . . Swe.	59.47 N	18.41 E
164	Norseman (nôrs′măn) . . . . . . Austl.	32.12 S	121.55 E
86	North Adams (ăd′ămz) . . . . . Mass.	42.42 N	73.5 W
169	North Adelaide (ăd′ê-lād) Austl. (Adelaide In.)	34.54 S	138.37 E
164	Northam (nôr′dhăm) . . . . Austl.	31.47 S	116.40 E
48	North America (ȧ-mĕr′ĭ-kȧ)		
91	North American Basin (Sea) Atl. O.	22.30 N	61.40 W
164	Northampton (nôr-thămp′tun) Austl.	28.47 S	114.40 E
116	Northampton . . . . Gt. Brit.	52.15 N	0.55 W
86	Northampton . . . . Mass.	42.20 N	72.40 W
85	Northampton . . . . Pa.	40.42 N	75.30 W
118	Northampton Co. . . . . Gt. Brit.	52.21 N	1.0 W
87	North Andover (ăn′dô-vẽr) Mass. (In.)	42.42 N	71.7 W
163	North Balabac Str. (bä-lä′bäk) P. I.	8.10 N	117.0 E
73	North Baldy (bôl′dĭ) Calif. (Los Angeles In.)	34.22 N	117.46 W
84	North Baltimore (bôl′tĭ-môr) . Ohio.	41.12 N	83.40 W
54	North Battleford (băt″l-fẽrd).Can.	52.50 N	108.29 W
55	North Bay . . . . Can.	46.16 N	79.30 W
70	North Bend . . . . Ore.	43.23 N	124.15 W
86	North Berwick (bûr′wĭk) . . . . . Me.	43.19 N	70.45 W
96	North Bight (bĭt) . . . . Ba. Is.	24.25 N	77.43 W
96	North Bimini I. (bê-mē′nê).Ba. Is.	25.46 N	79.17 W
87	Northboro (nôrth′bûr-ô) Mass. (In.)	42.19 N	71.38 W
86	Northbridge (nôrth′brĭj) . . . . Mass.	42.10 N	71.40 W
97	North Caicos I. (kī′kôs) . . . . Ba. Is.	1.57 N	72.0 W
87	North C. . . . . Can.	47.0 N	60.25 W
170	North Cape . . . . N. Z.	34.21 S	173.2 E
110	North Cape . . . . Nor.	71.5 N	26.0 E
6	North Cape . . . . . . Sta. Luc. (In.) .	14.5 N	60.54 W
83	North Carolina (State) (kăr-ô-lī′nȧ) . U. S.	35.40 N	78.50 W
84	North Channel . . . . Can.	46.5 N	83.0 W
116	North Channel . . . . Gt. Brit.	55.0 N	5.30 W
77	North Chicago (shĭ-kô′gō) . . . . . Ill.	42.19 N	87.51 W
169	Northcote (nôrth′kôt) Austl. (Melbourne In.)	37.46 S	144.59 E
170	Northcote. . . . . N. Z. (In.)	36.50 S	174.48 E
76	North Dakota (State) (dȧ-kō′tȧ) U. S.	47.40 N	100.20 W
116	North Downs (dounz). . . . Gt. Brit.	51.15 N	0.20 E
83	Northeast Cape Fear R. . . . . N. C.	34.45 N	77.55 W
89	Northeast Pass La. (New Orleans In.)	29.8 N	89.3 W
97	Northeast Pt. . . . . Ba. Is.	24.38 N	75.40 W
97	Northeast Pt. . . . . Ba. Is.	21.20 N	73.0 W
97	Northeast Pt. . . . . Ba. Is.	22.45 N	73.51 W
96	Northeast Providence Channel (prŏv′ĭ-dĕns) . Ba. Is.	25.42 N	77.0 W
122	Northeim (nôrt′hīm) . . . . Ger.	51.42 N	10.0 E
119	Northenden (nôr′dhĕn-dĕn) Gt. Brit. (Liverpool In.)	53.24 N	2.15 W
71	Northern Cheyenne Ind. Res. (shī-ĕn′) . Mont.	45.30 N	106.40 W
116	Northern Highlands . . . . . Gt. Brit.	57.20 N	5.0 W
116	Northern Ireland (īr′lănd)Gt. Brit.	55.0 N	7.0 W
149	Northern Land (Severnaya Zemlya) . . . Sov. Un.	79.0 N	103.0 E
77	Northern Light L. . . . . Can.	48.17 N	90.43 W
138	Northern Provinces . . . . Nig.	11.0 N	8.0 E
140	Northern Rhodesia (rô-dē′zhĭ-ȧ) Afr.	14.15 S	29.30 E
138	Northern Territories . . . . G. C.	10.0 N	1.45 W
164	Northern Territory . . . . Austl.	20.0 S	134.0 E
77	Northfield (nôrth′fēld) . . . . . Minn.	44.28 N	93.9 W
86	Northfield . . . . Vt.	44.10 N	72.39 W
117	North Foreland (fōr′lȧnd) Gt. Brit.	51.20 N	1.22 E
49	North Fork Reservoir Wash. (Portland In.)	46.1 N	122.27 W
80	North Franklin Park (frăŋ′klĭn) Tex.	31.55 N	106.30 W
169	North Fremantle (frē′măn-t′l) Austl. (Perth In.)	32.2 S	115.43 E
122	North Frisian I. (frĭzh′ȧn) . . . . Ger.	54.40 N	8.30 E
46	North Graham I. (grā′ăm).Ant. O.	65.0 S	62.0 W
157	North Han R. (hän) . . . . Cho.	38.10 N	127.52 E
170	North Havelock . . . . N. Z.	39.43 S	177.8 E
74	North I. . . . . Calif. (In.)	32.40 N	117.13 W
170	North I. . . . . N. Z.	38.0 S	174.0 E
84	North Judson (jŭd′sŭn) . . . . . . Ind.	41.13 N	86.47 W
79	North Little Rock . . . . Ark.	34.46 N	92.16 W
84	North Manchester (măn′chĕs-tẽr) Ind.	41.0 N	85.47 W
116	North Minch (Chan.) . . . . Gt. Brit.	58.10 N	6.0 W
167	North Mirboo (mĭr′bōō) . . . . Austl.	38.25 S	146.10 E
89	North Oakwood (ōk′wŏŏd) Va. (Norfolk In.)	36.55 N	76.15 W
119	North Ockendon (ŏk′ĕn-dŭn) Gt. Brit. (London In.)	51.32 N	0.18 E
73	North Ogden (ŏg′dĕn) Utah (Salt Lake City In.)	41.18 N	111.57 W
73	North Ogden Park Utah (Salt Lake City In.)	41.22 N	111.57 W
113	North Ossetia (Aut. Area) (ŏ-sē′-shȧ) . . . Sov. Un.	43.0 N	44.15 E
170	North Palmerston (päm′ẽr-stŭn) N. Z.	40.18 S	175.38 E
89	North Pass.La. (New Orleans In.)	29.12 N	89.3 W
78	North Platte (plăt) . . . . Neb.	41.09 N	100.46 W
58	North Platte R. . . . . U. S.	41.15 N	101.30 W
46	North Pole		
169	North Pt. . . . . . Austl. (Sidney In.)	33.49 S	151.19 E
95	North Pt. . . . . Barb. (In.)	13.20 N	59.37 W
84	North Pt. . . . . Mich.	45.0 N	83.15 W
82	Northport (nôrth′pōrt) . . . . Ala.	33.12 N	87.36 W
70	Northport . . . . Wash.	48.54 N	117.44 W
87	North Reading (rēd′ĭng) Mass. (In.)	42.34 N	71.4 W
118	North Riding (borough) (rĭd′ĭng) Gt. Brit.	54.12 N	1.9 W
116	North Ronaldshay (I.) (rŏn′ăld-shā) . Gt. Brit. (In.)	59.20 N	2.25 W
89	North St. Paul Minn. (Minneapolis In.)	45.0 N	93.0 W
73	North Salt Lake Utah (Salt Lake City In.)	40.51 N	111.56 W
110	North Sea . . . . Atl. O.	55.20 N	3.0 W
143	North Shepstone (shĕps′tŭn) U. S. Afr.	30.44 S	30.26 E
88	North Shore Channel Ill. (Chicago In.)	42.5 N	87.40 W
169	North Sydney (sĭd′nê) Austl. (Sidney In.)	33.49 S	151.11 E
87	North Sydney . . . . Can.	46.12 N	60.15 W
72	North Table Mt. Colo. (Denver In.)	39.48 N	105.12 W
170	North Taranaki Bight (tȧ-rȧ-nä′kĭ bĭt) . N. Z.	38.50 S	174.30 E
85	North Tonawanda (tŏn-ȧ-wŏn′dȧ) N. Y.	43.2 N	78.54 W
56	North Transcona (trăns-kō′nȧ) Can. (Winnipeg In.)	49.55 N	97.0 W
75	North Truchas Peaks (trōō′chäs) N. M.	35.38 N	105.47 W
163	North Ubian I. (ōō-bê-än′) . . . P. I.	6.9 N	120.28 E
116	North Uist (I.) (wĭst) . . . . Gt. Brit.	57.40 N	7.20 W
86	Northumberland (nôr-thŭm′bẽr-lȧnd) . N. H.	44.33 N	71.32 W
86	Northumberland, (B.) . . . . Can.	46.30 N	64.0 W
166	Northumberland C. . . . . Austl.	38.35 S	140.35 E
72	Northumberland Channel Can. (Vancouver In.)	49.12 N	123.55 W
165	Northumberland Is. . . . . Austl.	21.45 S	150.15 E
70	North Umpqua R. (ŭmp′kwȧ) Ore.	43.21 N	123.0 W
70	North Vancouver (văn-kōō′vẽr) Can.	49.18 N	123.6 W
84	North Vernon (vûr′nŭn) . . . . . Ind.	39.3 N	85.42 W
164	North West C. . . . . Austl.	21.50 S	114.10 E
96	Northwest Providence Channel (prŏv′ĭ-dĕns) . Ba. Is.	26.10 N	78.20 W
164	North West Region . . . . Austl.	24.0 S	117.30 E
54	Northwest Territories . . . . Can.	64.30 N	107.0 W
118	Northwich (nôrth′wĭch) . . Gt. Brit.	53.15 N	2.31 W
83	North Wilkesboro (wĭlks′bûrô) N. C.	36.10 N	81.10 W
76	Northwood . . . . N. D.	47.43 N	97.32 W
77	Northwood (nôrth′wŏŏd) . . . . . . Ia.	43.28 N	93.12 W
71	North Wood Cr. . . . . Wyo.	44.10 N	107.30 W
116	North York Moors (nôrth yôrk mŏŏrz′) . Gt. Brit.	54.20 N	1.0 W
78	Norton (nôr′tŭn) . . . . Kan.	39.49 N	99.54 W
83	Norton . . . . Va.	36.57 N	82.37 W
52	Norton B. . . . . Alsk.	64.30 N	161.30 W
52	Norton Sd. . . . . Alsk.	64.0 N	163.0 W
73	Norwalk (nôr′wôk) Calif. (Los Angeles In.)	33.54 N	118.5 W
85	Norwalk . . . . Conn.	41.7 N	73.26 W
84	Norwalk . . . . Ohio	41.14 N	82.36 W
120	Norway (nôr′wā) . . . . Eur.	61.0 N	8.0 E
86	Norway . . . . Me.	44.12 N	70.32 W
77	Norway . . . . Mich.	45.48 N	87.55 W
54	Norway House . . . . Can.	54.2 N	98.1 W
110	Norwegian Sea (nôr-wē′jăn) Atl. O.	65.40 N	1.30 E
87	Norwell (nôr′wĕl) . . . . . Mass. (In.)	42.10 N	70.47 W
85	Norwich (nôr′wĭch) . . . . Conn.	41.31 N	72.4 W
117	Norwich . . . . Gt. Brit.	52.40 N	1.20 E
85	Norwich . . . . N. Y.	42.32 N	75.32 W
169	Norwood (nôr′wŏŏd) Austl. (Adelaide In.)	34.55 S	138.38 E
86	Norwood . . . . Mass.	42.12 N	71.11 W
83	Norwood . . . . N. C.	35.14 N	80.8 W
84	Norwood . . . . Ohio	39.10 N	84.25 W
161	Norzagaray (nôr′zä-gä-rä′ê) P. I. (Manila In.)	14.55 N	121.2 E
158	Noshap C. (nō′shăp′) . . . . Jap.	43.28 N	145.40 E
158	Noshiro (nō′shê-rô) . . . . Jap.	40.11 N	140.2 E
140	Nosob R. (nô′sŏb)S. W. Afr.-Bech.	24.45 S	20.0 E
131	Nosovka (nô-sôf′kȧ) . . . . . Sov. Un.	50.56 N	31.34 E
141	Nossi Be (I.) (nô-sē′bā′) . . Madag.	13.15 S	48.15 E
141	Nossy-Vey (I.) (nô-sē′vā′).Madag.	23.32 S	43.32 E
123	Noteć R. (nô′tĕch) . . . . Pol.	53.4 N	17.23 E
120	Notodden (nô′tô-dĕn) . . . . Nor.	59.35 N	9.18 E
159	Noto Pen. (nô′tō) . . . . Jap.	37.15 N	137.0 E
83	Notoway R. (nŏt′ô-wā) . . . . Va.	36.52 N	77.30 W
87	Notre Dame B. (nō′t′r dàm′) Newf.	49.40 N	55.25 W
84	Nottawasaga B. (nŏt′ȧ-wȧ-sä′gȧ) Can.	44.40 N	80.30 W
55	Nottaway R. (nŏt′ȧ-wā) . . . . . Can.	51.0 N	7.28 W
116	Nottingham (nŏt′ĭng-ăm).Gt. Brit.	52.55 N	1.10 W
118	Nottingham Co. . . . . Gt. Brit.	53.8 N	1.0 W
135	Noual Sebkheten (L.) (sĕb′ĸĕt-ĕn-nōō-ȧl′) Tun. (In.)	34.23 N	9.45 E
165	Nouméa (nōō-mā′ä) . . . . . . N. Cal.	22.14 S	166.30 E
138	Noun C. (nô-ōōn′) . . . . R. de O.	28.45 N	11.15 W
86	Nouvelle (nōō-vĕl′) . . . . Can.	48.7 N	66.18 W
139	Nouvelle Anvers (nōō-vĕl′ äɴ-vâr′) . Bel. Cong.	1.39 N	19.7 E
124	Nouzonville (nōō-zôɴ-vēl′) . . . . Fr.	49.48 N	4.48 E
103	Nova (nō′vȧ) . . . . Braz.	20.20 S	42.28 W
99	Nova Friburgo (nō′vȧ frê-bōōr′ gōō) . Braz. (Rio de Janeiro In.)	22.20 S	42.33 W
151	Nova Goa (nô′vȧ-gō′ȧ) . . . . . . India	15.25 N	74.5 E
140	Nova Lisboa (Huambo) (nō′vȧ lêzh-bō′ȧ) . Ang.	12.45 S	15.47 E
128	Novara (nô-vä′rā) . . . . It.	45.26 N	8.38 E
55	Nova Scotia (Prov.) (nō′vȧ skō′shy-ȧ) . Can.	45.0 N	64.0 W
129	Nova Varoš (nô′vȧ vä′rôsh) .Yugo.	43.24 N	19.50 E
49	Novato (nô-vä′tō) Calif. (San Francisco In.)	38.5 N	122.32 W
131	Novaya Odessa (nô′vȧ-yȧ ô-dyĕs′ä) . . . Sov. Un.	47.18 N	31.47 E
131	Novaya Praga (nô′vȧ-yȧ prä′gȧ) Sov. Un.	48.34 N	32.55 E
131	Novaya Vodolaga (nô′vȧ-yȧ vô-dôl′á-gȧ) . . . Sov. Un.	49.42 N	35.51 E
149	Novaya Sibir I. (nô′vȧ-yȧ sê-bēr′) Sov. Un.	75.15 N	148.0 E
148	Novaya Zemlya (New Land) (nô′vȧ-yȧ zĕm-lyȧ′) . . . Sov. Un.	74.0 N	57.0 E
129	Nova Zagora (nô′vȧ zä′gô-rȧ).Bul.	42.29 N	26.1 E
127	Novelda (nō-vĕl′dȧ) . . . . Sp.	38.24 N	0.45 W
161	Noveleta (nō-vȧ-lā′tä) P. I. (Manila In.)	14.26 N	120.51 E
123	Nové Mesto (nô′vā myĕs′tō) Czech.	48.47 N	17.49 E
	Nové Zámky, see Érsekújvar, Hung.		
130	Novgorod (nôv′gô-rôt) . . . Sov. Un.	58.32 N	31.18 E
130	Novgorod (Dist.) . . . . Sov. Un.	58.30 N	32.30 E
131	Novgorod-Seversk (syĕ′vĕrsk) Sov. Un.	52.1 N	33.16 E
128	Novi (nô′vê) . . . . It.	44.45 N	8.49 E
131	Novi Bug (nô′vê bŏŏg′) . . Sov. Un.	47.41 N	32.30 E
131	Novie Senzhary (nô′vyȧ sĕn′zhȧ-rê) . . . Sov. Un.	49.18 N	34.18 E
128	Novi Grad (nô′vê gräd′) . . . . Yugo.	44.11 N	15.34 E
79	Novinger (nŏv′ĭn-jẽr) . . . . Mo.	40.14 N	92.43 W
131	Novi Oskol (nô′vê ôs-kôl′) Sov. Un.	50.46 N	57.52 E
129	Novi Pazar (nô′vê pȧ-zär′) . . Yugo.	43.7 N	20.31 E
129	Novi Sad (nô′vê säd′) . . . . . . Yugo.	45.16 N	19.51 E
131	Novo-Aidar (nô′vô-ī-där′) Sov. Un.	48.57 N	38.59 E
131	Novo Belaya (nô′vô byĕ′lȧ-yȧ) Sov. Un.	49.52 N	39.29 E
131	Novo Belenkaya (nô′vô byĕl-ĕŋ′-kȧ-yȧ) . . . Sov. Un.	49.44 N	39.5 E
131	Novocherkassk (nô′vô-chĕr-kȧsk′) Sov. Un.	47.25 N	40.5 E
140	Novo Lisboa (Huambo) (nô′vŏŏ lēzh bō′ȧ) (hwäm′bō) . Ang.	12.45 S	15.47 E
128	Novo Mesto (nô′vô mās′tô) . Yugo.	45.47 N	15.12 E
131	Novo Minskaya (nô′vô mên′skȧ-yȧ) . . . Sov. Un.	46.18 N	38.51 E
131	Novomirgorod (nô′vô-mēr′gô-rôt) Sov. Un.	48.46 N	31.42 E
131	Novomoskovsk (nô′vô-môs-kôfsk′) Sov. Un.	48.37 N	35.15 E
140	Novo Redondo (nô′vŏŏ rȧ-dôn′dŏŏ) Ang.	11.13 S	13.54 E
131	Novorossiisk (nô′vô-rô-sēsk′) Sov. Un.	44.42 N	37.48 E
130	Novorshev (nô′vô-rzhôf′) Sov. Un.	57.2 N	29.18 E
129	Novo-selo (nô′vô-sā′lô) . . . . Bul.	44.7 N	22.45 E
131	Novo Shcherbinovskaya (nô′vô shchĕr-bê-nôf′skȧ-yȧ) . . . Sov. Un.	46.27 N	38.32 E
148	Novo-Sibirsk (nô′vô-sê-bērsk′) Sov. Un.	55.10 N	82.59 E
130	Novosil (nô-vô-sēl′) . . . . . . Sov. Un.	52.58 N	37.1 E
130	Novo Sokolniki (nô′vô sô-kôl′nê-kê) Sov. Un.	56.18 N	30.2 E
148	Novo-Turukhansk (nô′vô-tōō-rōō-ĸänsk′) . . . Sov. Un.	65.55 N	88.30 E
131	Novo-Ukrainka (nô′vô-ōō-krä′ēn-kȧ) . . . Sov. Un.	48.17 N	31.32 E
131	Novoukrainsk (nô′vô-ōō-krä′ênsk) Sov. Un.	48.28 N	31.30 E
113	Novouzensk (nô′vô-ŏŏ-zĕnsk′) Sov. Un.	50.32 N	48.12 E
130	Novozybkov (nô′vô-zêp′kôf) Sov. Un.	52.32 N	31.53 E
122	Nový Bydžov (nô′vē bĕ′jôf)Czech.	50.14 N	15.30 E
	Novy Jičín, see Neu Titschein, Pol.		
79	Nowata (nô-wä′tȧ) . . . . Okla.	36.43 N	95.37 W
122	Nowawes (nō′vä-vĕs) . . . . Ger.	52.23 N	13.4 E
166	Nowingi (nô-wĭng′ĭ) . . . . Austl.	34.30 S	142.9 E
123	Nowogródek (nō′vō-grŏŏ′dĕk) . Pol.	53.36 N	25.51 E
167	Nowra (nou′rȧ) . . . . Austl.	34.52 S	150.38 E
123	Nowy Dwór (nô′vê dvŏŏr′) . . . Pol.	52.27 N	20.47 E
123	Nowy Sacz (nô′vê sôɴch) . . . . Pol.	49.37 N	20.43 E
123	Nowy Targ (nô′vê tärk) . . . . . . Pol.	49.29 N	20.1 E
82	Noxubee R. (nŏks′û-bē).Miss.-Ala.	33.0 N	88.28 W
126	Noya (nō′yä) . . . . Sp.	42.46 N	8.54 W
127	Noya R. . . . . Sp. (In.)	41.27 N	1.45 E
124	Noyon (nwȧ-yôɴ′) . . . . Fr.	49.37 N	3.0 E
143	Nqamakwe (′n-gä-mä′kwȧ) U. S. Afr.	32.9 S	27.58 E
143	Nqutu (′n-kōō′tōō) . . . . . U. S. Afr.	28.12 S	30.41 E
139	Nubian Des. (nōō′bĭ-ăn)A. E. Sud.	21.0 N	34.0 E
80	Nueces R. (nû-ā′sȧs) . . . . Tex.	28.30 N	99.40 W
54	Nuelton L. (nwĕl′tĭn) . . . . Can.	60.15 N	95.30 W
94	Nueva Armenia (nwā′vä är-mā′nê-ȧ) . Hond.	15.50 N	86.40 W
96	Nueva Gerona (nwā′vä ĸȧ-rō′nä) Isle of Pines	21.51 N	82.41 W
99	Nueva Palmira (nwā′vä päl-mē′ rä) . Ur. (Buenos Aires In.)	33.52 S	58.23 W
94	Nueva San Salvador (Santa Tecla) (nwā′vä sän′säl-vȧ-dōr′)Sal.	13.41 N	89.17 W
104	Nueve de Julio (nwā′vȧ dā hōō-lyô) . Arg.	35.30 S	61.00 W
96	Nuevitas (nwā-vē′tȧs) . . . . . . Cuba	21.34 N	77.16 W
96	Nuevitas B. . . . . Cuba	21.34 N	77.14 W
80	Nuevo Laredo (nwā′vō lȧ-rā′dhō) Mex.	27.29 N	99.30 W

ăt; finăl; rāte; senâte; ärm; ȧsk; sofȧ; fâre; ch-choose; dh-as th in other; bē; êvent; bĕt; recĕnt; cratẽr; g-go; gh-gutteral g; bĭt; ĭ-short neutral; rīde; ĸ-gutteral k as ch in German ich;

Page	Name Pronunciation Region	Lat. °′	Long. °′
80	Nuevo Leon (State) (nwā'vō lā-ōn')..Mex.	26.0 N	100.0 W
142	Nuganib R. (nōō'gȧ-nĕb) S. W. Afr.	27.5 S	17.28 E
153	Nuichwangcheng (Yinkow) (nu'-chwäng-chêng) Manch.	40.57 N	122.30 E
124	Nuits-St. George (nwē'săɴ-zhôrzh') Fr.	47.10 N	5.0 E
113	Nukha (nōō'ᴋä)..........Sov. Un.	41.15 N	47.12 E
52	Nulato (nōō-lä'tō)...........Alsk.	64.40 N	158.15 W
127	Nules (nōō'lås)...............Sp.	39.53 N	0.11 W
164	Nullarbor Plain (nŭ-lär'bôr).Austl.	30.45 S	130.40 E
164	Nullarbor Region..........Austl.	31.15 S	128.0 E
159	Numasu (nōō'mä-sōō) ....Jap.	35.8 N	138.52 E
120	Nummedalslaagen (R.) (nōōm'ĕ-dȧls-lôgh'ĕn).Nor.	60.0 N	9.18 E
167	Numurkah (nōō-mōōr'kȧ)...Austl.	36.5 S	145.26 E
118	Nuneaton (nŭn'ē-tŭn)...Gt. Brit.	52.30 N	1.30 W
57	Nun I. (nōōn).Can. (Montreal In.)	45.28 N	73.33 W
54	Nunivak (nōō'nĭ-văk).......Can.	68.15 N	135.20 W
53	Nunivak I.................Alsk.	60.5 N	166.30 W
153	Nünkiang (Mergen) (nün'kyäng') (mĕr'gĕn).Manch.	49.20 N	125.27 E
128	Nuoro (nwô'rō)............Sard.	40.20 N	9.19 E
148	Nur Ata (nōō-rȧ ät'ȧ)....Sov. Un.	40.30 N	65.30 E
148	Nura R. (nōō'rä).........Sov. Un.	50.0 N	74.0 E
122	Nürnberg (nürn'bĕrgh)......Ger.	49.27 N	11.5 E
122	Nürschan (Ny'řany) (nür'shän) (nĕrzh'ȧ-nĕ).Ger.	49.43 N	13.13 E
97	Nurse Cay (I.)............Ba. Is.	22.28 N	75.50 W
113	Nusaybin (nōō'sī-bĕn).......Tur.	37.5 N	41.10 E
151	Nushki (nŭsh'kê)...........India	29.29 N	66.0 E
85	Nutter Fort (nŭt'ĕr)......W. Va.	39.14 N	80.18 W
53	Nutzotin Mts. (nōōt'zô-tĭn) Alsk.-Can.	62.0 N	141.0 W
166	Nyang (nyäng)............Austl.	35.12 S	141.54 E
140	Nyangwe (nyäng'wâ)...Bel. Cong.	4.15 S	26.15 E
140	Nyassa L. (nyä'sä)..........Afr.	12.0 S	34.30 E
140	Nyasaland (nyä'sä-lănd).....Afr.	13.0 S	34.0 E
138	Nyasso (nyä'sō)......Fr. W. Afr.	14.47 N	4.46 W
120	Nyborg (nü'bôr")...........Den.	55.19 N	10.45 E
120	Nybro (nü'brô).............Swe.	56.44 N	15.56 E
120	Nyhem (nü'hĕm)...........Swe.	56.39 N	12.51 E
123	Nyíregyháza (nyē'rĕd-y'-hä'zô) Hung.	47.58 N	21.44 E
120	Nykōbing Fl. (nü'kû-bĭng)...Den.	54.45 N	11.54 E
120	Nykōbing S..................Den.	55.55 N	11.40 E
120	Nykōbing....................Den.	56.46 N	8.48 E
120	Nyköping (nü'chû-pĭng).....Swe.	58.46 N	17.0 E
119	Nylen (nē'lĕn)...Bel. (Anvers In.)	51.10 N	4.40 E
140	Nylstroom (nĭl'strōm)...U. S. Afr.	24.42 S	28.18 E
167	Nymagee (nī-mȧ-gē').......Austl.	32.2 S	146.19 E
169	Nymboida R. (nĭm-bô-ē'dȧ) Austl. (In.)	29.40 S	152.31 E
122	Nymburk (nĕm'bōōrk).....Czech.	50.11 N	15.2 E
77	Nymore (nī'mōr)..........Minn.	47.27 N	94.50 W
120	Nynäshamn (nü-nĕs-hȧm'n)..Swe.	58.54 N	17.58 E
167	Nyngan (nĭŋ'gȧn)..........Austl.	31.33 S	147.12 E
122	Nyon (nē-ôɴ')............Switz.	46.23 N	6.13 E
138	Nyong R. (nyông)..........Cam.	3.35 N	11.0 E
167	Nyora ('n-yō'rȧ)..........Austl.	38.19 S	145.40 E
	Nýřany, see Nürschan, Ger.		
131	Nystad (Uusikaupunki) (nü'stȧd) (ōō'sê-kou'pōōŋ-kĭ)...Fin.	60.49 N	21.28 E
149	Nyuya R. (nyōō'yȧ).....Sov. Un.	60.50 N	115.0 E
173	Oahu (I.) (ō-ä'hōō) (ō-ā'hû)..Haw.	21.25 N	158.0 W
56	Oak Bluff....Can. (Winnipeg In.)	49.47 N	97.20 W
78	Oak Creek (ōk-krēk').......Colo.	40.18 N	106.57 W
74	Oakdale (ōk'dāl)...........Calif.	37.45 N	120.52 W
84	Oakdale.....................Ky.	38.14 N	85.51 W
81	Oakdale.....................La.	30.49 N	92.39 W
89	Oakdale......Pa. (Pittsburgh In.)	40.24 N	80.12 W
82	Oakdale....................Tenn.	35.59 N	84.32 W
118	Oakengates (ōk'ĕn-gāts)..Gt. Brit.	52.41 N	2.27 W
76	Oakes (ōks)................N. D.	46.9 N	98.4 W
86	Oakfield (ōk'fēld)............Me.	46.8 N	68.10 W
73	Oak Flat..Calif. (Los Angeles In.)	34.14 N	117.18 W
88	Oak Forest......Ill. (Chicago In.)	41.36 N	87.44 W
118	Oakham (ōk'ăm)........Gt. Brit.	52.40 N	0.43 W
56	Oak HammockCan. (Winnipeg In.)	50.8 N	97.3 W
84	Oakharbor (ōk'här'bĕr)......Ohio	41.31 N	83.8 W
49	Oak Harbor...Wash. (Seattle In.)	48.17 N	122.38 W
77	Oak I.......................Wis.	46.55 N	90.45 W
74	Oakland (ōk'lănd)..........Calif.	37.48 N	122.15 W
79	Oakland....................Kan.	39.4 N	95.40 W
76	Oakland....................Neb.	41.51 N	96.27 W
84	Oakland City...............Ind.	38.20 N	87.22 W
167	Oaklands..................Austl.	35.34 S	146.9 E
169	Oakleigh (ōk'lê)...........Austl.	37.53 S	145.5 E
169	Oakley..............Austl. (In.)	27.24 S	151.42 E
71	Oakley (ōk'lĭ)...............Ida.	42.14 N	113.53 W
78	Oakley......................Kan.	39.6 N	100.49 W
82	Oakman (ōk'măn)...........Ala.	33.42 N	87.22 W
89	Oakmont (ōk'mŏnt) Pa. (Pittsburgh In.)	40.31 N	79.51 W
79	Oak Park.....................Ill.	41.53 N	87.43 W
81	Oakwood (ōk'wōōd).........Tex.	31.38 N	95.50 W
171	Oamaru (ô-ä'mä-rōō).......N. Z.	45.7 S	171.2 E
46	Oates Land (Reg.) (ōts).....Ant.	68.0 S	160.0 E
169	Oatlands (ōt'lăndz)Austl.(Tas. In.)	42.19 S	147.23 E
75	Oatman (ōt'măn)...........Ariz.	35.3 N	114.23 W
93	Oaxaca (State) (wä-hä'kä) ..Mex.	17.0 N	96.0 W
93	Oaxaca.....................Mex.	17.4 N	96.43 W
93	Oaxaca, Sierra de (Mts.)....Mex.	16.20 N	97.20 W
159	Obama (ō'bȧ-mä)...........Jap.	35.30 N	135.44 E
116	Oban (ō'băn)...........Gt. Brit.	45.25 N	5.30 W
161	Obando (ō-bän'dō) P. I. (Manila In.)	14.43 N	120.55 E
86	ObatogamauL.(ō-bȧ-tō'găm-ô) Can.	49.35 N	74.30 W
141	Obbia (ôb'byä)........It. E. Afr.	5.25 N	48.25 E
148	Obdorsk, see Sale Khard, Sov. Un.		
122	Oberhausen (ō'bĕr-hou'zĕn)...Ger.	51.30 N	6.49 E
122	Oberhollabrünn (ō'bĕr-hō'lä-brün) Ger.	48.34 N	16.4 E
78	Oberlin (ō'bĕr-lĭn)..........Kan.	39.48 N	100.31 W
84	Oberlin.....................Ohio	41.17 N	82.12 W
125	Obernai (ô-bĕr-nĕ')..........Fr.	48.30 N	7.30 E
167	Oberon (ō'bĕr-ŏn).........Austl.	33.43 S	149.52 E
148	Ob, G. of (ôp)..........Sov. Un.	69.0 N	73.30 E
103	Óbidos (ō'bê-dōōzh).........Braz.	1.59 S	55.30 W
161	Obi Is. (ō'bê)..........Neth. Ind.	1.30 S	127.45 E
82	Obion R. (ô-bī'ŏn).........Tenn.	36.10 N	89.20 W
82	Obion R., North Fork......Tenn.	36.26 N	88.40 W
82	Obion R., South Fork......Tenn.	36.5 N	88.45 W
161	Obira I. (ô-bē'rä)......Neth. Ind.	1.50 S	127.35 E
131	Obitochnaya, C. (ô-bē-tôch'-nȧ-yȧ).Sov. Un.	46.31 N	36.8 E
141	Obock (ō-bŏk)..........Fr. Som.	12.0 N	43.17 E
130	Obol R. (ô-bŏl')........Sov. Un.	55.25 N	29.32 E
131	Oboyan (ô-bô-yȧn') .....Sov. Un.	5.12 N	36.18 E
148	Ob' R. (ôp) ....Sov. Un.	61.20 N	70.0 E
49	O'Brien (ô-brī'ĕn) Wash. (Seattle In.)	47.25 N	122.15 W
131	Obukhov (ō'bōō-ᴋof).....Sov. Un.	50.7 N	30.35 E
83	Ocala (ô-kä'lȧ)...............Fla.	29.11 N	82.10 W
92	Ocampo (ô-käm'pō).........Mex.	22.50 N	99.20 W
102	Ocaña (ô-kän'yä)............Col.	8.0 N	73.30 W
126	Ocaña.......................Sp.	39.57 N	3.30 W
102	Occidental, Cordillera (Mts.) (ôk-sê-dĕn-täl').Col.	5.0 N	76.30 W
97	Ocean Bight..............Ba. Is.	21.15 N	73.15 W
85	Ocean City.................Md.	38.20 N	75.7 W
85	Ocean City.................N. J.	39.17 N	74.37 W
85	Ocean Grove...............N. J.	40.12 N	74.0 W
174	Oceania (ō-shê-ăn'ĭ-ă).....Pac. O.		
56	Oceanic (ō-shê-ăn'ĭk) Can. (Prince Rupert In.)	54.7 N	130.15 W
73	Ocean Park Calif.(Los Angeles In.)	33.59 N	118.29 W
74	Oceanside (ō'shăn-sīd)......Calif.	33.10 N	117.21 W
82	Ocean Springs.............Miss.	30.25 N	88.49 W
89	Ocean View.....Va. (Norfolk In.)	36.57 N	76.15 W
131	Ochakov (ô-chä'kôf).....Sov. Un.	46.37 N	31.31 E
82	Ochlockonee R. (ŏk-lô-kō'nē) Fla.-Ga.	30.36 N	84.20 W
119	Ochsenwärder (ôk'sĕn-vâr'dĕr) Ger. (Hamburg In.)	53.29 N	10.6 E
82	Ocilla (ô-sĭl'ȧ)...............Ga.	31.36 N	83.18 W
120	Ockelbo (ôk'ĕl-bô)..........Swe.	60.54 N	16.39 E
82	Ocmulgee R. (ôk-mŭl'gē).....Ga.	32.40 N	83.35 W
123	Ocna-Sibiului (ōk'nȧ-sê-byōō'lōō-ê).Rom.	45.53 N	24.3 E
129	Ocnele-Mari (ōk'nĕ-lĕ-mä'rê)Rom.	45.4 N	24.19 E
97	Ocoa B. (ô-kō'ȧ)......Dom. Rep.	18.25 N	70.38 W
82	Oconee R. (ô-kō'nē)..........Ga.	33.0 N	83.10 W
77	Oconomowoc (ô-kŏn'ô-mô-wŏk') Wis.	43.7 N	88.29 W
77	Oconto (ô-kŏn'tō)...........Wis.	44.54 N	87.52 W
77	Oconto Falls................Wis.	44.53 N	88.10 W
77	Oconto R....................Wis.	45.5 N	88.22 W
94	Ocós (ô-kōs')..............Guat.	14.33 N	92.12 W
94	Ocotal (ō-kô-täl')............Nic.	13.45 N	86.30 W
93	Ocotepec, Cerro (Mt.) (ô-kō-tâ-pĕk').Mex. (In.)	19.22 N	98.49 W
94	Ocotepeque (ô-kō-tâ-pā'kâ).Hond.	14.26 N	89.12 W
92	Ocotlán (ō-kô-tlän')..........Mex.	20.20 N	102.45 W
93	Ocotlán de Morelos (dā-mô-rā'lōs).Mex.	16.48 N	96.41 W
93	Ocozingo (ō-kō-zĭŋ'gō)......Mex.	17.3 N	92.12 W
93	Ocozocoautla (ô-kō'zô-kwä-ōō'tlä) Mex.	16.46 N	93.22 W
124	Octeville (ôkt'vēl')...........Fr.	49.35 N	1.35 W
102	Ocumare del Tuy (ō-kōō-mä'rā del twē').Ven.	10.2 N	66.45 W
110	Odádahraun (Plat.) (ō-dä'dhȧ-hroun').Ice.	65.20 N	17.20 W
159	Odawara (ō'dȧ-wä'rä)........Jap.	35.15 N	139.10 E
120	Odda (ôdh-ȧ)................Nor.	60.3 N	6.33 E
110	Oddi (ôdh'ē).................Ice.	63.43 N	20.20 W
76	Odebolt (ō'dê-bōlt)............Ia.	42.20 N	95.15 W
126	Odemira (ō-dâ-mē'rȧ).......Port.	37.36 N	8.39 W
113	Ödemiş (û'dĕ-mēsh).........Tur.	38.12 N	28.0 E
143	Odendaalsrust (ō'dĕn-däls-rûst') U. S. Afr.	27.51 S	26.51 E
120	Odense (ō'dhĕn-sĕ)..........Den.	55.23 N	10.22 E
73	Odenville (ō'dĕn-vĭl) Ala. (Birmingham In.)	33.41 N	86.24 W
122	Oder R. (ō'dĕr).............Ger.	51.50 N	15.43 E
80	Odessa (ô-dĕs'ȧ)............Tex.	31.51 N	102.21 W
131	Odessa (ô-dyĕs'ä)........Sov. Un.	46.27 N	30.48 E
70	Odessa (ô-dĕs'ȧ)...........Wash.	47.20 N	118.42 W
126	Odiel R. (ō-dē-ēl')............Sp.	37.30 N	6.56 W
138	Odienné (ō-dê-ĕn-nā')..Fr. W. Afr.	9.48 N	7.32 W
163	Odiongan (ō-dê-ôŋ'gän)......P. I.	12.24 N	121.59 E
127	Odivellas (ō-dê-vā'lyäs).Port. (In.)	38.48 N	9.10 W
123	Odobeşti (ō-dô-bĕsh't')......Rom.	45.46 N	27.5 E
149	Odoma R. (ō'dô-mȧ).....Sov. Un.	59.45 N	138.0 E
158	Odomari (ō'dô-mȧ'rē).......Kar.	46.38 N	142.45 E
80	O'Donnell (ō-dŏn'ĕl).........Tex.	32.57 N	101.50 W
123	Odorhei (ō'dôr-hā).........Rom.	46.18 N	25.17 E
103	Oeirás (ô-â'ê-räzh')..........Braz.	7.10 S	42.2 W
127	Oeirás...............Port. (In.)	38.42 N	9.19 W
119	Oeleghem (ōō'lĕgh-ĕm) Bel. (Anvers In.)	51.13 N	4.36 E
123	Oels (ûls)...................Ger.	51.12 N	17.23 E
122	Oelsnitz (ûl'snēts)...........Ger.	50.26 N	12.11 E
122	Oelsnitz....................Ger.	50.42 N	12.43 E
77	Oelwein (ōl'wīn)..............Ia.	42.41 N	91.55 W
71	O'Fallon Cr. (ō-făl'ŭn).....Mont.	46.30 N	104.50 W
128	Ofanto R. (ô-fän'tō)...........It.	41.10 N	15.55 E
122	Offenbach (ôf'ĕn-bäᴋ)........Ger.	50.6 N	8.45 E
122	Offenburg (ôf'ĕn-bōōrgh).....Ger.	48.27 N	7.57 E
110	Öfvertorneå (ûf'ĕr-tōr'nĕ-ô)...Swe.	66.18 N	23.35 E
159	Oga (ō'gȧ).......Jap. (Osaka In.)	34.49 N	135.6 E
159	Ogaki (ō'gä-kê)..............Jap.	35.22 N	136.32 E
76	Ogallala (ō-gä-lä'lä).........Neb.	41.8 N	101.41 W
7	Ogasawara Is. (ô-gä'sȧ-wä'rȧ) Pac. O.	28.0 N	141.30 E
138	Ogbomosho (ŏg-bô-mō'shō)...Nig.	8.7 N	4.9 E
77	Ogden (ŏg'dĕn)................Ia.	42.1 N	94.1 W
71	Ogden.....................Utah	41.14 N	111.59 W
73	Ogden Pk. Utah (Salt Lake City In.)	41.12 N	111.53 W
73	Ogden R. Utah (Salt Lake City In.)	41.15 N	111.53 W
73	Ogden R., Middle Fork Utah (Salt Lake City In.)	41.18 N	111.44 W
73	Ogden R., North Fork Utah (Salt Lake City In.)	41.23 N	111.53 W
73	Ogden R., South Fork Utah (Salt Lake City In.)	41.16 N	111.40 W
85	Ogdensburg (ŏg'dĕnz-bûrg)...Can.	44.41 N	75.30 W
83	Ogeechee R. (ô-gē'chē).......Ga.	32.48 N	82.0 W
53	Ogilvie (ō'g'l-vĭ)............Can.	63.20 N	129.30 W
79	Oglesby (ō'g'lz-bĭ)............Ill.	41.16 N	89.4 W
128	Oglio R. (ōl'yō)...............It.	45.10 N	10.20 E
88	Ogontz (ō'gŏnts) Pa. (Philadelphia In.)	40.4 N	75.8 W
140	Ogowe R. (ō-gô-wā')..Fr. Eq. Afr.	0.10 S	11.30 E
128	Ogulin (ō-gōō-lēn').........Yugo.	45.18 N	15.12 E
170	Ohakune (ô-hä'kōō-nê)......N. Z.	39.23 S	175.27 E
170	Ohariu R. (ô-hä'rê-ōō)..N. Z. (In.)	41.14 S	174.45 E
170	Ohau B. (ō-hä'ōō).....N. Z. (In.)	41.14 S	174.41 E
171	Ohau L.....................N. Z.	44.15 S	169.55 E
170	Ohau Pt..............N. Z. (In.)	41.14 S	174.40 E
84	Ohio (State) (ô'hī'ō).........U. S.	40.20 N	82.40 W
59	Ohio R......................U. S.	37.45 N	87.45 W
123	Ohlau (ō'lou)................Ger.	50.57 N	17.17 E
83	Ohoopee R. (ô-hōō'pē)........Ga.	32.30 N	82.30 W
129	Ohrid (ō'ᴋrēd)..............Yugo.	41.7 N	20.49 E
129	Ohrid, L..............Yugo.-Alb.	41.0 N	20.45 E
170	Ohura (ô-hōō'rä)...........N. Z.	38.55 S	175.3 E
159	Oigawa R. (ō'ê-gä'wȧ).......Jap.	35.10 N	138.10 E
85	Oil City......................Pa.	41.26 N	79.43 W
72	Oil Cr......Colo. (Colo. Sprs. In.)	38.38 N	105.13 W
7	Oil Is.....................Ind. O.	76.0 S	72.20 E
149	Oimekon (ô'ê-mĕ-kôn)....Sov. Un.	63.15 N	142.55 E
148	Oirat (Aut. Ter.) (ō-ē'rȧt) Sov. Un.	51.10 N	87.0 E
148	Oirat-Tura (Ulala) (tōō'rä) Sov. Un.	52.15 N	85.59 E
124	Oise R. (wäz)..................Fr.	49.25 N	2.40 E
158	Oita (ō'ê-tä)................Jap.	33.14 N	131.35 E
119	Öjendorf (û'yĕn-dôrf) Ger. (Hamburg In.)	53.33 N	10.8 E
120	Öjer, L. (û'yĕr)..............Nor.	59.50 N	11.0 E
159	Oji (ō'jê)........Jap. (Tokyo In.)	35.45 N	139.45 E
80	Ojinaga (ō-ᴋê-nä'gä)........Mex.	29.35 N	104.25 W
93	Ojitlán (San Lucas) (ōᴋê-tlän') Mex.	18.4 N	96.23 W
92	Ojo Caliente (ō'ᴋō käl-yĕn'tā) Mex.	21.52 N	100.43 W
92	Ojocaliente...................Mex.	22.38 N	102.14 W
96	Ojo del Toro, Pico (Pk.) (ō'ᴋō dĕl tō'rō).Cuba	19.57 N	77.29 W
170	Okahu (ô-kä'hōō)......N. Z. (In.)	36.51 S	174.50 E
140	Okakandja (ō'kä-kän'jä)S. W. Afr.	21.58 S	16.58 E
82	Okalona (ō-kȧ-lō'nȧ)........Miss.	33.59 N	88.44 W
158	Okamoya (ō'kȧ-mō'yȧ).......Jap.	36.0 N	138.0 E
54	Okanagan L. (ō'kȧ-näg'ȧn)...Can.	50.0 N	119.30 W
70	Okanogan...................Wash.	48.30 N	119.35 W
70	Okanogan R..................Wash.	48.30 N	119.30 W
138	Okano R. (ô'kä'nō)...Fr. Eq. Afr.	0.30 N	11.30 E
148	Oka R. (ô-kȧ')........Sov. Un.	54.0 N	102.0 E
130	Oka R..................Sov. Un.	54.52 N	39.40 E
82	Okatibbee Cr. (ō'kä-tĭb'ē)...Miss.	32.30 N	88.48 W
140	Okavango R. (ō'kä-väŋ'gō)...Afr.	18.0 S	20.50 E
140	Okavango Swamp..........Bech.	19.30 S	23.0 E
159	Okaya (ō'kȧ-yȧ)..............Jap.	36.4 N	138.1 E
159	Okayama (ō'kȧ-yä'mȧ).......Jap.	34.40 N	133.51 E
159	Okazaki (ō'kȧ-zä'kê).........Jap.	35.0 N	137.12 E
83	Okeechobee (ō-kê-chō'bē)Fla. (In.)	27.16 N	80.48 W
83	Okeechobee, L..........Fla. (In.)	27.0 N	80.50 W
78	Okeene (ô-kēn')............Okla.	36.7 N	98.19 W
83	Okefenokee Swamp (ō'kê-fê-nō'kē) Ga.	30.50 N	82.20 W
79	Okemah (ô-kē'mä)..........Okla.	35.25 N	96.18 W
149	Okhotsk (ô-ᴋôtsk').......Sov. Un.	59.25 N	143.20 E
149	Okhotsk, Sea of.........Sov. Un.	55.0 N	150.0 E
159	Oki I. (ō'kê)................Jap.	36.15 N	133.15 E
159	Oki Is......................Jap.	36.15 N	133.10 E
158	Okinawa I. (ō'kê-nä'wȧ) Ryukyu Is. (In.)	26.30 N	128.0 E
158	Okinawa Guntō (Is.) (ō'kī-nä'wȧ gōōn'tō').Ryukyu Is. (In.)	26.30 N	128.0 E
158	Okinoerabu I. (ō-kē'nô-â-rä'bōō) Jap. (In.)	27.28 N	128.40 E
78	Oklahoma (State) (ŏ-klȧ-hō'mȧ) U. S.	35.50 N	97.30 W
79	Oklahoma City.............Okla.	35.28 N	97.31 W
83	Oklawaha R. (ŏk-lȧ-wô'hô)....Fla.	29.10 N	82.0 W
79	Okmulgee (ok-mŭl'gē).......Okla.	35.36 N	95.58 W
79	Okolona (ō-kô-lō'nȧ)........Miss.	33.59 N	88.41 W
159	Okushiri I. (ō'kōō-shē'rê).....Jap.	42.15 N	139.30 E
73	Ola (ō'lȧ).......Ga. (Atlanta In.)	33.26 N	84.3 W
149	Ola (ō-lȧ').............Sov. Un.	59.35 N	151.10 E
173	Olaa (ō'lä'ä)...............Haw.	19.35 N	155.0 W
49	Olalla (ō-lä'lȧ).Wash. (Seattle In.)	47.25 N	122.33 W
94	Olanchito (ō'län-chē'tō)....Hond.	15.28 N	86.36 W
120	Öland (I.) (û-länd')..........Swe.	56.45 N	16.40 E
166	Olary (ō-lâ'rĭ).............Austl.	32.18 S	140.20 E
79	Olathe (ô-lā'thê)............Kan.	38.53 N	94.49 W
104	Olavarría (ō-lä-vär-rē'ä)......Arg.	36.59 S	60.25 W
96	Old Bahama Channel (bȧ-hā'mȧ) W. I.	22.20 N	77.40 W
118	Oldbury (ōld'bĕr-ĭ)......Gt. Brit.	52.30 N	2.1 W
126	Old Castile (Castilla la Vieja) (Prov.) (kăs-tēl') (käs-tēl'yä lä vyä'hä).Sp.	41.40 N	3.40 W
122	Oldenburg (State) (ôl'dĕn-bōōrgh) Ger.	52.55 N	8.3 E

ng-sing; ŋ-baŋk; ɴ-nasalized n; nŏd; cŏmmit; ōld; ôbey; ôrder; fōōd; fŏŏt; ou-out; s-soft; sh-dish; th-thin; pūre; ûnite; ûrn; stŭd; circŭs; ü-as "y" in study; '-indeterminate vowel.

Page	Name Pronunciation Region	Lat. °′	Long. °′
122	Oldenburg ... Ger.	53.7 N	8.12 E
119	Oldenfelde (ôl′dĕn-fĕlt′ĕ) Ger. (Hamburg In.)	53.37 N	10.9 E
85	Old Forge (ōld fôrj) ... Pa.	41.20 N	75.48 W
116	Oldham (ōld′ȧm) ... Gt. Brit.	53.30 N	2.10 W
89	Old Harbor Is. La. (New Orleans In.)	29.45 N	89.3 W
166	Old Man Plain ... Austl.	34.45 S	144.50 E
95	Old Providence I. ... W. I.	12.21 N	81.21 W
81	Old R. ... Tex. (In.)	29.52 N	94.50 W
86	Old Town ... Me.	44.57 N	68.40 W
85	Olean (ō-lê-ăn′) ... N. Y.	42.5 N	78.25 W
126	Oleiros (ô-lā′rōs) ... Sp.	43.20 N	8.20 W
149	Olekma R. (ô-lyĕk-mȧ′) .. Sov. Un.	55.20 N	120.0 E
149	Olekminsk (ô-lyĕk-mênsk′) Sov. Un.	60.30 N	120.40 E
149	Olenek R. (ô-lyĕ-nyôk′) .. Sov. Un.	70.0 N	120.40 E
124	Oleron, Ile d′ (ēl′ dō lā-rôN′) ... Fr.	46.0 N	1.20 W
127	Olesa de Montserrat (ô-lā′sä dā mōnt-sā-rät′) . Sp. (In.)	41.32 N	1.53 E
149	Olga (ôl′gȧ) ... Sov. Un.	43.45 N	135.25 E
158	Olga B. ... Sov. Un.	43.43 N	135.10 E
131	Olgopol (ôl-gô-pôl′y′) ... Sov. Un.	48.11 N	29.26 E
126	Olhão (ôl-youN′) ... Port.	37.1 N	7.51 W
142	Olifants Mts. (ŏl′ĭ-fănts) . U. S. Afr.	32.25 S	18.55 E
142	Olifants R. ... U. S. Afr.	32.0 S	18.48 E
140	Olifants R. ... U. S. Afr.-Moz.	24.0 S	31.15 E
92	Olinalá (ô-lē-nä-lä′) ... Mex.	17.45 N	98.48 W
73	Olinda (ô-lĭn′dȧ) Calif. (Los Angeles In.)	33.55 N	117.50 W
127	Oliva (ô-lē′vä) ... Sp.	38.55 N	0.7 W
126	Oliva de Jérez (ô-lē′vä dā hā′rāth) Sp.	38.17 N	6.55 W
127	Olivaes (ô-lê-vä′ĕzh) ... Port. (In.)	38.46 N	9.6 W
84	Olive Hill (ŏl′ĭv) ... Ky.	38.17 N	83.10 W
126	Olivenza (ō-lê-vĕn′thä) ... Sp.	38.42 N	7.5 W
77	Olivia (ō-lĭv′ê-ȧ) ... Minn.	44.48 N	94.58 W
99	Olivos (ō-lē′vōs) Arg. (Buenos Aires In.)	34.31 S	58.30 W
131	Olkhovets (ôl′Kô-vyĕts′) . Sov. Un.	49.3 N	30.50 E
123	Olkusz (ōl′ko͞osh) ... Pol.	50.16 N	19.40 E
102	Ollague (ô-lyä′gā) ... Chl.	21.2 S	68.15 W
118	Ollerton (ôl′ẽr-tŭn) ... Gt. Brit.	53.12 N	1.2 W
	Olmütz, see Olomouc, Czech.		
118	Olney (ŏl′nĭ) ... Gt. Brit.	52.9 N	0.42 W
88	Olney ... Ill.	38.45 N	88.6 W
49	Olney ... Ore. (Portland In.)	46.5 N	123.44 W
78	Olney ... Tex.	33.24 N	98.43 W
87	Olomanoshibo R. (ō′lô-mȧ′nô-shē′bō). Can.	50.40 N	50.25 W
123	Olomouc (ô′lô-mōts) ... Czech.	49.36 N	17.14 E
124	Oloron-Ste. Marie (ō-lō-rôN′-săNt mȧ-rē′) . Fr.	43.11 N	0.35 W
127	Olot (ô-lōt′) ... Sp.	42.12 N	2.30 E
131	Olshanka (ôl′shȧŋ-kȧ) ... Sov. Un.	48.12 N	30.50 E
131	Olshany (ôl′shȧn-ê) ... Sov. Un.	50.2 N	35.52 E
122	Olten (ôl′tĕn) ... Switz.	47.21 N	7.53 E
129	Oltenia (Prov.) (ôl-tā′nĭ-ȧ) .. Rom.	44.25 N	23.35 E
129	Oltenita (ôl-tā′nĭ-tsȧ) ... Rom.	44.5 N	26.38 E
129	Oltul R. (ôl′to͝ol) ... Rom.	44.30 N	24.10 E
163	Olutanga I. (ō-lo͞o-täng′ä) ... P. I.	7.22 N	122.53 E
126	Olvera (ôl-vā′rä) ... Sp.	36.56 N	5.16 W
123	Olyka (ō-wē′kȧ) ... Pol.	50.42 N	25.50 E
70	Olympia (ô-lĭm′pĭ-ȧ) ... Wash.	47.2 N	122.53 W
70	Olympic Mts. (ô-lĭm′pĭk) ... Wash.	47.52 N	123.40 W
104	Olympio (ô-lēm′pê-o͞o) . Braz. (In.)	22.51 S	42.59 W
129	Olympus, Mt. (ô-lĭm′pŭs) ... Grc.	40.3 N	22.20 E
70	Olympus, Mt. ... Wash.	47.47 N	123.43 W
85	Olyphant (ŏl′ĭ-fănt) ... Pa.	41.27 N	75.39 W
149	Olyutorsk, C. (ô′lyo͞o-tôrsk) Sov. Un.	59.50 N	170.10 E
149	Olyutorskoe (ôl′yo͞o-tôr-skô′yĕ) Sov. Un.	60.25 N	168.20 E
159	Omae, C. (ō′mȧ-å) ... Jap.	34.35 N	138.14 E
116	Omagh (ō′mä) ... Gt. Brit.	54.35 N	7.25 W
76	Omaha (ō′mȧ-hä) ... Neb.	41.17 N	95.57 W
150	Oman (ô-män′) ... Asia	22.0 N	58.30 E
150	Oman, G. of ... Oman	24.30 N	58.45 E
150	Oman, Trucial, see Trucial Coast (Dist.) Oman		
140	Omara R. (ō-mä′rä) Bech.-S. W. Afr.	21.45 S	22.30 E
140	Omaruru (ō-mä-ro͞o′ro͞o). S. W. Afr.	21.28 S	15.55 E
128	Ombrone R. (ôm-brō′nā) ... It.	42.50 N	11.18 E
139	Omdurman (ŏm-do͞or-män′) A. E. Sud.	15.40 N	32.30 E
93	Omealca (ō-må-äl′kō) ... Mex.	18.43 N	96.47 W
92	Ometepec (ô-mā-tå-pĕk′) ... Mex.	16.34 N	98.35 W
159	Omiya (ō′mê-yȧ) ... Jap.	35.57 N	139.38 E
94	Omoa (ô-mō′ä) ... Hond.	15.42 N	88.2 W
149	Omolon R. (ō-mô-lôn′) ... Sov. Un.	66.0 N	160.20 E
139	Omo R. (ō′mō) ... It. E. Afr.	6.30 N	36.30 E
94	Omotepe I. (ō-mô-tā′pā) ... Nic.	11.30 N	85.35 W
77	Omro (ŏm′rō) ... Wis.	44.1 N	88.44 W
148	Omsk (ômsk) ... Sov. Un.	55.15 N	73.25 E
158	Omu (ō′mo͞o′) ... Manch.	43.46 N	128.4 E
159	Omura (ō′mo͞o-rȧ) ... Jap.	32.56 N	129.58 E
112	Omutinsk (ô′mo͞o-tēnsk) . Sov. Un.	58.40 N	52.5 E
148	Ona (Biryusa) R. (ō-nȧ′) (bēr′-yo͞o-sȧ) . Sov. Un.	56.30 N	98.35 E
76	Onawa (ŏn-ȧ-wȧ) ... Ia.	42.4 N	96.5 W
84	Onaway (ŏn′ȧ-wā) ... Mich.	45.24 N	84.14 W
127	Onda (ōn′dä) ... Sp.	39.57 N	0.14 W
123	Ondava R. (ōn′dȧ-vȧ) ... Czech.	48.55 N	21.40 E
142	Onderste Doorns (ōn′dẽr-stĕ dōrns′) . U. S. Afr.	30.11 S	20.36 E
157	Ondin (ōn′dēn′) ... Cho.	37.56 N	125.20 E
112	Onega (ô-nyĕ′gȧ) ... Sov. Un.	63.50 N	38.15 E
112	Onega B. ... Sov. Un.	64.30 N	36.30 E
112	Onega, L. ... Sov. Un.	61.35 N	35.30 E
112	Onega R. ... Sov. Un.	63.15 N	39.15 E
170	Onehunga (ō-nȧ-ho͞on′gä) N. Z. (In.)	36.56 S	174.48 E
85	Oneida (ô-nī′dȧ) ... N. Y.	43.5 N	45.40 W
85	Oneida L. ... N. Y.	43.2 N	76.0 W
76	O′Neill (ō-nēl′) ... Neb.	42.28 N	98.38 W
85	Oneonta (ō-nê-ŏn′tȧ) ... N. Y.	42.27 N	75.7 W
170	Onerahi (ō-nå-rä′hê) ... N. Z.	35.46 S	174.20 E
152	Ongin (ŏn′gĭn′) ... Chn.	45.45 N	102.58 E
152	Ongin Gol (R.) (ŏn′gĭn gôl′) .. Chn.	45.42 N	103.30 E
141	Onitahy R. (ō-nê-tȧ-ē′) ... Madag.	23.28 S	45.0 E
138	Onitsha (ô-nĭt′shȧ) ... Nig.	6.12 N	6.41 E
159	Onomichi (ō′nô-mē′chê) ... Jap.	34.22 N	133.12 E
149	Onon R. (ô′nôn) ... Sov. Un.	50.30 N	115.0 E
164	Onslow (ŏnz′lō) ... Austl.	21.50 S	115.0 E
170	Onslow ... N. Z. (In.)	41.15 S	174.48 E
159	Ontake (Mt.) (ôn′tä-kĕ) ... Jap.	35.55 N	137.30 E
70	Ontario (ŏn-tā′rĭ-ō) ... Ore.	44.3 N	116.59 W
73	Ontario ... Calif. (Los Angeles In.)	34.4 N	117.39 W
55	Ontario (Prov.) ... Can.	50.15 N	89.0 W
85	Ontario, L. ... U. S.-Can.	43.35 N	77.30 W
127	Onteniente (ōn-tå-nyĕn′tā) ... Sp.	38.49 N	0.35 W
77	Ontonagon (ŏn-tô-năg′ŏn) ... Mich.	46.51 N	89.18 W
164	Oodnadatta (o͞od′nȧ-dä′tȧ) .. Austl.	27.30 S	135.32 E
142	O′okiep (ō-kēp′) ... U. S. Afr.	29.34 S	17.50 E
164	Ooldea (o͞ol-dā′ä) ... Austl.	30.30 S	132.0 E
119	Oorderen (ōr′dẽr-ĕn) Bel. (Anvers In.)	51.18 N	4.21 E
142	Oorlogs Kloof (R.) (ōr′lôks klōf′) U. S. Afr.	31.32 S	19.30 E
82	Oostanaula R. (o͞o-stȧ-nô′lȧ). . Ga.	34.25 N	85.5 W
148	Opalikha, see Kupino, Sov. Un.		
123	Opatów (ô-pä′to͝of) ... Pol.	50.47 N	21.25 E
...	Opava, see Troppau, Ger.		
120	Opdal (ôp′däl) ... Nor.	62.39 N	9.40 E
82	Opelika (ŏp-ê-lī′kȧ) ... Ala.	32.38 N	85.23 W
81	Opelousas (ŏp-ē-lo͞o′sȧs) ... La.	30.33 N	92.5 W
85	Opeongo L. (ŏp-ê-ôŋ′gō) ... Can.	45.45 N	78.20 W
52	Ophir (ō′fẽr) ... Alsk.	63.10 N	156.15 W
160	Ophir, Mt. (Talamau) (ō′fẽr) (tä-lä-mä′o͞o) ... Neth. Ind.	0.15 N	99.50 E
94	Opico (ô′pē′kō) ... Sal.	13.49 N	89.23 W
55	Opinaka R. (ŏp-ĭ-nä′kȧ) ... Can.	52.40 N	77.30 W
130	Opochka (ō-pôch′kȧ) ... Sov. Un.	56.42 N	28.40 E
123	Opoczno (ô-pōch′nô) ... Pol.	51.22 N	20.17 E
123	Opole (ô-pôl′å) ... Pol.	51.7 N	21.58 E
131	Oposhnya (ô-pôsh′nyȧ) ... Sov. Un.	49.57 N	34.33 E
170	Opotiki (ô-pō′tĭ-kê) ... N. Z.	38.0 S	177.20 W
82	Opp (ŏp) ... Ala.	31.17 N	86.17 W
123	Oppeln (ôp′ĕln) ... Ger.	50.41 N	17.55 E
170	Opunake (ō-po͞o-nȧ′kê) ... N. Z.	39.25 S	173.52 E
162	Oquendo (ô-kān′dō) ... P. I.	12.8 N	124.32 E
73	Oquirrh Mts. (ō′kwẽr) Utah (Salt Lake City In.)	40.35 N	112.12 W
123	Oradea (ô-räd′yä) ... Rom.	47.3 N	21.55 E
110	Öraefa-Jökull (Mt.) (û′rĕf-å-yû′ko͝ol) . Ice.	64.5 N	16.40 W
138	Oran (ō-rän′) (ô-räN′) ... Alg.	35.45 N	0.38 W
104	Orán ... Arg.	23.10 S	64.20 W
79	Oran (ôr′ȧn) ... Mo.	37.4 N	89.39 W
167	Orange (ŏr′ĕnj) ... Austl.	33.18 S	149.5 E
74	Orange ... Calif.	33.48 N	117.51 W
85	Orange ... Conn.	41.16 N	73.2 W
88	Orange ... N. J. (New York In.)	40.46 N	74.14 W
81	Orange ... Tex.	30.6 N	93.43 W
83	Orangeburg (ŏr′ĕnj-bûrg) ... S. C.	33.30 N	80.50 W
96	Orange Cay (I.) ... Ba. Is.	24.56 N	79.7 W
76	Orange City ... Ia.	43.0 N	96.5 W
143	Orange Free State ... U. S. Afr.	28.20 N	26.40 E
88	Orange Grove. Md. (Baltimore In.)	39.15 N	76.45 W
83	Orange L. ... Fla.	29.25 N	82.10 W
161	Orange Range ... Neth. Ind.	4.30 S	140.0 E
142	Orange R. ... Afr.	29.39 S	22.50 E
143	Orange River ... U. S. Afr.	29.40 S	24.12 E
85	Orangeville (ŏr′ĕnj-vĭl) ... Can.	43.55 N	80.2 W
94	Orange Walk ... Br. Hond. (In.)	18.10 N	88.32 W
162	Orani (ō-rä′nê) ... P. I.	14.48 N	120.32 E
130	Oranienbaum (ô-rä′nê-ĕn-boum) Sov. Un.	59.53 N	29.43 E
122	Oranienburg (ō-rä′nê-ĕn-bo͝orgh) Ger.	52.46 N	13.14 E
162	Oras (ō′räs) ... P. I.	12.9 N	125.27 E
162	Oras B. ... P. I.	12.10 N	125.30 E
129	Oraştie (ô-rûsh′tyå) ... Rom.	45.50 N	23.12 E
128	Orbetello (ôr-bȧ-tĕl′lō) ... It.	42.26 N	11.14 E
126	Orbigo R. (ôr-bē′gō) ... Sp.	42.20 N	5.53 W
167	Orbost (ôr-bōst′) ... Austl.	37.42 S	148.23 E
72	Orcas (ôr′kȧs) Wash. (Vancouver In.)	48.36 N	122.56 W
72	Orcas I. ... Wash. (Vancouver In.)	48.40 N	122.55 W
102	Orchilla I. (ôr-chē′lyä) ... Ven.	11.45 N	66.15 W
76	Ord (ôrd) ... Neb.	41.35 N	98.55 W
126	Órdenes (ōr′då-nās) ... Sp.	43.4 N	8.25 W
75	Ord Peak (ôrd) ... Ariz.	33.57 N	109.36 W
164	Ord R. ... Austl.	17.30 S	128.45 E
113	Ordu (ôr′do͞o) ... Tur.	40.58 N	37.55 E
126	Orduña (ôr-do͞o′nyä) ... Sp.	43.0 N	3.2 W
73	Ordway (ôrd′wā) Calif. (Los Angeles In.)	34.0 N	117.10 W
78	Ordway ... Colo.	38.13 N	103.46 W
113	Ordzhonikidze (Vladikavkaz) (ôrd′zhō-nĭ-kĭd′zĕ) (vlä-dĭ-käf′-käz) . Sov. Un.	43.5 N	44.32 E
131	Ordzhonikidze (Enakievo) Sov. Un.	48.14 N	38.12 E
130	Ordzhonikidzegrad (Bezhitsa) Sov. Un.	53.18 N	34.15 E
120	Örebro (û′rĕ-brō) ... Swe.	59.16 N	15.11 E
77	Oregon (ŏr′ê-gŏn) ... Ill.	42.2 N	89.20 W
70	Oregon (State) ... U. S.	44.10 N	120.0 W
70	Oregon Caves Natl. Mon. ... Ore.	42.5 N	123.0 W
70	Oregon City ... Ore.	45.21 N	122.37 W
120	Öregrund (û′rĕ-gro͝ond) ... Swe.	60.20 N	18.28 E
131	Orekhov (ôr-yĕ′Kôf) ... Sov. Un.	47.33 N	35.50 E
129	Orekhovo (ôr′yĕ′Kô-vô) ... Bul.	43.44 N	23.59 E
130	Orekhovo Zuevo (ôr′yĕ′Kô-vo zo͝o′å-vô) ... Sov. Un.	55.47 N	38.59 E
130	Orel (ôr-yôl′) ... Sov. Un.	52.56 N	36.5 E
130	Orel (Dist.) ... Sov. Un.	52.38 N	37.0 E
131	Orel R. ... Sov. Un.	49.5 N	34.40 E
75	Orem (ŏ′rĕm) ... Utah	40.16 N	111.46 W
122	Ore Mts. (ôr) ... Ger.	50.45 N	13.10 E
113	Orenburg (ô-rĕn-bo͝orgh′) Sov. Un.	51.48 N	55.10 E
126	Orense (ô-rĕn′sā) ... Sp.	42.19 N	7.51 W
120	Öresund (Sd.) (û′rĕ-so͝ond) ... Eur.	55.32 N	12.35 E
171	Oreti R. (ô-rā′tê) ... N. Z.	46.10 S	168.15 E
75	Organ Pipe Cactus National Monument . Ariz.	32.15 N	113.0 W
125	Orgeval (ôrzh-vȧl′) ... Fr. (In.)	48.55 N	1.58 E
131	Orhei (ôr-hā′) ... Rom.	47.22 N	28.49 E
102	Oriental, Cordillera (Mts.) (ō-rê-ĕn-täl′) . Col.	3.0 N	74.0 W
96	Oriente (State) (ō-rê-ĕn′tā) .. Cuba	20.30 N	76.30 W
127	Orihuela (ō′rê-wā′lä) ... Sp.	38.6 N	0.56 W
112	Orihvesi, L. (ô′rĭ-vĕ-sĭ) ... Fin.	62.20 N	29.45 E
55	Orillia (ô-rĭl′ĭ-ȧ) ... Can.	44.32 N	79.42 W
49	Orillia ... Wash. (Seattle In.)	47.27 N	122.15 W
103	Orinoco, Delta of the (ō-rĭ-nō′kō) Ven.	9.30 N	61.30 W
102	Orinoco, R. ... Ven.-Col.	5.0 N	67.45 W
162	Orion (ō-rê-ōn′) ... P. I.	14.37 N	120.34 E
128	Oristano, G. of (ō-rês-tä′nō). Sard.	39.50 N	8.30 E
93	Orizaba (ō-rê-zä′bä) ... Mex.	18.54 N	97.5 W
93	Orizaba (Vol.) ... Mex.	19.0 N	97.15 W
120	Örkedalen (ûr′kĕ-dä-lĕn) ... Nor.	63.18 N	9.53 E
120	Örken (L.) (ûr′kĕn) ... Swe.	57.8 N	15.0 E
129	Orkhanie (ôr-Kä′nyĕ) ... Bul.	42.54 N	23.38 E
152	Orkhon R. (ŏr-Kôn′) ... Chn.	49.0 N	105.0 E
120	Orkla R. (ôr′klȧ) ... Nor.	63.0 N	9.45 E
116	Orkney Is. (ôrk′nĭ) .. Gt. Brit. (In.)	59.0 N	2.30 W
83	Orlando (ôr-lăn′dō) ... Fla. (In.)	28.33 N	81.22 W
124	Orléans (ôr-lā-äN′) ... Fr.	47.55 N	1.57 E
84	Orleans (ôr-lēnz′) ... Ind.	38.40 N	86.27 W
86	Orleans I. (ôr-lā-äN′) ... Can.	46.56 N	71.0 W
138	Orléansville (ôr-lā-äN-vēl′) ... Alg.	36.14 N	1.20 E
163	Ormoc (ôr-mŏk′) ... P. I.	11.0 N	124.37 E
163	Ormoc B. ... P. I.	10.58 N	124.35 E
83	Ormond (ôr′mŏnd) ... Fla.	29.16 N	81.6 W
170	Ormondville (ôr′mŏnd-vĭl) ... N. Z.	40.8 S	176.12 E
118	Ormskirk (ôrmz′kẽrk) ... Gt. Brit.	53.34 N	2.53 W
124	Orne R. (ôrn′) ... Fr.	49.0 N	0.30 W
120	Orn I. (ôrn) ... Swe.	59.2 N	18.30 E
120	Örnskoldsvik (ûrn′skôlts-vêk). Swe.	63.14 N	18.41 E
102	Orocué (ô-rô-kwā′) ... Col.	4.58 N	71.28 W
170	Orongorongo R. (ô-rôŋ-gô-rôŋ′gō) N. Z. (In.)	41.23 S	174.56 E
116	Oronsay, Passage of (ō′rŏn-sā) Gt. Brit.	56.0 N	6.10 W
163	Oroquieta (ō-rô-kyā′tā) ... P. I.	8.29 N	123.48 E
99	Oro, R. del (rē′ō dĕl ō′rō) Chl. (Magallanes In.)	52.55 S	69.55 W
80	Oro, R. del ... Mex.	25.58 N	105.30 W
128	Orosei, G. of (ō-rô-sā′ē) ... Sard.	40.15 N	9.45 E
123	Orosháza (ô-rôsh-hä′zô) ... Hung.	46.33 N	20.41 E
95	Orosi (Vol.) (ō-rō′sē) ... C. R.	11.0 N	85.28 W
74	Oroville (ōr′ô-vĭl) ... Calif.	39.31 N	121.33 W
70	Oroville ... Wash.	48.54 N	119.27 W
119	Orrell (ŏr′ĕl) Gt. Brit. (Liverpool In.)	53.32 N	2.40 W
166	Orroroo (ŏr′ô-ro͞o) ... Austl.	32.45 S	138.39 E
84	Orrville (ôr′vĭl) ... Ohio	40.50 N	81.48 W
120	Orsa (ōr′sä) ... Swe.	61.9 N	14.38 E
125	Orsay (ôr-sĕ′) ... Fr. (In.)	48.41 N	2.11 E
130	Orsha (ôr′shȧ) ... Sov. Un.	54.30 N	30.27 E
113	Orsk (ôrsk) ... Sov. Un.	51.15 N	58.35 E
129	Orşova (ôr′shô-vȧ) ... Rom.	44.43 N	22.25 E
126	Ortegal C. (ôr-tå-gäl′) ... Sp.	43.46 N	7.55 W
123	Ortelsburg (ôr′tĕls-bo͝orgh) ... Ger.	53.33 N	20.59 E
124	Orthez (ôr-tĕz′) ... Fr.	43.28 N	0.48 W
126	Ortigueira (ôr-tê-gā′ē-rä) ... Sp.	43.41 N	7.50 W
49	Orting (ôrt′ĭng) Wash. (Seattle In.)	47.5 N	122.12 W
128	Ortona (ôr-tō′nä) ... It.	42.21 N	14.22 E
96	Ortonville (ôr′tŭn-vĭl) ... Minn.	45.19 N	96.25 W
102	Oruro (ô-ro͞o′rō) ... Bol.	17.58 S	67.3 W
128	Orvieto (ôr-vyå′tō) ... It.	42.43 N	12.7 E
120	Os (ôs) ... Nor.	60.11 N	5.29 E
148	Osa (ô-sȧ) ... Sov. Un.	53.30 N	103.59 E
77	Osage (ō′sāj) ... Ia.	43.18 N	92.48 W
79	Osage City ... Kan.	38.38 N	95.48 W
79	Osage Dam ... Mo.	38.10 N	92.45 W
79	Osage R. ... Mo.	38.12 N	93.0 W
159	Osaka (ō′zä-kä) ... Jap. (In.)	34.32 N	135.30 E
159	Osaka B. ... Jap.	34.30 N	135.15 E
77	Osakis (ô-sā′kĭs) ... Minn.	45.51 N	95.8 W
77	Osakis L. ... Minn.	45.55 N	95.5 W
95	Osa Pen. (ō′sā) ... C. R.	8.35 N	83.30 W
79	Osawatomia (ŏs-ȧ-wăt′ô-mê) . Kan.	38.29 N	94.56 W
78	Osborne (ŏz′bŭrn) ... Kan.	39.26 N	98.42 W
79	Osceola (ŏs-ê-ō′lȧ) ... Ark.	35.43 N	89.58 W
77	Osceola ... Ia.	41.2 N	93.45 W
79	Osceola ... Mo.	38.2 N	93.40 W
76	Osceola ... Neb.	41.12 N	97.33 W
122	Oschatz (ô′shäts) ...	51.17 N	13.6 E
122	Oschersleben (ôsh′ẽrs-lā-bĕn) .. Ger.	52.2 N	11.13 E
84	Oscoda (ŏs-kō′dȧ) ... Mich.	44.26 N	83.20 W
119	Osdorf (ôs′dôrf) Ger. (Hamburg In.)	53.34 N	9.51 E
120	Ose L. (o͞o′sĕ) ... Nor.	61.12 N	11.55 E
130	Osetr R. (ô′sĕt′r) ... Sov. Un.	54.25 N	38.25 E
84	Osgood (ŏz′go͝od) ... Ind.	39.7 N	85.19 W
148	Osh (ôsh) ... Sov. Un.	40.25 N	72.40 E
85	Oshawa (ŏsh′ȧ-wȧ) ... Can.	43.50 N	78.50 W
159	Oshima (I.) (ō′shē′mä) ... Jap.	34.45 N	139.25 E
158	Oshima Shotō (I.) (ō′shē′mä shō′tō) . Jap.	28.15 N	129.15 E
76	Oshkosh (ŏsh′kŏsh) ... Neb.	41.22 N	102.20 W
77	Oshkosh ... Wis.	44.0 N	88.30 W
129	Osijek (ôs′ĭ-yāk) ... Yugo.	45.33 N	18.41 E
77	Oskaloosa (ŏs-kȧ-lo͞o′sȧ) ... Ia.	41.18 N	92.38 W

ăt; finăl; rāte; senâte; ärm; ȧsk; sofȧ; fâre; ch-choose; dh-as th in other; bē; êvent; bĕt; recĕnt; cratẽr; g-go; gh-gutteral g; bĭt; ĭ-short neutral; rīde; K-gutteral k as ch in German ich:

Page	Name Pronunciation Region	Lat. °′	Long. °′
120	Oskarshamn (ôs'kärs-häm'n)..Swe.	57.16 N	16.26 E
120	Oskarsström (ôs'kärs-strûm)..Swe.	56.49 N	12.59 E
131	Oskol R. (ôs-kôl').......Sov. Un.	50.40 N	37.50 E
120	Oslo (ôs'lō)..............Nor.	59.57 N	10.42 E
163	Oslob (ôs-lōb')............P. I.	9.32 N	123.26 E
120	Oslo Fjord ....Nor.	59.10 N	10.35 E
126	Osma (ôs'mä)...............Sp.	41.34 N	3.3 W
121	Osmus (ôs'mōōs)............Est.	59.16 N	23.25 E
122	Osnabrück (ôs-nä-brük')......Ger.	52.16 N	8.3 E
104	Osorno (ô-sôr'nô)...........Chl.	40.40 S	73.2 W
165	Osprey Reef (ôs'prâ).......Austl.	13.45 S	146.38 E
85	Ossining (ŏs'ĭ-nĭng).........N. Y.	41.11 N	73.52 W
86	Ossipee (ŏs'ĭ-pē)............N. H.	43.40 N	71.8 W
130	Ostashkov (ôs-täsh'kôf)..Sov. Un.	57.7 N	33.5 E
84	Ostego (ŏs-tē'gô)..........Mich.	42.29 N	85.45 W
117	Ostende (ôst-ĕn'dē).........Bel.	51.12 N	2.55 E
131	Oster (ôs'tĕr)...........Sov. Un.	50.57 N	30.52 E
120	Öster Dal R. (ûs'tĕr däl).....Swe.	61.48 N	12.58 E
120	Öster Fjord (ûs'tĕr fyôr')....Nor.	60.38 N	5.30 E
123	Osterode (ôs-tē-rō'dē).......Ger.	53.41 N	19.58 E
120	Östersund (ûs'tĕr-sōōnd).....Swe.	63.11 N	14.40 E
120	Östhammar (ûst'häm'är).....Swe.	60.17 N	18.23 E
49	Ostrander (ŏs'trăn-dĕr) Wash. (Portland In.)	46.11 N	122.53 W
123	Ostróg (ôs-trôk')............Pol.	50.19 N	26.30 E
131	Ostrogozhsk (ôs-trô-gôzhk') Sov. Un.	50.53 N	39.4 E
123	Ostrołęka (ôs-trô-wôɴ'kà).....Pol.	53.4 N	21.36 E
131	Ostropol (ôs-trô-pôl')....Sov. Un.	49.49 N	27.31 E
129	Ostrov (ôs'trôv)............Rom.	44.56 N	28.11 E
130	Ostrov (ôs-trôf')........Sov. Un.	57.21 N	28.21 E
123	Ostrów (ôs'trōōf)............Pol.	51.38 N	17.48 E
123	Ostrów......................Pol.	52.47 N	21.54 E
123	Ostrów......................Pol.	51.33 N	22.52 E
123	Ostrowiec (ôs-trô'vyĕts).......Pol.	50.56 N	21.23 E
123	Ostrzeszów (ôs-tzhä'shōōf)....Pol.	51.26 N	17.56 E
129	Ostuni (ôs-tōō'nē)............It.	40.43 N	17.36 E
129	Osum R. (ō'sōōm)...........Alb.	40.33 N	20.10 E
158	Osumi Is. (ō'sōō-mē).........Jap.	30.28 N	130.45 E
159	Osumi (Van Diemen) Str......Jap.	30.55 N	131.0 E
126	Osuna (ô-sōō'nä)..............Sp.	37.14 N	5.6 W
118	Oswaldtwistle (ŏz-wald-twĭs''l) Gt. Brit.	53.44 N	2.24 W
85	Oswegatchie R. (ŏs-wē-găch'ĭ) N. Y.	44.15 N	75.10 W
79	Oswego (ŏs-wē'gō)..........Kan.	37.11 N	95.8 W
85	Oswego.....................N. Y.	43.26 N	76.30 W
70	Oswego.....................Ore.	45.25 N	122.42 W
123	Oświęcim (ôsh-vyăɴ'tsyĕm)...Pol.	50.3 N	19.16 E
123	Oszmiana (ôsh-myä'nà)........Pol.	54.26 N	25.56 E
131	Otachi (ô-täch")...........Rom.	48.26 N	27.47 E
171	Otago Harbor (ô-tä'gō).N. Z. (In.)	45.50 S	170.40 E
171	Otago Pen..........N. Z. (In.)	45.52 S	170.40 E
170	Otahuhu (ô-tä-hōō'hōō) N. Z. (In.)	36.57 S	174.51 E
171	Otaki (ô-tä'kē)..............N. Z.	40.40 S	175.10 E
170	Otari, Mt. (ô-tä'rē)....N. Z. (In.)	41.15 S	174.46 E
158	Otaru (ō'tà-rōō)............Jap.	43.10 N	140.59 E
158	Otaru B.....................Jap.	43.28 N	141.0 E
171	Otautau (ô-tou'tou)..........N. Z.	46.8 S	168.2 E
102	Otavalo (ô-tä-vä'lō)...........Ec.	0.10 N	78.15 W
140	Otavi (ô-tä'vē)........S. W. Afr.	19.45 S	17.25 E
74	Otay (ō'tā)...........Calif. (In.)	32.37 N	117.4 W
159	Otenjoyama (Mt.) (ō'tĕn-jô-yä'mä).Jap.	36.22 N	137.38 E
121	Otepää (ô'tĕ-pä)..............Est.	58.4 N	26.32 E
170	Oterongu (ō-tà-rôŋ'gōō) N. Z. (In.)	41.17 S	174.39 E
170	Oterongu B..........N. Z. (In.)	41.18 S	174.39 E
129	Othrys Mts. (ŏth'rĭs).........Grc.	39.0 N	22.30 E
171	Otira Pass (ō-tē'rà)..........N. Z.	42.53 S	171.38 E
140	Otjiwarongo (ŏt-jē-wà-rôŋ'gō) S. W. Afr.	20.27 S	16.32 E
118	Otley (ŏt'lĭ)...............Gt. Brit.	53.54 N	1.41 W
128	Otočac (ō'tô-chäts)..........Yugo.	44.50 N	15.16 E
163	Oton (ô-tōn')..................P. I.	10.42 N	122.28 E
170	Otorohanga (ô-tō-rō-häŋ'gä) N. Z.	38.8 S	175.12 E
129	Otranto (ô-trän-tō) (ô trän'tō).It.	40.9 N	18.29 E
129	Otranto, C.....................It.	40.6 N	18.32 E
129	Otranto, Str. of................It.	40.30 N	18.50 E
159	Otsu (ō'tsōō).................Jap.	35.2 N	135.52 E
119	Ottaiano (ōt-tä-yä'nō) It. (Napoli In.)	40.51 N	14.29 E
120	Ottavand (L.) (ôt'tà-vän)....Nor.	61.53 N	8.45 E
54	Ottawa............Can (In.)		
55	Ottawa (ŏt'à-wà)............Can.	45.30 N	75.44 W
79	Ottawa........................Ill.	41.21 N	88.50 W
79	Ottawa......................Kan.	38.37 N	95.16 W
84	Ottawa......................Ohio	41.2 N	84.4 W
55	Ottawa Is...................Can.	59.45 N	80.0 W
84	Ottawa Pt..................Mich.	44.15 N	83.25 W
55	Ottawa R....................Can.	46.30 N	78.30 W
75	Otter Cr. (ŏt'ĕr)............Utah	38.20 N	111.55 W
86	Otter Cr.......................Vt.	43.55 N	73.13 W
120	Otter R. (ôt'ĕr)...............Nor.	59.15 N	7.30 E
76	Otter Tail L.................Minn.	46.24 N	95.38 W
142	Ottery (ŏt'ĕr-ĭ)..........U. S. Afr.	34.1 S	18.31 E
143	Ottoshoop (ŏt'ōz-hōp)...U. S. Afr.	25.45 S	25.57 E
92	Otumba (ô-tŭm'bä)...........Mex.	19.41 N	98.47 W
77	Ottumwa (ô-tŭm'wà)...........Ia.	41.0 N	92.22 W
166	Otway, C. (ŏt'wā)..........Austl.	38.52 S	143.33 E
166	Otway Ra....................Austl.	38.30 S	143.35 E
104	Otway Water..................Chl.	53.0 S	71.30 W
123	Otwock (ôt'vôtsk)..............Pol.	52.5 N	21.17 E
79	Ouachita Mts. (wŏsh'ĭ-tô) Okla.-Ark.	34.30 N	94.30 W
59	Ouachita R....................Ark.	33.30 N	92.45 W
139	Ouada (Reg.) (wä'dà) Fr. Eq. Afr.-A. E. Sud.	13.0 N	21.0 E
138	Ouagadougou (wä-gà-dōō'gōō) Fr. W. Afr.	12.26 N	1.44 W
138	Ouahigouya (wä-ē-gōō'yä) Fr. W. Afr.	13.36 N	2.27 W
138	Oualata (wä-lä'tä)....Fr. W. Afr.	17.11 N	6.48 W
138	Ouallèn (Well) (wäl-lân')......Alg.	24.40 N	1.10 E
97	Ouanaminthe (wà-nà-măɴt')..Hai.	19.33 N	71.45 W
139	Ouanda Djalé (wän'dà ja-lā') Fr. Eq. Afr.	9.0 N	22.48 E
138	Ouargla (wär'glä)............Alg.	32.0 N	5.21 E
138	Oudjda (ōōj-dä') (ōōj'dä).....Mor.	34.40 N	2.0 W
142	Oudtshoorn (outs'hōrn).U. S. Afr.	33.35 S	22.11 E
138	Oued-Zem (wĕd-zĕm')...........Mor.	33.2 N	5.45 W
139	Oueita (wà-ē-tä') (wā'ē-tä) Fr. Eq. Afr.	17.40 N	20.27 E
139	Ouesso (wĕs-sô') (wĕs'sō) Fr. Eq. Afr.	1.32 N	16.0 E
138	Ouezzan (wē-zān')........Sp. Mor.	34.50 N	5.32 W
116	Oughter, Lough (L.) (lŏĸ-ŏĸ'tĕr) Ire.	54.0 N	7.30 W
138	Ouidah (wē-dä')......Fr. W. Afr.	6.28 N	2.2 E
114	Oulad Naïl, Mts. of the (ōō-lád' nà-ēl').Alg.	34.30 N	3.0 E
124	Oullins (ōō-lăɴ')...............Fr.	45.42 N	4.55 E
112	Oulu (ō'lōō)...................Fin.	65.0 N	25.32 E
112	Oulu, L.......................Fin.	64.25 N	27.30 E
112	Ounas R. (ō'nàs)..............Fin.	68.0 N	24.30 E
118	Oundle (ôn'd'l)..........Gt. Brit.	52.28 N	0.28 W
139	Ounianga Kebir (ōō-nē-äŋ'gà kē-bēr').Fr. Eq. Afr.	19.2 N	20.17 E
75	Ouray (ōō-rā')................Colo.	38.2 N	107.39 W
126	Ourique (ō-rē'kĕ)..............Port.	37.39 N	8.12 W
103	Ouro Preto (ō'rōō prā'tōō)...Braz.	20.28 S	43.30 W
169	Ouse R. (ōōz)....Austl. (Tas. In.)	42.15 S	146.50 E
116	Ouse, R..................Gt. Brit.	52.25 N	0.0
138	Outak-el-Had (ōō-tàk'-ĕl-häd') Mor.	33.25 N	3.38 W
55	Outarde R. (ōō-tàrd').........Can.	51.30 N	69.5 W
91	Outer Bras (I.) (bräs) (brä) Vir. Is.	18.24 N	64.58 W
116	Outer Hebrides (Is.) (hĕb'rĭ-dēz) Gt. Brit.	57.58 N	7.30 W
87	Outer I.......................Can.	51.5 N	58.35 W
77	Outer I......................U. S.	47.3 N	90.25 W
126	Outes (ō-ōō'täs)...............Sp.	42.51 N	8.55 W
140	Outjo (ōt'yō)...........S. W. Afr.	20.6 S	16.12 E
166	Outlet Cr. (out'lĕt)..........Austl.	35.43 S	141.55 E
124	Outreau (ōō-trō')...............Fr.	50.41 N	1.38 E
167	Outrim (ōō'trĭm)...............Austl.	38.31 S	145.42 E
166	Ouyen (ōō'yĕn)...............Austl.	35.4 S	142.18 E
6	Ovalau (I.) (ō-vä-lä'ōō) Fiji Is. (In.)	17.42 S	178.48 E
104	Ovalle (ō-väl'yä)...............Chl.	30.40 S	71.20 W
126	Ovar (ô-vär').................Port.	40.53 N	8.38 W
89	Overland (ō'vĕr-lănd) Mo. (St. Louis In.)	38.42 N	90.21 W
131	Ovidiopol (ô-vē-dē-ô-pôl') Sov. Un.	46.14 N	30.25 E
126	Oviedo (ô-vē-ā'dhō)...........Sp.	43.22 N	5.51 W
131	Ovruch (ôv'rōōch).........Sov. Un.	51.19 N	28.51 E
159	Owada (ō'wä-dà).Jap. (Tokyo In.)	35.44 N	140.6 E
85	Owasco, L. (ô-wăs'kō).........N. Y.	42.52 N	76.32 W
159	Owase (ō'wä-sà)...............Jap.	34.4 N	136.11 E
89	Owasso L. (ō-wăs'sō) Minn. (Minneapolis In.)	45.2 N	93.7 W
77	Owatonna (ō-wà-tŏn'à)......Minn.	44.5 N	93.12 W
85	Owego (ō-wē'gō).............N. Y.	42.6 N	76.17 W
77	Owen (ō'ĕn)...................Wis.	44.57 N	90.32 W
55	Owen Sd.......................Can.	44.40 N	80.57 W
84	Owensboro (ō'ĕnz-bŭr-ô).....Ky.	38.46 N	87.7 W
74	Owens L. (ō'ĕnz)............Calif.	36.25 N	117.45 W
74	Owens R.....................Calif.	37.15 N	118.18 W
161	Owen Stanley Ra. (ō'ĕn stăn'lē) Pap. Ter.	9.15 S	147.50 E
84	Owensville (ō'ĕnz-vĭl)........Ind.	38.27 N	87.40 W
79	Owensville....................Mo.	38.19 N	91.30 W
84	Owenton (ō'ĕn-tŭn)...........Ky.	38.34 N	84.55 W
138	Owerri (ô-wĕr'ē)..............Nig.	5.28 N	7.0 E
71	Owl Cr. (oul)..................Wyo.	43.42 N	108.40 W
84	Owosso (ô-wŏs'ō)............Mich.	42.0 N	84.12 W
70	Owyhee Reservoir (ô-wī'hē)...Ore.	43.25 N	117.20 W
70	Owyhee R.....................Ore.	42.40 N	117.10 W
70	Owyhee R., South Fork.......Ida.	42.18 N	116.53 W
93	Oxchuc (ôs-chōōk')..........Mex.	16.49 N	92.23 W
82	Oxford (ŏks'fērd)..............Ala.	33.36 N	85.50 W
86	Oxford........................Can.	45.43 N	63.51 W
73	Oxford.............Ga. (Atlanta In.)	33.37 N	83.53 W
116	Oxford...................Gt. Brit.	51.45 N	1.15 W
87	Oxford...............Mass. (In.)	42.7 N	71.52 W
84	Oxford.......................Mich.	42.52 N	83.16 W
79	Oxford.......................Miss.	34.22 N	89.31 W
171	Oxford.......................N. Z.	43.17 S	172.12 E
83	Oxford.......................N. C.	36.18 N	78.35 W
84	Oxford.......................Ohio	39.32 N	84.46 W
118	Oxford Co...............Gt. Brit.	52.6 N	1.24 W
167	Oxleys Pk. (ŏks'lēz)........Austl.	31.51 S	150.21 E
73	Oxmoor (ŏks'mōōr) Ala. (Birmingham In.)	33.26 N	86.51 W
74	Oxnard (ŏks'närd)............Calif.	34.12 N	119.11 W
159	Oyamazaki (ō'yà-mà-zä'kē) Jap. (Osaka In.)	34.54 N	135.40 E
103	Oyapock, R. (ô-yà-pŏk') Fr. Gui.-Braz.	2.30 N	52.30 W
157	Oye I. (ō'vā)...................Jap.	32.28 N	130.20 E
138	Oyem (ô-yĕm) (ô-yăɴ') Fr. Eq. Afr.	1.40 N	11.33 E
138	Oyo (ō'yō)....................Nig.	7.57 N	3.58 E
125	Oyonnax (ô-yô-nàks')...........Fr.	46.18 N	5.40 E
169	Oyster B. (ois'tĕr)Austl. (Tas. In.)	42.10 S	148.10 E
81	Oyster Bayou........Tex. (In.)	29.40 N	94.32 W
81	Oyster Creek.........Tex. (In.)	29.15 N	95.30 W
97	Ozama R. (ô-zä'mä)...Dom. Rep.	18.40 N	69.50 W
82	Ozark (ō'zärk)..................Ala.	31.28 N	85.28 W
79	Ozark.........................Ark.	35.29 N	93.48 W
79	Ozark Plat......................Mo.	38.10 N	93.0 W
79	Ozarks, L. of the...............Mo.	38.13 N	93.7 W
130	Ozery (ô-zyä'rē).........Sov. Un.	54.52 N	38.34 E
128	Ozieri (ô-zyä'rē)...............Sard.	40.35 N	9.1 E
125	Ozoir-la-Ferrière (ô-zwär'-là-fĕr-ê-âr').Fr. (In.)	48.46 N	2.40 E
123	Ozorków (ô-zôr'kōōf)...........Pol.	51.58 N	19.20 E
93	Ozuluama (ō'zōō-lōō-ä'mä)..Mex.	21.35 N	97.52 W
142	Paarl (pärl)...........U. S. Afr.	33.45 S	18.57 E
173	Paauilo (pä-ä-ōō'ē-lō)......Haw.	20.4 N	155.25 W
123	Pabjanice (pä-byà-nē'tsĕ)....Pol.	51.40 N	19.23 E
102	Pacaraíma, Serra (Mts.) (sĕr'rà pä-kä-rä-ē'mà).Ven.-Braz.	0.4 N	63.0 W
102	Pacasmayo (pä-käs-mä'yō)...Peru	7.0 S	79.30 W
154	Pachai (pä'chī')..............Chn.	26.8 N	107.40 E
156	Pachow (pä'chō')..............Chn.	39.13 N	116.21 E
152	Pachu (pä'chōō')..............Chn.	39.45 N	78.40 E
92	Pachuca (pä-chōō'kä).........Mex.	20.8 N	98.43 W
49	Pacific (pà-sĭf'ĭk) Wash. (Seattle In.)	47.15 N	122.15 W
74	Pacific Beach........Calif (In.)	32.47 N	117.0 W
74	Pacific Grove..............Calif.	36.36 N	121.55 W
172	Pacific O.		
73	Pacific Palisades Calif. (Los Angeles In.)	34.3 N	118.32 W
163	Pacijan I. (pä-sē'hän)........P. I.	10.40 N	124.20 E
160	Padang (pä-däng')......Neth. Ind.	0.59 S	100.29 E
145	Padang I.........Neth. Ind. (In.)	1.10 N	102.20 E
84	Paden City (pā'dĕn)......W. Va.	39.34 N	80.56 W
122	Paderborn (pä-dĕr-bôrn').....Ger.	51.43 N	8.45 E
118	Padiham (păd'ĭ-hăm).....Gt. Brit.	53.48 N	2.19 W
92	Padilla (pä-dēl'yä)...........Mex.	23.58 N	98.43 W
128	Padova (Padua) (pä'dô-vä) (păd'ū-à).It.	45.25 N	11.50 E
81	Padre I. (pä'drā).............Tex.	27.0 N	97.23 W
143	Padrone, C. (pä-drō'nä).U. S. Afr.	33.48 S	26.28 E
128	Padua (Padova) (păd'ū-à) (pä'dô-vä).It.	45.25 N	11.50 E
82	Paducah (pà-dū'kà)...........Ky.	37.4 N	88.35 W
104	Pae I. (pä'å)........Braz. (In.)	22.59 S	43.5 W
170	Paeroa (pä-å-rō'à)...........N. Z.	37.22 S	175.43 E
161	Paete (pä-ā'tå) P. I. (Manila In.)	14.22 N	121.33 E
128	Pag (I.) (päg)...............Yugo.	44.35 N	14.55 E
160	Paga I., North (pä'gä) Neth. Ind.	2.35 S	100.0 E
160	Paga I., South.........Neth. Ind.	3.0 S	100.25 E
6	Pago B. (pä'gō)..............Guam	13.24 N	144.48 E
75	Pagosa Springs (pà-gō'sà)....Colo.	37.16 N	107.2 W
161	Pagsanjan (päg-sän-hän') P. I. (Manila In.)	14.16 N	121.31 E
173	Pahala (pä-hä'lä)...........Haw.	19.11 N	155.29 W
170	Pahiatua (pä'hē-ä'tōō-ä)....N. Z.	40.27 S	175.50 E
157	Pahkchun (päk'chōōn')........Cho.	40.14 N	125.44 E
150	Pahlevi (Enzeli) (pä'lĕ-vē) (ĕn'zĕ-lē).Iran	37.30 N	49.29 E
83	Pahokee (pà-hō'kē)......Fla. (In.)	26.47 N	80.39 W
121	Paide (pī'dĕ)..................Est.	58.54 N	25.32 E
121	Päijänne L. (pĕ'ē-yĕn-nĕ).....Fin.	61.35 N	25.30 E
112	Pai-Koi Range (pī-kō'ē)..Sov. Un.	69.10 N	62.30 E
173	Pailolo Channel (pä-ē-lō'lō)..Haw.	21.5 N	156.40 W
84	Painesville (pānz'vĭl)..........Ohio	41.42 N	81.14 W
84	Paintsville (pānts'vĭl)...........Ky.	37.50 N	82.50 W
156	Paisiang (pī'syäng')............Chn.	37.32 N	114.46 E
116	Paisley (pāz'lĭ).............Gt. Brit.	55.50 N	4.29 W
102	Paita (pä-ē'tä)..................Peru	5.10 S	81.2 W
163	Paitan B. (pä-ē-tän').......B. N. B.	6.50 N	117.20 E
74	Paiute Ind. Res. (pī-ūt')......Calif.	37.35 N	118.30 W
75	Paiute Ind. Res.................Utah	38.15 N	113.50 W
93	Pajápan (pä-hä'pän)............Mex.	18.15 N	94.42 W
170	Paketutu (Neekes I.)..N. Z. (In.)	36.58 S	174.45 E
160	Pakhoi (päk'hoi')................Chn.	21.30 N	109.0 E
154	Paklow (päk'lō')................Chn.	22.52 N	110.18 E
160	Paknambo (päk-näm'bō)...Thai.	15.45 N	100.0 E
128	Pakrac (pä'kräts)...............Yugo.	45.26 N	17.13 E
123	Paks (pôksh)....................Hung.	46.38 N	18.53 E
81	Palacios (pä-lä'syōs)...........Tex.	28.43 N	96.12 W
127	Palafrugell (pä-lä-frōō-gĕl').....Sp.	41.55 N	3.4 E
125	Palaiseau (pä-lĕ-zō')......Fr. (In.)	48.42 N	2.15 E
127	Palamós (pä-lä-mōs')..............Sp.	41.51 N	3.7 E
162	Palanan B. (pä-lä'nän)..........P. I.	17.12 N	122.25 E
162	Palanan Pt.......................P. I.	17.9 N	122.30 E
129	Palanka (pä'län-kä)...........Yugo.	44.20 N	20.56 E
129	Palanka............................Yugo.	45.16 N	19.25 E
151	Palanpur (pä'lŭn-pōōr).........India	24.14 N	72.30 E
162	Palapag (pä-lä'päg)..............P. I.	12.33 N	125.7 E
140	Palapye (pà-läp'yĕ)..............Bech.	22.35 S	27.20 E
126	Palas de Rey (pä-läs' dä rā'ē)..Sp.	42.53 N	7.49 W
83	Palatka (pà-lăt'kà)...............Fla.	29.38 N	81.40 W
161	Palau Is. (pä-lä'ōō).........Pac. O.	7.30 N	134.35 E
162	Palaui I. (pä-lou'ē)...............P. I.	18.32 N	122.9 E
162	Palauig (pä-lou'ēg)...............P. I.	15.26 N	119.55 E
162	Palauig Pt.........................P. I.	15.26 N	119.53 E
6	Palauli (pä-lou'lē)......Sam. (In.)	13.46 S	172.18 W
163	Palawan (I.) (pä-lä'wän)......P. I.	9.35 N	118.30 E
128	Palazzola (pä-lät'sô-lō)..........It.	37.9 N	14.53 E
160	Palembang (pä-lĕm-bäng') Neth. Ind.	2.59 S	104.39 E
94	Palencia (pä-lĕn'sē-à)........Guat.	14.42 N	90.22 W
126	Palencia..............................Sp.	42.0 N	4.31 W
92	Palenque (pä-lĕŋ'kä)...........Mex.	17.33 N	91.58 W
97	Palenque Pt...............Dom. Rep.	18.14 N	70.10 W
128	Palermo (pä-lĕr'mō).................It.	38.7 N	13.23 E
145	Palestine (păl'ĕs-tīn).....Asia (In.)	32.0 N	35.0 E
81	Palestine...........................Tex.	31.47 N	95.37 W
151	Paletwa (pŭ-lĕt'wä).............India	21.12 N	92.50 E
94	Palín (pä-lēn')....................Guat.	14.24 N	90.42 W
74	Palisade (păl-ĭ-sād')..............Nev.	40.38 N	116.12 W
72	Palisade Mt....Colo. (Denver In.)	40.26 N	105.19 W
88	Palisades, The (Park) (păl-ĭ-sādz') N. J. (N. Y. In.)	40.52 N	73.58 W
93	Palizada (pä-lē-zä'dä)..........Mex.	18.17 N	92.3 W
151	Palk Str. (pôk)....................India	10.0 N	79.30 E
171	Palliser B. (pŏl'ĭ-sĕr)..........N. Z.	41.25 S	175.0 E
171	Palliser, C.........................N. Z.	41.37 S	175.17 E
141	Palma (päl'mä)....................Moz.	10.43 S	40.25 E

ng-sing; ŋ-baŋk; ɴ-nasalized n; nŏd; cŏmmit ōld; ôbey; ôrder; fōōd; fŏŏt; ou-out; s-soft; sh-dish; th-thin; pūre; ûnite; ûrn; stŭd; circŭs; ū-as "y" in study; '-indeterminate vowel.

Page	Name Pronunciation Region	Lat. °′	Long. °′
127	Palma ... Sp.	39.34 N	2.39 E
127	Palma B. ... Sp.	39.28 N	2.40 E
126	Palma del Río (päl'mä dĕl rē'ō) Sp.	37.42 N	5.18 W
138	Palma I. (päl'mä) ... Can. Is.	28.45 N	17.50 W
104	Palmas (päl'mäs) ... Braz.	26.28 S	52.0 W
163	Palmas I. ... P. I.	5.32 N	126.36 E
97	Palma Soriano (päl'mä sō-ré-ä'nō) .. Cuba	20.13 N	76.0 W
83	Palm Beach (päm bēch') Fla. (In.)	26.43 N	80.2 W
127	Palmela (päl-mā'lä) .... Port. (In.)	38.34 N	8.54 W
49	Palmer (päm'ẽr) Wash. (Portland In.)	45.33 N	122.7 W
46	Palmer Is. ... Ant. O.	64.30 S	63.0 W
72	Palmer L. .. Colo. (Colo. Sprs. In.)	39.8 N	104.55 W
89	Palmer L. Minn. (Minneapolis In.)	45.5 N	93.19 W
171	Palmerston (päm'ẽr-stŭn) ... N. Z.	45.30 S	170.43 E
165	Palmerville (päm'ẽr-vĭl) .... Austl.	16.5 S	144.14 E
83	Palmetto (păl-mĕt'ō) ..... Fla. (In.)	27.32 N	82.34 W
73	Palmetto .... Ga. (Atlanta In.)	33.31 N	84.41 W
97	Palmetto Pt. ... Ba. Is.	25.10 N	76.10 W
128	Palmi (päl'mē) ... It.	38.22 N	15.52 E
102	Palmira (päl-mē'rä) ... Col.	3.30 N	76.28 W
96	Palmira ... Cuba	22.13 N	80.23 W
92	Palmito de la Virgen (I.) (päl-mē'tō dā lä vēr-ĸān') .. Mex.	23.0 N	106.11 W
92	Palmito del Verde I. (päl-mē'tō dĕl vĕr'dā) .. Mex.	22.40 N	105.49 W
79	Palmyra (păl-mī'rȧ) ... Mo.	39.46 N	91.31 W
150	Palmyra (Ruins) ... Syr.	34.30 N	38.17 E
6	Palmyra I. ... Pac. O.	5.53 N	162.5 W
163	Palo (pä'lō) ... P. I.	11.9 N	12.5 E
74	Palo Alto (pä'lō äl'tō) ... Calif.	37.26 N	122.10 W
78	Paloduro Cr. (pā-lō-dōō'rō) .. Tex.	36.25 N	101.5 W
80	Paloma, L. (pä-lō'mä) ... Mex.	26.50 N	103.55 W
103	Palominos (I.) (pä-lō-mē'nōs) Peru (In.)	12.8 S	77.15 W
163	Palompon (pä-lōm-pōn') ... P. I.	11.3 N	124.23 E
127	Palos C. (pä'lōs) ... Sp.	37.37 N	0.41 W
88	Palos Park (pā'lōs) Ill. (Chicago In.)	41.40 N	87.50 W
70	Palouse (pȧ-lōōz') ... Wash.	46.55 N	117.5 W
70	Palouse R. ... Wash.	47.0 N	117.40 W
152	Palti, L. (Yamdok) (päl'tē) (yäm-dōk') . Chn.	29.0 N	90.45 E
113	Palu (pä-lōō') ... Tur.	38.48 N	40.8 E
162	Paluan (pä-lōō'än) ... P. I.	13.25 N	120.29 E
166	Pamamaroo, L. (pȧ-mä'mȧ-rōō) Austl.	32.16 S	142.28 E
162	Pambuhan (päm-bōō'än) .... P. I.	12.33 N	124.56 E
124	Pamiers (pȧ-myā') ... Fr.	43.8 N	1.35 E
152	Pamir (Highland) (pä-mēr') Sov. Un.-Chn.	38.0 N	73.50 E
83	Pamlico R. (păm'lĭ-kō) ..... N. C.	35.25 N	76.50 W
83	Pamlico Sd. ... N. C.	35.20 N	76.0 W
78	Pampa (păm'pȧ) ... Tex.	35.33 N	100.55 W
161	Pampanga (Prov.) (päm-päŋ'gä) P. I. (Manila In.)	15.2 N	120.35 E
162	Pampanga R. ... P. I.	15.20 N	120.55 E
104	Pampas (Reg.) (päm'päs) .... Arg.	33.30 S	62.0 W
126	Pampilhosa (päm-pē-lyō'sȧ) . Port.	40.21 N	8.25 W
102	Pamplona (päm-plō'nä) ... Col.	7.10 N	72.45 W
126	Pamplona ... Sp.	42.48 N	1.39 W
142	Pampoenpoort (päm'pōōn-pōrt) U. S. Afr.	31.5 S	22.40 E
85	Pamunkey R. (pȧ-mŭŋ'kĭ) .... Va.	37.45 N	77.20 W
79	Pana (pā'nȧ) ... Ill.	39.24 N	89.5 W
163	Panabutan B. (pä-nä-bōō'tän) P. I.	7.35 N	122.7 E
129	Panagyuriste (pȧ-nȧ-gyōō'rĕsh-tĕ) Bul.	42.29 N	24.11 E
95	Panama (păn-ȧ-mä') .... Cen. Am.	8.50 N	80.0 W
95	Panama ... Pan.	8.58 N	79.32 W
95	Panama, B. of ... Pan.	8.50 N	79.15 W
95	Panama Canal ... C. Z.	9.5 N	79.40 W
82	Panama City ... Fla.	30.9 N	85.39 W
95	Panama, G. of ... Pan.	7.50 N	79.20 W
95	Panama, Isth. of ... Pan.	9.30 N	79.55 W
163	Panaon I. (pä-nä-ōn') ... P. I.	10.3 N	125.12 E
128	Panaria (I.) (pä-nä'rē-ä) ... It.	38.39 N	15.4 E
128	Panaro R. (pä-nä'rō) ... It.	44.40 N	11.0 E
163	Panay (pä-nī') ... P. I.	11.34 N	122.48 E
163	Panay G. ... P. I.	10.20 N	122.20 E
163	Panay (I.) ... P. I.	11.10 N	122.30 E
163	Panay R. ... P. I.	11.20 N	122.40 E
129	Pančevo (pän'chĕ-vō) ... Yugo.	44.52 N	20.41 E
140	Panda (pän'dä') .... Bel. Cong.	10.52 S	27.13 E
163	Pandan (pän-dän') ... P. I.	11.43 N	122.6 E
162	Pandan ... P. I.	14.2 N	124.10 E
163	Pandaras Pt. (pän-dä'räs) B. N. B.	6.4 N	118.0 E
96	Pan de Guajaibon (Mt.) (pän dā gwä-hä-ē'bōn) . Cuba	22.41 N	83.27 W
95	Pando, Cerro (Mt.) (sĕr'rō pän'dō) Pan.	9.3 N	82.49 W
163	Panducan I. (pän-dōō'kän) .. P. I.	6.17 N	120.40 E
148	Pandzh R. (pändzh) Sov. Un.-Afg.	37.0 N	71.25 E
121	Panevežys (pä'nyĕ-väzh'ēs) .. Lith.	55.44 N	24.20 E
139	Panga (päŋ'gä) .... Bel. Cong.	1.51 N	26.40 E
162	Pangani (pän-gä'nē) ... Tan.	5.25 S	38.52 E
141	Pangani (Ruvu) R. (pän'gä'nē) (rōō'vōō) .. Tan.	5.0 S	38.6 E
167	Pangee (päŋ'gē) ... Austl.	32.1 S	146.45 E
161	Pangil (pän-gēl') . P. I. (Manila In.)	14.25 N	121.32 E
160	Pangkalpinang (päng-käl'pē-näng') Neth. Ind.	2.5 S	106.5 E
163	Panglao (pän-glä'ō) ... P. I.	9.35 N	123.47 E
163	Panglao I. ... P. I.	9.35 N	123.50 E
163	Panguil B. (pän-gēl') ... P. I.	8.2 N	123.45 E
75	Panguitch (päŋ'gwĭch) ...... Utah	37.51 N	112.28 W
163	Pangutarang Group (Is.) .... P. I.	6.20 N	120.30 E
163	Pangutarang I. (päŋ-gōō-tä'räng) P. I.	6.20 N	120.33 E
162	Paniqui (pä-nē'kē) ... P. I.	15.40 N	120.35 E
163	Panitan (pä-nē'tän) ... P. I.	11.28 N	122.45 E
160	Panjang R. (pän-yäng') Neth. Ind.	1.0 N	102.15 E
119	Pankow (päŋ'kō) . Ger. (Berlin In.)	52.35 N	13.24 E
170	Panmure (păn'mūr) .... N. Z. (In.)	36.54 S	174.52 E
161	Pantar (I.) (pän'tär) ... Neth. Ind.	8.20 S	124.15 E
114	Pantelleria (I.) (pän-tĕl-lȧ-rē'ä) . It.	36.52 N	11.58 E
93	Pantepec (pän-tȧ-pĕk') ... Mex.	17.10 N	93.0 W
125	Pantin (päɴ-tăɴ') .... Fr. (In.)	48.53 N	2.24 E
126	Pantón (pän-tōn') ... Sp.	42.31 N	7.36 W
163	Pantukan (pän-tōō'kän) ..... P. I.	7.8 N	125.54 E
92	Pánuco (pä'nōō-kō) ... Mex.	22.4 N	98.11 W
92	Pánuco ... Mex.	23.27 N	105.54 W
80	Pánuco de Coronado (pä'nōō-kō dā kō-rō-nä'dhō) . Mex.	24.31 N	104.20 W
92	Pánuco, R. ... Mex.	22.7 N	98.10 W
150	Panwel R. (pän-wĕl') India (Bombay In.)	18.58 N	72.58 E
94	Panzós (pän-zōs') ... Guat.	15.26 N	89.39 W
162	Paoay (pä-ō-ī') ... P. I.	18.4 N	120.31 E
154	Paoking (pou'kĭng') ... Chn.	27.6 N	111.20 E
128	Paola (pä'ō-lä) ... It.	39.21 N	16.3 E
79	Paola (pā-ō'lȧ) ... Kan.	38.34 N	94.52 W
84	Paoli (pȧ-ō'lĭ) ... Ind.	38.36 N	86.30 W
161	Paombong (pä-ōm-bông') P. I. (Manila In.)	14.51 N	120.45 E
75	Paonia (pā-ō'nyȧ) ... Colo.	38.51 N	107.37 W
152	Paoning (pä'ō-nĭng') ... Chn.	31.33 N	105.58 E
155	Paoshan (pä'ô-shän') ... Chn.	31.23 N	121.26 E
156	Paoti (pä'ô-tē') ... Chn.	39.44 N	117.15 E
156	Paoting (pä'ô-tĭng') ... Chn.	38.59 N	115.24 E
153	Paotowchen (pä'ô-tō'chĕn') .. Chn.	40.33 N	110.2 E
154	Paosting (pä'ô-stĭng) ... Chn.	28.43 N	109.35 E
156	Paoying (pä'ô-yĭng') ... Chn.	33.13 N	119.19 E
156	Paoying L. ... Chn.	33.0 N	119.15 E
123	Pápa (pä'pô) ... Hung.	47.18 N	17.28 E
75	Papago Ind. Res. (pä'pȧ-gō) .. Ariz.	32.30 N	115.0 W
92	Papagayo Lagoon ... Mex.	16.45 N	99.45 W
92	Papagayo, R. (pä-pä-gä'yō) .. Mex.	17.8 N	99.30 W
93	Papaloapan, R. (pä'pä-lō-ä'pän) Mex.	18.20 N	95.50 W
93	Papalotla (pä-pä-lōt'lä) Mex. (In.)	19.34 N	98.51 W
93	Papalotla, R. ... Mex. (In.)	19.35 N	98.55 W
93	Papantla (pä-pän'tlä) ... Mex.	20.27 N	97.18 W
171	Papanui (pä'pȧ-nōō'ē) .. N. Z. (In.)	43.29 S	172.36 E
171	Papanui, Inlet .... N. Z. (In.)	45.51 S	170.43 E
170	Papatoetoe (pä-pä-tō'tō) N. Z. (In.)	36.58 S	174.51 E
122	Papenburg (päp'ĕn-bōōrgh) ... Ger.	53.3 N	7.23 E
152	Papien R. (pä'pyĕn') Chn.-Fr. In. Chn.	23.0 N	101.45 E
127	Papiol (pä-pē-ōl') ...... Sp. (In.)	41.26 N	2.0 E
161	Papua (New Guinea) (I.) (pä'pōō-ä) (păp'ū-ȧ) Pac. O.	6.0 S	142.0 E
161	Papua, Ter. of ... Pap.	8.0 S	144.0 E
104	Paqueta I. (pä-kā'tä) . Braz. (In.)	22.45 S	43.6 W
103	Pará (State) (pä-rä') ... Braz.	5.0 S	50.0 W
103	Pará ... Braz.	19.58 S	44.40 W
103	Para (Belém) (pä-rä') (bā-lĕɴ') Braz. (In.)	1.28 S	48.29 W
162	Paracale (pä-rä-kä'lä) ... P. I.	14.17 N	122.47 E
103	Paracatú (pä-rä-kä-tōō') .... Braz.	17.15 S	46.58 W
160	Paracel Is. (China) (pȧ-rȧ-sĕl') Fr. In. Chn.	16.35 N	112.0 E
166	Parachilna (pȧ-rȧ-chĭl'nȧ) .. Austl.	31.9 S	138.26 E
92	Paracho (pä-rä'chō) ... Mex.	19.38 N	102.0 W
129	Paraćin (pȧ'rä-chēn) ... Yugo.	43.49 N	21.25 E
73	Paradise (păr'ȧ-dīs) Utah (Salt Lake City In.)	41.34 N	111.50 W
70	Paradise Valley ... Neb.	41.28 N	117.31 W
79	Paragould (păr'ȧ-gōōld) ... Ark.	36.3 N	90.29 W
102	Paraguano, Pen. of (pä-rä-gwä'nō) Ven.	11.45 N	70.0 W
103	Paraguassú, R. (pä'rä-gwä-sōō') Braz.	12.32 S	40.0 W
104	Paraguay (păr'ȧ-gwā) (pä-rä-gwī') S. A.	24.0 S	57.0 W
104	Paraguay, R. ... S. A.	22.30 S	57.50 W
103	Parahiba (State) (pä-rä-ē'bä) Braz.	7.0 S	36.30 W
99	Parahiba do Sul (pä-rä-ē'bȧ dōō sōōl') Braz. (Rio de Janeiro In.)	22.11 S	43.21 W
103	Parahiba (João Pessoa) (zhō-ouɴ' pĕ-sō'ȧ) .. Braz.	7.3 S	34.55 W
99	Parahiba, R. Braz. (Rio de Janeiro In.)	22.20 S	43.45 W
90	Paraíso (pä-rä-ē'sō) .... C. Z. (In.)	9.2 N	79.38 W
95	Paraíso ... C. R.	9.50 N	83.53 W
93	Paraíso ... Mex.	18.23 N	93.10 W
171	Parakanui, B. (pä-rä'kä-rōō'ē) N. Z. (In.)	45.45 S	170.39 E
138	Parakou (pä-rȧ-kōō') .. Fr. W. Afr.	9.27 N	2.33 E
103	Paramaribo (pä-rȧ-mä'rē-bō) . Sur.	5.45 N	55.15 W
124	Paramé (pȧ-rȧ-mā') ... Fr.	48.41 N	1.55 W
104	Paraná (pä-rä-nä') ... Arg.	31.45 S	60.31 W
103	Paraná (State) ... Braz.	24.0 S	51.30 W
103	Paranaguá (pä-rä-nä-gwä') .. Braz.	9.0 S	44.0 W
104	Paranaguá ... Braz.	25.30 S	48.30 W
103	Paranahiba R. (pä-rä-nä-ē'bȧ) Braz.	18.30 S	49.30 W
103	Paranápanema R. (pä-rä-nä'pä-nä'mȧ) Braz.	23.0 S	51.0 W
161	Paranaque (pä-rä-nä'kä) P. I. (Manila In.)	14.30 N	120.59 E
103	Paraná, R. (pä-rä-nä') ...... Braz.	13.0 S	47.0 W
104	Paraná, R. ... S. A.	30.0 S	59.30 W
103	Pará, R. (pä-rä') ... Braz.	0.30 S	48.28 W
130	Para R. ... Sov. Un.	53.56 N	41.0 E
99	Parati (pä-rä'tē) Braz. (Rio de Janeiro In.)	23.13 S	44.43 W
169	Parattah (pȧ-rät'ȧ) Austl. (Tas. In.)	42.23 S	147.28 E
124	Paray-le-Monial (pȧ-rĕ'lē-mō-nyȧl') Fr.	46.27 N	4.18 E
122	Parchim (pär'ĸĭm) ... Ger.	53.24 N	11.51 E
123	Parczew (pär'chĕf) ... Pol.	51.37 N	22.53 E
103	Pardo, R. (pär'dō) ... Braz.	15.15 S	40.30 W
122	Pardubice (pär'dōō-bĭt-sĕ) .. Czech.	50.2 N	15.47 E
103	Parecis, Serra dos (Mts.) (sĕr'rȧ dōs pä-rä'sēzh) .. Braz.	12.30 S	61.0 W
126	Paredes de Nava (pä-rā'dās dä nä'vä) .. Sp.	42.12 N	4.40 W
128	Parenzo (pä-rĕnt'sō) ... It.	45.11 N	13.37 E
127	Parets (pä-râts') ... Sp. (In.)	41.33 N	2.13 E
7	Paria, G. of (pä'rē-ä) .. Trin. (In.)	10.30 N	61.36 W
75	Paria R. (pär-ē-ȧ) ... Utah	37.15 N	111.55 W
80	Parida, R. de la (pä-rē'dä) ... Mex.	26.30 N	104.40 W
102	Parima, Serra (Mts.) (sĕr'rȧ pä-rē'mȧ) Ven.-Braz.	3.0 N	64.30 W
102	Pariña Pt. (pä-rēn'yä) ... Ec.	4.45 S	81.15 W
166	Paringa (pȧ-rĭng'ȧ) ... Austl.	34.11 S	140.48 E
103	Parintins (pä-rēɴ-tēɴzh') .... Braz.	2.45 S	56.33 W
79	Paris (păr'ĭs) ... Ark.	35.17 N	93.43 W
84	Paris ... Can.	43.13 N	80.24 W
125	Paris (pȧ-rē') ... Fr. (In.)	48.52 N	2.20 E
84	Paris (păr'ĭs) ... Ill.	39.37 N	87.40 W
84	Paris ... Ky.	38.14 N	84.16 W
79	Paris ... Mo.	39.27 N	92.0 W
82	Paris ... Tenn.	36.17 N	88.20 W
79	Paris ... Tex.	33.39 N	95.33 W
95	Parita G. (pä-rē'tä) ... Pan.	8.10 N	80.20 W
145	Parit Jawa (pä'rĕt jä'vȧ) Non-fed. Mal. St. (In.)	1.57 N	102.39 E
75	Park City ... Utah	40.38 N	111.30 W
72	Parker (pär'kẽr) Colo. (Denver In.)	39.31 N	104.45 W
76	Parker ... S. D.	43.24 N	97.9 W
75	Parker Dam ... Ariz.-Calif.	34.14 N	114.20 W
84	Parkersburg (pär'kẽrz-bûrg) W. Va.	39.16 N	81.32 W
167	Parkes (parks) ... Austl.	33.9 S	148.12 E
77	Park Falls ... Wis.	45.56 N	90.28 W
119	Parkgate (pärk'gāt) Gt. Brit. (Liverpool In.)	53.19 N	3.6 W
49	Parkland (pärk'lănd) Wash. (Seattle In.)	47.8 N	122.26 W
81	Park Place ... Tex. (In.)	20.41 N	95.16 W
78	Park Range ... Colo.	40.45 N	106.35 W
77	Park Rapids ... Minn.	46.55 N	95.2 W
76	Park River ... N. D.	48.22 N	97.43 W
169	Parkside (pärk'sīd) Austl. (Adelaide In.)	34.56 S	138.37 E
76	Parkston (pärks'tŭn) ... S. D.	43.24 N	97.59 W
75	Park View ... N. M.	36.43 N	106.32 W
127	Parla (pär'lä) ... Sp. (In.)	40.14 N	3.45 W
128	Parma (pär'mä) ... It.	44.47 N	10.20 E
84	Parma ... Ohio	41.24 N	81.45 W
103	Parnahiba (pär-nä-ē'bȧ) .... Braz.	3.0 S	41.42 W
103	Parnahiba, R. ... Braz.	4.0 S	42.50 W
129	Parnassus (Mt.) (pär-năs'ŭs) . Gre.	38.31 N	22.37 E
121	Pärnu (pĕr'nōō) ... Est.	58.22 N	24.30 E
121	Pärnu G. ... Est.	58.15 N	24.20 E
121	Pärnu R. ... Est.	58.30 N	24.55 E
165	Paroo R. (pä'rōō) ... Austl.	30.0 S	144.7 E
129	Paros (pä'rôs) (pä'rŏs) ... Grc.	37.4 N	25.10 E
129	Paros (I.) ... Grc.	37.5 N	25.12 E
75	Parowan (păr'ô-wăn) ... Utah	37.52 N	112.50 W
80	Parral (pär-räl') ... Mex.	26.55 N	105.40 W
80	Parral, R. ... Mex.	27.20 N	105.12 W
167	Parramatta (păr-ȧ-măt'ȧ) ... Austl.	33.48 S	150.59 E
169	Parramatta R. Austl. (Sydney In.)	33.50 S	151.4 E
80	Parras (pär-räs') ... Mex.	25.28 N	102.8 W
73	Pärrish (păr'ĭsh) Ala. (Birmingham In.)	33.43 N	87.18 W
86	Parrsborough (pärz'bŭr-ō) ... Can.	45.26 N	64.19 W
53	Parry, C. (păr'ĭ) ... Can.	70.0 N	123.38 W
85	Parry I. ... Can.	45.15 N	80.10 W
48	Parry Is. ... Can.	75.30 N	110.0 W
55	Parry Sound ... Can.	45.20 N	80.3 W
79	Parsons (pär's'nz) ... Kan.	37.20 N	95.16 W
85	Parsons ... W. Va.	39.6 N	79.43 W
124	Parthenay (pȧr-t'-nĕ') ... Fr.	46.39 N	0.15 W
128	Partinico (pär-tē'nê-kō) ... It.	38.2 N	13.7 E
103	Parú, R. (pä-rōō') ... Braz.	0.0	54.0 W
143	Parys (pȧ-rīs') ... U. S. Afr.	26.54 S	27.28 E
74	Pasadena (păs-ȧ-dē'nȧ) ... Calif.	34.9 N	118.10 W
81	Pasadena ... Tex. (In.)	29.42 N	95.12 W
162	Pasaleng B. (pä-sä'lĕng) ... P. I.	18.35 N	120.55 E
162	Pasay (pä'sä-ē) ... P. I.	14.32 N	121.0 E
82	Pascagoula (păs-kȧ-gōō'lȧ) .. Miss.	30.21 N	88.33 W
82	Pascagoula R. ... Miss.	30.50 N	88.45 W
123	Pascani (pȧsh'kän'') ... Rom.	47.16 N	26.43 E
70	Pasco (păs'kō) ... Wash.	46.13 N	119.7 W
169	Pascoe Vale (pȧs'kō vāl') Austl. (Melbourne In.)	37.44 S	144.55 E
102	Pasco, Nudo de (Mt.) (nōō'dô dā päs'kō) Peru	10.45 S	76.29 W
122	Pasewalk (pä'zē-välk) ... Ger.	53.31 N	14.1 E
158	Pashennaya (pȧsh'ĕn-nȧ-yȧ) Sov. Un.	47.47 N	134.48 E
149	Pashkova (pȧsh'kô-vȧ) .. Sov. Un.	48.59 N	130.59 E
131	Pashkovskaya (pȧsh-kôf'skȧ-yȧ) Sov. Un.	45.1 N	39.2 E
162	Pasig (pä'sĭg) ... P. I.	14.34 N	121.5 E
161	Pasig R. .... P. I. (Manila In.)	14.33 N	121.10 E
122	Pasing (pä'zĭng) ... Ger.	48.8 N	11.27 E
94	Pasión, R. de la (pä-syōn') Guat. (In.)	16.33 N	90.20 W
129	Pašmakli (päsh'mōk-lē) ... Bul.	41.35 N	24.35 E
166	Pasmore R. (păs'mōr) ... Austl.	31.25 S	139.28 E
92	Paso de Sotos (pä'sō dā sō'tōs) Mex.	21.38 N	102.40 W
160	Pasoeroean (pä-sōō-rōō'än) Neth. Ind.	7.41 S	121.55 E
74	Paso Robles (pä'sō rō'blĕs) .. Calif.	35.37 N	120.43 W
85	Passaic (pă-sā'ĭk) ... N. J.	40.52 N	74.8 W
88	Passaic R. ... N. J. (New York In.)	40.53 N	74.15 W

ăt; finȧl; rāte; senâte; ärm; ȧsk; sofȧ; fâre; ch-choose; dh-as th in other; bē; ēvent; bĕt; recĕnt; cratẽr; g-go; gh-guttural g; bĭt; ĭ-short neutral; rīde; ĸ-guttural k as ch in German ich;

Page	Name Pronunciation Region	Lat. °′	Long. °′
86	Passamaquoddy B. (păs′ȧ-mȧ-kwŏd′ĭ) Me.-Can.	45.5 N	66.58 W
140	Passa R. (pȧs′ȧ) . . . . . . Fr. Eq. Afr.	2.0 S	13.32 E
122	Passau (päs′ou) . . . . Ger.	48.34 N	13.27 E
82	Pass Christian (pȧs krĭs′tĭ-ăn) Miss.	30.19 N	89.17 W
163	Passi (päs′ē) . . . . P. I.	11.7 N	122.39 E
104	Passo Fundo (pä′sŏ fōōn′dōō) Braz.	28.15 S	52.28 W
102	Pastaza, R. (päs-tä′zä) . . . . Ec.	3.0 S	76.32 W
102	Pasto (päs′tō) . . . . Col.	1.2 N	77.15 W
102	Pasto (Vol.) . . . . Col.	1.0 N	77.15 W
126	Pasuquin (pȧ-sōō-kēn′) . . . . . . P. I.	18.20 N	120.37 E
121	Pasvalys (päs-vȧ′lēs) . . . . Lith.	56.3 N	24.24 E
104	Patagones (pä-tä-gō′nās) . . . . . Arg.	40.50 S	62.58 W
104	Patagonia (Reg.) (păt-ȧ-gō′nĭ-ȧ) Arg.	47.0 S	69.30 W
163	Pata I. (pä′tä) . . . . P. I.	5.48 N	121.10 E
88	Patapsco R. (pȧ-tăps′kō) Md. (Baltimore In.)	39.13 N	76.32 W
166	Patchewollock (pă-chē-wŏl′ŭk) Austl.	35.22 S	142.2 E
170	Patea (pä′tā-ä) (pȧ-tē′ȧ) . . . . . N. Z.	39.45 S	174.27 E
118	Pateley Bridge (păt′lĭ) . . . Gt. Brit.	54.5 N	1.45 W
143	Patentie (pȧ-tĕn′tē′) . . . . U. S. Afr.	33.48 S	24.47 E
127	Paterna de Rivera (pä-tĕr′nä dä rē-vä′rä) Sp. (In.)	36.31 N	5.51 W
128	Paternò (pä-tĕr-nô′) . . . . It.	37.34 N	14.52 E
85	Paterson (păt′ēr-sŭn) . . . . N. J.	40.57 N	74.12 W
167	Paterson, C. . . . . Austl.	38.40 S	145.35 E
71	Pathfinder Reservoir (păth′fīn-dēr) Wyo.	44.22 N	106.55 W
151	Patiala (pŭt-ē-ä′lŭ) . . . . India	30.16 N	76.17 E
151	Patna-Bankipore (pŭt′nŭ-băŋ′kē-pōr) India	25.35 N	85.15 E
162	Patnanongan I. (pät-nä-nôŋ′gän) P. I.	14.48 N	122.12 E
163	Patnongon (pät-nôŋ-gōn′) . . . P. I.	10.54 N	122.0 E
84	Patoka R. (pȧ-tō′kȧ) . . . . Ind.	38.23 N	87.10 W
103	Patos (pä′tōzh) . . . . Braz.	6.58 S	37.28 W
72	Patos I. (pä′tōs) Wash. (Vancouver In.)	48.48 N	122.57 W
104	Patos, Lagoa dos (L.) (lä-gō-ȧ dōzh pä′tōzh) . Braz.	31.0 S	51.15 W
129	Patrai (Patras) (pä-trī′) (pä-träs′) Grc.	38.14 N	21.48 E
129	Patras (Patrai) . . . . Grc.	38.14 N	21.48 E
129	Patras, G. of . . . . Grc.	38.15 N	21.35 E
103	Patrocinio (pä-trō-sē′nē-ōō) . . Braz.	18.58 S	46.49 W
160	Pattani (păt′ä-nē) . . . . Thai.	6.56 N	101.15 E
86	Patten (păt″n) . . . . Me.	45.59 N	68.28 W
81	Patterson (păt′ēr-sŭn) . . . . La.	29.40 N	91.19 W
85	Patton (păt″n) . . . . Pa.	40.41 N	78.42 W
95	Patuca Pt. (pä-tōō′kä) . . . . . Hond.	15.50 N	84.18 W
94	Patuca (R.) . . . . Hond.	15.0 N	85.0 W
154	Patung (pä′tōōng′) . . . . Chn.	31.2 N	110.17 E
170	Patutahi (pä-tōō′tä-hē) . . . . . N. Z.	38.38 S	177.52 E
85	Patuxent R. (pȧ-tŭk′sĕnt) . . . . Md.	39.0 N	76.45 W
92	Pátzcuaro (päts′kwä-rō) . . . . . Mex.	19.30 N	101.32 W
92	Pátzcuaro, L. . . . . Mex.	19.35 N	101.33 W
94	Patzún (pät-zōōn′) . . . . Guat.	14.40 N	91.0 W
124	Pau (pō) . . . . Fr.	43.18 N	0.21 W
84	Paulding (pôl′dĭng) . . . . Ohio	41.8 N	84.37 W
103	Paulista (pou-lēs′tä) . . . . Braz.	8.3 S	41.2 W
103	Paulo Affonso Falls (pou′lōō äf-fôɴ-sōō) . Braz.	9.28 S	38.15 W
143	Paul Pieters Burg (poul pē′tērz bōōrgh) . U. S. Afr.	27.28 S	30.49 E
79	Pauls Valley (pôlz) . . . . Okla.	34.43 N	97.14 W
124	Pau R. (pō) . . . . Fr.	43.10 N	0.10 W
173	Pauwela (pä-ōō-wä′lä) . . . . . . Haw.	20.55 N	156.23 W
128	Pavia (pä-vē′ä) . . . . It.	45.11 N	9.10 E
131	Pavoloch (pȧ-vô-lôch′) . . . Sov. Un.	49.52 N	29.21 E
148	Pavlodar (pȧv-lô-dȧr′) . . . Sov. Un.	53.15 N	77.10 E
131	Pavlograd (pȧv-lô-grȧt′) . . Sov. Un.	48.33 N	35.54 E
131	Pavlovsk (pȧv-lôfsk′) . . . . Sov. Un.	50.28 N	40.0 E
130	Pavlovski Posad (pȧv-lôf′skĭ pô-sȧt′) . Sov. Un.	55.46 N	38.38 E
104	Pavuna (pä-vōō′nȧ) . . . Braz. (In.)	22.49 S	43.20 W
79	Pawhuska (pô-hŭs′kȧ) . . . . Okla.	36.41 N	96.20 W
79	Pawnee (pô-nē′) . . . . Okla.	36.21 N	96.48 W
79	Pawnee City . . . . Okla.	40.6 N	96.9 W
84	Paw Paw (pô′ pô) . . . . Mich.	42.17 N	85.53 W
85	Pawtucket (pô-tŭk′ĕt) . . . . R. I.	41.52 N	71.25 W
129	Paxos (I.) (păk′sôs) . . . . Grc.	39.12 N	20.10 E
84	Paxton (păks′tŭn) . . . . Ill.	40.26 N	88.5 W
71	Paxton . . . . Mont.	47.39 N	105.21 W
155	Payang (pä-yäng) . . . . Chn.	29.5 N	116.40 E
158	Payen (pä′yĕn′) . . . . Manch.	46.0 N	127.29 E
70	Payette (pȧ-ĕt′) . . . . Ida.	44.5 N	116.56 W
70	Payette R., North Fork . . . . Ida.	44.20 N	116.5 W
70	Payette R., South Fork . . . . Ida.	44.9 N	115.45 W
55	Payne L. (pān) . . . . Can.	60.5 N	73.0 W
77	Paynesville (pānz′vĭl) . . . . Minn.	45.24 N	94.42 W
	Payo Obispo, see Ciudad Chetumal, Mex.		
104	Paysandú (pī-sän-dōō′) . . . . Ur.	32.25 S	58.1 W
75	Payson (pā′s′n) . . . . Utah	40.3 N	111.42 W
113	Pazar (pä′zär) . . . . Tur.	41.15 N	41.0 E
129	Pazardzik (pȧ-zȧr-dzhĕk′) . . . . . Bul.	42.11 N	24.19 E
79	Peabody (pē′bŏd-ĭ) . . . . Kan.	38.9 N	97.7 W
86	Peabody . . . . Mass.	42.31 N	70.58 W
83	Peace Cr. (pēs) . . . . Fla. (In.)	27.20 N	81.50 W
54	Peace R. . . . . Can.	58.0 N	117.0 W
88	Peach Haven (pēch) N. Y. (Niagara Falls In.)	43.3 N	78.58 W
167	Peak Hill (pēk-hĭl′) . . . . Austl.	32.44 S	148.12 E
167	Peak, The (Mt.) . . . . Austl.	31.33 S	145.53 E
118	Peak, The (Mt.) . . . . Gt. Brit.	53.23 N	1.52 W
82	Pea R. (pē) . . . . Ala.	31.27 N	86.0 W
81	Pearland (pûrl′ănd) . . . . Tex. (In.)	29.34 N	95.17 W
95	Pearl Lagoon . . . . Nic.	12.35 N	83.20 W
95	Pearl Lagoon (Las Perlas) (läs pĕr′-läs) . Nic.	12.20 N	83.41 W
154	Pearl R. (Chu Kiang) (pûrl) (chōō′ kyăng′) . Chn.	22.38 N	113.38 E
82	Pearl R. . . . . Miss.-La.	31.50 N	90.10 W
80	Pearsall (pēr′sôl) . . . . Tex.	28.53 N	99.6 W
49	Pearson (pēr′sŭn) Wash. (Seattle In.)	47.42 N	122.39 W
143	Pearston (pērs′tŭn) . . . . . U. S. Afr.	32.35 S	25.8 E
46	Peary Land (pēr′ĭ) . . . . Grnld.	82.0 N	40.0 W
78	Pease R. (pēz) . . . . Tex.	34.10 N	99.40 W
78	Pease R. North . . . . Tex.	34.20 N	100.32 W
81	Peason (pēz″n) . . . . La.	31.25 N	93.19 W
129	Peć (pĕch) . . . . Yugo.	42.39 N	20.19 E
80	Pecan Bayou (pē-kăn′) . . . . Tex.	31.50 N	99.0 W
103	Pecanha (pā-kän′yȧ) . . . . Braz.	18.30 S	42.40 W
77	Pecatonica R. (pĕk-ȧ-tŏn′ĭ-kȧ) . . Ill.	42.18 N	89.30 W
112	Pechora B. (pyĕ-chô′rȧ) . . Sov. Un.	68.45 N	54.30 E
112	Pechora R. . . . . Sov. Un.	66.0 N	52.30 E
72	Peckham (pĕk′ăm) Colo. (Denver In.)	40.17 N	104.45 W
80	Pecos (pā′kōs) . . . . Tex.	31.26 N	103.30 W
80	Pecos R. . . . . N. M.-Tex.	34.0 N	104.20 W
123	Pecs (pāch) . . . . Hung.	46.3 N	18.14 E
143	Peddie (pĕd′ĭ) . . . . U. S. Afr.	33.12 S	27.8 E
104	Pedra da Gavea (Mt.) (pā′drä dä gä′vā-ȧ) . Braz. (In.)	23.0 S	43.17 W
93	Pedregal de San Angel (Mt.) (pā-drä-gäl′ dā sän-än′häl) . Mex. (In.)	19.18 N	99.10 W
93	Pedregal R. (pā-drä-gäl′) . . . . Mex.	17.40 N	93.47 W
103	Pedro II (pā′drōō sā-gōōn′dōō) Braz.	4.28 S	41.28 W
94	Pedro Antonio Santos (Sta-Cruz Chico) (pā′drô än-tō′nē-ōō sän tozh) (sän′tä krōōz′ chē′kō) Mex. (In.)	18.50 N	88.15 W
96	Pedro Betancourt (pā′drō bā-täŋ-kōrt′) . Cuba	22.41 N	81.26 W
96	Pedro Bluff (pē′drō blŭf) . . . . Jam.	17.50 N	77.45 W
90	Pedro Miguel (pā′drō mē-gĕl′) C. Z. (In.)	9.1 N	79.37 W
49	Pedro Valley (pē′drō) Calif. (San Francisco In.)	37.35 N	122.30 W
166	Peebinga (pē-bĭng′ȧ) . . . . Austl.	34.52 S	140.52 E
116	Peebles (pē′b′lz) . . . . Gt. Brit.	55.40 N	3.10 W
83	Peedee R. (pē-dē′) . . . . S. C.	34.10 N	79.33 W
85	Peekskill (pēks′kĭl) . . . . N. Y.	41.17 N	73.56 W
171	Peel Mt. (pēl) . . . . N. Z.	43.48 S	171.10 E
167	Peel R. . . . . Austl.	31.0 S	150.51 E
54	Peel R. Can.	65.45 N	135.0 W
122	Peene R. (pā′nē) . . . . Ger.	53.55 N	13.25 E
166	Peery L. (pēr′ĭ) . . . . Austl.	30.45 S	143.36 E
171	Pegasus B. (pĕg′ȧ-sŭs) . . . . N. Z.	43.20 S	173.0 E
122	Pegnitz R. (pĕgh-nēts′) . . . . Ger.	49.32 N	11.30 E
127	Pego (pā′gō) . . . . Sp.	38.51 N	0.8 W
160	Pegu (pĕ-gōō′) . . . . India	17.15 N	96.29 E
160	Pegu Yoma (Mts.) (pĕ-gōō′ yō′mȧ) India	19.0 N	96.0 E
129	Pehčevo (pĕĸ′chĕ-vô) . . . . Yugo.	41.43 N	22.58 E
155	Pehkow Shan (Mts.) (pā′kō shän′) Chn.	29.18 N	114.25 E
156	Pehtaiho . . . . Chn.	39.50 N	119.30 E
156	Peihsien (pā′ē-hsyĕn′) . . . . Chn.	34.44 N	117.3 E
158	Peian (pā′ē-än) . . . . Manch.	48.15 N	126.25 E
122	Peine (pī′nē) . . . . Ger.	52.18 N	10.13 E
156	Peiping (Peking) (pā′ē-pĭng′) (pē-kĭng′) . Chn.	39.55 N	116.25 E
121	Peipsi (Chudskoe) L. (pīp′sĭ) (chōōt′skô-yĕ) . Eur.	58.40 N	27.30 E
156	Pei R. (pā′ē) . . . . Chn.	39.30 N	116.58 E
154	Pei R. . . . . Chn.	23.35 N	112.52 E
129	Peiraievs (Piraeus) (pī-rā-ĕfs′) (pī-rē′ŭs) . Grc.	37.58 N	23.39 E
156	Peisha R. (pā′ē-shä′) . . . . Chn.	32.54 N	120.29 E
156	Peitang R. (pā′ē-täng′) . . . . Chn.	39.40 N	117.28 E
156	Peiyang R. (pā′ē-yäng′) . . . . . . Chn.	33.39 N	120.40 E
79	Pekin (pē′kĭn) . . . . Ill.	40.34 N	89.38 W
88	Pekin . . . N. Y. (Niagara Falls In.)	43.10 N	78.54 W
156	Peking (Peiping) (pē-kĭng′) (pā′ē-pĭng′) . Chn.	39.55 N	116.25 E
128	Pelagosa Is. (pĕ-lä-gō′sä) . . . . . . It.	42.22 N	16.20 E
82	Pelahatchee (pĕl-ȧ-hăch′ē) . . Miss.	32.18 N	89.48 W
125	Pelat, Mt. (pē-lȧ′) . . . . Fr.	44.15 N	6.45 E
84	Pelée I. (pē′lē) . . . . Can.	41.55 N	82.30 W
6	Pelée (Mt.) (pē-lā′) . . . Mart. (In.)	14.48 N	61.9 W
84	Pelee Pt. (pē′lē) . . . . Can.	41.46 N	82.38 W
73	Pelham (pĕl′ăm) Ala. (Birmingham In.)	33.17 N	86.49 W
169	Pelham . . . . Austl. (In.)	26.23 S	150.20 E
82	Pelham . . . . Ga.	31.7 N	84.11 W
122	Pelhřimov (pĕl′hrzhē-mōf) . Czech.	49.26 N	15.13 E
96	Pelican Har. (pĕl′ĭ-kăn) . . . . Ba. Is.	26.21 N	77.0 W
77	Pelican L. . . . . Minn.	46.35 N	94.9 W
76	Pelican Rapids . . . . Minn.	46.35 N	96.5 W
112	Pelim R. (pyȧ-lēm′) . . . . . Sov. Un.	60.45 N	62.50 E
77	Pella (pĕl′ȧ) . . . . Ia.	41.25 N	92.52 W
142	Pella . . . . U. S. Afr.	29.2 S	19.8 E
122	Pellworm (I.) (pĕl′vôrm) . . . . . . Ger.	54.30 N	8.38 E
81	Pelly (pĕl-ĭ) . . . . Tex. (In.)	29.42 N	94.58 W
54	Pelly, L. . . . . Can.	65.50 N	102.0 W
53	Pelly Mts. . . . . Can.	61.20 N	131.30 W
54	Pelly R. Can.	62.35 N	135.0 W
129	Peloponnesos (pĕl-ō-pô-nä′sôs) Grc.	37.30 N	22.40 E
104	Pelotas (pā-lō′täzh) . . . . Braz.	31.40 S	52.20 W
135	Pelusium (Tina) B. (pē-lūzh′ĭ-ŭm) (tē′nȧ) . Eg. (In.)	31.15 N	32.40 E
135	Pelusium (Tina), Plain of . Eg. (In.)	30.55 N	32.40 E
125	Pelvoux, Mt. (pĕl-vōō′) . . . . Fr.	44.55 N	6.22 E
83	Pelzer (pĕl′zēr) . . . . S. C.	34.38 N	82.29 W
140	Pemba (pĕm′bȧ) . . . . N. Rh.	16.33 S	27.26 E
141	Pemba I. . . . . Zan.	5.10 S	39.45 E
76	Pembina (pĕm′bĭ-nȧ) . . . . N. D.	48.58 N	97.14 W
76	Pembina R. . . . . Can.-U. S.	49.0 N	98.10 W
118	Pembridge (pĕm′brĭj) . . . . Gt. Brit.	52.13 N	2.53 W
55	Pembroke (pĕm′brōk) . . . . Can.	45.45 N	77.31 W
116	Pembroke . . . . Gt. Brit.	51.40 N	4.57 W
87	Pembroke . . . . Mass. (In.)	42.4 N	70.48 W
126	Penafiel (pā-nȧ-fyĕl′) . . . . Port.	41.12 N	8.18 W
126	Peñafiel (pā-nyȧ-fyĕl′) . . . . Sp.	41.36 N	4.9 W
126	Peñalara (Mt.) (pā-nyȧ-lä′rä) . . Sp.	40.52 N	3.58 W
126	Penamacor (pā-nȧ-mȧ-kōr′) . . Port.	40.11 N	7.11 W
160	Penang (State) (pē-năng′) Strs. Sets.	4.30 N	100.0 E
160	Penang I. . . . . Strs. Sets.	5.21 N	100.15 E
162	Peñaranda (pā-nyȧ-rän′dä) . . . P. I.	15.20 N	121.0 E
126	Peñaranda de Bracamonte (pā-nyȧ-rän′dä dā brä-kä-mōn′tä) . Sp.	40.54 N	5.13 W
127	Peña Roya (Mt.) (pā′nyȧ rō′yȧ) Sp.	40.24 N	0.10 W
126	Peñas C. (pā′nyȧs) . . . . Sp.	43.40 N	5.51 W
78	Peñasco R. (pā-nyȧs′kō) . . . . N. M.	32.50 N	105.0 W
104	Peñas, G. of . . . . Chl.	47.30 S	75.0 W
154	Penchow (pĕn′chō′) . . . . Chn.	23.19 N	109.2 E
138	Pendembu (pĕn-dĕm′bōō) . . . . S. L.	8.15 N	10.47 W
76	Pender (pĕn′dēr) . . . . Neb.	42.8 N	96.41 W
72	Pender Is. . . . Can. (Vancouver In.)	48.47 N	123.18 W
70	Pendleton (pĕn′d′l-tŭn) . . . . . . Ore.	45.40 N	118.48 W
70	Pend Oreille L. (pĕnd ô-rĕl′) . . Ida.	48.12 N	116.30 W
70	Pend Oreille R. . . . . Wash.-Idaho	48.30 N	117.17 W
103	Penedo (pā-nā′dōō) . . . . Braz.	10.20 S	36.31 W
129	Peneios R. (pē′nĭ-ôs′) . . . . Grc.	39.35 N	22.10 E
85	Penetanguishene (pĕn′ē-tăŋ-gĭ-shēn′) . Can.	45.46 N	79.46 W
154	Pengk (pĕŋk) . . . . Chn.	30.48 N	105.55 E
156	Pengpu (pĕng′pōō′) . . . . Chn.	32.54 N	117.17 E
154	Pengshui (pĕng′shōō-ē′) . . . . . Chn.	29.20 N	108.14 E
155	Pengtze (pĕng′tzĕ′) . . . . Chn.	29.56 N	116.42 E
169	Penguin (pĕŋ′gwĭn) Austl. (Tas. In.)	41.6 S	146.3 E
126	Peniche (pĕ-nē′chĕ) . . . . Port.	39.22 N	9.23 W
118	Penistone (pĕn′ĭ-stŭn) . . . . Gt. Brit.	53.32 N	1.39 W
92	Penjamillo (pĕn-hä-mēl′yō) . . Mex.	20.6 N	101.56 W
92	Pénjamo (pān′hä-mō) . . . . Mex.	20.23 N	101.42 W
118	Penk, R. (pĕnk) . . . . Gt. Brit.	52.45 N	2.5 W
118	Penkridge (pĕnk′rĭj) . . . . . Gt. Brit.	52.43 N	2.7 W
128	Penne (pĕn′nä) . . . . It.	42.27 N	13.55 E
151	Penner R. (pĕn′ēr) . . . . India	14.30 N	79.0 E
116	Pennine Chain (Mts.) . . . . Gt. Brit.	54.20 N	2.10 W
84	Pennsboro (pĕnz′bŭr-ō) . . . . W. Va.	39.16 N	80.58 W
85	Pennsylvania (State) (pĕn-sĭl-vā′nĭ-ȧ) . U. S.	41.0 N	77.30 W
85	Penn Yan (pĕn yăn′) . . . . N. Y.	42.40 N	77.4 W
86	Penobscot B. (pē-nŏb′skŏt) . . . Me.	44.15 N	68.50 W
86	Penobscot R. . . . . Me.	45.25 N	68.40 W
130	Peno, L. (pā′nō) . . . . Sov. Un.	56.58 N	32.42 E
166	Penola (pē-nō′lȧ) . . . . Austl.	37.23 S	140.48 E
166	Penong (pē-nông′) . . . . Austl.	31.56 S	132.58 E
95	Penonome (pā-nō-nō-mā′) . . . . Pan.	8.28 N	80.17 W
167	Penrith (pĕn′rĭth) . . . . Austl.	33.46 S	150.42 E
82	Pensacola (pĕn-sȧ-kō′lȧ) . . . . . . Fla.	30.25 N	87.13 W
82	Pensacola B. . . . . Fla.	30.25 N	87.10 W
88	Pensauken Cr. (pĕn-sô′kĕn) Pa. (Philadelphia In.)	39.57 N	75.0 W
166	Penshurst (pĕnz′hûrst) . . . . . Austl.	37.52 S	142.20 E
165	Pentecost I. (pĕn′tē-kŏst) New Hebr.	15.45 S	168.10 E
104	Pentia (pĕn-tē′ȧ) . . . . . . Braz. (In.)	22.50 S	43.17 W
116	Pentland Firth (pĕnt′lănd) Gt. Brit. (In.)	58.40 N	3.0 W
118	Pen-y-ghent (Mt.) (pĕn-ĭ-gĕnt′) Gt. Brit.	54.9 N	2.14 W
113	Penza (pĕn′zȧ) . . . . Sov. Un.	53.10 N	45.0 E
116	Penzance (pĕn-zăns′) . . . . . Gt. Brit.	50.5 N	5.35 W
122	Penzberg (pĕnts′bĕrgh) . . . . Ger.	47.43 N	11.20 E
149	Penzhina (pĕn-zhē′nȧ) . . . . Sov. Un.	63.15 N	168.59 E
149	Penzhina R. . . . . Sov. Un.	63.0 N	168.0 E
149	Penzhinskaya B. (pĕn-zhĕnsk′ȧ-yȧ) . . Sov. Un.	61.0 N	162.0 E
79	Peoria (pē-ō′rĭ-ȧ) . . . . Ill.	40.41 N	89.37 W
92	Peotillos (pā-ō-tēl′yōs) . . . . . . Mex.	22.30 N	100.34 W
142	Pepani R. (pĕ-pä′nĭ) . . . . Bech.	25.50 S	23.10 E
96	Pepe, C. (pā′pā) . . . . . Isle of Pines	21.28 N	83.3 W
87	Pepperell (pĕp′ēr-ĕl) . . . Mass. (In.)	42.40 N	71.36 W
129	Peqin (pȧ-kēn′) . . . . Alb.	41.3 N	19.45 E
90	Pequiñi, R. (pȧ-kē′nyē) Pan. (C. Z. In.)	9.18 N	79.35 W
127	Perales R. (pā-rä′läs) . . . . Sp. (In.)	40.27 N	4.6 W
127	Perales de Tajuña (pā-rä′läs dā tä-hōō′nyä) . Sp. (In.)	40.13 N	3.21 W
86	Percé (pĕr-sā) . . . . Can.	48.31 N	64.15 W
119	Perchtoldsdorf (pĕrĸ′tōlts-dôrf) Aus. (Wien In.)	48.7 N	16.16 E
127	Perdido, Mt. (pĕr-dē′dō) . . . . Sp.	42.40 N	0.2 E
82	Perdido R. (pēr-dī′dō) . . . Ala.-Fla.	30.43 N	87.30 W
102	Pereira (pā-rā′rä) . . . . Col.	4.45 N	75.48 W
135	Perejil I. (pē-rȧ-kēl′) Sp. Mor. (Gib. In.)	35.54 N	5.36 E
131	Perekop (pĕr-ȧ-kôp′) . . . . . Sov. Un.	46.8 N	33.42 E
131	Pereshchipino (pâ′rȧsh-chē′pē-nô) Sov. Un.	49.1 N	35.18 E
130	Pereslavskoe, L. (pâ-rȧslȧf′-skō-yĕ) . Sov. Un.	56.45 N	38.47 E
130	Pereslavl-Zalesskii (pâ-rȧ-slȧv″l-zȧ-lyĕs′kĭ-ē) . Sov. Un.	56.43 N	38.52 E
89	Peres, R. des (dā pâr′) Mo. (St. Louis In.)	38.34 N	90.18 W
131	Pereyaslavl (pĕ-rȧ-yȧ′slȧv′l) Sov. Un.	50.5 N	31.28 E
104	Pergamino (pĕr-gȧ-mē′nō) . . . Arg.	33.58 S	60.40 W
76	Perham (pĕr′hăm) . . . . Minn.	46.36 N	95.32 W
55	Peribonka R. (pĕr-ĭ-bôŋ′kȧ) . . Can.	51.0 N	71.30 W
124	Périgueux (pā-rē-gû′) . . . . Fr.	45.11 N	0.45 E
145	Perim (I.) (pē-rēm′) Red Sea (In.)	12.39 N	43.26 E
95	Perlas Is. (pĕr′läs) . . . . Pan.	8.25 N	79.0 W
122	Perleberg (pĕr′lē-bĕrgh) . . . . Ger.	53.5 N	11.51 E
148	Perm (pĕrm) . . . . Sov. Un.	57.50 N	56.10 E
149	Perm . . . . Sov. Un.	50.45 N	137.5 E
158	Permskoe (pĕrm′skô-yĕ) . . Sov. Un.	43.43 N	135.1 E
103	Pernambuco (Recife) (pĕr-näm-bōō′kō) (rä-sē′fä) . Braz.	8.1 S	35.0 W
103	Pernambuco (State) . . . . Braz.	8.30 S	38.0 W
166	Pernatty Lagoon (pēr-năt′ĭ) . Austl.	31.30 S	137.13 E
129	Pernik (pĕr-nēk′) . . . . Bul.	42.35 N	23.2 E

ng-sing; ŋ-baŋk; ɴ-nasalized n; nŏd; cŏmmit ōld; ôbey; ôrder; fōōd; fŏŏt; ou-out; s-soft; sh-dish; th-thin; pūre; ūnite; ûrn; stŭd; circŭs; ü-as "y" in study; ′-indeterminate vowel.

Page	Name Pronunciation Region	Lat. °′	Long. °′
124	Péronne (pā-rôn′) Fr.	49.57 N	2.55 E
93	Perote (pâ-rō′tā) Mex.	19.34 N	97.14 W
124	Perpignan (pĕr-pē-nyäN′) Fr.	42.42 N	2.55 E
127	Perregaux (pĕr-rā-gō′) Alg.	35.35 N	0.5 E
73	Perris (pĕr′ĭs) Calif. (Los Angeles In.)	33.47 N	117.14 W
96	Perros B. (pā′rōs) Cuba	22.20 N	78.30 W
57	Perrot, Ile (pĕr′ŭt) Can. (Montreal In.)	45.23 N	73.55 W
82	Perry (pĕr′ĭ) Fla.	30.7 N	83.34 W
83	Perry Ga.	32.28 N	83.46 W
77	Perry Ia.	41.51 N	94.4 W
85	Perry N. Y.	42.55 N	78.0 W
79	Perry Okla.	36.17 N	97.18 W
73	Perry...Utah (Salt Lake City In.)	41.28 N	112.3 W
84	Perrysburg (pĕr′ĭz-bûrg) Ohio	41.35 N	83.37 W
78	Perryton (pĕr′ĭ-tŭn) Tex.	36.24 N	100.48 W
79	Perryville (pĕr′ĭ-vĭl) Mo.	37.43 N	89.53 W
150	Persepolis (Ruins) (pĕr-sĕp′ô-lĭs) Iran	29.55 N	53.0 E
150	Persia (Iran) (pûr′zhȧ) Asia	33.0 N	55.0 E
150	Persian G. (pûr′zhȧn) Asia	26.30 N	52.45 E
164	Perth (pûrth) Austl.	31.47 S	116.0 E
169	Perth Austl. (Tas. In.)	41.33 S	147.11 E
85	Perth Can.	44.53 N	76.15 W
116	Perth Gt. Brit.	56.25 N	3.25 W
85	Perth Amboy (pûrth ăm′boi) N. J.	40.32 N	74.16 W
169	Perth Water (L.) Austl. (Perth In.)	31.58 S	115.52 E
125	Pertuis (pĕr-tüē′) Fr.	43.43 N	5.30 E
124	Pertuis Breton (B.) pĕr-tüē′ brē-tôN′) Fr.	46.20 N	1.30 W
79	Peru (pē-rōō′) Ill.	41.19 N	89.9 W
84	Peru Ind.	40.47 N	86.3 W
102	Peru S. A.	10.0 S	75.0 W
128	Perugia (pā-rōō′jä) It.	43.17 N	12.23 E
131	Pervomaisk (pĕr-vô-mīsk′) Sov. Un.	48.4 N	30.52 E
128	Pesaro (pā′zä-rō) It.	43.55 N	12.54 E
158	Pescadores Channel (pĕs-kȧ-dō′-rĕs) Tai. (In.)	23.45 N	120.0 E
158	Pescadores Is. Tai. (In.)	23.40 N	119.35 E
93	Pescados, R. (pĕs-kä′dās) Mex.	19.18 N	96.40 W
128	Pescara (pās-kä′rä) It.	42.26 N	14.12 E
128	Pescara R. It.	42.12 N	13.40 E
113	Peschani, C. (pâs′chä-nĭ) Sov Un.	43.15 N	51.15 E
128	Pescia (pä′shä) It.	43.55 N	10.42 E
151	Peshawar (pĕ-shä′wŭr) India	33.59 N	71.43 E
77	Peshtigo (pĕsh′tē-gō) Wis.	45.4 N	87.48 W
77	Peshtigo R. Wis.	45.25 N	88.20 W
130	Pesochenski (pä-sô-chyĕn′skĭ-yĕ) Sov. Un.	54.4 N	34.17 E
126	Peso de Régua (pā-sōō dā rā′gwä) Port.	41.10 N	7.47 W
94	Pespire (pås-pē′rā) Hond.	13.38 N	87.22 W
103	Pesqueira (pĕs-kā′ē-rȧ) Braz.	8.15 S	36.32 W
80	Pesqueria, R. (pås-kā′rēä) Mex.	26.0 N	100.30 W
129	Peštera (pĕsh′tĕ-rȧ) Bul.	42.3 N	24.18 E
123	Pesterzsebet (pĕsht′ĕr-zhā′bĕt) Hung.	47.27 N	19.8 E
92	Petachalco B. (pā-tä-chäl′kō) Mex.	17.58 N	102.5 W
74	Petaluma (pĕt-ȧ-lōō′mȧ) Calif.	38.14 N	122.39 W
92	Petatlán (pā-tä-tlän′) Mex.	17.29 N	101.18 W
94	Petén (San Andres) L. (pā-tān′) (sän än-drās′) Guat. (In.)	17.0 N	89.50 W
166	Peterborough (pē′tēr-bŭr-ō) Austl.	32.59 S	138.50 E
55	Peterborough Can.	44.15 N	78.29 W
116	Peterborough Gt. Brit.	52.35 N	0.15 W
116	Peterborough, Soke of Gt. Brit.	52.37 N	0.21 W
116	Peterhead (pē-tēr-hĕd′) Gt. Brit.	57.30 N	1.50 W
46	Peter I. (pē′tēr) Ant. O.	69.0 S	90.0 W
85	Peter Pt. Can.	43.50 N	77.8 W
53	Petersburg (pē′tērz-bûrg) Alsk.	56.45 N	133.0 W
79	Petersburg Ill.	40.0 N	89.51 W
84	Petersburg Ind.	38.30 N	87.15 W
83	Petersburg Va.	37.12 N	77.24 W
73	Peterson (pē′tēr-sŭn) Utah (Salt Lake City In.)	41.7 N	111.46 W
153	Peter the Great B. Sov. Un.-Chn.	42.30 N	132.0 E
148	Petimskoe (pâ-tēm′skô-yĕ) Sov. Un.	74.20 N	84.30 E
86	Petitcodiac (pē-tē-kô-dyăk′) Can.	45.56 N	65.11 W
85	Petite Nation R. (pē-tēt′ nȧ-syôN′) Can.	45.45 N	75.8 W
95	Petite Terre (I.) (pē-tēt′ târ′) Guad. (In.)	16.10 N	61.8 W
97	Petit Goave (pē-tē′ gô-äv′) Hai.	18.26 N	72.53 W
79	Petit Jean Cr. (pē-tē′ zhäN′) Ark.	35.5 N	93.30 W
119	Petit Nethe R. (pē-tē′nât) Bel. (Anvers In.)	51.10 N	4.38 E
93	Petlalcingo (pĕ-tläl-sĕŋ′gō) Mex.	18.3 N	97.50 W
170	Petone (pĕ-tō′nē) N. Z. (In.)	41.14 S	174.53 E
99	Petorca (pā-tōr′kä) Chl. (Valparaiso In.)	32.14 S	70.59 W
99	Petorca, R. Chl. (Valparaiso In.)	32.20 S	71.20 W
84	Petoskey (pē-tŏs′kĭ) Mich.	45.23 N	85.58 W
89	Petre, Isle a (ēl-ȧ-pĕt′r′) La. (New Orleans In.)	30.9 N	89.9 W
129	Petrič (pā′trĭch) Bul.	41.23 N	23.12 E
75	Petrified Forest Natl. Mon. Ariz.	34.55 N	109.37 W
131	Petrikovka (pyĕ-trē-kôf′kä) Sov. Un.	48.43 N	34.29 E
131	Petrikovo (pyĕ-trē-kô′vô) Sov. Un.	52.8 N	28.32 E
128	Petrinja (pā′trēn-yȧ) Yugo.	45.26 N	16.19 E
	Petrograd, see Leningrad, Sov. Un.		
84	Petrolia (pē-trō′lĭ-ȧ) Mich.	42.52 N	82.10 W
103	Petrolina (pĕ-trō-lē′nȧ) Braz.	9.15 S	40.28 W
131	Petropavlovka (pyĕ′trô-päv′-lôf-kȧ) Sov. Un.	48.27 N	36.21 E
148	Petropavlovsk (pyĕ-trô-päv′-lôfsk) Sov. Un.	54.55 N	69.10 E
149	Petropavlovsk-Kamchatski Sov. Un.	53.20 N	158.50 E
103	Petrópolis (pā-trô-pô-lēzh′) Braz.	22.30 S	43.4 W
129	Petroşani (pā-trô-shän′′) Rom.	45.24 N	23.23 E
113	Petrovsk (pyĕ-trôfsk′) Sov. Un.	52.15 N	45.25 E
131	Petrovskaya (pyĕ-trôf′skȧ-yȧ) Sov. Un.	45.25 N	37.54 E
113	Petrovskoe (pyĕ-trôf′skô-yĕ) Sov. Un.	45.15 N	42.58 E
149	Petrovsk-Zabaikalski (pyĕ-trôfsk-zä-bī-käl′skĕ) Sov. Un.	51.15 N	108.40 E
143	Petrusburg (pä′trōōs-bōōrgh) (pē′trŭs-bûrg) U. S. Afr.	29.3 S	25.25 E
143	Petrus Steyn (pä′trōōs stän′) U. S. Afr.	27.42 S	28.8 E
143	Petrusville (pä′trōōs-vĭl) U. S. Afr.	30.7 S	24.41 E
121	Petseri (pĕt′sĕ-rē) Est.	57.48 N	27.40 E
88	Petty I. (pĕt′ĭ) N. J. (Philadelphia In.)	39.58 N	75.6 W
99	Peumo (pā-ōō′mō) Chl. (Valparaiso In.)	34.23 S	71.13 W
72	Peyton (pā′tŭn) Colo. (Colo. Sprs. In.)	39.2 N	104.29 W
88	Peyton Wis. (Duluth In.)	46.39 N	92.1 W
112	Peza R. (pyä′zȧ) Sov. Un.	65.35 N	46.35 E
124	Pézenas (pā-zē-nä′) Fr.	43.25 N	3.25 E
122	Pforzheim (pfôrts′hīm) Ger.	48.53 N	8.42 E
129	Phanos (I.) (fä nōs) Grc.	39.51 N	19.25 E
160	Phanrang (p′hän′räng′) Fr. In. Chn.	11.35 N	108.50 E
129	Pharsala (fär′sȧ-lȧ) Grc.	39.16 N	22.24 E
82	Phenix City (fē′nĭks) Ala.	32.29 N	85.1 W
...	Philadelphia, see Amman, Transj.		
82	Philadelphia (fĭl-ȧ-dĕl′phĭ-ȧ) Miss.	32.46 N	89.8 W
85	Philadelphia Pa.	40.0 N	75.10 W
142	Philadelphia U. S. Afr.	33.39 S	18.32 E
129	Philiatra (fĭ-lē-ä′trȧ) Grc.	37.10 N	21.36 E
76	Philip (fĭl′ĭp) S. D.	44.4 N	101.37 W
167	Philip I. Austl.	38.30 S	145.15 E
138	Philippeville (fē-lēp′vēl′) Alg.	36.58 N	6.58 E
162	Philippine Is. (fĭl′ĭ-pēn) Pac. O.	12.0 N	122.0 E
161	Philippine Trough (fĭl′ĭ-pēn) Pac. O.	9.30 N	127.0 E
143	Philippolis (fĭ-lĭp′ô-lĭs) U. S. Afr.	30.18 S	25.18 E
129	Philippopolis (Plovdiv) (fĭl-ĭp-ŏp′ô-lĭs) (plôv′dĭf) Bul.	42.8 N	24.42 E
71	Philipsburg (fĭl′ĭps-bûrg) Mont.	46.20 N	113.29 W
85	Philipsburg Pa.	40.54 N	78.12 W
143	Philipstown (fĭl′ĭps-toun) U. S. Afr.	30.25 S	24.30 E
85	Philippi (fĭ-lĭp′ĭ) W. Va.	39.9 N	80.3 W
77	Phillips (fĭl′ĭps) Wis.	45.41 N	90.22 W
78	Phillipsburg Kan.	39.45 N	99.19 W
85	Phillipsburg Pa.	40.42 N	75.10 W
119	Phlegrean Fields (flē-grē′ăn) It. (Napoli In.)	40.53 N	14.6 E
89	Phoebus (fē′bŭs) Va. (Norfolk In.)	37.1 N	76.19 W
75	Phoenix (fē′nĭks) Ariz.	33.27 N	112.4 W
70	Phoenix Can.	49.4 N	118.35 W
89	Phoenix La. (New Orleans In.)	29.39 N	89.56 W
172	Phoenix Is. Pac. O.	4.0 S	172.0 W
85	Phoenixville (fē′nĭks-vĭl) Pa.	40.9 N	75.31 W
128	Piacenza (pyä-chĕnt′sä) It.	45.2 N	9.41 E
102	Piacoa (pyä-kō′ä) Ven.	8.31 N	62.2 W
167	Pian Cr. (pyän) Austl.	30.0 S	148.57 E
119	Piano di Sorrento (pyä′nō dē sôr-rĕn′tō) It. (Napoli In.)	40.38 N	14.24 E
128	Pianosa (I.) (pyä-nō′sä) It.	42.35 N	10.5 E
128	Pianosa I. It.	42.14 N	15.44 E
119	Pianura (pyä-nōō′rä) It. (Napoli In.)	40.52 N	14.11 E
163	Piapayungan Mt. (pyä-pä-yōōŋ′gän) P. I.	7.39 N	124.32 E
123	Piatra-Neamt (pyä′trä-nä-ämts′) Rom.	46.55 N	26.23 E
103	Piauhi (State) (pyou′ē) Braz.	7.0 S	42.30 W
103	Piauhi, Serra do (Mts.) (sĕr′rä dōō pyou′ē) Braz.	9.30 S	43.15 W
128	Piave R. (pyä′vā) It.	45.47 N	12.20 E
128	Piazza Armerina (pyät′sä är-mā-rē′nä) It.	37.24 N	14.23 E
139	Pibor R. (pē′bôr) A. E. Sud.-Eth.	7.30 N	33.0 E
91	Picara Pt. (pē-kä′rä) St. Thomas (In.)	18.23 N	64.56 W
82	Picayune (pĭk′ȧ-yōōn) Miss.	30.31 N	89.41 W
152	Pichan (Shanshan) (pē′chän′) (shän′shän′) Chn.	42.40 N	90.4 E
79	Picher (pĭch′ēr) Okla.	36.58 N	94.49 W
135	Pichon (pē-shôN′) Tun. (In.)	35.39 N	9.41 E
93	Pichucalco (pē-chōō-käl′kō) Mex.	17.30 N	93.5 W
77	Pickerel L. (pĭk′ēr-ĕl) Can.	48.35 N	91.22 W
118	Pickering (pĭk′ēr-ĭng) Gt. Brit.	54.14 N	0.46 W
6	Pickering Pk. Fiji Is. (In.)	17.54 S	177.36 E
73	Pico (pē′kō) Calif. (Los Angeles In.)	34.0 N	118.5 W
138	Pico I. (pē′kōō) Az. Is. (In.)	38.25 N	28.20 W
166	Picola (pĭk′ō-lȧ) Austl.	36.0 S	145.8 E
103	Picos (pē′kōzh) Braz.	7.2 S	41.32 W
77	Pic R. (pēk) Can.	49.0 N	86.7 W
167	Picton (pĭk′tŭn) Austl.	34.10 S	150.38 E
85	Picton Can.	44.2 N	77.10 W
171	Picton N. Z.	41.17 S	174.0 E
87	Pictou (pĭk-tōō′) Can.	45.41 N	62.42 W
162	Piddig (pēd-dēg′) P. I.	18.10 N	120.43 E
151	Pidurutalagala, Mt. (pē′dōō-rōō-tä′lä-gä′lä) Cey. (In.)	7.5 N	80.45 E
93	Piedad (pyā-dhädh′) Mex. (In.)	19.24 N	99.9 W
104	Piedade (pyä-dä′dĕ) Braz. (In.)	22.41 S	43.3 W
104	Piedade Braz. (In.)	22.53 S	43.19 W
82	Piedmont (pēd′mŏnt) Ala.	33.56 N	85.37 W
128	Piedmont (Prov.) It.	44.59 N	7.30 E
79	Piedmont Mo.	37.8 N	90.41 W
83	Piedmont S. C.	34.42 N	82.27 W
85	Piedmont W. Va.	39.30 N	79.3 W
126	Piedrabuena (pyā-drä-bwā′nä) Sp.	39.2 N	4.10 W
97	Piedra Gran (Pk.) (pyā′drä grän′) Cuba	20.1 N	75.41 W
80	Piedras Negras (pyā′dräs nā′gräs) Mex.	28.41 N	100.31 W
77	Pie I. (pī) Can.	48.15 N	89.5 W
121	Pieksämäki (pyĕk′sĕ-mĕ-kē) Fin.	62.17 N	27.15 E
126	Piélagos (pyā′lä-gōs) Sp.	43.23 N	3.56 W
112	Piels (pyĕls) Fin.	63.15 N	29.30 E
169	Pieman (Corinna) (pī′măn) (kô-rĭn′ȧ) Austl. (Tas. In.)	41.45 S	145.20 E
76	Pierce (pērs) Neb.	42.12 N	97.31 W
85	Pierce W. Va.	39.13 N	79.32 W
76	Pierre (pēr) S. D.	44.22 N	100.20 W
125	Pierrefette (pyâr-fĕt′) Fr. (In.)	48.57 N	2.22 E
125	Pierrelaye (pyâr-lâ′) Fr. (In.)	49.1 N	2.9 E
123	Piešťany (pyĕsh′tyä-nûĭ) Czech.	48.36 N	17.48 E
112	Pietarsaari, see Jakobstad, Fin.		
143	Pietermaritzburg (pē-tēr-mâr′ĭts-bûrg) (pyä′tĕr-mä′rĕts-bōōrgh) U. S. Afr.	29.37 S	30.21 E
140	Pietersburg (pē′tērz-bûrg) U. S. Afr.	23.55 S	29.20 E
143	Piet Retief (pēt rĕ-tēf′) U. S. Afr.	27.2 S	30.49 E
128	Pieve di Cadore (pyā′vā dē kä-dō′rā) It.	46.27 N	12.22 E
56	Pigeon Bluff Can. (Winnipeg In.)	50.11 N	96.59 W
56	Pigeon L. (pĭj′ŭn) Can. (Winnipeg In.)	49.57 N	97.36 W
77	Pigeon R. Can.-U. S.	48.0 N	89.55 W
89	Pig Eye L. Minn. (Minneapolis In.)	44.55 N	93.1 W
79	Piggott (pĭg′ŭt) Ark.	36.23 N	90.11 W
143	Piggs Peak (pĭgs pēk′) Swaz.	25.58 S	31.12 E
112	Pihkva (Pskov) L. (pē′kvä) (pskôf) Eur.	58.0 N	28.0 E
93	Pijijiapan (pē-ĸē-ĸē-ä′pän) Mex.	15.41 N	93.13 W
78	Pikes Peak (pīks) Colo.	38.50 N	105.3 W
88	Pikesville (pīks′vĭl) Md. (Baltimore In.)	39.22 N	76.43 W
72	Pikeview (pīk′vū) Colo. (Colo. Sprs. In.)	38.55 N	104.50 W
84	Pikeville (pīk′vĭl) Ky.	37.26 N	82.32 W
161	Pila (pē′lä) P. I. (Manila In.)	14.15 N	121.25 E
99	Pilar (pē′lär) Arg. (Buenos Aires In.)	34.28 S	58.59 W
103	Pilar Braz.	14.43 S	49.32 W
104	Pilar Par.	26.50 S	58.28 W
162	Pilar P. I.	12.55 N	123.40 E
163	Pilar P. I.	11.28 N	123.0 E
162	Pilar P. I.	17.22 N	120.27 E
163	Pilar B. P. I.	11.30 N	123.0 E
99	Pilar, C. Chl. (Magallanes In.)	52.42 S	74.42 W
163	Pilas I. (pē′läs) P. I.	6.38 N	121.36 E
94	Pilas, Las (Vol.) (läs-pē′läs) Nic.	12.32 N	86.42 W
98	Pilcomaya R. (pēl-kō-mä′yō) S. A.	24.15 S	60.0 W
162	Pili (pē′lē) P. I.	13.33 N	123.17 E
123	Pilica R. (pē-lēt′sä) Pol.	51.30 N	20.0 E
130	Pilka R. (pēl-kä′) Sov. Un.	57.35 N	30.55 E
169	Pillar, C. (pĭl′ȧr) Austl. (Tas. In.)	43.12 S	148.0 E
123	Pillau (pĭl′ou) Ger.	54.40 N	19.54 E
161	Pillila (pē-lēl′ä) P. I. (Manila In.)	14.30 N	121.20 E
169	Pillinger (pĭl′ĭn-jēr) Austl. (Tas. In.)	42.18 S	145.33 E
126	Piloña (pē-lō′nyä) Sp.	43.22 N	5.22 W
80	Pilon, R. (pē-lōn′) Mex.	25.15 N	99.45 W
79	Pilot Cr. (pī′lŭt) Tex.	33.20 N	96.48 W
171	Pilot, Pt. N. Z. (In.)	45.46 S	170.42 E
79	Pilot Point Tex.	33.23 N	96.57 W
89	Pilottown La. (New Orleans In.)	29.11 N	89.15 W
	Pilsen, see Plzen, Czech.		
121	Pils Rauna (pēls rou′nȧ) Lat.	57.20 N	25.32 E
121	Piltene (pĕl′tĕ-nĕ) Lat.	57.16 N	21.42 E
92	Pimal, Cerro (sĕr′ō pē-mäl′) Mex.	22.58 N	104.18 W
166	Pimba (pĭm′bȧ) Austl.	31.12 S	136.45 E
162	Pinamalayan (pē-nä-mä-lä′yän) P. I.	13.4 N	121.30 E
163	Pinamungajan (pē-nä-mōōŋ-gä′-hän) P. I.	10.15 N	123.35 E
113	Pinarbaşi (pē′när-bä′shĭ) Tur.	38.40 N	36.12 E
96	Pinar del Rio (State) (pē-när′ dĕl rē′ō) Cuba	22.30 N	83.40 W
96	Pinar del Rio Cuba	22.21 N	83.38 W
162	Pinatubo Mt. (pē-nä-tōō′bō) P. I.	15.8 N	120.21 E
156	Pinchow (pĭn′chō′) Chn.	37.36 N	118.2 E
79	Pinckneyville (pĭnk′nĭ-vĭl) Ill.	38.5 N	89.22 W
123	Pinczów (pēn′′chōōf) Pol.	50.32 N	20.32 E
99	Pindamonhangaba (pēn-dä-mōn′än-gä′bȧ) Braz. (Rio de Janeiro In.)	22.58 S	45.30 W
129	Pindus (pĭn′dŭs) Grc.	39.35 N	21.30 E
79	Pine Bluff Ark.	34.13 N	92.1 W
87	Pine, C. Newf.	46.45 N	53.35 W
77	Pine City Minn.	45.49 N	92.59 W
72	Pine Cliffe (pīn′klĭf) Colo. (Denver In.)	39.57 N	105.27 W
164	Pine Cr. Austl.	13.50 S	131.59 E
70	Pine Forest Ra. Nev.	41.45 N	118.40 W
112	Pinega (pē-nyĕ′gȧ) Sov. Un.	64.40 N	43.30 E
112	Pinega R. Sov. Un.	64.10 N	42.30 E
72	Pine Grove Colo. (Denver In.)	39.25 N	105.19 W
83	Pine Is. Fla. (In.)	24.45 N	81.25 W

ăt; finȧl; rāte; senâte; ärm; ȧsk; sofȧ; fâre; ch-choose; dh-as th in other; bē; ēvent; bĕt; recĕnt; cratēr; g-go; gh-gutteral g; bĭt; ĭ-short neutral; rīde; ĸ-gutteral k as ch in German ich;

Page	Name Pronunciation Region	Lat. °′	Long. °′
83	Pine I. Sd. ....Fla. (In.)	26.35 N	82.10 W
73	Pine Knot. Calif. (Los Angeles In.)	34.14 N	116.55 W
76	Pine Ridge Ind. Res........S. D.	43.30 N	102.0 W
128	Pinerolo (pē-nä-rô'lō)........It.	44.52 N	7.20 E
96	Pines, Isle of..............Cuba	21.40 N	82.44 W
165	Pines, Isle of (Kunie I.) (pīnz) (kōō'nyě) (kü-nyā') . New Cal.	22.30 S	167.30 E
143	Pinetown (pīn'toun)....U. S. Afr.	29.51 S	30.51 E
82	Pineville (pīn'vĭl)...........Ky.	36.45 N	83.33 W
81	Pineville...................La.	31.19 N	92.25 W
154	Pingchow (pĭng'chō')........Chn	25.46 N	107.6 E
155	Pingho (pĭng'hō')..........Chn.	24.17 N	116.53 E
155	Pinghu (pĭng'hōō')..........Chn.	30.41 N	120.58 E
154	Pingkiang (pĭng'kyäng').....Chn.	28.40 N	113.25 E
152	Pingliang (pĭng'lyäng')......Chn.	35.27 N	106.35 E
154	Pinglo (pĭng'lō')...........Chn.	24.33 N	110.35 E
160	Ping, Me (R.) (mē' pĭng')...Thai.	18.0 N	98.35 E
154	Pingnan (pĭng'nän')..........Chn.	23.36 N	110.30 E
155	Pingnan.....................Chn.	27.3 N	119.2 E
156	Pingshan (pĭng'shän').......Chn.	38.18 N	114.13 E
154	Pingsiang (pĭng'syäng')......Chn.	27.38 N	113.42 E
156	Pingting (pĭng'tĭng')........Chn.	37.47 N	113.36 E
156	Pingtu (pĭng'tōō')..........Chn.	36.47 N	119.53 E
153	Pingyan (pĭng'yän')..........Chn.	36.0 N	111.30 E
155	Pingyang (pĭng'yäng').......Chn.	27.35 N	120.31 E
156	Pingyin (pĭng'yĭn')..........Chn.	36.16 N	116.21 E
156	Pingyüan (pĭng'yü-än')......Chn.	37.6 N	116.20 E
154	Pingyueh (pĭng'yōō-ā')......Chn.	26.43 N	107.20 E
103	Pinheiro (pē-nyā'rōō)..Braz. (In.)	1.20 S	48.28 W
126	Pinhel (pēn-yěl')...........Port.	40.45 N	7.5 W
127	Pinhel Novo (pēn-yěl nô'vōō) Port. (In.)	38.38 N	8.54 W
160	Pini (I.) (pē'nê).......Neth. Ind.	0.10 N	98.40 E
153	Pinkiang (Harbin) (pĭn'kyäng') (här'bēn) Chn.	45.40 N	126.31 E
74	Pinnacles Natl. Mon. (pĭn'ȧ-k'lz) Calif.	36.27 N	121.12 W
166	Pinnaroo (pĭn'ȧ-rōō).......Austl.	35.15 S	140.55 E
119	Pinnau, R. (pĭ-nou') Ger. (Hamburg In.)	53.40 N	9.36 E
119	Pinneberg (pĭn'ě-běrgh) Ger. (Hamburg In.)	53.40 N	9.48 E
119	Pinner (pĭn'ēr) Gt. Brit. (London In.)	51.36 N	0.24 W
93	Pinola (Las Rosas) (pē-nō'lȧ) (läs rō'zäs) Mex.	16.24 N	92.26 W
49	Pinole (pĭ-nō'lê) Calif. (San Francisco In.)	38.0 N	122.17 W
92	Pinos (pē'nōs).............Mex.	22.16 N	101.36 W
127	Pinoso (pê-nŏ'sō)............Sp.	38.24 N	0.59 W
126	Pinos-Puente (pē'nōs-pwān'tȧ) Sp.	37.15 N	3.45 W
92	Pinotepa Nacional (pē-nô-tā'pä nä-syô-näl') Mex.	16.21 N	98.4 W
123	Pińsk (pên'sk)..............Pol.	52.7 N	26.7 E
123	Pinsk Marshes......Pol.-Sov. Un.	52.10 N	27.30 E
102	Pinta (I.) (pēn'tä)...........Ec.	0.31 N	90.45 W
127	Pinto (pēn'tō)..........Sp. (In.)	40.14 N	3.42 W
75	Pioche (pī-ō'chê)...........Nev.	37.57 N	114.28 W
128	Piombino (pyôm-bē'nō).......It.	42.57 N	10.33 E
123	Piotrków (pyô't'r-kōōf)......Pol.	51.23 N	19.44 E
82	Piper (pī'pēr)..............Ala.	33.4 N	87.2 W
129	Piperi (I.) (pē'pěr-ê)........Grc.	39.18 N	24.19 E
75	Pipe Spring Natl. Mon......Ariz.	36.51 N	112.45 W
76	Pipestone (pīp'stōn).......Minn.	44.0 N	96.18 W
77	Pipestone R................Can.	48.40 N	92.10 W
171	Pipikariti, Pt. (pē'pē-kä'rê-tê) N. Z. (In.)	45.48 S	170.47 E
86	Pipmakan L. (pĭp-mä-kän')..Can.	49.40 N	70.15 W
84	Piqua (pĭk'wȧ)..............Ohio	40.11 N	84.16 W
142	Piquetberg (pĭk'ět-bûrg) U. S. Afr.	32.52 S	18.42 E
103	Piracicaba (pē-rä-sê-kä'bä)..Braz.	22.31 S	48.2 W
129	Piraeus (Peiraievs) (pī-rē'ŭs) (pī-rȧ-ěfs') Grc.	37.58 N	23.39 E
99	Pirahi (pê-rä'ē) Braz. (Rio de Janeiro In.)	22.38 S	43.55 W
128	Pirano (pē-rä'nō)..............It.	45.32 N	13.33 E
103	Pirapora (pē-rȧ-pō'rȧ)......Braz.	17.28 S	44.58 W
104	Piratininga, L. de (pē-rä-tē-nĭŋ-gȧ) Braz. (In.)	22.56 S	43.4 W
122	Pirmasens (pĭr-mä-zěns').....Ger.	49.12 N	7.35 E
122	Pirna (pĭr'nä)...............Ger.	50.58 N	13.52 E
161	Piroe (pê-rōō').........Neth. Ind.	2.59 S	128.18 E
129	Pirot (pē'rōt)..............Yugo.	43.9 N	22.34 E
75	Pirtleville (pûr't'l-vĭl).......Ariz.	31.24 N	109.33 W
131	Piryatin (pēr-yä-tēn')....Sov. Un.	50.14 N	32.31 E
128	Pisa (pē'sä)...................It.	43.43 N	10.24 E
102	Pisagua (pê-sä'gwä)..........Chl.	19.31 S	70.5 W
102	Pisco (pēs'kō)...............Peru	13.45 S	76.15 W
85	Piseco L. (pĭ-sā'kō)........N. Y.	43.25 N	74.35 W
122	Pisek (pē'sěk)............Czech.	49.18 N	14.9 E
128	Pisino (pê-sē'nō)..............It.	45.15 N	13.55 E
7	Piso Ruivo (Mt.) (pē'sō rōō-ē'vō) Madeira Is. (In.)	32.46 N	16.57 W
104	Pissis, Cerro (Vol.) (sěr'rō pē-sēs') Arg.	27.58 S	68.58 W
128	Pisticci (pês-tē'chē)...........It.	40.23 N	16.33 E
114	Pistoia (pês-tō'yä)............It.	43.56 N	10.55 E
87	Pistolet B. (pīs-tō-lā')......Newf.	51.35 N	55.45 W
126	Pisuerga R. (pê-swěr'gä)......Sp.	42.0 N	4.23 W
102	Pitalito (pē-tä-lē'tō).........Col.	2.2 N	75.47 W
166	Pitapunga, L. (pĭ-tȧ-pōōŋ'gȧ)) Austl.	34.22 S	143.28 E
6	Pitcairn I. (pĭt'kârn)......Pac. O.	24.4 S	130.6 W
7	Pitch L. (pĭch)........Trin. (In.)	10.14 N	61.36 W
110	Piteå (pē'tě-ô)..............Swe.	65.22 N	21.20 E
110	Pite R. (pē'tě)..............Swe.	65.52 N	20.0 E
129	Pitești (pê-těsht'')..........Rom.	44.51 N	24.51 E
124	Pithiviers (pē tē-vyā')........Fr.	48.12 N	2.18 E
70	Pit R. (pĭt)................Calif.	41.30 N	120.55 W
143	Pitsani (pêt-sȧ'nĭ)......Br. Bech.	25.45 S	25.4 E
119	Pitsea (pĭt'sē) Gt. Brit. (London In.)	51.34 N	0.30 E
143	Pitseng (pĭt-sěng')...........Bas.	28.3 S	28.12 E
157	Pitsuwo..................Kwan.	39.29 N	122.21 E
72	Pitt L. (pĭt) .Can. (Vancouver In.)	49.25 N	122.33 W
72	Pitt R......Can. (Vancouver In.)	49.14 N	122.44 W
49	Pittsburg (pĭts'bûrg) Calif. (San Francisco In.)	38.2 N	121.53 W
74	Pittsburg..................Calif.	38.1 N	121.54 W
79	Pittsburg...................Kan.	37.24 N	94.42 W
81	Pittsburg...................Tex.	33.0 N	95.0 W
79	Pittsburg...................Tex.	33.01 N	94.58 W
85	Pittsburgh...................Pa.	40.27 N	79.57 W
89	Pittsburgh.............Pa. (In.)		
89	Pittsburg L.....Ill. (St. Louis In.)	38.35 N	90.7 W
79	Pittsfield (pĭts'fēld)..........Ill.	39.37 N	90.47 W
86	Pittsfield...................Me.	44.46 N	69.28 W
85	Pittston (pĭts'tŭn)...........Pa.	41.18 N	75.46 W
169	Pittsworth (pĭts'wûrth) Austl. (In.)	27.42 S	151.39 E
102	Piura (pê-ōō'rä).............Peru	5.20 S	80.32 W
73	Placentia (plȧ-sěn'shĭ-ȧ) Calif. (Los Angeles In.)	33.52 N	117.54 W
87	Placentia..................Newf.	47.18 N	53.55 W
87	Placentia B................Newf.	47.25 N	54.30 W
163	Placer (plä'thēr).............P. I.	9.39 N	125.35 E
80	Placer......................Mex.	29.10 N	105.22 W
74	Placerville (plăs'ēr-vĭl)......Calif.	38.43 N	120.48 W
96	Placetas (plä-thā'täs) ......Cuba	22.17 N	79.39 W
85	Placid L. (plăs'ĭd)..........N. Y.	44.20 N	73.58 W
127	Pla del Panadés (plä' děl pä-nä-dās') Sp. (In.)	41.24 N	1.42 E
73	Plain (plān) Utah (Salt Lake City In.)	41.18 N	112.5 W
77	Plainesdale (plānz'dāl).....Mich.	47.2 N	88.40 W
85	Plainfield (plān'fēld)........N. J.	40.36 N	74.27 W
79	Plainview (plān'vū).........Ark.	34.58 N	93.18 W
72	Plainview.....Colo. (Denver In.)	39.54 N	105.17 W
77	Plainview..................Minn.	44.9 N	92.10 W
76	Plainview...................Neb.	42.21 N	97.46 W
78	Plainview...................Tex.	34.12 N	101.41 W
78	Plainville (plān'vĭl).........Kan.	39.12 N	99.18 W
84	Plainwell (plān'wěl)........Mich.	42.27 N	85.40 W
97	Plana (Flat) Cays (Is.) (plä'nä) Ba. Is.	22.37 N	73.35 W
81	Plano (plā'nō)...............Tex.	33.0 N	96.42 W
83	Plant City............Fla. (In.)	28.2 N	82.7 W
81	Plaquemine (plăk'mēn')......La.	30.17 N	91.13 W
163	Plaridel (plä-rê-děl')..........P. I.	8.36 N	123.43 E
126	Plasencia (plä-sěn'thê-ä)......Sp.	40.2 N	6.5 W
86	Plaster Rock (plȧs'tēr rŏk)..N. B.	46.53 N	67.24 W
158	Plastum B. (plȧs-tōōn')..Sov. Un.	44.45 N	136.22 E
104	Plata, R. de la (dā lä plä'tä) Arg.-Ur.	35.0 S	57.0 W
128	Platani R. (plä-tä'nē).........It.	37.28 N	13.40 E
72	Plateau........Colo. (Denver In.)	39.26 N	104.53 W
97	Platform Pt. (plăt'fôrm)......Hai.	19.36 N	73.22 W
92	Platón Sánchez (plä-tōn' sän'chěz) Mex.	21.16 N	98.18 W
76	Platte (plăt)...............S. D.	43.23 N	98.51 W
79	Platte R....................Mo.	39.50 N	94.42 W
79	Platte R...................Neb.	41.20 N	97.10 W
58	Platte R., North............Neb.	42.0 N	104.0 W
72	Platteville (plăt'vĭl) Colo. (Denver In.)	40.12 N	104.50 W
77	Platteville..................Wis.	42.45 N	90.29 W
79	Platt Natl. Park (plăt)......Okla.	34.30 N	96.58 W
79	Plattsburg (plăts'bûrg).......Mo.	39.33 N	94.27 W
85	Plattsburg.................N. Y.	44.42 N	73.38 W
76	Plattsmouth (plăts'mŭth) ...Neb.	41.1 N	95.53 W
122	Plauen (plou'ěn)............Ger.	50.30 N	12.6 E
93	Playa Vicente (plä'yä vê-thān'tä) Mex.	17.50 N	95.50 W
93	Playa Vicente R............Mex.	18.0 N	95.42 W
79	Pleasant Hill (plěz'ănt).......Mo.	38.47 N	94.17 W
89	Pleasant L. Minn. (Minneapolis In.)	45.6 N	93.4 W
85	Pleasant, L................N. Y.	43.28 N	74.24 W
49	Pleasanton (plěz'ăn-tŭn) Calif. (San Francisco In.)	37.39 N	121.53 W
79	Pleasanton.................Kan.	38.11 N	94.40 W
80	Pleasanton.................Tex.	28.57 N	98.30 W
171	Pleasant, Pt...............N. Z.	44.20 S	171.0 E
170	Plenty, B. of (plěn'tê) ......N. Z.	37.40 S	177.0 E
169	Plenty R...Austl. (Melbourne In.)	37.42 S	145.6 E
71	Plentywood (plěn'tê-wŏŏd) .Mont.	48.47 N	104.32 W
130	Ples (plyěs)............Sov. Un.	57.26 N	41.32 E
86	Plessisville (plě-sē'vēl')......Can.	46.13 N	71.47 W
123	Pleszew (plě'zhěf)...........Pol.	51.53 N	17.48 E
142	Plettenberg B. (plět'ěn-bûrg) U. S. Afr.	34.5 S	23.23 E
129	Pleven (plě'věn).............Bul.	43.24 N	24.35 E
129	Plevlje (Pljevlja) (plyěv'lyě) (plyěv'lyä) . Yugo.	43.21 N	19.22 E
123	Plock (pwôtsk) ....Pol.	52.34 N	19.44 E
125	Ploërmel (plô-ěr-měl').........Fr.	47.55 N	2.25 W
129	Ploești (plô-yěsht'').........Rom.	44.56 N	26.1 E
129	Plomarion (plô-mä'rĭ-ŏn).....Grc.	38.58 N	26.24 E
124	Plomb du Cantal (plôɴ' dü käɴ-täl') . Fr.	45.0 N	2.51 E
123	Plónsk (pwôn'sk)............Pol.	52.37 N	20.24 E
129	Plovdiv (Philippopolis) (plôv'dĭf) (fĭl-ĭp-ŏp'ô'lĭs) . Bul.	42.8 N	24.42 E
93	Pluma Hidalgo (plōō'mä ē-däl'gō) Mex.	15.54 N	96.27 W
72	Plum Cr.......Colo. (Denver In.)	39.29 N	105.0 W
72	Plummers (plŭm'ērz) Colo. (Denver In.)	40.36 N	105.1 W
121	Plunge (plŏŏn'gā)...........Lith.	55.56 N	21.47 E
116	Plymouth (plĭm'ŭth) ....Gt. Brit.	50.25 N	4.5 W
84	Plymouth....................Ind.	41.22 N	86.20 W
95	Plymouth............Le. Is. (In.)	16.43 N	62.13 W
86	Plymouth..................Mass.	41.55 N	70.41 W
86	Plymouth..................N. H.	43.45 N	71.42 W
83	Plymouth..................N. C.	35.51 N	76.43 W
85	Plymouth.....................Pa.	41.15 N	75.6 W
77	Plymouth...................Wis.	43.45 N	87.59 W
88	Plymouth Meeting Pa. (Philadelphia In.)	40.6 N	75.17 W
169	Plympton (plĭmp'tŭn) Austl. (Adelaide In.)	34.58 S	138.33 E
130	Plyusa R. (plyōō'sȧ).....Sov. Un.	58.45 N	28.10 E
122	Plzeń (p'l'zěn')............Czech.	49.46 N	13.23 E
160	Pnom Penh (p'nôm' pěn') Fr. In. Chn.	11.38 N	104.58 E
138	Pobé (pô-bā').........Fr. W. Afr.	6.48 N	2.32 E
127	Pobla de Lillet (pōb'lä dā lê-lyět') Sp.	42.16 N	1.57 E
79	Pocahontas (pō-kȧ-hŏn'tȧs) ..Ark.	36.15 N	91.1 W
77	Pocahontas....................Ia.	42.45 N	94.40 W
71	Pocatello (pō-kȧ-těl'ō) ....Ida.	42.51 N	112.27 W
130	Pochep (pô-chěp').......Sov. Un.	52.56 N	33.29 E
112	Pochinki (pô-chēn'kê)....Sov. Un.	54.40 N	44.50 E
130	Pochinok (pô-chê-nôk') ..Sov. Un.	54.22 N	32.25 E
156	Pochow (pō'chō')...........Chn.	33.51 N	115.44 E
93	Pochutla (San Pedro) (pō-chōō'tlä) (sän pā'drō) . Mex.	15.43 N	96.28 W
118	Pocklington (pŏk'lĭng-tŭn) Gt. Brit.	53.55 N	0.46 W
83	Pocolet R. (pō-kô-lět')......S. C.	35.0 N	81.50 W
85	Pocomoke City (pō-kō-mōk')..Md.	38.4 N	75.34 W
129	Podgorica (pôd'gô-rê-tsȧ)...Yugo.	42.25 N	19.17 E
131	Podgornoe (pôd'gôr-nô-yě) Sov. Un.	50.26 N	39.31 E
123	Podhajce (pôd-hä-ē'tsě)......Pol.	49.13 N	25.6 E
123	Podkarpatská Rus (Ruthenia) (Prov.) (pôd'kȧr-pȧt-skä rōōs') Czech.	48.28 N	23.20 E
	Podmokly, see Bodenbach, Ger.		
130	Podolsk (pô-dôl''sk) .....Sov. Un.	55.27 N	37.31 E
138	Podor (pō'dôr)........Fr. W. Afr.	16.35 N	15.3 W
123	Podwoloczyska (pôd-vō-wô-chēs' kȧ) . Pol.	49.33 N	26.9 E
128	Poggibonsi (pôd-jê-bôn'sē).....It.	43.27 N	11.12 E
149	Pogibi (pô'gê-bê)........Sov. Un.	52.15 N	141.50 E
130	Pogodino (Gorki) (pô'gô-dê-nō) (gôr'kĭ) . Sov. Un.	54.17 N	30.59 E
156	Pohai, Str. of...............Chn.	38.35 N	121.0 E
156	Pohsing (pō'hsĭng').........Chn.	37.14 N	118.13 E
89	Point Comfort I. La. (New Orleans In.)	29.49 N	89.12 W
89	Pointe a la Hache (poiɴt' ȧ lȧ ȧsh') La. (New Orleans In.)	29.35 N	89.48 W
91	Pointe à Pitre (pwăɴt' ȧ pē-tr') Guad.	16.15 N	61.30 W
57	Pointe aux Trembles (pwăɴt' ō träɴ'bl') . Can. (Montreal In.)	45.38 N	73.30 W
72	Point Roberts (point rŏb'ērts) Wash. (Vancouver In.)	48.59 N	123.5 W
57	Point Fortune (point fôr'tûn) Can. (Montreal In.)	45.34 N	74.23 W
72	Point Grey (point grā') Can. (Vancouver In.)	49.16 N	123.16 W
84	Point Pleasant...........W. Va.	38.50 N	82.8 W
124	Poissy (pwȧ-sē')..............Fr.	48.55 N	2.1 E
124	Poitiers (pwȧ-tyā')..........Fr.	46.35 N	0.20 E
124	Poitou Hills (pwȧ-tōō').......Fr.	46.50 N	0.50 W
103	Pojuca, R. (pō-hōō'kä) .Braz. (In.)	12.28 S	38.30 W
88	Pokegama (pō-kê-găm'ȧ) Wis. (Duluth In.)	46.39 N	92.9 W
155	Poklo (pŏk'lō')..............Chn.	23.8 N	114.17 E
157	Poko (Heunghai) (hě-ŏŏng'hī') . Cho.	36.1 N	129.20 E
153	Pokotu (pō'kô-tōō')......Manch.	48.37 N	122.0 E
130	Pokrov (pô'krôf)........Sov. Un.	55.55 N	39.9 E
131	Pokrovskaya (pô'krôf-skä'-yȧ) Sov. Un.	47.25 N	38.54 E
112	Pokrovskoe (pôk'rôf-skô'yě) Sov. Un.	57.18 N	61.0 E
128	Pola (pō'lä)....................It.	44.52 N	13.51 E
122	Poland (pō'lănd).............Eur.	52.0 N	22.0 E
162	Polangui (pô-läŋ'gē).........P. I.	13.18 N	123.29 E
130	Pola R.................Sov. Un.	57.45 N	31.55 E
123	Polgár (pôl'gär)...........Hung.	47.53 N	21.9 E
153	Poli (pô'lĭ)..............Manch.	45.50 N	130.40 E
128	Policastro, G. of (pō-lê-käs'trō) It.	39.55 N	15.35 E
125	Poligny (pō-lē-nyē')..........Fr.	46.50 N	5.42 E
162	Polillo (pô-lēl'yō)...........P. I.	14.41 N	121.56 E
162	Polillo I....................P. I.	14.50 N	121.55 E
162	Polillo Is...................P. I.	14.50 N	122.12 E
162	Polillo Str..................P. I.	15.0 N	121.42 E
128	Polistena (pō-lês-tā'nä)........It.	38.25 N	16.5 E
127	Pollensa (pōl-yěn'sä) ....Sp.	39.53 N	3.1 E
163	Polloc Har. (pōl-yôk').......P. I.	7.23 N	124.15 E
161	Polo (pō'lō) ....P. I. (Manila In.)	14.44 N	120.56 E
94	Polochic, R. (pō-lô-chēk')...Guat.	15.20 N	89.40 W
131	Polonnoe (pô'lô-nô-yě)...Sov. Un.	50.7 N	27.31 E
130	Polotsk (pô'lôtsk).......Sov. Un.	55.29 N	28.48 E
71	Polson (pōl'sŭn)...........Mont.	47.41 N	114.10 W
131	Poltava (pôl-tä'vä)......Sov. Un.	49.36 N	34.35 E
131	Poltavka (pôl-täv'kä)....Sov. Un.	47.31 N	32.27 E
121	Põltsamaa (pŏlt'sȧ-mä).......Est.	58.40 N	26.0 E
148	Polui R. (pôl'wê)........Sov. Un.	65.45 N	69.0 E
129	Polygyros (pŏ-lê-gē'rôs)......Grc.	40.23 N	23.24 E
129	Polykhnitos (pŏ-lê-ᴋnē'tôs)...Grc.	39.4 N	26.11 E
81	Polytechnic (pŏl-ĭ-těk'nĭk) ...Tex.	32.45 N	97.18 W
126	Pombal (pôm-bäl')..........Port.	39.54 N	8.38 W
122	Pomerania (Pommern) (Prov.) (pŏm-ê-rā'nĭ-ȧ) (pôm'ěrn) . Ger.	53.55 N	16.0 E
84	Pomeroy (pŏm'ēr-oi)........Ohio	39.4 N	82.2 W
70	Pomeroy...................Wash.	46.28 N	117.37 W
76	Pomme de Terre R. (pôm dē těr') Minn.	45.40 N	95.50 W
122	Pommern (Pomerania) (Prov.) (pôm'ērn) (pŏm-ê-rā'nĭ-ȧ) . Ger.	53.55 N	16.0 E
74	Pomona (pô-mō'nȧ)........Calif.	34.3 N	117.43 W
142	Pomona.............S. W. Afr.	27.9 S	15.15 E
116	Pomona (Mainland).....Gt. Brit.	59.0 N	2.50 W
83	Pompano (pŏm-pā'nō) Fla. (In.)	26.15 N	80.7 W

ng-sing; ŋ-baŋk; ɴ-nasalized n; nŏd; cŏmmit; ōld; ôbey; ôrder; fōōd; fŏŏt; ou-out; s-soft; sh-dish; th-thin; pūre; ûnite; ûrn; stŭd; circŭs; ü-as "y" in study; '-indeterminate vowel.

Page	Name Pronunciation Region	Lat. °'	Long. °'
119	Pompeii (pŏm-pā'yē) It. (Napoli In.)	40.45 N	14.29 E
125	Pompey (pôN-pā') Fr.	8.48 N	6.9 E
76	Ponca (pŏN'kȧ) Neb.	42.35 N	96.41 W
79	Ponca City Okla.	36.43 N	97.6 W
91	Ponce (pōn'sā) P. R. (In.)	18.1 N	66.39 W
119	Ponders End (pŏn'dērz) Gt. Brit. (London In.)	51.39 N	0.3 W
151	Pondichery (pôN'dē-shā-rē') (pŏn-dĭ-shĕr'ē) India	12.0 N	79.45 E
126	Ponferrada (pōn-fĕr-rä'dhä) Sp.	42.34 N	6.36 W
102	Pongo de Manseriche (Falls) (pōŋ'gō dā män-sā-rē'chā) Ec.	4.30 S	77.30 W
143	Pongola R. (pôŋ-gō'lȧ) U. S. Afr.	27.27 S	31.25 E
112	Ponoi (pō'nô-ĭ) Sov. Un.	67.0 N	41.25 E
112	Ponoi R. Sov. Un.	67.0 N	38.0 E
124	Pons (pôN) Fr.	45.35 N	0.35 W
163	Ponson I. (pŏn-sōn') P. I.	10.44 N	124.32 E
138	Ponta Delgada (pōŋ'tȧ dĕl-gä'dȧ) Az. (In.)	37.48 N	25.45 W
103	Ponta de Pedras (pōŋ'tȧ dā pā'-dräzh) Braz. (In.)	1.25 S	48.55 W
104	Ponta Grossa (pōŋ'tȧ grō'sȧ) Braz.	25.10 S	50.15 W
125	Pont-à-Mousson (pôN-tȧ-mōō-sôN') Fr.	48.55 N	6.3 E
125	Pontarlier (pôN'tȧr-lyā') Fr.	46.55 N	6.25 E
124	Pont-Audemer (pôN-tōd'mâr') Fr.	49.23 N	0.31 E
125	Pontault-Combault (pôN-tō'-kôN-bō') Fr. (In.)	48.46 N	2.36 E
125	Pontcarré (pôN-kȧ-rā') Fr. (In.)	48.47 N	2.42 E
81	Pontchartrain, L. (pôN-shȧr-trăN') La.	30.10 N	90.10 W
103	Ponte (pōŋ'tĕ) Braz.	19.58 S	44.0 W
128	Pontedera (pōn-tā-dā'rä) It.	43.40 N	10.38 E
126	Ponte de Sor (pōŋ'tĕ dā sōr') Port.	39.15 N	8.4 W
118	Pontefract (pŏn'tē-fräkt) Gt. Brit.	53.41 N	1.18 W
163	Pontevedra (pōn-tā-vā'drä) P. I.	11.28 N	122.50 E
126	Pontevedra Sp.	42.27 N	8.39 W
140	Ponthierville (pôN-tyā-vēl') Bel. Cong.	0.22 S	25.20 E
79	Pontiac (pŏn'tĭ-ăk) Ill.	40.53 N	88.36 W
84	Pontiac Mich.	42.40 N	83.18 W
160	Pontianak (pōn-tē-ä'näk) Neth. Ind.	0.5 S	109.28 E
119	Ponticelli (pōn-tē-chĕl'lē) It. (Napoli In.)	40.51 N	14.20 E
128	Pontine (Ponziane) Is. (pŏn'tīn) (pōnt-sē-ä'nä) It.	40.58 N	13.0 E
124	Pontivy (pôN-tē-vē') Fr.	48.5 N	2.58 W
124	Pont-l'Abbe (pôN-lȧ-bā') Fr.	47.53 N	4.11 W
125	Pontoise (pôN-twȧz') Fr. (In.)	49.2 N	2.6 E
82	Pontotoc (pŏn-tô-tŏk') Miss.	34.13 N	89.2 W
128	Pontremoli (pōn-trĕm'ō-lē) It.	44.21 N	9.55 E
124	Pont St. Esprit (pôN' săN tĕs-prē') Fr.	44.15 N	4.40 E
128	Ponza (I.) (pōnt'sä) It.	40.53 N	12.58 E
128	Ponziane (Pontine) Is. (pōnt-sē-ä'nä) (pŏn'tīn) It.	40.58 N	13.0 E
116	Poole (pōōl) Gt. Brit.	50.45 N	1.55 W
151	Poona (pōō'nă) India	18.30 N	73.45 E
166	Pooncaira (pōōn-kȧ-ē'rȧ) Austl.	33.23 S	142.35 E
166	Poopalloe L. (pōō-pȧ-lō-ē') Austl.	31.38 S	144.0 E
102	Poopó L. (pō-ō-pō') Bol.	18.45 S	67.0 W
170	Poor Knights I. N. Z.	35.30 S	174.45 E
102	Popayán (pō-pä-yän') Col.	2.18 N	76.45 W
166	Popilta, L. (pō-pĭl'tȧ) Austl.	33.9 S	141.42 E
71	Poplar (pŏp'lẽr) Mont.	48.6 N	105.10 W
79	Poplar Bluff Mo.	36.45 N	90.24 W
84	Poplar Plains Ky.	38.22 N	83.40 W
71	Poplar R. Mont.	48.35 N	105.20 W
71	Poplar R., West Fork Mont.	48.50 N	106.10 W
82	Poplarville Miss.	30.51 N	89.32 W
92	Popocatepetl (Cerro) (pō-pō-kä-tā'-pĕt'l) Mex.	19.2 N	98.37 W
140	Popokabaca (pō'pō-kȧ-bä'kȧ) Bel. Cong.	5.40 S	16.47 E
93	Popotla (pō-pō'tlä) Mex. (In.)	19.27 N	99.10 W
131	Popovka (pō'pôf-kȧ) Sov. Un.	47.13 N	36.32 E
131	Popovka Sov. Un.	50.3 N	33.38 E
131	Popovka Sov. Un.	51.13 N	33.5 E
129	Popovo (pô'pō-vō) Bul.	43.19 N	26.13 E
119	Poppenbüttel (pŏp'ĕn-büt-ĕl) Ger. (Hamburg In.)	53.40 N	10.5 E
88	Poquessing Cr. (pō-kwĕ'sĭng) Pa. (Philadelphia In.)	40.5 N	74.58 W
128	Po R. (pō) It.	44.55 N	10.30 E
151	Porbandar (pōr-bŭn'dŭr) India	21.38 N	69.37 E
99	Porcos, I. dos (dōzh pôr'kōzh) Braz. (Rio de Janeiro In.)	23.32 S	45.3 W
126	Porcuna (pôr-kōō'nä) Sp.	37.53 N	4.11 W
71	Porcupine Cr. (pôr'kû-pīn) Mont.	48.30 N	106.30 W
52	Porcupine R. Alsk.	67.0 N	142.30 W
128	Pordenone (pōr-dā-nō'nä) It.	45.57 N	12.38 E
130	Porechie (pō'ryĕch-yĕ) Sov. Un.	55.16 N	31.31 E
121	Pori (Björneborg) (pô'rē) (byûr'-nē-bôrgh) Fin.	61.30 N	21.48 E
110	Porjus (pôr'yōōs) Swe.	66.52 N	19.42 E
130	Porkhov (pôr'kôf) Sov. Un.	57.46 N	29.32 E
124	Pornic (pôr-nēk') Fr.	47.10 N	2.9 W
163	Poro I. (pō'rō) P. I.	10.40 N	124.27 E
122	Porrentruy (pô-răN-trüē') Switz.	47.25 N	7.3 E
120	Porsgrund (pôrs'grōōn') Nor.	59.8 N	9.40 E
102	Portachuelo (pôrt-ȧ-chwā'lō) Bol.	17.29 S	63.59 W
166	Port Adelaide (pōrt ăd'ē-lād) Austl.	34.50 S	138.30 E
169	Port Adelaide R. Austl. (Adelaide In.)	34.49 S	138.31 E
85	Portage (pōr'tāj) Pa.	40.24 N	78.40 W
77	Portage Wis.	43.34 N	89.28 W
56	Portage Cr. Can. (Winnipeg In.)	50.5 N	98.16 W
54	Portage-la-Prairie (pōr'tāj-lȧ-prā'rĭ) Can.	49.58 N	98.18 W
167	Port Albert (pōrt ăl'bẽrt) Austl.	38.40 S	146.41 E
170	Port Albert N. Z.	36.18 S	174.28 E
126	Portalegre (pōr-tȧ-lā'grĕ) Port.	39.18 N	7.27 W
78	Portales (pôr-tä'lĕs) N. M.	34.11 N	103.21 W
143	Port Alfred (ăl'frĕd) U. S. Afr.	33.35 S	26.55 E
85	Port Allegany (ăl-ē-gā'nĭ) Pa.	41.48 N	78.12 W
70	Port Angeles (ăn'jē-lĕz) Wash.	48.7 N	123.28 W
6	Port Apra (I.) (ä'prä) Guam I. (In.)	13.27 N	144.39 E
169	Port Arthur (är'thŭr) Austl. (Tas. In.)	43.9 S	147.50 E
55	Port Arthur Can.	48.30 N	89.10 W
156	Port Arthur (Riojun) ('r-yō'jōōn) Kwan.	38.51 N	121.7 E
81	Port Arthur Tex.	29.52 N	93.57 W
87	Port au Basque (pôr tō bȧsk') Newf.	45.30 N	59.10 W
166	Port Augusta (ô-gŭs'tȧ) Austl.	32.29 S	137.49 E
166	Port Augusta West Austl.	32.28 S	137.45 E
87	Port au Port B. (pôr'tō pōr') Newf.	48.35 N	58.50 W
97	Port Au Prince (pōr'tō präNs') Hai.	18.32 N	72.20 W
84	Port Austin (ôs'tĭn) Mich.	44.3 N	82.58 W
149	Port Ayan (ȧ-yän') Sov. Un.	56.25 N	138.15 E
142	Port Beaufort (bō'fērt) U. S. Afr.	34.22 S	20.47 E
163	Port Barton (bär'tŭn) P. I.	10.30 N	119.10 E
160	Port Blair (blâr) India	12.5 N	92.40 E
81	Port Bolivar (bŏl'ĭ-vȧr) Tex.	29.22 N	94.46 W
166	Port Broughton (brô'tŭn) Austl.	33.35 S	137.58 E
6	Port Castries (kȧs-trē') St. Lucia Is. (Martinique In.)	13.58 N	60.58 W
171	Port Chalmers (chä'mẽrs) N. Z.	45.49 S	170.39 E
49	Port Chicago Calif. (San Francisco In.)	38.3 N	122.1 W
102	Port Chicama (chē-kä'mä) Peru	7.45 S	79.28 W
84	Port Clinton (klĭn'tŭn) Ohio	41.30 N	82.57 W
85	Port Colborne (kōl'bōrn) Can.	42.55 N	79.10 W
72	Port Coquitlam (kô-kwĭt'lȧm) Can. (Vancouver In.)	49.15 N	122.46 W
49	Port Costa (kŏs'tȧ) Calif. (San Francisco In.)	38.2 N	122.11 W
85	Port Dalhousie (dăl-hōō'zĭ) Can.	43.10 N	79.16 W
124	Port-de-Bouc (pôr-dē-bōōk') Fr.	43.25 N	5.0 E
97	Port de Paix (pôr dē pĕ') Hai.	19.57 N	72.49 W
6	Port des Galets (pôr dā gȧ-lā') Réunion (In.)	20.57 S	55.20 E
145	Port Dickson (dĭk'sŭn) Fed. Mal. St. (In.)	2.32 N	101.49 E
49	Port Discovery (dĭs-kŭv'ẽr-ĭ) Wash. (Seattle In.)	48.1 N	122.52 W
86	Port Elgin (ĕl'jĭn) Can.	46.3 N	64.6 W
143	Port Elizabeth (pōrt ē-lĭz'ȧ-bĕth) U. S. Afr.	33.58 S	25.35 E
166	Port Elliot (ĕl'ĭ-ŭt) Austl.	35.30 S	138.42 E
73	Porter (pōr'tẽr) Ala. (Birmingham In.)	33.37 N	87.4 W
82	Porterdale (pōr'tẽr dāl) Ga.	33.34 N	83.54 W
74	Porterville (pōr'tẽr vĭl) Calif.	36.4 N	119.4 W
142	Porterville U. S. Afr.	33.0 S	18.59 E
138	Port Étienne (pôr tā-tyĕn') Fr. W. Afr.	20.58 N	17.2 W
166	Port Fairy Austl.	38.22 S	142.14 E
140	Port-Francqui (pôr-fräN-kē') Bel. Cong.	4.23 S	20.43 E
140	Port Gentil (pōr-zhäN-tē') Fr. Eq. Afr.	0.40 S	8.46 E
166	Port Germein (jẽr-măn') Austl.	33.1 S	138.0 E
82	Port Gibson (gĭb'sŭn) Miss.	31.57 N	91.0 W
138	Port-Gueydon (pôr-gā-dôN') Alg.	36.57 N	4.28 E
72	Port Guichon (gē-shôN') Can. (Vancouver In.)	49.5 N	123.6 W
167	Port Hacking (hăk'ĭng) Austl.	34.5 S	151.10 E
72	Port Hammond (hăm'ŭnd) Can. (Vancouver In.)	49.12 N	122.40 W
72	Port Haney (hā'nĭ) Can. (Vancouver In.)	49.13 N	122.35 W
138	Port Harcourt (hăr'kŭrt) Nig.	4.45 N	7.0 E
87	Port Hawkesbury (hôks'bẽr-ĭ) Can.	45.35 N	61.20 W
164	Port Hedland (hĕd'lănd) Austl.	20.31 S	118.25 E
140	Port Herald (hĕr'ăld) Nya.	16.58 S	35.13 E
87	Port Hood (hōōd) Can.	46.0 N	61.31 W
85	Port Hope (hōp) Can.	43.56 N	78.10 W
84	Port Huron (hū'rŏn) Mich.	42.57 N	82.27 W
135	Port Ibrahim (ē-brä-hēm') Eg. (Suez Can. In.)	29.57 N	32.33 E
119	Portici (pôr'tē-chē) It. (Napoli In.)	40.49 N	14.20 E
167	Port Jackson (jăk'sŭn) Austl.	33.49 S	151.14 E
85	Port Jervis (jûr'vĭs) N. Y.	41.25 N	74.41 W
72	Port Kells (kĕlz) Can. (Vancouver In.)	49.10 N	122.42 W
166	Portland (pōrt'lănd) Austl.	38.22 S	141.38 E
169	Portland Austl. (Tas. In.)	40.53 S	147.46 E
84	Portland Ind.	40.27 N	85.0 W
86	Portland Me.	43.40 N	70.15 W
84	Portland Mich.	42.52 N	84.58 W
49	Portland Ore. (In.)		
70	Portland Ore.	45.30 N	122.37 W
166	Portland B. Austl.	38.20 S	141.48 E
96	Portland Bight Jam.	17.50 N	77.6 W
116	Portland Bill Gt. Brit.	50.30 N	2.40 W
169	Portland, C. Austl. (Tas. In.)	40.43 S	147.57 E
170	Portland I. N. Z.	39.18 S	177.53 E
96	Portland Pt. Jam.	17.42 N	77.10 W
86	Portland, South Me.	43.38 N	70.13 W
81	Port Lavaca (lȧ-vä'kȧ) Tex.	28 37 N	96.38 W
171	Port Levy (lē'vĭ) N. Z. (In.)	43.38 S	172.51 E
166	Port Lincoln (lĭŋ'kŭn) Austl.	34.43 S	135.55 E
124	Port Louis (pôr lōō-ē') Fr.	47.42 N	3.20 W
6	Port Louis Mauritius (In.)	20.10 S	57.30 E
49	Port Ludlow (lŭd'lō) Wash. (Seattle In.)	47.55 N	122.41 W
138	Port-Lyautey (lĭ-ăw-tĭ) (Kenitra) Mor.	34.22 N	6.31 W
167	Port Macquarie (mȧ-kwŏ'rĭ) Austl.	31.25 S	152.55 E
49	Port Madison (măd'ĭ-sŭn) Wash. (Seattle In.)	47.42 N	122.31 W
72	Port Mann (măn) Can. (Vancouver In.)	49.13 N	122.50 W
96	Port Maria (mȧ-rī'ȧ) Jam.	18.22 N	76.54 W
169	Port Melbourne (mĕl'bŭrn) Austl. (Melbourne In.)	37.50 S	144.54 E
86	Port Menier (pôr mē-nyā') Can.	49.50 N	64.20 W
163	Port Misamis (mē-sä'mĭs) P. I.	8.10 N	123.54 E
72	Port Moody (mōōd'ĭ) Can. (Vancouver In.)	49.17 N	122.50 W
161	Port Moresby (mōrz'bē) Pap. Ter.	9.32 S	147.12 E
81	Port Neches (nĕch'ĕz) Tex.	30.0 N	93.58 W
54	Port Nelson (nĕl'sŭn) Can.	56.59 N	92.57 W
86	Portneuf (pôr-nûf') Can.	48.38 N	69.7 W
170	Port Nicholson (nĭk'ŭl-sŭn) N. Z. (In.)	41.17 S	174.48 E
142	Port Nolloth (nŏl'ŏth) U. S. Afr.	29.12 S	16.51 E
126	Pôrto (pōr'tōō) Port.	41.8 N	8.38 W
102	Porto Acre (pōr'tōō ä'krĕ) Braz.	9.30 S	67.33 W
104	Porto Alegre (pōr-tōō-ä-lā'grĕ) Braz.	30.1 S	51.10 W
140	Porto Alexandre (pōr'tōō ȧ-lĕ-zhän'drĕ) Ang.	15.55 S	11.47 E
141	Pôrto Amelia (pōr'tōō ȧ-mä'lyȧ) Moz.	12.55 S	40.30 E
95	Portobelo Pan.	9.33 N	79.40 W
141	Porto Durnford (Bur Gao) (pōr-tô dûrn'fōrd) It. E. Afr.	1.10 S	41.47 E
126	Pôrto de Mos (pōr'tōō dā mōzh') Port.	39.35 N	8.49 W
103	Porto de Pedras (pōr'tōō dā pā'dräzh) Braz.	9.2 S	35.20 W
135	Porto-Farina (pōr'tô-fä-rē'nä) Tun. (In.)	37.10 N	10.10 E
128	Portoferraio (pōr'tô-fĕr-rä'yō) It.	42.47 N	10.21 E
103	Port of Spain Trin.	10.40 N	61.31 W
7	Porto Grande (pōr'tō grän'dä) C. V. Is. (In.)	16.52 N	25.58 W
128	Portogruaro (pōr'tô-grōō-ä'rō) It.	45.48 N	12.49 E
74	Portola (pôr'tō-lȧ) Calif.	39.46 N	120.30 W
104	Porto Murtinho (pōr'tōō mōōr-tēn'yōō) Braz.	21.50 S	58.0 W
103	Porto Nacional (pōr'tōō nä-syō-näl') Braz.	10.44 S	48.28 W
138	Porto-Novo (pōr'tô-nō'vō) Fr. W. Afr.	6.31 N	2.31 W
49	Port Orchard (ôr'chẽrd) Wash. (Seattle In.)	47.32 N	122.38 W
91	Porto Rico (Puerto Rico) (pōr-tō rē'kō) (pwĕr'tō rē'kō) W. I. (In.)	18.0 N	66.0 W
138	Porto Santo I. (pōr'tōō säN'tōō) Madeira Is.	33.5 N	16.20 W
103	Porto Seguro (pōr'tōō sā-gōō'rōō) Braz.	16.28 S	39.14 W
128	Porto Torres (pōr'tō tŏr'rĕs) Sard.	40.49 N	8.55 E
124	Porto Vecchio (Corsica) (pōr'tō vĕk'ē-ō) Fr. (In.)	41.35 N	9.15 E
102	Porto Velho (pōr'tōō väl'yōō) Braz.	8.45 S	63.45 W
102	Portoviejo (pōr'tō vyā'hō) Ec.	1.0 S	80.20 W
116	Portpatrick (pōrt-păt'rĭk) Gt. Brit.	54.50 N	5.5 W
171	Port Pegasus (pĕg'ȧ-sŭs) N. Z.	47.13 S	167.45 E
166	Port Philip B. (fĭl'ĭp) Austl.	38.5 S	144.50 E
166	Port Pirie (pĭ'rē) Austl.	33.11 S	138.2 E
88	Port Richmond (rĭch'mŭnd) N. Y. (In.)	40.38 N	74.8 W
96	Port Royal (roi'ăl) Jam.	17.54 N	76.52 W
96	Port Sagua la Grande (sä'gwä lä grän'dä) Cuba	22.55 N	80.4 W
143	Port St. Johns U. S. Afr.	31.37 S	29.31 E
139	Port Said (sä-ēd') Eg.	31.14 N	32.11 E
97	Port San Antonio (săn ăn-tō'nĭ-ō) Jam.	18.11 N	76.26 W
114	Port Say (pōr sȧ'ē) Alg.	35.3 N	2.15 W
143	Port Shepstone (shĕps'tŭn) U. S. Afr.	30.46 S	30.25 E
56	Port Simpson (sĭmp'sŭn) Can. (Prince Rupert In.)	54.34 N	130.25 W
116	Portsmouth (pōrts'mŭth) Gt. Brit.	50.48 N	1.5 W
95	Portsmouth Le. Is. (In.)	15.34 N	61.28 W
86	Portsmouth N. H.	43.5 N	70.47 W
84	Portsmouth Ohio	38.45 N	83.0 W
85	Portsmouth Va.	36.47 N	76.20 W
167	Port Stephens (stē'vĕnz) Austl.	32.43 S	152.11 E
139	Port Sudan (sōō-dăn') A. E. Sud.	19.32 N	37.6 E
160	Port Swettenham (swĕt'ĕn-hăm) Strs. Sets.	3.5 N	101.30 E
83	Port Tampa (tăm'pȧ) Fla. (In.)	27.50 N	82.32 W
70	Port Townsend (tounz'ĕnd) Wash.	48.8 N	122.48 W
126	Portugal (pōr'tû-găl) Eur.	40.0 N	8.0 W
126	Portugalete (pōr-tōō-gä-lā'tä) Sp.	43.18 N	3.3 W
140	Portuguese East Africa (Mozambique) Afr.	18.15 S	35.0 E
138	Portuguese Guinea (gĭn'ē) Afr.	12.0 N	15.0 W
140	Portuguese West Africa (Angola) Afr.	12.30 S	18.30 E
148	Port Ust-Eniseiski (ōōst'yĕ-nĕ-sä ĕsk'ĭ-ē-ē) Sov. Un.	69.36 N	84.30 E
124	Port Vendres (pôr väN'dr') Fr.	42.32 N	3.5 E
166	Port Victoria (vĭk-tō'rĭ-ȧ) Austl.	34.29 S	137.31 E
119	Port Victoria Gt. Brit. (London In.)	51.26 N	0.42 E
165	Port Vila (vē'lä) New Hebr.	17.57 S	168.15 E
166	Port Wakefield (wāk'fēld) Austl.	34.13 S	138.12 E
77	Port Washington (wŏsh'ĭng-tŭn) Wis.	43.25 N	87.52 W
121	Porvoo (Borgå) (pôr'vō) Fin.	60.26 N	25.44 E
104	Posadas (pō-sä'dhäs) Arg.	27.20 S	55.59 W
126	Posadas Sp.	37.49 N	5.7 W
154	Poseh (pō'sä') Chn.	23.58 N	106.45 E
122	Posen (Poznań) (pō'zĕn) (pôz'nän') Pol.	52.25 N	16.53 E
156	Poshan (pō'shän') Chn.	36.31 N	117.54 E

ăt; finăl; rāte; senāte ärm; ȧsk; sofȧ; fâre; ch-choose; dh-as th in other; bē; ēvent; bĕt; recĕnt; cratẽr; g-go; gh-gutteral g; bĭt; ĭ-short neutral; rīde; K-gutteral k as ch in German ich;

Page	Name Pronunciation Region	Lat. °′	Long. °′
130	Poshekhono-Volodarsk (pô-shyĕĸ′-ô-nô-vôl′ô-dȧrsk) Sov. Un.	58.30 N	39.9 E
158	Posiet (pŏs-ĭ-ĕt′)........Sov. Un.	42.46 N	130.47 E
158	Posiet, B...............Sov. Un.	42.45 N	130.0 E
119	Posillipo C. (pô-zēl′lê-pō) It. (Napoli In.)	40.48 N	14.13 E
160	Poso, L. (pō′sō)........Neth. Ind.	1.50 S	120.38 E
78	Post (pōst)................Tex.	33.12 N	101.22 W
160	Postillion Is. (pŏs-tĭl′yŭn) Neth. Ind.	7.0 S	118.30 E
142	Postmasburg (pōst′mȧz-bûrg) Bech.	28.21 S	23.5 E
128	Postumia (pôs-tōō′myȧ).......It.	45.45 N	14.13 E
143	Potchefstroom (pŏch′ĕf-strōm) U. S. Afr.	26.42 S	27.4 E
79	Poteau (pô-tō′)............Okla.	35.4 N	94.36 W
79	Poteau R...................Okla.	35.0 N	94.36 W
80	Poteet (pô-tēt).............Tex.	29.3 N	98.35 W
128	Potenza (pô-tĕnt′sä)..........It.	40.38 N	15.48 E
128	Potenza R...................It.	43.17 N	13.20 E
171	Poteriteri, L. (pō-tĕ′rĭ-tĕ′rĭ)..N. Z.	46.5 S	167.5 E
140	Potgieters Rust (pŏt′gē-tērz rüst′) U. S. Afr.	24.13 S	28.57 E
113	Poti (pô′tê) ....Sov. Un.	42.10 N	41.40 E
85	Potomac R. (pô′tō-măk)..Md.-Va.	39.10 N	77.30 W
102	Potosí (pō-tô-sē′)...........Bol.	19.31 S	65.45 W
79	Potosi (pŏ-tō′sĭ).............Mo.	37.56 N	90.48 W
80	Potosí, R. (pō tô sē′)........Mex.	25.0 N	99.45 W
163	Pototan (pô-tō′tän).........P. I.	10.55 N	122.38 E
96	Potrerillo, Pico del (Pk.) (pō-trȧ-rēl′yō) Cuba	21.55 N	80.2 W
94	Potrerillos (pō-trȧ-rēl′yōs)..Hond.	15.13 N	87.58 W
122	Potsdam (pôts′däm).........Ger.	52.25 N	13.3 E
85	Potsdam (pŏts′dăm)........N. Y.	44.40 N	74.38 W
118	Potteries, The (pŏt′ēr-ĭz).Gt. Brit.	53.3 N	2.12 W
171	Potts, Mt. (pŏts)...........N. Z.	43.30 S	170.58 E
85	Pottstown...................Pa.	40.15 N	75.40 W
85	Pottsville (pŏts′vĭl)..........Pa.	40.42 N	76.12 W
85	Poughkeepsie (pô-kĭp′sĭ)....N. Y.	41.42 N	73.56 W
49	Poulsbo (pōlz′bo͝o) Wash. (Seattle In.)	47.44 N	122.38 W
118	Poulton-le-Fylde (pōl′tŭn-lē-fīld′) Gt. Brit.	53.50 N	2.59 W
99	Pouso Alegre (pō′zo͝o ā-lā′grĕ) Braz. (Rio de Janeiro In.)	22.5 S	45.55 W
112	Povenets (pô′vyĕ-nyĕts)..Sov. Un.	62.58 N	34.50 E
170	Poverty B. (pŏv′ĕr-tĭ)......N. Z.	38.43 S	178.0 E
126	Póvoa de Varzim (pô-vō′ȧ dā vär′zēɴ) Port.	41.23 N	8.47 W
71	Powder R. (pou′dēr)..Mont.-Wyo.	45.20 N	105.40 W
70	Powder R..................Ore.	44.55 N	117.30 W
71	Powder R., South Fork.....Wyo.	43.20 N	106.40 W
73	Powder Springs..Ga. (Atlanta In.)	33.52 N	84.41 W
71	Powell (pou′ĕl).............Wyo.	44.45 N	108.45 W
97	Powell Pt................Ba. Is.	24.53 N	76.23 W
82	Powell R.............Tenn.-Ky.	36.30 N	83.50 W
164	Powells Cr. (pou′ĕlz).......Austl.	18.2 S	133.30 E
155	Poyang L. (pō′yäng)........Chn.	29.4 N	116.15 E
89	Poydras (poi′drȧs) La. (New Orleans In.)	29.52 N	89.54 W
77	Poygan L. (poi′gȧn).........Wis.	44.9 N	88.45 W
119	Poynton (poin′tŭn) Gt. Brit. (Liverpool In.)	53.21 N	2.7 W
129	Požarevac (pô′zhȧ-rē-vȧts)..Yugo.	44.36 N	21.11 E
93	Pozas, Cerro (sĕr′ō pō′zäs) Mex. (In.)	19.24 N	99.22 W
129	Požega (pô′zhĕ-gȧ).........Yugo.	45.18 N	17.41 E
122	Poznań (Posen) (pôz′nän″) (pō′zĕn).Pol.	52.25 N	16.53 E
126	Pozoblanco (pô-thō-bläŋ′kō)...Sp.	38.23 N	4.51 W
92	Pozos (pô′zōs)..............Mex.	22.5 N	100.51 W
127	Pozuelo de Alarcón (pô-thwā′lō dā ä-lär-kōn′) Sp. (In.)	40.27 N	3.50 W
128	Pozzuoli (pôt-swô′lē).........It.	40.50 N	14.7 E
160	Prachin (prä′chên)..........Siam	13.58 N	101.15 E
124	Prades (prȧd)................Fr.	42.35 N	2.25 E
73	Prado (prä′dō) Calif. (Los Angeles In.)	33.54 N	117.38 W
122	Praha (Prague) (prä′hȧ) (präg) Czech.	50.5 N	14.26 E
138	Praia (prä′ê-ä).....C. V. Is. (In.)	14.59 N	23.31 W
70	Prairie City (prā′rĭ).........Ore.	44.26 N	118.42 W
77	Prairie du Chien (prā′rĭ do͞o shēn′) Wis.	43.2 N	91.9 W
57	Prairies, River des (rē-vyâr′ dā prȧ-rē′) Can. (Montreal In.)	45.35 N	73.40 W
130	Pra R. (prȧ)..........U. S. S. R.	54.55 N	40.18 E
127	Prat del Llobregat (prät′dĕl lyō-brȧ-gät′) Sp. (In.)	41.19 N	2.5 E
128	Prato (prä′tō)...............It.	43.53 N	11.4 E
124	Prats-de-Mollo (prȧ-dē-mô-lō′) Fr.	42.25 N	2.35 E
78	Pratt (prăt)...............Kans.	37.37 N	98.43 W
82	Prattville (prăt′vĭl)..........Ala.	32.28 N	86.28 W
126	Pravia (prä-vē′ä)............Sp.	43.29 N	6.9 W
123	Pregel R. (prā′gĕl)..........Ger.	54.38 N	21.25 E
127	Premiá de Mar (prā′mē-ä′ dā mär′).Sp. (In.)	41.29 N	2.21 E
80	Premont (prê-mŏnt′).........Tex.	27.20 N	98.10 W
73	Prenda (prĕn′dä) Calif. (Los Angeles In.)	33.55 N	117.22 W
122	Prenzlau (prĕnts′lou)........Ger.	53.19 N	13.51 E
123	Přerov (przhĕ′rôf).........Czech.	49.28 N	17.28 E
80	Presa di la Boquilla R. (prā-sä dā lä bô-kēl′yä).Mex.	27.32 N	105.30 W
118	Prescot (prĕs′kŭt).......Gt. Brit.	53.26 N	2.48 W
75	Prescott....................Ariz.	34.32 N	112.29 W
79	Prescott....................Ark.	33.46 N	93.23 W
85	Prescott....................Can.	44.42 N	75.32 W
56	Prescott I. Can. (Prince Rupert In.)	54.6 N	130.37 W
171	Preservation Inlet (prĕz-ēr-vā′-shŭn) N. Z.	46.5 S	166.40 E
76	Presho (prĕsh′ô).............S. D.	43.56 N	100.2 W
103	Presidente Epitacio (prā-sē-dĕn′tĕ ā-pê-tä′syo͞o).Braz.	21.45 S	52.1 W
80	Presidio (prā-sē′dê-ō)........Tex.	29.35 N	104.23 W
92	Presidio, R.................Mex.	23.50 N	105.50 W
123	Prešov (prĕ′shôf)..........Czech.	49.0 N	21.16 E
129	Prespa, L. (prĕs′pä)....Yugo.-Alb.	40.55 N	21.5 E
86	Presque Isle (prĕsk′ēl′).......Me.	46.31 N	67.57 W
119	Prestbury (prĕst′bēr-ê) Gt. Brit. (Liverpool In.)	53.17 N	2.9 W
116	Preston (prĕs′tŭn) ......Gt. Brit.	53.45 N	2.45 W
71	Preston.....................Ida.	42.4 N	111.53 W
77	Preston....................Minn.	43.41 N	92.6 W
84	Prestonburg (prĕs′tŭn-bûrg)...Ky.	37.38 N	82.50 W
169	Preston R..Austl. (Melbourne In.)	37.42 S	145.1 E
118	Prestwich (prĕst′wĭch)...Gt. Brit.	53.31 N	2.18 W
99	Preto, R. (prā′to͞o) Braz. (Rio de Janeiro In.)	22.30 S	43.55 W
143	Pretoria (prê-tō′rĭ-ȧ)....U. S. Afr.	25.45 S	28.15 E
129	Preveza (prĕ′vȧ-zä)..........Grc.	38.57 N	20.45 E
72	Prevost I. (prê-vō′) Can. (Vancouver In.)	48.50 N	123.23 W
52	Pribilof Is. (prē-bê-lŏf′)......Alsk.	57.0 N	170.0 W
129	Priboj (prē′bô-ê)...........Yugo.	43.34 N	19.33 E
122	Příbram (przhê′brȧm)......Czech.	49.42 N	14.0 E
75	Price (prīs)................Utah	39.37 N	110.47 W
75	Price R....................Utah	39.33 N	110.55 W
82	Prichard (prĭch′ērd).........Ala.	30.44 N	86.7 W
126	Priego (prê-ā′gō).............Sp.	37.26 N	4.11 W
121	Prienai (prê-ĕn′ī)...........Lith.	54.37 N	23.58 E
142	Prieska (prê-ĕs′kȧ).....U. S. Afr.	29.39 S	22.45 E
70	Priest L. (prēst)............Ida.	48.35 N	116.50 W
128	Prijedor (prē′yĕ-dôr).......Yugo.	44.58 N	16.43 E
113	Prikumsk (prē-ko͝omsk′).Sov. Un.	44.50 N	44.10 E
129	Prilep (prĭ′lĕp) ....Yugo.	41.20 N	21.34 E
131	Priluki (prê-lo͞o′kê)......Sov. Un.	50.35 N	32.21 E
78	Primero (prĭ-mē′rō).........Colo.	37.7 N	104.44 W
131	Primorsko Akhtarskii (prē-môr′skō äĸ-tär′skĭ-ê) Sov. Un.	46.2 N	38.10 E
54	Prince Albert...............Can.	53.12 N	105.35 W
142	Prince Albert..........U. S. Afr.	33.11 S	22.2 E
54	Prince Albert Sd............Can.	70.15 N	117.0 W
142	Prince Alfred's Hamlet..U. S. Afr.	33.15 S	19.19 E
55	Prince Edward I. (Prov.).....Can.	46.30 N	63.15 W
7	Prince Edward I..........Ind. O.	46.36 S	37.57 E
85	Prince Edward Pen..........Can.	44.0 N	77.15 W
54	Prince George...............Can.	53.51 N	122.50 W
52	Prince of Wales, C..........Alsk.	65.30 N	168.0 W
53	Prince of Wales I...........Alsk.	55.25 N	133.0 W
165	Prince of Wales I.......Pap. Ter.	10.44 S	142.8 E
56	Prince Rupert (ro͞o′pērt) Can. (In.)		
54	Prince Rupert...............Can.	54.18 N	130.15 W
165	Princess Charlotte B. (shär′lŏt) Austl.	14.0 S	144.0 E
53	Princess Royal I............Can.	52.40 N	129.0 W
7	Princes Town ....Trin. (In.)	10.18 N	61.20 W
49	Princeton (prĭns′tŭn) Calif. (San Francisco In.)	37.30 N	122.29 W
79	Princeton....................Ill.	41.22 N	89.28 W
84	Princeton...................Ind.	38.22 N	87.35 W
82	Princeton....................Ky.	37.6 N	87.53 W
77	Princeton..................Mich.	46.18 N	87.31 W
79	Princeton...................Mo.	40.24 N	93.34 W
77	Princeton..................Minn.	45.35 N	93.34 W
85	Princeton..................N. J.	40.21 N	74.39 W
83	Princeton................W. Va.	37.21 N	81.7 W
77	Princeton...................Wis.	43.50 N	89.9 W
53	Prince William Sd..........Alsk.	60.20 N	146.30 W
138	Principe I. (prēn′sê-pĕ).......Afr.	1.40 N	7.28 E
70	Prineville (prīn′vĭl)..........Ore.	44.18 N	120.50 W
72	Pring (prĭng) Colo. (Colo. Spgs. In.)	39.3 N	104.51 W
95	Prinzapolca (prēn-zä-pōl′kä)..Nic.	13.20 N	83.34 W
95	Prinzapolca, R..............Nic.	13.20 N	84.20 W
123	Pripyat (Pripet) R.......Sov. Un.	52.6 N	28.0 E
123	Pripet (Prypeć) R. (prē′pĕch) Pol.	51.52 N	25.40 E
129	Priština (prēsh′tĭ-nä).......Yugo.	42.38 N	21.10 E
78	Pritchett...................Colo.	37.23 N	102.50 W
122	Pritzwalk (prĭts′välk)........Ger.	53.9 N	12.10 E
124	Privas (prē-väs′)..............Fr.	44.45 N	4.39 E
131	Privolnoe (prê′vôl-nô-yĕ).Sov. Un.	47.28 N	32.14 E
129	Prizren (prē′zrĕn)...........Yugo.	42.12 N	20.43 E
129	Prjepolje (prĭ-yĕ′pôl-yĕ)....Yugo.	43.22 N	19.21 E
119	Procida (prô′chê-dä) It. (Napoli In.)	40.46 N	14.2 E
119	Procida Channel...It. (Napoli In.)	40.47 N	14.3 E
77	Proctor (prŏk′tēr).........Minn.	46.46 N	92.12 W
86	Proctor.....................Vt.	43.40 N	73.5 W
89	Proctor Pt..La. (New Orleans In.)	29.57 N	89.42 W
126	Proença-a-Nova (prô-än′sȧ-ä-nō′vȧ).Port.	39.45 N	7.55 W
93	Progreso (prô-grā′sō)........Mex.	21.16 N	89.40 W
80	Progreso....................Mex.	27.29 N	101.5 W
129	Prokuplje (prô′ko͝op′l-yĕ)...Yugo.	43.14 N	21.38 E
151	Prome (prōm)...............India	18.45 N	95.15 E
128	Promontore, C. (prō′môn-tô′rā) It.	44.46 N	13.55 E
73	Promontory Pt. (prŏm′ŭn-tô-rĭ) Utah (Salt Lake City In.)	41.13 N	112.26 W
130	Pronya R. (prô′nyä).....Sov. Un.	54.5 N	39.40 E
103	Propriá (prō-prê-ä′) ....Braz.	10.15 S	36.48 W
131	Proskurov (prô-sko͝o-rôf′) Sov. Un.	49.29 N	26.58 E
123	Prosna R. (prôs′nȧ)......Pol.-Ger.	51.40 N	18.7 E
169	Prospect (prŏs′pĕkt) Austl.(Adelaide In.)	34.53 S	138.36 E
72	Prospect L..Colo. (Colo. Spgs. In.)	38.45 N	104.42 W
88	Prospect Park Pa. (Philadelphia In.)	39.51 N	75.19 W
169	Prospect Reservoir Austl. (Sydney In.)	33.49 S	150.53 E
70	Prosser (prŏs′ēr)...........Wash.	46.10 N	119.47 W
123	Prostějov (prôs′tyĕ-yôf)....Czech.	49.28 N	17.8 E
169	Proston (prôs′tŭn)....Austl. (In.)	26.12 S	151.32 E
142	Protem (prō-tĕm′).......U. S. Afr.	34.15 S	20.5 E
131	Protoka R. (prôt′ô-kȧ)...Sov. Un.	45.25 N	38.5 E
130	Protva R. (prôt′vȧ)......Sov. Un.	55.5 N	36.35 E
129	Provadija (prō-väd′ê-yȧ).....Bul.	43.12 N	27.28 E
54	Providence (prŏv′ĭ-dĕns).....Can.	61.10 N	117.46 W
84	Providence...................Ky.	37.25 N	87.48 W
85	Providence.................R. I.	41.50 N	71.25 W
71	Providence.................Utah	41.43 N	111.49 W
97	Providenciales I. (prō-vê-dĕn-sê-ä′lās) (prŏ-vĭ-dĕn′ shȧlz) Ba. Is.	21.48 N	72.18 W
124	Provins (prô-văɴ′)............Fr.	48.35 N	3.15 E
75	Provo (prō′vō) ....Utah	40.14 N	111.40 W
128	Prozor (prô′zôr)............Yugo.	43.48 N	17.39 E
122	Prün (prün).................Ger.	50.13 N	6.25 E
121	Prunkkala (pro͝onk′ȧ-lȧ)......Fin.	60.39 N	22.36 E
122	Prussia (State) (prŭsh′ȧ).....Ger.	52.5 N	11.30 E
123	Prussia, East (Prov.)........Ger.	54.10 N	21.0 E
123	Pruszków (pro͝osh′ko͝of)......Pol.	52.9 N	20.50 E
131	Prut R. (pro͞ot)............Rom.	46.35 N	28.15 E
123	Pruzana (pro͝o-zhä′nȧ).......Pol.	52.33 N	24.28 E
79	Pryor (prī′ēr)..............Okla.	36.16 N	95.18 W
123	Prypeć (Pripet) R. (prē′pĕch) (prĭ′pĕt′).Pol.	51.52 N	25.40 E
123	Przasnysz (pzhȧs′nûēsh)......Pol.	53.1 N	20.53 E
123	Przedbórz (pzhĕd′bo͝ozh).....Pol.	51.4 N	19.53 E
123	Przemyśl (pzhĕ′mĭsh′l).......Pol.	49.47 N	22.45 E
129	Psara (I.) (psä′rȧ)..........Grc.	38.35 N	25.35 E
131	Psel R. (psĕl)...........Sov. Un.	50.58 N	34.50 E
130	Pskov (pskôf)...........Sov. Un.	57.48 N	28.19 E
130	Pskov (Dist.)...........Sov. Un.	56.50 N	30.0 E
130	Pskov (Pikhva), L.. (pĭĸ′vȧ) Est.-..Sov. Un.	58.2 N	28.20 E
130	Ptich R. (p′têch)........Sov. Un.	53.14 N	28.15 E
128	Ptuj (pto͞o′ê)..............Yugo.	46.26 N	15.51 E
145	Puah (po͞o′ä).....Neth. Ind. (In.)	1.39 N	102.30 E
155	Pucheng (po͞o′chĕng′)........Chn.	28.0 N	118.20 E
154	Puchi (po͞o′chē′)............Chn.	29.42 N	113.45 E
153	Puchow (po͞o′chō′)..........Chn.	34.53 N	110.29 E
156	Puchow.....................Chn.	35.51 N	115.42 E
163	Pucio Pt. (po͞o′thyô)........P. I.	11.46 N	121.51 E
123	Puck (po͝otsk)...............Pol.	54.42 N	18.23 E
143	Pudimoe (po͞o-dê-mō′ê).....Bech.	27.25 S	24.44 E
112	Pudozh (po͞o′dôzh).......Sov. Un.	61.48 N	36.35 E
92	Puebla (State) (pwā′blä)....Mex.	18.50 N	97.40 W
92	Puebla......................Mex.	19.2 N	98.11 W
126	Puebla de Don Fadrique (dā dōn fä-drē′kä).Sp.	37.57 N	2.25 W
126	Puebla del Caramiñal (dĕl kä-rä-mê-nyäl′).Sp.	42.37 N	8.58 W
99	Pueblo (pwā′blō) **Arg.** (Buenos Aires In.)	34.6 S	61.26 W
78	Pueblo.....................Colo.	38.15 N	104.36 W
92	Pueblo Nuevo (pwā′blō nwā′vō) Mex.	23.22 N	105.22 W
126	Pueblo Nuevo................Sp.	38.18 N	5.16 W
93	Pueblo Viejo (pwā′blō vyā′hō) Mex.	22.10 N	97.51 W
73	Puente (pwĕn′tā) Calif. (Los Angeles In.)	34.2 N	117.58 W
126	Puenteareas (pwĕn-tā-ä-rā′äs) .Sp.	42.9 N	8.31 W
126	Puente Ceso (pwĕn′tā thā′sō)..Sp.	43.15 N	8.55 W
126	Puentedeume (pwĕn-tā-dhâ-o͞o′mā).Sp.	43.24 N	8.11 W
126	Puente-Genil (pwĕn′tā-hâ-nēl′).Sp.	37.25 N	4.45 W
73	Puente Hills (pwĕn′tā hĭlz) Calif. (Los Angeles In.)	33.59 N	117.57 W
75	Puerco R. (pwĕr′kō).......N. M.	35.15 N	107.5 W
152	Puerh (po͞o′ĕr′).............Chn.	22.59 N	101.7 E
102	Puerto Colombia (pwĕr′tō kô-lôm′bê-ȧ).Col.	10.59 N	75.0 W
93	Puerto Ángel (äŋ′hȧl).......Mex.	15.40 N	96.30 W
95	Puerto Armuelles (är-mo͞o-ā′lyās) Pan.	8.18 N	82.52 W
94	Puerto Barrios (bär′rê-ōs)...Guat.	15.43 N	88.37 W
102	Puerto Bermudez (bĕr-mo͞o′dāz) Peru	10.5 S	74.58 W
102	Puerto Berrío (bĕr-rē′ō)......Col.	6.28 N	74.30 W
102	Puerto Cabello (kä-bĕl′yō)...Ven.	10.28 N	68.1 W
95	Puerto Cabezas (kä-bā′zäs)...Nic.	14.2 N	83.25 W
104	Puerto Casado (kä-sä′dō)....Par.	22.20 S	58.0 W
94	Puerto Castilla (käs-tēl′yō).Hond.	16.1 N	86.1 W
94	Puerto Cortés (kôr-tās′)....Hond.	15.48 N	87.57 W
78	Puerto de Luna (dā lo͞o′nä).N. M.	34.49 N	104.35 W
92	Puerto de Maruata (dā mä-ro͞o-ä′tä).Mex.	18.13 N	103.6 W
104	Puerto Deseado (dā-sȧ-ä′dhō) Arg.	47.40 S	66.0 W
138	Puerto Grande (grän′dā) C. V. Is. (In.)	16.52 N	25.1 W
126	Puertollano (pwĕr-tôl-yä′nō)...Sp.	38.42 N	4.6 W
104	Puerto Madryn (mä-drēn′)...Arg.	42.45 S	65.2 W
102	Puerto Maldonado (mäl-dō-nȧ′dô) Peru	12.35 S	69.3 W
93	Puerto México (mā-ĸê-kō) (māk′sê-kō).Mex.	18.9 N	94.20 W
104	Puerto Montt (mônt)........Chl.	41.29 S	72.59 W
102	Puerto Nutrias (no͞o-trê-äs′)..Ven.	8.2 N	69.12 W
96	Puerto Padre (pä′drā)......Cuba	21.11 N	76.36 W
97	Puerto Plata (plä′tä) ..Dom. Rep.	19.47 N	70.41 W
163	Puerto Princesa (prên-sā′sä)..P. I.	9.44 N	118.44 E
127	Puerto Real (rā-äl′)......Sp. (In.)	36.31 N	6.12 W
91	Puerto Rico (pwĕr′tō rē′kō) W. I. (In.)	18.0 N	66.0 W
104	Puerto San Julián (sän ho͞o-lyän′).Arg.	49.17 S	67.59 W
104	Puerto Santa Cruz (sän′ta kro͞oz′) Arg.	50.1 S	68.30 W
103	Puerto Suárez (swä′rāz)......Bol.	18.59 S	57.59 W
92	Puerto Vallarta (väl-yär′tā)..Mex.	20.36 N	105.15 W
104	Puerto Varas (vär′äs)........Chl.	41.20 S	73.0 W
102	Puerto Wilches (vēl′chĕs).....Col.	7.18 N	73.59 W
92	Puga (po͞o′gä)..............Mex.	21.37 N	104.51 W
113	Pugachev (po͞o-gȧ-chyôf′).Sov. Un.	51.58 N	48.45 E

ng-sing; ŋ-baŋk; ɴ-nasalized n; nŏd; cŏmmit; ōld; ôbey; ôrder; fo͞od; fo͝ot; ou-out; s-soft; sh-dish; th-thin; pūre; ûnite; ûrn; stŭd circŭs; ü-as "y" in study; ′-indeterminate vowel.

Page	Name Pronunciation Region	Lat. °'	Long. °'
49	Puget I. .... Wash. (Seattle In.)	46.10 N	123.23 W
70	Puget Sd. .... Wash.	47.40 N	122.25 W
125	Puget-Théniers (pü-zhĕ'-tâ-nyâ') Fr.	43.55 N	6.55 E
127	Puigcerdá (pwēg-thĕr-dä') .... Sp.	42.26 N	1.55 E
163	Pujada B. (pōō-hä'dä) .... P. I.	6.50 N	126.16 E
171	Pukaki, L. (pōō-kä'kĭ) ...... N. Z.	44.5 S	170.12 E
170	Pukekohe (pōō-kĕ-hō'hȧ) .... N. Z.	37.10 S	174.52 E
156	Pukow (pōō'kō') .... Chn.	32.8 N	118.38 E
102	Pulacayo (pōō-lä-kä'yō) ...... Bol.	20.28 S	66.44 W
163	Pulanduta Pt. (pōō-län-dōō'tä) P. I.	11.55 N	123.11 E
163	Pulangi R. (pōō-läŋ'gē) ...... P. I.	7.25 N	125.5 E
156	Pulantien (pōō'län'chĕn') ... Kwan.	39.28 N	121.55 E
82	Pulaski (pū-lăs'kĭ) .... Tenn.	35.12 N	87.3 W
83	Pulaski .... Va.	37.2 N	80.47 W
160	Pulau Kondor Is. (pōō-lä'ōō kōn-dōr') .Fr. In. Chn.	8.45 N	106.38 E
123	Pulawy (pōō-wä'vē) .... Pol.	51.24 N	21.59 E
161	Pulilan (pōō-lē'län) P. I. (Manila In.)	14.55 N	120.48 E
88	Pullman (pŏŏl'măn) Ill. (Chicago In.)	41.42 N	87.36 W
71	Pullman .... Wash.	46.44 N	117.12 W
161	Pulo Cambing (I.) (pōō'lō käm'-bĭng) ... Neth. Ind.	12.15 N	105.0 E
162	Pulog, Mt. (pōō'lŏg) .... P. I.	16.35 N	120.53 E
123	Pultusk (pōōl'tōōsk) .... Pol.	52.43 N	21.5 E
71	Pumpkin Cr. (pŭmp'kĭn) ... Mont.	45.40 N	105.50 W
151	Punaka (pōō-nŭk'ŭ) .... Bhu.	27.29 N	89.55 E
102	Punata (pōō-nä'tä) .... Bol.	17.31 S	66.1 W
92	Pungarabato (pōōŋ'gä-rä-bä'tō) Mex.	18.22 N	100.35 W
155	Puning (pōō'nĭng') .... Chn.	23.24 N	115.56 E
151	Punjab (Prov.) (pŭn-jäb') ... India	30.45 N	73.30 E
102	Puno (pōō'nō) .... Peru	15.58 S	70.1 W
94	Punta Gorda (pōōn'tä gôr'dä) Br. Hond.	16.6 N	88.52 W
83	Punta Gorda (pŭn'tȧ gôr'dȧ) Fla. (In.)	26.55 N	82.3 W
95	Puntarenas (pōōnt-ä-rā'näs) . C. R.	9.58 N	84.48 W
85	Punxsutawney (pŭnk-sōō-tô'nē) Pa.	40.58 N	78.9 W
79	Purcell (pûr-sĕl') .... Okla.	35.0 N	97.22 W
92	Purépero de Echaíz (pōō-rā'pā-rō dā ā-chä-ēz') . Mex.	19.55 N	102.2 W
119	Purfleet (pûr'flēt) Gt. Brit. (London In.)	51.29 N	0.14 E
78	Purgatoire R. (pûr-gȧ-twär') . Colo.	37.32 N	103.40 W
151	Puri (pōō'rē) .... India	19.45 N	85.50 E
97	Purial, Sierra de (Mts.) (pōō-rē-äl') Cuba	20.15 N	74.35 W
102	Purificación (pōō-rē-fē-kä-syōn') Col.	4.2 N	75.1 W
93	Purificación .... Mex. (In.)	19.31 N	98.48 W
92	Purificación .... Mex.	19.44 N	104.36 W
92	Purificación, R. .... Mex.	19.34 N	104.40 W
148	Pur R. (pōōr) .... Sov. Un.	66.0 N	78.0 E
160	Pursat (pōōr-sät') ... Fr. In. Chn.	12.28 N	103.45 E
92	Puruándiro de Calderón (pōō-rōō-än'dē-rō dā käl-dā-rōn') . Mex.	19.58 N	101.32 W
102	Purus R. (pōō-rōōs') .... Braz.	5.0 S	63.0 W
163	Pusan Pt. (pōō-sän') .... P. I.	7.17 N	126.38 E
130	Pushkino (pōōsh'kē-nô) ... Sov. Un.	56.1 N	37.51 E
123	Püspökladány (püsh'pû-klô'dän') Hung.	47.18 N	21.9 E
112	Pustozersk (pōōs-tô-zĕrsk') Sov. Un.	67.30 N	52.40 E
99	Putaendo (pōō-tä-ĕn'dō) Chl. (Valparaiso In.)	32.39 S	70.46 W
156	Putai (pōō'tī') .... Chn.	37.21 N	118.7 E
125	Puteaux (pü-tō') .... Fr. (In.)	48.52 N	2.0 E
160	Puting, C. (poo-tĭng') Neth. Ind.	3.35 S	111.55 E
131	Putivl (pōō-tēv''l) ...... Sov. Un.	51.20 N	33.52 E
93	Putla (pōō'tlä) .... Mex.	17.2 N	97.57 W
85	Putnam (pŭt'năm) .... Conn.	41.57 N	71.55 W
102	Putumayo, R. (pōō-tōō-mä'yō) Col.-Ec.	2.0 S	72.30 W
153	Putung (pōō'tōōng') Chn. (Shanghai In.)	31.00 N	121.29 E
70	Puyallup (pū-ăl'ŭp) .... Wash.	47.10 N	122.19 W
49	Puyallup R. ... Wash. (Seattle In.)	47.9 N	122.12 W
124	Puy-de-Carlitte (Pk.) (püē-dē-kär-lēt') . Fr.	42.35 N	1.55 E
124	Puy de Dome (Pk.) (püē' dē dōm') Fr.	45.45 N	3.0 E
140	Pweto (pwā'tō) .... Bel. Cong.	8.25 S	28.58 E
148	Pyasina R. (pyä-sē'nä) .. Sov. Un.	72.30 N	88.0 E
113	Pyatigorsk (pyä-tē-gôrsk') Sov. Un.	44.5 N	43.5 E
157	Pyengyang (Heijo) (pyĕng'yäng') (hā'jō') . Cho.	39.6 N	125.46 E
160	Pyinmana (pyēn-mä'nŭ) .... India	19.45 N	96.15 E
72	Pylades Chan. (pī'lȧ-dēz) Can. (Vancouver In.)	49.6 N	123.42 W
74	Pyramid L. (pī'rȧ-mĭd) ...... Nev.	40.0 N	119.35 W
74	Pyramid Lake Indian Res. ... Nev.	40.0 N	119.35 W
124	Pyrenees (Mts.) (pĭr-ē-nēz') Fr.-Sp.	42.50 N	1.0 E
103	Pyrenópolis (pē-rĕn-ō'pō-lēzh) Braz.	15.47 S	49.1 W
129	Pyrgos (pĭr'gōs) .... Grc.	37.41 N	21.27 E
122	Pyritz (pü'rĭts) .... Ger.	53.8 N	14.53 E
49	Pysht (pĭsht) .. Wash. (Seattle In.)	48.12 N	124.7 W
157	Pyungchang (pyōōng-chäng') . Cho.	37.22 N	128.23 E
157	Pyungkang (pyōōng'käng') ... Cho.	38.28 N	127.16 E
157	Pyungsan (pyōōng'sän') ..... Cho.	38.17 N	126.23 E
143	Qachasnek (kä'chäz-nĕk) ..... Bas.	30.8 S	28.45 E
150	Qain (kä'ēn) .... Iran	33.50 N	59.20 E
145	Qal'at 'Aneiza (käl'ät ȧ-nāz'ȧ) Transj. (In.)	30.28 N	35.50 E
145	Qal'at ed Dab'a (ĕd däb'ä) Transj. (In.)	31.37 N	36.2 E
145	Qal'at el Hasa (ĕl hä'sȧ) Transj. (In.)	30.52 N	35.53 E
139	Qallâbât (Gallabat) (kä-lä-bät') (gä-lä-bät') . A. E. Sud.	12.58 N	36.6 E
150	Qamaran Is. (kä-mä-rän') .... Asia	15.30 N	42.30 E
135	Qantara (kän'tä-rä) Eg. (Suez Can. In.)	30.52 N	32.21 E
113	Qara Boghaz, G. of (kä'rä bō'gäz) Sov. Un.	41.15 N	54.10 E
150	Qara Chai R. (kä-rä chä'ē) ... Iran	35.12 N	59.30 E
150	Qara Qum (Kara Kum) Des. (kä'rä kōōm') .. Sov. Un.	47.0 N	63.15 E
152	Qara Shahr (Yenki) (kä'rä shär') (yĕn'kē') . Chn.	42.2 N	86.28 E
152	Qargaliq (Yehcheng) (kär'gȧ-lēk) (yĕ-chĕng') . Chn.	37.28 N	79.41 E
150	Qasim (Reg.) (kä'sēm) ...... Nejd	26.30 N	43.30 E
145	Qasr el Azraq (käs''r-ĕl äz'räk) Transj. (In.)	31.50 N	36.18 E
150	Qatar (Dist.) (kä'tär) .... Asia	25.30 N	51.15 E
150	Qatif (kä'tēf) .... Sau. Ar.	26.35 N	50.0 E
139	Qattara Depression (kä-tä'rä) .. Eg.	29.30 N	27.50 E
139	Qena (kā'nȧ) .... Eg.	26.15 N	32.42 E
135	Qift (kĕft) .... Eg. (In.)	25.58 N	32.50 E
145	Qir Moav (El Kerak) (kēr'mō'äv) (ĕl kĕ-räk') . Transj. (In.)	31.10 N	35.42 E
150	Qishm (kĕsh''m) .... Iran	26.55 N	56.15 E
150	Qishm I. .... Iran	26.45 N	56.0 E
148	Qizil Qum (Kyzyl Kum) Des (kĭ'zĭl kōōm') .. Sov. Un.	44.0 N	64.0 E
150	Qizil Uzun (R.) (kĭz-ĭl ōō-zōōn') Iran	37.30 N	48.15 E
138	Qnitra (Kenitra) (k'nē'trȧ) (kĕ-nē'trȧ) . Mor.	34.22 N	6.31 W
152	Qomul (Hami) (kō-mōōl') (hä'mē') . Chn.	42.47 N	93.29 E
171	Quail I. (kwāl) .... N. Z. (In.)	43.37 S	172.43 E
169	Quaker Hill (kwā'kēr hĭl) Austl. (Sydney In.)	33.43 S	150.53 E
85	Quakertown (kwā'kēr-toun) ... Pa.	40.27 N	75.21 W
78	Quanah (kwä'nȧ) .... Tex.	34.17 N	99.44 W
160	Quangngãi (kwäng'n'gä'ē) Fr. In. Chn.	15.8 N	108.47 E
160	Quangtri (kwäng'trē') . Fr. In. Chn.	16.44 N	107.8 E
54	Qu'Appelle R. (kȧ-pĕl') ...... Can.	50.30 N	103.0 W
171	Quarantine I. (kwär'ăn-tēn) N. Z. (In.)	45.49 S	170.39 E
128	Quarnero, G. of (kwär-nâ'rō) .. It.	44.50 N	14.10 E
128	Quartú Sant Elena (kwär-tōō' sänt ā-lā'nä) . Sard.	39.15 N	9.11 E
143	Quathlamba (Drakensberg) (Mts.) (kwät-läm'bä) (drä'kĕns-bûrg) Bas.-U. S. Afr.	29.0 S	29.0 E
167	Queanbeyan (kwēn'bē-yăn) . Austl.	35.21 S	149.16 E
57	Quebec (kwē-bĕk') (kȧ-bĕk') Can. (In.)		
55	Quebec .... Can.	46.53 N	71.20 W
55	Quebec (Prov.) .... Can.	51.30 N	70.0 W
122	Quedlinburg (kvĕd'lĭn-bōōrgh) Ger.	51.48 N	11.10 E
104	Queen Adelaide Arch. (ăd'ē-lād) Chl.	52.0 S	74.30 W
46	Queen Alexandra Ra. (ăl-ĕg-zăn'drȧ) . Ant.	84.0 S	160.0 E
119	Queenborough (kwēn'bŭr-ō) Gt. Brit. (London In.)	51.25 N	0.44 E
164	Queen Channel .... Austl.	14.45 S	129.30 E
72	Queen Charlotte Chan. (shär'lŏt) Can. (Vancouver In.)	49.23 N	123.18 W
54	Queen Charlotte Is. .... Can.	53.0 N	132.30 W
54	Queen Charlotte Sd. .... Can.	51.5 N	129.0 W
46	Queen Mary Land .... Ant.	70.0 S	100.0 E
46	Queen Maud Ra. .... Ant.	86.0 S	150.0 W
166	Queenscliff (kwēnz'klĭf) .... Austl.	38.15 S	144.34 E
166	Queenscliffe .... Austl.	35.38 S	137.36 E
165	Queensland (State) (kwēnz'lănd) Austl.	22.45 S	144.0 E
88	Queenston (kwēnz'tŭn) Can. (Niagara Falls In.)	43.10 N	79.4 W
169	Queenstown (kwēnz'toun) Austl. (Tas. In.)	42.4 S	145.38 E
171	Queenstown .... N. Z.	45.2 S	168.42 E
143	Queenstown .... U. S. Afr.	31.53 S	26.51 E
	Queenstown, see Cobh, Ire.		
140	Quelimane (kā-lē-mä'nĕ) ..... Moz.	17.52 S	36.55 E
157	Quelpart (Saishu) I. (kwĕl'pärt) (sī'shōō) .. Jap.	33.28 N	126.30 E
103	Queluz (kȧ'lōōzh') .... Braz.	20.32 S	43.58 W
96	Quemada (kā-mä'dhä) .... Cuba	22.46 N	80.21 W
124	Quenilly (kā-nē-yē') .... Fr.	49.25 N	1.5 E
95	Quepos, Pt. (kā'pōs) .... C. R.	9.23 N	84.11 W
140	Queque (kwĕ'kwĕ) .... S. Rh.	19.0 S	29.45 E
92	Querétaro (kȧ-rā'tä-rō) ..... Mex.	20.36 N	100.23 W
92	Querétaro (State) .... Mex.	20.40 N	100.0 W
126	Quesada (kā-sä'dhä) .... Sp.	37.53 N	3.3 W
54	Quesnel (kä-nĕl') .... Can.	53.5 N	122.29 W
54	Quesnel L. .... Can.	52.28 N	121.0 W
77	Quetico Park (kwĕ'tĭ-kō) ..... Can.	48.30 N	91.30 W
151	Quetta (Shal) (kwĕt'ȧ) (shäl) India	30.20 N	67.12 E
94	Quezaltenango (kā-zäl'tā-näŋ'gō) Guat.	14.49 N	91.31 W
94	Quezaltepeque (kā-zäl'tā-pā'kā) Guat.	14.40 N	89.26 W
102	Quibdo (kēb'dō) .... Col.	5.32 N	76.32 W
124	Quiberon (kē-bē-rôɴ') .... Fr.	47.28 N	3.5 W
124	Quiberon Pen. .... Fr.	47.30 N	3.5 W
94	Quiché (kē-shā') .... Guat.	15.5 N	91.8 W
102	Quiciá (kē-sē-ä') .... Braz.	7.29 S	66.29 W
49	Quilcene (kwĭl-sēn') Wash. (Seattle In.)	47.49 N	122.52 W
124	Quillan (kē-yäɴ') .... Fr.	42.55 N	2.15 E
54	Quill Lakes (kwĭl) .... Can.	51.48 N	104.30 W
99	Quillota (kēl-yō'tä) Chl. (Valparaiso In.)	32.53 S	71.16 W
104	Quilmes (kēl'mās) ...... Arg. (In.)	34.43 S	57.16 W
151	Quilon (kwē-lōn') . India (Cey. In.)	9.0 N	76.35 E
165	Quilpie (kwĭl'pē) .... Austl.	26.45 S	144.25 E
124	Quimper (käɴ-pĕr') .... Fr.	47.59 N	4.5 W
124	Quimperlé (käɴ-pĕr-lā') .... Fr.	47.45 N	3.31 W
162	Quinabucasan Pt. (kē-nä-bōō-kä'sän) . P. I.	14.7 N	123.21 E
70	Quinault Ind. Res (kwē-nôlt') Wash.	47.25 N	124.30 W
70	Quinault R. .... Wash.	47.25 N	124.0 W
82	Quincy (kwĭn'sē) .... Fla.	30.35 N	84.36 W
79	Quincy .... Ill.	39.55 N	91.24 W
86	Quincy .... Mass.	42.15 N	71.0 W
84	Quincy .... Mich.	41.57 N	84.53 W
49	Quincy .... Ore. (Portland In.)	46.7 N	123.10 W
161	Quingua (kĭng'wä) P. I. (Manila In.)	14.53 N	120.50 E
161	Quingua R. .... P. I. (Manila In.)	14.55 N	120.45 E
160	Quinhon (kwĭ-nyôn') .. Fr. In. Chn.	13.55 N	109.0 E
163	Quiniluban Is. (kē-nē-lōō-bän') . P. I.	11.25 N	120.50 E
70	Quinn R. (kwĭn) .... Nev.	41.40 N	117.55 W
126	Quintana de la Serena (kēn-tä'nä dā lä sā-rā'nä) . Sp.	38.44 N	5.40 W
126	Quintanar (kēn-tä-när') .... Sp.	39.36 N	3.2 W
94	Quintana Roo .... Mex.	19.30 N	88.30 W
167	Quirindi (kwĭ-rĭn'dē) .... Austl.	31.31 S	150.42 E
92	Quiroga (kē-rō'gä) .... Mex.	19.40 N	101.27 W
126	Quiroga .... Sp.	42.28 N	7.19 W
161	Quisao (kē-sä'ō) . P. I. (Manila In.)	14.27 N	121.23 E
82	Quitman (kwĭt'măn) .... Ga.	30.47 N	83.33 W
82	Quitman .... Miss.	32.3 N	88.43 W
102	Quito (kē'tō) .... Ec.	0.10 S	78.30 W
103	Quixadá (kē-shä-dä') .... Braz.	4.59 S	39.1 W
152	Qulja (Ili) (kōōl'jä) (ē-lē') .... Chn.	43.55 N	81.0 W
135	Qulusna (kōō-lōōs'nä) .... Eg. (In.)	28.23 N	30.44 E
150	Qum (kōōm) .... Iran	34.31 N	50.58 E
143	Qumbu (kōōm'bōō) ..... U. S. Afr.	31.11 S	28.54 E
139	Qum Chalouba (kōōm shä-lōō'bä) Fr. Eq. Afr.	15.48 N	20.32 E
150	Qunfidha (Al Qunfidha) (kŭn'fēd'hä) .... Sau. Ar.	18.59 N	41.29 E
142	Quoin Pt. (kwoin) ...... U. S. Afr.	34.47 S	19.38 E
166	Quorn (kwôrn) .... Austl.	32.21 S	138.3 E
135	Qûs (kōōs) .... Eg. (In.)	25.54 N	32.46 E
139	Qusêr (kōō-sēr') .... Eg.	26.2 N	34.18 E
122	Raab R. (räp) .... Ger.	46.58 N	15.50 E
112	Raahe (rä'ĕ) .... Fin.	64.40 N	24.30 E
128	Rab (I.) (räb) .... Yugo.	44.45 N	14.45 E
138	Rabat (rä-bät') .... Mor.	34.6 N	6.51 W
161	Rabaul (rä'boul) ..... N. Gu. Ter.	4.10 S	152.18 E
150	Rabbath'Ammon (Amman) (rä-bät' äm'mōn) (äm'män) . Transj.	32.0 N	36.0 E
72	Rabbit Mt. (răb'ĭt) Colo. (Denver In.)	40.14 N	105.12 W
129	Rača (rä'chä) .... Yugo.	44.12 N	21.0 E
97	Raccoon Cay (I.) .... Ba. Is.	22.22 N	75.48 W
77	Raccoon R. .... Ia.	42.10 N	94.40 W
87	Race, C. (rās) .... Newf.	46.37 N	53.10 W
145	Rachaya (rȧ-chä'yȧ) .... Syr. (In.)	33.31 N	35.50 E
123	Rachov (rä'kôf) .... Czech.	48.3 N	24.12 E
77	Racine (rȧ-sēn') .... Wis.	42.44 N	87.48 W
123	Rădăuţi (rû-dû-ōōts'') .... Rom.	47.52 N	25.54 E
118	Radcliffe (răd'klĭf) ...... Gt. Brit.	53.34 N	2.20 W
122	Radeberg (rä'dē-bĕrgh) ...... Ger.	51.7 N	13.55 E
83	Radford (răd'fērd) .... Va.	37.7 N	80.35 W
120	Rad I. (räd) .... Nor.	60.42 N	5.0 E
116	Radnor Forest (răd'nēr) .. Gt. Brit.	52.10 N	3.10 W
123	Radom (rä'dôm) .... Pol.	51.24 N	21.9 E
129	Radomir (rä'dô-mēr) .... Bul.	42.33 N	22.58 E
123	Radomsko (rä'dôm-skô) .... Pol.	51.4 N	19.28 E
131	Radomysl (rä'dô-mēs'l) ... Sov. Un.	50.31 N	29.12 E
129	Radovište (rä'dô-vēsh-tĕ) ... Yugo.	41.38 N	22.27 E
131	Radul (rä-dōōl') .... Sov. Un.	51.52 N	30.45 E
121	Radviliškis (räd'vē-lēsh'kēs) .. Lith.	55.49 N	23.32 E
123	Radzyń (räd'zûn') .... Pol.	51.47 N	22.43 E
83	Raeford (rā'fērd) .... N. C.	34.57 N	79.12 W
164	Raeside, L. (rā'sīd) .... Austl.	29.15 S	121.45 E
54	Rae Str. (rā) .... Can.	95.30 N	69.0 W
170	Raetihi (rā-ĕ-tē'hē) .... N. Z.	39.23 S	175.18 E
145	Rafa (rä'fä) .... Eg. (In.)	31.5 N	34.10 E
104	Rafaela (rä-fä-ā'lä) .... Arg.	31.20 S	61.35 W
97	Rafael, C. (rä-fä-ĕl') ... Dom. Rep.	19.2 N	69.0 W
139	Rafai (rä-fä'ē) .... Fr. Eq. Afr.	4.58 N	24.0 E
71	Raft R. (răft) .... Ida.	42.10 N	113.28 W
162	Ragay (rä-gī') .... P. I.	13.49 N	122.45 E
162	Ragay G. .... P. I.	13.45 N	122.35 E
170	Raglan (răg'lăn) .... N. Z.	37.47 S	174.57 E
122	Ragnit (rägh'nēt) .... Ger.	55.1 N	22.2 E
120	Ragunda (rä-gōōn'dä) .... Swe.	63.7 N	16.18 E
129	Ragusa (Dubrovnik) (rä-gōō'sä) (dōō'brôv-nēk) . Yugo.	42.39 N	18.9 E
88	Rahway (rô'wā) N. J. (New York In.)	40.37 N	74.16 W
151	Raichur (rä-ē-chōōr') .... India	16.17 N	77.29 E
75	Rainbow Bridge Natl. Mon. (rān'bō) . Utah	37.4 N	110.57 W
119	Rainford (rān'fērd) ...... Gt. Brit.	53.30 N	2.47 W
119	Rainham (rān'ăm) Gt. Brit. (London In.)	51.32 N	0.12 E
70	Rainier (rā-nēr') .... Ore.	46.5 N	122.56 W
70	Rainier, Mt. .... Wash.	46.51 N	121.46 W
77	Rainy L. (rān'ē) .... Can.-U. S.	48.37 N	93.0 W
77	Rainy R. .... Can.-U. S. A.	48.37 N	94.0 W
151	Raipur (rä'ē-pōōr) .... India	21.8 N	81.45 E
84	Raisin, R. (rā'zĭn) .... Mich.	41.58 N	83.40 W
160	Rajaburi (rä-jŭ-bōō'rē) .... Thai.	13.29 N	99.45 E
151	Rajahmundry (räj-ŭ-mŭn'drē) India	17.0 N	81.50 E
160	Rajang R. (rä-jäng') .... Sar.	2.0 N	112.45 E
151	Rajkot (räj'kōt) .... India	22.15 N	70.47 E

ăt; finăl; rāte; senāte; ärm; àsk; sofȧ; fâre; ch-choose; dh-as th in other; bē; ēvent; bĕt; recĕnt; cratēr; g-go; gh-gutteral g; bĭt; ĭ-short neutral; rīde; ĸ-gutteral k as ch in German ich;

Page	Name Pronunciation Region	Lat. °′	Long. °′
151	Rajputana (Agency) (räj-pōō-tä'nŭ). India	27.30 N	73.30 E
171	Rakaia R. (rȧ-kī'ä) N. Z.	43.35 S	171.50 E
131	Rakitnoe (rȧ'kēt-nô-yĕ) Sov. Un.	50.51 N	35.50 E
123	Rákospalota (rä'kôs-pô'lô-tô) Hung.	47.34 N	19.11 E
122	Rakovnik (rä'kôv-nyêk) Czech.	50.6 N	13.43 E
123	Raków (rä'kŏŏf) Pol.	53.59 N	27.0 E
121	Rakvere (rȧk'vĕ-rĕ) Est.	59.20 N	26.21 E
83	Raleigh (rô'lȧ) N. C.	35.46 N	78.39 W
72	Ralston Cr. (rôls'tŭn) Colo. (Denver In.)	39.51 N	105.21 W
95	Rama (rä'mä) Nic.	12.10 N	84.16 W
95	Rama, R. Nic.	11.35 N	84.0 W
49	Ramapo Wash. (Seattle In.)	48.8 N	123.40 W
143	Ramathlabama (rä-mȧt-lȧ-bä'mȧ) Bech.	25.38 S	25.33 E
125	Rambersvillers (räɴ-bĕr-vē-yā')Fr.	48.22 N	6.38 E
124	Rambouillet (räɴ-bōō-yĕ') Fr.	48.38 N	1.48 E
130	Ramenskoe (rȧ'mĕn-skô-yĕ) Sov. Un.	55.34 N	38.10 E
167	Ram Head (răm) Austl.	37.45 S	149.30 E
145	Ramla (Er Ramle) (räm'lȧ) (ĕr räm'lĕ). Pal. (In.)	31.55 N	34.51 E
129	Râmnicul-Sărat (rûêm'nê-kŏŏl-sû-rȧt'). Rom.	45.23 N	27.5 E
129	Râmnicul-Vâlcea (rûêm'nê-kŏŏl-vûêl'chā-ȧ). Rom.	45.5 N	24.21 E
92	Ramos (rä'mōs) Mex.	22.49 N	101.55 W
80	Ramos Arizpe (rä'mōs ä-rēz'pā) Mex.	25.33 N	100.58 W
163	Ramos I. P. I.	8.7 N	117.2 E
104	Ramos Mejía (rä'mōs mā-ᴋē'ä) Arg. (In.)	34.39 S	58.34 W
80	Ramos, R. de Mex.	25.0 N	105.23 W
145	Rampah (räm'pä) Neth. Ind. (In.)	1.47 N	101.26 E
53	Rampart (răm'pȧrt) Alsk.	65.30 N	150.30 W
72	Rampart Ra. Colo. (Colo. Sprs. In.)	39.3 N	104.59 W
151	Rampur (räm'pōōr) India	28.43 N	79.8 E
151	Rampur Boalia (räm'pōōr bô-ä'lê-ä). India	24.20 N	88.40 E
118	Ramsbottom (rămz'bŏt-ŭm) Gt. Brit.	53.39 N	2.19 W
116	Ramsey (răm'zê) Gt. Brit.	54.18 N	4.20 W
117	Ramsgate (ramz'gāt) Gt. Brit.	51.20 N	1.23 E
120	Ramsjö (räm'shû) Swe.	62.12 N	15.41 E
161	Ramu R. (rä'mōō) N. Gu. Ter.	4.30 S	144.30 E
157	Ranan Cho.	41.50 N	129.35 E
160	Ranau, L. (rä-nä'ōō) Neth. E. Ind.	4.50 S	103.55 E
104	Rancagua (rän-kä'gwä) Chl.	34.10 S	70.55 W
124	Rance R. (räɴs) Fr.	48.15 N	2.10 W
151	Ranchi (rän'chē) India	23.20 N	85.29 E
99	Ranchos (rän'chōs) Arg. (Buenos Aires In.)	35.30 S	58.16 W
120	Randers (rän'ĕrs) Den.	56.28 N	10.2 E
143	Randfontein (rän'fôn-tān) U. S. Afr.	26.10 S	27.42 E
83	Randleman (răn'd'l-măn) N. C.	35.47 N	79.49 W
87	Randolph (răn'dôlf) Mass. (In.)	42.10 N	71.2 W
76	Randolph Neb.	42.23 N	97.22 W
86	Randolph Vt.	43.55 N	72.41 W
87	Random I. (răn'dŭm) Newf.	48.10 N	53.45 W
120	Rands Fjord (räns' fyôr) Nor.	60.35 N	10.15 E
130	Ranenburg (rä-nyĕn-bŏŏrg') Sov. Un.	53.14 N	39.58 E
170	Rangaunu B. (răŋ-gȧ-ōō'nŏŏ) N. Z.	34.50 S	173.12 E
86	Rangeley (rānj'lê) Me.	44.55 N	70.38 W
80	Ranger (rān'jēr) Tex.	32.27 N	98.41 W
171	Rangiora (răŋ'gê-ō'rȧ) N. Z.	43.17 S	172.38 E
170	Rangitaiki R. (răŋ-gê-tī'kê) N. Z.	38.30 S	176.40 E
171	Rangitata R. (răŋ-gē-tȧ'tȧ) N. Z.	43.45 S	171.18 E
170	Rangitikei R. (răŋ-gê-tē'kâ). N. Z.	40.0 S	175.32 E
170	Rangitoto (răŋ-gē-tō'tō) N. Z. (In.)	36.48 S	174.52 E
151	Rangoon (rȧŋ-gōōn') India	16.50 N	96.0 E
151	Rangpur (rŭng'pōōr) India	25.45 N	89.29 E
145	Rangsang (I.) (räng'säng') Neth. E. Ind. (In.)	1.0 N	102.55 E
151	Raniganj (rä-nē-gŭnj') India	23.35 N	87.0 E
54	Ranken Inlet (răŋ'kĕn) Can.	63.5 N	93.0 W
167	Rankins Sprs. (răŋ'kĭnz sprĭngz) Austl.	33.46 S	146.22 E
119	Rannersdorf (rän'ĕrs-dôrf) Aus. (Wien In.)	48.8 N	16.28 E
130	Ranova R. (rä'nô-vȧ) Sov. Un.	53.50 N	40.5 E
88	Ransomville (răn'sŭm-vĭl) N. Y. (Niagara Falls In.)	43 14 N	78.54 W
119	Ranst (ränst) Bel. (Anvers In.)	51.12 N	4.33 E
84	Rantoul (răn-tōōl') Ill.	40.25 N	88.8 W
169	Raoul, C. (rou'ŭl)Austl. (Tas. In.)	43.14 S	147.49 E
6	Rapa I. (rä'pä) Pac. O.	27.36 S	144.17 W
128	Rapallo (rä-päl'lô) It.	44.21 N	9.12 E
6	Rapa Nui (Easter) I. (rä'pä nōō'ê). Pac. O.	29.0 S	109.30 W
99	Rapel, R. (rä-pâl') Chl. (Valparaiso In.)	34.5 S	71.35 W
76	Rapid City (răp'ĭd) S. D.	44.5 N	103.13 W
77	Rapid R. Minn.	48.28 N	94.40 W
121	Rapla (räp'lȧ) Est.	59.1 N	24.48 E
85	Rappahannock R. (răp'ȧ-hăn'ŭk) Va.	38.10 N	77.10 W
162	Rapu-Rapu (rä-pōō-rä'pōō) P. I.	13.12 N	124.9 E
162	Rapu-Rapu I. P. I.	13.12 N	124.10 E
85	Raquette L. (răk'ĕt) N. Y.	43.50 N	74.40 W
85	Raquette R. N. Y.	44.45 N	75.0 W
88	Raritan B. (răr'ĭ-tăn) N. J.-N. Y. (In.)	40.28 N	74.14 W
6	Rarotonga (I.) (rä'rô-tŏŋ'gȧ) Pac. O.	21.14 S	159.46 W
163	Rasa I. (rä'sä) P. I.	9.14 N	118.27 E
139	Ras Dashan (Mt.) (räs dä-shän') It. E. Afr.	13.10 N	38.33 E
121	Raseiniai (rä-sā'nĭī) Lith.	55.22 N	23.6 E
141	Ras Hafun (C.) (räs hä-fōōn') It. E. Afr.	10.25 N	51.15 E
135	Rashîd (Rosetta) (rȧ-shēd') (rô-zĕt'ȧ). Eg. (In.)	31.23 N	30.25 E
158	Rashin (rä-shēn') Cho.	42.30 N	129.45 E
131	Rashkovo (rȧsh'kô-vô) Sov. Un.-Rom.	47.57 N	28.50 E
129	Raška (räsh'kȧ) Yugo.	43.14 N	20.38 E
141	Ras Kiuyu (Pt.) (räs' kyōō'yōō) Zan.	4.53 S	39.53 E
145	Ras Seilan (räs' sê-län'). Aden (In.)	13.4 N	45.25 E
113	Rasskazovo (rȧs'kȧ-zô'vô) Sov. Un.	52.35 N	41.50 E
122	Rastatt (rä shtät) Ger.	48.53 N	8.12 E
123	Rastenburg (räs'tĕn-bŏŏrgh) Ger.	54.5 N	21.24 E
141	Ras Upembe (Pt.) (räs' ōō-pĕm'bĕ) Zan.	5.26 S	39.43 E
81	Ratcliff (răt'klĭf) Tex.	31.22 N	95.10 W
122	Rathenow (rä'tē-nō) Ger.	52.36 N	12.20 E
116	Rathlin I. (răth'lĭn) Can.	55.15 N	6.15 W
123	Ratibor (rä'tê-bôr) Ger.	50.6 N	18.13 E
52	Rat Is. Alsk.	52.0 N	177.30 W
78	Raton (rȧ-tōn') N. M.	36.53 N	104.27 W
70	Rattlesnake Cr. Ore.	42.30 N	117.35 W
120	Rättvik (rĕt'vēk) Swe.	60.54 N	15.10 E
120	Raufoss (rou'fôs) Nor.	60.44 N	10.31 E
170	Raukumara Ra. (rou'kōō-mä'rȧ) N. Z.	38.0 S	177.50 E
121	Rauma (rä'ŏŏ-mȧ) Fin.	61.8 N	21.32 E
121	Rautilampo (rä'ŏŏ-tê-läm'pô). Fin.	62.38 N	26.51 E
73	Ravenna (rȧ-vĕn'ȧ) Calif. (Los Angeles In.)	34.27 N	118.14 W
128	Ravenna (rä-vĕn'nä) It.	44.25 N	12.13 E
76	Ravenna (rȧ-vĕn'ȧ) Neb.	41.01 N	98.52 W
84	Ravenna Ohio	41.10 N	81.20 W
122	Ravensburg (rä'vĕns-bŏŏrgh Ger.	47.47 N	9.36 E
84	Ravenswood, W. (rā'vĕnz-wŏŏd) Va.	38.57 N	81.47 W
151	Rawalpindi (rä-wŭl-pên'dê) India	33.45 N	73.2 E
123	Rawa Mazów (rä'vȧ mä'zŏŏf). Pol.	51.46 N	20.17 E
123	Rawa Ruska (rä'vȧ-rŏŏs'kȧ) Pol.	50.13 N	23.40 E
170	Rawene (rȧ-wē'nê) N. Z.	35.25 S	173.30 E
122	Rawicz (rä'vêch) Pol.	51.37 N	16.50 E
71	Rawlins (rô'lĭnz) Wyo.	41.46 N	107.13 W
104	Rawson (rô'sŭn) Arg.	43.20 S	65.15 W
118	Rawtenstall (rô'tĕn-stôl). Gt. Brit.	53.42 N	2.17 W
160	Raya, Mt. (rä'yȧ) Neth. Ind.	0.38 S	112.29 E
87	Ray, C. (rā) Newf.	47.35 N	59.18 W
119	Rayleigh (rā'lê) Gt. Brit. (London In.)	51.35 N	0.36 E
73	Raymond (rā'mŭnd) Ga. (Atlanta In.)	33.21 N	84.43 W
70	Raymond Wash.	46.42 N	123.44 W
167	Raymond Terrace Austl.	32.48 S	151.48 E
81	Raymondville (rā'mŭnd-vĭl) Tex.	26.30 N	97.45 W
81	Rayne (rān) La.	30.15 N	92.15 W
92	Rayón (rä-yōn') Mex.	21.50 N	99.38 W
81	Rayville (rā-vĭl) La.	32.28 N	91.45 W
131	Razdelnaya (rȧz'dĕl-nä'yȧ) Sov. Un.	46.48 N	30.2 E
158	Razdolnoe (rȧz'dôl-nô'yĕ) Sov. Un.	43.38 N	132.0 E
129	Razgrad (räz'grȧt) Bul.	43.30 N	26.30 E
129	Razlog (räz'lôk) Bul.	41.53 N	23.31 E
124	Raz, Pte. du (pwăɴt dü räz') Fr.	48.5 N	4.45 W
124	Ré, Ile de (ēl dē rā') Fr.	46.10 N	1.25 W
56	Reaburn (rā'bûrn) Can. (Winnipeg In.)	50.5 N	97.53 W
116	Reading (rĕd'ĭng) Gt. Brit.	51.25 N	1.0 W
87	Reading Mass. (In.)	42.32 N	71.6 W
84	Reading Mich.	41.47 N	84.47 W
84	Reading Ohio	39.16 N	84.28 W
85	Reading Pa.	40.22 N	75.56 W
102	Real, Cordilleras (Mts.) (rā-äl') Bol.	17.0 S	67.0 W
118	Rea, R. (rē) Gt. Brit.	52.24 N	2.28 W
158	Rebun I. (rē'bōōn) Jap.	45.25 N	141.0 E
128	Recanati (rā-kä-nä'tê) It.	43.26 N	13.33 E
164	Recherche, Arch. of the (rē-shârsh'). Austl.	34.0 S	122.30 E
130	Rechitsa (ryĕ'chēt-sȧ) Sov. Un.	52.21 N	30.25 E
103	Recife (Pernambuco) (râ-sē'fĕ) (pĕr-näm-bōō'kō). Braz.	8.1 S	35.0 W
143	Recife, C. U. S. Afr.	34.2 S	25.40 E
122	Recklinghausen (rĕk'lĭng-hou-zĕn) Ger.	51.34 N	7.2 E
104	Reconquista (rā-kōn-kēs'tä) Arg.	29.5 S	59.40 W
79	Rector (rĕk'tēr) Ark.	36.15 N	90.21 W
73	Redan (rê-dăn') (rĕd'ăn) Ga. (Atlanta In.)	33.44 N	84.8 W
74	Red Bluff Calif.	40.11 N	122.15 W
80	Red Bluff Reservoir N. M.-Tex.	32.0 N	103.59 W
77	Redby (rĕd'bê) Minn.	47.52 N	94.55 W
77	Red Cedar R. Wis.	45.5 N	91.43 W
78	Red Cloud Neb.	40.5 N	98.31 W
54	Red Deer Can.	52.17 N	113.46 W
54	Red Deer R. Can.	51.0 N	109.30 W
143	Reddersburg (rĕd'ērz-bûrg) U. S. Afr.	29.35 S	26.19 E
70	Redding (rĕd'ĭng) Calif.	40.35 N	122.25 W
119	Reddish (rĕd'ĭsh) Gt. Brit. (Liverpool In.)	53.26 N	2.9 W
118	Redditch (rĕd'ĭch) Gt. Brit.	52.19 N	1.56 W
166	Redesdale (rēdz'dāl) Austl.	37.1 S	144.29 E
76	Redfield (rĕd'fēld) S. D.	44.53 N	98.30 W
81	Red Fish Bar Tex. (In.)	29.31 N	94.5 W
166	Red Hill Austl.	33.33 S	138.15 E
87	Red Indian L. Newf.	48.45 N	56.50 W
76	Red Lake R. Minn.	47.48 N	96.40 W
76	Red Lake Falls Minn.	47.53 N	96.18 W
77	Red Lake Ind. Res. Minn.	48.0 N	95.20 W
74	Redlands (rĕd'lăndz) Calif.	34.4 N	117.13 W
85	Red Lion Pa.	39.54 N	76.34 W
71	Red Lodge Mont.	45.12 N	109.15 W
49	Redmond (rĕd'mŭnd) Wash. (Seattle In.)	47.40 N	122.8 W
73	Red Mt. Ala. (Birmingham In.)	33.35 N	86.41 W
76	Red Oak Ia.	41.1 N	95.12 W
124	Redon (rē-dôɴ') Fr.	47.40 N	2.5 W
95	Redonda (I.) (râ-dōn'dä) Le. Is. (In.)	16.56 N	62.18 W
126	Redondela (rā-dhôn-dā'lä) Sp.	42.16 N	8.36 W
126	Redondo (râ-dôn'dŏŏ) Port.	38.39 N	7.31 W
49	Redondo (rê-dŏn'dō) Wash. (Seattle In.)	47.21 N	122.20 W
74	Redondo Beach Calif.	33.47 N	118.25 W
76	Red River N. D.-Minn.	48.0 N	97.2 W
82	Red R. Tenn.	36.35 N	87.5 W
79	Red R. U. S.	33.42 N	96.20 W
78	Red R., North Fork Okla.	35.0 N	99.20 W
78	Red R., Prairie Dog Town Fork of Tex.	34.34 N	100.0 W
78	Red R., Salt Fork Okla.	34.51 N	100.0 W
71	Red Rock Cr. Mont.	44.45 N	112.25 W
150	Red Sea Asia-Afr.	20.0 N	39.0 E
138	Red Stony Des. (Hammada-el-Homra) (häm'ä-dä-ĕl-hôm'rä) Libya	29.30 N	12.0 E
71	Redwater Cr. (rĕd'wô-tēr) Mont.	47.35 N	105.40 W
77	Red Wing Minn.	44.33 N	92.32 W
74	Redwood City (rĕd'wŏŏd) Calif.	37.28 N	122.16 W
77	Redwood Falls Minn.	44.31 N	95.4 W
84	Reed City (rēd) Mich.	43.52 N	85.32 W
74	Reedley (rēd'lê) Calif.	36.36 N	119.28 W
77	Reedsburg (rēdz'bûrg) Wis.	43.33 N	90.0 W
70	Reedsport (rēdz'pôrt) Ore.	43.42 N	124.8 W
170	Reef Point (rēf) N. Z.	35.10 S	173.5 E
171	Reefton (rēf'tŭn) N. Z.	42.3 S	171.55 E
82	Reelfoot L. (rēl'fŏŏt) Tenn.	36.24 N	89.24 W
116	Ree, Lough (L.) (lŏᴋ' rē) Ire.	53.30 N	8.0 W
74	Reese R. (rēs) Nev.	39.40 N	117.15 W
82	Reform (rê-fôrm') Ala.	33.23 N	88.2 W
81	Refugio (râ-fōō'hyô) (rĕ-fū'jō) Tex.	28.19 N	97.15 W
122	Rega R. (rā'gȧ) Ger.	53.45 N	15.15 E
122	Regen R. (rā'ghĕn) Ger.	49.14 N	12.40 E
122	Regensburg (rā'ghĕns-bŏŏrgh). Ger.	49.2 N	12.4 E
128	Reggio (rĕ'jô) It.	44.41 N	10.38 E
128	Reggio Calabria (kä-lä'brê-ä) It.	38.7 N	15.40 E
123	Reghin (râ-gēn') Rom.	46.47 N	24.43 E
54	Regina (rê-jī'nȧ) Can.	50.29 N	104.40 W
90	Regla (rāg'lä) Cuba (Habana In.)	23.8 N	82.20 W
122	Regnitz R. (rĕgh'nēts) Ger.	49.30 N	10.58 E
126	Reguengos de Monsaraz (râ-gĕŋ'-gōzh dā mōn-sä-räzh'). Port.	38.25 N	7.30 W
140	Rehoboth (rê-hō-bôth) S. W. Afr.	23.20 S	17.18 E
122	Reichenbach (rī'ᴋĕn-bäᴋ) Ger.	50.36 N	12.17 E
123	Reichenbach Ger.	50.44 N	16.37 E
122	Reichenberg (Liberec) (rī'ᴋĕn-bĕrᴋ) (lē'bēr-ĕts) Ger.	50.46 N	15.4 E
122	Reichenhall, Bad (bät rī'ᴋĕn-häl) Ger.	47.43 N	12.52 E
157	Reichun (rā'ê-chōōn') Cho.	36.51 N	128.38 E
83	Reidsville (rēdz'vĭl) N. C.	36.21 N	79.39 W
157	Reigan Mojo Cho.	34.49 N	126.43 E
124	Reims (răɴs) Fr.	49.17 N	4.0 E
77	Reinbeck (rīn'bĕk) Ia.	42.22 N	92.42 W
54	Reindeer L. (rān'dēr) Can.	57.0 N	102.30 W
119	Reinickendorf (rī'nĭ-kĕn-dôrf) Ger. (Berlin In.)	52.34 N	13.20 E
126	Reinosa (râ-ê-nō'sä) Sp.	43.2 N	4.9 W
157	Reishu (rī'shōō') Cho.	37.17 N	127.40 E
157	Reisui (rī'sōōē) Cho.	34.45 N	127.40 E
143	Reitz (rīts) U. S. Afr.	27.48 S	28.32 E
157	Reizan (rī'zăn) Cho.	36.40 N	126.50 E
139	Rejaf (rĕ-jäf') A. E. Sud.	4.46 N	31.32 E
85	Relay (rē'lā) Md.	39.13 N	76.43 W
49	Reliance (rê-lī'ăns) Ore. (Portland In.)	45.41 N	123.21 W
138	Relizane (rē-lē-zȧn') Alg.	35.47 N	0.4 E
96	Remedios (rā-mā'dhê-ōs) Cuba	22.28 N	79.35 W
93	Remedios, R. Mex. (In.)	19.30 N	99.8 W
125	Remiremont (rē-mēr-môɴ') Fr.	48.1 N	6.38 E
122	Remscheid (rĕm'shīt) Ger.	51.11 N	7.10 E
165	Rendova I. (rĕn'dô-vȧ)Solomon Is.	8.30 S	157.20 E
122	Rendsburg (rĕnts'bŏŏrgh) Ger.	54.19 N	9.38 E
54	Renfrew (rĕn'frōō) Can.	45.28 N	76.58 W
145	Renggam (rĕng'gäm') Non-fed. Mal. States (In.)	1.56 N	103.27 E
99	Rengo (rĕŋ'gō) Chl. (Valparaiso In.)	34.23 S	70.54 W
131	Reni (rân') Rom.	45.25 N	28.19 E
129	Reni Rom.	45.28 N	28.20 E
166	Renmark (rĕn'märk) Austl.	34.10 S	140.43 E
165	Rennell I. (rĕn-nĕl') Solomon Is.	11.45 S	160.15 E
124	Rennes (rĕn) Fr.	48.19 N	1.41 W
74	Reno (rē'nō) Nev.	39.32 N	119.48 W
128	Reno R. (rā'nô) It.	44.30 N	11.17 E
85	Renovo (rê-nō'vō) Pa.	41.20 N	77.45 W
84	Rensselaer (rĕn'sē-lâr) Ind.	39.59 N	87.7 W
85	Rensselaer N. Y.	42.40 N	73.45 W
70	Renton (rĕn'tŭn) Wash.	47.27 N	122.15 W
77	Renville (rĕn'vĭl) Minn.	44.46 N	95.12 W
73	Republic (rê-pŭb'lĭk) Ala. (Birmingham In.)	33.27 N	86.54 W
70	Republic Wash.	48.39 N	118.45 W
78	Republican R. Colo.-Neb.	40.5 N	98.50 W
165	Repulse B. (rê-pŭls') Austl.	20.45 S	149.0 E
126	Requena (rā-kā'nä) Sp.	39.30 N	1.7 W
131	Reseni (râ-sĕn'') Rom.	47.43 N	28.54 E
131	Reshetilovka (ryĕ'shĕ-tê-lôf'kȧ) Sov. Un.	49.34 N	34.1 E
150	Resht (rĕsht) Iran	37.20 N	49.46 E
119	Resina (râ-sē'nä) It. (Napoli In.)	40.48 N	14.21 E
104	Resistencia (rā-sês-tĕn'syä) Arg.	27.29 S	59.0 W
129	Reşita (râ'shê-tȧ) Rom.	45.17 N	21.55 E
54	Resolution Can.	61.2 N	113.50 W
55	Resolution I. Can.	61.45 N	65.0 W

ng-sing; ŋ-baŋk; ɴ-nasalized n; nŏd; cŏmmit; ōld; ôbey; ôrder; fōōd; fŏŏt; ou-out; s-soft; sh-dish; th-thin; pūre; ûnite; ûrn; stŭd; circŭs; ü-as "y" in study '-indeterminate vowel.

6

Page	Name Pronunciation Region	Lat. °′	Long. °′
171	Resolution I. ... N. Z.	45.40 S	166.40 E
86	Restigouche R. (rĕs-tē-gōōsh') Can.	47.30 N	67.35 W
161	Restinga, Pt. (rĕs-tĭŋ'gä) P. I. (Manila In.)	14.17 N	120.35 E
94	Retalhulen (rā-täl-ōō-län')...Guat.	14.31 N	91.42 W
118	Retford (rĕt'fērd) ... Gt. Brit.	53.19 N	0.57 W
124	Rethel (rē-tĕl') ... Fr.	49.35 N	4.21 E
128	Rethymnon (rā'tēm-nōn) ... Grc.	35.21 N	24.29 E
6	Réunion (I.) (rā-ü-nyôɴ') Ind. O. (In.)	21.6 S	55.36 E
127	Reus (rā'ōōs) ... Sp.	41.9 N	1.5 E
122	Reuss R. (rois) ... Switz.	47.17 N	8.23 E
122	Reutlingen (roit'lĭng-ĕn) ... Ger.	48.30 N	9.13 E
121	Reval (Tallinn) (rē-väl') (tål'ĕn) Est.	59.26 N	24.46 E
124	Revel (rē-vĕl') ... Fr.	43.30 N	2.0 E
54	Revelstoke (rĕv'ĕl-stōk) ... Can.	51.0 N	118.1 W
95	Reventazon, R. (rā-vĕn-tä-zōn') C. R.	10.10 N	83.30 W
87	Revere (rē-vēr') ... Mass. (In.)	42.24 N	71.1 W
53	Revillagigedo (rā-vēl'yä-κē-κä'dō) Alsk.	55.30 N	131.30 W
90	Revilla Gigedo Is. ... Pac. O.	19.0 N	111.0 W
124	Revin (rē-văɴ') ... Fr.	49.45 N	4.40 E
151	Rewah (rā'wä) ... India	24.37 N	81.28 E
6	Rewa R. (rā'wä) ... Fiji Is. (In.)	17.54 S	178.26 E
151	Rewaz (rā'wäz) India (Bombay In.)	18.47 N	72.56 E
73	Rex (rĕks) ... Ga. (Atlanta In.)	33.35 N	84.16 W
71	Rexburg (rĕks'bûrg) ... Ida.	43.49 N	111.49 W
80	Rey, L. ... Mex.	27.0 N	103.25 W
102	Reyes (rā'yĕs) ... Bol.	14.2 S	67.2 W
74	Reyes, Pt. ... Calif.	38.0 N	123.0 W
95	Rey I. (rā'ē) ... Pan.	8.24 N	78.54 W
110	Reykjanes (Pt.) (rā'kyȧ-nĕs)..Ice.	63.45 N	22.45 W
110	Reykjavik (rā'kyȧ-vēk) ... Ice.	64.4 N	21.58 W
80	Reynosa (rā-ē-nō'sä) ... Mex.	26.5 N	98.17 W
150	Rezaieh (Urmia) (rĕ-zī'ȧ) (ōōr'mē-ȧ)...Iran	37.34 N	45.10 E
121	Rēzekne (rĕ'zĕk-nĕ) ... Lat.	56.30 N	27.21 E
99	Rezende (rā-zĕnd'ē) Braz. (Rio de Janeiro In.)	22.30 S	44.27 W
122	Rheden (rā'dĕn) ... Neth.	52.2 N	6.2 E
122	Rheine (rī'nĕ) ... Ger.	52.16 N	7.26 E
122	Rheinland (Prov.) (rīn'lănd)..Ger.	50.24 N	6.46 E
143	Rhenoster R. (rĕ'nŏs-tēr) U. S. Afr.	27.12 S	27.15 E
77	Rhinelander (rīn'lăn-dēr) ... Wis.	45.39 N	89.23 W
122	Rhine R. (rīn) ... Eur.	50.0 N	8.16 E
145	Rhio (Bintan) (I.) (rē'ō) (bĭn'tän)....Neth. Ind. (In.)	1.3 N	104.20 E
160	Rhio Arch. ... Neth. Ind.	0.40 N	104.20 E
145	Rhio Str. ... Neth. Ind. (In.)	0.45 N	104.25 E
85	Rhode Island (State) (rōd ī'lănd) U. S.	41.40 N	71.35 W
143	Rhodes (rōdz) ... U. S. Afr.	30.48 S	27.58 E
115	Rhodes (I.) ... Dodecanese Is.	36.15 N	28.0 E
129	Rhodope Mts. (rō'dō-pē) ... Bul.	41.40 N	24.35 E
116	Rhondda (rŏn'dhȧ) ... Gt. Brit.	51.40 N	3.30 W
124	Rhone R. (rōn) ... Fr.-Switz.	44.50 N	4.45 E
116	Rhyl (rĭl) ... Gt. Brit.	53.19 N	3.20 W
103	Riachão (rē-ä-shouɴ') ... Braz.	7.59 S	46.32 W
103	Riachão do Jacuhipe (rēȧ-chouɴ dōō hä-kōō-ē'pĕ).Braz. (In.)	11.51 S	39.20 W
73	Rialto (rē-äl'tō) Calif. (Los Angeles In.)	34.6 N	117.22 W
126	Rianjo (rē-än'hō) ... Sp.	42.39 N	8.49 W
126	Riaza R. (rē-ä'thä) ... Sp.	41.35 N	3.40 W
112	Ribachi Pen (rē'bách-ē)..Sov. Un.	69.45 N	32.50 E
126	Ribadavia (rē-bä-dhä'vē-ä)....Sp.	42.18 N	8.8 W
126	Ribadeo (rē-bä-dhā'ō) ... Sp.	43.33 N	7.5 W
116	Ribble R. (rĭb''l) ... Gt. Brit.	53.40 N	3.0 W
120	Ribe (rē'bĕ) ... Den.	55.19 N	8.45 E
125	Ribeauville (rē-bō-vēl') ... Fr.	48.10 N	7.18 E
126	Ribeira (rē-bā'ē-rä) ... Sp.	42.33 N	9.0 W
103	Ribeirão Preto (rē-bā-rouɴ' prā'tōō).Braz.	21.10 S	47.45 W
78	Ribera (rē-bā'rȧ) ... N. M.	35.23 N	105.26 W
102	Riberalta (rē-bä-räl'tä) ... Bol.	11.0 S	65.59 W
77	Rib L. ... Wis.	45.21 N	90.11 W
149	Ribnoe (rēb'nō-yĕ) ... Sov. Un.	72.45 N	106.0 E
114	Riçana, Er (ĕr rē-sä'nä)....Mor.	31.8 N	4.23 W
167	Ricardo, Pt. (rĭ-kär'dō) ... Austl.	37.48 S	148.42 E
85	Rice L. (rīs) ... Can.	44.10 N	78.8 W
89	Rice L....Minn. (Minneapolis In.)	44.55 N	93.14 W
77	Rice Lake ... Wis.	45.30 N	91.43 W
143	Richard B. (rĭch'ērd)....U. S. Afr.	28.50 S	32.5 E
53	Richard I. ... Can.	69.20 N	134.0 W
85	Richardson Park (rĭch'ērd-sŭn) Del.	39.42 N	75.37 W
85	Richelieu R. (rēsh'lyû') ... Can.	45.30 N	73.15 W
75	Richfield (rĭch'fēld) ... Utah	38.46 N	112.6 W
86	Richford (rĭch'fērd) ... Vt.	45.0 N	72.40 W
79	Rich Hill ... Mo.	38.6 N	94.12 W
86	Richibucto (rĭ-chĭ-bŭk'tō) ... Can.	46.42 N	64.54 W
82	Richland (rĭch'lănd) ... Ga.	32.6 N	84.41 W
77	Richland Center ... Wis.	43.20 N	90.23 W
167	Richmond (rĭch'mŭnd) ... Austl.	33.38 S	150.48 E
169	Richmond ... Austl. (Tas. In.)	42.46 S	147.36 E
74	Richmond ... Calif.	37.58 N	122.22 W
86	Richmond ... Can.	45.39 N	72.9 W
119	Richmond..Gt. Brit. (London In.)	51.27 N	0.19 W
84	Richmond ... Ind.	39.50 N	84.55 W
84	Richmond ... Ky.	37.45 N	84.20 W
79	Richmond ... Mo.	39.16 N	93.59 W
171	Richmond ... N. Z.	41.20 S	173.12 E
81	Richmond ... Tex.	29.35 N	95.45 W
143	Richmond ... U. S. Afr.	29.54 S	30.17 E
143	Richmond ... U. S. Afr.	31.25 S	23.57 E
71	Richmond ... Utah	41.55 N	111.50 W
85	Richmond ... Va.	37.34 N	77.26 W
49	Richmond Beach Wash. (Seattle In.)	47.46 N	122.23 W
89	Richmond Heights Mo. (St. Louis In.)	38.37 N	90.17 W
88	Richmond Hill ... N. Y. (In.)	40.43 N	73.52 W
169	Richmond Ra. ... Austl. (In.)	28.50 S	152.40 E
169	Richmond R. ... Austl. (In.)	28.45 S	152.57 E
82	Richten (rĭch'tĕn) ... Miss.	31.20 N	88.57 W
142	Richtersveld (rĭκ'tērs-vĕlt) U. S. Afr.	28.30 S	17.1 E
157	Richun (rī'chōōn') ... Cho.	37.17 N	127.27 E
84	Richwood (rĭch'wŏŏd) ... W. Va.	38.14 N	80.32 W
85	Rideau L. (rē-dō') ... Can.	44.40 N	76.20 W
148	Riderskoe (rē'dēr-skō-yĕ) Sov. Un.	50.30 N	83.20 E
49	Ridgefield (rĭj'fēld) Wash. (Portland In.)	45.48 N	122.45 W
88	Ridgefield Park N. J. (N. Y. In.)	40.52 N	74.2 W
85	Ridgeley (rĭj'lē) ... Va.	39.38 N	78.46 W
85	Ridgeway (rĭj'wā) ... Pa.	41.25 N	78.43 W
96	Riding Rocks (rīd'ĭng) ... Ba. Is.	25.14 N	79.10 W
143	Riebeek East (rē-bēk')..U. S. Afr.	33.11 S	26.12 E
122	Ried (rēd) ... Ger.	48.13 N	13.29 E
122	Riesa (rē'zä) ... Ger.	51.17 N	13.17 E
99	Riesco, Cordillera (Mts.) (rē-äs'kō).Chl. (Magallanes In.)	52.45 S	71.45 W
99	Riesco I.....Chl. (Magallanes In.)	52.55 S	72.20 W
142	Rietbron (rēt'brōn) ... U. S. Afr.	32.55 S	23.11 E
142	Rietfontein (rēt'fōn-tān) ... Bech	26.45 S	20.3 E
128	Rieti (rē-ä'tē) ... It.	42.24 N	12.52 E
143	Riet R. (rēt) ... Bech.	28.55 S	24.20 E
141	Riet Vley (L.) (rēt vlā).U. S. Afr.	33.50 S	18.30 E
75	Rifle (rī'f'l) ... Colo.	39.33 N	107.46 W
121	Riga (rē'gȧ) ... Lat.	56.58 N	24.5 E
121	Riga, G. of ... Lat.	57.30 N	23.35 E
57	Rigaud (rē-gō') Can. (Montreal In.)	45.28 N	74.18 W
71	Rigby (rĭg'bē) ... Ida.	43.40 N	111.55 W
123	Rika R. (rē'kȧ) ... Czech.	48.25 N	23.35 E
88	Rikers I. (rī'kērz) ... N. Y. (In.)	40.47 N	73.53 W
118	Rillington (rĭl'ĭng-tŭn) ... Gt. Brit.	54.10 N	0.41 W
102	Rimac, R. (rē-mäk')....Peru (In.)	12.2 S	77.6 W
123	Rimaszombat (Rimavská Sobota) (rē'mȧ-shôm-bät (rē'máf-skȧ) sô'bô-tȧ).Hung.	48.25 N	20.2 E
	Rimavská Sobota see Rimaszombat, Hung.		
120	Rimbo (rēm'bōō) ... Swe.	59.45 N	18.24 E
128	Rimini (rē'mē-nē) ... It.	44.3 N	12.33 E
86	Rimouski (rē-mōōs'kē) ... Can.	48.27 N	68.31 W
93	Rincón Antonio (rên-kōn' än-tō'nyō).Mex.	16.53 N	95.2 W
92	Rincón de Romos (dā rō'mōs) Mex.	22.14 N	102.19 W
157	Rinde (rĭn'dĕ') ... Cho.	38.4 N	128.7 E
169	Ringarooma R. (rĭŋ'gȧ-rōō'mȧ) Austl. (Tas. In.)	41.3 S	148.0 E
46	Ringgold I. (rĭng'gōld) ... Ant.	67.0 S	158.0 E
120	Ringkøbing (rĭng'kûb-ĭng)....Den.	56.6 N	8.15 E
120	Ringkøbing Fjord ... Den.	55.58 N	8.15 E
120	Ringsaker (rĭngs'äk-ēr) ... Nor.	60.56 N	10.41 E
120	Ringsted (rĭng'stĕdh) ... Den.	55.26 N	11.49 E
110	Ringvadsö (I.) (rĭng'vädhs û) Nor.	69.55 N	19.5 E
167	Ringwood (rĭng'wŏŏd) ... Austl.	37.49 S	145.12 E
102	Riobamba (rē'ō-bäm'bä) ... Ec.	1.45 S	78.32 W
99	Rio Bonito (rē'ōō bō-nē'tōō) Braz. (Rio de Janeiro In.)	22.42 S	42.36 W
102	Rio Branco (rē'ōō bräɴ'kōō).Braz.	9.59 S	67.50 W
99	Rio Claro (rē'ōō klä'rōō) Braz. (Rio de Janeiro In.)	22.26 S	47.33 W
104	Río Cuarto (rē'ō kwär'tō)....Arg.	33.15 S	64.20 W
99	Rio de Janeiro (rē'ōō dā zhä-nā'ē-rōō).Braz. (In.)		
104	Rio de Janeiro ... Braz. (In.)		
103	Rio de Janeiro ... Braz.	23.0 S	43.20 W
103	Rio de Janeiro (State) ... Braz.	23.0 S	42.30 W
138	Rio del Rey (rē'ō dĕl rā'ē)....Nig.	4.40 N	8.40 E
138	Rio de Oro (rē'ō dā ō'rō) ... Afr.	25.0 N	13.30 W
104	Río Gallegos (rē'ō gä-lā'gōs)..Arg.	51.40 S	69.15 W
92	Río Grande (rē'ō grän'dā)....Mex.	23.52 N	103.2 W
80	Riogrande (rē'ō grän'dā)....Tex.	26.22 N	98.50 W
103	Rio Grande do Norte (State) (rē'ōō grän'dē dōō nôr'tĕ).Braz.	6.0 S	36.30 W
104	Rio Grande (rē'ōō grän'dē)..Braz.	32.10 S	52.15 W
104	Rio Grande do Sul (State)...Braz.	29.0 S	53.0 W
95	Rio Grande (Matagalpa) R. (rē-ōgrän'dä mä-tä-gäl'pä).Nic.	13.0 N	84.20 W
102	Ríohacha (rē'ō-ä'chä) ... Col.	11.30 N	73.0 W
93	Río Hondo (rē'ō ōn'dō).Mex. (In.)	19.26 N	99.15 W
156	Riojun (Port Arthur), see Lushun, Kwan.		
124	Riom (rē-ôɴ') ... Fr.	45.55 N	3.8 E
126	Rio Maior (rē'ōō mä-yōr')...Port.	39.17 N	8.53 W
104	Rio Negro (rē'ōō nā'grōō)..Braz.	26.8 S	49.58 W
104	Rio Negro (State) (rē'ō nā'grō) Arg.	39.45 S	66.0 W
138	Rio de Oro (rē'ō dā ō'rō) ... Afr.	25.0 N	15.0 E
128	Rionero (rē-ō-nā'rō) ... It.	40.56 N	15.41 E
103	Rio Pardo (rē'ō pär'dō) ... Braz.	15.58 S	42.28 W
102	Riosucio (rē'ō-sōō'syō) ... Col.	5.20 N	75.58 W
103	Rio Verde (rē'ōō vĕr'dē) ... Braz.	17.45 S	50.47 W
92	Rioverde (rē'ō-vĕr'dā) ... Mex.	21.55 N	100.0 W
118	Ripley (rĭp'lē) ... Gt. Brit.	53.3 N	1.25 W
82	Ripley ... Tenn.	35.45 N	89.33 W
127	Ripoll (rē-pōl'') ... Sp.	42.13 N	2.10 E
118	Ripon (rĭp'ŏn) ... Gt. Brit.	54.8 N	1.31 W
77	Ripon ... Wis.	43.50 N	88.50 W
139	Ripon Falls (Simliki R.) (sêm-lē'kē).Ug.	0.32 N	33.4 E
164	Ripon I. (rĭp'ŏn) ... Austl.	20.15 S	119.0 E
169	Risdon (rĭz'dŭn)..Austl. (Tas. In.)	42.47 S	146.21 E
158	Rishiri I. (rē-shē'rē) ... Jap.	45.10 N	141.12 E
84	Rising Sun ... Ind.	38.58 N	84.52 W
124	Risle R. (rēl) ... Fr.	49.5 N	0.40 E
120	Risör (rēs'ûr) ... Nor.	58.44 N	9.14 E
121	Ristna (C.) (rēst'nȧ) ... Est.	58.56 N	22.2 E
56	Ritchot (rĭch'ŭt) Can. (Winnipeg In.)	49.47 N	97.5 W
84	Rittman (rĭt'măn) ... Ohio	40.58 N	81.47 W
70	Ritzville (rĭts'vĭl) ... Wash.	47.7 N	118.23 W
97	Riva (rē'vä) ... Dom. Rep.	19.10 N	69.54 W
128	Riva ... It.	45.53 N	10.50 E
126	Rivadesella (rē'vä-dā-säl'yä)...Sp.	43.27 N	5.5 W
94	Rivas (rē'väs) ... Nic.	11.26 N	85.52 W
124	Rive-de-Gier (rēv-dē-zhē-ā')...Fr.	45.32 N	4.37 E
104	Rivera (rē-vä'rȧ) ... Ur.	31.0 S	55.36 W
138	River Cess (rĭv'er sĕs) ... Lib.	5.45 N	9.50 W
73	Riverdale ... Ga. (Atlanta In.)	33.33 N	84.25 W
88	Riverdale ... Ill. (Chicago In.)	41.39 N	87.37 W
171	Riverdale ... N. Z.	45.53 S	168.45 E
73	Riverdale Utah (Salt Lake City In.)	41.11 N	111.59 W
82	River Falls ... Ala.	31.21 N	86.33 W
77	River Falls ... Wis.	44.52 N	92.38 W
88	River Forest.....Ill. (Chicago In.)	41.53 N	87.49 W
85	Riverhead ... N. Y.	40.55 N	72.40 W
167	Riverina (Reg.) (rĭv-ēr-ē'nȧ) Austl.	35.0 S	146.0 E
82	River Junction ... Fla.	30.42 N	84.50 W
84	River Rouge (rōōzh) ... Mich.	42.20 N	83.5 W
142	Riversdale ... U. S. Afr.	34.6 S	21.14 E
74	Riverside ... Calif.	33.58 N	117.22 W
88	Riverside ... Ill. (Chicago In.)	41.50 N	87.49 W
89	Riverside.....Mich. (Detroit In.)	42.21 N	82.56 W
166	Riverton ... Austl.	34.11 S	138.44 E
171	Riverton ... N. Z.	46.18 S	168.3 E
73	Riverton. Utah (Salt Lake City In.)	40.31 N	111.57 W
85	Riverton ... Va.	39.58 N	78.4 W
71	Riverton ... Wyo.	43.1 N	108.23 W
73	Rivertown ... Ga. (Atlanta In.)	33.37 N	84.44 W
124	Riversaltes (rēv'zält') ... Fr.	42.48 N	2.52 E
86	Rivière du Loup (rē-vyâr' dü lōō') Can.	47.49 N	69.33 W
57	Rivière Rouge (rē-vyâr' rōōzh') Can. (Montreal In.)	45.18 N	74.12 W
150	Riyadh (rē-yäd') ... Sau. Ar.	24.45 N	46.45 E
161	Rizal (Prov.) (rē-zäl') P. I. (Manila In.)	14.40 N	121.10 E
113	Rize (rē'zĕ) ... Tur.	41.0 N	40.32 E
129	Rizzuto, C. (rēt-sōō'tō) ... It.	38.53 N	17.4 E
120	Rjukan (ryōō'kän) ... Nor.	59.54 N	8.35 E
118	Roade (rōd) ... Gt. Brit.	52.9 N	0.53 W
124	Roanne (rō-än') ... Fr.	46.2 N	4.4 E
82	Roanoke (rō'ȧ-nōk) ... Ala.	33.8 N	85.22 W
83	Roanoke ... Va.	37.17 N	79.57 W
83	Roanoke Rapids ... N. C.	36.26 N	77.39 W
83	Roanoke R. ... Va.	36.33 N	77.0 W
94	Roatan (rō-ä-tän') ... Hond.	16.18 N	86.32 W
94	Roatan I. ... Hond.	16.20 N	86.30 W
141	Robben I. (rŏb'ĕn) ... U. S. Afr.	33.48 S	18.22 E
89	Robbinsdale (rŏb'ĭnz-dāl) Minn. (Minneapolis In.)	45.2 N	93.20 W
169	Robbins I. (rŏb'ĭnz) Austl. (Tas. In.)	40.40 S	144.57 E
6	Robert (rō-bĕr') ... Mart. (In.)	14.40 N	60.58 W
72	Roberts, Pt. (rŏb'ērts) Wash. (Vancouver In.)	48.58 N	123.6 W
142	Robertson (rŏb'ērt-sŭn).U. S. Afr.	33.47 S	19.51 E
87	Robertson L. ... Can.	51.0 N	59.10 W
138	Robertsport (rŏb'ērts-pōrt)...Lib.	6.48 N	11.30 W
166	Roberts Town ... Austl.	33.59 S	139.3 E
55	Roberval (rŏb'ēr-văl) (rō-bĕr-vál') Can.	48.35 N	72.14 W
84	Robinson (rŏb'ĭn-sŭn) ... Ill.	39.4 N	87.46 W
87	Robinsons ... Newf.	48.15 N	58.45 W
54	Robson, Mt. (rŏb'sŭn) ... Can.	53.2 N	118.15 W
81	Robstown (rŏbz'toun) ... Tex.	27.47 N	97.40 W
119	Roby (rō'bē) Gt. Brit. (Liverpool In.)	53.24 N	2.52 W
127	Roca, C. (rō'kȧ) ... Port. (In.)	38.47 N	9.30 W
103	Rocas (Is.) (rō'kȧs) ... Braz.	3.55 S	33.45 W
104	Rocha (rō'chäs) ... Braz. (In.)	22.50 S	43.3 W
104	Rocha ... Ur.	34.30 S	54.15 W
116	Rochdale (rŏch'dāl) ... Gr. Brit.	53.40 N	2.10 W
97	Roche à Bateau (rôsh ȧ bȧ-tō') Hai.	18.10 N	73.59 W
127	Roche, C. (rō'chā) ... Sp. (In.)	36.18 N	6.9 W
124	Rochefort (rôsh-fôr') ... Fr.	45.55 N	1.2 W
72	Roche Harbor (rōch) Wash. (Vancouver In.)	48.38 N	123.10 W
77	Rochelle (rō-shĕl') ... Ill.	41.55 N	89.3 W
166	Rochester (rŏch'ĕs-tēr) ... Austl.	36.22 S	144.39 E
117	Rochester ... Gt. Brit.	51.20 N	0.35 E
84	Rochester ... Ind.	41.6 N	36.12 W
77	Rochester ... Minn.	44.1 N	92.28 W
86	Rochester ... N. H.	43.20 N	71.0 W
85	Rochester ... N. Y.	43.8 N	77.35 W
119	Rochford (rŏch'fērd) Gt. Brit. (London In.)	51.35 N	0.43 E
85	Rockaway (rŏck'ȧ-wā) ... N. J.	40.54 N	74.35 W
88	Rockaway ... N. Y. (In.)	40.36 N	73.46 W
88	Rockaway Beach ... N. Y. (In.)	40.34 N	73.52 W
88	Rockaway Inlet ... N. Y. (In.)	40.34 N	73.54 W
73	Rockcastle. Ala. (Birmingham In.)	33.15 N	87.14 W
71	Rock Cr. ... Mont.	48.42 N	107.0 W
71	Rock Cr. ... Mont.	46.25 N	113.40 W
70	Rock Cr. ... Ore.	45.30 N	120.5 W
70	Rock Cr. ... Wash.	47.5 N	117.50 W
81	Rockdale (rŏck'dāl) ... Tex.	30.39 N	97.0 W
77	Rock Falls ... Ill.	41.46 N	89.42 W
77	Rockford (rŏck'fērd) ... Ill.	42.16 N	89.5 W
165	Rockhampton (rŏk-hămp'tŭn) Austl.	23.28 S	150.29 E
83	Rock Hill ... S. C.	34.55 N	81.2 W
83	Rockingham (rŏk'ĭng-hăm)..N. C.	34.56 N	79.46 W
118	Rockingham For. ... Gt. Brit.	52.32 N	0.39 W
54	Rockingham Station....Can. (In.)	44.41 N	63.39 W
79	Rock Island ... Ill.	41.30 N	90.35 W
70	Rock Island Dam Site ... Wash.	47.18 N	120.10 W
86	Rockland (rŏk'lănd) ... Me.	44.6 N	69.8 W
87	Rockland ... Mass. (In.)	42.8 N	70.55 W
82	Rock Mart (märt) ... Ga.	34.0 N	85.3 W
84	Rockport ... Ind.	37.52 N	87.5 W
87	Rockport ... Mass. (In.)	42.38 N	70.37 W
79	Rockport ... Mo.	40.25 N	95.30 W
81	Rockport ... Tex.	28.2 N	97.3 W

ăt; finăl; rāte; senāte; ärm; åsk; sofȧ; fâre; ch-choose; dh-as th in other; bē; ēvent; bĕt; recĕnt; cratēr; g-go; gh-gutteral g; bĭt; ĭ-short neutral; rīde; κ-gutteral k as ch in German ich;

Page	Name Pronunciation	Region	Lat. °'	Long. °'
76	Rock Rapids	Ia.	43.27 N	96.11 W
77	Rock R.	Ill.	41.50 N	89.30 W
76	Rock R.	Ia.-Minn.	43.22 N	96.10 W
97	Rock Sd.	Ba. Is.	24.52 N	76.10 W
171	Rocks Pt.	N. Z.	40.55 S	172.8 E
80	Rocksprings	Tex.	30.1 N	100.12 W
71	Rock Springs	Wyo.	41.35 N	109.12 W
103	Rockstone (rŏk'stōn)	Br. Gu.	5.58 N	58.31 W
76	Rock Valley	Ia.	43.12 N	96.18 W
84	Rockville (rŏck'vĭl)	Ind.	39.46 N	87.14 W
85	Rockville Center	N. Y.	40.40 N	73.42 W
81	Rockwall (rŏk'wôl)	Tex.	32.55 N	96.26 W
77	Rockwell City (rŏk'wĕl)	Ia.	42.24 N	94.36 W
86	Rockwood (rŏk'wŏŏd)	Me.	45.39 N	69.45 W
82	Rockwood	Tenn.	35.52 N	84.42 W
71	Rocky Boys Ind. Res. (rŏk'e)	Mont.	48.15 N	109.55 W
78	Rocky Ford	Colo.	38.3 N	103.44 W
169	Rocky Hd.	Austl. (Tas. In.)	40.50 S	145.30 E
83	Rocky Mount	N. C.	35.56 N	77.48 W
78	Rocky Mountain Natl. Park	Colo.	40.25 N	106.0 W
54	Rocky Mts.	N. A.	50.0 N	114.0 W
73	Rocky Pt.	Calif. (Los Angeles In.)	33.46 N	118.26 W
83	Rocky R.	N. C.	35.20 N	80.40 W
89	Rocky River	Ohio (Cleveland In.)	41.28 N	81.50 W
135	Rôda (rō'dà)	Eg. (In.)	27.48 N	30.51 E
96	Rodas (rō'dās)	Cuba	22.18 N	80.34 W
119	Rodaun (rō'doun)	Aus. (Wien In.)	48.7 N	16.16 E
118	Roden, R. (rō'dĕn)	Gt. Brit.	52.49 N	2.39 W
80	Rodeo (rō-dā'ō)	Mex.	25.10 N	104.34 W
124	Rodez (rô-dĕz')	Fr.	44.21 N	2.35 E
119	Roding, R. (rōd'ĭng)	Gt. Brit. (London In.)	51.37 N	0.3 E
123	Rodnei Mts. (rôd'nĕ-ê)	Rom.	47.37 N	24.30 E
130	Rodniki (rôd'nê-kê)	Sov. Un.	57.7 N	41.45 W
104	Rodrigo de Freitas, L. (rō-drē'gŏŏ dā frā'ē-tāzh)	Braz. (In.)	22.58 S	43.12 W
7	Rodrigues I. (rô-drē'gĕs)	Ind. O.	19.57 S	63.15 E
164	Roebourne (rō'bŭrn)	Austl.	20.50 S	117.10 E
164	Roebuck B. (rō'bŭck)	Austl.	18.5 S	122 10 E
117	Roermond (rōōr'mônt)	Neth.	51.10 N	6.0 E
55	Roes Welcome (Str.) (rōz)	Can.	64.45 N	86.45 W
130	Rogachev (rôg'á-chyôf)	Sov. Un.	53.5 N	30.2 E
169	Rogans Hill (rō'gănz)	Austl. (Sydney In.)	33.44 S	150.59 E
129	Rogačica (rō'gá-chēt-sà)	Yugo.	43.47 N	19.1 E
79	Rogers (rŏj-ĕrz)	Ark.	36.18 N	94.8 W
84	Rogers City	Mich.	45.26 N	83.50 W
82	Rogersville (rŏj'ĕrz-vĭl)	Tenn.	36.23 N	83.2 W
142	Roggeveld Mts. (rō'ghē-vĕlt)	U. S. Afr.	32.0 S	20.0 E
102	Rogoaguado, L. (rō'gō-â-gwā'dō)	Bol.	11.58 S	65.50 W
131	Rogovskaya (rô-gôf'skà-yà)	Sov. Un.	45.43 N	38.42 E
122	Rogozno (rô-gōzh'nô)	Pol.	52.44 N	16.54 E
70	Rogue R. (rōg)	Ore.	42.35 N	123.0 W
123	Rohatyn (rô-hā'tēn)	Pol.	49.25 N	24.38 E
119	Rohrbeck (rōr'bĕk)	Ger. (Berlin In.)	52.32 N	13.2 E
120	Rŏikenviken (rûē'kĕn-vēk-ĕn)	Nor.	60.28 N	10.29 E
125	Roissy-en-France (rwā-sē' äN-fräNs')	Fr. (In.)	49.0 N	2.30 E
99	Rojas (rō'hās)	Arg. (Buenos Aires In.)	34.8 S	60.44 W
93	Rojo, C. (rō'hō)	Mex.	21.34 N	97.20 W
91	Rojo, C.	P. R. (In.)	17.50 N	67.12 W
158	Rokko C. (rŏk'kō)	Jap.	37.30 N	137.18 E
159	Rokugogawa R. (rō'kōō-gō-gā'wā)	Jap. (Tokyo In.)	35.36 N	139.36 E
122	Rokycany (rô'kêt-sà-nê)	Czech.	49.44 N	13.36 E
79	Rolla (rŏl'á)	Mo.	37.56 N	91.45 W
76	Rolla	N. D.	48.52 N	99.30 W
120	Rollag (rō'lāgh)	Nor.	59.54 N	8.35 E
165	Roma (rō'mà)	Austl.	26.29 S	148.45 E
128	Roma (Rome) (rō'mä) (rōm)	It.	41.45 N	12.15 E
87	Romaine (rô-mĕn')	Can.	50.15 N	60.39 W
55	Romaine R.	Can.	52.0 N	63.45 W
123	Roman (rō'män)	Rom.	46.57 N	26.55 E
145	Romani (rô-mä'nê)	Eg. (In.)	30.57 N	32.46 E
129	Romania (rō-mä'nĕ-à)	Eur.	45.0 N	25.0 E
83	Romano, C. (rō-mä'nō)	Fla. (In.)	25.51 N	81.40 W
96	Romano Cay (I.)	Cuba	22.10 N	77.52 W
124	Romans (rô-mäN')	Fr.	45.4 N	5.3 E
142	Roman Vloer (L.) (rō'măn vlōōr')	U. S. Afr.	30.40 S	20.42 E
162	Romblon (rōm-blōn')	P. I.	12.34 N	122.15 E
162	Romblon I.	P. I.	12.33 N	122.16 E
82	Rome (rōm)	Ga.	34.15 N	85.10 W
128	Rome (Roma) (rōm) (rō'mä)	It.	41.45 N	12.15 E
85	Rome	N. Y.	43.14 N	75.30 W
84	Romeo (rō'mē-ō)	Mich.	42.50 N	83.0 W
119	Romford (rŭm'fērd)	Gt. Brit. (London In.)	51.35 N	0.11 E
119	Romiley (rŭm'ĭ-lē)	Gt. Brit. (Liverpool In.)	53.25 N	2.6 W
124	Romilly-sur-Seine (rô-mē-yē'-sür-sān')	Fr.	48.32 N	3.42 E
92	Romita (rō-mē'tä)	Mex.	20.54 N	101.32 W
131	Romny (rôm'nĭ)	Sov. Un.	50.46 N	33.31 E
120	Romö (I.) (rûm'û)	Den.	55.5 N	8.30 E
73	Romoland (rō'mō-lănd)	Calif. (Los Angeles In.)	33.45 N	117.10 W
124	Romorantin (rō-mō-räN-täN')	Fr.	47.25 N	1.45 E
71	Ronan (rō'năn)	Mont.	47.30 N	114.6 W
103	Roncador, Serra do (Mts.) (sĕr'rá dōō rôn-kā-dôr')	Braz.	11.30 S	52.0 W
85	Ronceverte (rŏn'sē-vûrt)	W. Va.	37.45 N	80.30 W
141	Rondebosch (rŏn'dĕ-bŏsh)	U. S. Afr.	33.57 S	18.28 E
126	Rondo (rŏn'dō)	Sp.	36.45 N	5.9 W
120	Rŏnne (rûn'ĕ)	Den.	55.5 N	14.42 E
120	Ronneby (rŏn'ĕ-bü)	Swe.	56.13 N	15.20 E
142	Roode Berg (Mt.) (rō'dĕ bĕrg)	U. S. Afr.	33.58 S	21.25 E
143	Roodepoort (rō'dĕ-pōrt)	U. S. Afr.	26.8 S	27.57 E
79	Roodhouse (rōōd'hous)	Ill.	39.28 N	90.20 W
117	Roosendaal (rō'zĕn-dāl)	Neth.	51.35 N	4.30 E
75	Roosevelt (rōz''vĕlt)	Utah	40.17 N	109.58 W
75	Roosevelt Dam	Ariz.	33.40 N	111.12 W
75	Roosevelt L.	Ariz.	33.40 N	111.10 W
103	Roosevelt, R.	Braz.	10.0 S	60.30 W
164	Roper R. (rōp'ēr)	Austl.	14.50 S	133.30 E
127	Roquetas (rō-kā'tās)	Sp.	40.50 N	0.31 E
103	Roraima Mt. (rô-rä-ē'mä)	Ven.-Br. Gu.	5.10 N	60.45 W
120	Rōros (rûr'ôs)	Nor.	62.35 N	11.21 E
122	Rorschach (rōr'shäk)	Switz.	47.27 N	9.28 E
135	Rosa, C. (rō'sä)	Tun. (In.)	36.55 N	8.31 E
80	Rosales (rō-za'lās)	Mex.	28.13 N	100.43 W
162	Rosales	P. I.	15.54 N	120.39 E
128	Rosa, Monte (Mt.) (mōn'tä rō'zä)	It.	45.56 N	7.51 E
92	Rosamorada (rō'zä-mō-rä'dhä)	Mex.	22.5 N	105.15 W
72	Rosa Mt. (rō'zä)	Colo. (Colo. Sprs. In.)	38.45 N	104.57 W
104	Rosario (rō-zä'rē-ō)	Arg.	33.0 S	60.45 W
103	Rosario (rô-zä'rē-ōō)	Braz.	2.58 S	44.18 W
104	Rosario	Braz. (In.)	22.41 S	43.16 W
92	Rosario (rô-zä'rê-ō)	Mex.	23.0 N	105.51 W
162	Rosario	P. I.	13.50 N	121.12 E
161	Rosario	P. I. (Manila In.)	14.26 N	120.50 E
99	Rosario	Ur. (Buenos Aires In.)	34.18 S	57.23 W
96	Rosario Cay (I.)	Cuba	21.37 N	81.54 W
103	Rosario Oeste (rô-zä'rê-ōō ō-ĕst'ĕ)	Braz.	14.45 S	56.28 W
72	Rosario Str.	Wash. (Vancouver In.)	48.35 N	122.45 W
127	Rosas, G. of (rō'zäs)	Sp.	42.10 N	3.10 E
49	Rosburg (rŏz'bûrg)	Wash. (Portland In.)	46.19 N	123.39 W
80	Roscoe (rŏs'kō)	Tex.	32.27 N	100.38 W
116	Roscommon (rôs-kŏm'ŭn)	Ire.	53.40 N	8.10 W
95	Roseau (rō-zō')	Le. Is. (In.)	15.17 N	61.23 W
76	Roseau	Minn.	48.51 N	95.46 W
71	Rosebud Cr.	Mont.	45.50 N	106.30 W
76	Rosebud Ind. Res.	S. D.	43.10 N	100.42 W
70	Roseburg (rōz'bûrg)	Ore.	43.11 N	123.20 W
72	Rosedale (rōz'dāl)	Can. (Vancouver In.)	49.10 N	121.48 W
79	Rosedale	Kan.	39.4 N	94.39 W
82	Rosedale	Miss.	33.49 N	91.1 W
49	Rosedale	Wash. (Seattle In.)	47.19 N	122.39 W
88	Rosehill (rōz'hĭl)	Can. (Niagara Falls In.)	42.53 N	78.59 W
124	Rosendael (rō-zäN-dāl')	Fr.	51.1 N	2.29 E
122	Rosenheim (rō'zĕn-hīm)	Ger.	47.51 N	12.6 E
119	Rosenthal (rō'zĕn-tāl)	Ger. (Berlin In.)	52.36 N	13.23 E
135	Rosetta (Rashîd) (rō-zĕt'á) (rä-shēd')	Eg. (In.)	31.23 N	30.25 E
74	Roseville (rōz'vĭl)	Calif.	38.43 N	121.18 W
153	Rosham (rō-shàm)	Manch.	48.50 N	126.0 E
80	Rosiclare (rōz'ĭ-klâr)	Ill.	37.28 N	88.17 W
129	Roşiorii de Vede (rô-shê-ôr-ĭ-ê dâ vä'dĕ)	Rom.	44.6 N	24.59 E
120	Roskilde (rôs'kêl-dĕ)	Den.	55.38 N	12.4 E
130	Roslavl (rôs'lâv'l)	Sov. Un.	53.58 N	32.52 E
70	Roslyn (rŏz'lĭn)	Wash.	47.13 N	121.0 W
143	Rosmead (rŏz'mēd)	U. S. Afr.	31.28 S	25.8 E
125	Rosny (rō-nē')	Fr. (In.)	48.52 N	2.29 E
169	Ross (rŏs)	Austl. (Tas. In.)	42.3 S	147.31 E
49	Ross	Calif. (San Francisco In.)	37.57 N	122.32 W
171	Ross	N. Z.	42.52 S	170.54 E
128	Rossano (rô-sä'nō)	It.	39.34 N	16.39 E
6	Ross Dependency	Pac. O.	70.0 S	170.0 W
55	Rosseau, L. (rôs-sō')	Can.	45.15 N	79.45 W
165	Rossel I. (rô-sĕl')	Pap. Ter.	11.30 S	154.0 E
56	Rosser (rŏs'sēr)	Can. (Winnipeg In.)	49.59 N	97.29 W
86	Rossignol L. (rô-sê-nyôl')	Can.	44.20 N	65.5 W
46	Ross I.	Ant.	76.0 S	169.0 E
54	Ross I.	Can.	54.15 N	98.15 W
70	Rossland (rôs'lănd)	Can.	49.4 N	117.47 W
131	Rossosh (rôs'sŭsh)	Sov. Un.	50.12 N	39.33 E
46	Ross Sea	Ant.	76.0 S	174.0 W
82	Rossville (rŏs'vĭl)	Ga.	34.58 N	85.22 W
119	Rostherne (rŏs'tērn)	Gt. Brit. (Liverpool In.)	53.21 N	2.24 W
122	Rostock (rôs'tŏk)	Ger.	54.5 N	12.6 E
131	Rostov (rôs-tôf')	Sov. Un	47.12 N	39.42 E
130	Rostov	Sov. Un	57.12 N	39.25 E
129	Rosul Pass (rō'zōōl)	Rom.	45.32 N	24.17 E
110	Rōs Water (L.) (rûs)	Nor.	65.48 N	14.0 E
72	Roswell (rŏz'wĕl)	Colo. (Colo. Sprs. In.)	38.53 N	104.50 W
82	Roswell	Ga.	34.3 N	84.24 W
78	Roswell	N. M.	33.23 N	104.31 W
127	Rota (rō'tä)	Sp. (In.)	36.37 N	6.21 W
80	Rotan (rō-tăn')	Tex.	32.50 N	100.30 W
122	Rothenburg (rō'tĕn-bōōrgh)	Ger.	49.22 N	10.12 E
116	Rotherham (rŏdh'ēr-ăm)	Gt. Brit.	53.25 N	1.20 W
86	Rothesay	Can.	45.24 N	65.59 W
116	Rothesay (rŏth'sā)	Gt. Brit.	55.50 N	5.0 W
118	Rothwell (rŏth'wĕl)	Gt. Brit.	53.44 N	1.29 W
161	Roti (I.) (rō'tē)	Neth. Ind.	10.45 S	123.0 E
167	Roto (rō'tō)	Austl.	33.11 S	145.31 E
124	Rotondo, Mt. (rō-tôn'dō)	Cor. (In.)	42.15 N	9.5 E
170	Rotorua (rō-tō-rōō'ä)	N. Z.	38.10 S	176.15 E
170	Rotorua L.	N. Z.	38.7 S	176.20 E
117	Rotterdam (rŏt-ēr-dăm')	Neth.	51.55 N	4.29 E
122	Rottweil (rōt'vīl)	Ger.	48.11 N	8.37 E
124	Roubaix (rōō-bĕ')	Fr.	50.41 N	3.10 E
124	Rouen (rōō-äN')	Fr.	49.25 N	1.5 E
89	Rouge, R. (rōōzh)	Mich. (Detroit In.)	42.19 N	83.10 W
117	Roulers (rōō-lā')	Bel	50.55 N	3.5 E
170	Round Back, Mt.	N. Z. (In.)	41.19 S	174.40 E
89	Round L.	Minn. (Minneapolis In.)	45.5 N	93.10 W
167	Round Mt.	Austl.	30.26 S	152.18 E
87	Round Pond	Newf.	48.10 N	56.5 W
71	Roundup	Mont.	46.26 N	108.34 W
74	Round Valley Ind. Res.	Calif.	39.50 N	123.20 W
116	Rousay (I.) (rōō'zá)	Gt. Brit. (In.)	59.5 N	3.0 W
169	Rous Hd. (rōōz)	Austl. (Perth In.)	32.3 S	115.44 E
143	Rouxville (rōō'vĭl)	U. S. Afr.	30.26 S	26.49 E
55	Rouyn (rōōn)	Can.	48.17 N	79.5 W
112	Rovaniemi (rō'và-nyĕ-mĭ)	Fin.	66.30 N	25.40 E
128	Rovato (rô-vä'tō)	It.	45.34 N	10.0 E
131	Rovenki (rô-vĕŋ'kê)	Sov. Un.	48.4 N	39.41 E
131	Rovenki	Sov. Un.	49.55 N	38.55 E
128	Rovereto (rô-vā-rā'tō)	It.	45.54 N	11.3 E
128	Rovigno (rô-vēn'yō)	It.	45.5 N	13.38 E
128	Rovigo (rô-vē'gō)	It.	45.4 N	11.46 E
131	Rovnoe (rôv'nô-yĕ)	Sov. Un.	48.11 N	31.43 E
87	Rowley (rou'lē)	Mass. (In.)	42.43 N	70.53 W
123	Równe (rōōv'nĕ)	Pol.	50.36 N	26.16 E
83	Roxboro (rŏks'bŭr-ō)	N. C.	36.23 N	78.58 W
171	Roxburgh (rŏks'bŭr-ō)	N. Z.	45.33 S	169.22 E
78	Roy (roi)	N. M.	35.55 N	104.11 W
73	Roy	Utah (Salt Lake City In.)	41.10 N	112.3 W
49	Roy	Wash. (Seattle In.)	47.1 N	122.33 W
96	Royal I. (roi'ăl)	Ba. Is.	25.32 N	76.50 W
167	Royal, Mt.	Austl.	32.9 S	151.20 E
84	Royal Oak	Mich.	42.29 N	83.11 W
84	Royalton (roi'ăl-tŭn)	Mich.	42.2 N	86.26 W
124	Royan (rwä-yäN')	Fr.	45.39 N	1.0 W
124	Roye (rwä)	Fr.	49.45 N	2.45 E
82	Royston (roiz'tŭn)	Ga.	34.17 N	83.9 W
118	Royton (roi'tŭn)	Gt. Brit.	53.34 N	2.7 W
123	Rózana (rōō-zhä'nä)	Pol.	52.51 N	24.53 E
123	Rozsnyó (Rožňava) (rōzh'nyō) (rōzh'nyà-và)	Hung.	48.40 N	20.32 E
113	Rtishchevo ('r-tēsh'chĕ-vō)	Sov. Un.	52.12 N	43.45 E
141	Ruaha R. (rōō'à-hä)	Tan.	7.40 S	37.0 E
170	Ruahine Ra. (rōō-à-hē'nē)	N. Z.	40.0 S	176.10 E
140	Ruanda Urundi (Prov.) (rōō-än'dä ōō-rōōn'dĭ)	Bel. Cong.	2.45 S	30.0 E
170	Ruapehu (Vol.) (rōō-à-pä'hōō)	N. Z.	39.18 S	175.33 E
171	Ruapuke I. (rōō-à-pōō'kĕ)	N. Z.	46.47 S	168.28 E
150	Rub al Khali (Great Sandy Desert) (rŭb äl kä'lē)	Asia	20.0 N	52.0 E
131	Rubanovka (rōō'băn-ôf-kà)	Sov. Un.	47.0 N	34.10 E
127	Rubí (rōō-bê')	Sp. (In.)	41.29 N	2.2 E
119	Rübke (rüp'kĕ)	Ger. (Hamburg In.)	53.29 N	9.46 E
148	Rubtsovsk (rōōp'tsôfsk)	Sov. Un.	51.30 N	81.15 E
52	Ruby (rōō'bê)	Alsk.	64.40 N	155.30 W
74	Ruby L.	Nev.	40.10 N	115.27 W
71	Ruby R.	Mont.	45.25 N	112.10 W
140	Ruchugi (rōō-chōō'gē)	Tan.	5.13 S	30.20 E
130	Rudabkina (rōō-däp'kê-nà)	Sov. Un.	52.44 N	29.0 E
120	Rudkŏbing (rōōdh'kûb-ĭng)	Den.	54.56 N	10.44 E
152	Rudok (rōō'dôk)	Chn.	33.28 N	77.44 E
139	Rudolph, L. (rōō'dŏlf)	Kenya-Eth.	4.0 N	36.0 E
122	Rudolstadt (rōō'dôl-shtät)	Ger.	50.43 N	11.19 E
124	Ruelle (rü-ĕl')	Fr.	45.41 N	0.15 E
139	Rufāa (rōō-fä'ä)	A. E. Sud.	14.40 N	33.28 E
124	Ruffec (rü-fĕk')	Fr.	46.3 N	0.11 E
141	Rufiji R. (rōō-fē'jē)	Tan.	7.45 S	38.0 E
99	Rufino (rōō-fē'nō)	Arg. (Buenos Aires In.)	34.13 S	62.43 W
138	Rufisque (rü-fēsk')	Fr. W. Afr.	14.42 N	17.8 W
118	Rugby (rŭg'bê)	Gt. Brit.	52.22 N	1.15 W
76	Rugby	N. D.	48.22 N	100.0 W
118	Rugeley (rŭj'lē)	Gt. Brit.	52.46 N	1.56 W
122	Rügen (I.) (rü'ghĕn)	Ger.	54.26 N	13.25 E
122	Rügenwalde (rüh-gĕn-väl'dĕ)	Ger.	54.26 N	16.23 E
121	Ruhno I. (rōō'nō)	Lat.	57.48 N	23.15 E
122	Ruhr R. (rōōr)	Ger.	51.28 N	8.10 E
121	Rūjeena (rōō'yà-nà)	Lat.	57.54 N	25.20 E
149	Rukhlovo (rōōk'lô-vô)	Sov. Un.	53.55 N	123.59 E
140	Rukwa, L. (rōōk-wä')	Tan.	8.18 S	32.42 E
116	Rum (I.) (rŭm)	Gt. Brit.	57.0 N	6.20 W
129	Ruma (rōō'mà)	Yugo.	45.0 N	19.51 E
139	Rumbek (rŭm'bĕk)	A. E. Sud.	6.52 N	29.40 E
97	Rum Cay (I.)	Ba. Is.	23.40 N	74.51 W
86	Rumford (rŭm'fērd)	Me.	44.33 N	70.35 W
123	Rummelsburg (rōōm'ĕls-bōōrgh)	Ger.	54.1 N	17.0 E
77	Rum R.	Minn.	45.25 N	93.20 W
171	Runanga (rōō-năŋ'gä)	N. Z.	42.22 S	171.15 E
170	Runaway, C. (rŭn'á-wā)	N. Z.	37.30 S	178.3 E
118	Runcorn (rŭŋ'kôrn)	Gt. Brit.	53.20 N	2.44 W
72	Running Cr.	Colo. (Denver In.)	39.34 N	104.32 W
145	Rupat I. (rōō'pät)	Neth. Ind. (In.)	1.50 N	101.35 E
71	Rupert (rōō'pērt)	Ida.	42.37 N	113.41 W
55	Rupert R.	Can.	51.35 N	77.45 W
119	Ruschwedel (rōōsh'vä-dĕl)	Ger. (Hamburg In.)	53.27 N	9.33 E
129	Rusčuk (Russe) (rōōs'chōōk) (rōō'sĕ)	Bul.	43.50 N	25.59 E
77	Rush City	Minn.	45.40 N	92.59 W
78	Rush Cr.	Colo.	38.40 N	103.10 W
118	Rushden (rŭsh'dĕn)	Gt. Brit.	52.18 N	0.35 W
79	Rushville (rŭsh'vĭl)	Ill.	40.7 N	90.34 W
84	Rushville	Ind.	39.35 N	85.37 W
76	Rushville	Neb.	42.42 N	102.26 W
166	Rushworth (rŭsh'wûrth)	Austl.	36.36 S	144.58 E
87	Rushy Pond (rŭsh'ĭ)	Newf.	48.58 N	55.41 W
81	Rusk (rŭsk)	Tex.	31.48 N	95.10 W
73	Russ (rŭs)	Calif. (Los Angeles In.)	34.27 N	118.20 W

ng-sing; ŋ-baŋk; N-nasalized n; nŏd; cŏmmit; ōld; ōbey; ôrder; fōōd; fŏŏt; ou-out; s-soft; sh-dish; th-thin; pūre; ūnite; ûrn; stŭd; circŭs; ü-as "y" in study; '-indeterminate vowel.

Page	Name Pronunciation Region	Lat. °′	Long. °′
129	Russe (Rusčuk) (ro͞o′sĕ) (ro͝os′cho͝ok). Bul.	43.50 N	25.59 E
54	Russell (rŭs′ĕl) .... Can.	50.48 N	101.1 W
78	Russell .... Kan.	38.53 N	98.51 W
84	Russell .... Ky.	38.30 N	82.45 W
170	Russell .... N. Z.	35.17 S	174.10 E
72	Russell Gulch (gŭlch) Colo. (Denver In.)	39.47 N	105.33 W
165	Russell I. .... Solomon Is.	9.8 S	159.0 E
82	Russellville (rŭs′ĕl-vĭl) .... Ala.	34.30 N	87.34 W
79	Russellville .... Ark.	35.16 N	93.8 W
82	Russellville .... Ky.	36.50 N	86.52 W
	Russia, see Soviet Union		
74	Russian R. .... Calif.	38.55 N	123.10 W
143	Rustenburg (rŭs′tĕn-bûrg) (ro͝os′tĕn-bo͝orgh). U. S. Afr.	25.41 S	27.16 E
81	Ruston (rŭs′tŭn) .... La.	32.31 N	92.39 W
122	Rüstringen (rüs′trĭng-ĕn) ..... Ger.	53.32 N	8.6 E
131	Rutchenkovo (ro͞ot′chĕn-kô-vô) Sov. Un.	47.53 N	37.34 E
126	Rute (ro͞o′tā) .... Sp.	37.20 N	4.21 W
74	Ruth (ro͞oth) .... Nev.	39.16 N	114.59 W
123	Ruthenia (Podkarpatská Rus) (Prov.) (ro͞o-thē′nê-à) .... Czech.	48.28 N	23.20 E
88	Rutherford (rŭdh′ẽr-fẽrd) N. J. (N. Y. In.)	40.50 N	74.6 W
83	Rutherfordton (rŭdh′ẽr-fẽrd-tŭn) N. C.	35.22 N	81.58 W
86	Rutland (rŭt′lănd) .... Vt.	43.35 N	73.0 W
118	Rutland Co. .... Gt. Brit.	52.39 N	0.42 W
140	Rutshuru (ro͞ot-sho͞o′ro͞o) Bel. Cong.	1.13 S	29.22 E
128	Ruvo (ro͞o′vô) .... It.	41.6 N	16.30 E
141	Ruvu (Kingani) R. (ro͞o′vo͞o) (kĭŋ′gä′nĭ). Tan.	6.40 S	38.45 E
141	Ruvu (Pangani) R. (päŋ-gä′nĭ) Tan.	5.0 S	38.6 E
141	Ruvuma R. (ro͞o-vo͞o′mä) Tan.-Moz.	11.15 S	38.15 E
150	Ruwanduz (ro͞o-wän′do͝oz) .... Iraq	36.38 N	44.40 E
139	Ruwenzori Ra. (ro͞o-wĕn-zō′rê) Ug.	0.15 N	30.30 E
89	Ruxton (rŭks′tŭn) Va. (Norfolk In.)	36.52 N	76.15 W
130	Ruza (ro͞o′zà) .... Sov. Un.	55.42 N	36.11 E
130	Ryazan (ryä-zän″) ...... Sov. Un.	54.38 N	39.42 E
130	Ryazan (Dist.) .... Sov. Un.	54.8 N	40.0 E
130	Ryazhsk (ryäzh′sk′) ..... Sov. Un.	53.42 N	40.2 E
130	Rybinsk (rê′bênsk) ...... Sov. Un.	58.1 N	38.41 E
123	Rybnik (rĭb′nêk) .... Pol.	50.6 N	18.33 E
131	Rybnitsa (rĭb′nêt-sà) .... Rom.	47.45 N	28.59 E
116	Ryde (rīd) .... Gt. Brit.	50.45 N	1.13 W
118	Rye, R. (rī) .... Gt. Brit.	54.10 N	0.51 W
131	Rylsk (rêl″sk) .... Sov. Un.	51.33 N	34.43 E
123	Rypin (rē′pên) .... Pol.	53.3 N	19.25 E
158	Ryukyu Is. (ryo͞o′kyo͞o′). Jap. (In.)	24.40 N	126.10 E
123	Rzeszów (zhå′sho͝of) .... Pol.	50.2 N	22.0 E
130	Rzhev (′r-zhĕf) .... Sov. Un.	56.15 N	34.20 E
131	Rzhishchev (′r-zhēsh′chĕf) Sov. Un.	49.58 N	31.2 E
122	Saale R. (sä′lĕ) .... Ger.	51.0 N	11.51 E
122	Saalfeld (säl′fĕlt) .... Ger.	50.38 N	11.20 E
72	Saanich Inlet (sô′nĭch) Can. (Vancouver In.)	48.38 N	123.30 W
125	Saarebourg (sär-bo͞org′) .... Fr.	48.45 N	7.5 E
121	Saaremaa (Ezel) (I.) (sä′rĕ-mä) (ĕt′sĕl). Est.	58.26 N	22.36 E
114	Saar, Wadi (R.) (wä′dê sä′är) Mor.	34.12 N	2.30 W
104	Saavedra (sä-ä-vā′drä) .... Arg.	37.45 S	62.20 W
122	Saaz (Žatec) (zäts) (zhä′tĕts). Ger.	50.19 N	13.32 E
95	Saba (I.) (sä′bä) ..... Le. Is. (In.)	17.38 N	63.14 W
129	Sabac (shä′bàts) .... Yugo.	44.45 N	19.43 E
127	Sabadell (sä-bä-dhål′) .... Sp. (In.)	41.32 N	2.6 E
97	Sabana de la Mar (dā lä mär′) Dom. Rep.	19.4 N	69.23 W
95	Sabana, R. (sä-bä′nä) .... Pan.	8.40 N	78.5 W
93	Sabancuy (sä-bäŋ-kwē′) ..... Mex.	18.58 N	91.6 W
97	Sabaneta (sä-bä-nā′tä). Dom. Rep.	19.28 N	71.23 W
160	Sabang (sä′bäng) ...... Neth. Ind.	5.52 N	95.26 E
128	Sabau dia (sä bà-o͞o′dê-à) ...... It.	41.19 N	13.0 E
139	Sabderat (säb-då-rät ... It. E. Afr.	15.28 N	36.41 E
79	Sabetha (sà-bĕth′à) .... Kans.	39.55 N	95.48 W
121	Sabile (sà′bê-lĕ) .... Lat.	57.2 N	22.36 E
80	Sabinal (sà-bī′nàl) .... Tex.	29.19 N	99.27 W
96	Sabinal Cay (I.) (sä-bē-näl′). Cuba	21.42 N	77.15 W
80	Sabinas Hidalgo (sä-bē′näs ê-däl′gō). Mex.	26.30 N	100.10 W
80	Sabinas, R. (sä-bē′näs) ...... Mex.	26.30 N	100.0 W
81	Sabine (sà-bēn′) .... Tex.	29.43 N	93.53 W
81	Sabine L. .... La.-Tex.	29.50 N	93.50 W
81	Sabine R. .... La.-Tex.	31.31 N	93.35 W
140	Sabi R. (sä′bê) .... Moz.-S. Rh.	21.17 S	34.0 E
162	Sablayan (säb-lä-yän′) .... P. I.	12.50 N	120.46 E
72	Sable (sā′b′l) ... Colo. (Denver In.)	39.46 N	104.50 W
124	Sablé (sà-blā′) .... Fr.	47.50 N	0.20 W
55	Sable, C. (sā′b′l) .... Can.	43.40 N	65.45 W
87	Sable I. .... Can.	43.55 N	60.0 W
86	Sable, Rivière du (rê-vyâr′ dü sà′bl′). Can.	49.12 N	70.25 W
112	Sablia, Mt. (sà-blē′yà) ... Sov. Un.	64.55 N	58.50 E
126	Sabor R. (sä-bōr′) .... Port.	41.28 N	7.40 W
103	Sabral (sä-bräl′) .... Braz.	3.43 S	40.18 W
162	Sabtang I. (säb-täng′) .. P. I. (In.)	20.20 N	121.43 E
85	Sacandoga R. (să′kăn-dō′gà) N. Y.	43.20 N	74.18 W
127	Sacavem (sä-kä-vĕN′) ... Port. (In.)	38.48 N	9.6 W
127	Sacavem R. .... Port. (In.)	38.51 N	9.8 W
128	Sacchia R. (säk′ê-ä) .... It.	44.35 N	10.46 E
77	Sac City (sôk) .... Ia.	42.25 N	94.59 W
157	Sachun (sä′cho͞on′) .... Cho.	35.6 N	128.7 E
85	Sacketts Harbor (săk′ĕts) ... N. Y.	43.55 N	76.6 W
86	Sackville (săk′vĭl) .... Can.	45.55 N	64.24 W
86	Saco (sô′kô) .... Me.	43.31 N	70.28 W
86	Saco R. .... Me.	43.55 N	70.50 W
79	Sac R. (sôk) .... Mo.	37.50 N	93.49 W
74	Sacramento (săk-rà-mĕn′tō).. Calif.	38.35 N	121.30 W

Page	Name Pronunciation Region	Lat. °′	Long. °′
80	Sacramento .... Mex.	27.3 N	101.45 W
80	Sacramento .... Mex.	25.45 N	103.21 W
58	Sacramento Mts. ...... N. M.-Tex.	32.0 N	104.30 W
74	Sacramento R. .... Calif.	38.15 N	121.35 W
159	Sada C. (sä′dä) .... Jap.	32.46 N	133.0 E
159	Sadamotu (sä′dà-mō′to͞o) Jap. (Tokyo In.)	35.20 N	139.54 E
141	Sadani (sä-dä′nê) .... Tan.	6.2 S	38.46 E
119	Saddleworth (săd″l-wûrth) Gt. Brit. (Liverpool In.)	53.33 N	2.0 W
160	Sadec (sà-dĕk′) ...... Fr. In. Chn	10.25 N	105.38 E
140	Sa′da Banderia .... Ang.	14.52 S	13.35 E
151	Sadiya (sŭ-dē′yä) .... India	27.55 N	95.40 E
158	Sado I. (sä′dō) .... Jap.	38.0 N	138.28 E
126	Sado R. (sä′do͝o) .... Port.	38.10 N	8.10 W
120	Saeby (sĕ′bü) .... Den.	57.21 N	10.30 E
145	Safed (Zefath) (sä′fĕd) (zĕ′fŭt) Pal. (In.)	32.58 N	35.29 E
135	Saff (säf) .... Eg. (In.)	29.34 N	31.20 E
120	Säffle (sĕf′lĕ) .... Swe.	59.8 N	12.56 E
75	Safford (săf′fẽrd) .... Ariz.	32.50 N	109.41 W
138	Safi (Asfi) (sä′fê) (äs′fê) ..... Mor.	32.24 N	9.12 W
141	Saft el Laban (säft ĕl lä′bàn) ... Eg.	30.2 N	31.10 E
159	Saga (sä′gä) .... Jap.	33.16 N	130.18 E
159	Sagami S. (sä′gä′mê) .... Jap.	35.2 N	139.20 E
122	Sagan (sä′gän) .... Ger.	51.36 N	15.19 E
77	Saganaga L. (să-gà-nă′gà) Can.-U. S.	48.13 N	90.57 W
163	Sagay (sä-gī′) .... P. I.	9.6 N	124.44 E
163	Sagay .... P. I.	10.56 N	123.27 E
88	Sag Bridge (săg) Ill. (Chicago In.)	41.41 N	87.56 W
73	Saginaw (săg′ĭ-nô) Ala. (Birmingham In.)	33.14 N	86.47 W
84	Saginaw .... Mich.	43.27 N	83.57 W
84	Saginaw B. .... Mich.	44.0 N	83.30 W
113	Sagiz (R.) (sä′gēz) .... Sov. Un.	48.28 N	54.30 E
75	Saguache (să-wăch′) (sà-gwä′chê) Colo.	38.5 N	106.9 W
75	Saguache Cr. .... Colo.	38.4 N	106.20 W
75	Saguaro Natl. Mon. (säg-wä′rō) Ariz.	32.8 N	110.33 W
55	Saguenay R. (săg-ē-nā′) ...... Can.	48.30 N	71.0 W
127	Sagunto (sä-go͞on′tō) .... Sp.	39.40 N	0.17 W
131	Saguny (sà′go͞o-nĭ) .... Sov. Un.	50.38 N	39.41 E
138	Sahara (Desert) (sà-hä′rà) .... Afr.	23.0 N	10.0 E
151	Saharanpur (sŭ-hä′rŭn-po͞or). India	29.58 N	77.31 E
92	Sahuayo (sä-wä′yō) .... Mex.	20.3 N	102.42 W
138	Saïda (sä′ê-dä) .... Alg.	34.49 N	0.5 E
150	Saidabad (sä-ê-dä′båd) ...... Iran	29.31 N	55.45 E
115	Saïda (Sidon) (sä′ê-dà) (sī′dŏn) Syr. (In.)	33.35 N	35.32 E
160	Saigon (sà-ê-gôN′) (sī-gŏn′) Fr. In. Chn.	10.46 N	106.38 E
150	Saihut (sä′ê-hŭt) .... Aden	15.17 N	51.29 E
159	Saijo (sä′ê-jô) .... Jap.	33.55 N	133.12 E
159	Saiki (sä′ê-kê) .... Jap.	33.0 N	131.46 E
121	Saima, L. (sä′ĭ-mà) .... Fin.	61.16 N	28.30 E
92	Sain Alto (sä-ēn′ äl′tō) ...... Mex.	23.35 N	103.13 W
56	St. Adolphe (sånt ā′dŏlf) (săN′tà dôlf′). Can. (Winnipeg In.)	49.40 N	97.5 W
124	St. Affrique (săN′tà frēk′) ...... Fr.	43.58 N	2.55 E
169	St. Albans (sånt ôl′bănz) Austl. (Melbourne In.)	37.45 S	144.48 E
116	St. Albans .... Gt. Brit.	51.45 N	0.20 W
86	St. Albans .... Vt.	44.49 N	73.8 W
84	St. Albans .... W. Va.	38.22 N	81.52 W
116	St. Albans Hd. .... Gt. Brit.	50.30 N	2.0 W
124	St. Amand (săN-tà măN′) ...... Fr.	50.30 N	3.40 E
124	St. Amand-Mont-Rond (săN-tà măN′-môN-rôN′). Fr.	46.45 N	2.30 E
95	St. Andrew (sånt ăn′dro͞o) Barb. (In.)	13.18 N	59.36 W
57	St. Andrews (ăn′dro͞oz) Can. (Montreal In.)	45.34 N	74.20 W
86	St. Andrews .... Can.	45.5 N	67.2 W
56	St. Andrews .. Can. (Winnipeg In.)	50.3 N	97.0 W
116	St. Andrews .... Gt. Brit.	56.20 N	2.45 W
82	St. Andrews B. .... Fla.	30.15 N	85.45 W
87	St. Andrews Channel .... Can.	46.5 N	60.30 W
95	St. Andrews I. .... W. I.	12.34 N	81.42 W
87	St. Ann B. (ăn) .... Can.	46.15 N	60.35 W
57	Ste. Annes (săNt àn′) (sånt ăn′) Can. (Montreal In.)	45.25 N	73.57 W
86	Ste. Anne de Beaupre (dē bō-prā′) Can.	47.1 N	70.57 W
86	Ste. Anne de la Pocatière (dē là pô-kà-tyâr′). Can.	47.23 N	70.0 W
86	Ste. Anne R. .... Can.	46.48 N	71.55 W
96	Ste. Anns B. .... Jam.	18.26 N	77.14 W
57	St. Anselme (săN′ tăN-sĕlm′) Can. (Quebec In.)	46.37 N	70.58 W
128	St. Antioco (I.) (sånt än-tē′ô-kō) Sard.	39.3 N	8.25 E
71	St. Anthony (sånt ăn′thô-nê) .. Ida.	43.59 N	111.42 W
57	St. Apollinaire (săN-tà pôl-ê-nâr′) Can. (Quebec In.)	46.37 N	71.31 W
166	St. Arnaud (sånt àr-nō′) .... Austl.	36.38 S	143.18 E
83	St. Augustine (ô′gŭs-tēn) ..... Fla.	29.54 N	81.20 W
125	St. Avold (săN-tà vôl′) .... Fr.	49.5 N	6.45 E
127	Ste. Barbe du Tlelat (săNt bärb dü tlē-là′). Alg.	35.34 N	0.25 W
87	St. Barbe Is. (sånt bärb′) .... Newf.	50.12 N	55.45 W
86	St. Barthélemi (săN′ bàr-tā-lĕ-mē′) Can.	46.11 N	73.8 W
95	St. Barthélemy (I.) .... W. I. (In.)	17.55 N	62.50 W
171	St. Bathans, Mt. (sånt bàth′ănz) N. Z.	44.43 S	169.47 E
116	St. Bees Hd. (sånt bēz′ hĕd) Gt. Brit.	54.30 N	3.40 W
54	St. Boniface (bŏn′ĭ-fās) ...... Can.	49.57 N	97.1 W
125	St. Brice (săN brēs′) ..... Fr. (In.)	49.0 N	2.21 E
116	St. Brides B. (sånt brīdz′). Gt. Brit.	51.50 N	5.15 W
124	St. Brieuc (săN brê-û′) .... Fr.	48.35 N	2.45 W

Page	Name Pronunciation Region	Lat. °′	Long. °′
57	St. Canut (săN′ kà-nü′) Can. (Montreal In.)	45.43 N	74.5 W
86	St. Casimir (kà-zê-mēr′) ..... Can.	46.38 N	72.14 W
57	Ste. Catherine (sånt kăth′ẽr-ĭn) Can. (Quebec In.)	46.53 N	71.35 W
89	St. Catherine, L. La. (New Orleans In.)	30.8 N	89.44 W
95	St. Catherine. Mt. .. Wind. Is. (In.)	12.10 N	61.42 W
85	St. Catherines .... Can.	43.10 N	79.13 W
124	St. Chamond (săN′ shà-môN′) .. Fr.	45.30 N	4.30 E
57	St. Charles .... Can. (In.)	46.47 N	70.56 W
77	St. Charles (sånt chärlz′) ...... Ill.	41.55 N	88.19 W
84	St. Charles .... Mich.	43.19 N	84.11 W
77	St. Charles .... Minn.	43.57 N	92.4 W
79	St. Charles .... Mo.	38.47 N	90.29 W
57	St. Charles R. .. Can. (Quebec In.)	46.53 N	71.22 W
124	St. Chély-d′ Apcher (săN shā-lē′ dàp-shā′). Fr.	44.45 N	3.15 E
91	St. Christopher, see St. Kitts		
84	St. Clair (klâr) .... Mich.	42.50 N	82.30 W
171	St. Clair .... N. Z. (In.)	45.55 S	170.30 E
49	St. Clair .... Wash. (Seattle In.)	47.2 N	122.43 W
55	St. Clair L. .... Can.	42.28 N	82.30 W
84	St. Clair, L. .... Mich.-Can.	42.35 N	82.30 W
84	St. Clair R. .... Mich.-Can.	42.50 N	82.28 W
73	St. Clair Springs Ala. (Birmingham In.)	33.46 N	86.24 W
125	St. Claude (săN klōd′) .... Fr.	46.25 N	5.51 E
57	St. Clet (klā′). Can. (Montreal In.)	45.22 N	74.14 W
83	St. Cloud (sånt kloud′) .. Fla. (In.)	28.14 N	81.17 W
125	St. Cloud (săN klo͞o′) .... Fr. (In.)	48.50 N	2.13 E
77	St. Cloud (sånt kloud′) .... Minn.	45.34 N	94.8 W
91	St. Croix (I.) (sånt kroi′) ... W. I.	17.45 N	64.45 W
77	St. Croix R. .... Minn.-Wis.	45.10 N	92.45 W
86	St. Croix R. .... U. S.-Can.	45.30 N	67.32 W
125	St. Cyr-l′ École (săN sēr′-lā kôl′) Fr. (In.)	48.47 N	2.7 E
57	St. Damien de Buckland (sånt dā′-mê-ĕn dē bŭk′lănd) Can. (Quebec In.)	46.38 N	70.40 W
57	St. Damien Station (săN dà-myăN′) Can. (Quebec In.)	46.36 N	70.43 W
116	St. Davids Hd. (sånt dā′vĭdz) Gt. Brit.	51.55 N	5.20 W
125	St. Denis (săN′ dē-nē′) .... Fr. (In.)	48.56 N	2.22 E
6	St. Denis .... Réunion (In.)	20.54 S	55.30 E
114	St. Denis-du-Sig (săN dē-nē′-dü-sēg′). Alg.	35.30 N	0.12 W
125	St. Dié (săN dê-ā′) .... Fr.	48.18 N	7.0 E
124	St. Dizier (săN dê-zyā′) .... Fr.	48.38 N	5.0 E
54	St. Elias, Mt. (sånt ê-lī′ăs) ... Can.	60.15 N	140.45 W
124	Saintes (săNt) .... Fr.	45.42 N	0.40 W
124	St. Etienne (săN-tā tyĕn′) ...... Fr.	49.25 N	1.10 E
124	St. Étienne .... Fr.	45.25 N	4.25 E
57	St. Eustache (săN-tû stàsh′) Can. (Montreal In.)	45.34 N	73.53 W
56	St. Eustache . Can. (Winnipeg In.)	49.58 N	97.48 W
95	St. Eustatius (I.) (sånt û-stā′shŭs) Le. Is. (In.)	17.30 N	62.58 W
57	Ste. Famille (săNt fà-mē′y′) Can. (Quebec In.)	46.59 N	70.58 W
86	St. Felicien (săN′ fā-lê-syăN′) . Can.	48.38 N	72.28 W
57	St. Féréol (fā-rā-ôl′) Can. (Quebec In.)	47.8 N	70.52 W
124	St. Florent-sur-Cher (săN flô-räN′-sür-shâr′). Fr.	46.59 N	2.15 E
125	St. Flour (săN flo͞or′) .... Fr.	45.1 N	3.10 E
143	St. Francis B. (sånt frăn′sĭs) U.S. Afr.	34.2 S	24.58 E
143	St. Francis, C. .... U. S. Afr.	34.12 S	24.50 E
79	St. Francis L. .... Ark.	35.40 N	90.25 W
85	St. Francis, L. .... Can.	45.5 N	74.30 W
79	St. Francis R. .... Ark.	36.30 N	90.10 W
86	St. Francis R. .... Can.	45.46 N	72.10 W
57	St. François (săN fräN-swä′) Can. (Quebec In.)	46.55 N	70.42 W
57	St. François d′Orléans (dôr-lâ-äN′) Can. (Quebec In.)	47.1 N	70.49 W
56	St. François Xavier (zà-vyā′) Can. (Winnipeg In.)	49.56 N	97.32 W
122	St. Gallen (sånt gäl′ĕn) (zänkt gäl′ĕn). Switz.	47.26 N	9.23 E
124	St. Gaudens (săN gō-dăNs′) .... Fr.	43.7 N	0.45 E
79	Ste. Genevieve (sånt jĕn′ĕ-vēv). Mo.	37.58 N	90.2 W
165	St. George (sånt jôrj) .... Austl.	28.0 S	148.35 E
86	St. George .... Can.	45.8 N	66.48 W
86	St. George (săN zhôrzh) ...... Can.	46.9 N	70.41 W
83	St. George (sånt jôrj) .... S. C.	33.11 N	80.35 W
75	St. George .... Utah	37.7 N	113.34 W
87	St. George B. .... Newf.	48.30 N	58.40 W
82	St. George, C. .... Fla.	29.35 N	85.4 W
87	St. George, C. .... Newf.	48.29 N	59.15 W
104	St. George, G. of .... Arg.	46.0 S	67.0 W
52	St. George I. .... Alsk.	56.30 N	169.30 W
87	St. Georges .... Newf.	48.28 N	58.25 W
95	St. Georges .... Wind. Is. (In.)	12.3 N	61.46 W
116	St. Georges Channel Gt. Brit.-Ire.	52.0 N	6.0 W
125	St. Germain, Fôret de (fô-rĕ′ dē săN′ zhĕr-măN′). Fr. (In.)	48.56 N	2.5 E
125	St. Germain-en-Laye (săN zhĕr-măN′-äN-lā′). Fr. (In.)	48.53 N	2.6 E
57	St. Gervais (săN zhĕr-vĕ′) Can. (Quebec In.)	46.43 N	70.54 W
124	St. Gilles (săN zhēl′) .... Fr.	43.40 N	4.28 E
119	St. Gilles Waes (väs′) Bel. (Anvers In.)	51.13 N	4.7 E
124	St. Girons (săN zhē-rôN′) ...... Fr.	43.0 N	1.9 E
122	St. Gotthard Tunnel (sånt gŏth′-àrd) (săN gô-tàr′). Switz.	46.37 N	8.37 E
87	St. Gregory, Mt. (sånt grĕg′ẽr-ê) Newf.	49.25 N	58.12 W
169	St. Helena (hĕ-lē′nà) .. Austl. (In.)	28.40 S	153.34 E

ăt finăl; rāte; senåte; ärm; àsk; sofà; fâre; ch-choose; dh-as th in other; bē; êvent; bĕt; recĕnt; cratẽr; g-go; gh-gutteral g; bĭt; ĭ-short neutral; rīde; K-gutteral k as ch in German ich;

Page	Name Pronunciation Region	Lat. °′	Long. °′
7	St Helena (I.)...Atl. O. (In.)	15.57 S	5.42 W
70	St. Helena...Ore.	45.51 N	122.49 W
142	St. Helena B....U. S. Afr.	32.45 S	18.5 E
116	St. Helens (sānt hĕl'ĕnz)..Gt. Brit.	53.25 N	2.50 W
70	St. Helens, Mt....Wash.	46.12 N	122.12 W
169	St. Helens Pt....Austl. (Tas. In.)	41.16 S	148.22 E
124	St. Helier (sānt hĕl'yẽr)..Gt. Brit.	49.10 N	2.5 W
57	St. Henry (hĕn'rē) Can. (Quebec In.)	46.42 N	71.4 W
57	St. Hubert (hū'bẽrt) Can. (Montreal In.)	45.31 N	73.24 W
86	St. Hyacinthe (săN'-tē-ā-săNt') (sānt hī'ȧ-sĭnth).Can.	45.38 N	72.55 W
77	St. Ignace (sānt ĭg'nȧs)....Mich.	45.52 N	84.40 W
77	St. Ignace I....Can.	48.45 N	87.55 W
86	St. Irénée (săN-tē-rā-nā')....Can.	47.33 N	70.13 W
57	St. Isidore (săN-tē zē-dōr') (sānt ĭz'ĭ-dôr).Can. (Montreal In.)	45.19 N	73.40 W
77	St. James (sānt jāmz')....Minn.	43.58 N	94.35 W
79	St. James....Mo.	37.59 N	91.37 W
57	St. Janvier (săN zhän-vyā') Can. (Montreal In.)	45.44 N	73.55 W
86	St. Jean (săN jäN')....Can.	45.18 N	73.17 W
124	St. Jean-d'Angély (săN zhäN' däN-zhā-lē').Fr.	45.55 N	0.32 W
124	St. Jean de Luz (dē lüz')....Fr.	43.25 N	1.39 W
57	St. Jean d'Orléans (dôr-lā-äN') Can. (Quebec In.)	46.56 N	70.54 W
85	St. Jerome (sānt jĕ-rōm') (săN zhā-rōm').Can.	45.47 N	74.2 W
57	St. Joachim (sānt jō'ȧ-kĭm) Can. (Quebec In.)	47.4 N	70.50 W
119	St. Jobint Goor (săN zhō-băN' gōr') Bel. (Anvers In.)	51.18 N	4.34 E
70	St. Joe R. (sānt jō')....Ida.	47.12 N	115.55 W
55	St. John (jŏn)....Can.	45.18 N	66.10 W
78	St. John....Kan.	38.0 N	98.45 W
76	St. John....N. D.	48.59 N	99.45 W
87	St. John, C....Newf.	50.0 N	55.30 W
91	St. John I....W. I. (P. R. In.)	18.15 N	64.42 W
55	St. John, L....Can.	48.55 N	72.0 W
55	St. John R....Can.	47.0 N	67.32 W
75	St. Johns (jŏnz)....Ariz.	34.31 N	109.23 W
55	St. Johns....Can.	45.27 N	73.19 W
95	St. Johns....Le. Is. (In.)	17.7 N	61.50 W
84	St. Johns....Mich.	43.2 N	84.33 W
87	St. Johns....Newf.	47.32 N	52.40 W
86	St. Johnsbury (jŏnz'bẽr-ē)....Vt.	44.25 N	72.2 W
83	St. Johns R....Fla.	30.0 N	81.40 W
86	St. Joseph....Can.	46.18 N	70.51 W
57	St. Joseph (jō'zĕf) Can. (Quebec In.)	46.49 N	71.11 W
84	St. Joseph....Mich.	42.3 N	86.30 W
79	St. Joseph....Mo.	39.45 N	94.50 W
84	St. Joseph I....Can.	46.15 N	83.57 W
81	St. Joseph I....Tex.	28.0 N	96.57 W
55	St. Joseph, L....Can.	51.14 N	90.45 W
84	St. Joseph R....Mich.-Ind.	41.40 N	86.0 W
82	St. Josephs B....Fla.	29.46 N	85.30 W
124	St. Junien (săN zhü-nyăN')....Fr.	45.52 N	0.58 E
57	Ste. Justine Station (sānt jŭs-tēn') Can. (Montreal In.)	45.22 N	74.25 W
169	St. Kilda (sānt kĭl'dȧ) Austl. (Melbourne In.)	37.52 S	145.0 E
116	St. Kilda....Gt. Brit.	57.50 N	8.35 W
171	St. Kilda....N. Z. (In.)	45.54 S	170.32 E
91	St. Kitts (Is.)....Le. Is.	17.15 N	62.45 W
86	St. Lambert (săN läN-bẽr') (sānt lăm'bẽrt).Can.	45.29 N	73.29 W
125	St. Lambert (săN läN-bẽr') Fr. (In.)	48.44 N	2.1 E
103	St. Laurent (săN lō-räN')...Fr. Gu.	5.28 N	54.0 W
124	St. Laurent-de-la-Salanque (dē-lá-sá-läNk').Fr.	42.50 N	3.0 E
55	St. Lawrence, G. of (sānt lŏ'rĕns) Can.	48.10 N	62.0 W
52	St. Lawrence I....Alsk.	63.20 N	170.0 W
55	St. Lawrence R....Can.-U. S.	49.0 N	68.0 W
57	St. Lazare (săN lá-zár') Can. (Montreal In.)	45.23 N	74.7 W
119	St. Léonard (săN lā-ō-nár') Bel. (Anvers In.)	51.21 N	4.40 E
86	St. Leonard (sānt lĕn'ȧrd)...Can.	47.8 N	67.55 W
124	St. Léonard-de-Noblat (săN lā-ō-nár'-dē-nō-blá').Fr.	45.50 N	1.30 E
125	St. Leu-Taverny (săN lû-tá-vĕr-nē') Fr. (In.)	49.1 N	2.15 E
57	St. Lin Junction (săN lăN) (sānt lĭn) Can. (Montreal In.)	45.39 N	73.50 W
124	Saint-Lô (săN-lō')....Fr.	49.10 N	1.5 W
138	St. Louis (săN lōō-ē') (sānt lōō'ĭs) Fr. W. Afr.	16.03 N	16.28 W
84	St. Louis (sānt lōō'ĭs) (lōō'ē) Mich.	43.26 N	84.33 W
89	St. Louis....Mo. (In.)		
79	St. Louis....Mo.	38.35 N	90.15 W
6	St. Louis (săN lōō-ē') Réunion (In.)	21.17 S	55.29 E
88	St. Louis B. (sānt lōō'ĭs) Minn.-Wis. (Duluth In.)	46.45 N	92.7 W
86	St. Louis, L. (săN lōō-ē')....Can.	45.23 N	73.50 W
89	St. Louis Park Minn. (Minneapolis In.)	44.56 N	93.21 W
77	St. Louis R. (sānt lōō'ĭs)...Minn.	46.58 N	92.50 W
91	St. Lucia (I.) (sānt lū'shĭ-ȧ) Wind. Is.	13.50 N	61.0 W
143	St. Lucia, C....U. S. Afr.	28.30 S	32.25 E
143	St. Lucia, L....U. S. Afr.	28.5 S	32.28 E
83	St. Lucie Canal (lū'sē)..Fla. (In.)	27.0 N	80.35 W
116	St. Magnus B. (sānt măg'nŭs) Gt. Brit. (In.)	60.25 N	1.30 W
124	St. Maixent-l'École (săN mĕk-săN'-lā-kôl').Fr.	46.25 N	0.11 W
124	St. Malo (săN má-lō')....Fr.	48.38 N	2.0 W
124	St. Malo, G. of....Fr.	48.50 N	2.20 W
97	St. Marc (săN márk')....Hai.	19.6 N	72.44 W
97	St. Marc Channel....Hai.	19.0 N	73.0 W
125	St. Marcellin (săN' mär-sē-lăN').Fr.	45.10 N	5.20 E
86	St. Margaret B. (sānt mär'gȧ-rĕt) Can.	44.40 N	60.0 W
86	St. Marguerite R. (săNt màr-gā-rĕt').Can.	50.42 N	66.50 W
97	St. Maria, C. (sānt mȧ-rē'ȧ) Ba. Is.	23.40 N	75.21 W
86	Ste. Marie (săNt mȧ-rē')....Can.	46.27 N	71.1 W
125	Ste. Marie aux-Mines (ō-mēn').Fr.	48.15 N	7.10 E
141	Ste. Marie, C....Madag.	25.30 S	45.15 E
141	Ste. Marie I....Madag.	16.40 S	49.55 E
70	St. Maries (sānt mā'rēz)....Ida.	47.17 N	116.34 W
143	St. Marks (sānt märks).U. S. Afr.	32.2 S	27.25 E
57	Ste. Marthe (márt') Can. (Montreal In.)	45.24 N	74.18 W
95	St. Martin (I.) (mär'tĭn) W. I. (In.)	18.3 N	63.5 W
57	St. Martin Junction Can. (Montreal In.)	45.35 N	73.43 W
125	St. Martin, Mont (môN' săN mär-tăN').Fr.	49.35 N	5.48 E
86	St. Martins (sānt mär'tĭnz)...Can.	45.22 N	65.32 W
142	St. Martins Pt....U. S. Afr.	32.42 S	17.55 E
81	St. Martinsville....La.	30.8 N	91.50 W
86	St. Mary B....Can.	44.30 N	66.10 W
119	St. Mary Cray (krā) Gt. Brit. (London In.)	51.23 N	0.7 E
87	St. Mary Is....Can.	50.18 N	59.40 W
169	St. Marys (sānt mā'rēz) Austl. (Tas. In.)	41.34 S	148.15 E
84	St. Marys....Can.	43.17 N	81.11 W
83	St. Marys....Ga.	30.43 N	81.33 W
79	St. Marys....Kan.	39.13 N	96.3 W
84	St. Marys....Ohio	40.33 N	84.24 W
85	St. Marys....Pa.	41.25 N	78.33 W
84	St. Mary's....W. Va.	39.22 N	81.13 W
87	St. Marys B....Newf.	47.5 N	53.40 W
88	St. Marys Falls Can.-U. S. (Sault Ste. Marie In.)	46.30 N	84.21 W
166	St. Marys Pk....Austl.	31.35 S	138.37 E
88	St. Marys R. Can.-U. S. (Sault Ste. Marie In.)	46.30 N	84.20 W
83	St. Marys R....Fla.-Ga.	30.34 N	82.0 W
52	St. Matthew I. (măth'ū)....Alsk.	60.20 N	172.30 W
84	St. Matthews (măth'ūz)....Ky.	38.16 N	85.40 W
83	St. Matthews....S. C.	33.40 N	80.47 W
55	St. Maurice R. (săN mō-rēs') (sānt mô'rĭs).Can.	47.50 N	73.12 W
125	St. Maur-les-Fossés (săN mōr'-lā-fō-sā').Fr. (In.)	48.48 N	2.28 E
124	Ste. Menehould (săNt mē-nōō') Fr.	49.5 N	4.55 E
52	St. Michael (sānt mī'kĕl)....Alsk.	63.28 N	162.5 W
57	St. Michel (săN mē-shĕl') Can. (Quebec In.)	46.53 N	71.27 W
124	St. Michel....Fr.	49.52 N	4.11 E
97	St. Michel....Hai.	19.22 N	72.20 W
57	St. Michel de Bellechasse (dē bĕl-shäs').Can. (Quebec In.)	46.53 N	70.55 W
125	St. Mihiel (săN mē-yĕl')....Fr.	48.52 N	5.31 E
169	St. Morang (sānt mō-răng') Austl. (Melbourne In.)	37.39 S	145.6 E
122	St. Moritz (sānt mō'rĭts) (zăŋkt mō'rēts).Switz.	46.31 N	9.50 E
124	St. Nazaire (săN ná-zâr')....Fr.	47.20 N	2.12 W
119	St. Nicolas (nē-kō-lá') Bel. (Anvers In.)	51.10 N	4.9 E
97	St. Nicolas, C....Hai.	19.45 N	73.28 W
125	St. Nom-la-Bretêche (săN nôN-lá-brē-tāsh').Fr. (In.)	48.51 N	2.2 E
56	St. Norbert (sānt nôr'bẽrt) Can. (Winnipeg In.)	49.46 N	97.9 W
124	St. Omer (săN tō-mâr')....Fr.	50.45 N	2.15 E
125	St. Ouen (săN tōō-äN')....Fr. (In.)	48.55 N	2.20 E
125	St. Ouen l'Aumône (lō-mōn') Fr. (In.)	49.2 N	2.6 E
119	St. Paul (săN' pôl') Bel. (Anvers In.)	51.11 N	4.6 E
89	St. Paul....Minn. (In.)		
77	St. Paul (sānt pôl')....Minn.	44.57 N	93.5 W
76	St. Paul....Neb.	41.13 N	98.27 W
52	St. Paul I....Alsk.	57.10 N	170.10 W
87	St. Paul I....Can.	47.15 N	60.10 W
7	St. Paul I....Ind. O.	38.43 S	77.31 E
89	St. Paul Park Minn. (Minneapolis In.)	44.51 N	93.0 W
98	St. Paul Rocks....Braz.	1.0 N	29.28 W
83	St. Pauls....N. C.	34.48 N	78.57 W
77	St. Peter (sānt pē'tẽr)....Minn.	44.19 N	93.55 W
55	St. Peter, L....Can.	46.16 N	72.35 W
87	St. Peters....Can.	45.38 N	60.48 W
83	St. Petersburg (pē'tẽrz-bûrg) Fla. (In.)	27.46 N	82.38 W
57	St. Philippe (săN fē-lēp') Can. (Montreal In.)	45.20 N	73.28 W
124	St. Pierre (sānt pyâr') (săN pyâr') Gt. Brit.	49.25 N	2.30 W
95	St. Pierre (săN pyâr'). Mart. (In.)	14.44 N	61.12 W
6	St. Pierre....Réunion (In.)	21.20 S	55.32 E
124	St. Pierre-des-Corps (dā-kôr')..Fr.	47.22 N	0.45 E
87	St. Pierre I....Newf.	46.45 N	56.15 W
124	St. Pierre-Quilbignon (kēl-bē-nyôN') Fr.	48.25 N	4.30 W
124	St. Pol (săN pôl')....Fr.	50.20 N	2.25 E
124	St. Pol-de-Léon (dē-lā-ôN')....Fr.	48.40 N	4.0 W
124	St. Pol-sur-Mer (sür-mâr')....Fr.	51.0 N	2.20 E
122	St. Pölten (zăŋkt-pûl'tĕn)....Ger.	48.12 N	15.38 E
124	St. Pourçain-sur-Sioule (săN-pōōr-săN' sür syōōl').Fr.	46.18 N	3.18 E
124	Ste.-Poy-la-Grande (săNt-pwá'-lá-gräNd').Fr.	44.48 N	0.15 E
124	St. Quentin (săN' käN-tăN')....Fr.	49.51 N	3.18 E
124	St. Raphael (săN rá-fá-ĕl')....Fr.	43.25 N	6.45 E
86	St. Raymond (săN rā-môN') (sānt rā'mȧnd).Can.	46.52 N	71.51 W
125	St. Remy-les-Chevreuse (săN rē-mē' lā-shē-vrûz').Fr. (In.)	48.42 N	2.5 E
102	St. Roman, C. (săn rō-mān').Ven.	12.30 N	71.0 W
86	St. Romuald (săN rô-mü-ál')..Can.	46.44 N	71.14 W
124	St. Savine (săN sá-vēn')....Fr.	48.18 N	4.2 E
57	Ste. Scholastique (skô-lás-tēk') Can. (Montreal In.)	45.39 N	74.5 W
142	St. Sebastian B. (sānt sē-băs'tyȧn) U. S. Afr.	34.25 S	20.50 E
124	St. Servan (săN sĕr-väN')....Fr.	48.40 N	2.0 W
57	Ste. Sophie (săNt sô-fē') Can. (Montreal In.)	45.50 N	73.55 W
86	St. Stephen (sānt stē'vĕn)...Can.	45.12 N	67.16 W
85	Ste. Thérèse (săNt tā-rĕz')....Can.	45.36 N	73.54 W
84	St. Thomas (sānt tŏm'ȧs)....Can.	42.46 N	81.14 W
	St. Thomas, see Charlotte Amalia, Vir. Is.		
91	St. Thomas (I.) Vir. Is. (P. R. In.)	18.21 N	64.55 W
125	St. Tropez (săN trō-pĕ')....Fr.	43.15 N	6.40 E
124	St. Valéry (săN vá-lā-rē')....Fr.	50.10 N	1.40 E
57	St. Vallier (săN vál-yā') Can. (Quebec In.)	46.54 N	70.50 W
124	St. Vallier....Fr.	45.10 N	4.50 E
57	St. Vallier Station Can. (Quebec In.)	46.53 N	70.47 W
122	St. Veit (zänkt vīt')....Ger.	46.47 N	14.21 E
86	St. Victor (sānt vĭk'tẽr)....Can.	46.9 N	70.55 W
126	St. Vincent, C....Port.	37.2 N	8.58 W
57	St. Vincent de Paul (săN' văN-săN' dē pôl').Can. (Montreal In.)	45.37 N	73.39 W
166	St.Vincent G. (sānt vĭn'sĕnt) Austl.	34.55 S	138.10 E
91	St. Vincent (I.) (sānt vĭn'sĕnt) Wind. Is.	13.15 N	61.10 W
7	St. Vincent I....C. V. Is. (In.)	16.51 N	25.3 W
72	St. Vrains (sānt vrānz') Colo. (Denver In.)	40.3 N	104.57 W
72	St. Vrains Cr., North Colo. (Denver In.)	40.13 N	105.25 W
124	St. Yrieix-la-Perche (săNt ē-rē-ĕ'-lā-pĕrsh').Fr.	45.30 N	1.10 E
152	Sairusu (sá'ẽr-ōō'sōō)....Chn.	44.51 N	106.52 E
157	Saishu....Cho.	33.30 N	126.31 E
157	Saishu (Quelpart) I. (sá'ē-shōō') (kwĕl'pärt)..Jap.	33.28 N	126.30 E
150	Saiun (sī-ōōn')....Aden.	16.0 N	44.0 E
102	Sajama (Vol.) (sā-hā'mā)....Bol.	18.2 S	68.59 W
159	Sakai (sā'kā-ē)....Jap.	35.21 N	133.15 E
159	Sakai....Jap.	34.30 N	135.30 E
140	Sakania (sá-kā'nĭ-á)....Bel. Cong.	12.40 S	28.38 E
113	Sakarya (R.) (sá-kär'yȧ)....Tur.	40.10 N	31.0 E
158	Sakata (sá'kā-tā)....Jap.	38.59 N	139.58 E
151	Sakchi (săk'chē)....India	22.28 N	85.59 E
149	Sakhalin (I.) (sá-ká-lēn').Sov. Un.	50.30 N	143.30 E
121	Šakiai (shä'kĭ-ī)....Lith.	54.58 N	23.1 E
145	Sakija (sá-kē'já)....Aden (In.)	12.45 N	43.38 E
158	Sakishima Rettō (Is.) (sá'kē-shē'-má rā'tō).Ryukyu Is. (In.)	24.31 N	124.30 E
113	Sakmara R. (sák-mä'rä)..Sov. Un.	51.40 N	56.30 E
119	Sakrow (sá'krō)..Ger. (Berlin In.)	52.26 N	13.6 E
151	Sakti (săk'tē)....India	21.59 N	82.50 E
163	Sakul I. (sä-kōōl')....P. I.	6.58 N	122.15 E
120	Sala (sô'lā)....Swe.	59.56 N	16.36 E
128	Sala Consilina (sä'lä kôn-sē-lē'nä) It.	40.24 N	15.35 E
104	Saladillo (sä-lä-dēl'yō)....Arg.	35.50 S	59.50 W
99	Saladillo, Arroyo (är-rō'yō sä-lä-dēl'yō).Arg. (Buenos Aires In.)	35.22 S	59.30 W
94	Salado (sä-lä'dhō)....Hond.	15.44 N	87.2 W
80	Salado de los Nadadores, R. (dā läs nä-dhä-dhō'räs).Mex.	27.30 N	101.30 W
104	Salado, R....Arg.	28.30 S	63.15 W
104	Salado, R....Arg.	34.0 S	66.45 W
96	Salado, R....Cuba	20.38 N	76.30 W
80	Salado, R....Mex.	27.9 N	100.0 W
127	Salado R....Sp. (In.)	36.45 N	6.0 W
94	Salama (sä-lä'mä)....Guat.	15.6 N	90.18 W
92	Salamanca (sä-lä-mäŋ'kä)...Mex.	20.34 N	101.12 W
85	Salamanca (sál-á-măŋ'kȧ)...N. Y.	42.10 N	78.44 W
126	Salamanca (sä-lä-mäŋ'kä)....Sp.	40.58 N	5.39 W
129	Salamis (săl'ȧ-mĭs)....Grc.	37.59 N	23.30 E
110	Salangen (sä-län'gĕn)....Nor.	68.58 N	17.55 E
126	Salas (sä'läs)....Sp.	43.26 N	6.16 W
102	Salaverry (sä-lä-vā'rē)....Peru	8.15 S	78.68 W
161	Salawati (I.) (sä-lä-wä'tē) Neth. Ind.	1.10 S	130.45 E
160	Salayar (I.) (sä-lä'yär).Neth. Ind.	6.15 S	120.30 E
98	Sala-y-Gomez (I.) (sä'lä-ē-gō'mäz) Pac. O.	26.30 S	105.50 W
97	Salcedo (säl-sā'dō)....Dom. Rep.	19.22 N	70.25 W
163	Salcedo....P. I.	11.8 N	125.39 E
142	Saldanha B. (säl-dän'yȧ) U. S. Afr.	33.4 S	17.55 E
121	Saldus (säl'dōōs)....Lat.	56.38 N	22.31 E
167	Sale (sāl)....Austl.	38.7 S	147.4 E
118	Sale....Gt. Brit.	53.25 N	2.21 W
138	Salé (sá-lā')....Mor.	34.10 N	6.48 W
6	Salealua (sä-lā-á-lōō'á) Samoa (In.)	13.45 S	172.35 W
148	Sale Khard (Obdorsk) (sä-lĕ kärd) Sov. Un.	66.30 N	66.55 E
72	Salem (sā'lĕm). Colo. (Denver In.)	39.39 N	104.38 W
79	Salem....Ill.	38.37 N	88.57 W
151	Salem....India	11.38 N	78.16 E
84	Salem....Ind.	38.36 N	86.4 W
86	Salem....Mass.	42.30 N	70.55 W
79	Salem....Mo.	37.37 N	91.31 W
85	Salem....N. J.	39.32 N	75.30 W
84	Salem....Ohio	40.56 N	80.50 W
70	Salem....Ore.	44.56 N	123.1 W
76	Salem....S. D.	43.44 N	97.23 W
83	Salem....Va.	37.18 N	80.34 W
84	Salem....W. Va.	39.15 N	80.34 W
160	Salembau (I.) (sä-lĕm-bä'ōō) Neth. Ind.	5.38 S	114.30 E
128	Salemi (sä-lä'mē)....It.	37.49 N	12.48 E

ŋg-sing; ŋ-bank; N-nasalized n; nŏd cŏmmit; ōld; ôbey; ôrder; fōōd; fŏŏt; ou-out; s-soft; sh-dish; th-thin; pūre; ûnite; ûrn; stŭd; circŭs; ü-as "y" in study; '-indeterminate vowel.

Page	Name Pronunciation	Region	Lat. °′	Long. °′
56	Sale, R. (rê-vyâr′ sȧl′)	Can. (Winnipeg In.)	49.48 N	97.41 W
128	Salerno (sä-lĕr′nô)	It.	40.41 N	14.43 E
128	Salerno, G. of	It.	40.25 N	14.45 E
116	Salford (săl′fērd)	Gt. Brit.	53.30 N	2.15 W
131	Salgir R. (sȧl′gēr)	Sov. Un.	45.20 N	34.18 E
123	Salgótarjan (sôl′gō-tôr-yän)	Hung.	48.6 N	19.50 E
138	Sal I. (säl)	C. V. Is. (In.)	16.45 N	22.55 W
75	Salida (sȧ-lī′dȧ)	Colo.	38.31 N	106.1 W
124	Salies (sȧ-lēs′)	Fr.	43.30 N	0.55 W
72	Salina (sȧ-lī′nȧ)	Colo. (Denver In.)	40.3 N	105.23 W
79	Salina	Kan.	38.51 N	97.36 W
75	Salina	Utah	38.57 N	111.51 W
128	Salina (I.) (sä-lē′nä)	It.	38.34 N	14.50 E
93	Salina Cruz (sä-lē′nä krōōz′)	Mex.	16.12 N	95.12 W
74	Salinas (sȧ-lē′nȧs)	Calif.	36.41 N	121.39 W
92	Salinas	Mex.	22.37 N	101.42 W
91	Salinas	P. R. (In.)	17.57 N	66.17 W
94	Salinas B.	Nic.-C. R.	11.0 N	85.50 W
127	Salinas, C.	Sp.	39.16 N	3.5 E
74	Salinas R.	Calif.	36.30 N	121.25 W
80	Salinas Victoria (sä-lē′näs vêk-tō′rê-ä)	Mex.	25.59 N	100.20 W
79	Saline R. (sȧ-lēn′)	Ark.	34.5 N	92.15 W
78	Saline R.	Kan.	39.12 N	99.0 W
95	Salines Pt. (sȧ-lēn′)	Mart. (In.)	14.23 N	60.53 W
125	Salins (sȧ-lăN′)	Fr.	46.55 N	5.52 E
166	Salisbury (sôlz′bēr-ê)	Austl.	34.45 S	138.38 E
86	Salisbury	Can.	46.2 N	65.3 W
116	Salisbury	Gt. Brit.	51.5 N	2.0 W
85	Salisbury	Md.	38.22 N	75.37 W
87	Salisbury	Mass. (In.)	42.50 N	70.55 W
79	Salisbury	Mo.	39.25 N	92.47 W
83	Salisbury	N. C.	35.39 N	80.28 W
140	Salisbury	S. Rh.	17.50 S	31.3 E
116	Salisbury Plain	Gt. Brit.	51.10 N	1.40 W
83	Salkehatchie R. (sô-kê-hăch′ê)	S. C.	33.5 N	81.10 W
145	Salkhad (säl′Kăd)	Syr. (In.)	32.32 N	36.39 E
79	Sallisaw (săl′ĭ-sô)	Okla.	35.27 N	94.48 W
139	Sallûm (säl-lōōm′)	Eg.	31.32 N	25.4 E
119	Salmannsdorf (säl′măns-dôrf)	Aus. (Wien In.)	48.15 N	16.18 E
71	Salmon (săm′ŭn)	Ida.	45.10 N	113.55 W
70	Salmon Falls Cr.	Ida.	42.25 N	114.50 W
164	Salmon Gums (săm′ŭn gŭmz)	Austl.	32.57 S	121.57 E
86	Salmon R.	Can.	46.12 N	65.46 W
70	Salmon R.	Ida.	45.28 N	115.40 W
85	Salmon R.	U. S.-Can.	44.45 N	74.15 W
70	Salmon R., Middle Fork	Ida.	44.50 N	114.46 W
70	Salmon R., South Fork	Ida.	44.20 N	114.30 W
70	Salmon River Mts.	Ida.	44.30 N	115.0 W
124	Salon-de-Province (sȧ-lôN′-dē-prô-văNs′)	Fr.	43.40 N	5.10 E
129	Salonika (Thessalonike) (sä-lô-nē′kȧ) (thĕs′ȧ-lô-nē′kê)	Grc.	40.35 N	22.55 E
123	Salonta (sä-lôn-tä′)	Rom.	46.47 N	21.39 E
128	Salpi, L. (lä′gō dē säl′pē)	It.	41.23 N	16.3 E
113	Sal R. (sȧl)	Sov. Un.	47.15 N	42.0 E
113	Salsk (sälsk)	Sov. Un.	46.30 N	41.35 E
104	Salta (säl′tä)	Arg.	24.45 S	65.28 W
104	Salta (State)	Arg.	24.0 S	63.30 W
73	Saltair (sôlt′âr)	Utah (Salt Lake City In.)	40.46 N	112.9 W
97	Salt Cay (I.)	Ba. Is.	21.21 N	71.12 W
88	Salt Cr.	Ill. (Chicago In.)	41.50 N	87.53 W
80	Saltillo (säl-tēl′yō)	Mex.	25.25 N	101.0 W
145	Salt (sält)	Transj. (In.)	32.2 N	35.44 E
138	Salt (El Juf) Desert (sält) (ĕl jōōf′)	Fr. W. Afr.	22.0 N	6.0 W
164	Salt L.	Austl.	24.15 S	113.40 E
164	Salt L.	Austl.	28.20 S	119.35 E
73	Salt Lake City (sôlt lāk)	Utah (In.)		
75	Salt Lake City	Utah	40.45 N	111.51 W
164	Salt Lake Reg.	Austl.	27.15 S	121.0 E
164	Salt Lakes	Austl.	29.15 S	131.0 E
99	Salto (säl′tō)	Arg. (Buenos Aires In.)	34.14 S	60.13 W
104	Salto	Ur.	31.29 S	58.2 W
103	Salto Grande de Paranápanema (säl′tō grän′ dā da-pä-rä-nä′pä-nä′mä)	Braz.	22.45 S	49.59 W
74	Salton Sea (sôlt′ŭn)	Calif.	33.20 N	115.50 W
138	Saltpond	G. C.	5.15 N	1.1 W
75	Salt R.	Ariz.	33.30 N	111.35 W
79	Salt R.	Mo.	39.40 N	91.55 W
142	Salt R.	U. S. Afr.	32.58 S	23.20 E
75	Salt River Indian Res.	Ariz.	33.40 N	111.40 W
97	Saltrou (sȧl-trōō′)	Hai.	18.13 N	71.58 W
120	Saltsjöbaden (säl-vȧ-dōr′) (sält′shû-bäd′ĕn)	Swe.	59.15 N	18.21 E
72	Saltspring I.	Can. (Vancouver In.)	48.47 N	123.30 W
83	Saltville (sôlt′vĭl)	Va.	36.[illegible]1 N	81.46 W
169	Salt Water R.	Austl. (Melbourne In.)	37.[illegible]3 S	144.51 E
83	Saluda (sȧ-lōō′dȧ)	S. C.	34.[illegible] N	81.47 W
83	Saluda R.	S. C.	34.20 N	82.12 W
128	Saluzzo (sä-lōōt′sō)	It.	44.37 N	7.30 E
94	Salvador (säl-va-dōr′) (săl′vȧ-dôr)	Cen. Am.	13.40 N	88.45 W
81	Salvador L.	La.	29.45 N	90.15 W
96	Salvador Pt.	Ba. Is.	24.27 N	77.45 W
92	Salvatierra (säl-vä-tyĕr′rä)	Mex.	20.14 N	100.53 W
126	Salvatierra	Sp.	42.5 N	8.31 W
152	Salween R. (săl-wēn′)	India-Chn.	25.0 N	98.45 E
113	Sālyany (sȧl-yä′nĭ)	Sov. Un.	39.35 N	49.0 E
122	Salzburg (sälts′bōōrgh)	Ger.	47.48 N	13.1 E
122	Salzwedel (sälts-vā′dĕl)	Ger.	52.51 N	11.10 E
161	Samal (sä′mäl)	P. I. (Manila In.)	14.45 N	120.28 E
63	Samales Group (Is.) (sä-mä′lās)	P. I.	6.2 N	121.52 E
163	Samal I. (sä′mäl)	P. I.	7.0 N	125.45 E
135	Samalut (sä-mä-lōōt′)	Eg. (In.)	28.18 N	30.43 E
97	Samaná (sä-mä-nä′)	Dom. Rep.	19.12 N	69.21 W
97	Samaná B.	Dom. Rep.	19.8 N	69.25 W
97	Samaná, C.	Dom. Rep.	19.18 N	69.10 W
97	Samana (Atwood) Cay (I.) (ăt′wōōd)	Ba. Is.	23.6 N	73.45 W
112	Samara, see Kuibishev, Sov. Un.			
161	Samarai (sä-mä-rä′ê)	Pap. Ter.	10.38 S	150.42 E
131	Samara R.	Sov. Un.	48.45 N	35.30 E
112	Samara R.	Sov. Un.	53.8 N	51.30 E
162	Samar I. (sä′mär)	P. I.	12.0 N	125.0 E
160	Samarinda (sä-mä-rēn′dä)	Neth. Ind.	0.29 S	117.8 E
148	Samarkand (sȧ-mȧr-känt′)	Sov. Un.	39.40 N	67.0 E
148	Samarovo (sȧ-mȧ-rô′vô)	Sov. Un.	61.0 N	69.0 E
162	Samar Sea (sä′mär)	P. I.	12.0 N	124.10 E
128	Samassu R. (sä-mäs′sōō)	Sard.	39.30 N	8.55 E
163	Samboan (säm-bō′än)	P. I.	9.32 N	123.20 E
159	Sambon Is. (säm′bôn)	Jap.	33.55 N	138.48 E
123	Sambor (säm′bôr)	Pol.	49.30 N	23.12 E
117	Sambre, R. (säN′br′)	Bel.	50.20 N	4.20 E
141	Same (sä′mā)	Tan.	4.3 S	37.46 E
155	Samhopa (säm′hō′pä′)	Chn.	24.20 N	116.25 E
113	Sam, L. (sȧm)	Sov. Un.	45.30 N	56.30 E
6	Samoa (I.) (sä-mō′ȧ)	Pac. O. (Samoa In.)	13.42 S	172.0 W
129	Samokov (sä′mô-kôf)	Bul.	42.20 N	23.33 E
127	Samora (sä-mô′rȧ)	Port. (In.)	38.56 N	8.53 W
129	Samos (I.) (sä′mŏs)	Grc.	37.45 N	26.50 E
129	Samothrace (I.) (săm′ô-thrās)	Grc.	40.25 N	25.35 E
162	Sampaloc Pt. (säm-pä′lôk)	P. I.	14.43 N	120.10 E
154	Samshui (säm′shwē′)	Chn.	23.12 N	112.48 E
120	Samsö (I.) (säm′sû)	Den.	55.50 N	10.35 E
82	Samson (săm′sŭn)	Ala.	31.5 N	86.2 W
158	Samsu (säm′sōō′)	Cho.	41.16 N	128.1 E
113	Samsun (sȧm-sōōn′)	Tur.	41.20 N	36.12 E
113	Samtredi (sȧm′trĕ-dê)	Sov. Un.	42.10 N	42.20 E
113	Samur R. (sä-mōōr′)	Sov. Un.	41.30 N	48.0 E
138	San (sän)	Fr. W. Afr.	13.35 N	4.41 W
150	San′a (sän′ä)	Yem.	15.44 N	44.5 E
138	Sanaga R. (sä-nä′gä)	Cam.	4.30 N	12.0 E
93	San Agustín (Loxicha) (sän ä-gōōs-tēn′) (lôk-sē′chä)	Mex.	16.3 N	96.46 W
163	San Agustin, C.	P. I.	6.17 N	126.12 E
98	San Ambrosio I. (sän äm-brō′zê-ō)	Pac. O.	26.40 S	80.0 W
74	San Andreas (săn ăn′drê-ās)	Calif.	38.10 N	120.42 W
93	San Andrés (sän än-drās′)	Mex.	18.59 N	97.32 W
93	San Andrés	Mex. (In.)	19.33 N	99.13 W
93	San Andrés (Miahuatlán) (mē-ȧ-wät-län′)	Mex.	16.20 N	96.36 W
94	San Andrés (Petén), L. (pȧ-tān′)	Guat. (In.)	17.0 N	89.50 W
127	San Andrés de Palomar (dā pä-lō-mär′)	Sp. (In.)	41.26 N	2.10 E
93	San Andrés Tuxtla (tōōs′tlä)	Mex.	18.26 N	95.13 W
93	San Ángel (sän än′Kāl)	Mex. (In.)	19.21 N	99.11 W
80	San Angelo (săn ăn′jĕ-lō)	Tex.	31.27 N	100.26 W
7	San Antonio (sän än-tō′nyō)	Az. Is. (In.)	38.31 N	28.22 W
104	San Antonio	Chl.	33.31 S	71.32 W
161	San Antonio (sän än-tō′nê-ō)	P. I. (Manila In.)	14.21 N	121.37 E
162	San Antonio	P. I.	14.58 N	120.5 E
80	San Antonio (săn ăn-tō′nê-ō)	Tex.	29.25 N	98.30 W
127	San Antonio Abad (sän än-tō′nyô ä-bäd′)	Sp.	38.59 N	1.19 E
163	San Antonio B.	P. I.	8.38 N	117.35 E
81	San Antonio B.	Tex.	28.20 N	96.45 W
96	San Antonio, C.	Cuba	21.55 N	84.55 W
99	San Antonio de Areco (sän än-tō′nyō dā ä-rā′kō)	Arg. (Buenos Aires In.)	34.13 S	59.30 W
96	San Antonio de los Baños (dā lōs bän′yōs)	Cuba	22.53 N	82.31 W
104	San Antonio de los Cobres (dā lōs kō′brās)	Arg.	24.0 S	66.20 W
73	San Antonio, Mt. (săn ăn-tō′nĭ-ō)	Calif. (Los Angeles In.)	34.17 N	117.39 W
162	San Antonio, Mt.	P. I.	13.20 N	122.0 E
104	San Antonio Oeste (ô-ĕs′tā)	Arg.	40.45 S	64.59 W
74	San Antonio R.	Calif.	36.0 N	121.15 W
81	San Antonio R.	Tex.	28.38 N	97.30 W
81	San Augustine (săn ô′gŭs-tēn)	Tex.	31.33 N	94.7 W
80	San Bartolo (sän bär-tō′lō)	Mex.	24.42 N	103.11 W
93	San Bartolomé (sän bär-tô-lô-mā′)	Mex.	16.21 N	92.34 W
128	San Bartolomeo (sän bär-tô-lô-mā′ō)	It.	41.24 N	15.1 E
93	San Bartolo Naucalpan (sän bär′tō-lō nou-käl′pän)	Mex. (In.)	19.28 N	99.14 W
127	San Baudilio de Llobregat sän bou-dē′lyō dā lyô-brȧ-gät′)	Sp. (In.)	41.21 N	2.3 E
153	San-Beisa-uRgo (Kerulen) (sȧn-bā′ê-sȧ-ōōr′gô)	Chn.	48.12 N	114.34 E
128	San Benedetto del Tronto (sän bā-nȧ-dĕt′tô dĕl trōn′tô)	It.	42.57 N	13.52 E
81	San Benito (săn bĕ-nē′tō)	Tex.	26.7 N	97.37 W
74	San Benito R.	Calif.	36.40 N	121.20 W
93	San Bernabé (sän bĕr-nä-bā′)	Mex. (In.)	19.19 N	99.15 W
93	San Bernardino (sän bĕr-när-dē′nō)	Mex. (In.)	19.29 N	98.54 W
74	San Bernardino (săn bûr-när-dē′-nō)	Calif.	34.7 N	117.18 W
74	San Bernardino Mts.	Calif.	34.5 N	116.30 W
162	San Bernardino Str. (sän bĕr-när-dē′nō)	P. I.	12.30 N	124.11 E
99	San Bernardo (sän bĕr-när′dō)	Chl. (Valparaiso In.)	33.34 S	70.44 W
92	San Blas (sän bläs′)	Mex.	21.33 N	105.18 W
82	San Blas, C.	Fla.	29.40 N	85.22 W
95	San Blas, Cordillera de (Mts.) (kôr-dēl-yā′rä dā sän-bläs′)	Pan.	9.20 N	78.30 W
95	San Blas, G. of	Pan.	9.30 N	79.0 W
93	San Borja, R. de (rē′ō-dā-sän bôr′hä)	Mex.	19.21 N	99.17 W
88	Sanborn (săn′bŭrn)	N. Y. (Niagara Falls In.)	43.8 N	78.54 W
80	San Buenaventura (sän bwā′nä-vĕn-tōō′rä)	Mex.	27.6 N	101.30 W
103	San Caetano de Odivelas (sän kä-ā-tä′nōō dā ô-dê-vā′läzh)	Braz. (In.)	0.42 S	48.5 W
93	San Carlos (sän kär′lōs)	Mex.	17.50 N	92.33 W
80	San Carlos	Mex.	24.35 N	98.58 W
162	San Carlos	P. I.	15.56 N	120.21 E
162	San Carlos	P. I.	10.30 N	123.25 E
102	San Carlos	Ven.	9.32 N	68.32 W
75	San Carlos Ind. Res.	Ariz.	33.28 N	110.10 W
75	San Carlos Reservoir	Ariz.	33.12 N	110.25 W
95	San Carlos, R.	C. R.	10.40 N	84.20 W
92	San Carlos, R.	Mex.	24.18 N	99.10 W
128	San Cataldo (sän kä-täl′dō)	It.	37.29 N	13.59 E
124	Sancerre (säN-sâr′)	Fr.	47.20 N	2.51 E
97	Sanchez (sän′chāz)	Dom. Rep.	19.13 N	69.38 W
162	Sanchez Mira (sän′chāz mē′rä)	P. I.	18.34 N	121.13 E
92	Sanchez Roman (Tlaltenango) (sän chāz-rō-män′) (tläl-tâ-näŋ′gō)	Mex.	21.48 N	103.25 W
92	San Ciro (sän sē′rō)	Mex.	21.39 N	99.49 W
126	San Clemente (sän klā-mĕn′tā)	Sp.	39.25 N	2.25 W
74	San Clemente I.	Calif.	32.55 N	118.30 W
104	San Clemente, Mt.	Chl.	46.35 S	73.28 W
163	Sanco Pt. (sän-kō′)	P. I.	8.15 N	126.28 E
94	San Cristóbal (sän krês-tō′bäl)	Guat.	15.23 N	90.27 W
102	San Cristóbal	Ven.	7.45 N	72.10 W
93	San Cristóbal	Mex.	16.43 N	92.38 W
102	San Cristóbal (I.)	Ec.	0.59 S	89.30 W
93	San Cristóbal Ecatepec (å-kä-tå-pĕk′)	Mex.	19.36 N	99.2 W
165	San Cristoval (I.) (sän krês-tō′väl)	Solomon Is.	10.45 S	161.45 E
128	San Croce, C. (sän krô′chā)	It.	37.15 N	15.4 E
96	Sancti Spíritus (säŋk′tē spē′rê-tōōs)	Cuba	21.55 N	79.27 W
159	Sanda (sän′dȧ)	Jap.	34.53 N	135.14 E
160	Sandakan (sȧn-dä′kȧn) (săn-dä′kăn)	B. N. B.	5.51 N	118.0 E
163	Sandakan Har. (sȧn-dä′kȧn)	B. N. B.	5.53 N	118.8 E
160	Sandalwood (Sumba) I. (săn′dăl-wōōd) (sōōm′bȧ)	Neth. Ind.	9.45 S	120.0 E
116	Sanday (I.) (sănd′ā)	Gt. Brit. (In.)	59.15 N	2.30 W
118	Sandbach (sănd′băch)	Gt. Brit.	53.8 N	2.22 W
72	Sand Cr.	Colo. (Colo. Sprs. In.)	38.55 N	104.42 W
120	Sandefjord (sän′dĕ-fyôr′)	Nor.	59.8 N	10.13 E
80	Sanderson (săn′dēr-sŭn)	Tex.	30.8 N	102.24 W
82	Sandersville (săn′dērz-vĭl)	Ga.	32.59 N	82.49 W
143	Sandflats (sănd′flăts)	U. S. Afr.	33.25 S	25.59 E
169	Sandgate (sănd′gāt)	Austl.	47.19 S	153.4 E
120	Sandhammar, C. (sänt′häm-ĕr)	Swe.	55.22 N	14.10 E
77	Sand I.	Wis.	46.58 N	90.58 W
74	San Diego (săn dê-ā′gō)	Calif. (In.)	32.44 N	117.10 W
80	San Diego	Tex.	27.47 N	98.14 W
92	San Diego de la Unión (dā lä ōō-nyōn′)	Mex.	21.27 N	100.52 W
74	San Diego R.	Calif.	32.55 N	117.0 W
93	San Dieguito (sän dê-ā-gē′tō)	Mex. (In.)	19.29 N	98.49 W
73	San Dimas (săn dē′mȧs)	Calif. (Los Angeles In.)	34.7 N	117.49 W
92	San Dimas	Mex.	24.7 N	105.57 W
73	Sand Mt.	Ala. (Birmingham In.)	33.43 N	86.42 W
120	Sandnes (sänd′nĕs)	Nor.	58.54 N	5.45 E
120	Sandoa (sän-dō′ȧ)	Bel. Cong.	9.40 S	23.0 E
123	Sandomierz (sȧn-dô′myĕzh)	Pol.	50.39 N	21.45 E
128	San Donà di Piave (sän dō-nȧ′ dē pyä′vā)	It.	45.38 N	12.33 E
169	Sandon Bluffs (săn′dŭn)	Austl. (In.)	29.40 S	153.19 E
151	Sandoway (sän-dô-wī′)	India	18.25 N	94.28 E
70	Sandpoint (sănd′point)	Ida.	48.16 N	116.33 W
169	Sandringham (săn′drĭng-ăm)	Austl. (Melbourne In.)	37.57 S	145.0 E
79	Sand Springs	Okla.	36.9 N	96.7 W
164	Sandstone (sănd′stōn)	Austl.	27.58 S	119.25 E
77	Sandstone	Minn.	46.9 N	92.51 W
73	Sandtown (sănd′toun)	Ga. (Atlanta In.)	33.43 N	84.34 W
84	Sandusky (săn-dŭs′kê)	Mich.	43.25 N	82.50 W
84	Sandusky	Ohio	41.27 N	82.41 W
84	Sandusky R.	Ohio	41.10 N	83.10 W
89	Sandwich (sănd′wĭch)	Mich. (Detroit In.)	42.18 N	83.3 W
165	Sandwich (Efate) I. (ā-fä′tā)	New Hebr.	17.50 S	168.15 E
73	Sandy (sănd′ê)	Utah (Salt Lake City In.)	40.35 N	111.54 W
165	Sandy C.	Austl.	24.30 S	153.15 E
169	Sandy C.	Austl. (Tas. In.)	41.26 S	144.45 E
167	Sandy Creek	Austl.	32.11 S	146.4 E
71	Sandy Cr.	Mont.	48.15 N	110.10 W
71	Sandy Cr.	Wyo.	42.5 N	109.35 W
164	Sandy Desert	Austl.	19.30 S	130.30 E
88	Sandy Hook B.	N. J. (New York In.)	40.26 N	74.2 W
85	Sandy Hook C.	N. J.	40.27 N	74.0 W
87	Sandy I.	Can.	51.10 N	58.25 W

ăt; finăl; rāte; senâte; ärm; ȧsk; sofȧ; fâre; ch-choose; dh-as th in other; bē; êvent; bĕt; recĕnt; cratēr; g-go; gh-gutteral g; bĭt; ĭ-short neutral; rīde; K-gutteral k as ch in German ich;

Page	Name Pronunciation Region	Lat. °′	Long. °′
87	Sandy L. . . . . Newf.	49.15 N	56.50 W
72	Sandy Pt. . . Wash. (Vancouver In.)	48.48 N	122.43 W
81	Sandy Point . . . . Tex. (In.)	29.22 N	95.27 W
104	San Estanislao (sän ĕs-tä-nēs-lä′ō) Par.	24.31 S	56.32 W
104	San Felipe (sän fâ-lē′pâ) . . . . . Chl.	32.50 S	71.50 W
93	San Felipe . . . . Mex. (In.)	19.31 N	98.54 W
92	San Felipe . . . . Mex.	22.21 N	105.24 W
161	San Felipe . . . . . P. I. (Manila In.)	14.36 N	121.1 E
102	San Felipe . . . . Ven.	10.20 N	68.45 W
99	San Felipe, B. Chl. (Magallanes In.)	52.45 S	70.0 W
96	San Felipe Cays (Is.) . . . . Cuba	22.0 N	83.20 W
74	San Felipe Cr. . . . . Calif.	33.10 N	116.0 W
75	San Felipe Ind. Res. . . . . N. M.	35.25 N	106.25 W
93	San Felipe (Jalápa de Diáz) (hä lä′pä dā dē-äz′) . Mex.	18.3 N	96.55 W
127	San Felíu de Guixols (sän fâ-lē′o͞o dā gē-hôls′) . Sp.	41.47 N	3.1 E
127	San Felíu de Llobregat (lyō-brä-gät′) . Sp. (In.)	41.22 N	2.2 E
98	San Felix I. (sän fâ-lēks) . . Pac. O.	26.20 S	80.10 W
99	San Fernando (sän fĕr-nän′dō) Arg. (Buenos Aires In.)	34.25 S	58.35 W
73	San Fernando Calif. (Los Angeles In.)	34.17 N	118.27 W
104	San Fernando . . . . Chl.	34.32 S	71.0 W
93	San Fernando . . . . Mex.	16.53 N	93.11 W
80	San Fernando . . . . Mex.	24.52 N	98.10 W
163	San Fernando . . . . P. I.	10.10 N	123.42 E
162	San Fernando . . . . P. I.	12.28 N	123.45 E
162	San Fernando . . . . P. I.	15.4 N	120.42 E
162	San Fernando . . . . P. I.	16.37 N	120.20 E
127	San Fernando . . . . Sp. (In.)	36.28 N	6.12 W
102	San Fernando de Apure (dā ä-po͞o′rä) . Ven.	7.45 N	67.28 W
102	San Fernando de Atabapo (ä-tä-bä′pō) . Ven.	3.59 N	67.44 W
127	San Fernando de Henares (ā-nä′räs) Sp. (In.)	40.24 N	3.31 W
80	San Fernando, R. . . . . Mex.	25.0 N	98.20 W
83	Sanford (săn′fērd) . . . . . . Fla. (In.)	28.46 N	81.17 W
86	Sanford . . . . Me.	43.25 N	70.45 W
83	Sanford . . . . N. C.	35.27 N	79.10 W
52	Sanford, Mt. . . . . Alsk. (In.)	62.10 N	144.10 W
104	San Francisco (sän frän-sēs′kō) Arg.	13.28 S	62.15 W
49	San Francisco (săn frăn-sĭs′kō) Calif. (In.)		
74	San Francisco . . . . Calif.	37.45 N	122.27 W
93	San Francisco (Ixhuatan) (ēks-wä-tän′) . Mex.	16.22 N	94.28 W
161	San Francisco (sän frän-sēs′kō) P. I. (Manila In.)	14.39 N	121.0 E
94	San Francisco (Gotera) (gô-tā′rä) Sal.	13.47 N	88.7 W
74	San Francisco B. . . . . Calif.	37.40 N	122.20 W
92	San Francisco de los Adames (sän frän-sēs′kō dā lōs ä-dā′mäs) Mex.	22.25 N	102.14 W
92	San Francisco del Rincón (dĕl rēn-kōn′) . Mex.	21.2 N	101.47 W
97	San Francisco de Macoris (dā mä-kō′rēs) . Dom Rep.	19.18 N	70.16 W
90	San Francisco de Paula (sän frän-sēs′kō dā pou′lä) Cuba (Habana In.)	23.4 N	82.16 W
75	San Francisco R. . . . . Ariz.-N. M.	33.20 N	109.0 W
73	San Gabriel (săn gā-brē-ĕl′) (gā′ brē-ĕl) Calif. (Los Angeles In.)	34.6 N	118.7 W
92	San Gabriel . . . . Mex.	19.46 N	103.46 W
93	San Gabriel Chilac (chē-läk′) Mex.	18.18 N	97.21 W
73	San Gabriel Mts. Calif. (Los Angeles In.)	34.23 N	118.0 W
73	San Gabriel R. Calif. (Los Angeles In.)	33.50 N	118.7 W
81	San Gabriel R. . . . . Tex.	30.40 N	97.20 W
73	San Gabriel R., West Fork Calif. (Los Angeles In.)	34.15 N	117.57 W
79	Sangamon R. (săŋ′gȧ-mŭn) . . . . Ill.	40.0 N	89.50 W
139	Sanga R. (säŋ-gä) Fr. Eq. Afr.-Cam.	3.30 N	16.0 E
163	Sanga Sanga I. (säng-ä′säng-ä′) P. I.	5.5 N	119.46 E
154	Sangchi (säng′chē′) . . . . Chn.	29.20 N	109.57 E
74	Sanger (săng′ẽr) . . . . Calif.	36.42 N	119.33 W
122	Sangerhausen (säng′ẽr-hou-zĕn) Ger.	51.28 N	11.17 E
161	Sangihe (I.) (säŋ′gē-hĕ) Neth. Ind.	3.30 N	125.30 E
126	Sangüesa (säŋ-gwā′sä) . . . . Sp.	42.36 N	1.15 W
127	San Ginés de Vilasar (sän Kē-näs′ dā vē-lä-sär′) . Sp. (In.)	41.30 N	2.19 E
119	San Giorgio a Cremona (sän jôr′jō ä krā-mō′nä) It. (Napoli In.)	40.49 N	14.20 E
119	San Giovanni a Teduccio (sän jō-vän′nē ä tā-do͞o′chō It. (Napoli In.)	40.49 N	14.19 E
128	San Giovanni in Fiore (sän jō-vän′nē ēn fyō′rä . . . . . It.	39.15 N	16.42 E
157	Sangju (säng′jo͞o′) . . . . Cho.	36.28 N	128.9 E
126	Sangonera R. (säŋ-gō-nä′rä) . . Sp.	37.40 N	1.40 W
73	San Gorgonio Mt. (săn gôr-gō′nĭ-ō) Calif. (Los Angeles In.)	34.6 N	116.50 W
78	Sangre de Cristo Mts. (säŋ′grä dā krēs′tō) . Colo.	37.40 N	105.40 W
128	Sangro R. (säŋ′grō) . . . . It.	42.0 N	14.20 E
83	Sanibel I. (săn′ĭ-bĕl) . . . . Fla. (In.)	26.27 N	82.5 W
93	San Ildefonso (sän ēl-dā-fōn′sō) Mex. (In.)	19.37 N	99.17 W
93	San Ildefonso (Villa Alta) (vēl′yä äl′tä) . Mex.	17.20 N	96.10 W
162	San Ildefonso, C. . . . . P. I.	16.3 N	122.2 E
126	San Ildefonso o la Granja (sän ēl-dā-fōn′sō ō lä grän′hä) . Sp.	40.55 N	4.1 W
76	Sanish (să′nĭsh) . . . . N. D.	47.59 N	102.32 W
163	San Isidro (sän ē-sē′drō) . . . . . P. I.	11.23 N	124.21 E
73	San Jacinto (săn jȧ-sĭn′tō) Calif. (Los Angeles In.)	33.47 N	116.58 W
95	San Jacinto (sän hä-sēn′tō) . . . Nic.	11.30 N	83.48 W
162	San Jacinto . . . . P. I.	12.32 N	123.42 E
73	San Jacinto R. (săn jȧ-sĭn′tō) Calif. (Los Angeles In.)	33.50 N	117.0 W
81	San Jacinto R. . . . . Tex.	30.0 N	95.8 W
93	San Jerónimo (sän hā-rō′nē-mō) Mex. (In.)	19.20 N	99.13 W
93	San Jerónimo (Ixtepec) (ēz-tā-pĕk′) . Mex.	16.35 N	95.5 W
102	San Jerónimo, Cerro (Mt.) (sän hā-rō′nē-mō) . Peru (In.)	12.0 S	77.3 W
92	San Jerónimo de Juárez (dā hwä′räz) . Mex.	17.8 N	100.34 W
93	San Joaquín (sän hō-ä-kēn′) Mex. (In.)	19.32 N	98.50 W
163	San Joaquin . . . . P. I.	10.36 N	122.9 E
74	San Joaquin R. (săn hwä-kēn′) Calif.	37.30 N	121.10 W
7	San Jorge I. (sän zhôr′ zhĕ) Az. Is. (In.)	38.39 N	28.6 W
103	San José (sän hō-sā′) . . . . Bol.	17.30 S	60.30 W
74	San Jose . . . . Calif.	37.20 N	121.55 W
95	San José (sän hō-sā′) . . . . C. R.	9.58 N	84.4 W
94	San José . . . . Guat.	13.57 N	90.49 W
162	San José . . . . P. I.	12.21 N	121.3 E
162	San José . . . . P. I.	13.41 N	123.31 E
162	San José . . . . P. I.	13.51 N	121.7 E
162	San José . . . . P. I.	15.47 N	120.59 E
104	San José . . . . Ur.	34.25 S	56.45 W
163	San José de Buenavista (dā buā-nä-vēs′tä) . P. I.	10.45 N	121.57 E
99	San José de la Esquina (dā lä ĕs-kē′nä) Arg. (Buenos Aires In.)	33.6 S	61.42 W
161	San Jose del Monte (sän hō-sā dĕl mōn′tā) . P. I. (Manila In.)	14.50 N	121.3 E
73	San Jose Hills (săn hō-sā′) Calif. (Los Angeles In.)	34.4 N	117.50 W
95	San José I. . . . . Pan.	8.17 N	79.7 W
75	San Jose R. . . . . N. M.	35.15 N	107.55 W
99	San José, R. . Ur. (Buenos Aires In.)	34.10 S	56.45 W
104	San Juan (sän hwän′) . . . . Arg.	31.40 S	68.35 W
104	San Juan (State) . . . . Arg.	31.0 S	69.0 W
97	San Juan . . . . Dom. Rep.	18.48 N	71.14 W
93	San Juan (Guichicovi) (gwē-chē-kō′vē) . Mex.	16.59 N	95.5 W
93	San Juan (Mazatlán) (mä-zä-tlän′) . Mex.	17.3 N	95.27 W
162	San Juan . . . . P. I.	16.40 N	122.20 E
91	San Juan . . . . P. R. (In.)	18.30 N	66.10 W
92	San Juan Bautista del Téul (sän hwän′bou-tēs′tä dĕl tā′o͞ol) Mex.	21.32 N	100.35 W
91	San Juan, C. . . . . P. R. (In.)	18.20 N	65.36 W
92	San Juan Capistrano (kä-pēs-trä′nō) . Mex.	22.36 N	104.5 W
74	San Juan Cr. (săn hwän′) . . . Calif.	35.30 N	120.10 W
80	San Juan de Guadalupe (dā gwä-dhä-lo͞o′pä) Mex.	24.38 N	102.43 W
80	San Juan del Mezquital (dĕl mĕz-kē-täl′) Mex.	24.20 N	103.20 W
95	San Juan del Norte (Greytown) (dĕl nôr′tā) (grā′toun) Nic.	10.56 N	83.46 W
95	San Juan del Norte B. . . . . Nic.	11.10 N	83.40 W
92	San Juan de los Lagos (dā lōs lä′ gōs) Mex.	21.16 N	102.17 W
92	San Juan del Río (dĕl rē′ō) . . Mex.	20.23 N	99.59 W
80	San Juan del Río . . . . Mex.	24.47 N	104.28 W
94	San Juan del Sur (dĕl so͞or′) . . Nic.	11.15 N	85.53 W
127	San Juan de Vilasar (dā vē-lä-sär′) Sp. (In.)	41.30 N	2.23 E
93	San Juan Evangelista (ā-väŋ-kä-lēs′tä) Mex.	17.54 N	95.7 W
72	San Juan I. Wash. (Vancouver In.)	48.33 N	123.5 W
163	San Juanico Str. (sän hwä-nē′kō) P. I.	11.25 N	124.59 E
92	San Juanito I. (sän hwä-nē′tō) Mex.	21.43 N	106.38 W
75	San Juan Mts. (săn hwän′) . . Colo.	37.40 N	107.10 W
93	San Juan, R. (sän hwän′) . . . . Mex.	18.0 N	95.13 W
80	San Juan, R. . . . . Mex.	26.0 N	99.12 W
94	San Juan, R. . . . . Nic.-C. R.	10.50 N	84.15 W
75	San Juan R. (săn hwän′) Utah-N. M.	37.15 N	110.20 W
80	San Juan Sabinas (sä-bē′näs) Mex.	27.55 N	101.17 W
96	San Juan y Martínez (ē mär-tē′nēz) Cuba	22.12 N	83.48 W
104	San Justo (sän ho͞os′tō) . Arg. (In.)	34.41 S	58.33 W
138	Sankarani R. (sän′kä-rä′nē) Fr. W. Afr.	11.0 N	8.30 W
154	Sankiang (sän′kyäng′) . . . . Chn.	26.41 N	109.2 E
140	Sankishia (sän-kē′shē-ä) Bel. Cong.	9.38 S	25.48 W
122	Sankt Joachimsthal (Jáchymov) (zängt yō′ä-kĭms-täl′) (yä′chĭ-môf) . Ger.	50.22 N	12.50 E
140	Sankuru R. (sän-ko͞o′ro͞o) Bel. Cong.	6.0 S	23.45 E
49	San Leandro (săn lē-ăn′drō) Calif. (San Francisco In.)	37.43 N	122.10 W
49	San Lorenzo (săn lō-rĕn′zō) Calif. (San Francisco In.)	37.41 N	122.8 W
94	San Lorenzo (sän lō-rĕn′zō) . Hond.	13.25 N	87.12 W
95	San Lorenzo . . . . Pan.	8.18 N	82.8 W
126	San Lorenzo del Escorial (sän lō-rĕn′thō dĕl ĕs-kō-rē-äl′) . . . Sp.	40.35 N	4.1 W
102	San Lorenzo I. (sän lō-rĕn′zō) Peru (In.)	12.6 S	77.14 W
127	Sanlúcar de Barrameda (sän-lo͞o′kär dā bär-rä-mā′dhä) Sp. (In.)	36.46 N	6.21 W
102	San Lucas (sän lo͞o′käs) . . . . . . Bol.	20.1 S	64.68 W
93	San Lucas . . . . Mex. (In.)	19.16 N	98.52 W
93	San Lucas (Ojitlan) (ō-Kē-tlän′) Mex.	18.4 N	96.23 W
104	San Luis (sän lo͝o-ēs′) . . . . Arg.	33.20 S	66.20 W
104	San Luis (State) . . . . Arg.	34.0 S	66.0 W
97	San Luis . . . . Cuba	20.11 N	75.51 W
161	San Luis . . . . P. I. (Manila In.)	15.3 N	120.44 E
161	San Luis . . . . . . P. I. (Manila In.)	13.50 N	120.53 E
92	San Luis de la Paz (dā lä päz′) Mex.	21.18 N	100.31 W
80	San Luis del Cordero (dĕl kôr-dā′rō) Mex.	25.25 N	104.20 W
74	San Luis Obispo (ō-bĭs′pō) . . . Calif.	35.18 N	120.40 W
74	San Luis Obispo B. . . . . Calif.	35.7 N	120.50 W
92	San Luis Potosí (pō-tō-sē′) . . Mex.	22.9 N	100.58 W
92	San Luis Potosí (State) . . . . . Mex.	22.40 N	100.50 W
74	San Luis Rey R. (rā′ē) . . . . . . Calif.	33.20 N	117.10 W
75	San Marcial (săn mär-syäl′) N. M.	33.42 N	106.59 W
128	San Marco (sän mär′kō) . . . . It.	41.43 N	15.38 E
94	San Marcos (sän mär′kōs) . . . Guat.	14.57 N	91.48 W
92	San Marcos . . . . Mex.	16.46 N	99.28 W
93	San Marcos . . . . Mex. (In.)	19.18 N	98.52 W
80	San Marcos (săn mär′kōs) . . . . Tex.	29.53 N	97.55 W
81	San Marcos R. . . . . Tex.	29.40 N	97.40 W
162	San Mariano (sän mä-rē-ä′nō) P. I.	17.0 N	121.59 E
128	San Marino (sän mä-rē′nō) . . . Eur.	43.56 N	12.25 E
128	San Marino . . . . San Marino	43.56 N	12.25 E
104	San Martín (sän mär-tēn′) Arg. (In.)	34.35 S	58.32 W
92	San Martín . . . . Mex.	21.24 N	98.39 W
93	San Martín (Vol.) . . . . Mex.	18.36 N	95.10 W
127	San Martín de la Vega (sän mär-tēn′ dā lä vā′gä) Sp. (In.)	40.12 N	3.34 W
92	San Martín Hidalgo (ē-däl′gō) Mex.	20.27 N	103.56 W
104	San Martín, L. . . . . Chl.-Arg.	48.45 S	72.40 W
74	San Mateo (săn mä-tā′ō) . . . . . Calif.	37.32 N	122.19 W
127	San Mateo (sän mä-tā′ō) . . . . . . Sp.	40.26 N	0.8 E
161	San Mateo . . . . . . P. I. (Manila In.)	14.42 N	121.8 E
93	San Mateo (Etlatongo) (ĕ-tlä-tōŋ′ gō) Mex.	17.1 N	97.1 W
104	San Matias, G. of (sän mä-tē′äs) Arg.	41.30 S	64.0 W
93	San Miguel (sän mē-gĕl′) . . . . Mex.	18.9 N	97.10 W
93	San Miguel Mex. (In.)	19.32 N	98.53 W
93	San Miguel . . . . Mex. (In.)	19.33 N	99.23 W
162	San Miguel . . . . P. I.	15.9 N	120.58 E
94	San Miguel . . . . Sal.	13.32 N	88.13 W
93	San Miguel (Sola de Vega) (sō′lä dā vā′gä) Mex.	16.30 N	96.58 W
93	San Miguel (Talea de Castro) (tä-lā′ä dā käs′trō) Mex.	17.22 N	96.15 W
94	San Miguel (Vol.) (sän mē-gĕl′) . Sal.	13.27 N	88.17 W
162	San Miguel B. . . . . P. I.	13.50 N	123.10 E
92	San Miguel de Allende (dā ä-lyĕn′ dā) Mex.	20.55 N	100.44 W
92	San Miguel de Mezquital (dĕl mĕz-kē-täl′) Mex.	24.17 N	103.27 W
92	San Miguel el Alto (ĕl äl′tō) Mex.	21.2 N	102.18 W
95	San Miguel G. . . . . Pan.	8.20 N	78.20 W
74	San Miguel I. . . . . Calif.	34.5 N	120.25 W
163	San Miguel I. . . . . P. I.	7.45 N	118.32 E
75	San Miguel R. (săn mē-gĕl′) . Colo.	38.12 N	108.25 W
155	Sanmun B. (sän′mo͞on′) . . . . . Chn.	29.8 N	121.40 E
162	San Narciso (sän när-sē′sō) . . P. I.	13.33 N	122.32 E
162	San Narciso . . . . P. I.	15.1 N	120.5 E
162	San Nicolas (sän nē-kō-läs′) . . P. I.	16.5 N	120.45 E
74	San Nicolas I. (săn nĭ′kō-lȧs) Calif.	33.15 N	119.30 W
125	Sannois (sȧ-nwä′) . . . . Fr. (In.)	48.58 N	2.16 E
135	Sannûris (săn-no͞o′rēs) . . . Eg. (In.)	29.27 N	30.51 E
123	Sanok (sä′nôk) . . . . Pol.	49.32 N	22.12 E
93	San Pablo (sän pä′blō) . Mex. (In.)	19.19 N	99.8 W
162	San Pablo . . . . P. I.	14.4 N	121.20 E
162	San Pablo . . . . P. I.	17.28 N	121.48 E
74	San Pablo B. . . . . Calif.	38.5 N	122.30 W
95	San Pablo, R. . . . . Pan.	8.10 N	81.15 W
162	San Pascual (sän päs-kwäl′) . . P. I.	13.8 N	123.0 E
99	San Pedro (sän pā′drō) Arg. (Buenos Aires In.)	33.39 S	59.38 W
74	San Pedro (săn pē′drō) . . . . . Calif.	33.45 N	118.25 W
93	San Pedro (sän pā′drō) . . . . . . Mex.	18.42 N	92.25 W
93	San Pedro . . . . Mex. (In.)	19.16 N	99.19 W
92	San Pedro (Amusgos) (ä-mo͞os′gōs) Mex.	16.38 N	98.6 W
93	San Pedro (Pochutla) (pō-cho͞o′tlä) Mex.	15.43 N	96.28 W
104	San Pedro . . . . Par.	24.5 S	57.10 W
161	San Pedro (sän pä′drō) P. I. (Manila In.)	14.23 N	121.4 E
94	San Pedro . . . . Sal.	13.48 N	88.58 W
73	San Pedro B. (săn pē′drō) Calif. (Los Angeles In.)	33.44 N	118.13 W
163	San Pedro B. (sän pä′drō) . . . . P. I.	11.10 N	125.6 E
94	San Pedro del Norte (dĕl nôr′tā) Nic.	13.0 N	84.59 W
97	San Pedro de Macorís (dā mä-kō-rēs′) Dom. Rep.	18.28 N	69.18 W
127	San Pedro de Ribas (dā rē′bäs) Sp. (In.)	41.15 N	1.47 E
127	San Pedro de Ruidevitlles (dā ro͞o-ē′dhā-vēt′lyäs) Sp. (In.)	41.26 N	1.43 E
92	San Pedro Lagunillas (lä-go͞o-nēl′ yäs) Mex.	21.12 N	104.46 W
80	San Pedro las Colonias (läs kō-lō′ nyäs) Mex.	25.45 N	103.0 W
75	San Pedro R. (săn pē′drō) . . . Ariz.	32.30 N	110.30 W
96	San Pedro R. (sän pä′drō) . . . Cuba	21.5 N	78.12 W
94	San Pedro, R. . . . . Guat. (In.)	17.10 N	90.20 W
93	San Pedro, R. . . . . Mex.	17.40 N	91.8 W
92	San Pedro, R. . . . . Mex.	22.16 N	105.0 W
80	San Pedro, R. . . . . Mex.	28.10 N	105.30 W
94	San Pedro Sula (so͞o′lä) . . . . Hond.	15.27 N	88.0 W
93	San Pedro y San Pablo (Teposcolula) (ē sän pä′blō) (tā-pō-skō-lo͞o′lä) Mex.	17.31 N	97.30 W

ng-sing; ŋ-baŋk; N-nasalized n; nŏd; cŏmmit; ōld; ôbey; ôrder; fo͞od; fo͝ot; ou-out; s-soft; sh-dish; th-thin; pūre; ûnite; ûrn; stŭd; circŭs; ü-as "y" in study; ′-indeterminate vowel.

Page	Name Pronunciation Region	Lat. °′	Long. °′
128	San Pietro (I.) (sän pyā′trō) . Sard.	39.9 N	8.15 E
162	San Quintin (sän kēn-tēn′) . . . P. I.	15.59 N	120.47 E
123	San R. (sän) . . . . Pol.	49.50 N	22.53 E
104	San Rafael (sän rä-fä-äl′) . . . . . Arg.	34.29 S	68.29 W
74	San Rafael (săn rȧ-fĕl′) . . . . . Calif.	37.59 N	122.31 W
93	San Rafael (sän rä-fä-äl′) Mex. (In.)	19.27 N	99.15 W
93	San Rafael . . . . Mex. (In.)	19.34 N	99.11 W
161	San Rafael (sän rä-fä-äl′) P. I. (Manila In.)	14.59 N	120.56 E
75	San Rafael R. (săn rȧ-fĕl′) . . . Utah	39.0 N	110.40 W
95	San Ramón (sän rä-mōn′) . . . C. R.	10.7 N	84.30 W
163	San Remigio (sän rā-mē′hyō) P. I.	11.5 N	123.57 E
128	San Remo (sän rā′mō) . . . . It.	43.49 N	7.46 E
161	San Roque (sän rō′kā) P. I. (Manila In.)	14.29 N	120.52 E
126	San Roque . . . . Sp.	36.13 N	5.22 W
80	San Saba (săn sä′ bȧ) . . . . Tex.	31.11 N	98.43 W
80	San Saba R. . . . . Tex.	31.0 N	99.18 W
138	San Sabastián (sän sȧ-bäs-tê-än′) Can. Is.	28.10 N	17.10 W
94	San Salvador (sän säl-vä-dōr′) Sal.	13.44 N	89.10 W
97	San Salvador (Watling) I. (săn săl′vȧ-dōr) Ba. Is.	24.0 N	74.0 W
138	Sansanné-Mango (sän-sȧ-nā′-mäɴ′ gō) Fr. W. Afr.	10.30 N	0.28 E
127	San Saturnino de Noya (sän sä-tōōr-nē′nō dā nō′yä) Sp. (In.)	41.24 N	1.47 E
126	San Sebastian (sän sȧ-bäs-tyän′) Sp.	43.19 N	1.59 W
93	San Sebastian (Tecomaxtlahuaca) (tā′kô-mäs-tlȧ-wä′kä) Mex.	17.41 N	96.56 W
119	San Sebastiano al Vesuvio (sän sā-bäs-tyä′nō äl vā-sōō′vê-ō) It. (Napoli In.)	40.50 N	14.25 E
127	San Sebastian de los Reyes (sän sā-bäs-tyän′ dā lōs rā′yĕs) Sp. (In.)	40.33 N	3.39 W
93	San Sebastián Zinacatepec (zē-nȧ-kä-tȧ-pĕk′) Mex.	18.18 N	97.14 W
128	Sansego (I.) (sän-sā′gô) . . . . It.	44.31 N	14.17 E
128	San Severo (sän sā-vȧ′rō) . . . . . . It.	41.41 N	15.23 E
161	San Simon (sän sê-mōn′) P. I. (Manila In.)	15.0 N	120.45 E
119	San Strato (sän strä′tô) It. (Napoli In.)	40.48 N	14.12 E
74	Santa Ana (săn′tȧ ăn′ȧ) . . . . . Calif.	33.44 N	117.51 W
92	Santa Ana (sän′tä ä′nä) . . . . . Mex.	19.18 N	98.10 W
94	Santa Ana . . . . Sal.	14.2 N	89.34 W
73	Santa Ana Mts. . . . . Calif.	33.50 N	117.37 W
74	Santa Ana R. (săn′tȧ ă′nȧ) Calif.	33.55 N	117.35 W
119	Santa Anastasia (sän′tä ä-näs-tä′ zê-ä) It. (Napoli In.)	40.52 N	14.24 E
80	Santa Anna (săn′tȧ ă′nȧ) . . . . . Tex.	31.43 N	99.20 W
99	Santa Anna B. (sän′tȧ ä′nȧ) Braz. (Rio de Janeiro In.)	22.40 S	41.50 W
119	Sant′ Agnello (sän-tä nyĕl′ō) It. (Napoli In.)	40.37 N	14.25 E
104	Sant′ Anna do Livramento (sän-tä′ nȧ dŏŏ lē-vrä-mĕŋ′tŏŏ) . Braz.	30.40 S	55.32 W
103	Sant′ Anna do Paranahiba (dŏŏ pä-rȧ-nä-ē′bȧ) . Braz.	19.43 S	51.2 W
103	Santa Barbara (sän′tȧ bär′bä-rȧ) Braz.	19.59 S	43.28 W
74	Santa Barbara (săn′tȧ bär′bȧ-rȧ) Calif.	34.25 N	119.41 W
80	Santa Barbara . . . . Mex.	26.47 N	105.49 W
163	Santa Barbara . . . . P. I.	10.48 N	122.31 E
74	Santa Barbara Chan. (săn′tȧ bär′bȧ-rȧ) . Calif.	34.13 N	120.0 W
74	Santa Barbara I. . . . . Calif.	33.28 N	119.2 W
74	Santa Barbara Is. . . . . Calif.	33.50 N	120.0 W
94	Santa Barbara, R. (sän′tä bär′-bä-rä) . Hond.	14.36 N	88.14 W
74	Santa Catalina I. (săn′tȧ kă-tȧ-lē′ nȧ) . Calif.	33.22 N	118.25 W
93	Santa Catarina (sän′tä kä-tä-rē′nä) . Mex. (In.)	19.19 N	98.58 W
93	Santa Catarina . . . . Mex. (In.)	19.29 N	98.46 W
80	Santa Catarina . . . . Mex.	25.40 N	100.27 W
93	Santa Catarina (Yosonotú) (yō-sô-nô-tōō′) . Mex.	16.53 N	97.34 W
93	Santa Catarina, Cerro (Mts.) Mex. (In.)	19.20 N	99.0 W
104	Santa Catharina (State) (kä-tä-rē′nȧ) . Braz.	27.0 S	51.0 W
74	Santa Clara (săn′tȧ klȧ′rȧ) . . Calif.	37.21 N	121.58 W
96	Santa Clara (sän′tä klä′rä) . . Cuba	22.22 N	79.58 W
96	Santa Clara (State) . . . . Cuba	22.20 N	80.30 W
02	Santa Clara . . . . Mex.	19.25 N	101.35 W
80	Santa Clara . . . . Mex.	24.27 N	103.20 W
94	Santa Clara (Vol.) . . . . Nic.	12.42 N	86.57 W
96	Santa Clara B. . . . . Cuba	23.5 N	80.55 W
93	Santa Clara Cuautitla (sän′tä klä′rä kwä-ōō-tē′tlä) . Mex. (In.)	19.43 N	99.4 W
78	Santa Clara Pueblo Ind. Res. (săn′tȧ klâ′rȧ pwĕb′lō) . N. M.	36.00 N	106.15 W
74	Santa Clara R. (săn′tȧ klâ′rȧ) Calif.	34.23 N	118.50 W
127	Santa Coloma de Farnés (sän′tä kō-lō′mä dā fär-nās′) . Sp.	41.52 N	2.40 E
126	Santa Comba (sän′tä kōm′bä) Sp.	43.3 N	8.49 W
104	Santa Cruz (State) (sän′tä krōōz′) Arg.	47.30 S	70.0 W
102	Santa Cruz . . . . Bol.	17.45 S	63.32 W
103	Santa Cruz . . . . Braz.	19.58 S	40.15 W
74	Santa Cruz (săn′tȧ krōōz′) . . . Calif.	36.58 N	122.3 W
99	Santa Cruz (sän′tä krōōz′) Chl. (Valparaiso In.)	34.38 S	71.24 W
94	Santa Cruz . . . . C. R.	10.17 N	85.37 W
92	Santa Cruz . . . . Mex.	20.38 N	101.1 W
80	Santa Cruz . . . . Mex.	25.48 N	105.25 W
163	Santa Cruz . . . . P. I.	6.50 N	125.25 E
162	Santa Cruz . . . . P. I.	13.28 N	122.1 E
162	Santa Cruz . . . . P. I.	14.17 N	121.25 E
162	Santa Cruz . . . . P. I.	15.46 N	119.54 E
162	Santa Cruz . . . . P. I.	17.5 N	120.28 E
93	Santa Cruz (Itundujia) (ê-tŏŏn-dŏŏ-ᴋê′ä) . Mex.	16.51 N	97.39 W
126	Santa Cruz de la Zarza (sän′tä krōōth′dä lä thär′thä) . Sp.	39.58 N	3.9 W
96	Santa Cruz del Sur (sän′tä krōōz dĕl sōōr′) . Cuba	20.42 N	78.1 W
138	Santa Cruz de Tenerife (dā tā-nȧ-rē′fä) . Can. Is.	28.32 N	16.14 W
74	Santa Cruz I. . . . . Calif.	34.1 N	119.50 W
165	Santa Cruz Is. (sän′tä krōōz′) Solomon Is.	11.0 S	166.0 E
104	Santa Cruz, R. . . . . Arg.	50.20 S	70.30 W
128	Santa Eufemia, G. of (sän′tä ȧ-ŏŏ-fā′mê-ä) . It.	38.50 N	16.10 E
127	Santa Eulalia del Río (sän′tä ȧ-ŏŏ-lä′lê-ä dĕl rē′ō) . Sp.	38.59 N	1.30 E
104	Santa Fé (sän′tä fā′) . . . . Arg.	31.40 S	60.45 W
104	Santa Fé (State) . . . . Arg.	30.0 S	61.0 W
96	Santa Fé, ... Isle of Pines	21.45 N	82.37 W
93	Santa Fé . . . . Mex. (In.)	19.23 N	99.11 W
75	Santa Fe (săn′tȧ fā′) . . . . N. M.	35.40 N	106.5 N
126	Santafe (sän′tä-fā′) . . . . Sp.	37.11 N	3.42 W
92	Santa Inés Ahuatempán (ä-hwä-tĕm-pän′) . Mex.	18.25 N	98.1 W
104	Santa Inès I. (ê-nās′) . . . . Chl.	53.45 S	73.0 W
99	Santa Isabel (ê-zä-bĕl′) Braz. (Rio de Janeiro In.)	23.19 S	46.15 W
138	Santa Isabel (ē-sä-bĕl′) . . . Sp. Gui.	3.50 N	8.45 E
94	Santa Isabel, R. . . . . Guat.	16.0 N	89.40 W
96	Santa Lucia (sän′tä lōō-sē′ä) . Cuba	21.21 N	77.32 W
162	Santa Lucia . . . . P. I.	17.8 N	120.28 E
96	Santa Lucia B. . . . . Cuba	22.41 N	83.59 W
99	Santa Lucia, R. Ur. (Buenos Aires In.)	34.30 S	56.25 W
93	Santa Lucrecia (sän′tä lōō-krā′-sê-ä) . Mex.	17.26 N	95.0 W
103	Santa Luzia (sän-tä lōō-zē′ȧ) Braz.	16.18 S	47.58 W
7	Santa Luzia I. . . . . . C. V. Is. (In.)	16.46 N	24.44 W
93	Santa Margarita (Huitepec) (mär-gä-rē′tä) (wē-tȧ-pĕk′) . Mex.	16.54 N	95.43 W
104	Santa Maria (mä-rē′ȧ) . . . . . . Braz.	29.35 S	53.40 W
74	Santa Maria (săn-tȧ mȧ-rē′ȧ) Calif.	34.58 N	120.29 W
128	Santa Maria (sän-tä mä-rē′ä) . . . It.	41.4 N	14.15 E
162	Santa Maria . . . . P. I.	14.48 N	120.58 E
161	Santa Maria . . . . P. I. (Manila In.)	14.32 N	121.29 E
93	Santa María (Huazolotlitlán) (wä-zô-lô-tlê-tlän′) . Mex.	16.18 N	97.54 W
93	Santa María (Zaachila) (zä-ä-chē′lä) . Mex.	16.57 N	96.45 W
93	Santa María Asunción (Tlaxiaco) (ä-sōōn-syōn′) (tläk-sê-ä′kō) . Mex.	17.15 N	97.40 W
126	Santa María, C. . . . . Port.	36.57 N	7.55 W
96	Santa Maria Cays (Is.) . . . . . Cuba	22.38 N	79.5 W
92	Santa María del Oro (dĕl ō′rō) Mex.	21.17 N	104.36 W
92	Santa María de los Ángeles (dā lōs äŋ′ᴋȧ-lās) . Mex.	22.15 N	103.18 W
92	Santa María del Río (dĕl rē′ō) Mex.	21.47 N	100.43 W
92	Santa María de Ocotán (dā ō-kô-tän′) . Mex.	22.56 N	104.30 W
129	Santa Maria di Leuca, C. (dē lā-ōō′kä) . It.	39.47 N	18.22 E
138	Santa Maria I. . . . . Az. Is. (In.)	36.55 N	25.5 W
92	Santa María, R. . . . . Mex.	21.30 N	100.8 W
161	Santa Maria R. . P. I. (Manila In.)	14.50 N	121.0 E
94	Santa María (Vol.) . . . . Guat.	14.45 N	91.34 W
102	Santa Marta (sän′tä mär′tä) . . Col.	11.15 N	74.10 W
126	Santa Marta . . . . Sp.	38.39 N	6.38 W
74	Santa Monica (săn′tȧ mŏn′ĭ-kȧ) Calif.	34.1 N	118.28 W
73	Santa Monica Bay . . . . Calif.	34.57 N	118.28 W
73	Santa Monica Mts. Calif. (Los Angeles In.)	34.7 N	118.32 W
93	Santa Monica (sän′tä mō′nê-kä) Mex. (In.)	19.27 N	98.52 W
126	Santander (sän-tän-dâr′) . . . . . . Sp.	43.28 N	3.49 W
127	Santañy (sän-tän′yê) . . . . Sp.	39.22 N	3.6 E
74	Santa Paula (săn′tȧ pô′lȧ) . . . Calif.	34.22 N	119.4 W
103	Santa Philomena (sän′tȧ fē-lô-mā′nȧ) . Braz.	9.0 S	45.45 W
103	Santarem (sän-tä-rĕɴ′) . Braz. (In.)	13.40 S	39.15 W
103	Santarem . . . . Braz.	2.28 S	54.32 W
126	Santarem . . . . Port.	39.14 N	8.42 W
127	Santarem (Prov.) . . . . . . Port. (In.)	38.52 N	8.48 W
96	Santaren Chan. (săn-tȧ-rĕn′) W. I.	23.50 N	79.30 W
75	Santa Rita (săn-tȧ rē′tȧ) . . . N. M.	32.47 N	108.4 W
161	Santa Rita (sän′tä rē′tä) P. I. (Manila In.)	15.2 N	120.32 E
90	Santa Rita Mt. . . . Pan (C. Z. In.)	9.19 N	79.47 W
74	Santa Rosa (săn′tȧ rō′zȧ) . . . Calif.	38.26 N	122.42 W
94	Santa Rosa (sän′tä rō′sä) . . . Guat.	14.22 N	90.15 W
94	Santa Rosa . . . . Hond.	14.42 N	88.48 W
93	Santa Rosa . . . . Mex.	18.48 N	97.12 W
78	Santa Rosa (săn′tȧ rō′zȧ) . . . N. M.	34.55 N	104.40 W
162	Santa Rosa (sän′tä rō′sä) . . . . P. I.	14.18 N	121.7 E
104	Santa Rosa de Toay (tō′ā) . . . . Arg.	36.40 S	64.20 W
84	Santa Rosa I. (săn′tȧ rō′zȧ) . Calif.	33.55 N	120.10 W
74	Santa Rosa Ind. Res. . . . . Calif.	33.30 N	116.42 W
80	Santa Rosalia (Camargo) (sän′tä rō-zä′lê-ä) (kä-mär′gō) . Mex.	27.40 N	105.10 W
93	Santa Rosa, Monte (Mts.) (mōn′-tȧ sän′tä rō′sä) Mex. (In.)	19.17 N	99.17 W
70	Santa Rosa Mts. (săn′tȧ rō′zȧ) Nev.	41.40 N	117.40 W
73	Santa Susana (săn′tȧ sōō-ză′nȧ) Calif. (Los Angeles In.)	34.17 N	118.43 W
73	Santa Susana Mts. Calif. (Los Angeles In.)	34.19 N	118.38 W
94	Santa Tecla (Nueva San Salvador) (sän′tä tĕk′lä) (nwā′vä sän säl-vȧ-dōr′) . Sal.	13.41 N	89.17 W
74	Santa Ynez R. (săn′tȧ ē-nĕz′) Calif.	34.37 N	120.10 W
74	Santa Ysabel Ind. Res. (săn-tȧ ē-zȧ-bĕl′) . Calif.	33.10 N	116.40 W
74	Santee (săn-tē′) . . . . Calif. (In.)	32.50 N	116.58 W
83	Santee Canal . . . . S. C.	33.20 N	80.12 W
83	Santee R. . . . . S. C.	33.30 N	80.0 W
92	Santelmo, Pt. (sän-tĕl′mō) . . . Mex.	18.22 N	103.32 W
99	Santiago . . . . Chl. (In.)		
104	Santiago (sän-tê-ä′gō) . . . . Chl.	33.28 S	70.45 W
102	Santiago (I.) . . . . Ec.	0.15 S	90.45 W
94	Santiago . . . . Hond.	15.17 N	87.56 W
92	Santiago (Juxtlahuaca) (hōōs′-tlä-wä′kä) . Mex.	17.18 N	98.2 W
93	Santiago (Trejúpam) (trȧ-hōō′-päm) . Mex.	17.40 N	97.25 W
93	Santiago (Zacatepec) (zä-kä′tȧ-pĕk′) . Mex.	17.10 N	95.53 W
92	Santiago . . . . Mex.	19.48 N	99.5 W
95	Santiago . . . . Pan.	8.6 N	80.58 W
161	Santiago, C. (sän-tê-ä′gō) P. I. (Manila In.)	13.47 N	120.36 E
162	Santiago . . . . P. I.	16.41 N	121.32 E
126	Santiago . . . . Sp.	42.52 N	8.33 W
97	Santiago de Cuba (dā kōō′bä) Cuba	20.0 N	75.49 W
96	Santiago de las Vegas (dā läs vā′gäs) . Cuba	22.58 N	82.24 W
104	Santiago del Estero (dĕl ĕs-tā′rō) Arg.	27.45 S	64.20 W
104	Santiago del Estero (State) . . . Arg.	28.0 S	63.30 W
97	Santiago de los Caballeros (dā lōs kä-bäl-yā′rōs) . Dom. Rep.	19.28 N	70.42 W
162	Santiago I. . . . . P. I.	16.25 N	119.55 E
92	Santiago Ixcuintla (ēs-kwēn′tlä) Mex.	21.48 N	105.12 W
80	Santiago Mts. . . . . Tex.	30.0 N	103.30 W
80	Santiago Papasquiaro (pä-päs-kê-ä′rō) . Mex.	25.3 N	105.25 W
73	Santiago Pk. Calif. (Los Angeles In.)	33.43 N	117.32 W
92	Santiago, R. . . . . Mex.	21.20 N	104.20 W
93	Santiago Tuxtla (tōōs′tlä) . . . Mex.	18.27 N	95.18 W
80	Santiaguillo, L. (sän-tê-ä-gēl′yō) Mex.	24.50 N	104.50 W
93	Santiaguito (sän-tê-ä-gē′tō) Mex. (In.)	19.30 N	99.15 W
70	Santiam R. (săn′tyăm) . . . . Ore.	44.50 N	122 50 W
127	Santi Petri Canal (sän′tê pā′trê) Sp (In)	36.24 N	6.11 W
126	Santisteban del Puerto (sän′tê-stȧ-bän′ dĕl pwĕr′tō) . Sp.	38.16 N	3.11 W
103	Santo Amaro (sän′tŏŏ ä-mä′rŏŏ) Braz. (In.)	12.33 S	38.45 W
7	Santo Antão I. (sän′tŏŏ än-touɴ′) C. V. Is. (In.)	17.3 N	25.9 W
140	Santo Antonio (sän′tŏŏ än-tō′-nê-ŏŏ) . Ang.	6.5 S	12.23 E
103	Santo Antonio da Bôa Vista (dä bō′ȧ vēs′tȧ) . Braz.	16.40 S	43.14 W
103	Santo Antonio de Balsas (dā bäl′-zäzh) . Braz.	7.0 S	45.59 W
96	Santo Domingo (sän′tō dō-mĭŋ′gō) Cuba	22.35 N	80.18 W
97	Santo Domingo (Ciudad Trujillo) Dom. Rep.	18.28 N	69.53 W
162	Santo Domingo . . . . P. I.	17.38 N	120.24 E
93	Santo Domingo (Tehuantepec) (tȧ-hwän′tȧ-pĕk′) . Mex.	16.20 N	95.14 W
93	Santo Domingo (Zanatepec) (zȧ-nä′tȧ-pĕk′) . Mex.	16.30 N	94.21 W
97	Santo Domingo Cay (I.) (sän-tō dô-mĭŋ′gō) . Ba. Is.	21.42 N	75.45 W
126	Santo Domingo de la Calzada (dā lä käl-thä′dä) . Sp.	42.26 N	2.57 W
126	Santoña (sän-tō′nyä) . . . . Sp.	43.27 N	3.28 W
103	Santos (sän′tōzh) . . . . Braz.	23.58 S	46.18 W
162	Santo Tomás (sän′tō tô-mäs′) P. I.	14.7 N	121.8 E
93	Santo Tomás (Tamazulapam) (tä-mä-zōō-lä′päm) . Mex.	17.42 N	97.34 W
162	Santo Tomás . . . . P. I.	16.20 N	120.33 E
155	Santuao (sän′tōō-ä′ō) . . . . Chn.	26.41 N	119.34 E
155	Santuao B. . . . . Chn.	26.30 N	119.45 E
159	Sanuki (sä′nōō-kê) Jap. (Tokyo In.)	35.16 N	139.54 E
124	Sanvic (säɴ-vēk′) . . . . Fr.	49.31 N	0.10 E
94	San Vicente (sän vê-sĕn′tȧ) . . . Sal.	13.41 N	88.43 W
126	San Vicente de Alcántara (sän vê-thĕn′tä dä äl-kän′tä-rä) Sp.	39.23 N	7.9 W
127	San Vicente de Sarriá (dä sär-rē-ȧ′) . Sp. (In.)	41.24 N	2.7 E
128	San Vito (sän vē′tō) . . . . It.	45.54 N	12.51 E
75	San Xavier Ind. Res. (sän ᴋä vyâr′) (zăv′ĭ-ēr) . Ariz.	32.7 N	111.0 W
140	Sanyati R. (sän-yä′tê) . . . . . S. Rh.	17.30 S	29.15 E
103	São Carlos do Pinhal (souɴ kär′lōzh dŏŏ pêɴ-häl′) . Braz.	22.1 S	47.59 W
103	São Domingos da Bôa Vista (souɴ dō-mĭŋ′gōsh dȧ bō′ȧ vēs′tȧ) . Braz. (In.)	1.41 S	47.48 W

ăt; finăl; rāte; senâte; ärm; ȧsk; sofȧ; fâre; ch-choose; dh-as th in other; bē; êvent; bĕt; recĕnt; cratẽr; g-go; gh-gutteral g; bĭt; ĭ-short neutral; rīde; ᴋ-gutteral k as ch in German ich;

Page	Name Pronunciation Region	Lat. °′	Long. °′
102	São Felipe (souN fȧ-lē′pĕ)...Braz.	0.18 N	67.3 W
102	São Felipe...Braz.	6.30 S	70.1 W
103	São Felix (souN fȧ-lēks′) Braz. (In.)	12.40 S	39.0 W
103	São Francisco (souN frăN-sēsh′kŏŏ) Braz.	15.59 S	44.45 W
104	São Francisco...Braz.	26.15 S	48.35 W
103	São Francisco, R....Braz.	12.0 S	43.15 W
102	São Gabriel (gä-brē-ĕl′)...Braz.	0.12 S	67.1 W
103	São Gonçalo (gōŋ-sä′lŏŏ) Braz. (In.)	12.25 S	38.55 W
104	São Gonçalo de Niteroi (dā nē-tȧ-rŏŏ′ĭ). Braz. (In.)	22.50 S	43.4 W
103	São João (souN zhô-ouN′)...Braz.	5.30 S	48.58 W
103	São Joao d'el Rey (dĕl rĕ′ē)..Braz.	2.12 S	44.20 W
127	São João dos Lampas (souN′ zhô-ouN′ dōzh lăN′pȧzh) Port. (In.)	38.53 N	9.24 W
99	São José dos Campos (souN zhô-zā′ dōzh kăN′pōzh) Braz. (Rio de Janeiro In.)	23.10 S	45.56 W
138	São Jorge I. (souN zhôr′zhĕ) Az. Is. (In.)	38.35 N	28.0 W
99	São Luiz (souN lōō-ēzh′) Braz. (Rio de Janeiro In.)	23.8 S	45.12 W
103	São Luiz (Maranhão) (mȧ-răn-youN′). Braz.	2.30 S	44.12 W
103	São Luis de Cáceres (souN lōō-ēzh′ dā kä′sȧ-rāzh). Braz.	16.2 S	57.45 W
103	São Manoel, R. (souN mä-nô-ĕl′) Braz.	12.0 S	56.0 W
103	São Matheus (mä-tā′ŏŏzh)...Braz.	18.30 S	39.45 W
103	São Miguel (mē-gĕl′)...Braz. (In.)	13.3 S	39.32 W
138	São Miguel I....Az. Is. (In.)	37.45 N	25.30 W
97	Saona I. (sä-ō′nä)...Dom. Rep.	18.9 N	68.40 W
124	Saône R. (sōn)...Fr.	46.10 N	4.50 E
104	Sao Nicolás (sä′ō nē-kō-läs′)..Arg.	33.30 S	60.10 W
138	São Nicolão I. (souN′ nē-kō-louN′). Cape Verde Is. (In.)	16.36 N	24.15 W
103	São Paulo (pou′lŏŏ)...Braz.	23.31 S	46.31 W
103	São Paulo (State)...Braz.	22.0 S	49.0 W
	São Paulo de Luanda, see Luanda, Angola.		
102	São Paulo de Olivença (souN′ pou′lŏŏ dā ô-lē-vĕŋ′sȧ). Braz.	3.30 S	68.59 W
103	São Raymundo Nonato (souN′ rä-ê-mōōn′dŏŏ nō-nä′tŏŏ). Braz.	9.0 S	42.29 W
103	São Roque (rō′kĕ)...Braz.	5.3 S	35.30 W
103	São Salvador (Bahia) (sä-vȧ-dōr′) (bä-ē′ä). Braz. (In.)	13.0 S	38.30 W
99	São Sebastião (souN sȧ-bäs-tē-ouN′) Braz. (Rio de Janeiro In.)	23.48 S	45.26 W
99	São Sebastiao, Ilha de (I.) (ēl′yȧ dā souN′sȧ-bäs-tē ouN′) Braz. (Rio de Janeiro In.)	23.50 S	45.20 W
138	São Thiago I. (souN tē-ä′gŏŏ) Cape Verde Is. (In.)	15.10 N	23.40 W
138	São Thomé (souN tô-mā′) São Thomé I.	0.25 N	6.38 E
138	São Thomé I....Atr.	0.15 N	6.35 E
103	São Vicente do Araguaia (vē-sĕn′tē dŏŏ ä-rȧ-gwä′yȧ). Braz.	5.58 S	48.15 W
138	São Vicente I. (vē-sĕn′tĕ) Cape Verde Is. (In.)	16.50 N	25.0 W
138	Sapele (sȧ-pā′lā)...Nig.	5.42 N	5.27 E
163	Sapian B. (sä-pē-än′)...P. I.	11.31 N	122.36 E
130	Sapozhok (sȧ-pô-zhôk′)...Sov. Un.	53.56 N	40.41 E
158	Sapporo (säp′ô-rō)...Jap.	43.2 N	141.16 E
130	Sapskoe (säp′skō-yĕ)...Sov. Un.	54.12 N	40.54 E
99	Sapucahi, R. (sä-pōō-kä′ē) Braz. (Rio de Janeiro In.)	22.40 S	45.40 W
104	Sapucaia I. (sä-pōō-kä′yȧ) Braz. (In.)	22.52 S	43.13 W
79	Sapulpa (sȧ-pŭl′pȧ)...Okla.	36.0 N	96.5 W
141	Saqqara Pyramids (sä′kä-rä)..Eg.	29.52 N	31.12 E
163	Sara (sä′rä)...P. I.	11.14 N	123.1 E
129	Sarajevo (sä-rä-yĕv′ô) (sä-rä′yȧ-vô)...Yugo.	43.50 N	18.26 E
103	Saramacca R. (sä-rä-mäk′kä).Sur.	5.0 N	56.0 W
85	Saranac L....N. Y.	44.15 N	74.15 W
85	Saranac Lake (săr′ȧ-năk)...N. Y.	44.22 N	74.6 W
104	Sarandi (sä-rän′dē)...Arg. (In.)	34.41 S	58.21 W
99	Sarandi....Ur. (Buenos Aires In.)	33.20 S	55.53 W
163	Sarangani B. (sä-rän-gä′nē)..P. I.	5.50 N	125.10 E
163	Sarangani I....P. I.	5.27 N	125.28 E
112	Saransk (sȧ-ränsk′)...Sov. Un.	54.8 N	45.10 E
104	Sarapuhi (sä-rä-pōō′ē)..Braz. (In.)	22.45 S	43.17 W
104	Sarapuhi, R....Braz. (In.)	22.44 S	43.20 W
148	Sarapul (sä-rä′pōōl′)...Sov. Un.	56.30 N	53.50 E
158	Sarapulskoe (sä-rä-pōōl-skō′yĕ) Sov. Un.	48.55 N	136.12 E
83	Sarasota (săr-ȧ-sō′tȧ)...Fla. (In.)	27.20 N	82.30 W
81	Saratoga (săr-ȧ-tō′gȧ)...Tex.	30.18 N	94.30 W
49	Saratoga Passage Wash. (Seattle In.)	48.6 N	122.30 W
85	Saratoga Springs...N. Y.	43.5 N	73.8 W
113	Saratov (sä-rä′tôf)...Sov. Un.	51.30 N	45.55 E
163	Saravia (sä-rä′ vyä)...P. I.	10.51 N	123.0 E
160	Sarawak (sä-rä′wäk)...Pac. O.	2.30 N	113.30 E
123	Sárbogárd (sär′bô-gärd)...Hung.	46.52 N	18.39 E
125	Sarcelles (sär-sĕl′)...Fr. (In.)	48.59 N	2.23 E
128	Sardinia (I.) (sär-dĭn′ĭ-ȧ)...It.	40.0 N	9.0 E
72	Sardis (sär′dĭs) Can. (Vancouver In.)	49.8 N	121.58 W
82	Sardis...Miss.	34.28 N	89.55 W
76	Sargent (sär′jĕnt)...Neb.	41.39 N	99.22 W
124	Sariat (sä-rē-ä′)...Fr.	44.53 N	1.15 E
161	Sariaya (sä-rē-ä′yä) P. I. (Manila In.)	13.59 N	121.35 E
113	Sarikamiş (sä-rē-kä′mēsh)...Tur.	40.30 N	42.48 E
127	Sariñena (sä-rēn-yā′nä)...Sp.	41.47 N	0.10 W
157	Sariwon (sä′rē-wŏn′)...Cho.	38.33 N	125.43 E
124	Sark (I.) (särk)...Chan. Is.	49.30 N	2.20 W
113	Şarkî-Karahisar (shär′kē-kä-rä′hĭ-sär′). Tur.	40.12 N	38.30 E
129	Şarköy (shär′kû-ē)...Tur.	40.38 N	27.8 E
104	Sarmiento, Mt. (sär-myĕn′tō).Chl.	54.30 S	70.58 W
55	Sarnia (sär′nē-ȧ)...Can.	42.58 N	82.27 W
123	Sarny (sär′nē)...Pol.	51.17 N	26.39 E
129	Saronic G. (Aegina, G. of) (sȧ-rō′nĭk) (ē-jī′nȧ). Grc.	37.35 N	23.40 E
129	Saros, G. of (sä′rôs)...Tur.	40.30 N	26.30 E
123	Sárospatak (shä′rôsh-pô′tôk) Hung.	48.20 N	21.35 E
120	Sarpsborg (särps′bôrg)...Nor.	59.17 N	11.9 E
162	Sarrat (sär-rät′)...P. I.	18.10 N	120.38 E
125	Sarreguemines (sär-gē-mēn′)...Fr.	49.5 N	7.8 E
126	Sarria (sär′rē-ä)...Sp.	42.46 N	7.25 W
94	Sarstoom, R. (sär-stoom′) Guat.-Br. Hond.	15.53 N	89.20 W
124	Sartène (sär-tĕn′)...Cor. (In.)	41.35 N	9.5 E
124	Sarthe R. (särt)...Fr.	47.50 N	0.20 W
120	Sartor (Store Sotra) (I.) (sär′tôr) (stô′rĕ sôt′rä). Nor.	60.18 N	5.8 E
158	Sartu (sär′tōō′)...Manch.	46.30 N	125.12 E
122	Sárvár (shär′vär)...Hung.	47.15 N	16.53 E
148	Sary Ishik-Otrau Des. (sä′rē ē′shĕk-ô′trou)...Sov. Un.	46.0 N	77.0 E
148	Sary-su (R.) (sä′rē-sōō)..Sov. Un.	47.30 N	68.0 E
128	Sarzana (särt-sä′nä)...It.	44.6 N	9.57 E
151	Sasaram (sŭs-ŭ-räm′)...India	24.55 N	84.5 E
159	Sasayama (sä′sä-yä′mä)...Jap.	35.5 N	135.12 E
159	Sasebo (sä′sä-bô)...Jap.	33.15 N	129.45 E
119	Sasel (sä′sĕl)..Ger. (Hamburg In.)	53.39 N	10.6 E
129	Saseno (I.) (sä-sä′nō)...It.	40.30 N	19.17 E
54	Saskatchewan (Prov.) (săs-kăch′ē-wăn). Can.	54.0 N	106.0 W
54	Saskatchewan R., North...Can.	54.0 N	111.0 W
54	Saskatoon (săs-kȧ-tōōn′)...Can.	52.12 N	106.44 W
121	Sasmaka (säs′mȧ-kȧ)...Lat.	57.22 N	22.36 E
112	Sasovo (sä′sô-vô)...Sov. Un.	54.20 N	41.50 E
138	Sassandra R. (sȧs-săn′drȧ) Fr. W. Afr.	6.0 N	6.47 W
128	Sassari (säs′sä-rē)...Sard.	40.45 N	8.35 E
122	Sassnitz (säs′nēts)...Ger.	54.32 N	13.36 E
138	Satadougou (sä-tȧ-dōō′gōō) Fr. W. Afr.	12.34 N	11.26 W
158	Satano C. (sä′tȧ-nō)...Jap.	31.1 N	130.40 E
72	Satellite Channel (săt′ĕl-līt) Can. (Vancouver In.)	48.43 N	123.32 W
120	Säter (sĕ′tĕr)...Swe.	60.21 N	15.43 E
83	Satilla R. (sȧ-tĭl′ȧ)...Ga.	31.16 N	82.0 W
148	Satkinskii (sät′kĕn-skē-ĭ).Sov. Un.	55.10 N	58.59 E
123	Sátoraljaújhely (shä′tô-rô-lyô-ōō′hĕl′).Hung.	48.24 N	21.39 E
123	Satu-Mare (sȧ′tōō-mȧ′rȧ)...Rom.	47.49 N	22.52 E
72	Saturna I. (sȧ-tûr′nȧ) Can. (Vancouver In.)	48.48 N	123.9 W
120	Saude (sou′dĕ)...Nor.	59.40 N	6.21 E
150	Saudi Arabia (Nejd)...Asia	25.0 N	43.0 E
84	Saugatuck (sô′gȧ-tŭk)...Mich.	42.42 N	86.10 W
84	Saugeen Pen. (sô′gēn)...Can.	44.50 N	81.10 W
84	Saugeen R....Can.	44.10 N	81.2 W
85	Saugerties (sô′gĕr-tēz)...N. Y.	42.7 N	73.57 W
151	Saugor (sä-gŭr′) (sô-gōr′)...India	23.42 N	78.35 E
73	Saugus (sô′gŭs) Calif. (Los Angeles In.)	34.25 N	118.33 W
87	Saugus...Mass. (In.)	42.28 N	71. 1 W
77	Sauk Center (sôk)...Minn.	45.45 N	94.56 W
77	Sauk City...Wis.	43.16 N	89.42 W
77	Sauk Rapids...Minn.	45.36 N	94.8 W
77	Sauk R....Minn.	45.35 N	94.45 W
55	Sault Ste. Marie (sōō sănt mȧ′rĭ) Can.	46.38 N	84.20 W
88	Sault Ste. Marie...Mich. (In.)		
77	Sault Ste. Marie...Mich.	46.29 N	84.18 W
97	Saumatre, L. (sô-mät′r′)...Hai.	18.37 N	72.0 W
88	Saunders (sôn′dĕrz) Wis. (Duluth In.)	46.38 N	92.6 W
171	Saunders, C....N. Z. (In.)	45.53 S	170.46 E
114	Saura, Wadi (R.) (wä′dē sä-ōō′rä). Alg.	29.0 N	1.48 W
140	Saurimo (sä-ōō-rē′mō)...Ang.	9.32 S	20.31 E
74	Sausalito (sô-sȧ-lē′tō)...Calif.	37.50 N	122.33 W
6	Savaii (I.) (sä-vī′ē)...Sam. (In.)	13.36 S	172.30 W
77	Savanna (sȧ-văn′ȧ)...Ill.	42.5 N	90.9 W
89	Savannah...Ga. (In.)		
83	Savannah...Ga.	32.4 N	81.7 W
79	Savannah...Mo.	39.57 N	94.50 W
82	Savannah...Tenn.	35.13 N	88.16 W
89	Savannah Beach Ga. (Savannah In.)	32.0 N	80.51 W
83	Savannah R....Ga.-S. C.	33.30 N	82.0 W
96	Savanna la Mar (sȧ-vän′ȧ lȧ mär′). Jam.	18.12 N	78.9 W
128	Sava R. (sä′vä)...Yugo.	45.5 N	18.0 E
160	Savargalok (sä-vär′gȧ-lŏk′)..Thai.	17.18 N	99.45 E
138	Savé (sȧ-vā′)...Fr. W. Afr.	8.12 N	2.30 E
138	Savelou (sȧ-vē-lōō′)...Fr. W. Afr.	8.0 N	2.2 E
124	Save R. (säv)...Fr.	43.20 N	0.50 E
125	Saverne (sȧ-vĕrn′)...Fr.	48.45 N	7.25 E
128	Savigliano (sä-vēl-yä′nō)...It.	44.37 N	7.39 E
126	Saviñao (sä-vēn-yä′ō)...Sp.	42.35 N	7.39 W
160	Savoe Is. (sä′vōō)...Neth. Ind.	10.30 S	121.55 E
128	Savona (sä-vō′nä)...It.	44.17 N	8.30 E
121	Savonlinna (sä′vŏn-lēn-nȧ)...Fin.	61.54 N	28.51 E
131	Savran (säv-rän′)...Sov. Un.	48.7 N	30.4 E
160	Savu Sea...Neth. Ind.	9.30 S	122.0 E
139	Sawākin (Suakin) (sŭ-wä′kĕn) (swä′kĕn) A. E. Sud.	19.3 N	37.20 E
80	Sawtooth Mt. (sô′tōōth)...Tex.	30.45 N	104.18 W
86	Sawyer L. (sô′yĕr)...Me.	45.5 N	70.59 W
138	Say (sä′ē)...Fr. W. Afr.	13.12 N	21.12 E
148	Sayanski Mts. (sä-yän′skē) Sov. Un.-Chn.	53.30 N	95.0 E
73	Sayre (sā′ĕr) Ala. (Birmingham In.)	33.43 N	86.58 W
78	Sayre...Okla.	35.20 N	99.37 W
85	Sayre...Pa.	41.58 N	76.30 W
73	Sayreton (sā′ĕr-tŭn) Ala. (Birmingham In.)	33.34 N	86.50 W
93	Sayula (sä-yōō′lä)...Mex.	17.52 N	94.57 W
92	Sayula...Mex.	19.53 N	103.34 W
92	Sayula, L....Mex.	19.56 N	103.32 W
85	Sayville (sā′vĭl)...N. Y.	40.44 N	73.6 W
122	Sázava R. (säz′ȧ-vä)...Czech.	49.43 N	15.15 E
88	Scajaquada Cr. (skȧ-jȧ-kwä′dȧ) N. Y. (Niagara Falls In.)	42.55 N	78.51 W
49	Scappoose (skă-pōōs′) Ore. (Portland In.)	45.56 N	122.52 W
54	Scarboro Junction (skär′bŭr-ô) Can. (In.)	43.44 N	79.14 W
116	Scarborough...Gt. Brit.	54.18 N	0.25 W
113	Scarpanto (I.) (skär-păn′tō) Dodecanese Is.	35.40 N	27.10 E
89	Scarsdale (skärz′dāl) La. (New Orleans In.)	29.51 N	89.59 W
87	Scatari I. (skăt′ȧ-rē)...Can.	46.0 N	59.45 W
125	Sceaux (sō)...Fr. (In.)	48.46 N	2.17 E
117	Schaerbeek (skär-bāk)...Bel.	55.51 N	4.21 E
122	Schaffhausen (shäf′hou-zĕn) Switz.	47.43 N	8.38 E
166	Schanck, C. (shănk)...Austl.	38.30 S	144.53 E
117	Scheldt R. (skĕlt)...Bel.	50.50 N	3.30 E
85	Schenectady (skĕ-nĕk′tȧ-dē).N. Y.	42.48 N	73.56 W
119	Schenefeld (shĕ′nĕ-fĕlt) Ger. (Hamburg In.)	53.36 N	9.49 E
119	Schiffbek (shĭf′bĕk) Ger. (Hamburg In.)	53.32 N	10.6 E
119	Schilde (skĕl′dĕ). Bel. (Anvers In.)	51.14 N	4.35 E
125	Schiltigheim (shĕl′tēgh-hĭm)...Fr.	48.40 N	7.50 E
128	Schio (skē′ō)...It.	45.43 N	11.22 E
122	Schivelbein (shĭ′fĕl-bīn)...Ger.	53.47 N	15.47 E
122	Schlawe (shlä′vĕ)...Ger.	54.21 N	16.39 E
122	Schlesien (Silesia) (Prov.) (shlā′zē-ĕn) (sĭ-lē′shȧ) Ger.	50.55 N	17.0 E
122	Schleswig (shlās′vēgh)...Ger.	54.31 N	9.33 E
122	Schleswig-Holstein (Prov.) (shlās′wēgh-hōl′shtīn) Ger.	54.25 N	9.30 E
122	Schmalkalden (shmäl′käl-dĕn) Ger.	50.43 N	10.27 E
122	Schneidemühl (shnī′dĕ-mül)..Ger.	53.8 N	16.42 E
119	Schnelsen (shnĕl′sĕn) Ger. (Hamburg In.)	53.38 N	9.55 E
77	Schofield (skō′fēld)...Wis.	44.55 N	89.35 W
122	Schönebeck (shû′nĕ-bĕk)...Ger.	52.1 N	11.42 E
119	Schöneberg (shû′nĕ-bĕrgh) Ger. (Berlin In.)	52.29 N	13.17 E
122	Schönlanke (shûn-läŋ′kĕ)...Ger.	53.3 N	16.26 E
143	Schoombie (skōm′byĕ)..U. S. Afr.	31.27 S	25.28 E
119	Schooten (skō′tĕn) Bel. (Anvers In.)	51.15 N	4.30 E
169	Schouten I. (shōō′tĕn) Austl. (Tas. In.)	42.20 S	148.20 E
161	Schouten Is. (skou′tĕn)Neth...Ind.	1.0 S	136.0 E
117	Schouwen (I.) (skou′vĕn)...Neth.	51.45 N	3.55 W
122	Schramberg (shräm′bĕrgh)...Ger.	48.14 N	8.24 E
85	Schroon L. (skrōōn)...N. Y.	43.50 N	73.46 W
119	Schulau (shōō′lou) Ger. (Hamburg In.)	53.34 N	9.42 E
76	Schuyler (skī′lĕr)...Neb.	41.27 N	97.5 W
85	Schuylkill Haven (skōōl′kĭl)...Pa.	40.37 N	76.12 W
88	Schuylkill R.Pa. (Philadelphia In.)	39.59 N	75.12 W
122	Schwabach (shvä′bäk)...Ger.	49.20 N	11.0 E
122	Schwandorf (shvän′dôrf)...Ger.	49.19 N	12.8 E
160	Schwaner Mts. (skvän′ĕr) Neth. Ind.	1.30 S	111.30 E
122	Schwaz (shväts)...Ger.	47.20 N	11.43 E
122	Schwechat (shvĕk′ät)...Ger.	48.8 N	16.28 E
122	Schwedt (shvĕt)...Ger.	53.3 N	14.16 E
122	Schweidnitz (shvīt′nēts)...Ger.	50.50 N	16.28 E
122	Schweinfurt (shvīn′fōōrt)...Ger.	50.3 N	10.13 E
143	Schweizer Reneke (shvīt-sĕr rĕn′ĕ-kē) U. S. Afr.	27.2 S	25.22 E
122	Schwenningen (shvĕn′ĭng-ĕn).Ger.	48.4 N	8.33 E
122	Schwerin (shvȧ-rēn′)...Ger.	52.35 N	15.31 E
122	Schwerin...Ger.	53.37 N	11.23 E
122	Schwerin, L....Ger.	53.42 N	11.27 E
122	Schwiebus (shvē′bōōs)...Ger.	52.16 N	15.36 E
122	Schwyz (shvēts)...Switz.	47.1 N	8.39 E
128	Sciacca (shē-äk′kä)...It.	37.30 N	13.5 E
116	Scilly I. (sĭl′ē)...Gt. Brit.	49.55 N	6.25 W
84	Scioto R. (sī-ō′tō)...Ohio	39.6 N	83.0 W
84	Sciotoville (sī-ō′tō-vĭl)...Ohio	38.45 N	82.46 W
87	Scituate (sĭt′ū-āt)...Mass. (In.)	42.12 N	70.45 W
71	Scobey (skō′bē)...Mont.	48.48 N	105.28 W
167	Scone (skōn)...Austl.	32.4 S	150.52 E
70	Scotia (skō′shȧ)...Calif.	40.29 N	124.5 W
116	Scotland (Division) (skŏt′lȧnd) Gt. Brit.	48.35 N	3.20 W
76	Scotland...S. D.	43.9 N	97.42 W
83	Scotland Neck...N. C.	36.8 N	77.24 W
86	Scotstown (skŏts′toun)...Can.	45.32 N	71.18 W
143	Scottburgh (skŏt′bûrg)..U. S. Afr.	30.19 S	30.44 E
54	Scott, C. (skŏt)...Can.	50.45 N	128.17 W
78	Scott City...Kan.	38.28 N	100.53 W
73	Scottdale (skŏt′dāl) Ga. (Atlanta In.)	33.47 N	84.16 W
46	Scott I....Ant. O.	67.0 S	179.0 W
70	Scott, Mt....Ore.	42.56 N	122.1 W
76	Scottsbluff (skŏts′blŭf)...Neb.	41.52 N	103.39 W
76	Scotts Bluff Natl. Mon....Neb.	41.50 N	103.42 W
82	Scottsboro (skŏts′bŭr-ô)...Ala.	34.40 N	86.3 W
84	Scottsburg (skŏts′bûrg)...Ind.	38.41 N	85.47 W
166	Scotts Cr....Austl.	30.33 S	138.18 E
169	Scottsdale (skŏts′dāl) Austl. (Tas. In.)	41.8 S	147.30 E
82	Scottsville (skŏts′vĭl)...Ky.	36.46 N	86.11 W
84	Scottville (skŏt′vĭl)...Mich.	43.59 N	86.19 W
85	Scranton (skrăn′tŭn)...Pa.	41.24 N	75.42 W
76	Scribner (skrĭb′nĕr)...Neb.	41.40 N	96.39 W
46	Scripps I. (skrĭps)...Ant. O.	70.0 S	64.0 W

ng-sing; ŋ-baŋk; N-nasalized n; nŏd; cŏmmit; ōld; ôbey; ôrder; fōōd; fŏŏt; ou-out; s-soft; sh-dish; th-thin; pūre; ûnite; ûrn; stŭd; circŭs; ü-as "y" in study; ′-indeterminate vowel.

Page	Name Pronunciation Region	Lat. °'	Long. °'
85	Scugog L. (skū'gôg) .... Can.	44.10 N	78.50 W
118	Scunthorpe (skŭn'thôrp) . Gt. Brit.	53.36 N	0.38 W
129	Scutari (Shkodër) (skōō'tä-rē) (shkō'dûr) Alb.	42.3 N	19.31 E
129	Scutari, L. .... Alb.-Yugo.	42.10 N	19.20 E
49	Seabeck (sē'bĕck) Wash. (Seattle In.)	47.37 N	122.49 W
81	Seabrook (sē'brŏŏk) .... Tex. (In.)	29.34 N	95.1 W
85	Seaford (sē'fērd) .... Del.	38.37 N	75.40 W
80	Seagraves (sē'grāvs) .... Tex.	32.55 N	102.34 W
72	Sea I. (Sē) .. Can. (Vancouver In.)	49.12 N	123.10 W
73	Seal Beach (sēl) Calif. (Los Angeles In.)	33.45 N	118.5 W
142	Seal, C. .... U. S. Afr.	34.6 S	23.23 E
97	Seal Cays (Is.) .... Ba. Is.	21.11 N	71.42 W
81	Sealey (sē'lē) .... Tex.	29.46 N	96.8 W
171	Seal Pt. (sēl) .... N. Z. (In.)	45.54 S	170.39 E
54	Seal R. .... Can.	59.0 N	96.30 W
141	Sea Pt. .... U. S. Afr.	33.54 S	18.23 E
79	Searcy (sûr'sē) .... Ark.	35.14 N	91.43 W
73	Searles (sûrlz) Ala. (Birmingham In.)	33.18 N	87.18 W
86	Searsport (sērz'pōrt) .... Me.	44.30 N	68.55 W
70	Seaside (sē'sīd) .... Ore.	45.59 N	123.55 W
49	Seattle (sē-ăt''l) ...... Wash. (In.)		
70	Seattle .... Wash.	47.45 N	122.25 W
49	Seaview (sē'vū) Wash. (Portland In.)	46.20 N	124.2 W
165	Seaview, Mt. .... Austl.	31.20 S	152.5 E
86	Sebago L. (sē-bā'gō) .... Me.	43.50 N	70.38 W
166	Sebastopol (sē-băs'tō-pōl) ... Austl.	37.35 S	143.49 E
74	Sebastopol .... Calif.	38.26 N	122.51 W
128	Sebenico (Šibenik) (sā-bā'nē-kō) (shē'bē-nēk) Yugo.	43.44 N	15.54 E
123	Sebeşul (sā-bā'shŏŏl) .... Rom.	45.57 N	23.33 E
160	Sebetik I. (sē-bē'tĭk) .... B. N. B.	4.15 N	117.45 E
84	Sebewaing (sē'bē-wăng) .... Mich.	43.45 N	83.26 W
130	Sebezh (syĕ'bĕzh) .... Sov. Un.	56.16 N	28.31 E
122	Sebnitz (zĕb'nēts) .... Ger.	51.0 N	14.14 E
84	Sebree (sē-brē') .... Ky.	38.37 N	87.31 W
83	Sebring (sē'brĭng) .... Fla. (In.)	27.30 N	81.26 W
84	Sebring .... Ohio	40.57 N	81.3 W
138	Sebu, Wadi (R.) (wăd'dē sā'bōō) Mor.	34.0 N	4.30 W
72	Sechelt (sē'chĕlt) Can. (Vancouver In.)	49.28 N	123.46 W
72	Sechelt Inlet Can. (Vancouver In.)	49.36 N	123.50 W
72	Sechelt Inlet, Salmon Arm Can. (Vancouver In.)	49.39 N	123.45 W
171	Secretary I. (sĕk'rē-tâ-rē) ... N. Z.	45.12 S	166.55 E
151	Secunderabad (sē-kŭn'dēr-ā-băd') India	17.30 N	78.29 E
72	Sedalia (sē-dā'lē-ā) Colo. (Denver In.)	39.27 N	104.58 W
79	Sedalia .... Mo.	38.43 N	93.12 W
166	Sedan (sē-dăn') .... Austl.	34.35 S	139.17 E
124	Sedan (sē-däN') .... Fr.	49.45 N	5.0 E
79	Sedan (sē-dăn') .... Kan.	37.7 N	96.10 W
118	Sedgley (sĕdj'lĭ) .... Gt. Brit.	52.32 N	2.7 W
70	Sedro-Woolley (sē'drō-wŏŏl'ē) Wash.	48.30 N	122.15 W
121	Šeduva (shĕ-dōō'vā) .... Lith.	55.44 N	23.48 E
119	Seeburg (zā'bŏŏrgh) Ger. (Berlin In.)	52.31 N	13.7 E
119	Seegefeld (zā'gē-fĕlt) Ger. (Berlin In.)	52.34 N	13.6 E
142	Seeheim (zā'hīm) ...... S. W. Afr.	26.48 S	17.48 E
114	Sefrou (sē-frōō') .... Mor.	33.42 N	4.45 W
163	Segama R. (sā-gä'mä) .... B. N. B.	5.10 N	118.22 E
145	Segamat (sā'gà-măt) Non-fed. Mal. St. (In.)	2.31 N	102.48 E
159	Segawa (sē'gā-wä) Jap. (Osaka In.)	34.49 N	135.27 E
138	Segiet el-Hamra (R.) (sē-gyĕt' ĕl-häm'rà) R. de O.	26.40 N	11.30 W
112	Seg, L. (syĕgh) .... Sov. Un.	63.20 N	33.30 E
127	Segorbe (sā-gōr'bā) .... Sp.	39.51 N	0.29 W
138	Ségou (sā-gōō') .... Fr. W. Afr.	13.30 N	6.23 W
126	Segovia (sā-gō'vē-ā) .... Sp.	40.57 N	4.7 W
94	Segovia, R. (R. Coco or Wanks) (rē'ō kō'kō, rē'ō wänks) Hond.-Nic.	14.30 N	85.0 W
124	Segré (sē-grā') .... Fr.	47.40 N	0.52 W
127	Segre R. (sā'grā) .... Sp.	41.40 N	0.40 E
138	Séguéla (sā-gā'lä) ..... Fr. W. Afr.	8.2 N	6.40 W
80	Seguin (sē-gēn') .... Tex.	29.35 N	97.58 W
126	Segura R. (sā-gōō'rä) .... Sp.	38.25 N	2.0 W
131	Seim R. (sā'ēm) .... Sov. Un.	51.19 N	33.0 E
121	Seinäjoka (sā'ē-nĕ-yō'kē) ..... Fin.	62.47 N	22.46 E
125	Seine (sān) .... Fr. (In.)	48.46 N	2.25 E
124	Seine, B. of the .... Fr.	49.30 N	0.30 W
77	Seine R. .... Can.	49.0 N	91.0 W
124	Seine R. .... Fr.	48.25 N	3.0 E
158	Seishin (sī'shĭn') .... Cho.	41.50 N	129.46 E
157	Seishu (sī'shōō') .... Cho.	36.40 N	127.29 E
127	Seixal (sā-ē-shäl') ...... Port. (In.)	38.38 N	9.6 W
138	Sekondi (sē-kōn'dē) .... G. C.	4.58 N	1.42 W
145	Selangor (State) (sā-läŋ'gōr) Fed. Mal. States (In.)	2.55 N	101.35 E
129	Selanovci (sāl'à-nôf-tsē) ...... Bul.	43.40 N	24.3 E
161	Selaroe (I.) (sā-lā'rōō) .. Neth. Ind.	8.20 S	131.10 E
160	Selatan, C. (sē-lä'tän) .. Neth. Ind.	4.14 S	114.44 E
122	Selb (zĕlp) .... Ger.	50.11 N	12.6 E
120	Selbu, L. (sĕl'bōō) .... Nor.	63.15 N	10.50 E
118	Selby (sĕl'bē) .... Gt. Brit.	53.47 N	1.3 W
53	Seldovia (sĕl-dō'vē-ā) .... Alsk.	59.25 N	151.30 W
149	Selegnyakh R. (sā-lĕk-nyäk') Sov. Un.	67.25 N	141.0 E
149	Selemdzha R. (sā-lĕmt-zhä') Sov. Un.	52.25 N	130.0 E
152	Selenga R. (sĕ-lĕŋ-gä') Chn.-Sov. Un.	49.30 N	104.0 E
125	Selestat (sā-lē-stä') .... Fr.	48.15 N	7.30 E
150	Seleucia (Ruins) (sē-lū'shĭ-ā) . Iraq.	33.0 N	44.30 E
138	Sélibaby (sā-lē-bà-bē') Fr. W. Afr.	15.20 N	12.9 W
130	Seliger, L. (sĕl'lē-gĕr) .... Sov. Un.	57.18 N	33.0 E
130	Selizharovo (sā'lē-zhä-rō-vō) Sov. Un.	56.49 N	33.28 E
54	Selkirk (sĕl'kûrk) .... Can.	50.12 N	96.59 W
54	Selkirk .... Can.	62.45 N	137.30 W
116	Selkirk .... Gt. Brit.	55.35 N	2.55 W
54	Selkirk Mts. .... Can.	50.48 N	117.30 W
139	Sella (sĕl'à) .... Libya	28.25 N	17.50 E
135	Selloum, Djebel (Mts.) (jĕb'ĕl sĕl-lōōm') . Tun. (In.)	35.0 N	8.55 E
149	Sellyakhskaya B. (sāl'lyäk-skà-yà) . Sov. Un.	71.35 N	139.50 E
82	Selma (sĕl'mà) .... Ala.	32.24 N	87.0 W
74	Selma .... Calif.	36.33 N	119.37 W
83	Selma .... N. C.	35.33 N	78.17 W
140	Selukwe (sē-lŭk'wē) .... S. Rh.	19.42 S	30.3 E
70	Selway R. (sĕl'wā) .... Ida.	46.5 N	115.10 W
54	Selwyn L. (sĕl'wĭn) .... Can.	60.0 N	104.50 W
160	Semarang (sē-mä'räng) Neth. Ind.	7.5 S	110.28 E
135	Semellawia (sē-mē-lä'wē-ā) Eg. (In.)	30.45 N	31.30 E
139	Semendria (Smederevo) (sē-mĕn'-drē-ä) (smĕ'dĕ-rē-vō) . Yugo.	44.38 N	20.57 E
129	Semeni Devol R. (sā'mĕ-nē dā'vōl) . Alb.	40.44 N	20.25 E
131	Semenovka (sā'mĕ-nôf-kà) Sov. Un.	52.9 N	32.36 E
160	Semeru Mt. (Vol.) (sĕm'ēr-ōō) Neth. Ind.	8.5 S	112.58 E
71	Seminoe Reservoir (sĕm'-ĭ-nō) Wyo.	42.20 N	106.53 W
79	Seminole (sĕm'ĭ-nōl) .... Okla.	35.13 N	96.39 W
83	Seminole Ind. Res. ...... Fla. (In.)	26.16 N	81.0 W
112	Semiostrovskaya (sē-mē-ôs'trôf-skà-yà) . Sov. Un.	68.40 N	37.32 E
148	Semipalatinsk (sā'mē-pà-lä-tĕnsk') Sov. Un.	50.25 N	80.20 E
163	Semirara I. (sā-mē'rä-rä) .... P. I.	12.3 N	121.23 E
163	Semirara Is. .... P. I.	11.55 N	121.33 E
148	Semiyarskaya (sā'mē-yär'skà-yà) Sov. Un.	50.59 N	78.25 E
139	Semliki R. (sĕm'lē-kē) Bel. Cong.-Ug.	1.30 N	30.30 E
129	Semlin (Zemun) (zĕm-lēn') (zā'mōōn) . Yugo.	44.50 N	20.25 E
122	Semmering Pass (zĕm'ēr-ĭng) . Ger.	47.38 N	15.50 E
82	Senatobia (sĕ-nà-tō'bē-ā) .... Miss.	34.36 N	89.58 W
158	Sendai (sĕn-dī') .... Jap.	38.17 N	140.55 E
79	Seneca (sĕn'ē-kà) .... Kan.	39.49 N	96.4 W
82	Seneca .... S. C.	34.40 N	83.0 W
85	Seneca Falls .... N. Y.	42.57 N	76.57 W
85	Seneca L. .... N. Y.	42.40 N	76.55 W
138	Senegal (Prov.) (sĕn-ē-gôl') Fr. W. Afr.	14.0 N	14.0 W
138	Senegal R. .... Fr. W. Afr.	15.30 N	13.0 W
143	Senekal (sĕn'ē-kăl) .... U. S. Afr.	28.19 S	27.39 E
122	Senftenberg (zĕnf'tĕn-bĕrgh) .. Ger.	51.32 N	14.1 E
128	Senigallia (sā-nē-gäl'lyä) .... It.	43.43 N	13.11 E
128	Senj (sĕn') .... Yugo.	44.59 N	14.54 E
110	Senjen (I.) (sĕn'yĕn) .... Nor.	69.15 N	17.30 E
159	Senju (sĕn'jōō) ... Jap. (Tokyo In.)	35.45 N	139.48 E
124	Senlis (säN-lēs') .... Fr.	49.15 N	2.35 E
125	Senlisse (säN-lēs') .... Fr. (In.)	48.41 N	1.58 E
139	Sennār (sĕn-när') .... A. E. Sud.	13.33 N	33.31 E
139	Sennar Dam .... A. E. Sud.	13.33 N	33.31 E
130	Senno (sā'nō) .... Sov. Un.	54.47 N	29.42 E
124	Sens (säNs) .... Fr.	48.11 N	3.18 E
123	Sensburg (zĕns'bōōrgh) .... Ger.	53.52 N	21.18 E
157	Sensen (Sunchun) (sĕn'sĕn sōōn'chōōn) .. Cho.	39.48 N	124.58 E
94	Sensuntepeque (sĕn-sōōn-tà-pā'-kā) . Sal.	13.53 N	88.33 W
129	Senta (sĕn'tä) .... Yugo.	45.55 N	20.5 E
127	Seo de Urgel (sā'ō dā ōōr-hāl') Sp.	42.23 N	1.28 E
157	Seoul (Keijo) (sē-ōōl') (kā'jō') Cho.	37.38 N	127.0 E
171	Separation Pt. (sĕp-à-rā'shŭn) N. Z.	40.45 S	173.0 E
99	Sepetiba B. (sā-pà-tē'bà) Braz. (Rio de Janeiro In.)	23.0 S	43.50 W
161	Sepik R. (sĕp-ēk') ..... N. Gu. Ter.	4.2 S	143.0 E
82	Sequatchie R. (sē-kwăch'ē) .. Tenn.	35.26 N	85.20 W
49	Sequim (sē'kwĭm) Wash. (Seattle In.)	48.5 N	123.7 W
74	Sequoia (sē-kwoi'à) .... Calif.	36.30 N	118.40 W
117	Seraing (sē-răN') .... Bel.	50.35 N	5.51 E
160	Serang (sā-räng') .... Neth. Ind.	6.8 S	106.8 E
126	Serantes (sā-rän'tās) .... Sp.	43.23 N	8.21 W
129	Serbia (Prov.) (sûr'bĭ-ā) .... Yugo.	43.40 N	20.40 E
113	Serdobsk (sĕr-dôpsk') ..... Sov. Un.	52.28 N	44.20 E
123	Sered (sĕr'ĕd) .... Czech.	48.17 N	17.43 E
130	Sereda (sĕ-rā-dà') .... Sov. Un.	57.15 N	41.9 E
131	Seredina-Buda (sā-rā-dē'nà-bōō'dà) ... Sov. Un.	52.10 N	34.2 E
145	Seremban (sĕr-ĕm-băn') Fed. Mal. States (In.)	2.44 N	101.55 E
104	Serena (sā-rā'nä) .... Chl.	29.50 S	71.20 W
140	Serenje (sē-rĕn'yē) .... N. Rh.	13.9 S	30.47 E
141	Serenli (sā-rĕn'lē) ...... It. E. Afr.	2.20 N	42.15 E
129	Seres (Serrai) (sĕr'ĕs) (sĕr'ĕ) .. Grc.	41.5 N	23.35 E
123	Seret R. (sĕr'ĕt) .... Pol.	49.16 N	25.40 E
112	Sergievsk (syĕr-gē'yĕfsk) . Sov. Un.	53.58 N	51.2 E
148	Sergiopol (syĕr-gē'ō-pōl) . Sov. Un.	48.5 N	80.20 E
151	Seringapatam (sē-rĭŋ-gà-pà-tăm') India	12.28 N	76.37 E
129	Seriphos (sē-rē'fôs) .... Grc.	37.8 N	24.31 E
129	Seriphos (I.) .... Grc.	37.10 N	25.30 E
103	Serilpe (State) (sĕr-zhē'pē) .. Braz.	11.0 S	37.15 W
143	Serobanyane (sē'rō-băn-yà'nâ) Bas.	29.18 S	29.5 E
126	Seron (sā-rōn') .... Sp.	37.21 N	2.29 W
140	Sercwe (sē-rō'wē) .... Bech.	22.25 S	26.40 E
126	Serpa (sĕr'pà) .... Port.	37.56 N	7.36 W
130	Serpukhov (syĕr'pŏŏ-kôf) Sov. Un.	54.55 N	37.25 E
129	Serrai (Seres) (sĕr'rĕ) (sĕr'ĕs) . Grc.	41.5 N	23.35 E
135	Serrat, C. (sĕr-rāt') .... Tun. (In.)	37.12 N	9.18 E
103	Serrinha (sĕr-sēn'yà) ... Braz. (In.)	11.39 S	38.58 W
103	Serro (sĕr'rō) .... Braz.	18.31 S	43.20 W
126	Serta (sĕr'tà) .... Port.	39.49 N	8.1 W
161	Serua (I.) (sē-rōō'à) .... Neth. Ind.	6.28 S	130.1 E
141	Sesebani (sĕ'sĕ-bà'nē) ... It. E. Afr.	8.0 N	43.40 E
128	Sesia R. (sâz'yä) .... It.	45.35 N	8.24 E
128	Sesto (sĕs'tō) .... It.	43.49 N	11.14 E
128	Sestri Levante (sĕs'trē lā-vän'tā) It.	44.16 N	9.24 E
124	Sète (Cette) (sĕt) .... Fr.	43.25 N	3.45 E
138	Sétif (sā-tēf') .... Alg.	36.18 N	5.22 E
159	Seto (sē'tō') .... Jap.	35.14 N	137.5 E
138	Settat (sĕt-ăt') (sē-tà') ...... Mor.	33.0 N	7.28 W
140	Sette-Cama (sā'tē-kà'mä) Fr. Eq. Afr.	2.29 S	9.45 E
118	Settle (sĕt''l) .... Gt. Brit.	54.4 N	2.16 W
96	Settlement Pt. (sĕt''l-mĕnt). Ba. Is.	26.42 N	79.0 W
127	Setúbal (sā-tōō'bāl) .... Port. (In.)	38.32 N	8.54 W
127	Setúbal, B. of .... Port. (In.)	38.26 N	8.54 W
55	Seul, Lac (L.) (lák sûl) ...... Can.	50.35 N	92.30 W
120	Sevalen (L.) (sē'vā-lĕn) ...... Nor.	62.16 N	10.28 E
131	Sevastopol (Akhiar) (syĕ-vás-tô'-pōl') (äk'yär) . Sov. Un.	44.35 N	33.32 E
86	Seven Islands .... Can.	50.12 N	66.23 W
159	Seven (Kozushima) Is. (kō'zōō-shē'mä) . Jap.	34.12 N	139.8 E
72	Severance (sĕv'ĕr-ăns) Colo. (Denver In.)	40.32 N	104.51 W
116	Severn (R.) .... Gt. Brit.	51.40 N	2.20 W
149	Severnaya Zemlya (Northern Land) (sā'vĕr-nà-yà zĕm'lya) ... Sov. Un.	79.0 N	103.0 E
169	Severn R. (sĕv'ĕrn) ... Austl. (In.)	29.23 S	151.20 E
55	Severn R. .... Can.	54.30 N	89.30 W
75	Sevier L. (sē-vēr') .... Utah	39.0 N	113.10 W
75	Sevier R. .... Utah	39.35 N	112.25 W
75	Sevier R., East Fork .... Utah	37.50 N	112.5 W
126	Sevilla (sā-vēl'yä) .... Sp.	37.25 N	5.58 W
129	Sevlievo (sĕv-lē'ĕ-vō) .... Bul.	43.2 N	25.6 E
125	Sevran (sĕ-vräN') .... Fr. (In.)	48.56 N	2.33 E
124	Sèvre Niortaise R. (sâ'vr' nyôr-tâz') . Fr.	46.20 N	0.50 W
124	Sèvre R. .... Fr.	47.5 N	1.15 W
131	Sevsk (syĕfsk) .... Sov. Un.	52.8 N	34.30 E
89	Sewall Pt. (sū'ăl) Va. (Norfolk In.)	36.57 N	76.19 W
52	Seward (sū'ārd) ...... Alsk. (In.)	60.7 N	149.20 W
76	Seward .... Neb.	40.55 N	97.5 W
52	Seward Pen. .... Alsk.	65.20 N	163.0 W
89	Sewickly (sē-wĭk'lē) Pa. (Pittsburgh In.)	40.32 N	80.12 W
161	Sexmoan (sĕx-mō-ăn') P. I. (Manila In.)	14.57 N	120.33 E
93	Seybaplaya (sā-ē-bà-plä'yà) .. Mex.	19.40 N	90.41 W
7	Seychelles (Is.) (sā-shĕl') .. Ind. O.	5.20 S	55.10 E
110	Seydisfjördur (sā'dēs-fyûr-dōōr) Ice.	65.22 N	13.58 W
167	Seymour (sē'mōr) .... Austl.	37.1 S	145.8 E
84	Seymour .... Ind.	38.57 N	85.52 W
77	Seymour .... Ia.	40.41 N	93.7 W
78	Seymour .... Tex.	33.35 N	99.15 W
143	Seymour .... U. S. Afr.	32.34 S	26.47 E
72	Seymour Cr. Can. (Vancouver In.)	49.30 N	123.0 W
124	Sézanne (sā-zăn') .... Fr.	48.40 N	3.42 E
128	Sezze (sĕt'sā) .... It.	41.30 N	13.3 E
123	Sfantul-Gheorghe (sfŭên'tōōl-gyôr'gā) . Rom.	45.53 N	25.47 E
138	Sfax (sfäks) .... Tun.	34.47 N	10.46 E
117	's Gravenhage (The Hague) ('s Krä-vĕn-hä'gē) (hāg) . Neth.	52.5 N	4.20 E
135	Sguenaia (sgē-nī'à) Sp. Mor. (Gib. In.)	35.40 N	5.52 W
73	Shades Cr. (shādz) Ala. (Birmingham In.)	33.18 N	86.58 W
73	Shades Mt. Ala. (Birmingham In.)	33.17 N	86.57 W
148	Shadrinsk (shà-drĕnsk') .. Sov. Un.	56.15 N	63.35 E
150	Shagra (shäg'rà) .... Sau. Ar.	25.15 N	45.15 E
46	Shag Rocks .... Ant. O.	52.0 S	43.0 W
151	Shahjahanpur (shä-jŭ-hän'pōōr) India	27.45 N	79.58 E
150	Shahreza (shä-rā'zä) .... Iran	32.0 N	51.59 E
150	Shahrud (shä'rōōd) .... Iran	36.15 N	54.47 E
155	Shahsien (shä'hsyĕn') .... Chn.	26.23 N	117.41 E
89	Shaker Heights (shā'kēr) Ohio (Cleveland In.)	41.29 N	81.32 W
113	Shakhova, C. (shä'kô-và) Sov. Un.	40.15 N	50.20 E
131	Shakhty (shäk'tē) .... Sov. Un.	47.43 N	40.12 E
156	Shakien (shä'kyĕn') .... Chn.	39.11 N	113.13 E
131	Shaknyal (shäk'nyăl) ..... Sov. Un.	45.2 N	34.40 E
77	Shakopee (shăk'ō-pē) .... Minn.	44.46 N	93.30 W
148	Shakrizyabs (shà-krē-zyăps') Sov. Un.	39.15 N	66.45 E
151	Shal (Quetta) (shäl) (kwĕt'ā) India	30.20 N	67.12 E
139	Shala, L. (shä'là) ...... It. E. Afr.	7.30 N	38.30 E
135	Shallufa (shăl'lōō-fà) Eg. (Suez Canal In.)	30.9 N	32.33 E
139	Shambe (shăm'bà) ...... A. E. Sud.	7.8 N	30.40 E
150	Sham, Jebel (Mt.) (jĕb'ĕl shăm') Oman	23.4 N	57.59 E
150	Shammar, Jebel (Mts.) (jĕb'ĕl shŭm'ăr) Sau. Ar.	27.15 N	41.30 E
152	Shamo, see Gobi		
85	Shamokin (shà-mō'kĭn) .... Pa.	40.47 N	76.33 W
78	Shamrock (shăm'rŏk) .... Tex.	35.14 N	100.14 W
140	Shamva (shăm'vā) .... S. Rh.	17.27 S	31.33 E
156	Shangcheng (shăng'chĕng') .. Chn.	31.54 N	115.23 E

ăt; finăl; rāte; senâte; ärm; ȧsk; sofȧ; fâre; ch-choose; dh-as th in other; bē; ēvent; bĕt; recĕnt; cratēr; g-go; gh-gutteral g; bĭt; ĭ-short neutral; rīde; K-gutteral k as ch in German ich;

Page	Name Pronunciation Region	Lat. °′	Long. °′
153	Shanghai, (shäng'hī') Chn. (In.)		
155	Shanghai ....Chn.	31.10 N	121.28 E
155	Shanghang (shäng'häng')....Chn.	24.59 N	116.12 E
156	Shangho (shäng'hō')........Chn.	37.18 N	117.6 E
155	Shangkao (shäng'kou')......Chn.	28.8 N	114.42 E
154	Shanglin (shäng'lēn') ....Chn.	23.30 N	107.25 E
154	Shanglin....Chn.	23.30 N	108.44 E
156	Shangshui (shäng'shwē').....Chn.	33.41 N	114.35 E
156	Shangtsai (shäng'tsī')......Chn.	33.16 N	114.14 E
154	Shangyü (shäng'yü) ....Chn.	25.59 N	114.5 E
155	Shangyu (shäng'yōō').......Chn.	29.58 N	120.58 E
156	Shanhaikwan (shän'hī'kwän') Chn.	39.59 N	119.30 E
156	Shanhsien (shän'hsyĕn').....Chn.	34.50 N	116.4 E
73	Shannon (shăn'ŭn)..........Ala.	33.24 N	86.52 W
170	Shannon....N. Z.	40.28 S	175.23 E
116	Shannon, R....Ire.	52.80 N	9.0 W
152	Shanshan (Pichan) (shän'shän') (pē'chän').Chn.	42.40 N	90.4 E
153	Shansi (Prov.) (shän'sē').....Chn.	37.0 N	112.0 E
149	Shantar I. (shän'tär) ....Sov. Un.	55.0 N	137.30 E
156	Shantung (Prov.) (shän'tŏŏng') Chn.	36.10 N	118.10 E
156	Shantung Pen....Asia	37.0 N	121.0 E
157	Shantung Pt....Chn.	37.25 N	122.38 E
155	Shaohing (shou'hĭng') ....Chn.	30.3 N	120.40 E
156	Shaopo (shä'ō-pō')..........Chn.	32.33 N	119.31 E
155	Shaowu (shou'wōō')..........Chn.	27.20 N	117.20 E
156	Sha R. (shä)....Chn.	32.47 N	116.0 E
156	Sha R....Chn.	38.40 N	114.27 E
153	Sharasume (shä-rä-sōō'mä) ..Chn.	47.48 N	88.5 E
150	Shardjah (shär'jä).........Oman	25.20 N	55.29 E
139	Shari R. (shä'rē).....Fr. Eq. Afr.	10.30 N	16.30 E
164	Shark B....Austl.	26.0 S	113.45 E
87	Sharon (shăr'ŏn)......Mass. (In.)	42.7 N	71.10 W
84	Sharon....Ohio	41.14 N	80.30 W
88	Sharon Hill . Pa. (Philadelphia In.)	39.54 N	75.16 W
78	Sharon Springs....Kan.	38.53 N	101.45 W
89	Sharpsburg (shärps'bûrg) Pa. (Pittsburgh In.)	40.30 N	79.55 W
154	Shasi (shä'sē')....Chn.	30.18 N	112.5 E
70	Shasta, Mt. (shăs'tȧ).......Calif.	41.25 N	122.12 W
112	Shatsk (shȧtsk)..........Sov. Un.	54.0 N	41.40 E
78	Shattuck (shăt'ŭk).........Okla.	36.16 N	99.54 W
82	Shaw....Miss.	33.35 N	90.47 W
77	Shawano (shȧ-wô'nō) ....Wis.	44.46 N	88.35 W
55	Shawinigan Falls (shô'ĭn-ĭ-găn) Can.	46.42 N	72.40 W
79	Shawnee (shô-nē')..........Okla.	35.19 N	96.55 W
84	Shawneetown (shô'nē-toun)....Ill.	37.42 N	88.8 W
72	Shawnigan L. (shô'nĭ-găn) Can. (Vancouver In.)	48.37 N	123.38 W
148	Shcheglovsk (shchĕg'lôfsk) Sov.Un.	55.30 N	85.55 E
130	Shchelkovo (shchĕl'kô-vô) Sov. Un.	55.53 N	38.2 E
131	Shcherbinovka (shchĕr'bē-nôf'kȧ) Sov. Un.	48.24 N	37.46 E
131	Shchetovo (shchĕ'tô-vô) .Sov. Un.	48.10 N	39.9 E
131	Shchigry (shchē'grē) .....Sov. Un.	51.52 N	36.55 E
141	Shebeli R. (shā'bå-lē)...It. E. Afr.	3.30 N	45.30 E
77	Sheboygan (shē-boi'găn).....Wis.	43.45 N	87.42 W
77	Sheboygan Falls....Wis.	43.45 N	87.50 W
86	Shediac (shĕ'dē-ăk).........Can.	46.17 N	64.35 W
116	Sheelin, L. (shēl'ĭn)..........Ire.	53.45 N	7.20 W
88	Sheenwater (shēn'wô-tēr) N. Y. (Niagara Falls In.)	43.0 N	79.0 W
88	Sheepshead B. (shēps'hĕd) N. Y. (In.)	40.35 N	73.57 W
117	Sheerness (shēr'nĕs).....Gt. Brit.	51.25 N	0.45 E
82	Sheffield (shĕf'fēld)..........Ala.	34.45 N	87.42 W
116	Sheffield....Gt. Brit.	53.20 N	1.30 W
145	Sheikh Sa'id (shĕk sä'ēd) Yemen (In.)	12.40 N	34.30 E
156	Shehsien (shĕ'hsyĕn') ....Chn.	36.39 N	113.48 E
145	Shekhem (Nablus) (shĕ'kĕm) (nä-blōōs').Pal. (In.)	32.13 N	35.16 E
154	Shekki (shĕk'kē')............Chn.	22.32 N	113.18 E
154	Sheklung (shĕk'lŏŏng') ......Chn.	23.1 N	113.55 E
130	Sheksna R. (shĕks'nȧ) ...Sov. Un.	58.45 N	38.12 E
79	Shelbina (shĕl-bī'nȧ).........Mo.	39.41 N	92.3 W
84	Shelburn (shĕl'bŭrn).........Ind.	39.10 N	87.28 W
85	Shelburne....Can.	44.3 N	80.8 W
86	Shelburne....Can.	43.47 N	65.19 W
84	Shelby (shĕl'bē)...........Mich.	43.33 N	86.24 W
82	Shelby....Miss.	33.57 N	90.47 W
71	Shelby....Mont.	48.27 N	111.50 W
83	Shelby....N. C.	35.16 N	81.34 W
84	Shelby....Ohio	40.54 N	82.40 W
79	Shelbyville (shĕl'bē-vĭl) ....Ill.	39.24 N	88.48 W
84	Shelbyville....Ind.	39.30 N	85.48 W
84	Shelbyville....Ky.	38.10 N	85.14 W
82	Shelbyville....Tenn.	35.30 N	86.28 W
76	Sheldon (shĕl'dŭn)............Ia.	43.11 N	95.50 W
81	Sheldon....Tex. (In.)	29.52 N	95.7 W
53	Shelikof Str. (shā'lē-kôf) ....Alsk.	58.30 N	153.30 W
89	Shell Beach .La. (New Orleans In.)	29.52 N	89.41 W
70	Shelley (shĕl'ē)..............Ida.	43.21 N	112.8 W
89	Shell I......La. (New Orleans In.)	29.15 N	89.39 W
164	Shellborough....Austl.	20.5 S	119.15 E
77	Shellrock R. (shĕl'rŏk).........Ia.	43.20 N	93.10 W
49	Shellville (shĕl'vĭl) (Calif. San Francisco In.)	38.13 N	122.26 W
130	Shelon R. (shå'lôn) .....Sov. Un.	57.55 N	29.40 E
85	Shelton (shĕl'tŭn) ....Conn.	41.18 N	73.6 W
76	Shelton....Neb.	40.48 N	98.42 W
70	Shelton....Wash.	47.13 N	123.8 W
113	Shemakha (shĕ-mȧ-kä')..Sov. Un.	40.40 N	48.40 E
76	Shenandoah (shĕn-ăn-dō'ȧ)....Ia.	40.47 N	95.00 W
85	Shenandoah....Pa.	49.48 N	76.12 W
85	Shenandoah....Va.	38.32 N	78.34 W
85	Shenandoah Natl. Park.......Va.	38.37 N	78.20 W
85	Shenandoah R....Va.	39.0 N	78.5 W
141	Shenbâb (shĕn-bäb') ....Eg.	29.51 N	31.14 E
154	Shenchow (shĕn'chō') ....Chn.	28.19 N	110.2 E
139	Shendi (shĕn'dē) ......A. E. Sud.	16.45 N	33.28 E
156	Shenkiu (shĕn'kvōō') ..Chn.	33.13 N	115.7 E
112	Shenkursk (shĕn-kōōrsk').Sov. Un.	62.5 N	42.58 E
152	Shensi (Prov.) (shĕn'sē').....Chn.	35.35 N	108.30 E
156	Shentseh (shĕn'tsĕ').........Chn.	38.23 N	115.13 E
153	Shenyang (Mukden) (shĕn'yäng') (mōōk'dĕn) Manch.	42.1 N	123.28 E
131	Shepetovka (shĕ-pĕ-tôf'kȧ) Sov. Un.	50.9 N	27.2 E
167	Shepparton (shĕp'pȧr-tŭn)..Austl.	36.24 S	145.25 E
139	Sherada (shĕ-rä'dä)....It. E. Afr.	7.18 N	36.25 E
87	Sherborn (shûr'bŭrn)..Mass. (In.)	42.14 N	71.22 W
55	Sherbrooke (shûr'brŏŏk).....Can.	45.23 N	71.46 W
118	Sherburn (shûr'bŭrn)....Gt. Brit.	53.48 N	1.15 W
114	Shergui I. (shĕr'gwē)...Medit. Sea	34.47 N	11.15 E
79	Sheridan (shĕr'ĭdăn).........Ark.	34.18 N	92.21 W
70	Sheridan....Ore.	45.7 N	123.22 W
71	Sheridan....Wyo.	44.49 N	106.57 W
130	Sherikhovichi (shå'rē-kôf-vē'-chē) ..Sov. Un.	58.45 N	33.31 E
135	Sherki, Esh (R.) (ĕsh-shĕr'kē) Eg. (In.)	30.50 N	31.17 E
73	Sherman (shûr'măn) Calif. (Los Angeles In.)	34.5 N	118.24 W
79	Sherman....Tex.	33.38 N	96.36 W
122	's Hertogenbosch (s'hĕr-tō'gĕn-bôs) . Neth.	51.41 N	5.20 E
118	Sherwood Forest (shûr'wŏŏd) Gt. Brit.	53.11 N	1.6 W
116	Shetland Is. (shĕt'lănd) Gt. Brit. (In.)	60.30 N	1.20 W
76	Sheyenne R. (shī-ĕn')......N. D.	47.30 N	98.0 W
84	Shiawassee R. (shī-ȧ-wôs'ē)..Mich.	43.0 N	84.12 W
150	Shibam (shē'bäm)..........Aden.	16.0 N	43.50 E
135	Shibin el Kom (shē-bēn' ĕl kōm') Eg. (In.)	30.31 N	31.0 E
135	Shibîn el Qanâtir (shē-bēn' ĕl kȧ-nä'tēr) . Eg. (In.)	30.18 N	31.20 E
159	Shibuya (shē'bŏŏ-yȧ) Jap. (Tokyo In.)	35.39 N	139.42 E
73	Shields (shēldz) Utah (Salt Lake City In.)	40.34 N	112.17 W
71	Shields R....Mont.	46.5 N	110.46 W
118	Shifnal (shĭf'năl)........Gt. Brit.	52.40 N	2.21 W
152	Shigatse (shē'gä-tsĕ')........Chn.	29.17 N	89.2 E
155	Shihcheng (shē'chĕng')......Chn.	26.22 N	116.18 E
155	Shihchiu L. (shē'chē-ōō')....Chn.	31.28 N	119.10 E
155	Shihma (shē'mä')..........Chn.	24.26 N	117.47 E
154	Shihmen (shē'mĕn')........Chn.	29.27 N	110.58 E
155	Shihmen....Chn.	30.33 N	120.23 E
154	Shihnan (shē'nän')........Chn.	30.18 N	109.6 E
156	Shih R. (shĭ)....Chn.	32.0 N	115.21 E
154	Shihshow (shē'shō')........Chn.	29.43 N	112.10 E
157	Shihtao (shĭ'tä'ō)...........Chn.	36.55 N	122.20 E
154	Shihtsien (shē'tsyĕn')........Chn.	27.32 N	108.10 E
151	Shikarpur (shē-kär'pōōr)....India	27.59 N	68.45 E
159	Shikoku (I.) (shē'kō-kōō).....Jap.	33.45 N	133.30 E
149	Shilka R. (shēl'kȧ).......Sov. Un.	53.0 N	119.0 E
151	Shillong (shēl-lông')........India	25.38 N	91.59 E
159	Shimabara (shē'mä-bä'rä)....Jap.	32.47 N	130.22 E
159	Shimada (shē'mä-dä)........Jap.	34.49 N	138.12 E
159	Shimizu (shē'mē-zōō)........Jap.	35.1 N	138.29 E
148	Shimki (shēm'kē)........Sov. Un.	51.45 N	102.20 E
159	Shimoda (shē'mō-dȧ)........Jap.	34.41 N	138.55 E
141	Shimoni (shē'mō-nē).......Kenya	4.37 S	39.23 E
159	Shimonoseki (shē'mō-nō-sä'kē) Jap.	34.0 N	131.0 E
159	Shinagawa (shĭ'nȧ-gä'wä).....Jap.	35.34 N	139.43 E
159	Shinanogawa R. (shē'nä-nō-gä'wä) Jap.	37.0 N	138.45 E
158	Shin-Anshu....Cho.	39.37 N	125.42 E
158	Shinasan (shē-nä-sän').......Cho.	42.30 N	130.30 E
158	Shinchiku (shĭn-chē'kōō).....Tai.	24.45 N	121.0 E
157	Shingishu (shĭn-gē'shōō).....Cho.	40.2 N	124.30 E
159	Shingu (shĭn'gōō)...........Jap.	33.43 N	135.59 E
159	Shinji, L. (shĭn'jē)...........Jap.	35.26 N	132.58 E
159	Shinjuku (shĭn'jōō'kōō) Jap. (Tokyo In.)	35.42 N	139.42 E
139	Shinko R. (shĭn'kō) ..Fr. Eq. Afr.	6.0 N	24.15 E
116	Shin, Loch (L.)(lŏk shĭn).Gt. Brit.	58.5 N	4.30 W
158	Shinomi C. (shē'nō-mē)......Jap.	33.31 N	135.47 E
157	Shinsen....Cho.	38.22 N	125.27 E
157	Shinshu (shĭn'shōō')........Cho.	35.15 N	128.5 E
140	Shinyanga (shĭn-yäŋ'gä).....Tan.	3.38 S	33.12 E
96	Ship Channel Cay. (I.)....Ba. Is.	24.49 N	77.50 W
118	Shipley (shĭp'lē).........Gt. Brit.	53.50 N	1.47 W
85	Shippensburg (shĭp'ĕnz-bûrg)..Pa.	40.3 N	77.31 W
86	Shippigan I. (shĭp'ĭ-găn).....Can.	47.48 N	64.36 W
86	Shipshaw R. (shĭp'shô)......Can.	48.40 N	71.2 W
118	Shipston-on-Stour (shĭp'stŭn-ŏn-stour') . Gt. Brit.	52.4 N	1.37 W
159	Shiranesan (Mt.) (shē'rä-nå-sän') Jap.	35.44 N	138.13 E
140	Shirati (shē-rä'tē)...........Tan.	1.15 S	34.3 E
150	Shiraz (shē-räz')............Iran	29.32 N	52.31 E
140	Shire R. (shē'rā)......Nya.-Moz.	16.0 S	34.45 E
158	Shiretoko C. (shē'rĕ-tō'kō)...Kar.	46.5 N	143.28 E
158	Shiriya C. (shē'rē-yä)........Jap.	41.22 N	141.22 E
72	Shirley (shûr'lē) Colo. (Colo. Sprs. In.)	38.54 N	104.39 W
87	Shirley....Mass. (In.)	42.33 N	71.38 W
131	Shirokoe (shē'rō-kō'yĕ)...Sov. Un.	47.39 N	33.15 E
154	Shiuchow (shū'chō')........Chn.	24.56 N	113.2 E
154	Shiuhing (shū'hĭng')........Chn.	23.5 N	112.24 E
75	Shivwits (Shebit) Ind. Res. (shĭv'wĭts) (shĕ'bĭt) . Utah	37.10 N	113.45 W
159	Shizuki (shĭ'zōō-kē).........Jap.	34.28 N	134.51 E
159	Shizuoka (shē'zōō-ō'kȧ)......Jap.	35.1 N	138.26 E
130	Shklov (shklôf).........Sov. Un.	54.11 N	30.20 E
129	Shkodēr (Scutari) (shkō'dûr) (skōō'tȧrē) . Alb.	42.3 N	19.31 E
149	Shkotovo (shkō'tō-vō)....Sov. Un.	43.20 N	132.30 E
130	Shlisselburg (shlĭs'sĕl-bōōrgh) Sov. Un.	59.55 N	31.5 E
79	Shoal Cr. (shōl)..............Ill.	38.45 N	89.30 W
167	Shoalhaven R. (shōl'hā-v'n).Austl.	35.5 S	150.0 E
84	Shoals (shōlz)...............Ind.	38.40 N	86.45 W
159	Shodo I. (shō'dō).............Jap.	34.30 N	134.15 E
119	Shoeburyness (shōō'bēr-ĭ-nĕs') Gt. Brit. (London In.)	51.32 N	0.47 E
158	Shojo....Cho.	40.30 N	125.2 E
151	Sholapur (shō'lä-pōōr)......India	17.45 N	75.59 E
159	Shomyo (shōm'yō)..........Jap.	34.23 N	131.9 E
77	Shorewood (shōr'wŏŏd)......Wis.	43.5 N	87.55 W
119	Shorne (shōrn) Gt. Brit. (London In.)	51.25 N	0.26 E
73	Short Cr...Ala. (Birmingham In.)	33.33 N	87.6 W
71	Shoshone (shō-shōn'ē)........Ida.	42.56 N	114.24 W
71	Shoshone Cavern Natl. Mon..Wyo.	44.30 N	109.0 W
71	Shoshone Ind. Res..........Wyo.	43.6 N	109.0 W
71	Shoshone L....Wyo.	44.25 N	110.45 W
71	Shoshone R....Wyo.	44.35 N	109.0 W
131	Shostka (shôst'kȧ) ....Sov. Un.	51.51 N	33.31 E
155	Showchang (shō'chäng')....Chn.	29.26 N	119.15 E
156	Shochang....Chn.	35.57 N	115.50 E
156	Showchow (shō'chō')........Chn.	32.34 N	116.42 E
156	Showkwang (shō'kwäng')....Chn.	36.56 N	118.42 E
155	Showning (shō'nĭng')........Chn.	27.32 N	119.17 E
156	Showyang (shō'yäng').......Chn.	37.52 N	113.10 E
131	Shpola (shpō'lȧ) ....Sov. Un.	49.0 N	31.26 E
81	Shreveport (shrēv'pōrt) ....La.	32.30 N	93.46 W
116	Shrewsbury (shrōōz'bēr-ĭ).Gt. Brit.	52.42 N	2.50 W
87	Shrewsbury.........Mass. (In.)	42.17 N	71.43 W
118	Shropshire (County) (shrŏp'shēr) Gt. Brit.	52.39 N	2.45 W
116	Shropshire Hills, South...Gt. Brit.	52.25 N	3.0 W
96	Shroud Cay (I.) (shroud)..Ba. Is.	24.22 N	76.39 W
154	Shuanen (shōō'ä-nĕn').......Chn.	30.3 N	109.4 E
152	Shufu (Kashgar) (shōō'fōō) (käsh'gär) . Chn.	39.28 N	76.2 E
72	Shukshan, Mt. (shŏŏk'shăn) Wash. (Vancouver In.)	48.50 N	121.36 W
152	Shuleh (Yangi Shahr) (shōō'lĕ') (yäŋ'gē shär') . Chn.	41.22 N	80.25 E
131	Shulginka (shŏŏl'gĭn-kȧ)..Sov. Un.	49.9 N	38.51 E
77	Shullsburg (shŭlz'bûrg)......Wis.	42.35 N	90.15 W
156	Shulu (shōō'lōō')............Chn.	37.56 N	115.20 E
52	Shumagin Is. (shōō'mȧ-gēn)..Alsk.	56.0 N	160.0 W
141	Shume (shōō'mȧ)............Tan.	4.42 S	38.12 E
154	Shumkai (shōōm'kī')........Chn.	22.58 N	111.2 E
155	Shunan (shōō'nän')..........Chn.	29.40 N	119.5 E
155	Shungchang (shŏŏng'chäng') . Chn.	26.47 N	117.42 E
52	Shungnak (shŭng'nȧk).......Alsk.	67.0 N	156.30 W
152	Shunking (shŭn'kĭng').......Chn.	30.50 N	106.0 E
152	Shunning (shŭn'nĭng').......Chn.	24.28 N	99.51 E
156	Shunteh (shŭn'tĕ')..........Chn.	37.5 N	114.40 E
156	Shunyi (shōōn'yĭ')..........Chn.	40.8 N	116.49 E
156	Shu R. (shōō)..............Chn.	34.30 N	118.26 E
150	Shurab R. (shōō'räb)........Iran	30.40 N	56.30 E
158	Shuri (shōō'rē)...Ryukyu Is. (In.)	26.14 N	127.45 E
150	Shur R. (shōōr)............Iran	35.45 N	50.0 E
150	Shushtar (shōōsh'tŭr)........Iran	31.59 N	48.47 E
156	Shuvang (shōō'wäng').......Chn.	34.5 N	118.52 E
130	Shuya (shōō'yȧ).........Sov. Un.	56.52 N	41.25 E
158	Shwangcheng (shwän-chûng) Manch.	45.27 N	126.29 E
158	Siakhin, L. (sē-äk'hĭn')......Chn.	45.17 N	132.34 E
155	Siakiang (syä'kyäng')........Chn.	27.28 N	115.10 E
145	Siak R. (sē-äk') ...Neth. Ind. (In.)	0.57 N	101.30 E
145	Siaksriindrapoera (sē-äks'rē-ēn'drȧ-pōō'rä) ..Neth. Ind. (In.)	0.45 N	102.3 E
151	Sialkot (sē-äl'kōt)..........India	32.28 N	74.29 E
	Siam, see Thailand.		
160	Siam, G. of (sī-ăm').Thai.-Fr. In.Chn.	10.0 N	102.0 E
152	Sian (syän') ....Chn.	34.17 N	108.57 E
158	Sian....Manch.	42.59 N	125.16 E
156	Siangho (syäng'hō') ....Chn.	39.44 N	116.59 E
154	Sianghsien (syäng'hsyĕn')....Chn.	24.3 N	109.46 E
155	Siangshan (syäng'shän').....Chn.	29.48 N	121.52 E
154	Siangsiang (syäng'syäng') ...Chn.	27.47 N	112.12 E
154	Siangtan (syäng'tän').......Chn.	27.53 N	112.40 E
154	Siangyin (syäng'yĭn') ....Chn.	28.38 N	112.35 E
156	Siaoching R. (syä'ō-chĭng') ..Chn.	37.0 N	117.30 E
155	Siaofeng (syä'ō-fĕng').......Chn.	30.30 N	119.37 E
158	Siaohaotze (syä'ō-hä'ō-tzĕ') Manch.	46.57 N	124.30 E
156	Siaohsien (syä'ō-hsyĕn') .....Chn.	34.11 N	117.3 E
155	Siao R. (syä'ō).............Chn.	29.5 N	114.40 E
161	Siaoe (I.) (sē-ä'ōō) ....Neth. Ind.	2.40 N	125.25 E
155	Siaoshan (syä'ō-shän').......Chn.	30.10 N	120.16 E
163	Siargao I. (sē-är-gä'ō).......P. I.	9.50 N	126.2 E
163	Siasi I. (sē-ä'sē)............P. I.	5.32 N	120.52 E
129	Siatista (syȧ'tĭs-tȧ)..........Grc.	40.15 N	21.32 E
163	Siaton (sē-ä'tôn) ....P. I.	9.3 N	123.3 E
163	Siaton Pt....P. I.	9.2 N	123.2 E
121	Šiauliai (shē-ou'lē-ī)........Lith.	55.58 N	23.20 E
156	Siayi (syä'yĭ') ....Chn.	34.18 N	116.14 E
163	Sibalon (sē-bä-lōn').........P. I.	10.47 N	122.1 E
163	Sibay I. (sē-bī')............P. I.	11.50 N	121.28 E
143	Sibayi, L. (sē-bä'yē)....U. S. Afr.	27.23 S	32.41 E
128	Sibenik (Sebenico) (shē-bā'nēk) (sā-bā'nē-kō) . Yugo.	43.44 N	15.54 E
148	Siberian Area (Reg.) (sī-bē'rĭ-ăn) Sov. Un.	60.0 N	90.0 E
160	Siberoet I. (sē'bå-rōōt) . Neth. Ind.	1.30 S	99.0 E
140	Sibiti (sē-bē-tē')......Fr. Eq. Afr.	3.42 S	13.17 E
123	Sibiu (sē-bē-ōō')...........Rom.	45.49 N	24.10 E
76	Sibley (sĭb'lē)................Ia.	43.25 N	95.42 W
160	Siboga (sē-bō'gä).......Neth. Ind.	1.50 N	98.50 E
163	Sibonga (sē-bôŋ'gä)..........P. I.	10.1 N	123.37 E
151	Sibsagar (sēb-sä'gär)........India	26.50 N	94.37 E
163	Sibuguey B. (sē-bōō-gä').....P. I.	7.37 N	122.40 E
163	Sibuku B. (sē-bōō'kōō) ......P. I.	7.19 N	122.3 E
163	Sibutu I. (sē-bōō'tōō) ....P. I.	4.47 N	119.28 E
163	Sibutu Passage....P. I.	5.0 N	119.35 E
162	Sibuyan I. (sē-bōō-yän').....P. I.	12.25 N	122.35 E
162	Sibuyan Sea....P. I.	12.30 N	122.40 E
162	Sicapoo, Mt. (sē-kä-pōō')....P. I.	18.1 N	120.51 E
153	Siccawei Cr. (sĭk'ȧ-wā'ē) Chn. (Shanghai In.)	31.9 N	121.24 E

ng-sing; ŋ-baŋk; ɴ-nasalized n; nŏd; cŏmmit; ōld; ôbey; ôrder; fōōd; fŏŏt; ou-out; s-soft; sh-dish; th-thin; pūre ûnite; ûrn; stŭd; circŭs; ü-as "y" in study; '-indeterminate vowel.

Page	Name Pronunciation Region	Lat. °′	Long. °′
166	Siccus R. (sĭk'ŭs) Austl.	31.42 S	139.22 E
128	Sicily (I.) (sĭs'ĭ-lē) It.	37.35 N	14.10 E
94	Sico (sē'kō) R. Hond.	15.33 N	85.30 W
102	Sicuani (sē-kwä'nē) Peru	14.28 S	71.1 W
139	Sidamo (Division) It. E. Afr.	5.0 N	38.30 E
119	Sidcup (sĭd'kŭp) Gt. Brit. (London In.)	51.25 N	0.6 E
99	Side, R. (sē'dā) Chl. (Magallanes In.)	52.46 S	69.20 W
128	Siderno Marina (sē-dĕr'nō mä-rē'nä) It.	38.7 N	16.18 E
129	Sidērokastron (sē-dē-rō-kàs'-trōn) Grc.	41.13 N	23.26 E
128	Sideron, C. (sē'dĕ-rōn) Grc.	35.19 N	26.20 E
138	Sidi-bel Abbès (sē'dē-bĕl-à-bĕs') Alg.	35.10 N	0.40 W
135	Sidi el Hani, Sebkra of (L.) (sĕb'krà sē-dē ĕl hä'nē) Tun. (In.)	35.35 N	10.20 E
72	Sidney Can. (Vancouver In.)	48.39 N	123.24 W
71	Sidney Mont.	47.44 N	104.9 W
76	Sidney Neb.	41.9 N	103.0 W
84	Sidney Ohio	40.21 N	84.7 W
72	Sidney I. Can. (Vancouver In.)	48.38 N	123.18 W
145	Sidon (saïda) (sī'dŏn) (sä'ē-dä) Syr. (In.)	33.33 N	35.23 E
139	Sidra, G. of (sēd'rȧ) Libya	31.30 N	18.0 E
119	Siebenhirten (zē'bĕn-hēr-tĕn) Aus. (Wien In.)	48.7 N	16.19 E
123	Siedlce (syĕd'l-tsĕ) Pol.	52.8 N	22.19 E
122	Siegburg (zēg'bŏŏrgh) Ger.	50.49 N	7.12 E
122	Siegen (zē'ghĕn) Ger.	50.53 N	8.1 E
122	Sieg River (zēg) Ger.	50.48 N	7.32 E
123	Siemiatycze (syĕm-yà-tē'chĕ). Poland	52.26 N	22.52 E
160	Siemréap-Angkor (syĕm-rä-äp'-äng-kōr') Fr. In. Chn.	13.25 N	103.59 E
128	Siena (syĕ'nä) It.	43.19 N	11.21 E
156	Sienhsien (syĕn'hsyĕn') Chn.	38.20 N	115.59 E
155	Sienku (syĕn'kōō') Chn.	28.51 N	120.42 E
155	Sienyu (syĕn'yōō') Chn.	25.18 N	118.38 E
123	Sieradz (syä'rädz) Pol.	41.35 N	18.44 E
126	Siero (syä'rō) Sp.	43.25 N	5.39 W
123	Sierpc (syĕrpts) Pol.	52.51 N	19.43 E
138	Sierra Leone (syĕr'ȧ lā-ō'nā) Afr.	8.30 N	12.0 W
72	Siesse, Mt. (sē-ĕs') Can. (Vancouver In.)	49.2 N	121.35 W
119	Sievering (sē'vẽr-ĭng) Aus. (Wien In.)	48.15 N	16.19 E
156	Sifei R. (sē'fä'ē) Chn.	33.10 N	116.4 E
158	Sifeng Manch.	42.50 N	128.30 E
49	Sifton (sĭf'tŭn) Wash. (Portland In.)	45.40 N	122.31 W
163	Sigaboy (sē-gä'boi) P. I.	6.37 N	126.5 E
163	Sigboye Passage (sēg-bō'yȧ) P. I.	5.25 N	120.30 E
120	Sigdal (sēgh'däl) Nor.	60.1 N	9.42 E
124	Sigean (sē-zhäN') Fr.	43.0 N	3.2 E
123	Sighet (sē-gât') Rom.	47.57 N	23.54 E
123	Sighișoara (sē-gē-shwä'rà) Rom.	46.12 N	24.48 E
129	Sighitikos, G. of (sē-ghē'tē-kōs) Grc.	40.15 N	23.55 E
126	Sigüenza (sē-gwĕn'thä) Sp.	41.4 N	2.39 W
110	Siglufjördur (sēgh'lōō-fyûr-dōōr) Ice.	66.10 N	18.50 W
113	Signakh (sēg-näK') Sov. Un.	41.38 N	45.50 E
171	Signal Hill (sĭg'nál) N. Z. (In.)	45.51 S	170.35 E
77	Sigourney (sĭg'ŭr-nē) Ia.	41.19 N	92.11 W
102	Sigsig (sēg-sēg') Ec.	3.10 S	78.30 W
120	Sigtuna (sēgh-tōō'nä) Swe.	59.38 N	17.40 E
96	Siguanea B. (sē-gwä-nā'ä) Isle of Pines	21.40 N	83.0 W
138	Siguiri (sē-gē-rē') Fr. W. Afr.	11.31 N	9.2 W
156	Sihwa (sĭ'hwä') Chn.	33.54 N	114.33 E
113	Siirt (sĭ-ērt') Tur.	38.2 N	42.2 E
152	Sikang (Prov.) (sĭ'käng') Chn.	29.45 N	98.0 E
138	Sikasso (sē-käs'sō) Fr. W. Afr.	11.20 N	5.36 W
79	Sikeston (sīks'tŭn) Mo.	36.52 N	89.35 W
149	Sikhota Alin (sē-Kō'tà à-lēn') Sov. Un.	47.0 N	137.20 E
129	Sikinos (I.) (sĭ'kĭ-nōs) Grc.	36.42 N	25.7 E
123	Siklós (sĭ'klōsh) Hung.	45.52 N	18.19 E
92	Silacayoápam (sē-lä-kä-yō-ä'päm) Mex.	17.31 N	98.0 W
163	Silam (sē-läm') B. N. B.	4.59 N	118.12 E
163	Silam, Mt. B. N. B.	4.59 N	118.10 E
162	Silang (sē-läng') P. I.	14.13 N	120.58 E
92	Silao (sē-lä'ō) Mex.	20.56 N	101.25 W
163	Silay (sē-lī') P. I.	10.47 N	122.59 E
151	Silchar (sĭl-chär') India	24.45 N	92.45 E
83	Siler City (sī'lẽr) N. C.	35.44 N	79.28 W
122	Silesia (Schlesien) (State) (sĭ-lē'shĭ-ȧ) (shlā'zē-ĕn) Ger.	50.55 N	17.0 E
135	Siliana, O. (R.) (sē-lē-ä'nä) Tun. (In.)	36.10 N	9.25 E
72	Silica (sĭl'ĭ-kȧ) Colo. (Denver In.)	39.27 N	105.4 W
163	Silingan, Mt. (sĭ-lĭŋ'gän) P. I.	7.44 N	122.30 E
129	Silistra (sē-lēs'trà) Rom.	44.5 N	27.16 E
120	Siljan, L. (sēl'yän) Swe.	60.50 N	14.45 E
120	Silkeborg (sĭl'kĕ-bôr') Den.	56.9 N	9.34 E
135	Silla del Papa (Mt.) (sēl'yä dĕl pä'pä) Sp. (Gib. In.)	36.8 N	5.15 E
79	Siloam Sprs. (sĭ-lōm') Ark.	36.11 N	94.32 W
126	Sil R. (sēl) Sp.	42.25 N	7.0 W
81	Silsbee (sĭlz'bē) Tex.	30.20 N	94.10 W
73	Siluria (sĭ-lū'rĭ-ȧ) Ala. (Birmingham In.)	33.14 N	86.49 W
121	Šilute (shĭ-lōō'tä) Lith.	55.21 N	21.11 E
49	Silvana (sĭl-văn'ȧ) Wash. (Seattle In.)	48.12 N	122.16 W
140	Silva Porto (Bihe) (sĭl'vȧ pôr'tōō) (bē-ā') Ang.	12.22 S	17.5 E
112	Silva R. (sĭl'vȧ) Sov. Un.	57.15 N	57.15 E
97	Silver Bank Ba. Is.	20.35 N	69.40 W
97	Silver Bank Passage Ba. Is.	20.50 N	70.10 W
75	Silver City N. M.	32.46 N	108.19 W
75	Silver Cr. (sĭl'vẽr) Ariz.	34.20 N	110.5 W
85	Silver Creek N. Y.	42.36 N	79.7 W
49	Silverdale (sĭl'vẽr-dāl) Wash. (Seattle In.)	47.38 N	122.43 W
70	Silver Mts. Ida.	43.15 N	116.50 W
72	Silver Pk. Can. (Vancouver In.)	49.8 N	121.30 W
166	Silverton (sĭl'vẽr-tŭn) Austl.	31.52 S	141.14 E
75	Silverton Colo.	37.50 N	107.40 W
70	Silverton Ore.	45.1 N	122.48 W
126	Silves (sēl'vĕzh) Port.	37.14 N	8.22 W
70	Silvies R. (sĭl'vēz) Ore.	43.40 N	119.0 W
135	Silwa (sēl'wä) Eg. (In.)	24.42 N	32.59 E
163	Simaddel I. (sē'mà-dĕl) B. N. B.	6.40 N	117.25 E
160	Simalur I. (sē-mä'lōōr) Neth. Ind.	2.30 N	96.15 E
162	Simara I. (sē-mä'rä) P. I.	12.48 N	122.3 E
139	Simba (sĭm'bà) Bel. Cong.	0.32 N	23.4 E
85	Simcoe (sĭm'kō) Can.	42.48 N	80.20 W
55	Simcoe, L. Can.	44.15 N	79.35 W
131	Simferopol (Akmechet) (sĕm-fĕ-rô'pôl') (àk-mĕch'ĕt) Sov. Un.	44.57 N	34.4 E
151	Simla (sĭm'là) India	31.5 N	77.5 E
123	Simleul-Silvaniei (shĕm-lā'ŏŏl-sēl-vä'nē-ĕ-ĭ) Rom.	47.15 N	22.46 E
121	Simola (sē'mō-là) Fin.	60.55 N	28.10 E
93	Simojovel (sē-mō-hō-vĕl') Mex.	17.8 N	92.42 W
163	Simonoc I. (sē-mô-nôc') P. I.	4.54 N	119.49 E
142	Simonstown (sī'mŭnz-toun) U. S. Afr.	34.11 S	18.23 E
122	Simplon Pass (sĭm'plŏn) (săN-plôN') Switz.	46.16 N	8.2 E
122	Simplon Tunnel Switz.-It.	46.16 N	8.8 E
54	Simpson (sĭmp'sŭn) Can.	61.50 N	121.31 W
77	Simpson I. Can.	48.45 N	87.41 W
54	Simpson Str. Can.	68.30 N	99.0 W
120	Simrishamn (sēm'rēs-häm'n) Swe.	55.33 N	14.20 E
81	Sims Bayou (sĭmz) Tex. (In.)	29.38 N	95.28 W
129	Sinaia (sē-nä'yà) Rom.	44.20 N	25.31 E
139	Sinai Pen. (sī'nī) Eg.	29.0 N	34.0 E
163	Sinait (sē-nä'ēt) P. I.	17.52 N	120.29 E
92	Sinaloa (State) (sē-nä-lō'ä) Mex.	23.0 N	105.50 W
150	Sinandij (sē-nän'dēj) Iran	35.29 N	46.55 E
102	Since (sēn'sà) Col.	9.15 N	75.15 W
102	Sincelejo (sēn-sà-lā'hō) Col.	9.15 N	75.28 W
155	Sinchang (sēn'chäng') Chn.	28.23 N	114.41 E
155	Sinchang Chn.	29.30 N	120.52 E
155	Sincheng (sēn'chĕng') Chn.	27.14 N	116.47 E
156	Sincheng Chn.	34.21 N	113.47 E
156	Sincheng Chn.	37.1 N	118.2 E
156	Sincheng Chn.	39.17 N	115.57 E
170	Sinclair Head (C.) (sĭn-klâr') N. Z. (In.)	41.22 S	174.44 E
72	Sinclair I. Wash. (Vancouver In.)	48.38 N	122.41 W
163	Sindangan B. P. I.	8.15 N	122.50 E
163	Sindangan Pt. (sēn-däŋ'gän) P. I.	8.9 N	122.40 E
121	Sindi (sēn'dē) Est.	58.24 N	24.41 E
131	Sinelnikovo (sē'nyĕl-nē-kô'vô) Sov. Un.	48.18 N	35.33 E
126	Sines (sē'nâzh) Port.	37.57 N	8.50 W
155	Sinfeng (sēn'fĕng') Chn.	25.22 N	114.30 E
139	Singa (sĭŋ'gä) A. E. Sud.	13.10 N	33.55 E
155	Singan R. (sĭŋ'gän') Chn.	29.43 N	118.35 E
160	Singapore (sĭŋ-gȧ-pōr') Strs. Sets.	1.14 N	103.55 E
145	Singapore I. Strs. Sets. (In.)	1.22 N	103.45 E
145	Singapore Str. Strs. Sets. (In.)	1.13 N	104.0 E
160	Singaradja (sĭŋ'gȧ-rä'jä) Neth. Ind.	8.17 S	115.5 E
160	Singkep I. (sĭng'kĕp) Neth. Ind.	0.30 S	104.30 E
167	Singleton (sĭŋ'g'l-tŭn) Austl.	32.38 S	151.11 E
154	Singling (sĭng'lĭng') Chn.	25.42 N	109.58 E
160	Singora (Songkhlä) (sĭn-gō'rä) (sông'klä') Thai.	7.8 N	100.35 E
156	Singtang (sĭng'täng') Chn.	38.31 N	114.30 E
151	Singu (sĭn'gŭ) India	22.29 N	95.50 E
156	Sinho (sĭn'hō') Chn.	37.35 N	115.17 E
154	Sinhwa (sēn'hwä') Chn.	27.44 N	111.3 E
131	Sinie Lipyagi (sēn'ē-ĕ lēp'yȧ-gē) Sov. Un.	51.23 N	38.26 E
161	Siniloan (sē-nē-lō'än) P. I. (Manila In.)	14.26 N	121.31 E
152	Sining (sē'nĭng') Chn.	36.40 N	101.40 E
128	Sinj (sēn') Yugo.	43.2 N	16.39 E
155	Sinkan (sēn'kän') Chn.	27.42 N	115.24 E
152	Sinkiang (Prov.) (sĭn'kyäng') Chn.	40.15 N	85.0 E
156	Sinlo (sĭn'lō') Chn.	38.29 N	114.48 E
157	Sinmi I. (sĭn'mē') Cho.	39.34 N	124.50 E
158	Sinmin (sĭn'mĭn') Manch.	41.58 N	122.52 E
128	Sinni R. (sēn'nē) It.	40.10 N	16.22 E
154	Sinning (sĭn'nĭng') Chn.	22.0 N	108.0 E
154	Sinning Chn.	26.27 N	110.43 E
160	Sinoia (sĭ-noi'ä) S. Rh.	17.22 S	30.8 E
113	Sinop (sē-nōp') Tur.	42.0 N	35.10 E
156	Sinpei (sĭn'pā'ē) Chn.	34.26 N	118.6 E
143	Sinqu (Orange) R. (sĭŋ-kōō') (ŏr'ĕnj) Bas.	29.30 S	28.50 E
155	Sin R. (sēn) Chn.	28.34 N	116.44 E
156	Sin R. (sĭn) Chn.	35.8 N	116.30 E
156	Sinsiang (sĭn'syăng') Chn.	35.17 N	114.3 E
156	Sinti (sēn'tē) Chn.	29.48 N	113.24 E
154	Sintien (sēn'tyĕn') Chn.	25.51 N	112.4 E
81	Sinton (sĭn'tŭn) Tex.	28.2 N	97.30 W
127	Sintra (sēn'trà) Port. (In.)	38.48 N	9.23 W
156	Sintsai (sĭn'tsī') Chn.	32.45 N	114.54 E
156	Sinyang (sĭn'yăng') Chn.	32.13 N	113.53 E
130	Sinyaya R. (sēn'yȧ-yȧ) Sov. Un.	56.42 N	28.20 E
155	Sinyü (sĭn'yü') Chn.	27.45 N	114.52 E
131	Sinyukha R. (sē'nyŏŏ-Kȧ) Sov. Un.	48.52 N	30.45 E
122	Sion (sē'ôN') Switz.	46.15 N	7.20 E
76	Sioux City (sōō) Ia.	42.30 N	96.22 W
76	Sioux Falls S. D.	43.33 N	96.42 W
129	Siphnos (I.) (sēf'nôs) Grc.	37.0 N	24.42 E
156	Siping (sē'pĭng') Chn.	33.23 N	113.57 E
129	Sipka Pass (shēp'kȧ) Bul.	42.3 N	25.19 E
160	Sipora (I.) (sē-pō'rä) Neth. Ind.	2.15 S	99.40 E
82	Sipsey R. (sĭp'sē) Ala.	33.10 N	87.48 W
92	Siqueros (sē-kä'rōs) Mex.	23.22 N	106.13 W
94	Siquia, R. (sē-kē'ä) Nic.	12.25 N	84.40 W
163	Siquijor (sē-kē-hōr') P. I.	9.12 N	123.32 E
163	Siquijor I. P. I.	9.10 N	123.35 E
154	Si R. (sē) Chn.	23.20 N	111.10 E
155	Si R. Chn.	26.10 N	117.38 E
128	Siracusa (Syracuse) (sē-rä-kōō'zä) (sĭr'ȧ-kūs) It.	37.5 N	15.17 E
135	Sirbon, L. (sēr'bōn) Eg. (In.)	31.5 N	32.55 E
148	Sir Darya (Yaxartes) R. (sēr där'yȧ) (yăks-ăr'tēz) Sov. Un.	45.0 N	65.0 E
164	Sir Edward Pellew Group (Is.) (pĕl'ū) Austl.	15.40 S	137.0 E
120	Sire R. (sē'rē) Nor.	58.45 N	6.45 E
123	Siret (sĭ-rĕt') Rom.	47.58 N	26.2 E
129	Siret R. Rom.	45.30 N	27.40 E
150	Sirhan, Wadi (R.) (wä'dē sēr'hän) Sau. Ar.-Transj.	30.20 N	37.45 E
149	Siriktakh R. (sē'rĭ-täK) Sov. Un.	65.20 N	141.0 E
87	Sir John H. Glover I. (glŭv'ẽr) Newf.	48.45 N	57.45 W
166	Sir Joseph Banks Group (Is.) Austl.	34.35 S	136.20 E
139	Sirte (sûr'tē) Libya	31.10 N	16.32 E
121	Sirvintai (sēr'vēn-tī) Lith.	55.1 N	24.55 E
128	Sisak (sē'sàk) Yugo.	45.29 N	16.21 E
93	Sisal (sē-säl') Mex.	21.8 N	90.1 W
112	Sisola R. (sē'sō-là) Sov. Un.	61.0 N	50.20 E
74	Sisquoc R. (sĭs'kwŏk) Calif.	34.48 N	120.15 W
76	Sisseton (sĭs'tŭn) S. D.	45.40 N	97.3 W
125	Sisteron (sēst'rôN') Fr.	44.10 N	5.55 E
169	Sisters (Is.) Austl. (Tas. In.)	39.38 S	147.38 E
84	Sisterville (sĭs'tẽr-vĭl) W. Va.	39.30 N	81.0 W
127	Sitges (sēt-käs') Sp. (In.)	41.14 N	1.48 E
128	Sitia (sē'tĭ-ȧ) Grc. (In.)	35.10 N	26.7 E
53	Sitka (sĭt'kȧ) Alsk.	57.10 N	135.30 W
94	Sittee River (sĭt-tē') Br. Hond. (In.)	16.55 N	88.16 W
154	Siulam (syōō'läm') Chn.	22.38 N	113.10 E
155	Siuning (syōō'nĭng') Chn.	29.48 N	118.10 E
156	Siuwu (syōō'wōō') Chn.	35.14 N	113.36 E
157	Siuyen (syōō'yĕn') Manch.	40.16 N	123.11 E
113	Sivas (sē'väs) Tur.	39.45 N	36.58 E
113	Siverek (sē'vĕ-rĕk) Tur.	37.48 N	39.18 E
130	Siverskaya (sē'vẽr-skȧ-yȧ) Sov. Un.	59.16 N	30.3 E
123	Sivica R. (shē-vē'tsä) Pol.	49.0 N	23.53 E
139	Siwa Oasis (sē'wä) Eg.	29.15 N	25.30 E
95	Sixaola, R. (sē-Kȧ-ō'lä) (sĕk-sä-ō'lä) C R.	9.34 N	83.0 W
88	Six Mile Cr. N. Y. (Niagara Falls In.)	43.14 N	78.59 W
120	Sjaelland (I.) (shĕl'lan') Den.	55.30 N	12.0 E
129	Sjenica (syĕ'nē-tsä) Yugo.	43.16 N	20.1 E
110	Sjönstad (syûn'städ) Nor.	67.11 N	15.43 E
131	Skadovsk (skä'dôfsk) Sov. Un.	46.8 N	32.52 E
120	Skagen (skägh'ĕn) Den.	57.48 N	10.34 E
120	Skagen (The Skaw) (skô) Den.	57.44 N	10.38 E
120	Skagerrak (Str.) (skägh-ĕ-räk') Eur	58.0 N	10.0 E
49	Skagit B. (skăg'ĭt) Wash. (Seattle In.)	48.19 N	122.30 W
70	Skagit R. Wash.	48.27 N	121.40 W
53	Skagway (skăg'wā) Alsk.	59.20 N	135.30 W
123	Skalat (skä'wàt) Pol.	49.26 N	25.58 E
120	Skaldervik (B.) (skäl'dĕr-vêk) Swe.	56.20 N	12.40 E
49	Skamania (skȧ-mā'nĭ-ȧ) Wash. (Portland In.)	45.37 N	122.3 W
49	Skamokawa (skȧ-mō-kō'wȧ) Wash. (Portland In.)	46.15 N	123.26 W
120	Skanderborg (skän'dĕr-bôrgh) Den.	56.3 N	9.55 E
85	Skaneateles (skăn-ĕ-ăt'lĕs) N. Y.	42.57 N	76.25 W
85	Skaneateles L. N. Y.	42.50 N	76.20 W
120	Skänninge (shĕn'ĭng-ĕ) Swe.	58.23 N	15.2 E
120	Skanör (skän'ûr) Swe.	55.23 N	12.50 E
129	Skantzoura (Is.) (skän'tsōō-rä) Grc.	39.3 N	24.5 E
120	Skara (skä'rä) Swe.	58.24 N	13.25 E
120	Skaw, The (Skagen) (skô) (skägh'ĕn) Den.	57.44 N	10.38 E
56	Skeena City Can. (Prince Rupert In.)	54.14 N	129.46 W
54	Skeena R. (skē'nȧ) Can.	54.30 N	129.0 W
110	Skellefteå (shĕl'ĕf-te-ô') Swe.	64.45 N	20.55 E
110	Skellefte R. (shĕl'ĕ-ftĕ) Swe.	65.5 N	20.30 E
119	Skelmersdale (skĕl'mẽrz-dāl) Gt. Brit. (Liverpool In.)	53.33 N	2.48 W
120	Skern R. (skĕrn) Den.	55.58 N	8.35 E
116	Skerries (Is.) (skĕr'ēz) Gt. Brit.	53.25 N	4.35 W
129	Skiathos (I.) (skē'ȧ-thôs) Grc.	39.8 N	23.28 E
116	Skibbereen (skĭb'ẽr-ēn) Ire.	51.40 N	9.20 W
81	Skidmore (skĭd'môr) Tex.	28.16 N	97.40 W
120	Skien (skē'ĕn) Nor.	59.13 N	9.38 E
123	Skierniewice (skyĕr-nyĕ-vēt'sĕ) Pol.	51.56 N	20.12 E
52	Skilak L. (skĭl'ák) Alsk. (In.)	60.25 N	150.35 W
72	Skinners (skĭn'ẽrz) Colo. (Colo. Spgs. In.)	38.47 N	104.45 W
118	Skipton (skĭp'tŭn) Gt. Brit.	53.58 N	2.0 W
120	Skive (skē'vĕ) Den.	56.33 N	9.0 E
110	Skjalfanda (R.) (skyäl'fänd-ô) Ice.	65.20 N	17.40 W
128	Skofja Loka (shkōf'yȧ lō'kȧ) Yugo.	46.10 N	14.18 E
123	Skole (skō'lĕ) Pol.	49.2 N	23.32 E
129	Skopelos (I.) (skō'pȧ-lôs) Grc.	39.5 N	23.40 E
129	Skoplje (skôp'lyĕ) Yugo.	42.1 N	21.28 E
130	Skopin (skō'pĕn) Sov. Un.	53.48 N	39.33 E
129	Skopo (skō'pō) Tur.	41.43 N	27.26 E
120	Skövde (shûv'dĕ) Swe.	58.24 N	13.50 E
86	Skowhegan (skou-hē'gȧn) Me.	44.46 N	69.44 W
128	Skradin (skrä'dĕn) Yugo.	43.50 N	15.55 E
120	Skreia (skrā'ä) Nor.	60.38 N	10.58 E
120	Skudeneshavn (skōō'dĕ-nĕs-houn') Nor.	59.11 N	5.19 E
120	Skulerud (skōō'lĕ-rōōdh) Nor.	59.39 N	11.32 E
75	Skull Valley Ind. Res. (skŭl) Utah	40.25 N	112.45 W
77	Skunk R. (skŭnk) Ia.	41.16 N	92.20 W
77	Skunk R., North Ia.	41.30 N	92.40 W

ăt; finăl; rāte; senāte; ärm; åsk; sofȧ; fâre; ch-choose; dh-as th in other; bē; ēvent; bĕt; recĕnt; cratẽr; g-go; gh-gutteral g; bĭt; ĭ-short neutral; rīde; K-gutteral k as ch in German ich;

Page	Name Pronunciation Region	Lat. °′	Long. °′
121	Skuodas (skwô'dȧs) Lith.	56.15 N	21.35 E
120	Skurup (skü'ro͝op) Swe.	55.28 N	13.29 E
131	Skvira (skvē'rȧ) Sov. Un.	49.43 N	29.40 E
116	Skye (I.) (skī) Gt. Brit.	57.25 N	6.20 W
104	Skyring Water (skī'ring) Chl.	52.35 S	72.0 W
129	Skyros (skē'rôs) Grc.	38.52 N	24.32 E
129	Skyros (I.) Grc.	38.50 N	24.35 E
120	Slagelse (slägh'ĕl-sĕ) Den.	55.25 N	11.19 E
160	Slamet, Mt. (Vol.) (slä'mĕt) Neth. Ind.	7.15 S	109.15 E
142	Slang Berg (Mt.) (slȧng bûrg) U. S. Afr.	31.37 S	20.51 E
129	Slănic (slǎ'nėk) Rom.	45.12 N	25.55 E
77	Slate Is. (slāt) Can.	48.40 N	87.0 W
79	Slater (slāt'ẽr) Mo.	39.13 N	93.2 W
129	Slatina (slä-tē'nä) Rom.	44.26 N	24.22 E
78	Slaton (slā'tŭn) Tex.	33.26 N	101.37 W
54	Slave R. (slāv) Can.	60.0 N	112.30 W
148	Slavgorod (sláf'gô-rôt) Sov. Un.	53.10 N	78.30 E
128	Slavonia (Prov.) (slȧ-vō'nĭ-ȧ) Yugo	45.25 N	18.0 E
131	Slavuta (slá-vo͞o'tȧ) Sov. Un.	50.18 N	26.53 E
131	Slavyansk (slȧv-yänsk') Sov. Un.	48.52 N	37.38 E
131	Slavyanskaya (slȧv-yȧn'skȧ'yȧ) Sov. Un.	45.16 N	38.4 E
76	Slayton (slā'tŭn) Minn.	43.59 N	95.34 W
118	Sleaford (slē'fẽrd) Gt. Brit.	53.0 N	0.24 W
166	Sleaford B. Austl.	34.55 S	135.50 E
77	Sleepy Eye Minn.	44.17 N	94.42 W
81	Slidell (slī-dĕl') La.	30.17 N	89.46 W
116	Sligo (slī'gō) Ire.	54.15 N	8.30 W
116	Sligo B Ire.	54.20 N	8.40 W
148	Slinkina (slĭŋ-kē'nȧ) Sov. Un.	58.55 N	68.45 E
120	Slite (slē'tĕ) Swe.	57.41 N	18.50 E
139	Sliten (slĭt'ĕn) Libya	32.27 N	14.30 E
129	Sliven (slē'vĕn) Bul.	42.39 N	26.19 E
88	Sloan (slōn) N. Y. (Niagara Falls In.)	42.53 N	78.48 W
112	Slobodskoi (slô'bôt-skô-ĭ) Sov. Un.	58.45 N	50.10 E
129	Slobozia (slô-bō'zyȧ) Rom.	44.34 N	27.24 E
121	Sloka (slô'kȧ) Lat.	56.57 N	23.40 E
123	Slonim (swō'nĕm) Pol.	53.4 N	25.19 E
139	Slonta (slŏn'tä) Libya	32.32 N	21.35 E
123	Slovakia (Slovensko) (Prov.) (slô-vȧk'ĭ-ȧ) (slô-vĕn'skô) Czech.	48.37 N	19.55 E
128	Slovenia (Prov.) (slô-vē'nĭ-ȧ) Yugo.	45.50 N	15.25 E
123	Slovensko (Slovakia) (Prov.) Czech.	48.37 N	19.55 E
130	Sluch R. (swo͝och) Pol.-Sov. Un.	52.40 N	27.20 E
123	Slucz R. (swo͝och) Pol.	51.10 N	26.47 E
128	Sluderno (slo͞o-dĕr'nō) It.	46.40 N	10.36 E
128	Slunj (slo͞on') Yugo.	45.7 N	15.35 E
123	Slupca (swo͞op'tsȧ) Pol.	52.16 N	17 52 E
123	Slutsk (slo͞otsk) Sov. Un.	53.2 N	27.35 E
130	Slutsk Sov. Un.	59.43 N	30.24 E
116	Slyne Head (slīn) Ire.	53.25 N	10.10 W
79	Smackover (smăk'ō-vẽr) Ark.	33.22 N	92.41 W
135	Smala des Souassi ('s-mä'lä dā so͞o-ȧ'sē) Tun. (In.)	35.22 N	10.28 E
143	Smaldeel (smäl'dāl) U. S. Afr.	28.22 S	26.42 E
119	Smay (smī) Bel. (Anvers In.)	51.10 N	4.3 E
129	Smederevo (Semendria) (smĕ'dĕ-rĕ-vô) (sĕ-mĕn'drĭ-ȧ) Yugo.	44.38 N	20.57 E
120	Smedjebacken (smĭ'dyĕ-bä-kĕn) Swe.	60.9 N	15.21 E
129	Smedovo (smĕ'dô-vô) Bul.	43.3 N	27.1 E
131	Smela (smyā'lȧ) Sov. Un.	49.14 N	31.52 E
131	Smeloe (smā'lô-ĕ) Sov. Un.	50.55 N	33.35 E
85	Smethport (smĕth'pōrt) Pa.	41.50 N	78.25 W
116	Smethwick (smĕdh'wĭk) Gt. Brit.	52.30 N	2.0 W
121	Smiltene (smēl'tĕ-nĕ) Lat.	57.26 N	25.54 E
78	Smith Center Kan.	39.46 N	98.47 W
169	Smithfield (smĭth'fēld) Austl. (Sydney In.)	33.51 S	150.55 E
83	Smithfield N. C.	35.30 N	78.20 W
143	Smithfield U. S. Afr.	30.14 S	26.31 E
71	Smithfield Utah	41.49 N	111.51 W
56	Smith I. (smĭth) Can. (Prince Rupert In.)	54.8 N	130.13 W
72	Smith I. Wash. (Vancouver In.)	48.19 N	122.50 W
84	Smithland (smĭth'lănd) Ky.	37.10 N	88.25 W
81	Smith Point Tex. (In.)	29.32 N	94.45 W
71	Smith R. Mont.	47.0 N	111.12 W
55	Smiths Falls (smĭths) Can.	44.51 N	76.0 W
87	Smith Sd. Newf.	48.20 N	53.45 W
169	Smithton (smĭth'tŭn) Austl. (Tas. In.)	40.51 S	145.6 E
81	Smithville (smĭth'vĭl) Tex.	30.0 N	97.9 W
70	Smoke Creek Des. Nev.	40.40 N	119.40 W
167	Smoky C. Austl.	30.53 S	153.8 E
79	Smoky Hill R. Kan.	38.44 N	99.0 W
53	Smoky R. Can.	55.0 N	118.30 W
120	Smölen (I.) (smûl'ĕn) Nor.	63.25 N	80.0 E
130	Smolensk (smô-lyĕnsk') Sov. Un.	54.45 N	32.1 E
130	Smolensk (Dist.) Sov. Un.	55.28 N	33.28 E
85	Smyrna (smûr'nȧ) Del.	39.18 N	75.38 W
78	Smyrna Ga. (Atlanta In.)	33.53 N	84.31 W
113	Smyrna (Izmir) (ĭz-mẽr') Tur.	38.25 N	27.10 E
99	Smyth Canal (smĭth) Chl. (Magallanes In.)	52.30 S	73.25 W
167	Snake I. Austl.	38.45 S	146.30 E
77	Snake R. Minn.	45.50 N	93.15 W
70	Snake R. U. S.	44.35 N	117.15 W
70	Snake River Plains Ida.	43.15 N	113.25 W
96	Snap Pt. Ba. Is.	23.44 N	77.35 W
122	Sneek (snāk) Neth.	53.1 N	5.40 E
143	Sneeuw Bergen (Mts.) (snēv' bĕrgh'ĕn) U. S. Afr.	31.45 S	24.35 E
75	Sneffels Pk. (snĕf'ĕlz) Colo.	38.1 N	107.48 W
120	Snehetten (Mt.) (snĕ'hĕt-ĕn) Nor.	62.20 N	9.15 E

Page	Name Pronunciation Region	Lat. °′	Long. °′
73	Snellville (snĕl'vĭl) Ga. (Atlanta In.)	33.52 N	84.1 W
123	Śniatyn (shnyä'tĭn) Pol.	48.27 N	25.35 E
70	Snohomish (snô-hō'mĭsh) Wash.	47.51 N	121.58 W
70	Snohomish R. Wash.	47.40 N	121.50 W
49	Snohomish (Tulalip) Indian Res. (to͞o'lȧ-lĭp) Wash. (Seattle In.)	48.8 N	122.20 W
131	Snovidovichi (snô'vê-dô-vē'chê) Sov. Un.	51.17 N	27.30 E
131	Snov R. (snôf) Sov. Un.	51.45 N	31.45 E
131	Snovsk (snôfsk) Sov. Un.	51.48 N	31.58 E
116	Snowdon, Mt. (snō'dŭn) Gt. Brit.	53.5 N	3.55 W
85	Snowhill (snō'hĭl) Md.	38.14 N	75.24 W
167	Snowy Mts. (snō'ê) Austl.	36.45 S	148.8 E
167	Snowy R. Austl.	37.10 S	148.20 E
78	Snyder (snī'dẽr) Okla.	34.39 N	98.57 W
80	Snyder Tex.	32.43 N	100.55 W
73	Snyderville (snī'dẽr-vĭl) Utah (Salt Lake City In.)	40.42 N	111.32 W
118	Soar, R. (sōr) Gt. Brit.	52.48 N	1.16 W
139	Sobat R. (sō'bȧt) A. E. Sud.	9.0 N	32.30 E
130	Sobinka (sô'bĭŋ-kȧ) Sov. Un.	55.58 N	40.0 E
159	Sobosan (Mt.) (sō'bō-sän') Jap.	32.46 N	131.30 E
119	Soccayo (sô-kä'yō) It. (Napoli In.)	40.51 N	14.12 E
123	Sochaczew (sô-kȧ'chĕf) Pol.	52.14 N	20.18 E
152	Soche (Yarkand) (sō'chē) (yär-kän') Chn.	38.12 N	77.30 E
113	Sochi (sôch'ĭ) Sov. Un.	43.38 N	39.45 E
156	Society B. Kwan.	39.25 N	121.20 E
6	Society Is. Pac. O.	16.30 S	152.0 W
56	Sockeye (sŏk'ī) Can. (Prince Rupert In.)	54.11 N	130.10 W
139	Socna (sôk'nȧ) Libya	29.7 N	15.47 E
93	Socoltenango (sô-kôl-tĕ-näŋ'gō) Mex.	16.17 N	92.18 W
93	Soconusco (sô-kô-no͞os'kō) Mex.	16.5 N	93.25 W
102	Socorro (sô-kôr'rō) Col.	6.12 N	73.45 W
75	Socorro N. M.	34.4 N	106.54 W
150	Socotra (I.) (sô-kō'trȧ) Asia	12.30 N	54.0 E
126	Socuéllamos (sô-ko͞o-āl'yä-mōs) Sp.	39.18 N	2.48 W
54	Soda Cr. (sō'dȧ) Can.	52.10 N	122.2 W
71	Soda Springs Ida.	42.39 N	111.37 W
120	Söderhamn (sû-dĕr-häm''n) Swe.	61.20 N	17.1 E
120	Söderköping (sû'dĕr-chû'pĭng) Swe.	58.30 N	16.15 E
120	Södertälje (sû-dĕr-tĕl'yĕ) Swe.	59.11 N	17.39 E
160	Soekaboemi (so͞o'kä-bo͞o'mĕ) Neth. Ind.	6.58 S	106.59 E
160	Soekadana (so͞o-kä-dä'nä) Neth. Ind.	1.15 S	109.59 E
160	Soemba (Sumba) (Sandalwood) I. (so͞om-bä) Neth. Ind.	9.45 S	120.0 E
161	Soela Is. (so͞o-lä') Neth. Ind.	1.50 S	126.0 E
160	Soembawa (so͞om-bä'wä) Neth. Ind.	8.35 S	117.25 E
160	Soembawa (Sumbawa) (I.) (so͞om-bä'wä) Neth. Ind.	8.45 S	118.0 E
160	Soerabaja (so͞o-rä-bä'yä) Neth. Ind.	7.22 S	112.40 E
122	Soest (zōst) Ger.	51.35 N	8.5 E
140	Sofala (sô-fä'lä) Moz.	20.7 S	34.40 E
114	Sofeggin, Wadi (R.) (wä'dê sô'f'ĕg-ĕn) Libya	31.22 N	14.0 E
129	Sofia (Sofija) (sô'fê-yȧ) (sô'fê-yȧ) (sô-fĭ'ȧ) Bul.	42.40 N	23.20 E
131	Sofievka (sô-fē'yĕf-kȧ) Sov. Un.	48.3 N	33.51 E
149	Sofiiskoe (sô-fē'ĕs-kô-yĕ) Sov. Un.	51.25 N	139.50 E
129	Sofija (Sofia) (sô'fê-yȧ) Bul.	42.40 N	23.20 E
159	Sogano (sō'gä-nō) Jap. (Tokyo In.)	35.35 N	140.9 E
120	Sogndal (sôghn'däl) Nor.	58.20 N	6.20 E
120	Sogndal Nor.	61.13 N	7.2 E
120	Sogne Fjord (sôgn'ĕ fyôr') Nor.	61.8 N	6.0 E
163	Sogod (sō'gōd) P. I.	10.23 N	125.0 E
163	Sogod B. P. I.	10.20 N	124.55 E
130	Sogozha R. (sō'gô-zhȧ) Sov. Un.	58.30 N	39.0 E
163	Sohoton Pt. (sō-hō-tōn') P. I.	9.59 N	122.27 E
124	Soissons (swä-sôN') Fr.	49.25 N	3.20 E
123	Sokal (sô'käl') Pol.	50.28 N	24.20 E
113	Söke (sû'kĕ) Tur.	37.45 N	27.25 E
138	Sokodé (sô-kô-dā') Fr. W. Afr.	8.58 N	1.4 E
123	Sokólka (sô-ko͞ol'kȧ) Pol.	53.23 N	23.31 E
138	Sokolo (sô-kô-lō) Fr. W. Afr.	14.52 W	69.0 W
123	Sokolów (sô-kô'wo͞of) Pol.	52.25 N	22.14 E
138	Sokoto (sô'kô-tō) Nig.	13.9 N	5.15 E
138	Sokoto (Prov.) Nig.	12.30 N	7.0 E
93	Sola de Vega (San Miguel) (sō'lä dā vā'gä) (sän mê-gāl') Mex.	16.30 N	96.58 W
162	Solana (sō-lä'nä) P. I.	17.39 N	121.41 E
162	Solano P. I.	16.30 N	121.11 E
102	Solar Pt. (sō-lär') Peru (In.)	12.12 S	77.3 W
92	Soledad Díez Gutiérez (sô-lā-dhädh'dē'äz go͞o-tyä'rĕz) Mex.	22.10 N	100.55 W
70	Soleduck R. (sōl'dŭk) Wash.	48.0 N	124.30 W
94	Solentiname Is. (sô-lĕn-tê-nä'mä) Nic.	11.10 N	85.0 W
130	Soligalich (sô-lê-gȧ-lēch') Sov. Un.	59.4 N	42.19 E
118	Solihull (sō'lē-hŭl) Gt. Brit.	52.25 N	1.46 W
112	Solikamsk (Ust-Usolka) (sô-lē-kȧmsk) Sov. Un.	59.35 N	56.45 E
122	Solingen (zō'lĭng-ĕn) Ger.	51.10 N	7.4 E
148	Solitude (Uedineniya) I. (sŏl'ĭ-to͞od) (o͞o'yĕ-dê-nyĕ-nē'yȧ) Sov. Un.	77.30 N	85.50 E
120	Sollefteå (sôl-lĕf'tĕ-ô) Swe.	63.9 N	17.14 E
127	Sóller (sōl'lyĕr) Sp.	39.46 N	2.42 E
160	Solo (sō'lō) Neth. Ind.	7.38 S	110.40 E
160	Solok (sō-lŏk') Neth. Ind.	0.45 S	100.44 E
94	Solola (sô-lō'lä) Guat.	14.45 N	91.12 W
165	Solomon Is. Prot. (sŏl'ô-mŭn) Pac. O.	9.0 S	159.0 E
78	Solomon R. Kan.	39.26 N	98.10 W
78	Solomon R., North Fork Kan.	39.38 N	99.25 W
78	Solomon R., South Fork Kan.	39.25 N	99.20 W
122	Solothurn (zō'lō-tho͞orn) Switz	47.13 N	7.32 E

Page	Name Pronunciation Region	Lat. °′	Long. °′
112	Solovetskie I. (sô'lô-vyĕt-skĭ-yĕ) Sov. Un.	65.10 N	36.0 E
122	Soltau (sôl'tou) Ger.	52.59 N	9.50 E
130	Soltsy (sôl'tsĕ) Sov. Un.	58.5 N	30.11 E
115	Soluch (sō'lo͞och) Libya	31.39 N	20.23 E
153	Solun (sô-lo͞on') Manch.	46.39 N	120.47 E
85	Solvay (sŏl'vā) N. Y.	43.5 N	76.14 W
120	Sölvesborg (sûl'vĕs-bôrg) Swe.	56.4 N	14.35 E
112	Solvychegodsk (sôl-vē-chĕ-gôtsk') Sov. Un.	61.20 N	46.50 E
116	Solway Firth (sŏl'wā fûrth) Gt. Brit.	54.45 N	3.40 W
124	Somain (sô-măN') Fr.	50.20 N	3.15 E
141	Somalia (sō-mä'lē-ä) (Division) It. E. Afr.	6.0 N	47.0 E
129	Sombor (sôm'bôr) Yugo.	45.47 N	19.8 E
92	Sombrerete (sōm-brā-rā'tā) Mex.	23.39 N	103.37 W
82	Somerset (sŭm'ẽr-sĕt) Ky.	37.6 N	84.37 W
85	Somerset Pa.	40.1 N	79.5 W
143	Somerset East U. S. Afr.	32.45 S	25.35 E
142	Somerset West U. S. Afr.	34.5 S	18.49 E
86	Somersworth (sŭm'ẽrz-wûrth) N. H.	43.18 N	70.55 W
75	Somerton (sŭm'ẽr-tŭn) Ariz.	32.35 N	114.43 W
169	Somerton Austl. (Melbourne In.)	37.39 S	144.56 E
88	Somerton Pa. (Philadelphia In.)	40.8 N	75.0 W
86	Somerville (sŭm'ẽr-vĭl) Mass.	42.25 N	71.5 W
82	Somerville Tenn.	35.14 N	89.22 W
81	Somerville Tex.	30.20 N	96.31 W
170	Somes I. (sōmz) N. Z. (In.)	41.15 S	174.52 E
123	Someşul R. (sô-mā'sho͞ol) Rom.	47.20 N	23.46 E
143	Somkele (sôm-kā'lȧ) U. S. Afr.	28.19 S	32.4 E
119	Somma, Mt. (sôm'mä) It. (Napoli In.)	40.49 N	14.25 E
119	Somma Vesuviana (sôm'mä vā-zo͞o-vē-ä'nä) It. (Napoli In.)	40.53 N	14.26 E
124	Somme R. (sôm) Fr.	50.0 N	2.0 E
122	Sommerfeld (zôm'ẽr-fĕlt) Ger.	51.48 N	14.57 E
72	Sommers (sŭm'ẽrz) Colo. (Colo. Sprs. In.)	38.58 N	104.50 W
94	Somoto Grande (sô-mō'tō grän'dĕ) Nic.	13.35 N	86.37 W
126	Son (sōn) Sp.	42.43 N	8.59 W
95	Sona (sō'nä) Pan.	8.0 N	81.20 W
120	Sönderborg (sûn''ẽr-bôrgh) Den.	54.55 N	9.48 E
122	Sondershausen (zôn'dẽrz-hou'zĕn) Ger.	51.17 N	10.45 E
158	Sondin Cho.	40.42 N	129.10 E
128	Sondrio (sôn'drê-ō) It.	46.11 N	9.51 E
120	Sonfjället (Nat. Park) (sōn'fyĕl-ĕt) Swe.	62.20 N	13.28 E
157	Songdo (Kaijo) (sông'dō') Cho.	38.1 N	126.30 E
140	Songea (sôn-gā'ȧ) Tan.	10.43 S	35.40 E
160	Songkhlâ (Singora) (sông'klä') (sĭŋ-gō'rȧ) Thai.	7.8 N	100.35 E
160	Song, Mt. (sông) Sar.	3.25 N	115.0 E
157	Songwha (sŏng'hwä') Cho.	38.23 N	125.7 E
122	Sonneberg (zôn'ē-bĕrgh) Ger.	50.22 N	11.11 E
74	Sonora (sō-nō'rȧ) Calif.	37.58 N	120.22 W
90	Sonora (State) Mex.	31.55 N	113.20 W
80	Sonora Tex.	30.33 N	100.40 W
74	Sonora Pk. Calif.	38.20 N	119.38 W
151	Son R. (sōn) India	24.30 N	83.0 E
126	Sonseca (sôn-sā'kȧ) Sp.	39.43 N	3.57 W
102	Sonsón (sôn-sôn') Col.	5.32 N	75.32 W
94	Sonsonate (sôn-sô-nä'tä) Sal.	13.46 N	89.43 W
161	Sonsorol Is. (sŏn-sô-rôl') Pac. O.	4.40 N	130.20 E
160	Sontay (sôN-tī') Fr. In. Chn.	21.8 N	105.28 E
155	Soochow (so͞o' chō') Chn.	31.15 N	120.32 E
72	Sooke Basin (so͞ok) Can. (Vancouver In.)	48.23 N	123.39 W
72	Sooke Har. Can. (Vancouver In.)	48.22 N	123.43 W
72	Sooke L. Can. (Vancouver In.)	48.33 N	123.42 W
157	Soonan (sō'ō-nän') Cho.	39.13 N	125.39 E
157	Soontyun (sō'ōn-tyo͞on') Cho.	34.58 N	127.31 E
153	Soping (sō'pĭng') Chn.	40.12 N	112.25 E
122	Sopron (shô'prôn) Hung.	47.42 N	16.33 E
128	Sora (sō'rä) It.	41.43 N	13.36 E
102	Sorato (Illampú) (Mt.) (sō-rä'tō) (ê-lyäm-po͞o') Bol.	15.58 S	68.30 W
130	Sorat R. (sō-rát') Sov. Un.	57.8 N	29.20 E
122	Sorau (zō'rou) Ger.	51.38 N	15.7 E
126	Sorbas (sôr'bäs) Sp.	37.5 N	2.6 W
86	Sorel (sô-rĕl') Can.	46.1 N	73.7 W
169	Sorell, C. (sô-rĕl') Austl. (Tas. In.)	42.10 S	145.11 E
169	Sorell, L. Austl. (Tas. In.)	42.8 S	147.11 E
128	Soresina (sō-rȧ-zē'nä) It.	45.14 N	9.44 E
126	Soria (sō'rê-ä) Sp.	41.46 N	2.28 W
99	Soriano (sō-rê-ä'nō) Ur. (Buenos Aires In.)	33.25 S	58.21 W
112	Sormovo (sôr'mô-vô) Sov. Un.	56.28 N	43.35 E
110	Sorö (I.) (sôr'ū) Nor.	70.35 N	22.15 E
131	Soroca (sô-rō'kȧ) Rom.	48.8 N	28.18 E
103	Sorocaba (sō-rô-kä'bȧ) Braz.	23.30 S	47.30 W
123	Soroksár (sō'rôk-shär) Hung.	47.23 N	19.9 E
161	Sorong (sō-rông') Neth. Ind.	1.0 S	131.28 E
139	Soroti (sō-rō'tê) Ug.	1.57 N	33.34 E
126	Sor R. (sôr) Port.	39.10 N	8.5 W
128	Sorraia R. (sôr-rī'ä) Port.	38.58 N	8.30 W
128	Sorrento (sôr-rĕn'tō) It.	40.37 N	14.21 E
162	Sorsogon (sôr-sō-gōn') P. I.	12.59 N	124.0 E
162	Sorsogon B. P. I.	12.50 N	123.50 E
121	Sortavala (sôr'tȧ-vȧ-lȧ) Fin.	61.44 N	30.42 E
131	Sosika R. (sō'sê-kȧ) Sov. Un.	46.25 N	39.20 E
131	Sosna R. (sôs'nȧ) Sov. Un.	50.42 N	38.30 E
131	Sosnitsa (sôs-nē'tsȧ) Sov. Un.	51.31 N	32.29 E
123	Sosnowiec (sôs-nô'vyĕts) Pol.	50.16 N	19.10 E
125	Sospel (sôs-pĕl') Fr.	43.54 N	7.27 E
158	Sosunova, C. (sô-so͞o-nô'vȧ) Sov. Un.	46.30 N	138.22 E
112	Sosva R. (sôs'vȧ) Sov. Un.	63.15 N	63.30 E
93	Soteapan (sō-tā-ȧ'pän) Mex.	18.14 N	94.53 W
92	Soto la Marina (sō'tō lä mä-rē'nä) Mex.	23.46 N	98.12 W

ng-sing; ŋ-baŋk; N-nasalized n; nŏd; cŏmmit; ōld; ôbey; ôrder; fo͞od; fo͝ot; ou-out; s-soft; sh-dish; th-thin; pūre; ûnite; ûrn; stŭd; circŭs; ü-as "y" in study; '-indeterminate vowel.

Page	Name Pronunciation Region	Lat. °'	Long. °'
93	Soto la Marina B. Mex.	23.46 N	96.47 W
92	Soto la Marina, R. Mex.	24.0 N	98.17 W
150	Soueïda (sōō-ā'ê-dȧ) Syr.	32.33 N	36.33 E
91	Soufrière (Vol.) (sōō-frê-âr') Guad.	16.7 N	61.39 W
95	Soufrière (Vol.) Le. Is. (In.)	16.43 N	62.10 W
95	Soufrière (Vol.) Wind. Is. (In.)	13.20 N	61.12 W
114	Souk-Ahras (sōōk-ä-räs') Alg.	36.20 N	7.52 E
135	Souk-el-Arba (sōōk-ĕl-är'bä) Tun. (In.)	36.28 N	8.55 E
57	Soulanges Canal (sōō-läNzh') Can. (Montreal In.)	45.19 N	74.5 W
129	Souphlion (sōōf'lĭ-ôn) Grc.	41.11 N	26.17 E
115	Sour (Tyre) (sōōr) (tīr) Syr.	33.18 N	35.15 E
103	Soure (sōr-ĕ) Braz. (In.)	0.40 S	48.32 W
126	Soure Port.	40.4 N	8.38 W
87	Souris (sōō-rē') Can.	46.20 N	62.17 W
54	Souris R. Can.	49.10 N	101.0 W
81	Sourlake (sour'läk) Tex.	30.8 N	94.24 W
138	Sousse (sōōs) Tun.	35.52 N	10.32 E
124	Soustons (sōōs-tôN') Fr.	43.45 N	1.20 W
119	Southall (soudh''l) Gt. Brit. (London In.)	51.31 N	0.24 W
88	South Amboy (ăm'boi) N. J. (N. Y. In.)	40.29 N	74.18 W
98	South America		
116	Southampton (south-ămp'tŭn) Gt. Brit.	50.55 N	1.25 W
55	Southampton I. Can.	64.35 N	84.30 W
164	South Australia Austl.	30.0 S	135.0 E
166	South B. Austl.	34.35 S	136.5 E
97	South B. Ba. Is.	20.57 N	73.38 W
84	South Bend Ind.	41.40 N	86.18 W
70	South Bend Wash.	46.39 N	123.49 W
96	South Bight Ba. Is.	24.13 N	77.38 W
96	South Bimini I. (bē'mê-nê) Ba. Is.	25.42 N	79.18 W
97	South Bluff (Pt.) Ba. Is.	22.17 N	74.10 W
87	Southboro (south'bŭr-ô) Mass. (In.)	42.18 N	71.32 W
83	South Boston (bôs'tŭn) Va.	36.43 N	78.56 W
72	South Boulder Cr. (bōl'dēr) Colo. (Denver In.)	39.57 N	105.23 W
86	Southbridge (south'brĭj) Mass.	42.5 N	72.5 W
171	Southbridge N. Z.	43.48 S	172.20 E
97	South Caicos I. (kī'kōs) Ba. Is.	21.31 N	71.31 W
171	South C. N. Z.	47.18 S	167.38 E
83	South Carolina (State) (kăr-ô-lī'nȧ) U. S.	34.10 N	81.0 W
118	South Cave Gt. Brit.	53.46 N	0.36 W
88	South Chicago (shĭ-kô'gō) Ill. (Chicago In.)	41.43 N	87.34 W
160	South China Sea Asia	15.0 N	115.0 E
76	South Dakota (State) (dȧ-kō'tȧ) U. S.	44.30 N	100.0 W
116	South Downs (dounz) Gt. Brit.	50.55 N	0.40 W
169	Southeast C. Austl. (Tas. In.)	43.39 S	146.51 E
89	Southeast Pass La. (New Orleans In.)	29.4 N	89.3 W
97	Southeast Pt. Ba. Is.	20.59 N	73.9 W
117	Southend-on-Sea (south-ĕnd') Gt. Brit.	51.32 N	0.42 E
171	Southern Alps (Mts.) N. Z.	43.30 S	170.20 E
164	Southern Cross Austl.	31.10 S	119.28 E
54	Southern Indian L. Can.	57.10 N	99.30 W
83	Southern Pines N. C.	35.8 N	79.22 W
138	Southern Provinces Nig.	7.0 N	5.30 E
140	Southern Rhodesia (rô-dē'zhĭ-ȧ) Afr.	19.0 S	30.0 E
138	Southern Territories (Div.) Alg.	29.0 N	3.0 E
116	Southern Uplands (ŭp'lăndz) Gt. Brit.	55.30 N	4.0 W
75	Southern Ute Ind. Res. (ūt) Colo.-N. M.	37.0 N	108.45 W
119	Southfleet (south'flēt) Gt. Brit. (London In.)	51.25 N	0.19 E
82	South Fulton Tenn.	36.28 N	88.54 W
46	South Georgia I. (jôr'jĭ-ȧ) Ant. O.	54.0 S	37.0 W
46	South Graham I. (grā'ăm) Ant. O.	68.0 S	65.0 W
84	South Haven (hā'v'n) Mich.	42.23 N	86.17 W
81	South Houston (hūs'tŭn) Tex. (In.)	29.40 N	95.13 W
85	Southington (sŭdh'ĭng-tŭn) Conn.	41.37 N	72.55 W
171	South Island N. Z.	44.0 S	170.0 E
83	South Jacksonville Fla.	30.17 N	81.39 W
76	South Loup R. Neb.	41.10 N	99.36 W
169	South Melbourne (mĕl'bŭrn) Austl. (Melbourne In.)	37.50 S	145.0 E
77	South Milwaukee (mĭl-wô'kê) Wis.	42.55 N	87.52 W
96	South Negril Pt. (nâ-grēl') Jam.	18.16 N	78.23 W
85	South Norfolk Va.	36.44 N	76.16 W
119	South Ockendon (ŏk''n-dŭn) Gt. Brit. (London In.)	51.32 N	0.18 E
88	South Orange (ŏr'ĕnj) N. J. (New York In.)	40.45 N	74.16 W
46	South Orkney Is. (ôrk'nê) Ant. O.	61.0 S	45.0 W
113	South Ossetia (Aut. Area) (ô-sē'shĭ-ȧ) Sov. Un.	42.20 N	44.30 E
86	South Paris (păr'ĭs) Me.	44.12 N	70.35 W
73	South Pasadena (păs-ȧ-dē'nȧ) Calif. (Los Angeles In.)	34.7 N	118.10 W
89	South Pass. La. (New Orleans In.)	29.0 N	89.8 W
78	South Pease R. (pēz) Tex.	34.10 N	100.20 W
169	South Perth (pûrth) Austl. (Perth In.)	31.58 S	115.52 E
82	South Pittsburgh (pĭts'bûrg) Tenn.	35.2 N	85.43 W
78	South Platte R. (plăt) Colo.-Neb.	39.45 N	105.0 W
95	South Pt. Barb. (In.)	13.3 N	59.33 W
97	South Pt. (C. Verde) Ba. Is.	22.50 N	74.54 W
84	South Pt. Mich.	44.52 N	85.18 W
89	South Point. La. (New Orleans In.)	30.9 N	89.52 W
46	South Pole		
165	Southport (south'pōrt) Austl.	27.59 S	153.25 E
116	Southport Gt. Brit.	53.38 N	2.55 W
83	Southport N. C.	33.56 N	78.2 W
73	South R. Ga. (Atlanta In.)	33.38 N	84.7 W
83	South R. N. C.	34.50 N	78.30 W
116	South Ronaldshay (rŏn'ăld-sā) Gt. Brit.	58.48 N	3.0 W
77	South St. Paul Minn.	44.52 N	93.2 W
72	South St. Vrains Cr. (sānt vrānz') Colo. (Denver In.)	40.10 N	105.20 W
6	South Sandwich Is. (sănd'wĭch) Ant. O.	58.30 S	26.0 W
49	South San Francisco Calif. (San Francisco In.)	37.39 N	122.25 W
54	South Saskatchewan R. (săs-kăch'ê-wăn) Can.	51.0 N	107.0 W
46	South Shetland Is. (shĕt'lănd) Ant. O.	62.0 S	58.0 W
116	South Shields (shēldz) Gt. Brit.	55.0 N	1.25 W
76	South Sioux City (sōō sĭt'ê) Neb.	42.28 N	96.25 W
170	South Taranaki Bight (tä-rä-nä'kê) N. Z.	39.40 S	174.0 E
116	South Uist I. (wĭst) Gt. Brit.	54.15 N	7.20 W
70	South Umpqua R. (ŭmp'kwȧ) Ore.	43.10 N	123.0 W
72	South Vancouver (văn-kōō'vēr) Can. (Vancouver In.)	49.13 N	123.5 W
46	South Victoria Land (vĭk-tō'rĭ-ȧ) Ant.	74.0 S	160.0 E
118	Southwell (south'wĕl) Gt. Brit.	53.4 N	0.56 W
140	Southwest Africa Afr.	22.0 S	17.0 E
169	South West C. Austl. (Tas. In.)	43.32 S	146.2 E
89	Southwest Pass La. (New Orleans In.)	29.0 N	89.21 W
72	South Westminster (wĕst'mĭn-stēr) Can. (Vancouver In.)	49.11 N	122.52 W
97	Southwest Pt. Ba. Is.	20.58 N	73.40 W
96	Southwest Pt. Ba. Is.	25.50 N	77.13 W
96	Southwest Pt. Ba. Is.	26.27 N	78.40 W
97	Southwest Pt. Ba. Is.	23.55 N	74.3 W
158	Soviet B. (sô-vyĕt') Sov. Un.	49.0 N	140.15 E
144	Soviet Union (sō-vĭ-ĕt') Eurasia	55.0 N	70.0 E
118	Sow, R. (sou) Gt. Brit.	52.49 N	2.9 W
93	Soyaltepec (sō-yäl-tâ-pĕk') Mex.	18.12 N	96.29 W
158	Soyami C. (sô-yä'mê) Jap.	45.29 N	141.55 E
158	Soya Str. (sō'yä) Jap.	45.45 N	142.0 E
158	Sozan Cho.	40.50 N	125.45 E
130	Sozh R. (sôzh) Sov. Un.	53.36 N	31.40 E
129	Sozopol (sôz'ô-pôl') Bul.	42.15 N	27.45 E
117	Spa (spä) Bel.	50.28 N	5.50 E
127	Spain (spān) Eur.	40.30 N	4.0 W
...	Spalato, see Split, Yugo.		
116	Spalding (spôl'dĭng) Gt. Brit.	52.45 N	0.10 W
76	Spalding Neb.	41.43 N	98.21 W
49	Spanaway (spăn'ȧ-wā) Wash. (Seattle In.)	47.6 N	122.27 W
122	Spandau (shpän'dou) Ger.	52.33 N	13.10 E
85	Spangler (spăng'lēr) Pa.	40.40 N	78.48 W
75	Spanish Fork Utah	40.7 N	111.40 W
138	Spanish Guinea (gĭn'ê) Afr.	3.0 N	9.30 E
96	Spanish Town Jam.	17.59 N	76.58 W
74	Sparks (spärks) Nev.	39.33 N	119.45 W
88	Sparrows Pt. (spăr'ō) Md. (Baltimore In.)	39.12 N	76.28 W
82	Sparta (spär'tȧ) Ga.	33.16 N	82.58 W
129	Sparta (Sparte) (spär'tē) Grc.	37.5 N	22.25 E
79	Sparta Ill.	38.7 N	89.40 W
84	Sparta Mich.	43.10 N	85.44 W
82	Sparta Tenn.	35.55 N	85.27 W
77	Sparta Wis.	43.57 N	90.48 E
83	Spartanburg (spär'tăn-bûrg) S. C.	34.57 N	81.57 W
129	Sparte (Sparta) (spär'tē) (spȧr'tȧ) Grc.	37.5 N	22.25 E
135	Spartel, C. (spär-tĕl') Tangier (Gibraltar In.)	35.46 N	5.6 E
128	Spartivento, C. (spär-tê-vĕn'tō) It.	37.55 N	16.5 E
128	Spartivento, C. Sard.	38.54 N	8.51 E
130	Spas Denmensk (spȧs dyĕ-mĕnsk') Sov. Un.	54.24 N	34.2 E
130	Spas Klepiki (spȧs klĕp'ê-kê) Sov. Un.	55.9 N	40.9 E
149	Spassk (spȧsk) Sov. Un.	44.40 N	132.50 E
130	Spassk Sov. Un.	54.24 N	40.26 E
128	Spathi, C. (spä'thê) Grc.	35.40 N	23.43 E
166	Spaulding (spôl'dĭng) Austl.	33.29 S	138.38 E
87	Spear, C. (spēr) Newfl.	47.30 N	52.40 W
76	Spearfish (spēr'fĭsh) S. D.	44.29 N	103.51 W
84	Spencer (spĕn'sēr) Ind.	39.16 N	86.48 W
77	Spencer Ia.	43.9 N	95.6 W
83	Spencer N. C.	35.42 N	80.25 W
85	Spencer W. Va.	38.52 N	81.20 W
166	Spencer, C. Austl.	35.15 S	136.55 E
166	Spencer G. Austl.	33.55 S	137.22 E
171	Spenser Mts. N. Z.	42.10 S	172.45 E
129	Sperkheios R. (spĕr'ĸê-ŏs) Grc.	38.52 N	22.20 E
116	Sperrin Mts. (spĕr'ĭn) Gt. Brit.	54.55 N	6.50 W
116	Spey, (R.) (spā) Gt. Brit.	57.20 N	3.20 W
122	Speyer (shpī'ēr) Ger.	49.19 N	8.25 E
128	Spezia (spät'sê-ä) It.	44.17 N	9.48 E
141	Sphinx (sfĭnks) Eg.	29.59 N	31.8 E
161	Spice Is. (Moluccas) (spīs) (mô-lŭk'ȧz) Neth. Ind.	1.0 S	128.0 E
128	Spinazzolo (spê-nät'zô-lō) It.	40.58 N	16.5 E
143	Spioen Kop (Mt.) (spê-ōōn' kŏp') U. S. Afr.	29.26 S	29.47 E
123	Spirding L. (shpēr'dĭng) Ger.	53.45 N	21.45 E
171	Spire Park, Mt. (spīr) N. Z.	45.22 S	167.30 E
70	Spirit L. (spĭr'ĭt) Ida.	47.57 N	116.53 W
77	Spirit Lake Ia.	43.25 N	95.5 W
123	Spišská Nová Ves (spĕsh'skä nō'vä vĕs) Czech.	48.57 N	20.33 E
119	Spital (spĭt'ăl) Gt. Brit. (Liverpool In.)	53.20 N	2.59 W
46	Spitsbergen (Svalbard) (spĭts'bûr-gĕn) (sväl'bärt) Arc. O.	79.0 N	16.0 E
122	Spittal (shpê-täl') Ger.	46.48 N	13.30 E
142	Spitzkop (Mt.) (spĕts'kŏp) U. S. Afr.	31.41 S	22.50 E
128	Split (Spalato) (splêt) (spä'lä-tō) Yugo.	43.31 N	16.26 E
70	Spokane (spō-kăn') Wash.	47.40 N	117.29 W
70	Spokane R. Wash.	47.45 N	118.0 W
128	Spoleto (spô-lā'tō) It.	42.45 N	12.43 E
77	Spooner (spōōn'ēr) Wis.	45.50 N	91.52 W
79	Spoon R. (spōōn) Ill.	40.45 N	90.10 W
129	Sporades (Is.) (spô'rȧ-dēz) Grc.	37.40 N	26.40 E
129	Sporades, Northern (Is.) Grc.	39.0 N	24.0 E
70	Sprague R. (sprāg) Ore.	42.30 N	121.40 W
70	Sprague R., North Fork Ore.	42.47 N	121.0 W
160	Spratley (Storm) I. (sprăt'lê) Asia	8.39 N	111.51 E
83	Spray (sprā) N. C.	36.31 N	79.45 W
122	Spree R. (shprā) Ger.	51.45 N	14.20 E
122	Spremberg (shprĕm-bĕrgh) Ger.	51.35 N	14.22 E
142	Springbok (sprĭng'bŏk) U. S. Afr.	29.39 S	17.51 E
88	Spring Brook N. Y. (Niagara Falls In.)	42.49 N	78.41 W
74	Spring Cr. Nev.	40.20 N	117.48 W
80	Spring Cr. Tex.	31.10 N	100.55 W
79	Springdale (sprĭng'dāl) Ark.	36.11 N	94.8 W
78	Springer (sprĭng'ēr) N. M.	36.21 N	104.35 W
78	Springfield (sprĭng'fēld) Colo.	37.25 N	102.37 W
79	Springfield Ill.	39.47 N	89.38 W
84	Springfield Ky.	37.43 N	85.12 W
86	Springfield Mass.	42.5 N	72.35 W
77	Springfield Minn.	44.15 N	94.59 W
79	Springfield Mo.	37.14 N	93.17 W
84	Springfield Ohio	39.56 N	83.48 W
70	Springfield Ore.	44.1 N	123.1 W
82	Springfield Tenn.	36.30 N	86.53 W
86	Springfield Vt.	43.18 N	72.30 W
143	Springfontein (sprĭng'fôn-tīn) U. S. Afr.	30.18 S	25.41 E
86	Springhill (sprĭng-hĭl') Can.	45.38 N	64.4 W
167	Springhurst (sprĭng'hûrst) Austl.	36.12 S	146.28 E
79	Spring R. Ark.-Mo.	36.25 N	91.32 W
143	Springs U. S. Afr.	26.15 S	28.26 E
56	Springstein (sprĭng'stīn) Can. (Winnipeg In.)	49.48 N	97.27 W
74	Spring Valley Calif. (In.)	32.46 N	117.1 W
79	Springvalley Ill.	41.19 N	89.14 W
77	Spring Valley Minn.	43.41 N	92.22 W
73	Springville (sprĭng'vĭl) Ala. (Birmingham In.)	33.47 N	86.28 W
75	Springville Utah	40.10 N	111.37 W
122	Sprottau (sprô'tou) Ger.	51.34 N	15.32 E
78	Spur (spûr) Tex.	33.27 N	100.51 W
116	Spurn Hd. (spûrn) Gr. Brit.	53.55 N	0.10 E
52	Spurr, Mt. Alsk. (In.)	61.20 N	152.10 W
72	Squamish (skwŏ'mĭsh) Can. (Vancouver In.)	49.42 N	123.11 W
128	Squillace, G. of (skwêl-lä'chā) It.	38.45 N	16.40 E
129	Srbobran (s'r'bô-brän) Yugo.	45.34 N	19.49 E
149	Sredne Kolymsk (s'ryĕd'nyĕ kô-lêmsk') Sov. Un.	67.20 N	154.55 E
123	Śrem (shrĕm) Pol.	52.7 N	17.2 E
149	Sretensk (s'r-yĕ'tĕnsk) Sov. Un.	52.15 N	117.20 E
151	Srinagar (srē-nŭg'ŭr) India	34.7 N	74.45 E
123	Środa (shrō'dä) Pol.	52.13 N	17.17 E
119	Staaken (shtä'kĕn) Ger. (Berlin In.)	52.32 N	13.9 E
119	Stabroeck (stä'brōōk) Bel. (Anvers In.)	51.20 N	4.21 E
122	Stade (shtä'dĕ) Ger.	53.36 N	9.29 E
120	Städjan (Mt.) (stĕd'yän) Swe.	61.53 N	12.52 E
119	Stadlau (shtät'lou) Aus. (Wien In.)	48.13 N	16.27 E
110	Stadur (stä'dōōr) Ice.	65.8 N	21.5 W
116	Stafford (stăf'fērd) Gt. Brit.	52.50 N	2.10 W
78	Stafford Kan.	37.57 N	98.37 W
118	Stafford Co. Gt. Brit.	52.50 N	2.0 W
119	Stahnsdorf (shtäns'dôrf) Ger. (Berlin In.)	52.23 N	13.13 E
125	Stains (stăN) Fr. (In.)	48.57 N	2.23 E
113	Stalin (stä'lēn) Sov. Un.	47.59 N	37.48 E
151	Stalin, Mt. Sov. Un.	39.0 N	72.0 E
148	Stalinabad (Dyushambe) (stä'lên-ȧ-bät) (dyōō-shäm'bĕ) Sov. Un.	38.45 N	68.50 E
113	Stalingrad (stä'lên-grät) Sov. Un.	48.40 N	44.30 E
148	Stalinsk (Kuznetsk) (stä'lênsk) Sov. Un.	53.55 N	87.10 E
123	Stallupönen (shtäl'ōō-pû-nĕn) Ger.	54.37 N	22.37 E
118	Stalybridge (stā'lê-brĭj) Gt. Brit.	53.29 N	2.3 W
77	Stambaugh (stăm'bô) Mich.	46.4 N	88.36 W
85	Stamford (stăm'fērd) Conn.	41.3 N	73.34 W
118	Stamford Gt. Brit.	52.38 N	0.28 W
80	Stamford Tex.	32.56 N	99.49 W
118	Stamford Bridge Gt. Brit.	53.59 N	0.54 W
119	Stammersdorf (shtäm'ērs dôrf) Aus. (Wien In.)	48.18 N	16.25 E
79	Stamps (stămps) Ark.	33.21 N	93.29 W
79	Stanberry (stăn'bĕr-ê) Mo.	40.12 N	94.33 W
143	Standerton (stăn'dēr-tŭn) U. S. Afr.	26.55 S	29.16 E
118	Standish (stăn'dĭsh) Gt. Brit.	53.35 N	2.39 W
72	Standley L. (stănd'lê) Colo. (Denver In.)	39.53 N	105.7 W
84	Stanford (stăn'fērd) Ky.	37.30 N	84.42 W
142	Stanford U. S. Afr.	34.27 S	19.22 E
119	Stanford-le-Hope (lē-hōp') Gt. Brit. (London In.)	51.31 N	0.26 E
143	Stanger (stăng'ēr) U. S. Afr.	29.19 S	31.20 E
120	Stangvik Fd. (stäng'vêk) Nor.	62.54 N	8.27 E
129	Stanimaka (stä-nê-mä'kä) Bul.	42.0 N	24.51 E
74	Stanislaus R. (stăn'ĭs-lô) Calif.	37.47 N	121.0 W
123	Stanisławów (stä-nê-swä'vōōf) Pol.	48.54 N	24.44 E
169	Stanley (stăn'lê) Austl. (Tas. In.)	40.45 S	145.16 E
54	Stanley Can.	55.25 N	104.29 W
86	Stanley Can.	46.18 N	66.45 W
76	Stanley N. D.	48.18 N	102.22 W
77	Stanley Wis.	44.57 N	90.55 W

ăt; finăl; rāte; senâte; ärm; ȧsk; sofȧ; fâre; ch-choose; dh-as th in other; bē; ēvent; bĕt; recĕnt; cratēr; g-go; gh-gutteral g; bĭt; ĭ-short neutral; rīde; ĸ-gutteral k as ch in German ich;

Page	Name Pronunciation Region	Lat. °′	Long. °′
104	Stanley................Falk. Is.	51.45 S	57.50 W
139	Stanley Falls..........Bel. Cong.	0.15 N	25.30 E
140	Stanley Pool Bel. Cong.-Fr. Eq. Afr.	4.10 S	15.35 E
166	Stanley Ra. (Main Barrier). Austl.	31.20 S	141.27 E
139	Stanleyville (stăn'lė-vĭl). Bel. Cong.	0.32 S	25.15 E
94	Stann Creek (stăn-krēk') Br. Hond. (In.)	17.0 N	88.14 W
149	Stanovoi Mts. (stä-nô-vô'ĭ) Sov. Un.	56.30 N	135.0 E
169	Stanthorpe (stăn'thōrp) Austl. (In.)	28.37 S	151.58 E
73	Stanton (stăn'tŭn) Calif. (Los Angeles In.)	33.49 N	118.0 W
76	Stanton....................Neb.	41.58 N	97.14 W
80	Stanton....................Tex.	32.7 N	101.47 W
49	Stanwood (stăn'wo͝od) Wash. (Seattle In.)	48.15 N	122.21 W
119	Stapelfeld (shtä'pĕl-fĕlt) Ger. (Hamburg In.)	53.36 N	10.13 E
77	Staples (stā'p'lz)..........Minn.	46.22 N	94.46 W
88	Stapleton (stā'p'l-tŭn). N. Y. (In.)	40.38 N	74.5 W
129	Stara Kanjiža (stä'rȧ kȧn'yê-zhȧ) Yugo.	46.5 N	20.2 E
130	Staraya Kazinka (stä'rȧ-yȧ kȧ'zêŋ-kȧ) Sov. Un.	52.50 N	40.8 E
130	Staraya Russa (stä'rȧ-yȧ ro͞os'sȧ) Sov. Un.	57.59 N	31.21 E
129	Stara Zagora (stä'rȧ zä'gô-rȧ). Bul.	42.25 N	25.38 E
56	Starbuck (stär'bŭk) Can. (Winnipeg In.)	49.46 N	97.35 W
6	Starbuck I...............Pac. O.	5.37 S	155.53 W
122	Stargard (shtär'gärt).........Ger.	53.20 N	15.3 E
129	Stari Bečej (stä'rê bĕ'chā-ê). Yugo.	45.36 N	20.2 E
130	Staritsa (stä'rê-tsȧ).......Sov. Un.	56.29 N	34.59 E
83	Starke (stärk)...............Fla.	29.57 N	82.7 W
78	Starkville (stärk'vĭl).........Colo.	37.6 N	104.33 W
82	Starkville..................Miss.	33.27 N	88.49 W
131	Starobelsk (stä-rô-byĕlsk') Sov. Un.	49.17 N	38.57 E
130	Starobino (stä'rô-bē'nô)..Sov. Un.	52.46 N	27.28 E
130	Starodub (stä-rô-do͞op')..Sov. Un.	52.35 N	32.49 E
123	Starogard (stä'rô-gär')........Pol.	53.53 N	18.32 E
131	Staro Shcherbinovka (stä'rô shchĕr'bê-nôf'kȧ)...Sov. Un.	46.37 N	38.37 E
131	Staroverovka (stä'rō-vyĕ'rôf-kȧ) Sov. Un.	49.32 N	35.44 E
116	Start Pt. (stärt).........Gt. Brit.	50.15 N	3.35 W
130	Stary Bykhov (stä'rê bēK'ôf) Sov. Un.	53.32 N	30.15 E
131	Stary-Oskol (stä'rê-ôs-kôl') Sov. Un.	51.18 N	37.50 E
123	Stary Sącz (stä-rê sôŋch')....Pol.	49.34 N	20.37 E
130	Stary Seslavino (stä'rê sĕs-lȧ'vê-nô) Sov. Un.	53.11 N	40.21 E
122	Staszfurt (shtäs'fo͝ort).......Ger.	51.53 N	11.33 E
123	Staszów (stä'sho͝of)..........Pol.	50.33 N	21.11 E
85	State College.................Pa.	40.48 N	77.56 W
104	Staten I. (stăt'ĕn)...........Arg.	54.45 S	64.0 W
88	Staten Island.........N. Y. (In.)	40.34 N	74.10 W
83	Statesboro (stāts'bŭr-ô).......Ga.	32.26 N	81.48 W
83	Statesville (stāts'vĭl)........N. C.	35.46 N	80.54 W
72	Statlu L. (stăt'lo͞o) Can. (Vancouver In.)	49.33 N	122.5 W
79	Staunton (stôn'tŭn)...........Ill.	39.0 N	39.47 W
85	Staunton......................Va.	38.10 N	79.5 W
120	Stavanger (stä'väng-ẽr)......Nor.	58.59 N	5.45 E
72	Stave Falls (stāv) Can. (Vancouver In.)	49.14 N	122.21 W
72	Stave L.....Can. (Vancouver In.)	49.20 N	122.17 W
118	Staveley (stāv'lė).......Gt. Brit.	53.16 N	1.21 W
72	Stave R.....Can. (Vancouver In.)	49.13 N	122.23 W
112	Stavropol (stäv'rô-pôl')..Sov. Un.	53.30 N	49.15 E
113	Stavropol..............Sov. Un.	45.5 N	42.0 E
166	Stawell (stā'wĕl)...........Austl.	37.5 S	142.48 E
78	Steamboat Springs..........Colo.	40.28 N	106.49 W
73	Stearn (stûrn) Calif. (Los Angeles In.)	33.53 N	117.48 W
131	Steblev (styĕp'lyôf).....Sov. Un.	49.23 N	31.4 E
77	Steel R. (stēl)...............Can.	49.0 N	86.51 W
85	Steelton (stēl'tŭn).............Pa.	40.14 N	76.46 W
143	Steenkamps Bert (Mts.) (stān'kämps). U. S. Afr.	25.20 S	30.10 E
70	Steens Mts. (stēnz)..........Ore.	42.30 N	118.45 W
164	Steep Pt....................Austl.	26.12 S	113.8 E
139	Stefanie (Chalbe), L. (stĕf-ȧ-nē') (chäl'bȧ). It. E. Afr.	4.45 N	36.50 E
46	Stefansson Str. (stĕ'făn-sōn) Ant. O.	70.0 S	60.0 W
84	Steger (stē'gẽr)...............Ill.	41.26 N	87.38 W
122	Steiermark (Prov.) (shtī'ẽr-märk) Ger.	47.15 N	15.0 E
49	Steilacoom (stê'lȧ-ko͞om) Wash. (Seattle In.)	47.10 N	122.36 W
122	Stein (shtīn).................Ger.	48.25 N	15.33 E
142	Steinkamp's Poort (Mt.) (stīn'kämps pōrt). U. S. Afr.	32.8 S	21.49 E
119	Steinkirchen (shtīn'kēr-Kĕn) Ger. (Hamburg In.)	53.34 N	9.36 E
142	Steinkopf (stīn'kôpf)....U. S. Afr.	29.15 S	17.42 E
119	Stekene (stĕk'ĕ-nĕ) Bel. (Anvers In.)	51.12 N	4.3 E
49	Stella (stĕl'ȧ) Wash. (Portland In.)	46.11 N	123.6 W
87	Stellarton (stĕl'ȧr-tŭn).......Can.	45.32 N	62.41 W
142	Stellenbosch (stĕl'ĕn-bōsh) U. S. Afr.	33.56 S	18.50 E
88	Stemmers Run (stĕm'ẽrz) Md. (Baltimore In.)	39.20 N	76.28 W
122	Stendal (shtĕn'däl)..........Ger.	52.36 N	11.50 E
110	Stenkjaer (stĭn'kyĕr).........Nor.	64.0 N	11.30 E
113	Stepanakert (styĕ'pän-ȧ-kĕrt) Sov. Un.	39.50 N	46.40 E
131	Stepantsi (styĕp'än-tsê)..Sov. Un.	49.43 N	31.14 E
56	Stephens I. (stē'vĕnz) Can. (Prince Rupert In.)	54.10 N	130.45 W
169	Stephenson, Mt. (stē'vĕn-sŭn) Austl. (In.)	27.53 S	152.20 E
167	Stephens Pt...............Austl.	32.45 S	152.12 E
80	Stephenville (stē'vĕn-vĭl).....Tex.	32.13 N	98.11 W
143	Sterkstroom (stĕrk'strōm) U.S. Afr.	31.32 S	26.32 E
78	Sterling (stûr'lĭng)..........Colo.	40.37 N	103.14 W
77	Sterling......................Ill.	41.47 N	89.42 W
78	Sterling.....................Kan.	38.13 N	98.12 W
87	Sterling.............Mass. (In.)	42.26 N	71.45 W
80	Sterling City.................Tex.	31.50 N	100.59 W
112	Sterlitamak (styĕr'lê-tȧ-mȧk') Sov. Un.	53.55 N	55.55 E
123	Sternberg (Sternberk) (shtĕrn'-bĕrK) (šhtĕrn'bĕrk). Ger.	49.43 N	17.18 E
	Sternberk, see Sternberg, Ger.		
73	Sterrett (stĕr'ĕt) Ala. (Birmingham In.)	33.27 N	86.28 W
122	Stettin (shtĕ-tēn')...........Ger.	53.26 N	14.32 E
122	Stettiner Hoff (Sea) (shtĕ'tē-nẽr hôf'). Ger.	53.45 N	14.15 E
84	Steubenville (stū'bĕn-vĭl)....Ohio	40.24 N	80.40 W
77	Stevens Point (stē'vĕnz).....Wis.	44.31 N	89.32 W
71	Stevensville (stē'vĕnz-vĭl)...Mont.	46.30 N	114.6 W
70	Steveston (stēvz'tŭn).........Can.	49.5 N	123.8 W
99	Stewart I. (stū'ẽrt) Chl. (Magallanes In.)	54.55 S	71.20 W
171	Stewart I....................N. Z.	47.0 S	168.0 E
54	Stewart R...................Can.	63.30 N	138.0 W
86	Stewiacke (stū'wê-ăk).......Can.	45.9 N	63.21 W
143	Steynsburg (stīnz'bûrg)..U. S. Afr.	31.19 S	25.48 E
143	Steynsdorp (stīnz'dôrf)..U. S. Afr.	26.9 S	30.58 E
122	Steyr (shtīr)..................Ger.	48.2 N	14.24 E
143	Steytlerville (stīt'lẽr-vĭl). U. S. Afr.	33.19 S	24.19 E
119	Stifford (stĭf'ẽrd) Gt. Brit. (London In.)	51.30 N	0.18 E
53	Stikine Mts. (stĭ-kēn')......Can.	59.0 N	129.0 W
54	Stikine R. (stĭ-kēn')........Can.	57.30 N	131.30 W
49	Stilaguamish R. (stĭl-ȧ-gwä'mĭsh) Wash. (Seattle In.)	48.12 N	122.20 W
142	Stil Bay (stĭl)..........U. S. Afr.	34.21 S	21.25 E
142	Stilbaai (stĭl'bā-ê)......U. S. Afr.	34.21 S	21.21 E
77	Stillwater (stĭl'wô-tẽr)......Minn.	45.4 N	92.49 W
79	Stillwater...................Okla.	36.7 N	97.3 W
70	Stillwater R................Mont.	48.45 N	114.40 W
70	Stillwater R................Mont.	45.30 N	109.50 W
129	Štip (shtĭp).................Yugo.	41.43 N	22.7 E
116	Stirling (stûr'lĭng).......Gt. Brit.	56.5 N	3.55 W
120	Stjördalen (styûr'dā-lĕn).....Nor.	63.27 N	10.58 E
123	Stochod R. (stôK-o͝ot)........Pol.	51.20 N	25.10 E
73	Stockbridge (stŏk'brĭj) Ga. (Atlanta In.)	33.33 N	84.14 W
122	Stockerau (shtô'kē-rou)......Ger.	48.24 N	16.12 E
86	Stockholm (stŏk'hōlm)........Me.	47.5 N	68.10 W
120	Stockholm (stôk'hôlm).......Swe.	59.20 N	18.0 E
116	Stockport (stŏk'pōrt)....Gt. Brit.	53.25 N	2.10 W
74	Stockton (stŏk'tŭn).........Calif.	37.56 N	121.18 W
116	Stockton................Gt. Brit.	54.35 N	1.22 W
78	Stockton....................Kan.	39.26 N	99.16 W
119	Stockton Heath Gt. Brit. (Liverpool In.)	53.22 N	2.34 W
77	Stockton I...................Wis.	46.55 N	90.35 W
120	Stöde (stû'dĕ)...............Swe.	62.28 N	16.38 E
116	Stoke-on-Trent (stōk-ŏn-trĕnt) Gt. Brit.	53.0 N	2.10 W
169	Stokes Pt. (stōks). Austl. (Tas. In.)	40.10 S	143.55 E
129	Stolac (stô'lȧts)............Yugo.	43.4 N	17.59 E
122	Stolberg (shtôl'bĕrgh)........Ger.	50.47 N	6.13 E
149	Stolbovoi I. (stô-lô-voi'). Sob. Un.	74.0 N	136.0 E
123	Stolin (stô'lēn)...............Pol.	51.53 N	26.50 E
123	Stolp (shtôlp)................Ger.	54.27 N	17.3 E
122	Stolpmünde (shtôlp'mün-dĕ)..Ger.	54.34 N	16.51 E
142	Stolzenfels (stôl'tsĕn-fĕls) S.W. Afr.	28.28 S	19.40 E
118	Stone (stōn)............Gt. Brit.	52.54 N	2.9 W
87	Stoneham (stōn'ăm)...Mass. (In.)	42.28 N	71.6 W
116	Stonehaven (stōn'hā-v'n). Gt. Brit.	56.55 N	2.13 W
73	Stone Mountain. Ga. (Atlanta In.)	33.48 N	84.10 W
56	Stonewall (stōn'wôl) Can. (Winnipeg In.)	50.9 N	97.18 W
73	Stonewall.......Ga. (Atlanta In.)	33.35 N	84.33 W
82	Stonewall...................Miss.	32.8 N	88.46 W
85	Stonington (stōn'ĭng-tŭn)..Conn.	41.20 N	71.56 W
74	Stony Cr. (stō'nė)..........Calif.	39.30 N	122.37 W
88	Stony Cr........Ill. (Chicago In.)	41.41 N	87.44 W
166	Stony Crossing..............Austl.	35.5 S	143.35 E
85	Stony Lake...................Can.	45.45 N	79.25 W
56	Stony Mountain Can. (Winnipeg In.)	50.5 N	97.13 W
167	Stony Point................Austl.	38.22 S	145.12 E
110	Stora Lule R. (sto͝o'rā-lo͞o'lĕ). Swe.	66.15 N	20.47 E
120	Stord I. (stôrd)..............Nor.	59.52 N	5.30 E
120	Storesotra (Sartor) (I.) (stô-rĕ-sô'trȧ) (sär'tôr). Nor.	60.18 N	5.8 E
120	Stor Fjord (stôr).............Nor.	62.23 N	6.15 E
120	Stor L........................Swe.	63.12 N	14.15 E
120	Stor L........................Nor.	61.35 N	11.12 E
169	Storm B.........Austl. (Tas. In.)	43.10 S	147.35 E
143	Stormberg R. (stôrm'bûrg) U.S. Afr.	31.0 S	26.20 E
160	Storm (Spratley) I. (sprăt'lė). Asia	8.39 N	111.51 E
77	Storm L. (stôrm)...............Ia.	42.40 N	95.10 W
72	Storm Mt......Colo. (Denver In.)	40.29 N	105.23 W
143	Storm Mts..............U. S. Afr.	31.25 S	27.0 E
91	Stormy Pt...........Vir. Is. (In.)	18.22 N	65.0 W
116	Stornoway (stôr'nô-wā)..Gt. Brit.	58.15 N	6.20 W
123	Storojinet (stô-rô-zhĭ'nĕts)..Rom.	48.11 N	25.45 E
120	Stor R........................Nor.	58.38 N	6.10 E
120	Storrsjö (stôr'shû)...........Swe.	62.50 N	13.2 E
120	Storvik (stôr'vêk)...........Swe.	60.37 N	16.31 E
89	Story (stō'rê) La. (New Orleans In.)	29.55 N	89.55 W
87	Stoughton (stō'tŭn)....Mass. (In.)	42.7 N	71.5 W
77	Stoughton....................Wis.	42.55 N	89.14 W
116	Stour (R.) (stour).......Gt. Brit.	50.55 N	2.0 W
118	Stourbridge (stour'brĭj)..Gt. Brit.	52.27 N	2.9 W
118	Stourport (stour'pōrt)....Gt. Brit.	52.20 N	2.16 W
87	Stow (stō)............Mass. (In.)	42.26 N	71.30 W
116	Strabane (strȧ-băn')........N. Ire.	54.52 N	7.22 W
165	Stradbroke I. (străd'brōk)..Austl.	27.35 S	153.29 E
169	Strahan (strā'ăn). Austl. (Tas. In.)	42.8 S	145.19 E
160	Straits Settlements...........Asia	4.0 N	102.0 E
122	Strakonice (strä'kô-nyê-tsĕ) Czech.	49.17 N	13.51 E
129	Straldža (sträl'dzhȧ)..........Bul.	42.35 N	26.38 E
122	Stralsund (shträl'so͝ont)......Ger.	54.19 N	13.3 E
120	Strand (stränd)...............Nor.	59.4 N	6.0 E
72	Strandell (strănd'ĕl) Wash. (Vancouver In.)	48.55 N	122.21 W
116	Strangford, Lough (L.) (lŏK străng'fẽrd). N. Ire.	54.25 N	5.40 W
120	Strångnås (strĕng'nĕs).......Swe.	59.22 N	17.0 E
116	Stranraer (străn-rär')....Gt. Brit.	54.50 N	5.0 W
125	Strasbourg (stràs-bo͞or').......Fr.	48.35 N	7.50 E
167	Stratford (străt'fẽrd).......Austl.	37.58 S	147.5 E
84	Stratford....................Can.	43.24 N	81.0 W
85	Stratford...................Conn.	41.8 N	73.8 W
119	Stratford...Gt. Brit. (London In.)	51.33 N	0.1 W
170	Stratford....................N. Z.	39.20 S	174.15 E
77	Stratford.....................Wis.	44.47 N	90.3 W
116	Stratford-on-Avon (ā'vŏn) Gt. Brit.	52.13 N	1.45 W
167	Strathbogie Ra. (străth-bō'gê) Austl.	36.53 S	145.50 E
169	Strathfield (străth'fēld) Austl. (Sydney In.)	33.52 S	151.6 E
122	Straubing (strou'bĭng)........Ger.	48.53 N	12.34 E
122	Strausberg (strous'bĕrgh).....Ger.	52.36 N	13.52 E
73	Strawberry Utah (Salt Lake City In.)	41.7 N	111.49 W
72	Strawberry Hill Can. (Vancouver In.)	49.9 N	122.54 W
75	Strawberry R ....Utah	40.5 N	111.0 W
80	Strawn (strôn)...............Tex.	32.34 N	98.28 W
123	Strážnice (sträzh'nyê-tsĕ)...Czech.	48.55 N	17.20 E
79	Streator (strē'tẽr).............Ill.	41.7 N	88.49 W
76	Streeter....................N. D.	46.39 N	99.22 W
129	Strehaia (strĕ-Kä'yȧ)........Rom.	44.36 N	23.11 E
123	Strehlen (shtrā'lĕn)..........Ger.	50.47 N	17.4 E
118	Stretford (strĕt'fẽrd).....Gt. Brit.	53.26 N	2.19 W
119	Stretton (strĕ'tŭn) Gt. Brit. (Liverpool In.)	53.20 N	2.34 W
161	Strickland R. (strĭk'lănd) Pap. Ter.	6.30 S	142.1 E
122	Striegau (shtrē'gou).........Ger.	50.58 N	16.20 E
73	Stringers (strĭng'ẽrz) Utah (Salt Lake City In.)	40.45 N	111.45 W
128	Stromboli (Vol.) (strôm'bô-lē)..It.	38.47 N	15.3 E
120	Strömstad (strûm'städ)......Swe.	58.58 N	11.8 E
82	Strong R. (strông)..........Miss.	32.0 N	89.53 W
116	Stronsay (I.) (strŏn'sā) Gt. Brit. (In.)	59.5 N	2.40 W
72	Strontia Sprs. (strŏn'shȧ) Colo. (Denver In.)	39.27 N	105.8 W
167	Stroud (stroud)............Austl.	32.26 S	151.59 E
85	Stroudsburg (stroudz'bûrg).....Pa.	40.59 N	75.13 W
129	Struma R. (stro͞o'mȧ).........Bul.	42.0 N	23.2 E
129	Strumica (stro͞o-mĭ'tsȧ).....Yugo.	41.26 N	22.39 E
84	Struthers (strŭdh'ẽrz).......Ohio	41.2 N	80.37 W
142	Struys Pt. (strīz).......U. S. Afr.	34.42 S	20.12 E
142	Strydenburg (strī'dĕn-bûrg) U. S. Afr.	29.58 S	23.42 E
123	Stryj (strē')...................Pol.	49.15 N	23.51 E
123	Stryj R.......................Pol.	49.10 N	23.45 E
129	Stryman, G. of (strē'mȧn)....Grc.	40.40 N	23.50 E
167	Strzelecki Ra. (stzhĕ-lă'tskê) Austl.	38.30 S	146.30 E
123	Strzelno (stzhăl'nô)...........Pol.	52.37 N	18.11 E
164	Stuart (Alice Sprs.) (stū'ẽrt) Austl.	23.38 S	133.50 E
83	Stuart..............Fla. (In.)	27.11 N	80.15 W
77	Stuart.........................Ia.	41.31 N	94.19 W
72	Stuart Chan. Can. (Vancouver In.)	48.57 N	123.40 W
72	Stuart I...Wash. (Vancouver In.).	48.41 N	123.12 W
164	Stuarts Ra..................Austl.	29.30 S	135.0 E
120	Struer (stro͞o'ẽr).............Den.	56.29 N	8.36 E
160	Stungtreng (sto͝ong'-trĕng') Fr. In. Chn.	13.38 N	105.53 E
77	Sturgeon B...................Wis.	44.51 N	87.21 W
77	Sturgeon R. (stûr'jŭn)......Mich.	46.45 N	88.36 W
84	Sturgis (stûr'jĭs)..............Ky.	37.35 N	87.59 W
84	Sturgis.....................Mich.	41.46 N	85.25 W
76	Sturgis.....................S. D.	44.25 N	103.30 W
166	Sturt B. (stûrt)............Austl.	35.10 S	137.25 E
164	Sturt Cr....................Austl.	19.30 S	128.0 E
143	Stutterheim (stŭt'ẽr-hīm) U. S. Afr.	32.35 S	27.26 E
79	Stuttgart (stŭt'gärt).........Ark.	34.30 N	91.33 W
122	Stuttgart (shto͝ot'gärt).......Ger.	48.50 N	9.11 E
119	Styal (stī'ăl) Gt. Brit. (Liverpool In.)	53.21 N	2.14 W
123	Styr R. (stêr)...............Pol.	51.3 N	25.30 E
139	Suakin (Sawakin) (swä'kên) (sä-wä'kên). A. E. Sud.	19.3 N	37.20 E
153	Sūanhwā (sü'ān-hwä') ......Chn.	40.37 N	115.6 E
121	Subata (so͞o'bȧ-tȧ)...........Lat.	56.1 N	25.55 E
169	Subiaco (so͞o-bê-ā'kō) Austl. (Perth In.)	31.57 S	115.50 E
162	Subic (so͞o'bĭk)..............P. I.	14.53 N	120.14 E
162	Subic B......................P. I.	14.40 N	120.12 E
129	Subotica (so͞o'bô-tê-tsȧ).....Yugo.	46.5 N	19.40 E
123	Suceava (so͞o-châ-ä'vȧ)......Rom.	47.39 N	26.17 E
123	Suceava R...................Rom.	47.45 N	26.3 E
123	Sucha (so͞o'Kȧ)...............Pol.	49.43 N	19.38 E
156	Sucheng (so͞o'chĕng')........Chn.	31.29 N	116.55 E
93	Suchiapa (so͞o-chê-ä'pä)......Mex.	16.38 N	93.5 W
94	Suchitoto (so͞o-chê-tō'tō)......Sal.	13.58 N	89.2 W
152	Suchow (so͞o'chō')...........Chn.	39.40 N	98.28 E
156	Süchow (sü'chō')...........Chn.	34.13 N	117.18 E
156	Suchow (so͞o'chō') ....Chn.	33.38 N	116.58 E
153	Suchow Cr....Chn. (Shanghai In.)	31.11 N	121.25 E

ng-sing; ŋ-baŋk; N-nasalized n; nŏd; cŏmmit; ōld; ôbey; ôrder; fo͞od; fo͝ot; ou-out; s-soft; sh-dish; th-thin; pūre; ûnite; ûrn; stŭd circŭs; ü-as "y" in study; '-indeterminate vowel.

Page	Name Pronunciation Region	Lat. °′	Long. °′
152	Suchow (Suifu) (sü'chō'sä')..Chn.	28.53 N	104.37 E
72	Sucia Is. (sōō'sē-*á*) Wash. (Vancouver In.)	48.46 N	122.54 W
116	Suck R. (sŭk)..............Ire.	53.15 N	8.15 W
102	Sucre (sōō'krā)..............Bol.	19.1 S	65.25 W
150	Sudair (sŭ-dā'ēr)........Sau. Ar.	25.50 N	45.30 E
138	Sudan (Reg.) (sōō-dän')......Afr.	12.0 N	10.0 E
130	Suda R. (sōō'dȧ)........Sov. Un.	59.0 N	37.0 E
55	Sudbury (sŭd'bēr-ē).........Can.	46.32 N	81.15 W
119	Sudbury...Gt. Brit. (London In.)	51.34 N	0.20 W
87	Sudbury.............Mass. (In.)	42.23 N	71.25 W
119	Süder Elbe (R.) (sü'dēr ĕl'bē) Ger. (Hamburg In.)	53.30 N	9.54 E
122	Sudetes (Mts.) (sōō-dē'tēz)...Ger.	50.25 N	16.40 E
130	Sudogda (sōō'dôk-dȧ)....Sov. Un.	55.58 N	40.51 E
130	Sudost R. (sōō-dôst')....Sov. Un.	52.40 N	33.20 E
57	Sud, R. du (rē-vyâr' dü süd') Can. (In.)	50.0 N	70.45 W
131	Sudzha (sōōd'zhȧ).......Sov. Un.	51.12 N	35.14 E
127	Sueca (swā'kä)..............Sp.	39.12 N	0.19 W
156	Suehfuchwang (swĕ'fōō-chwäng') Chn.	36.39 N	120.49 E
155	Suenping (swĕn'pĭng').......Chn.	28.38 N	119.34 E
139	Suez (sōō-ĕz')..............Eg.	29.59 N	32.28 E
135	Suez Canal............Eg. (In.)	30.36 N	32.21 E
139	Suez, G. of................Afr.	29.0 N	30.0 E
85	Suffolk (sŭf'ŭk)............Va.	36.40 N	76.35 W
79	Sugar Cr. (shŏŏg'ēr).........Ill.	40.25 N	89.15 W
84	Sugar Cr...................Ind.	39.57 N	87.5 W
78	Sugar City................Colo.	38.13 N	103.41 W
81	Sugarland Junction.....Tex. (In.)	29.30 N	95.31 W
72	Sugar Loaf....Colo. (Denver In.)	40.0 N	105.27 W
104	Sugar Loaf (Mt.)......Braz. (In.)	22.58 S	43.9 W
167	Sugarloaf Pt..............Austl.	32.29 S	152.34 E
139	Suhâg (sōō-häg')............Eg.	26.35 N	31.36 E
157	Suheung (sōō'hē-ōōng')......Cho.	38.28 N	126.14 E
122	Suhl (zōōl)................Ger.	50.37 N	10.42 E
155	Suian (sōō'ē-än')...........Chn.	29.32 N	118.53 E
157	Suian......................Cho.	38.43 N	126.21 E
155	Suichang (sōō'ē-chäng')......Chn.	28.33 N	119.22 E
156	Suichow (sōō'ē-chō')........Chn.	34.29 N	115.17 E
157	Suigen (sōō'e-gĕn)..........Cho.	37.17 N	127.3 E
158	Suihwa (sōō'ē-hwä')........Chn.	46.27 N	127.6 E
153	Suihwa..................Manch.	46.36 N	126.40 E
152	Suilai (sōō'ē-lī')..........Chn.	44.30 N	86.10 E
154	Suining (sōō'ē-nĭng').......Chn.	26.28 N	109.49 E
154	Suining...................Chn.	30.32 N	105.40 E
156	Suining...................Chn.	33.53 N	118.4 E
99	Suipacha (swē-pä'chä) Arg. (Buenos Aires In.)	34.42 S	59.38 W
156	Suiping (sōō'ē-pĭng').......Chn.	33.12 N	113.54 E
116	Suir, R. (Sūr)..............Ire.	52.20 N	7.30 W
49	Suisun B. (sōō-ē-sōōn') Calif. (San Francisco In.)	38.5 N	122.3 W
159	Suita (sōō'ē-tȧ)..Jap. (Osaka In.)	34.35 N	135.30 E
152	Suiting (sōō-ē'tĭng)........Chn.	31.5 N	107.38 E
152	Suiyan (Prov.) (sōō'ē-yän')...Chn.	41.30 N	108.30 E
154	Suiyang (sōō'ē-yäng').......Chn.	27.52 N	107.10 E
130	Sukhinichi (sōō'kē-nē-chē) Sov. Un.	54.6 N	35.21 E
112	Sukhona R. (sōō-kô'nȧ)..Sov. Un.	59.40 N	42.30 E
113	Sukhum (sōō-kōōm')......Sov. Un.	43.0 N	41.2 E
151	Sukkur (sŭk'ŭr)............India	27.40 N	68.55 E
159	Sukumo (sōō'kōō-mô)........Jap.	32.58 N	132.43 E
161	Sulabesi (I.) (sōō-lä-bä'sē) Neth. Ind.	2.15 S	126.0 E
94	Sulaco, R. (sōō-lä'kō)......Hond.	14.57 N	87.30 W
151	Sulaiman Ra. (sōō-lä-ē-män')India	29.30 N	69.38 E
113	Sulak R. (sōō-läk')......Sov. Un.	43.20 N	47.0 E
131	Sula R. (sōō-lä')........Sov. Un.	50.35 N	33.20 E
163	Sulat (sōō'lät)..............P. I.	11.47 N	125.27 E
163	Sulauan Pt. (sōō-lou'än)......P. I.	8.37 N	124.28 E
128	Sulet (I.) (sōō'lĕt)........Yugo.	43.23 N	16.20 E
131	Sulina (sōō-lē'nȧ)..........Rom.	45.7 N	29.30 E
110	Sulitelma (Mt.) (sōō-lē-tyĕl'mȧ) Swe.	67.5 N	16.30 E
102	Sullana (sōō-lyä'nä)........Peru	5.0 S	80.32 W
82	Sulligent (sŭl'ĭ-jĕnt).........Ala.	33.53 N	88.9 W
72	Sullivan (sŭl'ĭ-văn) Can. (Vancouver In.)	49.7 N	122.48 W
72	Sullivan.......Colo. (Denver In.)	39.40 N	104.53 W
79	Sullivan....................Ill.	39.35 N	88.36 W
84	Sullivan...................Ind.	39.6 N	87.22 W
79	Sullivan...................Mo.	38.13 N	91.8 W
128	Sulmona (sōōl-mō'nä).........It.	42.3 N	13.56 E
79	Sulphur (sŭl'fŭr)...........Okla.	34.31 N	96.58 W
79	Sulphur R..............Ark.-Tex.	33.24 N	94.55 W
143	Sulphur Spring.........U. S. Afr.	27.11 S	31.5 E
81	Sulphur Springs.............Tex.	33.8 N	95.36 W
80	Sulphur Springs Cr...........Tex.	32.58 N	102.32 W
150	Sultanabad (sōōl-tän-ä-bäd').Iran	28.15 N	55.29 E
92	Sultepec (sōōl-tȧ-pĕk')......Mex.	18.45 N	99.52 W
163	Suluan I. (sōō-lōō'än).......P. I.	10.44 N	125.58 E
163	Sulu Arch. (sōō'lōō).........P. I.	5.30 N	121.0 E
152	Sulu Ho (R.) (sōō'lōō hō')...Chn.	40.30 N	96.30 E
163	Sulu Sea....................P. I.	9.0 N	120.30 E
159	Suma (sōō'mä)...Jap. (Osaka In.)	34.39 N	135.6 E
72	Sumas (sü'mȧs) Wash. (Vancouver In.)	49.0 N	122.16 W
72	Sumas L....Can. (Vancouver In.)	49.4 N	122.8 W
72	Sumas R...Wash. (Vancouver In.)	48.57 N	122.15 W
160	Sumatra (I.) (sōō-mä'trȧ) Neth. Ind.	1.0 S	102.0 E
160	Sumba (Soemba) (Sandalwood) I. Neth. Ind.	9.45 S	120.0 E
160	Sumbawa (Soembawa) (I.) (sōōm-bä'wä)..Neth. Ind.	8.45 S	118.0 E
116	Sumburgh Pt. (sŭm'bŭr-ō) Gt. Brit. (In.)	59.55 N	1.20 W
123	Sümeg (shü'mĕg)...........Hung.	46.59 N	17.19 E
129	Sumen (shōō'mĕn)...........Bul.	43.15 N	26.55 E
159	Sumidagawa R. (sōō'mē-dȧ-gä'wä) Jap.	36.8 N	139.28 E
99	Sumidouro (sōō-mē-dō'rōō) Braz. (Rio de Janeiro In.)	22.0 S	42.39 W
73	Sumiton (sŭm'ĭ-tŭn) Ala. (Birmingham In.)	33.45 N	87.3 W
159	Sumiyoshi (sōō'mē-yō'shē) Jap. (Osaka In.)	34.36 N	135.29 E
157	Sumjin R. (sōōm'jĭn').......Cho.	35.16 N	127.23 E
70	Summer L. (sŭm'ēr)..........Ore.	42.50 N	120.50 W
86	Summerside (sŭm'ēr-sīd).....Can.	46.24 N	63.47 W
83	Summerton (sŭm'ēr-tŭn)....S. C.	33.37 N	80.22 W
83	Summerville (sŭm'ēr-vĭl)....S. C.	33.1 N	80.10 W
73	Summit (sŭm'ĭt) Calif. (Los Angeles In.)	34.20 N	117.25 W
70	Summit Lake Ind. Res.......Nev.	41.35 N	119.15 W
75	Summit Pk...................Colo.	37.18 N	106.42 W
171	Sumner (sŭm'nēr).....N. Z. (In.)	43.34 S	172.48 E
49	Sumner.......Wash. (Seattle In.)	47.12 N	122.14 W
171	Sumner Head.........N. Z. (In.)	43.34 S	172.48 E
	Sumperk, see Mährisch Schönberg, Ger.		
82	Sumrall (sŭm'rôl)...........Miss.	31.25 N	89.33 W
83	Sumter (sŭm'tēr)...........S. C.	33.56 N	80.20 W
131	Sumy (sōō'mē)..........Sov. Un.	50.55 N	34.48 E
166	Sunbury (sŭn'bēr-ē)........Austl.	37.33 S	144.42 E
85	Sunbury.....................Pa.	40.52 N	76.47 W
154	Sünchow (sün'chō')..........Chn.	23.28 N	110.4 E
157	Sunchun(Sensen)(sōōn'chōōn)Cho.	39.48 N	124.58 E
160	Sunda I. (sōōn'dȧ)..........E. I.	10.0 S	115.0 E
120	Sundals Fjord...............Nor.	62.50 N	8.10 E
120	Sundals L. (sōōn'däls).......Nor.	59.36 N	6.45 E
71	Sundance (sŭn'dăns)........Wyo.	44.25 N	104.30 W
160	Sunda Trough.........Neth. Ind.	10.0 S	111.0 E
164	Sunday Str..................Austl.	16.20 S	123.10 E
143	Sundays R.............U. S. Afr.	28.16 S	29.50 E
143	Sundays R.............U. S. Afr.	33.10 S	25.10 E
120	Sundbyberg (sōōn'bü-bĕrgh)..Swe.	59.22 N	17.58 E
116	Sunderland (sŭn'dēr-lănd)Gt. Brit.	54.55 N	1.25 W
160	Sundir Str. (sōōn'dēr)..Neth. Ind.	6.0 S	106.0 E
120	Sundsvall (sōōnds'väl).......Swe.	62.26 N	17.16 E
82	Sunflower R.................Miss.	33.0 N	90.35 W
153	Sungari R. (sōōn'gȧ-rē')..Manch.	46.0 N	127.0 E
161	Sungay Mt. (sōōŋ-gä'ē) P. I. (Manila In.)	14.10 N	121.2 E
157	Sungchun (sōōng'chōōn').....Cho.	39.17 N	126.11 E
155	Sungfow (sōōng'fō').........Chn.	31.5 N	114.44 E
157	Sungju (sōōng'jōō')..........Cho.	35.57 N	128.15 E
154	Sungkan (sōōng'kän').......Chn.	28.20 N	106.42 E
155	Sungki (sōōng'kē')..........Chn.	27.36 N	118.26 E
155	Sungkiang (sōōng'kyäng')....Chn.	30.55 N	121.8 E
154	Sungtze (sōōng'tsē')........Chn.	30.20 N	111.30 E
113	Sungurlu (sōōn'gōōr-lōō')....Tur.	40.8 N	34.28 E
155	Sungyang (sōōng'yäng')......Chn.	28.25 N	119.33 E
154	Sunhing (sōōn'hĭng')........Chn.	22.48 N	112.8 E
154	Sunhsien (sōōn'hsyĕn').....Chn.	35.41 N	114.53 E
154	Sunhwei (sōōn'hwī').........Chn.	22.28 N	112.56 E
120	Sunne (sōōn'ĕ)..............Swe.	59.50 N	13.10 E
154	Sunning (sōōn'nĭng')........Chn.	22.16 N	112.38 E
75	Sunnyside (sŭn'ĭ-sīd).......Utah	39.34 N	110.22 W
70	Sunnyside..................Wash.	46.18 N	120.0 W
159	Suno C. (sōō'nō)............Jap.	34.58 N	139.58 E
49	Sunol (sōō' nŭl) Calif. (San Francisco In.)	37.35 N	121.53 W
71	Sun R......................Mont.	47.28 N	112.10 W
73	Sunset Beach Calif. (Los Angeles In.)	33.44 N	118.5 W
75	Sunset Crater Natl. Mon.....Ariz.	35.40 N	111.30 W
169	Sunshine...Austl. (Melbourne In.)	37.48 S	144.50 E
149	Suntar (sōōn-tär')........Sov. Un.	62.10 N	117.30 E
121	Suojärvi (sōō'ō-jĕr-vē)........Fin.	62.17 N	32.35 E
75	Superior (sū-pē'rĭ-ēr).........Ariz.	33.17 N	111.8 W
72	Superior.......Colo. (Denver In.)	39.57 N	105.10 W
78	Superior....................Neb.	40.2 N	98.4 W
77	Superior....................Wis.	46.44 N	92.4 W
71	Superior....................Wyo.	41.46 N	108.59 W
88	Superior B. Minn.-Wis. (Duluth In.)	46.45 N	92.5 W
77	Superior, L...........U. S.-Can.	47.40 N	88.0 W
93	Superior, Laguna (lȧ-gōō'nȧ sōō-pȧ-rē-ōr').Mex.	16.20 N	94.55 W
154	Süpu (sü'pōō')..............Chn.	27.53 N	110.13 E
150	Sur (sōōr)..................Oman	22.32 N	59.29 E
	Surany, see Nagysurány, Hung.		
151	Surat (sōō'rŭt) (sōō-rät')....India	21.5 N	72.46 E
130	Surazh (sōō-räzh).......Sov. Un.	53.1 N	32.25 E
130	Surazh..................Sov. Un.	55.25 N	30.44 E
119	Surbiton (sûr'bĭ-tŭn) Gt. Brit. (London In.)	51.23 N	0.20 W
102	Surco (sōōr'kō)........Peru (In.)	12.9 S	77.1 W
125	Suresnes (sü-rân')........Fr. (In.)	48.51 N	2.13 E
124	Surgères (sür-zhâr').............Fr.	46.8 N	0.50 W
148	Surgut (sōōr'gōōt).......Sov. Un.	61.20 N	73.25 E
151	Suri (sōō'rē)...............India	23.46 N	87.48 E
163	Surigao (sōō-rē-gä'ō)........P. I.	9.46 N	125.30 E
163	Surigao Str...................P. I.	10.15 N	125.25 E
103	Surinam (Netherland Guiana) (sōō-rē-näm') (gē-än'ȧ).S. A.	4.0 N	56.0 W
103	Surinam R....................Sur.	5.0 N	55.2 W
169	Surrey (sŭr'ē)....Austl. (Tas. In.)	41.26 S	145.40 E
159	Suruga B. (sōō'rōō-gȧ).......Jap.	34.46 N	138.35 E
128	Susa (sōō'sä)..................It.	45.6 N	7.2 E
159	Susa.........................Jap.	34.39 N	131.40 E
128	Sušak (sōō'shäk)............Yugo.	45.17 N	14.28 E
159	Susaki (sōō'sä-kē)...........Jap.	33.22 N	133.15 E
157	Susan (sōō'sän')..............Cho.	36.47 N	126.27 E
74	Susanville (sōō'zăn-vĭl).......Calif.	40.23 N	120.42 W
122	Sušice (sōō'shē-tsĕ).........Czech.	49.14 N	13.31 E
53	Susitna (sōō-sĭt'nȧ)..........Alsk.	61.25 N	150.30 W
53	Susitna R....................Alsk.	62.40 N	150.0 W
85	Susquehanna (sŭs'kwē-hăn'ȧ)..Pa.	41.56 N	75.36 W
85	Susquehanna R.........Pa.-N. Y.	41.35 N	76.0 W
86	Sussex (sŭs'ĕks).............Can.	45.42 N	65.31 W
155	Susung (sōō'sōōng').........Chn.	30.10 N	116.7 E
169	Sutherland (sŭdh'ēr-lănd) Austl. (Sydney In.)	34.2 S	151.3 E
142	Sutherland............U. S. Afr.	32.22 S	20.39 E
151	Sutley R. (sŭt'lĕj)..........India	30.0 N	73.0 E
156	Sutsien (sōō'tsyĕn').........Chn.	33.56 N	118.22 E
119	Sutton (sŭt''n) Gt. Brit. (London In.)	51.22 N	0.12 W
87	Sutton..............Mass. (In.)	42.9 N	71.46 W
119	Sutton at Hone (hōn) Gt. Brit. (London In.)	51.25 N	0.14 E
118	Sutton Coldfield(kōld'fēld)Gt. Brit.	52.34 N	1.49 W
118	Sutton-in-Ashfield (ăsh'fēld) Gt. Brit.	53.7 N	1.15 W
6	Suva (sōō'vä)........Fiji Is. (In.)	18.8 S	178.25 E
123	Suwalki (sōō-väl'kē)..........Pol.	54.5 N	22.56 E
82	Suwannee R. (sōō-wô'nē).Fla.-Ga.	30.0 N	83.0 W
156	Suyi (sōō'yē')................Chn.	33.1 N	118.27 E
130	Suzdal (sōōz'dȧl)........Sov. Un.	56.25 N	40.28 E
46	Svalbard (Spitsbergen) (sväl'-bärt) (spĭts'bûr-gĕn).Arc. O.	79.0 N	16.0 E
120	Svaneke (svä'nĕ-kĕ).........Den.	55.7 N	15.9 E
110	Svappavaara (svä-pȧ-vä'rä)..Swe.	67.37 N	21.20 E
131	Svatova Luchka (svä'tô-vȧ lōōch'kȧ) Sov. Un.	49.24 N	38.2 E
120	Svedala (svä'dȧ-lä)..........Swe.	55.28 N	13.29 E
120	Svegsman (svāks'män).......Swe.	62.2 N	14.22 E
120	Svelvik (svĕl'vĭk)............Nor.	59.37 N	10.22 E
120	Svendborg (svĕn'bôrgh)......Den.	55.3 N	10.35 E
49	Svensen (svĕn'sĕn) Ore. (Portland In.)	46.10 N	123.40 W
148	Sverdlovsk (svĕrd-lôfsk').Sov. Un.	56.50 N	60.20 E
129	Svilajnac (svē'lȧ-ē-näts)....Yugo.	44.13 N	21.12 E
129	Svilengrad (svĕl'ĕn-grät)......Bul.	41.45 N	26.11 E
112	Svir R. (svēr)...........Sov. Un.	60.50 N	34.30 E
130	Svisloch R. (svēs'lŏk)....Sov. Un.	53.30 N	28.20 E
129	Svištov (svēsh'tôf)..........Bul.	43.35 N	25.20 E
	Svitavy, see Zwittau, Ger.		
149	Svobodny (svô-bôd'nĭ)...Sov. Un.	51.25 N	128.20 E
110	Svolvaer (svôl'vĕr)...........Nor.	68.15 N	14.30 E
149	Svyatoi, C. (svyȧ'tô-ē)...Sov. Un.	72.50 N	141.10 E
155	Swabue (swä'bōō'ē).........Chn.	22.47 N	115.19 E
118	Swadlincote (swŏd'lĭn-kōt)Gt. Brit.	52.47 N	1.34 W
165	Swain Reefs (swān).........Austl.	22.0 S	152.0 E
83	Swainsboro (swānz'bŭr-ō).....Ga.	32.36 N	82.20 W
142	Swakopmund (svä'kôp-mōōnt) (swä'kôp-mōōnd).S. W. Afr.	22.40 S	14.32 E
116	Swale, R. (swāl)........Gt. Brit.	54.10 N	1.10 W
87	Swampscott (swômp'skŏt) Mass. (In.)	42.28 N	70.55 W
166	Swan Hill..................Austl.	35.21 S	143.33 E
164	Swanland (Reg.) (swŏn'lănd) Austl.	31.30 S	120.0 E
164	Swan R. (swŏn)............Austl.	31.40 S	116.40 E
71	Swan R.....................Mont.	47.50 N	113.40 W
119	Swanscombe (swŏnz'kŏm) Gt. Brit. (London In.)	51.27 N	0.19 E
116	Swansea (swŏn'sē).......Gt. Brit.	51.37 N	3.55 W
116	Swansea B..............Gt. Brit.	51.35 N	3.50 W
170	Swanson (swŏn'sŭn)....N. Z. (In.)	36.52 S	174.35 E
155	Swatow (swä'tō')............Chn.	23.23 N	116.27 E
143	Swaziland (swä'zē-lănd)......Afr.	26.30 S	31.30 E
120	Sweden (swē'dĕn)............Eur.	60.0 N	15.0 E
71	Sweetgrass Cr. (swēt'gräs)..Mont.	46.10 N	109.55 W
82	Sweetwater (swēt'wô-tēr)....Tenn.	35.36 N	84.29 W
80	Sweetwater..................Tex.	32.28 N	100.25 W
135	Sweetwater Canal Eg. (Suez Can. In.)	30.14 N	30.25 E
73	Sweetwater Cr...Ga. (Atlanta In.)	33.48 N	84.47 W
76	Sweetwater L..................N. D.	48.12 N	98.48 W
74	Sweetwater Reservoir..Calif. (In.)	32.41 N	116.55 W
71	Sweetwater R.................Wyo.	42.25 N	108.40 W
142	Swellendam(swĕl'ĕn-dăm)U.S.Afr.	34.3 S	20.24 E
121	Święciany (shvyăŋ-tsyä'nē)...Pol.	55.8 N	26.10 E
123	Świecie (shvyā'tsyē)...........Pol.	53.24 N	18.26 E
54	Swift Current.................Can.	50.18 N	107.47 W
118	Swift, R...............Gt. Brit.	52.27 N	1.9 W
86	Swift R.......................Me.	44.45 N	70.41 W
116	Swindon (swĭn'dŭn)......Gt. Brit.	51.35 N	1.50 W
122	Swinemünde (svē'nĕ-mün-dĕ).Ger.	53.56 N	14.13 E
49	Swinomish Indian Res. (swĭ-nō'-mĭsh).Wash. (Seattle In.)	48.30 N	122.30 W
118	Swinton (swĭn'tŭn)......Gt. Brit.	53.29 N	2.19 W
122	Switzerland (swĭt'zēr-lănd)...Eur.	46.40 N	8.0 E
130	Syas R. (syäs)...........Sov. Un.	59.30 N	33.30 E
77	Sycamore (sĭk'ȧ-mōr)..........Ill.	42.0 N	88.40 W
130	Sychevka (sē-chĕf'kȧ)....Sov. Un.	55.51 N	34.17 E
169	Sydenham (sĭd'ĕn-ăm) Austl. (Melbourne In.)	37.42 S	144.47 E
169	Sydenham....Austl. (Sydney In.)	33.55 S	151.10 E
169	Sydney (sĭd'nē).......Austl. (In.)		
165	Sydney....................Austl.	34.0 S	151.0 E
55	Sydney......................Can.	46.18 N	60.14 W
87	Sydney Mines................Can.	46.15 N	60.15 W
139	Syene (Aswân) (sē-ā'nä) (ä-swän').Eg.	24.7 N	32.58 E
112	Syktyvkar (Ust Sysolsk) (sük-tüf'kär)..Sov. Un.	61.40 N	50.45 E
82	Sylacauga (sĭl-ȧ-kô'gȧ).......Ala.	33.9 N	86.14 W
120	Sylfjällen (Mt.) (sül'fyĕl-ĕn)..Swe.	63.0 N	12.12 E
120	Sylling (sül'lĭng)............Nor.	59.52 N	10.19 E
122	Sylt I. (sĭlt)................Ger.	54.53 N	8.30 E
83	Sylvania (sĭl-vā'nĭ-ȧ).........Ga.	32.44 N	81.38 W
82	Sylvester (sĭl-vĕs'tēr)........Ga.	31.32 N	83.52 W
158	Syokwa (syō-kwä).......Tai. (In.)	24.3 N	120.35 E
128	Syracuse (Siracusa) (sĭr'ȧ-kūs) (sē-rä-kōō'sä).It.	37.5 N	15.17 E
78	Syracuse....................Kan.	37.57 N	101.45 W
85	Syracuse....................N. Y.	43.5 N	76.10 W
73	Syracuse Utah (Salt Lake City In.)	41.5 N	112.7 W
150	Syria (sĭr'ĭ-ȧ)...............Asia	35.0 N	38.30 E

ăt; finăl; rāte; senâte; ärm; åsk; sofȧ; fâre; ch-choose; dh-as th in other; bē; ēvent; bĕt; recĕnt; cratēr; g-go; gh-gutteral g; bĭt; ĭ-short neutral; rīde; ĸ-gutteral k as ch in German ich;

Page	Name Pronunciation Region	Lat. °'	Long. °'
150	Syrian Des. ... Asia	31.0 N	40.0 E
129	Syros (I.) (sē'rôs) ... Grc.	37.25 N	24.55 E
113	Syzran (sėz-rän'') ... Sov. Un.	53.5 N	48.28 E
123	Szabadszállás (sô'bôd-sä'läs) Hung.	46.52 N	19.14 E
122	Szamotuly (shȧ-mô-tōō'wê) ... Pol.	52.36 N	16.33 E
123	Szarvas (sôr'vôsh) ... Hung.	46.51 N	20.35 E
123	Szczara R. (shchä'rȧ) ... Pol.	53.5 N	25.20 E
123	Szcyebrzeszyn (shchě-bzhā'shěn) Pol.	50.41 N	22.57 E
123	Szczuczyn (shchōō'chěn) ... Pol.	53.33 N	22.17 E
154	Szecheng (sä'chěng') ... Chn.	24.30 N	106.38 E
154	Szechow (sä'chō') ... Chn.	27.10 N	108.25 E
156	Szechow ... Chn.	33.29 N	117.48 E
154	Szechwan (Prov.) (sä'chwän') Chn.	30.5 N	106.45 E
123	Szeged (sě'gěd) ... Hung.	46.15 N	20.11 E
123	Székesfehérvár (sā'kěsh-fě'hār-vär) Hung.	47.12 N	18.24 E
123	Szekszárd (sěk'särd) ... Hung.	46.20 N	18.42 E
152	Szemao (sä'mä-'ō) ... Chn.	22.40 N	101.2 E
154	Szenan (sä'nän') ... Chn.	27.55 N	108.15 E
154	Szengjen (sěng'jěn') ... Chn.	24.55 N	108.20 E
123	Szentendre (sěnt'ěn-drě) ... Hung.	47.40 N	19.4 E
123	Szentes (sěn'těsh) ... Hung.	46.38 N	20.17 E
158	Szepingkai (sē'pĭng'kī') ... Manch.	43.26 N	124.15 E
123	Szereszów (shě-rā'shōōf) ... Pol.	52.32 N	24.10 E
156	Szeshui (sä'shōō'ê) ... Chn.	34.48 N	113.17 E
156	Szeshui ... Chn.	35.48 N	117.17 E
154	Szewui (sä'wōō'ē) ... Chn.	23.22 N	112.37 E
123	Szigetvár (sē'gět-vär) ... Hung.	46.5 N	17.50 E
123	Szolnok (sôl'nôk) ... Hung.	47.11 N	20.11 E
122	Szombathely (sôm'bôt-hěl') Hung.	47.13 N	16.35 E
123	Szydlowiec (shēd-wô'vyěts) ... Pol.	51.12 N	20.52 E
162	Taal (tä-äl') ... P. I.	13.51 N	120.55 E
162	Taal, L. ... P. I.	14.0 N	121.0 E
162	Taal, Vol. ... P. I.	14.1 N	121.0 E
162	Tabaco (tä-bä'kō) ... P. I.	13.21 N	123.42 E
143	Tabankulu (tȧ-bän-kōō'lä) U. S. Afr.	30.59 S	29.18 E
7	Tabaquite (tä-bä-kē'tä). Trin. (In.)	10.24 N	61.18 W
161	Tabar Is. (tä'bär) ... N. Gui. Ter.	2.40 S	152.3 E
135	Tabarka (tȧ-bär'kȧ) ... Tun. (In.)	36.55 N	8.55 E
95	Tabasara, Serranía de (Mts.) (sěr-rä-nē'ä dā tä-bä-sä'rä). Pan.	8.33 N	81.25 W
93	Tabasco (State) (tä-bäs'kō) .. Mex.	18.10 N	93.0 W
102	Tabatinga (tä-bä-tĭŋ'gä) ... Braz.	4.15 S	69.57 W
162	Tabayoc, Mt. (tä-bä-yôk') ... P. I.	16.41 N	120.53 E
126	Tabernas (tä-běr'näs) ... Sp.	37.3 N	2.22 W
104	Tablada (tä-blä'dhä) .... Arg. (In.)	34.42 S	58.31 W
162	Tablas Is. (tä'bläs) ... P. I.	12.20 N	122.0 E
162	Tablas Str. ... P. I.	12.30 N	121.45 E
141	Table B. ... U. S. Afr.	33.54 S	18.27 E
170	Table C. ... N. Z.	39.5 S	178.2 E
143	Table Mt. ... U. S. Afr.	33.18 S	23.57 E
141	Table Mt.. U. S. Afr. (Cape Town In.)	33.58 S	18.27 E
86	Tabletop (Jacques Cartier) (zhȧk kȧr-tyā') Mt. Can.	48.58 N	66.2 W
126	Taboada (tä-bō-ä'dä) ... Sp.	42.43 N	7.45 W
90	Taboga I. (tä-bō'gä) ... C. Z. (In.)	8.47 N	79.33 W
163	Tabogon (tä-bô-gōn') ... P. I.	10.57 N	124.1 E
122	Tábor (tä'bôr) ... Czech.	49.25 N	14.40 E
140	Tabora (tä-bō'rä) ... Tan.	5.5 S	32.47 E
138	Tabou (tȧ-bōō') ... Fr. W. Afr.	4.30 N	7.26 W
150	Tabriz (tȧ-brēz') ... Iran	38.4 N	46.15 E
92	Tacámbaro de Codallos (tä-käm'bä-rō dā kō-däl'yōs). Mex.	19.13 N	101.20 W
94	Tacaná (Vol.) (tä-kä-nä') ... Guat.	15.8 N	92.7 W
156	Tacheng (tä'chěng') ... Chn.	38.49 N	116.26 E
154	Tachu (tä'chōō') ... Chn.	30.43 N	107.9 E
54	Tacla L. (tăk-lȧ) ... Can.	55.30 N	126.15 W
163	Tacloban (tä-klō'bän) ... P. I.	11.13 N	125.0 E
102	Tacna (täk'nä) ... Chl.	17.45 S	69.45 W
70	Tacoma (tȧ-kō'mȧ) ... Wash.	47.15 N	122.30 W
85	Taconic Range (tȧ-kŏn'ĭk) .. N. Y.	42.0 N	73.40 W
88	Tacony (tȧ-kō'nê) Pa. (Philadelphia In.)	40.2 N	75.3 W
93	Tacotalpa (tä-kô-täl'pä) ... Mex.	17.37 N	92.50 W
104	Tacuarembo (tä-kwä-rěm'bō) .. Ur.	31.50 S	56.10 W
93	Tacuba (tä-kōō'bä) .... Mex. (In.)	19.28 N	99.10 W
93	Tacubaya (tä-kōō-bä'yä) Mex. (In.)	19.24 N	99.13 W
159	Tada (tä'dä) ... Jap. (Osaka In.)	34.52 N	135.24 E
118	Tadcaster (tăd'kȧs-tēr) ... Gt. Brit.	53.53 N	1.15 W
138	Tademait Plat. (tä-dê-mä'êt) . Alg.	28.30 N	3.0 E
141	Tadjoura (tȧd-zhōō'rȧ) ... Fr. Som.	11.50 N	42.53 E
159	Tadotsu (tä'dô-tsōō) ... Jap.	34.10 N	133.39 E
86	Tadoussac (tȧ-dōō-säk') ... Can.	48.9 N	69.43 W
148	Tadzhik (Aut. Rep.) (tät'zhĭk) Sov. Un.	39.0 N	71.0 E
126	Tafalla (tä-fäl'yä) ... Sp.	42.31 N	1.40 W
145	Tafel (Et Tafila) (tä'fěl) (ět tä'fê-lȧ). Transj. (In.)	30.50 N	35.37 E
143	Tafel Kop (Mt.) (tä'fěl kôp) U.S.Afr.	25.57 S	26.45 E
145	Tafila (tä-fē'la) ... Transj. (In.)	30.50 N	35.37 E
138	Tafilelt Oasis (tä-fē'lělt) ... Mor.	31.15 N	4.15 W
127	Tafna R. (täf'nä) ... Alg.	35.25 N	1.0 W
74	Taft (tȧft) ... Calif.	35.9 N	119.28 W
131	Taganrog (tȧ-gȧn-rôk') ... Sov. Un.	47.12 N	38.57 E
131	Taganrog, G. of ... Sov. Un.	47.5 N	38.30 E
163	Tagapula I. (tä-gä-pōō-lä') ... P. I.	12.4 N	124.12 E
163	Tagbilaran (täg-bê-lä'rän) ... P. I.	9.38 N	123.52 E
161	Tagig (tä-hēg') .. P. I. (Manila In.)	14.32 N	121.4 E
114	Tagiura (tä-jōō'rä) ... Libya	32.55 N	13.19 E
128	Tagliamento R. (täl-yä-měn'tō) . It.	46.0 N	12.54 E
163	Tagoloan (tä-gô-lō'än) ... P. I.	8.30 N	124.46 E
163	Tagoloan R. ... P. I.	8.21 N	125.0 E
163	Tagolo Pt. (tä-gō'lō) ... P. I.	8.42 N	123.24 E
163	Tagubud, Mt. (tä-gōō-bōōd') . P. I.	7.20 N	126.11 E
165	Tagula Is. (tä'gōō-lȧ) ... Pap. Ter.	11.30 S	153.15 E
163	Tagum (tä'gōōm) ... P. I.	7.19 N	125.44 E
163	Tagum R. ... P. I.	7.35 N	125.50 E
126	Tagus (Tajo) R. (tā'gŭs) (tä'hō) Sp.	39.50 N	5.0 W
138	Tahat, Mt. (tä-hät') ... Alg.	23.26 N	5.28 E
152	Tahcheng (Chuguchak) (tä'chěng') (chōō'gōō-chäk'). Chn.	46.48 N	83.5 E
6	Tahiti (I.) (tä'hê-tê) ... Pac. O.	17.53 S	148.5 W
79	Tahlequah (tă-lē-kwä') ... Okla.	35.55 N	94.58 W
74	Tahoe, L. (tä'hō) ... Calif.-Nev.	39.2 N	120.0 W
138	Tahoua (tä'ōō-ä) ... Fr. W. Afr.	14.55 N	5.20 E
135	Tahta (tä'tä) ... Eg. (In.)	26.49 N	31.30 E
171	Tahunanui (tä'hōō-nä-nōō'ê). N. Z.	41.18 S	173.17 E
156	Taian (tī'än') ... Chn.	36.9 N	117.8 E
171	Taiaroa Head (tä'ê-ä-rō'ä) N. Z. (In.)	45.47 S	170.45 E
157	Tai Bak San (Mts.) (tī'bäk'sän') Cho.	37.15 N	129.10 E
155	Tai Chang R. (tī'chäng') ... Chn.	25.37 N	118.28 E
155	Taichow (tī'chō') ... Chn.	28.52 N	121.7 E
156	Taichow ... Chn.	32.28 N	119.53 E
158	Taichu (tī'chōō') ... Tai. (In.)	24.15 N	120.45 E
157	Taichun (tī'chōōn') ... Cho.	39.58 N	125.28 E
157	Taiden (tī'děn) ... Cho.	36.20 N	127.26 E
156	Taierhchwang ... Chn.	34.35 N	117.45 E
171	Taieri R. (tä-ê-ä'rê) ... N. Z.	45.30 S	170.12 E
150	Taif (tīf) ... Sau. Ar.	21.10 N	40.50 E
148	Taiga (tä'ê-gȧ) ... Sov. Un.	56.0 N	85.40 E
149	Taigo, C. (tä'ê-gō) ... Sov. Un.	60.30 N	160.10 E
156	Taihang Shan (Mts.) (tī'häng'shän'). Chn.	35.50 N	113.28 E
170	Taihape (tä'ê-hä'pä) ... N. Z.	39.42 S	175.45 E
158	Taihasen Mt. (tī'hä-sěn') Tai. (In.)	24.29 N	121.15 E
156	Taihing (tī'hĭng') ... Chn.	32.9 N	119.59 E
155	Taiho (tī'hō') ... Chn.	26.46 N	114.37 E
156	Taiho ... Chn.	33.9 N	115.38 E
158	Taihoku (tī-hō'kōō) ... Tai. (In.)	25.1 N	121.30 E
155	Taihu (tī'hōō') ... Chn.	30.26 N	116.12 E
156	Taikang (tī'käng') ... Chn.	34.9 N	115.3 E
157	Taikyu (tī'kōō') ... Chn.	35.47 N	128.31 E
155	Tai L. (tī) ... Chn.	31.8 N	120.15 E
152	Tailagein Khara (Reg.) (tī'lȧ-gän ĸä'rä). Chn.	43.30 N	106.0 E
166	Tailem Bend (tāl'ěm) ... Austl.	35.14 S	139.28 E
154	Taileung (tī'lê-ōōng') ... Chn.	22.51 N	113.12 E
150	Taima (tä'ê-mä) ... Sau. Ar.	28.0 N	39.5 E
149	Taimyr I., Little (tȧ-ê-mêr') Sov. Un.	78.10 N	108.30 E
149	Taimyr, L. ... Sov. Un.	74.30 N	10.0 E
149	Taimyr Pen. ... Sov. Un.	75.30 N	105.0 E
148	Taimyr R. ... Sov. Un.	73.30 N	95.0 E
116	Tain (tān) ... Gt. Brit.	57.49 N	4.5 W
158	Tainan (tī'nän') ... Tai. (In.)	23.1 N	120.16 E
155	Taining (tī'nĭng') ... Chn.	26.55 N	117.0 E
154	Taiping (tī'pĭng') ... Chn.	22.28 N	107.32 E
155	Taiping ... Chn.	30.18 N	118.11 E
155	Taiping ... Chn.	31.36 N	118.28 E
156	Taiping ... Chn.	32.7 N	119.53 E
155	Taipu (tī'pōō') ... Chn.	24.27 N	116.29 E
145	Tais (tä'ēs) ... Yem. (In.)	13.35 N	43.57 E
156	Tai Shan (Mt.) (tī' shän') ... Chn.	36.18 N	117.18 E
156	Tai Shan (Mts.) ... Chn.	36.25 N	117.25 E
155	Taishun (tī'shōōn') ... Chn.	27.30 N	119.44 E
104	Taitao Pen. (tä-ê-tä'ō) ... Chl.	46.30 S	75.30 W
158	Taito (tī'tō') ... Tai. (In.)	22.46 N	121.5 E
155	Taitsang (tī'tsäng') ... Chn.	31.24 N	121.0 E
158	Taiwan (Formosa) (tī'wän') (fôr-mō'sȧ). Jap. (In.)	24.0 N	121.0 E
158	Taiwan (Formosa) Str. . Tai. (In.)	25.0 N	120.0 E
156	Taiyi (tī'yē') ... Chn.	34.15 N	119.19 E
153	Taiyüan (tī'yü-än') ... Chn.	37.50 N	112.30 E
126	Tajo (Tagus) R. (tä'hō) (tā'gŭs) Sp.	39.50 N	5.0 W
94	Tajumulco (Vol.) (tä-hōō-mōōl'kō) Guat.	15.2 N	91.55 W
126	Tajuna R. (tä-hōō'nä) ... Sp.	40.30 N	3.5 W
159	Takahashi (tä'kä-hä'shê) ... Jap.	34.48 N	133.35 E
159	Taka I. (tä'kä) ... Jap.	30.48 N	130.22 E
159	Takaido (tä'kä-ē'dō) Jap. (Tokyo In.)	35.39 N	139.36 E
171	Takaka (tä-kä'kȧ) ... N. Z.	40.52 S	172.48 E
159	Takamatsu (tä'kä-mä'tsōō) ... Jap.	34.14 N	134.0 E
159	Takamori (tä'kä-mō'rê) ... Jap.	32.50 N	131.8 E
160	Takao (tä'kä'ō) ... Jap.	22.35 N	120.30 E
158	Takao ... Tai. (In.)	22.44 N	120.21 E
159	Takaoka (tä'kä-ō'kä) ... Jap.	36.45 N	137.0 E
170	Takapuna (tä-kä-pōō'nä) N. Z. (In.)	36.48 S	174.46 E
159	Takasaki (tä'kä-sä'kê) ... Jap.	36.19 N	139.1 E
159	Takata (tä'kä-tä) ... Jap.	35.7 N	133.42 E
159	Takata ... Jap.	37.5 N	138.15 E
141	Takaungu (tä-kä-ōōŋ'gōō) .. Kenya	3.40 S	39.47 E
159	Takayama (tä'kä-yä'mä) ... Jap.	36.11 N	137.15 E
159	Takeda (tä'kě dä) ... Jap.	32.60 N	131.25 E
159	Takefu (tä'kě-fōō) ... Jap.	35.51 N	136.10 E
155	Takhing (täk'hĭng') ... Chn.	23.10 N	111.42 E
139	Takkaze R. (täk'ä-zä) .. It. E. Afr.	13.45 N	38.30 E
152	Takla Makan (Des.) (tä'klä mä-kän'). Chn.	39.20 N	83.0 E
138	Takoradi (tä-kô-rä'dê) ... G. C.	4.42 N	1.58 W
156	Taku (tä'kōō') ... Chn.	38.59 N	117.35 E
54	Taku R. (tä'kū) ... Can.	58.45 N	132.30 W
92	Tala (tä'lä) ... Mex.	20.39 N	103.40 W
163	Talacag (tä-lä-käg') ... P. I.	8.16 N	124.38 E
163	Talacogan (tä-lä-kō'gän) ... P. I.	8.30 N	125.40 E
95	Talamanca, Cordillera de (Mts.) (kôr-děl-yā'rä dā tä-lä-mäŋ'kä). C. R.-Pan.	9.20 N	83.30 W
160	Talamau (Ophir. Mt.) (tä-lä-mä'ōō) (ō'fēr). Neth. Ind.	0.15 N	99.50 E
140	Tala Mugongo (tä'lä mōō-gôŋ'gōō) Ang.	9.38 S	17.35 E
102	Talara (tä-lä'rä) ... Ec.	4.32 S	81.5 W
161	Talasea (tä-lä-sä'ä) ... N. Gui. Ter.	5.18 S	150.1 E
161	Talaur Is. (tä-lä'ōōr) ... Neth. Ind.	4.15 N	126.45 E
126	Talavera de la Reina (tä-lä-vä'rä dä lä rā-ē'nä). Sp.	39.58 N	4.49 W
73	Talbert (tôl'bûrt) Calif. (Los Angeles In.)	33.42 N	117.58 W
141	Talbia (täl'bĭ-ä) ... Eg.	30.0 N	31.10 E
166	Talbot (tôl'bŭt) ... Austl.	37.12 S	143.42 E
104	Talca (täl'kä) ... Chl.	35.28 S	71.45 W
104	Talcahuano (täl-kä-wä'nō) ... Chl.	36.45 S	73.1 W
148	Taldy-Kurgan (täl'dĭ kōōr-gän') Sov. Un.	45.10 N	78.25 E
93	Talea de Castro (San Miguel) (tä'lā-ä dä käs'trō). Mex.	17.22 N	96.15 W
124	Talence (tȧ-lôɴs) ... Fr.	44.48 N	0.35 W
152	Tali (tä'lē) ... Chn.	25.51 N	100.10 E
161	Taliabu (I.) (tä-lê-ä'bōō) Neth. Ind.	1.45 S	124.45 E
163	Talibon (tä-lē-bôn') ... P. I.	10.9 N	124.19 E
156	Talienwan (tä'lyěn-wän') ... Kwan.	39.4 N	121.37 E
163	Talikud I. (tä-lē-kōōd') ... P. I.	6.55 N	125.42 E
162	Talim I. (tä-lēm') ... P. I.	14.20 N	121.13 E
161	Talin, Pt. (tä-lēn') P. I. (Manila In.)	13.59 N	120.32 E
163	Talisay (tä-lē'sī) ... P. I.	10.13 N	123.51 E
163	Talisay ... P. I.	10.43 N	122.59 E
162	Talisay ... P. I.	14.8 N	122.56 E
161	Talisay ... P. I. (Manila In.)	14.7 N	121.1 E
163	Talisayan (tä-lē-sä'yän) ... P. I.	8.59 N	124.53 E
53	Talkeetna (tál-kēt'nȧ) ... Alsk.	62.20 N	150.0 W
52	Talkeetna Mts. ... Alsk. (In.)	62.10 N	149.0 W
82	Talladega (tăl-ȧ-dē'gȧ) ... Ala.	33.27 N	86.7 W
82	Tallahassee (tăl-ȧ-hăs'ē) ... Fla.	30.26 N	84.18 W
82	Tallahatchie R. (tăl-ȧ-hăch'ē) Miss.	34.32 N	89.30 W
167	Tallangatta (tă-lăŋ-gă'tȧ) ... Austl.	36.14 S	147.13 E
82	Tallapoosa (tăl-ȧ-pōō'sȧ) ... Ga.	33.45 N	85.17 W
82	Tallapoosa R. ... Ala.-Ga.	32.25 N	86.0 W
82	Tallassee (tăl'ȧ-sē) ... Ala.	32.31 N	85.55 W
121	Tallinn (Reval) (tál'lēn)(rā'väl) Est.	59.26 N	24.46 E
82	Tallulah (tȧ-lōō'lȧ) ... La.	32.25 N	91.11 W
131	Talnoe (täl'nô-yě) ... Sov. Un.	48.51 N	30.43 E
139	Talōdi (tä-lō'dê) ... A. E. Sud.	10.38 N	30.25 E
92	Talpa de Allende (täl'pä dā äl-yěn'dä). Mex.	20.25 N	104.49 W
121	Talsi (tál'sĭ) ... Lat.	57.15 N	22.38 E
104	Taltal (täl-täl') ... Chl.	25.20 S	70.35 W
131	Taly (täl'ĭ) ... Sov. Un.	49.51 N	40.2 E
166	Talyawalka Branch (R.) (tăl-yȧ-wôk'ȧ). Austl.	32.10 S	143.10 E
77	Tama (tā'mȧ) ... Ia.	41.57 N	92.35 W
170	Tamaki R. (tä-mä'kê) .. N. Z. (In.)	36.54 S	174.53 E
138	Tamale (tä-mä'lā) ... G. C.	9.24 N	0.50 W
77	Tamana Hill (Mt.) (tä-mä'nä) Trin. (In.)	10.29 N	61.12 W
131	Tamanskaya (tä'mán-skä-yä) Sov. Un.	45.11 N	36.41 E
138	Tamanr'aset, Wadi (R.) (wä'dê tä-män-räs'sět). Alg.	22.15 N	2.30 E
85	Tamaqua (tȧ-mô'kwȧ) ... Pa.	40.45 N	75.57 W
169	Tamar R. (tā'mär) Austl. (Tas. In.)	41.20 S	147.3 E
116	Tamar (R.) ... Gt. Brit.	50.35 N	4.15 W
127	Tamarite (tä-mä-rē'tä) ... Sp	41.53 N	0.25 E
161	Tamata (tä-mä'tä) P. I. (Manila In.)	14.55 N	121.40 E
141	Tamatave (tä-mȧ-täv') ... Madag.	18.10 S	49.20 E
92	Tamaulipas (State) (tä-mä-ōō-lē'päs). Mex.	23.30 N	99.0 W
92	Tamazula de Gordiano (tä-mä-zōō'lä dä gôr-dê-ä'nō). Mex.	19.38 N	103.8 W
93	Tamazulápam (Santo Tomas) (tä-mä-zōō-lä'päm) (sän'tō tô-mäs'). Mex.	17.42 N	97.34 W
92	Tamazunchale (tä-mä-zōōn-chä'lä) Mex.	21.17 N	98.46 W
138	Tambacounda (täm-bä-kōōn'dä) Fr. W. Afr.	13.52 N	13.45 W
160	Tambelan Is. (täm-bä-län') Neth. Ind.	0.38 N	107.0 E
165	Tambo (tăm'bō) ... Austl.	25.0 S	146.20 E
167	Tambo, R. ... Austl.	37.38 S	147.55 E
167	Tamboon Inlet (tăm-bōōn') . Austl.	37.46 S	149.8 E
167	Tamboritha Mt. (tăm-bô-rē'thȧ) Austl.	37.28 S	146.41 E
130	Tambov (tȧm-bôf') ... Sov. Un.	52.45 N	42.30 E
130	Tambov (Dist.) ... Sov. Un.	52.40 N	40.0 E
126	Tambre R. (täm'brā) ... Sp.	42.58 N	8.30 W
139	Tambura (täm-bōō'rä) .. A. E. Sud.	5.32 N	27.28 E
126	Tamega R. (tä'mä-gä) ... Port.	41.30 N	7.55 W
115	Tamel, Wadi (R.) (wä'dê täm'ěl) Libya	30.30 N	16.18 E
118	Tame, R. (tām) ... Gt. Brit.	52.31 N	1.45 W
92	Tamesí, R. (tä-mä-sē') ... Mex.	22.40 N	98.40 W
138	Tamgak Mts. (täm-gäk') Fr. W. Afr.	19.10 N	8.40 E
114	Tamgrout (täm-grōōt') ... Mor.	30.12 N	5.47 W
93	Tamiahua (tä-mê-ä'wä) ... Mex.	21.16 N	97.28 W
93	Tamiahua Lagoon ... Mex.	21.30 N	97.27 W
156	Taming (tä'mĭng') ... Chn.	36.20 N	115.20 E
121	Tammela (täm'ě-lä) ... Fin.	60.50 N	23.44 E
121	Tammisaari (Ekenas) (täm'ĭ-sä'rĭ) Fin.	59.58 N	23.28 E
161	Tamon, R. (tä-mōn') P. I. (Manila In.)	14.18 N	120.47 E
135	Tampa (tăm'pȧ) Bel. Cong. (Brazzaville In.)	4.45 S	15.23 E
72	Tampa (tăm'pȧ) Colo. (Denver In.)	40.8 N	104.27 W
83	Tampa ... Fla. (In.)	27.57 N	82.27 W
83	Tampa B. ... Fla. (In.)	27.40 N	82.35 W
121	Tampere (tám'pě-rě) ... Fin.	61.30 N	23.46 E
93	Tampico (täm-pē'kō) ... Mex.	22.14 N	97.51 W
93	Tampico Alto (äl'tō) ... Mex.	22.7 N	97.50 W
150	Tamrida (tám-rē'dȧ) ... Socotra	12.30 N	53.58 E
167	Tamworth (tăm'wûrth) ... Austl.	31.5 S	150.56 E
118	Tamworth ... Gt. Brit.	52.38 N	1.41 W
139	Tana, L. (tä'nä) ... It. E. Afr.	12.0 N	37.15 E
159	Tanabe (tä-nä'bā) ... Jap.	33.45 N	135.28 E
52	Tanaga I. (tä-nä'-gä) ... Alsk.	51.40 N	178.0 W

ng-sing; ŋ-baŋk; ɴ-nasalized n; nŏd; cŏmmit; ōld; ôbey; ôrder; fōōd; fōōt; ou-out; s-soft; sh-dish; th-thin; pūre; ůnite; ûrn; stŭd; circŭs ü-as "y" in study; '-indeterminate vowel.

Page	Name Pronunciation Region	Lat. °′	Long. °′
160	Tanahbala (I.) (tȧ-nȧ-bä′lä) Neth. Ind.	0.30 S	98.30 E
160	Tanahmasa (I.) (tȧ-nȧ-mä′sä) Neth. Ind.	0.10 S	38.30 E
164	Tanami (tȧ-nä′mē)..........Austl.	20.12 S	129.50 E
53	Tanana (tă-nȧ-nä′)..........Alsk.	65.10 N	152.0 W
53	Tanana R..................Alsk.	64.40 N	150.0 W
141	Tananarive (tȧ-nä-nȧ′rēv′).Madag.	18.50 S	47.33 E
141	Tana R. (tä′nä)...........Kenya	0.30 S	39.42 E
110	Tana R................Nor.-Fin.	69.50 N	26.15 E
128	Tanaro R. (tä′nä-rō)..........It.	44.41 N	8.0 E
163	Tanauan (tä-nä′wän)........P. I.	11.7 N	125.1 E
162	Tanauan....................P. I.	14.5 N	121.9 E
161	Tanay (tȧ-nä′ē) .P. I. (Manila In.)	14.31 N	121.19 E
92	Tancanhuitz (tän-kän-wēts′).Mex.	21.36 N	98.58 W
156	Tancheng (tän′chĕng′).......Chn.	34.47 N	118.23 E
92	Tancítaro (tän-sē′tä-rō).....Mex.	19.12 N	102.20 W
92	Tancitaro, Nudo de (Vol.) (nōō′dhō dā tän-cē′tä-rō).Mex.	19.12 N	102.23 W
93	Tancoco (tän-kō′kō)........Mex.	21.18 N	97.46 W
163	Tandag (tän′däg)...........P. I.	9.3 N	126.12 E
104	Tandil (tän-dēl′)............Arg.	37.20 S	59.15 W
160	Tandjongbalei (tän′jŏng-bȧ-lā′ē) Neth. Ind.	2.58 N	99.45 E
160	Tandjongpandan (tän′jŏng-pän-dän′).Neth. Ind.	2.42 S	107.52 E
145	Tandjongpinang (tän-jŏng-pē-näng′).Neth. Ind. (In.)	0.54 N	104.28 E
166	Tandou, L. (tăn′dou).......Austl.	32.38 S	142.5 E
163	Tandu (tän-dōō)............P. I.	6.0 N	121.20 E
159	Tanega I. (tä′nȧ-gä).........Jap.	30.30 N	130.59 E
138	Tanezrouft (Reg.) (tä′nĕz-rōōft) Alg.	24.0 N	0.30 E
141	Tanga (tăŋ′gȧ).............Tan.	5.7 S	39.7 E
92	Tangancícuaro (tăŋ-gän-sē′kwä-rō) Mex.	19.54 N	102.12 W
140	Tanganyika, L. (tăŋ-găn-yē-′kä) Bel. Cong.-Tan.	6.30 S	29.45 E
140	Tanganyika Ter.............Afr.	6.0 S	34.30 E
152	Tangar (täng′är)............Chn.	36.52 N	101.14 E
122	Tangermünde(täng′ĕr-mûn′dĕ)Ger.	52.33 N	11.57 E
138	Tangier (Neutral State) (tăn-jēr′) Afr.	35.50 N	5.52 W
135	Tangier, B. of Sp. Mor. (Gibraltar In.).	35.46 N	5.14 E
81	Tangipahoa R. (tăn′jē-pȧ-hō′ȧ)La.	30.50 N	90.30 W
155	Tangki (täng′kē′)...........Chn.	29.2 N	119.31 E
156	Tangku (taŋ′kōō′)...........Chn.	39.5 N	117.39 E
152	Tangla Mts.(täng′lä′).......Chn.	32.30 N	93.0 E
156	Tang R. (täng)..............Chn.	39.0 N	114.47 E
156	Tangshan (täng′shän′)......Chn.	34.24 N	116.31 E
154	Tangyang (täng′yäng′)......Chn.	30.50 N	111.38 E
156	Tangyin (täng′yĭn′).........Chn.	35.52 N	114.34 E
158	Tangyuan (täŋ-wän′).....Manch.	46.50 N	129.55 E
163	Tanjay (tän-hä′ē) ....P. I.	9.30 N	123.11 E
151	Tanjore (tăn-jôr′)..........India	10.40 N	79.8 E
154	Tankiang (tän′kyäng′)......Chn.	26.18 N	107.59 E
165	Tanna I. (tän′ä)......New Hebr.	18.25 S	169.20 E
153	Tann-bira R. (tän′-bē′rä)....Chn.	47.0 N	128.35 E
152	Tannu Ola (Mts.) (tä′nōō ō′lä)Chn.	50.30 N	95.0 E
152	Tannu Tuva (Dist.) (tä′nōō tōō′vä).Chn.	51.0 N	95.0 E
163	Tañon Str. (tän-yōn′).......P. I.	10.10 N	123.25 E
142	Tanqua R. (tän′kwä)...U. S. Afr.	32.25 S	20.0 E
93	Tanquijo Reef (tän-kē′hō)...Mex.	21.7 N	97.17 W
139	Tanta (tän′tä)..............Eg.	30.32 N	30.59 E
92	Tantoyuca (tän-tō-yōō′kä)...Mex.	21.21 N	98.13 W
145	Tantura (tän-tōō′rȧ)....Pal. (In.)	32.38 N	34.56 E
155	Tanyang (tän′yäng)........Chn.	31.57 N	119.37 E
157	Tanyang...................Cho.	36.58 N	128.20 E
157	Tanyo (tăn′yō′).............Cho.	35.20 N	126.57 E
162	Tanza (tän′zä)..............P. I.	14.24 N	120.51 E
158	Taoan (tä′ō-än′)..........Manch.	45.42 N	122.48 E
154	Taohsien (tä′ō-hsyĕn′).......Chn.	25.35 N	111.28 E
153	Taonan (tä′ō-nän′)........Manch.	45.27 N	122.31 E
155	Taoping (tä′ō-pĭng′)........Chn.	23.57 N	116.36 E
155	Tao R. (tä′ō)...............Chn.	25.12 N	114.32 E
128	Taormina (tä-ôr-mē′nä).......It.	37.52 N	15.16 E
78	Taos (tä′ōs)..............N. M.	36.25 N	105.32 W
138	Taoudenni Oasis (tä′ōō-dĕ-nē) Fr. W. Afr.	22.40 N	2.45 W
138	Taoulo (tä′ōō-lō)............Lib.	6.30 N	8.48 W
138	Taourirt (tä-ōō-rērt′).......Alg.	26.52 N	0.8 E
154	Taoyuan (tä′ō-yōō-än′)......Chn.	28.52 N	111.11 E
156	Taoyüan (tä′ō-yü-än′).......Chn.	33.38 N	118.42 E
121	Tapa (tȧ′pȧ)................Est.	59.12 N	25.55 E
103	Tapajoz, R. (tä-pä′zhōzh)...Braz.	5.28 S	56.30 W
171	Tapanui (tä-pȧ-nōō′ē)......N. Z.	45.55 S	169.18 E
103	Taperoá (tȧ-pä-rô-ä′)...Braz. (In.)	13.30 S	39.3 W
163	Tapiantana Group (Is.) (tä′pē-än-tä′nä).P. I.	6.18 N	122.0 E
170	Tapokopoko, Mt. (tä′pō-kô-pō′kô).N. Z. (In.)	41.23 S	174.59 E
158	Tappi C. (tăp′ē)............Jap.	41.10 N	140.25 E
151	Tapti R. (tăp′tē)...........India	21.0 N	76.0 E
170	Tapu I. (tä-pōō′)......N. Z. (In.)	36.47 S	174.55 E
163	Tapul Group (Is.) (tä-pōōl′)..P. I.	5.35 N	120.50 E
163	Tapul I....................P. I.	5.43 N	120.54 E
103	Taquari, R. (tä-kwä′rĭ).....Braz.	17.30 S	56.30 W
169	Tara (tä′rä)..........Austl. (In.)	27.12 S	150.31 E
148	Tara (tä′rȧ)............Sov. Un.	56.55 N	74.15 E
115	Tarabulus esh Sham (Tripoli) (tȧ-rä′bōō-lōōs ĕsh shäm′)(trĭp′ô-lē) Syr.	34.28 N	35.51 E
170	Taradale (tă′rȧ-dāl)........N. Z.	39.33 S	176.52 E
162	Tara I. (tä′rä)..............P. I.	12.18 N	120.22 E
158	Taraiki B. (tä′rä-ē′kē).......Kar.	49.0 N	143.30 E
126	Tarancón (tä-rän-kōn′).......Sp.	40.2 N	3.1 W
129	Taranto (tä′rän-tō)..........It.	40.28 N	17.12 E
129	Taranto, G. of................It.	40.10 N	17.10 E
148	Tara R................Sov. Un.	56.30 N	76.0 E
90	Tarará (tä-rä-rä′) Cuba (Habana In.)	23.11 N	82.14 W
96	Tarará Pt..................Cuba	23.10 N	82.15 W
124	Tarare (tȧ-rär′)...............Fr.	45.55 N	4.25 E
171	Tararua Ra. (tä-rȧ-rōō′ȧ)....N. Z.	40.50 S	175.20 E
124	Tarascon (tȧ-rȧs-kôɴ′).........Fr.	43.48 N	4.38 E
131	Tarashcha (tä′rȧsh-chȧ)..Sov. Un.	49.33 N	30.30 E
170	Tarawera L. (tä-rȧ-wā′rä)...N. Z.	38.12 S	176.28 E
170	Tarawhati (tä-rä-hwä′tē)....N. Z.	35.42 S	173.40 E
126	Tarazona (tä-rä-thō′nä).......Sp.	39.15 N	1.53 W
126	Tarazona....................Sp.	41.54 N	1.45 W
116	Tarbat Ness (tȧr′bȧt)....Gt. Brit.	57.50 N	3.45 W
124	Tarbes (tȧrb)...............Fr.	43.15 N	0.5 E
83	Tarboro (tär′bŭr-ô)........N. C.	35.54 N	77.33 W
167	Taree (tȧ-rē′)............Austl.	31.54 S	152.29 E
141	Tarfâya....................Eg.	29.50 N	31.16 E
129	Târgoviste (tĕr-gō′vēsh-tyĕ).Rom.	44.55 N	25.29 E
129	Târgul-Jiul (tĕr′gŏŏl-zhĭ′ŏŏl).Rom.	45.1 N	23.19 E
123	Târgul-Mureș (tĕr′gŏŏl-mōō′rĕsh) Rom.	46.33 N	24.35 E
123	Târgul-Neamț (tĕr′gŏŏl-nĕ-ämts′) Rom.	47.13 N	26.23 E
123	Târgul-Ocna (tĕr′gŏŏl-ôk′nȧ).Rom.	46.17 N	26.37 E
123	Târgul-Săcuesc (tĕr′gŏŏl-sȧ-kwĕsk′).Rom.	46.3 N	26.6 E
138	Tarhmanant (Well) (tär-mä-nänt′) Alg.	24.35 N	4.3 W
126	Tarifa (tä-rē′fä).............Sp.	36.2 N	5.35 W
162	Tarigtig Pt. (tä-rēg-têg′) ....P. I.	16.20 N	122.15 E
102	Tarija (tä-rē′hä)............Bol.	21.30 S	64.30 W
150	Tarim (tȧ-rēm′) ....Aden	16.10 N	44.10 E
152	Tarim Basin..............Chn.	39.50 N	83.0 E
152	Tarim R....................Chn.	41.0 N	83.0 E
143	Tarka R. (tär′kȧ).......U. S. Afr.	32.10 S	26.0 E
143	Tarkastad (tär′kȧ-städ).U. S. Afr.	31.59 S	26.14 E
131	Tarkhankut, C. (tȧr-ĸän′kŏŏt) Sov. Un.	45.22 N	32.31 E
79	Tarkio (tär′kĭ-ō)............Mo.	40.27 N	95.23 W
83	Tar R. (tär)...............N. C.	35.55 N	78.10 W
138	Tarkwa (tärk′wä)...........G. C.	5.18 N	2.0 W
162	Tarlac (tär′läk)............P. I.	15.30 N	120.36 E
102	Tarma (tär′mä).............Peru	11.28 S	75.45 W
123	Târnava Mică R. (tĕr-nä′vȧ mē′kȧ).Rom.	46.24 N	24.35 E
123	Târnava Sânmărtin (tĕr-nä′vȧ sĕn-mȧr-tēn′)..Rom.	46.20 N	24.18 E
123	Tarnopol (tȧr-nô′pôl′)........Pol.	49.33 N	25.37 E
124	Tarnos (tär-nô′)..............Fr.	43.35 N	1.27 W
123	Tarnów (tär′nŏŏf)............Pol.	50.1 N	20.59 E
124	Tarn R. (tärn)...............Fr.	43.40 N	1.25 E
169	Tarong (tä-rŏng′)..........Austl.	26.43 S	151.51 E
128	Taro R. (tä′rō)...............It.	44.37 N	10.0 E
138	Taroudant (tȧ-rōō-dänt′)....Mor.	30.32 N	8.50 W
82	Tarpon Springs (tär′pŏn)Fla. (In.)	28.8 N	82.46 W
118	Tarporley (tär′pēr-lē)....Gt. Brit.	53.9 N	2.40 W
97	Tarpum B. (tär′pŭm)......Ba. Is.	25.0 N	76.15 W
128	Tarquinia (Corneto) (tär-kwē′nē-ä) (kôr-nä′tō).It.	42.16 N	11.45 E
127	Tarragona (tär-rä-gō′nä)......Sp.	41.7 N	1.15 E
73	Tarrant (tăr′ănt) Ala. (Birmingham In.)	33.36 N	86.47 W
127	Tarrasa (tär-rä′sä).......Sp. (In.)	41.32 N	2.1 E
127	Tárrega (tä′rȧ-gä)...........Sp.	41.39 N	1.8 E
113	Tarsus (tȧr′sŏŏs) (tär′sŭs)....Tur.	37.0 N	34.55 E
115	Tartous (tȧr-tōōs′)..........Syr.	34.55 N	35.55 E
121	Tartu (Dorpat) (tär′tōō) (dôr′pät).Est.	58.24 N	26.48 E
130	Tarussa (tä′rŏŏ-sȧ)......Sov. Un.	54.43 N	37.9 E
138	Tasili (Ajer) Plat. (tä′sē-lē) (ä′zhĕr).Alg.	26.0 N	7.0 E
149	Tas-Kistabit Mts. (tȧs′-kēs-tȧ-bēt′) Sov. Un.	63.20 N	147.0 E
148	Tashkent (tȧsh′kĕnt).....Sov. Un.	41.30 N	69.20 E
171	Tasman B. (tăz′măn)........N. Z.	41.0 S	173.20 E
171	Tasman, Mt.................N. Z.	43.32 S	170.13 E
169	Tasmania (tăz-mā′nĭ-ȧ) Austl. (Tas. In.)	41.55 S	146.50 E
165	Tasman Sea..............Austl.	35.0 S	160.0 E
169	Tasmans Pen. (tăz′mănz) Austl. (Tas. In.)	43.5 S	147.50 E
92	Tasquillo (täs-kē′lyō).......Mex.	20.31 N	99.18 W
156	Tasung L. (tä′sŏŏng′).......Chn.	33.17 N	119.35 E
112	Tatar (Soviet Rep.) (tȧ-tär′) Sov. Un.	55.30 N	51.0 E
149	Tatar Str..........Sov. Un.-Jap.	49.0 N	141.0 E
148	Tatarsk (tȧ-tärsk′)......Sov. Un.	55.15 N	75.59 E
142	Tate Berg (Mt.) (tāt)...U. S. Afr.	32.12 S	20.51 E
140	Tati (tä′tē)................Bech.	21.22 S	27.38 E
155	Tatien (tä′tē-ĕn′)...........Chn.	25.40 N	117.50 E
167	Tatong (tȧ-tông′)..........Austl.	36.44 S	146.4 E
123	Tatra Mts., High (tä′trȧ) Pol.-Czech.	49.13 N	19.55 E
123	Tatra Mts., Low..........Czech.	48.55 N	19.40 E
152	Tatsienlu (tä′tsyĕn′lōō′).....Chn.	30.2 N	101.57 E
154	Tatsu (tä′tsōō′)............Chn.	29.52 N	105.45 E
159	Tatsuta (tăt′sōō-tȧ) Jap. (Osaka In.)	34.36 N	135.42 E
155	Tatung (tä′tŏŏng′)..........Chn.	30.48 N	117.48 E
153	Tatung....................Chn.	40.7 N	113.12 E
157	Tatungkow (tä′tŏŏng′kō′)...Chn.	39.54 N	124.9 E
99	Taubaté (tou-bȧ-tā′) Braz. (Rio de Janeiro In.)	23.4 S	45.35 W
139	Taufikia (tou-fēk′yȧ)...A. E. Sud.	9.28 N	31.41 E
170	Taumarunui (tou′mä-rŏŏ-nōō′ē) N. Z.	38.53 S	175.15 E
143	Taungs (tä′ŏŏngs)..........Bech.	27.31 S	24.47 E
116	Taunton (tôn′tŭn) (tän′tŭn) Gt. Brit.	51.0 N	3.10 W
86	Taunton...................Mass.	41.55 N	71.5 W
170	Taupaki (tä′ōō-pä′kē)..N. Z. (In.)	36.49 S	174.33 E
170	Taupo L. (tä′ōō-pō)........N. Z.	38.45 S	175.55 E
121	Taurage (tou-rä′gā).........Lith.	55.15 N	22.18 E
170	Tauranga (tä′ōō-räŋ′gȧ) ....N. Z.	37.40 S	176.10 E
170	Tauranga Harbor...........N. Z.	37.32 S	176.2 E
113	Taurus Mts. (tô′rŭs)........Tur.	37.15 N	34.30 E
126	Tauste (tä-ōōs′tȧ)............Sp.	41.55 N	1.16 W
149	Tavatama (tä′vȧ-tä′mä) .Sov. Un.	61.45 N	157.55 E
48	Tavda (tȧv-dȧ′).........Sov. Un.	58.20 N	65.0 E
148	Tavda R................Sov. Un.	58.15 N	65.0 E
125	Taverny (tȧ-vĕr-nē′).....Fr. (In.)	49.1 N	2.13 E
126	Tavira (tä-vē′rȧ)...........Port.	37.8 N	7.40 W
160	Tavoy (tä-voi′)............India	14.5 N	98.18 E
113	Tavşanli (tȧv′shän-lĭ)........Tur.	39.30 N	29.35 E
170	Tawa Flat (tä′wȧ).....N. Z. (In.)	41.11 S	174.50 E
159	Tawara (tä′wȧ-rȧ) Jap.(Osaka In.)	34.55 N	135.21 E
84	Tawas City (tô′wȧs).......Mich.	44.17 N	83.30 W
163	Tawitawi Group (Is.)........P. I.	5.0 N	120.0 E
163	Tawitawi I. (tä′wē-tä′wē)....P. I.	5.12 N	120.0 E
92	Taxco (El Vieja) (täs′kō) (ĕl vyā′hō).Mex.	18.32 N	99.36 W
116	Tay (R.) (tā)...........Gt. Brit.	56.35 N	3.30 W
161	Tayabas (tä-yä′bäs) P. I. (Manila In.)	14.2 N	121.40 E
161	Tayabas (Prov.).P. I. (Manila In.)	14.30 N	121.40 E
162	Tayabas B..................P. I.	13.45 N	121.40 E
163	Tayasan (tä-yä′sän) ....P. I.	9.56 N	123.11 E
155	Tayeh (tä′yĕ′)..............Chn.	30.5 N	114.52 E
116	Tay, Firth of...........Gt. Brit.	56.10 N	2.40 W
116	Tay, Loch (L.) (lŏĸ′tā′)..Gt. Brit.	56.30 N	4.10 W
85	Taylor (tā′lēr)...............Pa.	41.23 N	75.45 W
81	Taylor......................Tex.	30.35 N	97.25 W
72	Taylor Mt.....Colo. (Denver In.)	40.12 N	105.28 W
75	Taylor, Mt................N. M.	35.17 N	107.41 W
73	Taylorsville (tā′lērz-vĭl) Utah (Salt Lake City In.)	40.40 N	111.57 W
79	Taylorville (tā′lēr-vĭl).........Ill.	39.33 N	89.17 W
161	Taysan (tä-ē-sän′) P. I. (Manila In.)	13.51 N	121.10 E
163	Taytay (tī-tī′)...............P. I.	10.48 N	119.30 E
163	Taytay B...................P. I.	10.55 N	119.34 E
163	Taytay Pt...................P. I.	10.41 N	125.8 E
162	Tayug (tä-yōōg′) ....P. I.	16.1 N	120.44 E
155	Tayu Ling (Mts.) (tä′yōō-lĭng′) Chn.	26.8 N	116.15 E
138	Taza (tä′zä)...............Mor.	34.15 N	4.0 W
148	Taz, G. of (tȧz).........Sov. Un.	69.0 N	77.0 E
148	Taz R................Sov. Un.	65.30 N	82.0 E
140	Tchibanga (chē-băŋ′gä) Fr. Eq. Afr.	2.58 S	10.59 E
123	Tczew (tchĕf)...............Pol.	54.5 N	18.48 E
81	Teague (tēg)...............Tex.	31.39 N	96.17 W
170	Teana-Katuku (Mt.) (tā-ä′nä-kä-tōō′kōō).N. Z. (In.)	36.55 S	174.33 E
93	Teapa (tā-ä′pä).............Mex.	17.33 N	92.56 W
171	Te Arau L. (tā ä-rä′ōō) .....N. Z.	45.10 S	167.50 E
170	Te Aroha (tā ä-rō′hä).......N. Z.	37.33 S	175.47 E
170	Te Awamutu (tā ä-wä-mōō′tōō) N. Z.	37.59 S	175.20 E
138	Tébessa (tā-bĕs′ä)...........Alg.	35.25 N	8.6 E
145	Tebingtingga (teb′ĭng-tĭng′gä) Neth. Ind. (In.)	0.50 N	102.40 E
145	Tebnine (tĕb-nēn′)......Syr. (In.)	33.10 N	35.23 E
135	Teboursouk (tȧ-bŏŏr-sŏŏk′) Tun. (In.)	36.28 N	9.20 E
92	Tecalitlán (tā-kä-lē-tlän′)....Mex.	19.27 N	103.15 W
93	Tecamachalco (tā′kä-mä-chäl′kō) Mex. (In.)	19.22 N	98.57 W
92	Tecoanapa (tāk-wä-nä-pä′) ..Mex.	16.32 N	98.45 W
92	Tecolotlán (tā-kô-lô-tlän′)...Mex.	20.14 N	104.0 W
93	Tecolutla (tā-kô-lōō′tlä).....Mex.	20.30 N	97.2 W
93	Tecolutla, R...............Mex.	20.20 N	97.15 W
92	Tecomán (tā-kô-män′).......Mex.	18.56 N	103.53 W
93	Tecomaxtlahuaca (San Sebastian) (tā′kô-mäs′tlä-wä′kä (sän sā-bäs-tē-än′).Mex.	17.41 N	96.56 W
92	Tecozautla (tā′kô-zä-ōō′tlä)..Mex.	20.30 N	99.39 W
92	Tecpan de Galeana (tĕk′pän dā gä-lā-ä′nä).Mex.	17.17 N	100.33 W
93	Tecpatlán (tĕk-pä-tlän′).....Mex.	17.8 N	93.17 W
92	Tecuala (tā-kwä′lä).........Mex.	22.24 N	105.27 W
93	Tecuamulco (tā′kwä-mōōl′kō) Mex. (In.)	19.30 N	98.45 W
123	Tecuci (tȧ-kŏŏch′)..........Rom.	45.51 N	27.25 E
84	Tecumseh (tē-kŭm′sĕ)......Mich.	42.0 N	84.0 W
79	Tecumseh..................Neb.	40.23 N	96.12 W
79	Tecumseh..................Okla.	35.15 N	96.55 W
119	Teddington (tĕd′ĭng-tŭn) Gt. Brit. (London In.)	51.26 N	0.21 W
6	Teelani, Mt. (tĕ-ȧ-lä′nē)Sam. (In.)	13.40 S	172.27 W
116	Tees, R. (tēz)...........Gt. Brit.	54.35 N	1.50 W
102	Tefé (tĕf-ā′)...............Braz.	3.30 S	64.45 W
119	Tegel (tā′ghĕl)...Ger. (Berlin In.)	52.35 N	13.17 E
94	Tegucigalpa (tȧ-gōō-sē-gäl′pä) Hond.	14.12 N	87.23 W
156	Tehchow (tä′chō′)..........Chn.	37.33 N	116.18 E
155	Tehhing (tĕ′hĭng)...........Chn.	28.59 N	117.40 E
156	Tehping (tä′pĭng′)..........Chn.	37.39 N	117.0 E
150	Tehran (tĕ-hrän′)...........Per.	35.45 N	51.45 E
155	Tehtsing (tĕ′tsĭng′).........Chn.	30.35 N	120.3 E
93	Tehuacán (tā-wä-kän′)......Mex.	18.30 N	97.20 W
93	Tehuantepec (Santo Domingo) (tȧ-wän-tȧ-pĕk′).Mex.	16.20 N	95.14 W
93	Tehuantepec, G. of.........Mex.	16.0 N	94.40 W
93	Tehuantepec, Isth. of.......Mex.	16.50 N	94.30 W
93	Tehuantepec, R............Mex.	16.40 N	95.35 W
92	Tehuitzingo (tā-wē-tzĭŋ′gō)..Mex.	18.21 N	98.16 W
155	Tehwa (tĕ′wä′).............Chn.	25.26 N	118.11 E
155	Teian (tĕ′ē-än′).............Chn.	29.16 N	115.32 E
154	Teian......................Chn.	31.14 N	113.30 E
130	Teikovo (tā′kô-vô)......Sov. Un.	56.51 N	40.31 E
126	Tejo R. (tä′hŏŏ)............Port.	39.28 N	8.0 W
93	Tejúpam (Santiago) (tȧ-hōō′päm) (sän-tē-ä′gō).Mex.	17.40 N	97.25 W
92	Tejupilco de Hidalgo (tȧ-hōō-pēl′kō dā ē-dhäl′gō) . Mex.	18.53 N	100.8 W
76	Tekamah (tē-kā′mȧ)........Neb.	41.47 N	96.13 W

ăt; finăl; rāte; senâte; ärm; ȧsk; sofȧ; fâre; ch-choose; dh-as th in other; bē; ēvent; bĕt; recĕnt; cratẽr; g-go; gh-gutteral g; bĭt; ĭ-short neutral; rīde; ĸ-gutteral k as ch in German ich;

Page	Name Pronunciation Region	Lat. °′	Long. °′
171	Tekapo, L. (tĕ'kä-pō)........N. Z.	43.55 S	170.32 E
170	Te Karaka (tā-kä-rä'kä).....N. Z.	38.28 S	177.52 E
113	Tekirdağ (tĕk'ĕr-däg')........Tur.	41.0 N	27.30 E
70	Tekoa (tē-kō'à)...........Wash.	47.14 N	117.5 W
170	Te Kuiti (tā kōō-ē'tē).......N. Z.	38.20 S	175.10 E
94	Tela (tā'lä)..............Hond.	15.45 N	87.24 W
93	Telapon, Cerro (Mt.) (sĕr-rō tā-lä-pōn') Mex. (In.)	19.22 N	98.43 W
113	Telav (tyĕ-läf')..........Sov. Un.	41.55 N	45.30 E
145	Tel-Aviv (tĕl-ä-vēv').....Pal. (In.)	32.2 N	34.49 E
131	Teleneşti (tyĕ-lĕ-nĕsht'')....Rom.	47.31 N	28.18 E
74	Telescope Pk..............Calif.	36.11 N	117.7 W
94	Telica (Vol.) (tā-lē'kä)......Nic.	12.37 N	86.52 W
149	Telichiki (tyĕl'ê-chē-kê)..Sov. Un.	60.30 N	166.10 E
145	Tel Kerem (Tul Karm) (tĕl-kĕ-rĕm') (tŭl'kärm').Pal. (In.)	32.18 N	35.0 E
84	Tell City (tĕl)..............Ind.	37.58 N	86.46 W
52	Teller (tĕl'ĕr)..............Alsk.	65.10 N	166.15 W
75	Telluride (tĕl'û-rīd).........Colo.	37.57 N	107.49 W
160	Telokbetong (tā-lŏk'bà-tŏng') Neth. Ind.	5.31 S	105.7 E
92	Teloloapan (tā'lō-lō-ä'pän)...Mex.	18.15 N	99.56 W
112	Tel-pos-iz, Mt. (tyĕl'-pôs-ēz') Sov. Un.	63.50 N	59.25 E
121	Telšiai (tăl'shē-ī)...........Lith.	55.59 N	22.18 E
119	Teltow (tĕl'tō)...Ger. (Berlin In.)	52.24 N	13.16 E
92	Temascalcingo (tā-mäs-käl-sĭŋ'gō) Mex.	19.55 N	99.55 W
92	Temascaltepec (tā'mäs-käl'tà-pĕk').Mex.	19.2 N	100.3 W
118	Teme, R. (tēm).........Gt. Brit.	52.21 N	2.54 W
...	Temesvar, see Timişoara, Rom.		
148	Temir (tyĕ'mêr)..........Sov. Un.	49.25 N	57.15 E
86	Temiscouata L. (tĕ'mĭs-kōō-ä'tà) Can.	47.40 N	68.50 W
167	Temora (tē-mō'rà)..........Austl.	34.27 S	147.32 E
143	Tempe (tĕm'pê).........Sov. Un.	29.4 S	26.6 E
128	Tempio Pausania (tĕm'pê-ō pou-zä'nê-ä).Sard.	40.56 N	9.5 E
94	Tempisque, R. (tĕm-pēs'kä).C. R.	10.26 N	85.30 W
81	Temple (tĕm'p'l)..............Tex.	31.5 N	97.20 W
169	Templestowe (tĕm'p'l-stō) Austl. (Melbourne In.)	37.45 S	145.8 E
122	Templin (tĕm-plēn')..........Ger.	53.8 N	13.30 E
159	Tempozan (tĕm'pō-zän) Jap. (Osaka In.)	34.40 N	135.26 E
131	Temryuk (tyĕm-ryŏŏk')..Sov. Un.	45.15 N	37.22 E
104	Temuco (tà-mōō'kō)...........Chl.	38.45 S	72.32 W
171	Temuka (tê-mōō'kà)........N. Z.	44.13 S	171.20 E
88	Tenafly (tĕn'à-flī) N. J. (N. Y. In.)	40.56 N	73.58 W
92	Tenamaxtlán (tā'nä-mäs-tlän') Mex.	20.13 N	104.9 W
157	Ten-An....................Cho.	36.47 N	127.8 E
92	Tenancingo (tā-nän-sēŋ'gō)..Mex.	19.1 N	99.32 W
92	Tenango (tā-näŋ'gō).........Mex.	19.8 N	99.33 W
160	Tenasserim (tĕn-ăs'ĕr-ĭm)....India	12.5 N	99.0 E
125	Tenay (tē-nĕ')................Fr.	45.55 N	5.30 E
118	Tenbury (tĕn'bŭr-ĭ).....Gt. Brit.	52.18 N	2.35 W
131	Tendrovskaya Pen. (tĕn-drôf' skä-yà)...Sov. Un.	45.15 N	31.45 E
129	Tenedos (Bozcaada) (tĕn'ê-dhŏs) (bôz-kä'dä).Tur.	39.48 N	26.4 E
138	Tenerife (I.) (tā-nà-rē'fä) (tĕn-ĕr-ĭf').Can. Is.	28.18 N	16.30 W
7	Tenerife (Vol.) Can. Is. (Tenerife In.)	28.17 N	16.36 W
114	Ténès (tā-näs')...............Alg.	36.28 N	1.18 E
160	Tenga (Great Paternoster) Is. (tĕŋ'gä) (pā'tĕr-nŏs-tĕr) Neth. Ind.	7.35 S	117.30 E
156	Tengchow (tĕng'chō').......Chn.	37.49 N	120.41 E
145	Tenggaroh (tĕng'gä-rō') Non-fed. Mal. States (In.)	2.14 N	103.56 E
155	Tenghai (tĕng'hī')..........Chn.	23.30 N	116.32 E
154	Tenghsien (tĕng'hsē-ĕn').....Chn.	23.20 N	110.56 E
156	Tenghsien...................Chn.	35.17 N	117.8 E
152	Tengri Khan (Mt.) (tĕŋ'grê ᴋän').Chn.	42.22 N	80.27 E
152	Tengri Nor (Nam Tso) (L.) (tĕŋ'grê nōr) (näm'tsō').Chn.	30.45 N	90.30 E
140	Tenke (tĕŋ'kä).........Bel. Cong.	10.45 S	26.10 E
138	Tenkodogo (tĕŋ-kô-dō'gō) Fr. W. Afr.	11.46 N	0.28 W
164	Tennants Cr. (tĕn'ănts).....Austl.	19.40 S	134.0 E
82	Tennessee (State) (tĕn-ĕ-sē').U. S.	35.30 N	89.30 W
82	Tennessee R...............U. S.	35.0 N	88.15 W
82	Tennille (tĕn'ĭl)..............Ga.	32.56 N	82.50 W
159	Tenno (tĕn'nō)...Jap. (Osaka In.)	35.2 N	135.21 E
159	Tennoji (tĕn'nō-jê) Jap. (Osaka In.)	34.39 N	135.31 E
129	Tenos (I.) (tē'nŏs)..........Grc.	37.35 N	26.10 E
93	Tenosique (tā-nō-sē'kä).....Mex.	17.28 N	91.25 W
158	Tenryugawa R. (tĕn'rē-ōō-gä'wä) Jap.	35.30 N	137.50 E
81	Tensas R. (tĕn'sô)............La.	32.0 N	91.30 W
82	Tensaw R...................Ala.	31.0 N	87.55 W
71	Ten Sleep..................Wyo.	44.2 N	107.27 W
165	Tenterfield (tĕn'tĕr-fēld).....Austl.	29.0 S	152.0 E
92	Teocaltiche (tā'ô-käl-tē'chä).Mex.	21.25 N	102.36 W
93	Teocelo (tā-ô-sā'lō).........Mex.	19.23 N	96.58 W
92	Teocuitatlán de Corona (tā'ô-kwē' tä-tlän'dā kô-rō'nä).Mex.	20.6 N	103.22 W
99	Teodolina (tā-ô-dô-lē'nä) Arg. (Buenos Aires In.)	34.10 S	61.36 W
92	Teoloyucan (tā'ô-lô-yōō'kän).Mex.	19.44 N	99.11 W
93	Teopisca (tā-ô-pēs'kä).......Mex.	16.35 N	92.32 W
93	Teotitlán del Camino (tā-ô-tê-tlän').Mex.	18.8 N	97.4 W
93	Tepalcapan (tā-päl-kä-pän') Mex. (In.)	19.37 N	99.12 W
92	Tepalcatepec (tā'päl-kä'tà-pĕk') Mex.	19.10 N	102.50 W
92	Tepalcingo (tā-päl-sēŋ'gō)...Mex.	18.35 N	98.50 W
92	Tepatitlán de Morelos (tā-pä-tê-tlän' dā mô-rā'lōs)Mex.	20.50 N	102.42 W
93	Tepeaca (tā-pà-ä'kä).........Mex.	18.57 N	97.55 W
92	Tepecoacuilco de Trujano (tā'pà-kō'ä-kwēl'kō dā trōō-hä'nō).Mex.	18.15 N	99.30 W
92	Tepeji del Rio (tā-pà-kē' dĕl rē'ō).Mex.	19.55 N	99.22 W
93	Tepelmeme (tā'pĕl-mā'mà)...Mex.	17.50 N	97.25 W
93	Tepepan (tā-pā'pän)...Mex. (In.)	19.17 N	99.8 W
92	Tepetlaoxtoc (tā'pä-tlä'ôs-tŏk') Mex.	19.34 N	98.49 W
93	Tepexpan (tā-päs'pän)..Mex. (In.)	19.37 N	98.56 W
92	Tepezala (tā-pà-zä-lä').......Mex.	22.12 N	102.11 W
92	Tepic (tā-pēk')...............Mex.	21.31 N	104.53 W
122	Teplitz-Schönau (Teplice-Šanov) (tĕp'lĭts-shû'nou) (tĕp'lĭ-tsĕ-shä'nôf).Ger.	50.39 N	13.49 E
93	Teposcolula (San Pedro y San Pablo) (tā-pôs-kô-lōō'lä) (sän pä'drō ē sän pä'blō).Mex.	17.31 N	97.30 W
92	Tepoxtlán (tā-pôs-tlän')......Mex.	18.58 N	99.6 W
170	Te Puke (tā pōō'kā)........N. Z.	37.45 S	176.23 E
93	Tequezquinahuac (tā'käz-kē-nä-wäk').Mex. (In.)	19.29 N	98.49 W
92	Tequila (tā-kē'lä)............Mex.	20.53 N	103.48 W
92	Tequisquiapan (tā-kēs-kê-ä'pän) Mex.	20.31 N	99.55 W
128	Teramo (tā'rä-mō)............It.	42.39 N	13.40 E
166	Terang (tē-răng').........Austl.	38.14 S	142.54 E
126	Tera R. (tā'rä)...............Sp.	41.50 N	6.0 W
139	Terbu (tĕr'bōō)..............Libya	26.2 N	15.42 E
113	Tercan (tĕr'jän)...............Tur.	39.40 N	40.18 E
138	Terceira I. (tĕr-sā'rä).Az. Is. (In.)	38.40 N	27.15 W
152	Terek Pass (tyā'rĕk).Chn.-Sov. Un.	40.0 N	74.45 E
113	Terek R.................Sov. Un.	43.45 N	45.0 E
116	Terenure (tĕ'rĕ-nūr)..........Ire.	53.15 N	6.20 W
161	Teresa (tā-rā'sä) P. I. (Manila In.)	14.35 N	121.14 E
103	Teresina (tĕr-ā-sē'nà)........Braz.	5.2 S	42.45 W
99	Teresópolis (tĕr-ā-sô'pô-lēzh) Braz. (Rio de Janeiro In.)	22.25 S	42.59 W
113	Terme (tĕr'mĕ)...............Tur	41.10 N	37.2 E
151	Termez (tyĕr'mĕz)........Sov. Un.	37.29 N	66.59 E
73	Terminal I. (tûr'mĭ-năl) Calif. (Los Angeles In.)	33.45 N	118.15 W
128	Termini (tĕr'mê-nē)..........It.	37.57 N	13.40 E
128	Termoli (tĕr'mō-lē)...........It.	42.0 N	15.0 E
161	Ternate (tĕr-nä'tā).....Neth. Ind.	0.50 N	127.20 E
161	Ternate........P. I. (Manila In.)	14.19 N	120.41 E
128	Terni (tĕr'nê)..................It.	42.35 N	12.40 E
118	Tern, R. (tûrn)...........Gt. Brit.	52.48 N	2.31 W
131	Terny (tĕrn'ĭ)............Sov. Un.	50.58 N	33.57 E
127	Ter R. (tĕr)....................Sp.	41.58 N	2.30 E
128	Terracina (tĕr-rä-chē'nō).......It.	41.17 N	13.13 E
128	Terranova (tĕr-rä-nō'vä).......It.	37.4 N	14.14 E
128	Terranova...................Sard.	40.55 N	9.29 E
89	Terre aux Boeufs, Bayou (tĕr-ō-bûf').La. (New Orleans In.)	29.45 N	89.42 W
85	Terrebonne (tĕr-bŏn')........Can.	45.42 N	73.40 W
81	Terrebonne B...................La.	29.10 N	90.30 W
84	Terre Haute (tĕr-ê hōt').......Ind.	39.28 N	87.25 W
81	Terrell (tĕr'ĕl).................Tex.	32.42 N	96.17 W
70	Terry (tĕr'ĭ)...................Mont.	46.47 N	105.19 W
122	Terschelling (I.) (tĕr-sᴋĕl'ĭng) Neth.	53.24 N	5.20 E
126	Teruel (tā-rōō-ĕl')..............Sp.	40.21 N	1.7 W
166	Teryaweynya L. (tĕr-yà-wā'nyà) Austl.	32.20 S	143.22 E
129	Tešanj (tĕ'shän')..........Yugo.	44.35 N	17.59 E
93	Tesechoacán (tā-sà-chō-ä-kän').Mex.	18.10 N	95.40 W
158	Teshio R. (tĕsh'ê-ō).........Jap.	44.32 N	142.15 E
158	Teshiodake (Mt.) (tĕsh'ê-ō-dä'kä) Jap.	44.2 N	142.58 E
54	Teslin L. (tĕs'lĭn)..........Can.	60.0 N	132.30 W
54	Teslin R....................Can.	61.0 N	134.0 W
152	Tes R. (tĕs)..................Chn.	50.0 N	95.0 E
138	Tessaoua (tĕs-sä'ōō-ä).Fr. W. Afr.	13.48 N	8.2 E
128	Testa del Gargano (Pt.) (tās'tä dĕl gär-gä'nō).It.	41.48 N	16.13 E
116	Test, R. (tĕst)...........Gt. Brit.	51.10 N	1.20 W
140	Tete (tā'tĕ)...................Moz.	16.15 S	33.33 E
131	Teterev R. (tyĕ'tyĕ-rĕf)..Sov. Un.	50.40 N	29.33 E
122	Teterow (tā'tĕ-rō)............Ger.	53.46 N	12.33 E
129	Tetevene (tĕt'ĕ-vĕn-ĕ)..........Bul.	42.55 N	24.15 E
131	Tetkino (tyĕt'kê-nō).....Sov. Un.	51.18 N	34.16 E
70	Teton R. (tē'tŏn).............Mont.	47.55 N	111.50 W
129	Tetova (tā'tô-vô)............Yugo.	42.1 N	21.0 E
112	Tetrina (tyĕ-trē'nà).....Sov. Un.	66.4 N	38.0 E
122	Tetschen (Děčín) (tĕt'shĕn) (dyĕ'chēn).Ger.	50.47 N	14.13 E
118	Tettenhall (tĕt'ĕn-hôl)....Gt. Brit.	52.35 N	2.10 W
138	Tetuán (tā-twän')........Sp. Mor.	35.37 N	5.28 W
112	Tetyushi (tyĕt'yōō-shê)..Sov. Un.	54.55 N	48.48 E
128	Tevere (Tiber) R. (tā'vā-rä) (tī'bĕr).It.	42.42 N	12.14 E
171	Tewaewae B. (tà-wä'ĕ-wä'ĕ).N. Z.	46.15 S	167.30 E
169	Tewantin (tê-wŏn'tĭn).Austl. (In.)	26.19 S	153.1 E
87	Tewksbury (tūks'bĕr-ĭ)Mass. (In.)	42.37 N	71.13 W
79	Texarkana (tĕk-sär-kăn'à)....Ark.	33.25 N	94.1 W
79	Texarkana..................Tex.	33.25 N	94.3 W
80	Texas (State) (tĕk'sås).......U. S.	31.0 N	100.0 W
81	Texas City...................Tex.	29.24 N	94.55 W
92	Texcaltitlán (tās-käl'tê-tlän').Mex.	18.53 N	99.49 W
93	Texcoco (tās-kō'kō)....Mex. (In.)	19.31 N	98.53 W
93	Texcoco, L..............Mex. (In.)	19.28 N	99.0 W
93	Texcoco, R..............Mex. (In.)	19.28 N	98.48 W
122	Texel (I.) (tĕk'sĕl)..........Neth.	53.5 N	4.50 E
93	Texistepec (tĕk-sēs-tà-pĕk')..Mex.	17.52 N	94.48 W
92	Texmelucan (tās-mà-lōō'kän).Mex.	19.17 N	98.26 W
130	Teza R. (tā'zà)..........Sov. Un.	56.45 N	41.25 E
93	Teziutlán (tā-zē-ōō-tlän')....Mex.	19.48 N	97.21 W
93	Tezonco (tā-zōn'kō)....Mex. (In.)	19.19 N	99.4 W
92	Tezontepec (tā-zōn-tà-pĕk')..Mex.	19.51 N	98.49 W
92	Tezontepec de Aldama (dā äl-dä'mä).Mex.	20.11 N	99.25 W
54	Tha-anni R. (tà-ä'nĭ).........Can.	60.15 N	96.0 W
143	Thabanchu (tä'bä-n'chōō') U. S. Afr.	29.9 S	26.51 E
143	Thaba Putsua (Mt.) (tä'bä pōōt-sōō'ä).Bas.	29.45 S	27.55 E
160	Thailand(Siam)(tī'lănd)(sĭăm').Asia	16 0 N	102.30 E
160	Thakhoi (tä-koi')...........Thai.	9.0 N	99.20 E
135	Thala (tä'lä)..........Tun. (In.)	35.34 N	8.51 E
170	Thames (tĕmz).............N. Z.	37.7 S	175.35 E
170	Thames, Firth of...........N. Z.	37.5 S	175.25 E
119	Thames Haven Gt. Brit. (London In.)	51.31 N	0.30 E
84	Thames R...................Can.	42.40 N	81.50 W
116	Thames (R.)...............Gt. Brit.	51.35 N	1.0 W
170	Thames, R..................N. Z.	37.30 S	175.43 E
150	Thana R. (thä'nŭ) India (Bombay In.)	19.3 N	72.58 E
160	Thanh Hoa (tän' hō'ä) Fr. Ind. Chn.	19.38 N	105.40 E
125	Thann (tän)....................Fr.	47.50 N	7.5 E
125	Thaon (tà-ôɴ) (tōn)............Fr.	48.17 N	6.25 E
153	Thapingjau (tä'pĭng'jou') Chn. (Shanghai In.)	31.12 N	121.22 E
151	Thar (Indian) Des. (tŭr)....India	27.30 N	72.0 E
165	Thargomindah (thär-gō-mĭn'dà) Austl.	27.58 S	143.59 E
129	Thasos (I.) (thä'sôs)..........Grc.	40.40 N	24.38 E
91	Thatch Cay (I. (thăch) Vir.Is.(In.)	18.22 N	64.52 W
79	Thayer (thâ'ĕr)................Mo.	36.31 N	91.33 W
122	Thayer (Dyje) R. (tä'yĕr) (dē'yĕ) Ger.	48.50 N	15.55 E
129	Thebai (Thebes) (thä'bī) (thēbz) Grc.	38.21 N	23.18 E
139	Thebes (Ruins) (thēbz).......Eg.	25.46 N	32.32 E
70	The Dalles (dălz)..............Ore.	45.35 N	121.11 W
129	Theologos (thä-ō'lō-gôs)......Grc.	40.35 N	24.40 E
103	Theophilo Ottoni (tā-ô-fē'lōō ôt-tō'nī).Braz.	17.57 S	41.15 W
129	Thermaikos (Thessalonikē), G. of (thĕr-mä'ê-kôs) (thĕs-sä-lô-nē'kē).Grc.	40.10 N	22.50 E
70	Thermopolis (thēr-mŏp'ô-lĭs).Wyo.	43.38 N	108.11 W
167	The Rock..................Austl.	35.16 S	147.9 E
129	Thessalonikē (thĕs-sä-lô-nē'kē) Grc.	40.35 N	22.55 E
129	Thessalonikē (Thermaikos), G. of Grc.	40.10 N	22.50 E
129	Thessaly (Prov.) (thĕs'à-lê)...Grc.	39.40 N	22.20 E
86	Thetford Mines (thĕt'fērd)...Can.	46.4 N	71.19 W
72	Thetis I. (thē'tĭs) Can. (Vancouver In.)	49.0 N	123.41 W
81	Thibodaux (tê-bô-dō')........La.	29.47 N	90.49 W
76	Thief L......................Minn.	48.29 N	95.52 W
76	Thief R.....................Minn.	48.22 N	96.0 W
76	Thief River Falls............Minn.	48.6 N	96.11 W
124	Thiers (tyâr)...................Fr.	45.50 N	3.32 E
138	Thiès (tê-ĕs')..........Fr. W. Afr.	14.40 N	16.52 W
125	Thieux (tyû)...............Fr. (In.)	49.1 N	2.41 E
110	Thingvalla Water (tĭng-väl'ä).Ice.	64.10 N	21.12 W
125	Thionville (tyôɴ-vēl')...........Fr.	49.25 N	6.5 E
118	Thirsk (thērsk)..........Gt. Brit.	54.13 N	1.20 W
120	Thisted (tēs'tĕdh).............Den.	56.58 N	8.40 E
110	Thistil Fjord (tēs'tĕl fyôr')....Ice.	66.20 N	15.28 W
166	Thistle I. (thĭs''l)...........Austl.	34.59 S	136.11 E
110	Thjórsá (R.) (tyûr'sä)........Ice.	64.15 N	19.15 W
78	Thomas (tŏmăs)..............Okla.	35.45 N	98.45 W
49	Thomas.......Wash. (Seattle In.)	47.21 N	122.15 W
85	Thomas.....................W. Va.	39.10 N	79.30 W
96	Thomas B...................Ba. Is.	26.2 N	77.11 W
74	Thomas Cr..................Calif.	39.50 N	122.30 W
82	Thomaston (tŏm'ăs-tŭn)........Ga.	32.53 N	84.18 W
82	Thomasville (tŏm'ăs-vĭl).....Ala.	31.54 N	87.43 W
82	Thomasville.....................Ga.	30.50 N	83.59 W
83	Thomasville..................N. C.	35.52 N	80.4 W
96	Thompson Cay (I.)..........Ba. Is.	25.24 N	77.54 W
70	Thompson Falls..............Mont.	47.36 N	115.20 W
53	Thompson R. (tŏmp'sŭn)......Can.	51.0 N	120.30 W
72	Thompson R...Colo. (Denver In.)	40.24 N	105.25 W
79	Thompson R...............Mo.-Ia.	40.25 N	93.47 W
83	Thomson (tŏm'sŭn)..............Ga.	33.28 N	82.29 W
165	Thomson R..................Austl.	24.0 S	143.20 E
125	Thonon-les-Bains (tô-nôɴ'-lä-băɴ').Fr.	46.21 N	6.29 E
125	Thorigny (thô-rē-nyē')...Fr. (In.)	48.53 N	2.42 E
110	Thoris Water (L.) (tô'rĕs)....Ice.	64.12 N	18.50 W
116	Thornaby (thôr'nà-bê)...Gt. Brit.	54.33 N	1.20 W
72	Thornbrough Channel (thôrn'brŭ) Can. (Vancouver In.)	49.27 N	123.28 W
118	Thorne (thôrn)...........Gt. Brit.	53.37 N	0.58 W
119	Thornton (thôrn'tŭn) Gt. Brit. (Liverpool In.)	53.30 N	3.0 W
84	Thornton......................Ind.	40.6 N	86.36 W
88	Thorofare (thŭr'ô-fâr) N. J. (Philadelphia In.)	39.50 N	75.11 W
85	Thorold (thō'rōld)............Can.	43.5 N	79.12 W
110	Thorshavn (tōōrs-houn') The Faeroes	62.1 N	6.45 W
124	Thouars (tōō-är')................Fr.	47.0 N	0.15 W
117	Thourout (tōō-rōō')............Bel.	51.5 N	3.5 E
85	Thousand Is...................Can.	44.15 N	76.10 W
129	Thrace (Prov.) (thrās)..Grc.-Tur.	41.25 N	26.30 E
118	Thrapston (thrăp'stŭn)...Gt. Brit.	52.23 N	0.31 W
71	Three Forks..................Mont.	45.54 N	111.35 W
169	Three Hammock I..Austl.(Tas.In.)	40.24 S	144.55 E
170	Three Kings I................N. Z.	34.5 S	172.5 E
84	Three Oaks...................Mich.	41.48 N	86.40 W
138	Three Points, C................G. C.	4.42 N	2.0 W
55	Three Rivers (Trois Rivieres) (trwä' rē-vyâr')..Can.	46.29 N	72.22 W

ng-sing; ŋ-baŋk; ɴ-nasalized n; nŏd; cŏmmit; ōld; ôbey; ôrder; fōōd; fŏŏt; ou-out; s-soft; sh-dish; th-thin; pūre; ûnite; ûrn; stŭd; circŭs; ü-as "y" in study; '-indeterminate vowel.

Page	Name Pronunciation Region	Lat. °′	Long. °′
84	Three Rivers .... Mich.	41.58 N	85.40 W
88	Three Sisters Is. N. Y. (Niagara Falls In.)	43.5 N	79.4 W
88	Throgs Neck (thrŏgz)..N. Y. (In.)	40.49 N	73.46 W
124	Thuir (tü-ēr') .... Fr.	42.35 N	2.45 E
122	Thun (tōōn) .... Switz.	46.46 N	7.36 E
77	Thunder B. .... Can.	48.25 N	89.0 W
89	Thunderbolt..Ga. (Savannah In.)	32.2 N	81.3 W
122	Thun. L. .... Switz.	46.41 N	7.43 E
80	Thurber (thûr'bẽr) .... Tex.	32.31 N	98.22 W
122	Thüringen (State) (tü'rĭng-ĕn) Ger.	51.4 N	11.4 E
116	Thurles (thûrlz) .... Ire.	52.45 N	7.45 W
161	Thursday I. .... Pap. Ter.	10.35 S	42.10 E
116	Thurso (thûr'sô)...Gt. Brit. (In.)	58.35 N	3.30 W
135	Thysville (tēs-vēl') Bel. Cong. (Brazzaville In.)	5.20 S	14.52 E
123	Tiačevo (tē'á-chĕ-vô) ...... Czech.	48.1 N	23.42 E
74	Tia Juana (tē'ä hwä'nä) Calif. (In.)	32.32 N	117.3 W
162	Tiaong (tē-ä-ông') .... P. I.	13.57 N	121.19 E
138	Tiaret (tyä-rĕ') .... Alg.	35.29 N	1.15 E
104	Tibaji (tē-bä'zhĭ) .... Braz.	24.29 S	50.29 W
128	Tiber (Tevere) R. (tī'bẽr) (tā'vā-rā). It.	42.42 N	12.14 E
145	Tiberias (tī-bē'rĭ-ăs)....Pal. (In.)	32.48 N	35.30 E
139	Tibesti (Tu) (Reg.) (tē-bĕs'tē) (tōō).Fr. Eq. Afr.	21.0 N	18.0 E
139	Tibesti Massif (Reg.) (må-sēf') Fr. Eq. Afr.	20.10 N	17.30 E
152	Tibet (Dependency) (tĭ-bĕt') Chn.	31.0 N	88.0 E
152	Tibet, Plat. of .... Chn.	32.15 N	90.0 E
162	Tibiao (tē-bē-ä'ō) .... P. I.	11.17 N	122.2 E
49	Tiburon (tē-bōō-rōn') Calif. (San Francisco In.)	37.52 N	122.26 W
97	Tiburon .... Hai.	18.20 N	74.23 W
97	Tiburon, C. .... Hai.	18.23 N	74.28 W
95	Tiburon, C. .... Pan.	8.40 N	77.20 W
162	Ticao I. (tē-kä'ō) .... P. I.	12.30 N	123.42 E
162	Ticao Pass .... P. I.	12.30 N	123.55 E
118	Tickhill (tĭk'ĭl) .... Gt. Brit.	53.26 N	1.6 W
128	Ticino R. (tē-chē'nō) .... It.	45.23 N	8.50 E
85	Ticonderoga (tī-kŏn-dẽr-ō'gȧ) N. Y.	43.52 N	73.26 W
120	Tidaholm (tē'dȧ-hōlm) ...... Swe.	58.10 N	13.55 E
118	Tideswell (tīdz'wĕl) ...... Gt. Brit.	53.17 N	1.47 W
139	Tidichi (Tousidé Pk.) (tē-dē'chē) (tōō-sē-dā).Fr. W. Afr.	21.7 N	16.22 E
138	Tidikelt (Reg.) (tē-dē-kĕlt')...Alg.	26.0 N	2.30 E
138	Tidjikdja (tē-jĭk'jä)...Fr. W. Afr.	18.34 N	11.26 W
153	Tiehling (tyĕ'lĭng) .... Manch.	42.50 N	123.32 E
127	Tielmes (tyål-mās')......Sp. (In.)	40.15 N	3.20 W
156	Tienchang (tyĕn'chăng') ..... Chn.	32.42 N	118.57 E
154	Tienchu (tyĕn'chōō') .... Chn.	26.48 N	108.56 E
154	Tienho (tyĕn'hō') .... Chn.	24.48 N	108.49 E
153	Tienkaza (tyĕn'kä'zä') Chn. (Shanghai In.)	31.13 N	12.28 E
154	Tienkiang (tyĕn'kyăng') ..... Chn.	30.25 N	107.22 E
152	Tien, L. (tyĕn) .... Chn.	24.45 N	102.40 E
154	Tienmen (tyĕn'mĕn') .... Chn.	30.38 N	113.0 E
148	Tien Shan (Mts.)(tyĕn' shän) Sov. Un.-Chn.	43.0 N	80.0 E
155	Tientai (tyĕn'tī) .... Chn.	29.10 N	120.59 E
155	Tientang Shan (Mts.) (tyĕn'tăng' shän').Chn.	31.10 N	116.8 E
156	Tientsin (tyĕn'tsĕn') .... Chn.	39.13 N	117.3 E
120	Tierp (tyĕrp) .... Swe.	60.21 N	17.30 E
104	Tierra del Fuego (State) (tyĕr'rä dĕl fwā'gō).Arg.	54.30 S	67.30 W
126	Tiétar R. (tē-ā'tär) .... Sp.	40.5 N	5.30 W
103	Tieté, R. (tyā-tā') .... Braz.	21.15 S	50.0 W
84	Tiffin (tĭf'ĭn) .... Ohio	41.8 N	83.12 W
113	Tiflis (tĕf-lēs') .... Sov. Un.	41.45 N	44.50 E
82	Tifton (tĭf'tŭn) .... Ga.	31.26 N	83.32 W
162	Tigaon (tē-gä'ōn) .... P. I.	13.37 N	123.30 E
142	Tiger Berg (Mts.)......U. S. Afr.	31.0 S	20.40 E
95	Tiger Chan. .... Pan.	9.10 N	81.57 W
160	Tiger Is. .... Neth. E. Ind.	6.45 S	121.10 E
140	Tiger Pt. .... Ang.	16.30 S	11.42 E
131	Tighina (tē-gē'nä) .... Rom.	46.48 N	29.28 E
86	Tignish (tĭg'nĭsh) .... Can.	46.58 N	64.2 W
150	Tigris R. .... Asia	32.30 N	45.45 E
93	Tihuatlán (tē-wä-tlän') ...... Mex.	20.43 N	97.33 W
152	Tihwa (Urumchi) (tē'hwä') (ōō-rōōm'chē).Chn.	43.51 N	87.36 E
74	Tijuana (tē-hwä'nä) .... Mex.	32.32 N	117.1 W
104	Tijuca Pk. (tē-zhōō'kä).Braz. (In.)	22.57 S	43.17 W
104	Tijucas Is. (tē-zhōō'kȧzh) Atl. O. (In.)	23.2 S	43.18 W
94	Tikal (Ruins) (tē-käl').Guat. (In.)	17.12 N	89.36 W
113	Tikhoretsk (tē'kôr-yĕtsk) Sov. Un.	45.50 N	40.10 E
130	Tikhvin (têk-vēn')......Sov. Un.	59.37 N	33.38 E
150	Tikrit (tē-krēt') .... Iraq	34.38 N	43.45 E
122	Tilburg (tĭl'bûrg) .... Neth.	51.33 N	5.7 E
119	Tilbury (tĭl'bẽr-ē) Gt. Brit. (London In.)	51.27 N	0.23 E
138	Tillabéry (tē-yä-bā-rē') Fr. W. Afr.	14.15 N	1.30 E
70	Tillamook (tĭl'ȧ-mōōk) .... Ore.	45.27 N	123.50 W
70	Tillamook B. .... Ore.	45.30 N	124.0 W
49	Tillasana R. (tĭl-ȧ-săn'ȧ) Ore. (Portland In.)	46.8 N	123.33 W
120	Tillberga (tēl-bĕr'ghȧ) .... Swe.	59.39 N	16.34 E
123	Tilsit (tĭl'zĭt) .... Ger.	55.3 N	21.54 E
84	Tilsonburg (tĭl'sŭn-bûrg) ..... Can.	42.51 N	80.57 W
131	Tim (têm) .... Sov. Un.	51.38 N	37.2 E
171	Timaru (tē'mä-rōō) (tĭm'ȧ-rōō') N. Z.	44.23 S	171.18 E
81	Timbalier B. (tĭm'bȧ-lēr) ..... La.	29.10 N	90.20 W
103	Timbó (têŋ-bō') ......Braz. (In.)	11.52 S	37.54 W
138	Timbo (tĭm'bō) ......Fr. W. Afr.	10.34 N	11.46 W
166	Timboon (tĭm-bōōn') .... Austl.	38.31 S	143.0 E
138	Timbuktu (Tombouctou) (tĭm-bŭk'tōō) (tôn-bōōk-tōō') Fr. W. Afr.	16.57 N	2.58 W
120	Time (tē'mĕ) .... Nor.	58.46 N	5.38 E
138	Timimoun (tē-mē-mōōn') ..... Alg.	29.20 N	0.22 E
55	Timiskaming L. (tē-mĭs'kȧ-mĭng) Can.	47.0 N	79.0 W
123	Timişoara (tē-mĭsh-wä'rä)...Rom.	45.45 N	21.15 E
129	Timişul R. (tē'mĭsh-ōōl).....Rom.	45.42 N	21.20 E
138	Timmissao (Well) (tē-mē-sä'ō) Alg.	22.0 N	3.0 E
83	Timmonsville (tĭm'ŭnz-vĭl)...S. C.	34.8 N	79.57 W
72	Timnath (tĭm'năth) Colo. (Denver In.)	40.32 N	104.59 W
129	Timok R. (tē'môk) .... Yugo.	43.40 N	22.18 E
161	Timor (tē-mōr') .... Neth. Ind.	10.0 S	124.0 E
161	Timor (I.) .... Ind. O.	9.15 S	125.0 E
161	Timor Laut Is. (tē-mōr' lout') Neth. Ind.	7.20 S	131.20 E
161	Timor, Portuguese .... Pac. O.	8.50 S	126.0 E
161	Timor Sea .... Neth. Ind.	10.0 S	128.30 E
131	Timoshevskaya (tē-mô-shĕf'-skȧ-yȧ)...Sov. Un.	45.37 N	38.55 E
99	Timote (tē-mō'tä) Arg. (Buenos Aires In.)	35.12 S	62.4 W
75	Timpanogos Natl. Mon. (tĭm-pă-nō'gōs) Utah	40.28 N	111.45 W
81	Timpson (tĭmp'sŭn) .... Tex.	31.55 N	94.24 W
149	Timpton R. (tĕmp'tôn)..Sov. Un.	57.30 N	126.25 E
135	Timsah, L. (tĭm'sä) Eg. (Suez Canal In.)	30.33 N	32.19 E
135	Tina (Pelusium) B. (tē'nȧ) (pē-lū'zhĭ-ŭm).Eg. (In.)	31.15 N	32.40 E
135	Tina (Pelusium) Plain of Eg. (In.)	30.55 N	32.40 E
162	Tinaca Pt. (tē-nä'kä) .... P. I.	5.33 N	125.20 E
97	Tina, Mt. (tē'nä).....Dom. Rep.	18.43 N	70.41 W
143	Tina R. .... U. S. Afr.	31.0 S	28.53 E
138	Tindouf (tēn-dōōf') .... Alg.	27.35 N	7.41 W
126	Tineo (tē-nā'ō) .... Sp.	43.21 N	6.25 W
155	Tingchow (tĭng'chō') .... Chn.	25.45 N	116.9 E
156	Tingchow (tĭng'chō') .... Chn.	38.37 N	114.58 E
154	Tingfan (tĭng'făn') .... Chn.	26.5 N	106.25 E
169	Tingha (tĭn'gȧ) ......Austl. (In.)	29.58 S	151.12 E
155	Tinghai (tĭng'hī') .... Chn.	30.2 N	122.6 E
156	Tinghing (tĭng'hĭng') .... Chn.	39.20 N	115.38 E
156	Tingsiang (tĭng'syăng') .... Chn.	38.32 N	113.1 E
120	Tingsryd (tĭngs'rüd) .... Swe.	56.32 N	15.0 E
99	Tingua, Serra do (Mts.) (sĕr'rä dōō tĭŋ'gwȧ) Braz. (Rio de Janeiro In.)	22.45 S	43.25 W
92	Tinguindín (tēn-gēn-dēn')...Mex.	19.44 N	102.26 W
154	Tingyüan (tĭng'yü-än') ...... Chn.	30.25 N	106.18 E
156	Tingyüan .... Chn.	32.31 N	117.32 E
103	Tinhare I. (tē-nyä'rȧ)..Braz. (In.)	13.25 S	39.0 W
157	Tinnevelly (tĭn-ē-vĕl'ē) .... India	9.0 N	77.35 E
120	Tinn L. (tĕn) .... Nor.	59.50 N	9.0 E
120	Tinnosset (tĕn'nôs'sĕt) .... Nor.	59.42 N	9.2 E
104	Tinogasta (tē-nô-gäs'tä) ...... Arg.	28.5 S	67.50 W
151	Tinsukia (tĭn-sōō'kĭ-ȧ) .... India	27.28 N	95.27 E
116	Tintagel Hd. (tĭn-tăj'ĕl)..Gt. Brit.	50.40 N	4.50 W
166	Tintinara (tĭn-tĭ-nä'rȧ) ...... Austl.	35.53 S	139.58 E
139	Tin Toumma Steppe (tĭn-tōōm'ȧ) Fr. W. Afr.	16.0 N	14.0 E
94	Tipitapa R. (tē-pē-tä'pä) ..... Nic.	12.7 N	85.57 W
84	Tippecanoe R. (tĭp-ē-kȧ-nōō') Ind.	41.0 N	86.45 W
116	Tipperary (tĭp-ẽr-â'rē) .... Ire.	52.29 N	6.9 W
82	Tippo Bayou (tĭp'ō) .... Miss.	33.50 N	90.10 W
79	Tippo Bayou (Cr.) .... Miss.	33.55 N	90.07 W
118	Tipton (tĭp'tŭn) .... Gt. Brit.	52.32 N	2.4 W
84	Tipton .... Ind.	40.16 N	86.3 W
77	Tipton .... Ia.	41.48 N	91.9 W
129	Tiranë (tē-rä'nä) .... Alb.	41.18 N	19.50 E
128	Tirano (tē-rä'nō) .... It.	46.13 N	10.11 E
131	Tiraspol (tē-räs-pôl')...Sov. Un.	46.51 N	29.40 E
113	Tire (tē'rĕ) .... Tur.	38.5 N	27.48 E
116	Tiree (I.) (tī-rē') .... Gt. Brit.	56.30 N	6.50 W
117	Tirlemont (tēr-l' môn') .... Bel.	50.49 N	4.59 E
122	Tirol (Prov.) (tē-rōl') .... Ger.	47.10 N	11.0 E
128	Tirso R. (tēr'sō) .... Sard.	40.15 N	9.0 E
128	Tisa R. (tē'sä) .... Yugo.	45.30 N	20.5 E
123	Tisza R. .... Hung.	47.45 N	20.42 E
103	Titicaca L. (tē-tē-kä'kä) Bol.-Peru	16.0 S	69.30 W
170	Titirangi (tē-tē-räŋ'gē).N. Z. (In.)	36.57 S	174.38 E
83	Titusville (tī'tŭs-vĭl)...Fla. (In.)	28.37 N	80.47 W
85	Titusville .... Pa.	41.40 N	79.40 W
116	Tiverton (tĭv'ẽr-tŭn) ..... Gt. Brit.	50.55 N	3.30 W
128	Tivoli (tē'vô-lē) .... It.	41.57 N	12.48 E
162	Tiwi (tē'wē) .... P. I.	13.27 N	123.40 E
92	Tixtla de Guerrero (tēs'tlä dā gā-rā'rō).Mex.	17.36 N	99.25 W
92	Tizapán (tē-zä-pän')...Mex. (In.)	19.20 N	39.12 W
160	Tizard Bank & Reefs (tĭz'ȧrd) Asia	10.30 N	114.30 E
138	Tizi-n-Tamjurt (Mt.) (tē'zē-'n-tȧm'jōōrt).Mor.	31.25 N	7.55 W
138	Tizi-Ouzou (tē'zē-ōō-zōō')....Alg.	36.46 N	4.7 E
138	Tiznit (têz-nēt') .... Mor.	29.45 N	9.50 W
93	Tlacolula de Matamoros (tlä-kō-lōō'lä dä mä-tä-mō'rōs).Mex.	16.57 N	96.29 W
93	Tlacotálpan (tlä-kō-täl'pän).Mex.	18.37 N	95.40 W
92	Tlacotepec (tlä-kō-tä-pĕk')...Mex.	17.39 N	99.56 W
93	Tlacotepec .... Mex.	18.40 N	97.39 W
92	Tlacotepec .... Mex.	19.12 N	99.40 W
93	Tlahuac (tlä-wäk')......Mex. (In.)	19.16 N	99.0 W
92	Tlajomulco (tlä-hō-mōōl'kō) Mex.	20.28 N	103.28 W
92	Tlalchapa (tläl-chä'pä) ...... Mex.	18.21 N	100.27 W
93	Tlalixcoyan (tlä-lēs'kō-yän').Mex.	18.50 N	96.5 W
93	Tlalnepantla (tläl-nä-pän'tlä) Mex. (In.)	19.32 N	99.12 W
93	Tlalnepantla, R........Mex. (In.)	19.32 N	99.9 W
93	Tlaloc, Cerro (Mts.) (sĕr'rō tlä-lôk').Mex.	19.25 N	98.43 W
92	Tlálpam (tläl'päm) .... Mex.	19.16 N	99.10 W
92	Tlalpujahua de Rayón (tläl-pōō-hä'wä dä rä-yōn').Mex.	19.49 N	100.11 W
92	Tlaltenango (Sánchez Roman) (tläl-tā-näŋ'gō) (sän'chăz rō'män).Mex.	21.48 N	103.25 W
93	Tlaltenco (tläl-tĕŋ'kō)..Mex. (In.)	19.18 N	99.1 W
92	Tlapa (tlä'pä) .... Mex.	17.30 N	98.37 W
93	Tlapacoyan (tlä-pä-kō'yän)..Mex.	19.57 N	97.8 W
92	Tlapehuala (tläp-chwä'lä)...Mex.	18.18 N	100.33 W
93	Tlapisahua (tlä-pē-sä'wä) Mex. (In.)	19.20 N	98.57 W
92	Tlatlaya (tlä-tlä'yä) .... Mex.	18.35 N	100.12 W
92	Tlaxcala (tläs-kä'lä) .... Mex.	19.18 N	98.13 W
92	Tlaxcala (State) .... Mex.	19.20 N	98.0 W
92	Tlaxco (tläs'kō) .... Mex.	19.37 N	98.6 W
93	Tlaxiaco (St. María Asunción) (tläk-sē-ä'kō)(sän'tä mä-rē'ä ä-sōōn-syōn').Mex.	17.15 N	97.40 W
138	Tlemçen (tlĕm-sĕn') .... Alg.	34.55 N	1.21 W
93	Tlilán (tlē-län') .... Mex.	19.35 N	99.20 W
123	Tlumacz (twōō'mäch) .... Pol.	48.47 N	25.0 E
71	Toand Range (tō'ănd) ...... Nev.	40.50 N	114.10 W
97	Toa R. (tō'ä) .... Cuba	20.20 N	74.45 W
159	Toba (tō'bä) .... Jap.	34.28 N	136.50 E
103	Tobago (I.) (tō-bā'gō) .... Trin.	11.15 N	60.45 W
160	Toba, L. .... Neth. Ind.	2.35 N	98.50 E
126	Tobarra (tō-bär'rä) .... Sp.	38.36 N	1.41 W
148	Tobol R. (tō-bôl') ...... Sov. Un.	55.0 N	65.0 E
148	Tobolsk (tō-bôlsk') ...... Sov. Un.	58.15 N	68.30 E
139	Tobruk (tō-brōōk') .... Libya	32.0 N	24.0 E
103	Tocantins, R. (tō-kän-tēns').Braz.	3.30 S	49.32 W
82	Toccoa (tŏk'ō-ȧ) .... Ga.	34.35 N	83.20 W
159	Tochigi (tō'chē-gä) .... Jap.	36.24 N	139.48 E
104	Tocopilla (tō-kō-pēl'yä) ...... Chl.	22.0 S	70.10 W
139	Tocra (tôk'rä) .... Libya.	32.30 N	20.33 E
167	Tocumwal (tō-kŭm'wôl) ...... Austl.	35.48 S	145.34 E
118	Todmorden (tŏd'môr-dĕn). Gt. Brit.	53.43 N	2.6 W
54	Todmorden .... Can. (In.)	43.41 N	79.22 W
171	Toetoes B. (tō-ē-tō'ēz) ...... N. Z.	46.37 S	168.40 E
159	Toge (tō'gä)...Jap. (Osaka In.)	34.57 N	135.33 E
160	Togian (Turtle) Is.) (tō'gē-än) (tûr't'l)...Neth. Ind.	0.30 S	122.0 E
138	Togo (Reg.) (tō'gō)...Fr. W. Afr.	8.30 N	0.1 E
83	Tohopekaliga L. (tō'hō-pē'kä-lī'gȧ).Fla. (In.)	28.10 N	81.20 W
159	Toi C. (tō'ē) .... Jap.	31.28 N	131.20 E
121	Toijala (toi'yȧ-lä) .... Fin.	61.15 N	23.50 E
158	Tokachi R. (tō'kä-chē) ...... Jap.	42.59 N	143.0 E
123	Tokaj (tō'kō-ē) .... Hung.	48.7 N	21.25 E
171	Tokanui (tō-kȧ-nōō'ē) ...... N. Z.	46.33 S	168.58 E
139	Tokar (tō'kär) .... A. E. Sud.	18.30 N	37.45 E
158	Tokara Guntō (Is.) (gōōn'tō') Jap.	29.40 N	129.45 E
158	Tokara Str. (tō-kä'rä) .... Jap.	30.5 N	130.0 E
113	Tokat (tō-kät') .... Tur.	40.15 N	36.32 E
6	Tokelau (Union) Is. (tō-kē-lä'ōō) Pac. O.	9.0 S	172.0 W
148	Tokmak (tôk'măk) ...... Sov. Un.	42.45 N	75.30 E
131	Tokmak Bolshoi (Sea) (bŏl'zhô-ĭ tôk'măk)...Sov. Un.	47.15 N	35.46 E
158	Toko (tō'kō') .... Tai. (In.)	22.30 N	120.31 E
158	Tokuno I. (tō-kōō'nō) .... Jap.	27.45 N	129.0 E
159	Tokushima (tō'kōō-shē'mä)...Jap.	34.1 N	134.31 E
158	Tokuyama (tō'kōō-yä'mä)....Jap.	34.2 N	131.50 E
159	Tokyo (tō'kē-ō) .... Jap.	35.40 N	139.45 E
159	Tokyo .... Jap. (In.)		
159	Tokyo B. .... Jap.	35.21 N	139.46 E
170	Tolaga B. (tō-lä'gä) .... N. Z.	38.20 S	178.25 E
153	Tola R. (tō'lä') .... Chn.	45.45 N	122.15 E
92	Tolcayuca (tōl-kä-yōō'kä)...Mex.	19.55 N	98.55 W
77	Toledo (tō-lē'dō) .... Ia.	41.59 N	92.34 W
84	Toledo .... Ohio	41.40 N	83.30 W
70	Toledo .... Ore.	44.38 N	123.58 W
162	Toledo (tō-lā'dhō) .... P. I.	10.22 N	123.39 E
126	Toledo .... Sp.	39.53 N	4.2 W
102	Tolima (Vol.) (tō-lē'mä) ...... Col.	4.32 N	75.30 W
92	Tolimán (tō-lē-män') .... Mex.	20.53 N	99.57 W
139	Tolmeta (tōl-mā'tä) .... Libya	32.41 N	21.0 E
128	Tolmezzo (tōl-mĕt'sō) .... It.	46.26 N	13.2 E
128	Tolmino (tōl-mē'nō) .... It.	46.13 N	13.41 E
123	Tolna (tōl'nō) .... Hung.	46.25 N	18.47 E
160	Tolo, G. of (tō'lō) .....Neth. Ind.	2.0 S	122.30 E
163	Tolong (tō'lông') .... P. I.	9.22 N	122.49 E
163	Tolong B. .... P. I.	9.18 N	122.50 E
126	Tolosa (tō-lō'sä) .... Sp.	43.9 N	2.7 W
148	Tolstonosovskoe (tŏl'stō-nō-sôf-skō'yĕ)...Sov. Un.	70.10 N	83.10 E
79	Toluca (tō-lōō'kȧ) .... Ill.	40.59 N	89.8 W
92	Toluca .... Mex.	19.17 N	99.40 W
153	Tolunnoerh (tō'lōōn-ōr) ..... Chn.	42.20 N	116.25 E
122	Tölz, Bad (tûlts) .... Ger.	47.46 N	11.35 E
77	Tomah (tō'mȧ) .... Wis.	43.59 N	90.30 W
77	Tomahawk (tŏm'ȧ-hôk) ...... Wis.	45.29 N	89.42 W
131	Tomakovka (tō-mä-kôf'kä)Sov.Un.	47.48 N	34.40 E
126	Tomar (tō-mär') .... Port.	39.36 N	8.25 W
123	Tomaszów Lubelski (tō-mä'shōōf lōō-bĕl'skē)..Pol.	50.26 N	23.27 E
123	Tomaszów Mazowiecki .... Pol.	51.33 N	20.0 E
93	Tomatlán (tō-mä-tlän') Mex. (In.)	19.19 N	99.6 W
92	Tomatlán .... Mex.	19.55 N	105.16 W
92	Tomatlán, R. de .... Mex.	20.0 N	105.10 W
103	Tombador, Serra do (Mts.) (sĕr'rȧ dōō tōm-bä-dōr').Braz.	12.30 S	57.30 W
82	Tombigbee R. (tŏm-bĭg'bē) Ala.-Miss.	32.20 N	88.0 W
138	Tombouctou (Timbuktu) (tôn-bōōk-tōō') (tĭm-bŭk'tōō) (tĭm-bŭk-tōō').Fr. W. Afr.	16.57 N	2.58 W
75	Tombstone .... Ariz.	31.43 N	110.3 W
120	Tomelilla (tō'mĕ-lēl-ä) .... Swe.	55.32 N	13.57 E
126	Tomelloso (tō-mäl-lyō'sō) ...... Sp.	39.9 N	3.1 W
6	Tomil (I.) (tō-mēl') Pac. O. (Yap In.)	9.33 N	138.13 E

ăt; finăl; rāte; senâte; ärm; åsk; sofȧ; fâre; ch-choose; dh-as th in other; bē; êvent; bĕt; recĕnt; cratẽr; g-go; gh-gutteral g; bĭt; ĭ-short neutral; rīde; κ-gutteral k as ch in German ich;

Page	Name Pronunciation Region	Lat. °′	Long. °′
160	Tomini (Gorontalo), G. of (tō-mē'nē) (gō-rôn-tä'lō) Neth. Ind.	0.0	122.0 E
126	Tomiño (tō-mēn'yō) Sp.	41.59 N	8.45 W
159	Tomioka (tō'mē-ō'kä) Jap.	32.30 N	130.4 E
148	Tom R. (tŏm) Sov. Un.	55.0 N	87.0 E
148	Tomsk (tŏmsk) Sov. Un.	56.30 N	84.59 E
93	Tonalá (tō-nä-lä') Mex.	16.5 N	93.45 W
92	Tonalá Mex.	20.38 N	103.12 W
93	Tonalá R. Mex.	18.5 N	94.6 W
85	Tonawanda (tŏn-à-wŏn'dà) N. Y.	43.0 N	78.53 W
161	Tondano (tôn-dä'nō) Neth. Ind.	1.12 N	124.58 E
120	Tönder (tûn'nĕr) Den.	54.57 N	8.49 E
159	Tonegawa R. (tō'nā-gä'wä) Jap.	36.16 N	139.11 E
163	Tonejatan Pt. (tō-nä-hä'tän) P. I.	5.21 N	120.13 E
158	Tone R. (tō'nĕ) Jap.	36.0 N	139.50 E
6	Tonga Is. (tŏŋ'gȧ) Pac. O.	20.0 S	175.0 W
157	Tongchun (tŏng'chōōn') Cho.	38.54 N	127.57 E
104	Tongoy (tōn-goi') Chl.	30.20 S	71.31 W
71	Tongue R. Mont.-Wyo.	45.15 N	106.45 W
131	Tongue of Arabat (Arabatskaya Strelka) (ä-rä-bät') (ä-rä-bät' skä-yȧ strĕl'kȧ) Sov. Un.	45.50 N	35.0 E
157	Tongyung (tông'yōōng') Cho.	34.53 N	128.26 E
92	Tonila (tō-nē'lä) Mex.	19.23 N	103.30 W
139	Tonj R. (tônj) A. E. Sud.	6.30 N	28.25 E
151	Tonk (tŏŋk) India	26.5 N	75.59 E
79	Tonkawa (tŏŋ'kȧ-wô) Okla.	36.42 N	97.18 W
163	Tonkil I. (tôn-kēl') P. I.	6.2 N	121.50 E
160	Tonkin (Prov.) (tŏn-kēn') (tôN-käN') Fr. In. Chn.	21.30 N	105.0 E
160	Tonkin, G. of Fr. In. Chn.	20.0 N	108.0 E
148	Tonkova (tōn'kō-vȧ) Sov. Un.	60.40 N	89.55 E
160	Tonlé Sap (L.) (tôn'lā säp') Fr. In. Chn.	13.0 N	104.0 E
124	Tonneins (tô-năN') Fr.	44.25 N	0.20 E
124	Tonnerre (tô-nâr') Fr.	47.50 N	3.58 E
74	Tonopah (tō-nō-pä') Nev.	38.4 N	117.13 W
120	Tönsberg (tûns'bĕrg) Nor.	59.18 N	10.24 E
75	Tonto Cr. (tŏn'tō) Ariz.	33.55 N	111.15 W
75	Tonto Natl. Mon. Ariz.	33.38 N	111.9 W
93	Tonto, R. (tōn'tō) Mex.	18.30 N	96.40 W
72	Tonville (tŭn'vĭl) Colo. (Denver In.)	40.1 N	104.42 W
71	Tooele (tōō-ĕl'ē) Utah	40.31 N	112.19 W
166	Toolondo (tōō-lŏn'dō) Austl.	37.2 S	141.58 E
169	Toongabbie (tōōŋ-găb'ē) Austl. (Sydney In.)	33.47 S	150.57 E
165	Toowoomba (tōō-wōōm'bȧ) Austl.	27.35 S	152.0 E
120	Topdals R. (tôp'däls) Nor.	58.20 N	8.15 E
79	Topeka (tō-pē'kȧ) Kan.	39.3 N	95.40 W
112	Top, L. (tôp) Sov. Un.	65.45 N	31.30 E
129	Topola (tō-pō'lä) Yugo.	45.47 N	19.38 E
123	Topolčany (tō-pōl'chä-nū) Czech.	48.34 N	18.12 E
70	Toppenish (tŏp'ĕn-ĭsh) Wash.	46.21 N	120.21 W
157	Torai (tō'rī') Cho.	35.13 N	129.4 E
156	To R. (tō) Chn.	33.50 N	116.30 E
87	Torbay (tôr-bā') Newf.	47.39 N	52.45 W
84	Torch Lake Mich.	45.0 N	85.18 W
125	Torcy (tôr-sē') Fr.	48.51 N	2.38 E
120	Töreboda (tû'rĕ-bō'dȧ) Swe.	58.43 N	14.4 E
128	Torino (Turin) (tō-rē'nō) (tū'rĭn) It.	45.4 N	7.40 E
129	Torlak (tôr'läk) Bul.	43.45 N	26.14 E
126	Tórmes R. (tōr'mās) Sp.	41.0 N	5.44 W
110	Torne R. (tôr'nĕ) Swe.	67.42 N	21.0 E
110	Torne Träsk (L.) (tôr'nĕ trĕsk) Swe.	68.18 N	19.20 E
112	Tornio (tôr'nĭ-ō) Fin.	65.52 N	24.10 E
126	Toro (tō'rō) Sp.	41.32 N	5.23 W
167	Toronto (tō-rŏn'tō) Austl.	33.1 S	151.37 E
54	Toronto Can. (In.)		
55	Toronto Can.	43.38 N	79.27 W
84	Toronto Ohio	40.30 N	80.37 W
130	Toropets (tô'rō-pyĕts) Sov. Un.	56.31 N	31.39 E
127	Torote R. (tō-rō'tä) Sp. (In.)	40.35 N	3.26 W
120	Torp (tôrp) Swe.	62.31 N	16.3 E
120	Torpen (Åmot) (tôr'pĕn) (ô'mōt) Nor.	61.7 N	11.18 E
116	Torquay (tôr-kē') Gt. Brit.	50.30 N	3.30 W
119	Torre Annunziata (tôr'rä ä-nōōn-tsē-ä'tä) It. (Napoli In.)	40.45 N	14.27 E
126	Torre de Cerredo (Mt.) (tôr'rä dā thā-rā'dhō) Sp.	43.13 N	4.52 W
128	Torre del Greco (tôr'rä dĕl grā'kō) It.	40.47 N	14.22 E
126	Torredonjimeno (tôr'rā-dōn-kē-mā'nō) Sp.	37.47 N	3.58 W
126	Torrejoncillo (tôr'rā-hōn-thē'lyō) Sp.	39.55 N	6.27 W
127	Torrejón de Ardoz (tôr-rā-hōn' dā är'dōth) Sp. (In.)	40.28 N	3.29 W
126	Torrelavega (tôr-rā'lä-vā'gä) Sp.	43.21 N	4.1 W
127	Torrellas de Foix (tôr-rā'lyäs dā fō-ēsh') Sp. (In.)	41.22 N	1.34 E
128	Torre Maggiore (tôr'rā mäd-jō'rā) It.	41.41 N	15.28 E
169	Torrens I. (tŏr'ĕnz) Austl. (Adelaide In.)	34.47 S	138.32 E
166	Torrens L. Austl.	31.0 S	137.50 E
127	Torrente (tôr-rĕn'tä) Sp.	39.26 N	0.28 W
80	Torreón (tôr-rā-ōn') Mex.	25.33 N	103.25 W
127	Torre-Pacheco (tôr'rā-pä-chä'kō) Sp.	37.45 N	0.56 W
165	Torres Is. (tôr'rĕs) (tŏr'ĕz) New Hebr.	13.15 S	168.40 E
74	Torres Martinez Indian Res. (tôr'ĕz mär-tē'nĕz) Calif.	33.35 N	116.10 W
126	Tôrres Novas (tôr'rĕzh nō'väzh) Port.	39.28 N	8.33 W
161	Torres Str. (tôr'rĕs) Pap. Ter.	10.30 S	142.30 E
126	Torres Vedras (tôr'rĕzh vā'dräzh) Port.	39.6 N	9.15 W
127	Torrevieja (tôr-rā-vyā'hä) Sp.	37.58 N	0.40 W
162	Torrijos (tôr-rē'hōs) P. I.	13.19 N	122.4 E
76	Torrington (tŏr'ĭng-tŭn) Wyo.	42.3 N	104.10 W
166	Torrowangee (tôr-ō-wăŋ'gē) Austl.	31.23 S	141.31 E
126	Torrox (tôr-rōsh') Sp.	36.46 N	4.0 W
120	Torsby (tôrs'bü) Swe.	60.7 N	12.59 E
120	Torshälla (tôrs'hĕl-ä) Swe.	59.23 N	16.21 E
91	Tortola I. (tôr-tō'lä) W. I. (P. R. In.)	18.27 N	64.37 W
159	Totomi Sea (tō'tō-mē) Jap.	34.23 N	137.25 E
128	Tortona (tôr-tō'nä) It.	44.52 N	8.53 E
127	Tortosa (tôr-tō'sä) Sp.	40.49 N	0.34 E
97	Tortue Channel (tôr-tü') Hai.	20.0 N	72.50 W
97	Tortue I. Hai.	20.5 N	72.50 W
102	Tortuga I. (tôr-tōō'gä) Ven.	10.59 N	65.28 W
123	Toruń (tō'rōōn') Pol.	53.1 N	18.37 E
121	Tõrva (t'r'vȧ) Est.	58.0 N	25.54 E
116	Tory I. (tō'rē) N. Ire.	55.18 N	8.15 W
130	Torzhok (tôr'zhŏk) Sov. Un.	57.2 N	34.56 E
159	Tosa Sea (tō'sä) Jap.	33.20 N	133.45 E
149	Tosno (tôs'nō) Sov. Un.	59.33 N	30.50 E
140	Tostakh R. (tôs'täK) Sov. Un.	67.0 N	137.50 E
113	Tosya (tôz'yȧ) Tur.	41.5 N	34.5 E
126	Totana (tō-tä'nä) Sp.	37.46 N	1.27 W
123	Tótkomlós (tōt'kŭm-lōs) Hung	46.24 N	20.45 E
112	Totma (tôt'mȧ) Sov. Un.	59.58 N	42.45 E
94	Totonicapan (tō-tō-nē-kä'-pän) Guat.	14.56 N	91.20 W
167	Tottenham (tŏt'ĕn-ăm) Austl.	32.14 S	147.22 E
116	Tottenham Gt. Brit.	51.35 N	0.5 W
88	Tottenville (tŏt'ĕn-vĭl) N. Y. (In.)	40.31 N	74.15 W
159	Tottori (tō'tō-rē) Jap.	35.30 N	134.14 E
138	Touat (Reg.) (tōō'ät) Alg.	27.15 N	0.30 W
138	Touggourt (tōō-gōōrt') (tōō-gōōr') Alg.	33.10 N	6.3 E
114	Touil (Chelif), Wadi (R.) (wä'dē tōō-ēl') (shä-lēf') Alg.	34.30 N	2.12 E
125	Toul (tōōl) Fr.	48.38 N	5.50 E
125	Toulon (tōō-lôN') Fr.	43.8 N	5.56 E
124	Toulouse (tōō-lōōz') Fr.	43.35 N	1.28 E
160	Toungoo (tō-ōōŋ-gōō') India	19.0 N	96.28 E
160	Tourane (tōō-rän') Fr. In. Chn.	16.5 N	108.7 E
124	Tourcoing (tōōr-kwăng') Fr.	50.45 N	3.5 E
124	Tournon (tōōr-nôN') Fr.	45.5 N	4.50 E
124	Tournus (tōōr-nü') Fr.	46.35 N	4.55 E
124	Tours (tōōr) Fr.	47.20 N	0.40 E
139	Tousidé Pk. (Tidichi) (tōō-sē'dā) (tē-dē'chē) Fr. W. Afr.	21.7 N	16.22 E
142	Touws R. (tous) U. S. Afr.	33.32 S	20.25 E
142	Touws River U. S. Afr.	33.19 S	20.4 E
118	Tove. R. (tōv) Gt. Brit.	52.7 N	0.54 W
85	Towanda (tō-wăn'dȧ) Pa.	41.47 N	76.28 W
118	Towcester (tou'stēr) Gt. Brit.	52.7 N	0.59 W
102	Tower I. (tou'ēr) Ec.	0.25 N	89.59 W
76	Towner (tou'nēr) N. D.	48.20 N	100.22 W
87	Townsend (toun'zĕnd) Mass. (In.)	42.40 N	71.43 W
71	Townsend Mont.	46.18 N	111.31 W
164	Townsend Ra. Austl.	26.0 S	127.15 E
165	Townsville (tounz'vĭl) Austl.	19.14 S	146.45 E
85	Towson (tou'sŭn) Md.	39.20 N	76.38 W
160	Towuti L. (tō-wōō'tē) Neth. Ind.	2.15 S	121.30 E
80	Toyah (tô'yȧ) Tex.	31.20 N	103.48 W
159	Toyama (tō'yȧ-mä) Jap.	36.35 N	137.15 E
159	Toyama B. Jap.	37.0 N	137.5 E
154	Toyen Shan (Mts.) (tō'yĕn shän') Chn.	23.52 N	107.8 E
158	Toyohara (tō'yō-hä'rä) Kar.	46.55 N	142.42 E
159	Toyohashi (tō'yō-hä'shē) Jap.	34.45 N	137.27 E
114	Tozeur (tō-zûr') Tun.	34.5 N	7.47 E
135	Tozeur Tun. (In.)	33.55 N	8.28 E
126	Trabancos R. (trä-bäŋ'kōs) Sp.	41.0 N	5.5 W
113	Trabzon (Trebizond) (träb'zōn) (trĕb'ĭ-zŏnd) Tur.	40.58 N	39.45 E
72	Trachyte Mt. (trä'kīt) Colo. (Colo. Spgs. In.)	38.47 N	105.7 W
74	Tracy (trā'sē) Calif.	37.44 N	121.28 W
76	Tracy Minn.	44.14 N	95.37 W
82	Tracy City Tenn.	35.16 N	85.43 W
49	Tracyton (trā'sē-tŭn) Wash. (Seattle In.)	47.36 N	122.39 W
127	Trafalgar, C. (trăf-ăl-gär') (trȧ-făl'gȧr) Sp. (In.)	36.11 N	6.2 W
70	Trail (trāl) Can.	49.6 N	117.42 W
171	Training Wall N. Z. (In.)	45.52 S	170.35 E
116	Tralee (trȧ-lē') I. F. S.	52.15 N	9.42 W
120	Trälleborg (trĕl'ĕ-bôrg) Swe.	55.22 N	13.8 E
120	Tranås (trän'ôs) Swe.	58.3 N	14.59 E
92	Trancoso (träŋ-kō'sō) Mex.	22.40 N	102.22 W
126	Trancoso (träŋ-kō'sōō) Port.	40.46 N	7.23 W
161	Trangan (I.) (träŋ'gän) Neth. Ind.	6.45 S	134.15 E
128	Trani (trä'nē) It.	41.17 N	16.24 E
113	Transcaucasian (Sov. Rep.) (trăns-kô-kăzh'ăn) Sov. Un.	41.30 N	45.30 E
56	Transcona (trăns-kō'nȧ) Can.	49.55 N	97.0 W
152	Trans-Himalaya Ra. (hĭ-mä'lȧ-yȧ) Chn.	30.15 N	85.0 E
123	Transilvania (Prov.) (trăn-sĭl-vā'nĭ-ȧ) Rom.	46.30 N	23.20 E
150	Transjordan (trăns-jôr'dăn) Asia	30.0 N	36.30 E
140	Transvaal (Prov.) (trăns-väl') U. S. Afr.	24.45 S	29.15 E
128	Trapani (trä'pȧ-nē) It.	38.1 N	12.32 E
125	Trappes (trȧp) Fr. (In.)	48.46 N	2.0 E
167	Traralgor (trȧ-răl'gôr) Austl.	38.11 S	146.33 E
128	Trasimeno, L. (trä-sē-mā'nō) It.	43.10 N	12.5 E
126	Tras os Montes (Mts.) (träzh' ōzh môn'tăzh) Port.	41.35 N	7.0 W
126	Trasparga (trä-spär'gä) Sp.	43.12 N	7.49 W
122	Traun R. (troun) Ger.	48.12 N	14.8 E
122	Traunstein (troun'stīn) Ger.	47.53 N	12.38 E
122	Trautenau (Trutnov) (trou'tĕ-nou) (trōōt'nôf) Ger.	50.33 N	15.55 E
166	Travellers L. (trăv'ĕl-ĕrz) Austl.	33.18 S	141.59 E
84	Traverse City Mich.	44.45 N	85.40 W
76	Traverse L. (trăv'ērs) Minn.-S D	45.42 N	96.42 W
46	Traversey Is. (tră'vēr-sē) Ant. O.	57.0 S	27.0 W
128	Travnik (träv'nēk) Yugo.	44.13 N	17.41 E
122	Třebíč (t'rzhĕ'bēch) Czech.	49.13 N	15.53 E
129	Trebinje (trā'bēn-yĕ) Yugo.	42.43 N	18.21 E
123	Trebišov (trĕ'bē-shôf) Czech.	48.37 N	21.43 E
113	Trebizond (Trabzon) (trĕb'ĭ-zŏnd) (träb'zōn) Tur.	40.58 N	39.45 E
123	Trebnitz (trĕb'nĕts) Ger.	51.18 N	17.4 E
122	Třeboň (t'rzhĕ'bôn') Czech.	49.0 N	14.45 E
124	Tréboul (trā-bōōl') Fr.	48.5 N	4.20 W
122	Třebová (t'rzhĕ'bō-vä) Czech.	49.54 N	16.25 E
165	Tregrosse Is. (trē-grōs') Austl.	17.30 S	151.0 E
104	Treinta y Tres (trā-ēn'tä ē träs') Ur.	33.20 S	54.20 W
124	Trélazé (trā-lȧ-zā') Fr.	47.28 N	0.30 W
104	Trelew (trē'lū) Arg.	43.15 S	65.25 W
116	Tremadoc B. (trē-mă'dŏk) Gt. Brit.	52.50 N	4.15 W
125	Tremblay-les-Gonesse (träN-blĕ'-lā-gō-nĕs') Fr. (In.)	48.58 N	2.32 E
123	Trembowla (trĕm-bōv'lȧ) Pol.	49.18 N	25.43 E
128	Tremiti Is. (trā-mē'tē) It.	42.7 N	15.32 E
88	Tremont (trē-mŏnt') N. Y. (In.)	40.50 N	73.54 W
73	Tremonton (trē'mŏn-tŭn) Utah (Salt Lake City In.)	41.43 N	112.10 W
123	Trenčín (trĕn'chēn) Czech.	48.53 N	18.2 E
160	Trengganu (State) (trĕng-gä'nōō) Non-fed. Mal. St.	5.0 N	103.0 E
49	Trenholm (trĕn'hōlm) Ore. (Portland In.)	45.54 N	123.0 W
57	Trenholme Can. (Quebec In.)	46.45 N	71.35 W
118	Trent and Mersey Can. Gt. Brit.	53.0 N	2.10 W
128	Trentino (Prov.) (trĕn-tē'nō) It.	46.15 N	11.0 E
128	Trento (trĕn'tō) It.	46.4 N	11.9 E
163	Trento P. I.	8.2 N	126.3 E
55	Trenton (trĕn'tŭn) Can.	44.12 N	77.30 W
87	Trenton Can.	45.38 N	62.40 W
79	Trenton Mo.	40.5 N	93.36 W
85	Trenton N. J.	40.14 N	74.44 W
82	Trenton Tenn.	35.58 N	88.57 W
85	Trent R. (trĕnt) Can.	44.20 N	77.54 W
116	Trent (R.) Gt. Brit.	53.10 N	0.45 W
87	Trepassey (trē-păs'ē) Newf.	46.45 N	53.21 W
122	Treptow (trĕp'tō) Ger.	54.3 N	15.16 E
104	Tres Arroyos (träs' är-rō'yōs) Arg.	38.25 S	60.20 W
114	Tres Forcas, C. (träs' fōr'käs) Mor.	35.30 N	3.5 W
92	Tres Marias Is. (träs' mä-rē'äs) Mex.	21.25 N	106.25 W
72	Tretheway (Fivemile) Cr. (trĕdh'-ē-wā) Can. (Vancouver In.)	49.38 N	122.12 W
128	Treviglio (trā-vē'lyō) It.	45.31 N	9.36 E
126	Trevino (trā-vēn'yō) Sp.	42.44 N	2.43 W
128	Treviso (trā-vē'zō) It.	45.40 N	12.14 E
167	Trial B. (trī'ăl) Austl.	30.48 S	153.5 E
143	Trichard (trĭch'ērd) U. S. Afr.	26.29 S	29.11 E
151	Trichinopoly (trĭch-ĭ-nŏp'ō-lē) India	10.45 N	78.35 E
166	Trida (trī'dȧ) Austl.	33.1 S	145.2 E
125	Triel (trē-ĕl') Fr. (In.)	48.58 N	2.0 E
122	Trier (trēr) Ger.	49.45 N	6.39 E
128	Trieste (trē-ĕs'tä) It.	45.38 N	13.45 E
128	Trieste, G. of It.	45.35 N	13.35 E
126	Trigueros (trē-gā'rōs) Sp.	37.23 N	6.49 W
129	Trikhala (trē'kȧ-lȧ) Grc.	39.31 N	21.48 E
131	Trilessy (trē'lăs-sē) Sov. Un.	50.0 N	29.44 E
131	Trincomalee (trĭŋ-kō-mȧ-lē') Cey. (In.)	9.5 N	80.50 E
72	Trincomali Chan. (trĭŋ-kō-mȧ-lē') Can. (Vancouver In.)	48.54 N	123.28 W
102	Trinidad (trē-nē-dhädh') Bol.	14.32 S	64.57 W
78	Trinidad (trĭn'ĭ-dăd) Colo.	37.10 N	104.31 W
96	Trinidad (trē-nē-dhädh') Cuba	21.48 N	79.59 W
99	Trinidad Ur. (Buenos Aires In.)	33.32 S	56.59 W
7	Trinidad (trĭn'ĭ-dăd) W. I. (In.)	10.27 N	61.18 W
98	Trinidad I. Atl. O.	20.20 S	29.40 W
96	Trinidad Mts. (trē-nē-dhädh') Cuba	21.55 N	79.52 W
6	Trinité (trē-nē-tā') Mart. (In.)	14.44 N	60.58 W
87	Trinity (trĭn'ĭ-tē) Newf.	48.20 N	53.25 W
81	Trinity Tex.	30.57 N	95.23 W
87	Trinity B. Newf.	48.0 N	53.50 W
64	Trinity Is. Alsk.	56.20 N	154.30 W
70	Trinity R. Calif.	40.55 N	123.0 W
81	Trinity R. Tex.	31.30 N	95.43 W
79	Trinity R., West Fork of Tex.	33.25 N	98.0 W
128	Trino (trē'nō) It.	45.11 N	8.19 W
82	Trion (trī'ŏn) Ga.	34.33 N	85.19 W
139	Tripoli (trĭp'ō-lē) Libya	32.57 N	13.12 E
145	Tripoli (Tarabulus esh Sham) (tȧ-rä'bōō-lōōs ĕsh'shäm') Syr. (In.)	34.24 N	35.50 E
131	Tripolie (trē-pōl'ĭ-yĕ) Sov. Un.	50.5 N	30.46 E
129	Tripolis (trĭ'pō-lĭs) Grc.	37.30 N	22.23 E
139	Tripolitania (Prov.) (trē-pō-lē-tä'-nyȧ) Libya	31.15 N	13.30 E
76	Tripp (trĭp) S. D.	43.14 N	97.59 W
6	Tristan da Cunha (trēs-tän' dȧ kōōn'yȧ) Atl. O.	35.30 S	12.15 W
151	Trivandrum (trē-vŭn'drŭm) India (Cey. In.)	8.35 N	76.50 E
129	Trn (t'rn) Bul.	42.48 N	22.39 E
123	Trnava (t'r'nȧ-vȧ) Czech.	48.22 N	17.34 E
129	Trnovo (t'r'nō-vō) Bul.	43.5 N	25.7 E
161	Trobriand Is. (trō-brē-ănd') Pap. Ter.	8.30 S	151.5 E
128	Trogir (trō'gēr) Yugo.	43.33 N	16.16 E
86	Trois Pistoles (trwä' pēs-tōl') Can.	48.7 N	69.10 W
55	Trois Rivières (Three Rivers) (trwä rē-vyâr') Can.	46.29 N	72.22 W
148	Troitsk (trô'ĕtsk) Sov. Un.	54.15 N	61.40 E
123	Troki (trō'kē) Pol.	54.37 N	24.56 E
120	Troldheimen (Mts.) (trŏl'hā-mĕn) Nor.	62.48 N	9.20 E
120	Trollhätten (trôl'hĕt-ĕn) Swe.	58.17 N	12.20 E
103	Trombetas, R. (trŏm-bā'tȧzh) Braz.	0.0	56.45 W

ng-sing; ŋ-baŋk; N-nasalized n; nŏd; cŏmmit; ōld; ôbey; ôrder; fōōd; fŏŏt; ou-out; s-soft; sh-dish; th-thin; pūre; ûnite; ûrn; stŭd; circŭs; ü-as "y" in study; '-indeterminate vowel.

Page	Name Pronunciation Region	Lat. °′	Long. °′
143	Trompsburg (trŏmps'bûrg) U.S.Afr.	30.2 S	25.48 E
110	Tromsö (trôm'sû) Nor.	69.35 N	19.0 E
104	Tronador, Mt. (trō-nä'dôr) Chl.-Arg.	41.15 S	71.59 W
120	Trondheim (Nidaros) (trôn'hām) (nē'dhä-rôs) Nor.	63.26 N	10.21 E
120	Trondheims Fjord Nor.	63.26 N	10.10 E
123	Troppau (Opava) (trŏp'ou) (ō'pä-vä) Ger.	49.56 N	17.52 E
120	Trosa (trō'sä) Swe.	58.54 N	17.29 E
113	Trotsk (trôtsk) Sov. Un.	53.0 N	49.35 E
130	Trotsk (Krasnogvardeisk) Sov. Un.	59.38 N	30.6 E
72	Trout Cr. Colo. (In.)	39.3 N	105.7 W
70	Trout Cr. Ore.	42.15 N	118.30 W
49	Troutdale (trout'dāl) Wash. (Portland In.)	45.32 N	122.23 W
55	Trout L. Can.	51.15 N	93.15 W
55	Trout L. Can.	53.55 N	89.45 W
124	Trouville (trōō-vēl') Fr.	49.20 N	0.5 E
116	Trowbridge (trō'brĭj) Gt. Brit.	51.15 N	2.12 W
169	Trowulta (trō-wŭl'tȧ) Austl. (Tas. In.)	41.3 S	145.7 E
82	Troy (troi) Ala.	31.47 N	85.58 W
79	Troy Kans.	39.46 N	95.6 W
79	Troy Mo.	38.57 N	90.57 W
70	Troy Mont.	48.26 N	115.53 W
85	Troy N. Y.	42.46 N	73.42 W
83	Troy N. C.	35.22 N	79.54 W
84	Troy Ohio	40.2 N	84.15 W
124	Troyes (trwä) Fr.	48.18 N	4.5 E
129	Troy Ruins Tur.	39.58 N	26.15 E
129	Trstenik (t'r-stĕ'nĕk) Yugo.	43.34 N	21.0 E
130	Trubchevsk (trōōp'chĕfsk) Sov. Un.	52.35 N	33.48 E
150	Trucial Coast (Dist.) (trōō'shăl) Oman	24.30 N	55.0 E
74	Truckee (trŭk'ē) Calif.	39.20 N	120.11 W
74	Truckee R. Calif.-Nev.	39.25 N	120.7 W
94	Trujillo (trōō-ĸēl'yō) Hond.	15.56 N	85.58 W
102	Trujillo Peru	8.0 S	79.0 W
126	Trujillo Sp.	39.26 N	5.53 W
102	Trujillo Ven.	9.28 N	70.28 W
94	Trujillo B. Hond.	15.57 N	86.10 W
97	Trujin (trōō-ĸēn') Dom. Rep.	17.47 N	71.25 W
97	Trujin L. Dom. Rep.	17.45 N	71.24 W
79	Trumann (trōō'măn) Ark.	35.41 N	90.31 W
167	Trundle (trŭn'd'l) Austl.	32.54 S	147.43 E
166	Truro (trōō'rō) Austl.	34.23 S	139.9 E
55	Truro Can.	45.20 N	63.32 W
116	Truro Gt. Brit.	50.15 N	5.5 W
73	Trussville (trŭs'vĭl) Ala. (Birmingham In.)	33.37 N	86.37 W
	Trutnov, see Trautenau, Ger.		
152	Tsaidam Swamp (tsī'dăm) Chn.	37.0 N	95.0 E
83	Tsala Apopka L. (tsä'lȧ ȧ-pŏp'kȧ) Fla.	28.55 N	82.10 W
156	Tsangchow (tsäng'chō') Chn.	38.31 N	116.39 E
153	Tsangkapang (tsäng'kä-päng') Chn. (Shanghai In.)	31.10 N	121.29 E
156	Tsangkow (tsäng'kō') Chn.	36.9 N	120.21 E
152	Tsang Po (Brahmaputra) (tsäng'pō) (brä-mȧ-pōō'trȧ) Chn.-India	29.30 N	95.0 E
156	Tsaochow (tsä'ō-chō') Chn.	35.19 N	115.41 E
141	Tsaratanana, Mt. (tsä'rä-tä'nä-nä') Madag.	14.0 S	49.0 E
...	Tsaritsin, see Stalingrad, Sov. Un.		
154	Tsengshing (tsĕng'shĭng') Chn.	23.14 N	113.48 E
153	Tsetsen-Khan-Kure (tsĕ'tsĕn-kän-kōō'rȧ) Chn.	47.30 N	110.50 E
140	Tshela (tshä'lȧ) Bel. Cong.	5.17 S	13.50 E
140	Tshikapa (tshē-kä'pȧ) Bel. Cong.	6.30 S	20.50 E
140	Tshilongo (tshē-lŏŋ'gō) Bel. Cong.	10.28 S	26.5 E
149	Tshun Mt. (tshōōn) Sov. Un.	65.59 N	140.25 E
141	Tsiafajavona (Mt.) (tsē'ȧ-fȧ-yȧ-vō-nä') Madag.	19.20 S	47.18 E
155	Tsiahang (tsē'ä-häng') Chn.	24.3 N	115.49 E
141	Tsiandro (tsē-än-drō') Madag.	18.33 S	44.50 E
155	Tsianglo (tsī'äng-lō') Chn.	26.42 N	117.22 E
156	Tsienan (tsē'ĕn-än') Chn.	40.5 N	118.39 E
156	Tsienkiang (tsē'ĕn-kyäng') Chn.	23.38 N	109.7 E
154	Tsienkiang Chn.	30.24 N	112.40 E
155	Tsienshan (tsē'ĕn-shän') Chn.	30.37 N	116.34 E
155	Tsientang R. (tsē'ĕn-täng') Chn.	29.40 N	119.45 E
155	Tsienyün (tsē'ĕn-yün') Chn.	28.36 N	120.3 E
156	Tsiho (tsī'hō') Chn.	36.42 N	116.43 E
156	Tsimo (tsī'mō') Chn.	36.21 N	120.31 E
156	Tsinan (tsī'nän') Chn.	36.39 N	116.55 E
156	Tsingchang R. (tsĭng'chäng') Chn.	37.0 N	113.36 E
154	Tsingchen (tsĭng'chĕn') Chn.	26.25 N	106.17 E
156	Tsingcheng (tsĭng'chĕng') Chn.	37.9 N	117.47 E
154	Tsingchow (tsĭng'chō') Chn.	26.37 N	109.26 E
156	Tsingchow Chn.	36.46 N	118.34 E
156	Tsinghai (tsĭng'hī') Chn.	39.1 N	116.50 E
152	Tsinghai (tsĭng'hăĭ') (Div.) Chn.	34.45 N	95.0 E
156	Tsingho (tsĭng'hō') Chn.	37.8 N	115.40 E
156	Tsinghsien (tsĭng'hsyĕn') Chn.	38.47 N	116.35 E
154	Tsingkiang (tsĭng'kyäng') Chn.	26.42 N	108.30 E
156	Tsingkiang Chn.	31.58 N	120.12 E
156	Tsingkiangpo (tsĭng'kyäng'pō') Chn.	33.37 N	119.2 E
152	Tsinling Shan (Mts.) (tsĭn'lĭng' shän') Chn.	34.0 N	107.0 E
155	Tsingliu (tsĭng'lē-ōō') Chn.	26.5 N	116.47 E
154	Tsingping (tsĭng'pĭng') Chn.	26.37 N	107.38 E
155	Tsingpu (tsĭng'pōō') Chn.	31.3 N	120.59 E
154	Tsing R. (tsĭng') Chn.	30.22 N	109.44 E
156	Tsingsing (tsĭng'sĭng') Chn.	38.5 N	114.3 E
156	Tsingtao (tsĭng'tä'ō) Chn.	36.4 N	120.19 E
155	Tsingteh (tsĭng'tĕ') Chn.	30.18 N	118.29 E
155	Tsingtien (tsĭng'tyĕn') Chn.	28.8 N	120.17 E
154	Tsingyang (tsĭng'yäng') Chn.	30.38 N	117.52 E
154	Tsingyün (tsĭng'yün') Chn.	23.44 N	112.58 E
156	Tsinning (tsĭ'nĭng') Chn.	35.32 N	116.27 E
155	Tsinsien (tsĭn'syĕn') Chn.	28.20 N	116.5 E
141	Tsiribihina R. (tsē'rē-bē-hē-nä') Madag.	19.43 S	45.0 E
156	Tsisia (tsī'syä)' Chn.	37.16 N	120.56 E
143	Tsitsa R. (tsē'tsä) U. S. Afr.	31.10 S	28.42 E
153	Tsitsihar (Lungkiang) (tsē-tsē-här') (lōōng'kyäng') Manch.	47.28 N	123.57 E
156	Tsitung (tsī'tōōng') Chn.	37.6 N	117.24 E
156	Tsiyang (tsī'yäng') Chn.	36.57 N	117.3 E
154	Tso (tsō) Chn.	22.45 N	107.41 E
143	Tsolo (tsō'lō) U. S. Afr.	31.19 S	28.46 E
143	Tsombo (tsôm'bō) U. S. Afr.	32.0 S	27.47 E
156	Tsowhsien (tsō'hsyĕn') Chn.	35.33 N	117.1 E
156	Tsowping (tsō'pĭng') Chn.	36.54 N	117.41 E
159	Tsu (tsōō) Jap.	34.42 N	136.29 E
158	Tsugaru Str. (tsōō'gä-rōō) Jap.	41.20 N	140.15 E
157	Tsu Is. Jap.	34.17 N	129.20 E
140	Tsumeb (tsōō'mĕb) S. W. Afr.	19.15 S	17.45 E
154	Tsungfa (tsōōng'fä') Chn.	23.35 N	113.30 E
153	Tsunghochow (tsōōng'hō-chō') Chn. (Shanghai In.)	31.8 N	121.28 E
155	Tsungjen (tsōōng'jĕn') Chn.	27.39 N	115.56 E
155	Tsung Ming I. (tsōōng'mĭng') Chn.	31.35 N	121.28 E
154	Tsungyang (tsōōng'yäng') Chn.	29.32 N	113.54 E
154	Tsunyi (tsōō'nyē') Chn.	27.36 N	106.58 E
159	Tsuruga (tsōō'rōō-gä) Jap.	35.40 N	136.2 E
158	Tsurugaoka (tsōō-rōō-gä-ō'kȧ) Jap.	38.45 N	139.52 E
159	Tsurugi, C. (tsōō'rōō-gē) Jap. (Tokyo In.)	35.8 N	139.40 E
159	Tsurugiyama (Mt.) (tsōō'rōō-gē-yä'mȧ) Jap.	33.50 N	134.2 E
159	Tsurusaki (tsōō'rōō-sä'kē) Jap.	33.14 N	131.44 E
157	Tsushima Str. (tsōō'shē-mȧ) Jap.	33.53 N	129.20 E
159	Tsuwano (tsōō'wȧ-nō) Jap.	34.28 N	131.48 E
159	Tsuyama (tsōō'yȧ-mȧ) Jap.	35.2 N	134.0 E
152	Tsuyunga (tsōō'yōōng-ȧ') Chn.	25.2 N	101.31 E
139	Tu (Tibesti) (Reg.) (tōō) (tē-bĕs'tē) Fr. Eq. Afr.	21.0 N	18.0 E
102	Tuaja (tōō-ä'hä) Col.	5.30 N	73.40 W
170	Tuakau (tōō'ä-kä'ōō) N. Z.	37.16 S	17.50 E
6	Tuamotou (Low) Arch. (tōō-ä-mō'tōō) (lō) Pac. O.	17.0 S	145.0 W
162	Tuao (tōō-ä'ō) P. I.	17.44 N	121.26 E
95	Tuapi Lagoon (tōō-ä'pē) Nic.	14.10 N	83.25 W
113	Tuapse (tōō'äp-sĕ) Sov. Un.	44.5 N	39.10 E
126	Túa R. (tōō'ä) Port.	41.25 N	7.11 W
104	Tubarão (tōō-bä-rouɴ') Braz.	28.30 S	49.2 W
163	Tubigon (tōō-bē'gōn) P. I.	9.57 N	123.58 E
122	Tübingen (tü'bĭng-ĕn) Ger.	48.33 N	9.2 E
6	Tubuai (Austral) Is. (tōō-bōō-ä'ē) (ôs'trăl) Pac. O.	23.0 N	150.0 W
163	Tuburan (tōō-bōō'rän) P. I.	10.42 N	123.50 E
102	Tucacas (tōō-kä'käs) Ven.	10.45 N	68.28 W
155	Tuchang (tōō'chäng') Chn.	29.20 N	116.12 E
73	Tucker (tŭk'ĕr) Ga. (Atlanta In.)	33.51 N	84.13 W
75	Tucson (tōō-sŏn') Ariz.	32.14 N	110.57 W
104	Tucumán (tōō-kōō-män') Arg.	26.50 S	65.15 W
104	Tucumán (State) Arg.	27.0 S	65.30 W
78	Tucumcari (tōō'kŭm-kâr-ē) N. M.	35.10 N	103.43 W
126	Tudela (tōō-dhä'lä) Sp.	42.4 N	1.36 W
82	Tugaloo R. (tŭg'ȧ-lōō) Ga.	34.30 N	83.5 W
143	Tugela (tōō-gĕl'ȧ) U. S. Afr.	29.10 S	31.25 E
143	Tugela R. U. S. Afr.	28.50 S	31.0 E
84	Tug Fork (R.) (tŭg) W. Va.	37.40 N	82.15 W
167	Tuggerah Beach L. (tŭg'ĕr-ȧ) Austl.	33.12 S	151.35 E
163	Tugnug Pt. (tōōg-nōōg') P. I.	11.20 N	125.37 E
162	Tuguegarao (tōō-gā-gȧ-rä'ō) P. I.	17.36 N	121.43 E
156	Tuhai R. (tōō'hī') Chn.	37.8 N	117.0 E
156	Tuhshan (tōōk'shän') Chn.	25.49 N	107.24 E
73	Tujunga Cr. (tōō-jŭn'gȧ) Calif. (Los Angeles In.)	34.18 N	118.13 W
161	Tukangbesi Is. (tōō-käng-bä'sē) Neth. Ind.	5.30 S	124.0 E
154	Tukiang (tōō'kyäng') Chn.	25.47 N	108.2 E
170	Tukituki R. (tōō'kē-tōō'kē) N. Z.	39.50 S	176.50 E
121	Tukums (tōō'kōōms) Lat.	56.58 N	23.10 E
140	Tukuyu (tōō-kōō'yä) Tan.	9.15 S	33.38 E
49	Tukwila (tŭk'wĭ-lȧ) Wash. (Seattle In.)	47.28 N	122.16 W
92	Tula (tōō'lä) Mex.	20.4 N	99.21 W
92	Tula Mex.	23.0 N	99.42 W
130	Tula (tōō'lä) Sov. Un.	54.12 N	37.39 E
130	Tula (Dist.) Sov. Un.	53.40 N	37.30 E
165	Tulagi (I.) (tōō-lä'gē) Solomon Is.	9.6 S	160.20 E
49	Tulalip (tū-lă'lĭp) Wash. (Seattle In.)	48.4 N	122.18 W
70	Tulalip Ind. Res. Wash.	48.5 N	122.25 W
92	Tulancingo (tōō-län-sĭŋ'gō) Mex.	20.5 N	98.21 W
92	Tula, R. (tōō'lä) Mex.	20.20 N	99.13 W
74	Tulare (tōō-lä'rä) (tŭ-lâr') Calif.	36.12 N	119.21 W
74	Tulare Basin Calif.	36.5 N	119.50 W
75	Tularosa (tōō-lȧ-rō'zȧ) N. M.	33.4 N	106.3 W
142	Tulbagh (tōōl'bägh) (tŭl'băg) U. S. Afr.	33.15 S	19.6 E
102	Tulcán (tōōl-kän') Ec.	0.45 N	77.45 W
131	Tulcea (tōōl'chä) Rom.	45.8 N	28.49 E
131	Tulchin (tōōl'chĕn) Sov. Un.	48.41 N	28.54 E
92	Tulcingo (tōōl-sĭŋ'gō) Mex.	18.2 N	98.28 W
141	Tuléar (tōō-lä-är') Madag.	23.15 S	43.38 E
74	Tule R. (tōō'lā) Calif.	36.7 N	119.20 W
74	Tule River Ind. Res. Calif.	36.5 N	118.45 W
140	Tuli (tōō'lē) S. Rh.	21.55 S	29.10 E
78	Tulia (tōō'lĭ-ȧ) Tex.	34.33 N	101.47 W
145	Tul Karm (Tel Kerem) (tōōl kärm) (tĕl kĕ-rĕm') Pal. (In.)	32.18 N	35.0 E
82	Tullahoma (tŭl-ȧ-hō'mȧ) Tenn.	35.22 N	86.12 W
167	Tullamore (tŭl-ȧ-mōr') Austl.	32.39 S	147.38 E
116	Tullamore Ire.	53.15 N	7.25 W
124	Tulle (tül) Fr.	45.15 N	1.45 E
125	Tullins (tü-lăɴ') Fr.	45.18 N	5.30 E
122	Tulln (tōōln) Ger.	48.20 N	16.2 E
86	Tulmistuk R. (tŭl-mĭs'tŭk) Can.	50.10 N	67.49 W
93	Tulpetlac (tōōl-pȧ-tläk') Mex. (In.)	19.34 N	99.3 W
79	Tulsa (tŭl'sȧ) Okla.	36.9 N	95.59 W
157	Tulsan (tōōl'sän') Chn.	39.48 N	124.38 E
152	Tulufan (Turfan) (tōō'lōō-fän') (tōōr-fän') Chn.	43.0 N	89.2 E
148	Tulun (tōō-lōōn') Sov. Un.	54.30 N	100.30 E
93	Tulyehualco (tōōl-yȧ-wäl'kō) Mex. (In.)	19.15 N	99.1 W
75	Tumacacori Natl. Mon. (tōō-mä-kä'kō-rē) Ariz.	31.35 N	111.4 W
102	Tumaco (tōō-mä'kō) Col.	1.45 N	78.45 W
95	Tuma, R. (tōō'mä) Nic.	13.13 N	85.10 W
162	Tumauini (tōō-mou-ē'nē) P. I.	17.16 N	121.48 E
135	Tumba (tōōm'bä) Bel. Cong. (Brazzaville In.)	5.28 S	14.43 E
140	Tumba, L. (tōōm'bȧ) Bel. Cong.	0.45 S	18.5 E
135	Tumba Mani (tōōm'bȧ mä'nē) Bel. Cong. (Brazzaville In.)	5.55 S	15.37 E
167	Tumbarumba (tōōm-bȧ-rŭm'bȧ) Austl.	35.48 S	148.2 E
102	Tumbez (tōōm'bāz) Ec.	3.45 S	80.29 W
92	Tumbiscatío (tōōm-bē-skä-tē'ō) Mex.	18.32 N	102.30 W
166	Tumby B. (tŭm'bē) Austl.	34.21 S	136.0 E
103	Tumeremo (tōō-mā-rā'mō) Ven.	7.15 N	61.30 W
163	Tumindao I. (tōō-mĭn-dä'ō) P. I.	4.43 N	119.24 E
139	Tummo (tōōm'mō) Libya	22.40 N	14.19 E
138	Tummo Mts. Libya	23.30 N	12.30 E
103	Tumuc-Humac Mts. (tōō-mōōk'-ōō-mäk') S. A.	2.0 N	54.0 W
167	Tumut (tŭm'ŭt) Austl.	35.19 S	148.15 E
167	Tumut Ra. Austl.	35.18 S	148.30 E
167	Tumut R. Austl.	35.30 S	148.16 E
49	Tumwater (tŭm'wō-tĕr) Wash. (Seattle In.)	47.1 N	122.55 W
163	Tuna Pt. (tōō'nä) P. I.	6.23 N	124.3 E
96	Tunas de Zaza (tōō'näs dā zä'zä) Cuba	21.38 N	79.35 W
115	Tunbridge Wells (tŭn'brĭj wĕlz') Gt. Brit.	51.5 N	0.15 E
158	Tunchingcheng (tōōn'kĭng'chĕng') Manch.	44.6 N	129.6 E
129	Tundža R. (tōōnd'zhȧ) Bul.	42.30 N	26.30 E
155	Tungan (tōōn'gän') Chn.	24.44 N	118.1 E
154	Tungan Chn.	26.10 N	111.7 E
154	Tungan Chn.	30.23 N	105.46 E
156	Tungan Chn.	39.29 N	116.45 E
156	Tungchang (tōōng'chäng') Chn.	36.23 N	115.56 E
156	Tungcheng (tōōng'chĕng') Chn.	29.12 N	113.41 E
155	Tungcheng Chn.	31.3 N	116.55 E
152	Tungchow (tōōng'chō') Chn.	34.50 N	109.50 E
156	Tungchow Chn.	39.54 N	116.44 E
152	Tungchwan (tōōng'chwän') Chn.	31.0 N	104.55 E
155	Tunghu (tōōng'hōō') Chn.	29.50 N	119.42 E
155	Tunghu Chn.	30.12 N	117.2 E
153	Tunghwa (tōōng'hwä') Manch.	41.45 N	125.52 E
153	Tungjen (tōōng'jĕn') Chn.	27.35 N	108.51 E
153	Tungkiang (tōōng'kyäng') Manch.	47.35 N	132.41 E
154	Tungkun (tōōng'kōōn') Chn.	23.0 N	113.44 E
153	Tungkwan (tōōng'kwän) Chn.	34.55 N	110.30 E
156	Tungkwang (tōōng'kwäng') Chn.	38.3 N	116.22 E
154	Tunglan (tōōng'län') Chn.	24.30 N	107.20 E
155	Tungliang (tōōng'lyäng') Chn.	29.58 N	106.5 E
158	Tungliaochen (tōōng'lyä'ō-chĕn') Manch.	43.26 N	122.0 E
155	Tungliu (tōōng'lyōō') Chn.	28.31 N	114.3 E
156	Tungming (tōōng'mĭng') Chn.	35.16 N	115.25 E
154	Tung R. (tōōng) Chn.	23.8 N	114.8 E
158	Tungpei (tōōng'pī) Manch.	48.0 N	126.50 E
156	Tungsan B. (tōōng'sän') Chn.	23.50 N	117.32 E
155	Tungsan I. Chn.	23.45 N	117.20 E
155	Tungshan (tōōng'shän') Chn.	29.35 N	114.22 E
155	Tungsiang (tōōng'syäng') Chn.	28.15 N	116.33 E
156	Tungtai (tōōng'tī') Chn.	32.49 N	120.14 E
154	Tungtao (tōōng'tä'ō) Chn.	26.18 N	109.25 E
154	Tung Ting Hu (L.) (tōōng tĭng hōō) Chn.	29.0 N	112.15 E
154	Tungtse (tōōng'tsĕ') Chn.	28.0 N	106.42 E
149	Tungusk Ridge (tōōn-gōōsk') Sov. Un.	64.0 N	108.0 E
149	Tunguska R., Lower (tōōn-gōōs'kȧ) Sov. Un.	64.0 N	103.0 E
148	Tunguska R., Middle or Stony Sov. Un.	60.30 N	98.0 E
148	Tunguska R., Upper Sov. Un.	58.30 N	97.0 E
156	Tung Wan, Gulf of Chn.	40.20 N	121.10 E
155	Tungyang (tōōng'yäng') Chn.	29.15 N	120.11 E
153	Tunhwa (tōōn'hwä) Manch.	43.27 N	128.25 E
82	Tunica (tū'nĭ-kȧ) Miss.	34.42 N	90.26 W
138	Tunis (tū'nĭs) Tun.	37.0 N	10.10 E
135	Tunis, G. of Tun. (In.)	37.0 N	10.30 E
138	Tunisia (tū-nĭzh'ē-ȧ) Afr.	34.0 N	9.0 E
148	Tunka (tōōn'kä) Sov. Un.	51.50 N	103.10 E
85	Tunkhannock (tŭnk-hăn'ŭk) Pa.	41.36 N	75.58 W
73	Tunnel (tŭn'ĕl) Calif. (Los Angeles In.)	34.19 N	118.30 W
171	Tunnel N. Z.	43.34 S	172.44 E
169	Tunstall (tŭn'stȧl) Austl. (Melbourne In.)	37.49 S	145.10 E
154	Tunting L. (tōōn'tĭng') Chn.	29.8 N	112.20 E
74	Tuolumne R. (twō-lŭm'nē) Calif.	37.40 N	120.40 W
82	Tupelo (tū'pĕ-lō) Miss.	34.15 N	88.41 W
102	Tupiza (tōō-pē'zä) Bol.	21.28 S	65.30 W
85	Tupper Lake (tŭp'ĕr) N. Y.	44.15 N	74.28 W
104	Tupungato (Vol.) (tōō-pōōŋ-gä'tō) Arg.-Chl.	33.20 S	69.50 W
167	Turabeile Cr. (tōō'rȧ-bĕl) Austl.	31.22 S	149.52 E
170	Turakirae, C. (tōō'rȧ-kē-rä'ȧ) N. Z. (In.)	41.26 S	174.56 E
11	Tura R. (tōō'rȧ) Sov. Un.	58.45 N	62.0 E
102	Turbo (tōōr'bō) Col.	8.0 N	76.45 W
123	Turčiansky Svätý Martin (tōōr'chyȧn-skûē svä-tûē' mär'tyĕn) Czech.	49.3 N	18.50 E
123	Turda (tōōr'dȧ) Rom.	46.35 N	23.47 E

ăt; finăl; rāte; senâte; ärm; ȧsk; sofȧ; fâre; ch-choose; dh-as th in other; bē; ēvent; bĕt; recĕnt; cratēr; g-go; gh-gutteral g; bĭt; ĭ-short neutral; rīde; ĸ-gutteral k as ch in German ich;

Page	Name Pronunciation Region	Lat. °'	Long. °'
123	Turek (tōō'rĕk) Pol.	52.2 N	18.30 E
152	Turfan (Tulufan) (tōōr-fän') (tōō'lōō'fän'). Chn.	43.0 N	89.2 E
148	Turgai (tōōr'gä-ē) Sov. Un.	49.40 N	63.30 E
113	Turhal (tōōr'häl) Tur.	40.32 N	36.5 E
121	Türi (tü'rĭ) Est.	58.48 N	25.30 E
92	Turicato (tōō-rē-kä'tō) Mex.	18.52 N	101.18 W
96	Turiguano I. (tōō-rē-gwä'nō). Cuba.	22.18 N	78.40 W
128	Turin (Torino) (tū'rĭn) (tō-rē'nō). It.	45.4 N	7.40 E
112	Turinskie-Rudniki (tōō-rēn'skĭ-yĕ-rōōd'nĭ-kĭ)... Sov. Un.	59.50 N	60.15 E
123	Turja R. (tōōr'yȧ) Pol.	51.16 N	24.57 E
123	Turka (tōōr'kȧ) Pol.	49.8 N	23.1 E
150	Turkestan (Reg.) (tōōr-kĕ-stän') (tûr-kĕ-stăn')... Sov. Un.	42.0 N	57.0 E
148	Turkestan Sov. Un.	43.20 N	68.25 E
152	Turkestan, Eastern Chn.	37.30 N	83.0 E
123	Túrkeve (tōōr'kĕ-vĕ) Hung.	47.6 N	20.45 E
113	Turkey (tûrk'ē) Eur.-Asia.	38.30 N	32.40 E
73	Turkey Cr.. Ala. (Birmingham In.)	33.44 N	86.47 W
72	Turkey Cr. Colo. (Denver In.)	39.35 N	105.15 W
77	Turkey R. Ia.	43.0 N	91.40 W
150	Turkmen (Soviet Rep.) (tōōrk'mĕn)... Sov. Un.	40.20 N	54.30 E
97	Turks I. Passage (tûrks)... Ba. Is.	21.25 N	71.25 W
97	Turks Is. Ba. Is.	21.25 N	71.5 W
121	Turku (Åbo) (tōōr'kōō) (ō'bō) Fin.	60.29 N	22.14 E
74	Turlock (tûr'lŏk) Calif.	37.29 N	120.51 W
170	Turnagain, C. (tûrn'ȧ-gĕn).. N. Z.	40.28 S	176.40 E
94	Turneffe I. (tûr-nĕf'fē) Br. Hond. (In.)	17.20 N	87.52 W
96	Turner Sd. (tûr'nẽr) Ba. Is.	24.20 N	78.4 W
117	Turnhout (türn-hout') (tür-nōōt') Bel.	51.20 N	5.0 E
122	Turnov (tōōr'nôf) Czech.	50.35 N	15.12 E
129	Turnu Măgurele (tōōr'nōō mȧ-gōō'rĕ-ly'). Rom.	43.43 N	24.50 E
129	Turnu-Severin (tōōr'nōō-sĕ-vĕ-rēn'). Rom.	44.37 N	22.40 E
167	Turos R. (tōō'rōs) Austl.	36.14 S	149.50 E
96	Turquino, Pico de (Mt.) (pē'kō dā tōōr-kē'nō). Cuba	19.58 N	76.49 W
150	Turt-Kul (tōōrt'-kōōl')... Sov. Un.	41.37 N	61.15 E
81	Turtle B. (tûr't'l) Tex. (In.)	29.47 N	94.41 W
76	Turtle Cr. S. D.	44.40 N	98.38 W
89	Turtle I. S. C. (Savannah In.)	32.4 N	80.54 W
160	Turtle (Togian) Is. (tō'gē-än) Neth. Ind.	0.30 S	122.0 E
89	Turtle L.. Minn. (Minneapolis In.)	45.6 N	93.10 W
76	Turtle Mts. N. D.	48.50 N	100.10 W
129	Turtucaia (tōōr-tōō-kä'yȧ).. Rom.	44.2 N	26.36 E
170	Turua (tōō'rōō-ȧ) N. Z.	37.17 S	175.35 E
82	Tuscaloosa (tŭs-kȧ-lōō'sȧ) Ala.	33.11 N	87.35 W
128	Tuscany (Prov.) (tŭs'kȧ-nē) It.	43.25 N	11.20 E
70	Tuscarora (tŭs-kȧ-rō'rȧ) Nev.	41.18 N	116.15 W
88	Tuscarora Indian Res. N. Y. (Niagara Falls In.)	43.10 N	78.57 W
79	Tuscola (tŭs-kō'lȧ) Ill.	39.47 N	88.18 W
82	Tuscumbia (tŭs-kŭm'bĭ-ȧ) Ala.	34.43 N	87.42 W
82	Tuskegee (tŭs-kē'gē) Ala.	32.25 N	85.40 W
123	Tustanowice (tōōs'tä-nō-vē'tsĕ) Pol.	49.17 N	23.31 E
73	Tustin (tŭs'tĭn) Calif. (Los Angeles In.)	33.45 N	117.49 W
52	Tustumeno L. (tōōs-tōō-mē'nō) Alsk. (In.)	60.10 N	151.0 W
130	Tutayev (tōō'tȧ-yĕf) Sov. Un.	57.53 N	39.34 E
118	Tutbury (tŭt'bẽr-ē) Gt. Brit.	52.52 N	1.41 W
151	Tuticorin (tōō-tē-kō-rĭn') India	9.0 N	78.10 E
103	Tutoia (tōō-tō'yȧ) Braz.	2.35 S	42.20 W
122	Tuttlingen (tōōt'lĭng-ĕn) Ger.	47.58 N	8.49 E
6	Tutuila (I.) (tōō-tōō-ē'lä).. Pac. O.	14.19 S	170.50 W
82	Tutwiler (tŭt'wī-lẽr) Miss.	34.1 N	90.5 W
118	Tuxford (tŭks'fẽrd) Gt. Brit.	53.14 N	0.54 W
93	Túxpan (tōōs'pän) Mex.	20.57 N	97.24 W
93	Túxpan Reef Mex.	21.2 N	97.13 W
93	Túxpan R. Mex.	20.55 N	97.40 W
92	Tuxpan (tōōs'pän) Mex.	19.30 N	103.18 W
92	Tuxpan Mex.	21.56 N	105.19 W
92	Tuxtepec (tōōs-tȧ-pĕk') Mex.	18.5 N	96.8 W
93	Tuxtla Gutiérrez (tōōs'tlä gōō-tyâr'räz). Mex.	16.45 N	93.23 W
161	Tuy (tōō-ē') P. I. (Manila In.)	14.2 N	120.40 E
126	Tuy Sp.	42.3 N	8.40 W
129	Tuya R. (tōō'yȧ) Sov. Un.	58.0 N	112.0 E
95	Tuyra, R. (tōō-ē'rȧ) Pan.	8.0 N	77.30 W
154	Tuyün (tōō'yün') Chn.	26.13 N	107.22 E
113	Tuz L. (tōōz) Tur.	38.45 S	33.30 E
129	Tuzla (tōōz'lȧ) Yugo.	44.33 N	18.47 E
120	Tvedestrand (tvĭ'dhĕ-stränd). Nor.	58.38 N	8.57 E
120	Tveitsund (tvåt'sōōnd) Nor.	59.1 N	8.30 E
...	Tver, see Kalinin, Sov. Un.		
130	Tver (Dist.) Sov. Un.	57.30 N	35.30 E
155	Twanfeng (twăn'fĕng) Chn.	30.36 N	114.48 E
116	Tweed (R.) (twēd) Gt. Brit.	55.35 N	2.30 W
88	Twelve Mile Cr. N. Y. (Niagara Falls In.)	43.15 N	79.56 W
119	Twielenfleth (tvē'lĕn-flĕt) Ger. (Hamburg In.)	53.36 N	9.33 E
87	Twillingate (twĭl'ĭn-gāt) Newf.	49.40 N	54.49 W
87	Twillingate I. Newf.	49.35 N	54.45 W
49	Twin Wash. (Seattle In.)	48.9 N	123.56 W
71	Twin Bridges Mont.	45.33 N	112.18 W
71	Twin Falls Ida.	42.33 N	114.29 W
89	Twin Lakes Minn. (Minneapolis In.)	45.3 N	93.19 W
73	Twin Peaks Calif. (Los Angeles In.)	34.15 N	117.15 W
73	Twin Pks. (Mt.) Utah (Salt Lake City In.)	40.33 N	111.40 W
78	Two Butte Cr. (būt) Colo.	37.40 N	102.28 W
79	Two Prairie Bayou (Cr.) Ark.	34.25 N	91.40 W
167	Twofold B. (tōō'fōld) Austl.	37.5 S	149.53 E
77	Two Harbors Minn.	47.1 N	91.40 W
57	Two Mountains, L. of Can. (Montreal In.)	45.28 N	74.0 W
77	Two Rivers Wis.	44.9 N	87.35 W
157	Tyansan Pt. (tĭän'sän') Cho.	38.10 N	124.45 E
131	Tyasmin R. (tyȧs'mĭn).. Sov. Un.	49.10 N	32.25 E
89	Tybee I. (tĭ'bē) Ga. (Savannah In.)	32.0 N	80.53 W
89	Tybee R. Ga. (Savannah In.)	31.58 N	80.56 W
89	Tybee Roads (Inlet) S. C.-Ga. (Savannah In.)	32.3 N	80.53 W
56	Tyee (tī'ē) Can. (Prince Rupert In.)	54.12 N	129.56 W
141	Tygerberg (tī'gẽr-bûrg).. U. S. Afr.	33.51 S	18.29 E
143	Tylden (tĭl'dĕn) U. S. Afr.	32.7 S	27.5 E
118	Tyldesley (tĭldz'lē) Gt. Brit.	53.31 N	2.28 W
76	Tyler (tī'lẽr) Minn.	44.18 N	96.8 W
81	Tyler Tex.	32.21 N	95.18 W
82	Tylertown (tī'lẽr-toun) Miss.	31.7 N	90.8 W
76	Tyndall (tĭn'dăl) S. D.	42.59 N	97.51 W
116	Tyne (R.) (tīn) Gt. Brit.	54.55 N	2.10 W
116	Tynemouth (tīn'mŭth)... Gt. Brit.	55.0 N	1.30 W
87	Tyngsboro (tĭngz'bŭr-ō) Mass. (In.)	42.41 N	71.25 W
120	Tynset (tün'sĕt) Nor.	62.18 N	10.48 E
145	Tyr (Sour) (tĭr) (sōōr)... Syr. (In.)	33.17 N	35.11 E
120	Tyri Fjord (tü'rē) Nor.	60.2 N	10.10 E
129	Tyrnavos (tẽr'nȧ-vōs) Grc.	39.30 N	22.11 E
73	Tyrone (tĭ-rōn').. Ga. (Atlanta In.)	33.28 N	84.36 W
75	Tyrone N. M.	32.38 N	108.22 W
85	Tyrone Pa.	40.42 N	78.15 W
166	Tyrrell Cr. (tĭr'ĕl) Austl.	35.45 S	143.10 E
166	Tyrrell L. Austl.	35.22 S	142.52 E
128	Tyrrhenian Sea (tĭr-rē'nĭ-ăn)... It.	40.0 N	12.0 E
121	Tyrvää (tür'vä) Fin.	61.20 N	22.52 E
123	Týsmienica (tĭsh-myĕ-nĭ'tsä).. Pol.	48.53 N	24.53 E
148	Tyukalinsk (tyōō'kȧ-lĭnsk) Sov. Un.	55.55 N	71.30 E
149	Tyukyan R. (tyōōk'yȧn) Sov. Un.	65.30 N	117.0 E
113	Tyulenii Is. (tyōō-lĕ'nĭ-ē) Sov. Un.	44.30 N	47.30 E
157	Tyulwon (tyōōl'wŏn') Cho.	38.16 N	127.11 E
148	Tyumen (tyōō'mĕn) Sov. Un.	57.15 N	65.25 E
149	Tyungili R. (tyōōn'gē-lē). Sov. Un.	65.30 N	120.0 E
157	Tyungju (tyōōng'jōō') Cho.	39.43 N	125.13 E
129	Tyurk-Arnautlar (tyōōrk-är-nä'-ōōt-lär). Bul.	43.19 N	27.21 E
156	Tzechwan (chĕ'wăn') Chn.	36.44 N	118.1 E
154	Tzeli (tzē'lē') Chn.	29.10 N	110.52 E
156	Tzuchow (tzōō'chō') Chn.	36.20 N	114.33 E
154	Tzu R. (tzōō) Chn.	28.17 N	110.48 E
135	Uad Zaryon (wăd thär-yōn') Mor. (Gib. In.)	35.43 N	5.34 E
102	Uaupes, R. (wä-ōō'päs) Braz.	0.1 N	68.30 W
139	Ubangi R. (ōō-bäŋ'gē) Afr.	3.0 N	18.30 E
139	Ubangi-Shari (Prov.) (ōō-bäŋ'gē-shä'rē). Fr. Eq. Afr.	6.30 N	21.30 E
99	Ubatuba (ōō-bȧ-tōō'bȧ) Braz. (Rio de Janeiro In.)	23.27 S	45.6 W
158	Ube (ōō'bā) Jap.	40.8 N	141.45 E
126	Úbeda (ōō'bȧ-dä) Sp.	38.1 N	3.21 W
103	Uberara (ōō-bȧ-rä'rȧ) Braz.	19.45 S	48.0 W
148	Ubogan, L. (ōō'bō-gän).. Sov. Un.	52.25 N	64.45 E
160	Ubol (ōō-bōl') Thai.	15.15 N	104.50 E
143	Ubombo (ōō-bōm'bō)... U. S. Afr.	27.35 S	32.4 E
131	Ubort R. (ōō-bōrt') Sov. Un.	51.25 N	27.53 E
126	Ubrique (ōō-brē'kā) Sp.	36.42 N	5.36 W
152	Ubsa Nor (L.) (ōōb'sȧ nōr').. Chn.	50.30 N	92.30 E
102	Ucayali, R. (ōō'kä-yä'lē) Peru	6.30 S	75.3 W
117	Uccle (ü'kl') Bel.	50.45 N	4.22 E
148	Uch Aral (ōōch' ȧ-räl')... Sov. Un.	46.15 N	81.10 E
159	Uchinoko (ōō'chē-nō'kō) Jap.	33.30 N	132.39 E
159	Uchinoura (ōō'chē-nō-ōō'rȧ).. Jap.	31.16 N	131.3 E
158	Uchiura B. (ōō-chē-ōō'rȧ) Jap.	42.15 N	140.45 E
152	Uch Turfan (Wushih) (ōōch' tōōr-fän') (wōō'shē'). Chn.	41.7 N	79.30 E
122	Ückermünde (ü'kẽr-mün-dĕ).. Ger.	53.43 N	14.1 E
151	Udaipur (ōō-dŭ'ē-pōōr) India	24.30 N	73.45 E
131	Udai R. (ōō-dĭ') Sov. Un.	50.30 N	32.35 E
149	Uda R. (ōō'dȧ) Sov. Un.	54.10 N	132.0 E
120	Uddevalla (ōōd'dĕ-väl-ȧ) Swe.	58.22 N	11.57 E
141	Uddur (ōō-dōōr') It. E. Afr.	4.8 N	43.50 E
138	Udeni (ōō-dä'nē) Nig.	8.1 N	8.9 E
112	Udima (ōō'dē-mȧ) Sov. Un.	61.7 N	46.30 E
128	Udine (ōō'dē-nä) It.	46.4 N	13.13 E
149	Udskaya B. (ōōt-skä'yȧ) Sov. Un.	55.0 N	136.0 E
149	Udskii Ostrog (ōōt'skĭ-ē ôs-trôk') Sov. Un.	54.30 N	134.30 E
159	Ueda (wä'dä) Jap.	36.20 N	138.15 E
165	Uea (I.) (ōō-ä'ȧ) N. Cal.	20.30 S	166.45 E
139	Ueb Gestro (wĕb gĕs'trō) It. E. Afr.	6.30 N	41.10 E
139	Uele R. (ōō-ä'lȧ) Bel. Cong.	3.30 N	25.0 E
112	Ufa (ōō'fȧ) Sov. Un.	54.45 N	56.0 E
112	Ufa R. Sov. Un.	55.30 N	56.30 E
140	Ugab R. (ōō'gäb) S. W. Afr.	20.45 S	15.0 E
140	Ugala R. (ōō-gä'lä) Tan.	6.15 S	32.30 E
139	Uganda (ōō-gän'dȧ) (ū-găn'dȧ) Afr.	2.0 N	32.30 E
52	Ugashik, L. (ōō'gȧ-shēk) Alsk.	57.40 N	156.30 W
129	Ugerčin (ōō'gĕr-chēn) Bul.	43.5 N	24.25 E
143	Ugie (ōō'gē) U. S. Afr.	31.12 S	28.15 E
130	Uglich (ōōg'lĕch) Sov. Un.	57.32 N	38.19 E
130	Uglovka (ōōg-lôf'kȧ) Sov. Un.	58.13 N	33.30 E
130	Ugra R. (ōōg'rȧ) Sov. Un.	54.50 N	34.30 E
123	Uherské Hradiště (ōō-hĕr-skä hrä'dēsh-tyĕ). Czech.	49.4 N	17.30 E
84	Uhrichsville (ū'rĭks-vĭl) Ohio	40.25 N	81.21 W
113	Uil R. (ōō-ēl') Sov. Un.	48.58 N	54.0 E
73	Uintah (ū-ĭn'tȧ) Utah (Salt Lake City In.)	41.8 N	111.55 W
71	Uintah Mts. Utah	40.47 N	110.10 W
75	Uintah R. Utah	40.23 N	110.0 W
143	Uitenhage (ū'tĕn-häg) (ŭĕ'tĕn-hä-ghĕ). U. S. Afr.	33.45 S	25.25 E
140	Ujiji (ōō-jē'jē) Tan.	4.55 S	29.42 E
159	Uji Yamada (ōō'jē yä'mȧ-dä) Jap.	34.28 N	136.44 E
151	Ujjain (ōō-jŭ'ēn) India	23.10 N	75.59 E
123	Ujpest (ōō'ē-pĕsht) Hung.	47.34 N	19.7 E
142	Ukamas (ōō-kä'mäs)... S. W. Afr.	28.4 S	19.45 E
112	Ukhta (ōōκ'tȧ) Sov. Un.	65.25 N	31.15 E
71	Ukiah (ū-kī'ȧ) Calif.	39.8 N	123.14 W
121	Ukmerge (ōōk-mĕr'ghä) Lith.	55.18 N	24.46 E
131	Ukraine (Soviet Rep.) (ū'krān) Sov. Un.	49.30 N	34.0 E
159	Uku (I.) (ōōk'ōō) Jap.	33.15 N	129.8 E
148	Ulala (Oirat-Tura) (ōō'lȧ-lȧ) Sov. Un.	52.15 N	85.59 E
152	Ulan-Bator-Khoto (Urga) (ōō'län-bä'tôr-Kô'tō) (ōōr'gȧ) Chn.	47.56 N	106.55 E
149	Ulan Ude (Verkhneudinsk) (ōō'län ōō'dȧ).. Sov. Un.	51.55 N	107.30 E
152	Ulankom (ōō-län-kōm') Chn.	50.12 N	92.10 E
152	Ulasutai (ōō'lȧ-sōō-tä'ē) Chn.	47.50 N	96.50 E
161	Ulawun (Mt.) (ōō-lä'wŭn) N. Gui. Ter.	5.0 S	151.28 E
129	Ulčinj (Dulcigno) (ōōl'tsēn') (dōōl-chēn'yō).. Yugo.	41.56 N	19.12 E
153	Uldza, R. (ōōl'dzä) Chn.	49.0 N	113.15 E
140	Ulindi R. (ōō-lĭn'dē)... Bel. Cong.	2.40 S	27.0 E
112	Ul'yanovsk (ōō'lē-yä-nôfsk') Sov. Un.	54.12 N	48.25 E
130	Ulla (ōōl'ȧ) Sov. Un.	55.13 N	29.12 E
116	Ullapool (ŭl'ȧ-pōōl) Gt. Brit.	57.55 N	5.10 W
130	Ulla R. Sov. Un.	54.56 N	28.55 E
126	Ulla R. (ōō'lä) Sp.	42.50 N	8.20 W
127	Ulldecona (ōōl'dā-kō'nä) Sp.	40.37 N	0.27 E
122	Ulm (ōōlm) Ger.	48.24 N	9.59 E
120	Ulricehamn (ōōl-rē'sĕ-häm).. Swe.	57.48 N	13.26 E
94	Ulúa, R. (ōō-lōō'ä) Hond.	15.35 N	87.50 W
163	Ulugan B. (ōō-lōō'gän) P. I.	10.10 N	118.45 E
113	Ulukişla (ōō-lōō-kēsh'lä) Tur.	37.35 N	34.30 E
169	Ulverstone (ŭl'vẽr-stŭn) Austl. (Tas. In.)	41.10 S	146.12 E
120	Ulvik (ōōl'vĕk) Nor.	60.35 N	7.0 E
78	Ulysses (ū-lĭs'ēz) Kan.	37.34 N	101.25 W
122	Ülzen (ült'sĕn) Ger.	52.57 N	10.33 E
93	Umán (ōō-män') Mex.	20.53 N	89.38 W
131	Uman (ōō-mȧn'') Sov. Un.	48.44 N	30.12 E
131	Umanskaya (ōō-män'skȧ-yȧ) Sov. Un.	46.19 N	39.20 E
70	Umatilla Ind. Res. (ū-mȧ-tĭl'ȧ) Ore.	45.37 N	118.40 W
163	Umayam R. (ōō-mȧ-yäm')... P. I.	8.10 N	125.27 E
86	Umbagog L. (ŭm-bā'gŏg) Me.-N. H.	44.45 N	71.2 W
143	Umbeluzi (ōōm-bȧ-lōō'zĭ) Moz.	26.3 S	32.23 E
161	Umbo (I.) (ŭm'bō)... N. Gui. Ter.	5.40 S	147.50 E
96	Umbrella Pt. (ŭm-brĕl'ȧ) Jam.	18.30 N	77.56 W
128	Umbria (Prov.) (ŭm'brĭ-ȧ) It.	42.55 N	12.35 E
110	Umeå (ōō'mĕ-ō) Swe.	63.48 N	20.20 E
110	Ume R. (ōō'mĕ) Swe.	64.38 N	18.30 E
143	Umfolozi (ōōm-fō-lō'zē). U. S. Afr.	28.45 S	31.54 E
143	Umgeni R. (ōōm-gā'nē). U. S. Afr.	29.30 S	30.30 E
143	Umhlatuzi R. (ōōm'hlȧ-tōō'zĭ) U. S. Afr.	28.46 S	31.30 E
143	Umkomaas R. (ōōm-kō'mäs) U. S. Afr.	29.50 S	30.0 E
143	Umkusi R. (ōōm-kōō'sĭ) U. S. Afr.	27.38 S	31.35 E
143	Umlalazi (ōōm-lȧ-lä'zĭ).. U. S. Afr.	28.57 S	31.45 E
52	Umnak I. (ōōm'nȧk) Alsk.	53.20 N	168.0 W
52	Umnak Pass Alsk.	53.20 N	167.30 W
70	Umpqua R. (ŭmp'kwȧ) Ore.	43.43 N	123.50 W
140	Umtali (ōōm-tä'lē) S. Rh.	18.57 S	32.35 E
143	Umtamvuna R. (ōōm-täm-vōō'nȧ) U. S. Afr.	31.5 S	30.11 E
143	Umtata (ōōm-tä'tä) U. S. Afr.	31.35 S	28.46 E
143	Umtata R. U. S. Afr.	31.40 S	28.50 E
143	Umvoti R. (ōōm-vō'tĭ).. U. S. Afr.	29.12 S	30.45 E
143	Umzimkulu (ōōm-zēm-kōō'lōō) U. S. Afr.	30.18 S	29.57 E
143	Umzimkulu R. U. S. Afr.	30.30 S	30.0 E
143	Umzinto (ōōm-zĭn'tō) U. S. Afr.	30.18 S	30.40 E
143	Umzunvubu R. (ōōm-zēm-vōō'bōō) U. S. Afr.	30.59 S	29.18 E
52	Unalakleet (ū-nȧ-lăk'lēt) Alsk.	64.0 N	160.45 W
52	Unalaska (ū-nȧ-lăs'kȧ) Alsk.	53.50 N	166.25 W
52	Unalaska I. Alsk.	53.30 N	166.30 W
128	Una R. (ōō'nȧ) Yugo.	44.55 N	16.10 E
49	Uncas (ŭŋ'kȧs) Wash. (Seattle In.)	47.57 N	122.53 W
102	Uncia (ōōn'sē-ȧ) Bol.	18.30 S	66.31 W
75	Uncompahgre Pk. (ŭn-kŭm-pä'grē) Colo.	38.3 N	107.25 W
75	Uncompahgre R. Colo.	38.25 N	107.48 W
143	Underberg (ŭn'dẽr-bûrg) U. S. Afr.	29.49 S	29.32 E
130	Unecha (ōō-nä'chȧ) Sov. Un.	52.51 N	32.42 E
55	Ungava R. (ŭŋ-gȧ'vȧ) Can.	59.40 N	67.30 W
155	Ungkung (ōōng'kōōng') Chn.	23.41 N	116.50 E
123	Ungvár (Užhorod) (ōōng'vär) (ōōzh'hō-rōt). Hung.	48.38 N	22.19 E
103	União (ōō-nē-ouN') Braz.	9.2 S	36.0 W
93	Unidos, R. (ōō-nē'dōs) Mex.	19.26 N	99.4 W
128	Unie (I.) (ōō'nē-ä) It.	44.37 N	14.13 E
52	Unimak Is. (ōō-nē-mäk') Alsk.	54.40 N	164.0 W
52	Unimak Pass Alsk.	54.20 N	165.0 W
82	Union (ūn'yŭn) Miss.	32.35 N	89.9 W
79	Union Mo.	38.27 N	91.0 W
87	Union N. Y.	42.6 N	76.6 W
70	Union Ore.	45.12 N	117.52 W
83	Union S. C.	34.42 N	81.40 W
49	Union Wash. (Seattle In.)	47.21 N	123.6 W
73	Union City Ga. (Atlanta In.)	33.34 N	84.33 W
84	Union City Ind.	40.10 N	84.50 W
84	Union City Mich.	42.3 N	85.6 W
88	Union City.. N. J. (New York In.)	40.47 N	74.2 W
85	Union City Pa.	41.54 N	79.50 W
82	Union City Tenn.	36.25 N	89.3 W
142	Uniondale (ūn'yŭn-dăl)... U.S.Afr.	33.40 S	23.8 E

ng-sing; ŋ baŋk; N-nasalized n; nŏd; cŏmmit; ōld; ōbey; ôrder; fōōd; fŏŏt; ou-out; s-soft; sh-dish; th-thin; pūre; ūnite; ûrn; stŭd; circŭs; ü-as "y" in study; '-indeterminate vowel.

Page	Name Pronunciation Region	Lat. °′	Long. °′
96	Unión de Reyes (ōō-nê-ōn′ dā rā′ĕs) Cuba	22.45 N	81.33 W
92	Unión de San Antonio (sän än-tō′-nyō) Mex.	21.8 N	58.0 W
92	Unión de Tula (tōō′lä)......Mex.	19.59 N	104.14 W
93	Unión Hidalgo (ê-däl′gō)....Mex.	16.28 N	94.50 W
6	Union (Tokelau) Is. (ūn′yŭn) (tō-kĕ-lä′ōō) Pac. O.	9.0 S	172.0 W
144	Union of Socialistic Soviet Republics, see Soviet Union		
142	Union of South Africa........Afr.	30.0 S	25.0 E
82	Union Point.............. ..Ga.	33.37 N	83.7 W
82	Union Springs...............Ala.	32.9 N	85.43 W
82	Uniontown (ūn′yŭn-toun)....Ala.	32.27 N	87.31 W
85	Uniontown..................Pa.	39.55 N	79.43 W
79	Unionville (ūn′yŭn-vĭl).......Mo.	40.28 N	92.59 W
162	Unisan (ōō-nē′sän) ....P. I.	13.50 N	121.59 E
151	United Provinces (States)...India	27.0 N	80.0 E
58	United States..............N. A.		
84	Universal (ū-nĭ-vûr′sȧl)......Ind.	39.37 N	86.29 W
126	Universales, Mts. (ōō-nê-vĕr-sä′lås) Sp.	40.20 N	1.25 W
89	University City Mo. (St. Louis In.)	38.40 N	90.20 W
169	Unley (ŭn′lê). Austl. (Adelaide In.)	34.57 S	138.37 E
157	Unneul (ōōn′nĕ-ōōl′)........Cho.	38.32 N	125.9 E
163	Unsang Pt. (ōōn′säng)...B. N. B.	5.26 N	119.14 E
116	Unst (I.) (ōōnst)...Gt. Brit. (In.)	60.45 N	1.30 W
157	Unyang (ōōn′yäng′).........Cho.	36.39 N	129.7 E
113	Ünye (ün′yĕ)...............Tur.	41.10 N	37.18 E
112	Unzha R. (ōōn′zhȧ).....Sov. Un.	57.45 N	43.50 E
139	Uorra Hailu (vō′rä hä ē lōō) It. E. Afr.	10.37 N	39.29 E
93	Upanapa, R. (ōō-pā-nä′pä)...Mex.	17.50 N	94.11 W
130	Upa R. (ōō′pȧ).........Sov. Un.	53.58 N	36.40 E
102	Upata (ōō-pä′tä)...........Ven.	8.0 N	62.31 W
119	Upholland (ŭp-hŏl′ănd) Gt. Brit. (Liverpool In.)	53.32 N	2.42 W
161	Upig R. (ōō′pĕg) P. I. (Manila In.)	15.3 N	121.0 E
142	Upington (ŭp′ĭng-tŭn)......Bech.	28.25 S	21.15 E
73	Upland (ŭp′lănd) Calif. (Los Angeles In.)	34.6 N	117.40 W
119	Upminster (ŭp′mĭn-stẽr) Gt. Brit. (London In.)	51.33 N	0.15 E
6	Upolu (I.) (ōō′pô-lōō)..Sam. (In.)	13.54 S	171.42 W
173	Upolu Pt..................Haw.	20.17 N	155.50 W
79	Upper Alton (ôl′tŭn)..........Ill.	38.55 N	90.8 W
54	Upper Arrow L............Can.	50.30 N	117.59 W
171	Upper Hutt (hŭt)..........N. Z.	41.7 S	175.5 E
70	Upper Klamath L. (klăm′ȧth) Ore.	42.20 N	121.30 W
70	Upper L...................Calif.	48.0 N	120.19 W
77	Upper Red L..............Minn.	48.6 N	94.45 W
171	Upper Riccarton (rĭk′ȧr-tŭn) N. Z. (In.)	43.31 S	172.34 E
84	Upper Sandusky (săn-dŭs′kê) Ohio	40.50 N	83.22 W
118	Uppingham (ŭp′ĭng-ăm)..Gt. Brit.	52.35 N	0.43 W
120	Uppsala (ōōp′sȧ-lä).........Swe.	59.53 N	17.40 E
87	Upton (ŭp′tŭn).......Mass. (In.)	42.10 N	71.36 W
118	Upton-on-Severn (sĕv′ẽrn) Gt. Brit.	52.4 N	2.13 W
159	Uraga (ōō′rȧ-gȧ). Jap. (Tokyo In.)	35.15 N	139.38 E
159	Uraga Str.......Jap. (Tokyo In.)	35.12 N	139.45 E
148	Ural (Aut. Area) (ōō-räl″) (ū-rôl) Sov. Un.	61.0 N	68.0 E
167	Uralla (û-rä′lȧ)............Austl.	30.38 S	151.31 E
112	Ural Mts..............Sov. Un.	56.0 N	57.45 E
113	Ural R.................Sov. Un.	51.18 N	52.0 E
113	Uralsk (ōō-rȧlsk′).......Sov. Un.	51.10 N	51.29 E
151	Uran (ōō-rän′) India (Bombay In.)	18.53 N	72.57 E
167	Urana (û-rä′nȧ)...........Austl.	35.19 S	146.17 E
167	Urana, L..................Austl.	35.18 S	146.12 E
167	Uranquinty (ū-rȧn-kwĭn′tê). Austl.	35.12 S	147.15 E
159	Urawa (ōō′rä-wä)...........Jap.	35.50 N	139.40 E
131	Urazovo (ōō′rȧ-zô-vô)....Sov. Un.	50.5 N	38.0 E
113	Urbakh (ōōr′bäĸ) ....Sov. Un.	51.12 N	46.55 E
84	Urbana (ûr-băn′ȧ)............Ill.	40.7 N	88.12 W
84	Urbana...................Ohio	40.6 N	83.46 W
128	Urbino (ōōr-bē′nō)............It.	43.44 N	12.37 E
149	Urchur R. (ōōr-chōōr′)...Sov. Un.	57.0 N	132.0 E
113	Urda (Khanskaya Stavka) (ōōr′dȧ) (ĸän′skȧ-yȧ stäf′kȧ)...Sov. Un.	48.48 N	47.40 E
162	Urdaneta (ōōr-dä-nā′tä).....P. I.	15.59 N	120.35 E
148	Urdzhar (ōōrd-zhȧr′) ....Sov. Un.	47.25 N	81.50 E
118	Ure, R. (ûr)............Gt. Brit.	54.8 N	1.30 W
113	Urfa (ōōr′fȧ)..............Tur.	37.12 N	38.50 E
152	Urga (Ulan-Bator-Hoto) (ōōr′gä) (ōō′län-bä′tôr-hô′tô). Chn.	47.56 N	106.55 E
113	Urla (ōōr′lȧ)..............Tur	38.25 N	26.55 E
150	Urmia (Rezaieh) (ōōr′mê-ä) (rĕ-zī′ȧ). Iran	37.34 N	45.7 E
158	Urmi R. (ōōr′mê)........Sov. Un.	48.40 N	134.0 E
119	Urmston (ûrmz′tŭn) Gt. Brit. (Liverpool In.)	53.27 N	2.21 W
130	Urod R. (ōō′rôt) ....Sov. Un.	56.44 N	41.5 E
130	Urshel (ōōr-shĕl′)........Sov. Un.	55.38 N	40.10 E
92	Uruapan (ōō-rōō-ä′pän).....Mex.	19.25 N	101.56 W
102	Urubamba, R. (ōō-rōō-bäm′bä) Peru	11.0 S	73.0 W
104	Uruguaiana (ōō-rōō-gwī-ä′nȧ) Braz.	29.45 S	57.10 W
104	Uruguay (ōō-rōō-gwī′) (ū′rōō-gwā) S. A.	32.45 S	56.0 W
104	Uruguay, R................S. A.	28.0 S	55.30 W
152	Urumchi (Tihwa) (ōō-rōōm′chê) (tī′hwä′). Chn.	43.51 N	87.36 E
150	Urumlyeh (Urmia), L. (ōō-rōōm′′l-yȧ) (ōōr′mê-ä) Iran	37.45 N	45.30 E
167	Urunga (ōō-rōōŋ′gȧ) ....Austl.	30.28 S	153.2 E
152	Urungu R. (ōō-rōōŋ′gōō) ....Chn.	46.15 N	88.30 E
157	Urusan....................Cho.	35.40 N	129.21 E
161	Urville, C. d′ (kāp dúr-vēl′) Neth. Ind.	1.23 S	137.42 E
113	Uryupinskaya (ōōr′yōō-pēn-skä′yȧ) Sov. Un.	50.48 N	42.2 E
112	Urzhum (ōōr′zhōōm) .. Sov. Un.	57.5 N	50.0 E
129	Urziceni (ōōr-zē-chā′nê) ....Rom.	44.42 N	26.31 E
113	Uşak (ōō′shȧk)..............Tur.	38.42 N	29.15 E
140	Usakos (ōō-sä′kōs).....S. W. Afr.	22.5 S	15.40 E
112	Usa R. (ōō′sȧ)..........Sov. Un.	66.30 N	59.0 E
99	Useless B. ..Chl. (Magallanes In.)	53.30 S	69.50 W
159	Ushimado (ōō′shê-mä′dō) ....Jap.	34.36 N	134.9 E
158	Ushoro (ōō-shō′rô)..........Kar.	48.48 N	141.58 E
104	Ushuaia (ōō-shōō-ī′ä)........Arg.	54.50 S	68.28 W
113	Üsküdar (üs′kü-där)..........Tur.	41.0 N	29.10 E
130	Usman (ōōs′mȧn)........Sov. Un.	52.1 N	39.40 E
148	Usol′e (ōō-sô′lyĕ)........Sov. Un.	52.40 N	103.45 E
148	Usol′e..................Sov. Un.	59.35 N	56.55 E
104	Uspallata Pass..........Arg.-Chl.	32.50 S	70.15 W
124	Ussel (üs′ĕl)..................Fr.	45.32 N	2.20 E
158	Ussuri (ōō-sōō′rē).......Sov. Un.	45.1 N	133.1 E
149	Ussuri R. (ōō-sōō′rê) Manch.-Sov. Un.	47.0 N	134.0 E
148	Ust Abakanskoe (ōōst ȧ-bȧ-kän′-skô-yĕ)...Sov. Un.	53.50 N	91.25 E
	Ústí, see Aussig, Ger.		
128	Ustica (I.) (ōōs′tê-kä).........It.	38.42 N	13.10 E
131	Ustinovka (ōōs-tê-nôf′kȧ) Sov. Un.	47.59 N	32.29 E
148	Ust Kamenogorsk (ōōst kȧ-mĕn′ô-gôrsk)...Sov. Un.	50.0 N	82.35 E
112	Ust-Kulom (ōōst-kōō′lŭm) Sov. Un.	61.40 N	53.45 E
152	Ust Kyakhta (Kyakhta) (ōōst kyäĸ′tȧ)..Sov. Un.	50.35 N	105.55 E
149	Ust Maiskaya (ōōst′ mā-ê-skä′yȧ) Sov. Un.	60.30 N	134.30 E
113	Ust-Medveditskaya (ōōst-mĕd-vyĕ′-dêt-skä′yȧ)...Sov. Un.	49.35 N	42.50 E
149	Ust Olemskoe (ōōst ô′lĕm-skô′yĕ-′ Sov. Un.	72.59 N	120.10 E
149	Ust Orda (ōōst′ ôr′dȧ)....Sov. Un.	52.45 N	104.40 E
112	Ust-Sysolsk (Syktyvkar) (ōōst′sê-sôlsk′)..Sov. Un.	61.40 N	50.45 E
112	Ust-Tsylma (tsēl′mȧ)....Sov. Un.	65.29 N	52.28 E
150	Ust Urt Plat. (ōōst′ ōōrt′). Sov. Un.	44.30 N	56.45 E
112	Ust-Usolka (Solikamsk) (ōō-sôl′kȧ) Sov. Un.	59.35 N	56.45 E
149	Ust Yansk (yȧnsk)......Sov. Un.	70.50 N	136.25 E
130	Ustyuzhna (ōōst-yōōzh′nȧ) Sov. Un.	58.48 N	36.21 E
159	Usuki (ōō′sōō-kê) ....Jap.	33.5 N	131.48 E
94	Usulatán (ōō-sōō-lä-tän′).....Sal.	13.22 N	88.24 W
93	Usumacinta, R. (ōō′sōō-mä-sēn′tō) Mex.	17.20 N	91.23 W
140	Usumbura (ōō-sōōm-bōō′rȧ) Bel. Cong.	3.22 S	29.22 E
158	Utsuryo I. (Woolleng).......Jap.	37.31 N	130.52 E
143	Usutu R. (ōō-sōō′tōō) Swaz.-U. S. Afr.	26.38 S	31.20 E
143	Usutu R., Little..Swaz.-U. S. Afr.	26.24 S	31.10 E
143	Usutu (Maputo) R. (mä-pōō′tô) Moz.	26.30 S	32.35 E
75	Utah (State) (ū′tô).........U. S.	39.0 N	111.50 W
75	Utah L....................Utah	40.15 N	111.50 W
78	Ute Cr. (ût)..............N. M.	36.0 N	103.45 W
121	Utena (ōō-tā′nȧ)...........Lith.	55.31 N	25.40 E
141	Utete (ōō-tā′tȧ)............Tan.	8.0 S	38.43 E
85	Utica (ū′tĭ-kȧ).............N. Y.	43.7 N	75.13 W
126	Utiel (ōō-tyål′) ....Sp.	39.35 N	1.13 W
94	Utila I. (ōō′tê-lä)..........Hond.	16.6 N	86.56 W
159	Uto (ōō′tō) ....Jap.	32.45 N	130.43 E
122	Utrecht (ü-trĕĸt′) (ū′trĕkt)..Neth.	52.5 N	5.9 E
143	Utrecht..............U. S. Afr.	27.41 S	30.19 E
126	Utrera (ōō-trā′rä)............Sp.	37.12 N	5.46 W
120	Utsire (I.) (ōōt-sē′rĕ)........Nor.	59.20 N	4.52 E
159	Utsunomiya (ōōt′sōō-nô-mē′yȧ) Jap.	36.31 N	139.47 E
160	Uttara (ōō′tä-rä) ....Thai.	17.35 N	102.50 E
118	Uttoxeter (ŭt-tôk′sê-tẽr) .Gt. Brit.	52.54 N	1.52 W
91	Utuado (ōō-tōō-ä′dhō) .P. R. (In.)	18.15 N	66.40 W
121	Uusikaupunki (Nystad) (ōō′sĭ-kou-pōōŋ-kĭ) (nü′städh). Fin.	60.49 N	21.28 E
80	Uvalde (û-văl′dê)...........Tex.	29.13 N	99.48 W
140	Uvira (ōō-vē′rä).......Bel. Cong.	3.28 S	29.3 E
159	Uwajima (ōō′wä-jē′mä)......Jap.	33.15 N	132.31 E
87	Uxbridge (ŭks′brĭj) ...Mass. (In.)	42.4 N	71.38 W
102	Uyuni (ōō-yōō′nê)............Bol.	19.29 S	66.48 W
148	Uzbek (Sov. Rep.) (ōōz′bĕk) Sov. Un.	40.30 N	69.0 E
113	Uzen R., Great (ōō′zĕn) .Sov. Un.	49.45 N	49.30 E
124	Uzès (ü-zĕs′)..................Fr.	44.2 N	4.25 E
	Užhorod, see Ungvár, Hung.		
131	Uzh R. (ōōzh)..........Sov. Un.	51.0 N	28.45 E
129	Užice (ōō′zhĭ-tsĕ)..........Yugo.	43.51 N	19.51 E
169	Uzunga (ōō-zōōŋ′gȧ) ..Austl. (In.)	30.27 S	153.3 E
129	Uzunköprü (ōō′zōōn-kû′prü)..Tur.	41.15 N	26.41 E
120	Vaads (I.) (vôds)............Nor.	61.58 N	5.5 E
143	Vaal R. (väl)..........U. S. Afr.	26.55 S	27.0 E
121	Vaasa (vä′sȧ)................Fin.	63.5 N	21.40 E
123	Vac (väts)................Hung.	47.47 N	19.10 E
97	Vache I. (väsh)..............Hai.	18.4 N	73.40 W
112	Vadsö (vädhs′û).............Nor.	70.5 N	29.45 E
120	Vadstena (vôd′stĭn′ȧ)........Swe.	58.27 N	14.55 E
122	Vaduz (vä′dōōts)..........Liech.	47.9 N	9.32 E
112	Vaga R. (vä′gȧ).........Sov. Un.	61.20 N	42.30 E
123	Vágfarkasd (Farkašd) (väg′fär-käsht) (fär′käsht). Hung.	42.2 N	17.56 E
126	Vagos (vä′gōzh).............Port.	40.33 N	8.41 W
123	Váh R. (väĸ)...............Czech.	49.16 N	18.40 E
112	Vaigach I. (vī-gȧch′).....Sov. Un.	70.0 N	59.30 E
148	Vakh R. (vȧĸ)...........Sov. Un.	60.30 N	82.10 E
131	Vâlcov (vûl′kôv).............Rom.	45.25 N	29.36 E
130	Valdai (vȧl-dī′)...........Sov. Un.	57.58 N	33.12 E
130	Valdai Hills............Sov. Un.	57.35 N	33.0 E
120	Valdemarsvik (väl′dĭ-märs-vēk′) Swe.	58.12 N	16.41 E
127	Valdemorillo (väl-dȧ-mô-rēl′yō) Sp. (In.)	40.30 N	4.5 W
126	Valdepeñas (väl-dȧ-pān′yäs)...Sp.	38.46 N	3.22 W
163	Valderrama (väl-dĕr-rä′mä) ..P. I.	11.0 N	122.7 E
72	Valdes I. (vȧl′dĕs) Can. (Vancouver In.)	49.5 N	123.39 W
53	Valdez (văl′dĕz)............Alsk.	61.5 N	146.5 W
104	Valdez Pen. (väl′dåz)........Arg.	42.30 S	64.0 W
127	Valdilecha (väl-dê-lā′chä) Sp. (In.)	40.17 N	3.18 W
104	Valdivia (väl-dē′vê-ä).......Chl.	39.45 S	73.10 W
82	Valdosta (văl-dŏs′tȧ).........Ga.	30.50 N	83.18 W
126	Valdovino (väl-dô-vē′nō)......Sp.	43.36 N	8.6 W
70	Vale (vāl)..................Ore.	43.59 N	117.15 W
103	Valença (vä-lĕɴ′sȧ) ....Braz. (In.)	13.20 S	39.6 W
99	Valença. Braz. (Rio de Janeiro In.)	22.13 S	43.44 W
126	Valença....................Port.	42.2 N	8.38 W
124	Valence (vȧ-läɴs′).............Fr.	44.55 N	4.55 E
163	Valencia (vä-lĕn′syä)........P. I.	9.37 N	124.13 E
126	Valencia (vä-lĕn′thê-ä)........Sp.	39.25 N	7.15 W
127	Valencia....................Sp.	39.28 N	0.22 W
127	Valencia (Prov.).............Sp.	39.30 N	0.40 W
102	Valencia (vä-lĕn′syä)........Ven.	10.12 N	68.1 W
116	Valencia I. (vȧ-lĕn′shȧ).......Ire.	51.55 N	9.25 W
124	Valenciennes (vȧ-läɴ-syĕn′)....Fr.	50.25 N	3.5 E
125	Valentigny (vȧ-läɴ-tê-nyē′)....Fr.	47.30 N	6.50 E
76	Valentine (văl′ĕn-tīn)........Neb.	42.52 N	100.33 W
102	Valera (vä-lā′rä)............Ven.	9.15 N	70.30 W
95	Valientes, C. (vä-lyĕn′tås)....Pan.	9.10 N	81.55 W
71	Valier (vă-lēr′).............Mont.	48.17 N	112.15 W
129	Valjevo (väl′yȧ-vō) ....Yugo.	44.17 N	19.54 E
121	Valka (wäl′kä)..............Est.	57.46 N	26.1 E
131	Valki (väl′kê)...........Sov. Un.	49.48 N	35.39 E
126	Valladolid (väl-yä-dhô-lēdh′) ..Sp.	41.40 N	4.41 W
125	Vallauris (vȧl-lô-rēs′) ....Fr.	43.35 N	7.1 E
127	Vall de Uxó (väl dā ōō-ĸô′) ....Sp.	39.50 N	0.15 W
127	Valldigna (väl-dēn′yä)........Sp.	39.5 N	0.17 W
74	Valle, Arroyo del (ä-rō′yō dĕl väl′yā). Calif.	37.35 N	121.40 W
127	Vallecas (väl-yä′kås).....Sp. (In.)	40.23 N	3.38 W
80	Valle de Allende (väl′yā dā äl-yĕn′-dā). Mex.	26.55 N	105.25 W
92	Valle de Bravo (väl′yā dā brä′vô) Mex.	19.12 N	100.7 W
92	Valle de Santiago (väl′yā dā sän-tê-ä′gō). Mex.	20.23 N	101.11 W
102	Valledupar (väl′yā-dōō-pär′)..Col.	10.2 N	73.30 W
102	Vallegrande (väl-yā-grän′dā)..Bol.	18.33 S	64.15 W
163	Vallehermoso (väl′yȧ-ĕr-mō′sō) P. I.	10.19 N	123.19 E
74	Vallejo (väl-yā′hō) (vă-lā′hō) Calif.	38.6 N	122.15 W
104	Vallenar (väl-yȧ-när′)........Chl.	28.40 S	70.50 W
7	Valletta (väl-lĕt′ä)....Malta (In.)	35.55 N	14.29 E
73	Valley Cr. (văl′ê) Ala. (Birmingham In.)	33.28 N	87.10 W
76	Valley City...............N. D.	46.56 N	98.0 W
79	Valley Falls................Kan.	39.21 N	95.27 W
55	Valleyfield (văl′ê-fēld).......Can.	45.18 N	74.0 W
97	Vallière (väl-yâr′).....Dom. Rep.	19.28 N	71.54 W
127	Valls (väls)..................Sp.	41.16 N	1.12 E
121	Valmiera (vȧl′myĕ-rȧ).......Lat.	57.34 N	25.25 E
72	Valmont (văl′mŏnt) Colo. (Denver In.)	40.2 N	105.12 W
124	Valognes (vȧ-lôn′y′)..........Fr.	49.30 N	1.25 W
57	Valois (vȧ-lwä′) Can. (Montreal In.)	45.27 N	73.48 W
129	Valona (Vlonë) (vä-lō′nä) (vlō′nā). Alb.	40.28 N	19.30 E
104	Valparaíso (väl′pä-rä-ē′sō)....Chl.	33.0 S	71.40 W
84	Valparaiso (văl-pȧ-rā′zō).....Ind.	41.28 N	87.2 W
92	Valparaíso (väl′pä-rä-ē′sō)...Mex.	22.58 N	103.38 W
124	Valréas (vȧl-rā-ä′)............Fr.	44.25 N	4.59 E
161	Valsch, C. (välsk)......Neth. Ind.	8.25 S	137.40 E
143	Valsch R. (välsh).......U. S. Afr.	28.30 N	26.45 E
131	Valuiki (vȧ-lōō-ē′kē).....Sov. Un.	50.13 N	38.5 E
73	Val Verde (văl vûr′dê) Calif. (Los Angeles In.)	33.50 N	117.15 W
126	Valverde (väl-vĕr′dā).........Sp.	37.35 N	6.46 W
113	Van (vȧn)..................Tur.	38.32 N	43.18 E
79	Van Buren (văn bū′rĕn)......Ark.	35.25 N	94.21 W
86	Van Buren...................Me.	47.9 N	67.58 W
84	Vanceburg (văns′bûrg).......Ky.	38.36 N	83.20 W
56	Vancouver.............Can. (In.)		
70	Vancouver (văn-kōō′vẽr)....Can.	49.16 N	123.5 W
70	Vancouver................Wash.	45.37 N	122.40 W
70	Vancouver I...............Can.	48.52 N	124.0 W
79	Vandalia (văn-dā′lĭ-ȧ)........Ill.	38.57 N	89.6 W
79	Vandalia....................Mo.	39.17 N	91.30 W
164	Van Diemen, C. (văn dē′mĕn) Austl.	11.5 S	130.29 E
164	Van Diemen G............Austl.	12.0 S	132.0 E
73	Vandiver (văn′dĭ-vẽr) Ala. (Birmingham In.)	33.28 N	86.31 W
110	Vandö (I.) (vänd′û).........Nor.	70.10 N	19.45 E
120	Väner, L. (vĕ′nẽr)...........Swe.	59.0 N	13.0 E
120	Vänersborg (vĕ′nẽrs-bôr′)....Swe.	58.23 N	12.18 E
141	Vanga (väŋ′gä)...........Kenya	4.38 S	39.10 E
119	Vange (văn′jê) Gt. Brit. (London In.)	51.33 N	0.28 E
113	Van, L. (vȧn)...............Tur.	38.45 N	43.0 E
84	Van Lear (văn lēr′)..........Ky.	37.45 N	82.50 W
124	Vannes (vȧn).................Fr.	47.40 N	2.45 W
142	Van Rhyn's Dorp (vȧn rīnz′ dôrp). U. S. Afr.	31.36 S	18.42 E
6	Vanua Levu (I.) (vä′nōō-ä lā′vōō) Fiji Is. (In.)	16.54 S	178.48 E
84	Van Wert (văn wûrt′).......Ohio	40.50 N	84.38 W
142	Van Wyk's Vlei (vȧn wīks′ vlī) U. S. Afr.	30.21 S	21.50 E
72	Van Zandt (văn zănt′) Wash. (Vancouver In.)	48.48 N	122.12 W
120	Vara (vä′rä)...............Swe.	58.18 N	12.56 E
128	Varallo (vä-räl′lō)............It.	45.46 N	8.16 E
110	Varanger Fjord (vä-räng′gẽr fyôr′). Nor.	69.55 N	30.30 E
128	Varano, L. of (vä-rä′nô).......It.	41.53 N	15.45 E
128	Varaždin (vä′räzh-dên) .....Yugo.	46.19 N	16.21 E
128	Varazze (vä-rät′sä)...........It.	44.22 N	8.37 E
120	Varberg (vär′bĕr′)..........Swe.	57.6 N	12.16 E

ăt; finȧl; rāte; senâte; ärm; ȧsk; sofȧ; fâre; ch-choose; dh-as th in other; bē; êvent; bĕt; recĕnt; cratẽr; g-go; gh-gutteral g; bĭt; ĭ-short neutral; rīde; ĸ-gutteral k as ch in German ich

Page	Name Pronunciation	Region	Lat. °′	Long. °′
129	Vardar R. (vär-där′)	Yugo.	41.33 N	22.0 E
120	Varde (vär′dě)	Den.	55.38 N	8.30 E
120	Varde R.	Den.	55.45 N	8.40 E
112	Vardö (värd′û)	Nor.	70.25 N	31.0 E
121	Varena (vä-rā′nȧ)	Lith.	54.16 N	24.32 E
57	Varennes (vȧ-rĕn′)	Can. (In.)	45.41 N	73.25 W
129	Vareš (vä′rĕsh)	Yugo.	44.11 N	18.21 E
128	Varese (vä-rā′sā)	It.	45.48 N	8.50 E
121	Varkaus (vär′kous)	Fin.	62.20 N	27.57 E
121	Varklāni (värk′lā-nê)	Lat.	56.36 N	26.48 E
129	Varna (vär′nȧ)	Bul.	43.12 N	27.56 E
120	Värnamo (vĕr′nȧ-mô)	Swe.	57.10 N	14.3 E
...	Varnsdorf, see Warnsdorf, Ger.			
83	Varnville (värn′vĭl)	S. C.	32.51 N	81.4 W
128	Varoš (vä′rôsh)	Yugo.	44.37 N	17.23 E
121	Värtsilä (vĕrt′sē-lĕ)	Fin.	62.10 N	30.40 E
131	Varvaropolie (vȧr′vȧr-ô-pô′lyĕ)	Sov. Un.	48.37 N	38.35 E
123	Văscăuti (vĕs-kĕ-ōōts′′)	Rom.	48.21 N	25.34 E
126	Vascongadas (Prov.) (väs-kôn-gä′däs)	Sp.	43.5 N	2.35 W
112	Vashka R. (vȧsh′kȧ)	Sov. Un.	64.15 N	47.20 E
49	Vashon (văsh′ŭn)	Wash. (In.)	47.26 N	122.27 W
49	Vashon I.	Wash. (In.)	47.25 N	122.30 W
150	Vasht (väsht)	Iran	28.17 N	61.2 E
131	Vasilkov (vȧ-sêl′-kôf′)	Sov. Un.	50.10 N	30.21 E
123	Vaslui (vȧs-lōō′ê)	Rom.	46.39 N	27.43 E
84	Vassar (văs′ẽr)	Mich.	43.23 N	83.35 W
99	Vassouras (väs-sō′räzh)	Braz. (Rio de Janeiro In.)	22.25 S	43.41 W
120	Västanfors (vĕst′ȧn-fôrs)	Swe.	59.59 N	15.50 E
120	Västerås (vĕs′tĕr-ôs)	Swe.	59.38 N	16.30 E
120	Västervik (vĕs′tĕr-vēk)	Swe.	57.46 N	16.38 E
128	Vasto (väs′tō)	It.	42.6 N	14.41 E
148	Vasyugan R. (vȧs-yōō-gȧn′)	Sov. Un.	59.20 N	78.0 E
129	Vathy (vä′thê)	Grc.	37.45 N	26.59 E
128	Vatican City (Città del Vaticano) (văt′ĭ-kăn sĭt′ê) (chē-tȧ′del vä-tê-kä′nō)	It.	41.53 N	12.28 E
128	Vaticano, C. (vä-tê-kä′nō)	It.	38.37 N	15.50 E
110	Vatna-Jökull (Klofa-Jökull) (Glacier) (vät-nȧ-yû′kool) (klō′fȧ-yû′kool)	Ice.	64.30 N	16.45 W
123	Vatra Dornei (vät′rȧ dôr′nĕ-ê)	Rom.	47.23 N	25.30 E
120	Vätter, L. (vĕt′ẽr)	Swe.	58.20 N	14.30 E
85	Vaudreuil (vô-drû′y′)	Can.	45.24 N	74.2 W
78	Vaughn (vôn)	N. M.	34.36 N	105.13 W
49	Vaughn	Wash. (Seattle In.)	47.21 N	122.46 W
125	Vaujours (vô-zhōōr′)	Fr. (In.)	48.56 N	2.35 E
120	Vaxholm (väks′hōlm)	Swe.	59.25 N	18.20 E
120	Växjö (vĕks′shû)	Swe.	56.53 N	14.48 E
120	Veblungsnaes (vib′loongs-nĕs)	Nor.	62.33 N	7.44 E
121	Vecgulbene (vĕts′gool′bĕ-nĕ)	Lat.	57.9 N	26.49 E
90	Vedado (vȧ-dhä′dhō)	Cuba (Habana In.)	23.9 N	82.24 W
72	Vedder Crossing (vĕd′ẽr)	Can. (Vancouver In.)	49.5 N	121.58 W
129	Vedea R. (vȧ′dyȧ)	Rom.	44.20 N	24.45 E
84	Veedersburg (vē′dẽrz-bûrg)	Ind.	40.5 N	87.16 W
49	Vega (vā′gȧ)	Wash. (Seattle In.)	47.7 N	122.42 W
93	Vega de Alatorre (vā′gä dā ä-lä-tōr′rȧ)	Mex.	20.2 N	96.40 W
97	Vega Real (Mts.) (vā′gä rā-äl′)	Hai.	19.20 N	70.40 W
110	Vegen (I.) (vȧgh′ĕn)	Nor.	65.37 N	11.55 E
99	Veinticinco de Mayo (vȧ-ēn′tê-sēŋ′kō dā mä′yō)	Arg. (Buenos Aires In.)	35.23 S	60.10 W
127	Vejer de la Frontera (vā-κĕr′ dā lä frôn-tā′rä)	Sp. (In.)	36.15 N	5.57 W
120	Vejle (vī′lĕ)	Den.	55.40 N	9.30 E
	Vejprty, see Weipert, Ger.			
128	Velebit Mts. (vā′lĕ-bêt)	Yugo.	44.25 N	15.20 E
129	Veles (vā′lĕs)	Yugo.	41.42 N	21.49 E
126	Vélez Blanco (vā′lāth bläŋ′kō)	Sp.	37.42 N	2.5 W
126	Vélez de la Gomera I. (dā lä gô-mā′rä)	Mor.	35.12 N	4.18 W
126	Vélez-Málaga (vā′lāth-mä′lä-gä)	Sp.	36.47 N	4.5 W
126	Vélez Rubio (vā′lāth rōō′bê-ō)	Sp.	37.39 N	2.5 W
129	Velika Kikinda (vȧ-lē′kȧ kê-kēn′dȧ)	Yugo.	45.48 N	20.29 E
130	Velikaya R. (vȧ-lē′kȧ-yȧ)	Sov. Un.	57.30 N	28.10 E
129	Veliki Beckerek (vȧ-lē′kê bĕch′kȧ-rĕk)	Yugo.	45.22 N	20.25 E
130	Velikie Luki (vȧ-lē′kyĕ lōō′kê)	Sov. Un.	56.19 N	30.32 E
112	Veliki Ustyug (vȧ-lē′kyĕ ōōs-tyoog′)	Sov. Un.	60.45 N	46.15 E
130	Velikoe (vȧ-lē′kô-yĕ)	Sov. Un.	57.18 N	39.45 E
130	Velikoe, L.	Sov. Un.	55.12 N	40.8 E
130	Velikoe, L.	Sov. Un.	56.58 N	36.35 E
123	Veliký Bočkov (vĕl′ê-kê bôch′kôf)	Czech.	47.59 N	24.2 E
130	Velizh (vȧ-lēzh′)	Sov. Un.	55.37 N	31.10 E
122	Velké Mezříčí (vĕl′kā mĕz′ê-rē-chē)	Czech.	49.22 N	16.1 E
165	Vella Lavella I. (väl′yä lä-väl′yä)	Solomon Is.	7.45 S	156.30 E
7	Vellas (vä′läzh)	Az. Is. (In.)	38.41 N	28.12 W
128	Velletri (vĕl-lā′trē)	It.	41.42 N	12.47 E
151	Vellore (vĕl-lōr′)	India	12.46 N	79.8 E
117	Velsen (vĕl′sĕn)	Neth.	52.28 N	4.40 E
112	Velsk (vĕlsk)	Sov. Un.	61.5 N	42.10 E
124	Venaco (vȧ-nä′kō)	Cor. (In.)	42.30 N	9.22 E
92	Venado (vȧ-nä′dō)	Mex.	22.55 N	101.5 W
125	Vence (väNs)	Fr.	43.45 N	7.5 E
124	Vendôme (väN-dōm′)	Fr.	47.45 N	1.5 E
127	Vendrell (vĕn-dräl′)	Sp.	41.14 N	1.31 E
128	Venetian Alps (Mts.) (vĕ-nē′shăn ălps)	It.	46.5 N	12.30 E
130	Venev (vĕn-ĕf′)	Sov. Un.	54.19 N	38.10 E
128	Venezia (Prov.) (vä-nĕt′sê-ä)	It.	45.50 N	12.0 E
128	Venezia (Venice) (vĕn′ĭs)	It.	45.26 N	12.20 E
102	Venezuela (vĕn-ê-zwē′lȧ)	S. A.	8.0 N	65.0 W
102	Venezuela, G. of	Ven.	11.30 N	71.0 W
73	Venice (vĕn′ĭs)	Calif. (Los Angeles In.)	33.58 N	118.27 W
89	Venice	Ill. (St. Louis In.)	38.40 N	90.10 W
128	Venice (Venezia) (vā-nĕt′sê ä)	It.	45.26 N	12.20 E
89	Venice	La. (New Orleans In.)	29.17 N	89.22 W
128	Venice, G. of	It.	45.20 N	13.0 E
121	Venta R. (vĕn′tȧ)	Lat.	57.4 N	21.45 E
143	Ventersdorp (vĕn′tērs-dôrp)	U. S. Afr.	26.19 S	26.49 E
143	Venterskroon (vĕn′tērs-krōn)	U. S. Afr.	26.52 S	27.15 E
143	Venterstad (vĕn-tēr-shtät)	U. S. Afr.	30.48 S	25.46 E
128	Ventimiglia (vĕn-tê-mēl′yä)	It.	43.47 N	7.37 E
85	Ventnor (vĕnt′nẽr)	N. J.	39.20 N	74.30 W
121	Ventspils (vĕnt′spêls)	Lat.	57.24 N	21.36 E
74	Ventura (vĕn-tōō′rȧ)	Calif.	34.17 N	119.19 W
102	Ventuari, R. (vĕn-tōō-ä′rê)	Ven.	5.0 N	66.28 W
126	Vera (vā′rä)	Sp.	37.14 N	1.51 W
93	Veracruz (vā-rä-krōōz′)	Mex.	19.10 N	96.10 W
92	Veracruz (State)	Mex.	19.0 N	96.20 W
151	Veraval (vĕr-ŭ′väl)	India	21.10 N	70.12 E
131	Verbki (vĕrp′kê)	Sov. Un.	48.37 N	35.52 E
128	Vercelli (vĕr-chĕl′lē)	It.	45.18 N	8.25 E
57	Verchères (vĕr-shâr′)	Can. (In.)	45.47 N	73.21 W
138	Verde, C. (vûrd) (vĕr′dȧ)	Fr. W. Afr.	14.42 N	12.30 W
97	Verde C. (South Pt.)	Ba. Is.	22.50 N	74.52 W
97	Verde, Cay (I.)	Ba. Is.	22.3 N	75.11 W
162	Verde I. (vĕr′dā)	P. I.	13.33 N	121.4 E
122	Verden (fĕr′dĕn)	Ger.	52.57 N	9.15 E
75	Verde R. (vûrd)	Ariz.	34.5 N	111.40 W
93	Verde, R. (vĕr′dā)	Mex.	16.20 N	97.10 W
92	Verde, R.	Mex.	21.2 N	102.43 W
92	Verde, R.	Mex.	21.40 N	99.46 W
79	Verdigris R. (vûr′dê-grēs)	Okla.	36.40 N	95.34 W
162	Verdi Island Passage (vĕr′dē)	P. I.	13.35 N	120.50 E
124	Verdun (vĕr-dŭN′)	Fr.	49.10 N	5.22 E
79	Vere, Bayou de (bī′yōō dê vēr′)	Ark.	35.25 N	91.0 W
143	Vereeniging (vĕ-rā′nĭ-gĭng)	U. S. Afr.	26.41 S	27.59 E
76	Verendrye Natl. Mon. (vē-räN-drē′)	N. D.	47.57 N	102.32 W
130	Vereya (vĕ-rȧ′yȧ)	Sov. Un.	55.21 N	36.9 E
126	Vergara (vĕr-gä′rä)	Sp.	43.8 N	2.25 W
126	Verín (vȧ-rēn′)	Sp.	41.57 N	7.25 W
131	Verkhnee (vyĕrκ′nyĕ)	Sov. Un.	48.54 N	38.25 E
149	Verkne Kamchatsk (vyĕrκ′nyĕ kȧm-chȧtsk′)	Sov. Un.	54.30 N	158.30 E
149	Verkhne Kol-ymsk (kôl-êmsk′)	Sov. Un.	65.35 N	151.0 E
149	Verkhneudinsk (Ulan Ude (vyĕrk′nye-ōō-dênsk′)	Sov. Un.	51.55 N	107.30 E
148	Verkne-Uralsk (ōō-rȧlsk′)	Sov. Un.	53.55 N	59.20 E
149	Verkholensk (vyĕr-κô-lyĕnsk′)	Sov. Un.	54.15 N	105.40 E
149	Verkhoyansk (vyĕr-κô-yänsk′)	Sov. Un.	67.30 N	133.30 E
149	Verkhoyanski Ridge	Sov. Un.	64.30 N	130.0 E
149	Verkon R. (vyĕr′kôn)	Sov. Un.	68.30 N	174.0 E
142	Verloren R. (vĕr-lō′rĕn)	U. S. Afr.	32.30 S	18.35 E
54	Vermilion (vẽr-mĭl′yŭn)	Can.	53.26 N	111.0 W
81	Vermilion B.	La.	29.40 N	92.0 W
77	Vermilion L.	Minn.	47.51 N	92.20 W
86	Vermilion R.	Can.	47.25 N	73.20 W
79	Vermilion R.	Ill.	41.0 N	88.46 W
77	Vermilion R.	Minn.	48.5 N	92.30 W
76	Vermilion R.	S. D.	43.20 N	97.0 W
76	Vermillion	S. D.	42.48 N	96.55 W
86	Vermont (State) (vẽr-mŏnt′)	U. S.	43.50 N	72.46 W
75	Vernal (vûr′nȧl)	Utah	40.27 N	109.35 W
124	Verneuil (vĕr-nû′y′)	Fr.	48.45 N	0.59 E
142	Verneuk Pan (L.) (vĕr-nûk′)	U. S. Afr.	29.58 S	21.9 E
54	Vernon (vûr′nŭn)	Can.	50.12 N	119.15 W
124	Vernon (vĕr-nôN′)	Fr.	49.5 N	1.31 E
84	Vernon (vûr′nŭn)	Ind.	39.0 N	85.40 W
78	Vernon	Tex.	34.9 N	99.16 W
148	Verny (Alma Ata) (vyĕr′nê) (äl′′mȧ ȧ′tȧ)	Sov. Un.	43.30 N	77.0 E
83	Vero Beach (vē′rô)	Fla. (In.)	27.37 N	80.25 W
128	Verona (vā-rō′nä)	It.	45.27 N	11.0 E
89	Verona (vê-rō′nȧ)	Pa. (Pittsburgh In.)	40.30 N	79.51 W
70	Veronia (vê-rō′nĭ-ȧ)	Wash.	46.2 N	122.53 W
119	Verrebroek (vĕr′rĕ-brook)	Bel. (Anvers In.)	51.15 N	4.11 E
125	Verrières-le-Buisson (vĕr-yâr′ lē-bwē-sôN′)	Fr. (In.)	48.45 N	2.16 E
129	Verroia (vĕr-rē′ä)	Grc.	40.31 N	22.12 E
125	Versailles (vĕr-sī′y′)	Fr. (In.)	48.47 N	2.8 E
84	Versailles (vẽr-sālz′)	Ky.	38.4 N	84.45 W
79	Versailles	Mo.	38.25 N	92.51 W
86	Verte, B. (vûrt)	Can.	46.2 N	63.55 W
143	Verulam (vĕr′oo-lăm)	U. S. Afr.	29.39 S	31.2 E
117	Verviers (vĕr-vyā′)	Bel.	50.35 N	5.50 E
136	Ves′egonsk (vyĕ-syĕ-gônsk′)	Sov. Un.	58.40 N	37.15 E
131	Veseloe (vyĕ′sĕ-lô-yĕ)	Sov. Un.	46.59 N	34.55 E
125	Vesoul (vē-sōōl′)	Fr.	47.40 N	6.11 E
110	Vester Aalen (Is.) (vĕs′tĕr ô′lĕn)	Nor.	68.50 N	15.30 E
120	Vester Dal R. (vĕs′tĕr däl)	Swe.	61.0 N	13.20 E
110	Vestmannaeyjar (vĕst′män-ä-ā′yär)	Ice.	63.20 N	20.16 W
112	Vestnik I. (vyĕst′nêk)	Sov. Un.	69.28 N	54.50 E
128	Vesuvius (Vol.) (vê-sū′vê-ŭs)	It.	40.49 N	14.23 E
123	Veszprém (vĕs′prām)	Hung.	47.4 N	17.53 E
123	Vesztő (vĕs′tû)	Hung.	46.55 N	21.17 E
130	Vetka (vyĕt′kȧ)	Sov. Un.	52.35 N	31.8 E
120	Vetlanda (vĕt-län′dä)	Swe.	57.27 N	15.5 E
112	Vetluga (vyĕt-lōō′gȧ)	Sov. Un.	57.50 N	45.45 E
129	Vetovo (vā tô-vô)	Bul.	43.40 N	26.16 E
143	Vet. R. (vĕt)	U. S. Afr.	28.10 S	26.30 E
129	Vetren (vĕt′rĕn′)	Bul.	42.16 N	24.3 E
84	Vevay (vē′vā)	Ind.	38.45 N	85.4 W
122	Vevey (vē-vā′)	Switz.	46.28 N	6.52 E
125	Veynes (vĕn′)	Fr.	44.32 N	5.48 E
124	Vézère R. (vā-zâr′)	Fr.	45.0 N	1.0 E
128	Viadana (vê-ä-dä′nä)	It.	44.56 N	10.32 E
79	Vian (vī′ăn)	Okla.	35.30 N	94.58 W
126	Viana del Bollo (vê-ä′nä dĕl bôl′yô)	Sp.	42.12 N	7.8 W
126	Viana do Alentejo (vê-ä′nȧ dōō ä-lĕN-tā′hōō)	Port.	38.21 N	8.1 W
126	Viana do Castelo (vê-ä′nȧ dōō käs-tā′lōō)	Port.	41.41 N	8.50 W
103	Vianna (vê-än′nȧ)	Braz.	3.15 S	44.35 W
128	Viannos (vyä′nôs)	Grc.	35.3 N	25.23 E
126	Viara R. (vê-ä′rä)	Sp.	37.50 N	5.55 W
128	Viareggio (vê-ä-rĕd′jô)	It.	43.53 N	10.16 E
90	Vibora, Cerro (Mt.) (vê-bō′rä)	Cuba (Habana In.)	23.7 N	82.22 W
120	Viborg (vē′bôr′)	Den.	56.27 N	9.24 E
121	Viborg (Viipuri) (vē′pōō-rĭ)	Fin.	60.44 N	28.42 E
127	Vicálvaro (vê-käl′vä-rō)	Sp. (In.)	40.25 N	3.37 W
128	Vicenza (vê-chĕnt′sä)	It.	45.33 N	11.31 E
127	Vich (vēch)	Sp.	41.56 N	2.15 E
112	Vichegda R (vē-chĕg′dȧ)	Sov. Un.	62.10 N	49.0 E
130	Vichuga (vē-chōō′gȧ)	Sov. Un.	57.0 N	41.0 E
124	Vichy (vê-shē′)	Fr.	46.8 N	3.29 E
84	Vicksburg (vĭks′bûrg)	Mich.	42.10 N	85.32 W
82	Vicksburg	Miss.	32.20 N	90.54 W
119	Vico Equense (vē′kô ā-kwĕn′sȧ)	It. (Napoli In.)	40.40 N	14.26 E
72	Victor (vĭk′tēr)	Colo. (Colo. Sprs. In.)	38.43 N	105.8 W
166	Victor Harbor	Austl.	35.32 S	138.38 E
166	Victoria (State) (vĭk-tō′rĭ-ȧ)	Austl.	37.0 S	145.0 E
103	Victoria (vêk-tō′rĭ-ȧ)	Braz.	20.15 S	40.28 W
70	Victoria (vĭk-tō′rĭ-ȧ)	Can.	48.25 N	123.21 W
154	Victoria	Hong Kong	22.18 N	114.5 E
138	Victoria	Nig.	4.3 N	9.16 E
162	Victoria	P. I.	15.34 N	120.41 E
140	Victoria	S. Rh.	20.10 S	30.45 E
81	Victoria	Tex.	28.47 N	97.0 E
83	Victoria	Va.	36.58 N	78.13 W
142	Victoria B.	U. S. Afr.	34.2 S	22.35 E
96	Victoria de las Tunas (vêk-tō′rê-ä dā läs tōō′näs)	Cuba	20.56 N	77.2 W
140	Victoria Falls (vĭk-tō′rĭ-ȧ)	S. Rh.	17.55 S	25.50 E
99	Victoria I. (vêk-tō′rê-ȧ)	Braz. (Rio de Janeiro In.)	23.49 S	45.9 W
54	Victoria I. (vĭk-tō′rĭ-ȧ)	Can.	70.10 N	109.0 W
140	Victoria, L.	Afr.	1.0 S	33.0 E
166	Victoria L.	Austl.	34.0 S	141.15 E
167	Victoria L.	Austl.	38.0 S	147.35 E
6	Victoria, Mt.	Fiji Is. (In.)	17.33 S	178.4 E
169	Victoria Park	Austl. (Perth In.)	31.58 S	115.55 E
94	Victoria Peak	Br. Hond. (In.)	16.46 N	88.40 W
163	Victoria Peaks	P. I.	9.23 N	118.18 E
164	Victoria R.	Austl.	16.0 S	131.10 E
164	Victoria River Downs	Austl.	16.30 S	130.58 E
54	Victoria Str.	Can.	69.0 N	101.0 W
86	Victoriaville (vĭk-tō′rĭ-ȧ-vĭl)	Can.	46.3 N	71.58 W
142	Victoria West	U. S. Afr.	31.25 S	23.5 E
102	Victorino (vêk-tō-rē′nō)	Col.	2.45 N	67.35 W
83	Vidalia (vĭ-dā′lĭ-ȧ)	Ga.	32.12 N	82.16 W
81	Vidalia	La.	31.33 N	91.27 W
129	Vidin (vĭ′dên)	Bul.	43.59 N	22.52 E
104	Viedma (vyād′mä)	Arg.	41.0 S	63.0 W
104	Viedma, L.	Arg.	49.32 S	72.30 W
94	Viejo, El (Vol.) (vyā′hō)	Nic.	12.42 N	87.0 W
94	Viejo. R.	Nic.	12.50 N	86.15 W
122	Vienna (Wien)	Aus.	48.14 N	16.20 E
82	Vienna (vê-ĕn′ȧ)	Ga.	32.4 N	83.51 W
79	Vienna	Ill.	37.25 N	88.54 W
124	Vienne (vyĕn′)	Fr.	45.31 N	4.52 E
124	Vienne R.	Fr.	47.5 N	0.15 W
160	Vientiane (vyĕN′tyän′)	Fr. Ind. Chn.	18.8 N	102.38 E
91	Vieques (vyā′käs)	P. R. (In.)	18.8 N	65.26 W
91	Vieques I.	P. R.	18.8 N	65.22 W
143	Vierfontein (vēr′fôn-tān)	U. S. Afr.	27.5 S	26.44 E
119	Viersel (vēr′zĕl)	Bel. (Anvers In.)	51.12 N	4.39 E
124	Vierzon-Forges (vyâr-zôN′-fôrzh′)	Fr.	47.15 N	2.8 E
124	Vierzon-Village (vyâr-zôN′ vê-lȧzh′)	Fr.	47.18 N	2.5 E
124	Vierzon-Ville (vyâr-zôN′vēl′)	Fr.	47.15 N	2.5 E
80	Viesca (vê-ās′kä)	Mex.	25.20 N	102.48 W
80	Viesca L.	Mex.	25.30 N	102.45 W
128	Vieste (vyĕs′tȧ)	It.	41.52 N	16.10 E
162	Viga (vē′gä)	P. I.	13.52 N	124.19 E
162	Vigan (vē′gän)	P. I.	17.34 N	120.23 E
128	Vigevano (vê-jȧ-vä′nō)	It.	45.18 N	8.51 E
103	Vigia (vê-zhē′ȧ)	Braz. (In.)	0.51 S	48.8 W
112	Vig, L. (vēk)	Sov. Un.	63.40 N	35.45 E
125	Vigny (vên-yē′)	Fr. (In.)	49.3 N	1.55 E
126	Vigo (vē′gō)	Sp.	42.14 N	8.44 W
121	Vihti (vē′tĭ)	Fin.	60.28 N	24.19 E
121	Viipuri (Viborg) (vē′pōō-rĭ) (vē′-bôr′)	Fin.	60.44 N	28.42 E
121	Viipuri B.	Fin.	60.30 N	28.20 E
120	Viki Sogn (vēk′ ê sōghn′)	Nor.	61.5 N	6.37 E
127	Viladecáns (vê-lä-dȧ-käns′)	Sp. (In.)	41.19 N	2.2 E

ng-sing; ŋ-bank; N-nasalized n; nŏd; cŏmmit; ōld; ôbey; ôrder; fōōd; foot; ou-out; s-soft; sh-dish; th-thin; pūre; ûnite; ûrn; stŭd; circŭs; ü-as "y" in study; ′-indeterminate vowel.

Page	Name Pronunciation Region	Lat. °′	Long. °′
140	Vila de João Belo (vē′lȧ dā zhô-ouɴ′ bā′lô)..Moz.	25.3 S	33.40 E
126	Vila de Rei (vē′lȧ dā rā′ĭ) ....Port.	39.42 N	8.4 W
126	Vila do Conde (vē′lȧ do͝o kôn′dĕ) Port.	41.22 N	8.46 W
126	Vila Franca de Xira (vē′lȧ frāŋ′kȧ dā shē′rȧ).Port.	38.58 N	8.59 W
124	Vilaine R. (vē-lĕn′)...........Fr.	47.35 N	2.15 W
140	Vilanculos (vē-lāŋ-ko͞o′lōzh)..Moz.	22.7 S	35.12 E
121	Vilani (vē′lȧ-nĭ).............Lat.	56.33 N	26.57 E
126	Vila Nova de Fozcoa (vē′lȧ nō′vȧ dā fôz-kō′ȧ).Port.	41.6 N	7.10 W
126	Vila Nova de Gaia (vē′lȧ nō′vȧ dā gā′yȧ).Port.	41.8 N	8.38 W
126	Vila Nova de Milfontes (vē-lȧ nō′-vȧ dā mêl-fôn′tāzh).Port.	37.45 N	8.47 W
126	Vila Nova de Portimão (vē′lȧ nō′-vȧ dā pôr-tê-mouɴ′).Port.	37.8 N	8.33 W
126	Vila Real (vē′lȧ rā-äl′)......Port.	41.18 N	7.46 W
126	Vila Real de Santo Antonio (dā sāŋ′to͞o ān-tō′nê-o͞o).Port.	37.12 N	7.27 W
126	Vila Viçosa (vē′lȧ vê-sō′zȧ)...Port.	38.47 N	7.25 W
125	Vilennes-sur-Seine (vê-lĕn′-sür-sān′) Fr. (In.)	48.56 N	2.0 E
121	Viljandi (vēl′yȧn-dê).........Est.	58.22 N	25.36 E
121	Vilkaviškis (vēl-kȧ-vêsh′kês).Lith.	54.39 N	23.2 E
148	Vilkitskogo I. (vêl′kēts-kô-gô) Sov. Un.	73.25 N	76.0 E
102	Villa (vēl′yä)..........Peru (In.)	12.12 S	77.1 W
80	Villa Ahumada (vē′lyä ȧ-o͞o-mä′dä) Mex.	30.44 N	106.30 W
93	Villa Alta (San Ildefonso) (vēl′yä äl′tä) (sän ēl-dȧ-fōn′sō).Mex.	17.20 N	96.10 W
102	Villa Bella (vē′lȧ bȧl′ȧ).....Braz.	10.29 S	65.29 W
99	Villa Bella .Braz. (Rio de Janeiro)	23.45 S	45.20 W
126	Villablino (vēl-yä-blē′nō)......Sp.	42.57 N	6.18 W
126	Villacañas (vēl-yä-kän′yäs)....Sp.	39.38 N	3.20 W
126	Villacarrillo (vēl-yä-kä-rēl′yō) .Sp.	38.7 N	3.6 W
99	Villa Casilda (vĭl-yä kä-sēl′dä) Arg. (Buenos Aires In.)	33.0 S	61.12 W
122	Villach (fē′läᴋ)............Ger.	46.37 N	13.50 E
128	Villacidro (vē-lä-chē′drô)....Sard.	39.27 N	8.46 E
138	Villa Cisneros (vēl′yä thês-nā′rōs) R. de O.	23.45 N	16.0 W
99	Villa Constitución (vēl′yä kōn-stê-to͞o-syōn′).Arg. (Buenos Aires In.)	33.13 S	60.20 W
80	Villa Coronado (vēl′yä kō-rō-nä′-dhō).Mex.	26.45 N	105.10 W
93	Villa de Acala (vēl′yä dā ȧ-kä′lä) Mex.	16.37 N	92.48 W
80	Villa de Allende (dā äl-yĕn′dȧ) Mex.	25.18 N	100.1 W
92	Villa de Álvarez (äl′vä-rāz)...Mex.	19.19 N	103.47 W
80	Villa de Fuente (fwān′tȧ) ....Mex.	28.39 N	100.34 W
92	Villa de Guadalupe (gwä-dhä-lo͞o′-pā).Mex.	23.22 N	100.44 W
92	Villa del Refugio (dĕl rā-fo͞o′ᴋê-ō) Mex.	21.47 N	103.6 W
92	Villa de Reyes (dā rā′yĕs)....Mex.	21.46 N	100.54 W
104	Villa Dolores (dô-lō′rās).......Arg.	32.0 S	65.25 W
104	Villa Dominico (dō-mê-nē′kō) Arg. (In.)	34.41 S	58.20 W
127	Villafamés (vēl′yä-fȧ-mās′)....Sp.	40.7 N	0.5 W
93	Villa Flores (flō′rās).........Mex.	16.13 N	93.16 W
128	Villafranca (vēl-lä-fräŋ′kä).....It.	45.22 N	10.52 E
126	Villafranca del Bierzo (vēl-yä-fräŋ′kä dĕl byĕr′thō).Sp.	42.37 N	6.49 W
126	Villafranca de los Barros (dā lōs bär′rōs).Sp.	38.33 N	6.20 W
127	Villafranca del Panades (dĕl pä-nä-dās′).Sp. (In.)	41.20 N	1.42 E
92	Villa García (gär-sē′ä) ......Mex.	22.7 N	101.57 W
126	Villagarciá (vēl′yä-gär-thē′ä) ..Sp.	42.36 N	8.39 W
73	Village Springs (vĭl′ȧj sprĭngz′) Ala. (Birmingham In.)	33.46 N	86.38 W
92	Villagrán (vēl-yä-grän′).....Mex.	24.26 N	99.29 W
84	Villa Grove (vĭl′ȧ grōv′).......Ill.	39.55 N	88.14 W
104	Villa Hayes (vēl′yä ä′yās) (hāz) Par.	25.10 S	57.35 W
93	Villahermosa (vēl′yä-ĕr-mō′sä) Mex.	17.59 N	92.55 W
93	Villa Hidalgo (Yalálag) (vēl′yä ē-däl′gō) (yä-lä′läg).Mex.	17.12 N	96.11 W
127	Villajoyosa (vēl′yä-hô-yō′sä) ..Sp.	38.32 N	0.12 W
93	Villa Juárez (Ixtlan de Juarez) (hwä′rȧz) (ēs-tlän′ dā hwä′rȧz).Mex.	17.20 N	96.30 W
104	Villa Klein (vēl′yä klīn) .Arg. (In.)	34.33 S	58.33 W
126	Villalba (vēl-yäl′bä)..........Sp.	43.17 N	7.42 W
80	Villaldama (vēl-yäl-dä′mä) ..Mex.	26.30 N	100.26 W
80	Villa López (vēl′yä lō′päz)...Mex.	27.0 N	105.1 W
126	Villalpando (vēl-yäl-pän′dō)...Sp.	41.53 N	5.23 W
104	Villa Maria (mä-rē′ä) ....Arg.	32.20 S	63.15 W
126	Villamartín (vēl′yä-mär-tēn′)..Sp.	36.52 N	5.38 W
104	Villa Mercedes (vēl′yä mĕr-sā′dās) Arg.	33.45 S	65.29 W
94	Villanueva (vēl′yä-nwā′vä) .Hond.	15.19 N	88.1 W
92	Villanueva.................Mex.	22.25 N	102.58 W
126	Villanueva de Córdoba (dā kôr′dō-bä).Sp.	38.18 N	4.38 W
126	Villanueva del Arzobispo (dĕl är-thō-bēs′pō).Sp.	38.12 N	3.0 W
126	Villanueva de la Serena (dā lä sā-rā′nä).Sp.	38.58 N	5.48 W
127	Villanueva Y Geltru (ē ᴋĕl-tro͞o′) Sp. (In.)	41.14 N	1.44 E
80	Villa Ocampō (ô-käm′pō)....Mex.	26.26 N	105.30 W
125	Villard-Bonnot (vēl-yär′ bôn-nô′) Fr.	45.25 N	5.52 E
163	Villareal (vēl-yä-rā-äl′) ......P. I.	11.33 N	124.56 E
127	Villarreal................... .Sp.	39.56 N	0.6 W
104	Villarrica (vēl-yä-rē′kä)......Par.	25.50 S	56.29 W
126	Villarrobledo (vēl-yär-rô-blā′dhō) Sp.	39.16 N	2.36 W
126	Villarrubia (vēl-yär-ro͞o′bē-ä)..Sp.	39.14 N	3.38 W
92	Villa Unión (o͞o-nyōn′).......Mex.	23.11 N	106.13 W
126	Villaviciosa (vēl′yä-vê-thê-ō′sä) Sp.	43.29 N	5.25 W
127	Villaviciosa de Odón (dā ō-dōn′) Sp. (In.)	40.22 N	3.54 W
124	Villefranche (vēl′-fräɴsh′).....Fr.	46.0 N	4.45 E
125	Villefranche.................Fr.	43.41 N	7.19 E
124	Villefranche-de-Rouergue (dē-ro͞o-ĕrg′).Fr.	44.20 N	2.5 E
125	Villejust (vēl-zhüst′).....Fr. (In.)	48.41 N	2.14 E
127	Villena (vē-lyā′nä)............Sp.	38.37 N	0.51 W
124	Villeneuve (vēl′nûv′)..........Fr.	48.5 N	3.19 E
124	Villeneuve-le-Comte (vēl′nûv′-lē-kôɴt′).Fr.	48.48 N	2.50 E
125	Villeneuve-le-Roi (lē-rwä′) Fr. (In.)	48.41 N	2.25 E
125	Villeneuve-St. Georges (săɴ zhôrzh′).Fr. (In.)	48.41 N	2.26 E
124	Villeneuve-sur-Lot (sür-lô′)....Fr.	44.25 N	0.40 E
125	Villeparisis (vēl′pȧ-rê-sē′) Fr. (In.)	48.56 N	2.37 E
125	Villepinte (vēl′păɴt′).....Fr. (In.)	48.57 N	2.32 E
81	Ville Platte (vēl plȧt′).........La.	30.40 N	92.16 W
124	Villers-Cotterêts (vē-lâr′ kô-tē-rĕ′) Fr.	49.20 N	3.1 E
125	Villerupt (vēl-rüp′)...........Fr.	49.28 N	5.52 E
124	Villeurbanne (vēl-ûr-bān′).....Fr.	45.45 N	4.55 E
143	Villiersdorp (vê-lērz′dôrp) U. S. Afr.	27.4 S	28.38 E
142	Villiersdorp............U. S. Afr.	33.59 S	19.16 E
125	Villiers-le-Bel (vê-lyâr′lē-bĕl′) Fr. (In.)	49.1 N	2.23 E
122	Villingen (fĭl′ĭng-ĕn).........Ger.	48.4 N	8.28 E
77	Villisca (vĭ-lĭs′kȧ).............Ia.	40.56 N	94.58 W
121	Vilppula (vĭl′pŭ-lȧ)...........Fin.	62.1 N	24.29 E
	Vilna, see Wilno, Pol.		
149	Vilyui R. (vê-lyo͞o′ĭ).....Sov. Un.	63.0 N	114.0 E
149	Vilyukisk (vê-lyo͞o′ĭsk)...Sov. Un.	63.35 N	121.50 E
149	Vilyuiski Ridge.........Sov. Un.	66.30 N	110.0 E
126	Vimianzo (vê-myän′thō)......Sp.	43.7 N	9.0 W
120	Vimmerby (vĭm′ĕr-bü) ......Swe.	57.41 N	15.51 E
	Vimperk, see Winterberg, Ger.		
112	Vim R. (vêm)..........Sov. Un.	63.0 N	50.45 E
104	Viña del Mar (vē′nyä dĕl mär′) Chl.	33.0 S	71.32 W
86	Vinalhaven (vī-năl-hā′vĕn)....Me.	44.3 N	68.49 W
127	Vinaroz (vē-nä′rōth)..........Sp.	40.30 N	0.28 E
125	Vincennes (văɴ-sĕn′).....Fr. (In.)	48.50 N	2.27 E
84	Vincennes (vĭn-sĕnz′).........Ind.	38.42 N	87.30 W
82	Vincent (vĭn′sĕnt)............Ala.	33.22 N	86.24 W
110	Vindeln (vĭn′dĕln)...........Swe.	64.10 N	19.45 E
110	Vindel R. (vĭn′dĕl)...........Swe.	65.16 N	18.0 E
151	Vindhya Range (vĭnd′yä)...India	22.45 N	77.30 E
85	Vineland (vīn′lănd)..........N. J.	39.30 N	75.3 W
160	Vinh (vên′y′)........Fr. In. Chn.	18.17 N	105.52 E
126	Vinhais (vên-yä′ēzh)........Port.	41.50 N	7.1 W
160	Vinhlong (vên-y′lŏng′) Fr. In. Chn.	10.18 N	106.5 E
73	Vinings (vī′nĭngz) Ga. (Atlanta In.)	33.52 N	84.28 W
79	Vinita (vĭ-nē′tȧ)...........Okla.	36.37 N	95.8 W
129	Vinkovci (vēn′kôv-tsê).....Yugo.	45.17 N	18.48 E
131	Vinnitsa (vê′nêt-sȧ)......Sov. Un.	49.12 N	28.31 E
77	Vinton (vĭn′tŭn)..............Ia.	42.10 N	92.0 W
81	Vinton.....................La.	30.12 N	93.35 W
83	Vinton.....................Va.	37.18 N	79.54 W
129	Vir (vêr)................Yugo.	42.15 N	19.5 E
162	Virac (vê-räk′)............P. I.	13.34 N	124.13 E
121	Virbalis (vêr′bȧ-lês).........Lith.	54.38 N	22.52 E
79	Virden (vûr′dĕn).............Ill.	39.27 N	89.45 W
124	Vire (vēr)....................Fr.	48.50 N	0.50 W
77	Virginia (vēr-jĭn′yȧ).......Minn.	47.31 N	92.32 W
85	Virginia (State)............U. S.	37.0 N	78.0 W
74	Virginia City...............Nev.	39.18 N	119.39 W
91	Virgin Is. (vûr′jĭn).........W. I.	18.25 N	65.0 W
75	Virgin R..................Nev.	36.25 N	114.20 W
121	Virmo (vĭr′mô)..............Fin.	60.42 N	21.59 E
125	Viroflay (vê-rô-flĕ′)......Fr. (In.)	48.47 N	2.12 E
77	Viroqua (vĭ-rō′kwȧ).........Wis.	43.35 N	90.52 W
128	Virovitica (vē-rô-vē′tê-tsȧ)..Yugo.	45.49 N	17.24 E
121	Virrat (vĭr′ät)..............Fin.	62.15 N	23.50 E
120	Virserum (vĭr′sē-ro͝om)......Swe.	57.22 N	15.36 E
121	Virts, L. (vĭrts).............Est.	58.14 N	26.0 E
128	Vis (vês)..................Yugo.	43.4 N	16.11 E
128	Vis (I.)...................Yugo.	43.3 N	16.10 E
74	Visalia (vĭ-sā′lĭ-ȧ)..........Calif.	36.20 N	119.18 W
162	Visayan Is. (vê-sä′yän)......P. I.	11.0 N	124.0 E
163	Visayan Sea................P. I.	11.30 N	123.45 E
120	Visby (vĭs′bü)..............Swe.	57.39 N	18.21 E
129	Višegrad (vē′shĕ-gräd).....Yugo.	43.46 N	19.20 E
126	Viseu (vê-zȧ′o͞o)............Port.	40.39 N	7.55 W
130	Vishnii Volochek (vēsh′nĭ-ê vôl-ô-chôk′) Sov. Un.	57.35 N	34.36 E
120	Viske R. (vĭs′kĕ)...........Swe.	57.33 N	12.40 E
121	Viski (vēs′kĭ)...............Lat.	56.2 N	26.46 E
129	Visoko (vē′sô-kô)..........Yugo.	43.59 N	18.11 E
128	Viso, Mt. (vē′zō)..........It.-Fr.	44.40 N	7.5 E
129	Vistonis, L. (vês′tô-nĭs)......Grc.	41.3 N	25.8 E
129	Vistritsa (Aliakmon) R. (vês-trē′-tsȧ) (ä-lê-äk′mōn) Grc.	40.20 N	22.10 E
123	Vistula (Wisla) R. (vĭs′tû-lȧ) (vēs′wȧ) Pol.	51.4 N	21.50 E
163	Vitali I. (vē-tä′lē)...........P. I.	7.20 N	122.22 E
129	Vitanovac (vê-tä′nô-vȧts)...Yugo.	43.43 N	20.47 E
130	Vitebsk (vē′tyĕpsk)......Sov. Un.	55.11 N	30.11 E
128	Viterbo (vê-tĕr′bō)............It.	42.15 N	12.7 E
6	Viti Levu (Great Fiji) (I.) (vē′tê lā′vo͞o) Fiji Is. (In.)	17.48 S	178.0 E
149	Vitim (vē′têm)..........Sov. Un.	59.25 N	112.40 E
149	Vitim R...............Sov. Un.	56.0 N	115.50 E
126	Vitoria (vê-tō′rê-ä)...........Sp.	42.51 N	2.39 W
128	Vitré (vê-trā′)...............Fr.	48.10 N	1.10 W
124	Vitry-le-François (vê-trē′-lē-fräɴ-swȧ′) Fr.	48.45 N	4.35 E
128	Vittorio (vê-tô′rê-ô)..........It.	45.59 N	12.19 E
161	Vitu Is. (vē′to͞o).....N. Gui. Ter.	4.50 S	149.13 E
126	Vivero (vê-vā′rō).............Sp.	43.39 N	7.37 W
81	Vivian (vĭv′ĭ-ȧn).............La.	32.51 N	93.59 W
166	Vivonne B. (vê-vôn′).......Austl.	36.0 S	137.15 E
151	Vizagapatam (vē-zŭg′ŭ-pŭ-tŭm′) India	17.45 N	83.15 E
129	Vize (vē′zĕ).................Tur.	41.34 N	27.47 E
151	Vizianagram (vē-zê-ăn′ȧ-grŭm′) India	18.0 N	83.30 E
128	Vizzini (vêt-sē′nê)............It.	37.12 N	14.44 E
117	Vlaardingen (vlär′dĭng-ĕn)..Neth.	51.55 N	4.20 E
113	Vladikavkaz (Ordzhonikidze) (vlȧ-dê-käf′ᴋȧz) (ôrd′zhô-nê-kē-dzĕ) Sov. Un.	43.5 N	44.32 E
130	Vladimir (vlȧ-dē′mēr)....Sov. Un.	56.8 N	40.22 E
130	Vladimir (Dist.).........Sov. Un.	56.2 N	39.50 E
149	Vladimiro Aleksandrovskoe (vlȧ-dē′mē-rô ä-lyĕk-sän′drôf-skô-yĕ) Sov. Un.	42.45 N	132.59 E
149	Vladivostok (vlȧ-dê-vôs-tôk′) Sov. Un.	43.15 N	131.50 E
129	Vlasenica (vlä′sĕ-nêt′sȧ)....Yugo.	44.12 N	18.58 E
129	Vlasotince (vlä′sô-tên-tsĕ)...Yugo.	42.57 N	22.7 E
129	Vlčedrma (v′l′chĕd′r-mȧ).....Bul.	43.41 N	23.26 E
122	Vlieland (I.) (vlē′länt)......Neth.	53.16 N	4.57 E
117	Vlissingen (Flushing) (vlĭs′sĭng-ĕn) Neth.	51.35 N	3.35 E
129	Vlonē (Valona) (vlō′nā) (vȧ-lō′nā) Alb.	40.28 N	19.30 E
122	Vltava R. (v′l′tȧ-vȧ).......Czech.	49.14 N	14.24 E
112	Vodl, L. (vôd″l) ....Sov. Un.	62.15 N	37.0 E
143	Vogel River (fō′gĕl).....U. S. Afr.	32.51 S	25.10 E
170	Vogeltown (vō′gĕl-toun) N. Z. (In.)	41.19 S	174.47 E
128	Voghera (vô-gā′rä)...........It.	44.59 N	9.1 E
141	Vohémar (vô-ā-mär′).....Madag.	13.30 S	50.3 E
125	Voiron (vwȧ-rôɴ′)............Fr.	45.22 N	5.38 E
125	Voisins-le-Bretonneux (vwä-săɴ′-lē-brĕ-tôn-nû′) Fr. (In.)	48.0 N	2.3 E
131	Volchansk (vôl-chänsk′)..Sov. Un.	50.17 N	36.57 E
131	Volchya R. (vôl-chyȧ)....Sov. Un.	49.35 N	34.35 E
131	Volegotsulovo (vô-lĕ-gôt′so͝o-lô-vō) Sov. Un.	47.28 N	29.52 E
113	Volga-German (Soviet Rep.) (vôl′gȧ-jēr′măn) Sov. Un.	51.0 N	46.30 E
113	Volga R...............Sov. Un.	51.45 N	47.0 E
130	Volkhov R. (vôl′ᴋôf).....Sov. Un.	59.0 N	31.48 E
130	Volkhovstroi (vôl′ᴋôf-strô-ĭ) Sov. Un.	59.52 N	32.21 E
119	Volksdorf (fôlks′dôrf) Ger. (Hamburg In.)	53.39 N	10.10 E
143	Volksrust (vôlks′rûst)...U. S. Afr.	27.22 S	29.55 E
130	Vologda (vô′lôg-dȧ)......Sov. Un.	59.11 N	39.51 E
130	Vologda (Dist.).........Sov. Un.	59.10 N	40.0 E
130	Volokolamsk (vô-lô′kō-lämsk′) Sov. Un.	56.2 N	35.59 E
131	Volokopovka (vô′lô-kô-pôf′kȧ) Sov. Un.	50.28 N	37.49 E
129	Volos (vô′lôs)...............Grc.	39.21 N	22.58 E
129	Volos, G. of................Grc.	38.15 N	23.0 E
113	Volsk (vôl′sk)..........Sov. Un.	52.0 N	47.30 E
138	Volta R. (vŏl′tȧ)..........G. C.	8.30 N	0.45 W
128	Volterra (vôl-tĕr′rä)..........It.	43.23 N	10.53 E
128	Voltri (vōl′trē)..............It.	44.26 N	8.45 E
128	Volturno R. (vôl-to͞or′nō)......It.	41.12 N	14.30 E
129	Volvi, L. (vôl′vê)..........Grc.	40.38 N	23.30 E
121	Vōōbsu (vēb′so͝o)............Est.	58.5 N	27.31 E
130	Vop R. (vôp)...........Sov. Un.	55.15 N	32.52 E
120	Vordingborg (vôr′dĭng-bôr′) .Den.	55.0 N	11.55 E
131	Vorochilovgrad (Lugansk) (vō-rô-chĭ-lôf′gräd)..Sov. Un.	48.35 N	39.19 E
121	Vorms I. (vôrms)............Est.	59.0 N	23.15 E
131	Voronezh (vô-rô′nyĕzh)..Sov. Un.	51.40 N	39.10 E
131	Voronezh (Dist)........Sov. Un.	51.15 N	39.30 E
130	Voronezh R............Sov. Un.	52.15 N	39.21 E
131	Vorontsovo-Gorodishche (vô-rônt′sô-vô-gô-rôd-êsh′chĕ)..Sov. Un.	49.18 N	31.26 E
112	Voronya R. (vô-rô′nyȧ)..Sov. Un.	68.30 N	35.30 E
121	Vōru (vĕ′ro͞o)...............Est.	57.51 N	27.1 E
142	Vosburg (vŏs′bûrg).....U. S. Afr.	30.31 S	22.52 E
124	Vosges (Mts.) (vōzh).........Fr.	48.20 N	7.10 E
120	Voss (vôs)..................Nor.	60.40 N	6.25 E
112	Votkinsk (vôt-kēnsk) ....Sov. Un.	54.0 N	57.10 E
112	Votsk (Aut. Ter.) (vôtsk) Sov. Un.	57.50 N	53.0 E
126	Vouga R. (vō′gȧ)...........Port.	40.45 N	8.0 W
124	Vouziers (vo͞o-zyā′)..........Fr.	49.25 N	4.40 E
129	Voyutsa R. (vô′yo͞o-tsȧ)......Alb.	40.20 N	20.0 E
112	Vozhe, L. (vôzh′yĕ)......Sov. Un.	60.30 N	39.0 E
131	Voznesensk (vôz-nyĕ-sĕnsk′) Sov. Un.	47.33 N	31.23 E
119	Vracene (vrȧ′sĕ-nĕ) Bel. (Anvers In.)	51.13 N	4.12 E
129	Vranje (vrän′yĕ)...........Yugo.	42.33 N	21.54 E
129	Vratca (vrät′tsȧ)............Bul.	43.12 N	23.32 E
129	Vrbas (v′r′bäs).............Yugo.	45.35 N	19.42 E
128	Vrbas R..................Yugo.	44.40 N	17.10 E
	Vrchlabi, see Hohenelbe, Ger.		
143	Vrede (vrĭ′dĕ) (vrēd)...U. S. Afr.	27.25 S	29.12 E
143	Vredefort (vrĭ′dĕ-fôrt) (vrēd′fōrt) U. S. Afr.	26.59 S	27.22 E
142	Vredenburg (vrĭ′dĕn-bo͝orgh) (vrē′dĕn-bûrg) U. S. Afr.	32.51 S	17.57 E
119	Vremde (vrĕm′dĕ) Bel. (Anvers In.)	51.11 N	4.31 E
129	Vršac (v′r′shȧts)...........Yugo.	45.16 N	21.18 E
123	Vrutky (vro͞ot′kê)........Czech.	49.8 N	18.54 E
143	Vryburg (vrī′bûrg)........Bech.	26.58 S	24.42 E
143	Vryheid (vrī′hīt).......U. S. Afr.	27.48 S	30.46 E
123	Vsetín (fsĕt′yēn)..........Czech.	49.21 N	18.1 E
96	Vuelta Abajo (Mts.) (vwĕl′tā ä-bä′hō) Cuba	22.15 N	83.55 W
141	Vugha (vo͞o′gȧ)..............Tan.	4.55 S	38.20 E
129	Vukovar (vo͞o-kô′vär)......Yugo.	45.20 N	19.0 E
128	Vulcano (I.) (vo͞ol-kä′nō)......It.	38.23 N	14.57 E
112	Vyatka (vyȧt′kȧ)........Sov. Un.	58.35 N	49.35 E
112	Vyatka R..............Sov. Un.	59.25 N	51.30 E
130	Vyazma (vyȧz′mȧ).......Sov. Un.	55.11 N	34.19 E
112	Vyazniki (vyȧz′nê-kê)....Sov. Un.	56.12 N	42.10 E
123	Výškov (vêsh′kôf).........Czech.	49.17 N	17.0 E
122	Vysoké Myto (vûê′sô-kā mē′tô) Czech.	49.57 N	16.9 E

ăt; finăl; rāte; senâte; ärm; ȧsk; sofȧ; fâre; ch-choose; dh-as th in other; bē; êvent; bĕt; recĕnt; cratēr; g-go; gh-gutteral g; bĭt; ĭ-short neutral; rīde; ᴋ-gutteral k as ch in German ich;

Page	Name Pronunciation Region	Lat. °'	Long. °'
130	Vysokovo Nekrasovo (vē'sô-kô-vô nĕk'rȧ-sô-vô) Sov. Un.	56.13 N	36.32 E
112	Vytegra (vē'tĕg-rȧ) Sov. Un.	61.0 N	36.30 E
122	Waal R. (väl) Neth.	51.53 N	5.26 E
84	Wabash (wô'băsh) Ind.	40.48 N	85.50 W
77	Wabasha (wä'bȧ-shô) Minn.	44.24 N	92.2 W
84	Wabash R. Ill.-Ind.	39.15 N	87.30 W
123	Wąbrzeżno (vôṉ-bzhĕzh'nô) Pol.	53.17 N	18.58 E
83	Waccamaw R. (wăk'ȧ-mô) S. C.	33.45 N	79.3 W
82	Waccassassa B. (wă-kȧ-să'sȧ) Fla.	29.0 N	83.0 W
81	Waco (wā'kō) Tex.	31.35 N	97.7 W
159	Wadayama (wä'dȧ-yȧ'mȧ) Jap.	35.16 N	134.49 E
139	Wadelai (wä-dĕ-lä'ē) Ug.	2.36 N	31.30 E
77	Wadena (wŏ-dē'nȧ) Minn.	46.26 N	95.6 W
83	Wadesboro (wādz'bŭr-ō) N. C.	34.59 N	80.5 W
141	Wadi Digla (R.) (wä'dē dēg'lȧ) Eg.	29.57 N	31.24 E
139	Wādi Halfa (wä'dē häl'fȧ) A. E. Sud.	21.57 N	31.25 E
127	Wadi Sli (R.) (wä'dē slē') Alg.	35.40 N	1.10 E
141	Wadi Tih (R.) (wä'dē tē') Eg.	29.58 N	31.21 E
83	Wadley (wŏd'lē) Ga.	32.53 N	82.24 W
139	Wad Medani (wäd mē-dä'nē) A. E. Sud.	14.25 N	33.30 E
123	Wadowice (vȧ-dô-vēt'sĕ) Pol.	49.53 N	19.31 E
84	Wadsworth (wŏdz'wûrth) Ohio	41.2 N	81.44 W
54	Wager B. (wā'jẽr) Can.	65.45 N	90.30 W
167	Wagga Wagga (wŏg'ȧ wŏg'ȧ) Austl.	35.6 S	147.25 E
142	Waggenaarskraal (väg'ĕ-närz-kräl') U. S. Afr.	31.51 S	22.49 E
76	Wagner (wăg'nẽr) S. D.	43.5 N	98.18 W
79	Wagoner (wăg'ŭn-ẽr) Okla.	35.57 N	95.23 W
78	Wagon Mound N. M.	36.0 N	104.42 W
123	Wągrowiec (vôṉ-grô'vyĕts) Pol.	52.47 N	17.13 E
139	Wahat el Dakhla (Oasis) (wȧ-hät' ĕl däk'lȧ) Eg.	25.45 N	28.50 E
139	Wahat el Kharga (Oasis) (kär-gȧ) Eg.	25.26 N	30.36 E
167	Wahgunyan (wȧ-gōōn'yȧn) Austl.	36.2 S	146.26 E
173	Wahiawa (wä-hē-ȧ'wȧ) Haw.	21.30 N	158.3 W
72	Wahl (wôl) Wash. (Vancouver In.)	48.50 N	122.22 W
72	Wahleach L. (wä'lĭch) Can. (Vancouver In.)	49.13 N	121.37 W
76	Wahoo (wȧ-hōō') Neb.	41.13 N	96.38 W
76	Wahpeton (wô'pē-tŭn) N. D.	46.17 N	96.36 W
73	Waialeale, Mt. (wä'ē-ä'lā-ä'lā) Haw.	22.5 N	159.31 W
173	Waialua (wä'ē-ȧ-lōō'ȧ) Haw.	21.34 N	158.8 W
173	Waianae (wä'ē-ȧ-nä'ā) Haw.	21.25 N	158.9 W
171	Waiau R. (wä'ē-ä'ōō) N. Z.	45.50 S	167.40 E
171	Waiau-uha (Dillon) R. (wä'ē-ä'ōō-ōō'hȧ) (dĭl'ŭn) N. Z.	42.38 S	173.0 E
155	Waichow (wī'chō) Chn.	23.10 N	114.24 E
122	Waidhofen (vīd'hôf-ĕn) Ger.	47.58 N	14.47 E
170	Waiheki I. (wä'ē-hä'kē) N. Z.	36.48 S	175.8 E
161	Waigeoe (I.) (wä-ē-gä'ōō) Neth. Ind.	0.15 S	131.0 E
170	Waihi (wä'ē-hē) N. Z.	37.22 S	175.52 E
171	Waihola (wä'ē-hō'lȧ) N. Z.	46.2 S	170.8 E
170	Waikara, L. (wä'ē-kȧ-rä) N. Z.	38.45 S	177.10 E
170	Waikato R. (wä'ē-kä-tō) N. Z.	38.20 S	175.50 E
166	Waikerie (wī'kē-rē) Austl.	34.11 S	139.59 E
170	Waikomiti (wä-ē-kō-mē'tē) N. Z. (In.)	36.54 S	174.39 E
171	Waikouaiti (wä-ē-kō-ōō-ä'ē-tē) N. Z.	45.37 S	170.42 E
173	Wailuku (wä-ē-lōō'kōō) Haw.	20.55 N	156.31 W
171	Waimakariri R. (wä'ē-mä'kȧ-rē'rē) N. Z.	43.27 S	172.30 E
173	Waimanalo (wä-ē-mä'nȧ-lō) Haw.	21.19 N	157.43 W
171	Waimate (wä'ē-mä'tä) N. Z.	44.43 S	171.5 E
173	Waimea (wä-ē-mä'ȧ) Haw.	21.57 N	159.39 W
151	Wainganga R. (wä-ēn-gŭn'gȧ) India	21.0 N	79.40 E
160	Waingapoe (wä-ēn-gä-pō'ȧ) Neth. Ind.	9.38 S	120.8 E
170	Wainuiomata R. (wä'ē-nōō'ē-ō-mä'tä) N. Z. (In.)	41.22 S	174.56 E
170	Waipa R. (wä'ē-pä) N. Z.	37.50 S	175.12 E
173	Waipahu (wä'ē-pä'hōō) Haw.	21.20 N	157.2 W
171	Waipapa Pt. (wä'ē-pȧ'pȧ) N. Z.	42.10 S	175.58 E
171	Waipara (wä-ē-pä'rä) N. Z.	43.3 S	172.47 E
170	Waipawa (wä-ē-pä'wȧ) N. Z.	39.53 S	176.42 E
170	Waipukurau (wä'ē-pōō'kōō-rä'ōō) N. Z.	40.0 S	176.35 E
171	Wairarapa, L. (wä'ē-rȧ-rä'pȧ) N. Z.	41.10 S	175.18 E
171	Wairau R. (wä'ē-rä'ōō) N. Z.	41.37 S	173.30 E
170	Wairoa (wä'ē-rō'ȧ) N. Z.	39.3 S	177.22 E
170	Wairoa R. N. Z.	36.8 S	174.0 E
171	Waitaki (wä'ē-tä'kē) N. Z.	44.57 S	171.8 E
171	Waitaki, R. N. Z.	44.45 S	170.35 E
170	Waitara (wä'ē-tä'rä) N. Z.	39.0 S	174.15 E
170	Waitemata Chan. (wä'ē-tȧ-mä'tȧ) N. Z. (In.)	36.49 S	174.50 E
170	Waitemata Har. N. Z. (In.)	36.51 S	174.43 E
66	Waitsburg (wāts'bûrg) Wash.	46.16 N	118.10 W
170	Waiuku (wä'ē-ōō'kōō) N. Z.	37.15 S	174.45 E
159	Wajima (wä'jē-mȧ) Jap.	37.24 N	136.52 E
140	Waka (wä'kä) Bel. Cong.	0.40 S	20.10 E
158	Wakamatsu (wä'kȧ-mät'sōō) Jap.	37.29 N	139.59 E
158	Wakamatsu Jap.	33.55 N	130.44 E
159	Wakasa B. (wä'kȧ-sä) Jap.	35.45 N	135.40 E
171	Wakatipu L. (wä-kȧ-tē'pōō) N. Z.	45.10 S	168.45 E
159	Wakayama (wä'kȧ-yä'mȧ) Jap.	34.10 N	135.15 E
78	Wakeeney (wô-kē'nē) Kan.	39.0 N	99.54 W
116	Wakefield (wāk'fēld) Gt. Brit.	53.40 N	1.30 W
87	Wakefield Mass. (In.)	42.30 N	71.4 W
77	Wakefield Mich.	46 29 N	89.55 W
76	Wakefield Neb.	42.16 N	96.51 W
83	Wake Forest N. C.	35.58 N	78.30 W
7	Wake I. (wāk) Pac. O.	19.11 N	166.31 E
159	Wakimachi (wä'kē-mä'chē) Jap.	34.5 N	134.10 E
143	Wakkerstroom (väk'ẽr-strōm) (wăk'ẽr-strōōm) U. S. Afr.	27.21 S	30.11 E
166	Wakool R. (wä'kōōl) Austl.	35.25 S	144.0 E
129	Walachia (Prov.) (wŏ-lā'kĭ-ȧ) (wô-lä'chĭ-ȧ) Rom.	44.45 N	25.0 E
88	Walbridge (wôl'brĭj) Wis. (Duluth In.)	46.37 N	92.14 W
167	Walcha (wôl'chȧ) Austl.	30.59 S	151.35 E
122	Waldenburg (väl'dĕn-bōōrgh) Ger.	50.46 N	16.16 E
86	Waldoboro (wôl'dô-bŭr-ō) Me.	44.6 N	69.21 W
70	Waldo L. (wôl'dō) Ore.	43.45 N	122.10 W
72	Waldron (wôl'drŭn) Wash. (Vancouver In.)	48.42 N	123.2 W
72	Waldron I. Wash. (Vancouver In.)	48.43 N	123.2 W
116	Wales (Div.) (wālz) Gt. Brit.	52.30 N	3.30 W
167	Walgett (wôl'gĕt) Austl.	30.1 S	148.10 E
167	Walhalla (wŏl-hăl'ȧ) Austl.	37.58 S	146.25 E
82	Walhalla Ga.	34.46 N	83.4 W
119	Walkden (wôk'dĕn) Gt. Brit. (Liverpool In.)	53.31 N	2.24 W
72	Walker (wôk'ẽr) Colo. (Denver In.)	40.16 N	104.57 W
77	Walker Minn.	47.5 N	93.36 W
142	Walker B. U. S. Afr.	34.32 S	19.15 E
86	Walker L. Can.	50.17 N	67.12 W
74	Walker L. Nev.	38.40 N	118.45 W
74	Walker R. Nev.	39.9 N	119.10 W
74	Walker Riv. Indian Reservation Nev.	39.0 N	118.52 W
74	Walker River Range Nev.	38.40 N	119.0 W
71	Walkerville (wôk'ẽr-vĭl) Mont.	46.2 N	112.33 W
169	Walkerville Austl. (Adelaide In.)	34.53 S	138.38 E
89	Walkerville Junction Mich. (Detroit In.)	42.19 N	82.57 W
151	Walkeshwar (wô'kĕsh-wär) India (Bombay In.)	18.56 N	72.48 E
70	Wallace (wŏl'ȧs) Ida.	47.28 N	115.55 W
169	Wallangarra (wŏl-ăṉ-găr'ȧ) Austl. (In.)	28.54 S	151.55 E
166	Wallaroo (wŏl-ȧ-rōō') Austl.	33.56 S	137.37 E
166	Wallaroo B. Austl.	33.55 S	137.35 E
116	Wallasey (wŏl'ȧ-sē) Gt. Brit.	53.25 N	3.5 W
167	Walla Walla (wŏl'ȧ wŏl'ȧ) Austl.	35.46 S	146.43 E
70	Walla Walla Wash.	46.4 N	118.21 W
142	Walle Kraal (väl'ĕ kräl) U. S. Afr.	30.21 S	17.26 E
167	Wallendbeen (wŏl'ĕnd-bĭn) Austl.	34.32 S	148.11 E
167	Wallerawang (wŏl'ẽr-ȧ-wăng) Austl.	33.25 S	150.3 E
86	Wallingford (wŏl'ĭng-fẽrd) Vt.	43.30 N	72.55 W
119	Wallington (wŏl'ĭng-tŭn) Gt. Brit. (London In.)	51.21 N	0.10 W
167	Wallis L. (wŏl'ĭs) Austl.	32.17 S	152.30 E
81	Wallisville (wŏl'ĭs-vĭl) Tex. (In.)	29.50 N	94.45 W
70	Wallowa (wŏl'ō-wȧ) Ore.	45.34 N	117.32 W
70	Wallowa Mts. Ore.	45.8 N	117.15 W
70	Wallowa R. Ore.	45.30 N	117.30 W
167	Wallsend (wôlz'ĕnd) Austl.	32.55 S	151.38 E
114	Wallsend Gt. Brit.	55.0 N	1.32 W
88	Walmore (wôl'mōr) N. Y. (Niagara Falls In.)	43.7 N	78.57 W
116	Walney (I.) (wôl'nē) Gt. Brit.	54.5 N	3.15 W
73	Walnut (wôl'nŭt) Calif. (Los Angeles In.)	34.0 N	117.52 W
75	Walnut Canyon Nat. Mon. Ariz.	35.10 N	111.30 W
78	Walnut Cr. Kan.	38.27 N	99.20 W
49	Walnut Creek Calif. (San Francisco In.)	37.54 N	122.3 W
73	Walnut Grove Ga. (Atlanta In.)	33.44 N	83.52 W
79	Walnut R. Kan.	37.35 N	97.0 W
79	Walnut Ridge Ark.	36.5 N	90.57 W
87	Walpole (wôl'pōl) Mass. (In.)	42.8 N	71.15 W
86	Walpole N. H.	43.5 N	72.25 W
116	Walsall (wôl'sôl) Gt. Brit.	52.35 N	2.0 W
78	Walsenburg (wôl'sĕn-bûrg) Colo.	37.37 N	104.48 W
83	Walterboro (wôl'tẽr-bŭr-ō) S. C.	32.52 N	80.40 W
78	Walters (wôl'tẽrz) Okla.	34.21 N	98.19 W
87	Waltham (wôl'thȧm) Mass. (In.)	42.23 N	71.14 W
116	Walthamstow (wôl'tȧm-stō) Gt. Brit.	51.35 N	0.5 W
85	Walton (wôl'tŭn) N. Y.	42.11 N	75.7 W
118	Walton-le-Dale (lē-dāl') Gt. Brit.	53.44 N	2.40 W
119	Walton-on-the-Hill Gt. Brit. (Liverpool In.)	53.28 N	2.57 W
140	Walvis B. (wôl'vĭs) S. W. Afr.	22.53 S	14.25 E
140	Walvis Bay S. W. Afr.	22.55 S	14.35 E
77	Walworth (wôl'wûrth) Wis.	42.32 N	88.35 W
139	Wamba Bel. Cong.	2.12 N	28.3 E
140	Wamba R. (wäm'bȧ) Bel. Cong.	6.45 S	17.45 E
79	Wamego (wŏ-mē'gō) Kan.	39.13 N	96.17 W
141	Wami R. (wä'mē) Tan.	6.13 S	38.0 E
155	Wanan (wä'nän') Chn.	26.44 N	114.12 E
166	Wanbi (wăn'bē) Austl.	34.46 S	140.29 E
155	Wanchih (wän'chĭ') Chn.	31.5 N	118.35 E
153	Wanchuan (wän'chōō-än') Chn.	41.0 N	114.35 E
122	Wandsbek (vänts'bĕk) Ger.	53.35 N	10.4 E
170	Wanganui (wôṉ'gȧ-nōō'ē) N. Z.	39.55 S	175.3 E
170	Wanganui R. N. Z.	39.30 S	175.5 E
167	Wangaratta (wôṉ-gȧ-rä'tȧ) Austl.	36.22 S	146.18 E
166	Wangatarra L. (wôṉ-gȧ-tär'ȧ) Austl.	31.33 S	144.4 E
158	Wangching (wäng'kēng) Manch.	43.20 N	129.30 E
167	Wangen (wôṉ'gĕn) Austl.	30.36 S	149.1 E
122	Wangeroog (I.) (väṉ-gē-rōg') Neth.	53.47 N	7.55 E
155	Wangkiang (wäng'kyäng') Chn.	30.9 N	116.45 E
156	Wangtu (wäng'tōō') Chn.	38.47 N	115.1 E
154	Wanhsien (wän'hsyĕn') Chn.	31.4 N	108.32 E
140	Wankie (wäṉ'kē) S. Rh.	18.35 S	26.30 E
94	Wanks, R. (Coco or Segovia) (wăṉks) (kō'kō; sē-gō'vē-ȧ) Hond.-Nic.	14.30 N	85.0 W
171	Wanoka L. (wȧ-nō'kȧ) N. Z.	44.30 S	169.12 E
155	Wansai (wän'sī') Chn.	27.57 N	114.10 E
157	Wanto (wän'tō') Cho.	34.19 N	126.43 E
84	Wapakoneta (wä'pȧ-kō-nĕt'ȧ) Ohio	40.34 N	84.12 W
77	Wapello (wŏ-pĕl'ō) Ia.	41.12 N	91.13 W
85	Wappingers Falls (wŏp'ĭn-jẽrz) N. Y.	41.36 N	73.55 W
77	Wapsipinicon R. (wŏp'sĭ-pĭn'ĭ-kŏn) Ia.	42.11 N	91.30 W
151	Warangal (wŭ'rŭṉ-gŭl) India	17.59 N	79.40 E
167	Waratah B. (wŏr'ȧ-tȧ) Austl.	38.55 S	146.5 E
167	Warburton (wŏr'bûr-tŭn) Austl.	37.46 S	145.42 E
164	Warburton (R.), The Austl.	27.30 S	138.30 E
119	Warden (wôr'dĕn) Gt. Grit. (London I.)	51.25 N	0.53 E
143	Warden U. S. Afr.	27.50 S	29.11 E
151	Wardha (wŭr'dȧ) India	20.45 N	78.32 E
151	Wardha R. India	20.30 N	78.30 E
170	Ward I. (wôrd) N. Z. (In.)	41.18 S	174.53 E
84	War Eagle Ky.	37.32 N	81.56 W
122	Waren (vä'rĕn) Ger.	53.32 N	12.42 E
169	Warialda (wôr-ē-ăl'dȧ) Austl. (In.)	29.34 S	150.36 E
56	Wark Channel (wårk) Can. (Prince Rupert In.)	54.25 N	130.10 W
170	Warkworth (wärk'wûrth) N. Z.	36.25 S	174.40 E
151	Warli (wŭr'lē) India (Bombay In.)	19.2 N	72.49 E
142	Warmbad (värm'bäd) (wôrm'băd) S. W. Afr.	28.28 S	18.41 E
70	Warm Springs Reservoir Ore.	43.40 N	118.17 W
122	Warnemünde (vär'nē-mün-dē) Ger.	54.11 N	12.4 E
73	Warner (wôr'nẽr) Utah (Salt Lake City In.)	40.32 N	112.20 W
70	Warner Range Calif.-Ore.	41.50 N	120.15 W
122	Warnow R. (vär'nō) Ger.	53.50 N	11.57 E
122	Warnsdorf (Varnsdorf) (värns'dôrf) Ger.	50.55 N	14.35 E
166	Warracknabeal (wôr'răk-nȧ-bēl') Austl.	36.15 S	142.25 E
167	Warragul (wôr'ȧ-gŭl) Austl.	38.10 S	145.55 E
141	Warraq el Arab (wȧ'răk ĕl ăr'ăb) Eg.	30.6 N	31.13 E
165	Warrego R. (wôr'ē-gō) Austl.	28.0 S	145.50 E
79	Warren (wŏr'ĕn) Ark.	33.36 N	92.4 W
167	Warren Austl.	31.42 S	147.51 E
84	Warren Ind.	40.42 N	85.25 W
76	Warren Minn.	48.11 N	96.45 W
84	Warren Ohio	41.15 N	80.55 W
49	Warren Ore. (Portland In.)	45.50 N	122.51 W
85	Warren Pa.	41.50 N	79.7 W
73	Warren Utah (Salt Lake City In.)	41.17 N	112.8 W
167	Warren Cr. Austl.	31.5 S	147.50 E
79	Warrensburg (wŏr'ĕnz-bûrg) Mo.	38.46 N	93.43 W
143	Warrenton (wŏr'ĕn-tŭn) Bech.	28.8 S	24.52 E
56	Warrenton Can. (Winnipeg In.)	50.8 N	97.32 W
83	Warrenton Ga.	33.25 N	82.40 W
49	Warrenton Ore. (Portland In.)	46.10 N	123.55 W
85	Warrenton Va.	38.45 N	77.50 W
138	Warri (wär'ē) Nig.	5.32 N	5.41 E
82	Warrington (wŏr'ĭng-tŭn) Fla.	30.21 N	87.17 W
116	Warrington Gt. Brit.	53.25 N	2.35 W
73	Warrior (wôr'yẽr) Ala. (Birmingham In.)	33.49 N	86.49 W
166	Warrnambool (wôr'nȧm-bōōl) Austl.	38.23 S	142.31 E
77	Warroad (wôr'rōd) Minn.	48.55 N	95.18 W
167	Warrumbungle Ra. (wôr'ŭm-bŭṉ-g'l) Austl.	31.35 S	149.45 E
79	Warsaw (wôr'sô) Ill.	40.21 N	91.25 W
84	Warsaw Ind.	41.13 N	85.50 W
85	Warsaw N. Y.	42.47 N	78.10 W
83	Warsaw N. C.	35.0 N	78.7 W
123	Warsaw (Warszawa) (vȧr-shä'vȧ) Pol.	52.14 N	21.0 E
118	Warsop (wôr'sŭp) Gt. Brit.	53.12 N	1.9 W
123	Warszawa (Warsaw) Pol.	52.14 N	21.0 E
123	Warta (vär'tȧ) Pol.	51.42 N	18.38 E
122	Warta R. Pol.	52.12 N	18.30 E
122	Warthe R. (vär'tē) Ger.	52.44 N	15.20 E
165	Warwick (wŏr'ĭk) Austl.	28.10 S	152.5 E
116	Warwick Gt. Brit.	52.15 N	1.40 W
85	Warwick R. I.	41.38 N	71.22 W
118	Warwick County Gt. Brit.	52.21 N	1.30 W
71	Wasatch Range (wô'săch) Utah	41.35 N	11.30 W
143	Waschbank (väsh'bȧnk) U. S. Afr.	28.19 S	30.9 E
70	Wasco (wăs'kō) Ore.	45.35 N	120.43 W
77	Waseca (wô-sē'kȧ) Minn.	44.5 N	93.29 W
86	Washburn (wŏsh'bŭrn) Me.	46.45 N	68.10 W
77	Washburn Wis.	46.41 N	90.53 W
71	Washburn, Mt. Wyo.	44.50 N	110.24 W
82	Washington (wŏsh'ĭng-tŭn) Ga.	33.43 N	82.45 W
84	Washington Ind.	38.38 N	87.10 W
79	Washington Ia.	41.18 N	91.40 W
79	Washington Kans.	39.48 N	97.4 W
79	Washington Mo.	38.34 N	91.0 W
83	Washington N. C.	35.33 N	77.3 W
85	Washington Pa.	40.10 N	80.20 W
70	Washington (State) U. S.	47.25 N	120.38 W
84	Washington Court House Ohio	39.34 N	83.27 W
3	Washington, D. C. U. S.	38.55 N	77.0 W
84	Washington Heights Mich.	42.23 N	85.15 W
6	Washington, I. Pac. O.	4.43 N	160.25 W
77	Washington I. Wis.	45.24 N	86.55 W
49	Washington, L. Wash. (Seattle In.)	47.37 N	122.17 W
86	Washington, Mt. N. H.	44.15 N	71.20 W
72	Washington Sd. Wash. (Vancouver In.)	48.35 N	123.0 W
79	Washita R. (wŏsh'ĭ-tô) Tex.-Okla.	35.5 N	98.20 W
49	Washougal (wŏ-shōō'gȧl) Wash. (Portland In.)	45.35 N	122.21 W
49	Washougal R. Wash. (Portland In.)	45.38 N	122.16 W
117	Wash, The (wŏsh) Gt. Brit.	53.0 N	0.30 E
123	Wasilków (vȧ-sēl'kŏŏf) Pol.	53.12 N	23.13 E
52	Wasilla (wŏ'sĭl-ȧ) Alsk. (In.)	61.35 N	149.25 W
89	Wassaw Sd. (wŏs'sô) Ga. (Savannah In.)	31.56 N	80.58 W

ng-sing; ṉ-baṉk; N-nasalized n; nŏd; cŏmmit; ōld; ôbey; ôrder; fōōd; fŏŏt; ou-out; s-soft; sh-dish; th-thin; pūre; ůnite; ûrn; stŭd; circŭs; ü-as "y" n study; '-indeterminate vowel.

Page	Name Pronunciation	Region	Lat. °′	Long. °′
135	Wasta (wäs'tä)	Eg. (In.)	29.20 N	31.14 E
85	Waterbury (wô'tēr-bĕr-ē)	Conn.	41.32 N	73.2 W
86	Waterbury	Vt.	44.21 N	72.46 W
97	Water Cay (I.)	Ba. Is.	23.0 N	75.45 W
83	Wateree R. (wô'tēr-ē)	S. C.	34.20 N	80.45 W
169	Waterford	Austl. (In.)	27.41 S	153.10 E
116	Waterford (wô'tēr-fērd)	Ire.	52.15 N	7.5 W
143	Waterford	U. S. Afr.	33.5 S	25.0 E
169	Waterhouse I. (wô'tēr-hous)	Austl. (Tas. In.)	40.47 S	147.39 E
91	Water I. (wô'tēr)	Vir. Is. (In.)	18.19 N	64.57 W
84	Waterloo (wô-tēr-lōō')	Can.	43.27 N	80.39 W
86	Waterloo	Can.	45.21 N	72.32 W
79	Waterloo	Ill.	38.19 N	90.9 W
77	Waterloo	Ia.	42.30 N	92.20 W
85	Waterloo	N. Y.	42.55 N	76.52 W
119	Waterloo Seaforth (sē'fōrth)	Gt. Brit. (Liverpool In.)	53.28 N	3.3 W
73	Waterman Mt. (wô'tēr-măn)	Calif. (Los Angeles In.)	34.20 N	117.55 W
72	Waters (wô'tērz)	Colo. (Colo. Sprs. In.)	38.51 N	105.9 W
71	Waterton-Glacier Intl. Peace Park	U. S.-Can.	48.50 N	114.0 W
71	Waterton Lakes Nat. Park (wô'tēr-tŭn)	Can.	49.5 N	114.0 W
87	Watertown (wô'tēr-toun)	Mass. (In.)	42.22 N	71.11 W
85	Watertown	N. Y.	43.58 N	75.56 W
76	Watertown	S. D.	44.55 N	97.5 W
77	Watertown	Wis.	43.13 N	88.42 W
82	Water Valley	Miss.	34.9 N	89.39 W
86	Waterville (wô'tēr-vĭl)	Me.	44.34 N	69.38 W
77	Waterville	Minn.	44.12 N	93.32 W
70	Waterville	Wash.	47.37 N	120.5 W
85	Watervliet (wô-tēr-vlēt')	N. Y.	42.46 N	73.46 W
72	Watkins (wŏt'kĭnz)	Colo. (Denver In.)	39.45 N	104.35 W
85	Watkins	N. Y.	42.25 N	76.52 W
154	Watlam (wät'läm)	Chn.	22.48 N	110.12 E
97	Watling (San Salvador) I. (wŏt'lĭng')	Ba. Is.	24.1 N	74.0 W
78	Watonga (wŏ-tôŋ'gȧ)	Okla.	35.51 N	98.26 W
124	Watrelos (vȧ-tr'-lō')	Fr.	50.41 N	3.11 E
139	Watsa (wät'sä)	Bel. Cong.	2.59 N	29.32 E
84	Wateska (wŏt-sē'kȧ)	Ill.	40.46 N	87.42 W
73	Watson (wŏt'sŭn)	Ala. (Birmingham In.)	33.38 N	86.53 W
74	Watsonville (wŏt'sŭn-vĭl)	Calif.	36.55 N	121.47 W
72	Wattenberg (wŏt'ĕn-bērg)	Colo. (Denver In.)	40.1 N	104.50 W
73	Watts (wŏts)	Calif. (Los Angeles In.)	33.56 N	118.15 W
139	Wau (wä'ōō)	A. E. Sud.	7.40 N	28.0 E
76	Waubay (wô'bā)	S. D.	45.19 N	97.18 W
166	Waubra (wô'brȧ)	Austl.	37.20 S	143.38 E
167	Wauchope (wô'chŏ-pē)	Austl.	31.25 S	152.45 E
83	Wauchula (wô-chōō'lȧ)	Fla. (In.)	27.33 N	81.47 W
77	Waukegan (wô-kē'găn)	Ill.	42.22 N	87.50 W
77	Waukesha (wô-kē-shô)	Wis.	43.0 N	88.15 W
77	Waukon (wô'kŏn)	Ia.	43.15 N	91.29 W
77	Waupaca (wô-păk'ȧ)	Wis.	44.21 N	89.4 W
77	Waupun (wô-pŭn')	Wis.	43.36 N	88.42 W
166	Wauraltee I. (wô'răl-tē)	Austl.	34.28 S	137.21 E
78	Waurika (wô-rē'kȧ)	Okla.	34.9 N	97.59 W
77	Wausau (wô'sô)	Wis.	44.58 N	89.38 W
77	Wausaukee (wô-sô'kē)	Wis.	45.23 N	87.59 W
84	Wauseon (wô'sē-ŏn)	Ohio	41.30 N	84.13 W
77	Wautoma (wô-tō'mȧ)	Wis.	44.4 N	89.18 W
77	Wauwatosa (wô-wȧ-tō'sȧ)	Wis.	43.4 N	88.0 W
95	Wava (wä'vä)	Nic.	14.0 N	83.58 W
164	Wave Hill	Austl.	17.15 S	131.10 E
117	Waveney R. (wāv'nē)	Gt. Brit.	52.30 N	1.30 E
170	Waverley (wā'vēr-lē)	N. Z.	39.45 S	174.40 E
77	Waverly	Ia.	42.45 N	92.28 W
82	Waverly	Tenn.	36.5 N	87.47 W
84	Wawasee L. (wô-wô'sē)	Ind.	41.24 N	85.42 W
81	Waxahachie (wăk-sȧ-hăch'ē)	Tex.	32.23 N	96.50 E
83	Waycross (wā'krôs)	Ga.	31.11 N	82.23 W
82	Wayland (wā'lănd)	Ky.	37.26 N	82.49 W
87	Wayland	Mass. (In.)	42.22 N	71.22 W
76	Wayne (wān)	Neb.	42.14 N	97.2 W
83	Waynesboro (wānz'bŭr-ō)	Ga.	33.6 N	82.3 W
85	Waynesboro	Pa.	39.55 N	80.12 W
85	Waynesboro	Va.	38.5 N	78.50 W
85	Waynesburg (wānz'bûrg)	Pa.	39.54 N	80.12 W
82	Waynesville (wānz'vĭl)	N. C.	35.29 N	82.59 W
78	Waynoka (wā-nō'kȧ)	Okla.	36.35 N	98.51 W
153	Wayun (wä'yōōn')	Chn.	49.1 N	130.1 E
119	Wealdstone (wēld'stŭn)	Gt. Brit. (London In.)	51.36 N	0.21 W
116	Weald, The (wēld)	Gt. Brit.	51.0 N	0.1 E
78	Weatherford (wĕ-dhēr-fērd)	Okla.	35.32 N	98.42 W
81	Weatherford	Tex.	32.45 N	97.49 W
118	Weaver R. (wē'vēr)	Gt. Brit.	53.12 N	2.31 W
70	Weaverville (wē'vēr-vĭl)	Calif.	40.44 N	122.56 W
79	Webb City (wĕb)	Mo.	37.9 N	94.26 W
86	Webster (wĕb'stēr)	Mass.	42.5 N	71.52 W
76	Webster	S. D.	45.20 N	97.30 W
81	Webster	Tex. (In.)	29.32 N	95.7 W
77	Webster City	Ia.	42.28 N	93.48 W
79	Webster Grove	Mo.	38.35 N	90.20 W
85	Webster Springs	W. Va.	38.28 N	80.22 W
46	Weddell Sea (wĕd'ĕl) (wĕd-dĕl')	Ant. O.	73.0 S	40.0 W
166	Wedderburn (wĕd'ēr-bûrn)	Austl.	36.24 S	143.38 E
119	Wedel (vä'dĕl)	Ger. (Hamburg In.)	53.35 N	9.42 E
119	Wedeler Au (R.) (vä'dĕ-lēr ou')	Ger. (Hamburg In.)	53.36 N	9.45 E
86	Wedgeport (wĕj'pōrt)	Can.	43.45 N	66.0 W
116	Wednesbury (wĕd''nz-bŭr-ē)	Gt. Brit.	52.35 N	2.2 W
118	Wednesfield (wĕd''nz-fēld)	Gt. Brit.	52.36 N	2.4 W
70	Weed (wēd)	Calif.	41.25 N	122.21 W
143	Weenen (vā'nĕn)	U. S. Afr.	28.52 S	30.5 E
157	Weensan (wē'ĕn-sän')	Cho.	39.57 N	125.47 E
123	Węgrów (văn'grōōf)	Pol.	52.23 N	22.3 E
123	Wehlau (vā'lou)	Ger.	54.37 N	21.16 E
153	Weichang (wā'chäng')	Chn.	42.20 N	117.48 E
122	Weiden (vī'dĕn)	Ger.	49.42 N	12.8 E
119	Weidling (vīd'lĭng)	Aus. (Wien In.)	48.17 N	16.19 E
156	Weihaiwei (wā'hī-wā')	Chn.	37.32 N	122.2 E
152	Weihsi (wā'hsē')	Chn.	27.20 N	99.32 E
156	Weihsien (wā'hsyĕn')	Chn.	36.46 N	119.7 E
156	Weihwei (wā'hwā')	Chn.	35.20 N	114.21 E
122	Weilheim (vīl'hīm')	Ger.	47.50 N	11.6 E
154	Weilnan (Saining) (wāl'nän') (sĭ'nĭng')	Chn.	23.4 N	111.24 E
122	Weimar (vī'mär)	Ger.	50.59 N	11.18 E
122	Weinheim (vīn'hīm)	Ger.	49.36 N	8.39 E
156	Wei R. (wā'ē)	Chn.	36.10 N	115.17 E
122	Weipert (Vejprty) (vī'pērt) (vā'p'r-tē)	Ger.	50.29 N	13.3 E
169	Weir R. (wēr)	Austl. (In.)	27.50 S	150.22 E
84	Weirton (wēr'tŭn)	Ohio	40.27 N	80.37 W
70	Weiser (wē'zēr)	Ida.	44.15 N	116.59 W
70	Weiser R.	Ida.	44.30 N	116.45 W
122	Weiszenburg (vīs'sĕn-bōōrgh)	Ger.	49.4 N	11.20 E
122	Weiszenfels (vīs'sĕn-fĕls)	Ger.	51.12 N	11.58 E
119	Weiszensee (vīs'sĕn-sā)	Ger. (Berlin In.)	52.34 N	13.27 E
150	Wejh (wĕj)	Sau. Ar.	26.25 N	36.40 E
123	Wejherowo (vā-ē-hä-rô'vô)	Pol.	54.36 N	18.14 E
73	Welby (wĕl'bē)	Utah (Salt Lake City In.)	40.35 N	111.59 W
83	Welch (wĕlch)	W. Va.	37.24 N	81.38 W
72	Weld Can. (wĕld)	Colo. (Denver In.)	40.34 N	104.35 W
83	Weldon (wĕl'dŭn)	N. C.	36.25 N	77.36 W
79	Weldon R.	Ia.-Mo.	40.25 N	93.35 W
79	Weleetka (wē-lēt'kȧ)	Okla.	35.18 N	96.9 W
165	Welford (wĕl'fērd)	Austl.	25.8 S	143.38 E
85	Welland (wĕl'ănd)	Can.	43.0 N	79.10 W
116	Welland (R.)	Gt. Brit.	52.35 N	0.30 W
87	Wellesley (wĕlz'lē)	Mass. (In.)	42.17 N	71.17 W
164	Wellesley Is.	Austl.	16.45 S	139.30 E
118	Wellingborough (wĕl'ĭng-bŭr-ō)	Gt. Brit.	52.18 N	0.42 W
167	Wellington	Austl.	32.35 S	148.58 E
166	Wellington	Austl.	35.19 S	139.22 E
72	Wellington	Can. (Vancouver In.)	49.6 N	123.52 W
118	Wellington	Gt. Brit.	52.42 N	2.30 W
79	Wellington	Kan.	37.15 N	97.25 W
170	Wellington	N. Z. (In.)	41.17 S	174.47 E
84	Wellington	Ohio	41.10 N	82.12 W
78	Wellington	Tex.	34.51 N	100.14 W
142	Wellington	U. S. Afr.	33.37 S	18.59 E
104	Wellington I.	Chl.	49.15 S	74.30 W
167	Wellington, L.	Austl.	38.5 S	147.17 E
167	Wellington, Mt.	Austl.	37.34 S	146.48 E
169	Wellington, Mt.	Austl. (Tas. In.)	42.53 S	147.11 E
77	Wells (wĕlz)	Minn.	43.45 N	93.41 W
70	Wells	Nev.	41.8 N	115.0 W
85	Wellsboro (wĕlz'bŭr-ō)	Pa.	41.46 N	77.18 W
84	Wellsburg	W. Va.	40.14 N	80.38 W
102	Wells I.	Peru (In.)	12.7 S	77.14 W
164	Wells, L.	Austl.	26.45 S	123.15 E
84	Wellston (wĕlz'toun)	Ohio	39.8 N	82.37 W
79	Wellsville (wĕlz'vĭl)	Mo.	39.3 N	91.34 W
85	Wellsville	N. Y.	42.9 N	77.57 W
84	Wellsville	Ohio	40.37 N	80.42 W
71	Wellsville	Utah	41.38 N	111.56 W
122	Wels (vĕls)	Ger.	48.10 N	14.1 E
116	Welshpool (wĕlsh'pōōl)	Gt. Brit.	52.52 N	3.5 W
72	Welty	Colo. (Denver In.)	40.20 N	105.2 W
143	Welverdiend (vĕl-vēr-dēnd')	U. S. Afr.	26.24 S	27.20 E
118	Wem (wĕm)	Gt. Brit.	52.52 N	2.44 W
156	Wenan (wĕn'än')	Chn.	39.2 N	116.29 E
71	Wenatchee (wē-năch'ē)	Wash.	47.24 N	120.19 W
155	Wenchow (wĕn'chō')	Chn.	28.1 N	120.38 E
155	Wenchow B.	Chn.	27.55 N	121.4 E
87	Wenham (wĕn'ăm)	Mass. (In.)	42.36 N	70.53 W
156	Wenhsien (wĕn'hsyĕn')	Chn.	34.56 N	113.9 E
102	Wenman I. (wĕn'măn)	Galápagos Is.	1.30 N	91.45 W
118	Wenning, R. (wĕn'ĭng)	Gt. Brit.	54.7 N	2.30 W
156	Wen R. (wĕn)	Chn.	36.1 N	116.50 E
166	Wensleydale (wĕnz'lē-dāl)	Austl.	38.20 S	144.1 E
152	Wensuh (Aqsu) (wĕn'sōō') (äk'sōō')	Chn.	41.40 N	80.5 E
117	Wensum, R. (wĕn'sŭm)	Gt. Brit.	52.40 N	1.30 E
156	Wenteng (wĕn'tĕng')	Chn.	37.12 N	121.59 E
118	Went, R. (wĕnt)	Gt. Brit.	53.39 N	1.6 W
166	Wentworth	Austl.	34.5 S	141.54 E
118	Weobley (wē'ō-blē)	Gt. Brit.	52.9 N	2.53 W
143	Wepener (wā'pĕn-ēr) (vä'pĕn-ēr)	U. S. Afr.	29.41 S	27.2 E
122	Werdau (vĕr'dou)	Ger.	50.44 N	12.22 E
122	Wernigerode (vĕr-nē-gē-rō'dē)	Ger.	51.51 N	10.47 E
122	Werra R. (vĕr'ä)	Ger.	50.51 N	10.0 E
167	Werris Creek (wĕr'ĭs)	Austl.	31.22 S	150.39 E
122	Wertach R. (vĕr'täĸ)	Ger.	48.15 N	10.45 E
122	Wesel (vā'zĕl)	Ger.	51.39 N	6.38 E
122	Wesermünde (vā'zēr-mün-dē)	Ger.	53.32 N	8.36 E
122	Weser R. (vā'zēr)	Ger.	52.23 N	9.0 E
122	Weser Canal	Ger.	52.18 N	9.0 E
80	Weslaco (wĕs-lā'kō)	Tex.	26.9 N	98.0 W
85	Weslemkoon L. (wĕs'lĕm-kōōn)	Can.	45.3 N	77.26 W
164	Wessel Is. (vĕs'ĕl)	Austl.	11.30 S	136.30 E
76	Wessington Springs (wĕs'ĭng-tŭn)	S. D.	44.6 N	98.33 W
49	West (wĕst)	Ore. (Portland In.)	46.4 N	123.55 W
77	West Allis (ăl'ĭs)	Wis.	43.0 N	87.59 W
46	West Antarctica (ănt-ärk'tĭ-kȧ)	Ant.	76.0 S	84.0 W
88	West Arlington (är'lĭng-tŭn)	N. J. (N. Y. In.)	40.47 N	74.8 W
89	West B.	La. (New Orleans In.)	29.6 N	89.21 W
81	West B.	Tex.	29.15 N	95.0 W
77	West Bend	Wis.	43.26 N	88.11 W
87	Westboro (wĕst'bŭr-ō)	Mass. (In.)	42.16 N	71.37 W
87	West Boylston (boil-stŭn)	Mass. (In.)	42.22 N	71.47 W
84	West Branch	Mich.	44.18 N	84.12 W
118	West Bridgford (brĭj'fērd)	Gt. Brit.	52.56 N	1.8 W
86	Westbrook (wĕst'brŏŏk)	Me.	43.42 N	70.21 W
77	Westby (wĕst'bē)	Wis.	43.39 N	90.51 W
97	West Caicos I. (kä-ē'kōs)	Ba. Is.	21.40 N	72.28 W
85	West Chester (chĕs'tēr)	Pa.	38.58 N	75.36 W
83	West Columbia	S. C.	33.58 N	81.5 E
81	West Columbia	Tex.	29.9 N	95.36 W
81	West Cote Blanche B. (kōt blănch)	La.	29.40 N	91.45 W
89	Westcott (wĕst'kŭt)	Minn. (Minneapolis In.)	44.50 N	93.6 W
77	West Des Moines R. (dē-moin')	Ia.	43.30 N	94.52 W
77	West Des Moines	Ia.	41.34 N	93.41 W
88	West Duluth (dōō-lōōth')	Minn. (Duluth In.)	46.45 N	92.10 W
85	Westerly (wĕs'tēr-lē)	R. I.	41.20 N	71.50 W
164	Western Australia	Austl.	25.0 S	120.00 E
116	Western Downs	Gt. Brit.	51.0 N	2.0 W
167	Western Port	Austl.	38.29 S	145.10 E
85	Western Port	Md.	39.32 N	79.5 W
88	Western Springs	Ill. (Chicago In.)	41.49 N	87.54 W
84	Westerville (wĕs'tēr-vĭl)	Ohio	40.8 N	82.58 W
122	Westerwald (Reg.) (vĕs'tēr-väld)	Ger.	50.45 N	8.7 E
122	Westfalen (State) (vĕst-fä'lĕn)	Ger.	51.50 N	7.40 E
85	Westfield (wĕst'fēld)	N. Y.	42.20 N	70.38 W
110	West Fd.	Nor.	67.40 N	14.0 E
87	Westford (wĕst'fērd)	Mass. (In.)	42.35 N	71.27 W
79	West Frankfort (frănk'fŭrt)	Ill.	37.55 N	88.56 W
122	West Frisian Is.	Neth.	53.22 N	4.57 E
72	Westham (wĕst'ăm)	Can. (Vancouver In.)	49.5 N	123.9 W
116	West Ham (wĕst hăm)	Gt. Brit.	51.30 N	0.5 E
72	Westham I.	Can. (Vancouver In.)	49.5 N	123.10 W
85	West Hartford (härt'fērd)	Conn.	41.44 N	72.44 W
116	West Hartlepool (här't'l-pōōl)	Gt. Brit.	54.40 N	1.0 W
79	West Helena (hĕl'ē-nȧ)	Ark.	34.32 N	91.38 W
88	West Hoboken (hō'bō-kĕn)	N. J. (New York In.)	40.46 N	74.2 W
119	Westhoughton (wĕst'hô-tŭn)	Gt. Brit. (Liverpool In.)	53.33 N	2.32 W
96	West Indies (ĭn'dēz)	N. A.		
155	West Kienning (kyĕn'nĭng')	Chn.	26.47 N	116.42 E
118	West Kirby (kûr'bē)	Gt. Brit.	53.22 N	3.10 W
84	West Lafayette (lä-fā-yĕt')	Ind.	40.27 N	86.57 W
79	West Liberty	Ia.	41.31 N	91.18 W
70	West Linn (lĭn)	Ore.	45.22 N	122.37 W
119	Westmalle (vĕst-mäl')	Bel. (Anvers In.)	51.18 N	4.40 E
73	Westminster (wĕst'mĭn-stēr)	Calif. (Los Angeles In.)	33.45 N	118.0 W
72	Westminster	Colo. (Denver In.)	39.50 N	105.3 W
85	Westminster	Md.	39.37 N	77.58 W
82	Westminster	S. C.	34.40 N	83.6 W
167	West Molong (mō'lŏng)	Austl.	33.5 S	148.50 E
72	West Monument Cr.	Colo. (Colo. Sprs. In.)	38.58 N	104.55 W
118	Westmorland Co. (wĕst'mōr-lănd)	Gt. Brit.	54.14 N	2.45 W
57	Westmount (wĕst'mount)	Can. (Montreal In.)	45.31 N	73.55 W
88	West New Brighton (brī'tŭn)	N. Y. (In.)	40.58 N	74.7 W
87	West Newbury (nū'bĕr-ē)	Mass. (In.)	42.48 N	71.0 W
88	West New York	N. J. (New York In.)	40.48 N	74.0 W
77	West Nishnabotna R. (nĭsh-nȧ-bŏt'nȧ)	Ia.	41.15 N	95.27 W
89	West Norfolk (nôr'fŏk)	Va. (Norfolk In.)	36.52 N	76.21 W
87	Weston (wĕs'tŭn)	Mass. (In.)	42.21 N	71.17 W
84	Weston	W. Va.	39.0 N	80.30 W
116	Weston-super-Mare (sū'pēr-mā'rē)	Gt. Brit.	51.20 N	2.55 W
88	West Orange (ŏr'ĕnj)	N. J. (New York In.)	40.47 N	74.15 W
73	Westover (wĕst'ō-vēr)	Ala. (Birmingham In.)	33.20 N	86.32 W
83	West Palm Beach	Fla. (In.)	26.42 N	80.4 W
84	West Park	Ohio	41.26 N	81.50 W
79	Westplains (wĕst-plānz')	Mo.	36.43 N	91.51 W
86	West Pt.	Can.	49.53 N	64.34 W
87	West Pt.	Hai.	18.56 N	73.18 W
83	West Point	Ga.	32.53 N	85.10 W
82	West Point	Miss.	33.36 N	88.39 W
76	Westpoint (wĕst'point)	Neb.	41.51 N	96.41 W
85	West Point	N. Y.	41.26 N	74.0 W
85	West Point	Va.	37.32 N	76.48 W
116	Westport (wĕst'pōrt)	Ire.	53.45 N	9.32 W
171	Westport	N. Z.	41.48 S	171.47 E
49	Westport	Ore. (Portland In.)	46.8 N	123.23 W
116	Westray (I.) (wĕs'trā)	Gt. Brit. (In.)	59.15 N	2.55 W
118	West Riding (Borough) (rīd'ĭng)	Gt. Brit.	53.54 N	2.3 W
89	West St. Paul	Minn. (Minneapolis In.)	44.54 N	93.4 W
97	West Sand Spit	Ba. Is.	21.22 N	72.9 W
117	West Scheldt R. (skĕlt)	Neth.	51.25 N	3.40 E

ăt; finăl; rāte, senāte; ärm; ȧsk; sofȧ; fâre; ch-choose; dh-as th in other; bē; ēvent; bĕt; recĕnt; cratēr; g-go; gh-gutteral g; bĭt; ĭ-short neutral; rīde; ĸ-gutteral k as ch in German ich;

Page	Name Pronunciation Region	Lat. °′	Long. °′
72	Westsound (wĕst'sound) Wash. (Vancouver In.)	48.38 N	122.58 W
84	West Terre Haute Ind.	39.28 N	87.28 W
77	West Union Ia.	42.58 N	91.48 W
89	Westview (wĕst'vū) Pa. (Pittsburgh In.)	40.31 N	80.2 W
87	Westville (wĕst'vĭl) Can.	45.35 N	62.45 W
84	Westville Ill.	40.3 N	87.39 W
88	Westville N. J. (Philadelphia In.)	39.52 N	75.8 W
84	West Virginia (State) (vẽr-jĭn'ĭ-ȧ). U. S.	39.0 N	80.30 W
74	West Walker R. (wôk'ẽr) Calif.-Nev.	38.20 N	119.25 W
85	West Warwick (wŏr'ĭk) R. I.	41.40 N	71.30 W
73	West Weber (wĕb'ẽr) Utah (Salt Lake City In.)	41.15 N	112.5 W
74	Westwood (wĕst'wŏŏd) Calif.	40.18 N	121.3 W
87	Westwood Mass. (In.)	42.13 N	71.13 W
161	Wetar (I.) (wĕt'är) Neth. Ind.	7.45 S	126.15 E
54	Wetaskiwan (wĕ-tăs'kē-wŏn). Can.	53.3 N	113.28 W
118	Wetherby (wĕdh'ẽr-bē) Gt. Brit.	53.55 N	1.23 W
141	Weti (wä'tē) Zan.	5.3 S	39.44 E
82	Wetumpka (wē-tŭmp'kȧ) Ala.	32.33 N	86.13 W
122	Wetzlar (vĕts'lär) Ger.	50.33 N	8.31 E
79	Wewoka (wē-wō'kȧ) Okla	35.7 N	96.30 W
116	Wexford (wĕks'fẽrd) Ire.	52.20 N	6.30 W
86	Weymont (wā'mŏnt) Can.	47.55 N	73.48 W
116	Weymouth (wā'mŭth) Gt. Brit.	50.37 N	2.30 W
86	Weymouth Mass.	42.15 N	70.59 W
170	Whakatane (whä-kä-tä'nā) N. Z.	37.55 S	177.5 E
170	Whakatane R. N. Z.	38.20 S	177.3 E
96	Whale Cay (I.) Ba. Is.	25.24 N	77.48 W
96	Whale Cay Channels Ba. Is.	26.42 N	77.13 W
170	Whale I. N. Z.	37.50 S	177.2 E
141	Whale Rock U. S. Afr.	33.49 S	18.23 E
46	Whales, B. of Ant.	78.0 S	165.0 W
119	Whaley Bridge (hwā'lē) Gt. Brit. (Liverpool In.)	53.20 N	1.59 W
170	Whangerei (hwăn'gẽr-ē) N. Z.	35.43 S	174.20 E
170	Whangarei Harbor (hwăn-gä-rā'ē). N. Z.	35.52 S	174.35 E
153	Whangpu, R. (whäng'pōō') Chn. (Shanghai In.)	31.12 N	121.30 E
116	Wharfe (R.) (hwôr'fē) Gt. Brit.	53.55 N	1.30 W
81	Wharton (hwôr'tŭn) Tex.	29.19 N	96.7 W
77	What Cheer Ia.	41.23 N	92.21 W
72	Whatcom, L. (hwăt'kŭm) Wash. (Vancouver In.)	48.46 N	122.13 W
71	Wheatland (hwēt'lănd) Wyo.	42.4 N	104.56 W
71	Wheatland Reservoir Wyo.	41.52 N	105.30 W
76	Wheaton (hwē'tŭn) Minn.	45.48 N	96.29 W
72	Wheat Ridge Colo. (Denver In.)	39.46 N	105.5 W
78	Wheeler Natl. Mon. Colo.	37.53 N	106.47 W
75	Wheeler Pk. (hwē'lẽr) Nev.	38.56 N	114.15 W
84	Wheeling (hwēl'ĭng) W. Va.	40.3 N	80.43 W
118	Whernside (Mt.) (hwẽrn'sīd) Gt. Brit.	54.13 N	2.25 W
119	Whetstone (hwĕt'stŭn) Gt. Brit. (London In.)	51.38 N	0.11 W
49	Whidbey I. (hwĭd'bē) Wash. (Seattle In.)	48.10 N	122.40 W
140	Whimo (hwē'mō) Tan.	3.50 S	32.36 E
82	Whistler (hwĭs'lẽr) Ala.	30.46 N	88.10 W
85	Whitby (hwĭt'bē) Can.	43.50 N	78.58 W
116	Whitby Gt. Brit.	54.30 N	0.40 W
118	Whitchurch (hwĭt'chûrch). Gt. Brit.	53.58 N	2.40 W
171	Whitcombe Pass (hwĭt'kŏm). N. Z.	43.12 S	171.0 E
87	White B. Newf.	50.0 N	56.40 W
87	White Bear B. Newf.	47.40 N	57.20 W
89	White Bear L. Minn. (Minneapolis In.)	45.5 N	92.59 W
89	White Bear Lake Minn. (Minneapolis In.)	45.5 N	93.0 W
81	White Castle La.	30.11 N	91.10 W
171	Whitecliff (whĭt'klĭf) N. Z.	43.27 S	171.55 E
84	White Cloud Mich.	43.35 N	85.45 W
76	White Earth R. N. D.	48.20 N	102.45 W
77	Whiteface R. Minn.	47.10 N	92.20 W
119	Whitefield. Gt. Brit. (Liverpool In.)	53.33 N	2.17 W
86	Whitefield N. H.	44.22 N	71.38 W
71	Whitefish Mont.	48.23 N	114.21 W
77	Whitefish Bay Wis.	43.5 N	87.89 W
77	Whitefish B. Mich.	46.35 N	84.45 W
88	Whitefish I. Can. (Sault Ste. Marie In.)	46.31 N	84.21 W
77	White Fish R. Mich.	46.0 N	86.53 W
79	White Hall Ill.	39.26 N	90.24 W
84	Whitehall (hwĭt'hôl) Mich.	43.23 N	86.20 W
85	Whitehall N. Y.	43.33 N	73.26 W
116	Whitehaven (hwĭt'hā-vĕn). Gt. Brit.	54.35 N	3.32 W
54	Whitehorse Can.	60.35 N	134.59 W
116	White Horse Hills Gt. Brit.	51.30 N	1.40 W
170	White I. N. Z.	37.30 S	177.13 E
148	White (Belii) I. (byâl'ĭ-ē) Sov. Un.	73.20 N	71.0 E
77	White L. Can.	48.50 N	85.35 W
85	White L. Can.	45.16 N	76.32 W
81	White L. La.	29.45 N	92.30 W
74	White Mountain Pk. Calif.	37.37 N	118.12 W
86	White Mts. N. H.	44.20 N	71.15 W
76	Whitemouth L. (hwĭt'mŭth). Can.	49.14 N	95.38 W
139	White Nile (Bahr el Abyad) (R.) (bär ĕl ä-byäd'). A. E. Sud.	13.0 N	32.45 E
77	White Otter L. (ŏt'ẽr) Can.	49.10 N	91.55 W
53	White Pass Alsk.-Can.	59.50 N	135.30 W
74	White Pine Pk. Nev.	38.55 N	115.30 W
85	White Plains N. Y.	41.2 N	73.48 W
79	White R. Ark.-Mo.	35.56 N	92.0 W
77	White R. Can.	48.40 N	85.40 W
75	White R. Colo.	40.8 N	108.55 W
84	White R. Ind.	39.10 N	86.51 W
76	White R. S. D.	43.46 N	101.20 W
78	White R. Tex.	34.10 N	101.40 W
86	White R. Vt.	43.45 N	72.45 W
70	White R. Wash.	47.5 N	121.50 W
84	White R., East Fork Ind.	38.45 N	86.10 W
72	White Rock. Can. (Vancouver In.)	49.1 N	122.48 W
130	White Russia (Soviet Rep.) Sov. Un.	53.30 N	29.30 E
80	White Sands Natl. Mon. N. M.	32.45 N	106.15 W
112	White Sea Sov. Un.	66.0 N	40.0 E
99	Whiteside Canal Chl. (Magallanes In.)	53.55 S	70.20 W
88	Whitestone (hwĭt'stōn). N. Y. (In.)	40.47 N	73.49 W
71	White Sulphur Springs Mont.	46.33 N	110.53 W
143	White Umfolozi R. (ŭm-fō-lō'zē) U. S. Afr.	28.25 S	31.40 E
83	Whiteville (hwīt'vĭl) N. C.	34.18 N	78.43 W
77	Whitewater Wis.	42.50 N	88.44 W
83	Whitewater B. Fla. (In.)	25.15 N	80.57 W
71	Whitewater Cr. Mont.	48.50 N	107.40 W
76	Whitewater L. Can.	49.16 N	100.20 W
79	Whitewright (hwīt'rīt) Tex.	33.31 N	96.24 W
167	Whitfield (hwĭt'fēld) Austl.	36.42 S	146.24 E
84	Whiting (hwīt'ĭng) Ind.	41.42 N	87.28 W
87	Whitman (hwĭt'mȧn) Mass. (In.)	42.5 N	70.56 W
83	Whitmire (hwĭt'mīr) S. C.	34.31 N	81.39 W
74	Whitney, Mt. (hwĭt'nē) Calif.	36.33 N	118.18 W
73	Whittier (hwĭt'ĭ-ẽr) Calif. (Los Angeles In.)	33.59 N	118.2 W
166	Whittlesea (hwĭt''l-sē) Austl.	37.30 S	145.8 E
143	Whittlesea U. S. Afr.	32.10 S	26.49 E
165	Whitsunday I. (hwĭt's'n-dā) Austl.	20.8 S	148.52 E
82	Whitwell (hwĭt'wĕl) Tenn.	35.12 N	85.32 W
118	Whitworth (hwĭt'wŭrth). Gt. Brit.	53.40 N	2.10 W
72	Whonnock (hwŏn'nŭk) Can. (Vancouver In.)	49.10 N	122.30 W
166	Whyalla (hwī-ăl'ȧ) Austl.	33.2 S	137.35 E
72	Whytecliff (hwīt'klĭf) Can. (Vancouver In.)	49.22 N	123.16 W
84	Wiarton (wī'ȧr-tŭn) Can.	44.45 N	81.10 W
79	Wichita (wĭch'ĭ-tô) Kan.	37.41 N	97.21 W
78	Wichita Falls Tex.	33.54 N	98.29 W
78	Wichita Mts. Okla.	34.55 N	98.50 W
78	Wichita R. Tex.	33.45 N	99.10 W
116	Wick (wĭk) Gt. Brit.	58.25 N	3.10 W
171	Wickcliffe B. (wĭk'klĭf). N. Z. (In.)	45.50 S	170.46 E
119	Wickford (wĭk'fẽrd) Gt. Brit. (London In.)	51.37 N	0.31 E
116	Wicklow (Cill Mantain) (wĭk'lō) (kĭl wŏn'tô-ĭn). Ire.	53.0 N	6.5 W
116	Wicklow Mts. (wĭk'lō) Ire.	53.0 N	6.20 W
72	Widefield (wīd'fēld) Colo. (Colo. Sprs. In.)	38.45 N	104.44 W
84	Widen (wī'dĕn) W. Va.	38.26 N	80.54 W
118	Widnes (wĭd'nĕs) Gt. Brit.	53.21 N	2.45 W
122	Widze (vēd'zĕ) Pol.	55.23 N	26.39 E
123	Wieliczka (vyĕ-lēch'kȧ) Pol.	49.58 N	20.7 E
123	Wieluń (vyĕ'lōōn') Pol.	51.12 N	18.33 E
122	Wien (Vienna) (vēn) (vē-ĕn'ä). Ger.	48.14 N	16.20 E
119	Wien (Vienna) Ger. (In.)		
122	Wiener Neustadt (vē'nẽr noi'-shtät). Ger.	47.48 N	16.15 E
123	Wieprz (vyĕpzh) Pol.	51.0 N	23.10 E
81	Wiergate (wẽr'gāt) Tex.	31.2 N	93.43 W
123	Wierzbnik (vyäzh'bnēk) Pol.	51.3 N	21.6 E
122	Wiesbaden (vēs'bä-dĕn) Ger.	50.5 N	8.14 E
116	Wigan (wĭg'ăn) Gt. Brit.	53.30 N	2.38 W
82	Wiggins (wĭg'ĭnz) Miss.	30.53 N	89.9 W
116	Wight, Isle of (wīt) Gt. Brit.	50.40 N	1.20 W
116	Wigtown (wĭg'tŭn) Gt. Brit.	54.52 N	4.25 W
116	Wigtown B. Gt. Brit.	54.50 N	4.10 W
72	Wigwam (wĭg'wôm) Colo. (Colo. Sprs. In.)	38.32 N	104.38 W
79	Wilber (wĭl'bẽr) Neb.	40.28 N	96.59 W
79	Wilburton (wĭl'bẽr-tŭn) Okla.	34.55 N	95.18 W
166	Wilcannia Austl.	31.32 S	143.25 E
106	Wilde (wĭld) Arg. (In.)	34.41 S	58.19 W
73	Wildomar (wĭl'dō-mär) Calif. (Los Angeles In.)	33.36 N	117.17 W
77	Wild Rice R. Minn.-N. D.	47.17 N	96.5 W
72	Wilds (wīldz) Colo. (Denver In.)	40.25 N	105.10 W
85	Wildwood (wīld'wŏŏd) N. J.	38.58 N	74.52 W
123	Wilejka (vē-lā'ē-kȧ) Pol.	54.30 N	26 55 E
78	Wiley (wī'lē) Colo.	38.7 N	102.42 W
143	Wilge R. (wĭl'gē) U. S. Afr.	25.46 S	28.55 E
110	Wilhelmina (vĕl-hĕl-mē'nȧ) Swe.	64.37 N	16.42 E
161	Wilhelmina, Mt. (vĕl-hĕl-mē'nȧ) Neth. Ind.	4.5 S	138.36 E
119	Wilhelmsburg (vĕl'hĕlms-bŏŏrgh) Ger. (Hamburg In.)	53.30 N	10.0 E
122	Wilhelmshaven (vĕl-hĕlms-hä'fĕn) Ger.	53.31 N	8.9 E
123	Wilja R. (vĕl'yȧ) Pol.	54.41 N	25.17 E
85	Wilkes-Barre (wĭlks'-băr-ē) Pa.	41.14 N	75.52 W
46	Wilkes Land (wĭlks) Ant.	68.0 S	126.0 E
89	Wilkinsburg (wĭl'kĭnz-bûrg) Pa. (Pittsburgh In.)	40.26 N	79.53 W
70	Willamette R. (wĭ-lăm'ĕt) Ore.	44.35 N	123.15 W
70	Willamette R., Middle Fork Ore.	43.55 N	123.10 W
167	Willandra Billabong Cr. (wĭl-lăn'-drȧ bĭl'ȧ-bŏng). Austl.	33.11 S	145.0 E
70	Willapa B. (wĭ-lăp'ȧ) (wĭl'ȧ-pȧ) Wash.	46.40 N	124.5 W
84	Willard (wĭl'ȧrd) Ohio	41.3 N	82.47 W
73	Willard. Utah (Salt Lake City In.)	41.24 N	112.2 W
75	Willcox (wĭl'kŏks) Ariz.	32.13 N	109.51 W
102	Willemstad (vĭl'ĕm-stät) Curaçao	12.5 N	68.59 W
118	Willenhall (wĭl'ĕn-hôl) Gt. Brit.	52.35 N	2.4 W
116	Willesden (wĭlz'dĕn) Gt. Brit.	51.30 N	0.15 W
164	William Creek (wĭl'yȧm) Austl.	28.45 S	136.15 E
75	Williams (wĭl'yȧmz) Ariz.	35.17 N	112.11 W
82	Williamsburg (wĭl'yȧmz-bûrg). Ky.	36.43 N	84.12 W
85	Williamsburg Va.	37.15 N	76.40 W
96	Williams I. Ba. Is.	24.39 N	78.28 W
83	Williamson (wĭl'yȧm-sŭn) N. C.	35.52 N	77.4 W
84	Williamson W. Va.	37.40 N	82.15 W
85	Williamsport (wĭl'yȧmz-pōrt). Md.	39.36 N	77.48 W
85	Williamsport Pa.	41.13 N	77.2 W
75	Williams R. Ariz.	34.14 N	113.50 W
83	Williamston (wĭl'yȧmz-tŭn). S. C.	34.36 N	82.29 W
166	Williamstown (wĭl'yȧmz-toun) Austl.	37.49 S	144.50 E
84	Williamstown W. Va.	39.22 N	81.30 W
85	Willimantic (wĭl-ĭ-măn'tĭk). Conn.	41.40 N	72.10 W
81	Willis (wĭl'ĭs) Tex.	30.25 N	95.28 W
165	Willis Is. Austl.	16.15 S	150.8 E
76	Williston (wĭl'ĭs-tŭn) N. D.	48.8 N	103.39 W
142	Williston U. S. Afr.	31.20 S	20.56 E
74	Willits (wĭl'ĭts) Calif.	39.26 N	123.21 W
77	Willmar (wĭl'mär) Minn.	45.7 N	95.2 W
84	Willoughby (wĭl'ō-bē) Ohio	41.39 N	81.22 W
89	Willoughby B. Va. (Norfolk In.)	36.57 N	76.18 W
166	Willoughby, C. Austl.	35.48 S	138.5 E
71	Willow Creek (wĭl'ō) Mont.	48.45 N	111.30 W
70	Willow Cr. Ore.	45.35 N	119.55 W
70	Willow Cr. Ore.	44.10 N	117.40 W
142	Willowmore (wĭl'ō-mōr). U. S. Afr.	33.18 S	23.29 E
74	Willows (wĭl'ōz) Calif.	39.31 N	122.12 W
88	Willow Springs. Ill. (Chicago In.)	41.44 N	87.52 W
79	Willow Springs Mo.	37.0 N	91.57 W
143	Willowvale (wĭl'ō-văl) U. S Afr.	32.17 S	28.31 E
81	Wills Point (wĭlz) Tex.	32.42 N	96.2 W
166	Willunga (wĭ-lŭn'gȧ) Austl.	35.15 S	138.35 E
166	Willyama (Broken Hill) (wĭl-yä'mȧ). Austl.	31.57 S	141.28 E
119	Wilmarsdonck (vĕl'märz-dŏnk) Bel. (Anvers In.)	51.17 N	4.22 E
77	Wilmette (wĭl-mĕt') Ill.	42.4 N	87.43 W
166	Wilmington (wĭl'mĭng-tŭn). Austl.	32.41 S	138.8 E
73	Wilmington Calif. (Los Angeles In.)	33.47 N	118.18 W
85	Wilmington Del.	39.44 N	75.32 W
87	Wilmington Mass. (In.)	42.33 N	71.10 W
83	Wilmington N. C.	34.14 N	77.57 W
84	Wilmington Ohio	39.21 N	83.49 W
89	Wilmington I. Ga. (Savannah In.)	32.0 N	80.58 W
89	Wilmington R. Ga. (Savannah In.)	32.0 N	81.0 W
84	Wilmore (wĭl'mōr) Ky.	37.50 N	84.40 W
118	Wilmslow (wĭlmz'lō) Gt. Brit.	53.20 N	2.14 W
123	Wilno (Vilna) (vĕl'nô) (vĭl'nȧ) Pol.	54.41 N	25.17 E
119	Wilryck (vĕl'rĭk). Bel. (Anvers In.)	51.10 N	4.23 E
79	Wilson (wĭl'sŭn) Ark.	35.34 N	90.3 W
83	Wilson N. C.	35.43 N	77.56 W
79	Wilson Okla.	34.9 N	97.26 W
72	Wilson Cr. Colo. (Colo. Sprs. In.)	38.40 N	105.11 W
77	Wilson I. Can.	48.44 N	87.29 W
82	Wilson L. Ala.	34.48 N	87.30 W
73	Wilson Mt. Calif. (Los Angeles In.)	34.14 N	118.4 W
71	Wilson Peak Utah	40.47 N	110.48 W
167	Wilson Promontory Austl.	39.5 S	146.12 E
73	Wilsonville. Ala. (Birmingham In.)	33.14 N	86.29 W
76	Wilton (wĭl'tŭn) N. D.	47.9 N	100.47 W
164	Wiluna (wĭ-lōō'nȧ) Austl.	26.32 S	120.18 E
116	Wimbledon (wĭm'b'l-dŭn) Gt. Brit.	51.25 N	0.10 W
166	Wimmera R. (wĭm'ẽr-ȧ) Austl.	36.38 S	142.22 E
84	Winamac (wĭn'ȧ-măk) Ind.	41.5 N	86.40 W
143	Winburg (wĭn'bûrg) U. S. Afr.	28.29 S	27.1 E
73	Winchester (wĭn'chĕs-tẽr) Calif. (Los Angeles In.)	33.43 N	117.4 W
116	Winchester Gt. Brit.	51.5 N	1.20 W
70	Winchester Ida.	46.13 N	116.38 W
84	Winchester Ky.	37.59 N	84.12 W
87	Winchester Mass.	42.27 N	71.8 W
86	Winchester N. H.	42.45 N	72.25 W
84	Winchester Ohio	40.10 N	84.50 W
82	Winchester Tenn.	35.11 N	86.7 W
85	Winchester Va.	39.10 N	78.12 W
166	Windabout L. (wĭnd'ȧ-bout) Austl.	31.20 S	137.5 E
85	Windber (wĭnd'bẽr) Pa.	40.15 N	78.48 W
76	Wind Cave Natl. Park S. D.	43.33 N	103.29 W
82	Winder (wīn'dẽr) Ga.	33.58 N	83.43 W
116	Windermere (wĭn'dẽr-mẽr) Gt. Brit.	54.25 N	2.55 W
85	Windham (wĭnd'ăm) Conn.	41.44 N	72.6 W
140	Windhoek (vĭnt'hŏŏk). S. W. Afr.	22.33 S	17.10 E
77	Windom (wĭn'dŭm) Minn.	43.52 N	95.5 W
165	Windora (wĭn-dō'rȧ) Austl.	25.29 S	142.40 E
71	Wind R. (wĭnd) Wyo.	43.25 N	109.15 W
71	Wind River Range Wyo.	43.0 N	109.30 W
167	Windsor (wĭn'zẽr) Austl.	33.38 S	150.51 E
55	Windsor Can.	45.5 N	64.14 W
55	Windsor Can.	42.18 N	82.50 W
78	Windsor Colo.	40.27 N	104.54 W
116	Windsor Gt. Brit.	51.25 N	0.35 W
79	Windsor Mo.	38.32 N	93.29 W
83	Windsor N. C.	35.59 N	76.57 W
86	Windsor Vt.	43.30 N	72.25 W
143	Windsorton (wĭn'zẽr-tŭn) Bech.	28.18 S	24.42 E
97	Windward Channel (wĭnd'wẽrd) W. I.	19.50 N	73.50 W
95	Windward Is. W. I. (In.)		
91	Windward Is. W. I.	13.0 N	61.30 W
73	Wineville (wīn'vĭl) Calif. (Los Angeles In.)	34.2 N	117.32 W
79	Winfield (wĭn'fēld) Kan.	37.14 N	97.0 W
88	Winfield Junction N. Y. (In.)	40.44 N	73.54 W
167	Wingham (wĭng'ăm) Austl.	31.51 S	152.23 E
154	Wingsun (wĭng'sōōn') Chn.	22.52 N	109.2 E
55	Winisk R. (wĭn'ĭsk) Can.	54.32 N	87.0 W
80	Wink (wĭŋk) Tex.	31.48 N	103.9 W
142	Winkelhaaks R. (vĭŋ'kĕl-häks) U. S. Afr.	32.50 S	19.30 E
138	Winneba (wĭn'ē-bȧ) G. C.	5.28 N	0.38 W
77	Winnebago (wĭn-ē-bā'gō) Minn.	43.47 N	94.8 W
77	Winnebago L. Wis.	44.0 N	88.25 W
70	Winnemucca (wĭn-ē-mŭk'ȧ) Nev.	40.59 N	117.43 W
86	Winnepesaukee, L. (wĭn'ē-pē-sô'kē). N. H.	43.40 N	71.25 W

ng-sing; ŋ baŋk; N-nasalized n; nŏd; cŏmmit; ōld; ôbey; ôrder; fōōd; fŏŏt; ou-out; s-soft; sh-dish; th-thin; pūre; ûnite; ûrn; stŭd; circŭs; ü-as "y" in study; '-indeterminate vowel.

Page	Name Pronunciation	Region	Lat. °′	Long. °′
76	Winner (wĭn'ẽr)	S. D.	43.22 N	99.51 W
77	Winnetka (wĭ-nĕt'kȧ)	Ill.	42.5 N	87.43 W
71	Winnett (wĭn'ĕt)	Mont.	47.1 N	108.20 W
81	Winnfield (wĭn'fēld)	La.	31.55 N	92.39 W
77	Winnibigoshish L. (wĭn'ĭ-bĭ-gō'shĭsh)	Minn.	47.25 N	94.10 W
54	Winnipeg (wĭn'ĭ-pĕg)	Can.	49.47 N	97.15 W
54	Winnipeg L.	Can.	53.0 N	97.0 W
54	Winnipegosis (wĭn'ĭ-pê-gō'sĭs)	Can.	51.42 N	99.59 W
54	Winnipegosis, L.	Can.	52.40 N	99.58 W
81	Winnsboro (wĭnz'bŭr-ô)	La.	32.8 N	90.43 W
83	Winnsboro	S. C.	34.22 N	81.6 W
81	Winnsboro	Tex.	32.57 N	95.18 W
77	Winona (wĭ-nō'nȧ)	Minn.	44.3 N	91.38 W
82	Winona	Miss.	33.28 N	89.43 W
86	Winooski (wĭ-nōōs'kê)	Vt.	44.31 N	73.11 W
118	Winsford (wĭnz'fẽrd)	Gt. Brit.	53.11 N	2.30 W
75	Winslow (wĭnz'lō)	Ariz.	35.1 N	110.43 W
49	Winslow	Wash. (Seattle In.)	47.37 N	122.32 W
85	Winsted (wĭn'stĕd)	Conn.	41.55 N	73.5 W
118	Winster (wĭn'stẽr)	Gt. Brit.	53.8 N	1.38 W
73	Winston (wĭn'stŭn)	Ga. (Atlanta In.)	33.43 N	84.50 W
83	Winston-Salem (sā'lĕm)	N. C.	36.5 N	80.14 W
122	Winterberg (Vimperk) (vĭn'tĕr-bĕrĸ) (vĭm'pĕrk)	Ger.	49.3 N	13.41 E
142	Winterberg (Mt.) (wĭn'tẽr-bûrg)	U. S. Afr.	33.7 S	19.5 E
143	Winterberg (Mts.)	U. S. Afr.	32.25 S	26.30 E
83	Winter Garden	Fla. (In.)	28.32 N	81.34 W
83	Winter Haven	Fla. (In.)	28.2 N	81.43 W
143	Winterhoek (vĭn'tẽr-ho͝ok)	U.S.Afr.	33.32 S	25.0 E
83	Winter Park	Fla. (In.)	28.36 N	81.20 W
80	Winters (wĭn'tẽrz)	Tex.	31.59 N	99.58 W
77	Winterset (wĭn'tẽr-sĕt)	Ia.	71.19 N	94.1 W
122	Winterthur (vĭn'tẽr-to͞or)	Switz.	47.30 N	8.42 E
143	Winterton (wĭn'tẽr-tŭn)	U. S. Afr.	28.49 S	29.32 E
86	Winthrop (wĭn'thrŭp)	Me.	44.19 N	70.0 W
87	Winthrop	Mass. (In.)	42.22 N	70.59 W
77	Winthrop	Minn.	44.32 N	94.20 W
165	Winton	Austl.	22.14 S	143.0 E
171	Winton (wĭn'tŭn)	N. Z.	46.8 S	168.20 E
119	Winwick (wĭn'wĭk)	Gt. Brit. (Liverpool In.)	53.25 N	2.36 W
71	Wiota (wī-ō'tä)	Mont.	48.7 N	106.14 W
118	Wirksworth (wûrks'wûrth)	Gt. Brit.	53.5 N	1.35 W
166	Wirrega (wĭr'ê-gȧ)	Austl.	36.13 S	140.35 E
116	Wisbech (wĭz'bêch)	Gt. Brit.	52.40 N	0.10 E
85	Wisconisco (wĭs-kŏn-ĭs'kō)	Pa.	40.35 N	76.43 W
77	Wisconsin (State) (wĭs-kŏn'sĭn)	U. S.	44.40 N	89.40 W
77	Wisconsin Dells	Wis.	43.38 N	89.45 W
77	Wisconsin R.	Wis.	44.10 N	89.54 W
77	Wisconsin Rapids	Wis.	44.23 N	89.48 W
76	Wishek (wĭsh'ĕk)	N. D.	46.16 N	99.34 W
123	Wisla (Vistula) R. (vês'wȧ) (vĭs'tû-lȧ)	Pol.	51.4 N	21.50 E
123	Wisloka R. (vês-wô'kȧ)	Pol.	49.50 N	21.23 E
103	Wismar (wĭz'mȧr) (vĭs'mär)	Br. Gu.	5.58 N	58.15 W
122	Wismar (vĭs'mär)	Ger.	53.54 N	11.26 E
76	Wisner (wĭz'nẽr)	Neb.	42.0 N	96.54 W
123	Wisniowiec (vêsh-nyō'vyĕts)	Pol.	49.55 N	25.46 E
88	Wissahickon Cr. (wĭs-ȧ-hĭk'ŭn)	Pa. (Philadelphia In.)	40.3 N	75.13 W
125	Wissembourg (vē-säɴ-bo͞or')	Fr.	49.1 N	7.59 E
140	Wissmar Pool (L.) (vĭs'mär)	Bel. Cong.	3.12 S	17.20 E
143	Witbank (wĭt'băŋk)	U. S. Afr.	25.54 S	29.11 E
116	Witham (R.) (wĭdh'ăm)	Gt. Brit.	53.0 N	0.10 W
116	Withernsea (wĭdh'ẽrn-sē)	Gt. Brit.	53.40 N	0.5 E
119	Withington (wĭdh'ĭng-tŭn)	Gt. Brit. (Liverpool In.)	53.26 N	2.13 W
82	Withlacoochee R. (wĭth-lȧ-ko͞o'chē)	Fla.	31.0 N	83.18 W
143	Witteberg (Mts.) (wĭt'ê-bẽrg)	U. S. Afr.	30.40 S	27.30 E
119	Wittenau (vĭt'ē-nou)	Ger. (Berlin In.)	52.36 N	13.20 E
	Wittenberg, see Lutherstadt.			
122	Wittenberge (vĭt-ĕn-bĕr'gē)	Ger.	53.0 N	11.43 E
122	Wittlich (vĭt'lĭĸ)	Ger.	49.58 N	6.53 E
122	Wittstock (vĭt'shtôk)	Ger.	53.11 N	12.26 E
141	Witu (wē'too)	Kenya	2.18 S	40.28 E
143	Witzieshoek (wĭt'sêz-ho͝ok)	U. S. Afr.	28.31 S	28.51 E
123	Wkra (Dzialdowka) R. (v'krȧ) (jyȧl-do͞of'kȧ)	Pol.	52.50 N	20.48 E
123	Wloclawek (vwôts-wä'vĕk)	Pol.	52.38 N	19.6 E
123	Wlodawa (vwô-dä'vä)	Pol.	51.33 N	23.33 E
123	Wlodzimierz (vwô-jê-myĕ'zhĕts)	Pol.	50.49 N	24.20 E
123	Wloszczowa (vwôsh-chō'vä)	Pol.	50.51 N	19.58 E
87	Woburn (wo͞o'bŭrn) (wō'bŭrn)	Mass. (In.)	42.28 N	71.9 W
167	Wodonga (wō-dŏŋ'gȧ)	Austl.	36.8 S	146.52 E
122	Wolfenbüttel (vôl'fĕn-büt-ĕl)	Ger.	52.10 N	10.31 E
85	Wolf I. (wo͝olf)	Can.	44.10 N	76.25 W
88	Wolf L.	Ill.-Ind. (Chicago In.)	41.40 N	87.32 W
82	Wolf R.	Tenn.-Miss.	35.5 N	89.40 W
77	Wolf R.	Wis.	44.50 N	88.38 W
71	Wolf Point	Mont.	48.6 N	105.40 W
86	Wolfville (wo͝olf'vĭl)	Can.	45.5 N	64.21 W
122	Wolgast (vôl'gäst)	Ger.	54.4 N	13.45 E
123	Wolkowysk (vôl-kō'vêsk)	Pol.	53.9 N	24.28 E
164	Wollall (wo͝ol'ôl)	Austl.	19.45 S	120.58 E
54	Wollaston L. (wo͝ol'ȧs-tŭn)	Can.	58.15 N	103.30 W
167	Wollondilly R. (wo͝ol'ŏn-dĭl-ê)	Austl.	34.25 S	150.8 E
167	Wollongong (wo͝ol'ŭn-gŏng)	Austl.	34.24 S	150.54 E
143	Wolmaransstad (vôl'mä-rän-stät)	U. S. Afr.	27.11 S	25.58 E
123	Wolomin (vô-wō'mên)	Pol.	52.19 N	21.15 E
166	Wolseley (wo͝olz'lê)	Austl.	36.24 S	140.54 E
118	Wolstanton (wo͝ol-stăn'tŭn)	Gt. Brit.	53.2 N	2.13 W
116	Wolverhampton (wo͝ol'vẽr-hămp-tŭn)	Gt. Brit.	52.35 N	2.10 W
118	Wolverton (wo͝ol'vẽr-tŭn)	Gt. Brit.	52.4 N	0.48 W
119	Wommelghem (vŏm'ĕl-gĕm)	Bel. (Anvers In.)	51.12 N	4.31 E
157	Wonju (wôn'jo͞o')	Cho.	37.21 N	127.56 E
157	Wonsan (Gensan) (wôn'sän') (gĕn'sän)	Cho.	39.11 N	127.28 E
167	Wonthaggi (wônt-hăg'ê)	Austl.	38.37 S	145.33 E
76	Wood	S. D.	43.28 N	100.24 W
76	Woodbine (wo͝od'bīn)	Ia.	41.45 N	95.42 W
70	Woodburn (wo͝od'bŭrn)	Ore.	45.9 N	122.51 W
88	Woodbury (wo͝od'bĕr-ê)	N. J. (Philadelphia In.)	39.50 N	75.9 W
119	Woodchurch (wo͝od'chûrch)	Gt. Brit. (Liverpool In.)	53.23 N	3.6 W
119	Woodford (wo͝od'fẽrd)	Gt. Brit. (London In.)	51.36 N	0.1 E
119	Wood Green	Gt. Brit. (London In.)	51.36 N	0.8 W
49	Woodinville (wo͝od'ĭn-vĭl)	Wash. (Seattle In.)	47.45 N	122.10 W
89	Wood L.	Minn. (Minneapolis In.)	44.52 N	93.16 W
74	Woodland (wo͝od'lănd)	Calif.	38.40 N	121.48 W
56	Woodland	Can. (Winnipeg In.)	50.12 N	97.40 W
49	Woodland	Wash. (Portland In.)	45.53 N	122.45 W
72	Woodland Park	Colo. (Colo. Sprs. In.)	38.59 N	105.4 W
161	Woodlark (Murua) (I.) (wo͝od'lärk) (mo͞o'ro͞o-ȧ)	Pap. Ter.	9.0 S	152.45 E
164	Woodroffe, Mt. (wo͝od'rŭf)	Austl.	26.0 S	132.0 E
83	Woodruff (wo͝od'rŭf)	S. C.	34.44 N	82.2 W
73	Woods Cross	Utah (Salt Lake City In.)	40.53 N	111.55 W
84	Woodsfield (wo͝odz'fēld)	Ohio	39.45 N	81.9 W
167	Woodside (wo͝od'sīd)	Austl.	38.32 S	146.52 E
164	Woods, L. (wo͝odz)	Austl.	17.50 S	133.30 E
77	Woods, L. of the	Can.-U. S.	49.10 N	94.40 W
73	Woodstock (wo͝od'stŏk)	Ala. (Birmingham In.)	33.13 N	87.9 W
55	Woodstock	Can.	46.1 N	67.37 W
84	Woodstock	Can.	43.8 N	80.50 W
77	Woodstock	Ill.	42.20 N	88.28 W
85	Woodstock	Va.	38.54 N	78.29 W
86	Woodsville (wo͝odz'vĭl)	N. H.	44.9 N	72.0 W
169	Woodville (wo͝od'vĭl)	Austl. (Adelaide In.)	34.53 S	138.33 E
82	Woodville	Miss.	31.6 N	91.18 W
170	Woodville	N. Z.	40.20 S	175.55 E
81	Woodville	Tex.	30.47 N	94.25 W
73	Woodward (wo͝od'wẽrd)	Ala. (Birmingham In.)	33.25 N	86.57 W
78	Woodward	Okla.	36.26 N	99.25 W
157	Wooljin (wo͝ol'jĭn')	Cho.	37.1 N	129.20 E
158	Woolleng (Matsu) I. (wo͝ol'lĕng') (mät'so͞o)	Jap.	37.31 N	130.52 E
73	Woolsey (wo͝ol'sê)	Ga. (Atlanta In.)	33.22 N	84.24 W
171	Woolston (wo͝ol'stŭn)	N. Z. (In.)	43.32 S	172.43 E
119	Woolton (wo͝ol'tŭn)	Gt. Brit. (Liverpool In.)	53.22 N	2.52 W
119	Woolwich (wo͝ol'ĭj)	Gt. Brit. (London In.)	51.29 N	0.2 E
86	Woonsocket (wo͞on-sŏk'ĕt)	R. I.	42.0 N	71.31 W
76	Woonsocket	S. D.	44.4 N	98.16 W
84	Wooster (wo͝os'tẽr)	Ohio	40.49 N	81.56 W
155	Woosung (wo͞o'so͝ong')	Chn.	31.21 N	121.30 E
116	Worcester	Gt. Brit.	52.10 N	2.10 W
86	Worcester	Mass.	42.15 N	71.50 W
142	Worcester	U. S. Afr.	33.39 S	19.22 E
118	Worcester Co.	Gt. Brit.	52.19 N	2.15 W
116	Workington (wûr'kĭng-tŭn)	Gt. Brit.	54.35 N	3.30 W
118	Worksop (wûrk'sŭp) (wûr'sŭp)	Gt. Brit.	53.18 N	1.7 W
71	Worland (wûr'lănd)	Wyo.	44.1 N	107.57 W
123	Wormditt (vōrm'dĕt)	Ger.	54.6 N	20.10 E
122	Worms (vōrms)	Ger.	49.37 N	8.21 E
81	Wortham (wûr'dhăm)	Tex.	31.46 N	96.28 W
116	Worthing (wûr'dhĭng)	Gt. Brit.	50.50 N	0.25 W
84	Worthington (wûr'dhĭng-tŭn)	Ind.	39.6 N	87.0 W
76	Worthington	Minn.	43.38 N	95.35 W
73	Worthville (wûrth'vĭl)	Ga. (Atlanta In.)	33.22 N	83.54 W
160	Wowoni I. (wō-wō'nê)	Neth. Ind.	4.0 S	123.0 E
118	Wragby (răg'bê)	Gt. Brit.	53.17 N	0.19 W
149	Wrangel I. (răŋ'gĕl)	U. S. S. R.	70.45 N	180.0 E
53	Wrangell	Alsk.	56.25 N	132.30 W
53	Wrangell, Mt.	Alsk.	62.5 N	144.0 W
116	Wrath, C. (răth)	Gt. Brit.	58.35 N	5.0 W
78	Wray (rā)	Colo.	40.5 N	102.15 W
118	Wreak, R. (rēk)	Gt. Brit.	52.44 N	1.0 W
167	Wreck B. (rĕk)	Austl.	35.12 S	150.36 E
165	Wreck Reef	Austl.	22.15 S	155.30 E
118	Wrekin, The (Mt.) (rĕk'ĭn)	Gt. Brit.	52.40 N	2.33 W
83	Wrens (rĕnz)	Ga.	33.13 N	82.23 W
87	Wrentham (rĕn'thăm)	Mass. (In.)	42.3 N	71.20 W
116	Wrexham (rĕk'săm)	Gt. Brit.	53.0 N	2.55 W
122	Wriezen (vrē'zĕn)	Ger.	52.44 N	14.6 E
163	Wright (rīt)	P. I.	11.47 N	125.2 E
89	Wrights R. (rīts)	S. C. (Savannah In.)	32.6 N	80.58 W
83	Wrightsville (rīts'vĭl)	Ga.	32.43 N	82.43 W
54	Wrigley (rĭg'lê)	Can.	63.20 N	124.15 W
123	Wrzésnia (vzhăsh'nyȧ)	Pol.	52.18 N	17.33 E
156	Wuan (wo͞o'än')	Chn.	36.46 N	114.18 E
155	Wuchang (wo͞o'chăng')	Chn.	30.32 N	114.10 E
158	Wuchang	Manch.	44.50 N	127.12 E
155	Wuchanghsien (wo͞o'chăng'hsyĕn')	Chn.	30.22 N	114.45 E
156	Wucheng (wo͞o'chĕng')	Chn.	37.8 N	115.53 E
156	Wuchih (wo͞o'chĭ')	Chn.	35.3 N	113.28 E
156	Wuching (wo͞o'chĭng')	Chn.	39.32 N	116.51 E
154	Wuchow (wo͞o'chō')	Chn.	23.28 N	111.20 E
154	Wuchwan (wo͞o'chwän')	Chn.	28.22 N	108.2 E
154	Wufeng (Changlo) (wo͞o'fĕng') (chăng'lō')	Chn.	30.18 N	110.35 E
156	Wuho (wo͞o'hō')	Chn.	33.8 N	117.50 E
156	Wuhsien (wo͞o'hsyĕn')	Chn.	38.6 N	113.26 E
155	Wuhu (wo͞o'ho͞o')	Chn.	31.20 N	118.23 E
154	Wukang (wo͞o'kăng')	Chn.	26.40 N	110.25 E
155	Wukang	Chn.	30.33 N	119.57 E
156	Wukao R. (wo͞o'kä'ō)	Chn.	36.35 N	120.13 E
156	Wuki (wo͞o'kĭ')	Chn.	38.16 N	114.56 E
156	Wukiang (wo͞o'kyăng')	Chn.	38.10 N	115.21 E
156	Wukiao (wo͞o'kyä'ō)	Chn.	37.45 N	116.23 E
158	Wukon R. (wo͞o'kôn')	Manch.	46.27 N	130.27 E
155	Wu Kung Shan (Mts.) (wo͞o'ko͝ong'shän')	Chn.	27.0 N	115.40 E
158	Wulachieh (wo͞o'lä-kī-ê')	Manch.	44.4 N	126.30 E
155	Wuning (wo͞o'nĭng')	Chn.	29.10 N	114.43 E
95	Wuonta (wo͞o ôn'tä)	Nic.	13.31 N	83.32 W
75	Wupatki Natl. Mon. (wo͞o-păt'kĭ)	Ariz.	35.45 N	111.35 W
155	Wuping (wo͞o'pĭng')	Chn.	25.3 N	115.54 E
122	Wuppertal (vo͝op'ẽr-täl)	Ger.	51.16 N	7.10 E
	Wu R., see Yu R., China.			
154	Wu R.	Chn.	29.20 N	107.42 E
155	Wu R.	Chn.	28.6 N	120.25 E
122	Württemberg (State) (vür'tĕm-bĕrgh)	Ger.	48.35 N	9.20 E
122	Würzburg (vürts'bo͝orgh)	Ger.	49.48 N	9.56 E
122	Wurzen (vo͝ort'sĕn)	Ger.	51.23 N	12.45 E
154	Wushan (wo͞o'shän')	Chn.	31.10 N	109.45 E
152	Wushih (Vch Turfan) (wo͞o'shĭ) (o͞och' to͝or-fän')	Chn.	41.7 N	79.30 E
155	Wusih (wo͞o'sĭ')	Chn.	31.32 N	120.18 E
152	Wusu (Kweitun) (wo͞o'so͞o') (kwā'to͞on')	Chn.	44.29 N	84.28 E
155	Wusueh (wo͞o'so͞o'ȧ')	Chn.	29.46 N	115.52 E
	Wusung, see Woosung, China.			
156	Wutai (wo͞o'tī')	Chn.	38.46 N	113.23 E
156	Wutai Shan (Mts.) (shän')	Chn.	39.5 N	113.30 E
156	Wutaishan (Mt.)	Chn.	38.47 N	113.47 E
156	Wuting (wo͞o'tĭng')	Chn.	37.32 N	117.32 E
155	Wuwei (wo͞o'wā')	Chn.	31.17 N	117.52 E
155	Wuyi (wo͞o'yĭ')	Chn.	28.53 N	119.52 E
156	Wuyi	Chn.	37.56 N	115.53 E
156	Wuyi	Chn.	32.15 N	118.27 E
155	Wuyuan (wo͞o'yo͞o-än')	Chn.	29.17 N	117.50 E
153	Wuyun (wo͞o-yün')	Manch.	49.5 N	130.1 E
167	Wyalong (wī'ȧ lông)	Austl.	33.55 S	147.16 E
84	Wyandotte (wī'ăn-dŏt)	Mich.	42.12 N	83.10 W
73	Wyatt (wī'ăt)	Ala. (Birmingham In.)	33.41 N	87.4 W
116	Wycombe (wĭ'kŭm)	Gt. Brit.	51.40 N	0.50 W
118	Wye, R. (wī)	Gt. Brit.	53.13 N	1.42 W
79	Wymore (wī'mōr)	Neb.	40.9 N	96.39 W
142	Wynberg (wīn'bĕrg)	U. S. Afr.	33.59 S	18.25 E
164	Wyndham (wīnd'ăm)	Austl.	15.30 S	128.10 E
171	Wyndham	N. Z.	46.30 S	168.50 E
119	Wyneghem (vī'nĕ-gĕm)	Bel. (Anvers In.)	51.14 N	4.31 E
79	Wynne (wĭn)	Ark.	35.13 N	90.47 W
79	Wynne Wood	Okla.	34.37 N	97.10 W
79	Wynona (wī-nō'nȧ)	Okla.	36.33 N	96.19 W
169	Wynyard (wĭn'yẽrd)	Austl. (Tas. In.)	41.0 S	145.43 E
71	Wyoming (State) (wī-ō'mĭng)	U. S.	41.05 N	105.30 W
71	Wyoming Ra.	Wyo.	42.40 N	110.40 W
169	Wyreema (wī-rē'mȧ)	Austl. (In.)	27.36 S	151.54 E
118	Wyre Forest (wīr)	Gt. Brit.	52.26 N	2.26 W
118	Wyre, R.	Gt. Brit.	53.51 N	2.57 W
123	Wysokie Mazowieckie (vê-sō'kyȧ mä-zô-vyĕt'skyȧ)	Pol.	52.56 N	22.43 E
123	Wyszków (vêsh'ko͝of)	Pol.	52.36 N	21.28 E
83	Wytheville (wĭth'vĭl)	Va.	36.57 N	81.6 W
96	Xagua Bank (sä'gwä)	Cuba	21.40 N	81.0 W
129	Xanthē (ksän'thê)	Grc.	41.8 N	24.53 E
84	Xenia (zē'nĭ-ȧ)	Ohio	39.43 N	83.55 W
129	Xerokhorios (I.) (ksē-rô-ĸō'rĭ-ōs)	Grc.	39.10 N	23.59 E
92	Xicotencatl (hē-kô-tĕŋ-kät''l)	Mex.	23.0 N	98.56 W
92	Xilitla (hē-lē'tlä)	Mex.	21.23 N	99.2 W
103	Xingú, R. (zhĕŋ-go͞o')	Braz.	3.0 S	52.15 W
93	Xochaque (hō-chä'kȧ)	Mex. (In.)	19.25 N	98.56 W
92	Xochihuehuetlán (hō'chē-wȧ-wĕ-tlän')	Mex.	17.55 N	98.33 W
93	Xochimilco (hō-chê-mēl'kō)	Mex. (In.)	19.16 N	99.6 W
93	Xochinahuac (hō-chê-nä-wäk')	Mex. (In.)	19.30 N	99.11 W
93	Xochitepec (hō-chê-tȧ-pĕk')	Mex. (In.)	19.15 N	99.8 W
93	Xocoyahualco (hō-kô-yä-wäl'kō)	Mex. (In.)	19.31 N	99.13 W
166	Yaapeet (yä-pāt')	Austl.	35.41 S	142.2 E
149	Yablonovoi Ridge (Mts.) (yȧ-blô-nô-vô'ĭ)	Sov. Un.	53.30 N	115.0 E
152	Yachow (yä'chō')	Chn.	29.56 N	102.50 E
152	Yachu (Yalung Ho) (R.) (yä'cho͞o') (yä'lo͝ong' hō')	Chn.	30.0 N	101.6 E
167	Yackandandah (yă-kăn-dăn'dȧ)	Austl.	36.18 S	146.51 E
49	Yacolt (yă'kôlt)	Wash. (Portland In.)	45.52 N	122.24 W
102	Yacuiba (yä-ko͞o-ē'bä)	Bol.	21.58 S	64.0 W
83	Yadkin R. (yăd'kĭn)	N. C.	35.40 N	80.20 W
131	Yagotin (yä'gô-tên)	Sov. Un.	50.17 N	31.45 E
96	Yaguajay (yä-guä-hä'ê)	Cuba	22.17 N	79.18 W
159	Yahata	Jap.	35.42 N	139.56 E
92	Yahualica (yä-wä-lē'kä)	Mex.	21.9 N	102.57 W
93	Yahuatengo (yä-wä-tĕŋ'gō)	Mex. (In.)	19.38 N	98.54 W
131	Yaila Range (yä'ê-lä)	Sov. Un.	44.50 N	34.30 E
93	Yajalón (yä-hä-lōn')	Mex.	17.17 N	92.10 W

ăt; finăl; rāte; senâte; ärm; ȧsk; sofȧ; fâre; ch-choose; dh-as th in other; bē; êvent; bĕt; recĕnt; cratẽr; g-go; gh-gutteral g; bĭt; ĭ-short neutral; rīde; ĸ-gutteral k as ch in German ich;

Page	Name Pronunciation Region	Lat. °′	Long. °′
70	Yakima (yăk'ĭ-mȧ)........Wash.	46.36 N	120.30 W
70	Yakima R................Wash.	46.45 N	120.21 W
159	Yaku I. (yä'ko͞o)............Jap.	30.15 N	130.30 E
149	Yakut (Aut. Rep.) (yȧ'ko͝ot) Sov. Un.	65.0 N	125.0 E
53	Yakutat (yȧk'o͞o-tȧt).......Alsk.	59.35 N	139.48 W
149	Yakutsk (yȧ-ko͝otsk')....Sov. Un.	62.0 N	129.50 E
93	Ya'álag (Villa Hidalgo) (yä-lä' läg) (vēl'yä ê-däl'gō).Mex.	17.12 N	96.11 W
72	Yale (yāl)...Can. (Vancouver In.)	49.33 N	121.25 W
84	Yale.....................Mich.	43.8 N	82.46 W
79	Yale.....................Okla.	36.7 N	96.43 W
49	Yale........Wash. (Portland In.)	45.58 N	122.19 W
83	Yale, L....................Fla.	28.55 N	81.45 W
139	Yalinga (yä-lĭŋ'gȧ) ....Fr. Eq. Afr.	6.50 N	23.27 E
82	Yalobusha R. (yă-lô-bo͝osh'ȧ) Miss.	33.47 N	89.30 W
158	Yal R. (yäl)...............Chn.	48.0 N	122.35 E
131	Yalta (Krasnoarmeisk) (yäl'tȧ) (krȧs-nô-ȧr-mā'ĭsk)...Sov. Un.	44.29 N	34.10 E
152	Yalung Ho (Yachu) (R.) yä'lo͝ong' hō') (yä'cho͞o').Chn.	30.0 N	101.6 E
157	Yalu R. (yä'lo͞o')......Chn.-Cho.	40.10 N	124.30 E
148	Yalutorovsk (yä-lo͞o'tô-rôfsk) Sov. Un.	56.40 N	66.25 E
159	Yamabe(yä'mȧ-bȧ) Jap.(OsakaIn.)	34.59 N	135.23 E
159	Yamadanochi (yä'mȧ-dȧ-nō'chê) Jap.	33.36 N	133.40 E
158	Yamagata (yä-mȧ-gä'tȧ).....Jap.	38.14 N	140.21 E
159	Yamaguchi (yä-mȧ-go͞o'chê)..Jap.	34.11 N	131.30 E
148	Yamal Pen. (yä-mäl')....Sov. Un.	71.0 N	71.0 E
97	Yamasa (yä-mä'sä)....Dom. Rep.	18.47 N	70.2 W
159	Yamasaki (yä'mȧ-sä'kê)......Jap.	35.1 N	134.32 E
159	Yamatogawa R. (yä'mȧ-tô-gä'wä) Jap. (Osaka In.)	34.36 N	135.33 E
161	Yamdena (I.) (yăm-dā'nä) Neth. Ind.	7.30 S	131.30 E
152	Yamdok (Palti), L. (yȧm-dôk) (päl'tê).Chn.	29.0 N	90.45 E
160	Yamethin (yŭ-mē'thên).....India	20.15 N	96.28 E
162	Y'ami I. (ê-ä'mê)......P. I. (In.)	21.5 N	121.58 E
165	Yamma Yamma, L. (yăm'ȧ yăm'ȧ).Austl.	26.30 S	141.30 E
78	Yampa R. (yăm'pȧ)........Colo.	40.28 N	107.10 W
149	Yamsk (yȧmsk).........Sov. Un.	59.35 N	154.0 E
166	Yanac (yăn'ȧk)............Austl.	36.9 S	141.29 E
159	Yanagawa (yä'nȧ-gä'wȧ).....Jap.	33.11 N	130.23 E
149	Yana R. (yä'nȧ)........Sov. Un.	68.0 N	134.10 E
151	Yanaon (yȧ'nȧ'ôɴ')........India	16.44 N	82.12 E
167	Yanco (yăŋ'kō)............Austl.	34.36 S	146.25 E
167	Yanda Cr. (yăn'dȧ)........Austl.	30.55 S	145.47 E
154	Yanfa (yän'fä')..............Chn.	25.14 N	113.10 E
156	Yangcheng (yäng'chĕng')....Chn.	33.51 N	113.38 E
156	Yangchow (yäng'chō').......Chn.	32.26 N	119.23 E
157	Yangchun (yäng'cho͞on').....Cho.	38.7 N	127.7 E
157	Yangduk (yäng'do͞ok').......Cho.	39.13 N	126.52 E
152	Yangihissar (Yingkisha) (yäŋ'gê-hĭs'är) (yĭng'kĭ-shä').Chn.	39.2 N	75.37 E
152	Yangi Shahr (Shuleh) (yäŋ'gê shär') (sho͞o'lȧ').Chn.	41.22 N	80.25 E
156	Yangku (yäng'ko͞o').........Chn.	36.8 N	115.53 E
153	Yangkyung (yäng'kyo͝ong') Chn. (Shanghai In.)	31.11 N	121.31 E
154	Yangli (yäng'lē').............Chn.	22.52 N	107.19 E
157	Yangpyung (yäng'pyo͝ong')...Cho.	37.32 N	127.31 E
154	Yangshan (yäng'shän')......Chn.	24.27 N	112.23 E
156	Yangsin (yäng'sĭn')..........Chn.	37.46 N	117.28 E
154	Yangso (yäng'sō')...........Chn.	24.40 N	110.24 E
153	Yangtze Kiang (R.) (yäng'tsĕ kyȧng').Chn.	30.0 N	116.30 E
154	Yangtze Kiang (Great R.)...Chn.	30.10 N	108.0 E
152	Yangtze Kiang (Dichu) (R.) (dē'cho͞o').Chn.	33.0 N	97.30 E
156	Yangwu (yäng'wo͞o')........Chn.	35.1 N	114.11 E
157	Yangyang (yäng'yäng')......Cho.	38.2 N	128.32 E
49	Yankton (yănk'tŭn) Ore. (Portland In.)	45.52 N	122.52 W
76	Yankton...................S. D.	42.53 N	97.23 W
129	Yannina (Ioannina) (yä'nê-nȧ) (yô-ä'nê-nȧ).Grc.	39.38 N	20.53 E
131	Yanushpol (yȧ'no͝osh-pôl') Sov. Un.	49.53 N	28.12 E
139	Yao (yä'ō)..........Fr. Eq. Afr.	13.0 N	17.36 E
138	Yaoundé (yȧ-o͞on-dā')........Cam.	3.58 N	11.40 E
6	Yap (I.) (yăp)......Pac. O. (In.)	9.30 N	138.10 E
97	Yaque del Norte, R. (yä'kȧ dĕl nôr'tȧ).Dom. Rep.	19.40 N	71.8 W
97	Yaque del Sur, R. (dĕl so͞or') Dom. Rep.	1.840 N	71.8 W
97	Yaque, Pico del (Mt.) (pē'kō dĕl yä'kȧ).Dom. Rep.	19.2 N	70.58 W
165	Yaraka (yȧ-răk'ȧ).........Austl.	24.50 S	144.5 E
112	Yaransk (yä-ränsk').....Sov. Un.	57.15 N	47.50 E
139	Yarda (yär'dȧ).......Fr. Eq. Afr.	18.30 N	19.13 E
158	Yarigadake (Mt.) (yä'rê-gȧ-dä'kĕ).Jap.	36.28 N	137.35 E
152	Yarkand (Soche) (yär-känt') (sō'chĕ').Chn.	38.12 N	77.30 E
55	Yarmouth (yär'mŭth).......Can.	43.57 N	66.5 W
169	Yarra, R. (yăr'ȧ) Austl. (Melbourne In.)	37.50 S	144.57 E
169	Yarraville (yăr'ȧ-vĭl) Austl. (Melbourne In.)	37.49 S	144.53 E
167	Yarrawonga (yăr-rȧ-wôŋ'gȧ) Austl.	36.2 S	146.1 E
169	Yarra Yarra Cr. (yăr'ȧ yăr'ȧ) Austl. (Melbourne In.)	37.45 S	145.5 E
167	Yarra Yarra R.............Austl.	37.40 S	145.20 E
112	Yarro-to, L. (yȧ'rô-tô')...Sov. Un.	68.30 N	71.30 E
130	Yartsev (yärt'sôf).......Sov. Un.	55.2 N	32.40 E
102	Yarumal (yä-ro͞o-mäl').......Col.	6.32 N	75.32 W
6	Yasawa Group (Is.) (yä-sä'wä) Fiji Is. (In.)	17.0 S	177.20 E
167	Yass (yȧs).................Austl.	34.50 S	148.55 E
97	Yateras (yä-tā'räs)..........Cuba	19.59 N	74.58 W
79	Yates Center (yāts) ....Kan.	37.53 N	95.44 W
55	Yathkyed L. (yȧth-kī-ăd')...Can.	62.45 N	97.32 W
159	Yatsugatake (Mt.) (yät'so͞o-gä-tä'kä).Jap.	35.58 N	138.22 E
159	Yatsushiro (yät'so͞o-shē'rō)...Jap.	32.30 N	130.35 E
151	Yatung (yä'to͝ong).........India	27.28 N	88.59 E
157	Yatushiro B. (yä'to͞o-shē'rō)..Jap.	32.23 N	130.27 E
92	Yautepec (yä-o͞o-tȧ-pĕk')....Mex.	18.53 N	99.4 W
159	Yawata (yä'wä-tä)..........Jap.	33.47 N	130.46 E
159	Yawata.....................Jap.	34.50 N	135.40 E
159	Yawatahama (yä'wȧ-tȧ-hä'mä) Jap.	33.25 N	132.25 E
148	Yaxartes (Sir Darya) R. (yăks-ăr'tēz) (sêr där'yä) Sov. Un.	45.0 N	65.0 E
82	Yazoo City (yă'zo͞o)........Miss.	32.50 N	90.25 W
82	Yazoo R...................Miss.	33.0 N	90.20 W
167	Yea (yē)..................Austl.	37.14 S	145.23 E
88	Yeadon (yē'dŭn) Pa. (Philadelphia In.)	39.56 N	75.15 W
126	Yecla (yā'klä)..............Sp.	38.36 N	1.8 W
166	Yeelanna (yê-lăn'ȧ)........Austl.	34.9 S	135.50 E
152	Yehcheng (Qargaliq) (yĕ'chĕng') (kär'gȧ-lĭk).Chn.	37.28 N	79.41 E
116	Yell (I.) (yĕl)......Gt. Brit. (In.)	60.40 N	1.5 W
73	Yellowleaf Cr. (yĕl'ô-lēf) Ala. (Birmingham In.)	33.17 N	86.35 W
156	Yellow R. (Hwang Ho) (hwäng' hō').Chn.	36.0 N	115.58 E
82	Yellow R...................Fla.	31.0 N	85.32 W
73	Yellow R.......Ga. (Atlanta In.)	33.47 N	84.4 W
157	Yellow Sea (Hwang Hai) (hwäng'hī').Chn.	36.0 N	123.0 E
71	Yellowstone L. (yĕl'ô-stōn)..Wyo.	44.25 N	110.25 W
71	Yellowstone Natl. Park.....Wyo.	44.45 N	110.40 W
71	Yellowstone R.......Mont.-N. D.	46.0 N	107.0 W
49	Yelm (yĕlm) ..Wash. (Seattle In.)	46.57 N	122.36 W
149	Yelovka (Elovka) (yĕ-lôf'kȧ) Sov. Un.	56.59 N	160.45 E
126	Yéltes R. (yāl'tĕs)............Sp.	41.0 N	6.30 W
138	Yelwa (yĕl'wä)..............Nig.	8.58 N	9.46 E
150	Yemen (yĕm'ĕn)............Asia	15.0 N	44.15 E
152	Yenan (yĕn'än')............Chn.	36.35 N	109.35 E
157	Yen-An.....................Cho.	37.55 N	126.10 E
150	Yenbo (yĕn'bô).........Sau. Ar.	24.0 N	38.10 E
156	Yencheng (yĕn'chĕng')......Chn.	33.20 N	120.5 E
156	Yencheng...................Chn.	33.35 N	113.57 E
153	Yenchi (Chultzuchien) (yĕn'kĭ') (cho͝ol'tzo͝o-chyĕn').Manch.	43.0 N	129.32 E
155	Yenchow (yĕn'chō')..........Chn.	29.36 N	119.36 E
156	Yenchow....................Chn.	35.43 N	116.53 E
138	Yendi (yĕn'dê)...............G. C.	9.28 N	0.2 E
129	Yenişehir (yĕ-nê-shĕ'hĭr).....Tur.	39.59 N	26.11 E
152	Yenisei R. (yĕ-nê-sĕ'ê)......Chn.	52.30 N	95.0 E
148	Yenisei (Enisei) R.......Sov. Un.	61.30 N	90.0 E
152	Yenki (Qara Shahr) (yĕn'kĭ') (kä'rä shär').Chn.	42.2 N	86.28 E
156	Yenling (yĕn'lĭng')..........Chn.	34.11 N	114.17 E
72	Yennadon (yĕn'ȧ-dŭn) Can. (Vancouver In.)	49.15 N	122.35 W
155	Yenping (yĕn'pĭng').........Chn.	26.38 N	118.3 E
156	Yen R. (yĕn)...............Chn.	33.50 N	119.20 E
156	Yenshan (yĕn'shän')........Chn.	38.15 N	117.4 E
52	Yenta R. (yĕn'tȧ).....Alsk. (In.)	61.40 N	150.35 W
156	Yentsing (yĕn'tsĭng')........Chn.	35.7 N	114.24 E
164	Yeo, L. (yō)...............Austl.	27.27 S	124.20 E
167	Yeoval (yō'vȧl)............Austl.	32.48 S	148.41 E
116	Yeovil (yō'vĭl)...........Gt. Brit.	50.55 N	2.50 W
167	Yeo Yeo (yō' yō) ....Austl.	34.31 S	147.59 E
74	Yerington (yê'rĭng-tŭn)......Nev.	38.58 N	119.10 W
125	Yerres (yĕr')............Fr. (In.)	48.42 N	2.30 E
125	Yerres R................Fr. (In.)	48.42 N	2.30 E
126	Yeste (yĕs'tȧ)................Sp.	38.22 N	2.19 W
166	Yetta (yĕt'ȧ)...............Austl.	34.8 S	141.54 E
124	Yeu d' Ile (yû dēl')...........Fr.	46.40 N	2.20 W
150	Yezd (yĕzd')..................Iran	31.59 N	54.20 E
156	Yichow (yĭ'chō')............Chn.	39.29 N	115.17 E
156	Yihsien (yĭ-hsyĕn')..........Chn.	34.45 N	117.45 E
154	Yingcheng (yĭng'chĕng').....Chn.	30.54 N	113.23 E
156	Yingchow (yĭng'chō')........Chn.	32.55 N	115.46 E
156	Yingchow...................Chn.	39.35 N	113.20 E
152	Yingkisha (Yangihissar) (yĭng'kĭ-shä') (yäŋ'gĭ-hĭs'är).Chn.	32.2 N	75.37 E
153	Yingkow (Niuchwangcheng) (yĭng'kō')..Manch.	40.50 N	122.25 E
156	Yingkow (yĭng'kō').......Manch.	40.40 N	122.12 E
158	Yingpan (yĭng'pän') ......Manch.	41.59 N	124.27 E
156	Ying R. (yĭng)..............Chn.	33.12 N	115.0 E
155	Yingshan (yĭng'shän').......Chn.	30.45 N	115.43 E
156	Yingshang (yĭng'shäng').....Chn.	32.37 N	116.11 E
154	Yingtak (yĭng'täk')..........Chn.	24.9 N	113.6 E
166	Yinkanie (yĭŋ-kä'nê).......Austl.	34.24 S	140.19 E
154	Yinkiang (yĭn'kyȧng').......Chn.	28.5 N	108.29 E
156	Yi, R. (yĭ)...................Chn.	34.50 N	118.20 E
99	Yi, R. (rē'ō-yē') Ur. (Buenos Aires In.)	33.15 S	57.0 W
154	Yiyang (yê'yäng')...........Chn.	28.33 N	112.2 E
81	Yoakum (yō'kŭm)............Tex.	29.17 N	97.9 W
154	Yochih (yō'chĭ')............Chn.	30.39 N	106.26 E
154	Yochow (yō'chō')...........Chn.	29.21 N	112.46 E
82	Yocona R. (yô-kō'nȧ).......Miss.	34.10 N	89.42 W
159	Yodo (yō'dō).....Jap. (Osaka In.)	34.54 N	135.42 E
159	Yodogawa R. (yō'dô-gä'wä) Jap. (Osaka In.)	34.48 N	135.36 E
162	Yog Pt. (yōg)................P. I.	14.6 N	124.13 E
54	Yoho Natl Park (yō' hō).....Can.	51.0 N	116.0 W
94	Yojoa, L. (yô-hō'ä)........Hond.	14.50 N	88.0 W
82	Yokahockany Cr. (yôk-ȧ-hŏk'ȧ-nê) Miss.	33.0 N	89.35 W
79	Yokahockany R............Miss.	33.15 N	89.25 W
159	Yokkaichi (yôk'kä-ê-chê).....Jap.	35.1 N	136.32 E
159	Yokohama (yō'kô-hä'mȧ).....Jap.	35.22 N	139.37 E
159	Yokosuka (yō'kô-so͞o'kȧ).....Jap.	35.17 N	139.41 E
159	Yokota (yō'kô-tȧ)..Jap. (Tokyo In.)	35.24 N	140.2 E
138	Yola (yō'lä).................Nig.	9.18 N	12.26 E
95	Yolaina, Cordillera de (Mts.) (yō-lä-ē'nä).Nic.	11.45 N	84.25 W
82	Yolande (yô-lăn'dê).........Ala.	33.18 N	87.12 W
159	Yonago (yō'nä-gō)...........Jap.	35.25 N	133.20 E
158	Yonezawa (yō'nĕ-zä'wȧ)......Jap.	37.52 N	140.2 E
157	Yongsan (yŏng'sän')........Cho.	37.34 N	126.57 E
157	Yonhunman B...............Cho.	39.15 N	127.30 E
85	Yonkers (yŏŋ'kērz).........N. Y.	40.57 N	73.53 W
124	Yonne R. (yôn)..............Fr.	48.10 N	3.20 E
159	Yono (yō'nō).....Jap. (Osaka In.)	34.55 N	135.30 E
73	Yorba (yôr'bä) Calif. (Los Angeles In.)	33.52 N	117.48 W
82	York (yôrk) ....Ala.	32.28 N	88.18 W
164	York.....................Austl.	31.50 S	116.50 E
169	York...........Austl. (Tas. In.)	41.9 S	146.46 E
116	York..................Gt. Brit.	53.55 N	1.5 W
76	York......................Neb.	40.52 N	97.35 W
85	York.......................Pa.	39.58 N	76.42 W
83	York.....................S. C.	34.59 N	81.4 W
165	York, C..................Austl.	10.45 S	142.25 E
48	York, C..................Grnld.	76.0 N	68.0 W
118	York Co...............Gt. Brit.	54.0 N	1.30 W
166	Yorke Pen. (yôrk).........Austl.	34.30 S	137.42 E
166	Yorketown (yôrk'toun).....Austl.	35.2 S	137.37 E
55	York Factory..............Can.	56.58 N	92.31 W
116	Yorkshire Wolds (Hills) (yôrk'-shĭr).Gt. Brit.	54.0 N	0.30 W
54	Yorkton (yôrk'tŭn).........Can.	51.13 N	102.31 W
81	Yorktown (yôrk'toun).......Tex.	28.58 N	97.30 W
85	Yorktown...................Va.	37.12 N	76.32 W
94	Yoro (yō'rô)...............Hond.	15.8 N	87.4 W
74	Yosemite Natl. Park (yô-sĕm'ĭ-tê) Calif.	37.55 N	119.40 W
159	Yoshida (yō'shê-dȧ).........Jap.	34.39 N	132.41 E
159	Yoshinogawa R. (yō'shê-nô-gä'wȧ).Jap.	34.3 N	133.50 E
159	Yoshiwara (yō'shê-wä'rä).....Jap.	35.11 N	138.41 E
159	Yosii (yō'sē-ē)..............Jap.	33.25 N	130.45 E
93	Yosonotú (Santa Catarina) (yô-sō-nô-to͞o') (sän'tä kä-tä-rē'nä).Mex.	16.53 N	97.34 W
155	Yotsing (yŏt'sĭng')..........Chn.	28.9 N	120.55 E
116	Youghal (yo͞o'ôl) (yôl)........Ire.	51.45 N	7.50 W
116	Youghal B..................Ire.	51.55 N	7.50 W
89	Youghiogheny R. (yŏk-yô-gā'nê) Pa. (Pittsburgh In.)	40.20 N	79.52 W
139	Youkadouma (yo͞o-kȧ-do͞o'mä) Cam.	3.28 N	15.2 E
167	Young (yŭng)..............Austl.	34.18 S	148.18 E
155	Youngfeng (yō'o͝ong'fĕng')...Chn.	27.17 N	115.18 E
157	Youngheung (yō'o͝ong'hĕ-o͝ong') Cho.	39.31 N	127.15 E
166	Younghusband Pen.........Austl.	36.0 S	139.30 E
49	Youngs R. (yŭngz) Ore. (Portland In.)	46.8 N	123.48 W
88	Youngstown (yŭngz'toun) N. Y. (Niagara Falls In.)	43.15 N	79.3 W
84	Youngstown................Ohio	41.5 N	80.40 W
157	Youngtuk (yō'o͝ong-to͞ok')....Cho.	36.26 N	129.23 E
157	Youngyou (yō'o͝ong-yō'o͞o)...Cho.	39.20 N	125.36 E
113	Yozgat (yôz'gȧd)............Tur.	39.50 N	34.48 E
117	Ypres (ē'pr')................Bel.	50.50 N	2.50 E
84	Ypsilanti (ĭp-sĭ-lăn'tĭ)......Mich.	42.14 N	83.37 W
70	Yreka (ê-rē'kȧ)............Calif.	41.43 N	122.38 W
165	Ysabel I. (ē'zȧ-bĕl)...Solomon Is.	8.0 S	159.0 E
80	Ysleta (êz-lē'tȧ)............Tex.	31.42 N	106.18 W
124	Yssingeau (ē-săɴ-zhō')........Fr.	45.10 N	4.10 E
120	Ystad (ü'städ)..............Swe.	55.25 N	13.49 E
120	Ytre Sullen (I.) (ü'trĕ so͞o'lĕn) Nor.	61.2 N	4.50 E
154	Yuanan (yo͞o'ä-nän')........Chn.	31.3 N	111.29 E
154	Yuanchow (yo͞o'än-chō').....Chn.	27.18 N	109.22 E
155	Yüanchow (yü'än-chō')......Chn.	27.37 N	114.16 E
154	Yüankiang (yü'än-kyäng')...Chn.	28.45 N	112.8 E
154	Yuan R. (yo͞o'än')..........Chn.	28.32 N	110.15 E
155	Yuan R.....................Chn.	27.40 N	114.50 E
152	Yuan R........Chn.-Fr. In. Chn.	22.30 N	103.55 E
155	Yüanshan (yü'än-shän').....Chn.	28.13 N	117.41 E
156	Yuanshih (yü'än-shĭ')........Chn.	37.50 N	114.33 E
159	Yuasa (yo͞o'ȧ-sȧ).............Jap.	34.2 N	135.10 E
74	Yuba City (yo͞o'bȧ).........Calif.	39.8 N	121.38 W
138	Yubi, C (yo͞o'bē)........R. de O.	28.0 N	12.52 W
73	Yucaipa (yo͞o-kȧ-ē'pȧ) Calif. (Los Angeles In.)	34.4 N	117.3 W
93	Yucatan (yo͞o-kä-tän')......Mex.	20.45 N	89.0 W
90	Yucatan, Channel of....Cen. Am.	21.30 N	86.30 W
75	Yucca House Nat. Mon. (yŭk'ȧ) Colo.	37.14 N	108.42 W
154	Yücheng (yü'chĕng')........Chn.	25.30 N	113.16 E
156	Yücheng...................Chn.	36.56 N	116.31 E
156	Yüchow (yü'chō')...........Chn.	34.9 N	113.29 E
156	Yüchow....................Chn.	39.50 N	114.28 E
129	Yugoslavia (Serb-Croat-Slovene-State) (yo͞o-gô-slä-vĭ-ȧ).Eur.	43.0 N	20.0 E
112	Yug R. (yo͝ok)..........Sov. Un.	60.0 N	46.0 E
155	Yuhang (yo͞o'häng')..........Chn.	30.18 N	119.55 E
154	Yuhsien (yo͞o'hsyĕn').........Chn.	26.58 N	113.4 E
155	Yuhwan I. (yo͞o'hwän')......Chn.	28.2 N	121.20 E
155	Yuhwanting (yo͞o'hwän-tĭng') Chn.	28.10 N	121.12 E
155	Yukan (yo͞o'kän')...........Chn.	28.43 N	116.40 E
130	Yukhnov (yo͝oĸ'nôf).....Sov. Un.	54.45 N	35.12 E
155	Yuki (yo͞o'kê')..............Chn.	26.12 N	118.3 E
154	Yuking (yo͞o'kĭng')..........Chn.	27.9 N	107.39 E
157	Yuko (Rashin) (yo͞o'kō).....Cho.	42.30 N	129.45 E

ng-sing; ŋ-baŋk; ɴ-nasalized n; nŏd; cŏmmit; ōld; ôbey; ôrder; fo͞od; fo͝ot; ou-out; s-soft; sh-dish; th-thin; pūre; ûnite; ûrn; stŭd; circŭs; ü-as "y" in study; '-indeterminate vowel.

Page	Name Pronunciation Region	Lat. °′	Long. °′
54	Yukon (Ter.) (yo͞o'kŏn)...Can.	63.0 N	136.0 W
52	Yukon R....Alsk.	65.20 N	151.0 W
152	Yulin (yo͞o'lĭn')...Chn.	38.15 N	109.34 E
74	Yuma (yo͞o'mä)...Ariz.	32.41 N	114.37 W
78	Yuma...Colo.	40.7 N	102.44 W
97	Yuma B....Dom. Rep.	18.20 N	68.35 W
152	Yümen (yü'mĕn')...Chn.	40.9 N	97.2 E
97	Yuna R. (yo͞o'nä')...Dom. Rep.	79.8 N	70.0 W
155	Yungan (yo͝on'gän')...Chn.	23.37 N	115.5 E
155	Yungan...Chn.	25.51 N	117.20 E
152	Yungchang (yo͝ong'chäng')...Chn.	25.8 N	99.10 E
154	Yungchang (yo͝ong'chäng')...Chn.	29.35 N	105.33 E
156	Yüncheng (yün'chĕng)...Chn.	35.33 N	116.2 E
154	Yungchow (yo͝ong'chō')...Chn.	26.10 N	111.29 E
155	Yungchun (yo͝ong'cho͞on')...Chn.	25.20 N	118.12 E
157	Yungchun...Cho.	35.58 N	128.56 E
154	Yungchwan (yo͝ong'chwän')...Chn.	29.33 N	105.54 E
154	Yungfu (yo͝ong'fo͞o')...Chn.	24.58 N	109.59 E
155	Yungfu...Chn.	25.44 N	118.43 E
154	Yungfu R....Chn.	24.35 N	109.50 E
154	Yunghing (yo͝ong'hĭng')...Chn.	26.4 N	112.41 E
154	Yungkang (yo͝ong'käng')...Chn.	22.56 N	108.1 E
155	Yungkang...Chn.	28.56 N	120.3 E
154	Yungming (yo͝ong'nĭng')...Chn.	25.14 N	111.18 E
154	Yungning...Chn.	26.53 N	113.40 E
154	Yungshun (yo͝ong'sho͞on')...Chn.	28.57 N	109.44 E
154	Yungsin (yo͝ong'sĭn')...Chn.	27.0 N	113.55 E
154	Yungsui (yo͝ong'swē')...Chn.	28.37 N	109.15 E
155	Yungting (yo͝ong'tĭng')...Chn.	24.47 N	116.33 E
154	Yungting...Chn.	28.58 N	110.21 E
156	Yungting R. (Hun R.) (yo͝ong'-tĭng').Chn.	39.40 N	116.10 E
154	Yungtsong (yo͝ong'tsông')...Chn.	25.58 N	108.59 E
154	Yungyün (yo͝ong'yün')...Chn.	24.28 N	113.18 E
155	Yunho (yo͝ong'hō')...Chn.	28.5 N	119.34 E
157	Yunil B. (yo͞o'nĭl)...Cho.	36.5 N	129.25 E
155	Yün Ling (Mts.) (yün' lĭng').Chn.	27.55 N	117.45 E
154	Yünmeng (yün'mĕng')...Chn.	31.0 N	113.32 E
152	Yünnan (Prov.) (yün'nän')...Chn.	24.0 N	102.0 E
154	Yunnan (Prov.) (yo͞on'nän')...Chn.	23.52 N	106.10 E
152	Yünnanfu (yün'nän'fo͞o')...Chn.	25.1 N	102.34 E
152	Yünnan, Plat. of...Chn.	25.45 N	103.0 E
156	Yunping (yo͞on'pĭng')...Chn.	39.57 N	118.51 E
155	Yun R (yo͝on)...Chn.	30.4 N	120.50 E
156	Yun R. (Grand Canal) (yo͞on).Chn.	35.50 N	116.10 E
155	Yunsiao (yo͝on'syou')...Chn.	23.59 N	117.8 E
166	Yunta (yo͞on'tȧ)...Austl.	32.36 S	139.33 E
154	Yun Wu Shan (Mts.) (yo͞on'wo͞o' shän').Chn.	26.5 N	107.10 E
154	Yünyang (yün'yäng')...Chn.	31.10 N	109.2 E
153	Yünyang (yün'yäng')...Chn.	33.0 N	110.56 E
154	Yüping (yü'pĭng')...Chn.	27.10 N	108.35 E
154	Yu R. (yo͞o)...Chn.	23.23 N	107.45 E
159	Yura (yo͞o'rä)...Jap.	34.18 N	134.55 E
92	Yurécuaro (yo͞o-rā'kwä-rō)...Mex.	20.19 N	102.15 W
130	Yur'ev (yo͞o'ryĕf)...Sov. Un.	56.31 N	39.41 E
112	Yurievets (yo͞o'ryĕ-vyĕts) Sov. Un.	57.15 N	43.0 E
102	Yurimaguas (yo͞o-rē-mä'gwäs) Peru	5.58 S	76.2 W
92	Yuriria (yo͞o'rē-rē'ä)...Mex.	20.12 N	101.7 W
92	Yuriria, L....Mex.	20.15 N	101.5 W
94	Yuscarán (yo͞os-kä-rän')...Hond.	13.55 N	86.53 W
155	Yushan (yo͞o'shän')...Chn.	28.40 N	118.18 E
156	Yüshih (yü'shĭ')...Chn.	34.25 N	114.18 E
156	Yutai (yo͞o'tī')...Chn.	34.54 N	116.28 E
156	Yütien (yü'tyĕn')...Chn.	39.53 N	117.38 E
152	Yutien (Keriya) (yo͞o'tyĕn') (kē'rē-yȧ).Chn.	36.32 N	81.20 E
155	Yutsien (yo͞o'tsyĕn')...Chn.	30.13 N	119.30 E
155	Yütu (yü'to͞o')...Chn.	25.52 N	115.10 E
104	Yuty (yo͞o-tē')...Par.	26.45 N	56.20 W
154	Yuyang (yo͞o'yäng')...Chn.	28.53 N	108.39 E
155	Yüyao (yü'you')...Chn.	30.4 N	121.10 E
112	Yuzha (yo͞o'zhȧ)...Sov. Un.	56.40 N	42.10 E
122	Yverdon (ē-vĕr-dôɴ')...Switz.	46.46 N	6.40 E
125	Yvette R. (ē-vĕt')...Fr. (In.)	48.42 N	2.15 E
124	Yvetot (ēv-tō')...Fr.	49.38 N	0.45 E
93	Zaachila (Santa Maria) (zä-ä-chē'-lȧ) (sän'tä mä-rē'ä).Mex.	16.57 N	96.45 W
122	Zaandam (zän'dȧm)...Neth.	52.57 N	4.50 E
94	Zacapa (zä-kä'pä)...Guat.	14.57 N	89.31 W
93	Zacapoaxtla (zä-kä-pō-äs'tlä).Mex.	19.53 N	97.35 W
92	Zacapú (zä-kä-po͞o')...Mex.	19.45 N	101.45 W
92	Zacatecas (zä-kä-tā'käs)...Mex.	22.46 N	102.33 W
92	Zacatecas (State)...Mex.	23.0 N	103.0 W
94	Zacatecoluca (zä-kä-tȧ-kô-lo͞o'kä) Sal.	13.30 N	88.50 W
92	Zacatelco (zä-kä-tĕl'kō)...Mex.	19.13 N	98.13 W
93	Zacatepec (Santiago) (zä-kä-tȧ-pĕk') (sän-tē-ä'gō).Mex.	17.10 N	95.53 W
93	Zacatlán (zä-kä-tlän')...Mex.	19.56 N	97.57 W
92	Zacoalco de Torres (zä-kô-äl'kō dā tōr'rĕs).Mex.	20.13 N	103.33 W
92	Zacualpán (zä-ko͞o-äl-pän')...Mex.	18.43 N	99.46 W
92	Zacualtipán (zä-ko͞o-äl-tē-pän') Mex.	20.38 N	98.38 W
130	Zadonsk (zä'dônsk)...Sov. Un.	52.23 N	38.57 E
121	Žagere (zhä'gĕ-rā)...Lith.	56.22 N	23.15 E
138	Zaghouan (zȧ-gwäɴ')...Tun.	36.28 N	10.3 E
135	Zaghouan, Djebel (Mt.) (jĕb'ĕl zȧ-gwäɴ').Tun. (In.)	36.20 N	10.9 E
129	Zagora (zä'gô-rȧ)...Grc.	39.28 N	23.3 E
130	Zagorsk (zä-gôrsk')...Sov. Un.	56.18 N	38.7 E
128	Zagreb (zä'grĕb)...Yugo.	45.49 N	15.58 E
135	Zahara (thä'ȧ-rä)...Sp. (Gib. In.)	36.9 N	5.11 E
150	Zahedan (Duzdab) (zä'hȧ-dän) (do͝oz'däb).Per.	29.32 N	60.34 E
115	Zahlé (zä-lā')...Syr.	33.45 N	35.52 E
150	Zaindeh Rud (R.) (zä'ēn-dĕ ro͞od')..Iran	32.30 N	51.32 E
148	Zaisan Nor (L.) (zī'sȧn-nôr) Sov. Un.	48.0 N	84.0 E
126	Zájar R. (thä'gär)...Sp.	38.55 N	5.20 W
129	Zaječar (zä'yĕ-chär)...Yugo.	43.53 N	22.16 E
148	Zakarovskoe (Bakhty) (zȧ'kȧ-rôf-skô'yĕ) (bȧκ'tê) Sov. Un.	46.58 N	82.50 E
123	Zakopane (zȧ-kô-pä'nĕ)...Pol.	49.18 N	19.57 E
142	Zak R. (zȧk)...U. S. Afr.	30.30 S	20.30 E
142	Zak River...U. S. Afr.	30.52 S	20.25 E
129	Zakynthos (zȧ'kĭn-thôs)...Grc.	37.47 N	20.53 E
129	Zakynthos (Zante) (I.) (zän'tĕ) Grc.	37.45 N	20.48 E
122	Zalaegerszeg (zô'lô-ĕ'gĕr-sĕg) Hung.	46.50 N	16.47 E
126	Zalamea de la Serena (thä-lä-mā'ä dā lä sā-rā'nä).Sp.	38.37 N	5.39 W
126	Zalamea la Real (lä-rā-äl')...Sp.	37.42 N	6.40 W
123	Zalău (zä'lȧ-o͝o)...Rom.	47.11 N	23.4 E
140	Zambezi R. (zȧm-bā'zê) (zăm-bē'zê).Afr.	18.0 S	27.0 E
163	Zamboanga (zäm-bô-äŋ'gä)...P. I.	6.54 N	122.5 E
123	Zambrów (zäm'bro͝of)...Pol.	52.58 N	22.16 E
92	Zamora (zä-mō'rä)...Mex.	19.59 N	102.15 W
126	Zamora (thä-mō'rä)...Sp.	41.31 N	5.45 W
123	Zamość (zä'môshch)...Pol.	50.42 N	23.17 E
93	Zanatepec (Santo Domingo) (zä-nä-tȧ-pĕk') (sän-tô dō-mĭŋ'gô) Mex.	16.30 N	94.21 W
143	Zand R. (zȧnd)...U. S. Afr.	28.6 S	27.0 E
84	Zanesville (zānz'vĭl)...Ohio	39.56 N	82.2 W
129	Zante (Zakynthos) (I.) (zän-tĕ) (zä'kĭn-thôs)..Grc.	37.45 N	20.48 E
141	Zanzibar (I.) (zăn'zĭ-bär)...Afr.	5.30 S	39.30 E
141	Zanzibar...Zan.	6.5 S	39.13 E
114	Zanzur (zän-zo͞or')...Libya	32.53 N	13.3 E
138	Zaouri, Wad (R.) (zä'o͝o-rê)...Alg.	29.30 N	1.30 W
104	Zapala (zä-pä'lä)...Arg.	38.50 S	70.2 W
93	Zapaluta (La Trinitaria) (zä-pä-lo͞o'tä) (lä trē-nê-tä'rê-ä).Mex.	16.7 N	92.2 W
80	Zapata (zä-pä'tä)...Tex.	26.52 N	99.19 W
96	Zapata Pen....Cuba	22.18 N	81.30 W
96	Zapata Swamp...Cuba	22.23 N	81.15 W
94	Zapatero I. (zä-pä-tā'rō)...Nic.	11.45 N	85.50 W
92	Zapopan (zä-pō'pän)...Mex.	20.43 N	103.22 W
131	Zaporozh'e (zä-pô-rôzh'ĭ-yĕ) Sov. Un.	47.45 N	35.11 E
92	Zapotiltic (zä-pô-têl-tēk')...Mex.	19.37 N	103.23 W
92	Zapotitlán (zä-pô-tê-tlän')...Mex.	17.18 N	98.49 W
93	Zapotitlán...Mex. (In.)	19.18 N	99.2 W
93	Zapotitlán, C....Mex.	18.33 N	94.48 W
92	Zapotlanejo (zä-pô-tlä-nā'hō) Mex.	20.37 N	103.5 W
139	Zaqazîq (zä-kȧ-zēk')...Eg.	30.33 N	31.32 E
128	Zara (dzä'rä)...Yugo.	44.7 N	15.4 E
92	Zaragoza (zä-rä-gō'sä)...Mex.	23.58 N	99.48 W
80	Zaragoza...Mex.	26.7 N	103.26 W
80	Zaragoza...Mex.	28.28 N	100.54 W
127	Zaragoza (thä-rä-gō'thä)...Sp.	41.39 N	0.52 W
130	Zaraisk (zä'rȧ-ĭsk)...Sov. Un.	54.46 N	38.56 E
121	Zarasai (Ežerēnai) (zȧ-rȧ-sī) (ĕ-zhĕ-rā'nī).Lith.	55.44 N	26.17 E
104	Zarate (zä-rä'tā)...Arg.	34.15 S	59.0 W
138	Zaria (zä'rê-ä)...Nig.	11.8 N	7.45 E
149	Zashiversk (zȧ'shĭ-vĕrsk) Sov. Un.	67.0 N	143.50 E
123	Zastavna (zȧs-täv'nȧ)...Rom.	48.32 N	25.50 E
143	Zastron (zȧs'trŭn)...U. S. Afr.	30.18 S	27.5 E
	Žatec, see Saaz, Ger.		
149	Zavitaya (zȧ'vê-tȧ-yȧ)...Sov. Un.	50.15 N	129.40 E
139	Zawia (zä'wê-ä)...Libya	32.38 N	12.51 E
123	Zawiercie (zȧ-vyĕr'tsyĕ)...Pol.	50.28 N	19.25 E
96	Zaza R. (zȧ'zȧ)...Cuba	21.58 N	79.20 W
123	Zbaraż (zbȧ'rȧsh)...Pol.	49.39 N	25.48 E
123	Zbrucz R. (zbro͝och) Pol.-Sov. Un.	49.15 N	26.15 E
123	Zdolbunów (zdôl-bo͞o'no͝of)...Pol.	50.31 N	26.16 E
123	Zduńska Wola (zdo͞on''skȧ vō'lȧ) Pol.	51.36 N	18.56 E
143	Zeakoe R. (zē'kō)...U. S. Afr.	0.52 S	24.40 E
145	Zebdany (zĕb'dȧ-nê)...Syr. (In.)	33.44 N	36.4 E
117	Zeebrugge (zā'bro͝og'ĕ)...Bel.	51.20 N	3.10 E
169	Zeehan (zē'ăn)...Austl. (Tas. In.)	41.54 S	145.24 E
169	Zeehan, Mt....Austl. (Tas. In.)	42.0 S	145.15 E
84	Zeeland (zē'lănd)...Mich.	42.50 N	86.2 W
143	Zeerust (zā'rŭst)...U. S. Afr.	25.31 S	26.5 E
145	Zefath) Safed) (zĕ-făt') (sȧ-fēd') Pal. (In.)	32.58 N	35.29 E
122	Zehdenick (tsā'dē-nêk)...Ger.	52.59 N	13.20 E
119	Zehlendorf) tsā'lĕn-dôrf) Ger. (Berlin In.)	52.26 N	13.15 E
139	Zeila (zā'lä)...Br. Som.	11.15 N	43.26 E
122	Zeitz (tsīts)...Ger.	51.3 N	12.7 E
123	Żelechów (zhĕ-lā'κo͝of)...Pol.	51.47 N	21.54 E
122	Zella-Mehlis (tsĕl'ȧ-mā'lês)...Ger.	50.40 N	10.39 E
135	Zembra I. (zĕm'brā)...Tun. (In.)	37.8 N	10.40 E
139	Zémio (zā'mê-ō)...Fr. Eq. Afr.	5.2 N	25.11 E
93	Zempoala, Pt. (zĕm-pô-ä'lä) Mex.	19.27 N	96.19 W
93	Zempoatlépetl (Mt.) (zĕm-pô-ä-tlā'pĕt'l).Mex.	17.15 N	95.57 W
129	Zemun (Semlin) (zĕ'mo͞on) (sĕm'lĭn).Yugo.	44.50 N	20.25 E
129	Zenica (zĕ'nêt-sȧ)...Yugo.	44.10 N	17.54 E
150	Zenjan (zĕn-jän')...Per.	36.32 N	48.32 E
131	Zenkov (zĕŋ'kôf)...Sov. Un.	50.12 N	34.22 E
157	Zenshu (Jyunju) (zĕn-sho͞o')..Cho.	35.52 N	127.5 E
129	Žepče (zhĕp'chĕ)...Yugo.	44.25 N	18.1 E
122	Zerbst (tsĕrbst)...Ger.	51.57 N	12.3 E
145	Zerga (zēr'gă)...Transj. (In.)	32.5 N	36.6 E
149	Zeya (zȧ'yȧ)...Sov. Un.	53.45 N	127.15 E
149	Zeya R....Sov. Un.	53.0 N	127.30 E
113	Zeytun (zā-to͝on')...Tur.	37.55 N	30.50 E
126	Zêzere R. (zĕ'zȧ-rĕ)...Port.	40.0 N	7.58 W
123	Zgierz (zgyĕzh)...Pol.	51.51 N	19.26 E
145	Zgorta (zgôr'tȧ)...Syr. (In.)	34.21 N	35.52 E
131	Zgurovka (zgo͞o-rôf'kȧ)...Sov. Un.	50.32 N	31.43 E
131	Zhadov (zhȧ'dôf)...Sov. Un.	52.2 N	32.50 E
69	Zhelaniya, C. (zhĕ'lä-nĭ-yȧ) Sov. Un.	76.45 N	69.0 E
149	Zhigalovo (zhĭ'gȧ-lô-vô)..Sov. Un.	54.50 N	105.10 E
149	Zhigansk (zhē-gȧnsk')...Sov. Un.	66.40 N	123.30 E
131	Zhitomir (zhê'tô-mĭr)...Sov. Un.	50.15 N	28.40 E
130	Zhizdra (zhêz'drȧ)...Sov. Un.	53.46 N	34.44 E
130	Zhizhitskoe, L. (zhê'zhêt-skô'yĕ) Sov. Un.	56.10 N	31.15 E
131	Zhmerinka (zhmyĕ'rêŋ-kȧ) Sov. Un.	49.3 N	28.8 E
123	Ziegenhals (tsē'gĕn-häls)...Ger.	50.19 N	17.23 E
138	Ziguincher (zĭ-gwĭn'chēr) (zê-găɴ-shā').Fr. W. Afr.	12.32 N	16.20 W
113	Zile (zê-lĕ')...Tur.	40.15 N	36.0 E
123	Žilina (zhê'lĭ-nȧ)...Czech.	49.13 N	18.45 E
152	Ziling Tso (L.) (zĭ'lĭng' tsō') Chn.	31.45 N	88.30 E
148	Zima (zē'mȧ)...Sov. Un.	53.59 N	101.59 E
92	Zimapan (zē-mä'pän)...Mex.	20.44 N	99.22 W
93	Zimatlán de Álvarez (zē-mä-tlän' dā äl'vä-rāz).Mex.	16.53 N	96.48 W
129	Zimnicea (zêm-nē'chȧ)...Rom.	43.38 N	25.22 E
92	Zinapécuaro (zē-nä-pā'kwȧ-rō) Mex.	19.51 N	100.47 W
138	Zinder (zĭn'dēr)...Fr. W. Afr.	13.57 N	8.58 E
131	Zinovievsk (Kirovo) (zê-nô'vyĕfsk) Sov. Un.	48.31 N	32.15 E
77	Zion (zī'ŭn)...Ill.	42.26 N	87.50 W
75	Zion Natl. Mon....Utah	37.35 N	112.50 W
75	Zion Natl. Park...Utah	37.20 N	113.0 W
102	Zipaquirá (zē-pä-kē-rä')...Col.	4.58 N	14.10 W
92	Zirandaro (zē-rän-dä'rō)...Mex.	18.28 N	100.59 W
112	Ziryan (Komi) (Aut. Area) (zêr'yän) (κō'mê)...Sov. Un.	64.0 N	55.0 E
92	Zitacuaro (zē-tȧ-kwä'rō)...Mex.	19.23 N	100.22 W
92	Zitlala (zê-tlä'lä)...Mex.	17.42 N	99.14 W
122	Zittau (tsê'tou)...Ger.	50.54 N	14.49 E
131	Zlatopol (zlȧ'tô-pôl')...Sov. Un.	48.48 N	31.42 E
148	Zlatoust (zlȧ-tô-o͝ost)...Sov. Un.	55.20 N	59.40 E
123	Zloczew (zwô'chĕf)...Pol.	51.23 N	18.37 E
123	Zloczów (zwô'cho͝of...Pol.	49.49 N	24.55 E
130	Zlynka (zlêŋ'kȧ)...Sov. Un.	52.29 N	31.41 E
122	Znaim (Znojmo) (tsnīm) (znoi'mō) Ger.	48.52 N	16.2 E
131	Znamenka (znȧ-mĕŋ'kȧ) Sov. Un.	48.42 N	32.31 E
	Znojmo, see Znaim, Ger.		
123	Żolkiew (zho͝ol'kyĕf)...Pol.	50.3 N	23.58 E
131	Zolotonosha (zô'lô-tô-nô'shȧ) Sov. Un.	49.39 N	32.1 E
140	Zomba (zôm'bȧ)...Nya.	15.22 S	35.15 E
142	Zonder Einde R. (zôn'dēr īn'dē) U. S. Afr.	34.8 S	19.50 E
139	Zongo (zŏŋ'gô)...Bel. Cong.	4.24 N	18.35 E
113	Zonguldak (zôn'go͝ol-dȧk)...Tur.	41.30 N	31.50 E
123	Zoppot (tsôp'ôt)...Dan.	54.26 N	18.33 E
93	Zoquitlán (zō-kēt-län')...Mex.	18.18 N	97.1 W
126	Zorita (thō-rē'tä)...Sp.	39.17 N	5.40 W
142	Zout River Vlei (zout' rĭv'ēr vlī') U. S. Afr.	32.22 S	23.3 E
139	Zuare (zwā'rȧ)...Libya	33.0 N	12.3 E
130	Zubtsov (zo͝op'tsôf)...Sov. Un.	56.11 N	34.38 E
127	Zuera (thwā'rä)...Sp.	41.50 N	0.50 W
122	Zug (tso͞og)...Switz.	47.9 N	8.32 E
122	Zug, L....Switz.	47.7 N	8.30 E
143	Zululand (zo͞o'lo͞o-lănd)..U. S. Afr.	28.0 S	32.0 E
163	Zumarraga (zo͞o-mär-rä'gä)...P. I.	11.38 N	124.51 E
140	Zumbo (zo͞om'bo͝o)...Moz.	15.35 S	30.28 E
77	Zumbro, R. (zŭm'brō)...Minn.	44.15 N	92.20 W
77	Zumbrota (zŭm-brō'tȧ)...Minn.	44.17 N	92.38 W
92	Zumpango (zo͞om-päŋ'gō)...Mex.	19.47 N	99.6 W
138	Zungeru (zo͞oŋ-gā'ro͞o)...Nig.	9.48 N	6.8 E
75	Zuni Ind. Res. (zo͞o'nê)...N. M.	35.9 N	108.40 W
75	Zuni R....Ariz.	34.40 N	109.30 W
128	Zupanjac (zho͞o-pän'yȧts)...Yugo.	43.42 N	17.15 E
122	Zürich (tsü'rĭκ)...Switz.	47.21 N	8.31 E
122	Zürich, L. of...Switz.	47.14 N	8.42 E
130	Zusha R. (zo͞o'shȧ)...Sov. Un.	53.10 N	36.40 E
122	Zutphen (zŭt'fĕn) (tso͝ot'fĕn) Neth.	52.7 N	6.12 E
143	Zuur Berg (Mts.) (zo͞or' bûrg) U. S. Afr.	31.15 S	25.40 E
130	Zvenigorod (zvȧ'nĭ-gô-rôt) Sov. Un.	55.44 N	36.52 E
131	Zvenigorodka (zvȧ'nĭ-gô-rôt'kȧ) Sov. Un.	49.6 N	30.59 E
123	Zvolen (zvō'lĕn)...Czech.	48.35 N	19.10 E
129	Zvornik (zvôr'nēk)...Yugo.	44.23 N	19.7 E
131	Zvyagel (zvyȧ'gĕl)...Sov. Un.	50.35 N	27.38 E
142	Zwaartmodder (zvärt'mô-dēr) Bech.	28.2 S	20.31 E
139	Zwai, L. (zwä'ê)...It. E. Afr.	8.0 N	38.50 E
143	Zwart Berg (Mt.) (zvärt'bûrg) U. S. Afr.	30.8 S	29.25 E
142	Zwarte Bergen (Mts.) (zvär'tĕ bĕr'gĕn).U. S. Afr.	32.50 S	19.35 E
142	Zwart Doorn (zvärt dōrn') U. S. Afr.	30.35 S	18.25 E
143	Zwart Krans (Mt.) (kräns) U. S. Afr.	28.31 S	28.1 E
122	Zweibrücken (tsvī-brük'ĕn)...Ger.	49.16 N	7.22 E
122	Zwickau (tsvĭk'ou)...Ger.	50.44 N	12.30 E
122	Zwolle (zvôl'ĕ)...Neth.	52.31 N	6.4 E
122	Zwittau (Svitavy) (tsvĭt'ou) (svē'tȧ-vê).Ger.	49.46 N	16.27 E
119	Zwyndrecht (zvĭn'drĕκt) Bel. (Anvers In.)	51.13 N	4.19 E
123	Zydaczów (zhê-dä'cho͝of)...Pol.	49.22 N	24.11 E
123	Zyrardów (zhê-rär'do͝of)...Pol.	52.4 N	20.28 E
123	Zywiec (zhē'vyĕts)...Pol.	49.41 N	19.12 E

ăt; finăl; rāte; senâte; ärm; ȧsk; sofȧ; fâre; ch-choose; dh-as th in other; bē; êvent; bĕt; recĕnt; cratēr; g-go; gh-gutteral g; bĭt; ĭ-short neutral; rīde; κ-gutteral k as ch in German ich;